D1571445

ELECTRONIC CIRCUITS MANUAL

BOOKS by JOHN MARKUS

ELECTRONIC CIRCUITS MANUAL

ELECTRONICS DICTIONARY

ELECTRONICS FOR ENGINEERS

ELECTRONICS MANUAL FOR RADIO ENGINEERS

ELECTRONICS AND NUCLEONICS DICTIONARY

HANDBOOK OF ELECTRONIC CONTROL CIRCUITS

HANDBOOK OF INDUSTRIAL ELECTRONIC CIRCUITS

HANDBOOK OF INDUSTRIAL ELECTRONIC CONTROL CIRCUITS

HOW TO GET AHEAD IN THE TELEVISION AND RADIO SERVICING BUSINESS

HOW TO MAKE MORE MONEY IN YOUR TV SERVICING BUSINESS

SOURCEBOOK OF ELECTRONIC CIRCUITS

TELEVISION AND RADIO REPAIRING

WHAT ELECTRONICS DOES

ELECTRONIC CIRCUITS MANUAL

Over 3,100 modern electronic circuits, complete with values of all parts, organized in 99 logical chapters for quick reference and convenient browsing

JOHN MARKUS

Consultant, McGraw-Hill Book Company
Senior Member, Institute of Electrical and Electronics Engineers
Editorial Board, American Society for Information Science

McGRAW-HILL BOOK COMPANY

New York St. Louis San Francisco Düsseldorf Johannesburg
Kuala Lumpur London Mexico Montreal New Delhi
Panama Rio de Janeiro Singapore Sydney Toronto

ELECTRONIC CIRCUITS MANUAL

 Library of Congress Catalog Card Number 70–152007

07-040444-5

1234567890 HDAH 754321

This book was set in Spartan heavy by Brown Brothers
Linotypers, Inc., printed by Halliday Lithograph
Corporation, and bound by A. Horowitz & Son Bookbinders.
The editors were Tyler G. Hicks and Lila M. Gardner. George E. Oechsner supervised production.

Preface

More than 3,100 electronic circuits, published largely within the past 5 years in the United States and abroad, are presented here in 99 chapters, logically organized for convenient reference and browsing by practical electronics engineers, technicians, and experimenters. Each circuit has the values of all significant components, an identifying title, a concise description, performance data, and suggestions for applications. At the end of each description is a citation giving the title of the original article or book, its author, and the exact location in the source. After a circuit is selected, the construction details, performance graphs, and calibration procedures can usually be found in the original publication if needed.

The circuits in this book are completely different from those in the highly successful predecessor volume, "Sourcebook of Electronic Circuits," published by McGraw-Hill in 1968. New chapters provide easy access for the first time to circuits for Audio Control, Automotive Control, Flashers, Lamp Control, Lasers, Metal Detectors, Opamps, Optoelectronics, Tachometers, Voltage-Level Detectors, and 14 other new categories. Internal connections for the most-used IC chips are given in the Integrated Circuits chapter as an extra aid for analyzing the modern solid-state circuits that dominate this book.

This electronic circuit compendium serves as a highly effective desk-top information retrieval system for tested practical electronic circuits developed throughout the world. Engineering libraries, particularly in foreign countries, will find it a welcome substitute for the original sources when facing limitations on budgets, shelving, or searching manpower. The circuits for this new book were located by cover-to-cover searching of five years of back issues of 39 U.S. and foreign electronics periodicals, the published literature of several hundred manufacturers, and hundreds of recent books, together filling well over 100 feet of shelving. This same search would take weeks or even months at a large engineering library, plus the time required to write for manufacturer literature and locate elusive sources.

To find a desired circuit quickly, start with the alphabetically arranged table of contents at the front of the book. Note the chapters most likely to contain the desired type of circuit, and look in these first. Remember that most applications use combinations of basic circuits, and could therefore be placed in any of several different chapters.

If a quick scan of these chapters does not give the exact circuit desired, use the index at the back of the book. Here the circuits are indexed in depth under the different names by which they are known. In addition, the index contains hundreds of cross references that speed up your search.

In most cases, you can locate a desired circuit in a few minutes. It should be free of drafting errors, because corrections pointed out in subsequently published errata notices have been made; this alone can save many frustrating hours of troubleshooting.

Values of important components are given for every circuit, because these help in reading the circuit and redesigning it for other requirements. The development of a circuit for a new application is speeded when design work can be started with a working circuit, instead of starting from scratch. Research and experimentation are thereby cut to a minimum, so even a single use of this circuit-retrieval book could pay for its initial cost many times over.

This book is organized to provide a maximum of circuit information per page, with minimum repetition. The chapter title, heading, and original title in the citation should therefore be considered along with the description when studying a circuit.

Abbreviations are used extensively to conserve space. Their meanings are given after the table of contents. Abbreviations on diagrams and in original article titles were unchanged, but their meanings can be deduced by context.

Few publications are able to maintain a supply of back issues, but many are willing to make copies of individual articles. A charge is usually made for this service, per page or per article. Similarly, libraries are usually willing to make copies of articles in publications brought to their copying machines.

Mailing addresses of some U.S. electronics publications are given after the list of abbreviations for convenience in writing for back issues or copies of articles. Addresses for foreign sources are generally included with the citations for the 420 foreign circuits given.

To artist and orchid-hybridizer Jack Quint, more active than ever in Florida retirement, goes full credit for arranging the circuits so well on these pages, each unmistakably associated with its text. Secretaries Joyce MacIntyre and Diane Jacobs deserve recognition for perseverance in learning the language of electronics and typing it exactly as dictated, hyphens, kHzs, and all. Other co-workers for this book include Claire del Aguila, Joan Clough, Barbara Jankowski, and Pat Qualls (typing), Ann Fioto (retyping), Debbie Zlendick (editing), and Mike Wechsberg (140 abstracts).

To the original publications cited and to their authors and editors should go the real credit, however, for making possible this contribution to electronic circuit design.

John Markus

Contents

ABBREVIATIONS USED

a atto (10^{-18})
A ampere
a-c alternating current
a-c/d-c alternating current and direct current
a-f audio frequency
afc automatic frequency control
aft automatic fine tuning
agc automatic gain control
a-m amplitude modulation
bcd binary coded decimal
bfo beat-frequency oscillator
b-w black-and-white
c centi- (10^{-2})
C Centigrade; capacitance; capacitor
CATV Community Antenna Television
CB Citizens Band
CCTV Closed-Circuit Television
cm centimeter
cr cathode-ray
cro cathode-ray oscilloscope
crt cathode-ray tube
c-w continuous-wave
d-a digital-analog
d-c direct current
d deci- (10^{-1})
dB decibel
dBm decibels above 1 milliwatt
deg degree
diac diode a-c switch
DTL diode-transistor logic
dvm digital voltmeter
ecg electrocardiograph
eeg electroencephalograph
emf electromotive force
f femto- (10^{-15})
fet field-effect transistor
f-m frequency modulation
fsk frequency shift keying
ft feet
G giga (10^{9})
GHz gigahertz
G-M Geiger-Muller
hp horsepower
hr hour
Hz hertz
IC integrated circuit
i-f intermediate frequency
IR infrared
k kilo- (10^{3})
K kilohm (,000 ohms)
kHz kilohertz
kV kilovolt
kW kilowatt
L inductance; inductor
las light-activated switch
lascr light-activated scr
lascs light-activated scs
m milli- (10^{-3})
M mega- (10^{6})
meg megohm
mH millihenry
MHz megahertz
mil 0.001 inch (10^{-3} inch)
min minute
ms millisecond
mm millimeter
modem modulator-demodulator
mono monostable multivibrator
mosfet metal-oxide semiconductor field-effect transistor
μ micro- (10^{-6})
μA microampere
μF microfarad
μH microhenry
μs microsecond
mV millivolt
mvbr multivibrator
mW milliwatt
n nano- (10^{-9})
nA nanoampere
nF nanofarad
npn negative-positive-negative
ns nanosecond
nW nanowatt
opamp operational amplifier
p pico- (10^{-12})
pA picoampere
pam pulse-amplitude modulation
pcm pulse-code modulation
pep peak envelope power
pF picofarad
piv peak inverse voltage
p-m phase modulation; permanent magnet
pnp positive-negative-positive
p-p peak-to-peak
ppi plan position indicator
ppm pulse per minute
pps pulse per second
preamp preamplifier
prf pulse repetition frequency
prr pulse repetition rate
psc permanent split capacitor
pW picowatt
pwm pulse-width modulation
R resistance; resistor
RCTL resistor-capacitor-transistor logic
RDTL resistor-diode-transistor logic
r-f radio frequency
rfi radio frequency interference
rms root-mean-square
rpm revolutions per minute
RTL resistor-transistor logic
sbs silicon bilateral switch
scope oscilloscope
scr silicon controlled rectifier
scs silicon controlled switch
s second
s/n signal-to-noise
spdt single-pole double-throw
sq cm square centimeter
ssb single-sideband
ssl solid-state lamp
sus silicon unilateral switch
s-w short-wave
sync synchronizing
T tera- (10^{12})
td tunnel diode
t-r transmit-receive
triac triode a-c switch
TTL transistor-transistor logic
tv television
twt traveling-wave tube
uhf ultrahigh frequency
ujt unijunction transistor
V volt; voltage
VA voltampere
vco voltage-controlled oscillator
vdr voltage-dependent resistor
vfo variable-frequency oscillator
vhf very high frequency
vlf very low frequency
v-o-m volt-ohm-milliammeter
vswr voltage standing wave ratio
vu volume unit
W watt; wattage
Z impedance

ADDRESSES OF ELECTRONICS PUBLICATIONS

CQ, 14 Vanderventer Avenue, Port Washington, L.I., New York 11050

EDN (now *EDN/EEE*), Cahners Publishing Company, 270 St. Paul Street, Denver, Colorado 80206

EEE (now *EDN/EEE*), Cahners Publishing Company, 270 St. Paul Street, Denver, Colorado 80206

Electronic Design, Hayden Publishing Company, 850 Third Avenue, New York, New York 10222

Electronic News, 7 E. 12th Street, New York, New York 10003

Electronic Products, 645 Stewart Avenue, Garden City, New York 11530

Electronics, 330 W. 42d Street, New York, New York 10036

Electronics World, P.O. Box 1093, Flushing, New York 11352

Electronic Technician, 1 East First Street, Duluth, Minnesota 55802

Elementary Electronics, 229 Park Avenue South, New York, New York 10003

IEEE Publications, 345 East 47th Street, New York, New York 10017

Popular Electronics, Ziff-Davis Publishing, 1 Park Ave., New York, New York 10016

QST, 225 Main St., Newington, Connecticut 06111

Radio-Electronics, Boulder, Colorado 80302

CHAPTER 1
Alarm Circuits

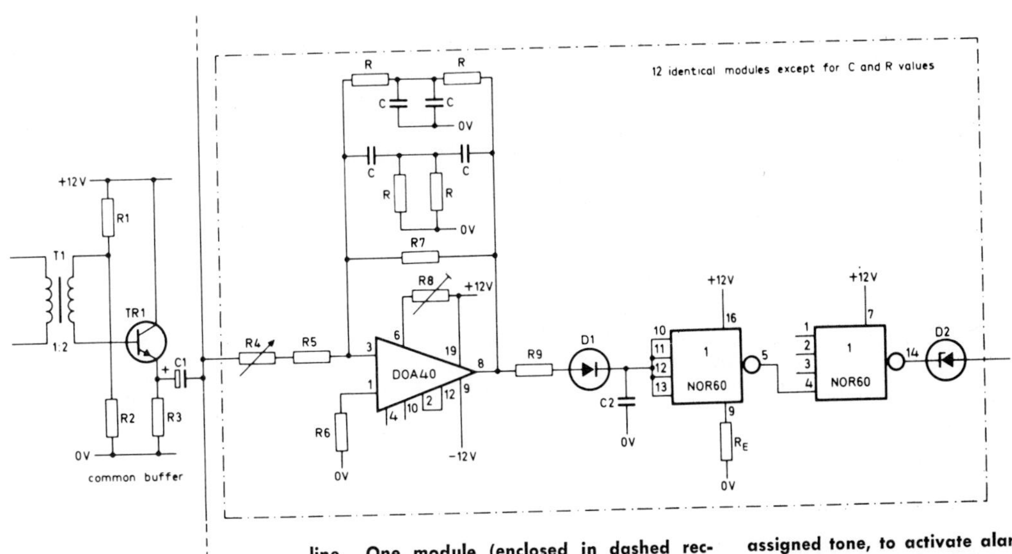

MULTITONE ALARM RECEIVER—Input consists of 12 different audio tones in range from 330 to 2,850 Hz, coming from remote monitoring points over 600-ohm double-core transmission line. One module (enclosed in dashed rectangle) is used for each tone frequency. Report gives values of R and C for the 12 frequencies used. Twin-T network converts Philips DOA40 opamp into selective amplifier that delivers 6.5-V rms output only for its assigned tone, to activate alarm through pair of NOR60 gates connected as Schmitt trigger. —L. J. Lemmens, Single-Line Multitone Transmission for Alarm and Warning Systems, Philips, Pub. Dept., Elcoma Div., Eindhoven, The Netherlands, No. 75.

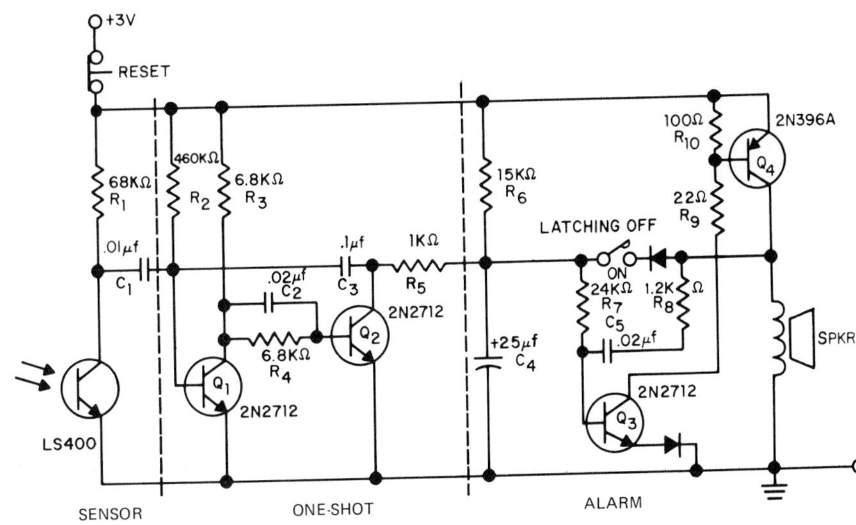

PULSED-LIGHT INTRUSION ALARM RECEIVER—Can be used up to 10 ft away from pulsed-light transmitter. Sounds alarm only if no light pulses reach LS400 phototransistor for predetermined time. One-shot pulse generator stretches received pulses. Alarm consists of 200-Hz audio oscillator Q3-Q4 driving small p-m speaker. Optical filter is not required as long as ambient light is not strong enough to saturate phototransistor. If latching switch is closed, alarm will continue sounding after intruder passes through light beam.—L. M. Hertz, Solid State Lamps—Part II, General Electric, Cleveland, Ohio, No. 3-0121, 1970, p 30.

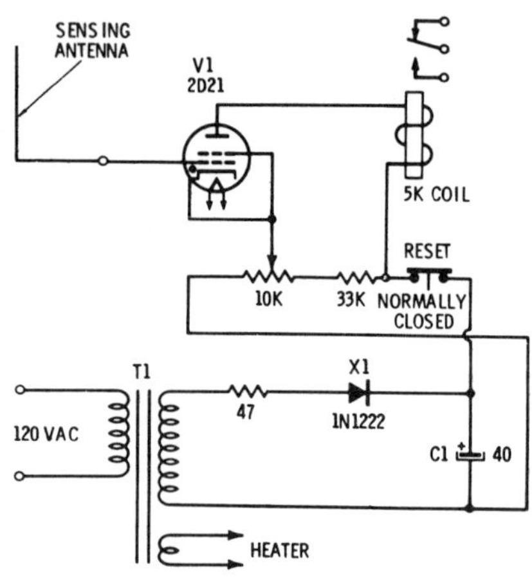

TOUCH SWITCH—Touching of sensing antenna wire with tip of finger is enough to fire 2D21 thyratron and pull in relay that can actuate burglar alarm or close any other circuit.—J. P. Shields, "Novel Electronic Circuits," H. W. Sams & Co., Indianapolis, Ind., 1968, p 78.

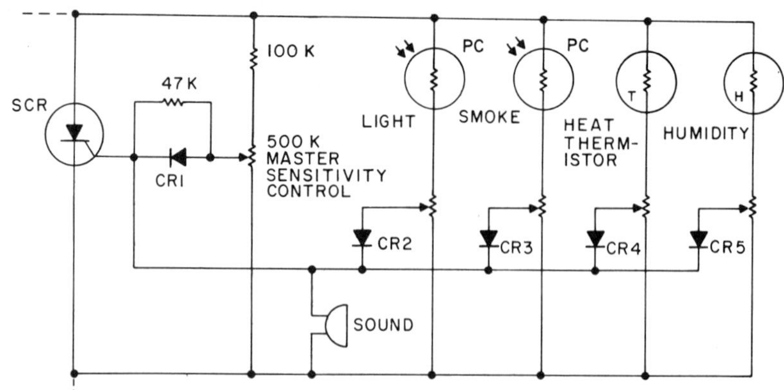

MULTIPLE-SENSOR ALARM—When connected as shown between electrodes of scr in oscillator circuit driving alarm speaker, alarm will respond to flame, smoke, heat, or sound of fire. Response to humidity is optional. Can also be used to wake up bird watchers at sunrise without causing loss of sleep on cloudy days.—"Hobby Manual," General Electric, Owensboro, Ky., 1965, p 127.

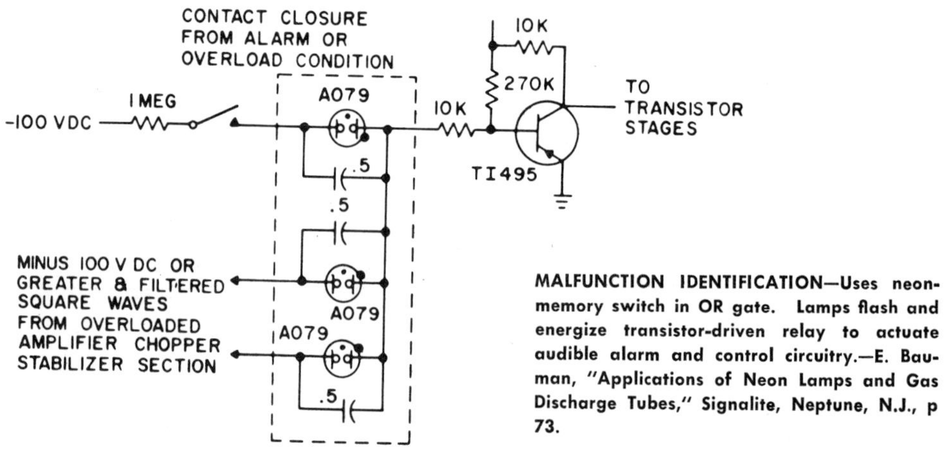

MALFUNCTION IDENTIFICATION—Uses neon-memory switch in OR gate. Lamps flash and energize transistor-driven relay to actuate audible alarm and control circuitry.—E. Bauman, "Applications of Neon Lamps and Gas Discharge Tubes," Signalite, Neptune, N.J., p 73.

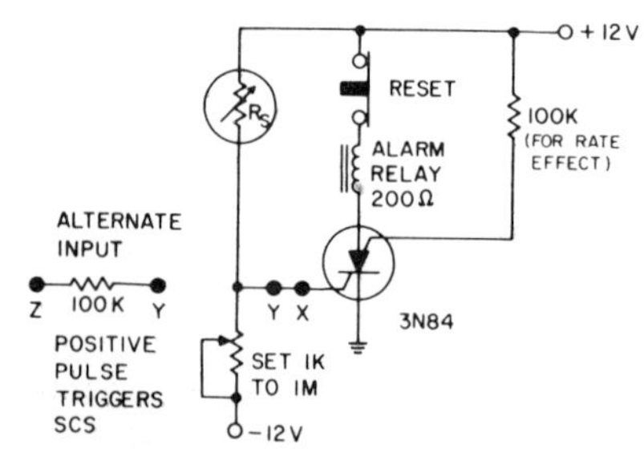

BASIC SCS ALARM—Transducer can be any resistor sensitive to temperature, light, or radiation, up to 1 meg. Alarm is triggered whenever resistance of transducer drops below setting of preset potentiometer. Alternatively, alarm can be triggered by 0.75 V applied to scs through 100K. Interchanging RS and pot gives triggering for increase in transducer resistance.—Planar Silicon Controlled Switch 3N84/3N85, General Electric, Syracuse, N.Y., No. 65.18, 1964.

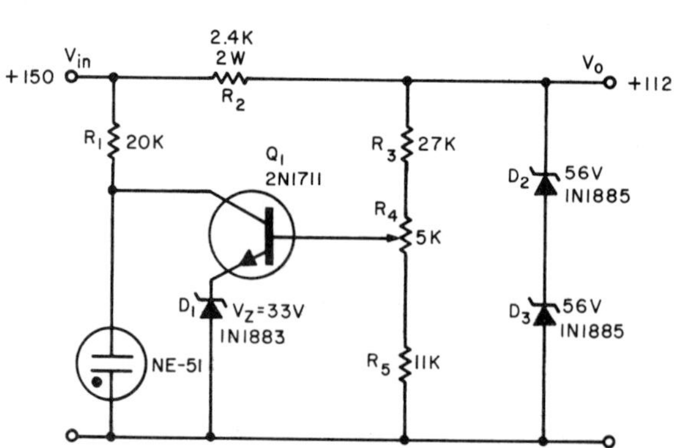

OVERLOAD—Inexpensive overload indicator uses neon lamp, three zeners, and transistor. Neon glows to indicate overload whenever output voltage drops below 112 V. If R4 is properly adjusted, lamp will glow for only 1 V drop.—M. R. Johnson, Overload Indicator Utilizes Inexpensive Neon Bulb, *Electronic Design*, June 8, 1964, p 74–75.

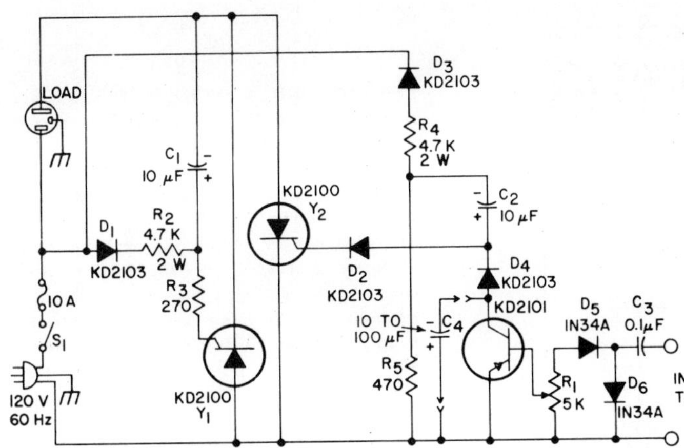

BURGLAR NOISE ALARM—When sound level, as produced by burglar breaking into home or any other cause, exceeds predetermined level set by R1, circuit turns on alarm horn for other load up to 1 kW and keeps it on until sound level drops in monitored area. Input terminals require 1-V audio signal, which requires use of preamplifier or amplifier along with microphone. Circuit becomes self-latching if mike picks up sound of alarm. —"Silicon Controlled Rectifier Experimenter's Manual," RCA, Harrison, N.J., 1967, p 127.

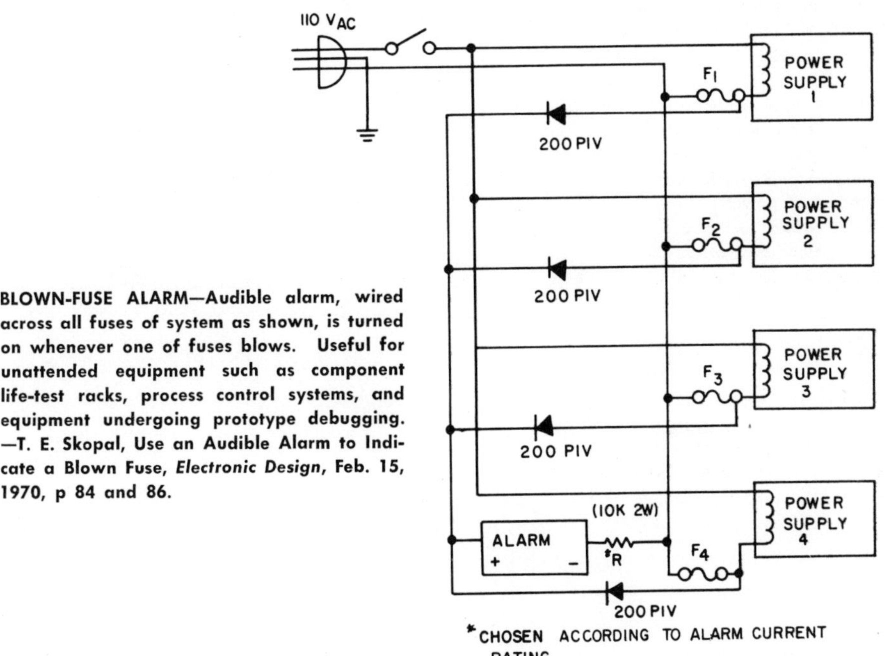

BLOWN-FUSE ALARM—Audible alarm, wired across all fuses of system as shown, is turned on whenever one of fuses blows. Useful for unattended equipment such as component life-test racks, process control systems, and equipment undergoing prototype debugging. —T. E. Skopal, Use an Audible Alarm to Indicate a Blown Fuse, *Electronic Design*, Feb. 15, 1970, p 84 and 86.

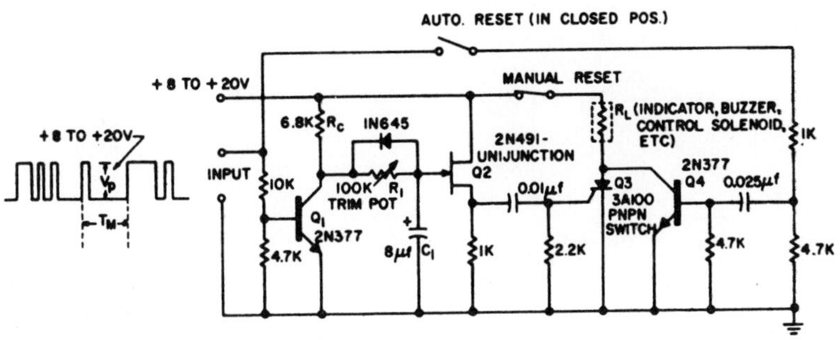

MISSING-PULSE DETECTOR—Circuit actuates indicator, alarm buzzer, or control solenoid when interval between consecutive pulses at input exceeds preset time determined by setting of R1. Has been used to detect misfeed of answer sheet in test-scoring machine and shut off feed before jam occurs. Will also detect momentary dropout longer than preset period, if monitoring d-c line. Reset can be either manual or automatic. Uses diode in ujt timing circuit to provide alternate discharge path without interfering with normal charging cycle of C1. R1 can be set for intervals of 100 ms to 1.5 s.—J. V. McMillin, Versatile Transistorized Alarm Detects Pulse Dropouts, "400 Ideas for Design Selected from Electronic Design," Hayden Book Co., N.Y., 1964, p 113–114.

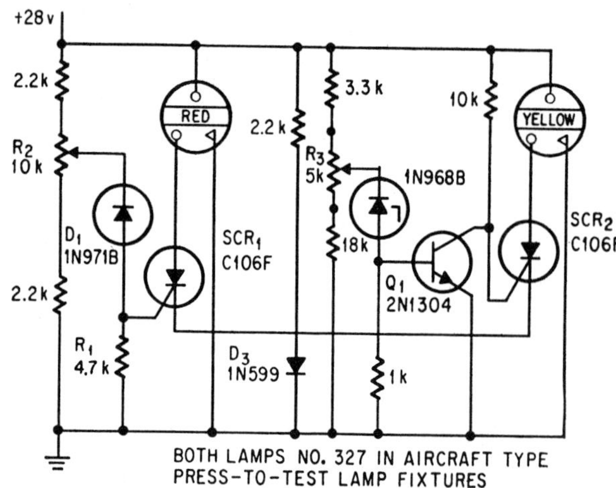

AIRCRAFT D-C OVERVOLTAGE—Red lamp comes on when 28-V supply voltage rises to 32 V because of voltage regulator malfunction, so repairs can be made before aircraft storage battery is damaged. Yellow undervoltage warning lamp comes on when voltage drops below 24 V. With appropriate changes of lamps and semiconductor devices, circuit can monitor voltages up to 600 V.—R. L. Nuckolls III, Warning Lights Monitor D-C Supply Voltage, *Electronics*, Dec. 12, 1966, p 106.

TEMPERATURE ALARM—Will ring bell, turn on lamp, or turn on attic ventilating fan when temperature exceeds predetermined adjustable value in room. Once relay pulls in, alarm cannot be turned off until temperature is reduced or battery switch is opened. If bell or buzzer is operated from battery instead of 12-24 V secondary of bell transformer, alarm becomes independent of power failure. L1 is 7,000 turns No. 38 wound on reed switch.—"Hobby Manual," General Electric, Owensboro, Ky., 1965, p 152.

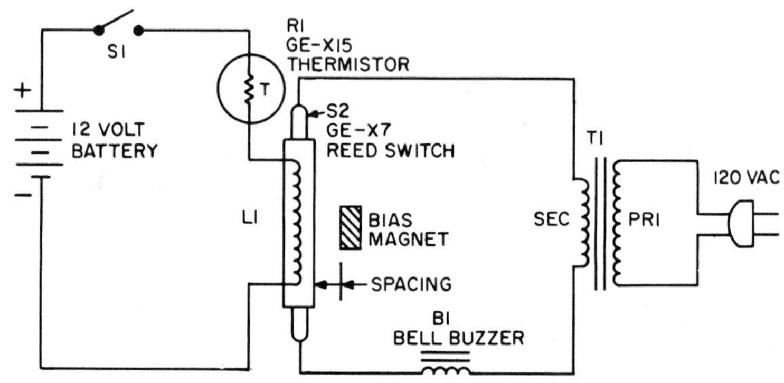

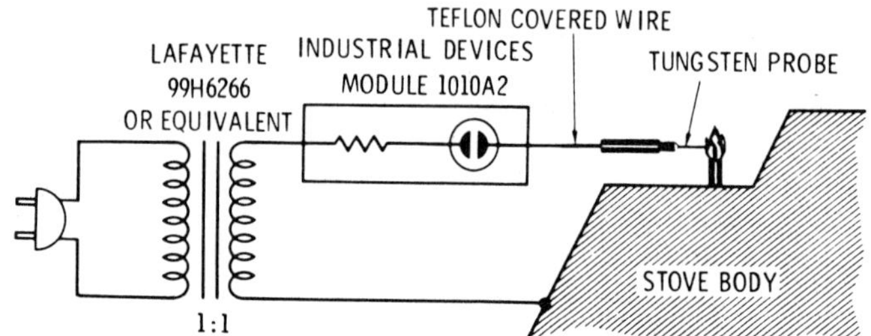

PILOT FLAME MONITOR—Utilizes flame as high-impedance conductor to keep neon lamp lit. When pilot flame goes out, lamp extinguishes.—W. G. Miller, "Using and Understanding Miniature Neon Lamps," H. W. Sams & Co., Indianapolis, Ind., 1969, p 24.

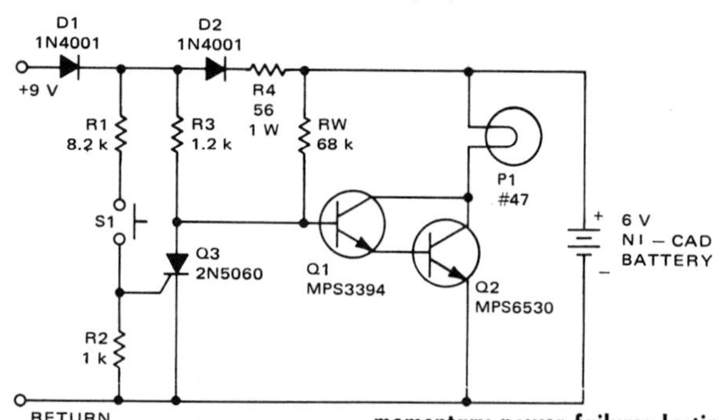

POWER-FAILURE INDICATOR—Lamp comes on whenever 9-V power source fails either because of open or short, and stays on after power is restored, until circuit is reset with S1. Lamp will also come on and stay on for momentary power failures lasting longer than 5-μs recovery time of scr. When circuit is reset, power source will trickle-charge lamp battery to keep it at full charge.—"Semiconductor Power Circuits Handbook," Motorola, Phoenix, Ariz., 1968, p 6–40.

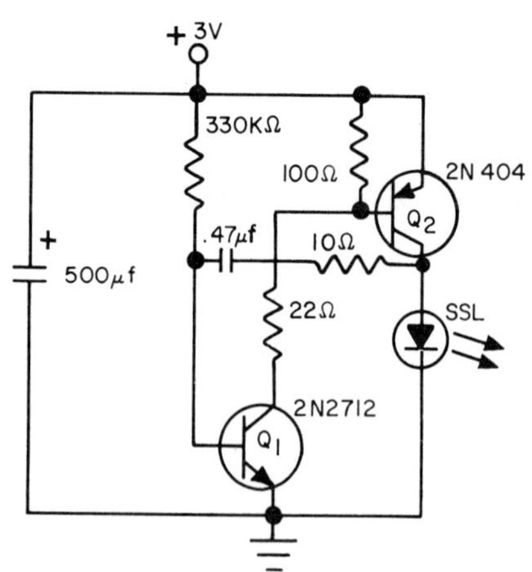

PULSED-LIGHT INTRUSION ALARM TRANSMITTER—Operates from pair of D flashlight cells, drawing only 0.7 mA. Relaxation oscillator applies 1-A current pulses to SSL-4 gallium arsenide lamp at rate of 10 pps. Used with receiver up to 10 feet away, which sounds alarm if no light pulses are received for predetermined time.—L. M. Hertz, Solid State Lamps—Part II, General Electric, Cleveland, Ohio, No. 3-0121, 1970, p 29.

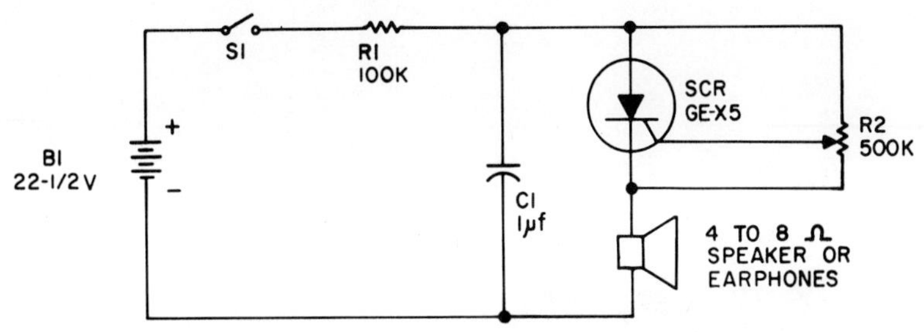

ALARM BOX—Single scr in relaxation oscillator circuit drives speaker to produce series of loud clicks for use as fire, smoke, or intrusion alarm controlled by switch. Setting of R2 determines frequency of clicks.—"Hobby Manual," General Electric, Owensboro, Ky., 1965, p 124.

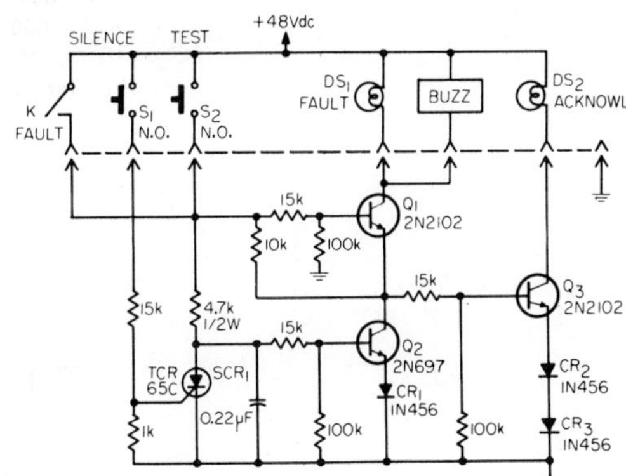

AUDIBLE-VISUAL FAULT ALARM—When fault closes contact K by any means, fault-indicating lamp and buzzer both come on. When silence switch is closed, or when fault is removed, lamp and buzzer go off. ACKNOWLEDGE lamp then comes on only if fault is still present.—R. Breazzano, Fault Alarm Circuit, *EEE*, May 1967, p 180.

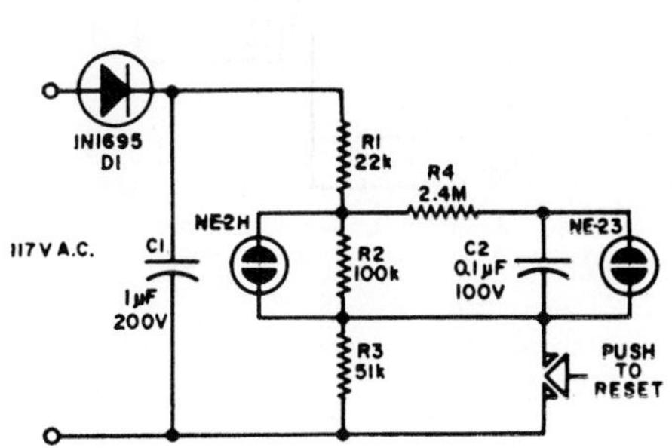

A-C POWER FAILURE—Neon lamp NE-23 begins blinking when a-c line voltage drops below 100 V or power fails, and continues blinking until reset switch is closed. Intended for use with electronic equipment that is left operating unattended for long periods of time. —C. D. Geilker, A. C. Line Voltage Monitor, *Electronics World*, Jan. 1969, p 85.

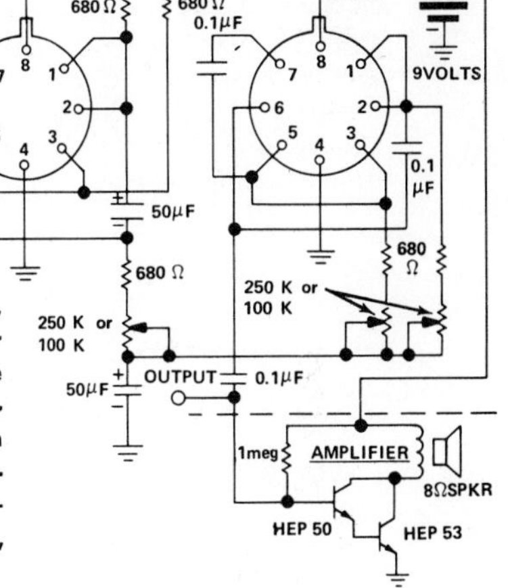

IC SIREN—Can be used for burglar, intrusion, and auto tamper alarms, or as toy siren for bicycles. Potentiometer settings determine type of siren sound obtained. Omit amplifier section (below dashed line) if using siren to feed external audio or p-a amplifier. Operates from 9-V transistor radio battery.—"Tips on Using IC's," HMA-32, Motorola, Phoenix, Ariz., 1968.

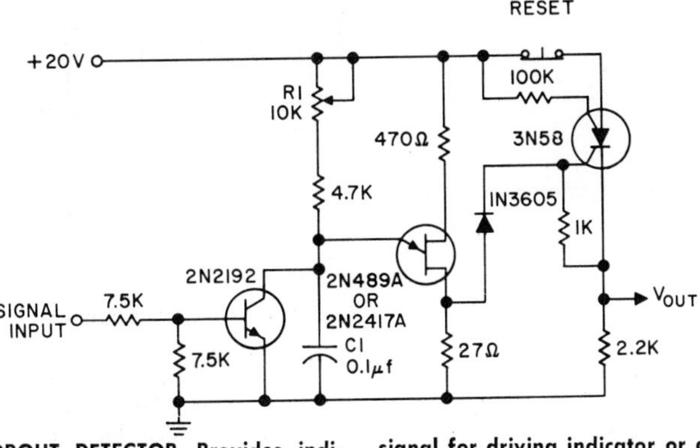

SIGNAL DROPOUT DETECTOR—Provides indication of momentary dropout of d-c, a-c, or pulse input voltage. R1 permits adjusting interval between signal disappearance and triggering of 3N58 scs to give d-c output signal for driving indicator or alarm. Output signal remains until scs is turned off by momentarily opening reset switch.—"Unijunction Circuit Hints," General Electric, Syracuse, N.Y., Fig. 4.

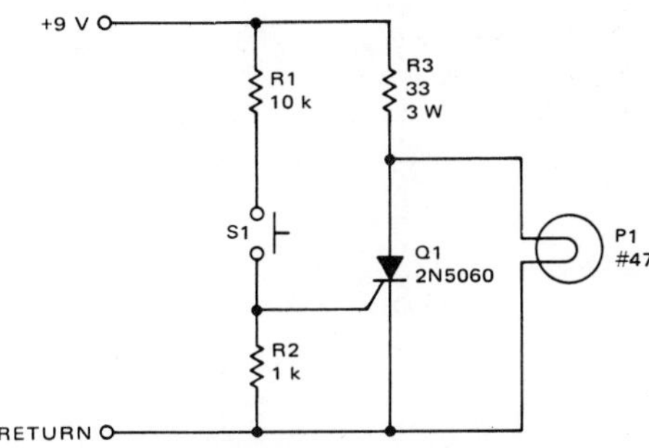

POWER-INTERRUPTION INDICATOR—Lamp glows to indicate momentary interruption of power from source. Closing S1 momentarily turns on scr Q1, which shunts lamp and keeps it off. If power is interrupted longer than 50-μs recovery time of scr, scr will turn off and stay off. When power service is resumed, lamp will come on to indicate there has been an interruption. Switch must then be closed to turn on scr again and turn off lamp.—"Semiconductor Power Circuits Handbook," Motorola, Phoenix, Ariz., 1968, p 6—39.

CHAPTER 2
Amplifier Circuits

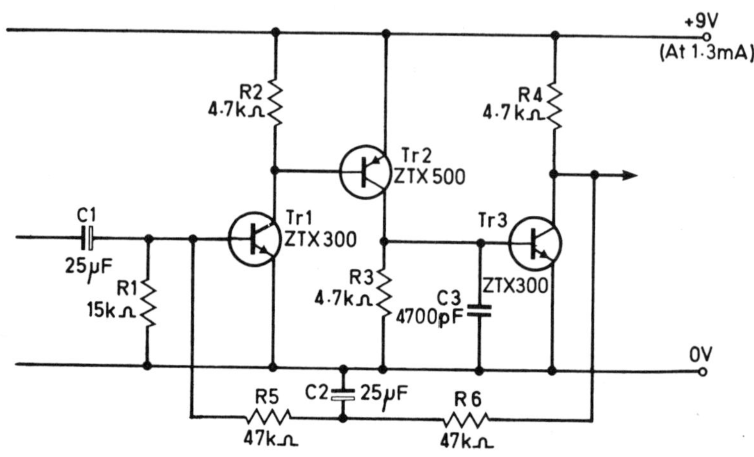

DIRECT-COUPLED RING-OF-THREE—Provides voltage gain of 90 dB, which rises 4.5 dB at 40 Hz and drops 3 dB at 25 kHz. C3 determines high-frequency gain, while low-frequency gain is determined by C1, C2, and source resistance. Complementary transistors give simple circuit.—E-Line Transistor Applications, Ferranti Ltd., Oldham, Lancs., England, 1969, p 49.

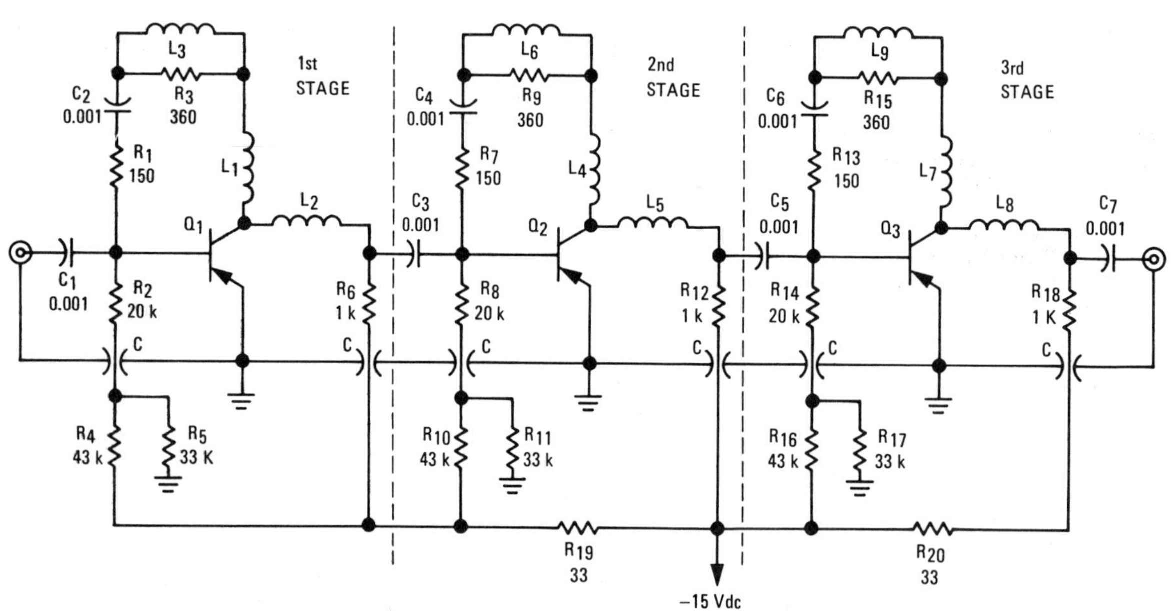

L_1, L_4, & L_7 = 3.5 turns #20 soft-drawn, ID = ¼ inch, Length = 1 inch

L_2, L_5, & L_8 = 6 turns #20 soft-drawn, ID = ¼ inch, Length = ¾ inch

L_3, L_6, & L_9 = 6 turns #24 tinned wire on CF103, Q_3 toroid with teflon sleeve.

C = 500 pF Erie button capacitor with 0.02 μF ceramic disk. - all other capacitors are ceramic disk.

Bandwidth: 3.1 - 405 MHz at 3 dB point

Gain: 31 dB ± 1 dB

Sensitivity: 100 uV $\left(\frac{S+N}{N} = 10 \text{ dB}\right)$

I_C = 5 mA, V_{CE} = 10 Vdc for all devices

400-MHZ BROADBAND—Consists of three identical transistor stages using 2N4957 pnp silicon transistors. Both input and output have 50-ohm terminations. Gain is 30 dB, with 3-dB-down points at 3.1 MHz and 405 MHz. Report gives detailed design procedure based on use of Smith charts.—S. P. Kwok, UHF Broadband Amplifier Design, Motorola, Phoenix, Ariz., No. AN-406, 1967.

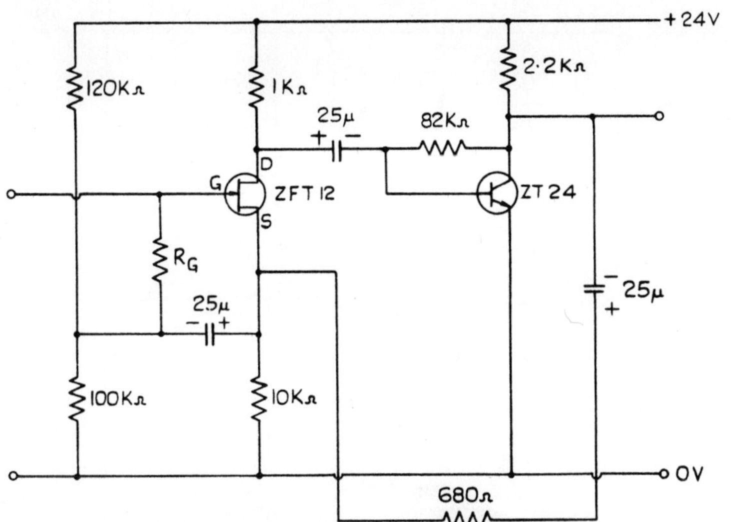

FET WITH NEGATIVE FEEDBACK—First stage is high-input-impedance bootstrapped source follower with drain load, giving gain well below unity. Output is capacitor-coupled to high-gain amplifier stage using conventional bipolar transistor, with almost entire output signal fed back to source of fet. This makes input impedance of complete amplifier much higher than that of fet first stage, while giving over-all unity gain. Input impedance is 65 meg when RG is 1 meg, and 500 meg when RG is 10 meg.—Field Effect Transistors and Applications, Ferranti Ltd., Oldham, Lancs., England, No. 22, 1965.

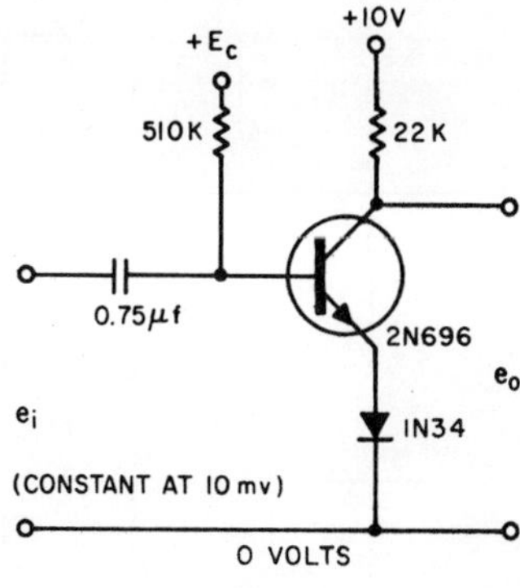

VARIABLE GAIN—Voltage-controlled common-emitter amplifier can be used for remote adjustment of gain, amplitude modulation of wideband signals, and avc. Control voltage range of 6 V for Ec provides 40-dB change in voltage gain, independently of frequency from 100 Hz to beyond 100 kHz. Action is based on use of diode in place of emitter resistor.—M. L. Patterson, Amplifier Provides Voltage-Controlled Gain, *Electronic Design*, Nov. 23, 1964, p 60.

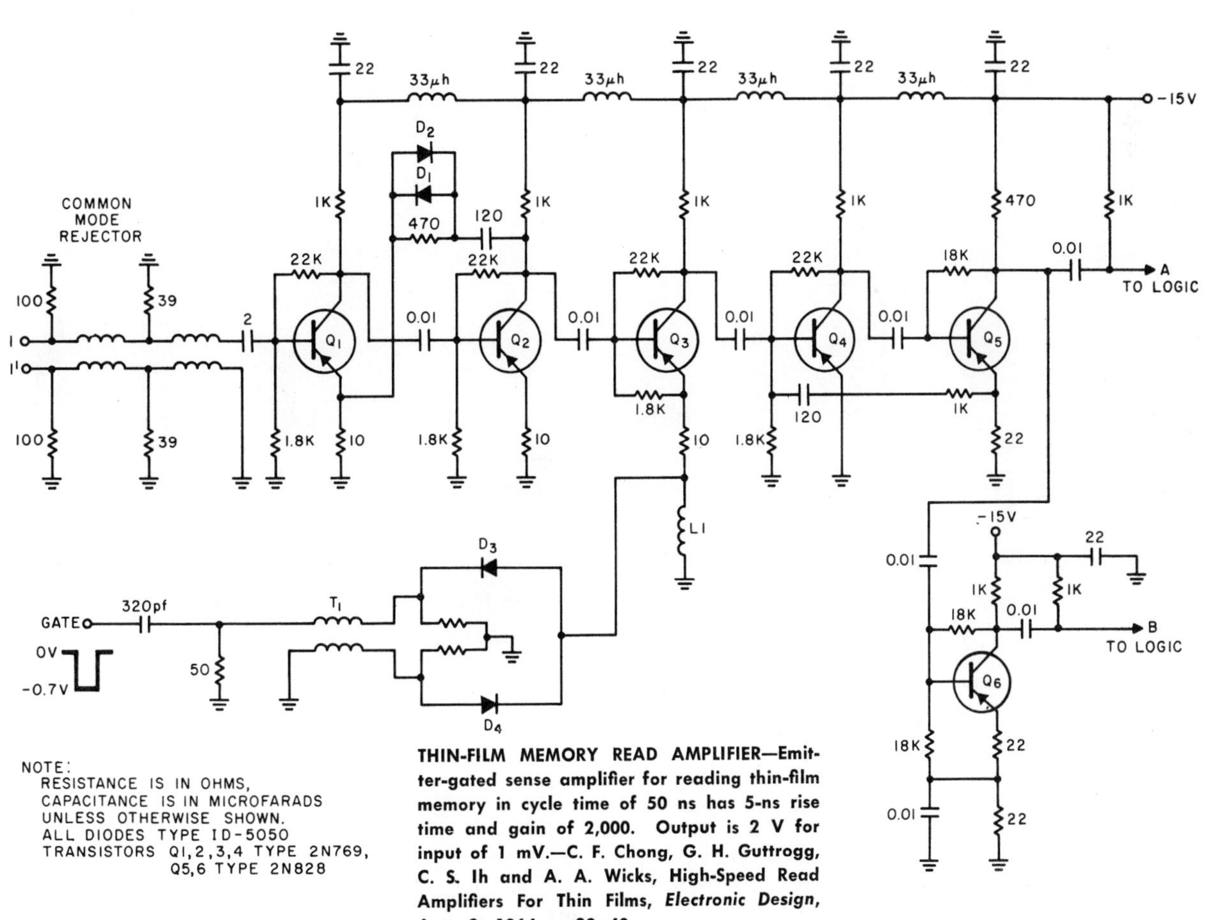

THIN-FILM MEMORY READ AMPLIFIER—Emitter-gated sense amplifier for reading thin-film memory in cycle time of 50 ns has 5-ns rise time and gain of 2,000. Output is 2 V for input of 1 mV.—C. F. Chong, G. H. Guttrogg, C. S. Ih and A. A. Wicks, High-Speed Read Amplifiers For Thin Films, *Electronic Design*, Aug. 3, 1964, p 38–40.

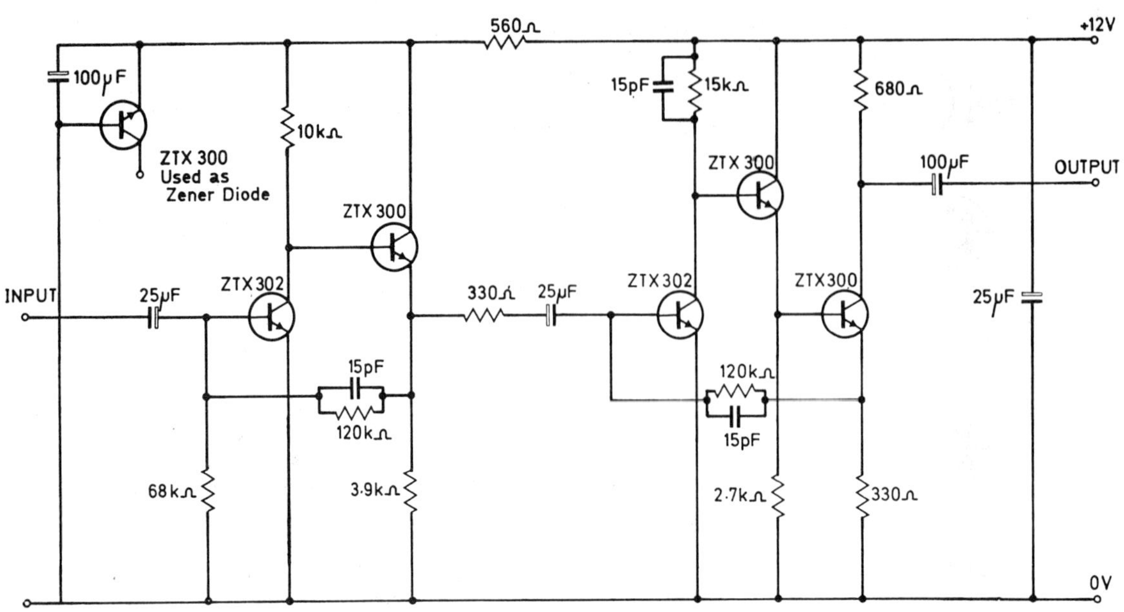

20 HZ—150 KHZ—Provides power gain of 86 dB, with p-p noise below 10 μV referred to input. Developed for use in balanced chopper amplifier of microammeter.—E-Line Transistor Applications, Ferranti Ltd., Oldham, Lancs., England, 1969, p 47.

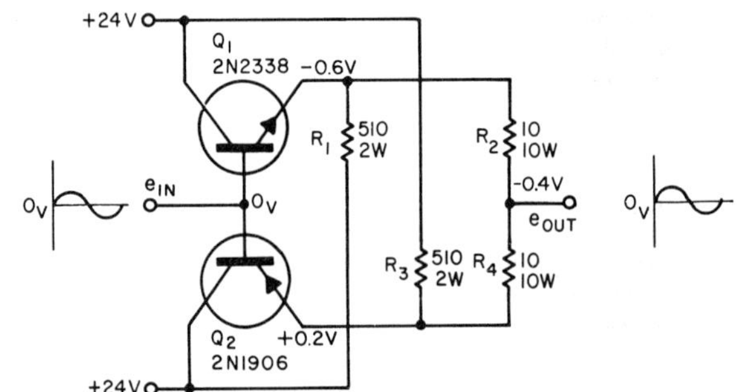

COMPLEMENTARY PUSH-PULL—Simple push-pull emitter-follower with single input gives high drive power, symmetrical around 0 V, with very low quiescent power.—R. Zane, Single-Ended Input Provides Push-Pull Output, *Electronic Design*, July 20, 1964, p 77.

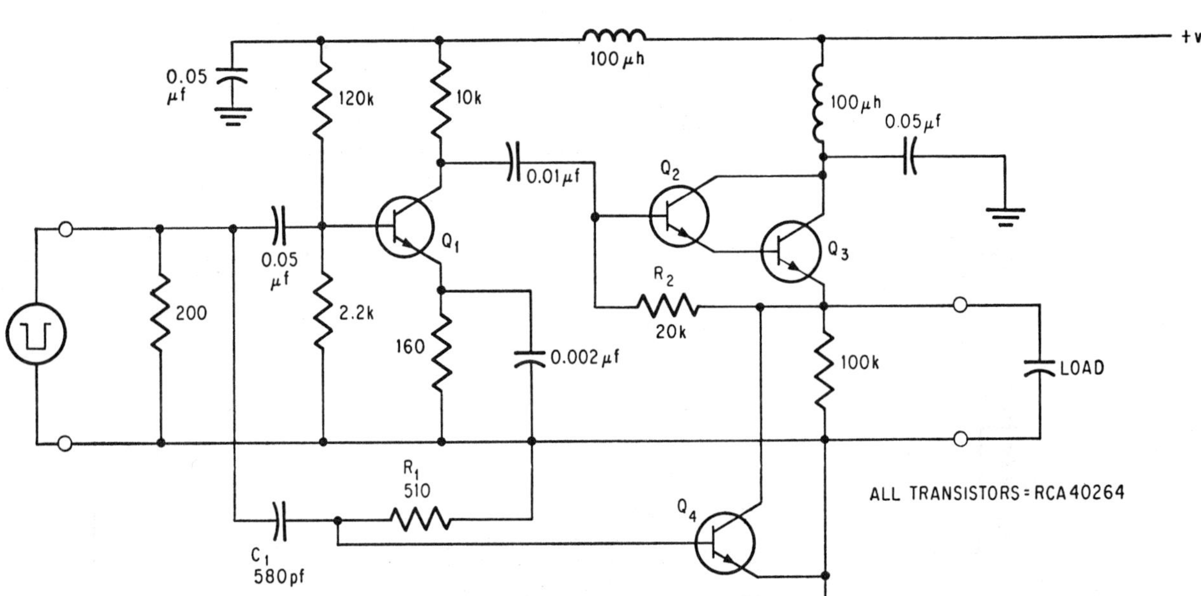

SPIKES INTO CAPACITIVE LOAD—Delivers train of high-voltage high-duty-cycle pulses to capacitive load, with low output impedance for transferring charge rapidly to and from load. Common-emitter amplifier Q1 drives Darlington Q2-Q3. Output impedance is controlled by R1-C1 connected across input and by Q4 shunting load.—D. Perlman, NPN Amplifier Delivers Fast, High-Voltage Pulses, *Electronics*, June 26, 1967, p 109–110.

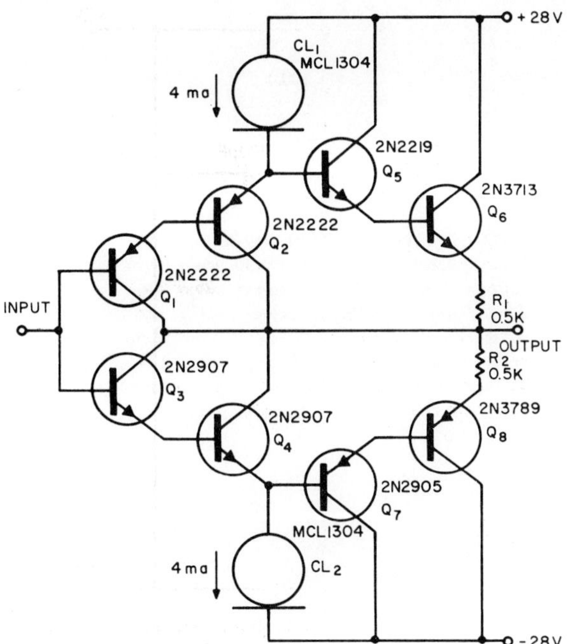

UNITY-GAIN BALANCED AMPLIFIER—Uses field-effect constant-current-source diodes CL1 and CL2 for full temperature compensation, minimum crossover distortion, and unity gain. Can handle signal peaks nearly equal to supply voltages, or 40 V p-p into 5-ohm load. Input impedance at low frequencies is above 1 meg. Can be used to increase power of opamp, either inside or outside feedback loop.—C. F. Andren, Symmetry Amplifier Compensated by FET Current-Source Diodes, *Electronic Design*, Oct. 25, 1965, p 70.

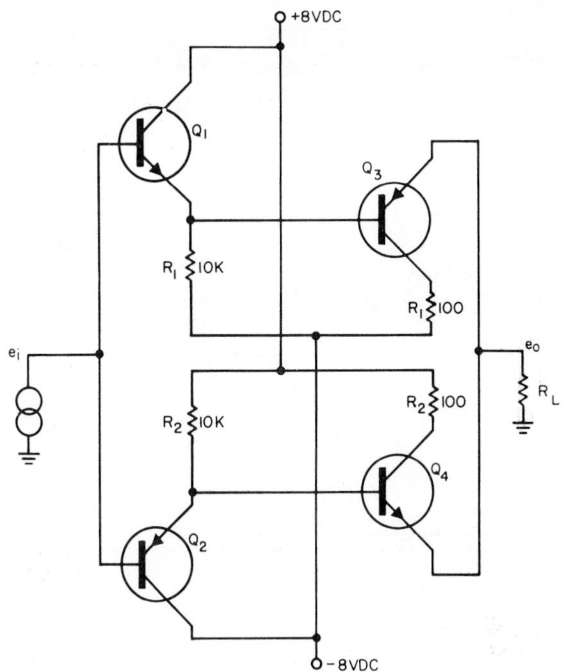

DUAL-FOLLOWER—Use of additional complementary pair of transistors in place of balanced diodes in dual emitter-follower gives increased input impedance and higher current gain while eliminating crossover distortion problem. No trimming adjustment is needed. 100-ohm resistors provide overload protection by limiting short-circuit current.—J. P. Chidester, Complementary Dual-Follower Increases Input Impedance, *Electronic Design*, Nov. 8, 1965, p 58–59.

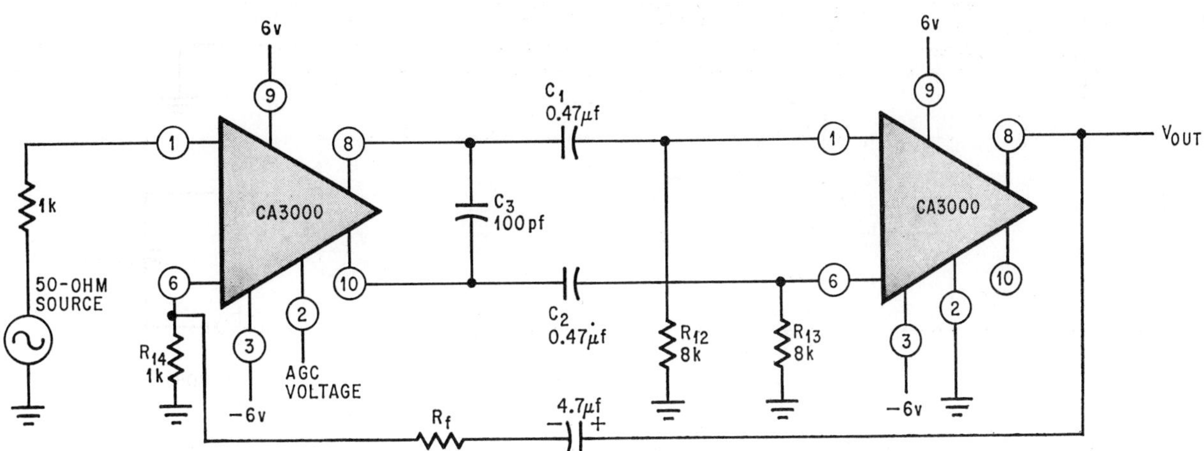

62 DB GAIN WITH IC PAIR—Uses two RCA IC video amplifiers, the first connected as a double-ended differential amplifier and the other single-ended, with R-C interconnecting network for frequency-shaping. Low-frequency rolloff starts at 22 Hz and high-frequency rolloff at 1 MHz. Can be adapted for agc. Bandwidth can be increased by changing feedback to reduce gain.—J. P. Keller, Linear IC's: Part 3—Differential Amplifiers At Work, *Electronics*, Sept. 18, 1967, p 96–104.

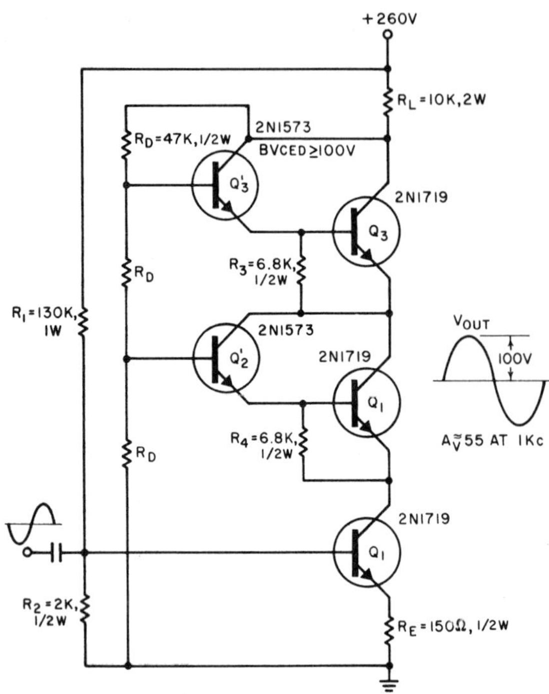

LINEAR DARLINGTON—Uses low-cost Darlington-connected series transistors in linear high-voltage amplifier. Arrangement gives high current gain and good power, along with satisfactory voltage division for transistors during quiescence.—V. Glover, Using Low-Voltage Transistors in High-Voltage Circuits, *Electronic Design*, July 20, 1964, p 62–67.

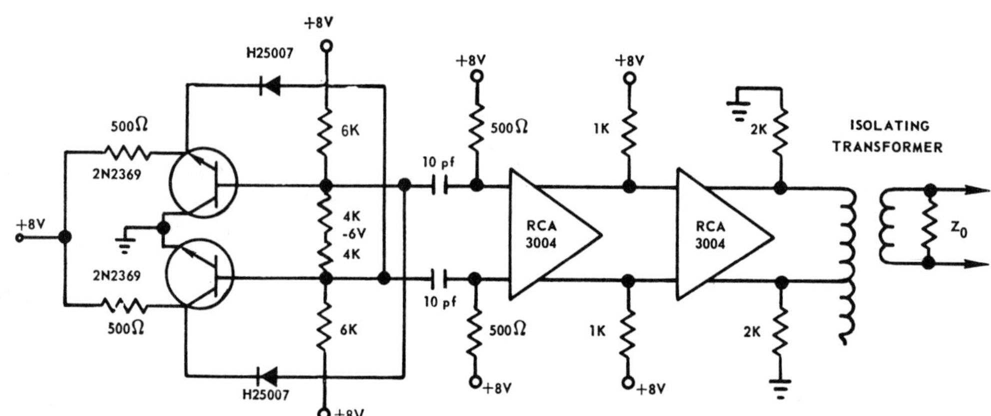

SENSE AMPLIFIER—Used in high-speed read-only memory of computer, in which information is stored by means of mutual inductive coupling between two concentric solenoids. Winding pattern determines points at which read and sense wires meet as solenoid pair for storing information pattern. Circuit also includes output latch.—Y. Hsia, Solenoid-Coupled READ-ONLY Memory, *IEEE Transactions on Electronic Computers*, June 1970, p 344–350.

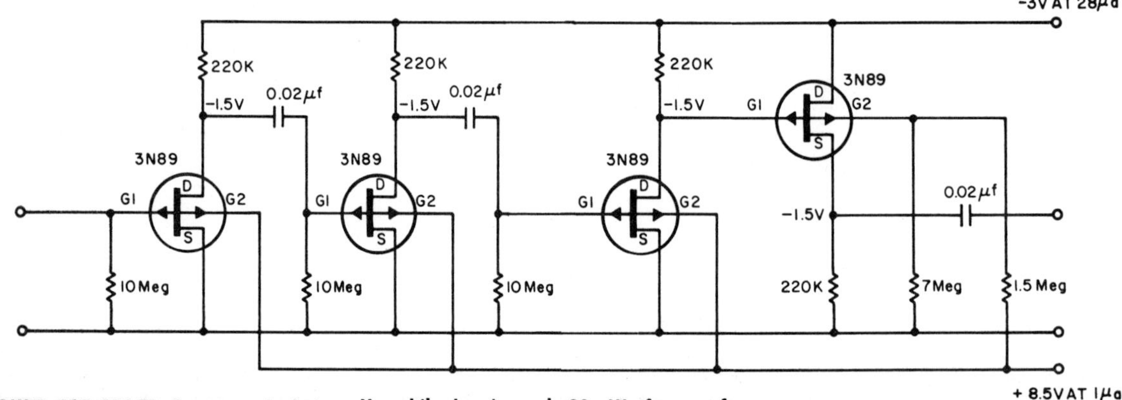

MICROPOWER FOR SPACE—Four tetrode fet's provide voltage gain of over 1,000 and 0.5 V rms output over bandwidth of 1 to 30,000 Hz, while drawing only 90 μW of power from spacecraft supply.—J. S. Sherwin, Need High Z and Low C? Turn to the Tetrode FET for HF Design, *Electronic Design*, June 7, 1965, p 20–25.

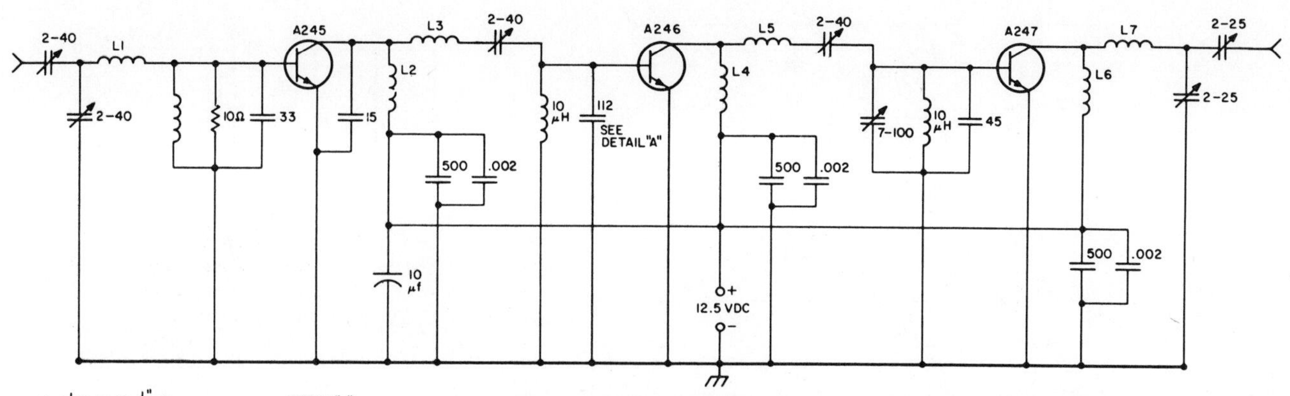

L1 – $1\frac{1}{2}$T, NO.16, $\frac{1}{4}$" I.D.
L2,L3 – $3\frac{1}{2}$T, NO.16, $\frac{1}{4}$" I.D.
L4,L5 – $4\frac{1}{2}$T, NO.16, $\frac{1}{4}$" I.D.
L6 – $3\frac{1}{2}$T, NO.16, $\frac{1}{4}$" I.D.
L7 – 2T, NO.14, $\frac{1}{4}$" I.D.
10μH – MILLER NO.9330-24

DETAIL "A"
A246
56
E
B
C
56
E

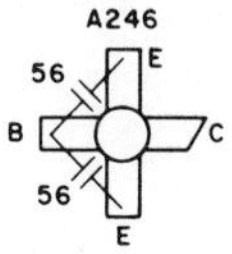

25-W THREE-TRANSISTOR POWER AMP—Provides excellent stability and minimum of harmonic and unwanted signal components, with bandwidth of 20 MHz. Power output increases about 8% at low end of 150–175 MHz mobile band. Drive power required is 100 mW. Requires 50-ohm load.—Two 175 MHz 12.5 Volt Mobile Communication Power Amplifiers for 25W and 40W Power Output, Amperex, Slatersville, R.I., No. S-140, 8/68.

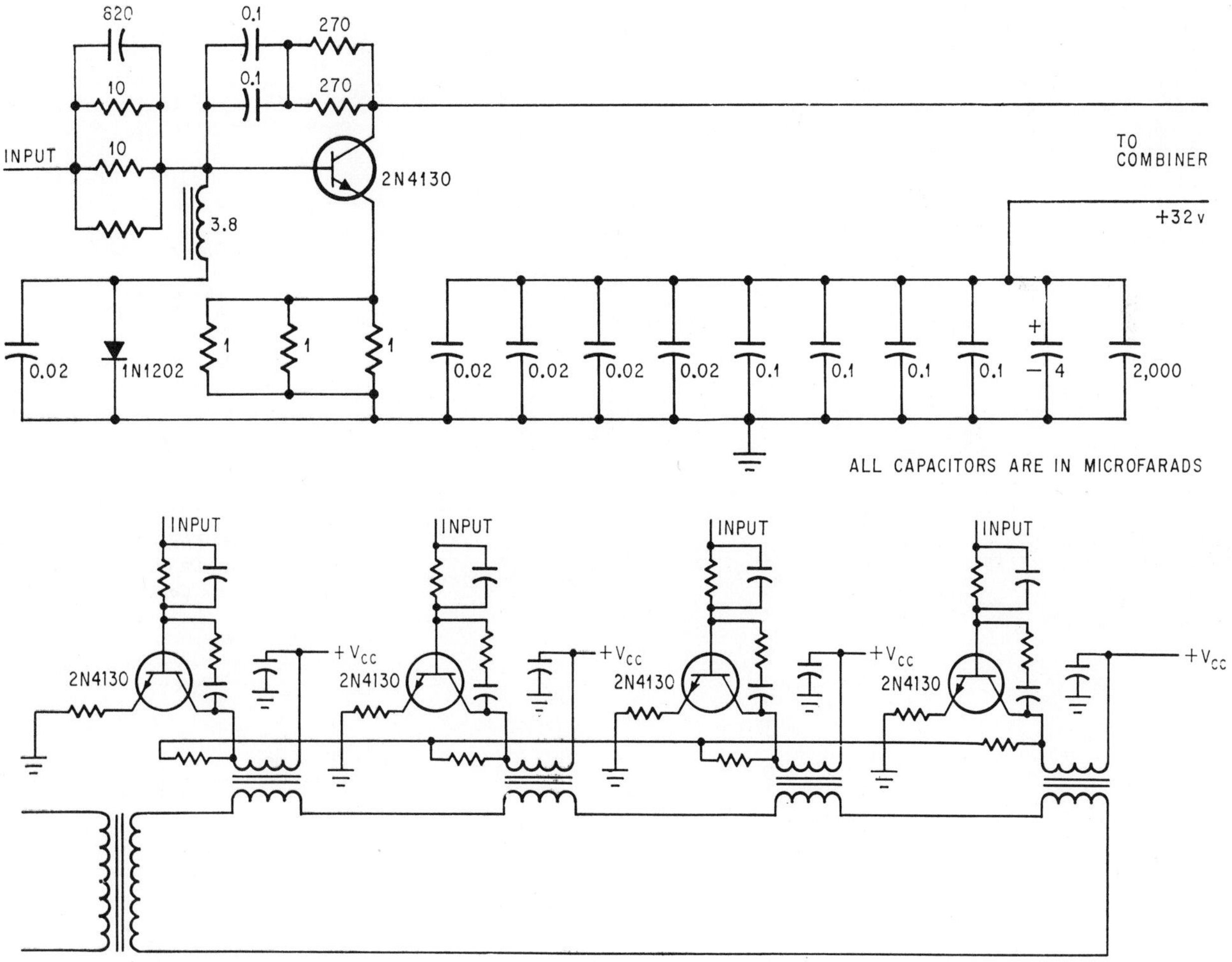

ALL CAPACITORS ARE IN MICROFARADS

1 KW FROM 60 TRANSISTORS—Circuit developed by Westinghouse under Air Force contract, for use in communication systems, keeps transistors electrically isolated so outputs can be paralleled. With input drive as low as 0.25 W, peak envelope power output is 1 kW for bandwidth of 2 to 32 MHz. Basic four-transistor module consists of four 2N4130 IT&T transistors each connected as in upper circuit, with their outputs combined by transformers as in lower circuit to form module that can in turn be paralleled with similar modules to give desired power output. Resulting power output amplifier can be tuned as single unit.—C. H. Wood Jr., A. W. Morse, and G. R. Brainerd, Transistors Share the Load in a Kilowatt Amplifier, *Electronics*, Dec. 11, 1967, p 100–105.

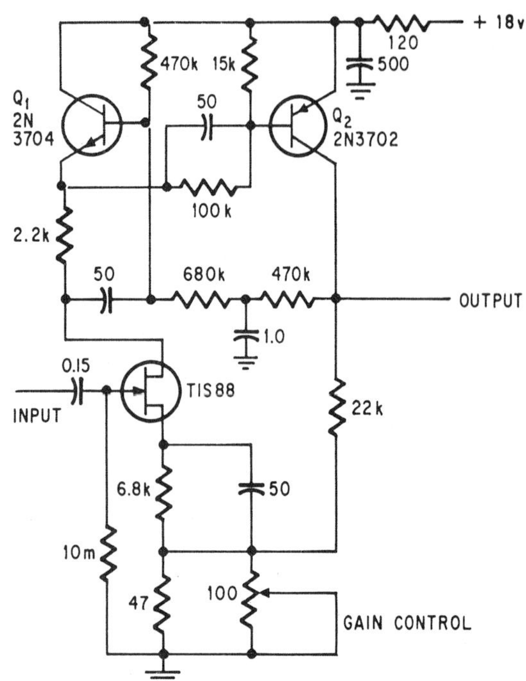

0.5 HZ TO 300 KHZ—Fet and only two other transistors give wide bandwidth and gain of 1,000, with low distortion. Npn stage Q1 controls fet. Stabilization is achieved with 20 dB negative feedback. Input impedance is 10 meg at 1 kHz and output impedance 2K. Current drain is about 1.5 mA. All capacitor values are μF.—T. C. Penn, High-Precision Preamp Built from 3 Transistors, *Electronics*, Dec. 23, 1968, p 58.

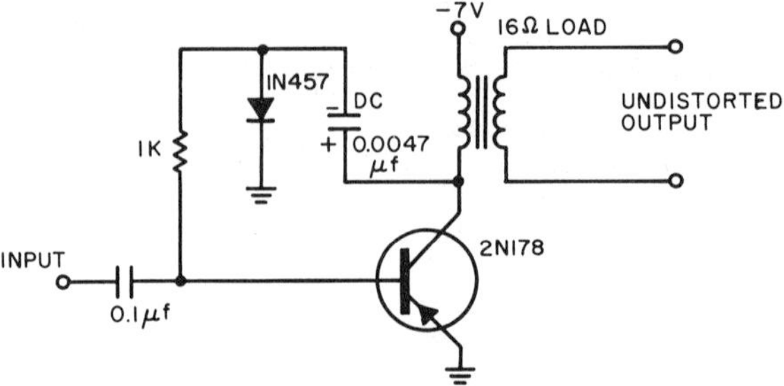

DISTORTIONLESS CLASS A—Self-generated bias voltage, developed by capacitor charging through diode, is proportional to input signal. Permits use of single-transistor output stage, with low d-c drain on battery through transformer primary.—C. G. Dorn, Capacitor Charge Sets Transistor Bias Point, *Electronic Design*, March 16, 1964, p 105.

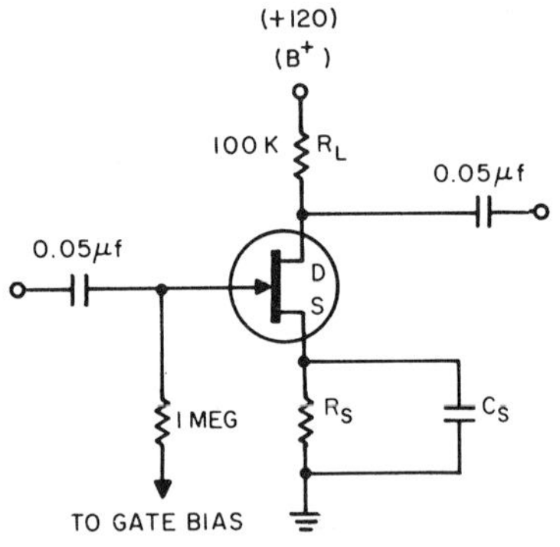

SELF-BIASING FOR FET—Voltage drop produced by drain current through RS serves as gate bias. Value of CS is chosen to prevent feedback at signal frequencies. Article discusses stabilization achieved with self-bias, and other design procedures for improving fet performance in linear voltage amplifiers. —W. A. Rheinfelder, FETs Outperform Bipolars, Pentodes in Linear Voltage Amplifiers, *Electronic Design*, Dec. 20, 1965, p 24–26 and 28–29.

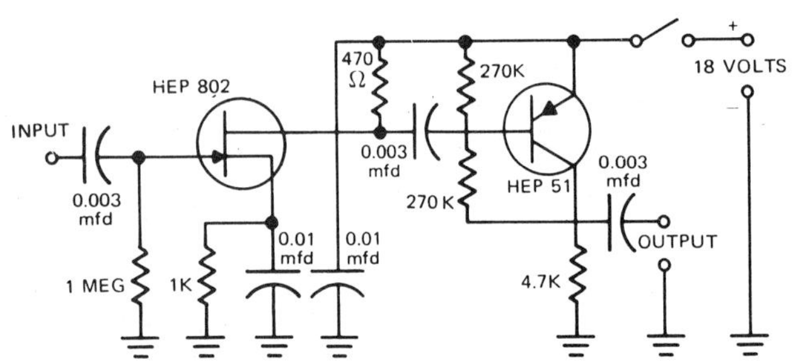

BROADBAND R-F FET—Covers range of 1–40 MHz with high s/n ratio, using two 9-V batteries in series. Gain drops from 100 at 1 MHz to about 20 at 40 MHz.—"Tips on Using FET's," HMA-33, Motorola, Phoenix, Ariz., 1969.

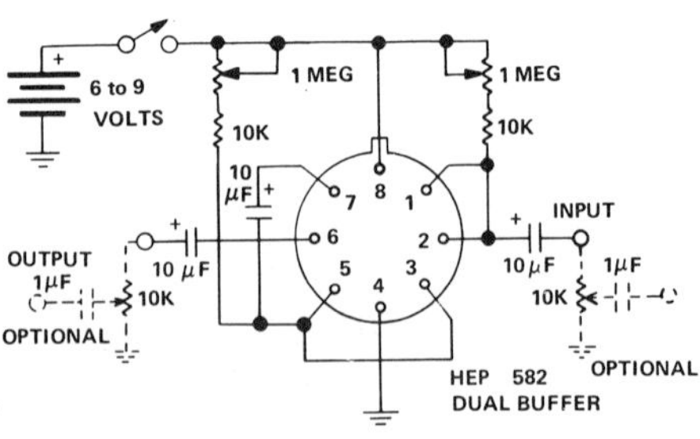

HIGH-GAIN IC—Takes input of 0.4 mV p-p and gives output of 2.5-6 V p-p for use as audio or low-frequency r-f amplifier or as preamp to increase cro sensitivity. Gain is 5,000 to 10,000. Adjust 1-meg pots for maximum undistorted output. May also be used with HEP580 2-input gate IC, using 1-meg resistors in place of 1-meg pots in series with 10K.—"Tips on Using IC's," Motorola, Phoenix, Ariz., HMA-32, 1968.

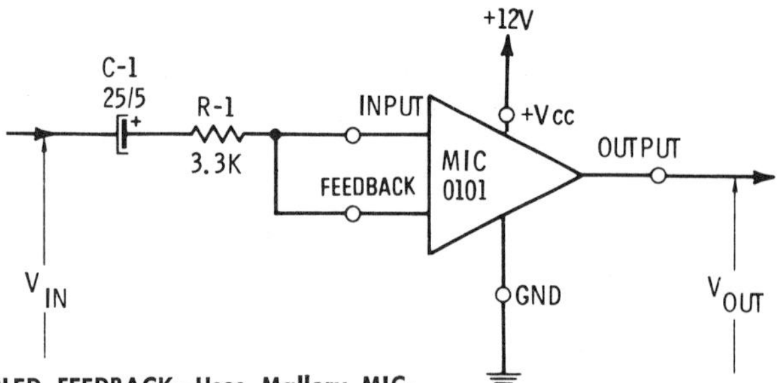

R-C COUPLED FEEDBACK—Uses Mallory MIC-0101 preamp with feedback terminal open with respect to a-c ground but returned to IC input terminal to maintain correct d-c bias. Feedback extends 3-dB bandwidth to almost 3 MHz and down to 10 Hz, but at sacrifice of voltage gain. With 3.3K feedback resistor, overall gain is 100 or 40 dB. Can be used as low-level video amplifier where source is either video tape head or another amplifier. —M. L. Deschler, Integrated Circuit Preamplifiers, Mallory, Indianapolis, Ind., APPN-2, 1968.

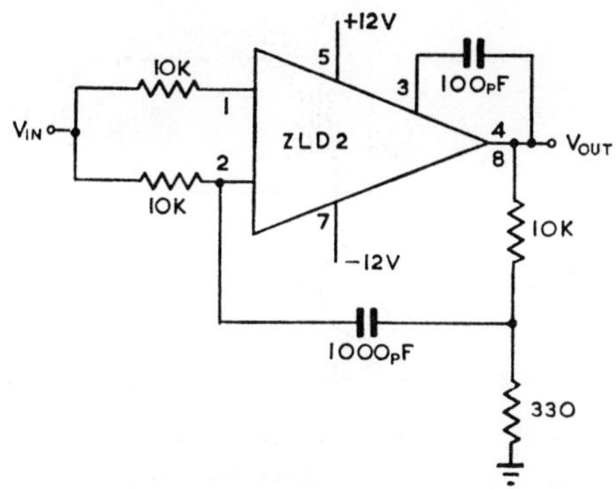

NONINVERTING WIDEBAND—Gives high input impedance, but is direct coupled and signal source must supply necessary base current for Ferranti ZLD2 IC differential-input d-c amplifier. Gain is 3 dB down at 220 Hz and 600 kHz.—Microlin Amplifiers ZLD2S and ZLD2T, Ferranti Ltd., Oldham, Lancs., England, No. 11, 1967.

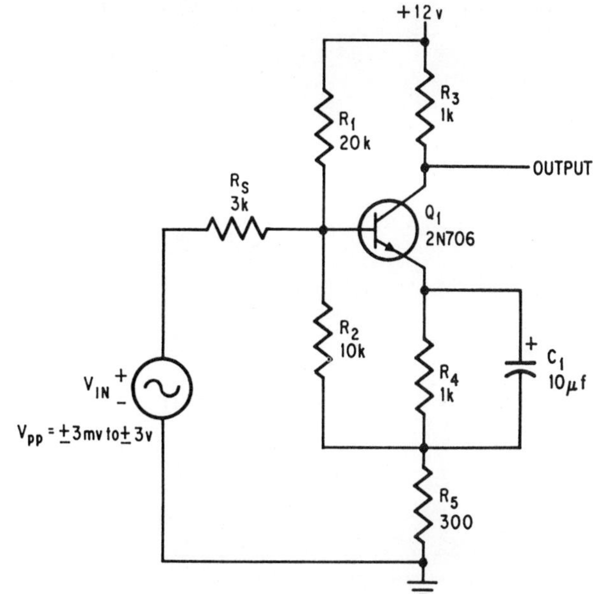

BOOTSTRAPPING—Combining positive and negative feedback in bootstrap amplifier gives both high input impedance and high voltage gain. Bootstrapping resistor R2 provides positive feedback. Article gives design equations.—G. P. Klein, Combined Feedback Builds Gain and Input Impedance, *Electronics*, Oct. 16, 1967, p 99.

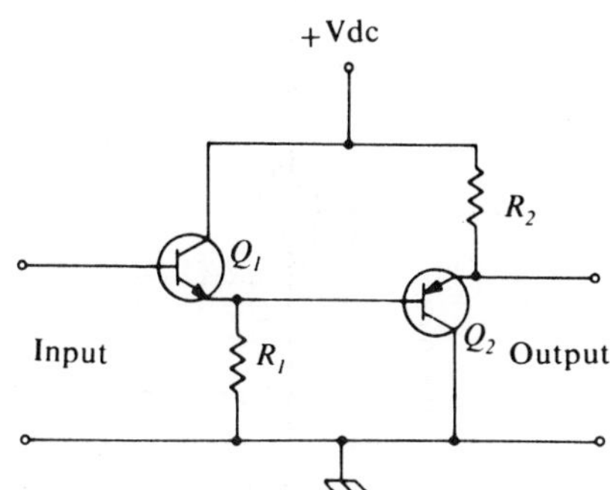

TEMPERATURE-STABLE EMITTER-FOLLOWER—With 2N780 for Q1 and 2N869 for Q2, average variation in output voltage will be only about 25 mV for temperature range of −20 to 200 F when R1 and R2 are 20K.—"Selected Electronic Circuitry," NASA SP-5046, 1966, Government Printing Office, Washington, D.C., p 65.

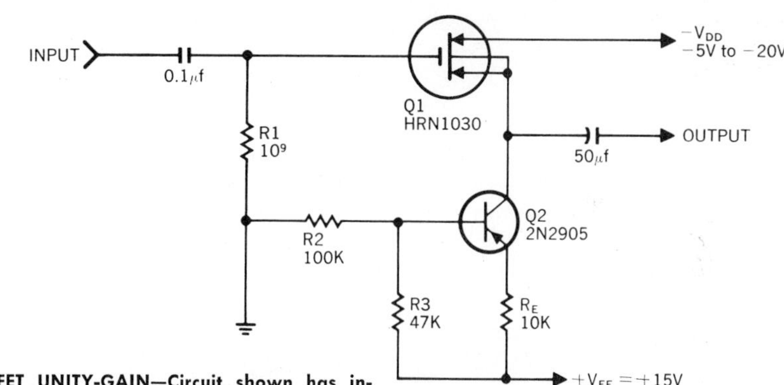

MOSFET UNITY-GAIN—Circuit shown has input impedance above 1,000 meg. Mosfet functions as source follower with constant-current generator instead of source resistance. —C. R. Perkins, "Application of MOSFET Devices to Electronic Circuits," Hughes, Newport Beach, Cal., 1968, p 10.

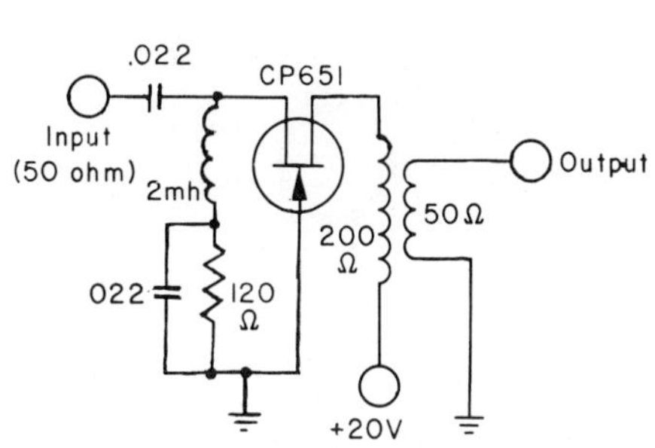

BROADBAND FET PREAMP—Gives bandwidth of 0.5 to 40 MHz for maximum input signal of 3 V p-p. Voltage gain is 10 dB, and dynamic range 140 dB.—FET Broadband R. F. Preamplifiers, Crystalonics, Cambridge, Mass., TMF1.

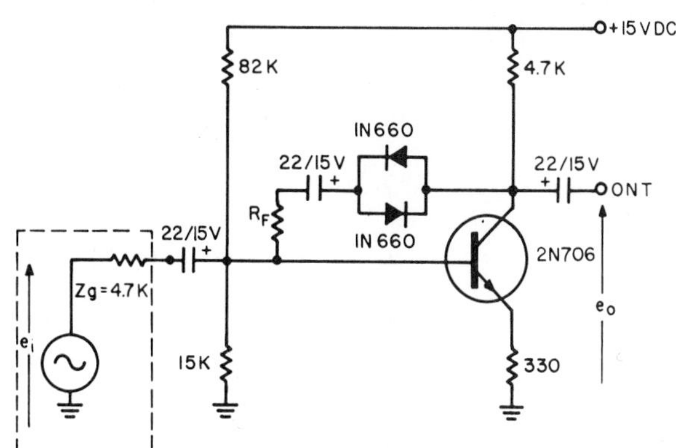

NONLINEAR GAIN—Diodes in feedback network are biased into conduction when signal excursions exceed 0.6 V p-p, and resulting negative feedback reduces gain of stage. Value of feedback resistor RF determines gain change at levels above break-point; typical values range from 470 to 10,000 ohms. Used to emphasize specific input levels.—J. K. Hickman, Complementary Diode Feedback Produces Nonlinear Gain, *Electronic Design*, June 7, 1965, p 42.

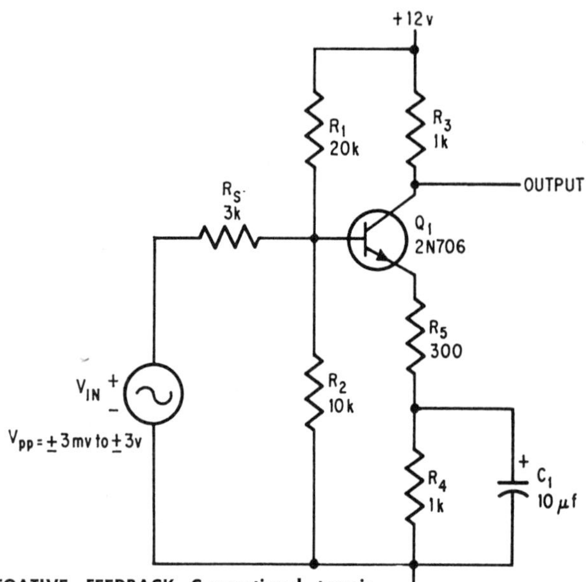

NEGATIVE FEEDBACK—Conventional transistor amplifier circuit shown uses negative feedback by R5 to increase input impedance, but does not give high voltage gain. Article gives design equations and tells how to add positive feedback for higher gain.—G. P. Klein, Combined Feedback Builds Gain and Input Impedance, *Electronics*, Oct. 16, 1967, p 99.

15-MHZ TUNED R-F IC—Designed for use in military receiver covering frequency range of 2 to 30 MHz. Deliberate mismatching gives stability. Total gain is 20 dB, bandwidth is 315 kHz, noise figure at full gain 7.4 dB, and power dissipation is only 1.8 mW. Uses CA3018 four-transistor IC.—"Linear Integrated Circuits," RCA, Harrison, N.J., IC-41, p 312.

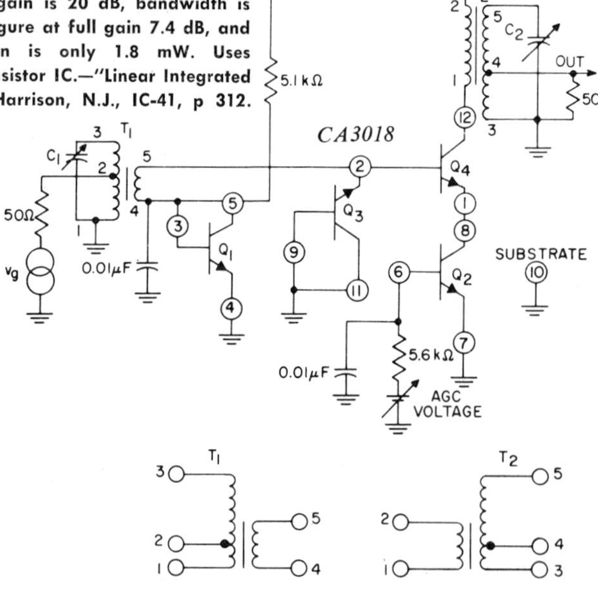

T1	T2
$L = 0.8\ \mu H$	$L = 0.8\ \mu H$
$Q_o = 200$	$Q_o = 200$
$T_{1\text{-}3} = 6T$	$T_{3\text{-}5} = 6T$
$T_{1\text{-}2} = 1T$	$T_{1\text{-}2} = 4T$
$T_{4\text{-}5} = 2T$	$T_{3\text{-}4} = 1T$

#22 wire on Q-2 material, CF107 Toroid from Indiana General.
C_1, C_2 = Arco 425 or equiv.

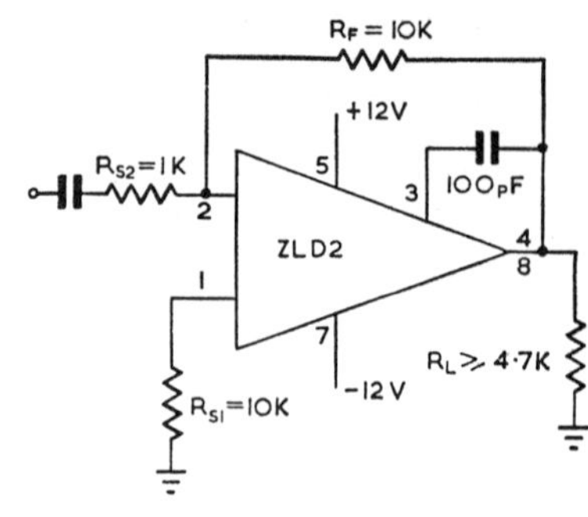

IC INVERTING A-C AMPLIFIER—Uses Ferranti ZLD2 IC differential-input d-c amplifier connected to give gain of 10 with negative feedback. Intended for applications where d-c component is not required, so capacitance coupling is used at input. This unbalances values of RS1 and RS2, for which correction is made by making RS1 equal to RF. Alternatively, RS1 can be 910 ohms and an additional 1K resistor connected between terminal 2 and ground.—Microlin Amplifiers ZLD2S and ZLD2T, Ferranti Ltd., Oldham, Lancs., England, No. 11, 1967.

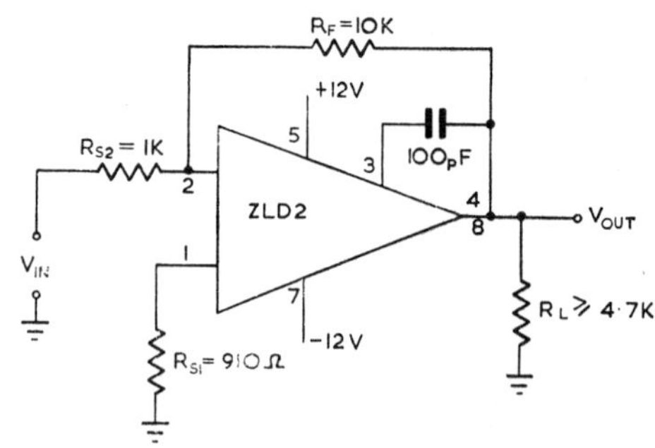

INVERTING A-C OR D-C AMPLIFIER—Uses Ferranti ZLD2 IC differential-input d-c amplifier connected to give gain of 10 with negative feedback. Values shown give bandwidth of 1.5 MHz.—Microlin Amplifiers ZLD2S and ZLD2T, Ferranti Ltd., Oldham, Lancs., England, No. 11, 1967.

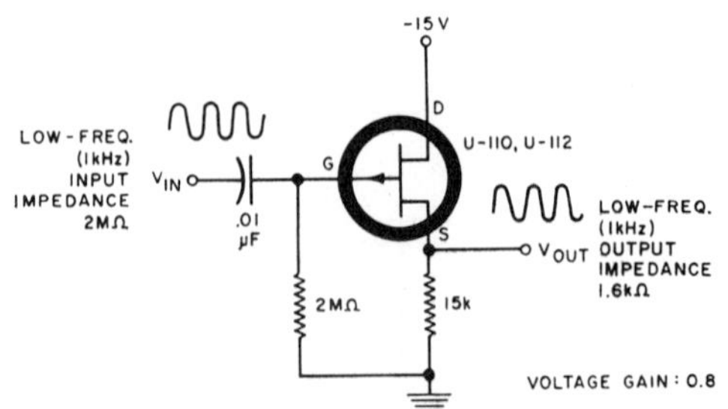

SOURCE-FOLLOWER FET—Circuit is analogous to tube cathode-follower or transistor emitter-follower. Gives high input impedance, relatively low output impedance, and voltage gain close to unity. Frequency response is flat to 1 MHz.—J. H. Wujek, Jr. and M. E. McGee, Field-Effect Transistor Circuits, *Electronics World*, May 1967, p 32–33 and 75.

8-MHZ 3-W AMPLIFIER—Uses pair of BFY50 transistors connected in parallel common-emitter configuration. Power gain is 8.9 dB, efficiency is 61%, and both input and output impedances are 50 ohms.—*Applications of the BFY50, BFY51, and BFY52*, Philips, Pub. Dept., Elcoma Div., Eindhoven, The Netherlands, No. 428, 1965.

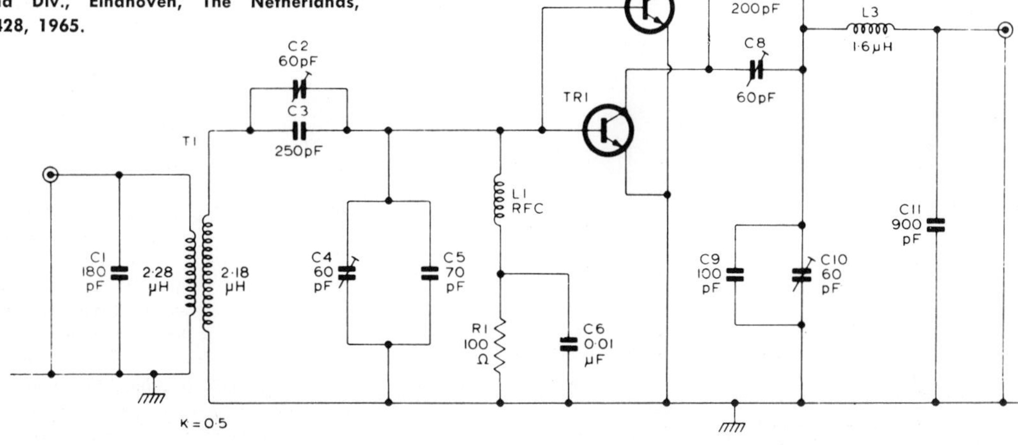

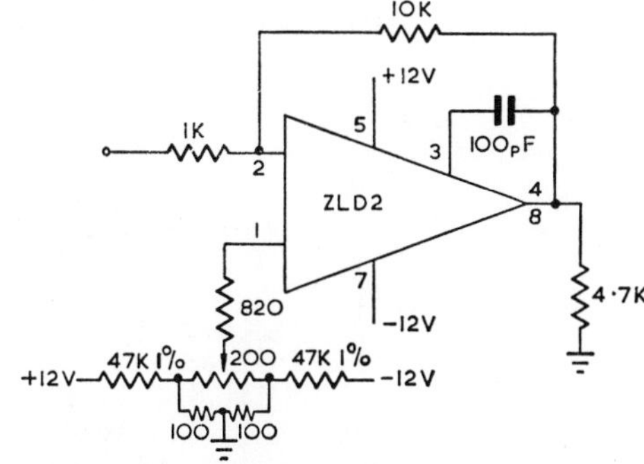

INVERTING AMPLIFIER WITH ADJUSTABLE INPUT BIAS—Provides gain of 10 and bandwidth of 1.5 MHz for either a-c or d-c inputs, with adjustable bias voltage applied to input for correcting offset voltage of amplifier, which may typically be about 20 mV.—*Microlin Amplifiers ZLD2S and ZLD2T*, Ferranti Ltd., Oldham, Lancs., England, No. 11, 1967.

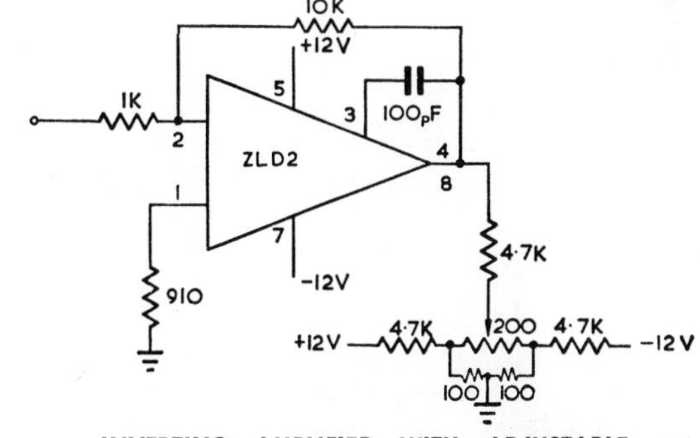

INVERTING AMPLIFIER WITH ADJUSTABLE OUTPUT BIAS—Provides gain of 10 and bandwidth of 1.5 MHz for either a-c or d-c inputs, with adjustable bias voltage applied to output for correcting offset voltage of amplifier, which may typically be about 20 mV.—*Microlin Amplifiers ZLD2S and ZLD2T*, Ferranti Ltd., Oldham, Lancs., England, No. 11, 1967.

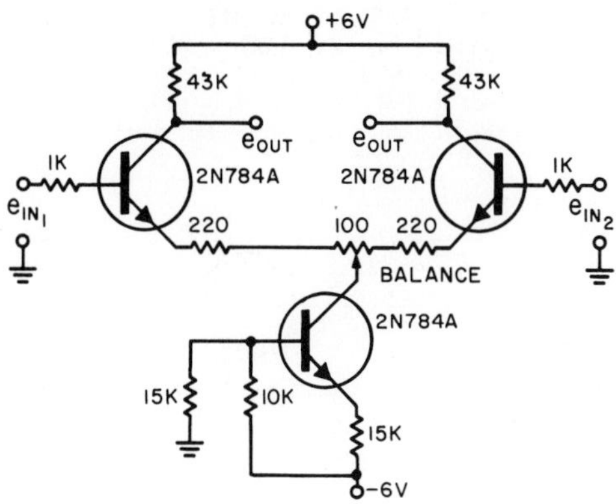

LONG LONG-TAIL PAIR—Drift is less than 75 μV per deg C referred to input, and differential mode voltage gain is 30. Addition of third transistor to differential pair improves common-mode rejection while requiring only extra −6 V source.—Differential Amplifier, *Electronic Design*, Feb. 3, 1964, p 44.

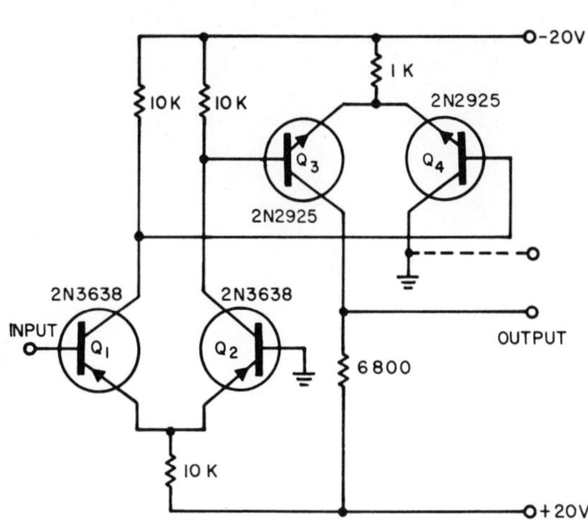

DIFFERENTIAL OUTPUT—Conventional differential-pair shown is often used as output stage of amplifier even though only one output phase is used. Q4 maintains gain at frequencies down to d-c without resorting to zener diode or large bypass capacitor.—S. G. Freshour, Differential Amplifier Offers Efficient, Dual Outputs, *Electronic Design*, July 19, 1965, p 37–38.

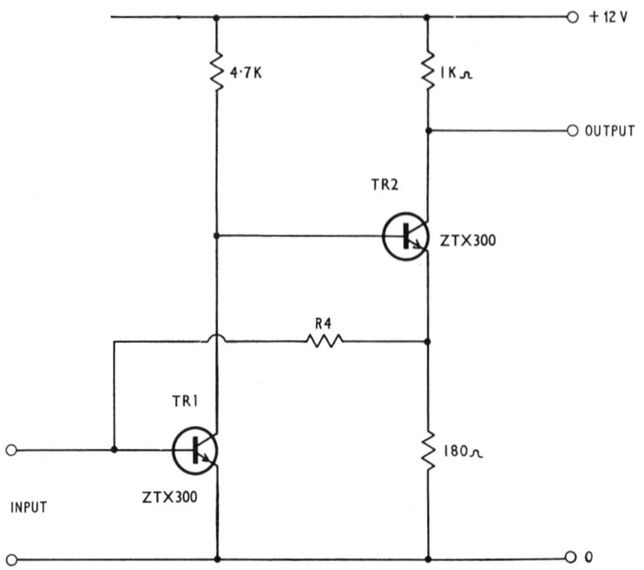

WIDEBAND CURRENT AMPLIFIER—Bandwidth is over 6 MHz, input impedance about 15 ohms, and output impedance 1K. Report gives design procedure. R4 determines current gain; 1.8K gives gain of 10 and bandwidth of 9 MHz, while 3.6K gives current gain of 20 and bandwidth of 6.5 MHz.—E-Line Transistor Applications, Ferranti Ltd., Oldham, Lancs., England, 1969, p 29.

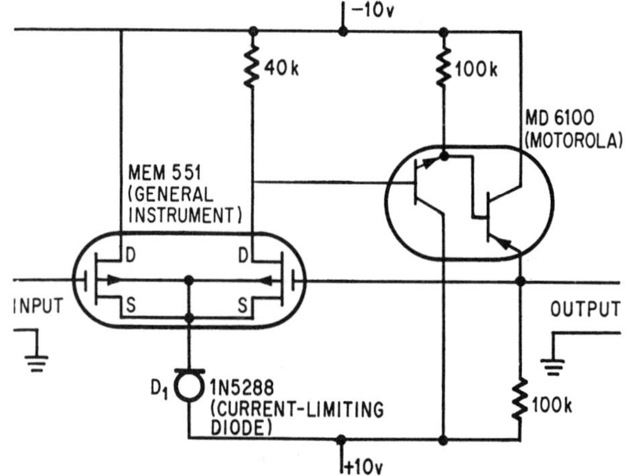

BUFFER—Dual mosfet coupled to complementary transistor pair has excellent thermal stability and almost infinite impedance, for isolating high-impedance circuits. Maximum input current drawn is less than 0.1 pA.—T. H. Lynch, MOS FET Amplifier Provides Almost Infinite Impedance, *Electronics*, July 24, 1967, p 88.

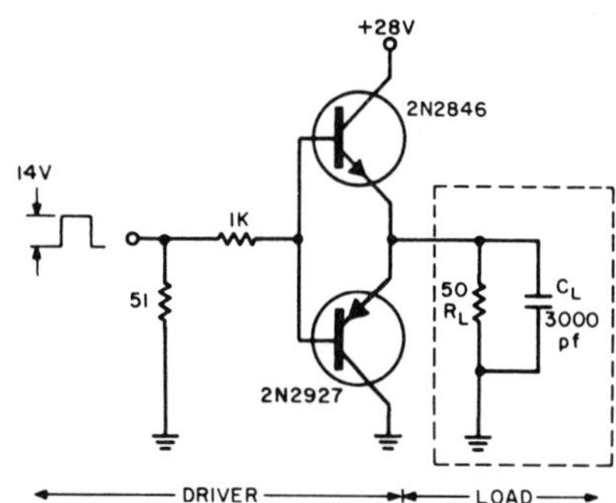

CABLE-DRIVING PULSE AMPLIFIER—Upper transistor is turned on by pulse to drive 50-ohm line, and lower transistor turns on at end of pulse to discharge line capacitance, to improve waveshape and permit driving of longer lines. Area enclosed in dashed lines simulates worst-case line-load situation. With 2N2927 pnp, 14-V pulse decays in 75 ns; if 2N1132 is used instead, decay is 110 ns.—Cable Driver Amplifier, *Electronic Design*, Feb. 3, 1964, p 44.

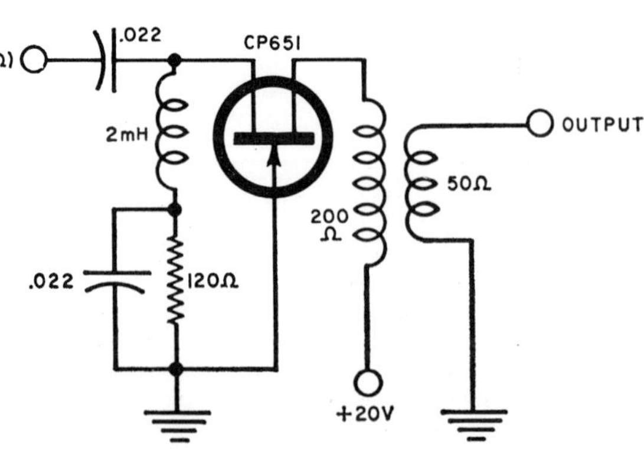

POWER-FET FRONT END—Covers 0.5 to 40 MHz. Broadband noise figure is below 3 dB, with sufficient dynamic range to handle signals above 2 V with little distortion. Receiver sensitivity and selectivity are significantly better than that achieved with bipolar devices.—J. Tamosaitis, The Power FET, *Electronics World*, June 1969, p 34–35 and 82.

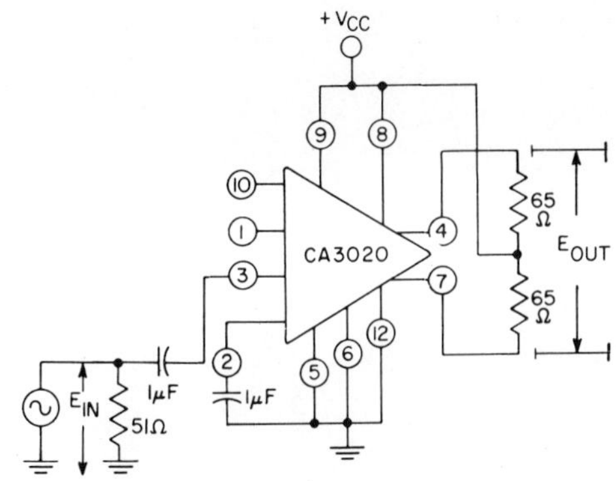

WIDEBAND CONTROL AMPLIFIER—Voltage gain is 44 dB at 1 kHz. Highly efficient as power amplifier in control systems requiring a-c amplification.—"Linear Integrated Circuits," RCA, Harrison, N.J., IC-41, p 274.

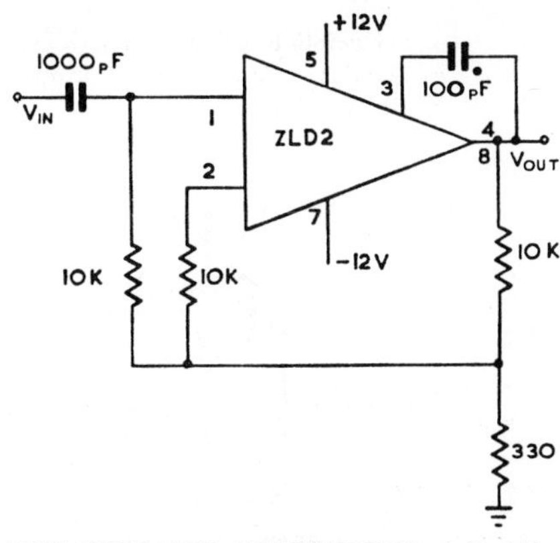

HIGH-IMPEDANCE NONINVERTING A-C AMPLIFIER—Arrangement of resistors used with Ferranti ZLD2 IC differential-input d-c amplifier gives high input impedance (400,000 ohms), because feedback is applied to both inputs. Voltage gain is 30. Gives reasonably good low-frequency response without requiring large-value capacitors; gain is 3 dB down at 240 Hz and 440 kHz.—Microlin Amplifiers ZLD2S and ZLD2T, Ferranti Ltd., Oldham, Lancs., England, No. 11, 1967.

THREE-STAGE CASCADED IC—Symmetrical cascading of three IC video amplifiers gives stable gain of 65 dB with minimum supply decoupling. Operates equally well from either 4.5-V or 6-V supplies, except for larger output swing capability with higher voltage.

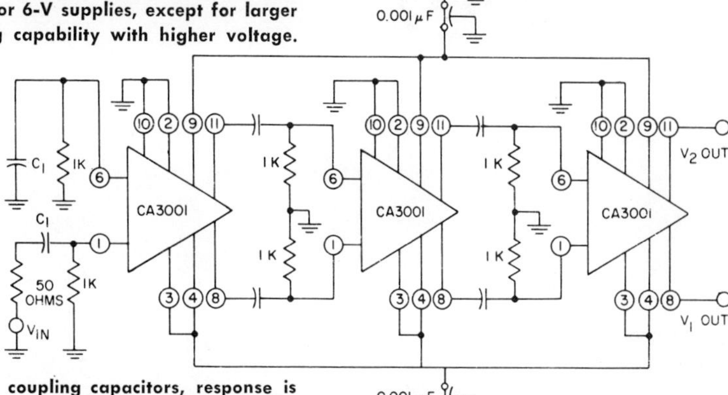

With 0.02-µF coupling capacitors, response is flat within 1 dB from 0.02 to about 5 MHz. With 100-pF coupling, gain drops to 60 dB maximum at 3 MHz, and 1-dB-down bandwidth is only about 2 MHz.—"Linear Integrated Circuits," RCA, Harrison, N.J., IC-41, p 145.

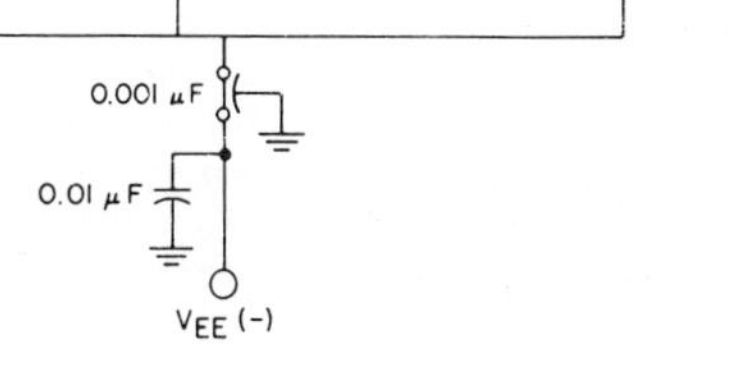

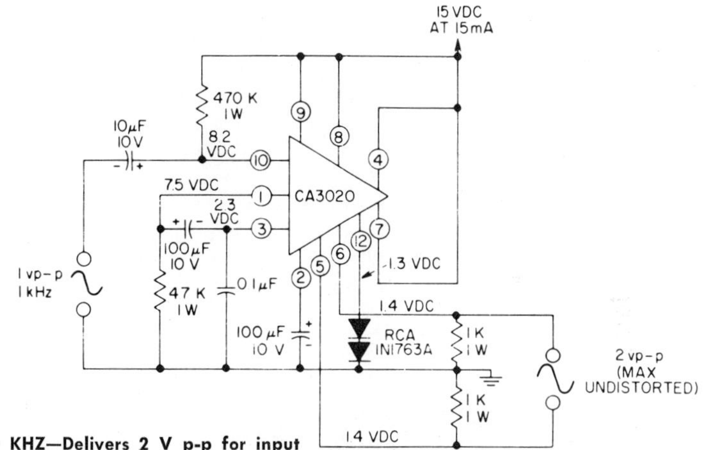

D-C TO 100 KHZ—Delivers 2 V p-p for input of 0.1 V p-p at 1 kHz, and covers entire frequency range from 100 kHz down to d-c.—"Linear Integrated Circuits," RCA, Harrison, N.J., IC-41, p 276.

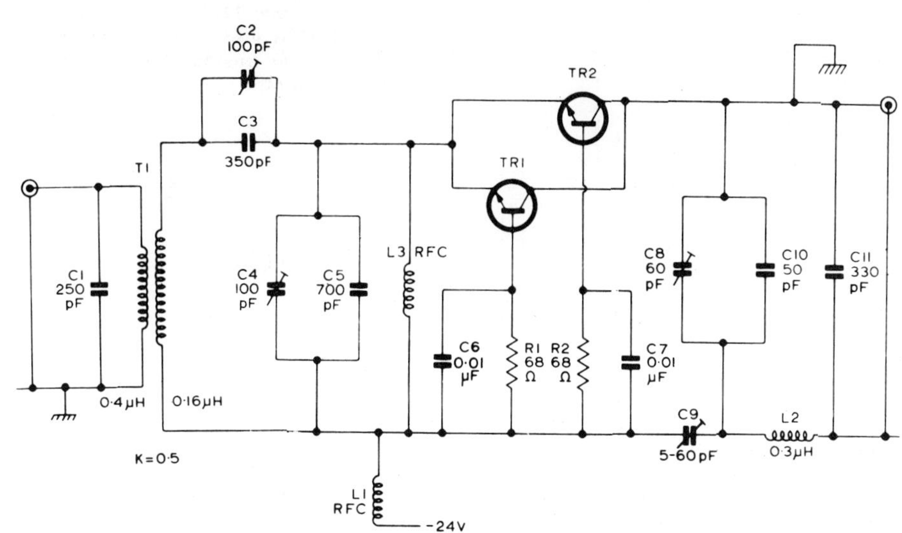

30-MHZ 3-W AMPLIFIER—Provides power gain of 7 dB and 48% efficiency with BFY50 transistors. Input and output impedances are 50 ohms.—Applications of the BFY50, BFY51, and BFY52, Philips, Pub. Dept., Elcoma Div., Eindhoven, The Netherlands, No. 428, 1965.

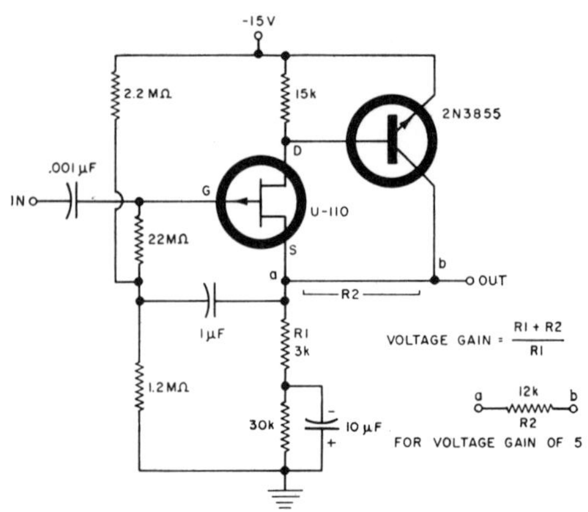

FET WITH TRANSISTOR—Gives very high input impedance and low output impedance. Voltage gain can be made greater than unity by inserting resistor R2 in feedback path. Bandwidth decreases as impedance of driving source increases.—J. H. Wujek, Jr., and M. E. McGee, Field-Effect Transistor Circuits, *Electronics World*, May 1967, p 32–33 and 75.

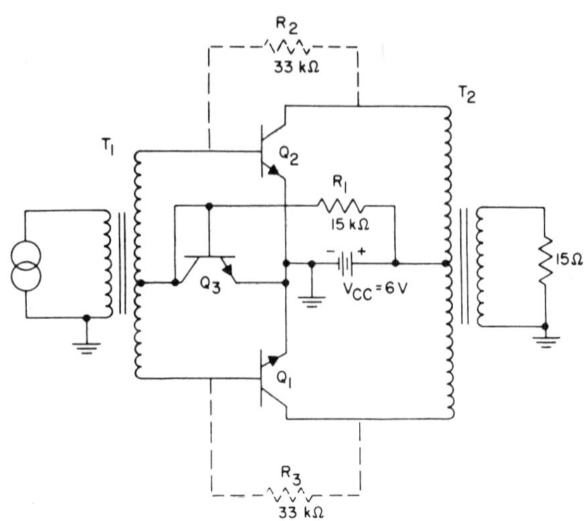

LOW-LEVEL CLASS B—Uses RCA CA3018 transistor array to give maximum output power of 40 mW and total idling current that varies only from 0.5 to 0.6 mA over entire military temperature range. Uses both a-c and d-c feedback. T1 is ADC Products 5SX1322, and T2 is Chicago Standard TA-10. R1 is removed when R2 and R3 are added.—"Linear Integrated Circuits," RCA, Harrison, N.J., IC-41, p 315.

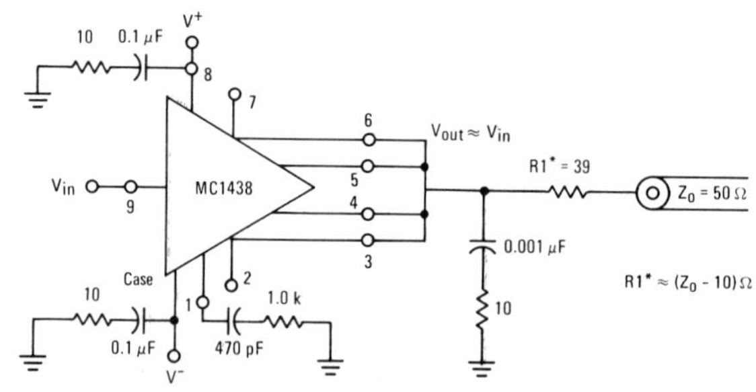

LINE DRIVER—Uses Motorola IC amplifier providing 70 dB current gain, with unity voltage gain, as either digital or analog driver for 50-ohm line.—Power Booster MC1438R, Motorola, Phoenix, Ariz., ADI-14R1, 1969.

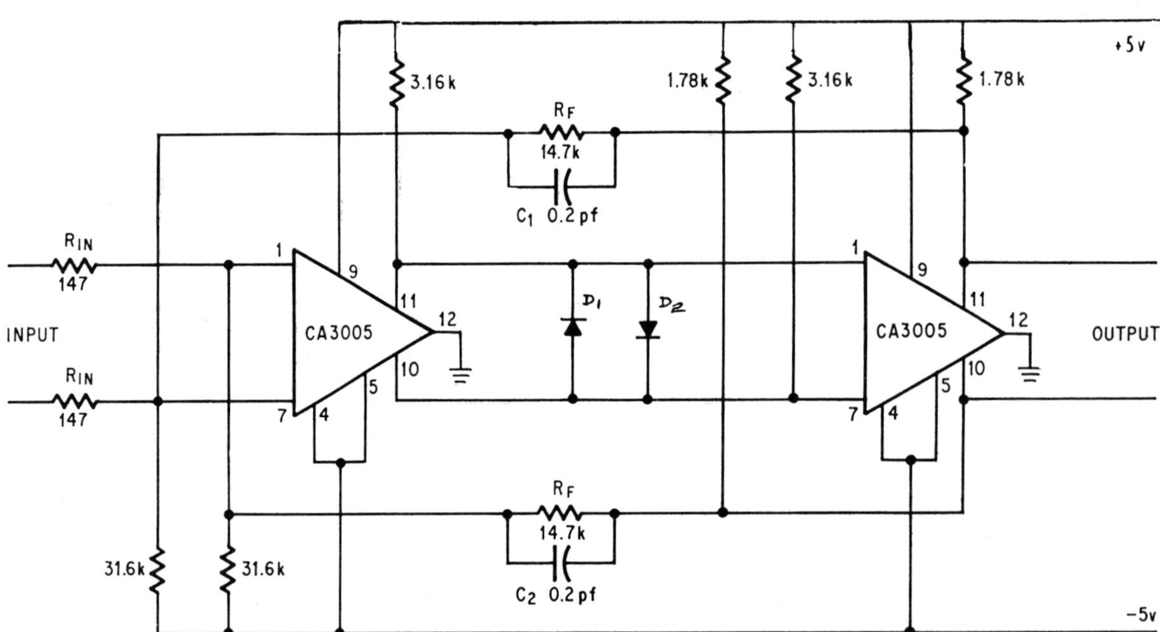

20-MHZ BANDWIDTH—Two IC r-f amplifiers are combined to form stable, reliable wideband differential amplifier. Gain, determined by ratio of RF to RIN, is 100 for values shown. Bandwidth is 20 MHz, and delay time is 20 ns. Clamp diodes D1 and D2 are required if amplifier is overloaded by large differential inputs. Diodes cause output to clip symmetrically and insure fast recovery.—C. J. Ulrick, Differential Amplifier Uses Two IC's, *Electronics*, Nov. 11, 1968, p 120–121.

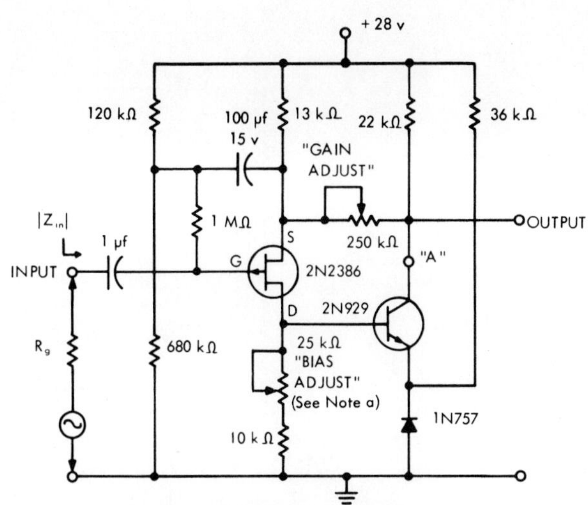

NOTES: a. Adjust for + 18 v at Point "A".
b. All resistors ± 5% tolerance, 1/2 watt.

HIGH-Z INPUT—Use of p-channel diffused planar silicon fet gives input impedance of 70 meg up to 100 Hz, 50 meg at 1 kHz, and 10 meg at 10 kHz. Intended for small-signal applications. Voltage gain is adjustable from 1 to 20.—"Preferred Semiconductors and Components," Texas Instruments, Dallas, Texas, CC101, 1968, p 6302.

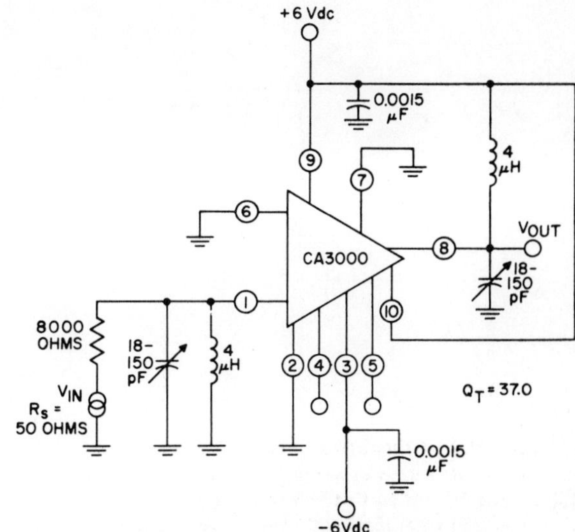

10-MHZ NARROW-BAND—With tuned input and tuned output, IC d-c amplifier provides narrow-band response, with gain dropping from about 30 dB down to 0 dB at about 1.2 MHz off from center frequency in either direction. Can be used in tuned amplifiers up to 30 MHz.—"Linear Integrated Circuits," RCA, Harrison, N.J., IC-41, p 128.

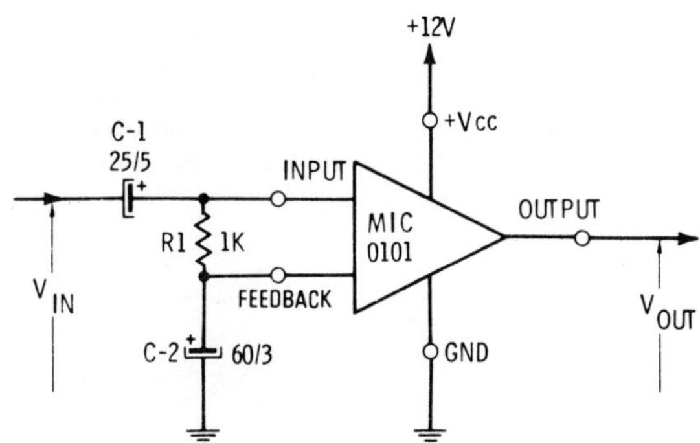

R-C COUPLING—Uses Mallory MIC0101 preamp to provide voltage gains from 57 to 53 dB. 3-dB bandwidth extends up to 700 kHz. Distortion is under 5% for outputs up to 1 V rms.—M. L. Deschler, Integrated Circuit Preamplifiers, Mallory, Indianapolis, Ind., APPN-2, 1968.

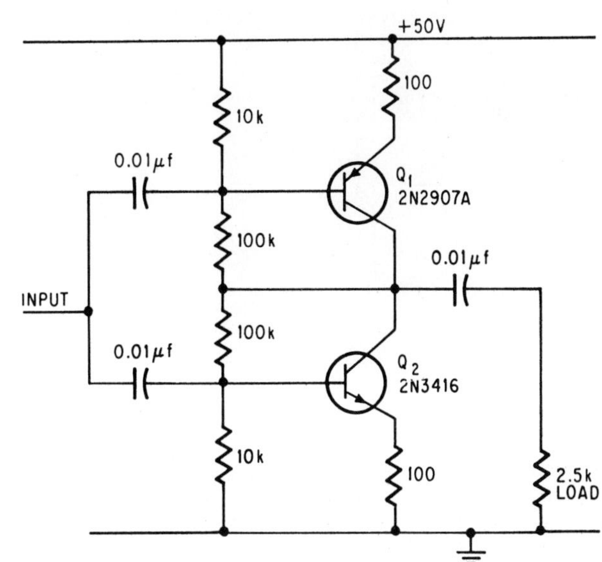

IMPROVING SIGNAL TRANSFER—Complementary arrangement of amplifier transistors, with each operating class A as both amplifier and collector load, improves efficiency and reduces distortion. Each transistor serves as collector impedance for the other. Delivers 0.5 W at 22 V to load.—M. J. Wright, Transistor Replaces Resistor and Improves Amplifier, *Electronics*, Jan. 8, 1968, p 92.

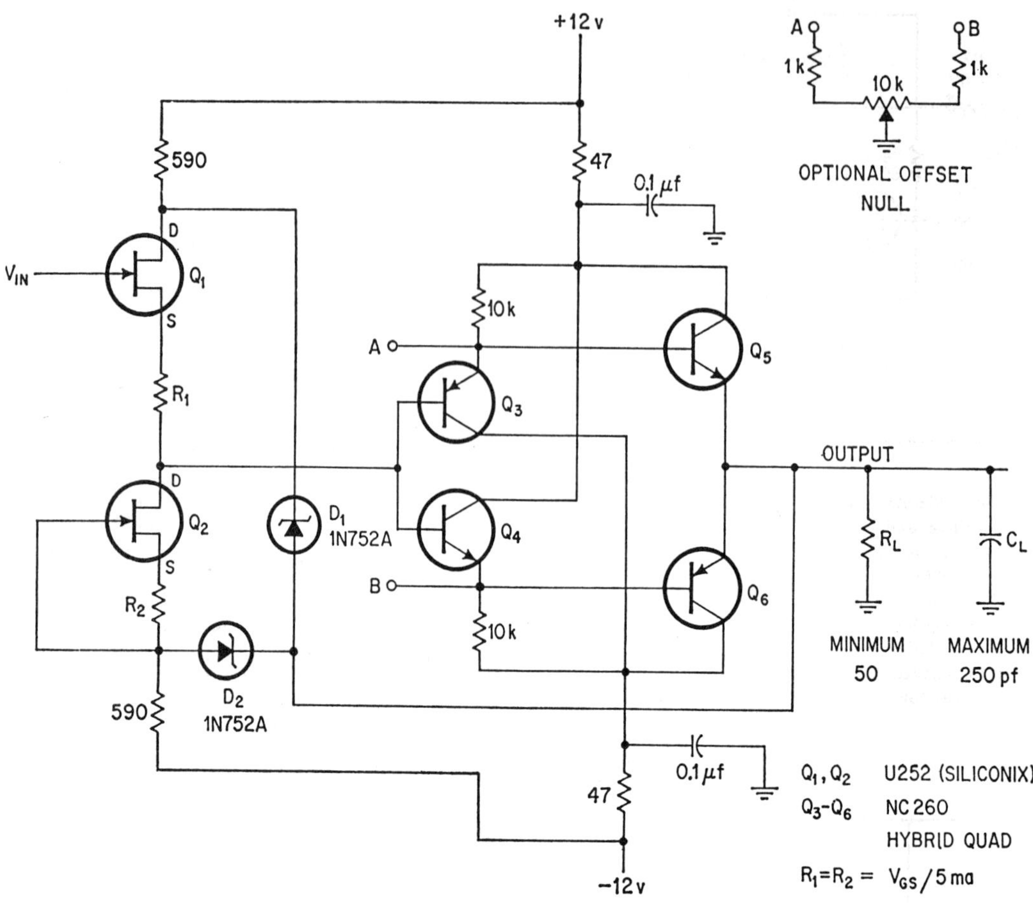

FAST-SETTLING BUFFER—Simple transistor circuit outperforms high-speed fet opamps used in sampling circuits and analog memories by settling to 0.1% of final value in 50 ns. Circuit is stable with moderate capacitive loading and will slew at up to 300 V per μs. Potentiometer can be connected to A and B to null the offset voltage. Bode plot is flat from d-c to 40 MHz.—D. Atlas, FET Buffer Boasts High Speed and Performance, *Electronics*, July 21, 1969, p 82–83.

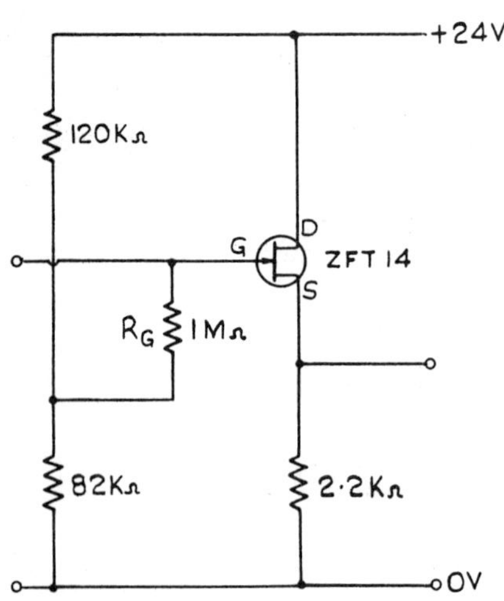

FET SOURCE FOLLOWER—Uses voltage divider to provide bias for gate. Input impedance is 1 meg.—Field Effect Transistors and Applications, Ferranti Ltd., Oldham, Lancs., England, No. 22, 1965.

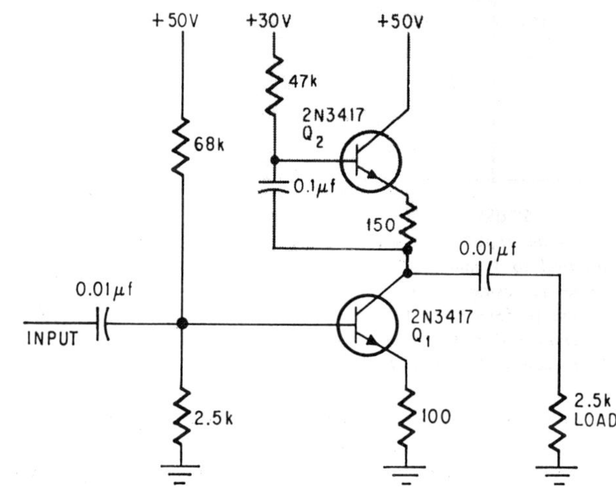

CONSTANT-CURRENT SOURCE—Q2 offers high impedance to amplifier, and requires only bias current to develop output voltage. Practically all of collector-current modulation of Q1 is delivered to load; thus, collector current of 2 mA p-p produces 1-mA p-p in load, whereas 2.5K resistor in place of Q2 would require 4-mA p-p input for same output. Maximum output power is over 0.2 W at 22 V.—M. J. Wright, Transistor Replaces Resistor and Improves Amplifier, *Electronics*, Jan. 8, 1968, p 92.

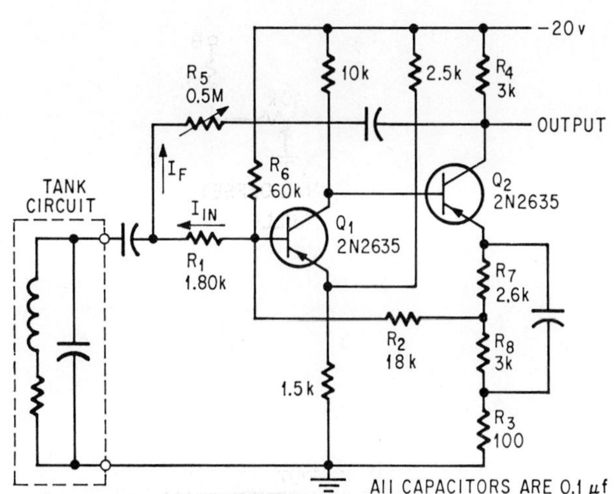

INFINITE IMPEDANCE—Simple two-stage amplifier with both positive and negative feedback can serve either as Q multiplier or infinite-impedance amplifier, by appropriate adjustment of interstage feedback. Basically, this circuit is a negative-impedance converter. Article gives design equations.—G. Marosi, Negative Impedance Converter Does Double Duty, *Electronics*, July 24, 1967, p 87–88.

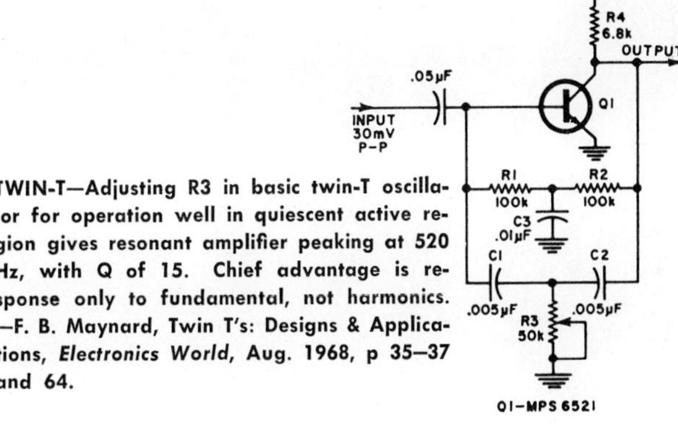

TWIN-T—Adjusting R3 in basic twin-T oscillator for operation well in quiescent active region gives resonant amplifier peaking at 520 Hz, with Q of 15. Chief advantage is response only to fundamental, not harmonics. —F. B. Maynard, Twin T's: Designs & Applications, *Electronics World*, Aug. 1968, p 35–37 and 64.

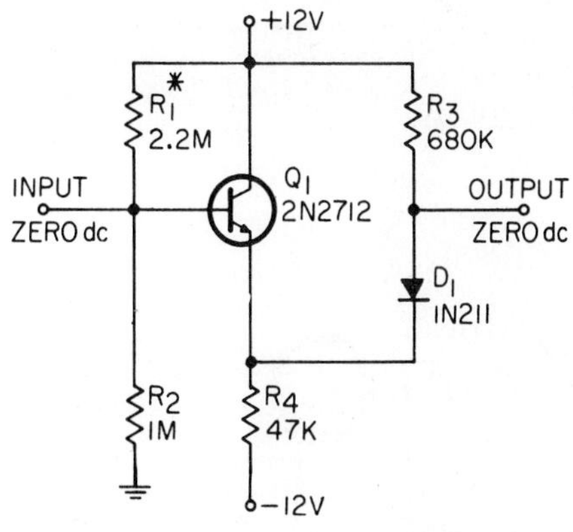

EMITTER-FOLLOWER WITHOUT OFFSET—D-c levels at input and output are equal, with offset eliminated by diode. Suitable for both d-c and a-c applications.—A. C. Caggiano, Modified Emitter Follower Has No Offset, *EEE*, March 1967, p 164.

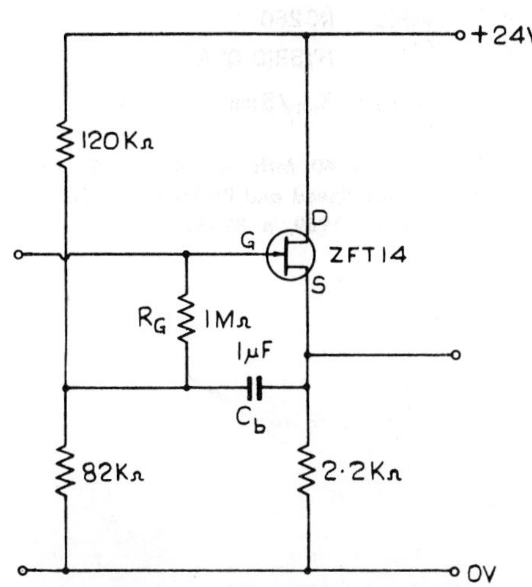

BOOTSTRAPPED FET SOURCE FOLLOWER—Bootstrapping increases input impedance to 5.5 meg as compared to 1 meg for conventional source follower using same resistor values, for improved performance stability.—Field Effect Transistors and Applications, Ferranti Ltd., Oldham, Lancs., England, No. 22, 1965.

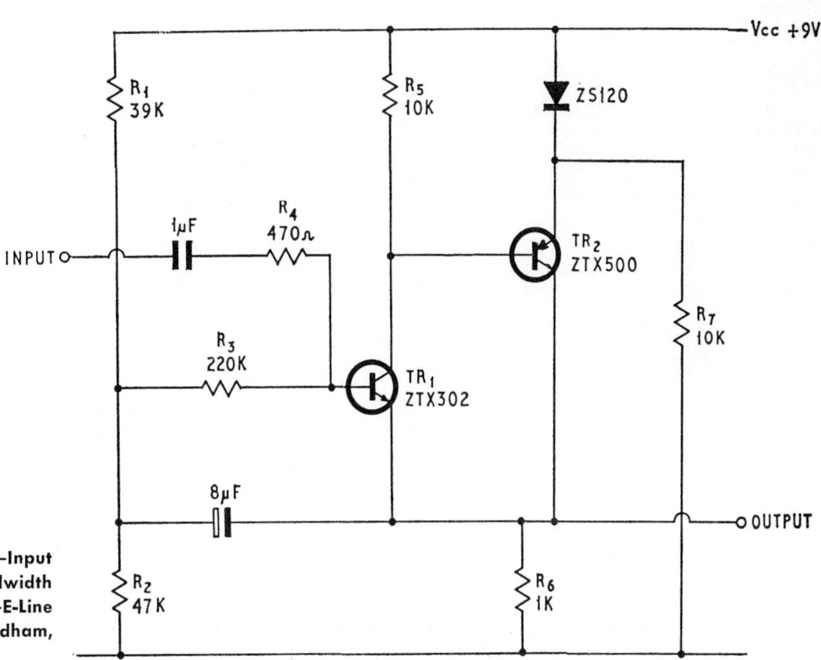

UNITY GAIN AT HIGH IMPEDANCE—Input impedance is at least 1 meg and bandwidth is above 1 MHz at 1 V rms output.—E-Line Transistor Applications, Ferranti Ltd., Oldham, Lancs., England, 1969, p 31.

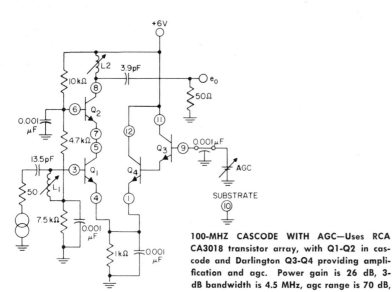

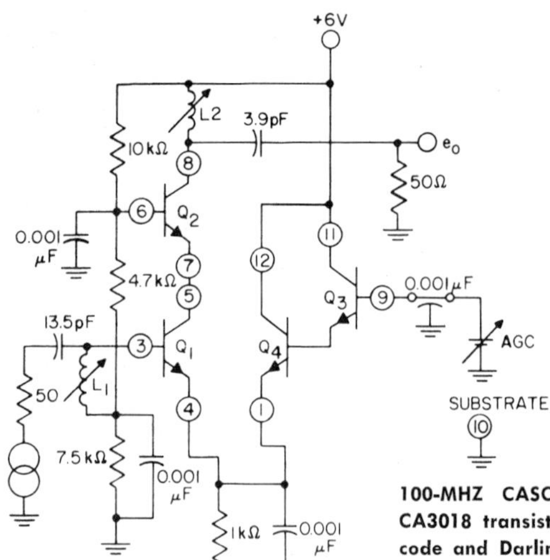

$L_1 = 0.11$ to $0.17\ \mu H$
$L_2 = 0.5$ to $0.8\ \mu H$

100-MHZ CASCODE WITH AGC—Uses RCA CA3018 transistor array, with Q1-Q2 in cascode and Darlington Q3-Q4 providing amplification and agc. Power gain is 26 dB, 3-dB bandwidth is 4.5 MHz, agc range is 70 dB, and noise figure is 6.8 dB.—"Linear Integrated Circuits," RCA, Harrison, N.J., IC-41, p 316.

PROBE AMPLIFIER—Input impedance is well above 10 meg and input current about 1.5 mA. Power supply and output are combined in one lead, and coax shield provides ground, so amplifier requires only two conductors. Uses fet and bipolar transistor. Can easily drive several feet of coax.—J. F. Teixeira, Unity-gain Amplifier in Probe Needs Only Two Conductors, *Electronics*, June 9, 1969, p 99.

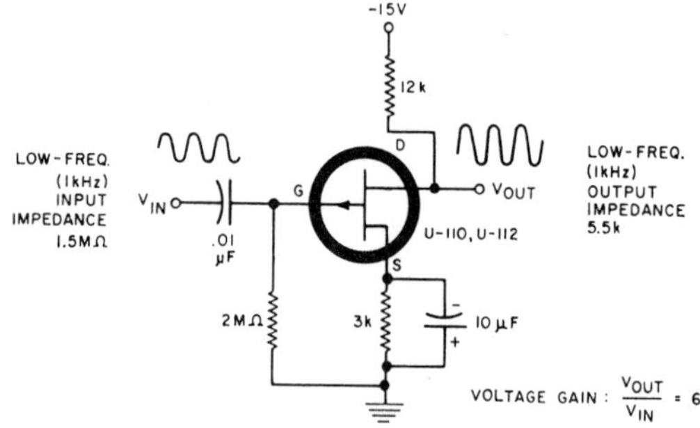

COMMON-SOURCE FET—Circuit is analogous to common-emitter transistor and common-cathode tube circuits. Voltage gain can be greater than unity up to 1 MHz.—J. H. Wujek, Jr. and M. E. McGee, Field-Effect Transistor Circuits, *Electronics World*, May 1967, p 32—33 and 75.

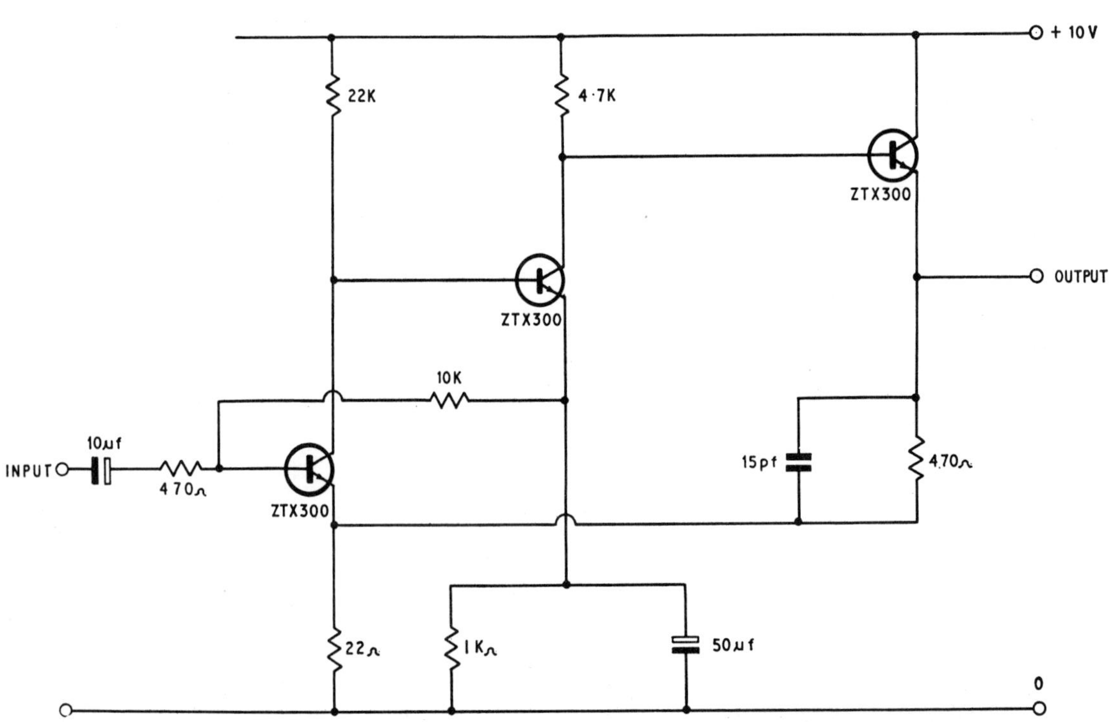

WIDEBAND VOLTAGE AMPLIFIER—Bandwidth for 3 dB down is 14 MHz, with 10K input impedance and voltage gain of 20. Report gives design procedure.—S-Line Transistor Applications, Ferranti Ltd., Oldham, Lancs., England, 1969, p 31.

CHAPTER 3
Audio Amplifier Circuits

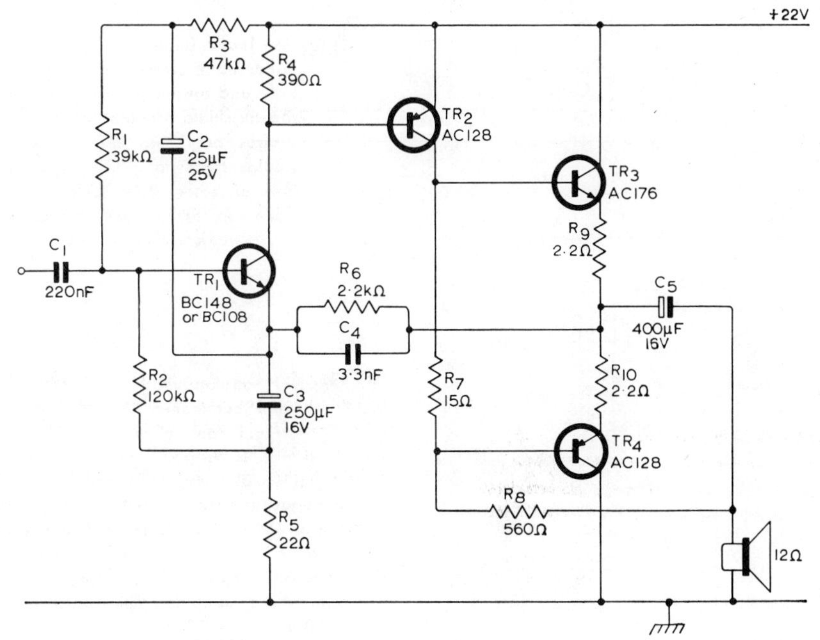

3-W AUDIO AMP—Response is flat within 3 dB from 40 to 20,000 Hz because circuit uses 20-dB feedback. Sensitivity is 70 mV for rated power output into 12-ohm speaker.—"Transistor Audio and Radio Circuits," Mullard Ltd., London, 1969, p 35.

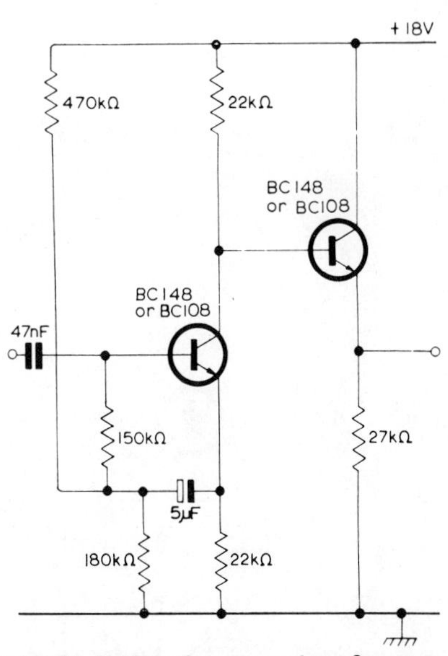

2-STAGE BUFFER—Common-emitter first stage has heavy feedback. Voltage gain of buffer is unity, response is flat within 3 dB from 20 to 20,000 Hz, distortion is below 0.5% for outputs up to 2.5 V, input impedance is 3.6 meg, and output impedance is 250 ohms.—"Transistor Audio and Radio Circuits," Mullard Ltd., London, 1969, p 122.

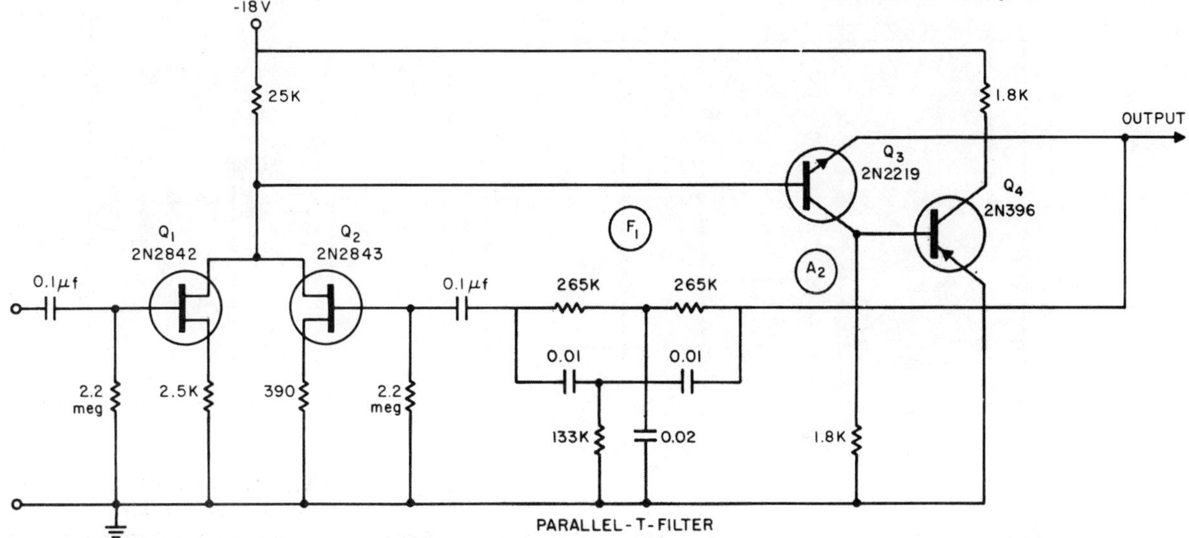

60-HZ NARROW BANDPASS—Amplifies 60-Hz input signal 4 times, while attenuating 30-Hz and 120-Hz signals 12 dB. Response at 600 Hz is down over 20 dB. Output is inverted. First stage is summing amplifier using two fet's in class A connected to common load. Components in section F1 eliminate 60-Hz component to keep negative feedback at zero.—J. M. Howe, Low-Frequency FET Amplifier has Narrow Bandpass, *Electronic Design*, Jan. 4, 1965, p 72.

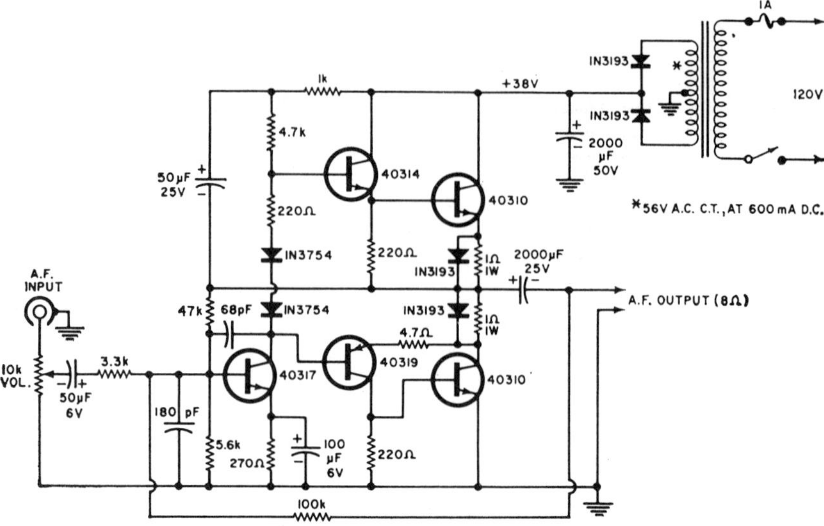

10-W HI-FI—Quasi-complementary circuit uses 1N3754 diodes in input of driver to compensate for effect of high-temperature variations of output transistors. Diodes shunting 1-ohm resistors in output stage reduce losses when operating at rated power, while resistors provide degeneration for circuit stability. Response is flat within 1 dB from 15 to 20,000 Hz.—R. D. Gold and J. C. Sondermeyer, Designing Silicon-Transistor Hi-Fi Amplifiers, *Electronics World*, Nov. 1966, p 47–50 and 80–81.

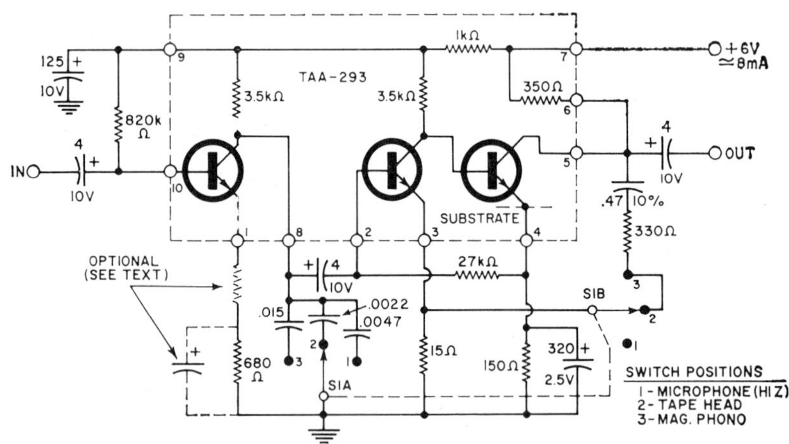

IC PREAMP—Uses Amperex TAA-293 integrated circuit containing three transistors and four resistors, priced under $3. S1 gives choice of three types of equalization. To obtain higher gain for tape playback, add 125-μF capacitor across 560-ohm resistor used in place of 680 ohms, and insert 180-ohm unbypassed series resistor as per dotted lines. Output is 0.5 V.—D. R. Pryce, Integrated Circuit Equalized Preamplifier, *Electronics World*, July 1968, p 29 and 73.

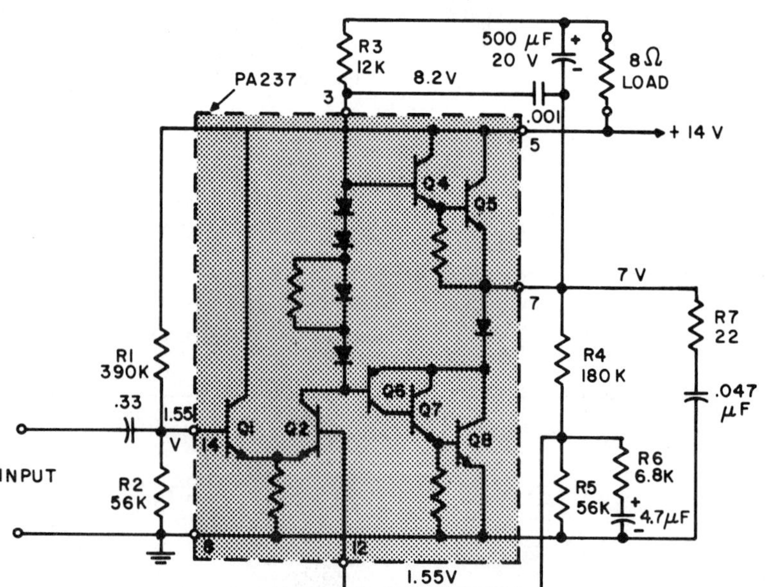

1-W IC AMPLIFIER—Uses GE PA-237 monolithic integrated circuit with external components shown. Can drive 8-ohm speaker directly. With 22-V supply, will deliver 1.5 W into 22-ohm load. Total harmonic distortion is 1% at 1 kHz.—Dwight V. Jones, Monolithic 2 Watt Integrated Amplifier—Characteristics and Applications, General Electric, Syracuse, N.Y., No. 90.73, 1968, p 10.

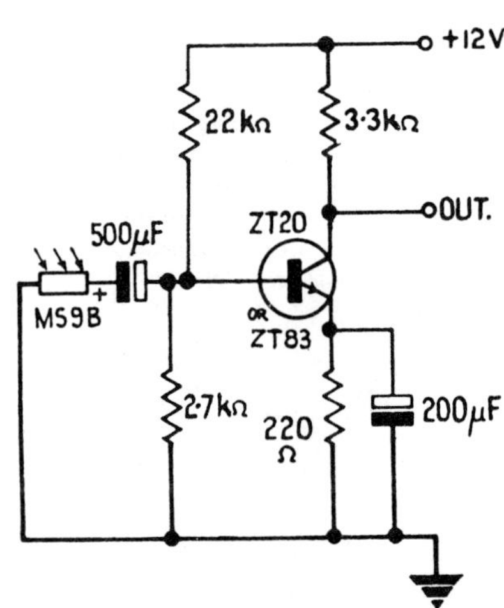

MOVIE SOUND PICKUP—Silicon photocell and single-transistor amplifier give essentially flat frequency response from d-c to well above 20,000 Hz for sound-on-film track of movie projector.—Silicon Photocell Applications, Ferranti Ltd., Oldham, Lancs., England, No. 9, 5/67, p 16.

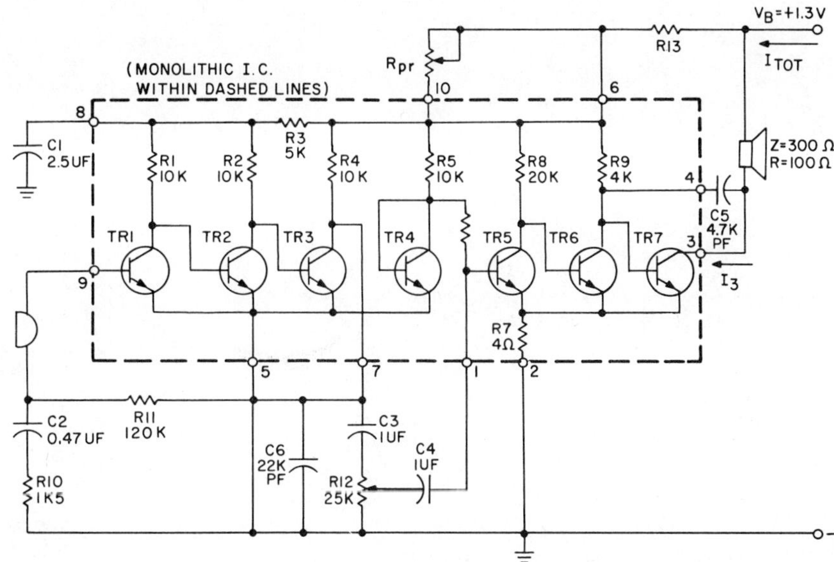

IC HEARING AID—Uses TAA370 IC developed especially for body and behind-the-ear hearing aids. Heavy negative feedback keeps spread in gain very small for battery aging and other factors. Output power is 1 mW. Frequency response is determined largely by values of C2, C5, and C6; for those shown, response is flat within 3 dB from 200 Hz to above 9,000 Hz. R10 is 1.5K.—The Amperex TAA 370 as a Hearing Aid Amplifier, Amperex, Slatersville, R.I., S-139, 1968.

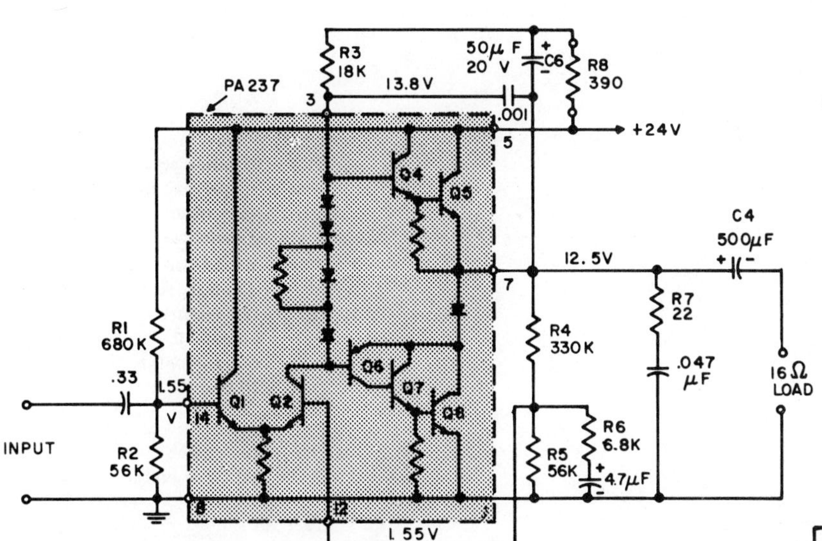

2-W IC AMPLIFIER—Uses GE PA-237 integrated circuit for driving 16-ohm load that is returned to ground. Total harmonic distortion is 1% at 1 kHz.—Dwight V. Jones, Monolithic 2 Watt Integrated Amplifier—Characteristics and Applications, General Electric, Syracuse, N.Y., No. 90.73, 1968, p 11.

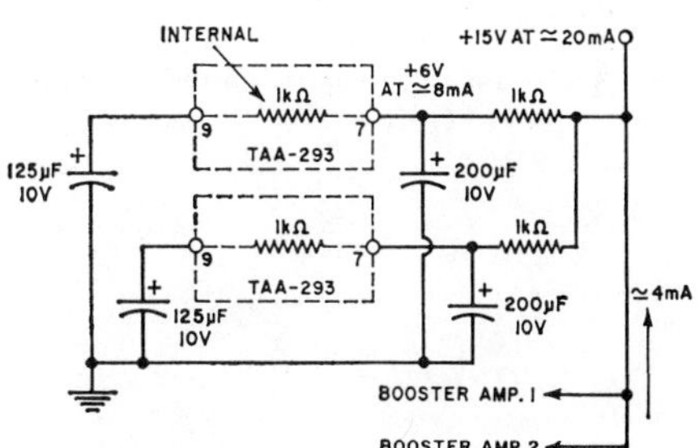

DECOUPLER—Used to prevent feedback and crosstalk problems when two preamps, with or without booster amplifiers, are used in stereo system having Amperex TAA-293 IC in each channel. Only power supply connections for IC's are shown here.—D. R. Pryce, Integrated Circuit Equalized Preamplifier, *Electronics World*, July 1968, p 29 and 73.

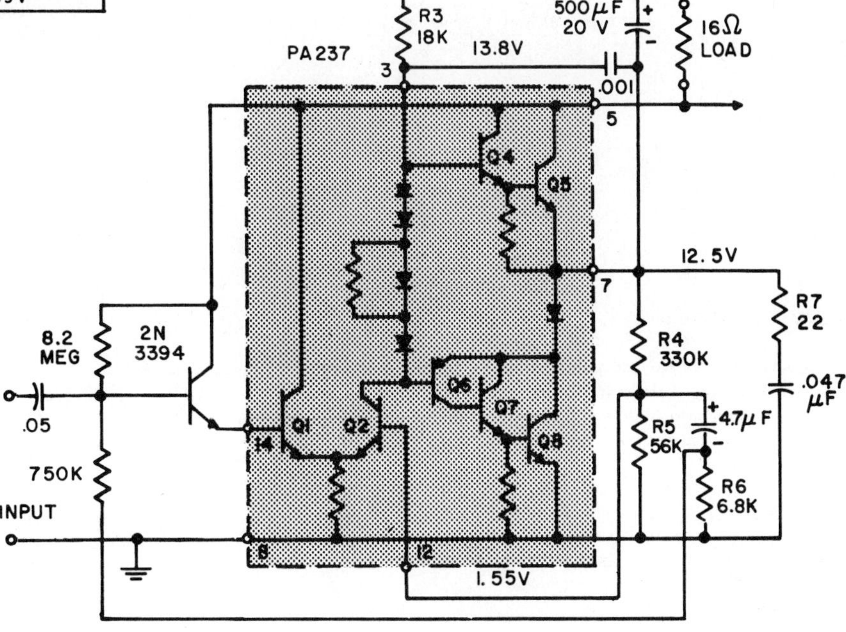

2-W IC WITH 2-MEG INPUT—Uses GE PA-237 integrated circuit with additional transistor at input to give input impedance between 2 and 3 meg.—Dwight V. Jones, Monolithic 2 Watt Integrated Amplifier—Characteristics and Applications, General Electric, Syracuse, N.Y., No. 90.73, 1968, p 13.

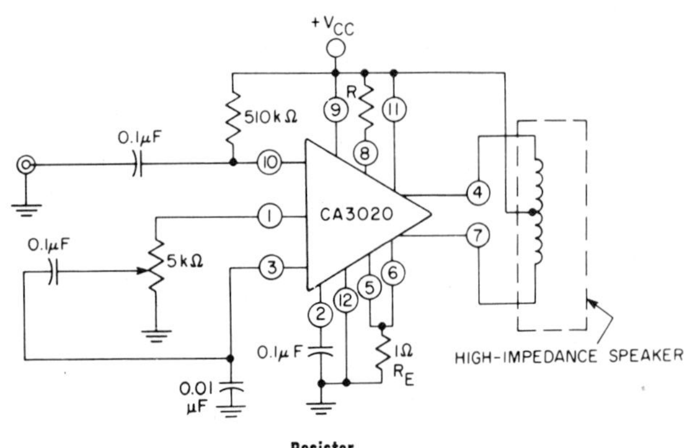

Supply Voltage Vcc (V)	Idling Current I_{do} (mA)	Resistor between Terminals 8 and 11 (ohms)	Power Output P_{out} (mW)	Total Harmonic Distortion (%)
3	10	220	50	2.0
6	21	1000	200	2.0
9	24	∞	400	2.5

LOW-DISTORTION IC AMPLIFIER—Table gives optimum value of resistor R, connected between wideband IC amplifier terminals 8 and 11, for minimizing total harmonic distortion. —"Linear Integrated Circuits," RCA, Harrison, N.J., IC-41, p 270.

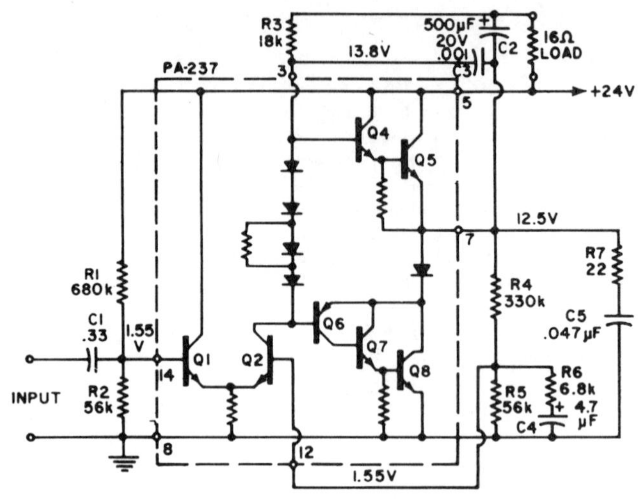

2-W AUDIO IC—G-E monolithic amplifier has quasi-complementary output circuit, shown inside dashed square, to give push-pull output. Input is differential amplifier.—D. V. Jones, Audio-Frequency Integrated Circuits, *Electronics World*, July 1968, p 54–56.

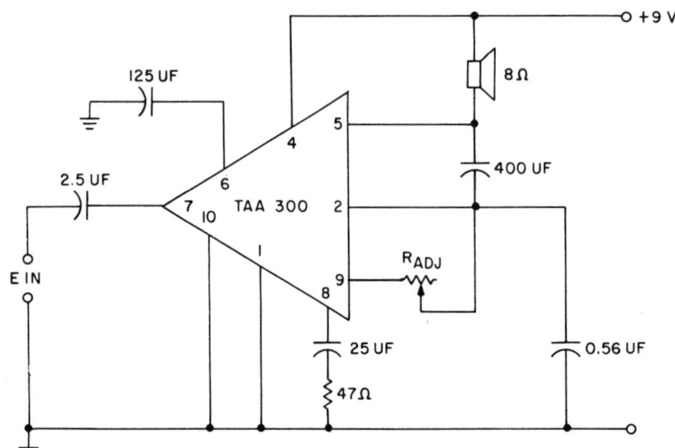

1-W IC AUDIO AMP—Gives high gain and low current consumption for portable radios, phonographs, TV sets, tape cassette systems, and walkie-talkies. Uses Amperex TAA300 IC. Frequency response is down 3 dB at 120 and 23,000 Hz with feedback. Select R-adj for 8-mA no-signal total current drain. —The Amperex TAA 300 Monolithic Integrated Circuits Used as a Complete Audio Amplifier, Amperex, Slatersville, R.I., S-138, 1968.

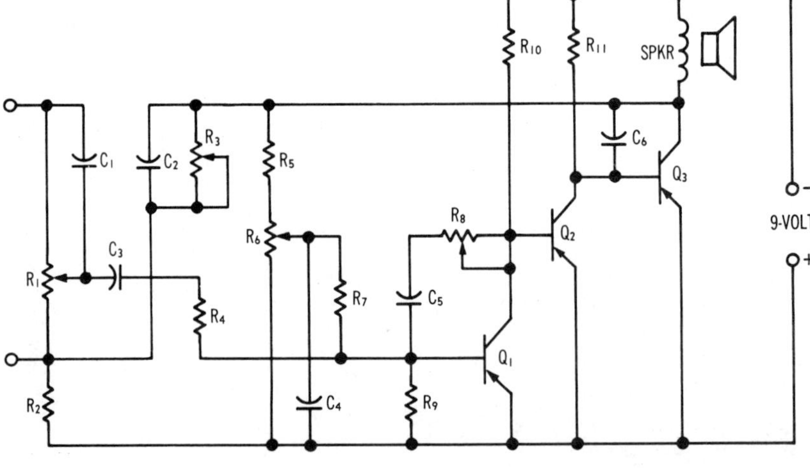

0.5-W AMPLIFIER—Serves as center of inexpensive mono hi-fi system. Uses external 9-V supply for power, and a-m/f-m tuner or ceramic cartridge phonograph as program source feeding into 32-ohm speaker. Article gives construction details. Parts values are: R1 2.5 meg; R2 270; R3 10K bass pot; R4 200K; R5, R9 10K; R6-R7-R8 100K; R10 22K; R11 1.2K; C1 75 μμF; C2 0.1 μF; C3 0.02 μF; C4 15 μF; C5 0.01 μF; C6 0.05 μF; Q1 HEP-253; Q2 HEP254; Q3 HEP230.—"Solid State Projects Manual," Motorola, Phoenix, Ariz., 1968, p 37.

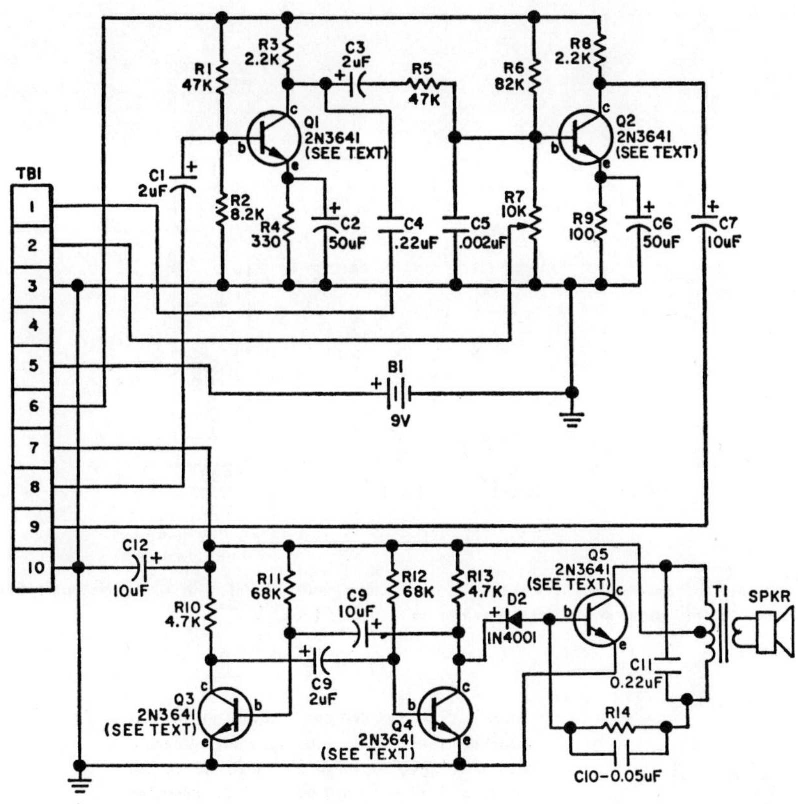

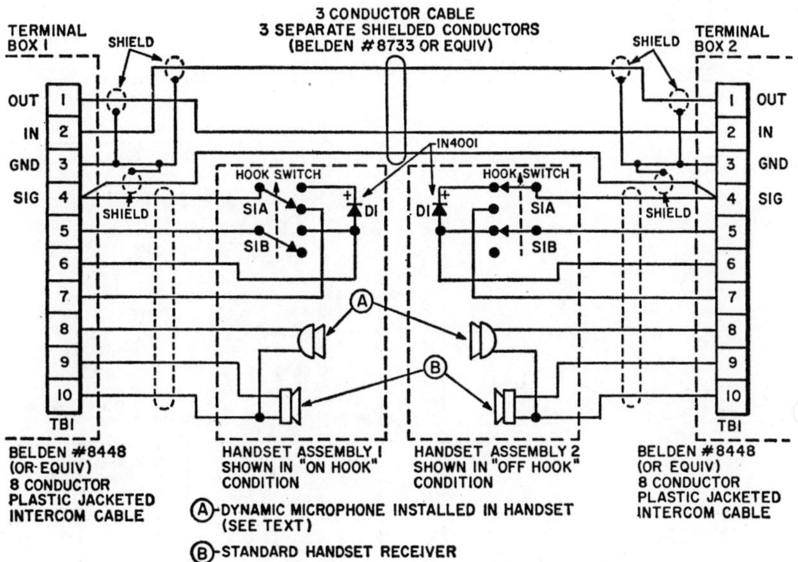

TWO-STATION INTERCOM WITH PRIVACY— Has no on-off or talk-listen switches yet neither party can listen in on room conversations at other station when handset at one station is hung up. When one party picks up handset, beep tone at other station calls other party. When that handset is picked up, tone stops and normal two-way conversation can take place, with both parties talking and listening just as with standard telephone. Cost of parts for two stations is about $50. Any equivalent transistor can be used, such as 2N697, 2N3705, SK3020, GE21, or HEP54. Article tells where to buy handset, cradle, and dynamic microphone to be used in place of handset transmitter cartridge in each of the identical stations or terminals.—E. A. Morris, Phonecom—The Hot Line Intercom, *Elementary Electronics*, Mar.–Apr. 1970, p 35–40 and 99–100.

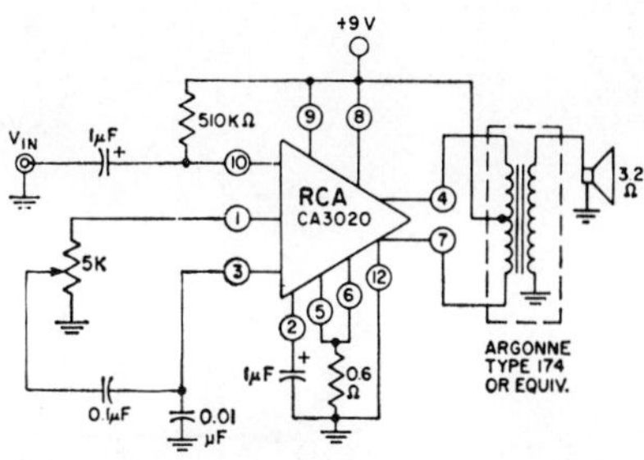

IC AUDIO OUTPUT—Delivers up to 1 W, either to center-tapped speaker or to output transformer and ordinary speaker as shown. Same integrated circuit can also drive higher-power audio amplifiers. Power gain is 58 dB.—D. E. Lancaster, Audio Integrated Circuits—What's Available?, *Electronics World*, Oct. 1967, p 34–36.

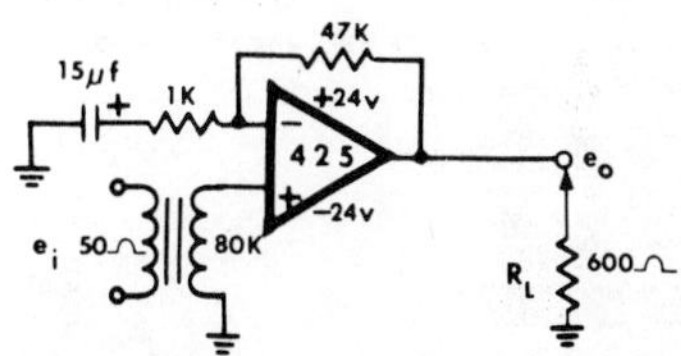

OPAMP PREAMP—Input transformer for microphone provides voltage step-up for Model 425 d-c opamp. Serves to reduce overall noise, because total noise becomes equal to noise of transformer plus noise of IC, divided by transformer gain. Low-frequency cutoff is 10 Hz. Output level of IC is +22 dBm and overall gain is 1,000 (60 dB). May also be used as tape preamp.—B. J. Losmandy, Operational Amplifier Applications for Audio Systems, Opamp Labs, Los Angeles, Cal., 1968.

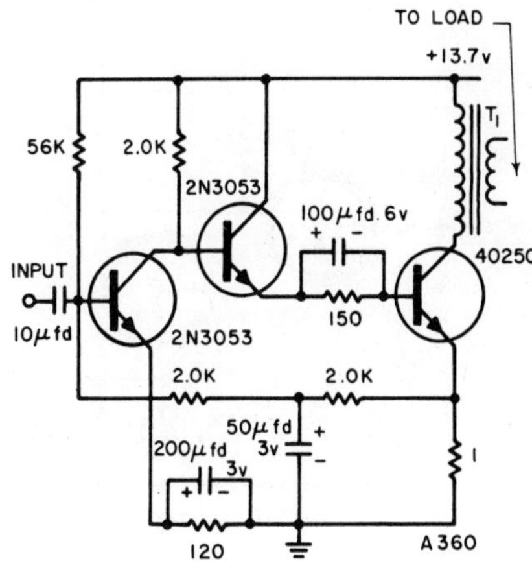

12-V OUTPUT STAGE—Provides medium power for audio applications. Converter and inverter applications for 40250 are given in RCA Application Note SMA-35.—Amplifiers and Converters, *Electronic Design*, March 15, 1965, p 217.

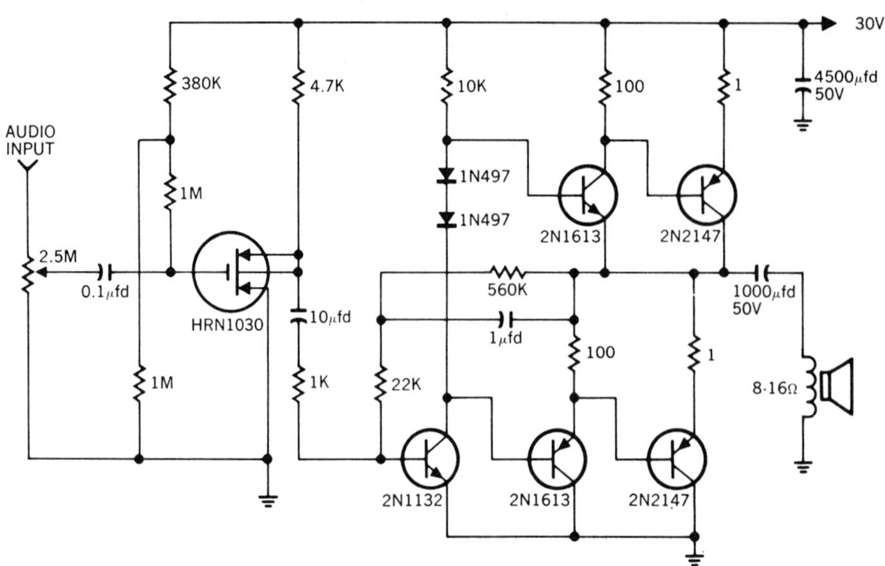

5-W HI-FI AMPLIFIER—Uses single mosfet input stage, for which two-mosfet tone control circuit may be substituted if desired.—C. R. Perkins, "Application of MOSFET Devices to Electronic Circuits," Hughes, Newport Beach, Cal., 1968, p 8.

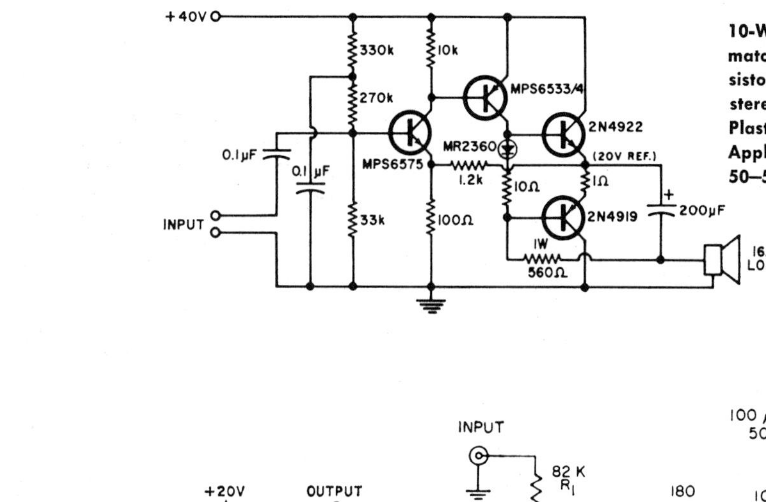

10-W COMPLEMENTARY AMPLIFIER—Uses matched pair of pnp and npn Motorola transistors to give high-fidelity performance for stereo and other applications.—D. E. Lancaster, Plastic Power Transistors—Advantages and Applications, *Electronics World*, Feb. 1968, p 50–52.

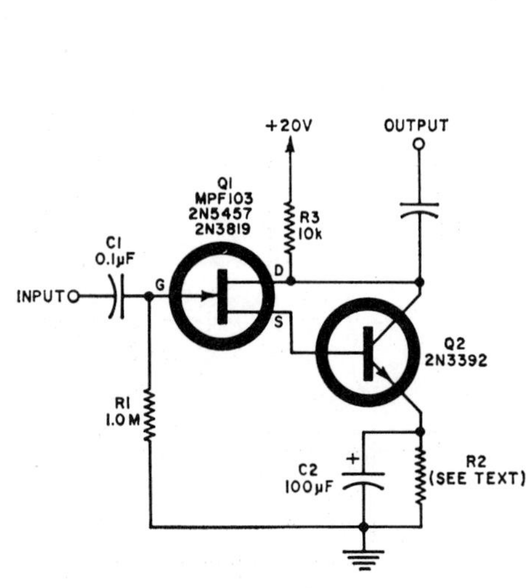

FET INPUT—Used when high audio voltage gain is more important than hi-fi quality. Signal voltage gain is 120, and frequency response is down 2 dB at 30 Hz and 10,000 Hz. R2 is between 560 and 1,200 ohms, selected to produce d-c stage current of 1 mA at 20 V.—F. H. Tooker, High-Gain Audio Input Stage, *Electronics World*, July 1969, p 77.

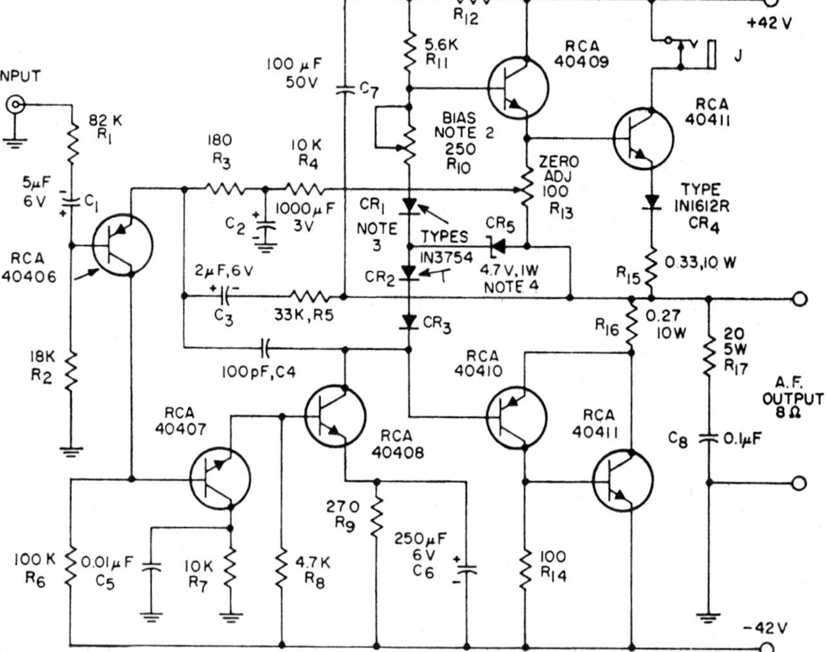

70-W 20-HZ QUASI-COMPLEMENTARY—Developed for amplifying 20-Hz sine-wave input and feeding 225-W peak power into 8-ohm load. Zener CR5 is 1M1519.—"Silicon Power Circuits Manual," RCA, Harrison, N.J., SP-5, p 100.

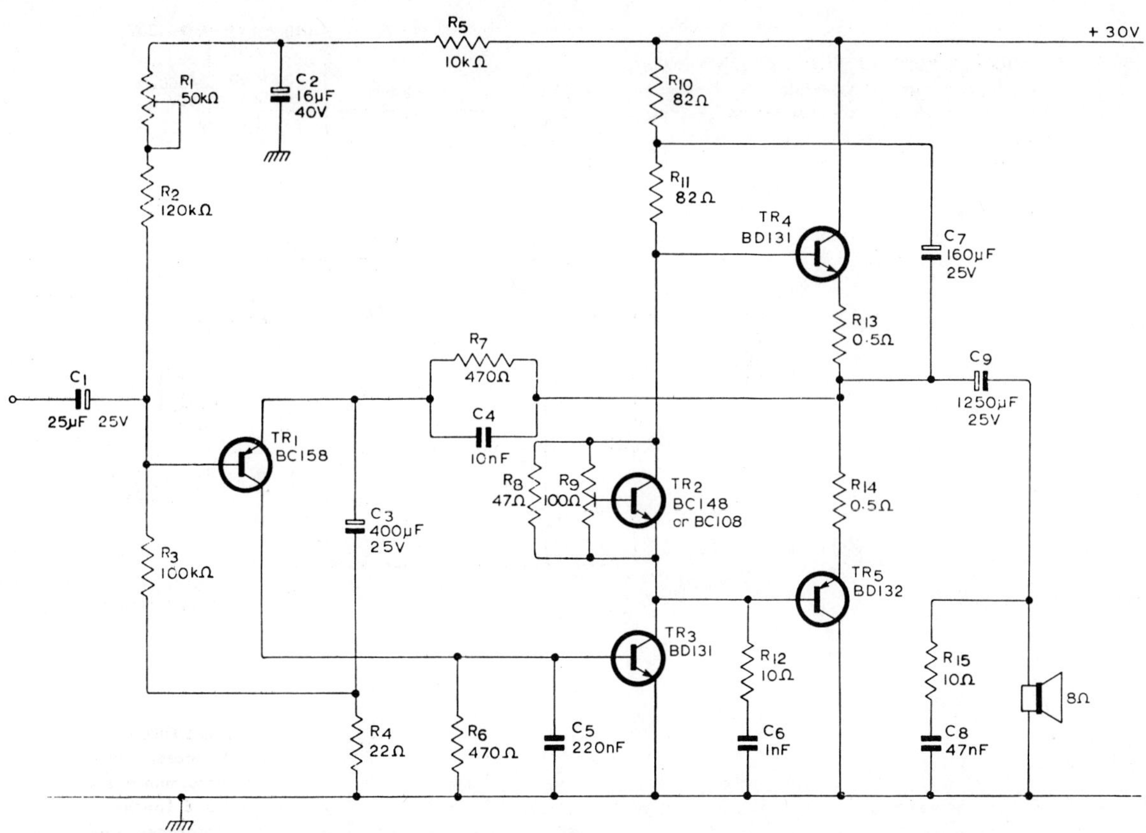

10-W HI-FI AMPLIFIER—Response is flat within 3 dB from 20 to 35,000 Hz for 2-W output. Distortion at rated output is less than 0.1%. Complementary pair of output transistors drives 8-ohm speaker directly. Book gives recommendations for layout of components to ensure high quality without hum.—"Transistor Audio and Radio Circuits," Mullard Ltd., London, 1969, p 102.

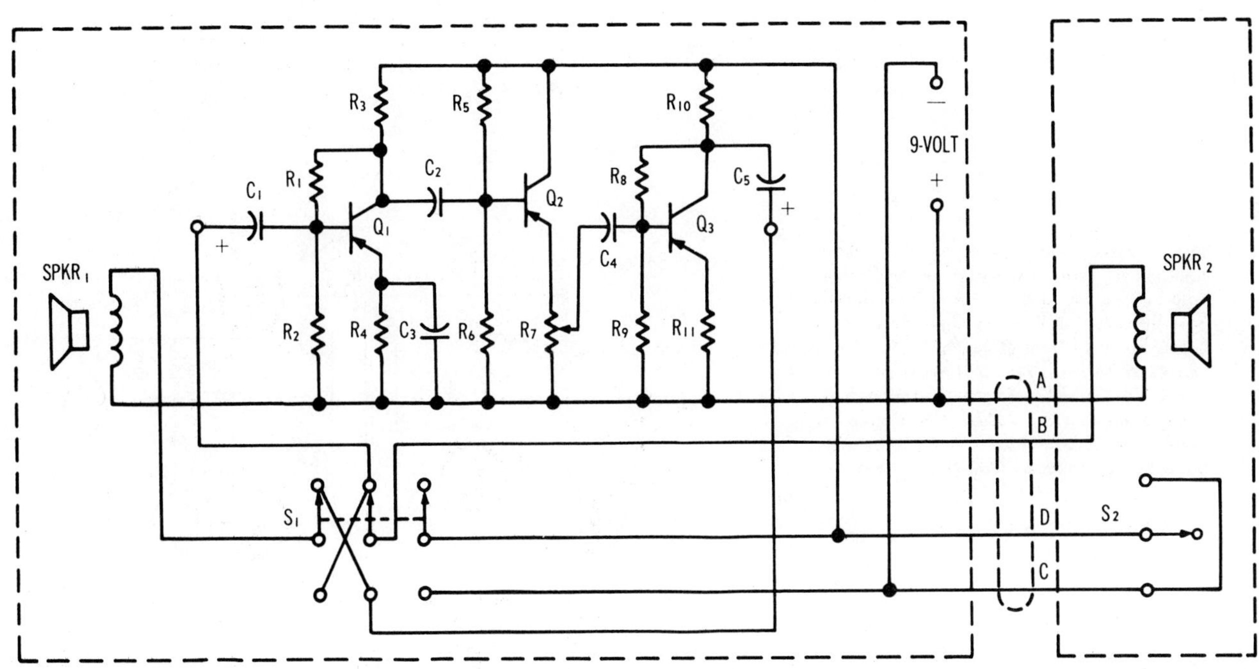

TWO-STATION INTERCOM—Can provide communication over distance of 100 feet, using 9 to 12 V voltage source. Circuit draws power only when message is being sent, thereby increasing battery life. Article gives construction details. Both speakers are 45 ohms. Parts values are: R1 100K; R2, R5, R6 10K; R3, R7 2K; R4 51; R8 1.5K; R9 100; R10 56; R11 0.47; C1, C2 5 μF; C3 25 μF; C4, C5 10 μF; Q1 HEP253; Q2 HEP254; Q3 HEP230.—"Solid State Projects Manual," Motorola, Phoenix, Ariz., 1968, p 45–50.

AUDIO FOR PORTABLE COLOR TV—Uses low-cost high-voltage glassivated D40N power transistor in class A common-emitter output stage having direct coupling to common-emitter driver. Maximum power output at 400 Hz is 2 W. At 1 W, distortion is about 10%.—E. L. Haas and D. V. Jones, Portable TV Sound System, General Electric, Syracuse, N.Y., No. 90.78, 1969.

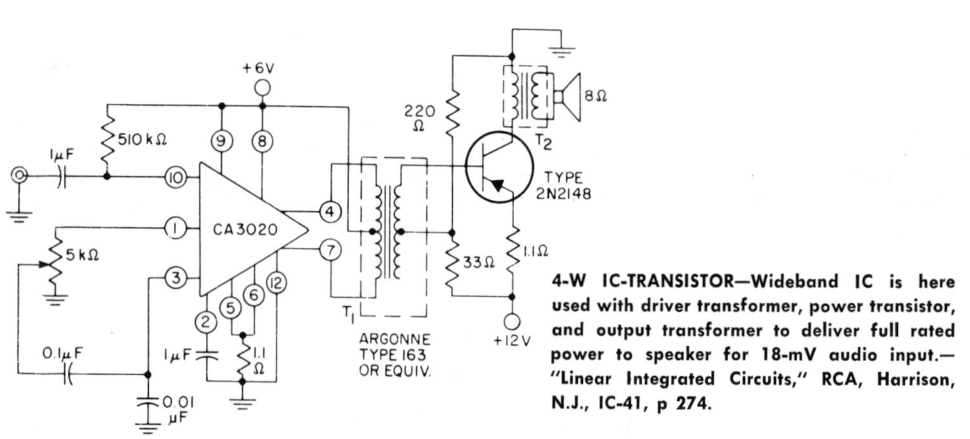

4-W IC-TRANSISTOR—Wideband IC is here used with driver transformer, power transistor, and output transformer to deliver full rated power to speaker for 18-mV audio input.—"Linear Integrated Circuits," RCA, Harrison, N.J., IC-41, p 274.

80-W POWER AMPLIFIER—Uses high-voltage high-power audio transistors in half-bridge push-pull output to drive 8-ohm load directly from balanced 50-V d-c supply. Response is flat within 1 dB from 20 to 20,000 Hz at 1 W and 20 W output. For 50 W per channel, d-c supply can be reduced to 35 V and bias resistor changed from 750 to 550 ohms.—160 Watt Stereo Audio Power Amplifier Design, Delco Radio, Kokomo, Ind., No. 35, 1968.

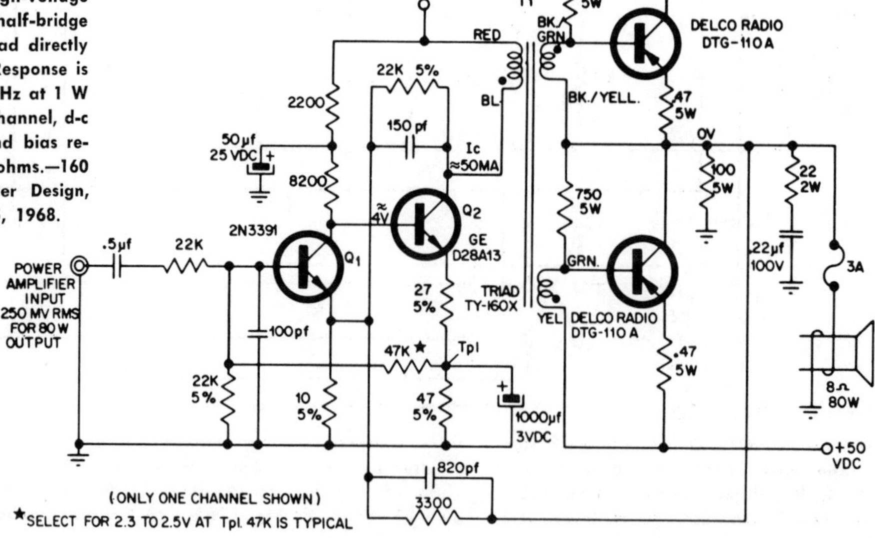

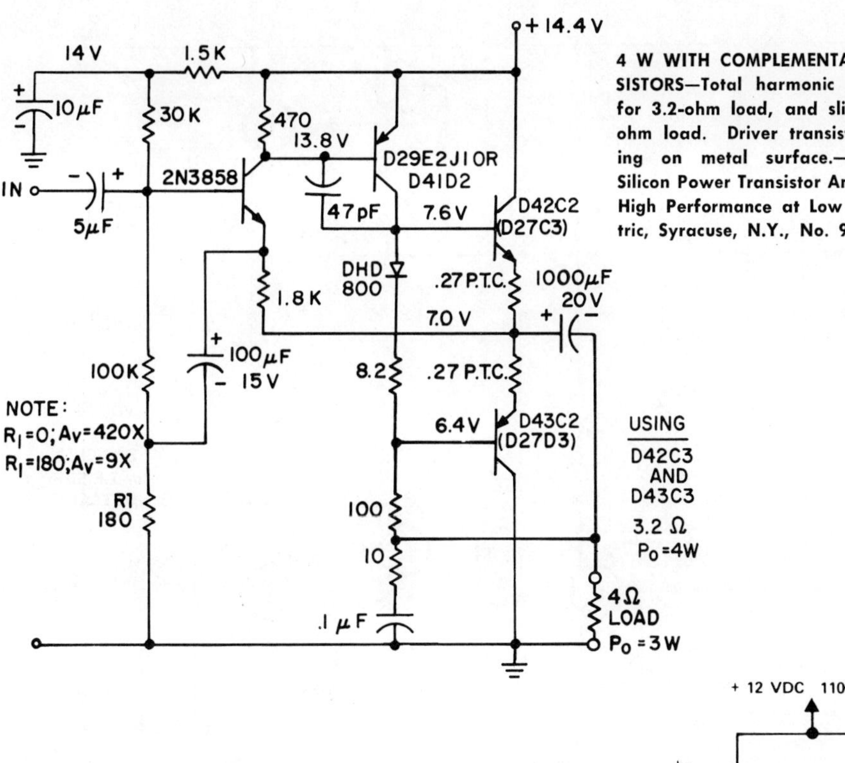

4 W WITH COMPLEMENTARY OUTPUT TRANSISTORS—Total harmonic distortion is 1.6% for 3.2-ohm load, and slightly higher for 4-ohm load. Driver transistor requires mounting on metal surface.—Dwight V. Jones, Silicon Power Transistor Amplifier Circuits with High Performance at Low Cost, General Electric, Syracuse, N.Y., No. 90.79, 1969.

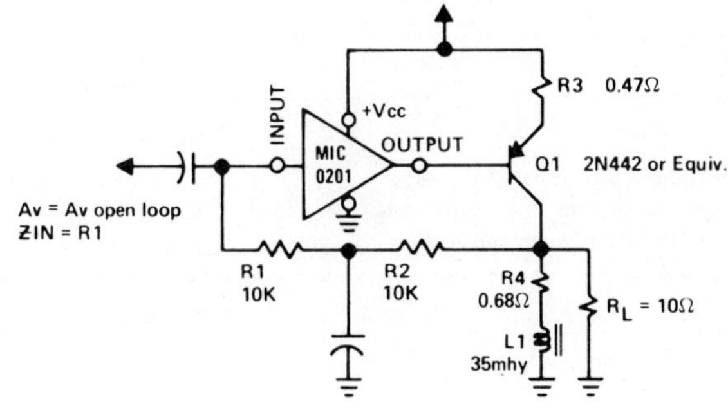

6-W IC WITHOUT A-C FEEDBACK—Provides high gain, with distortion still less than 10% at full power. Feeds 10-ohm speaker. Used in auto radios, tape players, and mobile power amplifiers. IC is Mallory MIC0201.—M. L. Deschler, Integrated Circuit Audio Driver Amplifier, Mallory, Indianapolis, Ind., APPN-1, 1968.

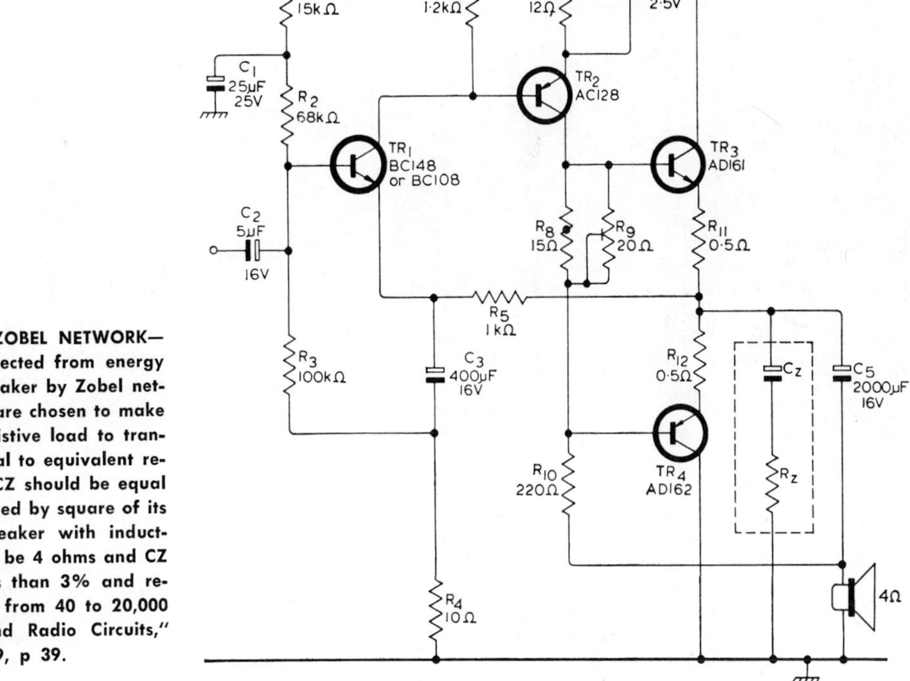

10-W AUDIO AMP WITH ZOBEL NETWORK—Output transistors are protected from energy stored in inductance of speaker by Zobel network RZ-CZ whose values are chosen to make speaker present purely resistive load to transistors. RZ should be equal to equivalent resistance of speakers, and CZ should be equal to speaker inductance divided by square of its resistance. For 4-ohm speaker with inductance of 200 μH, RZ should be 4 ohms and CZ 12.5 μF. Distortion is less than 3% and response is flat within 3 dB from 40 to 20,000 Hz.—"Transistor Audio and Radio Circuits," Mullard Ltd., London, 1969, p 39.

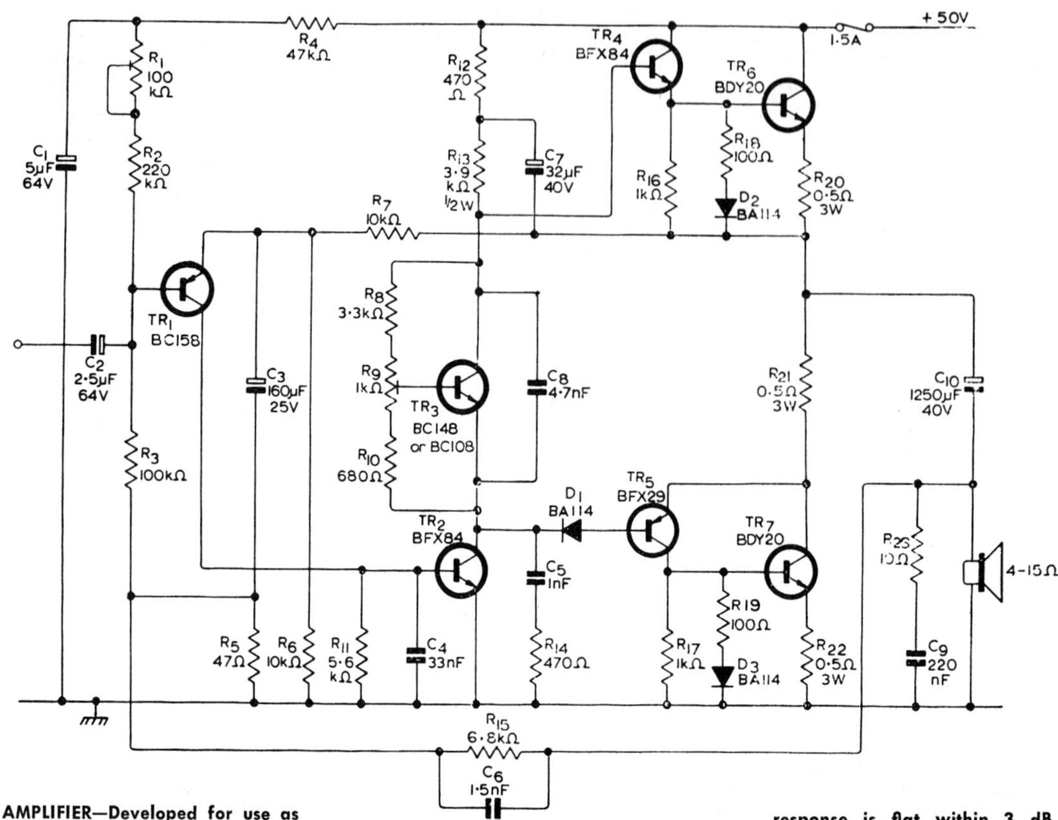

25-W HI-FI AMPLIFIER—Developed for use as one channel of stereo system. Matched output transistors are driven by matched complementary pair. Three diodes ensure that distortion in crossover region (at low output power) is very low. R1 is preset for symmetrical clipping in output stage. Frequency response is flat within 3 dB from 10 to 30,000 Hz, and distortion at full output is only 0.2%.—"Transistor Audio and Radio Circuits," Mullard Ltd., London, 1969, p 106.

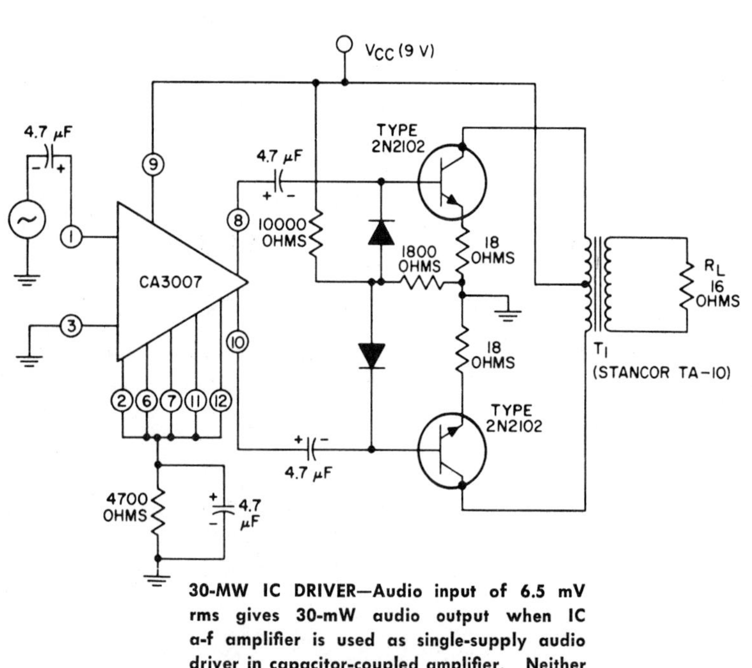

30-MW IC DRIVER—Audio input of 6.5 mV rms gives 30-mW audio output when IC a-f amplifier is used as single-supply audio driver in capacitor-coupled amplifier. Neither a-c nor d-c feedback loops are used.—"Linear Integrated Circuits," RCA, Harrison, N.J., IC-41, p 135.

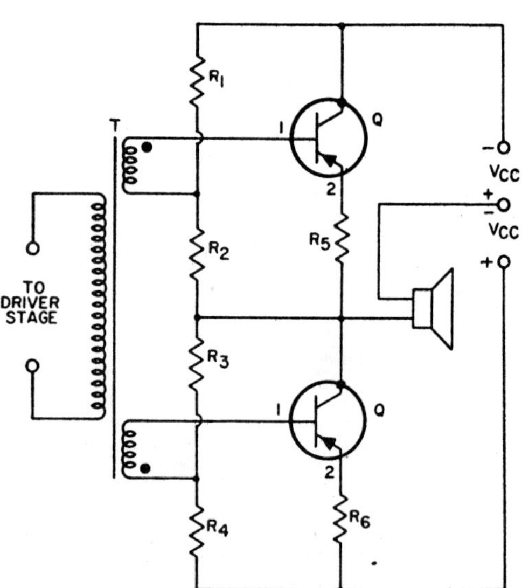

SINGLE-ENDED PUSH-PULL CLASS B—With 2N2147 power transistors, EIA music power output rating is 45 W and power gain 33 dB. Chief drawback is need for driver transformer. Values: R1, R3 330; R2, R4 3.9; R5, R6 0.27; Vcc 22 V.—"Transistor Manual," RCA, Harrison, N.J., SC-13, p 192.

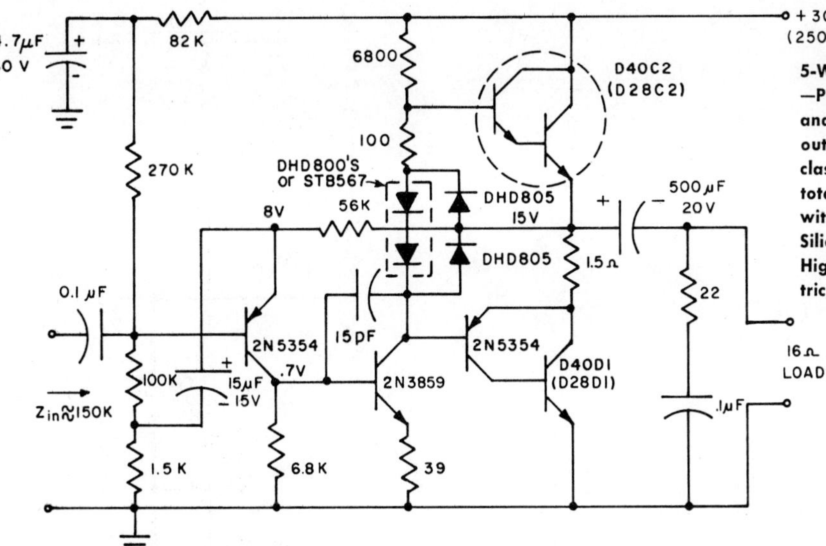

5-W AMPLIFIER WITH DARLINGTON OUTPUT—Pre-driver stage increases both sensitivity and input impedance. Power Darlington in output eliminates need for bootstrapping class A drive load resistor. At rated output, total harmonic distortion at 1 kHz is 1.5% with 280-mV input signal.—Dwight V. Jones, Silicon Power Transistor Amplifier Circuits with High Performance at Low Cost, General Electric, Syracuse, N.Y., No. 90.79, 1969.

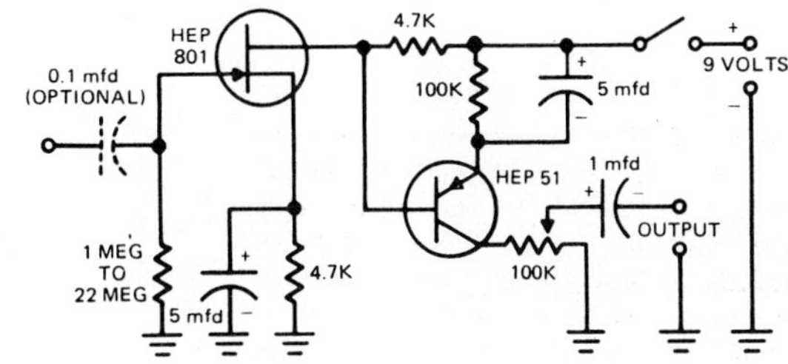

VERSATILE FET—Amplifies low-level audio signals over frequency range of 10 Hz to 30 kHz. Current drain is only 200 to 400 μA. Typical gain is 200 to 400. Has high input impedance and low output impedance.—"Tips on Using FET's," HMA-33, Motorola Semiconductor Products Inc., Phoenix, Ariz., 1969.

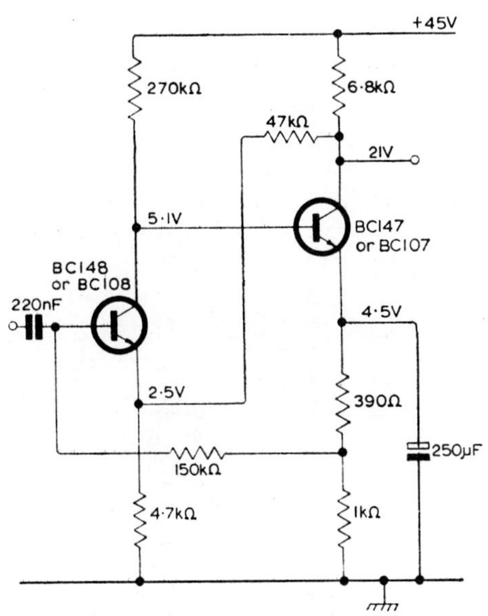

AMPLIFIER WITH HIGH VOLTAGE OUTPUT—Voltage gain is 20 dB and maximum output voltage 10 V, with 45-V supply. Input impedance is 140K and output impedance is 200 ohms. Response is flat within 3 dB from 20 to 20,000 Hz.—"Transistor Audio and Radio Circuits," Mullard Ltd., London, 1969, p 127.

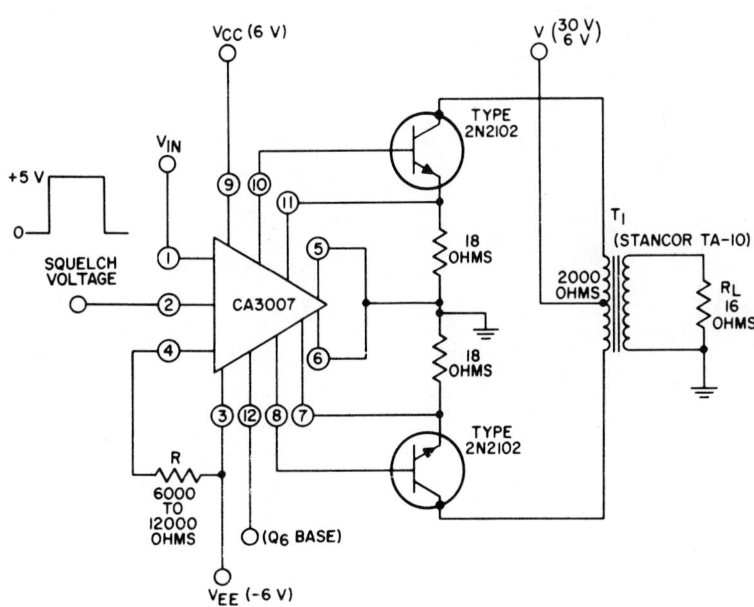

300-MW IC DRIVER—IC a-f amplifier is used as dual-supply audio driver in direct-coupled audio amplifier delivering 300 mW for audio input of 0.3 V rms with 30-V supply for output stage, and about 100 mW for 6-V supply. If audio squelch is not desired, terminal 2 must be grounded.—"Linear Integrated Circuits," RCA, Harrison, N.J., IC-41, p 133.

50-W POWER AMPLIFIER—Provides high performance at low cost for commercial home entertainment systems. Can be used after tone control or preamp stage providing 0.1 V signal. Bandwidth is flat within 1 dB from 20 to 20,000 Hz at 5 W. Total harmonic distortion is 2% at 1 kHz up to full output, and intermodulation distortion below 3% up to 40 W.—50 Watt Audio Power Amplifier Design, Delco Radio, Kokomo, Ind., No. 36, 1967.

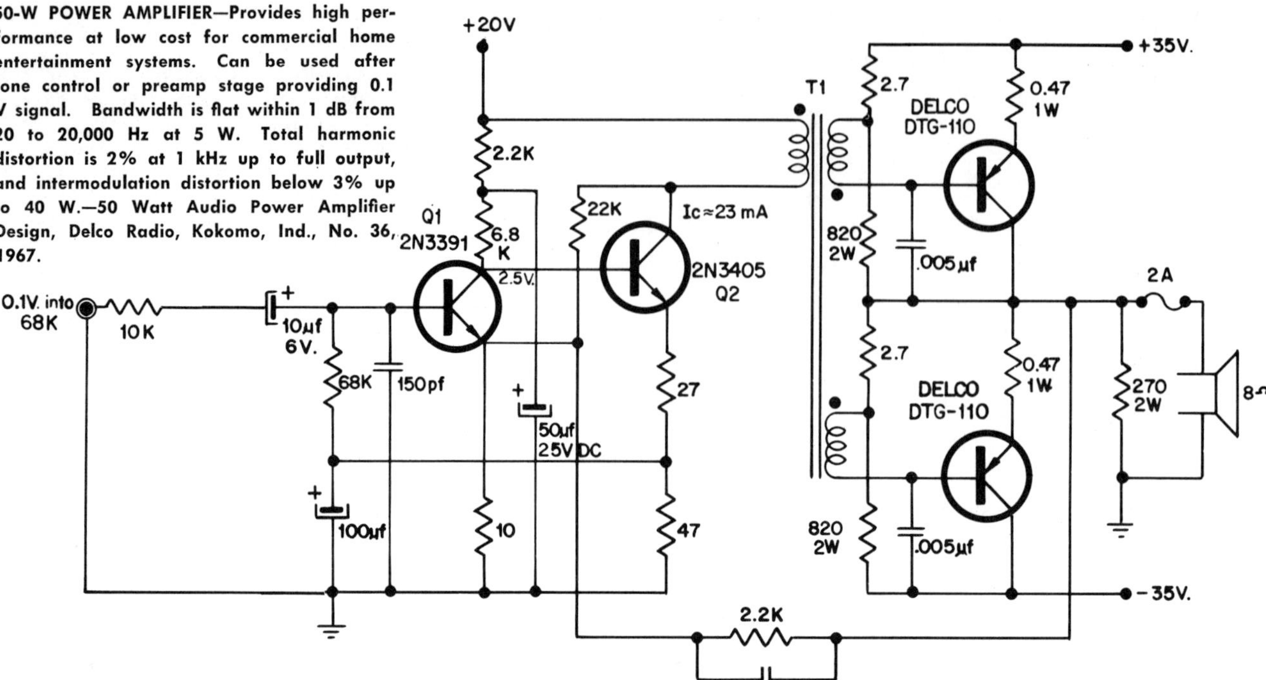

AUDIO BOOSTER—Single-transistor audio amplifier operating from 1.5-V alkaline cell can be mounted in base of desk-stand microphone for use as preamp, to give more modulation for any transmitter and less hum pickup even when using long microphone cable. T1 is miniature audio transformer having 100,000-ohm primary (for use with high-impedance mike) and 1,000-ohm secondary. For low-impedance mike, omit T1 and connect directly to C1. Book gives construction details.—E. A. Morris, Modulation Booster, "Bench-Tested Communications Projects," Hayden Book Co., N.Y., p 51–54.

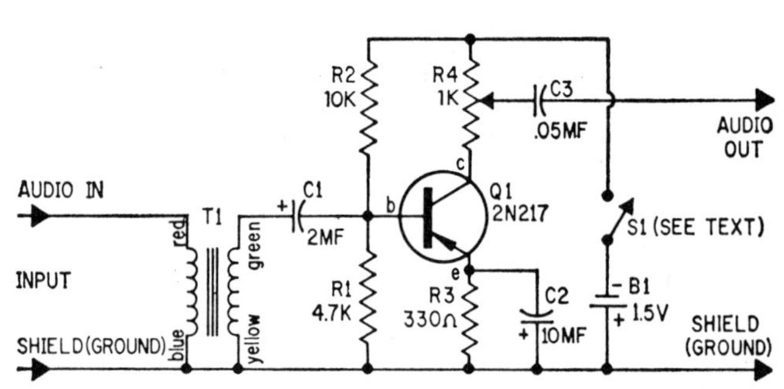

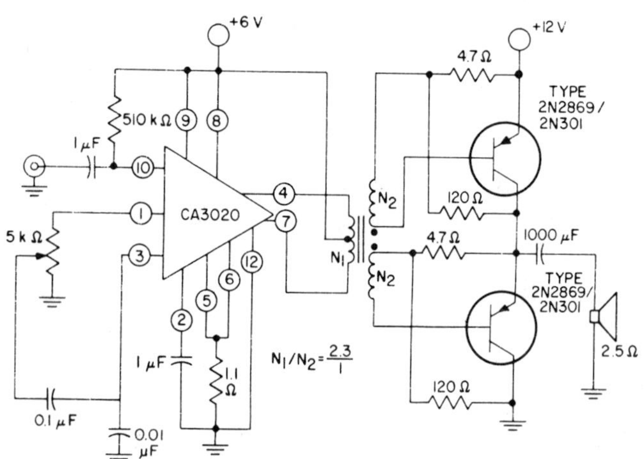

7-W SINGLE-ENDED CLASS B—Two power transistors in single-ended output stage drive 2.5-ohm speaker directly with full rated power for input of 14.2 mV to IC wideband amplifier.—"Linear Integrated Circuits," RCA, Harrison, N.J., IC-41, p 274.

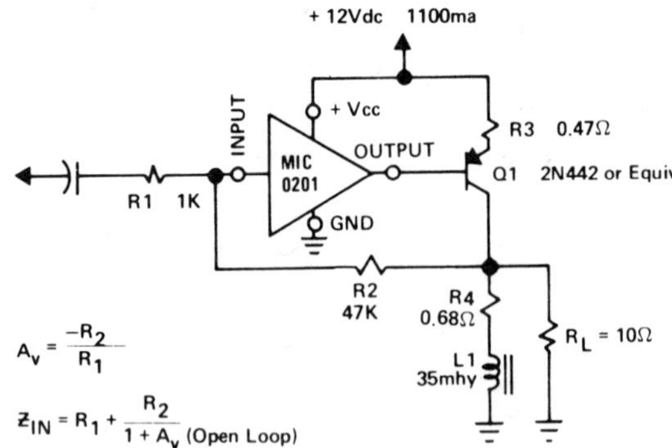

6-W IC WITH SHUNT A-C FEEDBACK—Uses Mallory MIC0201 audio driver IC with minimum number of external components. Distortion is less than 1% for outputs up to 3.5 W. Distortion increases to 10% for outputs above 6 W. Used in auto radios, tape players, and mobile power amplifiers.—M. L. Deschler, Integrated Circuit Audio Driver Amplifier, Mallory, Indianapolis, Ind., APPN-1, 1968.

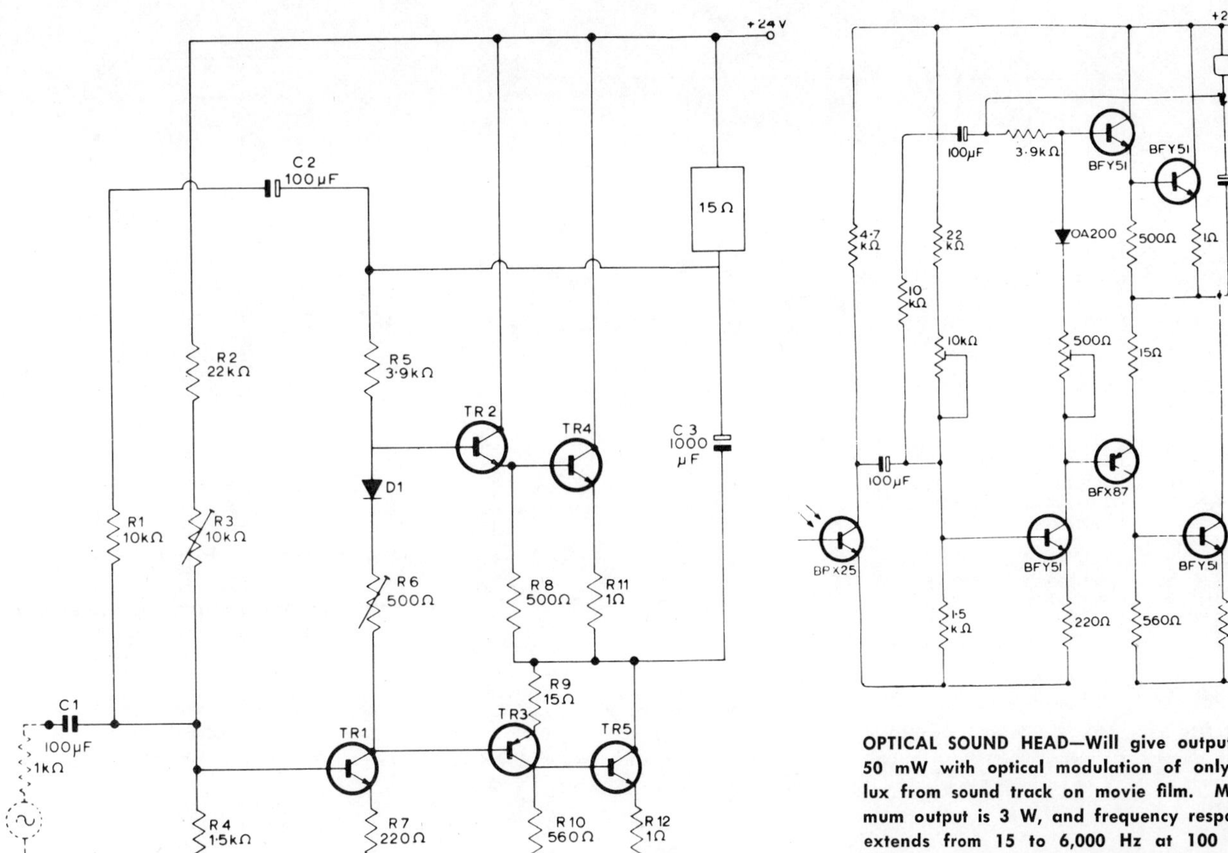

3-W UTILITY AMPLIFIER—Power gain is 38 dB, voltage gain 20 dB, and response is flat within 3 dB from 15 Hz to 50,000 Hz. Will drive loudspeaker directly. TR3 is BCY32 and other transistors are BFY51. Diode is OA200.—Applications of the BFY50, BFY51 and BFY52, Philips, Pub. Dept., Elcoma Div., Eindhoven, The Netherlands, No. 428, 1965.

OPTICAL SOUND HEAD—Will give output of 50 mW with optical modulation of only 50 lux from sound track on movie film. Maximum output is 3 W, and frequency response extends from 15 to 6,000 Hz at 100 lux. Required intensity through 0.08 × 0.01-inch slot, for bandwidth of 6 Hz and full output, can be obtained by focusing 1-W miniature lamp on slot.—Applications of Silicon Planar Phototransistor BPX25, Philips, Pub. Dept., Elcoma Div., Eindhoven, The Netherlands, No. 316, 1967.

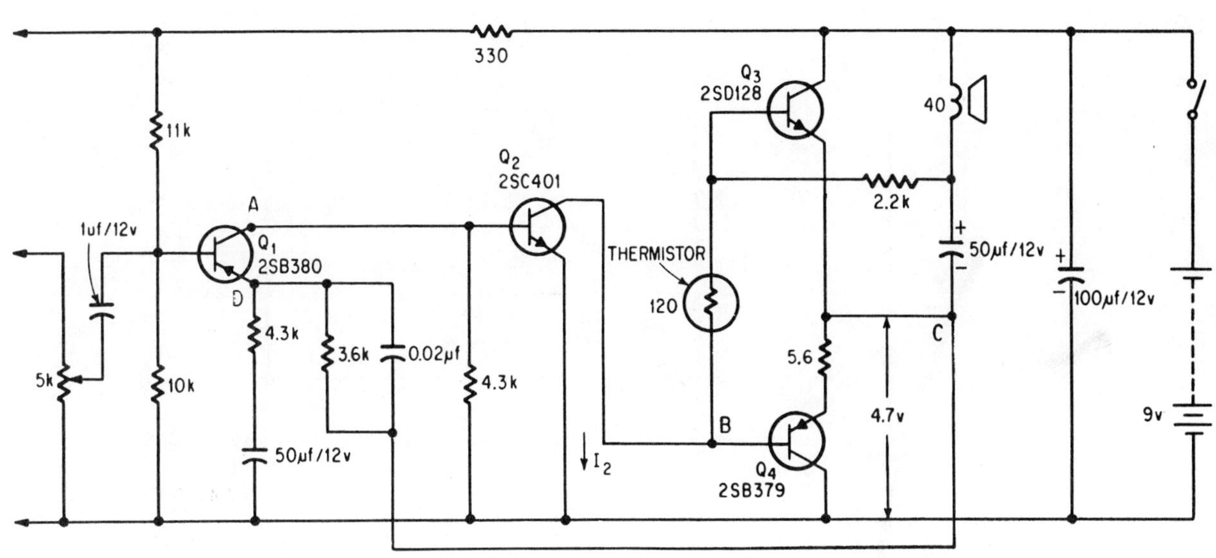

DIRECT-COUPLED OUTPUT—Direct coupling in Sony model 2R-27 a-m portable radio eliminates two coupling transformers and reduces no-signal battery drain to 5.5 mA, thus increasing battery life 30%. First two stages use complementary-symmetry cascade connection, while output stage is class B push-pull complementary symmetry. High stability is obtained by 100% d-c negative feedback from output stage through 3.6K resistor to Q1.—Ceramic Filters Edge Out Costly I-F Transformers, *Electronics*, Nov. 14, 1966, p 160—163.

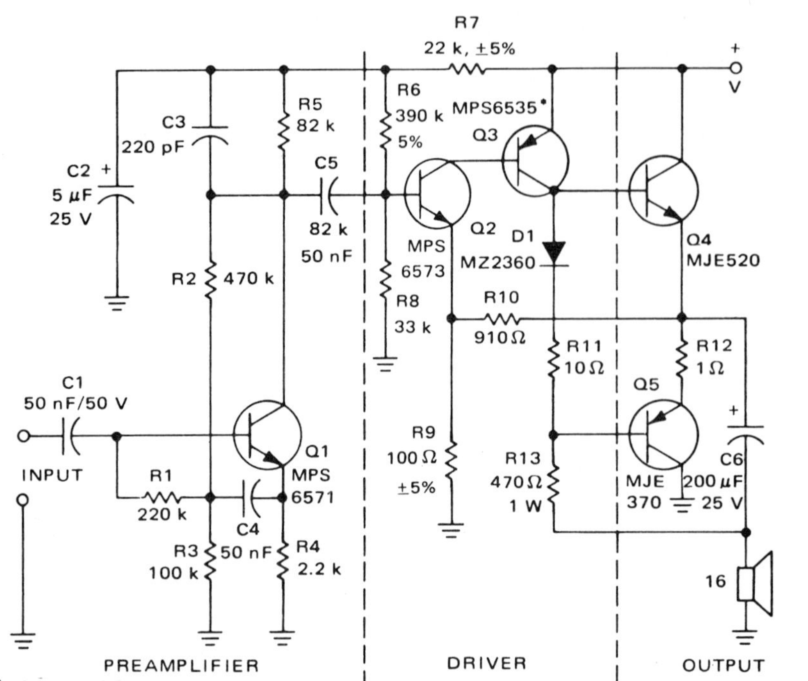

5 W FOR 16 OHMS—Simple and economical audio power amplifier delivers rated output for input of 0.1 V rms. Response is down 3 dB at 40 Hz and well above 20 kHz. Book gives changes needed for 10-W output.—"Semiconductor Power Circuits Handbook," Motorola, Phoenix, Ariz., 1968, p 5–34.

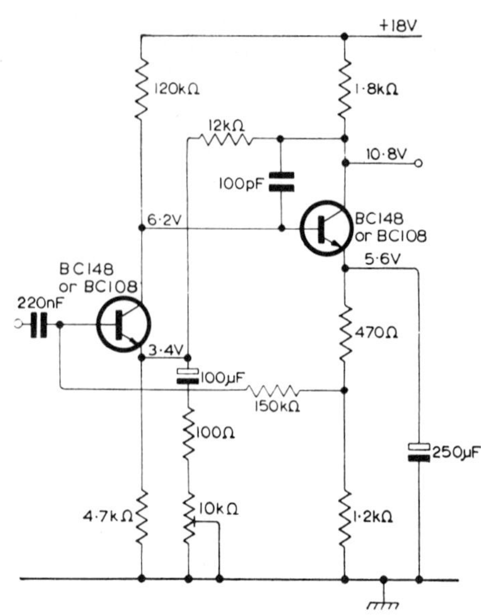

MICROPHONE AMPLIFIER—Voltage gain is adjustable between 13 and 40 dB by varying feedback with 10K pot. Distortion at maximum gain is 0.75% for 2-V output, input impedance is 120K, and output impedance is 120 ohms.—"Transistor Audio and Radio Circuits," Mullard Ltd., London, 1969, p 124.

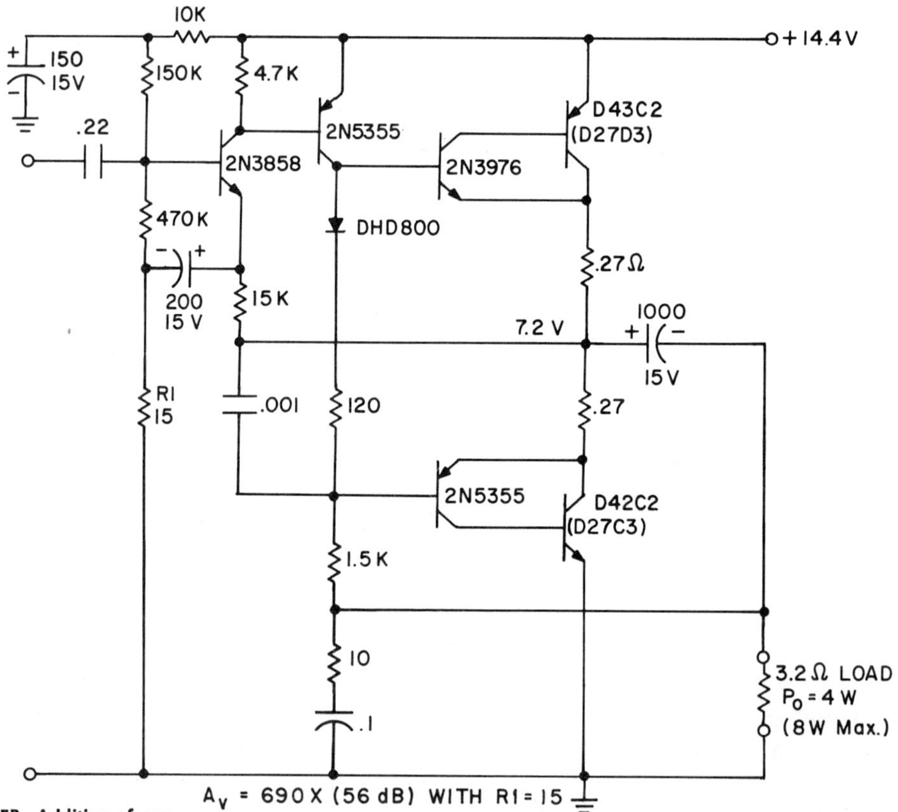

4-W HIGH-GAIN AMPLIFIER—Addition of complementary push-pull drive stage to basic complementary output transistor arrangement permits class A drive stage to be operated at lower current and power dissipation. This gives higher voltage gain and permits use of lower-cost transistors. Added sensitivity reduces distortion. Total harmonic distortion at 1 kHz is 1.8% for 5.4-mV input signal.—Dwight V. Jones, Silicon Power Transistor Amplifier Circuits with High Performance at Low Cost, General Electric, Syracuse, N.Y., No. 90.79, 1969.

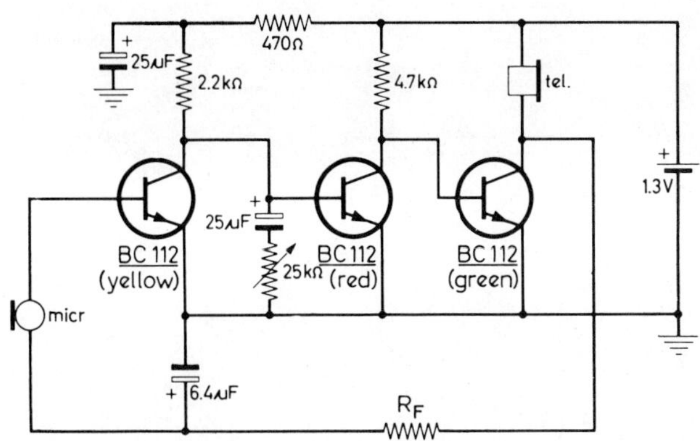

1-MW HEARING AID—Three-transistor circuit provides adequate power for conventional behind-the-ear hearing aid. Requires only 25K volume control, low enough to be reliable as miniature pot. Input can range from 100 μV to 5 mV. Value of RF depends on transistor currents; average value is 350K.—A. M. Aelbers and A. M. Peters, The Microminiature Transistor BC112 Employed in a Direct Coupled Hearing Aid Amplifier with 1 mW Output, Philips, Pub. Dept., Elcoma Div., Eindhoven, The Netherlands, No. 135, 1966.

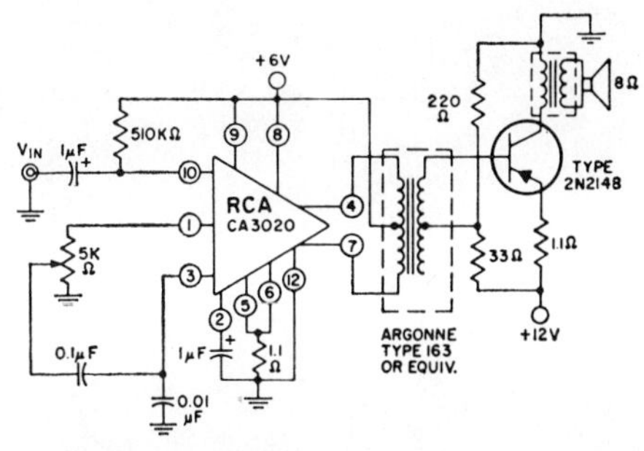

4-W CLASS-A AMPLIFIER WITH IC—Integrated circuit provides 58 dB power gain in driving transistor output stage through coupling transformer.—D. E. Lancaster, Audio Integrated Circuits—What's Available?, *Electronics World*, Oct. 1967, p 34–36.

SEISMIC AMPLIFIER—Can amplify faint echoes of distant explosive charge without being saturated by direct sound of underground explosion used in geophysical prospecting. Gain is about 25 for microvolt inputs, and decreases automatically as input increases to millivolt levels. Only first stage is shown; five stages give maximum overall gain of 1,000,000 and input dynamic range of 60 dB from 1-μV minimum signal. Third stage has manual level control that adjusts gain without affecting frequency response or dynamic range.—G. S. Lehsten, Audio Amplifier Adjusts Gain to Input Levels, *Electronics*, May 29, 1967, p 86–87.

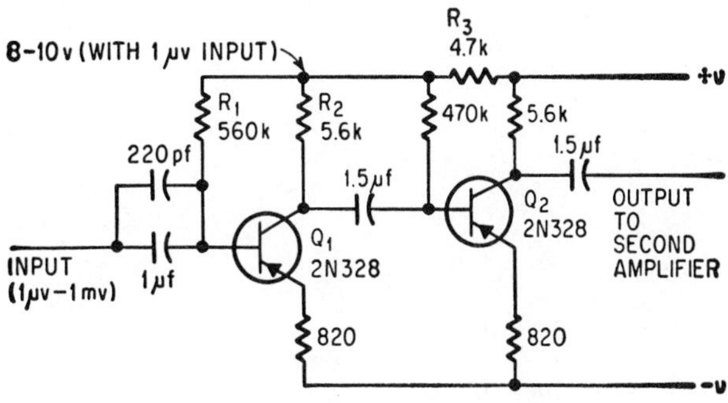

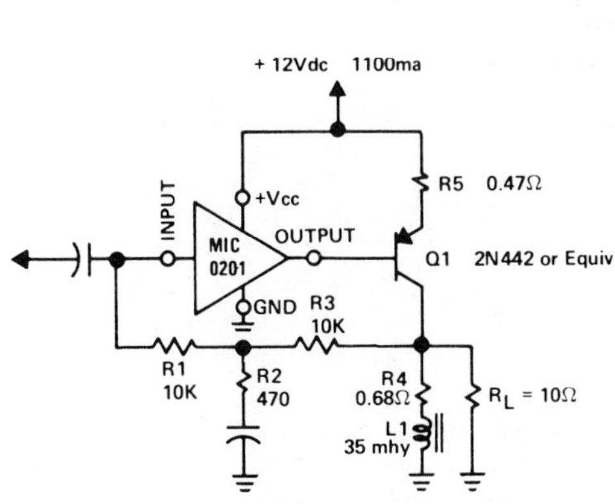

6-W IC WITH SERIES-SHUNT A-C FEEDBACK—Input impedance is 1K but circuit retains high sensitivity (20 mV input for 2 W output) even with feedback from output transistor to Mallory MIC0201 IC input. Distortion is about 10% for 6 W but less than 5% up to 4.5 W. —M. L. Deschler, Integrated Circuit Audio Driver Amplifier, Mallory, Indianapolis, Ind., APPN-1, 1968.

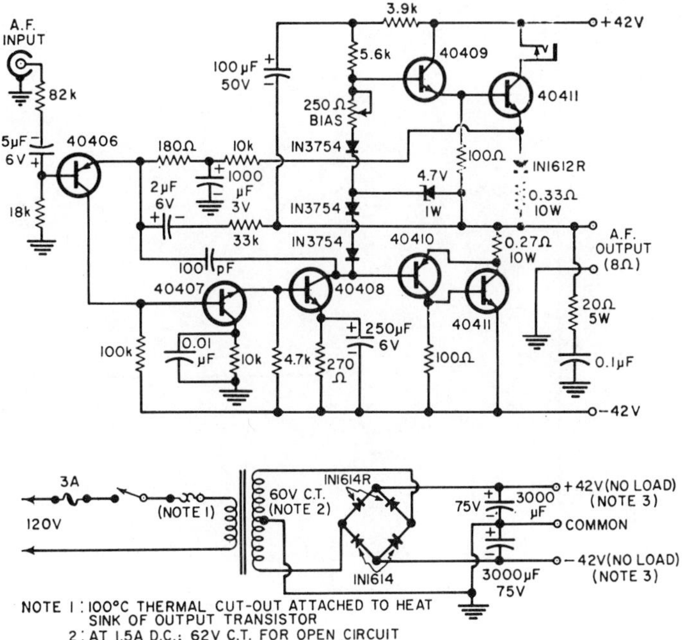

70-W HI-FI—Response is flat within 1 dB from 5 to 25,000 Hz. Diodes in driver stage are thermally connected to output transistor heat sinks, to maintain preset 20 mA of quiescent output current at case temperatures up to 100 C. Other circuit features contribute to stability and reliability.—R. D. Gold and J. C. Sondermeyer, Designing Silicon-Transistor Hi-Fi Amplifiers, *Electronics World*, Nov. 1966, p 47–50 and 80–81.

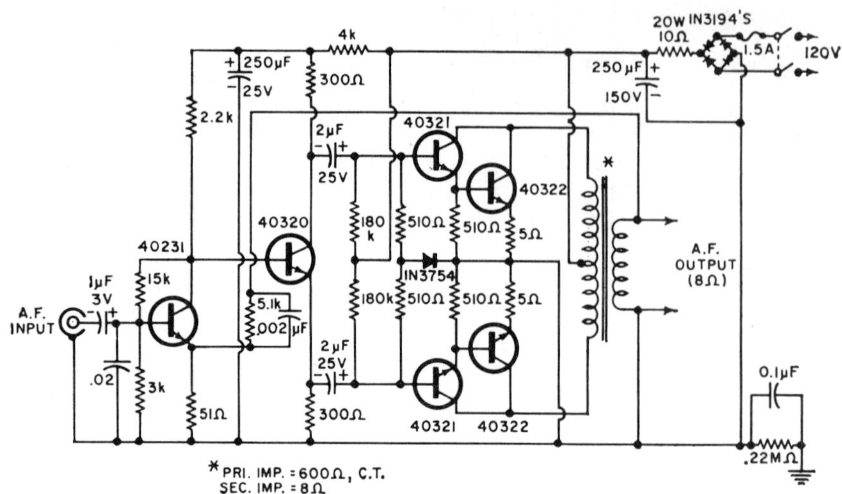

25-W PUBLIC ADDRESS—Transformer-coupled a-c/d-c class-AB audio amplifier provides output impedance flexibility. Drivers use Darlington arrangement to output transistors. Input impedance is 2,500 ohms. Response is flat within 3 dB from about 30 to 10,000 Hz.—R. D. Gold and J. S. Sondermeyer, Designing Silicon-Transistor Hi-Fi Amplifiers, *Electronics World*, Nov. 1966, p 47–50 and 80–81.

0.8-MW IC HEARING AID—Uses TAA370 IC driving 1,000-ohm earpiece. Total current drain is 1.65 mA from 1.55-V silver oxide cell. R10 is 3.3K. Report gives performance curves.—The Amperex TAA 370 as a Hearing Aid Amplifier, Amperex, Slatersville, R.I., S-139, 1968.

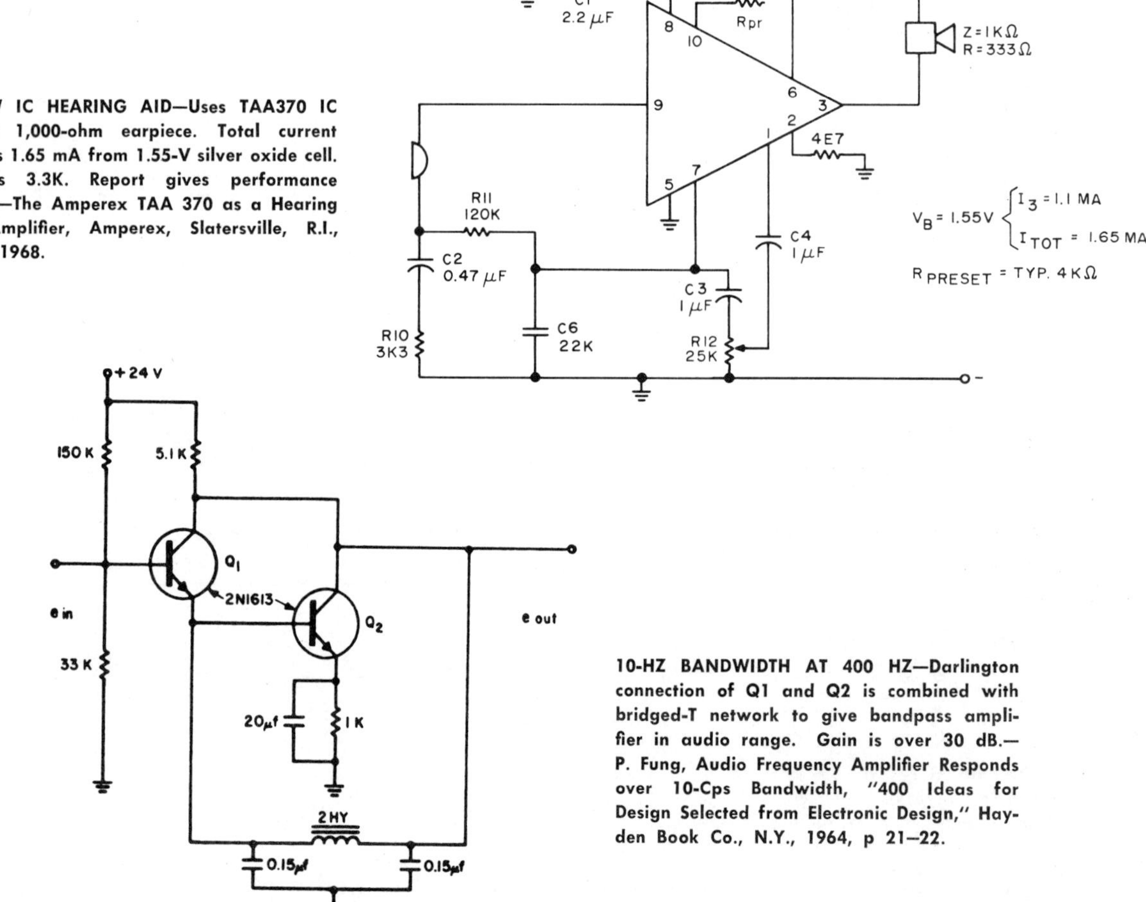

10-HZ BANDWIDTH AT 400 HZ—Darlington connection of Q1 and Q2 is combined with bridged-T network to give bandpass amplifier in audio range. Gain is over 30 dB.—P. Fung, Audio Frequency Amplifier Responds over 10-Cps Bandwidth, "400 Ideas for Design Selected from Electronic Design," Hayden Book Co., N.Y., 1964, p 21–22.

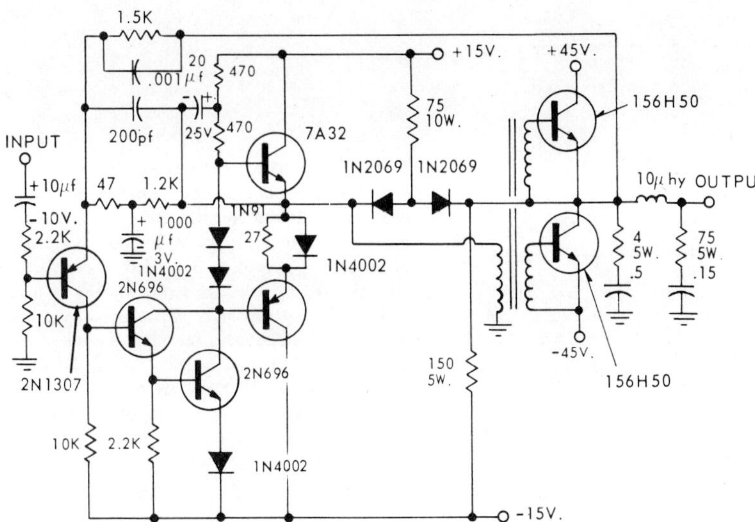

100 W PER CHANNEL—Intermodulation distortion is below 0.3% at any power level, and total harmonic distortion below 0.5% from 20 to 20,000 Hz. Latching diode circuit is used ahead of power stage to disconnect it from driver when instantaneous voltage across output terminals is greater than 15-V supply voltage of driver. Power stage efficiency is 78%.—"Silicon Power Transistor Handbook," Westinghouse, Youngwood, Pa., p 6–17.

15-W QUASI-COMPLEMENTARY—Provides hi-fi performance for mono or in pairs for stereo, while requiring only npn transistors in output stage. Fet serves as high-input-impedance preamplifier.—D. E. Lancaster, Plastic Power Transistors—Advantages and Applications, *Electronics World*, Feb. 1968, p 50–52.

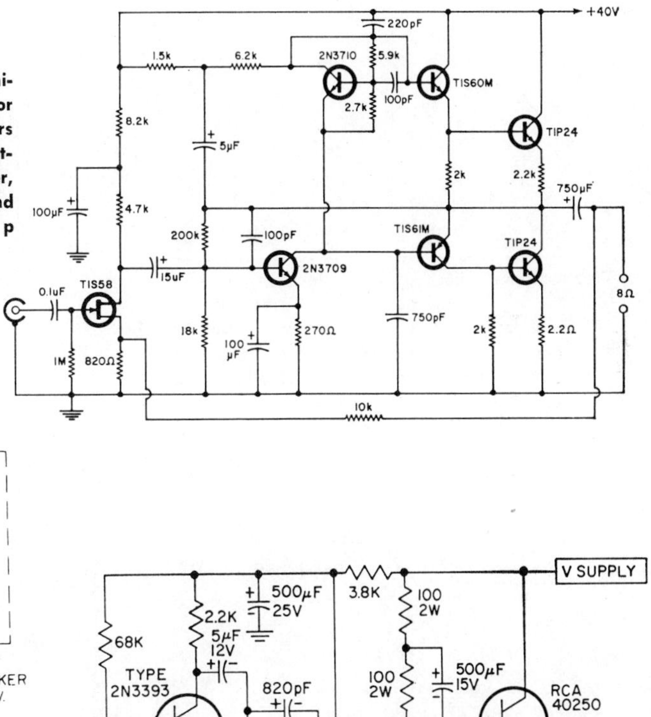

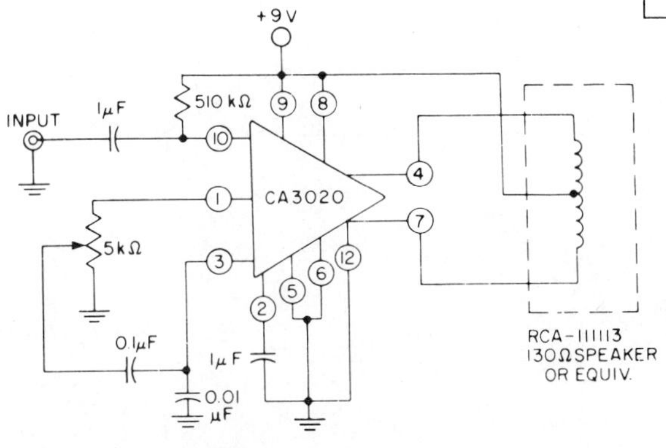

310-MW IC TRANSFORMERLESS—Can be used with most a-m and f-m detectors, because full power is developed for 45-mV input voltage. Total harmonic distortion is only 1%.—"Linear Integrated Circuits," RCA, Harrison, N.J., IC-41, p 272.

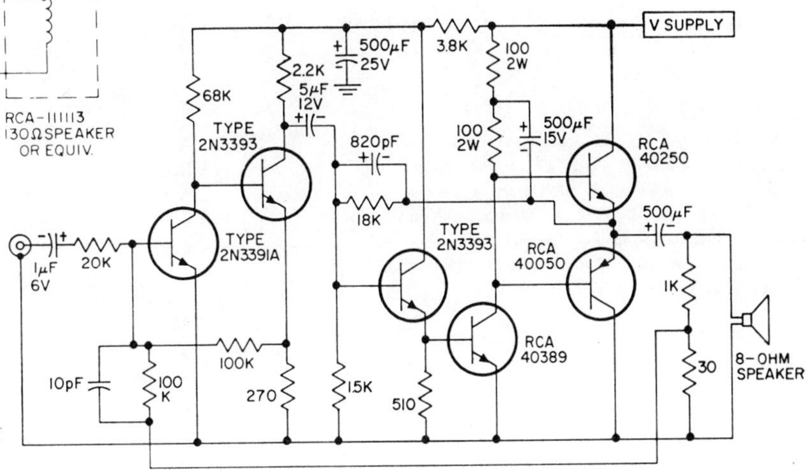

CLASS-B COMPLEMENTARY-SYMMETRY POWER AMPLIFIER—Book gives detailed design procedure for overcoming bias dissipation. Storage effects are reduced as result of reverse bias provided for OFF transistor by ON transistor in complementary symmetry.—"Silicon Power Circuits Manual," RCA, Harrison, N.J., SP-51, p 402.

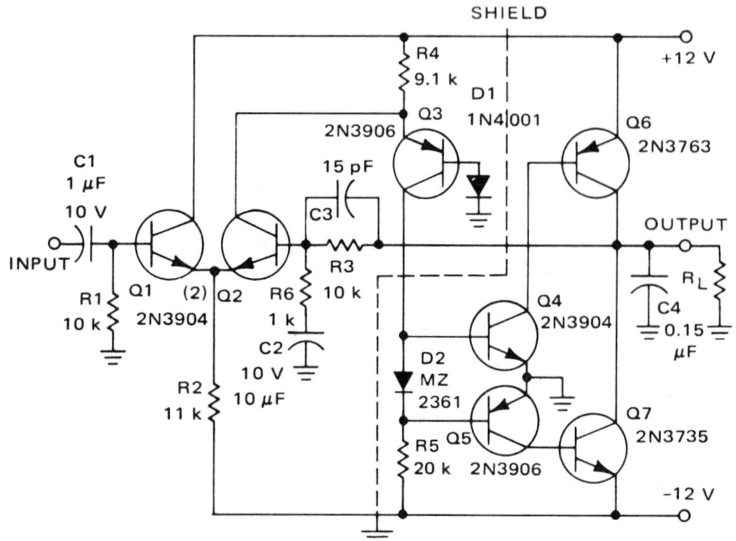

4-W WIDEBAND AMPLIFIER—Bandwidth is 100 kHz and minimum power output 2 W. Beta product of Q4-Q6 and Q5-Q7 complementary pairs should be matched to give low d-c offset at amplifier output and minimize distortion. At 4-W output, response is flat within — 1 dB from 45 Hz to 100 kHz. Distortion limits are more than adequate for hi-fi applications. Can be used as d-c amplifier with excellent stability if C1 and C2 are shorted out.—"Semiconductor Power Circuits Handbook," Motorola, Phoenix, Ariz., 1968, p 5—30.

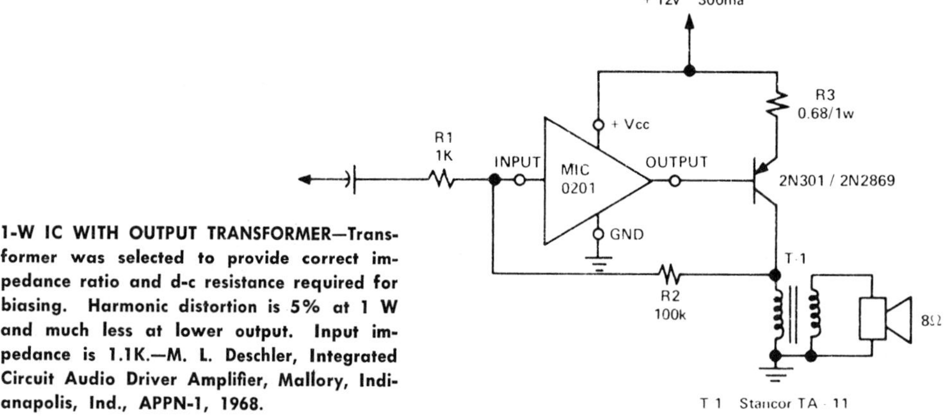

1-W IC WITH OUTPUT TRANSFORMER—Transformer was selected to provide correct impedance ratio and d-c resistance required for biasing. Harmonic distortion is 5% at 1 W and much less at lower output. Input impedance is 1.1K.—M. L. Deschler, Integrated Circuit Audio Driver Amplifier, Mallory, Indianapolis, Ind., APPN-1, 1968.

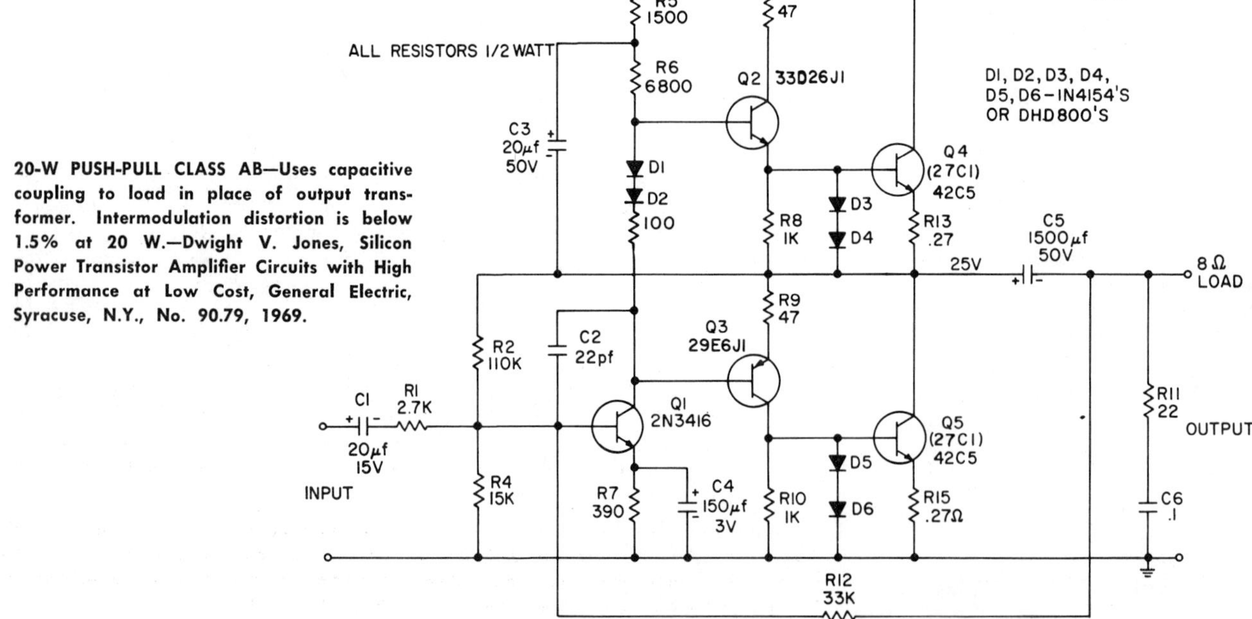

20-W PUSH-PULL CLASS AB—Uses capacitive coupling to load in place of output transformer. Intermodulation distortion is below 1.5% at 20 W.—Dwight V. Jones, Silicon Power Transistor Amplifier Circuits with High Performance at Low Cost, General Electric, Syracuse, N.Y., No. 90.79, 1969.

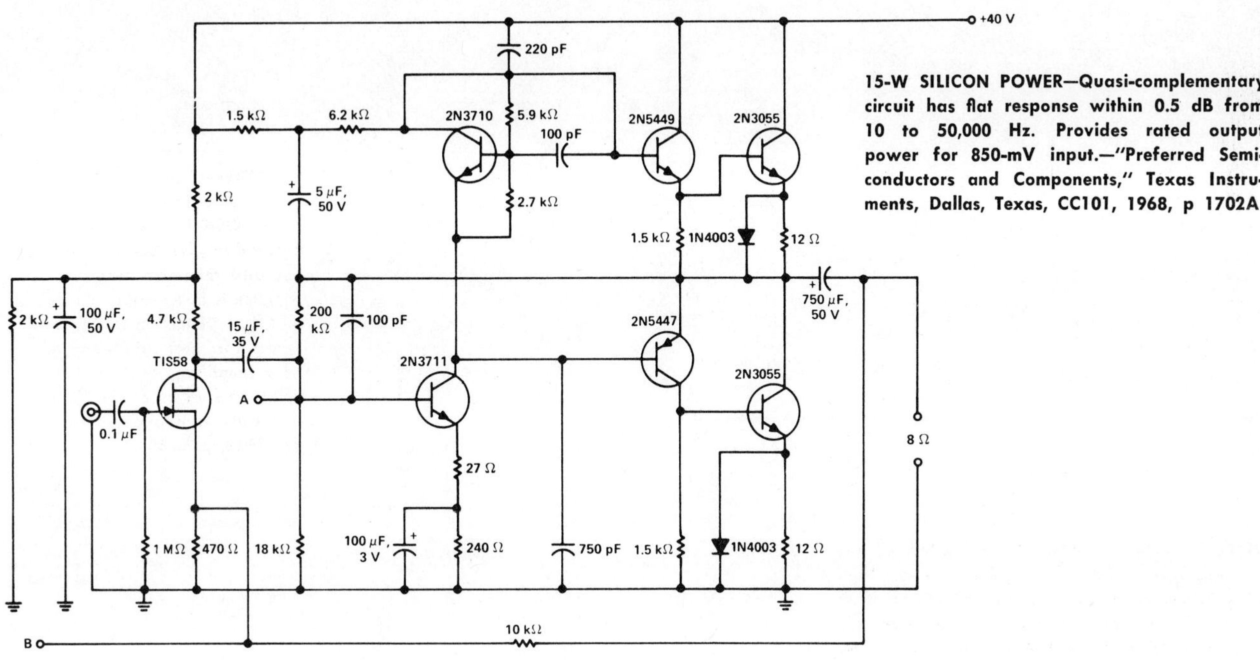

15-W SILICON POWER—Quasi-complementary circuit has flat response within 0.5 dB from 10 to 50,000 Hz. Provides rated output power for 850-mV input.—"Preferred Semiconductors and Components," Texas Instruments, Dallas, Texas, CC101, 1968, p 1702A.

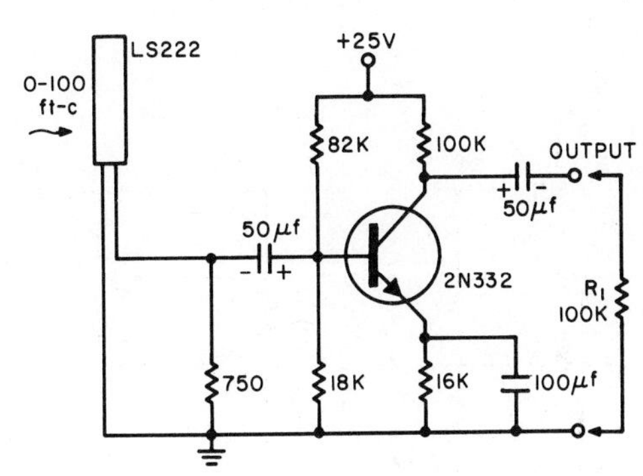

SOUND-ON-FILM HEAD—Uses silicon photovoltaic sensor producing 26.7 μA output at 0 Hz and 21.3 μA at 20 kHz, boosted by preamp to 1.8 V p-p at 20 Hz and 1.2 V p-p at 10 kHz. Output is linear within 3 dB from — 40 to 75 C.—Light Sensor and Preamplifier, *Electronic Design*, Feb. 3, 1964, p 44.

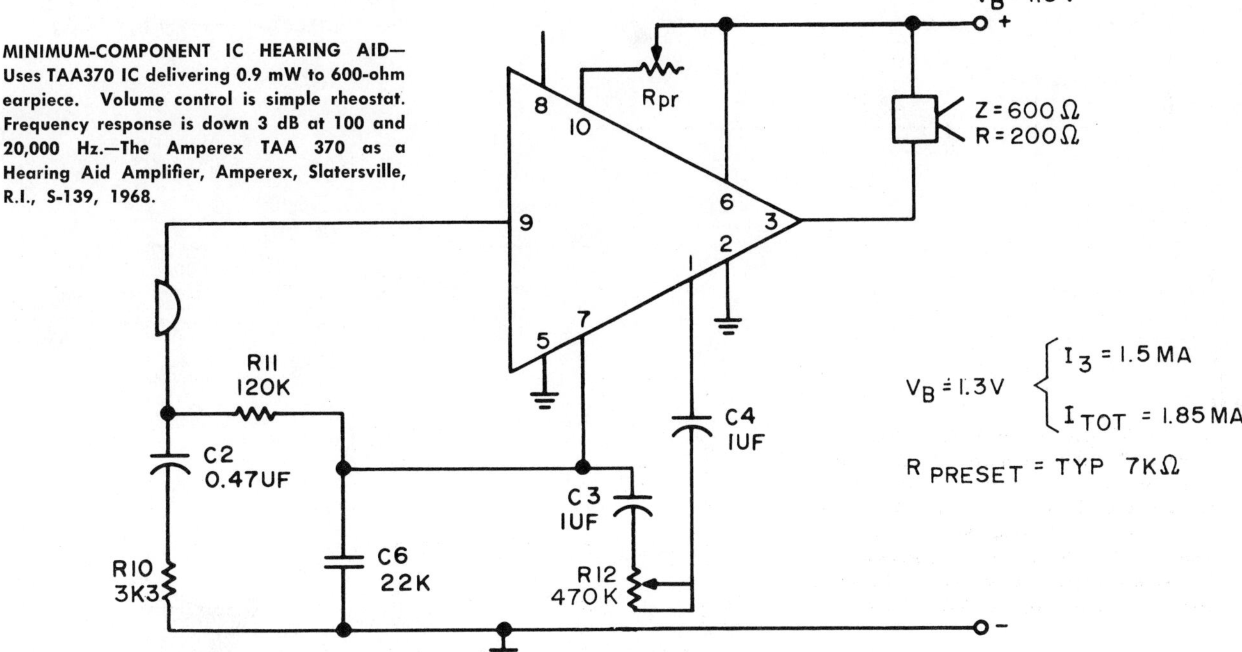

MINIMUM-COMPONENT IC HEARING AID—Uses TAA370 IC delivering 0.9 mW to 600-ohm earpiece. Volume control is simple rheostat. Frequency response is down 3 dB at 100 and 20,000 Hz.—The Amperex TAA 370 as a Hearing Aid Amplifier, Amperex, Slatersville, R.I., S-139, 1968.

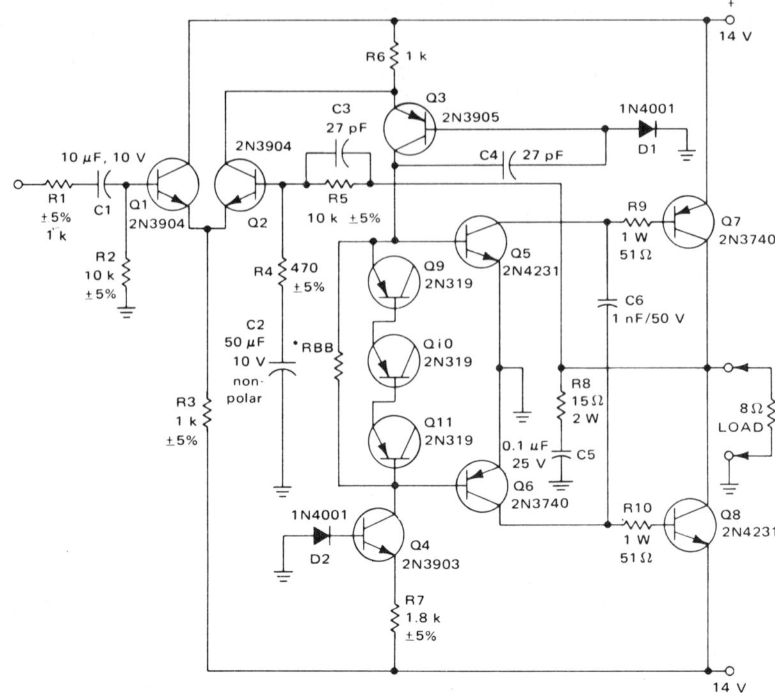

10 W FOR 8 OHMS—Direct-coupled class-B complementary-output amplifier has less than 1% distortion from 20 to 20,000 Hz, with response no more than 0.3 dB down over this frequency range at 1-W output level. Input impedance is about 10K.—"Semiconductor Power Circuits Handbook," Motorola, Phoenix, Ariz., 1968, p 5–37.

*RBB — AS REQUIRED TO GIVE 15-30 MILLIAMPS QUIESCENT CURRENT IN Q7 AND Q8.

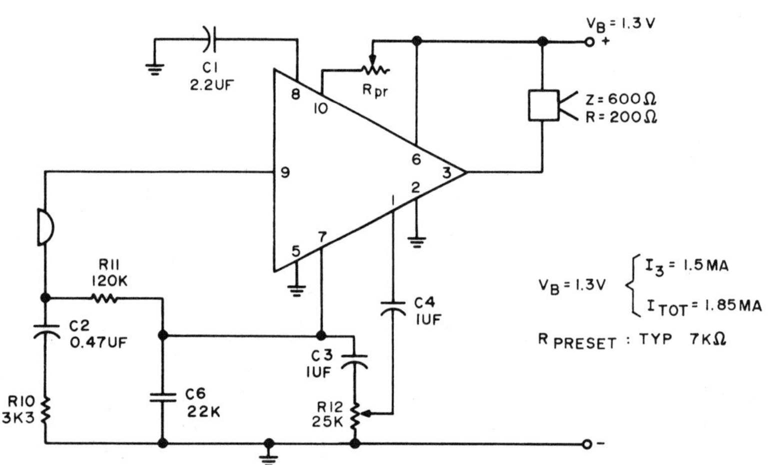

0.9-MW IC HEARING AID—Uses TAA370 IC driving 600-ohm earpiece. Frequency response is flat within 3 dB from 150 to 30,000 Hz. R10 is 3.3K.—The Amperex TAA 370 as a Hearing Aid Amplifier, Amperex, Slatersville, R.I., S-139, 1968.

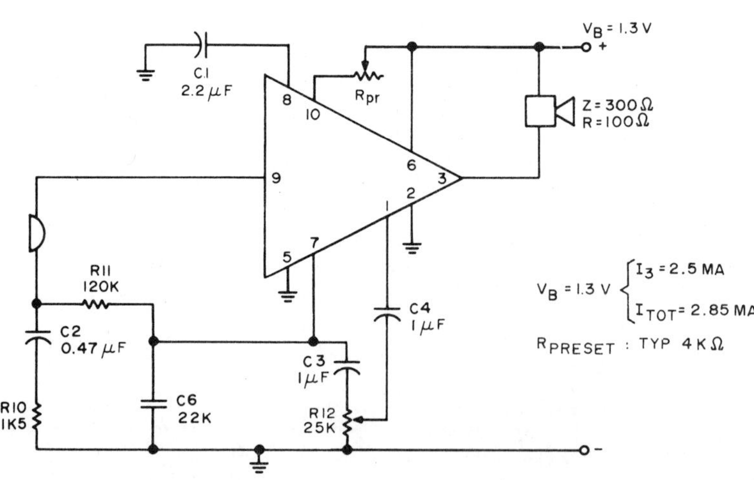

1.5-MW IC HEARING AID—Uses TAA370 IC driving 300-ohm earpiece. Total battery drain at 1.3 V is 2.85 mA. Volume control is conventional continuous type. Report includes graphs showing how performance varies with voltage and temperature.—The Amperex TAA 370 as a Hearing Aid Amplifier, Amperex, Slatersville, R.I., S-139, 1968.

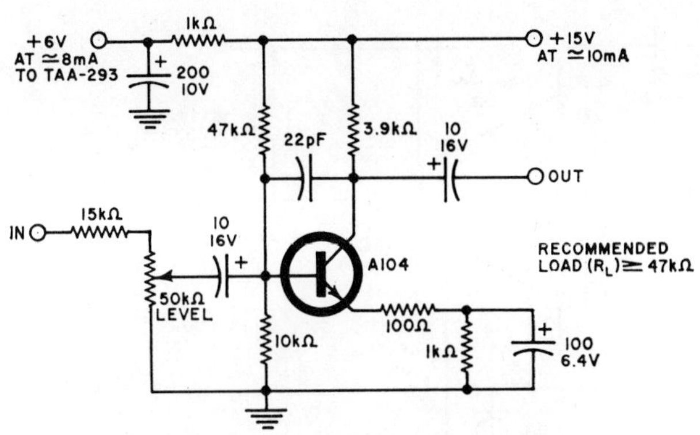

BOOSTER FOR PREAMP—Provides additional 18 dB of gain, or about 4 V output for input of 0.5 V from preamp. Amperex A104 transistor may be replaced by any silicon npn type with beta over 150.—D. R. Pryce, Integrated Circuit Equalized Preamplifier, *Electronics World*, July 1968, p 29 and 73.

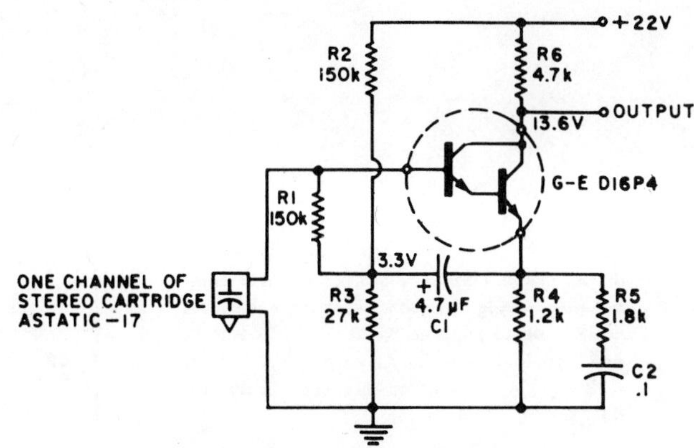

DARLINGTON IC AUDIO PREAMP—Response is flat within 2 dB from 40 to 12,000 Hz. High input impedance makes circuit ideal for ceramic cartridges or microphones. Output reference level is 1.9 V.—D. V. Jones, Audio-Frequency Integrated Circuits, *Electronics World*, July 1968, p 54–56.

4.5-W IC WITHOUT A-C FEEDBACK—Uses Mallory MIC0201 IC audio driver with output transistor. Input impedance goes up to 18K without a-c feedback, in tradeoff for reduced bandwidth of 30 to 10,000 Hz. Used in low-cost auto radios and tape players.—M. L. Deschler, Integrated Circuit Audio Driver Amplifier, Mallory, Indianapolis, Ind., APPN-1, 1968.

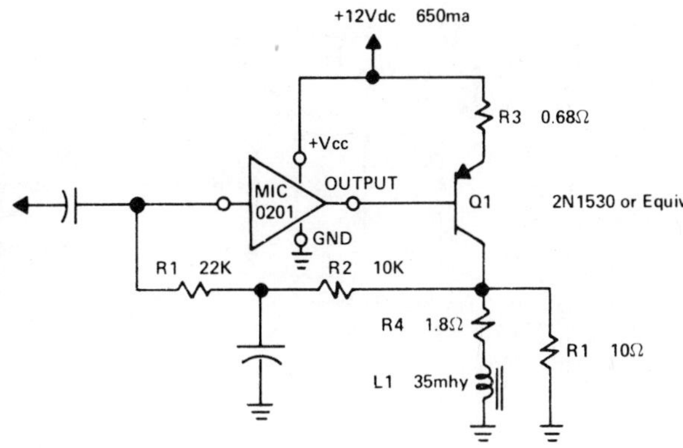

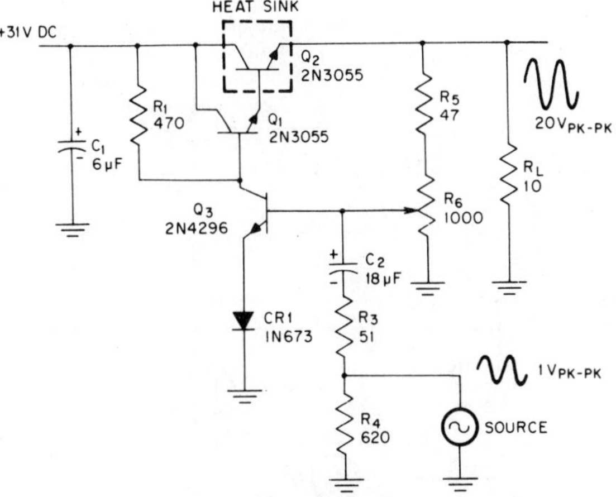

MODULATED SERIES REGULATOR—With C2, R3, R4, and 600-ohm source added, basic series regulator for d-c output of power supply becomes audio amplifier providing gain of 20, with cutoff at 20 kHz. Frequency response falls off below 1 kHz because of C2, but can be extended to d-c if C2 is shorted, R3 is made larger, and larger modulating voltage is used for base drive to Q3.—R. L. Starliper and R. D. Clement, Modulated DC Voltage Regulator, *EEE*, Feb. 1970, p 114.

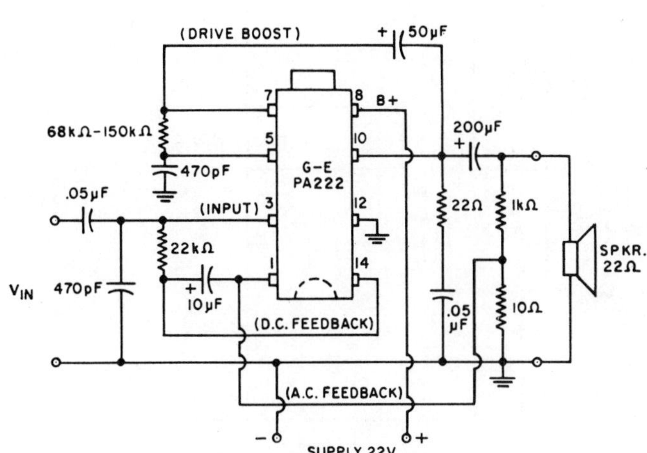

1-W IC OUTPUT—Delivers 1 W into 22-ohm load at 10% distortion, fom 55 to 15,000 Hz. Can deliver up to 2 W but with lower fidelity, provided external heatsinking is added to heatsink tab on IC. External components shown serve chiefly to prevent parasitic oscillation. Ideal for intercoms and other average-fidelity applications.—D. E. Lancaster, Audio Integrated Circuits—What's Available?, *Electronics World*, Oct. 1967, p 34–36.

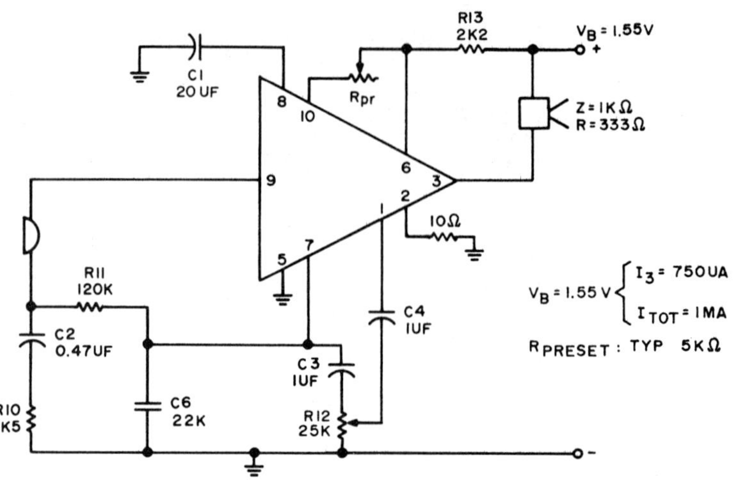

0.5-MW IC HEARING AID—Uses TAA370 IC driving 1,000-ohm earpiece, and circuit components giving frequency response that is down 3 dB at 200 and 8,000 Hz. R13 is 2.2K and R10 is 1.5K.—The Amperex TAA 370 as a Hearing Aid Amplifier, Amperex, Slatersville, R.I., S-139, 1968.

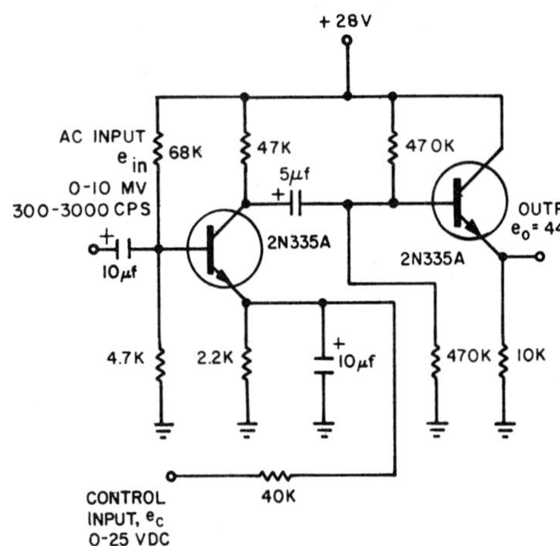

INTERCOM REMOTE GAIN—Control signal of 0 to 25 V d-c changes voltage gain of two-stage audio amplifier from 440 to 0. Control is linear within 2% and distortion is negligible.—P. Cooper, External Signal Controls Audio Voltage Gain, *Electronic Design*, Aug. 31, 1964, p 48.

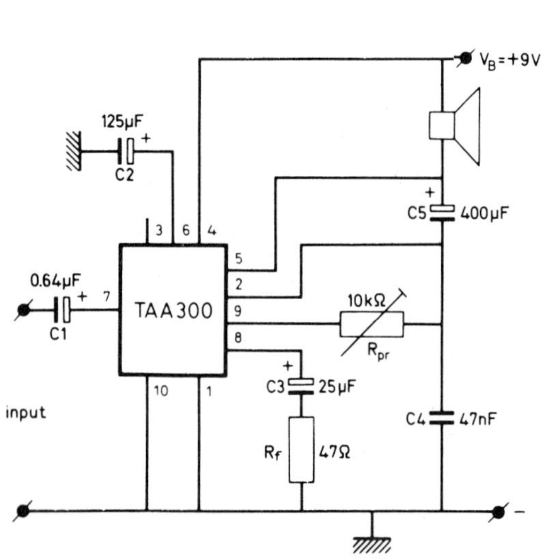

1-W IC AMPLIFIER—IC drives speaker directly, with minimum number of additional components. Input may be from ceramic phono pickup or from detector in portable radio. Total battery drain is 150 mA just before clipping, and 180 mA at full output with 10% distortion.—A. M. Peters, TAA300 Integrated 1 W Class B A. F. Amplifier, Philips, Pub. Dept., Elcoma Div., Eindhoven, The Netherlands, No. 136, 1969.

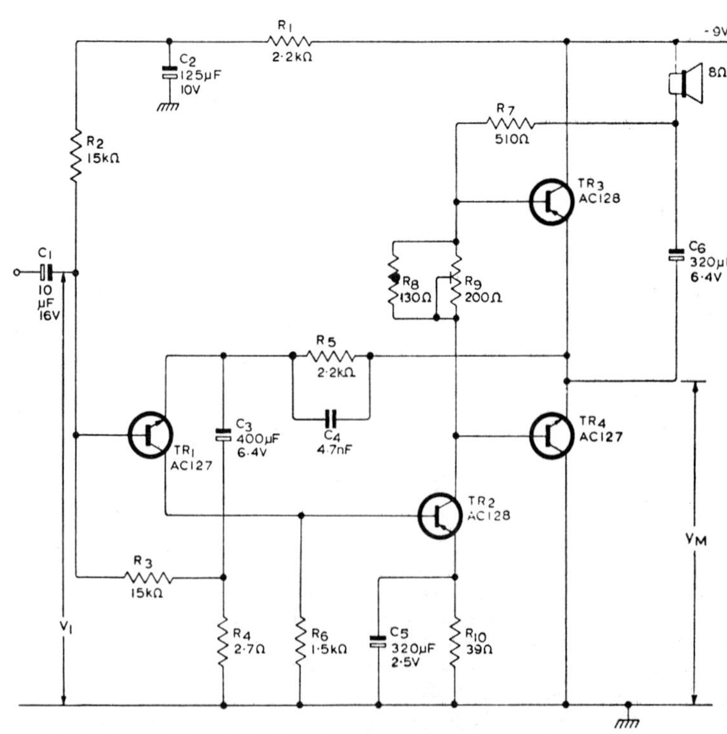

1-W TRANSFORMERLESS AUDIO AMP—Frequency response is flat within 3 dB from 100 to 20,000 Hz. Has good d-c stability while using minimum number of components.—"Transistor Audio and Radio Circuits," Mullard Ltd., London, 1969, p 35.

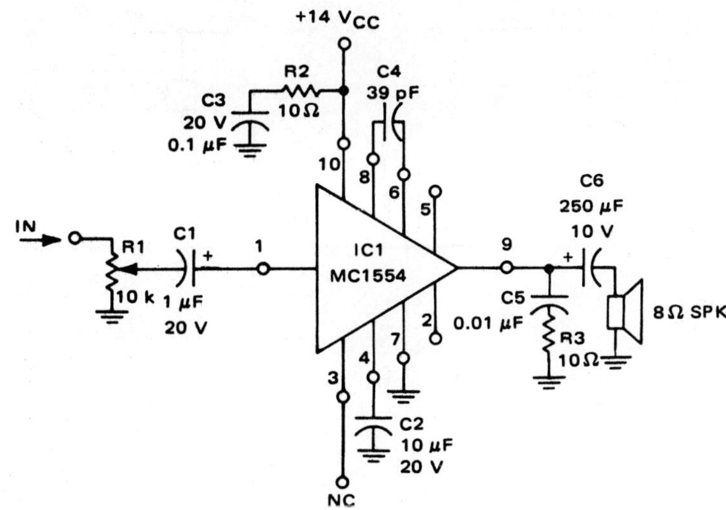

1-W IC AMPLIFIER—Will amplify signals up to 300 kHz. Total harmonic distortion from 20 to 20,000 Hz for 1 W into 16-ohm load, with voltage gain of 10, is typically 0.4%, and for 8-ohm speaker is 1% at 1,000 Hz.—"Semiconductor Power Circuits Handbook," Motorola, Phoenix, Ariz., 1968, p 5–28.

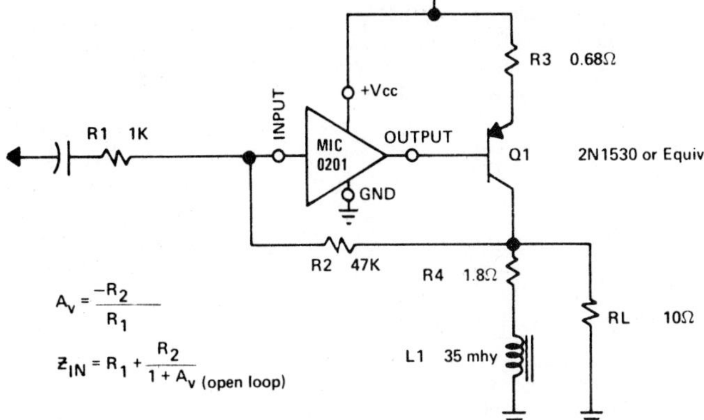

4.5-W IC WITH SHUNT FEEDBACK—Uses Mallory MIC0201 IC audio driver with power output transistor to deliver rated output at 10% distortion, for use in low-cost auto radios, tape players, and other mobile equipment. Response is 3 dB down from 30 to 20,000 Hz at 3 W output.—M. L. Deschler, Integrated Circuit Audio Driver Amplifier, Mallory, Indianapolis, Ind., APPN-1, 1968.

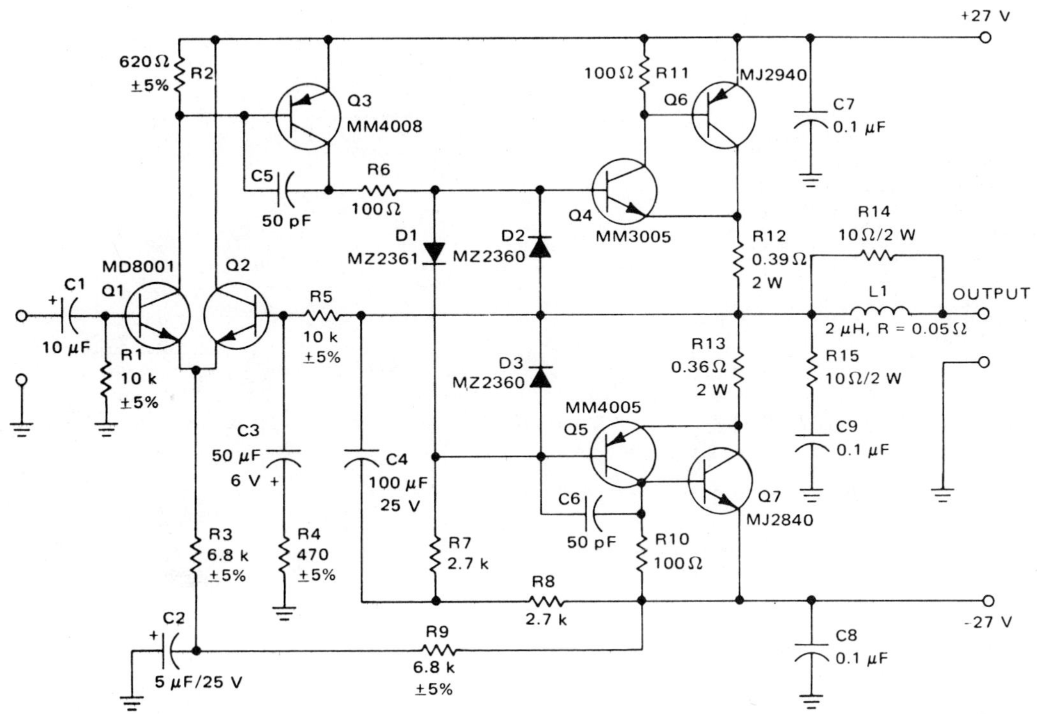

35 W FOR 8 OHMS—Has less than 0.1% total harmonic distortion and less than 0.2% intermodulation distortion at full power output, with 3-dB bandwidth of 10 Hz to 100 kHz. Book gives changes required in values to boost output to 60 W. Diodes provide load-fault protection.—"Semiconductor Power Circuits Handbook," Motorola, Phoenix, Ariz., 1968, p 5–45.

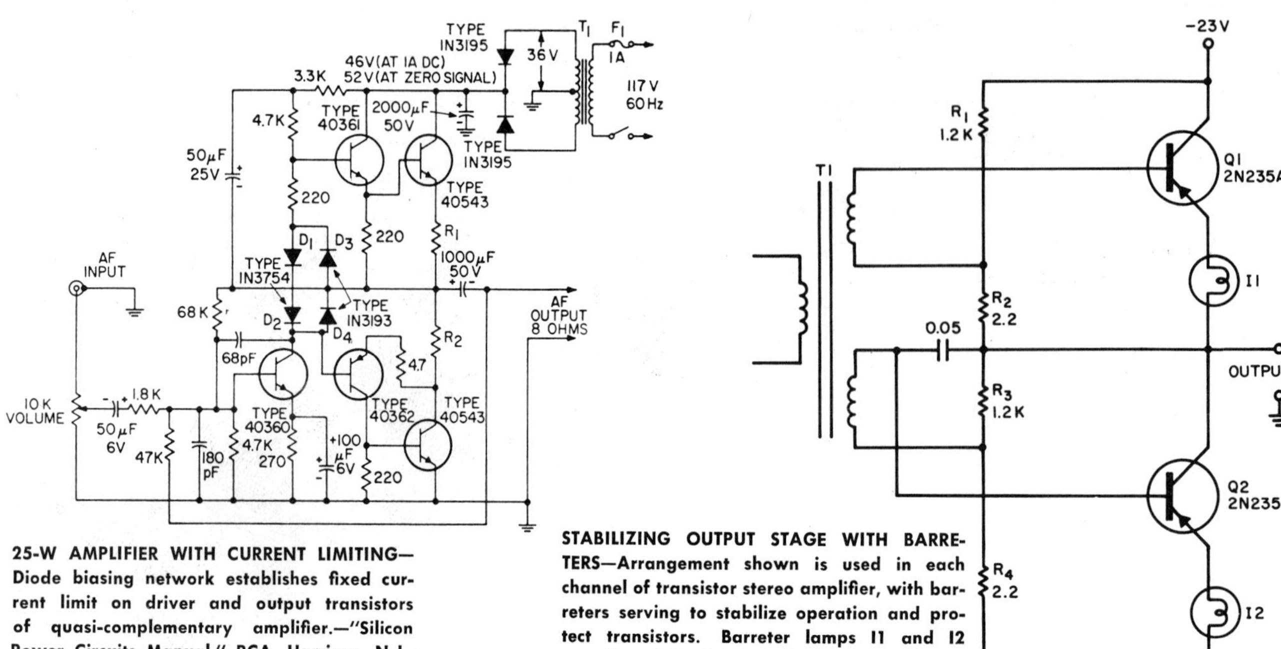

25-W AMPLIFIER WITH CURRENT LIMITING— Diode biasing network establishes fixed current limit on driver and output transistors of quasi-complementary amplifier.—"Silicon Power Circuits Manual," RCA, Harrison, N.J., SP-51, p 409.

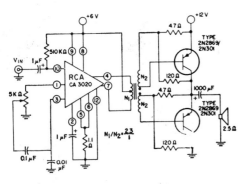

STABILIZING OUTPUT STAGE WITH BARRETERS— Arrangement shown is used in each channel of transistor stereo amplifier, with barreters serving to stabilize operation and protect transistors. Barreter lamps I1 and I2 are Tung-Sol CE101, whose resistance increases exponentially with current from 0.2 ohm until burnout at about 1.5 A. Barreters thus serve as fuses.—Using Barreters for Stabilizing an Output Stage, *Electronic Design*, June 8, 1964, p 68.

7-W CLASS-B AMPLIFIER WITH IC— Low-cost integrated circuit drives two-transistor single-ended output stage through coupling transfomer.—D. E. Lancaster, Audio Integrated Circuits—What's Available?, *Electronics World*, Oct. 1967, p 34–36.

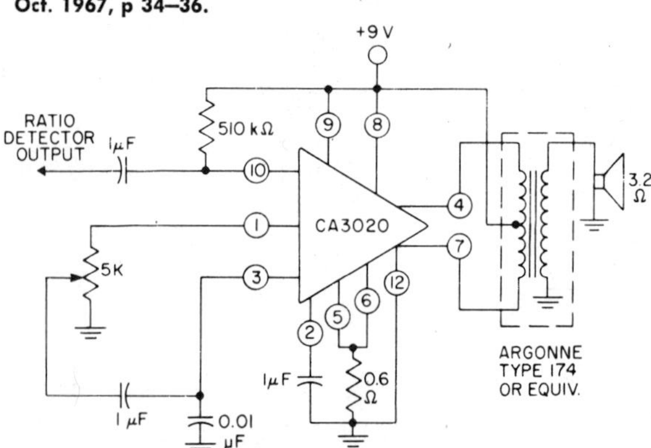

545-MW IC OUTPUT— With change in output transformer, wideband IC amplifier may be used to drive 8-ohm or 16-ohm speaker. Input of 45 mV gives full power output. Developed for use with portable f-m radio.—"Linear Integrated Circuits," RCA, Harrison, N.J., IC-41, p 273.

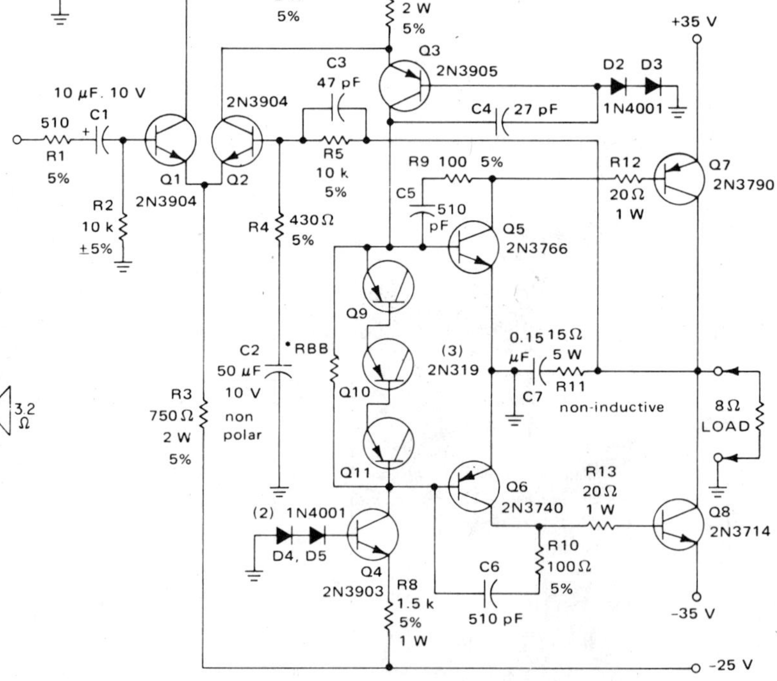

*RBB – AS REQUIRED TO GIVE 20-40 mA QUIESCENT CURRENT IN Q7 AND Q8.

50 W FOR 8 OHMS— Low-cost 1N4728 zener at collector of Q1 limits applied voltage, allowing use of low-cost plastic-encapsulated transistor. Frequency response and distortion meet requirements for hi-fi applications.—"Semiconductor Power Circuits Handbook," Motorola, Phoenix, Ariz., 1968, p 5–49.

50-W QUASI-COMPLEMENTARY—Ideal for either monaural or stereo applications. Frequency response is flat within 1 dB from 15 Hz to 100 kHz at rated output. Total harmonic distortion is less than 0.1% at 1 kHz up to rated output, and intermodulation distortion less than 0.2% at 60 Hz and 6 kHz up to rated output. Differential amplifier at input keeps output at d-c ground by compensating bias of output silicon power transistors. Q4 is RCA 40409 and Q5 is RCA 40410.—Direct-Coupled 50-Watt Audio Amplifier, Delco Radio, Kokomo, Ind., No. 43, 1968.

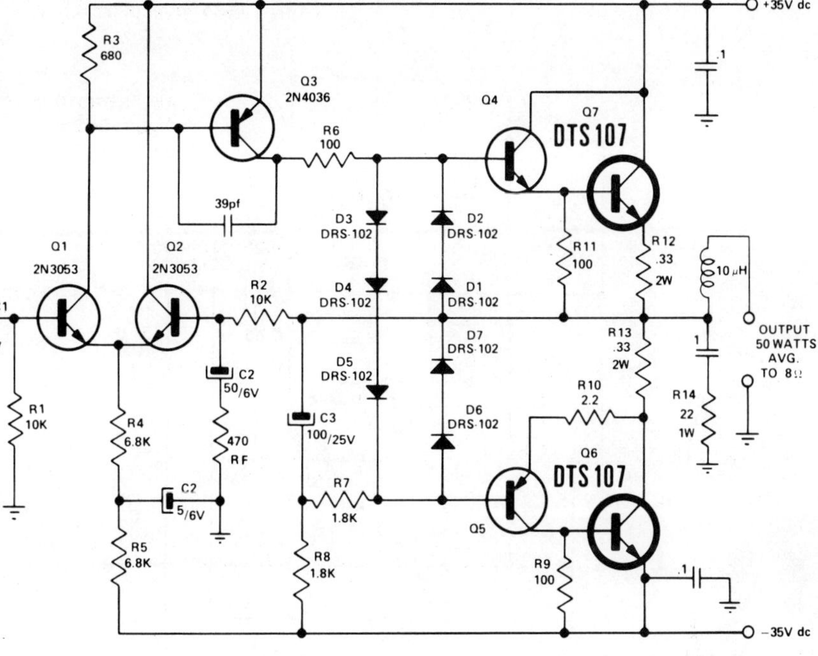

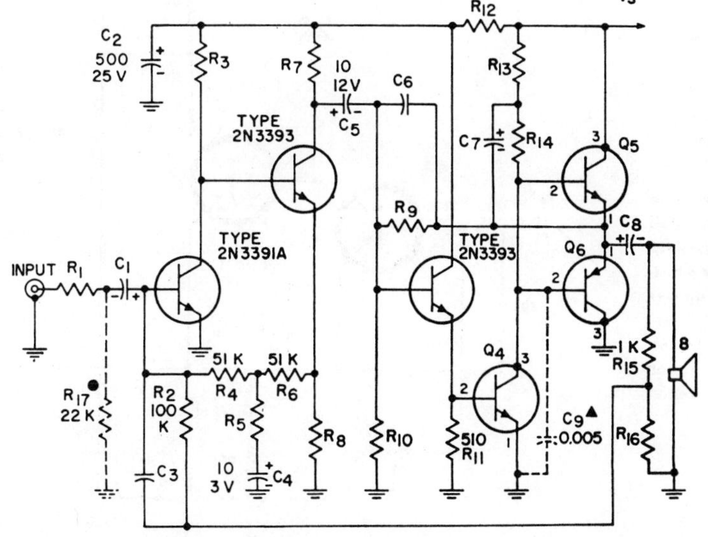

TRUE-COMPLEMENTARY-SYMMETRY AMPLIFIER—Basic circuit can be used for nine different audio amplifiers in power output range of 3 to 20 W. Frequency response is flat well beyond 20 kHz for each, with total harmonic distortion of 1%. Operation approximates that of true class B amplifier. Book gives parts values and supply voltages for each combination of power output and transistor complement.—"Silicon Power Circuits Manual," RCA, Harrison, N.J., SP-51, p 411.

4-W IC POWER AMPLIFIER—Uses Philips IC driver to feed complementary output stage. Both d-c and a-c feedback are applied to input differential amplifier in IC. Circuit includes stabilization against supply voltage fluctuations. Will operate with supply between 10 and 18 V.—Complementary Output Stages Driven By the TAA435, Philips, Pub. Dept., Elcoma Div., Eindhoven, The Netherlands, No. 18, 1968.

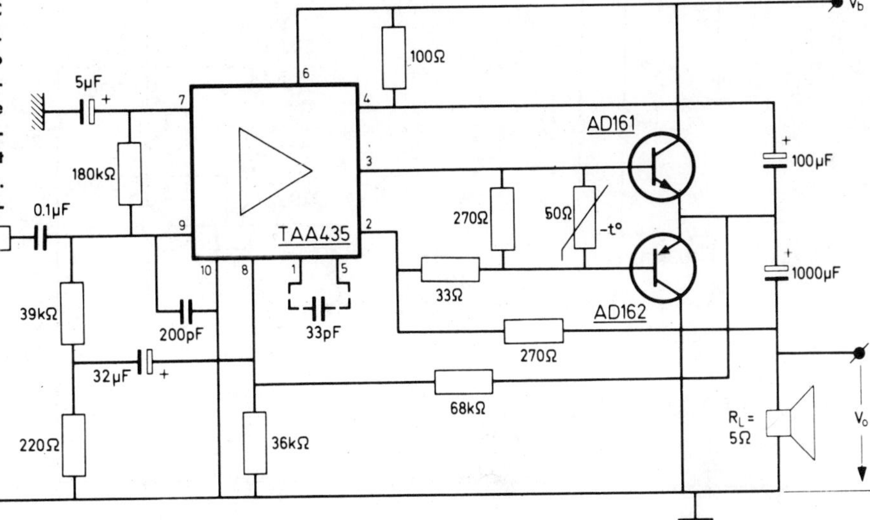

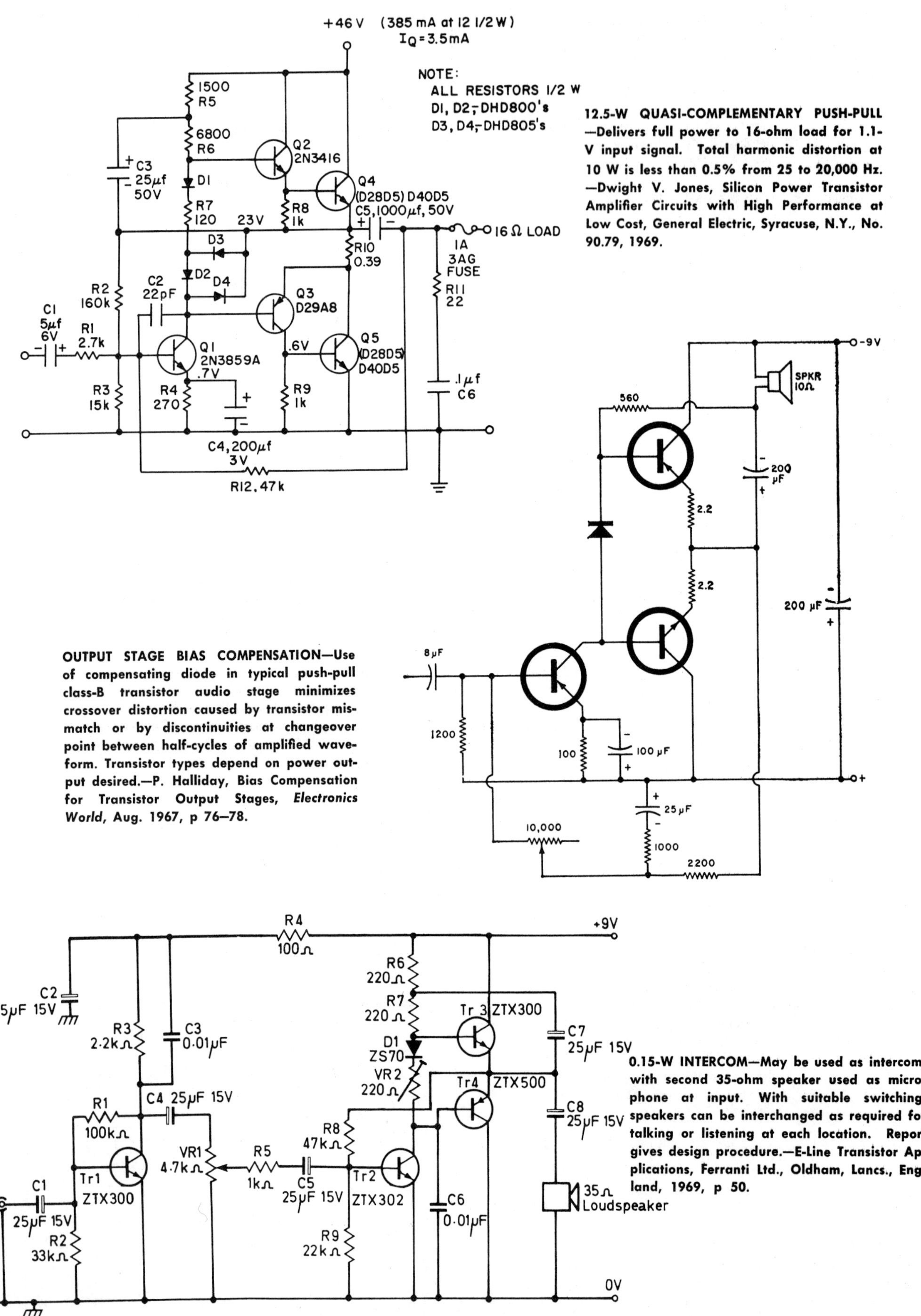

12.5-W QUASI-COMPLEMENTARY PUSH-PULL—Delivers full power to 16-ohm load for 1.1-V input signal. Total harmonic distortion at 10 W is less than 0.5% from 25 to 20,000 Hz.—Dwight V. Jones, Silicon Power Transistor Amplifier Circuits with High Performance at Low Cost, General Electric, Syracuse, N.Y., No. 90.79, 1969.

OUTPUT STAGE BIAS COMPENSATION—Use of compensating diode in typical push-pull class-B transistor audio stage minimizes crossover distortion caused by transistor mismatch or by discontinuities at changeover point between half-cycles of amplified waveform. Transistor types depend on power output desired.—P. Halliday, Bias Compensation for Transistor Output Stages, *Electronics World*, Aug. 1967, p 76–78.

0.15-W INTERCOM—May be used as intercom, with second 35-ohm speaker used as microphone at input. With suitable switching, speakers can be interchanged as required for talking or listening at each location. Report gives design procedure.—E-Line Transistor Applications, Ferranti Ltd., Oldham, Lancs., England, 1969, p 50.

CHAPTER 4
Audio Control Circuits

3-W WITH BASS AND TREBLE CONTROLS—R10 cuts and boosts treble, while R13 controls bass. Input transistor is chosen to give improvement in bass response and reduce distortion.—"Transistor Audio and Radio Circuits," Mullard Ltd., London, 1969, p 47.

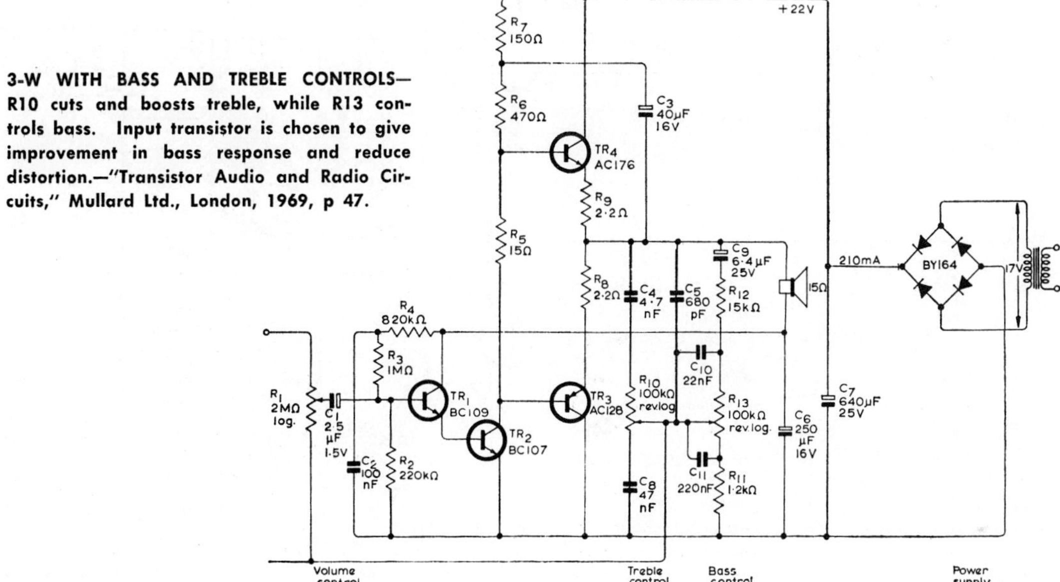

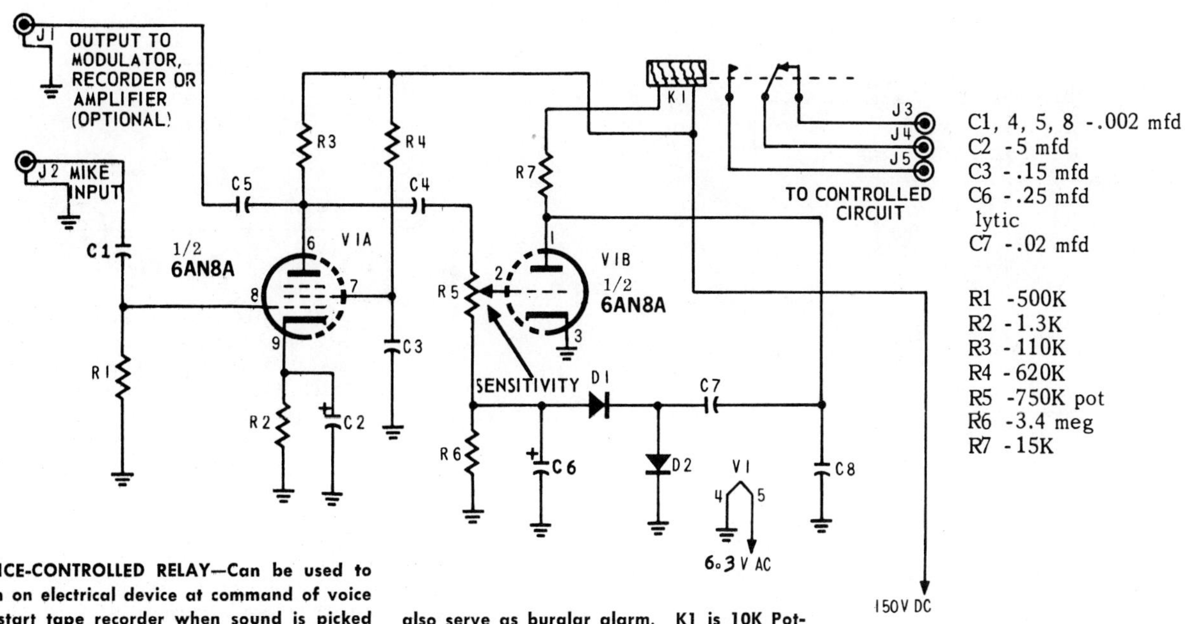

VOICE-CONTROLLED RELAY—Can be used to turn on electrical device at command of voice or start tape recorder when sound is picked up by microphone. If alarm is connected to relay, and R5 adjusted for faint noise, can also serve as burglar alarm. K1 is 10K Potter & Brumfield PW5LS relay. Both diodes are 1N2071.—R. M. Brown, "104 Simple One-Tube Projects," Tab Books, Blue Ridge Summit, Pa., 1969, p 71.

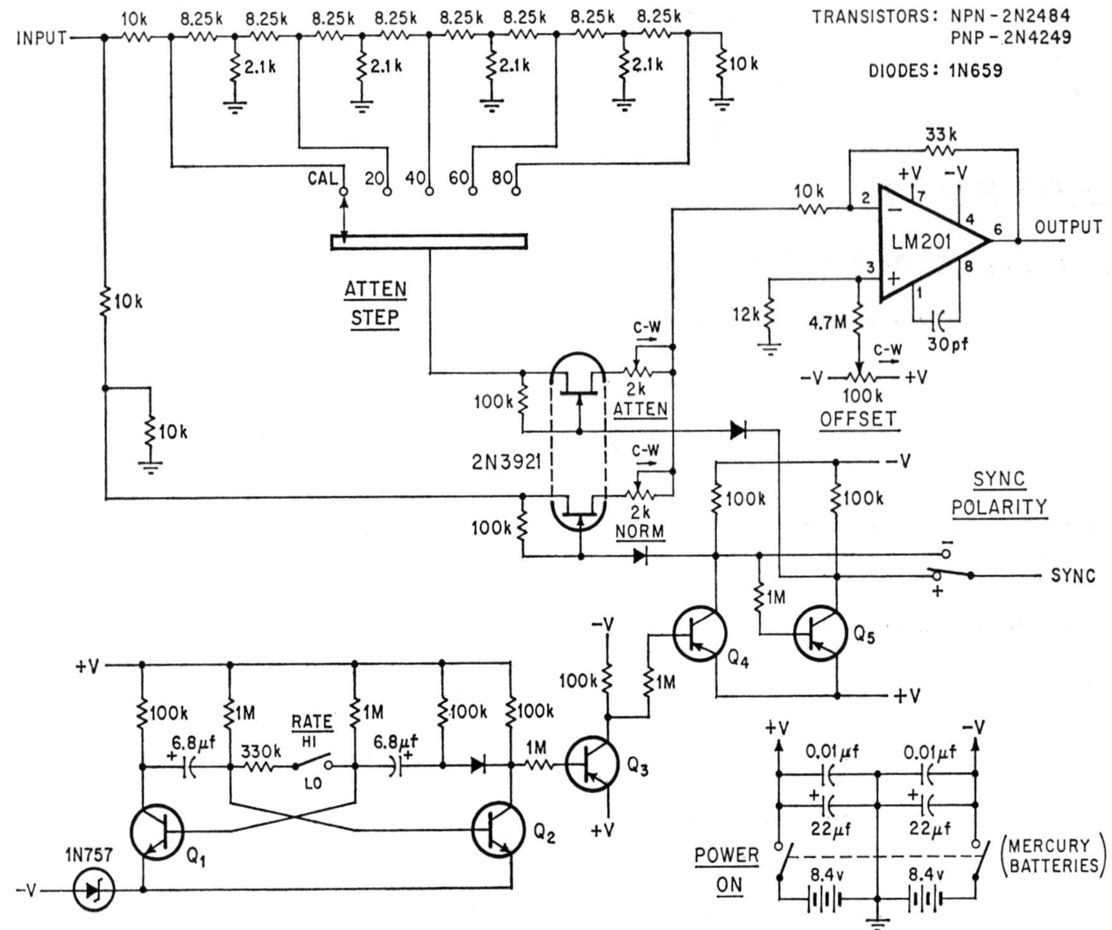

FAST-ACTING ATTENUATOR—Will shift level of audio signal in less than 10 μs, to give up to 80 dB of attenuation in audio amplifier. Incoming signal is split between ladder attenuator and straight-through 6-dB loss network. Dual fet acts as spst switch for selecting either channel to drive astable mvbr followed by inverters Q4 and Q5. Rate of astable can be either 1.2 or 5 s per sample. Signal from fet goes to opamp providing voltage gain of 6 dB to 50-ohm load. Sync output gives 16-V pulses with 10-μs rise time. Use of battery supply isolates circuit from line noise. Can be used to measure response of agc networks.—T. E. O'Brien, Automatic Attenuator Rapidly Changes Signal Level, *Electronics*, Sept. 15, 1969, p 120.

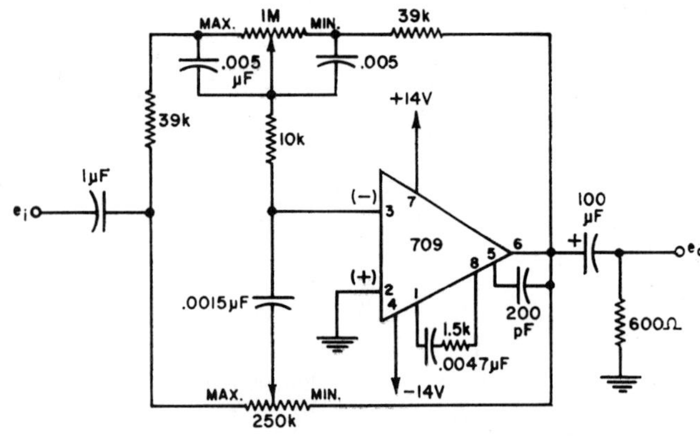

IC TONE CONTROL—Uses Fairchild μA709 or National LM709 IC opamp as unity-gain inverter when both pots are at mid-positions. At maximum positions, provides about 20 dB of attenuation or boost at low and high frequencies.—S. L. Silver, IC Op Amps Boost Audio Circuit Performance, *Electronics World*, Sept. 1968, p 30–32.

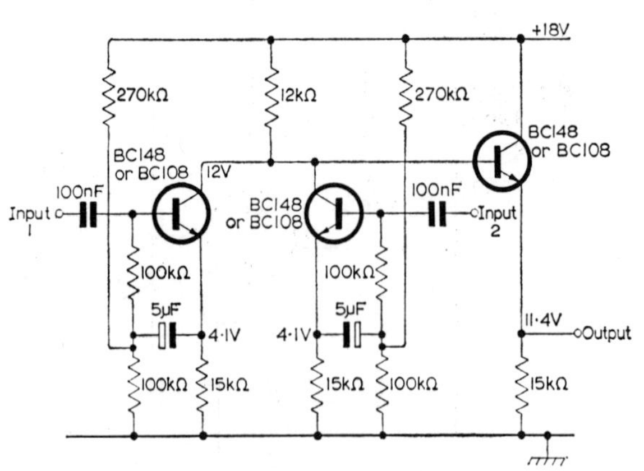

TWO-INPUT MIXER—Input transistors use common 12K collector load resistor. Input impedance is 2.5 meg, output is 70 ohms, voltage gain is unity, and distortion is 0.5% for 2 V output.—"Transistor Audio and Radio Circuits," Mullard Ltd., London, 1969, p 126.

PHONO TONE CONTROL—Provides separate bass and treble controls for phonograph using crystal or ceramic cartridge. Input mosfet Q1 is connected as source-follower amplifier providing extremely high input impedance to avoid loading transducer.—C. R. Perkins, "Application of MOSFET Devices to Electronic Circuits," Hughes, Newport Beach, Cal., 1968, p 5.

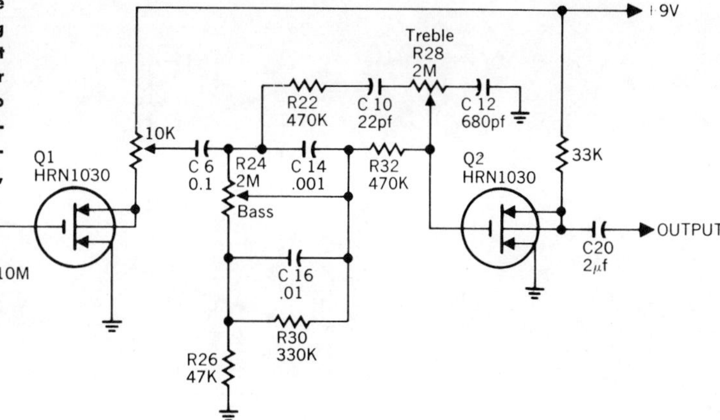

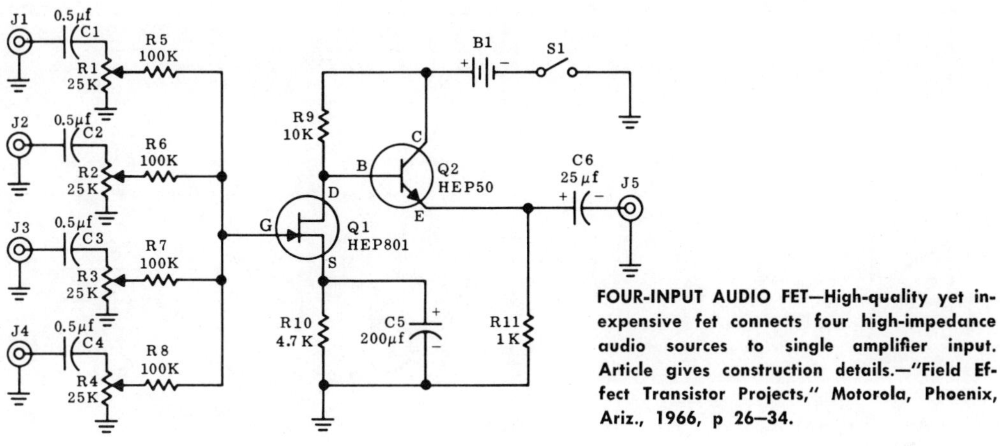

FOUR-INPUT AUDIO FET—High-quality yet inexpensive fet connects four high-impedance audio sources to single amplifier input. Article gives construction details.—"Field Effect Transistor Projects," Motorola, Phoenix, Ariz., 1966, p 26–34.

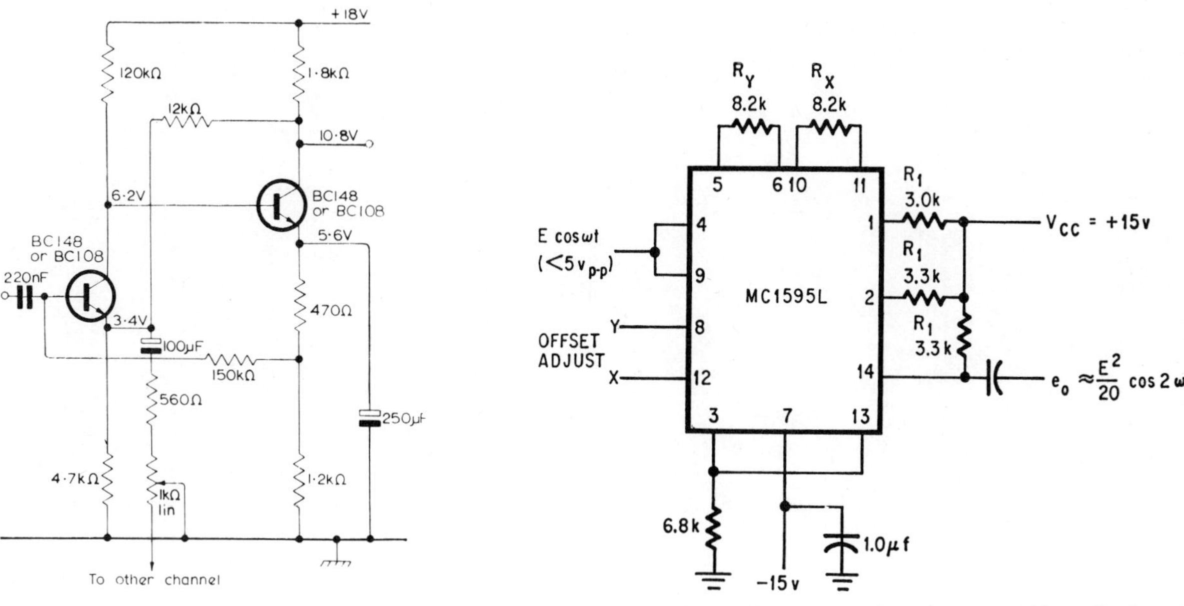

BALANCE CONTROL—When used in each stereo channel, permits varying voltage gain in both channels by 6 dB in opposite directions. Control potentiometer is in feedback circuit.—"Transistor Audio and Radio Circuits," Mullard Ltd., London, 1969, p 129.

DOUBLING 10 KHZ—Motorola monolithic multiplier gives second harmonic directly when two equal cosine waves are applied to inputs X and Y. A-c coupling removes d-c term. Dynamic range of input is 5 V p-p. Doubled output frequency has less than 1% distortion even without filtering. Will operate well above 200 kHz.—E. Renschler and D. Weiss, Try the Monolithic Multiplier as a Versatile A-C Design Tool, *Electronics*, June 8, 1970, p 100–105.

$$e_o \approx \frac{E^2}{20} \cos 2\omega t$$

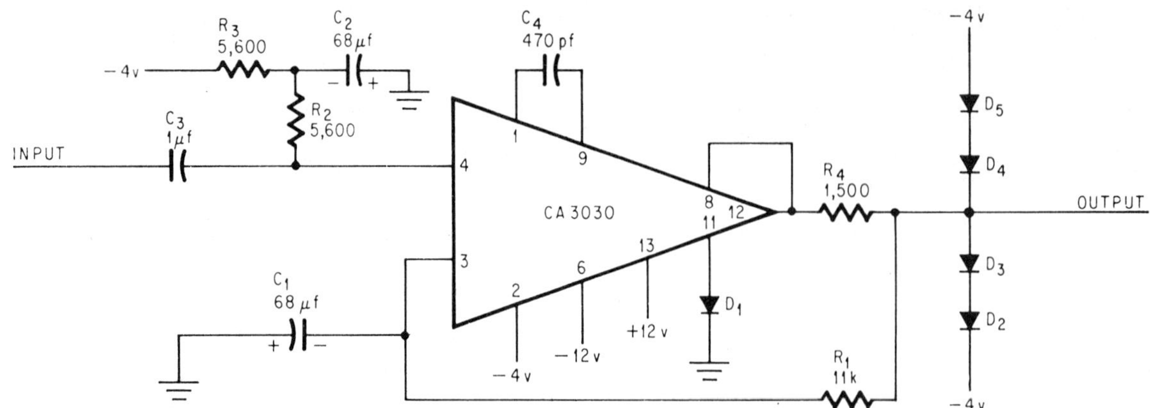

78-DB RANGE—Wideband audio limiter, built around RCA IC opamp, delivers clean sine waves below limiting threshold and symmetrical square waves for higher input voltages. Limiting begins at 0.4 mV input. Can handle up to 6 V p-p. Second harmonic distortion is 0.3% over dynamic range of 54 dB, and 2% for 78 dB.—R. Glasgal, Low-Distortion Limiter Uses IC Operational Amplifier, *Electronics*, October 14, 1968, p 120–121.

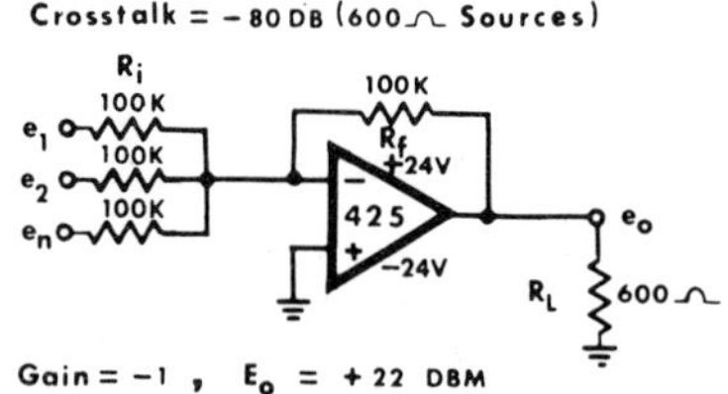

20-CHANNEL MIXER—Active mixer using Model 425 IC opamp connected for unity gain has no insertion loss, because negative input summing point is driven to virtual zero. Up to 20 input channels may be used. Output voltage across 600-ohm load is 22 dBm.—B. J. Losmandy, Operational Amplifier Application for Audio Systems, Opamp Labs, Los Angeles, Cal., 1968.

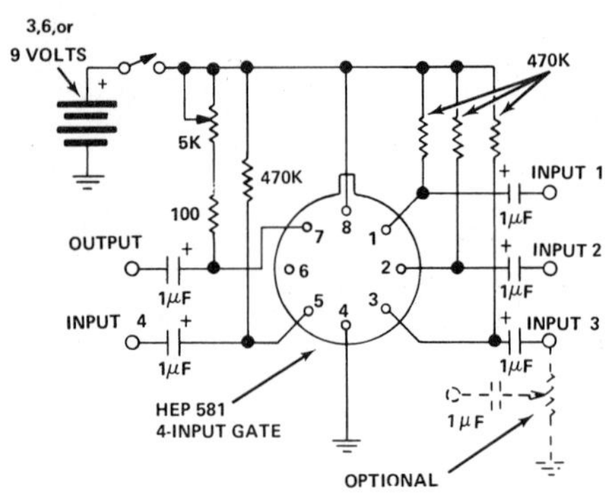

FOUR-INPUT AUDIO IC—Output is about 3 V p-p on input of 0.3 V p-p from low-level microphone or phono. Optional 10K pot and capacitor can be added to each input, as shown by dashed lines for input 3. Adjust 5K pot for maximum undistorted output.—"Tips on Using IC's," Motorola, Phoenix, Ariz., HMA-32, 1968.

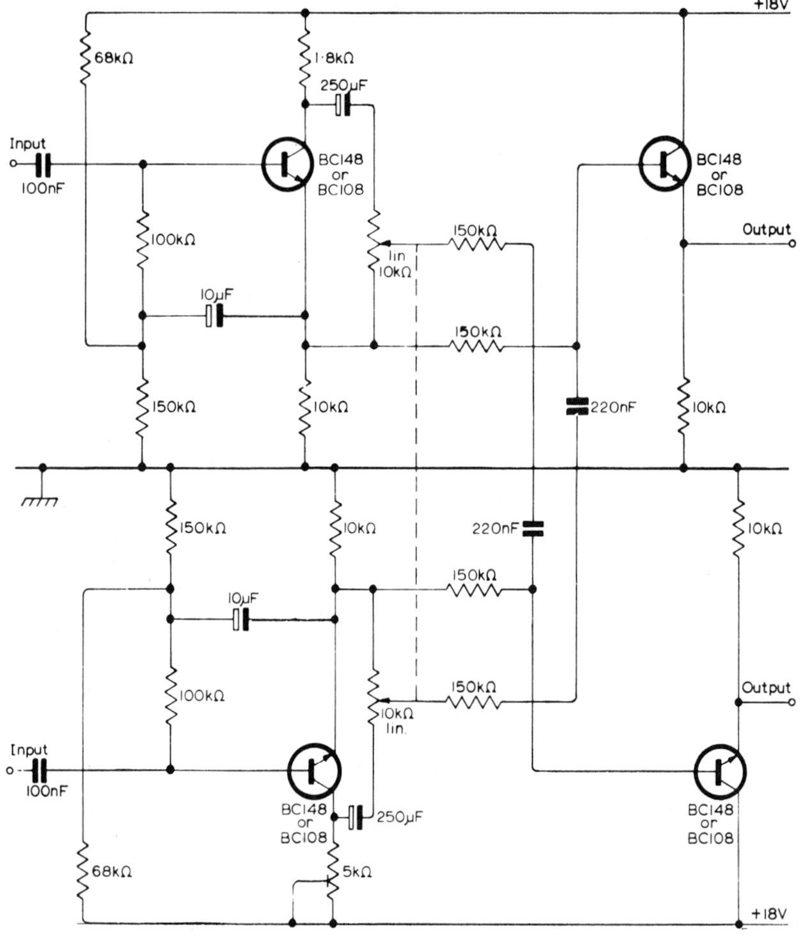

SOUND SOURCE WIDTH CONTROL—Ganged controls give effect of moving stereo sound pickup microphones continuously between in-phase crosstalk of 100% (corresponding to monophonic recording), and anti-phase crosstalk of 24%. Greater anti-phase crosstalk is unnecessary because sound impression falls apart and effect becomes that of two independent sources rather than stereo. Channels are balanced with 5K preset pot.—"Transistor Audio and Radio Circuits," Mullard Ltd., London, 1969, p 134.

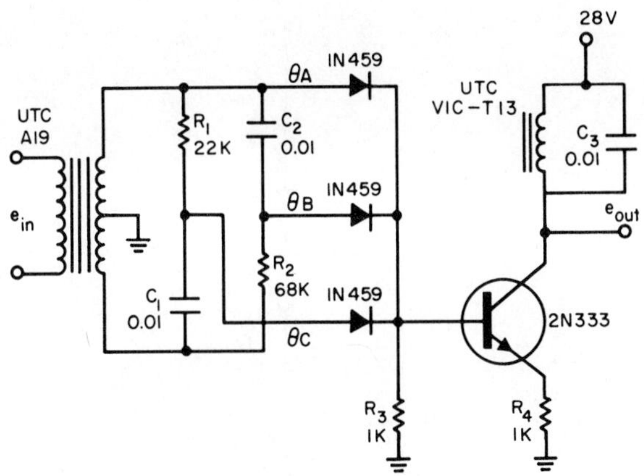

TRIPLER FOR 400-HZ SOURCE—Simple pulser feeding tank network delivers equal-energy pulses at triple-frequency rate to provide good 1,200-Hz sine-wave output with no fundamental-frequency modulation. Values of R1, R2, C1, C2, and C3 may be chosen for any other standard audio frequency. Article gives detailed description of circuit operation, along with design equations.—J. B. Messmer, Precise Frequency-Tripler Uses 400 CPS Standard Source, *Electronic Design*, Nov. 22, 1965, p 61–62.

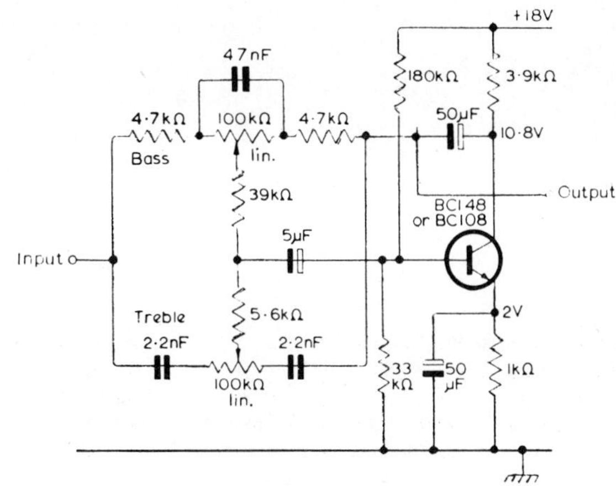

ACTIVE TONE CONTROL—Operates with frequency-dependent feedback network between collector and base of tone-control transistor. At 30 Hz, control range is −22 dB to 19.5 dB, and at 20 Hz is −19 dB to 19.5 dB. Frequency response is flat when both pots are centered.—"Transistor Audio and Radio Circuits," Mullard Ltd., London, 1969, p 131.

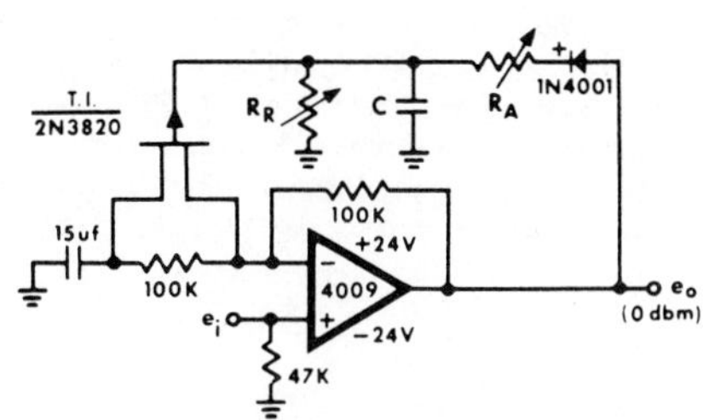

20-DB AUDIO COMPRESSOR—Uses Model 4009 IC opamp in circuit having adjustable attack-time and release-time pots. For most applications, RA is set for attack time between 10 μs and perhaps 20 ms, while RR is set for release times somewhere between 20 and 200 ms. FET is inside electronic feedback path and automatically adjusts gain of amplifier as function of output voltage. At low signal levels, gain is about 10.—B. J. Losmandy, Operational Amplifier Application for Audio Systems, Opamp Labs, Los Angeles, Cal., 1968.

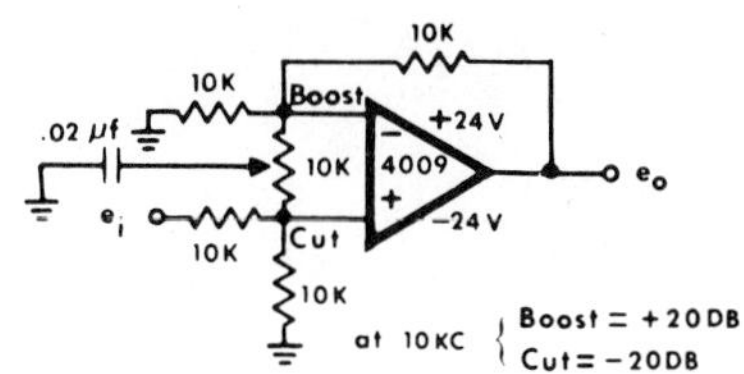

TREBLE CONTROL—Uses Model 4009 IC opamp to provide wide range of treble boost and cut, with turn-over frequency of about 800 Hz for values shown.—B. J. Losmandy, Operational Amplifier Application for Audio Systems, Opamp Labs, Los Angeles, Cal., 1968.

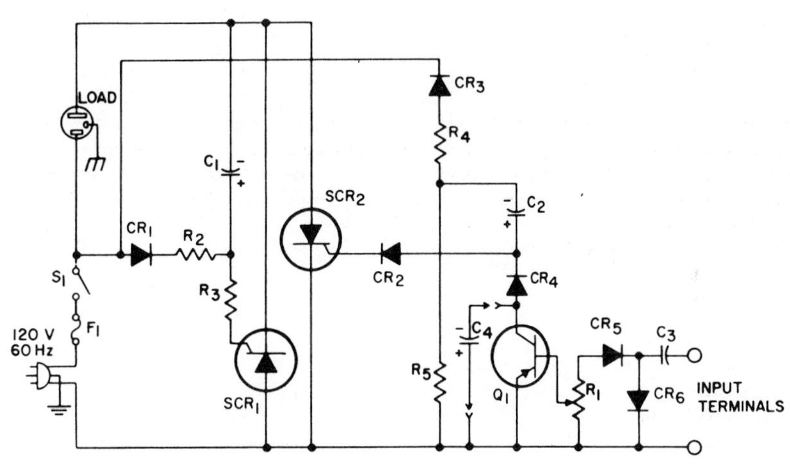

$C_1 C_2$ = 10 microfarads, 15 volts, electrolytic
C_3 = 0.1 microfarad, 25 volts or greater
C_4 = 10 to 100 microfarads, 12 volts, electrolytic, to increase release time
$CR_1 CR_2 CR_3 CR_4$ = silicon rectifier, RCA SK3030
$CR_5 CR_6$ = silicon rectifier, type 1N34A
F_1 = fuse, 125 volts, ampere rating depends on load
Q_1 = transistor, RCA SK3005
R_1 = potentiometer, 5000 ohms, 2 watts, linear taper
$R_2 R_4$ = 4700 ohms, 2 watts, 10%
R_3 = 270 ohms, 1/2 watt, 10%
R_5 = 470 ohms, 1/2 watt, 10%
S_1 = switch, 125 volts, 15 amperes, single-pole, single-throw toggle
$SCR_1 SCR_2$ = silicon controlled rectifier, RCA KD2100

SOUND-OPERATED SWITCH—Will turn on load up to 1 kW for as long as sound or noise signal fed to input by microphone and preamp remains above predetermined level set by R1. Release time can be increased by adding capacitor (up to 100 μF) between emitter and collector of Q1 so switch does not open for momentary interruptions in sound such as between syllables of speech.—"Hobby Circuits Manual," RCA, Harrison, N.J., HM-90, p 164.

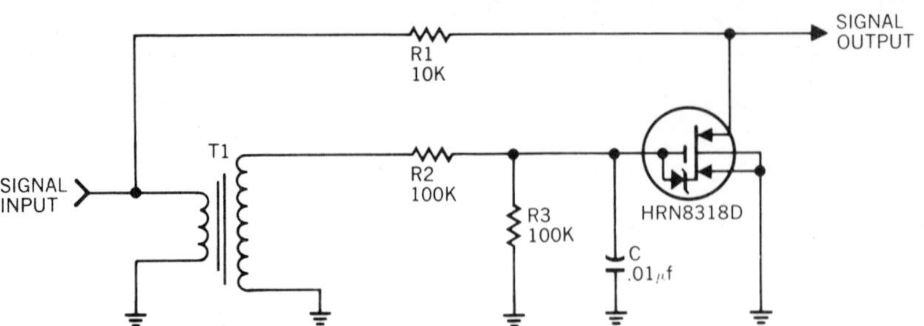

VOLUME COMPRESSOR—Mosfet acts as variable resistance shunting audio line, with increasing signal level causing resistance to decrease and thereby provide compression. Audio signal itself develops negative voltage at mosfet gate, eliminating need for power supply for compressor. With −3 V on gate, mosfet resistance is above 10K, dropping to 300 ohms for −10 V. Turns ratio of T1 should be at least 20:1, to step up signal level enough to operate mosfet. Clamping diode is integral part of mosfet.—C. R. Perkins, "Application of MOSFET Devices to Electronic Circuits," Hughes, Newport Beach, Cal., 1968, p 14.

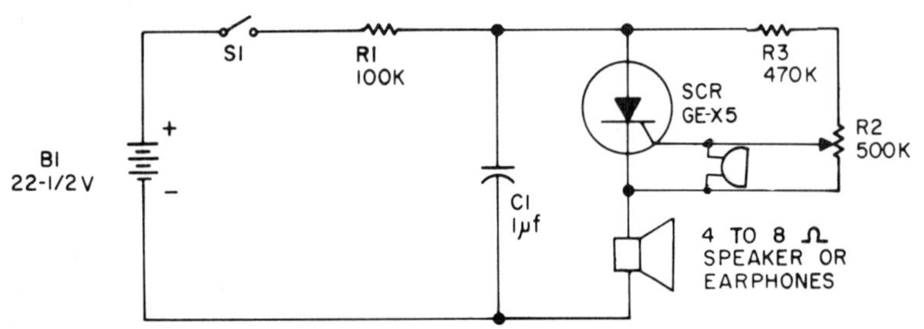

SOUND-CONTROLLED OSCILLATOR—Ceramic contact microphone or phono pickup connected between gate and cathode of scr oscillator as shown will respond to vibrations produced on floor or wall by footsteps or other sound-producing source, to give alarm sound from speaker.—"Hobby Manual," General Electric, Owensboro, Ky., 1965, p 126.

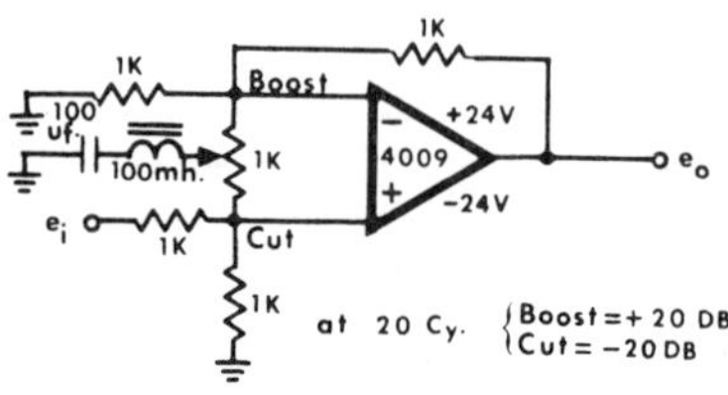

BASS CONTROL—Uses Model 4009 IC opamp to provide wide range of bass boost and cut, with turn-over frequency of 1,600 Hz for values shown. L-C circuit between arm of pot and ground resonates at 50 Hz.—B. J. Losmandy, Operational Amplifier Application for Audio Systems, Opamp Labs, Los Angeles, Cal., 1968.

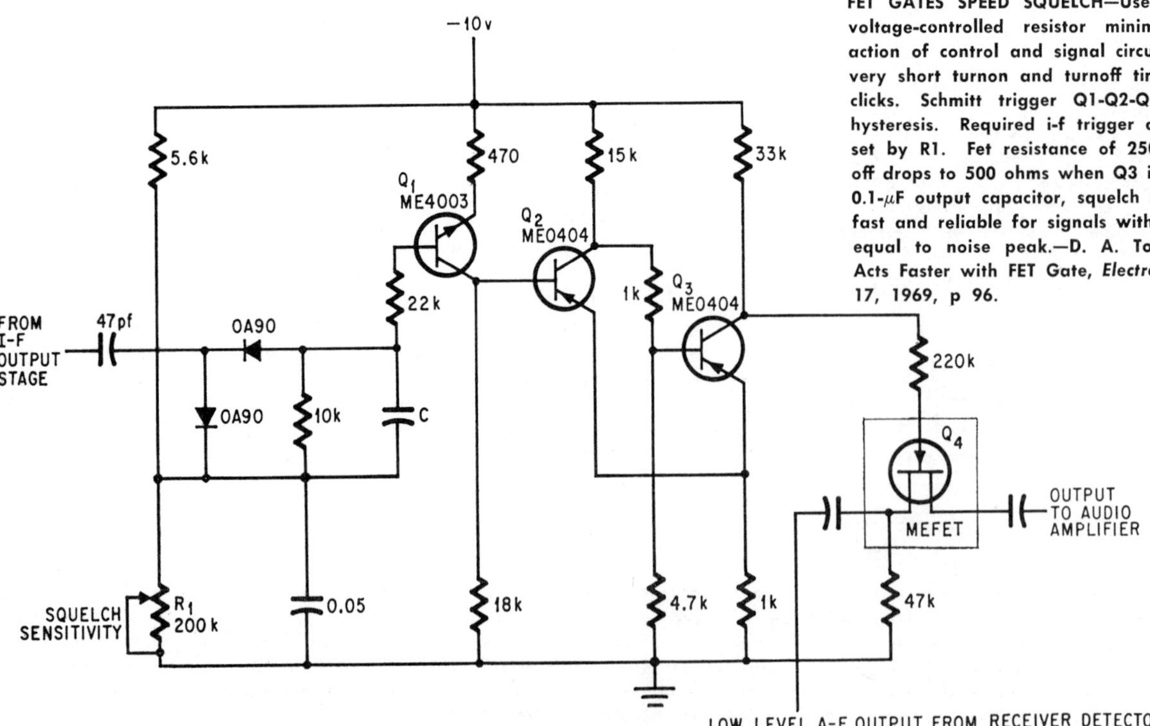

FET GATES SPEED SQUELCH—Use of fet as voltage-controlled resistor minimizes interaction of control and signal circuits, to give very short turnon and turnoff times and no clicks. Schmitt trigger Q1-Q2-Q3 has low hysteresis. Required i-f trigger amplitude is set by R1. Fet resistance of 250K with Q3 off drops to 500 ohms when Q3 is on. With 0.1-μF output capacitor, squelch operation is fast and reliable for signals with amplitudes equal to noise peak.—D. A. Tong, Squelch Acts Faster with FET Gate, *Electronics*, March 17, 1969, p 96.

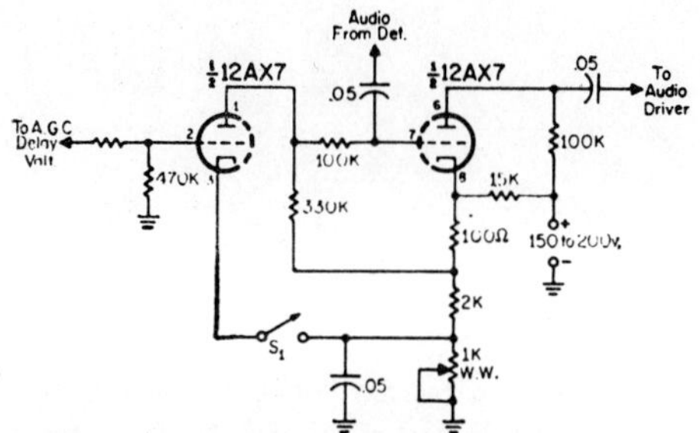

SIMPLE SQUELCH—Can be easily added to practically any a-m receiver between detector and input to audio amplifier. Setting of 1K pot determines amount of squelch when S1 is closed.—"Electronic Circuits Handbook," Vol. II, Cowan Pub. Corp., Port Washington, N.Y., 1966, p 38.

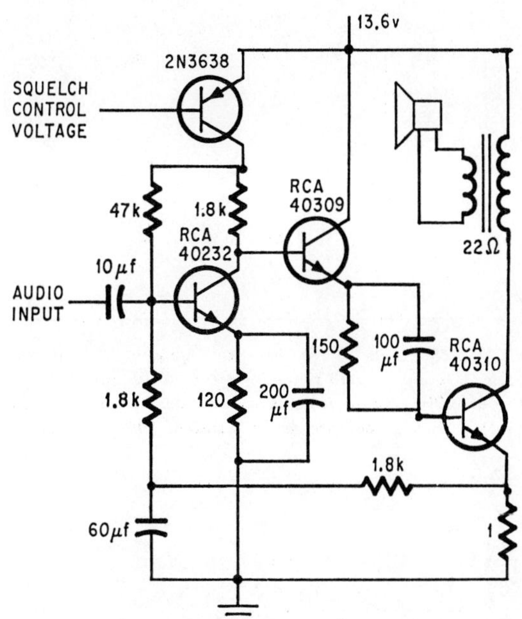

SQUELCHED AUDIO GATE—Three-stage direct-coupled amplifier has single-ended output and squelched audio gate using 2N3638, for police, emergency, and other receivers operating in standby or squelched condition most of the time. Current drain is fraction of mA when squelched. D-c feedback gives stability for temperature changes and varying transistor parameters. Squelch gate removes bias from output stage. Power output is 2.5 W, power gain 87 dB, current drain 550 mA, and harmonic distortion 2% at 1 kHz.—A. T. Lehmann, Squelch Gate Reduces Amplifier's Standby Drain, *Electronics*, Dec. 9, 1968, p 83.

REMOTE AUDIO SWITCH—Applying +72 V to gate input fires neon V1, making it provide low-impedance path for practically all of audio spectrum. For 300-3,000 Hz communication channel, smaller capacitors can be used.—W. G. Miller, "Using and Understanding Miniature Neon Lamps," H. W. Sams & Co., Indianapolis, Ind., 1969, p 75.

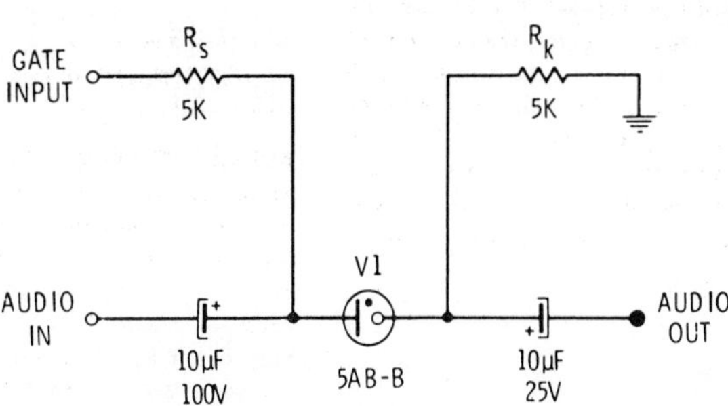

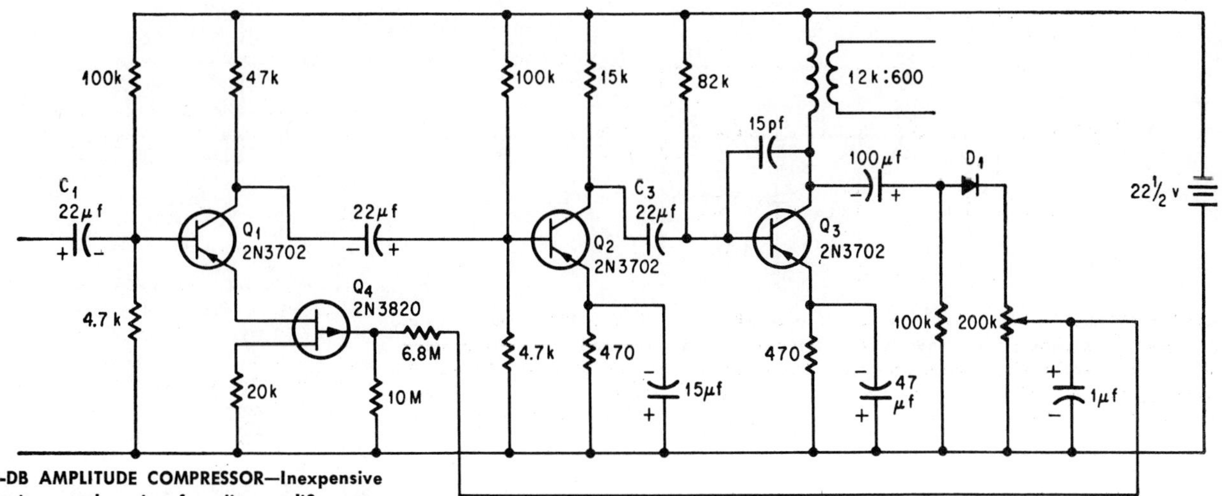

30-DB AMPLITUDE COMPRESSOR—Inexpensive circuit controls gain of audio amplifier over large dynamic input range by making input signal vary source-drain resistance of fet. Used to provide essentially constant amplification for wide range of signals picked up by acoustical transducer. Both input and output impedances are 600 ohms.—D. L. Pippen, Audio Amplifier Compresses Input Signal by 30 Decibels, *Electronics*, Jan. 9, 1967, p 105–106.

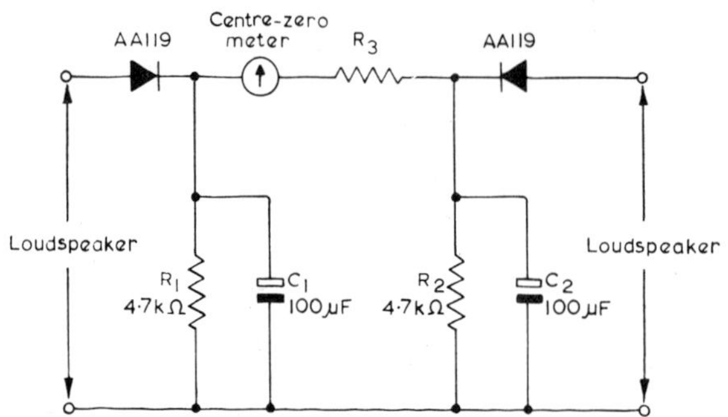

SPEAKER BALANCE METER—Value of R3 is selected to suit current rating of zero-center meter and output of amplifier; typical value is 10K for 1-mA meter. Used to balance the two outputs in a stereo system. Capacitors serve to damp meter movement.—"Transistor Audio and Radio Circuits," Mullard Ltd., London, 1969, p 183.

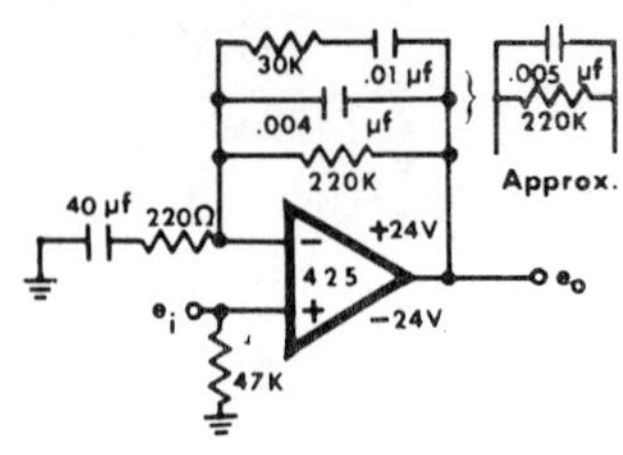

RIAA EQUALIZATION—Uses Model 425 IC opamp in network giving standard equalization for LP records. Simpler network at right will serve for less critical applications. Large capacitor may be electrolytic because voltage across it is few millivolts as summing point of opamp is driven to virtual zero.—B. J. Losmandy, Operational Amplifier Application for Audio Systems, Opamp Labs, Los Angeles, Cal., 1968.

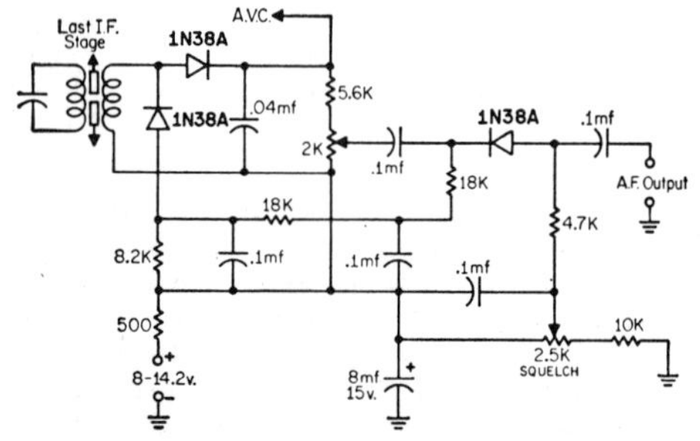

DETECTOR WITH SQUELCH—Circuit is designed to replace conventional detector of a-m receiver. Diode types are not critical, but all three should be the same. Noise limiting is achieved primarily with diode connected through capacitor to center of 2K pot. Squelch threshold is set by 2.5K pot.—"Electronic Circuits Handbook," Vol. II, Cowan Pub. Corp., Port Washington, N.Y., 1966, p 38.

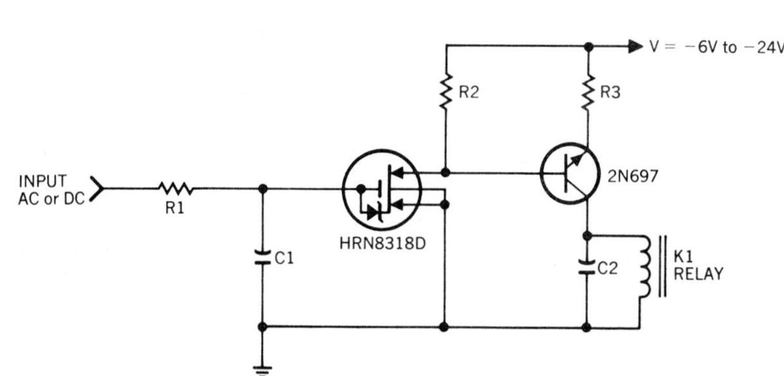

Attack time constant, A = R1C1
Decay time constant, D = $R_{K1}C_2$

AUDIO-ACTIVATED RELAY—Used to detect audio signals and energize relay to feed signals to telephone line or tape recorder. Input mosfet provides very high input impedance, permitting use of high values for time constant circuit R1-C1; typical values are 1 meg and 0.01 μF, giving 1-ms delay in energizing relay, to avoid triggering on noise spikes and other high-frequency signals. Time for relay to drop out after audio signals cease is determined by C2 and inductance of relay. With 100 μF for C2, delay is 2 s.—C. R. Perkins, "Application of MOSFET Devices to Electronic Circuits," Hughes, Newport Beach, Cal., 1968, p 36.

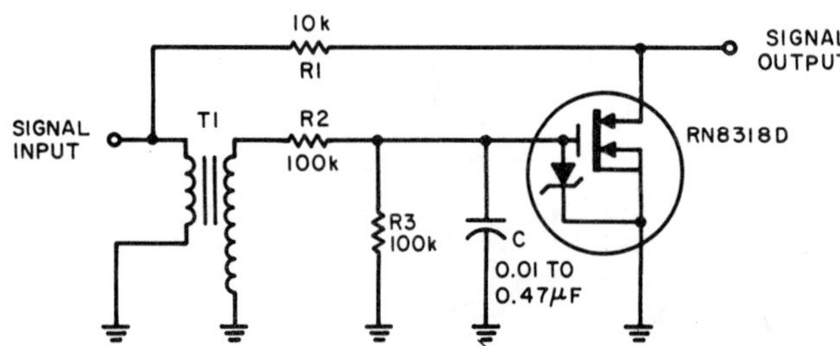

VOLUME COMPRESSOR—Mosfet acts as variable resistance, changing from several hundred ohms to several million ohms depending on value of negative voltage at its gate terminal. With −3 V, resistance is above 10K, and with −10 V it is 300 ohms. Signal source provides required bias. Transformer turns ratio should be at least 20:1.—C. R. Perkins, Volume Compressor Needs No Power Supply, *Electronic Design*, Dec. 20, 1967, p 110.

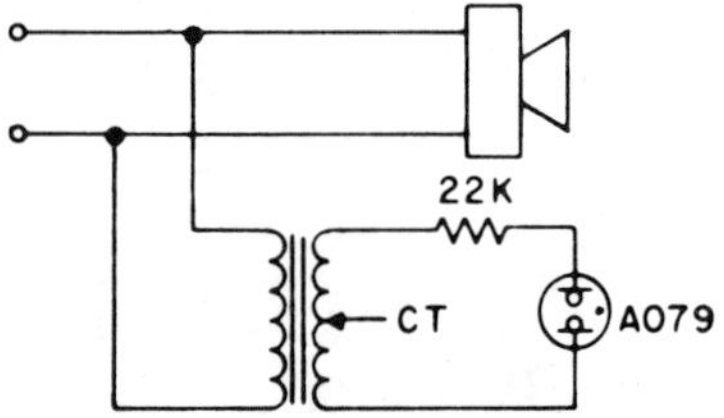

ANNUNCIATOR INDICATOR—Neon indicates which of several remote speakers in communications system is active. Transformer is a-f output transformer wired backwards.—E. Bauman, "Applications of Neon Lamps and Gas Discharge Tubes," Signalite, Neptune, N. J., p. 152.

NOTE: To locate additional circuits in the category of this chapter, use the index at the back of this book. Check also the author's "Sourcebook of Electronic Circuits," published by McGraw-Hill in 1968.

CHAPTER 5
Automatic Gain Control Circuits

1,000:1 GAIN RANGE—Insulated-gate fet increases controlled gain range to about 60 dB. Opamp A1 is connected noninverting to prevent loading of variable attenuator R1-R2-Q1. Output is full-wave rectified by A2 and fed to A3 along with reference from 2K output-level pot. A3 integrates sum and applies it to Q1 to complete feedback loop. Clamp circuit around A3 prevents saturation by zero or overload input signals.—E. Guenther, MOS-FET Provides 60-dB Dynamic Range Low-Frequency AGC Circuit, *EEE*, Nov. 1969, p 107.

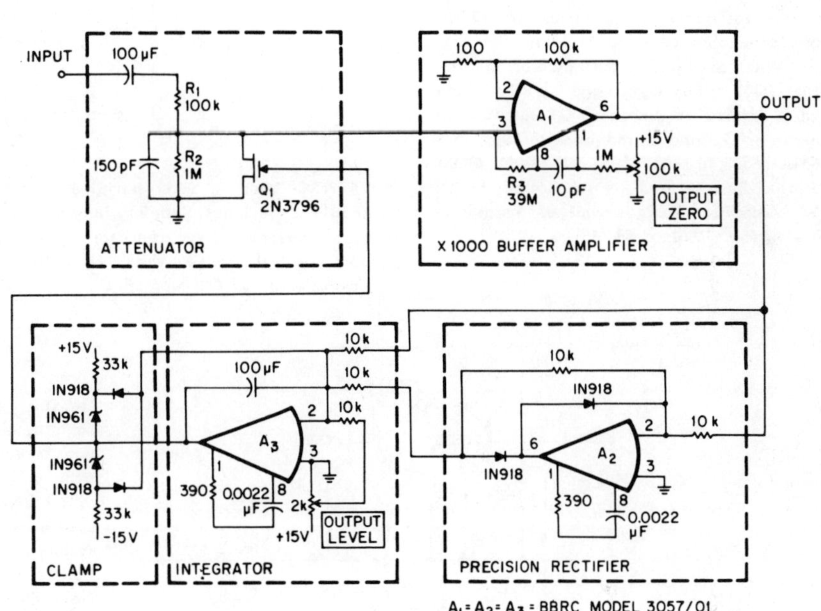

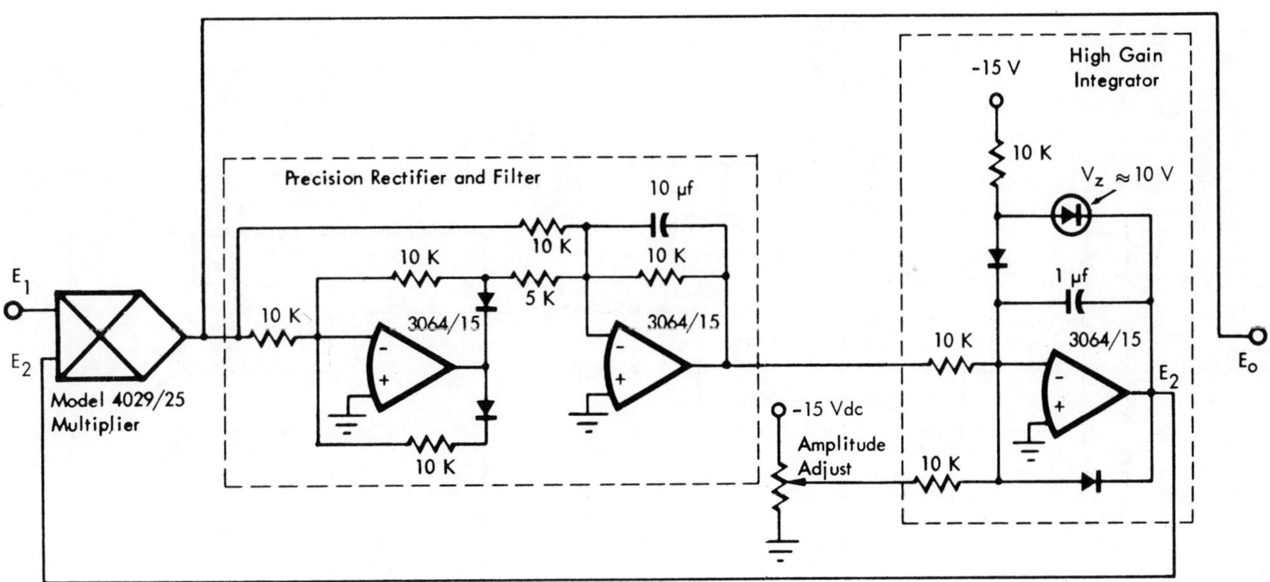

MULTIPLIER MODULE FOR AGC—Burr-Brown 4029/25 quarter-square multiplier-divider is combined with amplifier module to give stable, reliable, and accurate agc loop for such military applications as stabilizing oscillator signal amplitude or holding amplitude constant while phase angle is varied by filtering. Designed for frequency range of 10–500 Hz. Amplitude of output signal is converted to d-c and compared with reference voltage to generate error signal for integrator whose output is multiplied by input signal to vary gain. Rate of restabilization of loop after sudden change in input level depends on time constant of integrator and rectifier-filter. —Quarter-Square Multiplier/Dividers, Burr-Brown Research, Tucson, Ariz., PDS-201C, 1969.

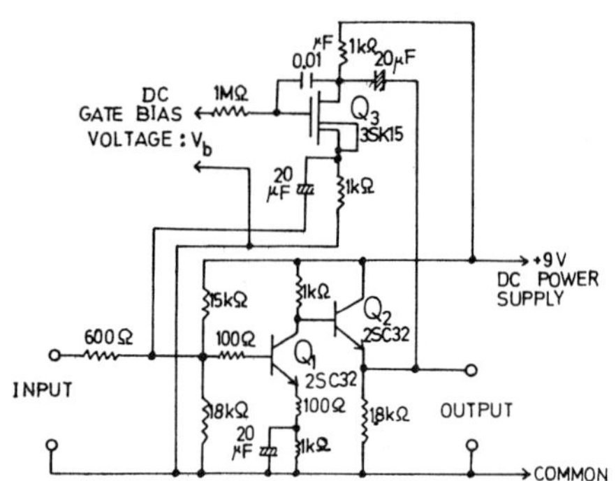

MOS TRANSISTOR AS VARIABLE RESISTOR—Provides resistance range of 0.8 to 50,000 ohms depending on strength of applied signal. When used in feedback path of agc amplifier (Q3), gives agc range of 3:1. Input signal applied to base of Q1 appears at emitter of Q2 and is fed back through mos transistor Q3 to base of Q1.—H. Ikeda, MOST Variable Resistor and Its Application to an AGC Amplifier, *IEEE Journal of Solid-State Circuits*, Feb. 1970, p 43–45.

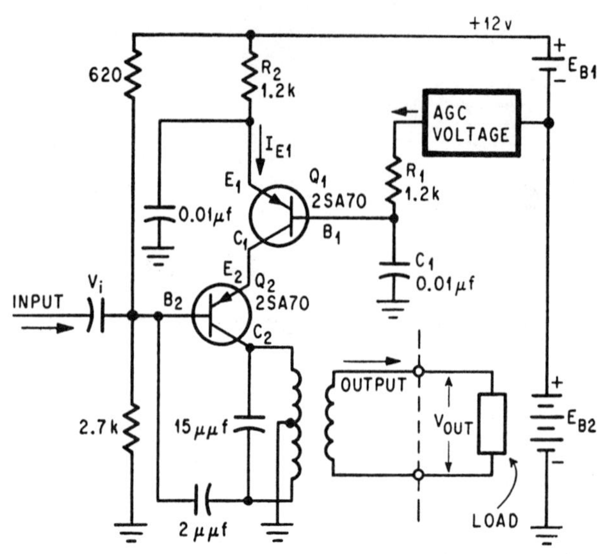

50-DB AGC—Used in Sony portable tv sets to handle large input signals without distortion or overload. Two transistors give far greater control range than conventional single-stage agc. Q2 amplifies, while Q1 serves are variable impedance in emitter circuit of Q2 and controls bias of Q2.—Two-Stage Gain Control for Portable TV Set, *Electronics*, Nov. 14, 1966, p 171–172.

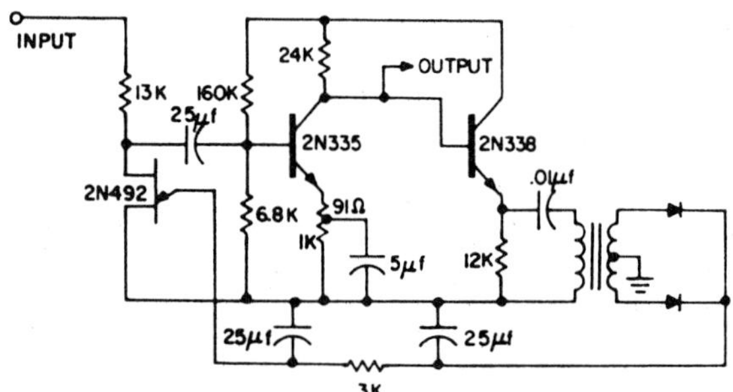

LIMITED AGC FOR OSCILLATOR—Ujt compensates oscillator whose output varies inversely with frequency, to keep output essentially constant at 7-V p-p over frequency range of 2.8 to 3.1 kHz. Operation is based on negative resistance characteristic of ujt.—R. S. Hughes, Automatic Gain Control Circuit Uses Unijunction Transistor, "400 Ideas for Design Selected from Electronic Design," Hayden Book Co., N.Y., 1964, p 111.

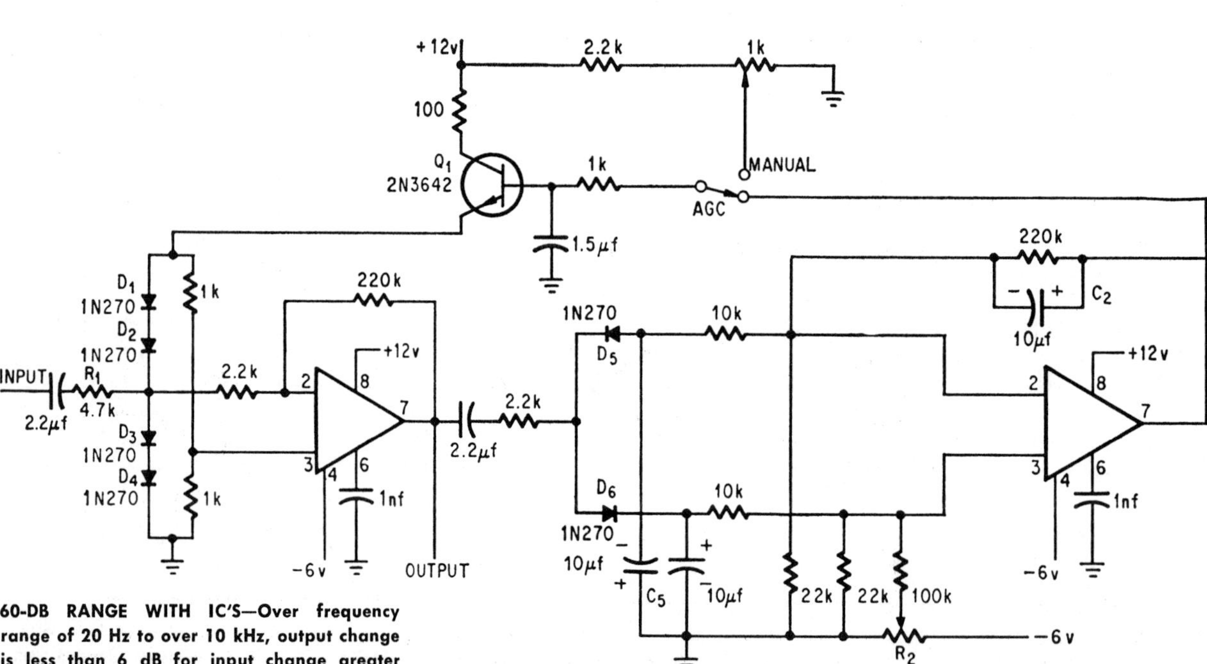

60-DB RANGE WITH IC'S—Over frequency range of 20 Hz to over 10 kHz, output change is less than 6 dB for input change greater than 60 dB. Signal from voltage divider R1-D1-D2-D3-D4 is amplified by first IC opamp having gain of 100, rectified by D5-D6, then fed back to input through second opamp and buffer Q1. For manual control, switch inserts potentiometer in feedback loop. Input signal should be several volts, for maximum agc range.—W. H. Ellis, Jr., AGC Circuit Possesses 60-Decibel Gain, *Electronics*, Dec. 12, 1966, p 107–108.

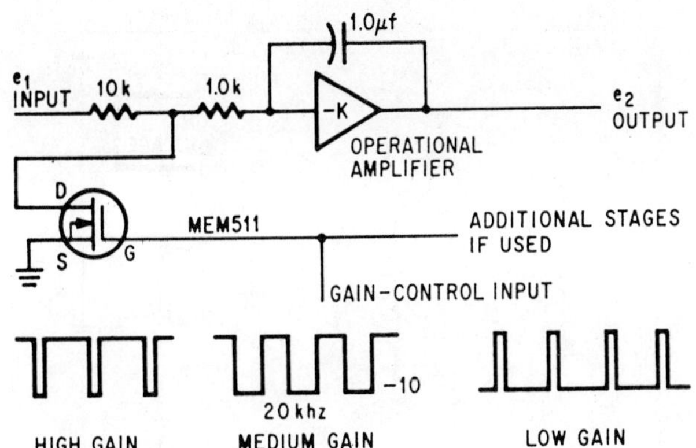

CHOPPER-CONTROLLED GAIN—Gain of any opamp may be varied over 32-dB range by varying ratio of OFF and ON times of 20-kHz pulse-width-modulated source applied to single fet. Resulting chopping of input to opamp, at significantly higher rate than upper cutoff frequency of amplifier, attenuates input signal during pulse ON time while giving normal gain during OFF time.—D. E. Lancaster, Operational Amplifier Gain Varied by FET Chopper, *Electronics*, Oct. 2, 1967, p 98.

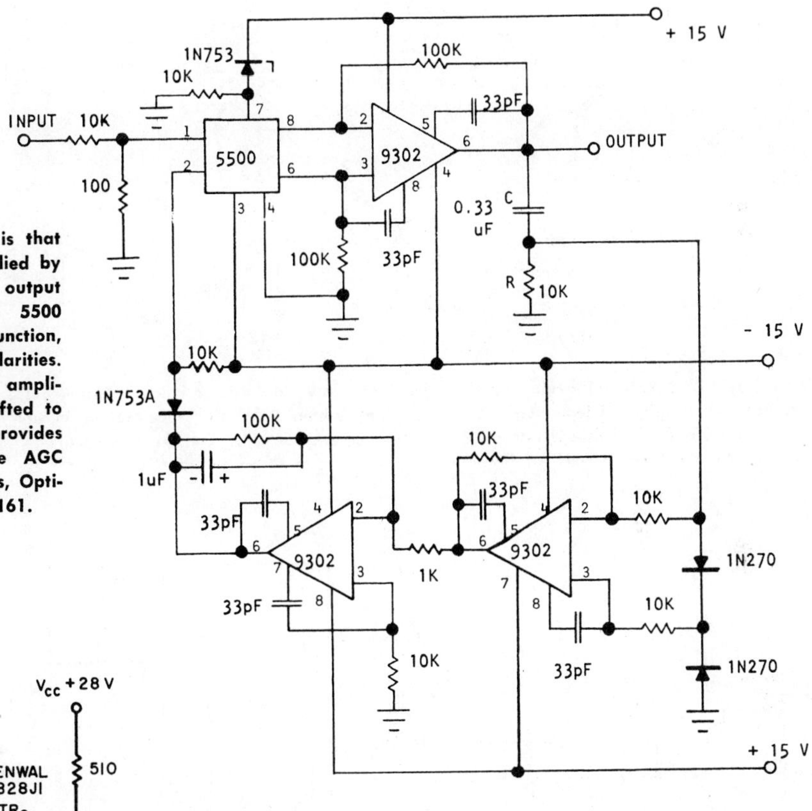

HIGH-ACCURACY AGC—Arrangement is that of multiplier, with input signal multiplied by corrective d-c voltage required to keep output level constant. Uses two-quadrant 5500 multiplier with 9302 opamp for this function, giving 10 V output level of both polarities. Output a-c signal is full-wave rectified, amplified, integrated, and its d-c level shifted to control multiplier. 1N753A diode provides d-c level compatibility.—An Accurate AGC Amplifier Using OEI Monolithic Circuits, Optical Electronics, Tucson, Ariz., No. 10161.

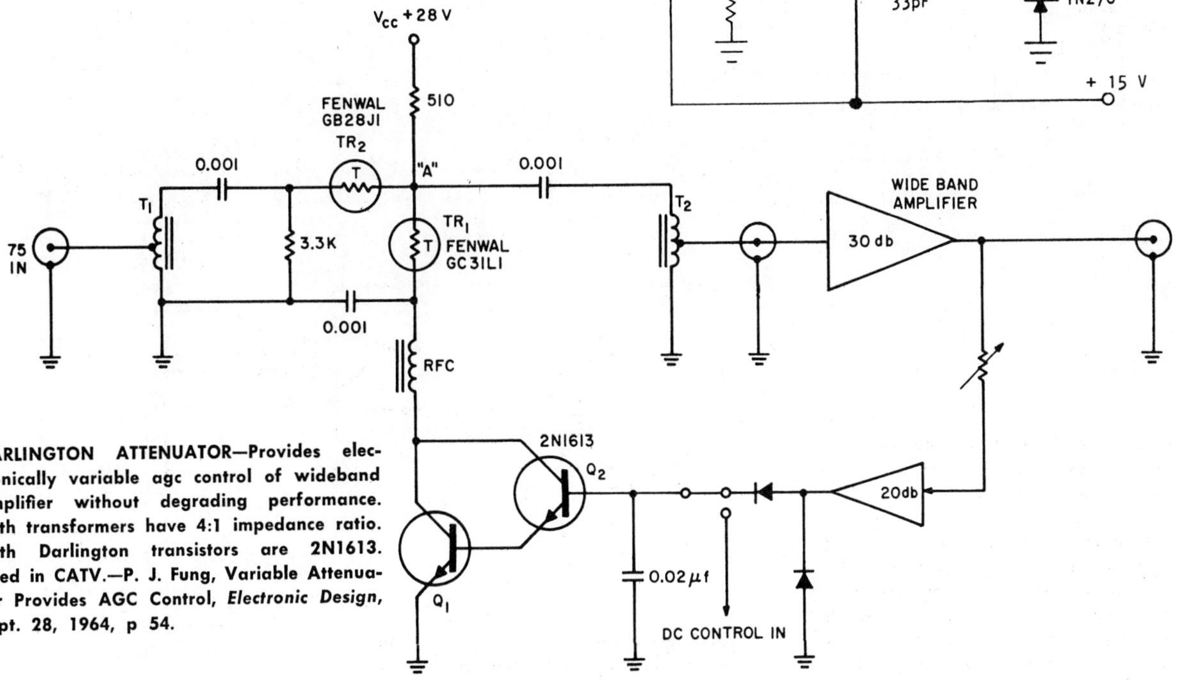

DARLINGTON ATTENUATOR—Provides electronically variable agc control of wideband amplifier without degrading performance. Both transformers have 4:1 impedance ratio. Both Darlington transistors are 2N1613. Used in CATV.—P. J. Fung, Variable Attenuator Provides AGC Control, *Electronic Design*, Sept. 28, 1964, p 54.

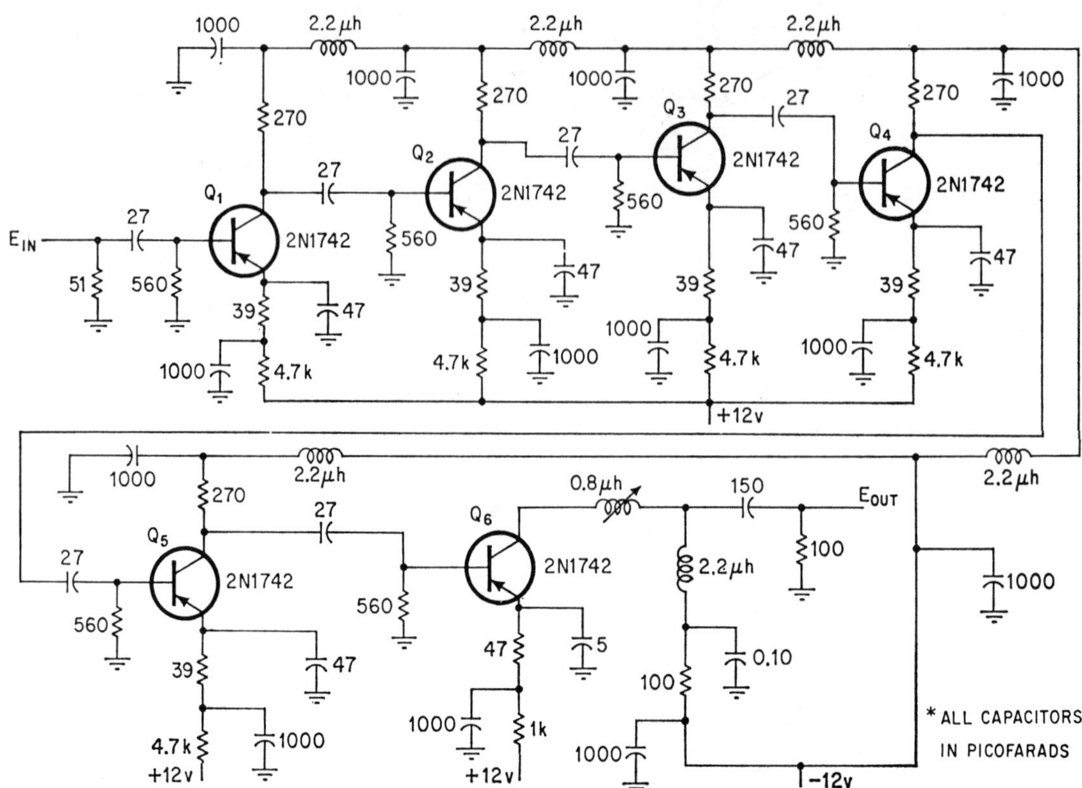

CONSTANT-OUTPUT LIMITER—Provides constant output essentially independent of changes in input amplitude, without introducing phase shift. Limiting begins at input level of 9 mV, and circuit holds output level constant within 0.06 dB even though input level increases 50 dB. Output stage Q6 has resonant circuit tuned to 80 MHz and drives 50-ohm or 100-ohm cable. Upper cutoff frequency of 100 MHz is limited only by transistors used.—R. J. Turner, Transistors Improve High-Frequency Limiter, *Electronics*, Oct. 13, 1969, p 94.

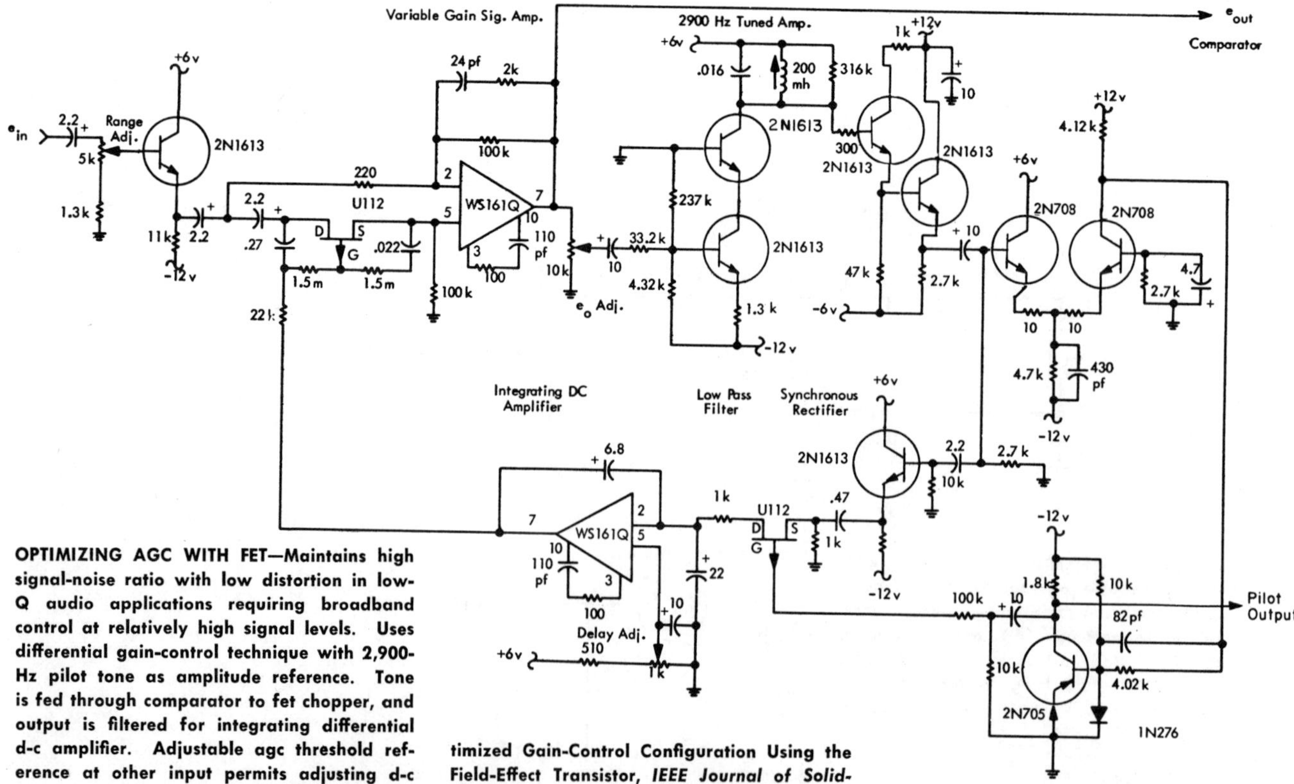

OPTIMIZING AGC WITH FET—Maintains high signal-noise ratio with low distortion in low-Q audio applications requiring broadband control at relatively high signal levels. Uses differential gain-control technique with 2,900-Hz pilot tone as amplitude reference. Tone is fed through comparator to fet chopper, and output is filtered for integrating differential d-c amplifier. Adjustable agc threshold reference at other input permits adjusting d-c output of amplifier.—H. N. Leighton, An Optimized Gain-Control Configuration Using the Field-Effect Transistor, *IEEE Journal of Solid-State Circuits*, Dec. 1968, p 441–447.

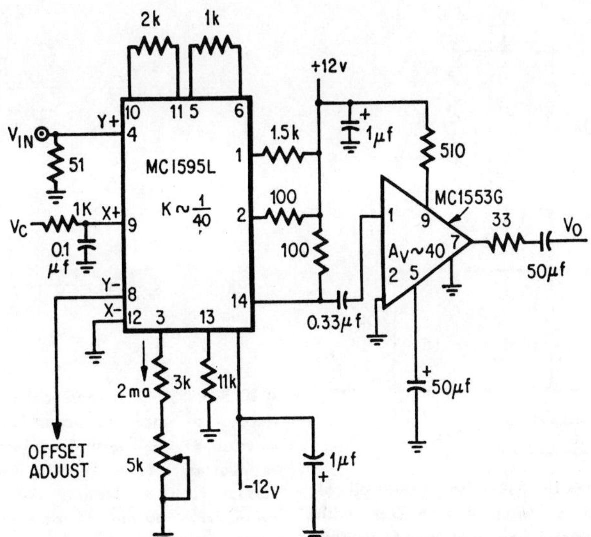

AGC WITH IC MULTIPLIER—Circuit requires 0-1 V d-c control voltage to provide linear gain control of 1-V p-p signal at 200 kHz. Peak-to-peak value of output is thus exactly the same as value of control voltage. Gain is recovered with IC video amplifier having gain of 40.—E. Renschler and D. Weiss, Try the Monolithic Multiplier as a Versatile A-C Design Tool, *Electronics*, June 8, 1970, p 100–105.

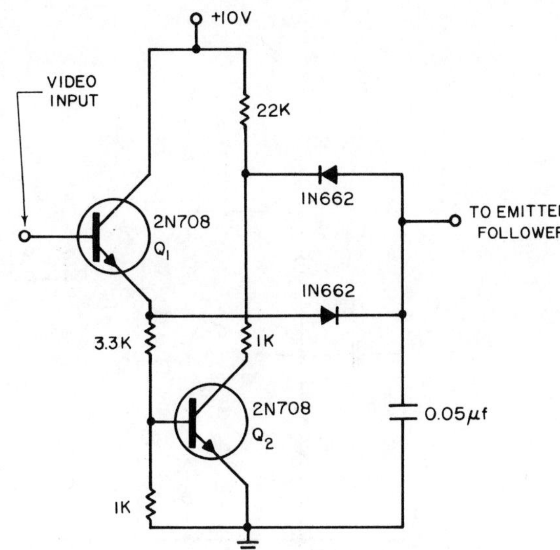

BOXCAR FOR PULSE AGC—Provides control over gain of video amplifier when both pulse width and frequency are variable. Used to keep amplitude of r-f burst constant despite variations in signal amplitude, frequency, or pulse width. Boxcar circuit is sample-and-hold integrator. Output of standard emitter-follower is desired agc voltage to be applied to controlled amplifier. With values shown, circuit will handle inputs of 2 to 8 V at 1 to 50 kHz and pulse widths of 5 to 500 µs.—G. P. Klein, Boxcar Circuit Provides Pulse Amplifier AGC, *Electronic Design*, Sept. 13, 1965, p 83–84.

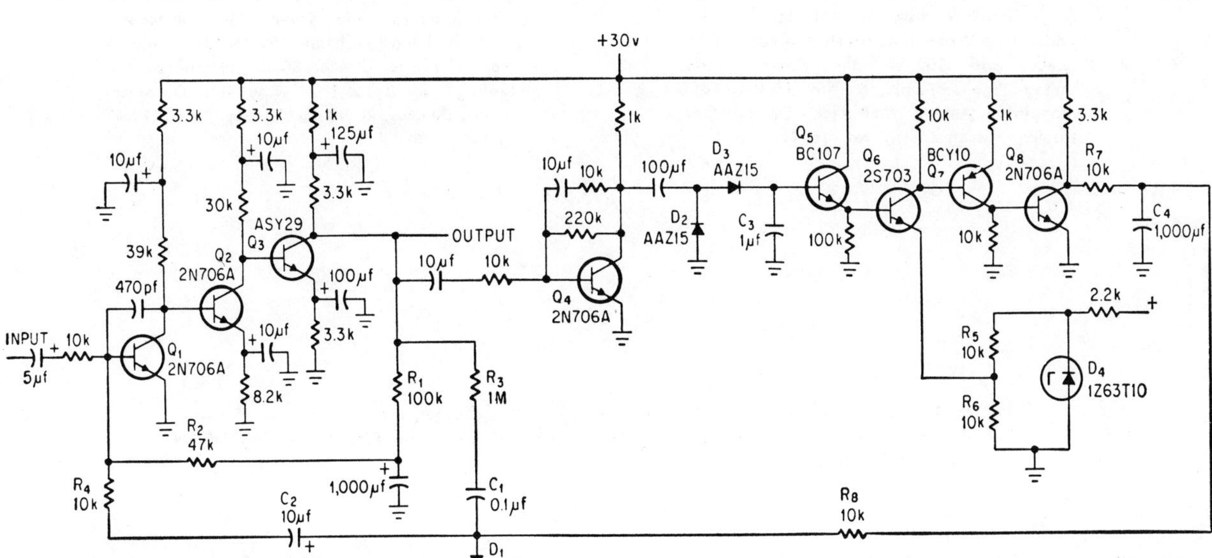

ERASING 19-DB SIGNAL SWINGS—A-c gain of 10–50,000 Hz amplifier is automatically controlled by error signal that changes dynamic resistance of diode D1 in feedback loop. Used in system for determining density of plasma in microwave cavity. Maximum gain of amplifier is 10,000, and noise level is 20 µV.—C. A. J. van der Geer, Amplifier Erases Swing of 19-DB in Input Signals, *Electronics*, May 29, 1967, p 85–86.

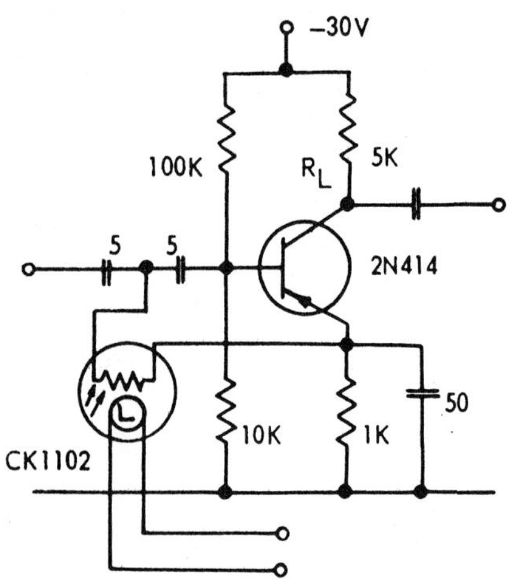

10-DB OPTOELECTRONIC—Uses photocell of Raysistor to shunt input of transistor, with one end of Raysistor tied to emitter to protect low-frequency response. Requires d-c control voltage of 0 to 1 V.—Raysistor Optoelectronic Devices, Raytheon, Quincy, Mass., 1967, p 12.

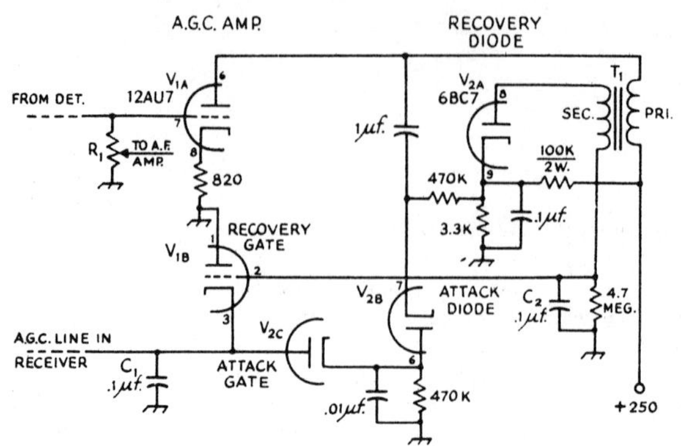

AGC FOR SSB—Provides fast attack and slow decay, for improved reception with ssb receiver. R1 is normal volume control in receiver and T1 is 1:3 step-up audio transformer such as Stancor A-53. Uses audio drive from output of detector in receiver. Requires receiver having good skirt selectivity, with no d-c return from agc line to ground.—G. W. Luick, Improved A. G. C. For S. S. B. Reception, "Single Sideband for the Radio Amateur," ARRL, Newington, Conn., 1965, p 180.

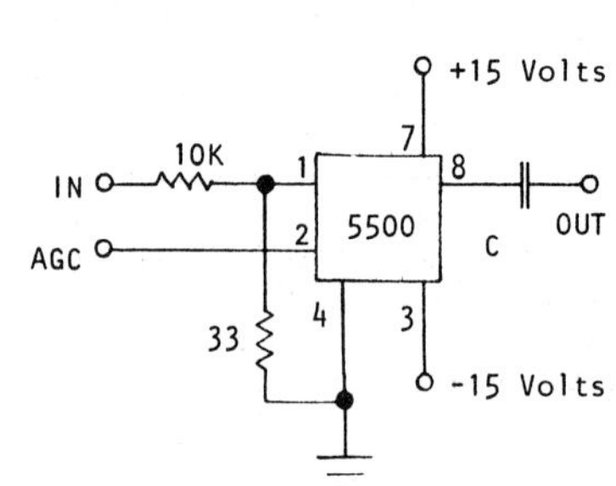

VOLTAGE-CONTROLLED GAIN—Analog multiplier makes agc voltage act on input signal up to 100 kHz, to give over 40 dB of agc range with low distortion. If signal level is under 10 mV at input, resistive divider is not needed and 5500 will then provide useful voltage gain.—Applying the Model 5500 Monolithic Analog Multiplier, Optical Electronics, Tucson, Ariz., No. 10138.

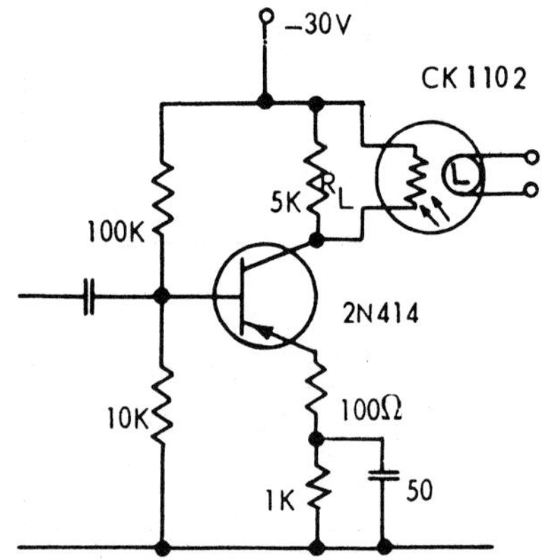

15-DB OPTOELECTRONIC—Uses Raysistor in collector circuit, so collector load decreases and reduces gain when input increases. Changing load resistance RL to 15K increases control range to over 30 dB for d-c control voltage of 0 to 1 V.—Raysistor Optoelectronic Devices, Raytheon, Quincy, Mass., 1967, p 12.

NOTE: To locate additional circuits in the category of this chapter, use the index at the back of this book. Check also the author's "Sourcebook of Electronic Circuits," published by McGraw-Hill in 1968.

CHAPTER 6
Automotive Control Circuits

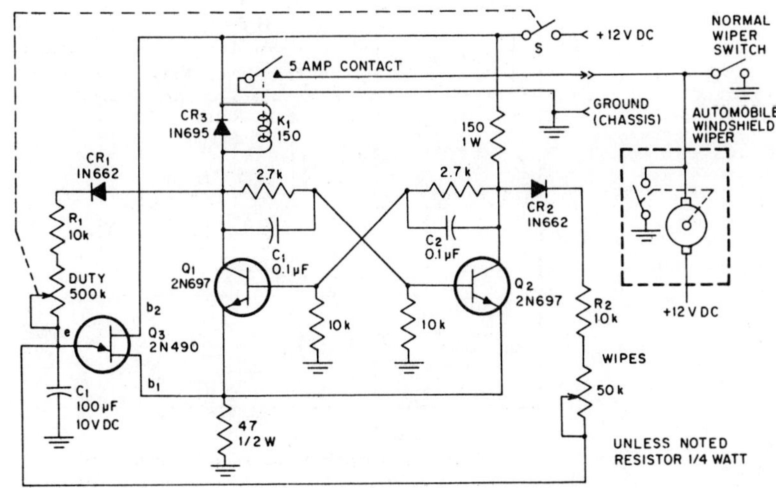

VARIABLE WIPER—Flip-flop drives ujt timer and wiper motor relay. Setting of duty pot determines interval, in range of 1 to 80 s, at which ujt timer Q3 will be activated and power applied to wiper motor through flip-flop. Setting of WIPES pot determines interval before flip-flop is switched back, in range of 1 to 8 s. Typical setting is 1 s for single wiping action. Chief advantage is ability to set wiper for operation at long time intervals, such as once every 30 s, for very light rain.—J. L. Shagena and T. H. Miller, Variable Control for Automobile Windshield Wiper, *EEE*, June 1969, p 140–141.

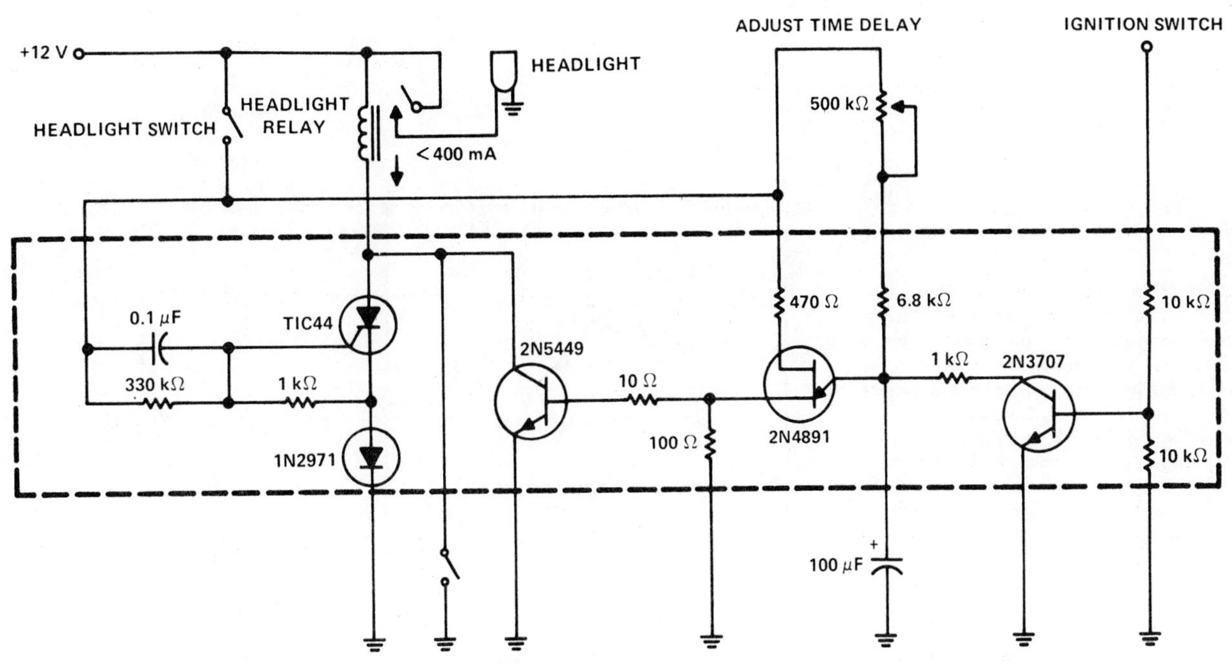

AUTOMATIC HEADLIGHT SWITCH—Headlights in car are turned off automatically in from 1 s to 15 minutes after ignition is turned off, with amount of delay being adjustable with 500K pot. Ujt is used as timer. —"Preferred Semiconductors and Components," Texas Instruments, Dallas, Texas, CC101, 1968, p 24114A.

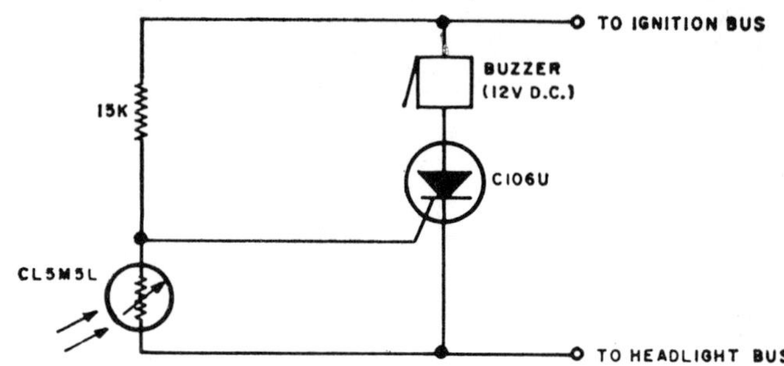

SCR HEADLIGHT-OFF ALARM—Sounds buzzer until headlights are turned on after dark. Mount photocell on inside of windshield facing out. If buzzer sounds too early, before it is dark enough for headlights, increase resistor value. Circuit is for negative ground; for positive ground, interchange connections to headlight and ignition bus.—J. G. Rabinowitz, Photocells—Types, Characteristics, and Applications, *Electronics World*, Sept. 1968, p 23–26.

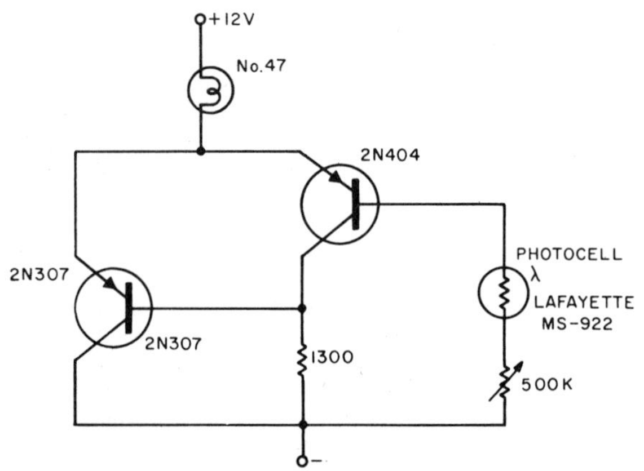

HEADLIGHT BURNOUT INDICATOR—Turns on pilot lamp on dashboard if photocell mounted near edge of headlight does not pick up light when headlight switch is turned on. Circuit is Schmitt trigger. Designed for 12-V battery with negative ground. Can also be used to monitor tail-light or stoplight.—M. Dickey, Inexpensive Circuit Makes Remote Light Indicator, *Electronic Design*, Sept. 14, 1964, p 75–76.

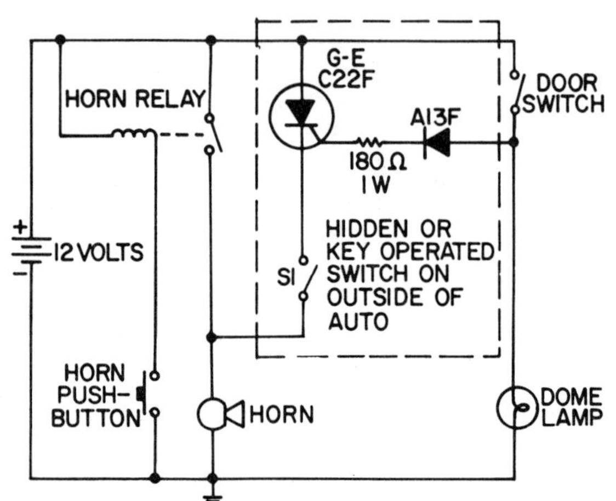

AUTO THEFT ALARM—Simple scr control, energized by closing S1, latches in when door of car is opened by thief and keeps horn blowing continuously until S1 is opened. Used in many London taxis; police have master key for key switch S1 mounted on left front fender, to turn off horn after catching thief. —F. W. Gutzwiller and E. K. Howell, Economy Power Semiconductor Applications, General Electric, Syracuse, N.Y., No. 671.1, 1965, p 4.

ELECTRIC CAR FUEL GAGE—Monitors discharge rate of 24-V battery in electrically powered vehicle. Turns on lamp to warn that battery has discharged enough to require immediate attention, and disconnects motor before battery is damaged. Includes override button that can be held down to get vehicle out of hazardous traffic situation. Action of voltage sensor can be adjusted to allow for age, history, and nominal output voltage of individual batteries. Report describes auxiliary measuring circuit that displays battery output voltage against expanded scale covering important range from nominal maximum charge to critical discharge (corresponding to fuel gage indication).—Battery Discharge Sensor for Electrically Powered Vehicles, Philips, Pub. Dept., Elcoma Div., Eindhoven, The Netherlands, No. 434, 1966.

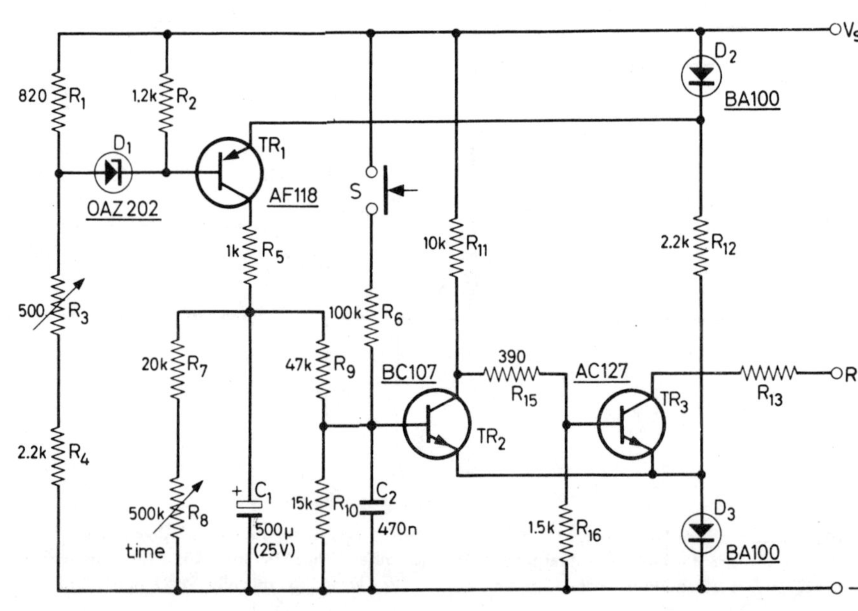

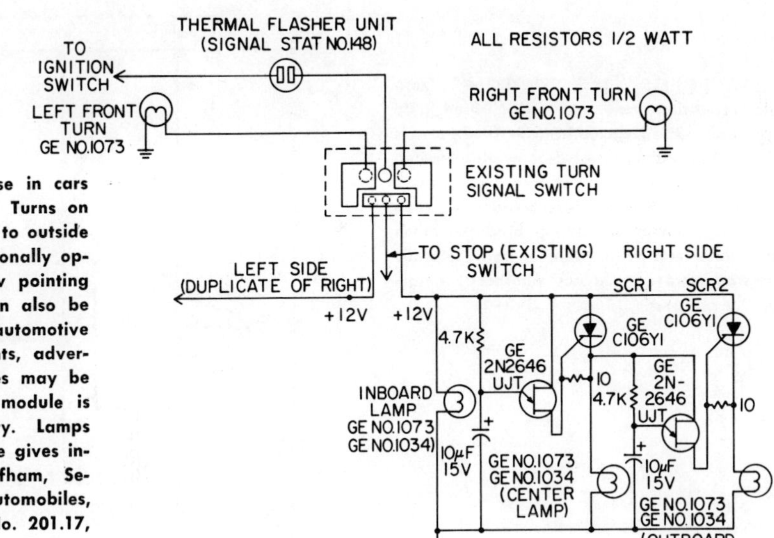

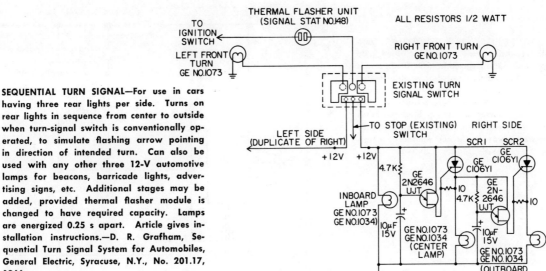

SEQUENTIAL TURN SIGNAL—For use in cars having three rear lights per side. Turns on rear lights in sequence from center to outside when turn-signal switch is conventionally operated, to simulate flashing arrow pointing in direction of intended turn. Can also be used with any other three 12-V automotive lamps for beacons, barricade lights, advertising signs, etc. Additional stages may be added, provided thermal flasher module is changed to have required capacity. Lamps are energized 0.25 s apart. Article gives installation instructions.—D. R. Grafham, Sequential Turn Signal System for Automobiles, General Electric, Syracuse, N.Y., No. 201.17, 1966.

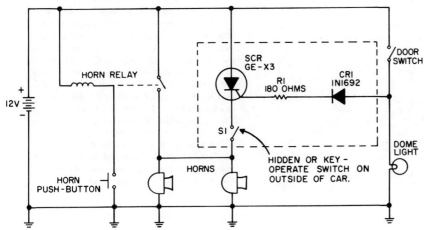

BURGLAR ALARM—Circuit is activated by closing S1 after leaving car. When any door is then opened that has switch for turning on dome light, scr is triggered and applies power to horns. Once activated, horns can be turned off only by opening concealed or key-operated switch S1. To prevent horns from going off when returning to car, open S1 before opening door. Arrangement shown applies only to negative-grounded cars.—"Hobby Manual," General Electric, Owensboro, Ky., 1965, p 50.

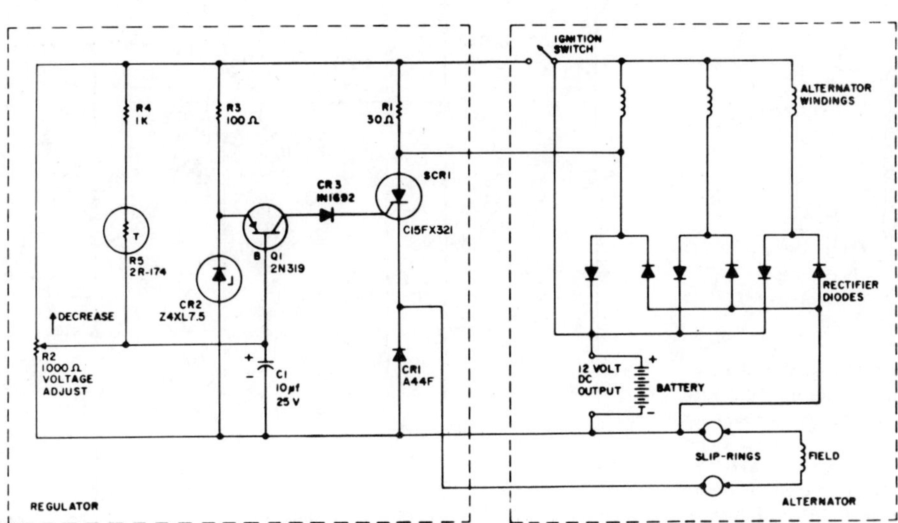

ALTERNATOR REGULATOR—Scr control circuit applies rectified output of alternator to 12-V auto battery whenever it is in need of charge, and automatically opens when battery is fully charged. To adjust, connect voltmeter across battery, with engine running at moderate speed, and turn R2 in direction of higher voltage until battery voltage levels off at 14.5 V for normal room temperature (use 15 V if adjusting outdoors at 0 F).—Automotive Alternator Regulator, General Electric, Auburn, N.Y., No. 630.15.

SCR WINDSHIELD WIPER CONTROL—R2 controls repetition rate at which windshield wiper motor is energized to drive blade across windshield and back at full wiping speed. Connections shown are for negative ground. Used to operate wiper less frequently when rain is light, without slowing blade so much that it interferes with vision or perhaps stalls part-way across.—"Circuits Manual," Motorola, Phoenix, Ariz., 1965, p 6–3–2.

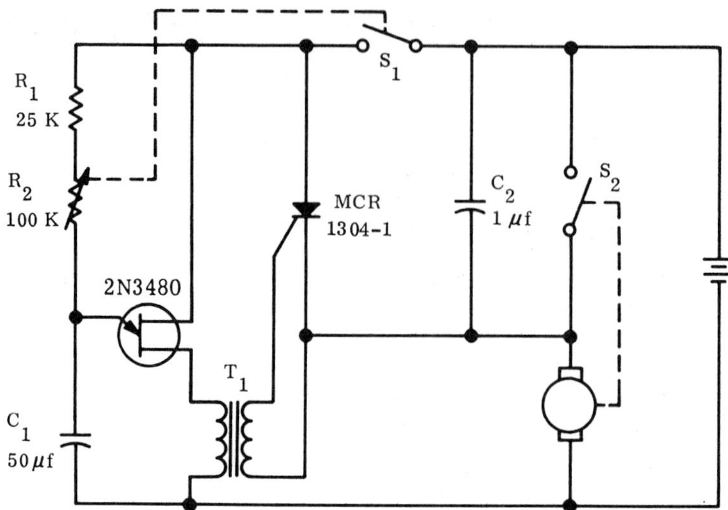

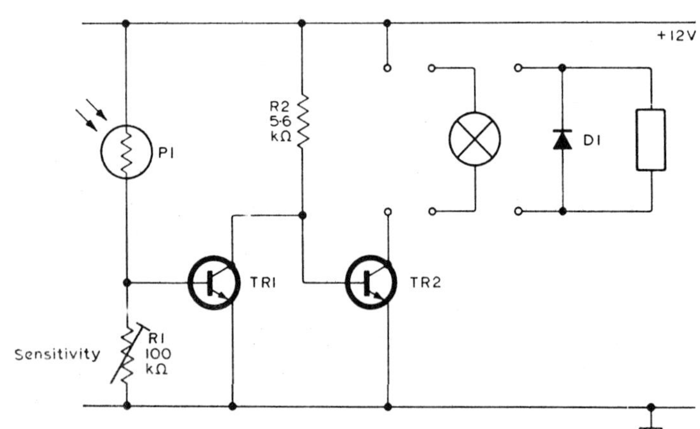

PARKING-LIGHT TURN-ON—Simple two-transistor d-c amplifier requires only two resistors and photocell to energize lamp or relay load. Can be used to turn on 12-V 2.2-W automobile parking light automatically when darkness falls. Power limitation is due to fact that current in TR2 increases gradually as light is reduced, making dissipation in transistor high during transitional period. With maximum setting of sensitivity control, lamp is energized at 1 lux and deenergized at 3.3 lux. At minimum sensitivity, lamp comes on at 0.1 lux and goes off at 0.5 lux. Transistors are BFY52 and P1 is ORP60 or ORP61.—Applications of the BFY50, BFY51 and BFY52, Philips, Pub. Dept., Elcoma Div., Eindhoven, The Netherlands, No. 428, 1965.

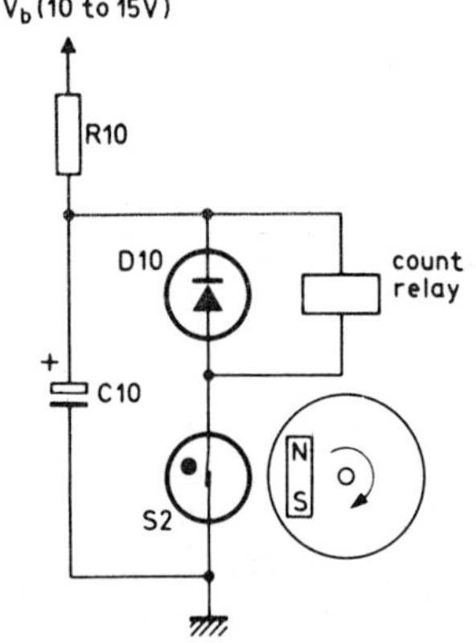

ODOMETER—Magnet on transmission shaft or driveshaft trips reed relay once per 100 revolutions to actuate electromechanical count relay that, in European version, advances count once per 100 meters of distance moved by car. Uses 100:1 reduction gear between shaft and rotating magnet. Diode is BAX13, S2 is reed contact, R10 is 1K, and C10 is 470 μF.—A. G. Korteling, Electronic Speedometer/Odometer Using Reed Contact Type Signal Transmitter, Philips, Pub. Dept., Elcoma Div., Eindhoven, The Netherlands, No. 89, 1970.

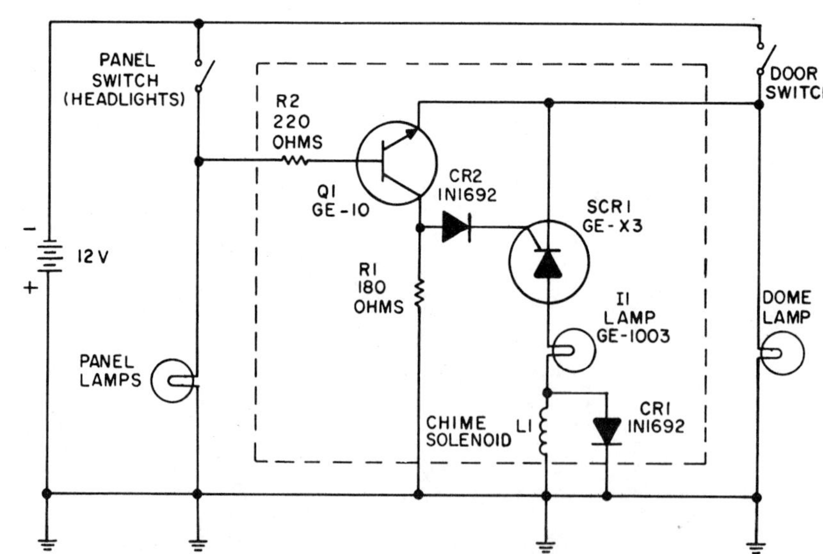

POSITIVE-GROUND LIGHTS-ON CHIME—Scr circuit actuates chime once when car door is open with lights on, as reminder to turn lights off. Single-stroke feature gives gentle reminder without becoming nuisance when door is kept open for loading or unloading passengers. Lamp in series with chime provides supplemental continuous visual indication without overheating chime solenoid, because lamp has much higher resistance when hot than when cold.—"Hobby Manual," General Electric, Owensboro, Ky., 1965, p 46.

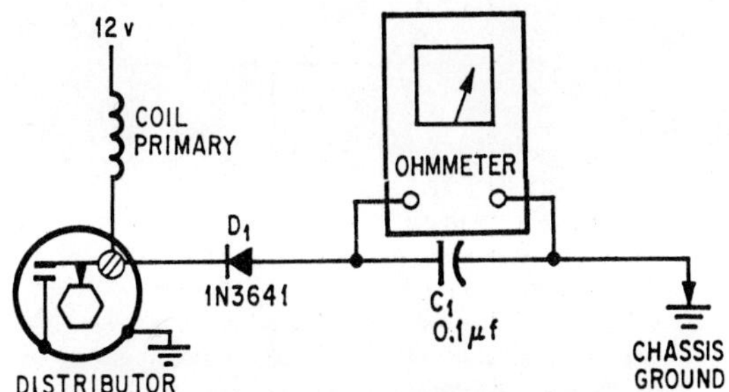

DWELL ANGLE—Simple diode-capacitor arrangement permits use of ohmmeter to measure breaker-point dwell angle (portion of rotation during which points are closed). With engine running, ohmmeter reads average of infinite resistance when points are open and zero resistance when closed. Article tells how to calculate dwell angle for engines with four, six, and eight cylinders.—E. W. Horrigan, Ohmmeter and Diode Measure Dwell Angle, *Electronics*, Aug. 5, 1968, p 105–106.

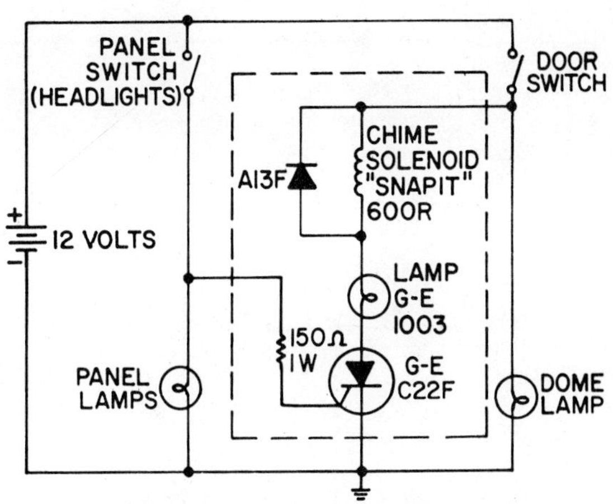

BATTERY-SAVER—Simple scr circuit makes chime ring if car door is opened while headlights are on, as reminder to turn them off. —F. W. Gutzwiller and E. K. Howell, Economy Power Semiconductor Applications, General Electric, Syracuse, N.Y., No. 671.1, 1965, p 4.

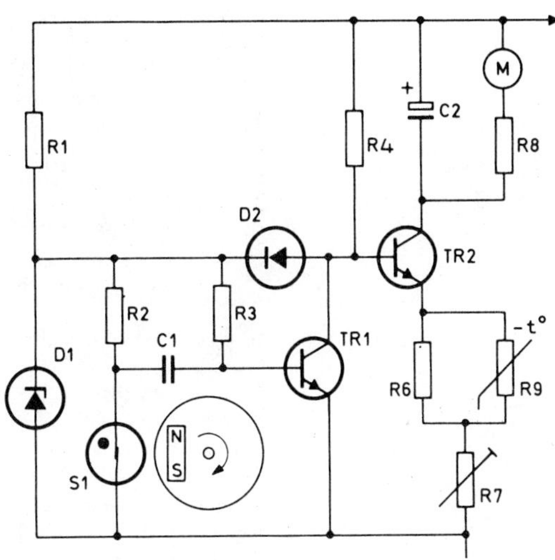

SPEEDOMETER—Monostable mvbr is driven by magnetically actuated reed contact in signal transmitter coupled either to transmission or driveshaft of auto, eliminating need for speedometer-odometer cable. Meter indication is proportional to rate at which pulses arrive from transmitter when car is in motion. In European version, speed of transmitter input spindle was such that reed contacts S1 produced one pulse per meter of distance covered.—A. G. Korteling, Electronic Speedometer/Odometer Using Reed Contact Type Signal Transmitter, Philips, Pub. Dept., Elcoma Div., Eindhoven, The Netherlands, No. 89, 1970.

R1 = 680 Ω
R2 = 10 kΩ
R3 = 10 kΩ
R4 = 1.5 kΩ
R6 = 68 Ω
R7 = 100 Ω, potentiometer
R8 = 1 kΩ
R9 = 130 Ω, NTC thermistor

C1 = 270 nF
C2 = 330 μF
D1 = BZY88-C5V6
D2 = BAX13
TR1, TR2 = BC147
S1 = Reed contact RI-12
M = Moving coil meter 5 mA, 0.6 V

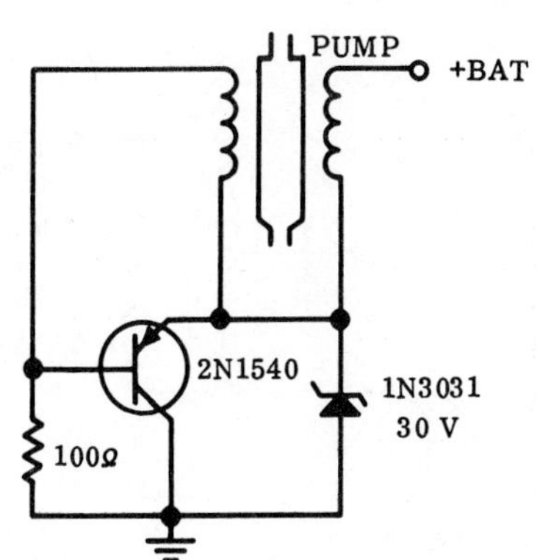

FUEL PUMP OSCILLATOR WITH ZENER—30-V zener across transistor speeds decay of solenoid current after plunger has been pulled in, thereby increasing frequency of operation and pumping rate. Designed to give 16 strokes of plunger per second with battery voltage of 13.5 V.—"Circuits Manual," Motorola, Phoenix, Ariz., 1965, p 7–3–3.

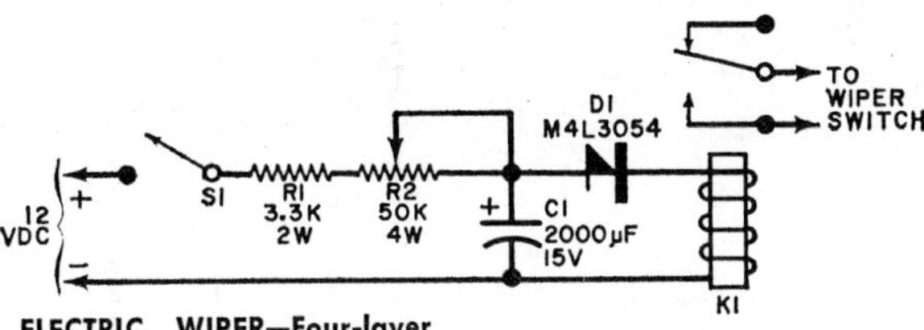

SLOWING UP ELECTRIC WIPER—Four-layer diode D1 in simple relaxation oscillator drives relay K1 which in turn controls switch of electric windshield wiper motor. R2 determines rate at which C1 is charged to point where it breaks down D1 and operates wiper. When C1 discharges below 1 mA, D1 turns off and relay drops out for start of new cycle. Will work with either ground polarity. —C. A. Huber, Slow-Kick Windshield Wiper, *Popular Electronics*, April 1970, p 86.

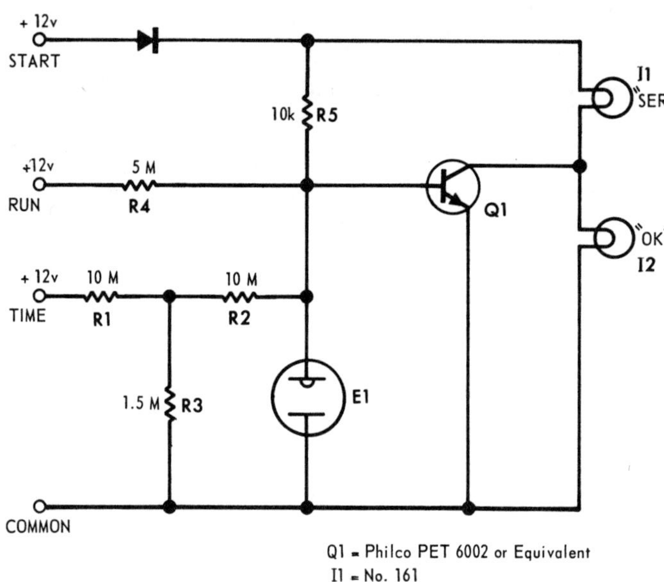

OIL-CHANGE COMPUTER—Simple electrochemical-cell circuit turns on lamp I1 when oil in auto engine should be changed. Factors involved are running time of engine, time oil is in engine, and number of cold starts made by engine. All three factors are weighted by resistors and used to control rate of transfer of platable material in cell E1.—J. Rose, E-Cell Computer Solves Oily Problem, *EDN*, Sept. 6, 1967, p 42–43.

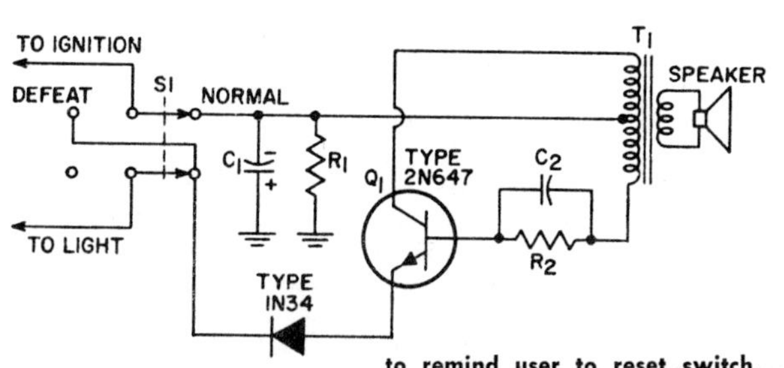

POSITIVE-GROUND HEADLIGHT ALARM—Speaker howls if ignition is turned off but lights left on. Can be defeated with S1, but alarm then sounds when ignition is turned on, to remind user to reset switch. C1 is 0.22 μF, C2 30 μF, R1 15K, and R2 680. Secondary of audio output transformer T1 should match speaker.—"Transistor Manual," RCA, Harrison, N.J., SC-13, p 517.

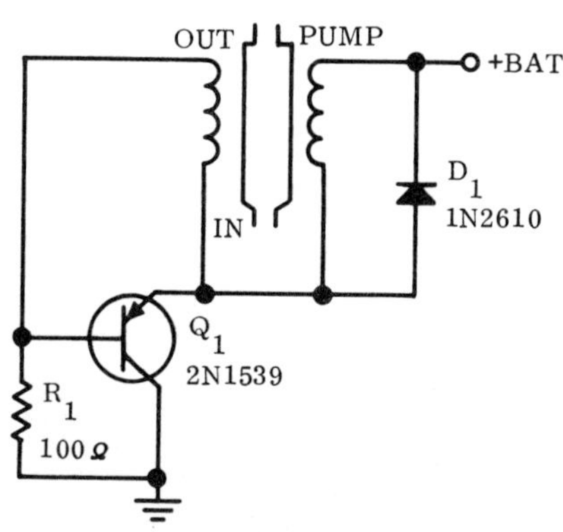

ELECTRIC FUEL PUMP—Basic blocking oscillator drives solenoid of Bendix plunger-type electric fuel pump, with feedback winding added to complete oscillator circuit. Transistor conducts for 25 ms to make plunger move full distance back into solenoid.—"Circuits Manual," Motorola, Phoenix, Ariz., 1965, p 7–3–1.

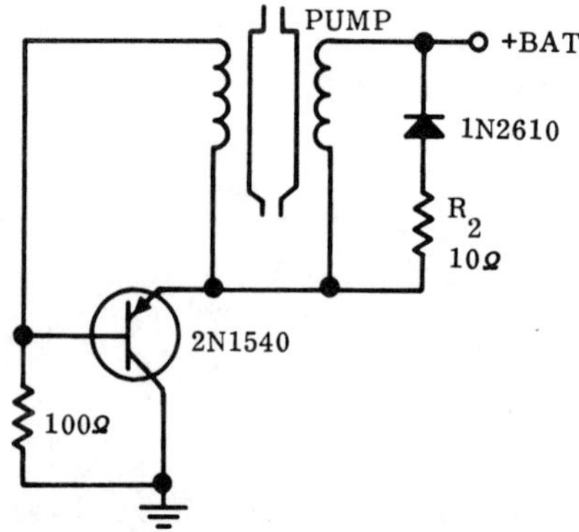

HIGH-SPEED ELECTRIC FUEL PUMP—Use of 10-ohm resistor R2 in series with diode across feedback winding of oscillator decreases off time of solenoid, thereby increasing frequency of operation and pumping rate.—"Circuits Manual," Motorola, Phoenix, Ariz., 1965, p 7–3–2.

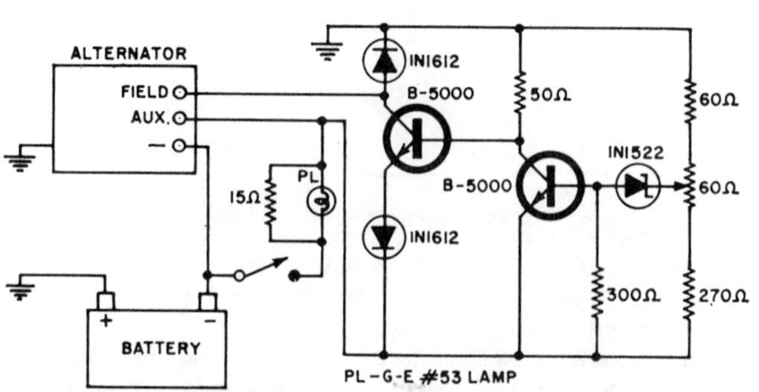

ALTERNATOR VOLTAGE REGULATOR—Uses two inexpensive Bendix plastic-encased power transistors rated at 25 W each and 35 V.—D. E. Lancaster, Plastic Power Transistors—Advantages and Applications, *Electronics World*, Feb. 1968, p 50–52.

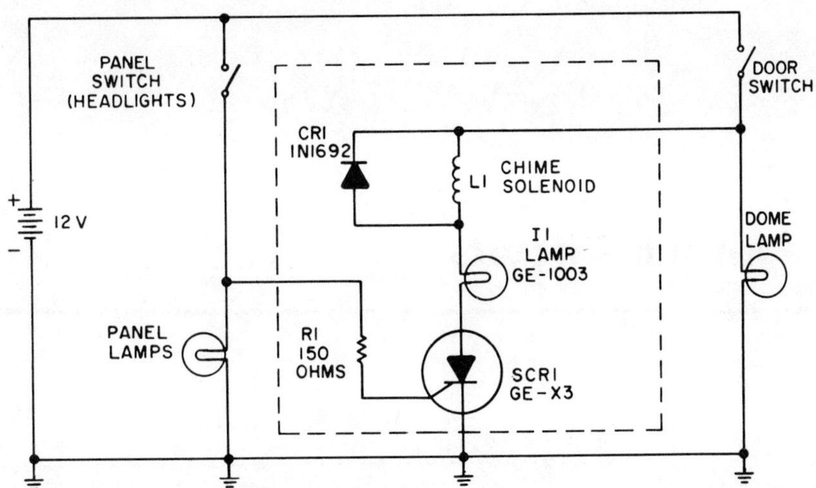

NEGATIVE-GROUND LIGHTS-ON CHIME—Scr circuit actuates chime once when car door is open with lights on, as reminder to turn lights off. Single-stroke feature gives gentle reminder without becoming nuisance when door is kept open for loading or unloading passengers. Lamp in series with chime provides supplemental continuous visual indication without overheating chime solenoid, because lamp has much higher resistance when hot than when cold.—"Hobby Manual," General Electric, Owensboro, Ky., 1965, p 46.

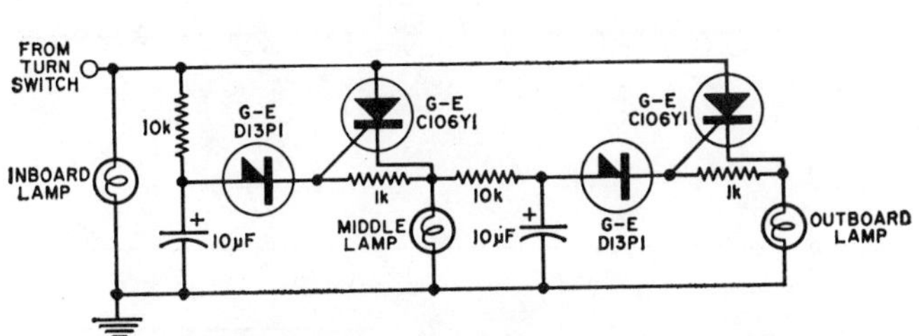

SEQUENTIAL TAIL-LIGHTS—Uses scr's to create sequential tail-light flashing, in combination with D13P1 four-layer breakdown diodes to open the circuit and reset the scr's. Breakover occurs at 6 to 10 V.—R. M. Brown, Automotive Electronics, *Electronics World*, May 1967, p 23–29.

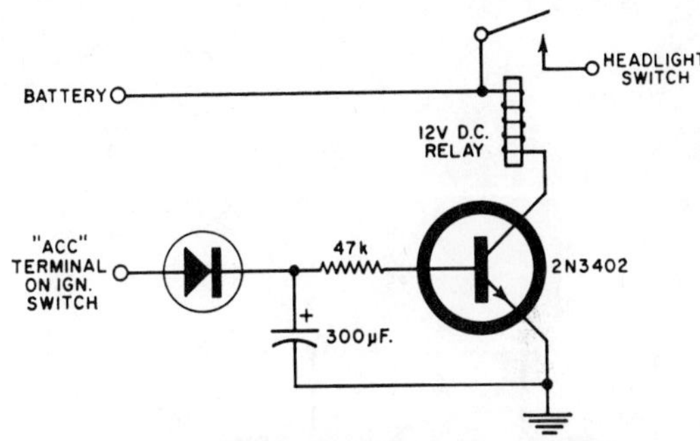

HEADLIGHT-OFF TIME DELAY—Gives 60 to 90 s after ignition switch is turned off, before turning off headlights automatically if driver forgets them or wants driveway lighted while he unlocks door to house.—R. M. Brown, Automotive Electronics, *Electronics World*, May 1967, p 23–29.

NEGATIVE-GROUND HEADLIGHT ALARM—Speaker howls if auto lights are on when ignition is turned off. Can be defeated with S1 if lights are left on intentionally, but alarm then sounds when ignition is turned back on to remind user that switch should be returned to normal position. C1 is 0.22 μF, C2 30 μF, R1 15K, and R2 680. Secondary of audio output transformer T1 should match speaker. —"Transistor Manual," RCA, Harrison, N.J., SC-13, p 517.

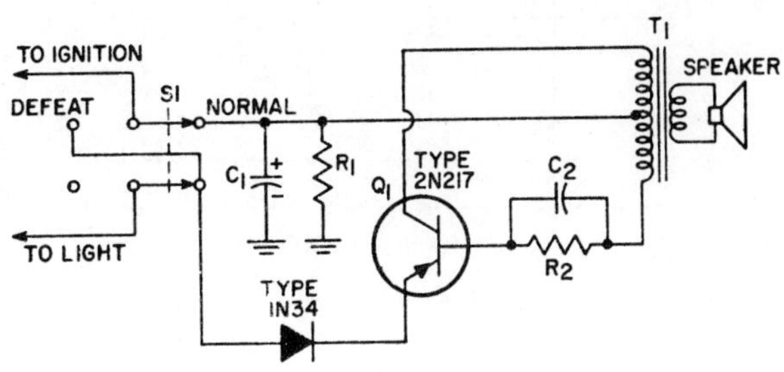

NOTE: To locate additional circuits in the category of this chapter, use the index at the back of this book. Check also the author's "Sourcebook of Electronic Circuits," published by McGraw-Hill in 1968.

CHAPTER 7
Automotive Ignition Circuits

TRIGGERED ONE-SHOT IGNITION—Uses silicon gate control switch that turns on like scr but is turned off by small reverse voltage pulse applied to gate. Trigger can be obtained from magnetic pickup as shown, or from photoelectric pickup actuated by distributor shaft.—"Circuits Manual," Motorola, Phoenix, Ariz., 1965, p 11–18.

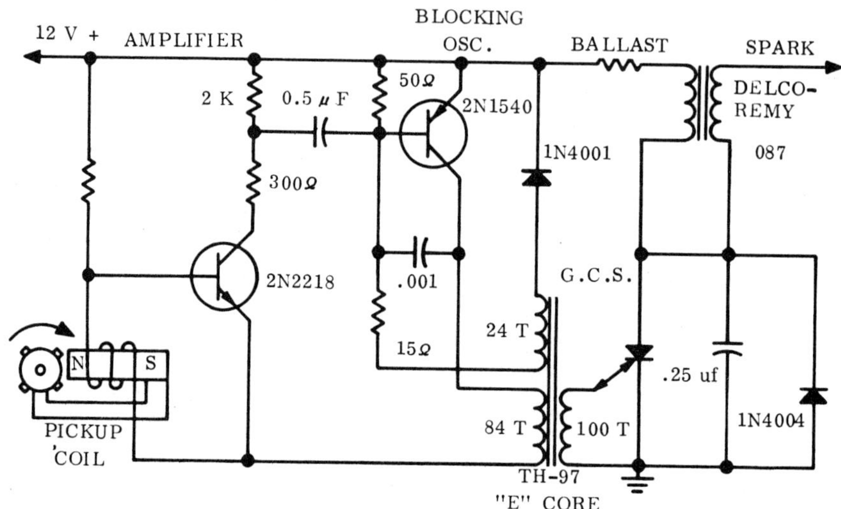

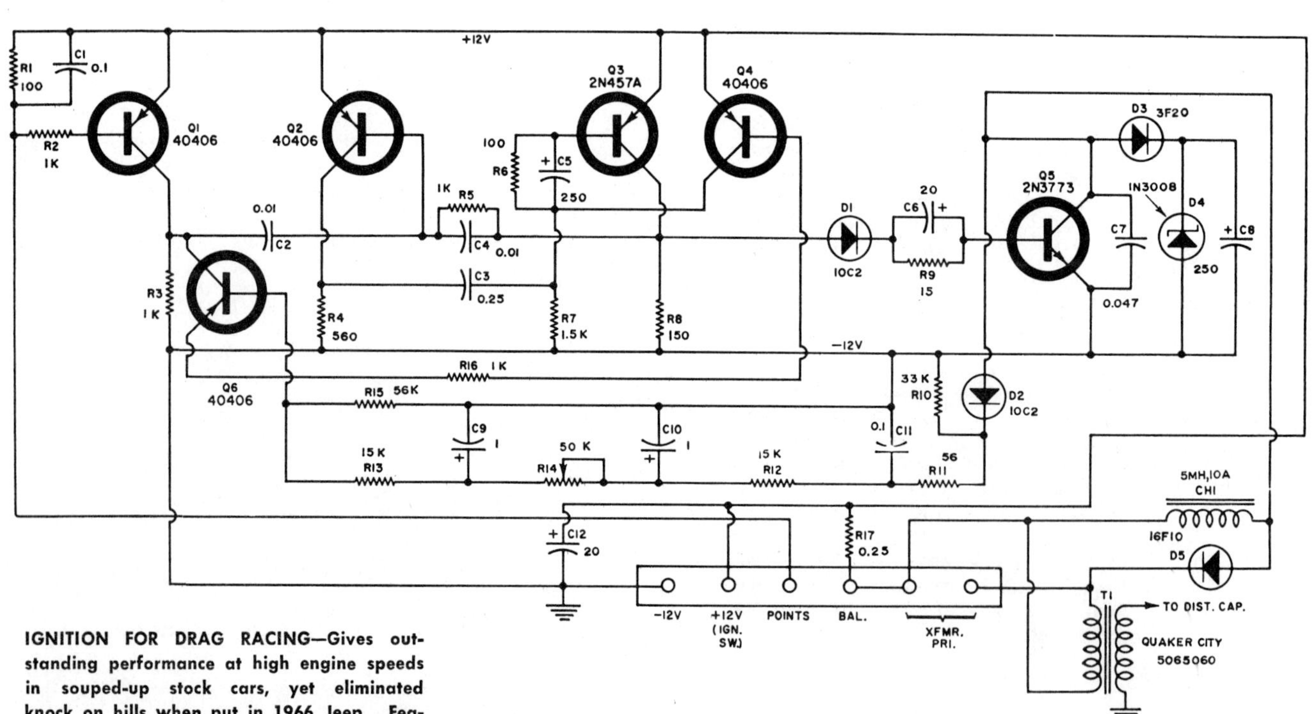

IGNITION FOR DRAG RACING—Gives outstanding performance at high engine speeds in souped-up stock cars, yet eliminated knock on hills when put in 1966 Jeep. Features include special storage choke coil and high-voltage pulse transformer that together provide hot spark long enough to assure complete ignition. Article describes system operation and adjustment procedures.—H. I. Keroes, High-"Q" Inductive Electronic Ignition System, *Electronics World*, July 1969, p 32–34 and 61–62.

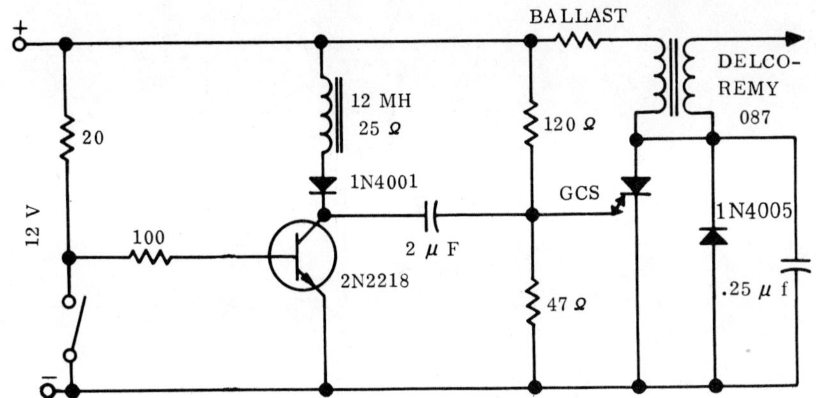

CAPACITOR-TURN-OFF IGNITION—Uses silicon gate control switch that turns on much like scr, but can be turned off by relatively small reverse voltage pulse applied to gate. Can turn off 7-A coil current at voltage levels approaching 500 V. Capacitor charges to voltage level of 25–30 V, dependent on energy stored in inductance while transistor is on.—"Circuits Manual," Motorola, Phoenix, Ariz., 1965, p 11–17.

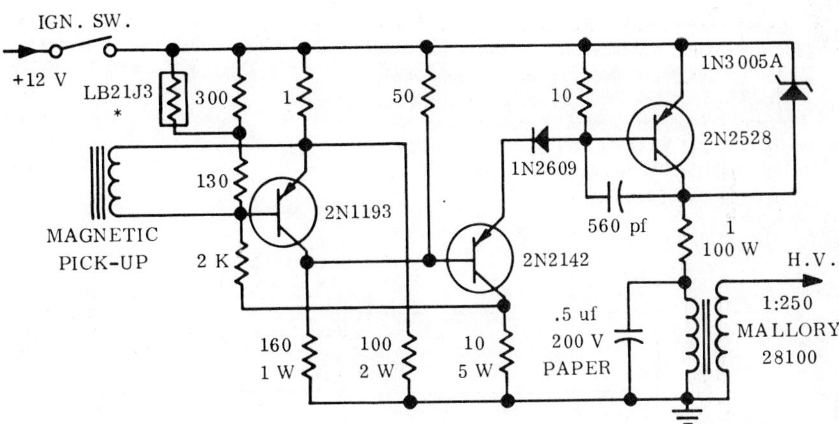

CONTACTLESS IGNITION—Magnetic pickup triggered by rotating teeth on distributor shaft serves in place of distributor contacts. Fenwal thermistor in bias circuit of 2N1193 ensures proper operation of circuit at low temperatures and low ignition speeds where pickup trigger signals are very low.—"Circuits Manual," Motorola, Phoenix, Ariz., 1965, p 11–4.

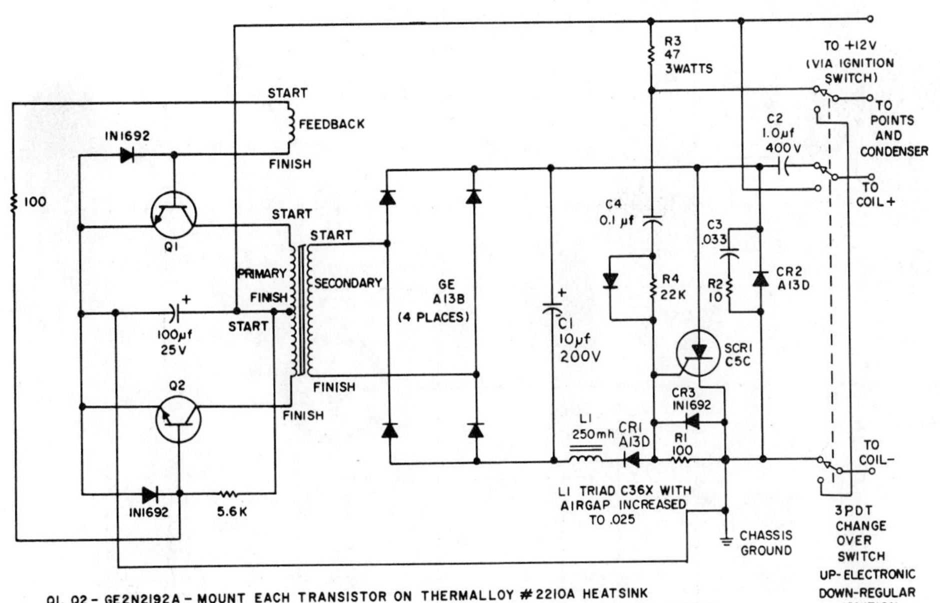

Q1, Q2 - GE2N2192A - MOUNT EACH TRANSISTOR ON THERMALLOY #2210A HEATSINK
T1 - FERROXOCUBE 206F440 - 3C5 "E" CORES (2 REQUIRED); FERROXCUBE 595F425 BOBBIN
WIND 140 TURNS SEC FIRST (4 LAYER)#30AWG FORMVAR WIRE; INSULATE WITH 1 LAYER MYLAR TAPE
WIND 9 TURNS FEEDBACK NEXT (1 LAYER) #30 AWG FORMVAR WIRE
BIFILAR WIND (2 X 9 TURNS) PRIMARY LAST (2 LAYERS) #20 AWG FORMVAR WIRE.

SCR CAPACITOR-DISCHARGE IGNITION—Delivers relatively constant ignition voltage over entire speed range of idling to maximum rpm limit (about 5,500 rpm for 4-stroke V8 engine of most modern automobiles. Eliminates distributor contact wear from arcing because contacts handle only low-current scr trigger signal. Alternatively, scr can be triggered by pulse output of magnetic pickup attached to distributor in place of contacts.—D. R. Grafham, Using Low Current SCR's, General Electric, Syracuse, N.Y., No. 200.19, 1967, p 32.

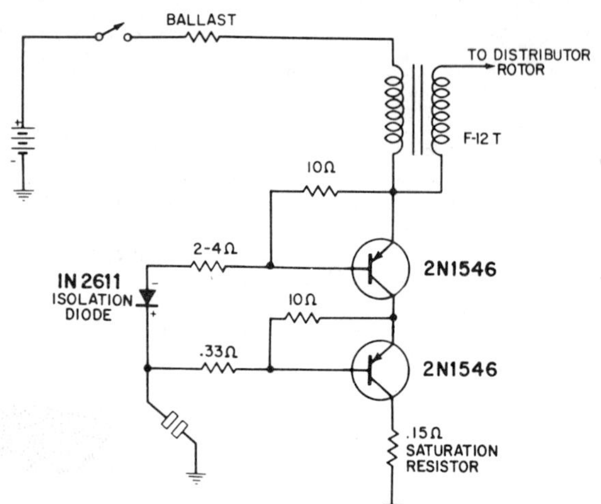

DUAL-TRANSISTOR IGNITION—Use of two low-voltage transistors in place of much more costly high-voltage unit gives comparable reliability. Possible drawback is lack of zener diode protection. Circuit is Slep Electronics Co. TS-14.—B. Ward, "Transistor Ignition Systems Handbook," H. W. Sams & Co., Indianapolis, Ind., 1966, p 93.

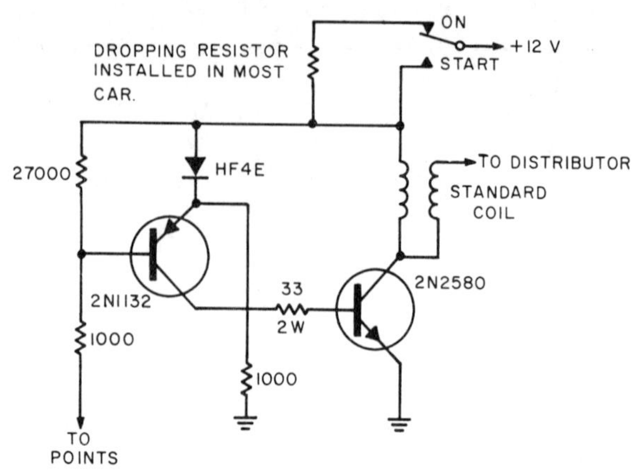

ELECTRONIC IGNITION WITH STANDARD COIL—Uses existing wiring and standard ignition coil, improves gas mileage at high speeds, is not affected by high temperature, and extends life of points to that of car itself.—A. M. Hildebrant, Transistor Auto Ignition Uses Standard Coil, *Electronic Design*, May 11, 1964, p 83.

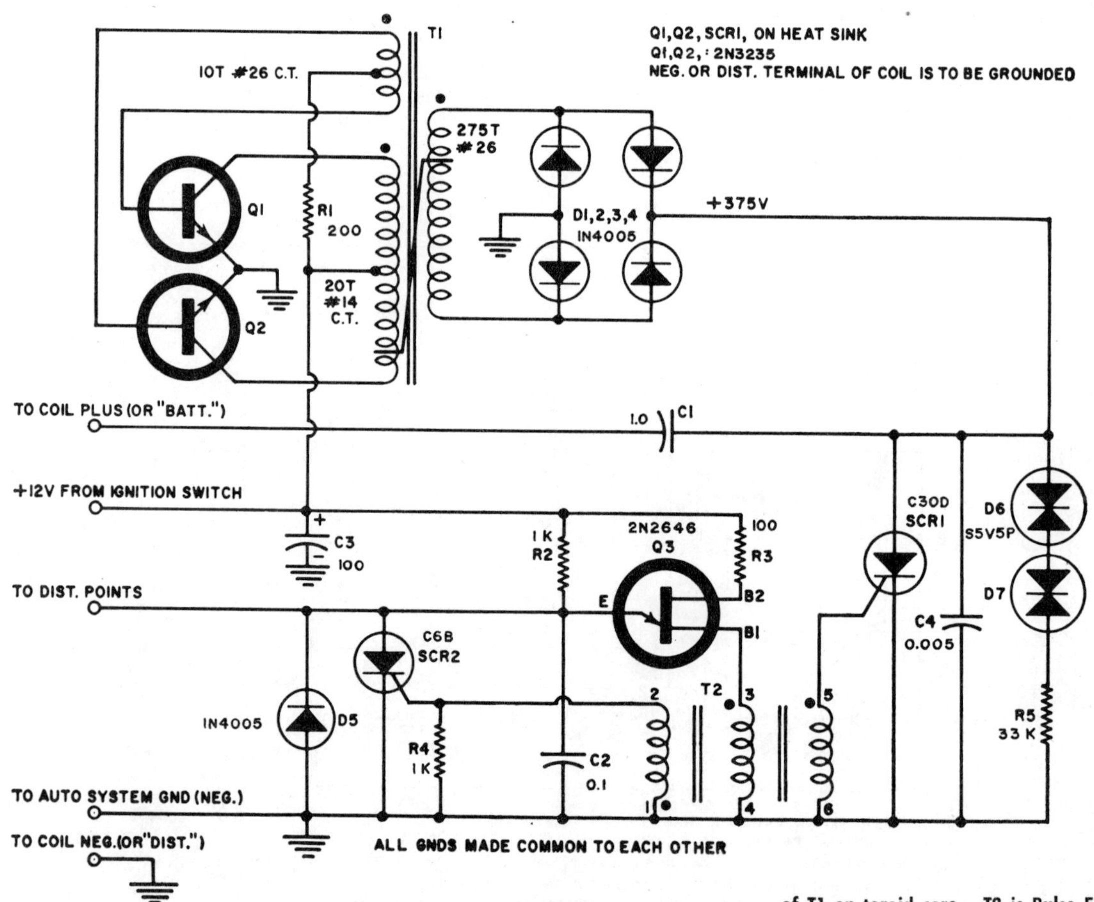

TWO-SCR IGNITION—Improves engine performance, increases miles per gallon, and prevents multiple firing or misfiring caused by point bounce. Power supply uses inverter and bridge to step up battery voltage from 12 V to 375 V for charging energy storage capacitor C1. Opening of distributor points triggers SCR1 into conduction, thereby discharging C1 through ignition coil. Article gives construction details, including winding of T1 on toroid core. T2 is Pulse Engineering PE2225 or Sprague 11Z13 1:1:1 pulse transformer. Works only on cars with negative ground.—C. C. Morris and R. D. Morton, Unique Capacitor-Discharge Ignition System, *Electronics World*, Jan. 1969, p 45–48 and 56.

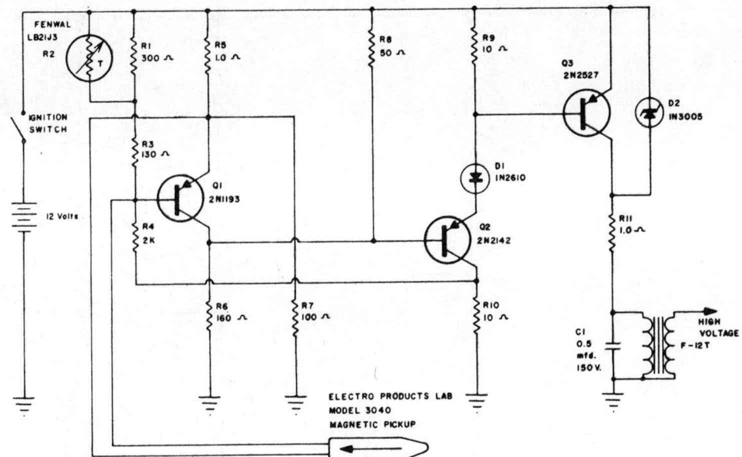

BREAKERLESS IGNITION—Motorola system, using magnetic pickup in place of distributor points, was used in somewhat similar form on Pontiac Grand Prix. Requires 8-tooth iron or steel star wheel for 8-cylinder engine (6 for 6-cylinder) mounted on rotor of distributor, with each spoke as wide at tip as dwell angle specified for car in which it will be used. Magnetic pickup is mounted on breaker plate, using bracket, with sufficiently wide relief hole in distributor case to permit movement by centrifugal and vacuum advance mechanisms. Pickup coil contains small permanent magnet in tip.—B. Ward, "Transistor Ignition Systems Handbook," H. W. Sams & Co., Indianapolis, Ind., 1966, p 63.

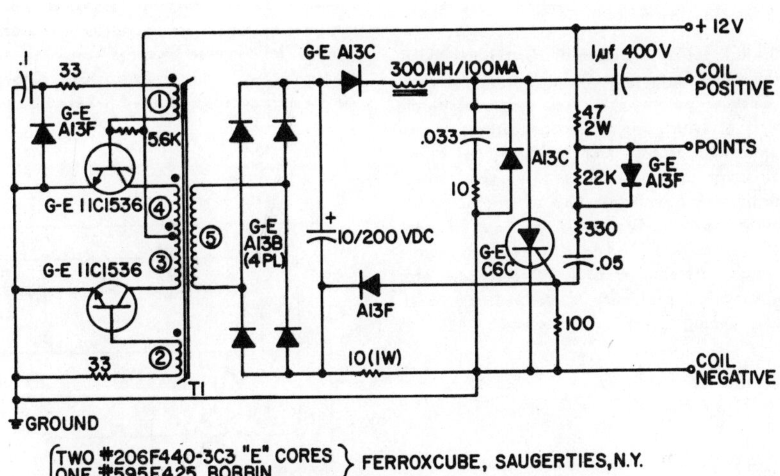

SCR CAPACITOR-DISCHARGE IGNITION—Driven by silicon-transistor inverter, drawing less than 2 A from battery over entire speed range. Will provide full spark voltage for speeds up to 6,000 rpm on 8-cylinder engine. Distributor points carry very little current so there is no arcing and very little wear. Existing points, capacitor, ballast, and coil of car are used. Lockout circuit in scr gate prevents false triggering by contact bounce, eliminating misfiring.—F. W. Gutzwiller and E. K. Howell, Economy Power Semiconductor Applications, General Electric, Syracuse, N.Y., No. 671.1, 1965, p 25.

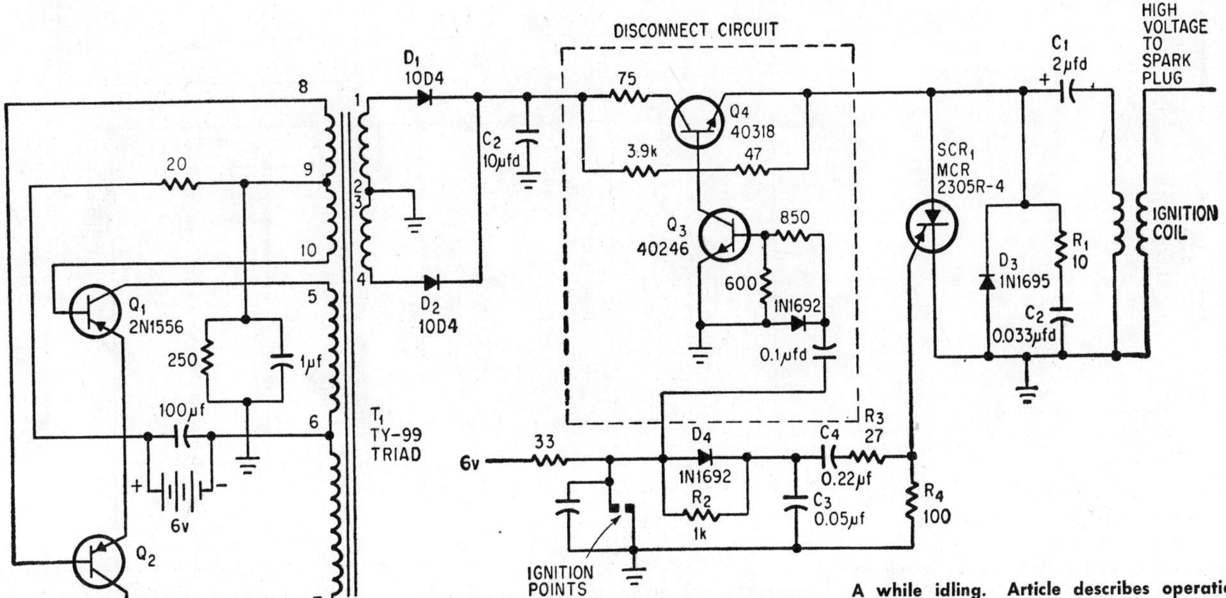

LOW-DRAIN ELECTRONIC IGNITION—Addition of transistors Q3 and Q4 to capacitor-discharge ignition system improves performance at high speeds and cuts current drain to 1 A while idling. Article describes operation.—K. W. Scheel, Two Added Transistors Reduce Ignition-System Current Drain, *Electronics*, May 29, 1967, p 87.

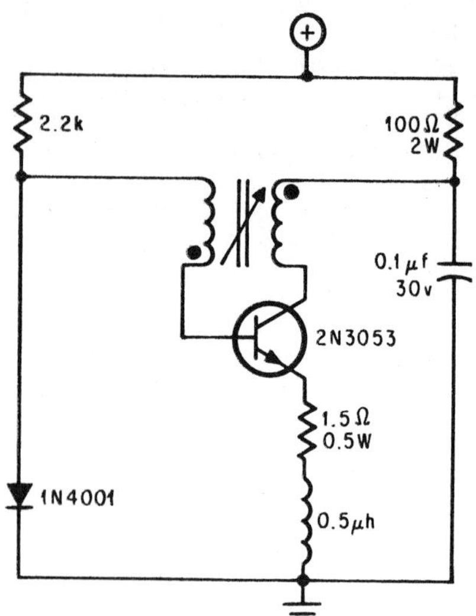

BREAKERLESS TRIGGER FOR IGNITION—Eliminates need for engine retiming and resetting of breaker point gap. Uses simple oscillator circuit in which high average current is obtained with transformer feedback. Fits into distributor housing in place of breaker points. Rotation of cam in air gap of trigger transformer makes circuit go in and out of nonlinear oscillation, producing square wave through 100-ohm resistor. Circuit can also be used as proximity switch.—R. L. Ronci, Good Timing, *Electronics*, Sept. 18, 1967, p 50.

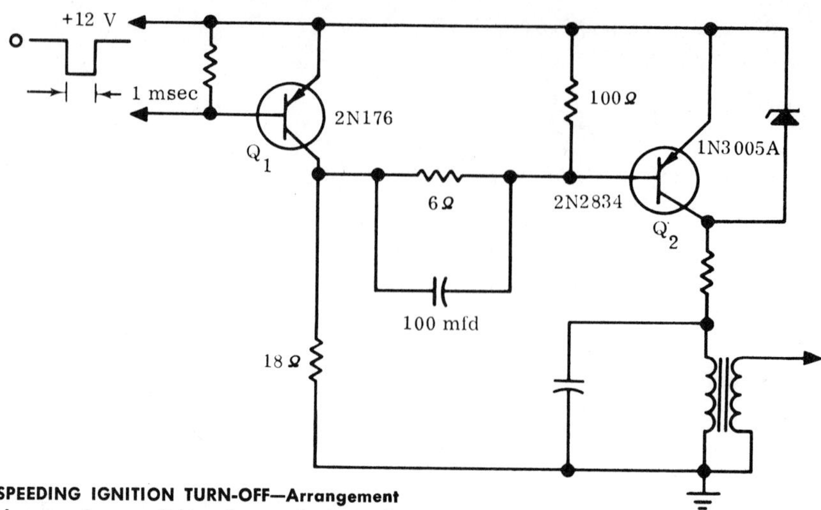

SPEEDING IGNITION TURN-OFF—Arrangement shown reduces switching losses of electronic ignition system and increases ignition coil output, by reverse-biasing transistor to decrease turn-off time of transistor. Charge on 100-μF capacitor, obtained when Q1 is nonconducting, supplies reverse bias for Q2 when Q1 is triggered on. Reduces erosion at gap of spark-plug electrodes.—"Circuits Manual," Motorola, Phoenix, Ariz., 1965, p 11–10.

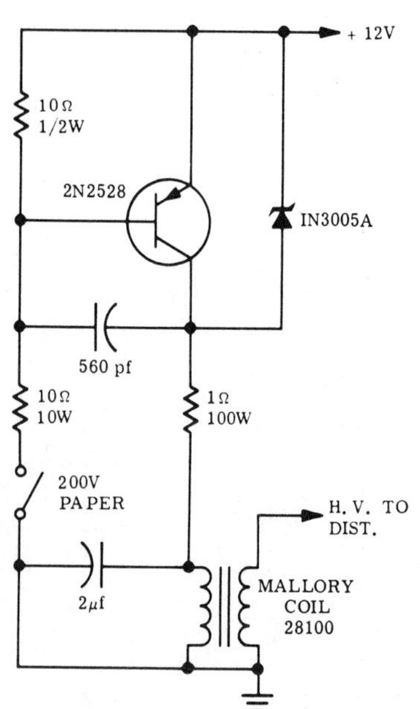

100-V ZENER PROTECTS IGNITION TRANSISTOR—Zener is connected between emitter and collector of transistor in electronic ignition system, with voltage rating chosen for protection against surges without affecting reliability of circuit operation.—"Zener Diode Handbook," Motorola, Phoenix, Ariz., 1967, p 7–9.

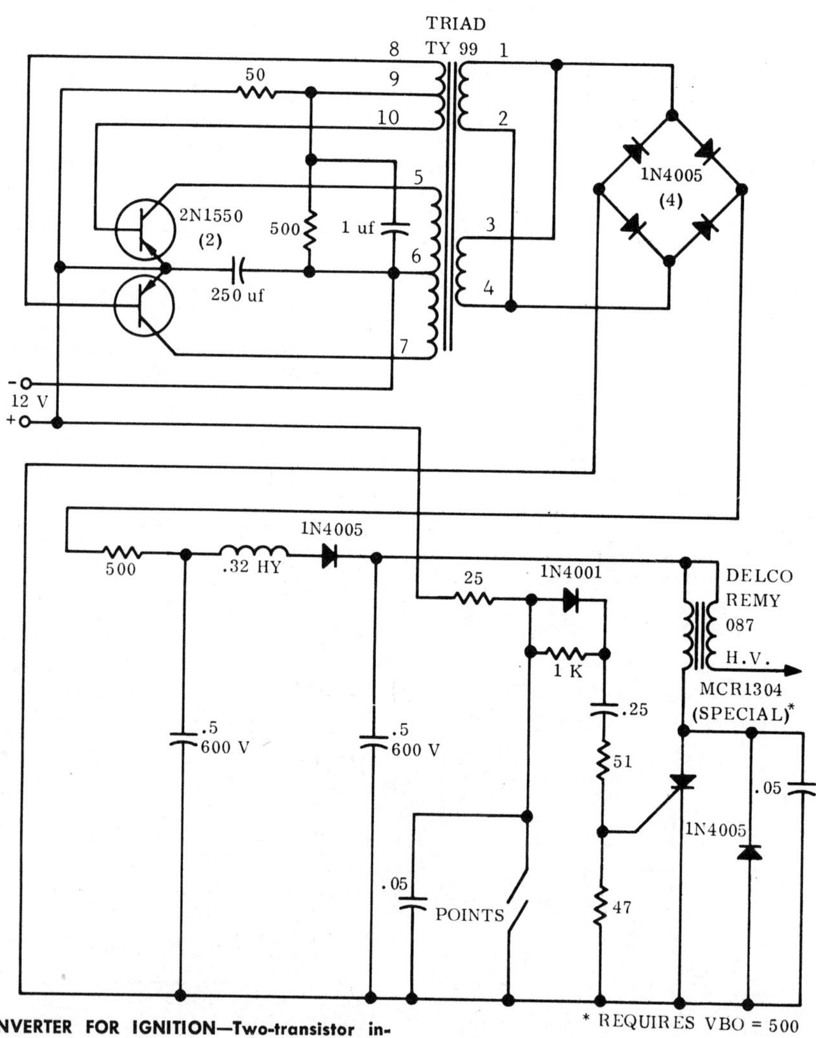

INVERTER FOR IGNITION—Two-transistor inverter drives bridge rectifier to give d-c/d-c converter providing 200 to 400 V d-c for more efficient operation of scr capacitor-discharge ignition system.—"Circuits Manual," Motorola, Phoenix, Ariz., 1965, p 11–13.

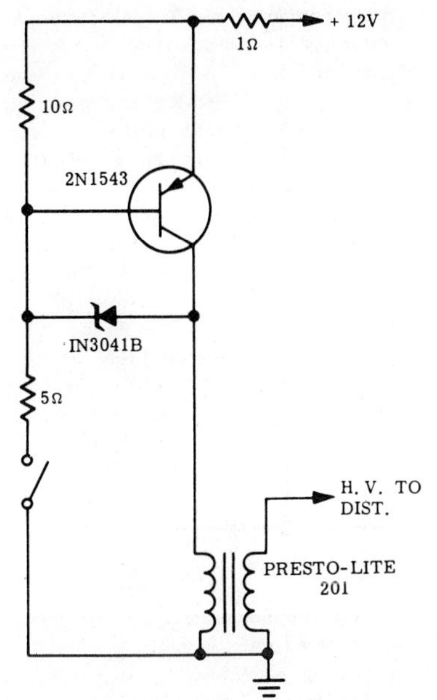

75-V ZENER PROTECTS IGNITION TRANSISTOR—Zener is connected between base and collector of transistor in electronic ignition system, with voltage rating chosen for protection against surges without affecting reliability of circuit operation.—"Zener Diode Handbook," Motorola, Phoenix, Ariz., 1967, p 7–9.

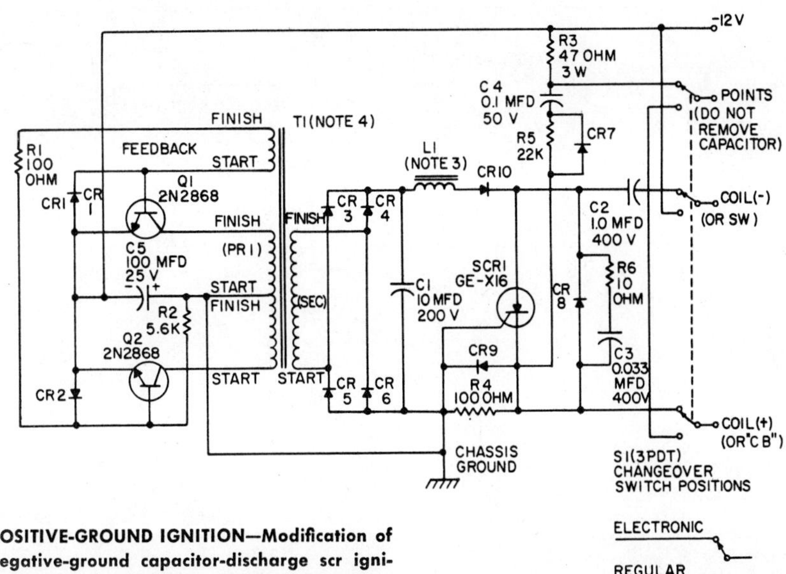

POSITIVE-GROUND IGNITION—Modification of negative-ground capacitor-discharge scr ignition system will operate on cars having positive ground. Diodes CR3-CR6 are 1N1693, CR8 and CR10 are 1N1695, and all others 1N1692. Book gives construction details, including winding data for T1.—"Hobby Manual," General Electric, Owensboro, Ky., 1965, p 63.

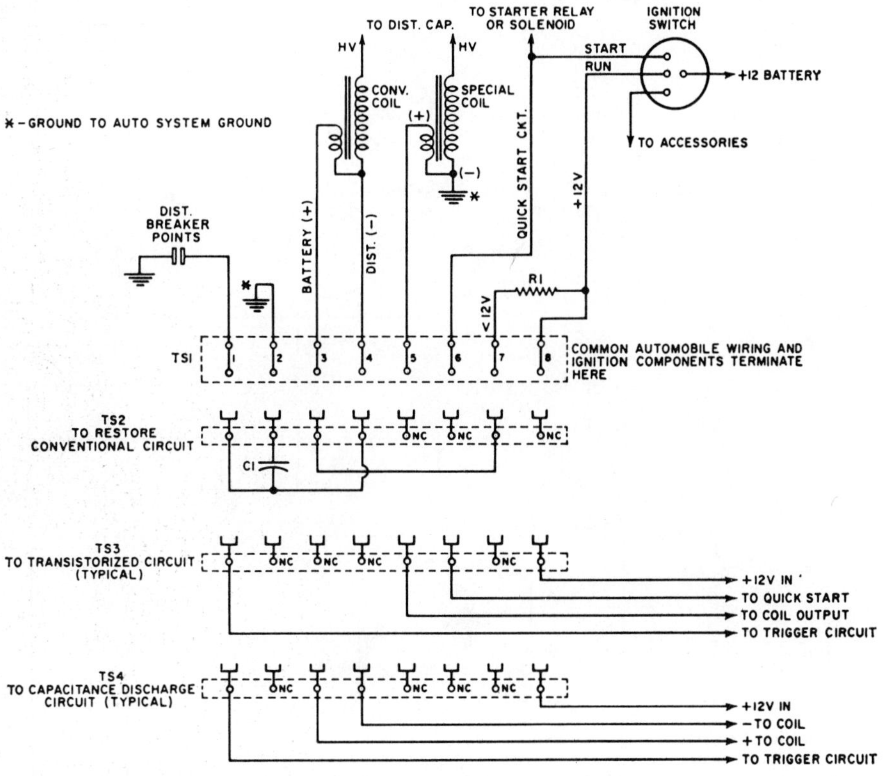

ELECTRONIC IGNITION ADAPTER—Permits testing all types of transistor and capacitor-discharge ignition systems on automobile and returning to conventional system without rewiring. All wires needed for installation are terminated in central location, using screw-type terminal strip. R1 is original ballast resistor, and C1 is original capacitor removed from distributor housing.—C. C. Morris, Universal Wiring for Automotive Ignition Systems, *Electronics World*, Aug. 1967, p 48.

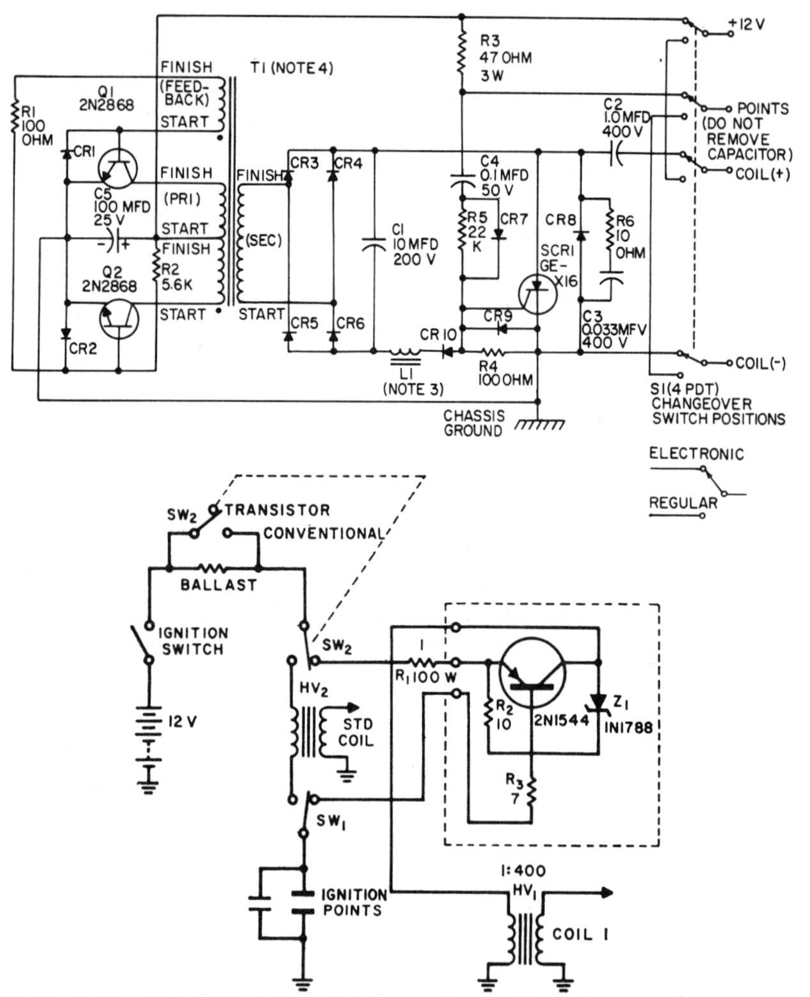

CAPACITOR-DISCHARGE SCR IGNITION—Circuit includes inverter and bridge rectifier for charging capacitor to 175 V d-c and scr triggering circuit for discharging capacitor through primary of ignition coil. Inverter Q1—Q2 converts negative-ground auto battery voltage to high-voltage a-c at about 8,000 Hz. Delivers about 23,000 Hz peak output from standard 12.6-V ignition coil, yet will operate on 6.5-V d-c input for good cold-weather starting. Book gives constructions details, including winding data for T1. Diodes CR3-CR6 are 1N1693, CR8 and CR10 are 1N1695, and all others 1N1692.—"Hobby Manual," General Electric, Owensboro, Ky., 1965, p 60.

QUICK-CHANGEOVER TRANSISTOR IGNITION—Single-transistor ignition improves performance and increases life of breaker points. Conventional ignition can be restored by operating both switches and moving high-voltage cable back to standard ignition coil.—J. Nawracaj, Transistor Ignition System Improves Engine Performance, "400 Ideas for Design Selected from Electronic Design," Hayden Book Co., N.Y., 1964, p 232.

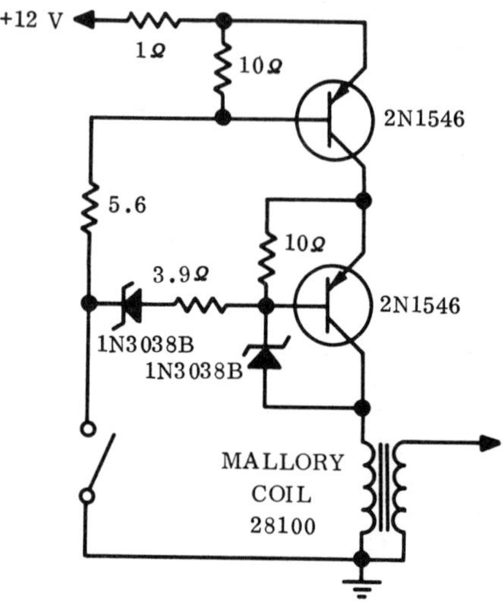

TWO-TRANSISTOR IGNITION—Medium-voltage transistors in series meet 120-V switching requirement for ignition coil having low turns ratio (below 325:1) and requiring between 7 and 12 A of collector current.—"Circuits Manual," Motorola, Phoenix, Ariz., 1965, p 11–3.

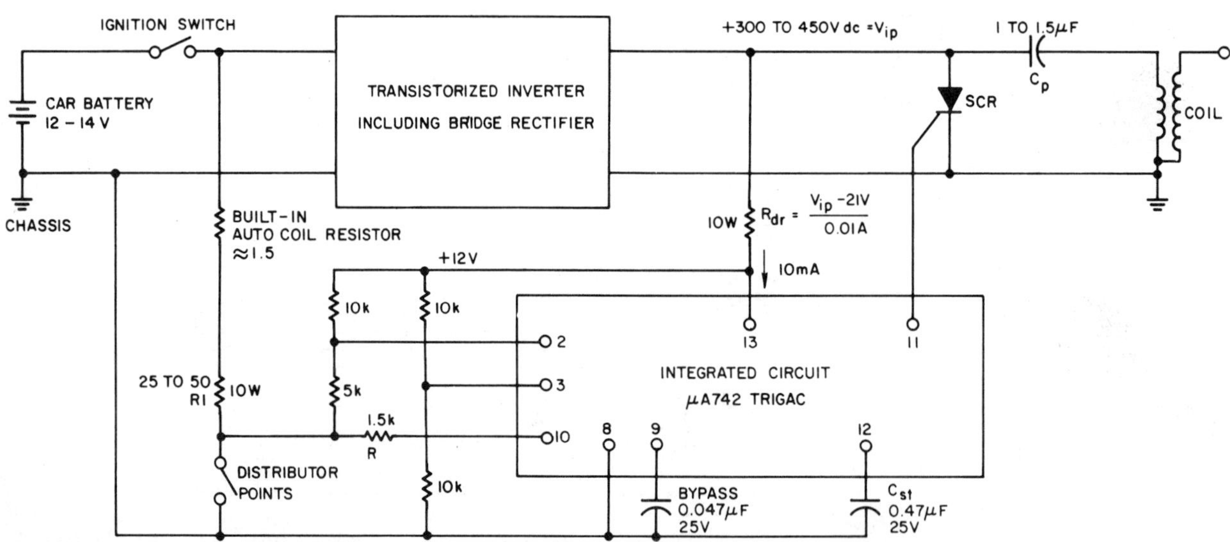

IC-SCR IGNITION—IC provides peak current of 2 A for firing almost any scr of capacitor-discharge electronic ignition system. Circuit prevents multiple firing caused by distributor points bounce at very low cranking speeds and at high speeds.—W. L. Brown, Improved IC Fires SCRs Used in Auto Ignition, *Electronic Design*, July 5, 1970, p 68 and 70.

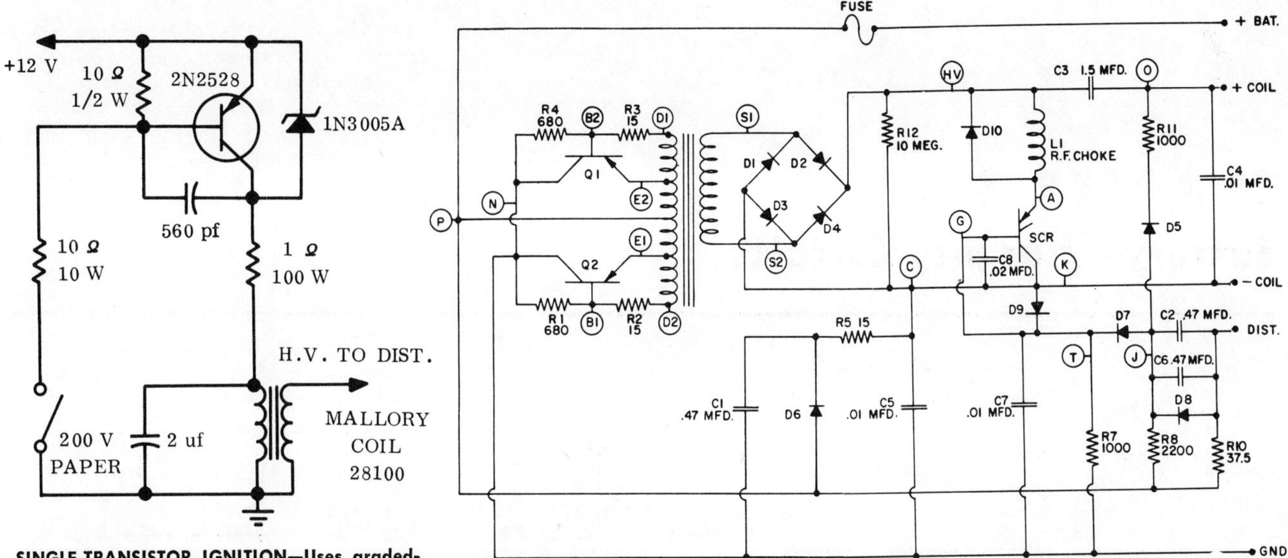

SINGLE-TRANSISTOR IGNITION—Uses graded-base high-voltage transistor for switching load line up to 120 V for ignition coil having low turns ratio (below 325:1) and requiring between 7 and 12 A of collector current.—"Circuits Manual," Motorola, Phoenix, Ariz., 1965, p 11–3.

SCR IGNITION—Consists of d-c/d-c converter for stepping up auto battery voltage to about 400 V for charging C3. When first cylinder comes up on compression to position where spark plug should be fired, points open and current through D7 switches on scr to discharge C3 through ignition coil. Brochure describes operation in detail.—MARK TEN—A New Ignition System for All Motor Vehicles, Delta Products, Grand Junction, Colo., 1969.

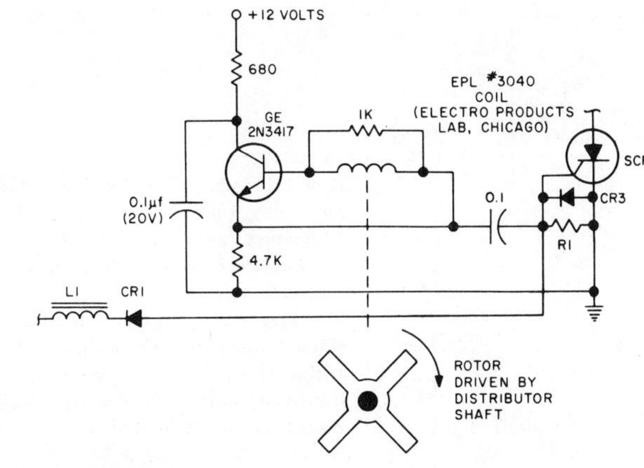

CONTACTLESS IGNITION TRIGGER—Four-pole permanent magnet mounted on distributor rotor generates scr trigger pulses in pickup coil, for driving scr of capacitor-discharge automotive ignition. Distributor contacts are then unnecessary. Circuit shown amplifies and differentiates pulse before it is applied to gate of scr. Magnet-coil combination is commercially available.—D. R. Grafham, Using Low Current SCR's, General Electric, Syracuse, N.Y., No. 200.19, 1967, p 33.

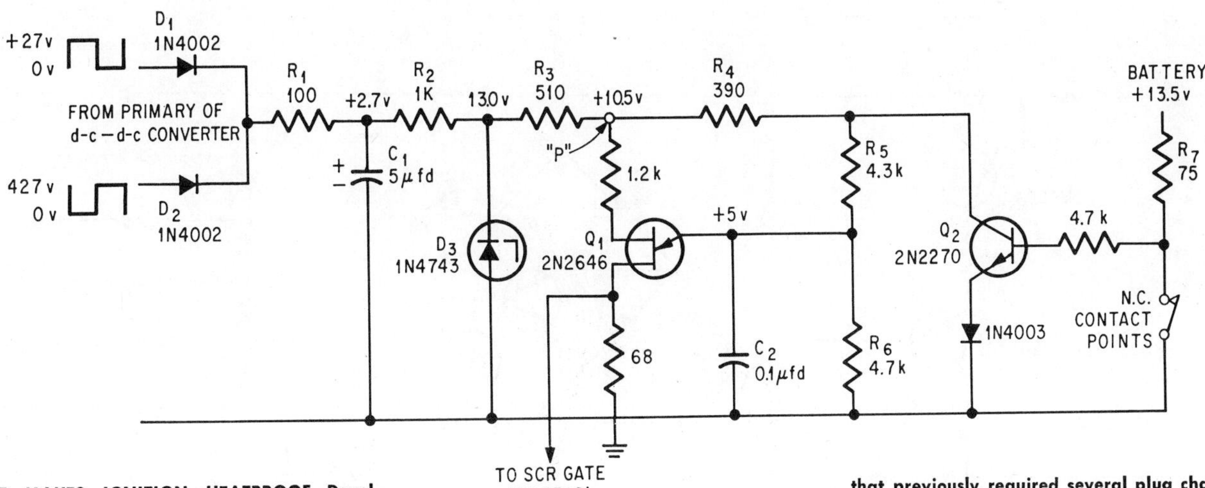

UJT MAKES IGNITION HEATPROOF—Developed for sports cars used in racing. Ujt trigger in capacitor-discharge ignition maintains quality of ignition pulse over temperature range of −30 to 160 F with simultaneous supply voltage variations of more than 30% above and below battery voltage. Entire ignition system costs less than $50. Race cars that previously required several plug changes in 6-hour race can run entire season on one set of plugs.—F. Honey, Unijunction Trigger Boosts Ignition Reliability, *Electronics*, Sept. 18, 1967, p 107–108.

CHAPTER 8
Battery-Charging Circuits

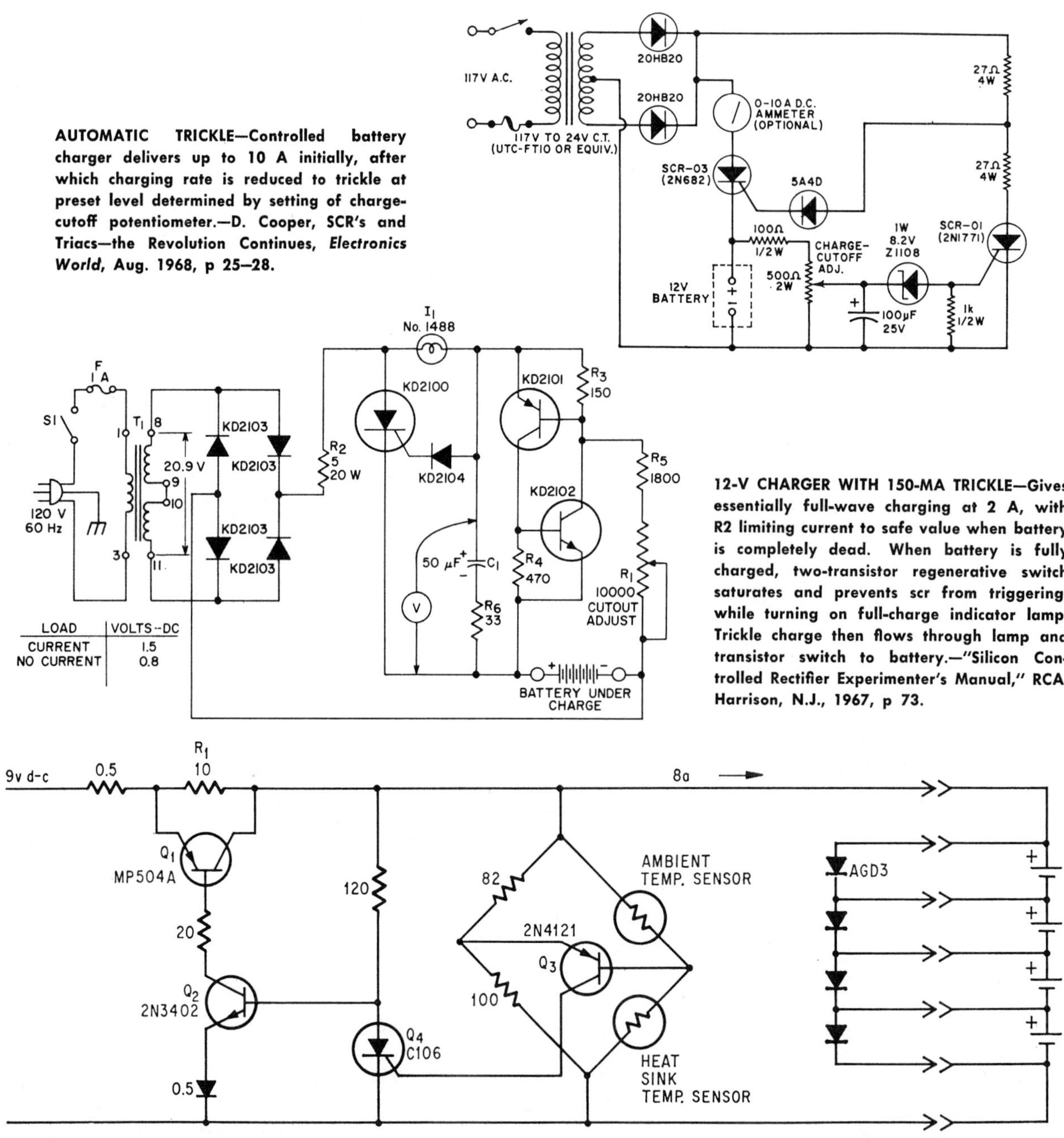

AUTOMATIC TRICKLE—Controlled battery charger delivers up to 10 A initially, after which charging rate is reduced to trickle at preset level determined by setting of charge-cutoff potentiometer.—D. Cooper, SCR's and Triacs—the Revolution Continues, *Electronics World*, Aug. 1968, p 25–28.

12-V CHARGER WITH 150-MA TRICKLE—Gives essentially full-wave charging at 2 A, with R2 limiting current to safe value when battery is completely dead. When battery is fully charged, two-transistor regenerative switch saturates and prevents scr from triggering, while turning on full-charge indicator lamp. Trickle charge then flows through lamp and transistor switch to battery.—"Silicon Controlled Rectifier Experimenter's Manual," RCA, Harrison, N.J., 1967, p 73.

PROTECTING NICKEL-CADMIUM CELLS—Special diodes, called Amp-Gates by Mallory, shunt individual nickel-cadmium cells during fast recharge to prevent cells from overheating and rupturing. Two thermistors in bridge circuit sense when battery is fully charged and terminate charging, to protect diodes from overheating that would result if they carried full charging current. Developed for use with cordless appliances.—J. V. Ball, There's No Overcharge For Fast-Charged Batteries, *Electronics*, Jan. 22, 1968, p 97–100.

12-V ON-OFF BATTERY CHARGER—Automatically switches off when battery is fully charged, and switches itself back on just before battery is fully discharged. To adjust, connect fully charged battery and adjust R1 until charging just stops.—"Hobby Manual," General Electric, Owensboro, Ky., 1965, p 52.

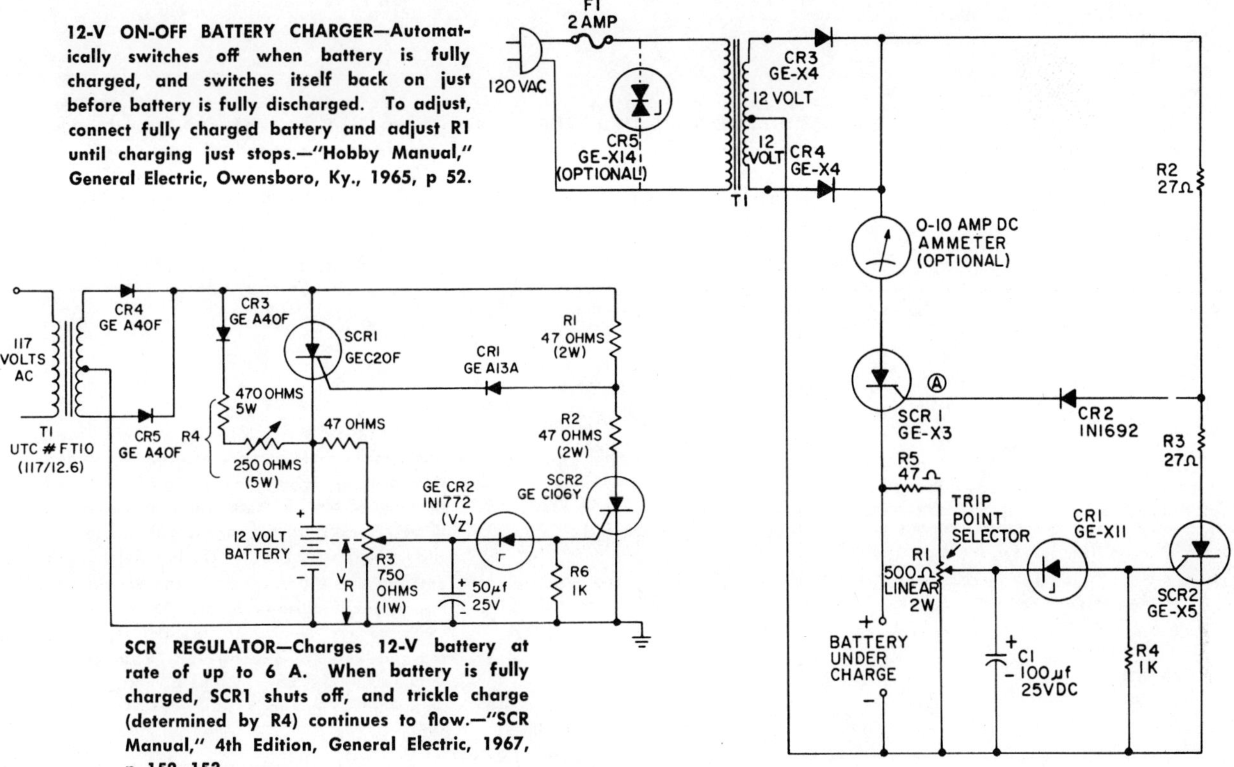

SCR REGULATOR—Charges 12-V battery at rate of up to 6 A. When battery is fully charged, SCR1 shuts off, and trickle charge (determined by R4) continues to flow.—"SCR Manual," 4th Edition, General Electric, 1967, p 152–153.

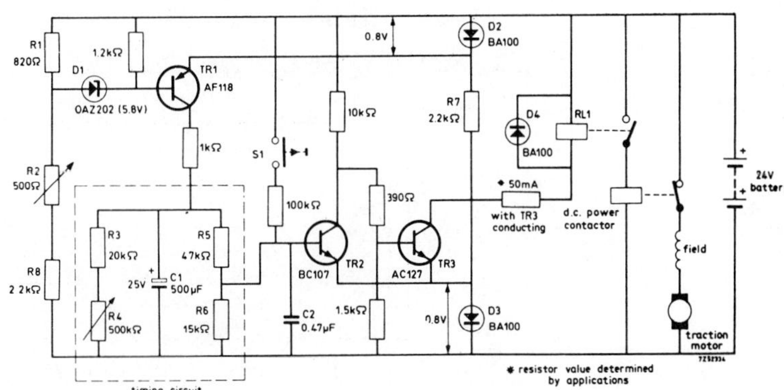

BATTERY VOLTAGE SENSOR—Used on electric golf carts and other electric vehicles to cut out traction motor when battery voltage is low and/or trip a warning device. Timing circuit prevents sensor from responding to short-duration voltage drops. Delay can be set by R4 between 15 and 40 s. Override S1 permits driving to nearest charging station on low battery.—"Rectifier Diodes," Philips, Pub. Dept., Elcoma Div., Eindhoven, The Netherlands, 1969, p 221.

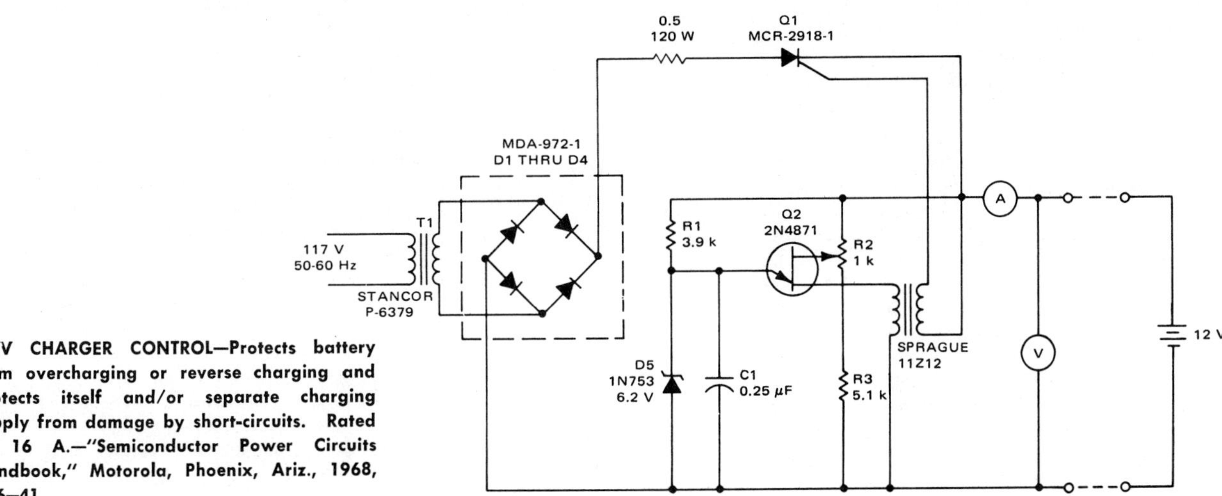

12-V CHARGER CONTROL—Protects battery from overcharging or reverse charging and protects itself and/or separate charging supply from damage by short-circuits. Rated at 16 A.—"Semiconductor Power Circuits Handbook," Motorola, Phoenix, Ariz., 1968, p 6–41.

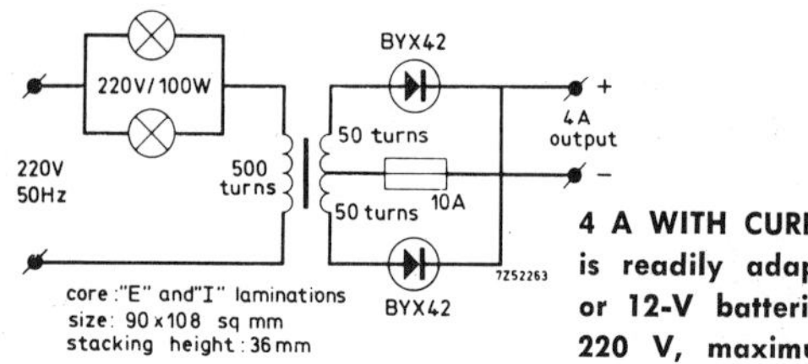

4 A WITH CURRENT-LIMITING LAMPS—Circuit is readily adapted for charging either 6-V or 12-V batteries from 115-V a-c line. On 220 V, maximum output current for direct short is 7 A. 10-A fuse protects against reverse connection of battery.—"Rectifier Diodes," Philips, Pub. Dept., Elcoma Div., Eindhoven, The Netherlands, 1969, p 217.

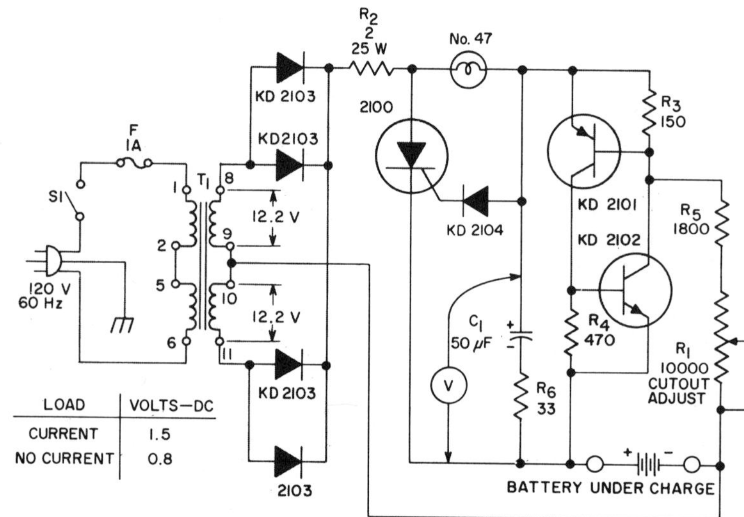

6-V CHARGER WITH 150-MA TRICKLE—Silicon rectifiers in full-wave center-tapped connection provide 3.2 A for charging, with R2 limiting current to safe value if battery is dead. Two-transistor regenerative switch at right opens scr when battery is fully charged, and passes 150-mA trickle charge through battery and indicator lamp. R1 is adjusted so lamp just begins to brighten for fully charged battery (reading 7.15 V across its terminals).—"Silicon Controlled Rectifier Experimenter's Manual," RCA, Harrison, N.J., 1967, p 76.

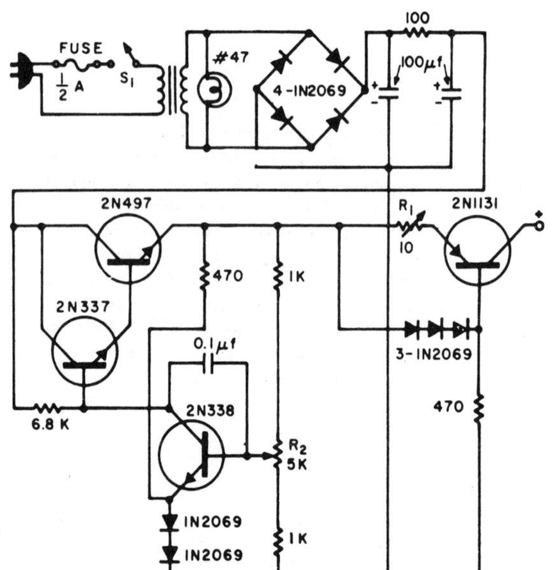

PROTECTION FOR NICKEL-CADMIUM CELLS—Uses constant-current source to provide recommended maximum charge rate of 120 mA for small three-cell rechargeable nickel-cadmium battery, and simple series voltage regulator for holding voltage limit down to 4.5 V so maximum charge voltage of 1.5 V per cell is never exceeded. R1 is adjusted for 120 mA while output is shorted with ammeter having appropriate current range, and open-circuit voltage is similarly adjusted with R2 and voltmeter across output.—R. M. Mann, Battery Charger Protects Small Nickel-Cadmium Cells, "400 Ideas for Design Selected from Electronic Design," Hayden Book Co., N.Y., 1964, p 210.

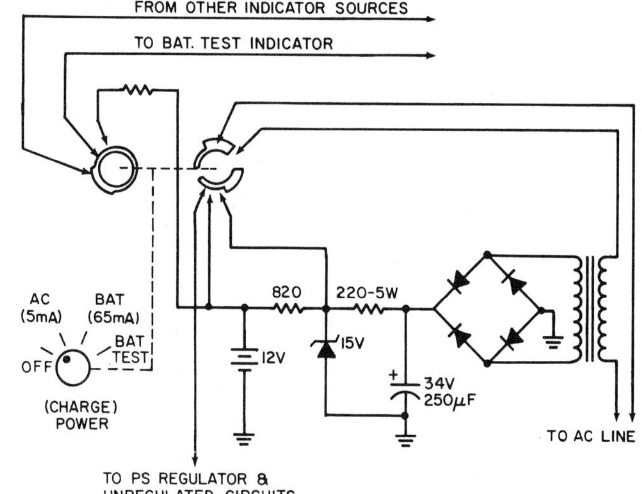

BATTERY-FAILURE PROTECTION—Battery-charging circuit for 12-V nickel-cadmium battery doubles as 12-V d-c power supply if battery fails. With switch at AC, charger furnishes 5-mA trickle current to battery and low-ripple 15-V d-c to regulator. With switch at BAT, 820-ohm trickle-charge resistor is shorted out and regulator operates directly from 12-V battery. Fast battery charging is obtained by plugging in a-c line cord with switch at BAT position. At BAT TEST position, battery is checked while under load but with a-c power removed.—J. Collins and W. Whitaker, Fail-Safe Unit Operates from NiCad Batteries or A-C Line, *Electronic Design*, Oct. 11, 1967, p 98 and 100.

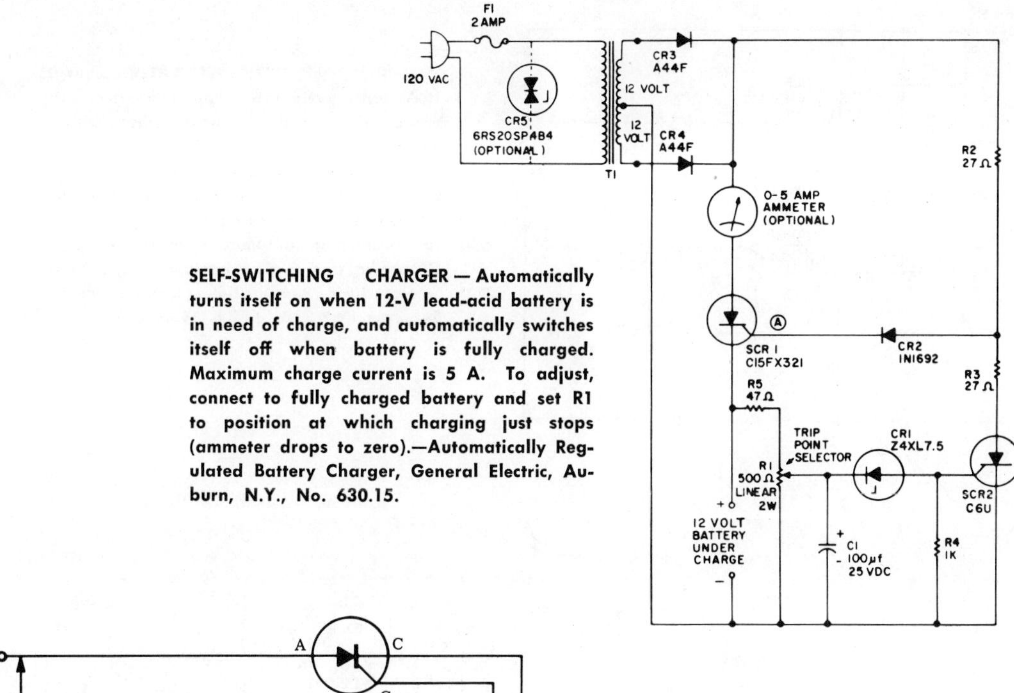

SELF-SWITCHING CHARGER—Automatically turns itself on when 12-V lead-acid battery is in need of charge, and automatically switches itself off when battery is fully charged. Maximum charge current is 5 A. To adjust, connect to fully charged battery and set R1 to position at which charging just stops (ammeter drops to zero).—Automatically Regulated Battery Charger, General Electric, Auburn, N.Y., No. 630.15.

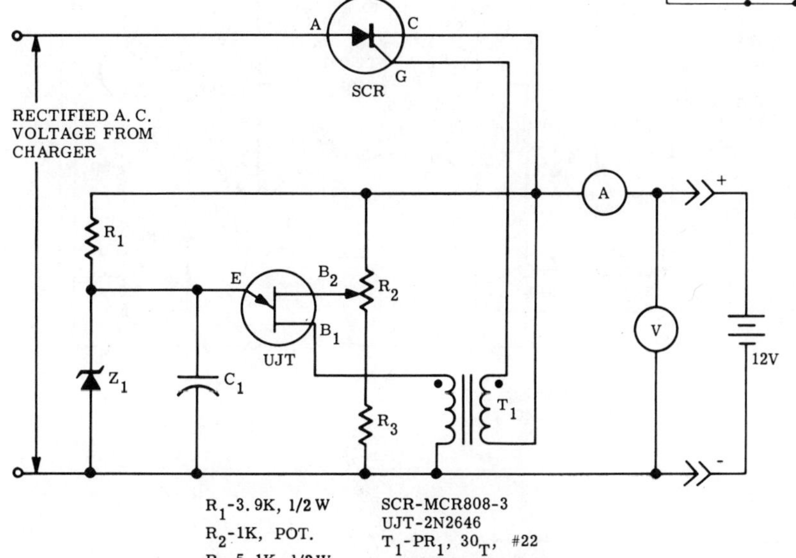

12-V CLAMPED-EMITTER UJT SENSING—Will not operate unless battery is properly connected to charger. Charging stops when zener in ujt circuit senses that battery is properly charged. Triggering pulses for scr are generated by ujt oscillator when battery voltage is low.—"Zener Diode Handbook," Motorola, Phoenix, Ariz., May 1967, p 8–7.

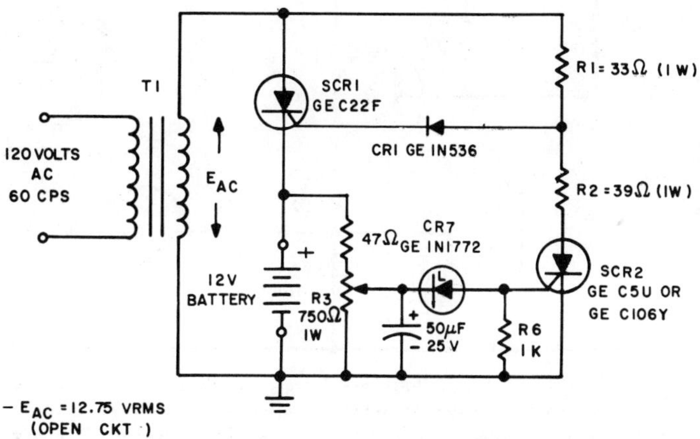

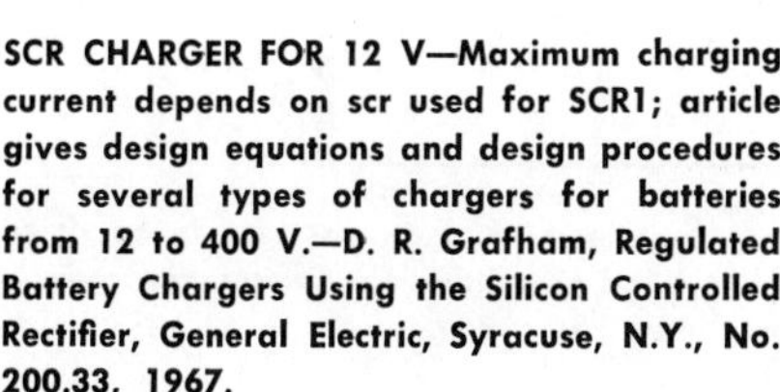
SCR CHARGER FOR 12 V—Maximum charging current depends on scr used for SCR1; article gives design equations and design procedures for several types of chargers for batteries from 12 to 400 V.—D. R. Grafham, Regulated Battery Chargers Using the Silicon Controlled Rectifier, General Electric, Syracuse, N.Y., No. 200.33, 1967.

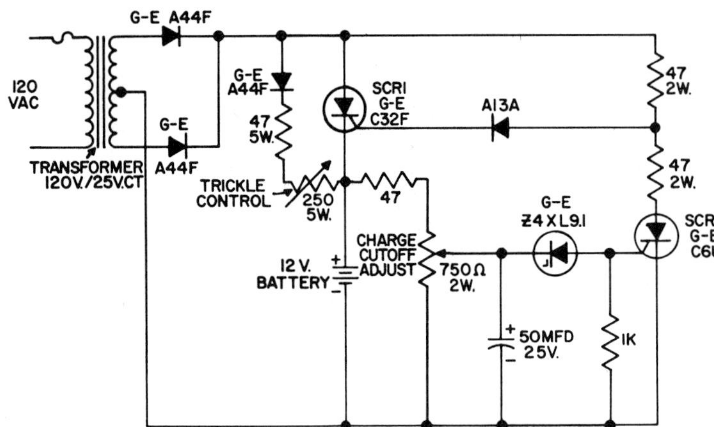

15-A CHARGER WITH REGULATOR—Charges 12-V battery from a-c line. Changes automatically to trickle charge when battery voltage reaches preset level, and starts heavy charging again when voltage falls below preset level. Ideal for use on trailers and boats, for emergency power systems, and for recharging automotive batteries.—F. W. Gutzwiller and E. K. Howell, Economy Power Semiconductor Applications, General Electric, Syracuse, N.Y., No. 671.1, 1965, p 7.

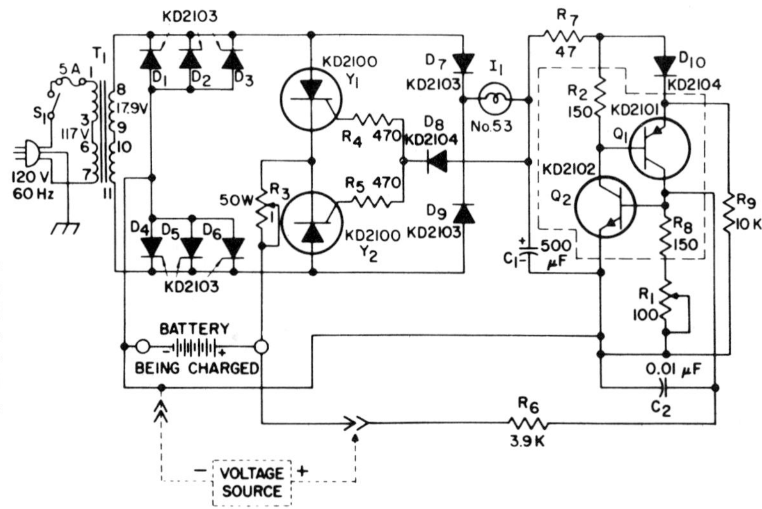

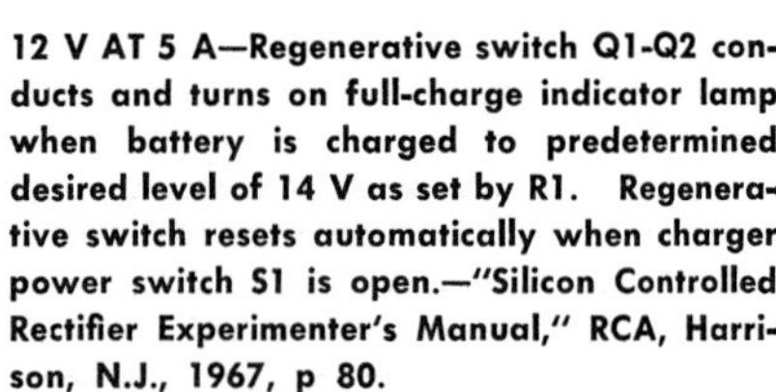

12 V AT 5 A—Regenerative switch Q1-Q2 conducts and turns on full-charge indicator lamp when battery is charged to predetermined desired level of 14 V as set by R1. Regenerative switch resets automatically when charger power switch S1 is open.—"Silicon Controlled Rectifier Experimenter's Manual," RCA, Harrison, N.J., 1967, p 80.

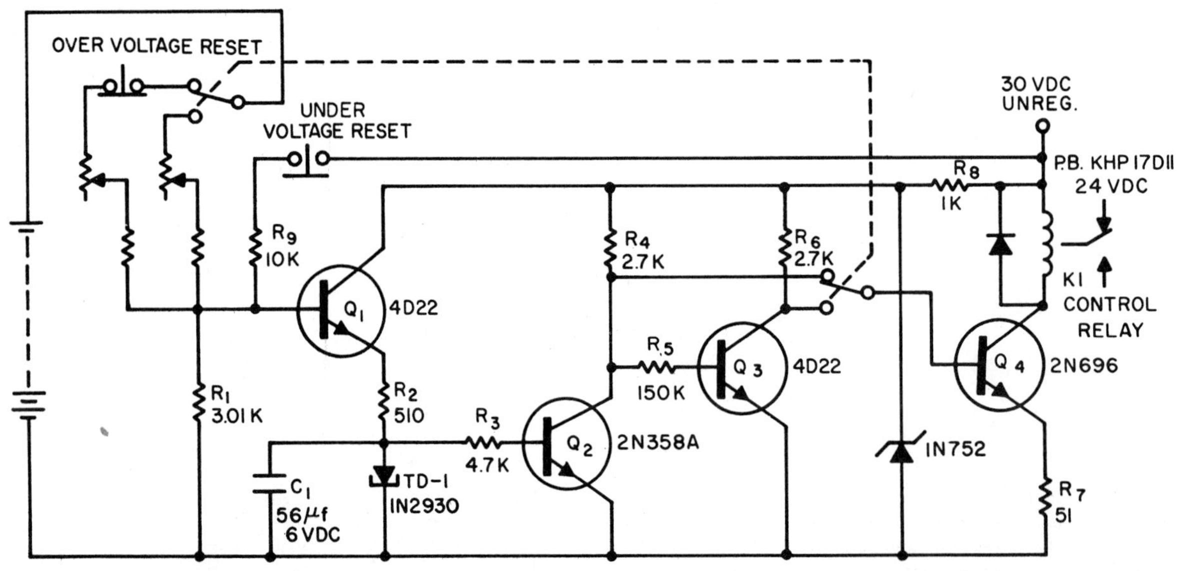

AUTOMATIC CHARGER SWITCH—Voltage detector circuit using tunnel diode operates relay to disconnect charger at preselected battery overvoltage value. In discharge mode, battery is disconnected from load when preselected undervoltage condition exists. Repeatability is within 0.1 V over temperature range of 32 to 90 F. Voltage-divider network values depend on voltages to be detected.—H. Layte, Ideas For Design, *Electronic Design*, Aug. 30, 1965, p 44.

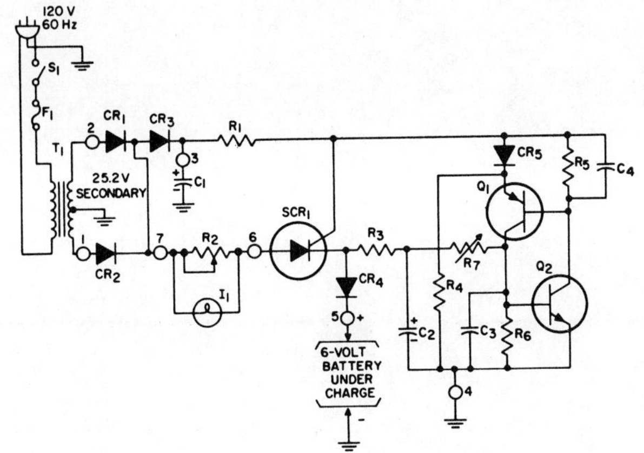

C_1 = 500 microfarads, 25 volts, electrolytic
C_2 = 100 microfarads, 12 volts, electrolytic
C_3C_4 = 0.01 microfarad, ceramic disc
CR_1 through CR_5 = silicon rectifier, RCA SK3030
F_1 = fuse, 1 ampere, 125 volts
I_1 = lamp, No. 47
Q_1 = transistor, RCA SK3005
Q_2 = transistor, RCA SK3020
R_1 = 330 ohms, 1/2 watt, 10%
R_2 = adjustable resistor, 5 ohms, 10 watts, 10%
R_3 = 4700 ohms, 1/2 watt, 10%
R_4 = 10,000 ohms, 1/2 watt, 10%
R_5 = 150 ohms, 1/2 watt, 10%
R_6 = 470 ohms, 1/2 watt, 10%
R_7 = miniature trimmer control, 5000 ohms, Mallory No. MTC-1 or equivalent
SCR_1 = silicon controlled rectifier, RCA SK2100
S_1 = switch, 125 volts, 1 ampere, single-pole, single-throw
T_1 = transformer, primary 117 volts, secondary 25.2 volts at 1 ampere, Stancor No. TP-4 or equivalent.

6-V CHARGER—For motorcycle and photoflash storage batteries. Charging rate of 1 A is automatically terminated when battery is fully charged. Adjust R7 in voltage-sensing circuit at right so scr is turned off for fully charged battery, which is 7 V for lead-acid batteries.—"Hobby Circuits Manual," RCA, Harrison, N.J., HM-90, p 114.

NOTE: To locate additional circuits in the category of this chapter, use the index at the back of this book. Check also the author's "Sourcebook of Electronic Circuits," published by McGraw-Hill in 1968.

CHAPTER 9
Bridge Circuits

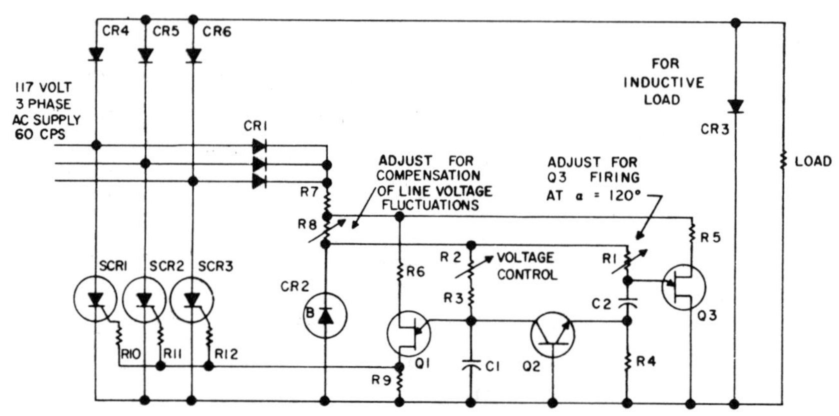

THREE-PHASE SCR CONTROL—Simple three-transistor scr firing circuit provides stepless control of d-c output voltage of three-phase bridge between 25% and 100% of maximum output voltage, or from 40 to 150 V. With 93-V output for line voltage of 130 V a-c, drop to 100 V a-c reduces d-c output only 1 V.—"SCR Manual," 4th Edition, General Electric, 1967, p 202–204.

CR1 — (3) G E IN1695
CR2 — 20 VOLT, 1 WATT ZENER DIODE, IN1527
CR3, CR4, CR5, CR6 — AS REQUIRED FOR LOAD (e.g. IN2156)
SCR1, SCR2, SCR3 — AS REQUIRED FOR LOAD (e.g. C35B)
Q1, Q3 — G E 2N2646 Q2 — G E 2N2923
R1 — 10K POT
R2 — 20K POT
R3 — 470 Ω

R4 — 100 Ω
R5, R6 — 390 Ω
R7 — 3.3K, 2W
R8 — 500 Ω POT, 2W
R9 — 100 Ω
R10, R11, R12 — 25 Ω
C1 — 0.5 MFD
C2 — 1.0 MFD

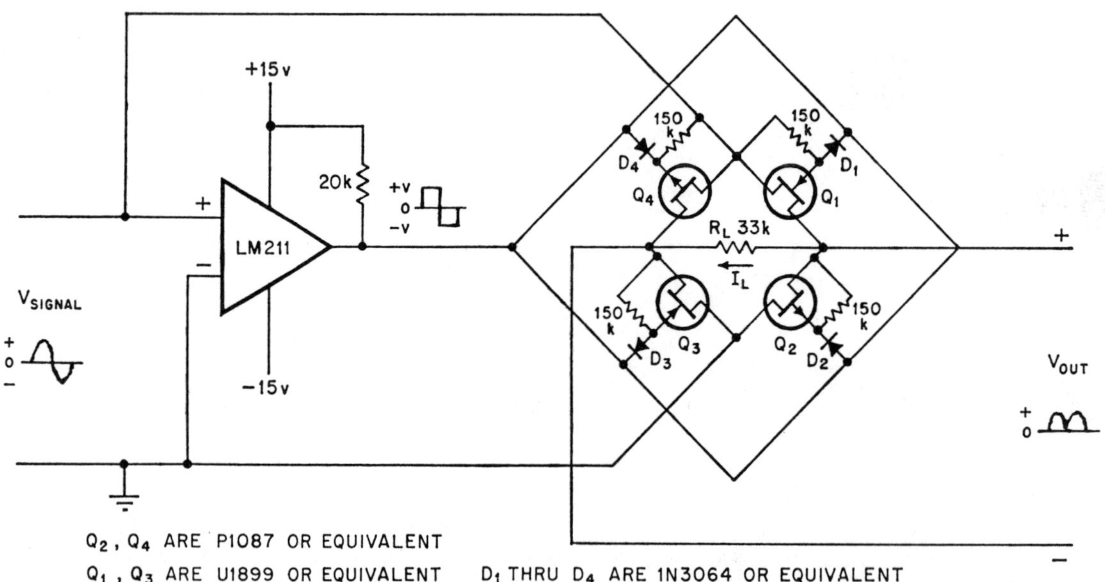

COMPARATOR-CONTROLLED FET BRIDGE—Diodes have secondary role of simply switching fet's. With zero offset voltage for fet's, output closely follows or inverts half of sine-wave input signal, to give full-wave rectification with no distortion.—L. Accardi, Diode-Switched FET's Rectify the Full Wave, *Electronics*, Aug. 3, 1970, p 76.

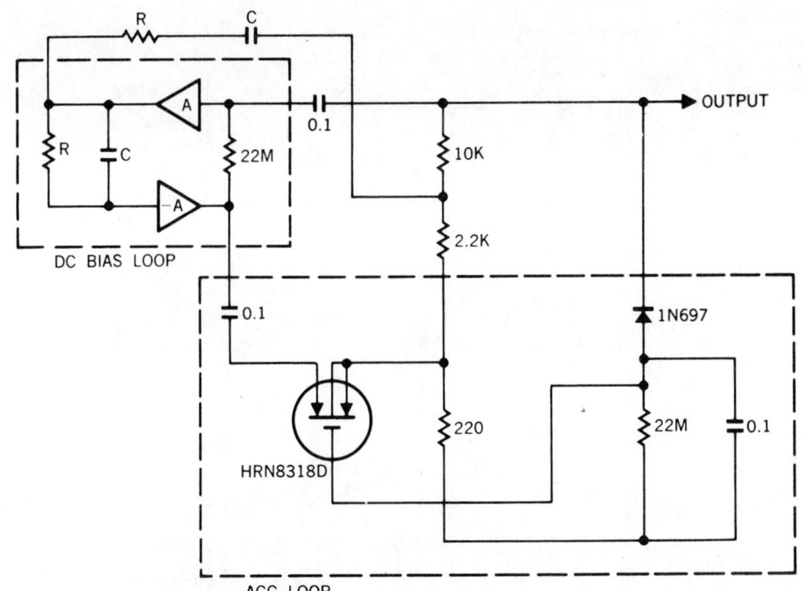

WIEN-BRIDGE OSCILLATOR—Mosfet is used as linear resistance whose value depends on level of oscillator output signal. Increase in output level gives bias voltage for mosfet by detection of peak negative value, for controlling gain in oscillator automatically.—C. R. Perkins, "Application of MOSFET Devices to Electronic Circuits," Hughes, Newport Beach, Cal., 1968, p 29.

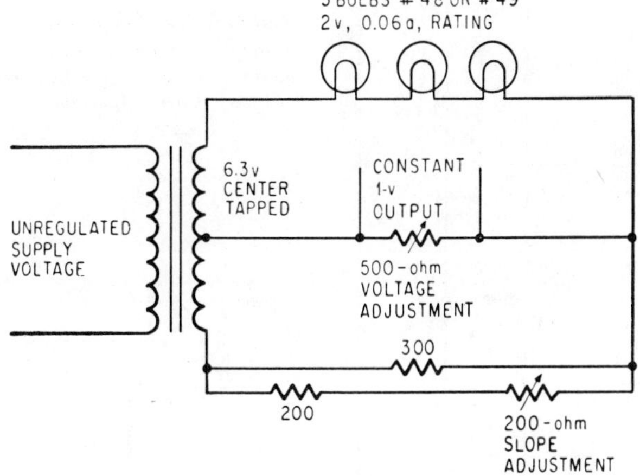

LAMPS REGULATE 1-V A-C—Inexpensive voltage-regulating bridge depends on ballast action of 2-V lamps operated at about 0.6 V to give 1-V a-c output that varies only 0.25% for line voltage change of 105 to 125 V. Regulation is independent of frequency over range of 25 to 800 Hz. Thermal inertia makes correction slow, so large input change may require almost 1 s for full correction, but this is usually not serious drawback. Bulbs should be soldered into circuit.—D. Kelly, Small Lamp Bridge Regulates Line Voltage, *Electronics*, March 20, 1967, p 89–90.

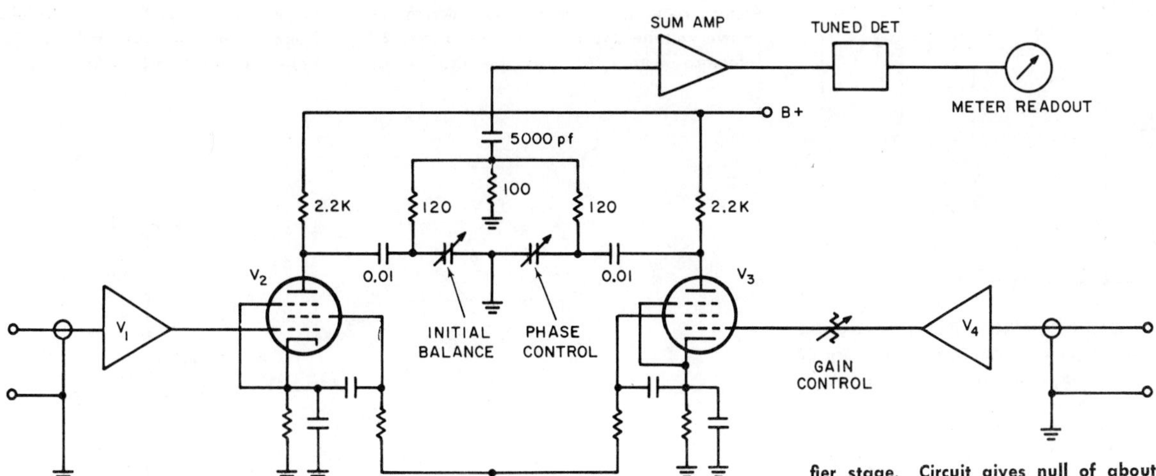

MEASURING PHASE AT 100 MHZ—Broad null of conventional balanced bridge is sharpened in Teltronics PD-200 phase detector by using two similar channels exactly 180 deg out of phase. Pentode types for V2 and V3 are not critical, and component values for tube circuits are those of conventional pentode amplifier stage. Circuit gives null of about −55 dB, permitting phase measurement accuracy to within 0.1 deg in frequency range of 15 to 100 MHz.—R. O. Goodwin, Unbalanced Bridge Simplifies Phase Measurements, *Electronic Design*, March 15, 1965, p 52–53.

10-V BIPOLAR FROM BRIDGE—Grounding common point of two zeners connected across output of power supply eliminates need for two secondary windings on power transformer and provides protection against short-circuits. If unsymmetrical voltages are required, use zeners with different ratings.—S. Ritterman, Single Transformer Provides Positive and Negative Voltages, *Electronic Design*, Jan. 18, 1970, p 86.

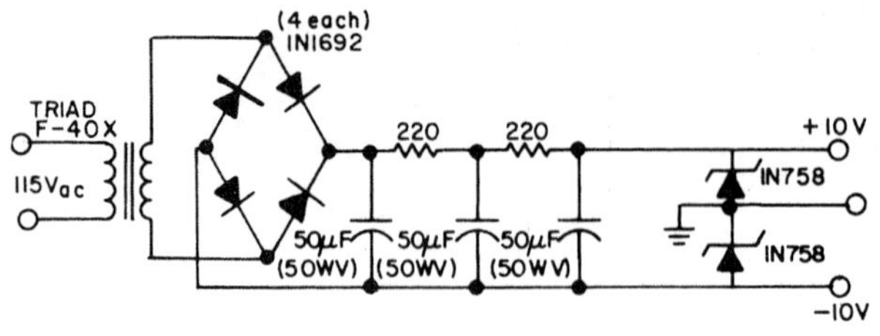

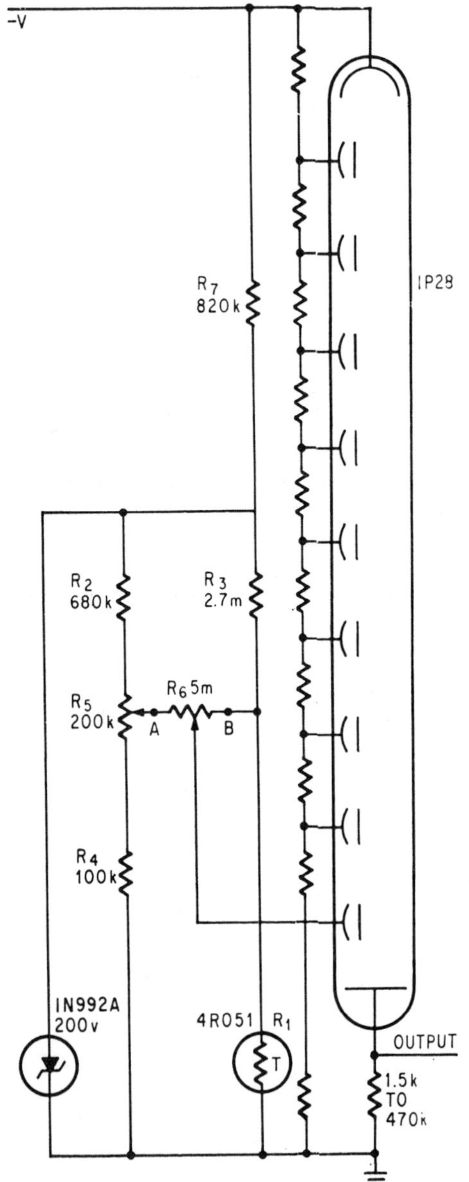

TUBE WARMUP CONTROL—Thermistor mounted on socket of photomultiplier forms one leg of bridge used to compensate for decrease in gain of tube as ambient temperature increases during warm-up period. Control circuit acts on voltage of last dynode. Output amplitude is constant within 2% from 24 to 40 C with compensation, as compared to 8% variation without compensation. Article gives calibration procedure.—A. E. Martens, Photomultiplier's Gain is Temperature Compensated, *Electronics*, April 14, 1969, p 97–98.

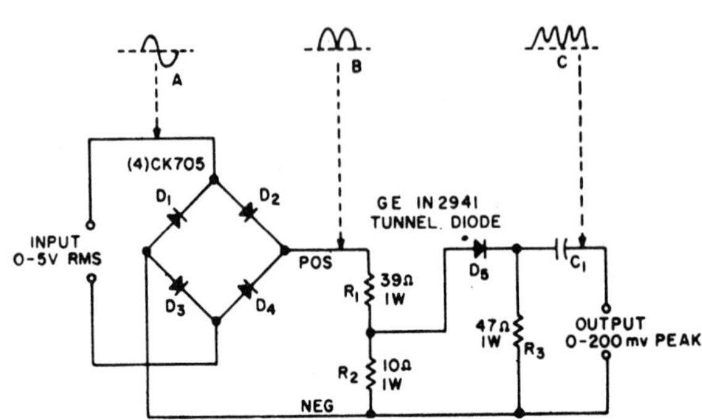

QUADRUPLER—Tunnel diode doubles double-frequency output of bridge rectifier. Adjust input voltage to give best output waveform on cro. Circuit operates up to several MHz. —R. P. Turner, Tunnel Diode Doubles Doubled Frequency, "400 Ideas for Design Selected from Electronic Design," Hayden Book Co., N.Y., 1964, p 170.

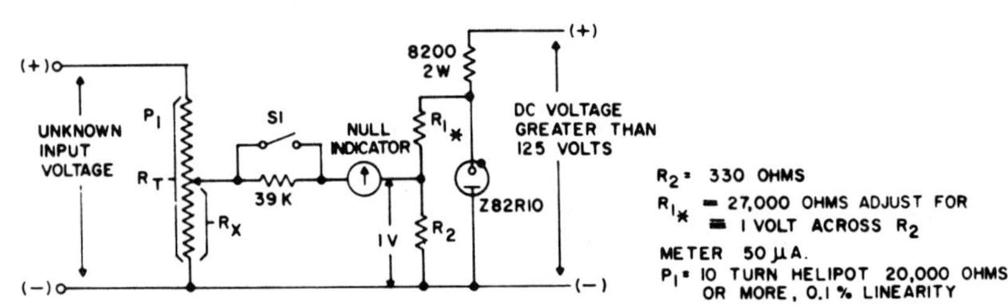

POTENTIOMETER BRIDGE—Uses precision neon voltage regulator. Potentiometer divides unknown voltage down and compares it to 1-V reference across R2. As balance is approached, S1 is closed to increase sensitivity of null meter.—E. Bauman, "Applications of Neon Lamps and Gas Discharge Tubes," Signalite, Neptune, N.J., p 89.

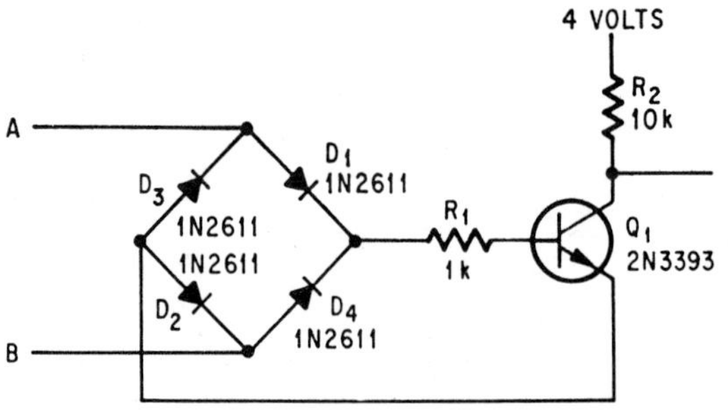

EXCLUSIVE-OR—Simple circuit gives output of 1 when input A or input B is 1, but no output (0) when both inputs are 1.—R. C. Hoyler, Bridge and Transistor are Exclusive-or Gate, *Electronics*, Aug. 19, 1968, p 88.

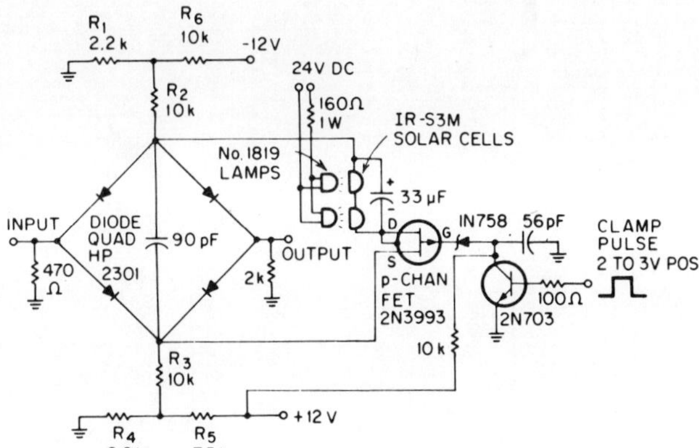

SOLAR-CELL ISOLATION—Cells provide floating low-impedance bias source supplying 1.6 V to turn on fast-response hot-carrier-diode bridge. Bridge input will accept signal voltages up to 4 V p-p. On-off ratios of 60 dB are possible up to 20 MHz. Response is down 5 dB at 40 MHz. Corners of diode bridge are switched simultaneously by low-impedance source, to minimize transients in output. Gating period can range from several ns to several hours.—J. J. Contus, A Broadband Low-Noise Gate Using Hot-Carrier Diodes, *EEE*, March 1969, p 122 and 124.

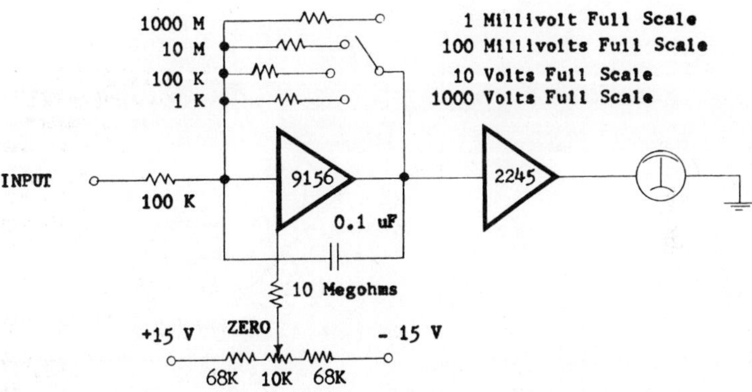

LOGARITHMIC NULL VOLTMETER—May be used as indicator for Wheatstone bridge, comparison bridge, or differential voltmeter. Will also serve as solid-state galvanometer for laboratory use. Model 9156 IC operates as active attenuator for 1,000-V full-scale setting. Precision resistors are not required because absolute measurements are seldom made off null. Meter should be 10—0—10 V. Model 2245 IC provides four-decade bipolar log function.—A Logarithmic Null-Voltmeter Design, Optical Electronics, Tucson, Ariz., No. 10084.

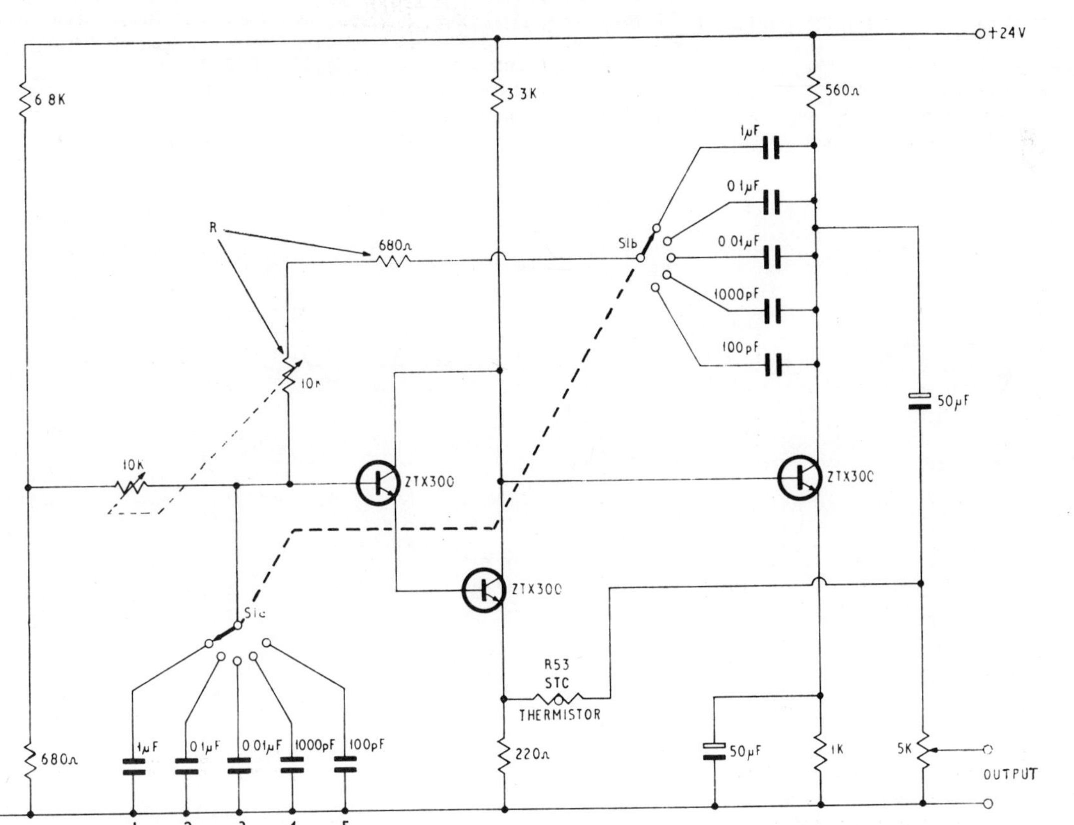

10 HZ–5 MHZ WIEN-BRIDGE OSCILLATOR—Output is 1 V rms, with less than 0.2% total harmonic distortion at 1 kHz. Switch gives five ranges: 15–200 Hz; 150–2,000 Hz; 1.5–20 kHz; 15–200 kHz; 150–2,000 kHz.—"E-Line Transistor Applications," Ferranti Ltd., Oldham, Lancs., England, 1969, p 35.

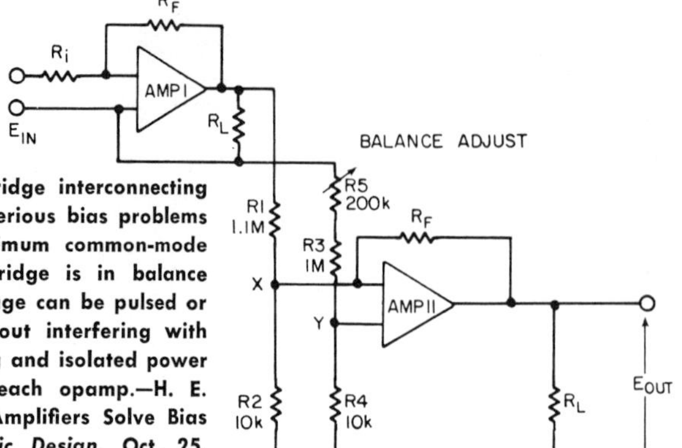

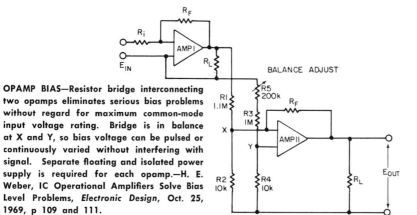

OPAMP BIAS—Resistor bridge interconnecting two opamps eliminates serious bias problems without regard for maximum common-mode input voltage rating. Bridge is in balance at X and Y, so bias voltage can be pulsed or continuously varied without interfering with signal. Separate floating and isolated power supply is required for each opamp.—H. E. Weber, IC Operational Amplifiers Solve Bias Level Problems, *Electronic Design*, Oct. 25, 1969, p 109 and 111.

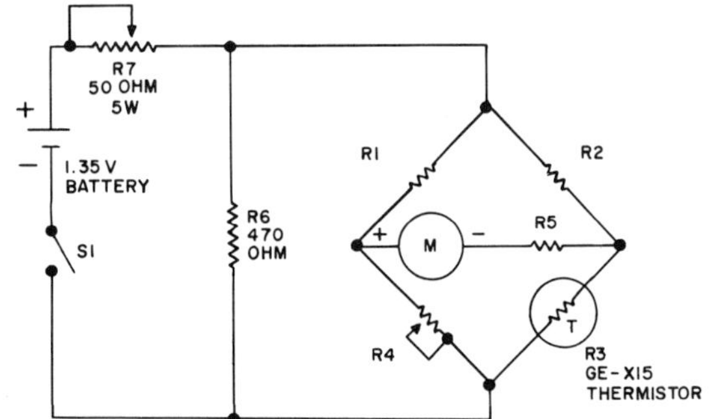

THERMISTOR THERMOMETER—Will indicate on meter the temperature inside deep freeze, solution temperature in darkroom, or any other temperature measurable with thermistor that can be connected into bridge-meter circuit shown. For range of 32 to 122 F, R1 and R2 are 1,000, R4 is 5,000, and R5 is 9,500 ohms. For low-temperature range of −40 to +32 F, R1 and R2 are 7,300, R4 is 50,000, and R5 is 4,850 ohms, with battery changed to 1.5-V mercury cell. Both ranges use 50-μA d-c meter (GE type DW-91 having 1,500 ohms resistance). Resistor values in bridge are critical. Calibrate with crushed ice in water and with calibrating resistors supplied with thermistor.—"Hobby Manual," General Electric, Owensboro, Ky., 1965, p 150.

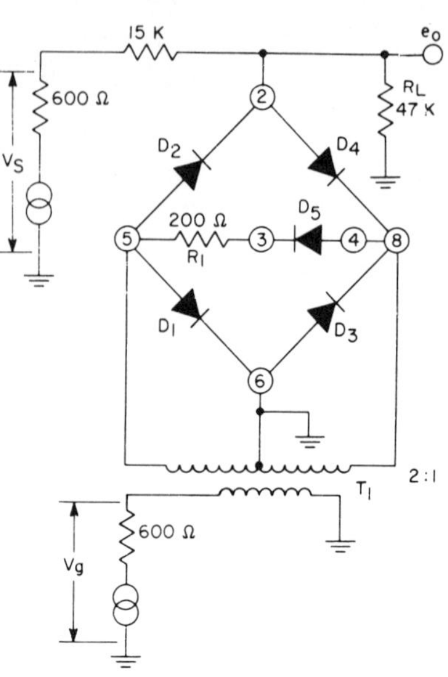

SHUNT GATE—Uses CA3019 diode IC array with diode bridge shunting load resistance and balancing out gating signal to provide pedestal-free output. When gating voltage Vg is of sufficient amplitude, bridge conducts for half of each gating cycle and prevents input signal Vs from reaching output. Gating voltage should be 0.8 to 1.2 V rms at 1 to 100 kHz, and input signal 0 to 1 V rms from d-c to 500 kHz.—"Linear Integrated Circuits," RCA, Harrison, N.J., IC-41, p 303.

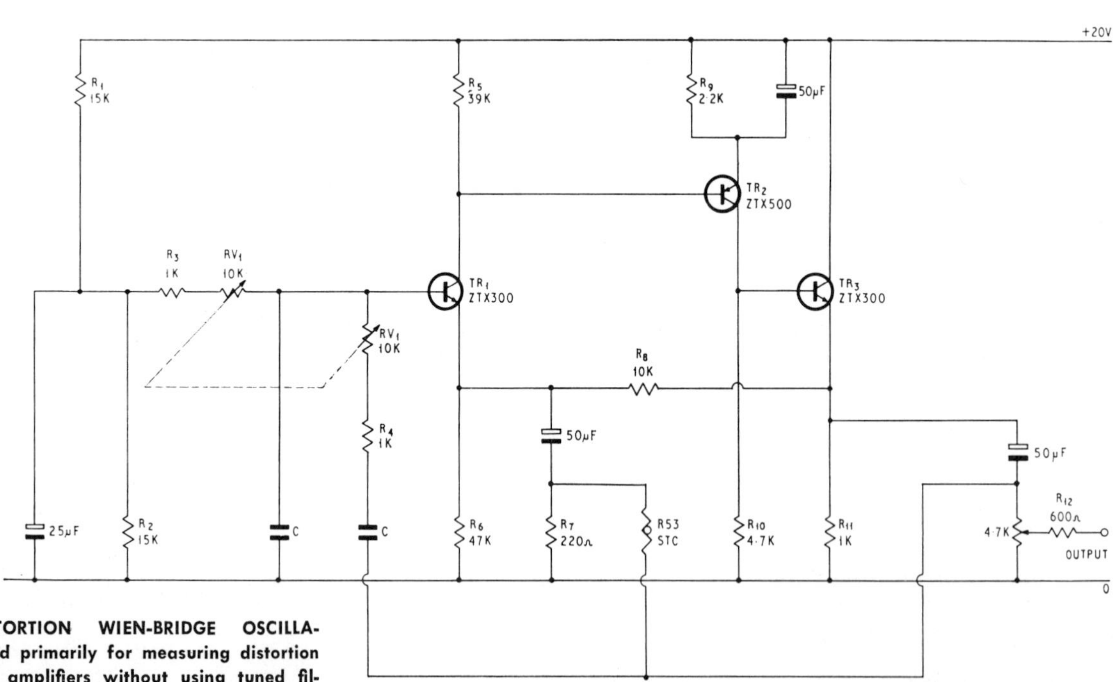

LOW-DISTORTION WIEN-BRIDGE OSCILLATOR—Used primarily for measuring distortion in audio amplifiers without using tuned filters. Delivers pure sine wave with very low distortion. Values of R3 and R4 determine frequency ratio covered on each range; 1K gives maximum to minimum frequency ratio of 11:1, for small overlap on decade ranges. Output is 1 V rms into 600 ohms over frequency range of 10 Hz to 100 kHz.—"E-Line Transistor Applications," Ferranti Ltd., Oldham, Lancs., England, 1969, p 36.

BRIDGE BALANCE DETECTOR—Design goal is simplest circuit giving sufficient sensitivity and linearity, since gain stability is unimportant for application. Report gives design procedure.—"E-Line Transistor Applications," Ferranti Ltd., Oldham, Lancs., England, 1969, p 38.

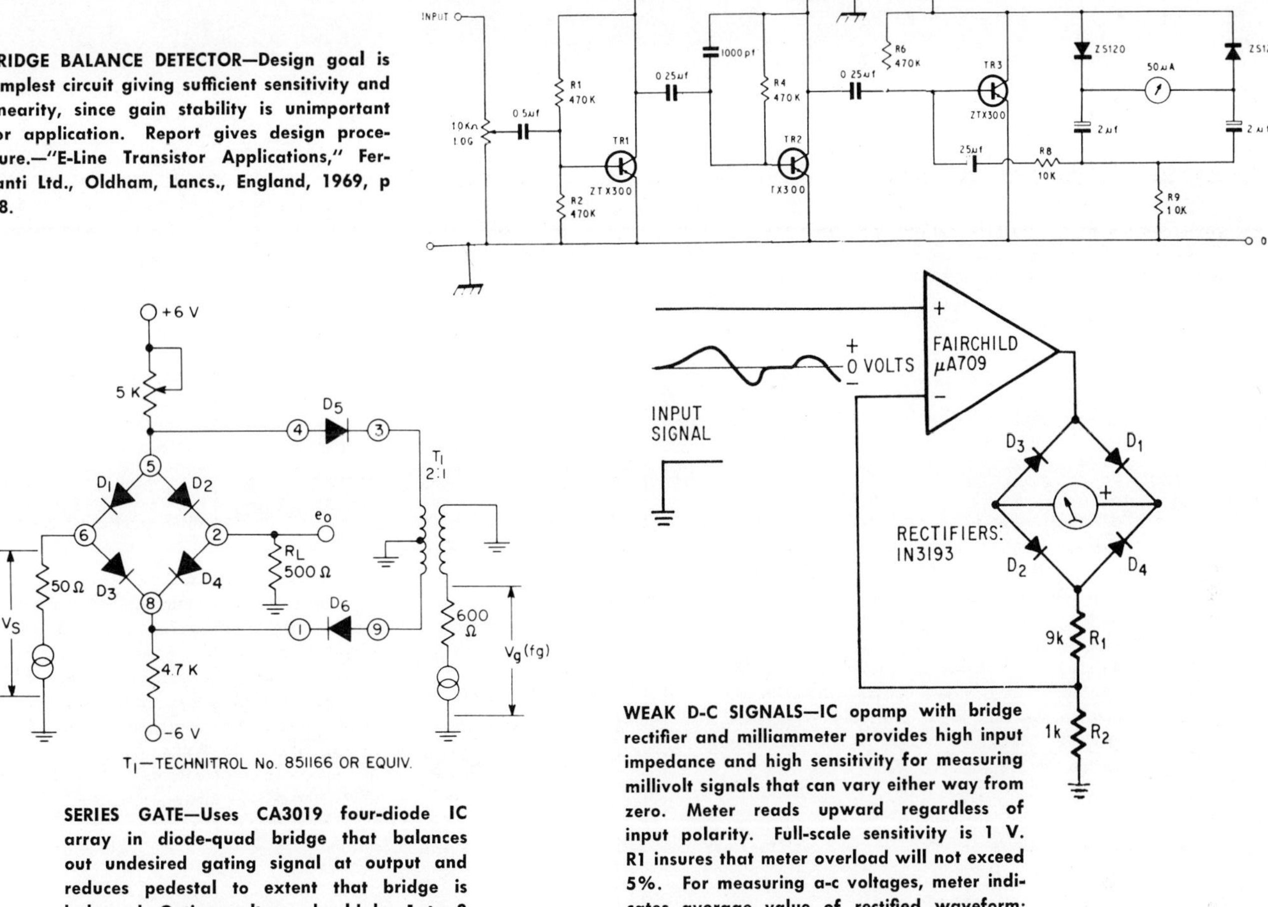

SERIES GATE—Uses CA3019 four-diode IC array in diode-quad bridge that balances out undesired gating signal at output and reduces pedestal to extent that bridge is balanced. Gating voltage should be 1 to 3 V rms at 1 to 500 kHz.—"Linear Integrated Circuits," RCA, Harrison, N.J., IC-41, p 301.

WEAK D-C SIGNALS—IC opamp with bridge rectifier and milliammeter provides high input impedance and high sensitivity for measuring millivolt signals that can vary either way from zero. Meter reads upward regardless of input polarity. Full-scale sensitivity is 1 V. R1 insures that meter overload will not exceed 5%. For measuring a-c voltages, meter indicates average value of rectified waveform; for rms readings, reduce R2 by 11%.—J. P. Budlong, Bridge and Amplifier Monitor D-c Level, *Electronics*, Sept. 2, 1968, p 71–72.

DIAMOND GATE—Used in Paramatrix system for preprocessing analog information, chiefly photos and graphs, while converting to digital signals under computer control. System can enlarge or shrink picture, move it around, rotate it, correct blurs, and fill in gaps. Cuts computer requirements by factor of 10. Can also be applied to automatic drafting. Article presents theory and many block diagrams along with examples of results achieved. Circuit shown is used in interpolator, and requires input signals at both gates before diode bridge transmits analog voltage.—W. J. Poppelbaum, M. Faiman, and E. Carr, Paramatrix Puts Digital Computer In Analog Picture, And Vice Versa, *Electronics*, Sept. 4, 1967, p 99–108.

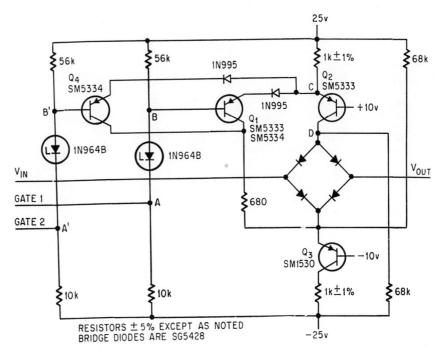

RESISTORS ±5% EXCEPT AS NOTED
BRIDGE DIODES ARE SG5428

CHAPTER 10
Capacitance Control Circuits

NO-PUSH ELEVATOR BUTTON—Finger near button, even if gloved, actuates appropriate relay in modern elevator control system and turns on lamp behind button. Screen behind button picks up hum signal from building ground, capacitively coupled through body of person. This signal is passed to MEM511 mosfet which in turn makes GE C106 scr turn on No. 1829 lamp and relay.—F. G. Geil, MOS FET Takes the Push Out of Elevator Push Button, *Electronics*, Oct. 30, 1967, p 70–71.

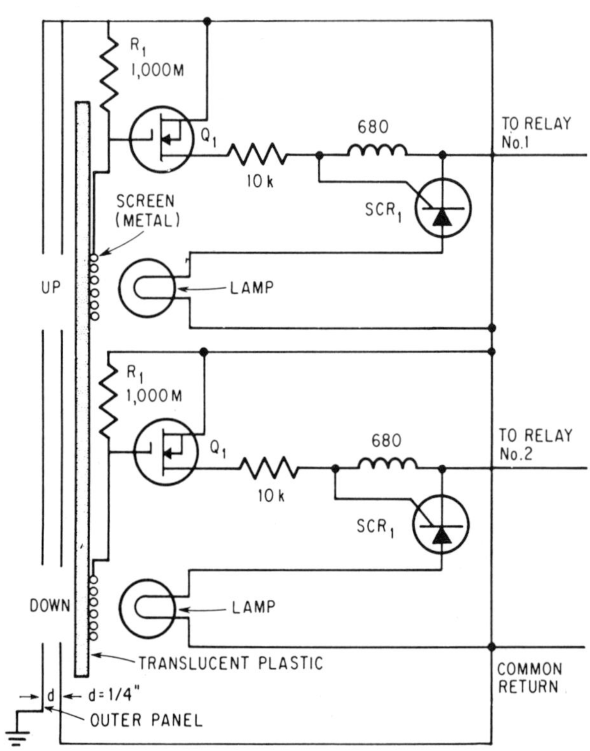

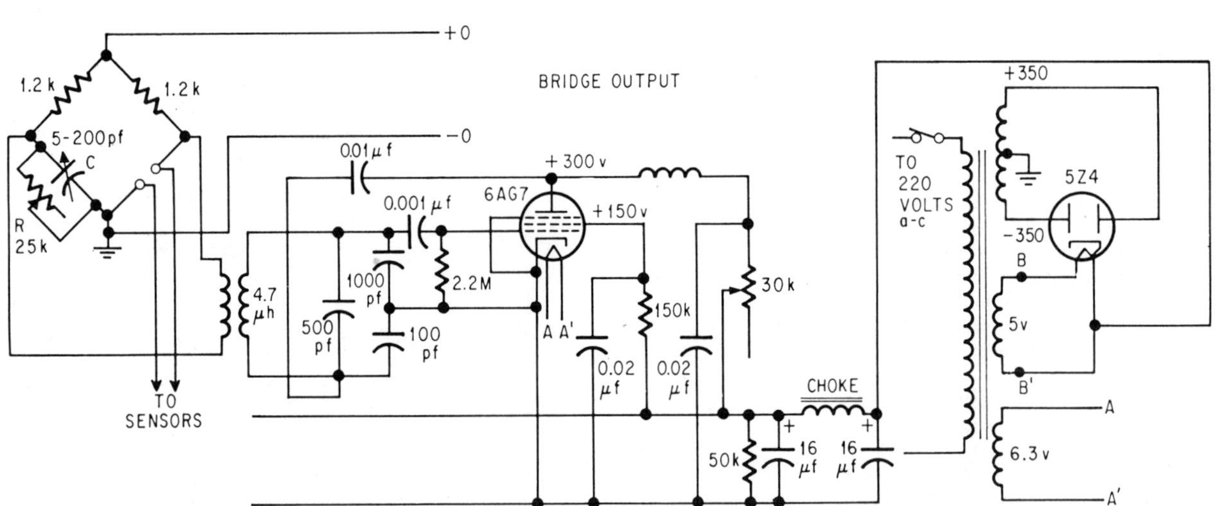

LIQUID LEVEL IN TANK—Movement of liquid in glass gage tube outside tank changes capacitance between liquid and metal-band sensor around glass. Sensor is connected in one arm of bridge, which is first balanced by adjusting C and R with liquid at top of the two sensor electrode rings. Bridge receives 10-V excitation from 3.2-MHz oscillator using 6AG7 tube. Article gives detection sensitivity for ten different liquids.—P. K. Mital, Capacitance Sensor Monitors Stored Liquid Levels, *Electronics*, Oct. 30, 1967, p 71–72.

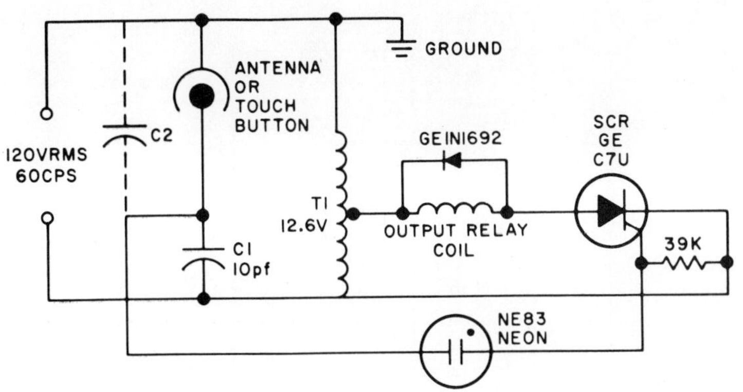

T1 :- 117/12.6 VOLT AUTO TRANSFORMER (OR FILAMENT TRANSFORMER)

PROXIMITY SWITCH—Can be used for elevator call buttons, supermarket and other door controls, burglar alarms, and other applications where load is to be energized by momentary touch of finger on button. C2 represents capacitance between touch button and ground that is provided by body of person. Size of touch button or sensing plate depends on distance to object being sensed; if distance is small, as with touch control, sensing plate need be no larger than a penny. For latching action, drive scr anode circuit only with d-c.—D. R. Grafham, Using Low Current SCR's, General Electric, Syracuse, N.Y., No. 200.19, 1967, p 30.

BODY-CAPACITANCE CONTROL—Bistable neon mvbr is triggered by momentary finger contact with ON touch point, to pull in relay. Relay releases when other point is touched. Chief requirement is sufficient capacitance between circuit and ground. With a-c/d-c supply, ground side of power line should go to circuit ground. With battery supply, larger touch points are needed and circuit ground should be metal chassis.—W. G. Miller, "Using and Understanding Miniature Neon Lamps," H. W. Sams & Co., Indianapolis, Ind., 1969, p 74.

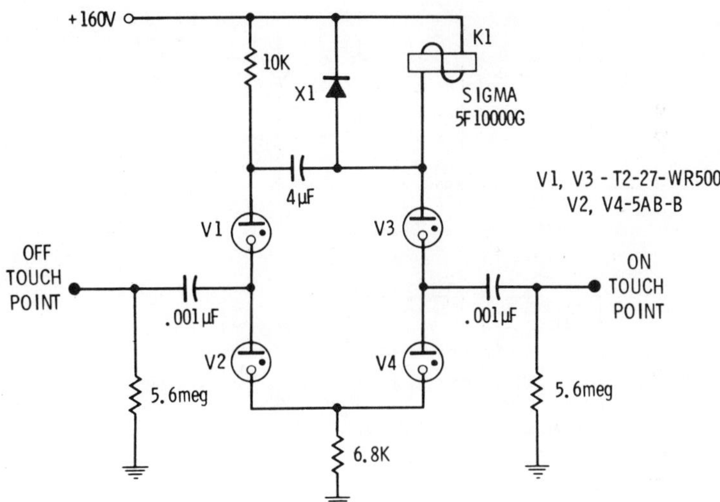

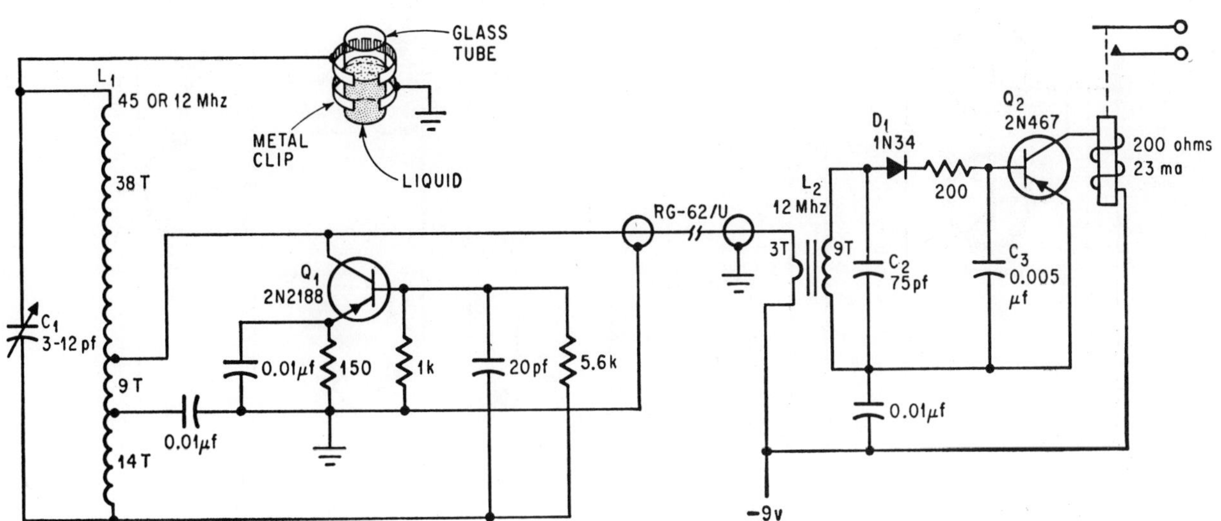

LIQUID-SENSING CAPACITOR—Conventional Hartley oscillator resonates at 45 MHz when glass tube is empty. When liquid reaches critical level inside metal bands surrounding tube, increased dielectric constant of liquid column changes capacitance enough to reduce frequency to 12 MHz. Circuit will trigger reliably with differential capacitance of 0.1 pF between sensing point and ground.—J. K. Marsh, Two-Frequency Oscillator Detects Level of Liquid, *Electronics*, March 20, 1967, p 90.

PROXIMITY SWITCH—Load is energized as long as button of sensor plate capacitor C2 is touched. When button is released, load is de-energized. Latching action can be obtained by replacing CR1 with connection shown as dashed line. Reset will then require auxiliary contact in series with SCR1. Used for door safety controls and floor selector buttons in elevators, supermarket door control, safe monitor in banks, flow switches, and conveyor counting systems.—"SCR Manual," 4th Edition, General Electric, 1967, p 169.

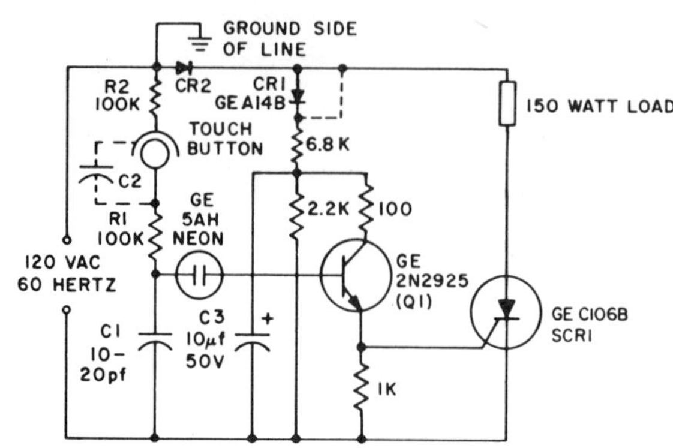

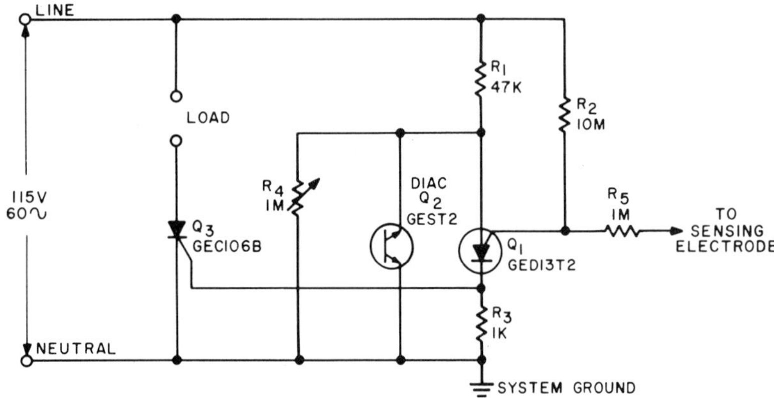

100-W A-C PROXIMITY SWITCH—High sensitivity of D13T2 programmable ujt makes triggering of circuit possible with only about 10 pF capacitance between sensing electrode and ground. This means that finger does not have to touch sensing button. Circuit is nonlatching, and will therefore open when body or other capacitance is removed. R4 adjusts sensitivity. Applications include counting freshly painted objects moving past on conveyor line.—E. K. Howell, Small Scale Integration in Low Cost Control Circuits, General Electric, Syracuse, N.Y., No. 671.9, 1968, p 19.

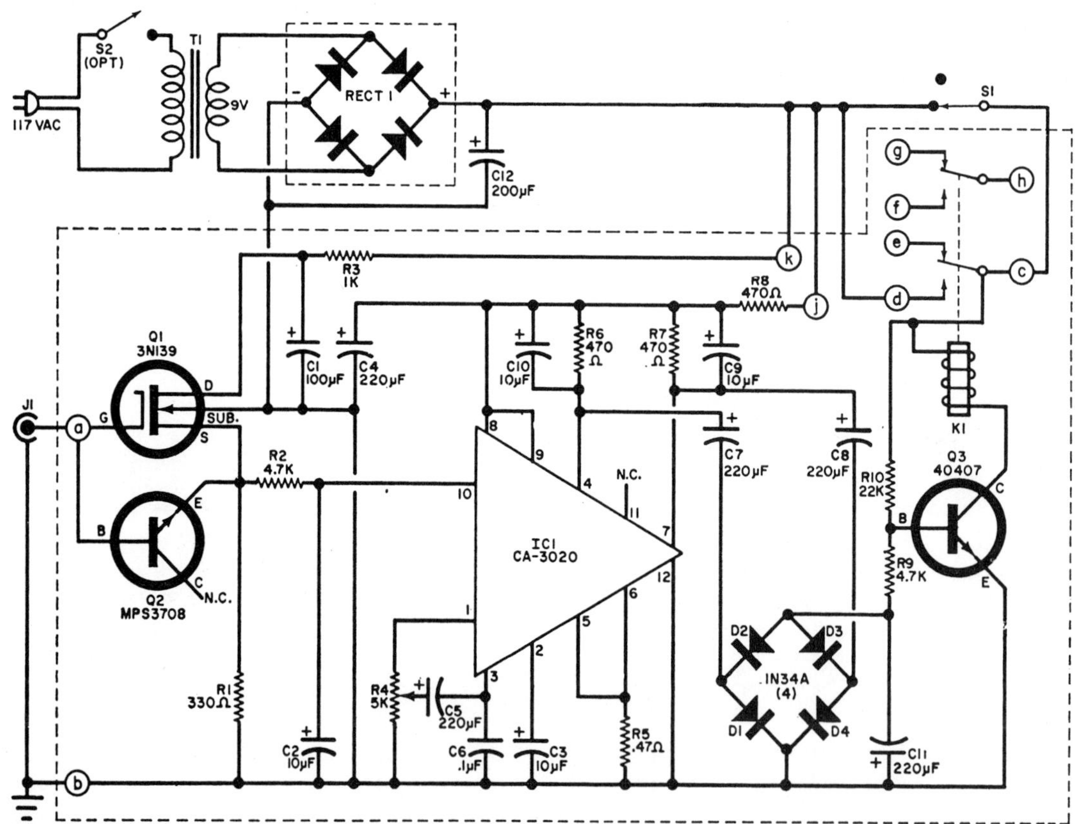

INTRUSION DETECTOR—Responds to change in capacitance between sensor antenna (J1) and ground when person is within several feet of antenna, to energize relay that trips local or remote alarm, turns on lights, summons guard, or applies output of auto ignition coil to intruder. Antenna may be decorative metal art object. For fail-safe operation, Q3 may be biased to energize relay under normal conditions. Presence of intruder or failure of power will then release relay and set off alarm. For protection against burglars in stores, antenna can be safe or cash register.—L. E. Garner, Jr., The Amazing "People Detector," *Popular Electronics*, June 1968, p 27–32 and 93.

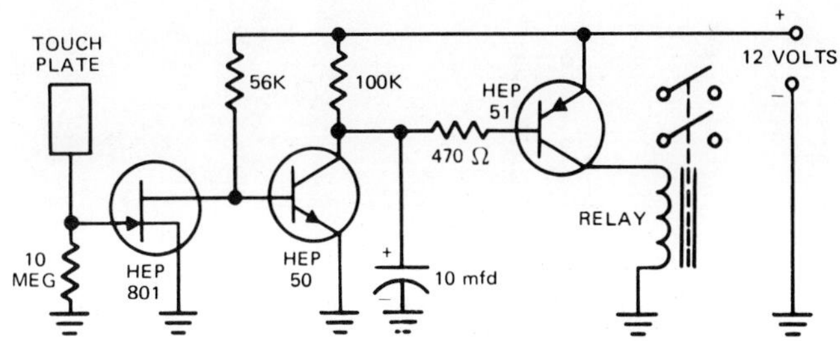

TOUCH SWITCH—Can be used to turn on or off variety of circuits, depending on type of relay used. Touching metal plate, which should be kept close to gate of fet, operates relay.—"Tips on Using FET's," Motorola, Phoenix, Ariz., HMA-33, 1969.

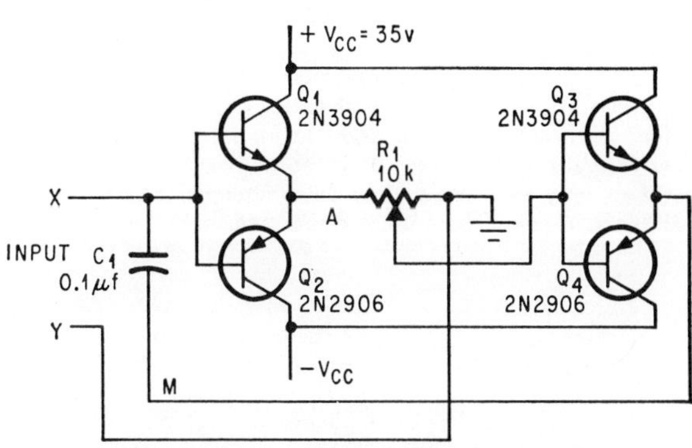

1,000:1 VARIABLE CAPACITOR—Potentiometer R1, buffered on both sides by complementary emitter-followers, reduces effective value of fixed capacitor C1 over much greater range than with conventional variable capacitors. Useful for capacitive tuning of tank circuits over wide frequency ranges.—J. Gaon, Feedback Turns Fixed Capacitor into Variable Capacitance, *Electronics*, Nov. 28, 1966, p 80–81.

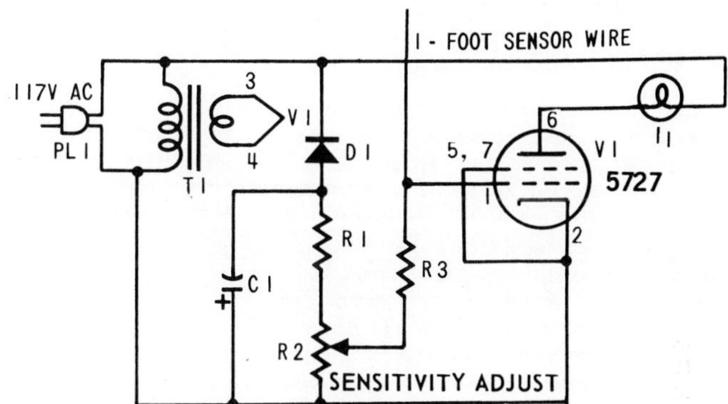

PROXIMITY DETECTOR—Turns on light when person approaches sensor wire. R2 should be well insulated because it is connected to one side of power line when at lower end of range. Values are: I1 10-W lamp; T1 Stancor P-6134; D1 125-V 65-mA selenium rectifier; C1 10 μF; R1 39K; R2 15K pot; R3 3.9 meg.—R. M. Brown, "104 Simple One-Tube Projects," Tab Books, Blue Ridge Summit, Pa., 1969, p 144.

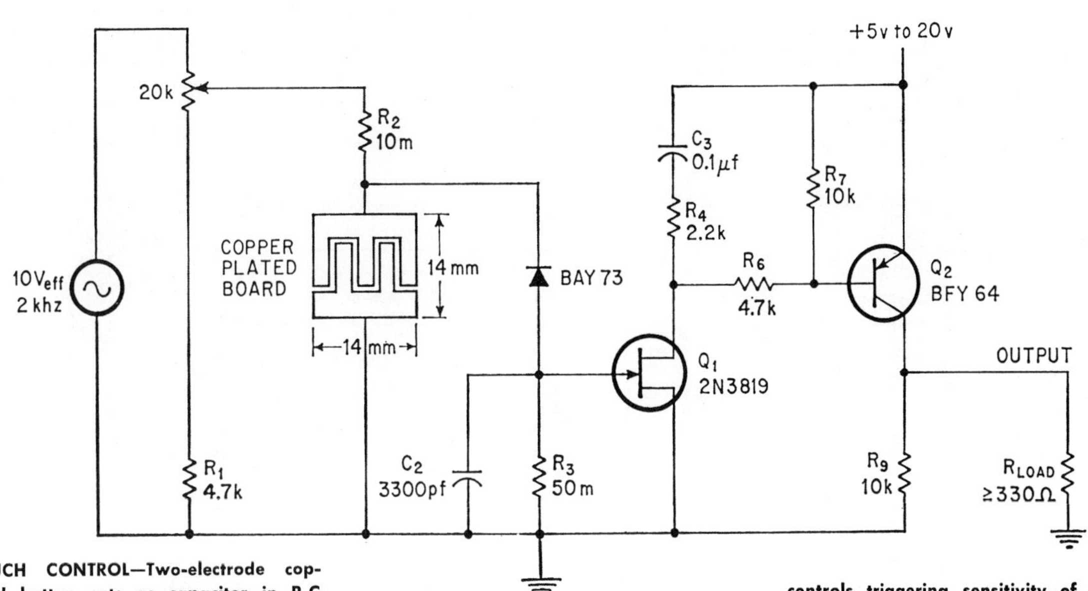

SOFT-TOUCH CONTROL—Two-electrode copper-plated button acts as capacitor in R-C reactive bleeder circuit connected to 2-kHz 10-V source. With button not touched, fet Q1 and transistor Q2 are off and output is at ground or logic zero. When button is touched, its capacitance increases about five times, triggering both transistors on and giving positive output voltage or logic one. Pot controls triggering sensitivity of circuit and triggering level. May be used for elevators, typewriters, and computers.—F. Minder, Touch-Activated Switch Built With Copper-Plated Board, *Electronics*, Sept. 1, 1969, p 79.

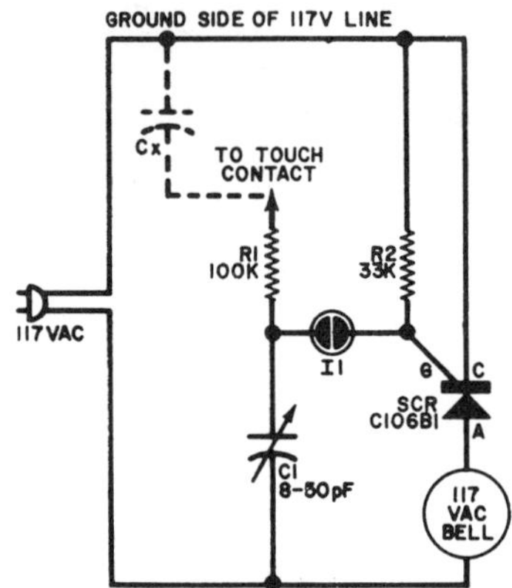

TOUCH ALARM—When intruder touches metal plate or other metal object connected to free end of R1, scr is triggered on and alarm is energized. May be connected to doorknob, metal screen door, foil strip on window sill, or other metal object that is not too large. Object must not be grounded through building structure, because alarm depends on change in capacitance between R1 and ground. Alarm stops when touch contact is broken.—R. F. Graf, Build Low-Cost Touch Alarm, *Popular Electronics*, Feb. 1969, p 92–93.

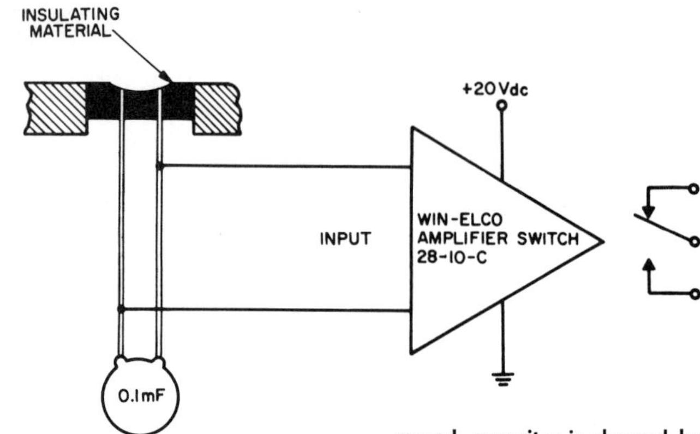

TOUCH SWITCH—Finger in depression of switch plate discharges capacitor and energizes double Darlington amplifier driving reed switch. Relay remains energized as long as finger makes contact. When finger is removed, capacitor is charged by IC and relay stays energized for about 10 s until charging current drops below threshold current of amplifier.—J. H. Still, Time Delay Touch Switch Uses Body Stray Voltage, *Electronic Design*, July 19, 1967, p 106.

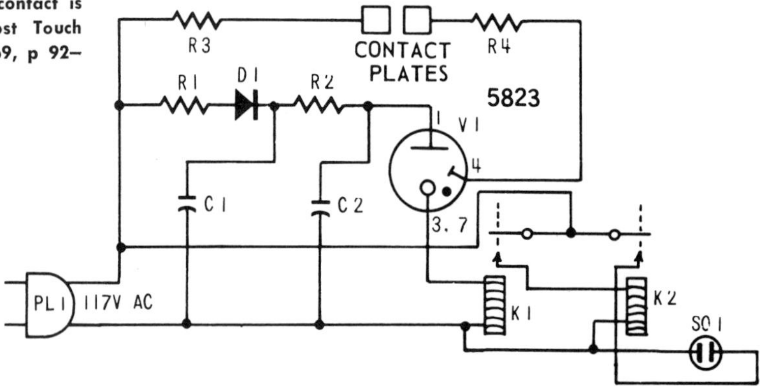

TOUCH CONTROL—Lamp, appliance, tv, or stereo set can be turned on simply by touching two small pieces of tin foil or metal with finger to bridge gap between them. Uses grid-glow tube. Relays are 2.5K. When V1 pulls in K1, its contacts pull in K2 to apply power to lamp or other appliance plugged into socket. Once fired, V1 stays on and relays remain energized until power from a-c line is interrupted. Values are: D1 125-V 65-mA selenium rectifier; C1 0.47 μF; C2 2μF; R1 27; R2 110K; R3 1.1 meg; R4 110K. Warning: if R3 is shorted or much smaller resistor used, circuit can be dangerous for one position of plug because one contact plate goes to a-c line.—R. M. Brown, "104 Simple One-Tube Projects," Tab Books, Blue Ridge Summit, Pa., 1969, p 140.

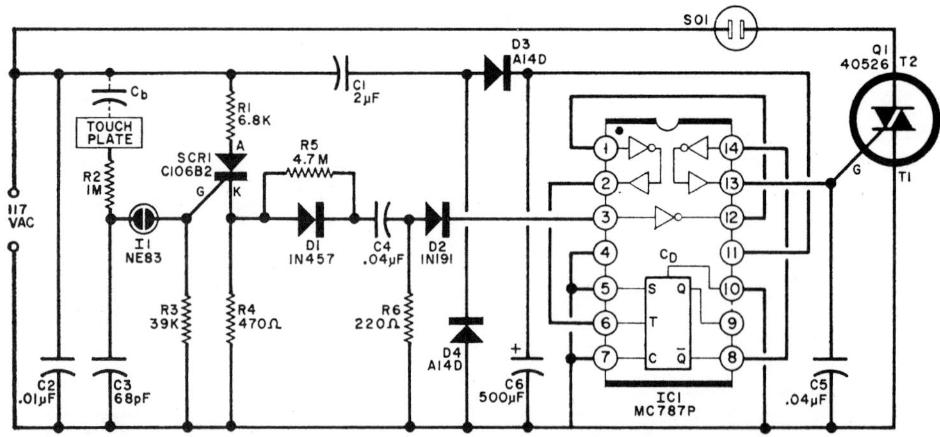

TOUCH SWITCH—Body capacitance is sufficient to trigger scr through neon and energize load through IC and triac Q1, which will handle up to 150 W. Alternate touches of metal plate will turn load on and off. Reversing line cord plug at wall outlet may improve operation.—J. Bechtold, TC Switch For Remote Control, *Popular Electronics*, April 1970, p 52–55.

CHAPTER 11
Cathode-Ray Circuits

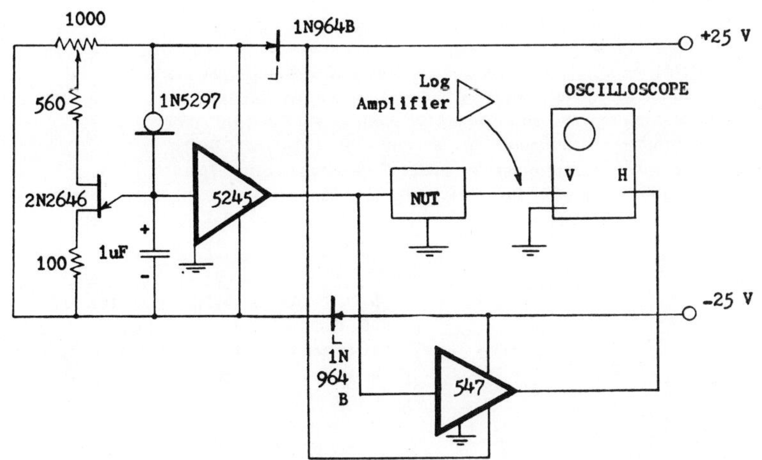

SWEEP GENERATOR—Uses OEI Model 5245 voltage-frequency transducer having output frequency range of 10 Hz to 100 kHz for input of 0 to 5 V. Output is pseudo-sinusoidal, adequate for driving L-C and R-C filter-type networks under test (NUT). OEI 547 frequency-voltage transducer has log response, with d-c output equal to log of input over frequency range of 1 Hz to 100 kHz. Ujt generates low-frequency sawtooth that slews output frequency of 5245 over entire audio spectrum. Arrangement gives log-log display on cro, but with modifications will give lin-lin display.—A Wide Range Sweep Generator, Optical Electronics, Tucson, Ariz., No. 10100.

150-MHZ CRO HORIZONTAL DEFLECTION AMPLIFIER—Provides linear 13-cm deflection, with provision for expanding selected portion of trace tenfold. Writing speed of 5 ns/cm is available at maximum rate of output. Circuit is broadly symmetrical, with long-tailed pairs used in all stages.—K. Hart and F. G. Oude Moleman, Horizontal Deflection Amplifier for 150 MHz Oscilloscopes, *Mullard Technical Communications*, Sept. 1968, p 167–174.

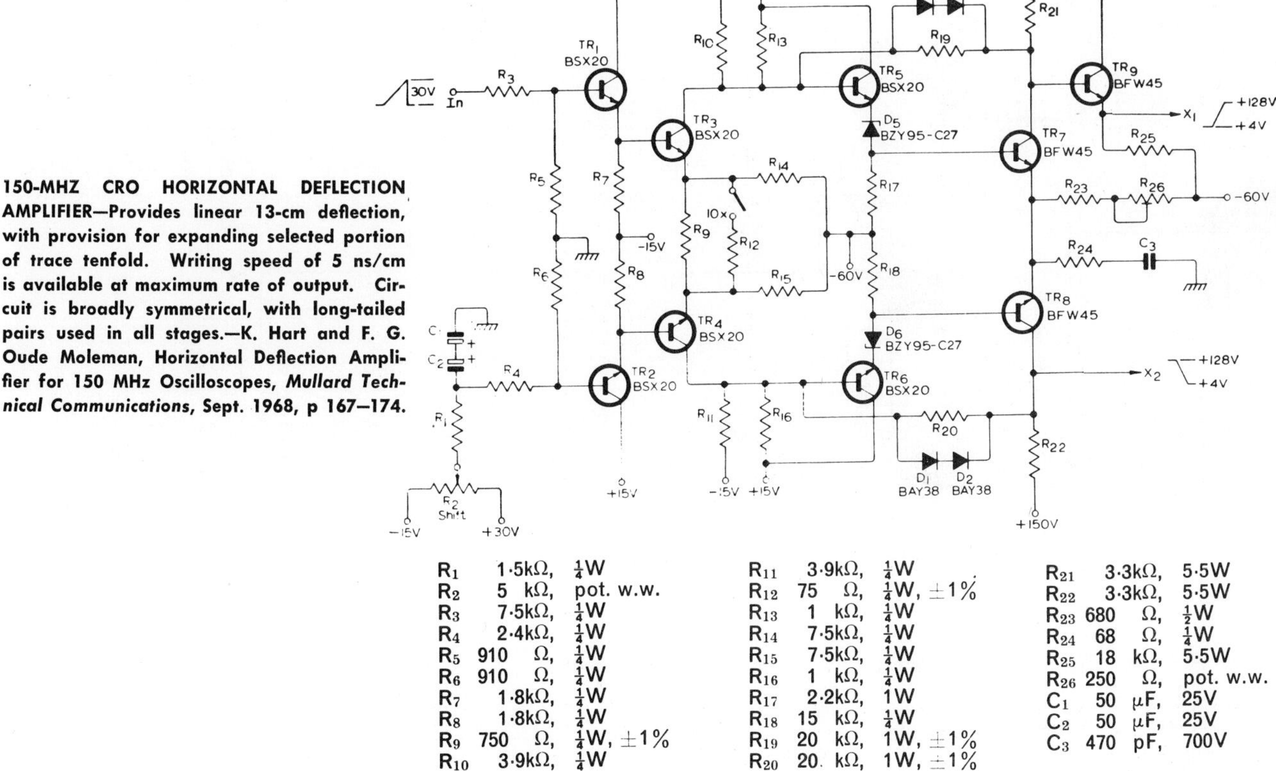

R_1	1·5kΩ,	¼W	R_{11}	3·9kΩ,	¼W	R_{21}	3·3kΩ,	5·5W
R_2	5 kΩ,	pot. w.w.	R_{12}	75 Ω,	¼W, ±1%	R_{22}	3·3kΩ,	5·5W
R_3	7·5kΩ,	¼W	R_{13}	1 kΩ,	¼W	R_{23}	680 Ω,	½W
R_4	2·4kΩ,	¼W	R_{14}	7·5kΩ,	¼W	R_{24}	68 Ω,	¼W
R_5	910 Ω,	¼W	R_{15}	7·5kΩ,	¼W	R_{25}	18 kΩ,	5·5W
R_6	910 Ω,	¼W	R_{16}	1 kΩ,	¼W	R_{26}	250 Ω,	pot. w.w.
R_7	1·8kΩ,	¼W	R_{17}	2·2kΩ,	1W	C_1	50 μF,	25V
R_8	1·8kΩ,	¼W	R_{18}	15 kΩ,	¼W	C_2	50 μF,	25V
R_9	750 Ω,	¼W, ±1%	R_{19}	20 kΩ,	1W, ±1%	C_3	470 pF,	700V
R_{10}	3·9kΩ,	¼W	R_{20}	20. kΩ,	1W, ±1%			

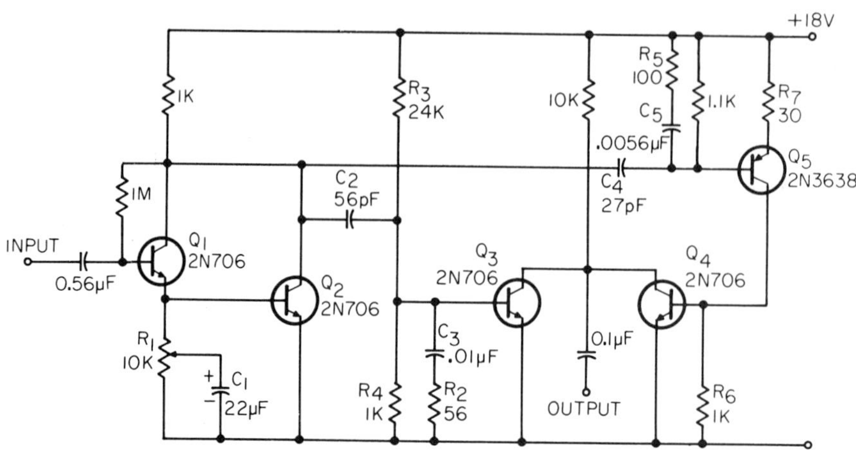

AUTOMATIC TRACE INTENSITY CONTROL—Differentiating circuit, with output feeding cathode of crt, gives increased gain at high frequencies to compensate for loss of brightness. With input of 50 mV rms, output is 17 V peak above 100 MHz. Below 100 MHz, output voltage decreases in direct proportion to frequency. Gain control R1 is used to balance intensity initially for vertical and horizontal deflections.—W. J. Godsey, Differentiating Amplifier Intensifies Scope Trace, *EEE*, Jan. 1967, p 115–116.

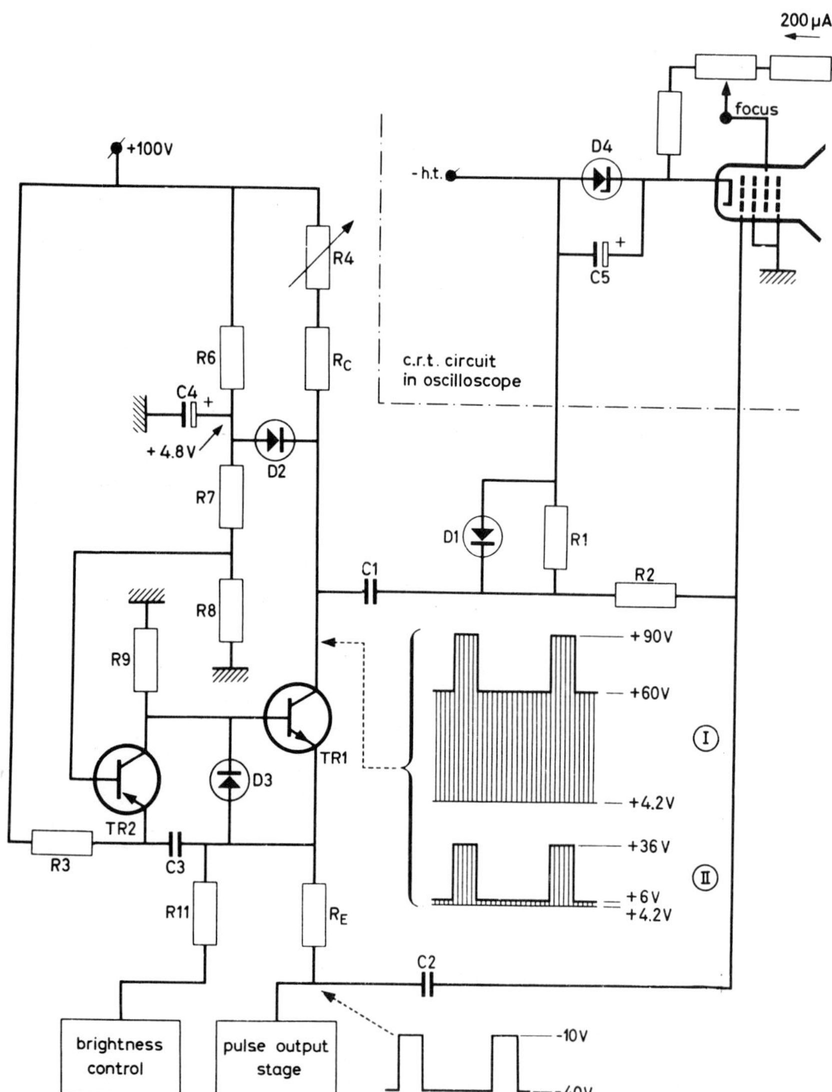

D-C RESTORER WITH POSITIVE CRT GRID DRIVE—Used with inexpensive D7-190 crt in oscilloscope having bandwidth up to 10 MHz. Brightness control adjusts grid drive over range of 2 to 36 V during unblanking periods. Values are: R1 1 meg; R2 470K; R3 120K; R4 4.7K; R6 22K; R7 1K; R8 100; R9 470; R11 15K; RE, RC 15K; C1, C2 180 pF; C3 3.3 nF; C4 16 μF; C5 6.4 μF; D1, D2 BAX16; D3 OA79; D4 BZY95/C75; TR1 BSX21; TR2 BC187.—G. W. Broekema, A New CRT-Grid Drive Circuit Using D. C. Restoration of the Unblanking Signal, Philips, Pub. Dept., Elcoma Div., Eindhoven, The Netherlands, No. 326, 1968.

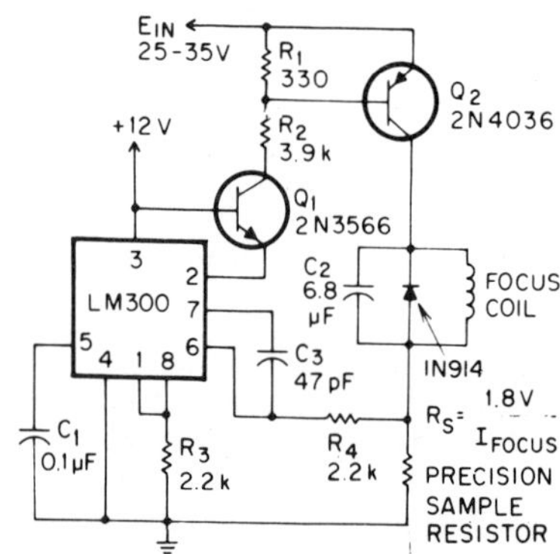

FOCUS CURRENT REGULATOR—Regulates control current through focus coil of cathode-ray tube. Use of separate supply for National Semiconductor IC current regulator makes it unnecessary to restrict unregulated input voltage to maximum 30-V rating of IC. Line regulation is better than 0.02% and load regulation better than 0.05%. Intended for focus coils within 10% of 400 ohms and maximum focus current of 50 mA.—W. G. Jung, An Efficient Focus-Current Regulator Using the LM300, *EEE*, Feb. 1969, p 113–114.

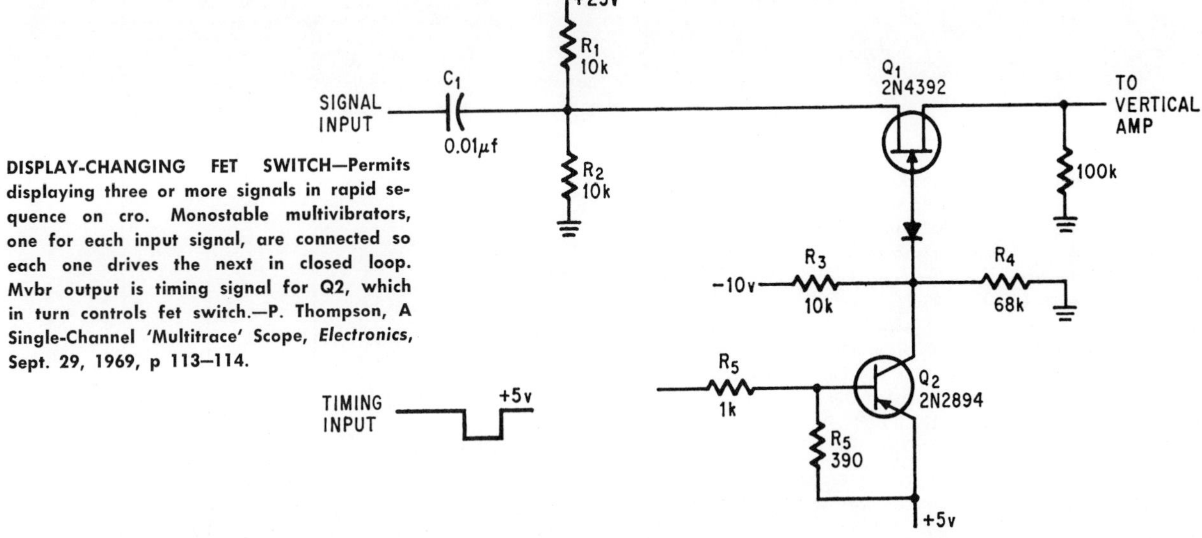

DISPLAY-CHANGING FET SWITCH—Permits displaying three or more signals in rapid sequence on cro. Monostable multivibrators, one for each input signal, are connected so each one drives the next in closed loop. Mvbr output is timing signal for Q2, which in turn controls fet switch.—P. Thompson, A Single-Channel 'Multitrace' Scope, *Electronics*, Sept. 29, 1969, p 113–114.

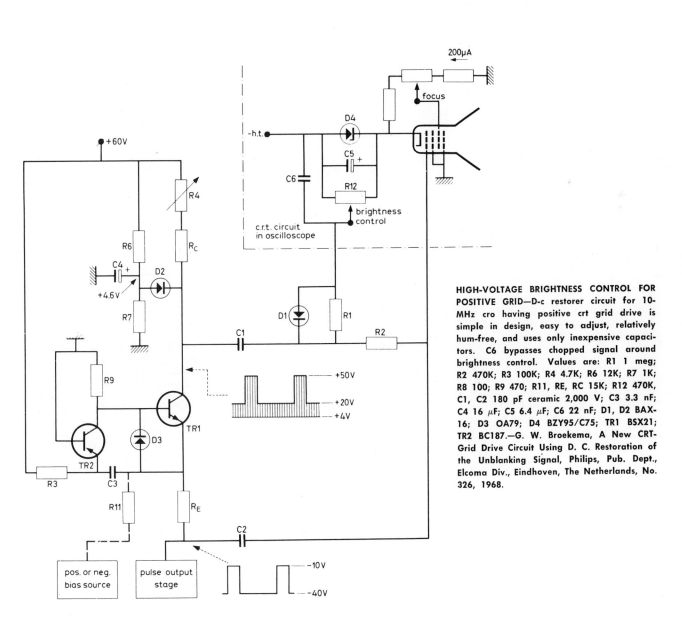

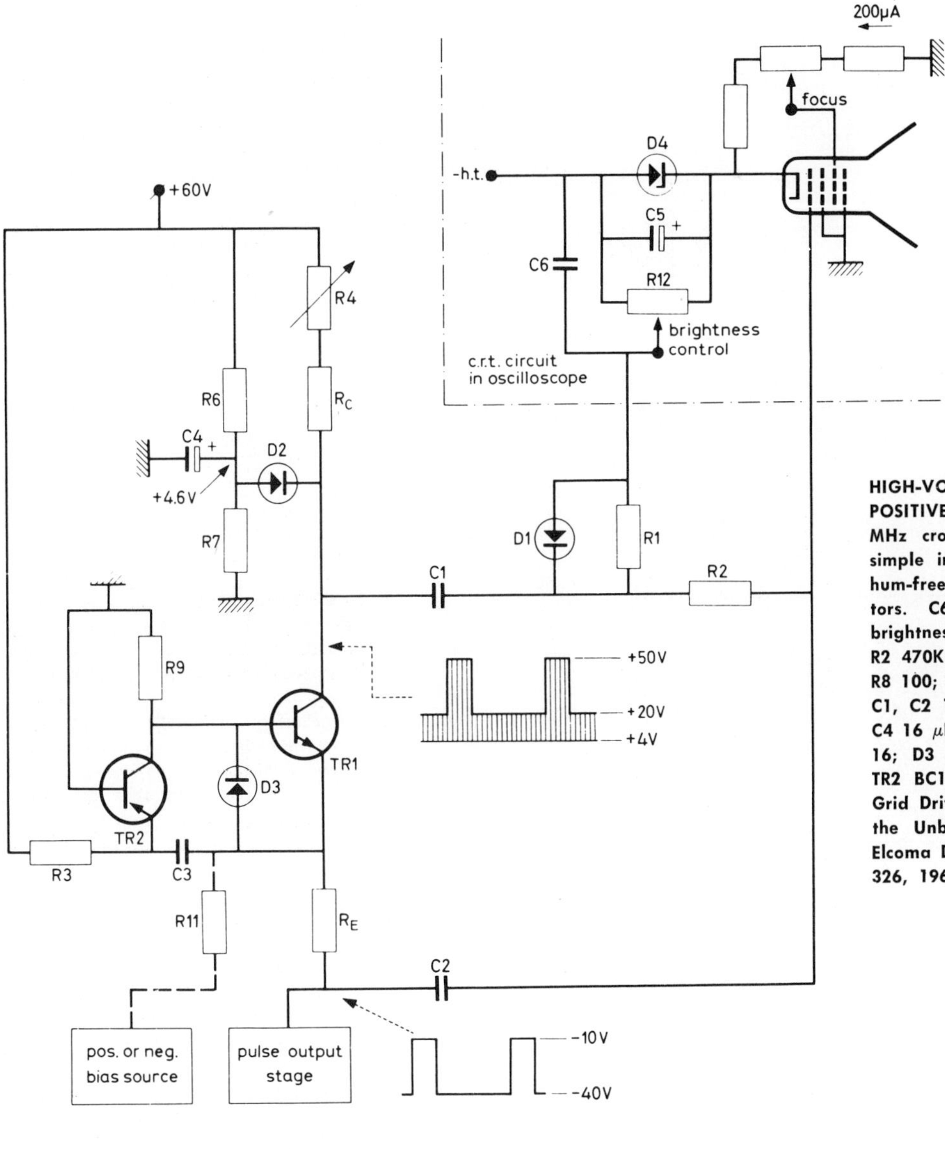

HIGH-VOLTAGE BRIGHTNESS CONTROL FOR POSITIVE GRID—D-c restorer circuit for 10-MHz cro having positive crt grid drive is simple in design, easy to adjust, relatively hum-free, and uses only inexpensive capacitors. C6 bypasses chopped signal around brightness control. Values are: R1 1 meg; R2 470K; R3 100K; R4 4.7K; R6 12K; R7 1K; R8 100; R9 470; R11, RE, RC 15K; R12 470K, C1, C2 180 pF ceramic 2,000 V; C3 3.3 nF; C4 16 μF; C5 6.4 μF; C6 22 nF; D1, D2 BAX-16; D3 OA79; D4 BZY95/C75; TR1 BSX21; TR2 BC187.—G. W. Broekema, A New CRT-Grid Drive Circuit Using D. C. Restoration of the Unblanking Signal, Philips, Pub. Dept., Elcoma Div., Eindhoven, The Netherlands, No. 326, 1968.

CHARACTERISTIC CURVE ROTATOR—Inexpensive two-port negative-impedance converter varies characteristic curve of component by revolving it about an origin. Oscilloscope at input port displays rotated characteristic curve, as aid to designer in building new circuits having functions not attainable with conventional components. Article gives design criteria and equations for R, L, and C rotators and examples of curves that can be obtained.—L. O. Chua, A Good Turn for Old Components, *Electronics*, May 29, 1967, p 109–122.

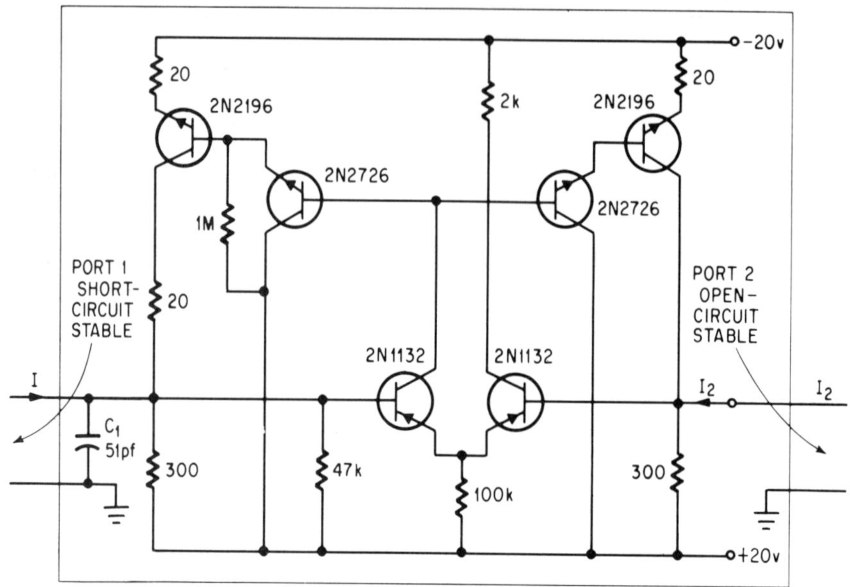

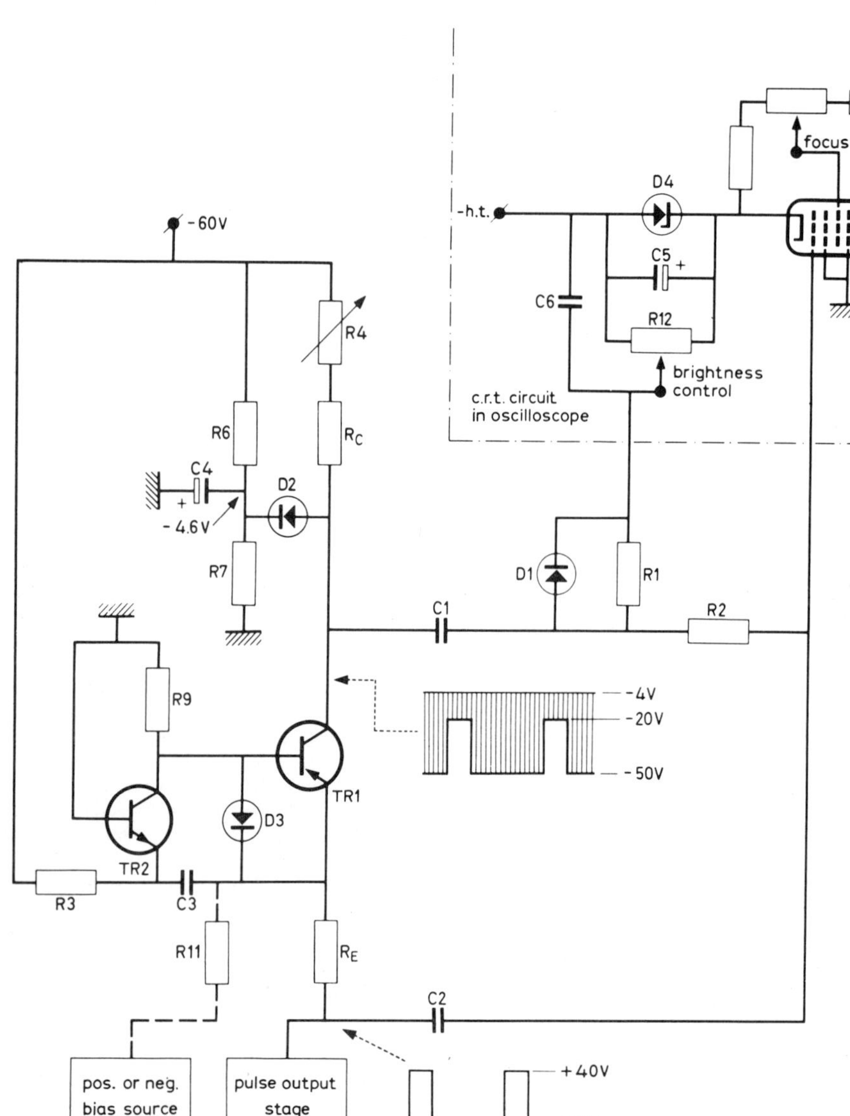

HIGH-VOLTAGE BRIGHTNESS CONTROL—D-c restorer circuit for crt having negative grid drive controls brightness at high-voltage level. Chopper supply voltage is only 60 V, because chopping pulses are not varied in magnitude by shifting chopped signal. Instead, chopped signal varies symmetrically about center of available collector voltage swing for TR1. Values are: R1 1 meg; R2 470K; R3 100K; R4 4.7K; R6 12K; R7 1K; R8 100; R9 470; R11, RE, RC 15K; R12 470K; C1, C2 180 pF ceramic 2,000 V; C3 3.3 nF; C4 16 µF; C5 1 µF; C6 22 nF; D1, D2 BAX16; D3 OA79; D4 BZY95/C30; TR1 AF118; TR2 BF194.—G. W. Broekema, A New CRT-Grid Drive Circuit Using D. C. Restoration of the Unblanking Signal, Philips, Pub. Dept., Elcoma Div., Eindhoven, The Netherlands, No. 326, 1968.

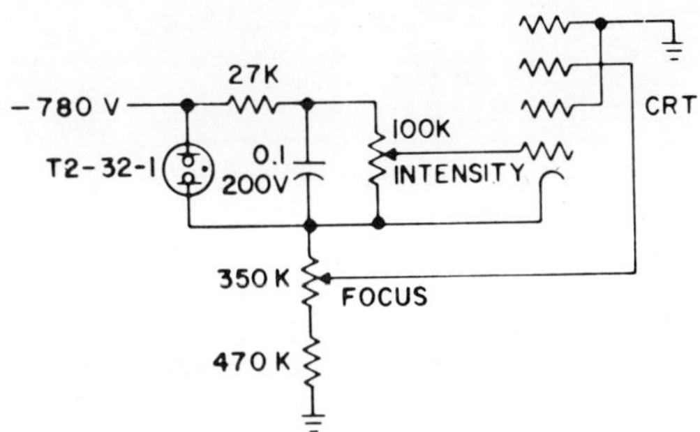

PILOT LIGHT AND BIAS REGULATOR—Single neon lamp acts both as pilot light and as bias regulator for grid 1 of the crt.—E. Bauman, "Applications of Neon Lamps and Gas Discharge Tubes," Signalite, Neptune, N.J., p 151.

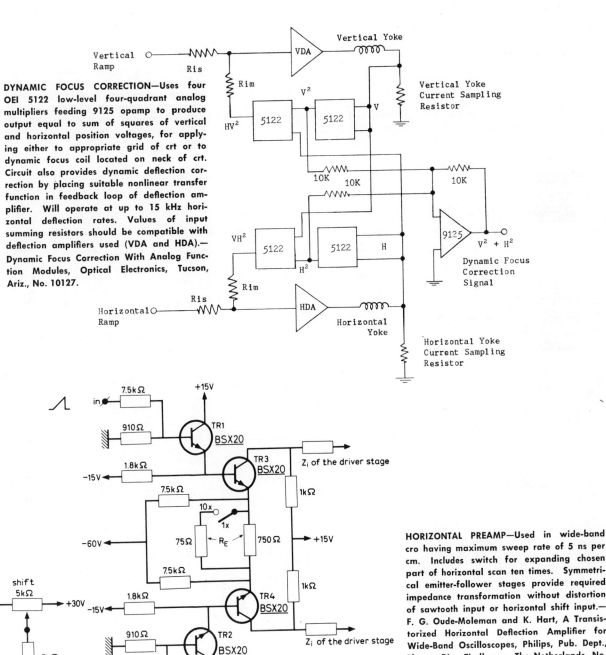

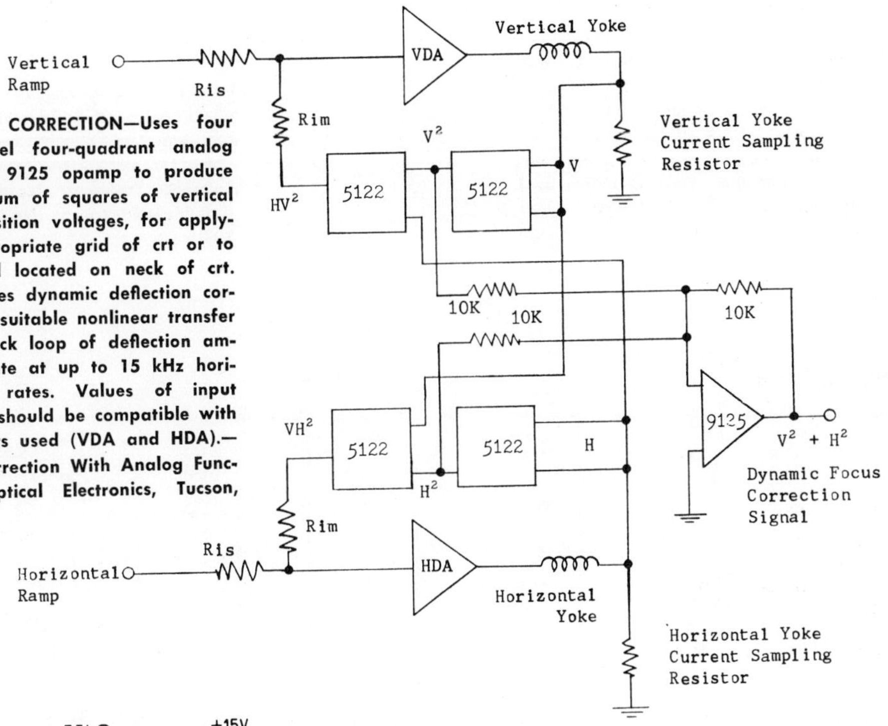

DYNAMIC FOCUS CORRECTION—Uses four OEI 5122 low-level four-quadrant analog multipliers feeding 9125 opamp to produce output equal to sum of squares of vertical and horizontal position voltages, for applying either to appropriate grid of crt or to dynamic focus coil located on neck of crt. Circuit also provides dynamic deflection correction by placing suitable nonlinear transfer function in feedback loop of deflection amplifier. Will operate at up to 15 kHz horizontal deflection rates. Values of input summing resistors should be compatible with deflection amplifiers used (VDA and HDA).—Dynamic Focus Correction With Analog Function Modules, Optical Electronics, Tucson, Ariz., No. 10127.

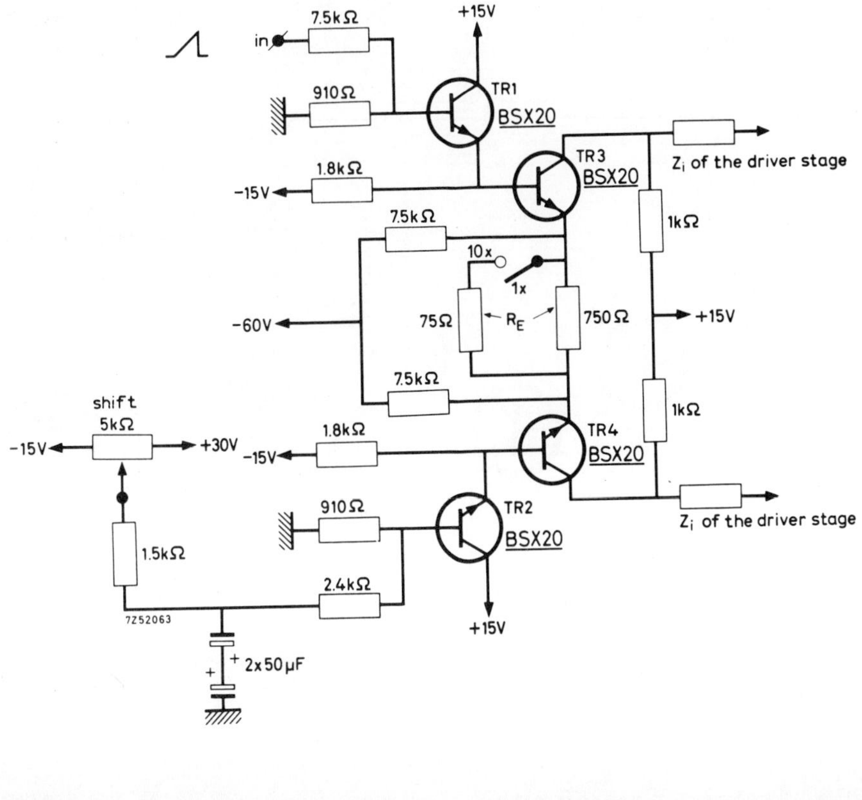

HORIZONTAL PREAMP—Used in wide-band cro having maximum sweep rate of 5 ns per cm. Includes switch for expanding chosen part of horizontal scan ten times. Symmetrical emitter-follower stages provide required impedance transformation without distortion of sawtooth input or horizontal shift input.—F. G. Oude-Moleman and K. Hart, A Transistorized Horizontal Deflection Amplifier for Wide-Band Oscilloscopes, Philips, Pub. Dept., Elcoma Div., Eindhoven, The Netherlands, No. 317, 1967.

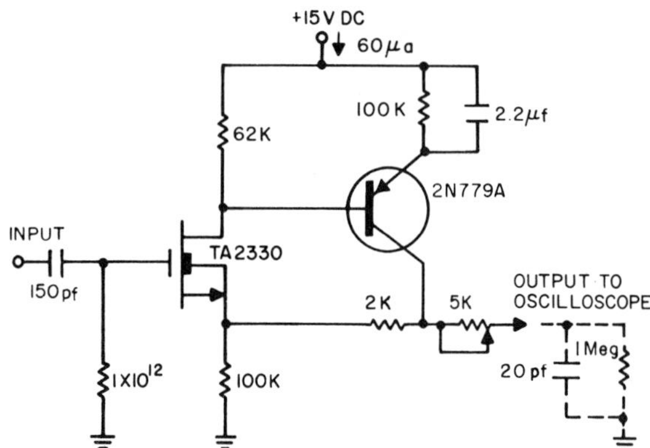

MILLION-MEG SCOPE PROBE—Insulated-gate fet as input stage of oscilloscope probe gives unusually high input impedance of 1,000,000 meg in parallel with 2 pF, although at expense of higher output noise than when using junction fet in probe. Gain is unity.—E. J. Kennedy, FET Used For Unity-Gain, High-Impedance Scope Probe, *Electronic Design*, Aug. 30, 1965, p 46–47.

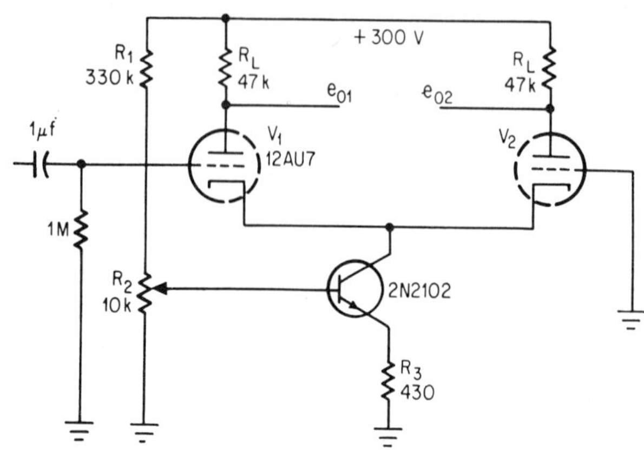

PARAPHASE AMPLIFIER—Adding transistor eliminates need for negative supply voltage and improves balance of output signal amplitudes for electrostatic cathode-ray tubes.—P. Salomon, Transistor Replaces Supply in CRT Amplifier, *Electronics*, Nov. 13, 1967, p 102–103.

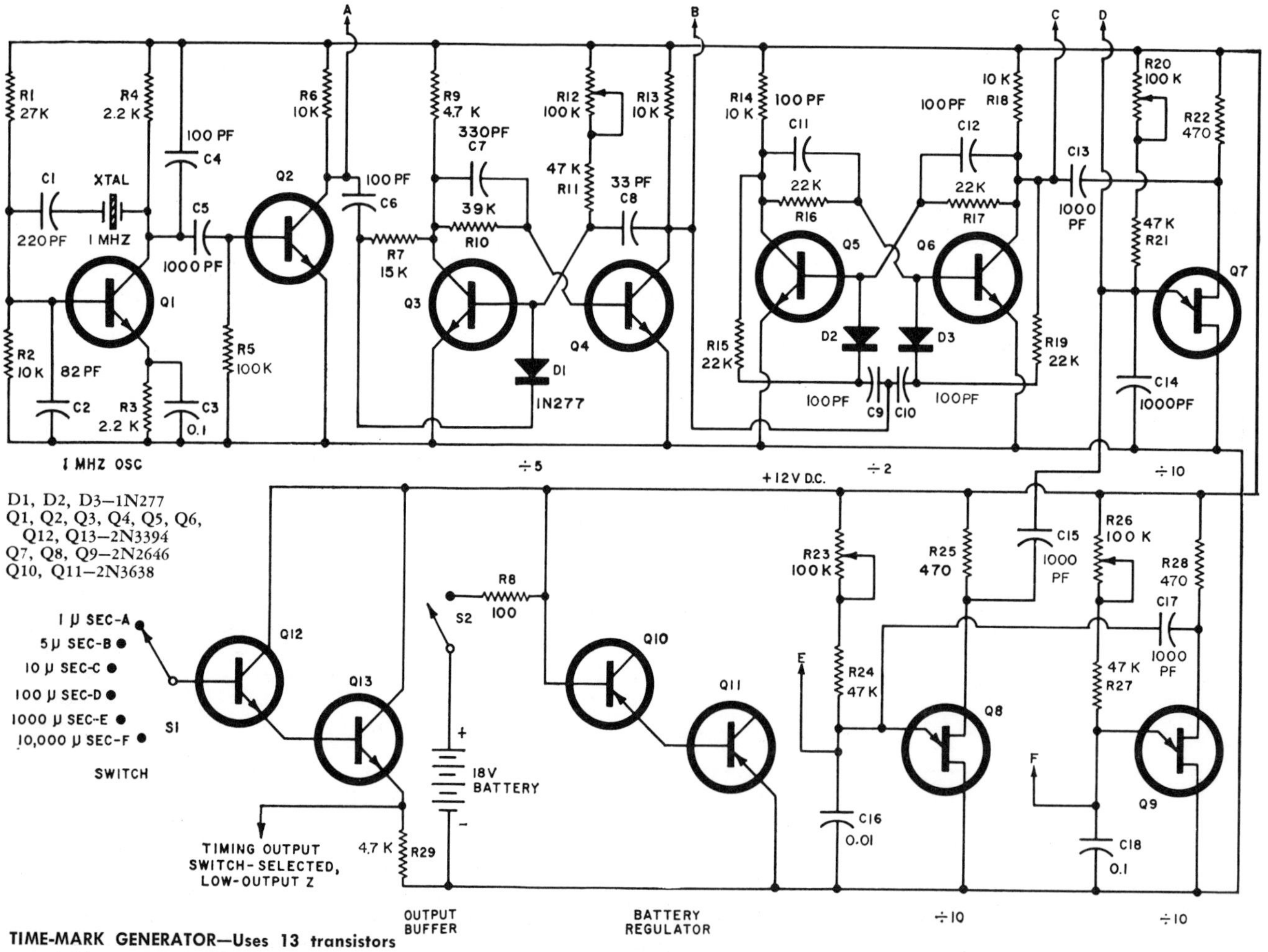

D1, D2, D3—1N277
Q1, Q2, Q3, Q4, Q5, Q6, Q12, Q13—2N3394
Q7, Q8, Q9—2N2646
Q10, Q11—2N3638

TIME-MARK GENERATOR—Uses 13 transistors to provide accurate calibration points of 1, 5, 10, 100, 1,000, and 10,000 μs for calibrating horizontal sweep of oscilloscope. Primary accuracy is provided by 1-MHz crystal oscillator Q1. Regulator transistors Q10 and Q11 can be omitted if mercury battery or regulated power supply is used.—R. G. Teeter, Scope Sweep Generator, *Electronics World*, Feb. 1967, p 80–81.

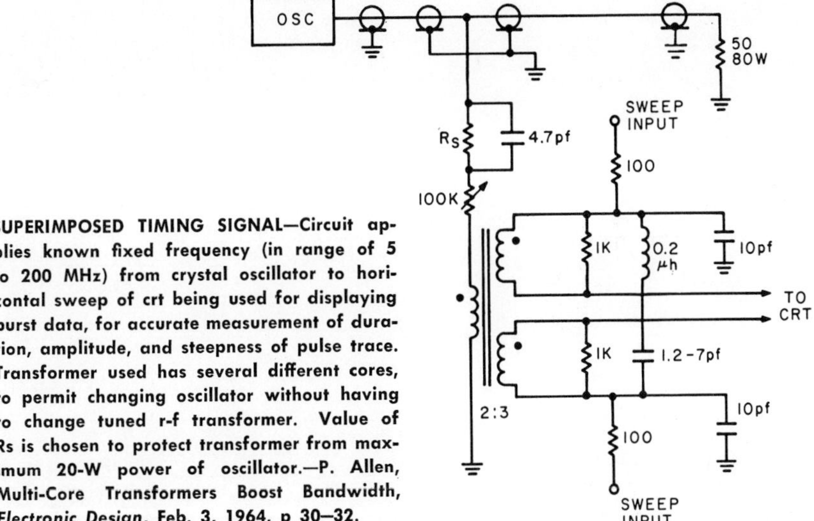

SUPERIMPOSED TIMING SIGNAL—Circuit applies known fixed frequency (in range of 5 to 200 MHz) from crystal oscillator to horizontal sweep of crt being used for displaying burst data, for accurate measurement of duration, amplitude, and steepness of pulse trace. Transformer used has several different cores, to permit changing oscillator without having to change tuned r-f transformer. Value of Rs is chosen to protect transformer from maximum 20-W power of oscillator.—P. Allen, Multi-Core Transformers Boost Bandwidth, *Electronic Design*, Feb. 3, 1964, p 30–32.

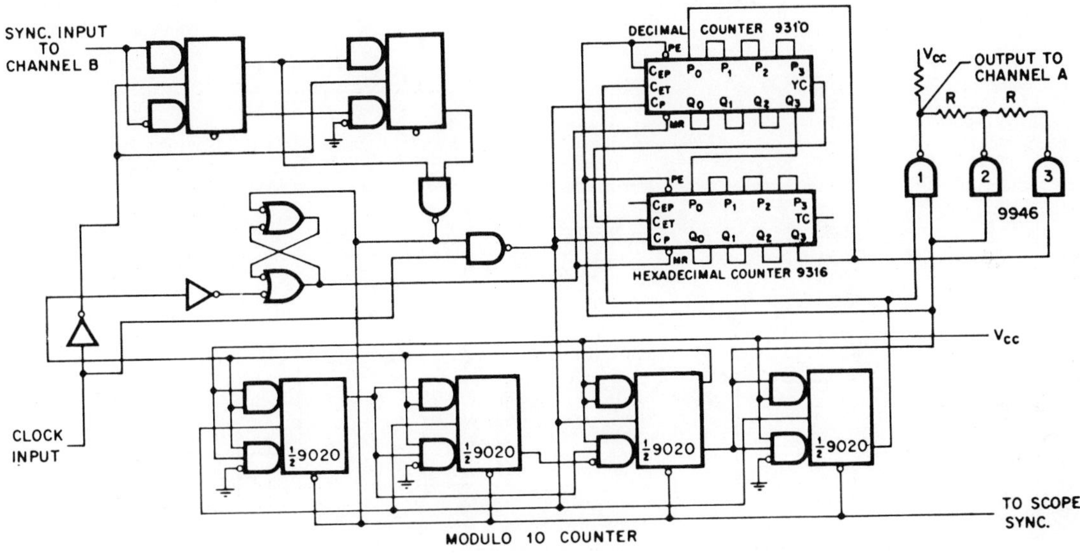

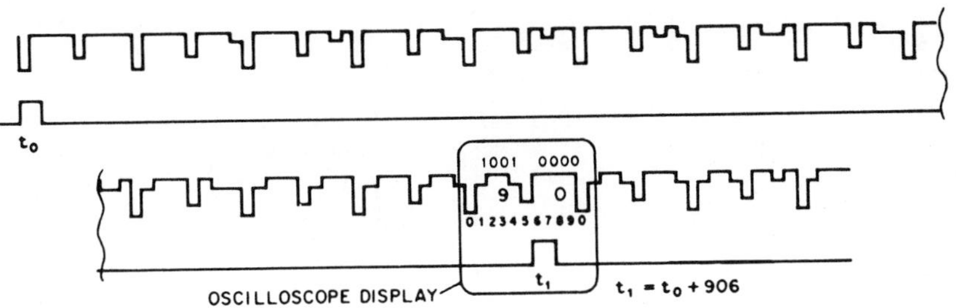

CODED REFERENCE WAVEFORM—Pulse generator connected to sync input of cro can be driven either by master clock of digital system or by any external signal source. If period in seconds of reference waveform is known, then delay in pulse on cro trace can be measured directly by projecting leading edge of pulse down to reference waveform and reading delay in increments of clock (in μs if clock is 1 MHz). Reference waveform, as generated by IC units shown, has long pulse marking beginning of each period. Following four bit positions determine most significant digit in hexadecimal code. Two more four-bit decimal codes follow.—J. L. Nichols, Reference Waveform Adds to Scope's Measuring Capability, *Electronics*, Dec. 22, 1969, p 77–78.

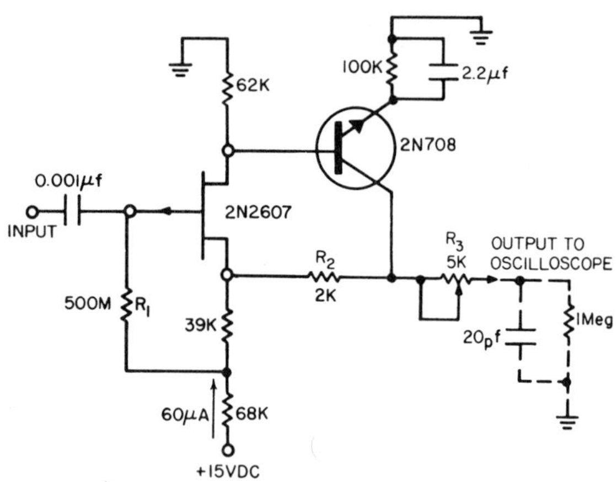

1,200-MEG SCOPE PROBE—Bootstrap action of transistor pair gives effective input impedance of 1,200 meg in parallel with 3.5 pF for unity-gain probe to be used in extremely high impedance circuits. Can handle up to 2-V input signals of either polarity without appreciable distortion. Low power drain of input fet permits battery operation.—E. J. Kennedy, FET Used For Unity-Gain, High-Impedance Scope Probe, *Electronic Design*, Aug. 30, 1965, p 46–47.

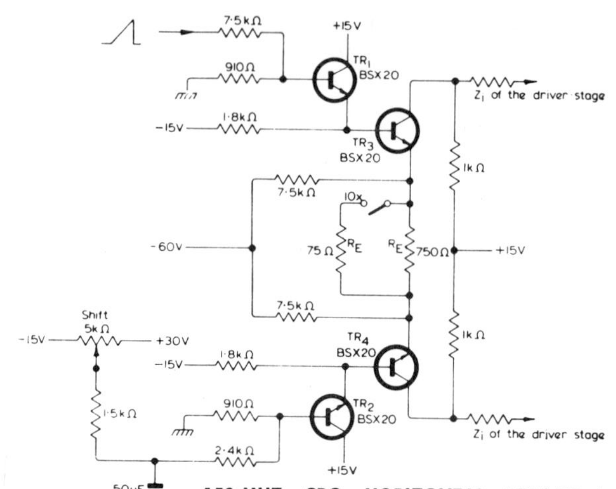

150-MHZ CRO HORIZONTAL PREAMP—Includes phase inverter, provisions for X-expansion and shift, and sufficient output for driver stage of horizontal amplifier in oscilloscope having sufficient bandwidth for detailed study of fast transients. Requires sawtooth with 3.26 V p-p and peak current of 3.58 mA at input going to base of TR1.—K. Hart and F. G. Oude Moleman, Horizontal Deflection Amplifier for 150 MHz Oscilloscopes, *Mullard Technical Communications*, Sept. 1968, p 167–174.

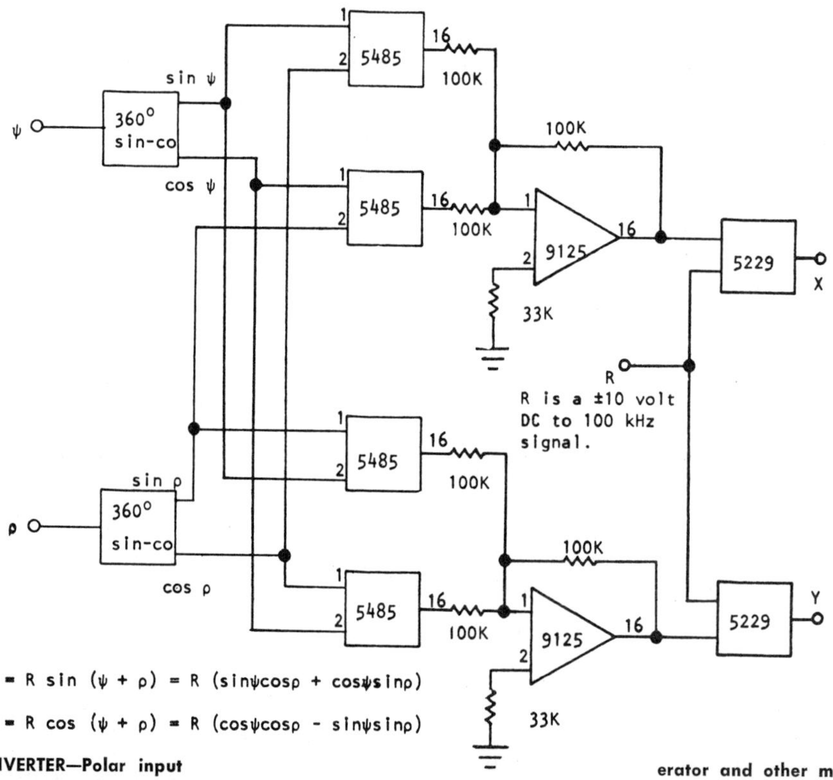

PPI TO X-Y SCAN CONVERTER—Polar input from radar ppi display consists of azimuth heading angle psi, direction angle rho of radar antenna with respect to direction of target travel, and range or distance R. Output voltages X and Y, each up to 10 V full-scale in either polarity, are derived from polar coordinates with OEI sine function modules in 360-deg sine-cosine function generator and other modules shown, in accordance with trig relationship given below circuit. —Polar Coordinates to Rectangular Coordinates Scan Converter, Optical Electronics, Tucson, Ariz., No. 10155.

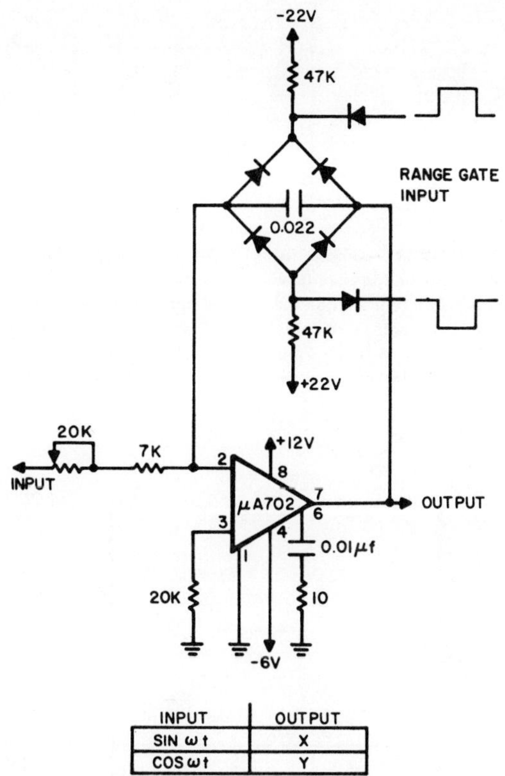

INPUT	OUTPUT
SIN ωt	X
COS ωt	Y

PPI SWEEP GENERATOR—Two Fairchild IC opamps connected identically for X and Y axes (only one shown) generate waveforms required for radial plan position indicator display. Advantages are high linearity, uniform bilateral integration, rapid reset time, and sufficient output for deflection driver. IC opamp is connected as independent integrator that is diode-clamped to zero until range-gate pulse arrives and allows sweep waveform to start. Values shown give several thousand radial sweeps for 40-rpm antenna.—D. E. Lancaster, The Integrated Operational Amplifier: A Versatile and Economical Circuit, "Microelectronic Design," Hayden Book Co., N.Y., 1966, p 189–194.

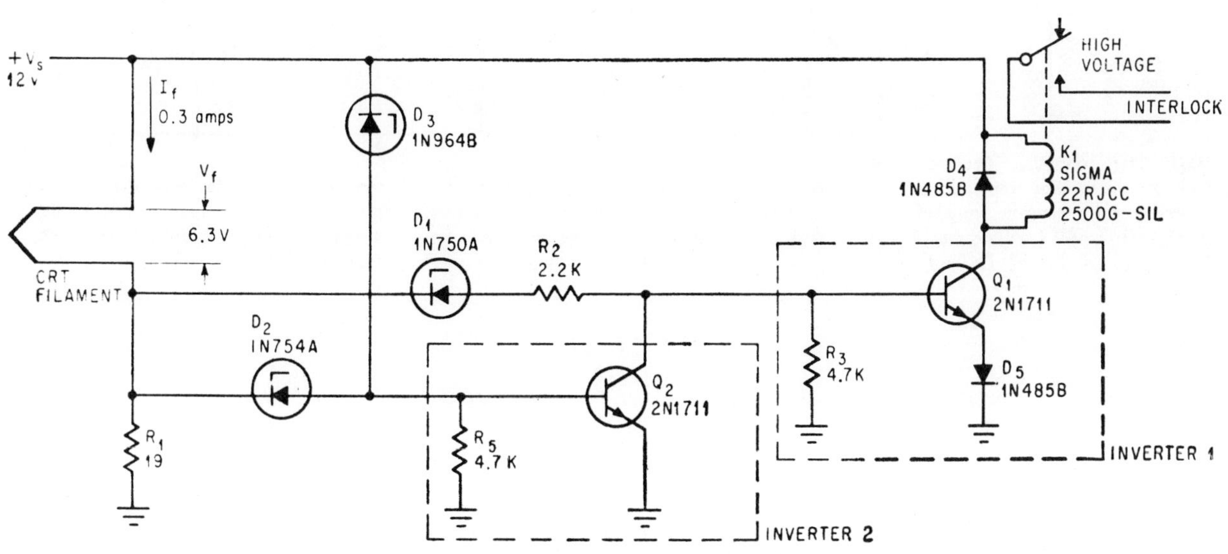

PROTECTIVE INTERLOCK—Protective circuit is activated, to prevent application of high voltage to cathode-ray tube, for four possible system faults: (1) Low filament supply voltage; (2) High filament supply voltage; (3) Open filament feed lines; (4) Shorted filament feed lines.—K. E. Springer, Interlock Protects Display Tube, *Electronics*, Sept. 19, 1966, p 125–126.

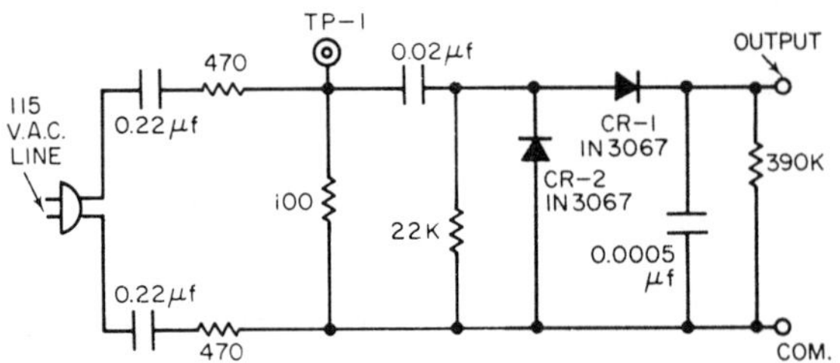

TRANSIENT-WIDENING NETWORK—Simple, inexpensive differentiator and voltage doubler together serve to detect and widen narrow and fast nonrepetitive transients that may occur on either side of a-c power line. Storage capacitor at right of diodes charges almost completely in 400 ns and holds its charge for over 200 μs to give at least 500-to-1 widening and brightening of scope trace.—P. Lefferts, Differentiator-Divider Network Analyzes Power-Line Transients, *Electronic Design*, Dec. 6, 1965, p 52 and 54.

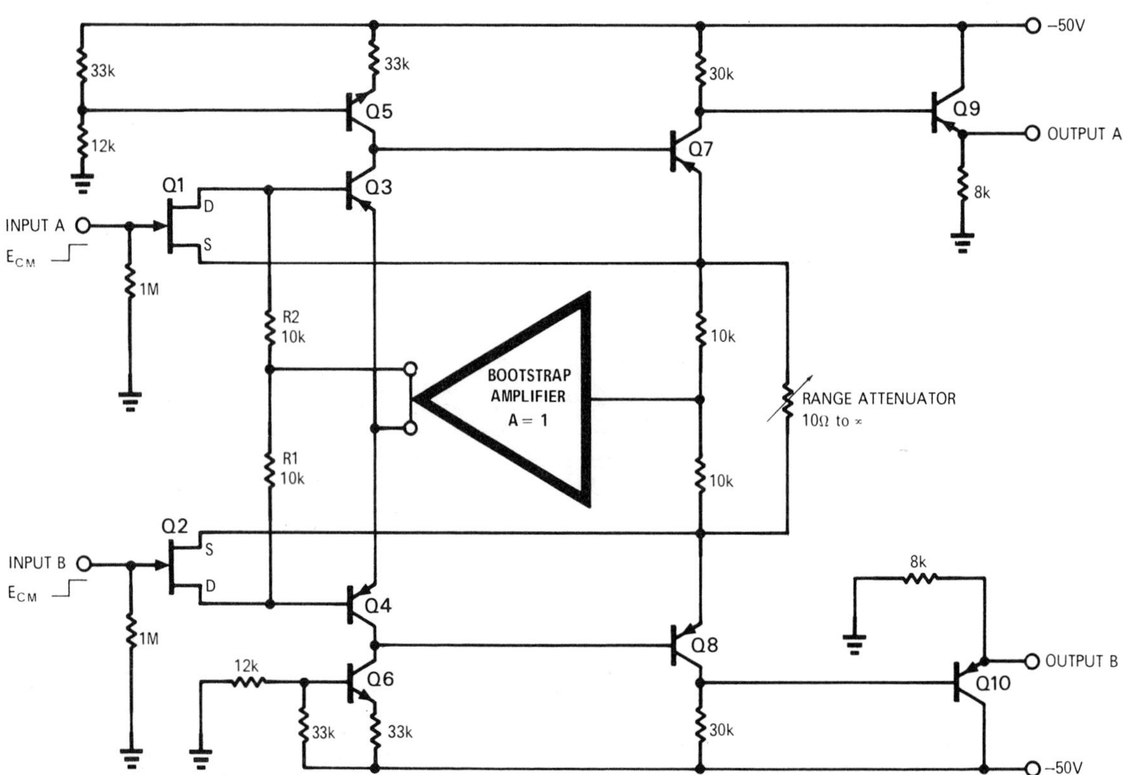

LOW-COST CRO VERTICAL PREAMP—Bootstrapping of differential fet-input preamp gives common-mode-rejection ratio of over 100,000 to 1 (100 dB), from d-c to 10 kHz. Designed for use in Hewlett-Packard Model 1200 series low-frequency oscilloscopes. Transistor types are not given in article. With unity-gain bootstrapped preamp, common-mode signal appears equally on each terminal of input fet, virtually nullifying amplification of this signal.—J. E. Kluge, Bootstrapped Preamp Exhibits High CMRR, *EDN*, Mar. 1, 1970, p 61–62.

NOTE: To locate additional circuits in the category of this chapter, use the index at the back of this book. Check also the author's "Sourcebook of Electronic Circuits," published by McGraw-Hill in 1968.

CHAPTER 12
Chopper Circuits

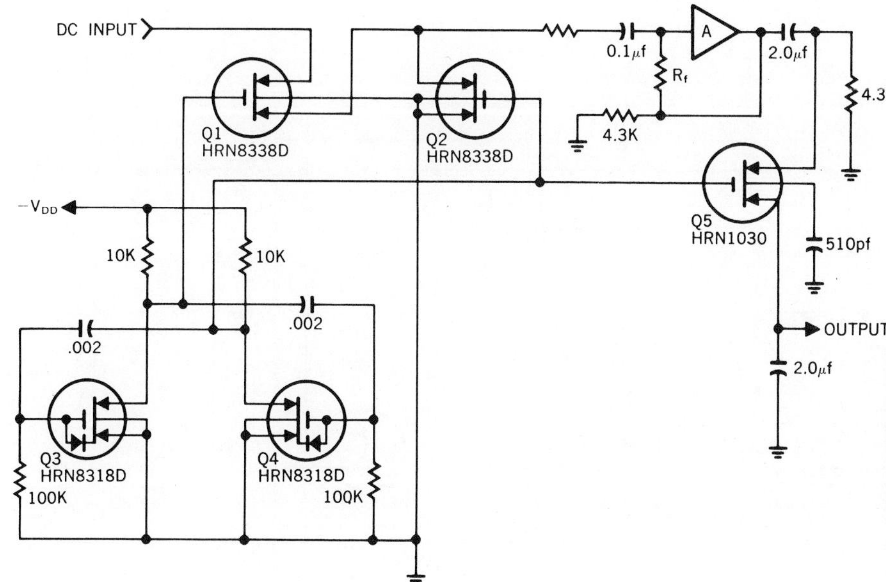

SERIES-SHUNT CHOPPER—Series switch Q1 and shunt switch Q2 are driven by astable mvbr Q3-Q4 for detection of signal levels as low as 30 μV and amplification by opamp. Demodulator Q5 is simple series switch. Arrangement gives stable and accurate detection of very small d-c signals.—C. R. Perkins, "Application of MOSFET Devices to Electronic Circuits," Hughes, Newport Beach, Cal., 1968, p 22.

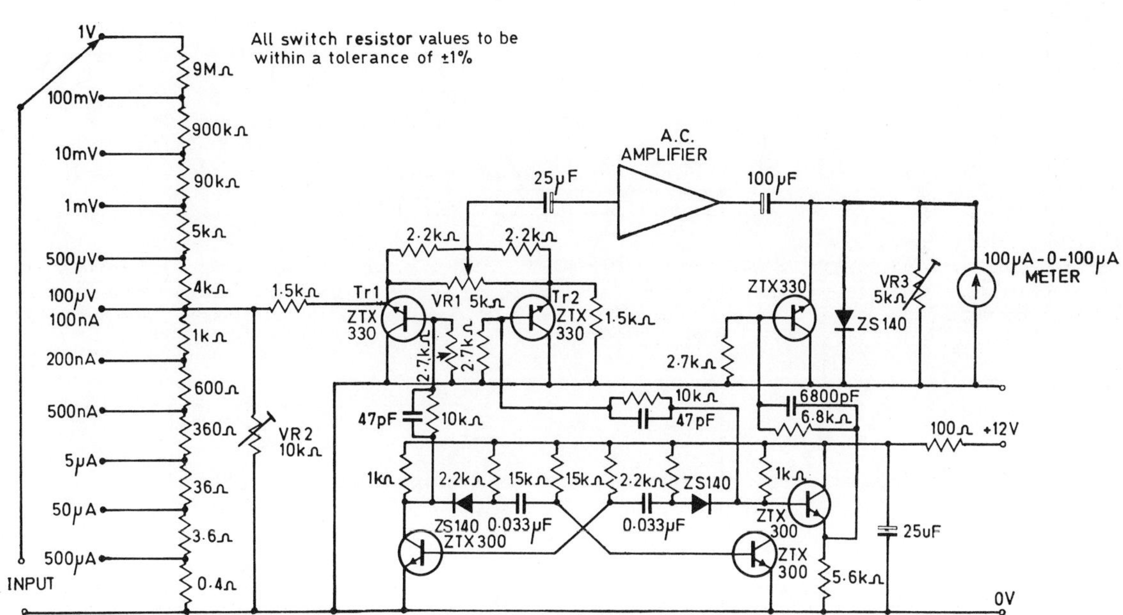

BALANCED CHOPPER—Used here as combination microvoltmeter and microammeter. A-c amplifier can be discrete components or IC having power gain of 86 dB, bandwidth of 20 Hz to 150 kHz at 3 dB down, and p-p noise less than 10 μV referred to input. Chopping frequency is 1.5 kHz. Input impedance on voltage ranges is 10 meg per V. Requires regulated power supply providing 12 V at about 35 mA. Accuracy depends on initial adjustment procedure, as given in report.—E-Line Transistor Applications, Ferranti Ltd., Oldham, Lancs., England, 1969, p 46.

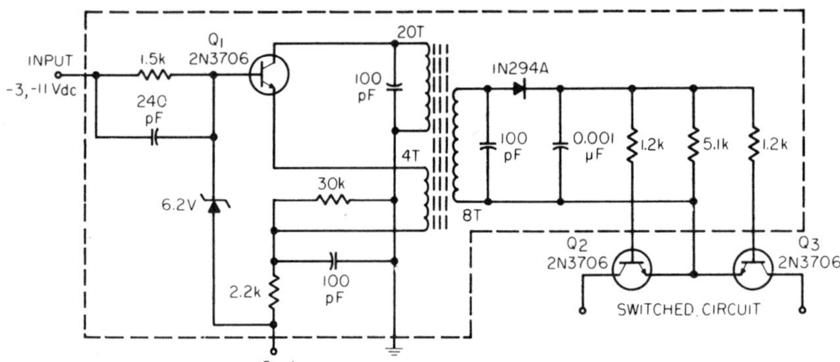

CHOPPER-DRIVER—Switches at rates from d-c to 10 kHz, with output completely isolated from input control signal just as in conventional relay. Q1 is 10-MHz common-base oscillator receiving bias from input logic signals. Rectified and filtered transformer secondary voltage controls bipolar switch Q2-Q3 having ON resistance of about 20 ohms and OFF leakage below 1 μA. Transformer is wound on Arnold A4-134P toroidal core.—J. E. Frecker, Solid-State Relay, *EEE*, June 1967, p 136.

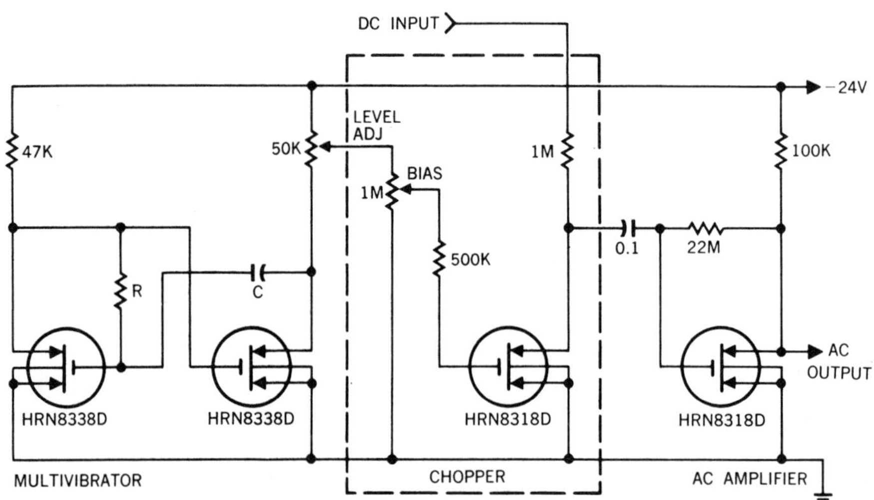

D-C MODULATOR—Useful for modulating or chopping low-level d-c signals for further amplification or for detection of d-c level. Left-hand pair of mosfets forms astable mvbr whose period of oscillation is determined by values of R and C used. Mvbr output drives simple shunt mosfet chopper switch, while mosfet at right provides signal gain and transforms high impedance of chopper to low impedance for a-c output.—C. R. Perkins, "Application of MOSFET Devices to Electronic Circuits," Hughes, Newport Beach, Cal., 1968, p 21.

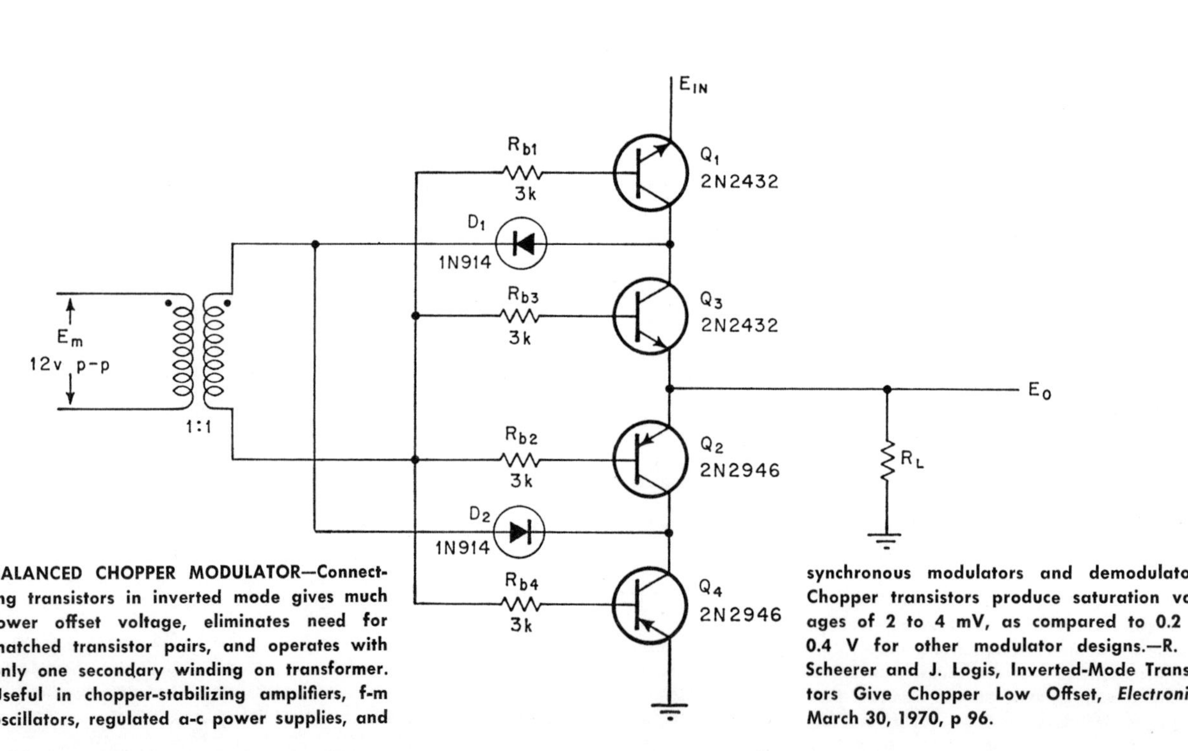

BALANCED CHOPPER MODULATOR—Connecting transistors in inverted mode gives much lower offset voltage, eliminates need for matched transistor pairs, and operates with only one secondary winding on transformer. Useful in chopper-stabilizing amplifiers, f-m oscillators, regulated a-c power supplies, and synchronous modulators and demodulators. Chopper transistors produce saturation voltages of 2 to 4 mV, as compared to 0.2 to 0.4 V for other modulator designs.—R. C. Scheerer and J. Logis, Inverted-Mode Transistors Give Chopper Low Offset, *Electronics*, March 30, 1970, p 96.

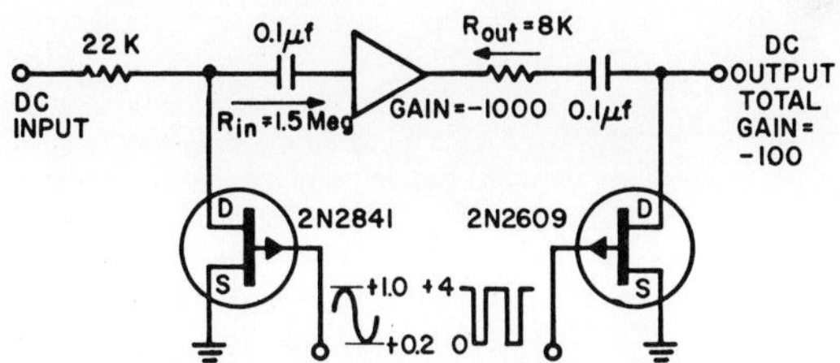

FET CHOPPERS GIVE GAIN OF 100—Input fet chopper is driven by sine wave, and output by 4-V p-p square wave. Input current is less than 20 pA, input impedance is 33K, and offset is less than 4.5 μV at room temperature. Any IC amplifier having gain of 1,000 can be used.—DC Amplifier With FET Chopper, *Electronic Design*, April 13, 1964, p 66.

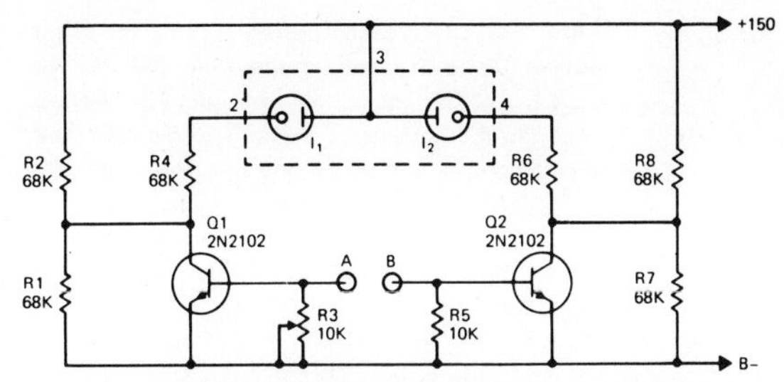

LAMP DRIVER FOR CHOPPER—Used with full-wave laboratory-type photoelectric chopper amplifier. Lamps are neons.—The Dual Photocell, Hewlett Packard, No. 924.

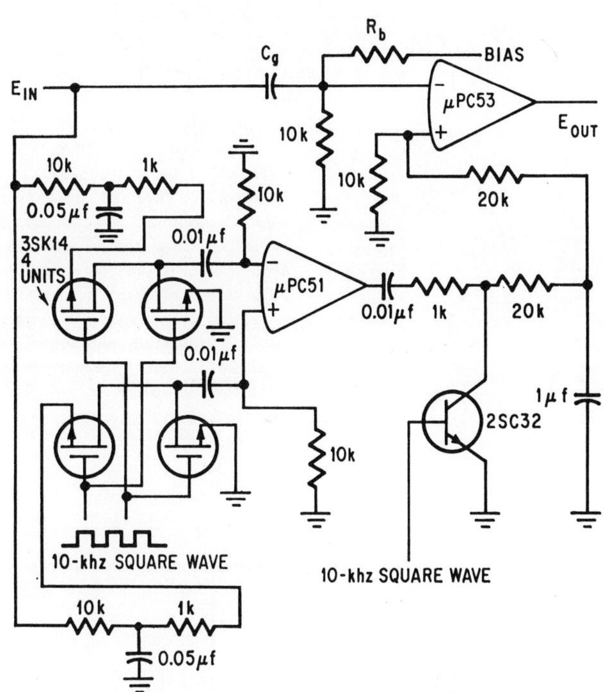

CHOPPER STABILIZATION—Four mosfet's in double-twin 10-kHz chopper are used to stabilize opamp integrator to give required accuracy of 0.1%, increase gain of opamp, and reduce drift. Integrator operates in 2 minutes for standard slow computing time, and in repetitive periods of 100, 50, 25, 12.5, 10, 5, and 2.5 ms for fast operation. Overall gain of chopper-stabilized opamp is 125 dB and input impedance is 20K. Used in IC analog computer.—K. Kurokawa, All-IC Hybrid Computer Eliminates the Patchwork from Programing, *Electronics*, March 17, 1969, p 100–107.

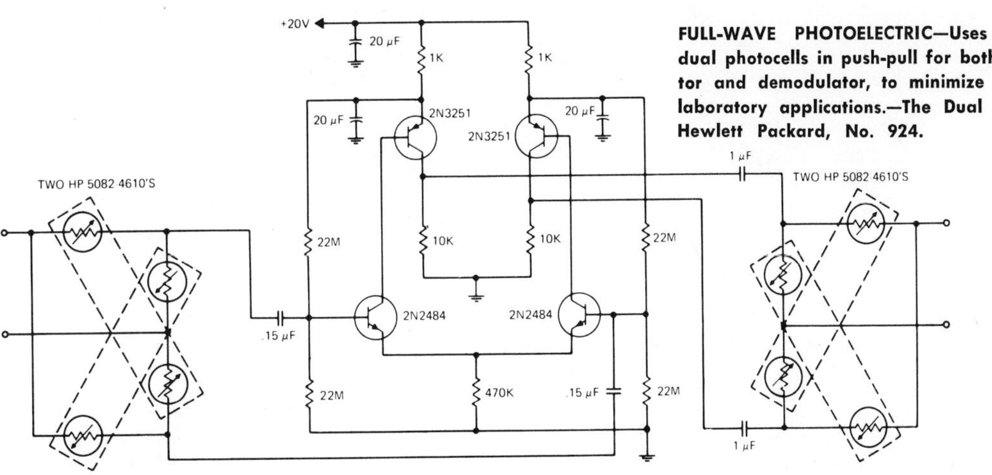

FULL-WAVE PHOTOELECTRIC—Uses pair of dual photocells in push-pull for both modulator and demodulator, to minimize noise for laboratory applications.—The Dual Photocell, Hewlett Packard, No. 924.

FAST SWITCH—Chops analog signals by using output of pulse-saving network (C1-D1) to switch fet on and off, without introducing common-mode noise. Pulse transformer can maintain 6-V on or off signals for over 100 ms. Transformer is Pulse Engineering Co. model 2228.—C. A. Walton, Pulse-Saving Network Permits Signal Switching, *Electronics*, Sept. 18, 1967, p 108–109.

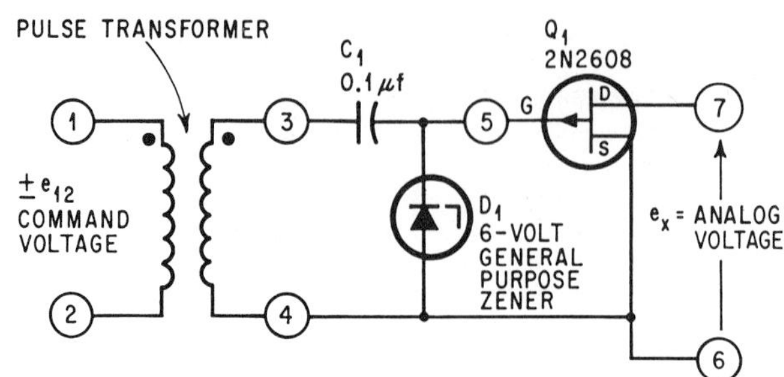

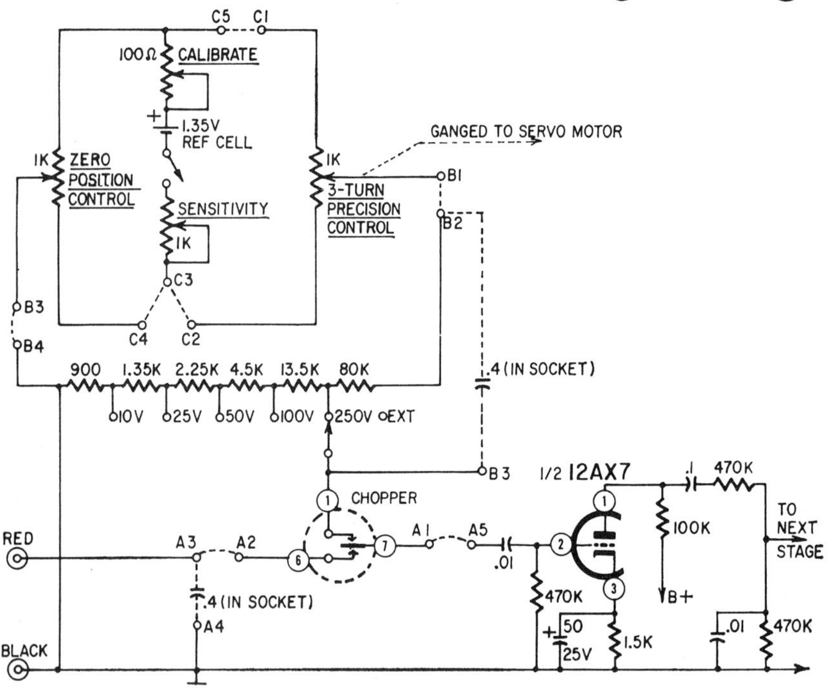

SERVO-DRIVEN PEN—Uses potentiometric metering system, in which input voltage is continuously compared with reference voltage from mercury cell by means of 3-turn slide-wire pot ganged to servo motor. Voltage difference is chopped, and resulting a-c voltage is amplified. Second pot, at left, is used to set marking pen at any desired point on strip chart paper for zero input voltage. Four stages of amplification round off corners of square-wave chopper output so drive for servo is practically sine wave.—E. Leslie, Low-Cost Strip-Chart Recorders, *Radio-Electronics*, June 1965, p 58–59.

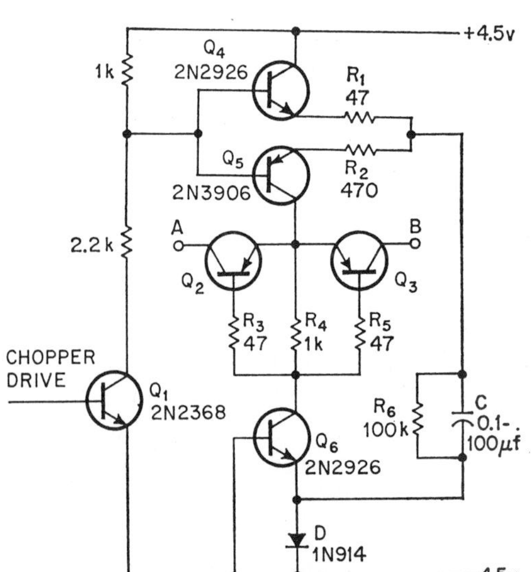

TRANSFORMERLESS WIDEBAND CHOPPER—Provides high isolation and reliable operation over wide range of mark-space ratios and repetition frequencies. During positive half-cycles of square-wave chopper drive, signals are transferred from A to B, but blocked during negative half-cycles.—H. Riddle, Transformer is Eliminated in Transistor Chopper, *Electronics*, Dec. 22, 1969, p 77.

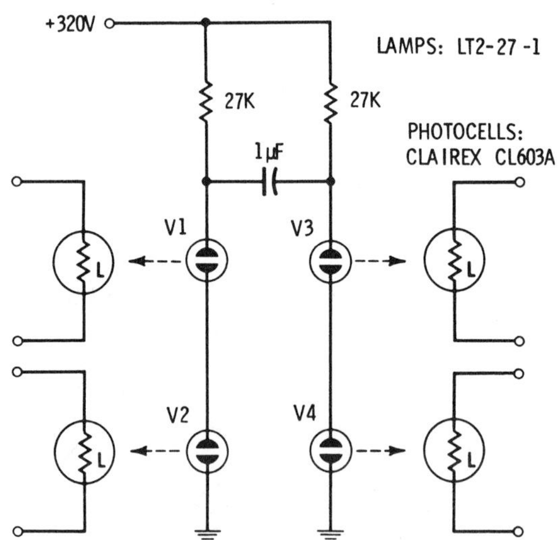

20-HZ PHOTOCHOPPER—Four neons in astable mvbr act on four photocells to provide synchronous chopping at 20 Hz. Developed for use in voltmeters and chopper-stabilized power supplies.—W. G. Miller, "Using and Understanding Miniature Neon Lamps," H. W. Sams & Co., Indianapolis, Ind., 1969, p 68.

NONINVERTING CHOPPER OPAMP—Noninverting mode of operation gives greatly improved accuracy when handling signals from high-impedance sources. Applications include microvolt measurements in biological and research applications. Maximum current drift of opamp is 10 pA per degree C and common-mode rejection ratio is 300,000. Report also covers differential and off-ground applications, and use with bridge signals.—P. Zicko, Designing With Chopper Stabilized Operational Amplifiers, Analog Devices, Cambridge, Mass., 1970.

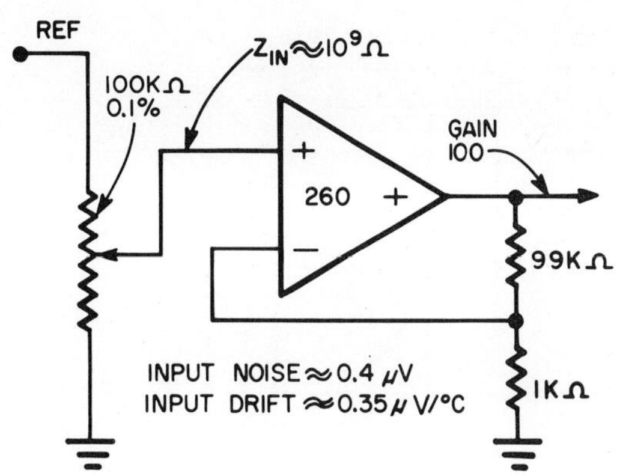

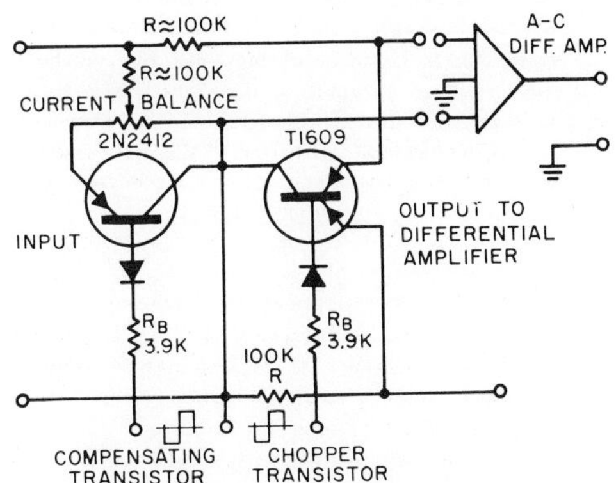

NOISE CANCELLER—Arrangement provides almost complete cancelling of switching spikes and voltage offsets. Dual emitters of chopper transistor convert these noise sources into common-mode noise, which is rejected by differential amplifier.—S. W. Holcomb, F. Opp, and J. A. Walston, Low-Noise Chopper, *Electronic Design*, Jan. 6, 1964, p 78.

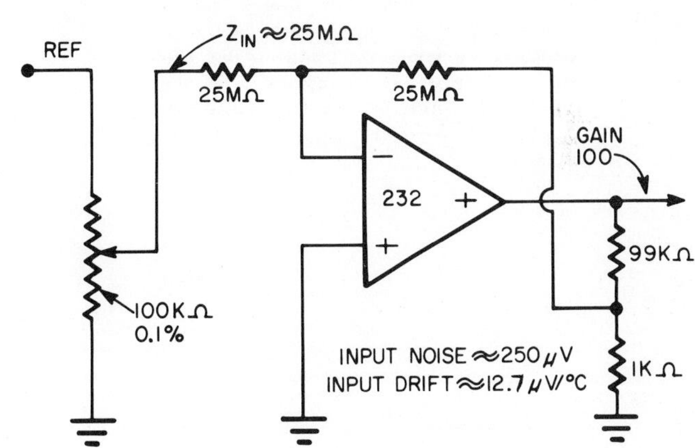

INVERTING-ONLY CHOPPER OPAMP—Used for high-accuracy low-level measurements where low noise and low drift are major requirements, as when measuring signals from 100K precision pot. Common-mode rejection ratio is 300,000.—P. Zicko, Designing With Chopper Stabilized Operational Amplifiers, Analog Devices, Cambridge, Mass., 1970.

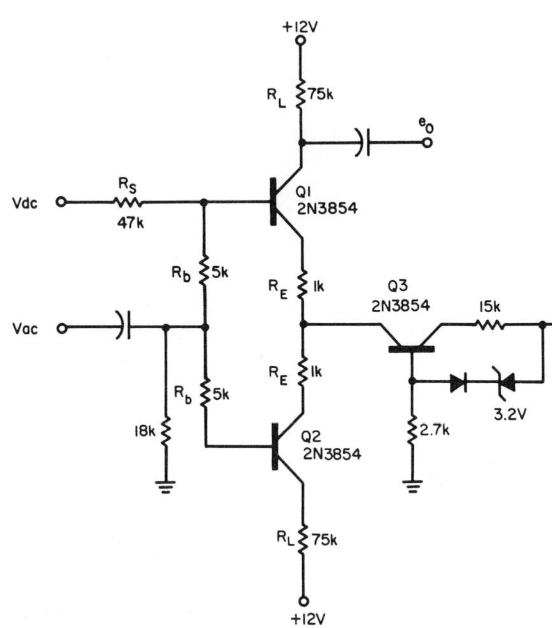

TRANSFORMERLESS CHOPPER—Uses differential amplifier Q1-Q2 and constant-current source Q3. Differential input stage has good temperature and drift stabilization. For optimum conversion of very small d-c signals, differential amplifier should be operated at currents of about 10 μA.—A. C. Caggiano, Transformerless Chopper Circuit Built With a Differential Amplifier, *Electronic Design*, Oct. 11, 1967, p 106.

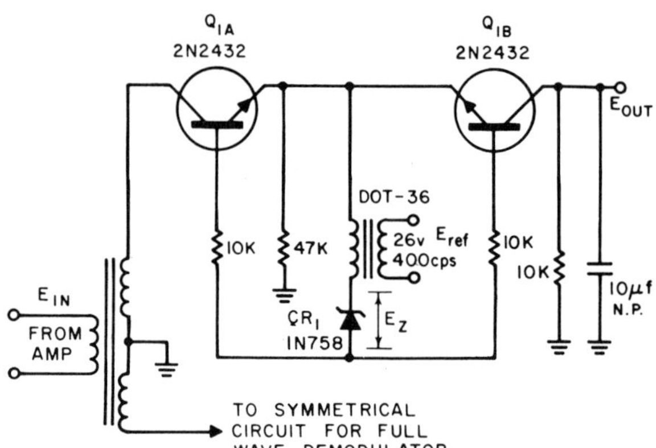

AMPLIFYING LOW-LEVEL D-C—Chopper-amplifier converts d-c signal to a-c at 400 Hz, passes signal through a-c narrow-band amplifier, and synchronously demodulates to give amplified d-c signal. Zener in chopper switching leg suppresses transients and minimizes drift and offset errors.—T. B. Hooker, Zener Diode Aids Chopper in Demodulator Application, *Electronic Design*, April 12, 1965, p 56–57.

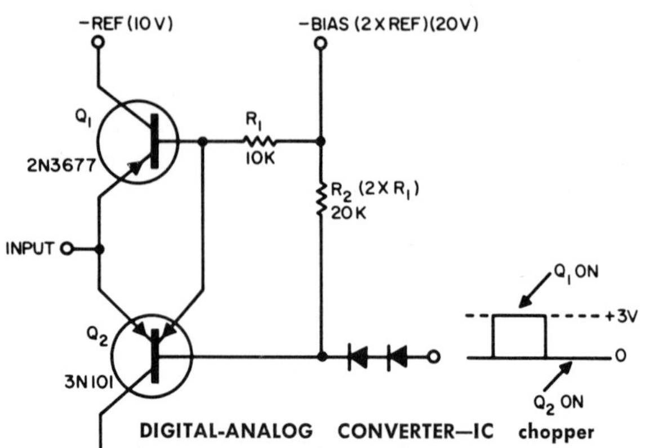

DIGITAL-ANALOG CONVERTER—IC chopper Q2 acts as spdt switch operating from single-polarity drive between logic levels of 0 and +3 V, to give digital-to-analog conversion without complex drive circuit or multiplicity of supply voltages. Input terminal is connected to leg in ladder network, for switching between ground and minus reference voltage.—Integrated Chopper Forms Simple Digital-to-Analog Converter, "Microelectronic Design," Hayden Book Co., N.Y., 1966, p 135.

NOTE: To locate additional circuits in the category of this chapter, use the index at the back of this book. Check also the author's "Sourcebook of Electronic Circuits," published by McGraw-Hill in 1968.

CHAPTER 13
Clock Circuits

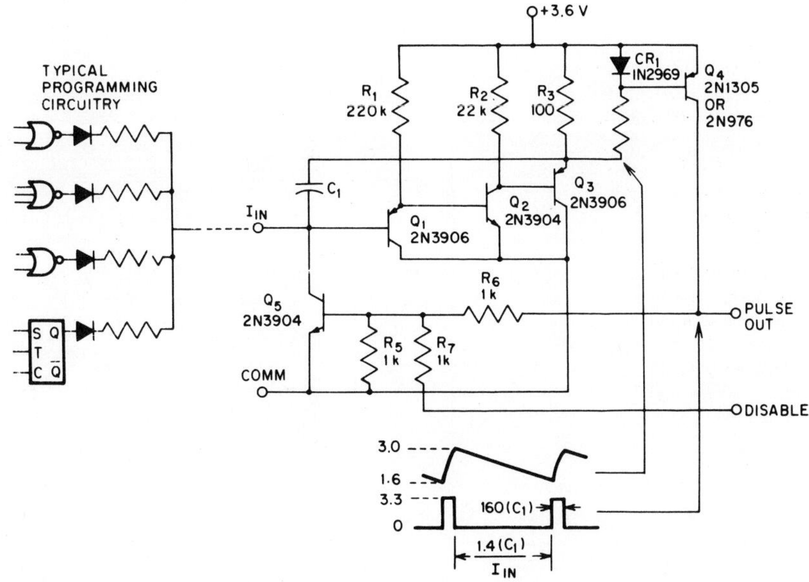

2–10,000 HZ PROGRAMMABLE—Repetition rate can be programmed over four decades by input current changes. Works with 3.6 V RTL logic. Linearity of current-frequency conversion is about 1% from 0.1 to 100 μA.—R. W. Fergus, Wide-Range Programmable Clock for Low-Voltage Logic, *EEE*, Sept. 1969, p 132–133.

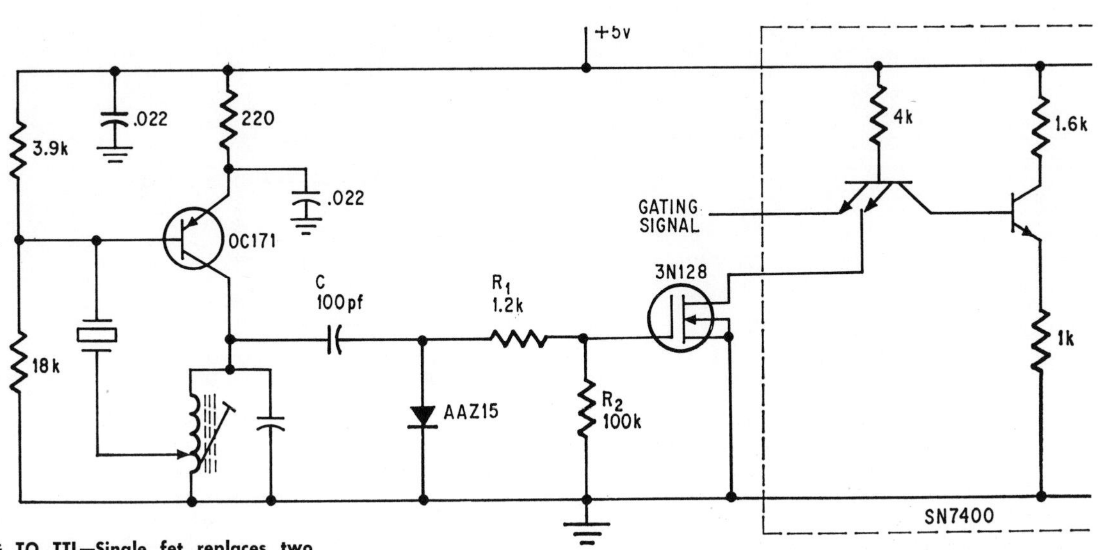

COUPLING TO TTL—Single fet replaces two or more driver stages and allows clock generator to operate from same 5-V supply as TTL. Crystal oscillator provides 4-V p-p sine wave at 12 MHz.—C. S. L. Keay and I. C. Graham, FET Links Oscillator to TTL Circuit, *Electronics*, Feb. 17, 1969, p 97.

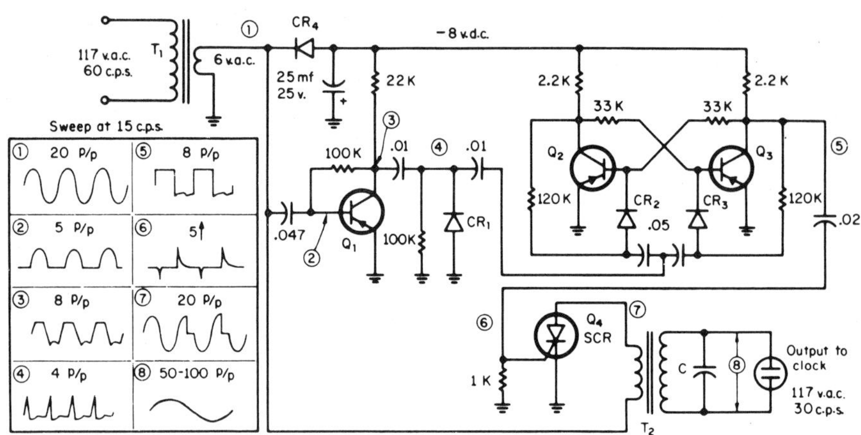

24-HOUR CLOCK—Frequency divider cuts 60-Hz line frequency to 30 Hz for driving standard electric clock at half speed, so hour hand takes 24 hours for one revolution. With appropriate change in clock face, Greenwich Mean Time can be read directly. CR4 is any top-hat diode rated at 400 piv and 750 mA. Other diodes are 1N34, Q1-Q3 2N404, and Q4 is International Rectifier 50-V 2-A scr. T2 is same as T1.—D. L. Jones, A 24-Hour Clock for the Shack, *CQ*, May 1970, p 20–21.

RESYNCHRONIZER—Ujt Q4, triggered by one-shot mvbr G1-G2-G3-Q2, reconstructs clock signal from incoming data, such as NRZ signal, that has no accompanying clock. NAND gates keep cost far below that of packaged one-shot. Designed for data rate of 30 kHz, though maximum operating frequency is 50 kHz.—F. Badal, UJT Oscillator Reconstructs Clock Signals, *EEE*, Aug. 1968, p 140.

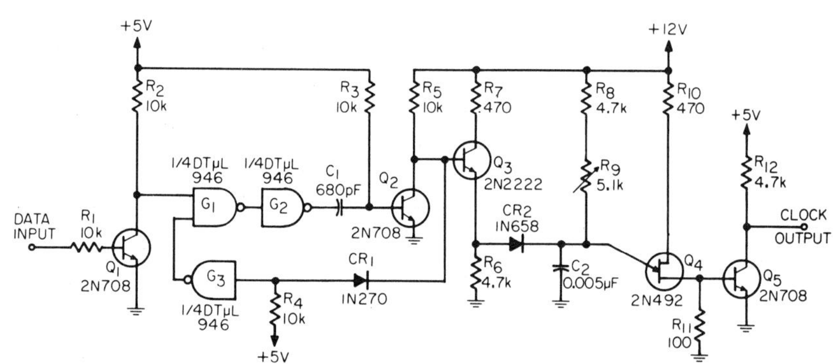

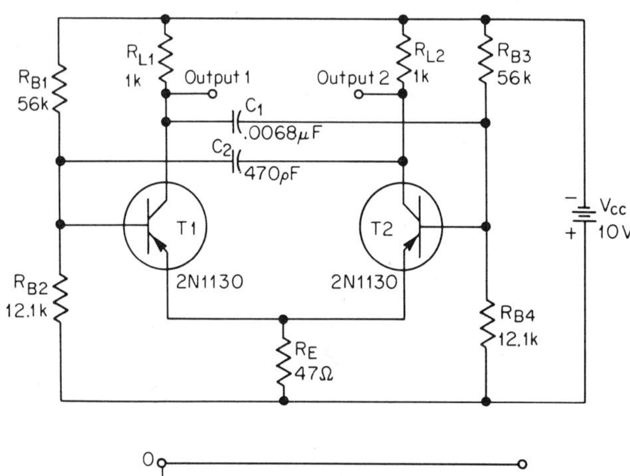

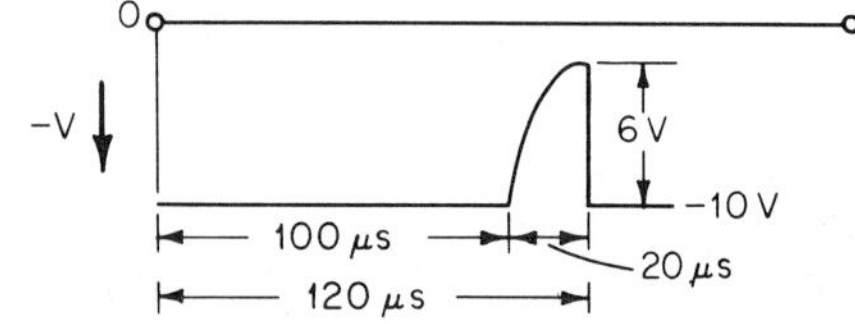

NONSYMMETRICAL ASTABLE—As waveform indicates, transistor conducting times are made unequal by making cross-coupling capacitors C1 and C2 unequal. For values shown, one transistor conducts for only 20 μs out of total period time of 120 μs. Frequently used as clock for frequency control. Collector waveform is shown.—A. C. Gillie, "Pulse and Logic Circuits," McGraw-Hill, N.Y., 1968, p 213.

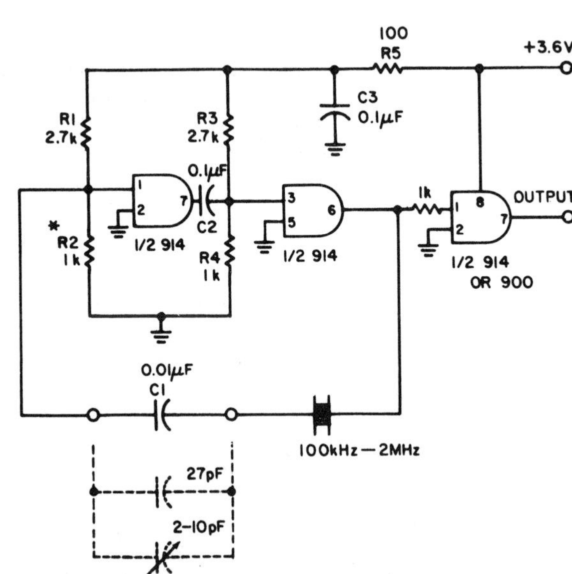

*ADJUST R2 SLIGHTLY TO OBTAIN SYMMETRICAL WAVEFORM

DIGITAL CLOCK—Provides square-wave output of 0.2 to 3.6 V at any frequency from 100 kHz to 2 MHz while requiring only 3.6-V d-c supply. Intended for digital logic applications. Stability approaches that of crystal used.—L. Roque, Accurate Digital Clock Uses Inexpensive IC Gates, *Electronic Design*, Aug. 16, 1969, p 242 and 244.

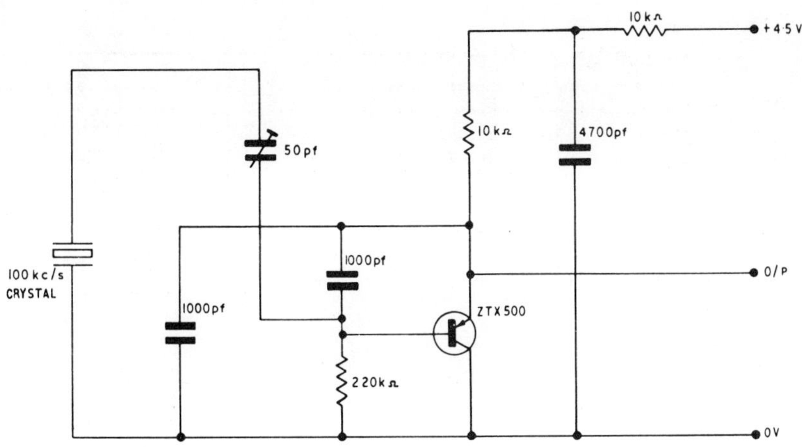

100-KHZ CRYSTAL FOR CLOCK—Used with ten frequency divider stages to give pulse every half-minute for driving ratchet mechanism of battery-powered clock. Accuracy is about 1 s per week. Report gives circuits for divider stages and ratchet coil drive.—A Crystal Clock Using Plastic Transistors, Ferranti Ltd., Oldham, Lancs., England, No. 34, 1968.

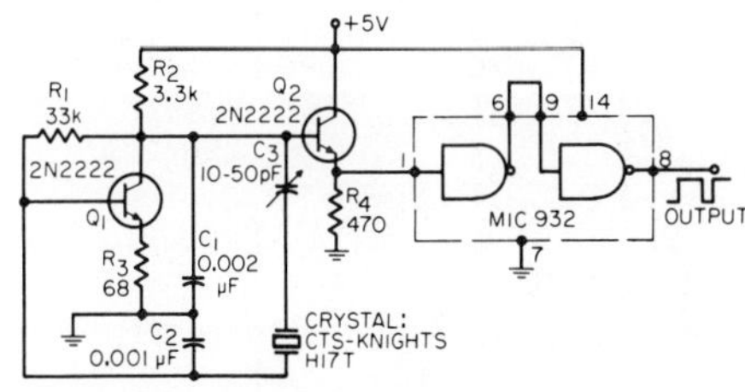

100-KHZ COLPITTS CRYSTAL—Operates from single 5-V supply. Consists of oscillator Q1, emitter-follower Q2, and DTL buffer gate. Output is square wave with rise and fall times under 50 ns. Will drive 25 DTL loads or 12 TTL loads. Stability is that of crystal. —D. Jones, Stable Clock Oscillators are DTL/TTL Compatible, *EEE*, May 1968, p 123–124.

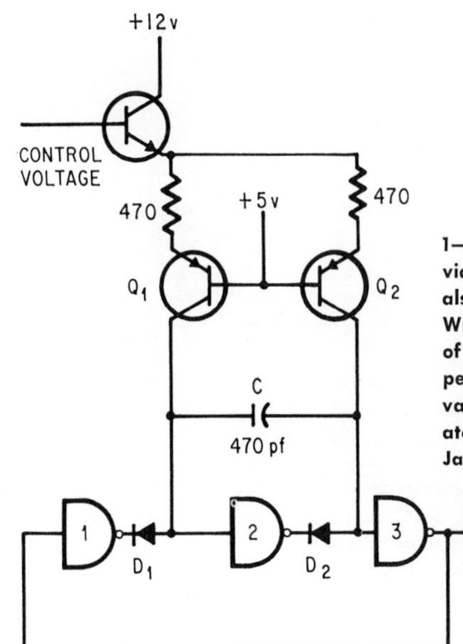

1–10 MHZ CONTINUOUSLY VARIABLE—Provides good timing for digital system, and can also be used as voltage-frequency converter. With SN7400 TTL quad gate, frequency range of square-wave output is 1 to 15 MHz depending on constant-current source Q1-Q2 and value of C.—P. Westphal, Digital Clock Operates in Low Megahertz Range, *Electronics*, Jan. 20, 1969, p 87.

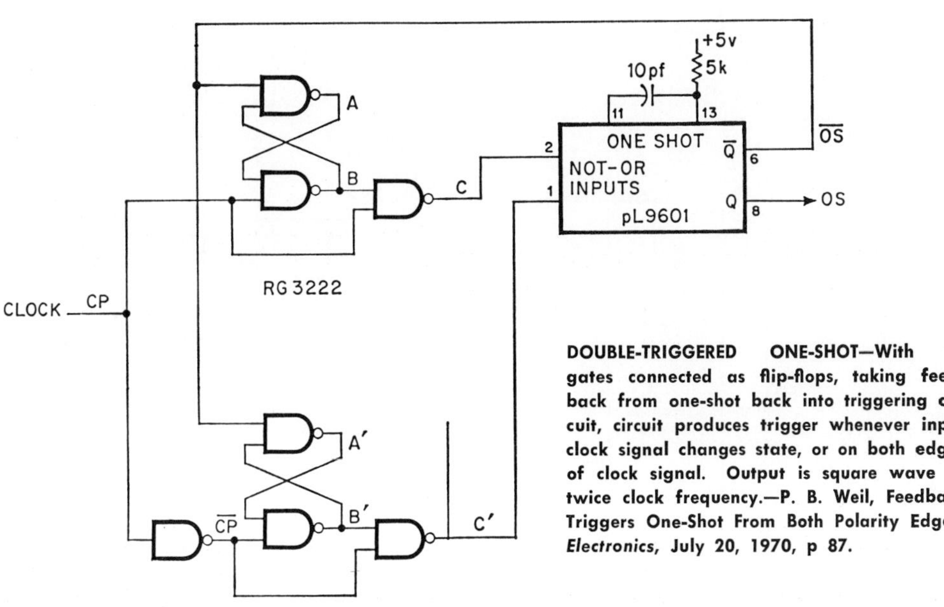

DOUBLE-TRIGGERED ONE-SHOT—With IC gates connected as flip-flops, taking feedback from one-shot back into triggering circuit, circuit produces trigger whenever input clock signal changes state, or on both edges of clock signal. Output is square wave at twice clock frequency.—P. B. Weil, Feedback Triggers One-Shot From Both Polarity Edges, *Electronics*, July 20, 1970, p 87.

MANUAL CLOCK PULSES—Useful for testing counters, adders, and other types of digital circuits. Eliminates effects of switch bounce that could cause false triggering. Provides complementary set-reset voltages at collectors of Q1 and Q2, and manual clock pulse each time mono is triggered by change in state of Q2 collector voltage from low to high. With 2N706 transistors, total latching time is less than 200 ns.—T. Carmody, Low-Cost Manual Pulser, *EEE*, Oct. 1967, p 143–144.

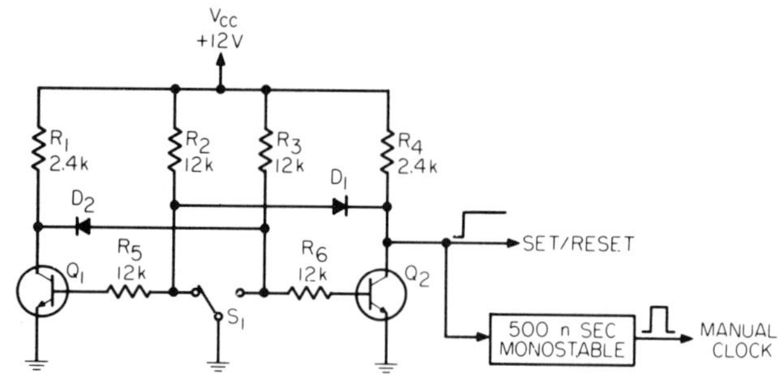

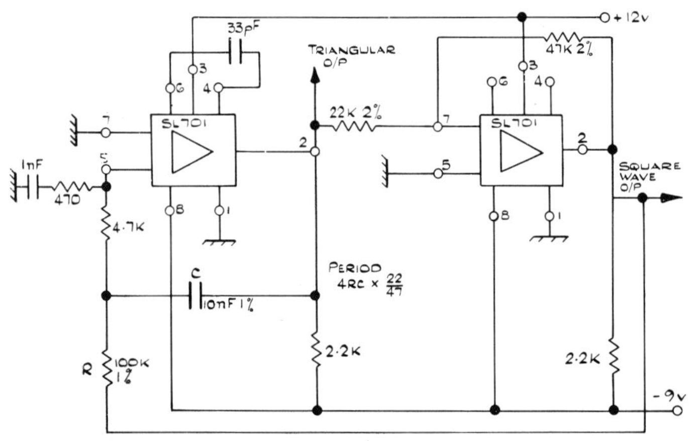

SQUARE-TRIANGULAR CLOCK—Uses Plessey high-gain d-c amplifiers as clock providing choice of two waveforms at frequency that is held constant within 2% over 50 deg C temperature range and 0.5-V change in supply voltages. Second amplifier uses positive feedback to achieve precision trigger circuit. —R. C. Foss and B. J. Green, The SL700 Series and Applications, Plessey, Swindon, England, No. 7.

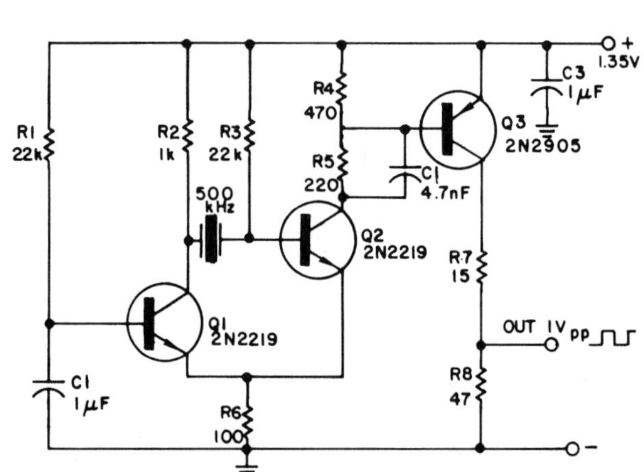

500-KHZ CRYSTAL—Operates from single 1.35-V mercury cell and delivers 1 V p-p square-wave output for clock generators, lab standards, or cro calibrators.—R. L. Billion, Crystal-Controlled Oscillator Operates From One Mercury Cell, *Electronic Design*, Nov. 8, 1969, p 109.

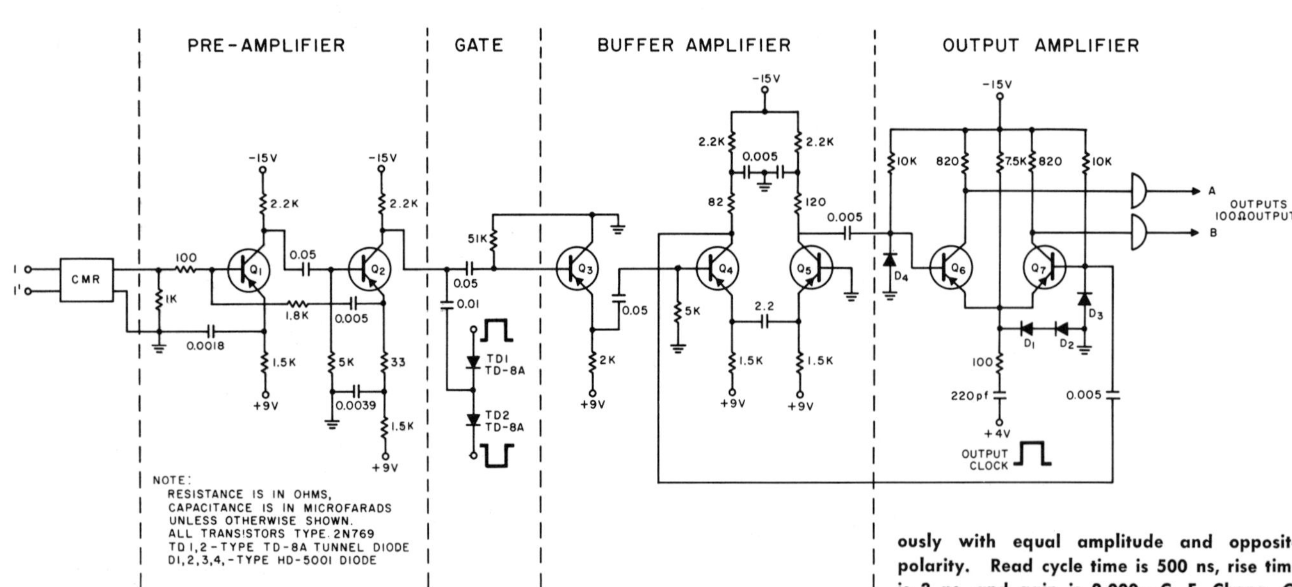

DOUBLE-CLOCK MEMORY READ AMPLIFIER—Proper timing of clocks gives maximum signal gain for reading thin-film memory, with transient noise completely rejected in output stage. Clock signals are applied to tunnel-diode gate connected as Goto pair, simultaneously with equal amplitude and opposite polarity. Read cycle time is 500 ns, rise time is 3 ns, and gain is 2,000.—C. F. Chong, G. H. Guttrogg, C. S. Ih and A. A. Wicks, High-Speed Read Amplifiers For Thin Films, *Electronic Design*, Aug. 3, 1964, p 38–40.

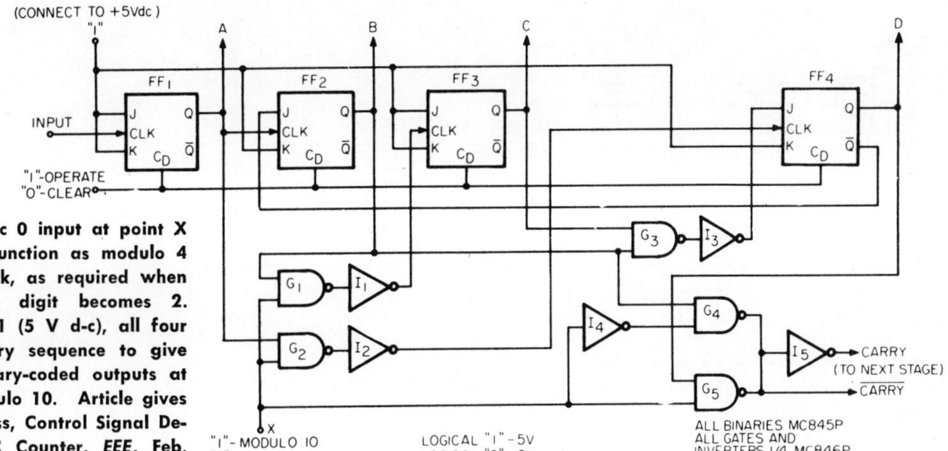

MODULO 10 OR 4—Logic 0 input at point X makes digital counter function as modulo 4 in electronic digital clock, as required when most significant hours digit becomes 2. When point X is logic 1 (5 V d-c), all four flip-flops count in binary sequence to give 1—2—4—8 weighted binary-coded outputs at A, B, C, and D for modulo 10. Article gives truth tables.—I. P. Breikss, Control Signal Determines Modulo of EC Counter, *EEE*, Feb. 1968, p 126 and 128.

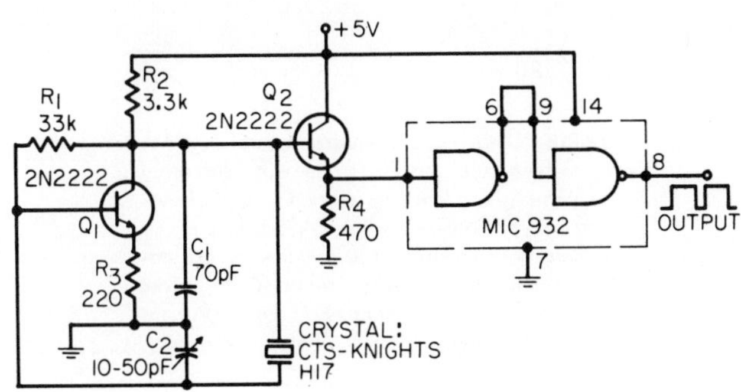

1-MHZ COLPITTS CRYSTAL—Operates from single 5-V supply and provides output levels completely compatible with digital IC's. Frequency stability approaches that of crystal alone, from 0 to 70 C.—D. Jones, Stable Clock Oscillators are DTL/TTL Compatible, *EEE*, May 1968, p 123—124.

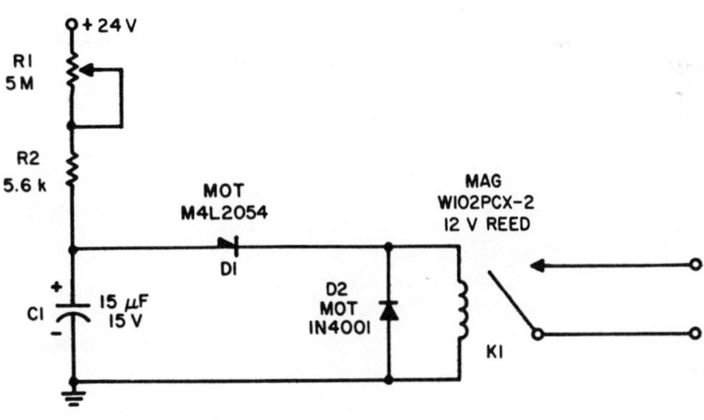

PROCESS CONTROL PULSER—Simple clock, using four-layer diode as timing control, provides repetitive closures of relay at rates from 1 to 600 ppm. Closure time is about 10 ms at all rates. Applications include cycling of components on life test.—D. T. Krausman, Four-Layer Diode Clock Has Relay Closure Output, *Electronic Design*, May 10, 1967, p 92 and 94.

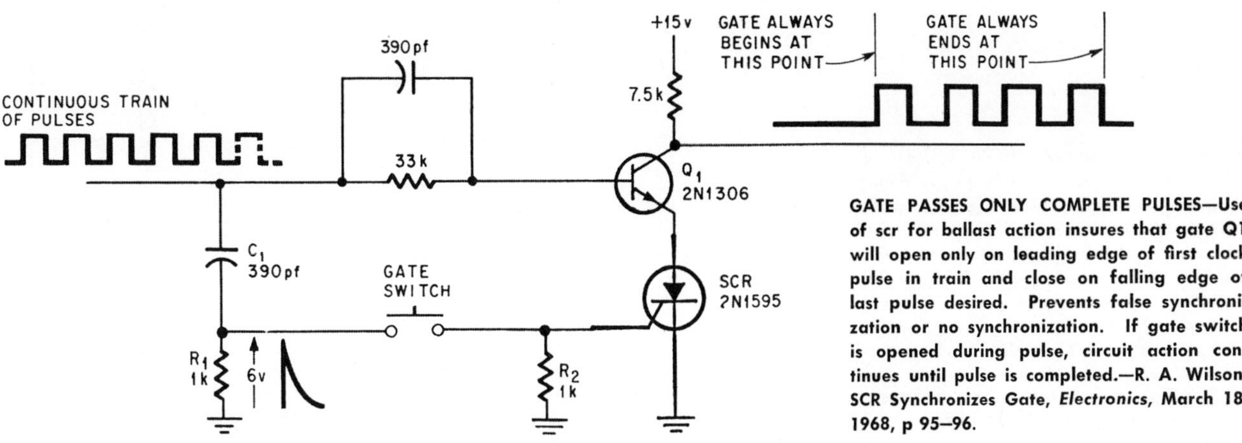

GATE PASSES ONLY COMPLETE PULSES—Use of scr for ballast action insures that gate Q1 will open only on leading edge of first clock pulse in train and close on falling edge of last pulse desired. Prevents false synchronization or no synchronization. If gate switch is opened during pulse, circuit action continues until pulse is completed.—R. A. Wilson, SCR Synchronizes Gate, *Electronics*, March 18, 1968, p 95—96.

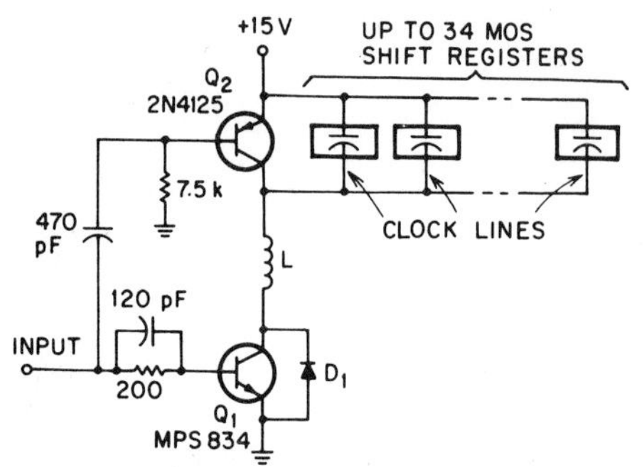

CLOCK-LINE DRIVER—Inductor L and transistor switch are connected in series with clock line to form series resonant tank circuit capable of handling 34 256-bit mos registers operating at clock frequency of 620 kHz. L is 6.8 μH.—R. O. Brink, Resonant Clock-Line Driver for MOS ICs, *EEE*, April 1969, p 118 and 120.

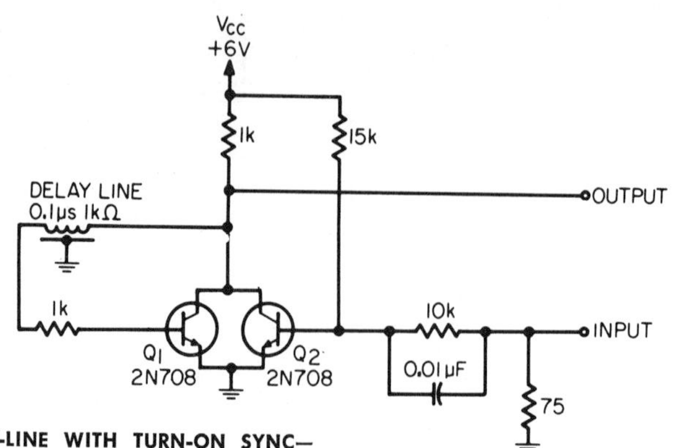

5-MHZ DELAY-LINE WITH TURN-ON SYNC—Clock pulses always start in phase with leading edge of input gate pulse, and always stop with trailing edge. Gives square-wave output. Delay line is PCA Electronics type DL-1000-0.1-2289 having 1K impedance and 100-ns delay. Circuit is designed for 5-V gate pulse. Eliminates possible range error of one count occurring with crystal-controlled clock oscillators.—P. E. Dingwell, Gated Delay-Line Oscillator Eliminates Range Error, *EEE*, Sept. 1968, p 108 and 110.

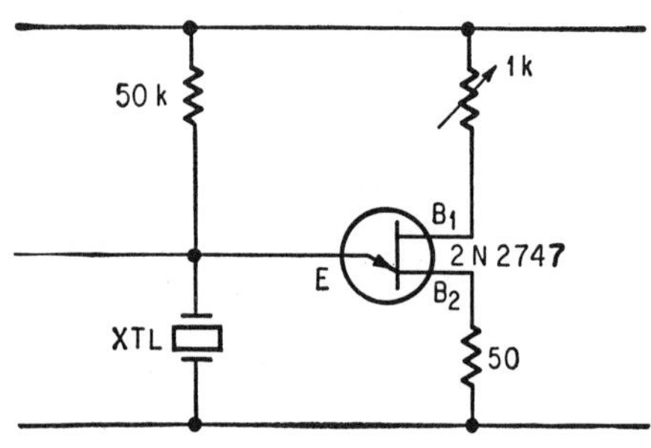

SIMPLE CLOCK—Use of quartz crystal in place of conventional capacitor in ujt relaxation oscillator gives low-cost clock for digital systems. With 100-kHz crystal, clock has excellent stability at either 100 or 50 kHz. Shunting crystal with several hundred pF gives 33.33 kHz.—R. G. Damaye, Quartz Crystal Synchronizes Relaxation Oscillator, *Electronics*, Jan. 9, 1967, p 104.

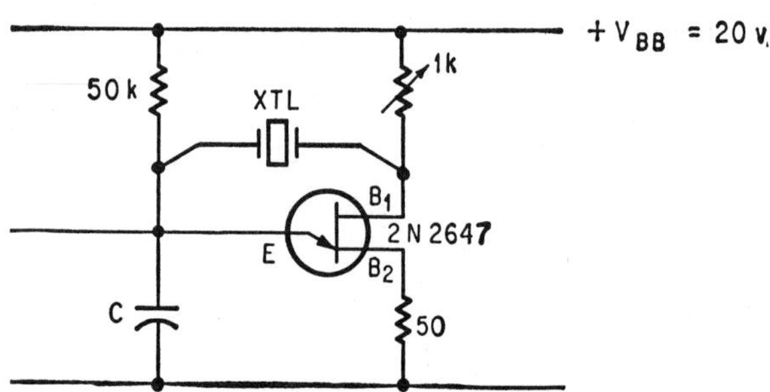

CRYSTAL-UJT—With quartz crystal connected between emitter and base of relaxation oscillator, lock-in occurs at fundamental or submultiples of crystal frequency. External pulses are not required for synchronization. Serves as inexpensive 100, 50, or 33.33 Hz clock for digital systems, with high stability for both voltage and temperature variations. —R. G. Damaye, Quartz Crystal Synchronizes Relaxation Oscillator, *Electronics*, Jan. 9, 1967, p 104.

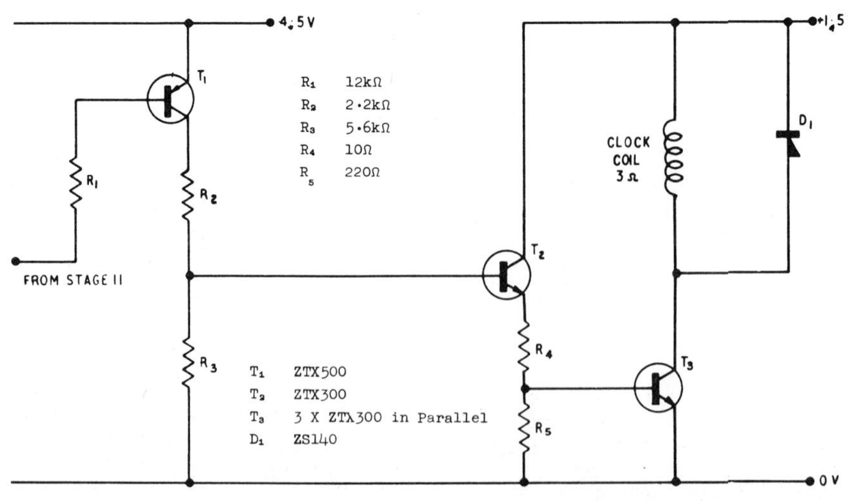

IMPULSE CLOCK DRIVE—Circuit receives narrow pulse every 30 s from frequency divider of battery-powered 100-kHz quartz crystal oscillator and delivers 300-mA current to coil of ratchet that advances clock hands half a minute. Output stage operates from separate 1.5-V cell so negative pulses on its supply line do not affect earlier stages. Impulse clock used is made by English Clock Systems, a branch of Smiths Clocks.—A Crystal Clock Using Plastic Transistors, Ferranti Ltd., Oldham, Lancs., England, No. 34, 1968.

CHAPTER 14
Code Circuits

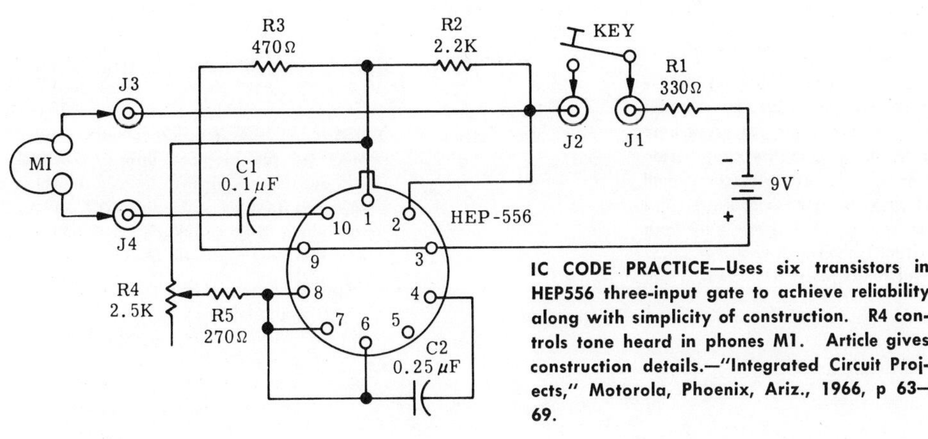

IC CODE PRACTICE—Uses six transistors in HEP556 three-input gate to achieve reliability along with simplicity of construction. R4 controls tone heard in phones M1. Article gives construction details.—"Integrated Circuit Projects," Motorola, Phoenix, Ariz., 1966, p 63–69.

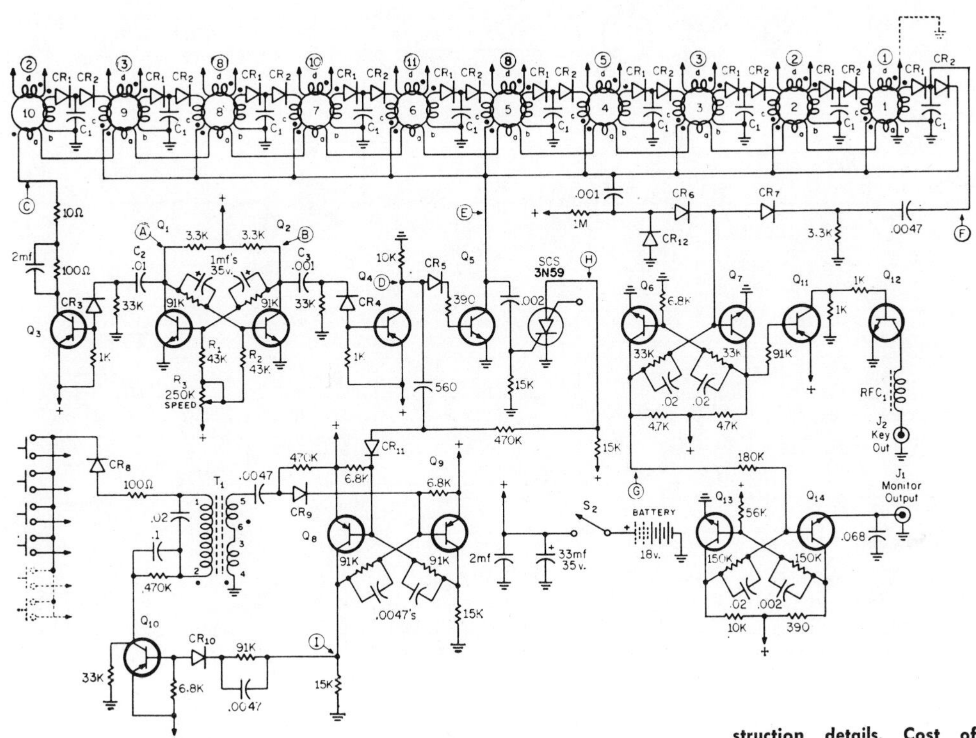

CODE-GENERATING C-W KEYBOARD—Generates corresponding Morse code automatically when key for letter or numeral is pressed. Microswitches under keys control magnetic-core shift register in which astable mvbr Q1-Q2 runs continuously to provide shift and switching pulses. Article gives interconnection diagram for shift register set windings that generate required combination of dots and dashes for each character, and gives construction details. Cost of components is about $130. C1 is 0.1 μF; CR1-CR11 1N645; CR12 1N191; Q1-Q2, Q5-Q7, Q13-Q14 2N1252; Q3-Q4 2N1131; Q8-Q11 2N404; Q12 2N657.—H. Granberg, A Push-Button Keyer, CQ, Sept. 1964, p 28–31 and 92.

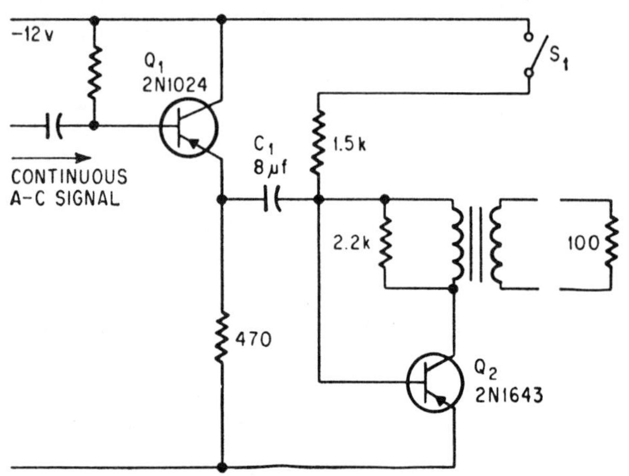

SWITCHING AUDIO TONES NOISELESSLY—Two-transistor circuit with 1:1 transformer makes key clicks negligible at switching speeds up to 50 bauds. Signal suppression during off periods is 70 dB. Operates well with up to 0.2 μF across switch contacts, permitting remote control of keying with long cable.—J. M. Little, Transistor Switch For Clickless Keying, *Electronics*, Oct. 31, 1966, p 68.

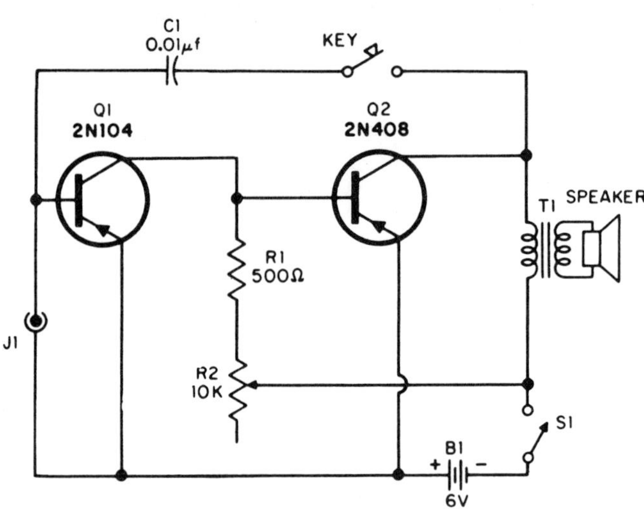

CODE PRACTICE SET—R2 controls tone. Earphone can be plugged into phono jack J1. T1 is output transformer having 500-ohm primary and 3.2-ohm secondary, for driving 3.2-ohm 6-inch p-m speaker.—"A Modern Transistor Workbook," Radio Shack, Boston, Mass., 1965, p 10.

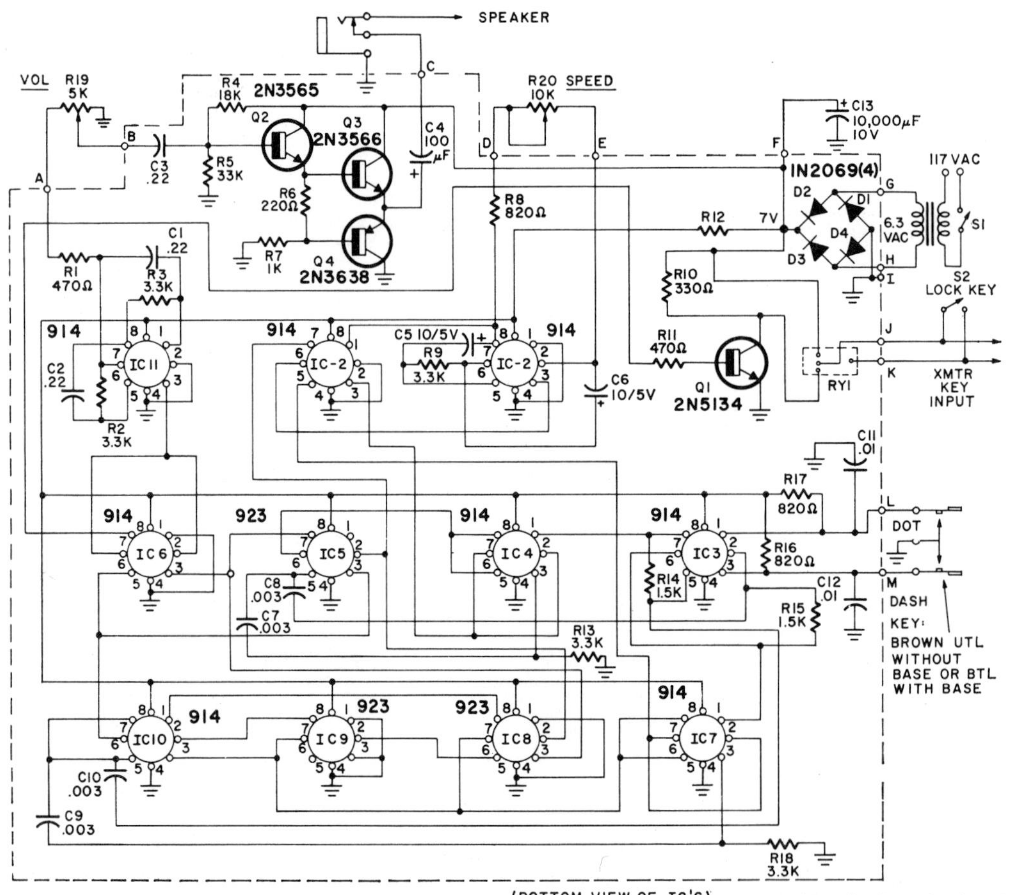

ELECTRONIC KEYER—Generates perfect Morse-code dots and dashes, with dashes always three times longer than dots and with each dot or dash self-completing even though key is released. Circuit uses Fairchild or ITT type 923 JK IC flip-flops in combination with type 914 dual RTL IC gates and three transistors. Keying-relay output may be connected to any transmitter keying circuit. Operating speed is set by R20. Article gives construction details. R12 is about 21 ohms.—W. O. Hamlin, Build Perfect Electronic Keyer, *Radio-Electronics*, Nov. 1969, p 69–72.

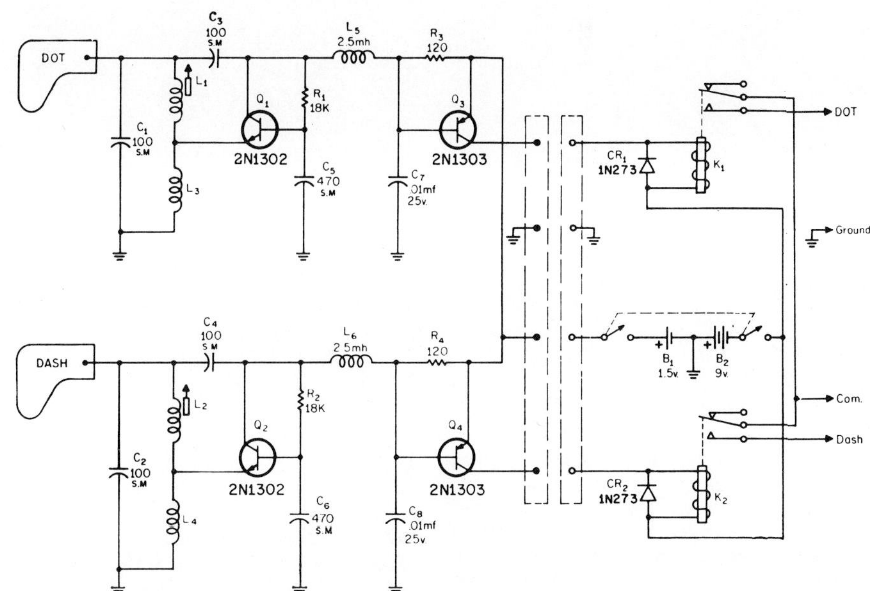

MOTIONLESS KEY—Resembles and is operated like conventional paddle key but responds to slightest touch of either stationary paddle for triggering capacitance-sensing dot or dash generator of electronic keyer. Both paddles are grounded for d-c. Action is fast and reliable with normally moist skin. For dry skin, glycerine rubbed between thumb and fingers will increase conductivity enough for reliable triggering. Article gives construction details. A-c power supply and long-dash circuit (described in CQ, Feb. 1965, p 59 and 104–105) are desirable options.—A. H. Jackson, The Touch-Key, CQ, Nov. 1964, p 28–31 and 137.

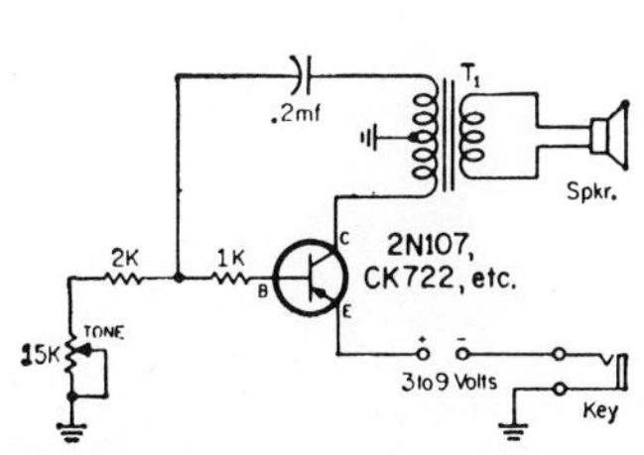

PRACTICE SET WITH SPEAKER—Any expensive pnp transistor may be used. T1 is Lafayette TR-109 transistor output transformer or equivalent.—"Electronic Circuits Handbook," Vol. II, Cowan Pub. Corp., Port Washington, N.Y., 1966, p 84.

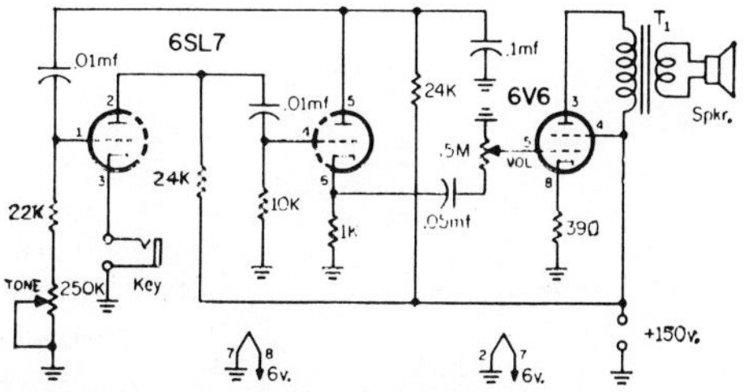

THREE-TUBE PRACTICE SET—Provides sufficient loudspeaker volume for classroom use. Almost any other dual-triode and pentode may be used by changing pin connections and filament voltage. T1 is any 50L6-type output transformer.—"Electronic Circuits Handbook," Vol. II, Cowan Pub. Corp., Port Washington, N.Y., 1966, p 85.

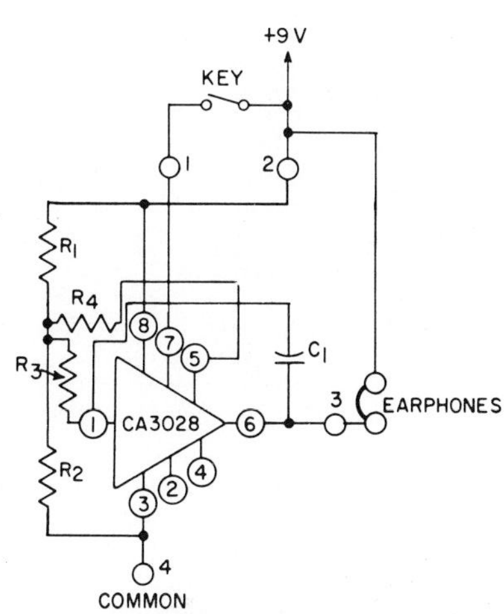

IC CODE PRACTICE OSCILLATOR—Current drain with key down is only 5.5 mA from 9-V transistor radio battery. Values are: C1 0.47 μf; R1, R3, R4 1K; R2 2K; phones 2K magnetic.—"Hobby Circuits Manual," RCA, Harrison, N.J., HM-90, p 59.

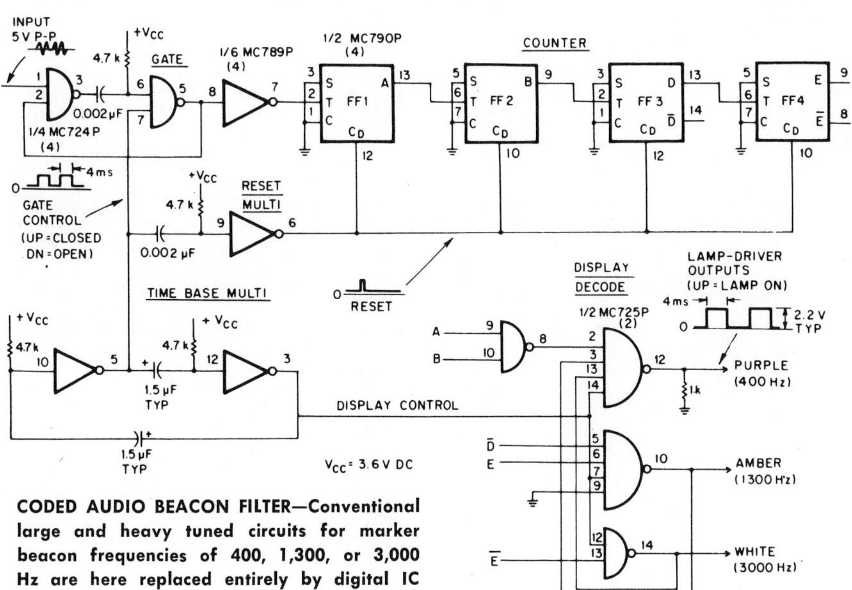

CODED AUDIO BEACON FILTER—Conventional large and heavy tuned circuits for marker beacon frequencies of 400, 1,300, or 3,000 Hz are here replaced entirely by digital IC frequency counter. Counting and display periods are about 4 ms each. When gate control line is positive, gate is closed, and previous count activates lamp corresponding to frequency. In typical 4-ms count, input of 250 to 1,000 Hz gives count of 1 to 3 and purple light, 1,000 to 2,000 Hz gives 4–7 and amber light, and 2,000 to 4,000 gives 8–15 and white light. Lamps are disabled during counting period to prevent flicker.—R. J. Battes, Digital ICs Serve as Audio Filters, *EEE*, Sept. 1969, p 131.

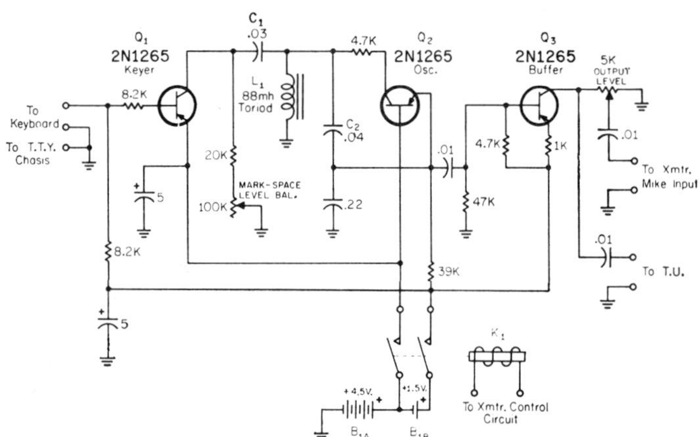

AUDIO FSK—Developed for radioteletype work on vhf bands, in which transmitter must be modulated at 2,975 Hz for space signal and at 2,125 Hz for mark signal. Frequency shift keyer circuit shown uses inexpensive components, is free from capacitive loading effects of keying circuit, has provisions for balancing mark and space output levels, and has good frequency stability. Space signal is transmitted when keyboard contacts are open. Article gives construction procedure. —R. P. Brickey, A Transistorized A. F. Shift Keyer, CQ, Nov. 1964, p 90–91, 124, and 126.

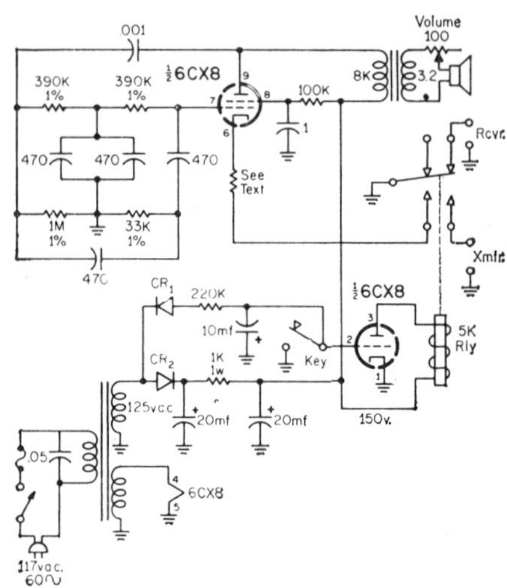

KEYING RELAY—With key and keying relay open, receiver contacts are closed and receiver is operating, while grid of keyer tube is blocked by negative voltage. With key closed, monitor and transmitter are operational. Use 500-ohm pot for cathode resistor of tetrode and adjust until oscillator functions. Diodes should be rated 300 piv.—"Electronic Circuits Handbook," Vol. II, Cowan Pub. Corp., Port Washington, N.Y., 1966, p 84.

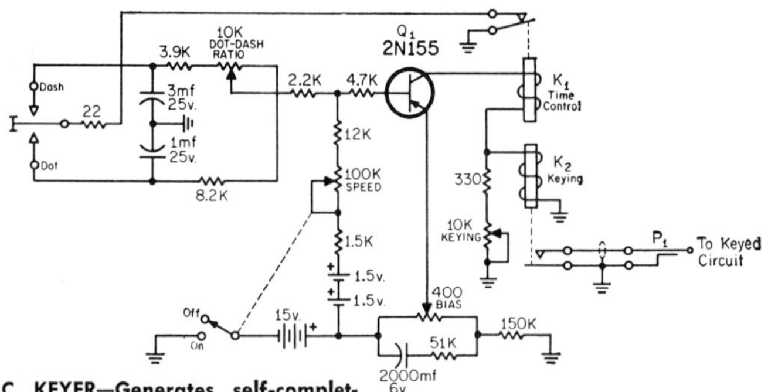

ELECTRONIC KEYER—Generates self-completing dash when paddle is pushed to left and released. Speed control determines length of dash. If dot is sent before dash is completed, keyer automatically completes dash and following space before producing dot and its space.—H. J. Sartori, An Electronic Keyer for Every C. W. Operator, CQ, April 1964, p 37–39 and 102.

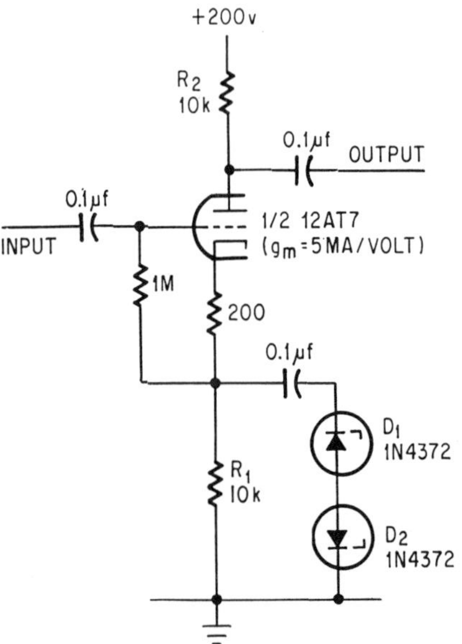

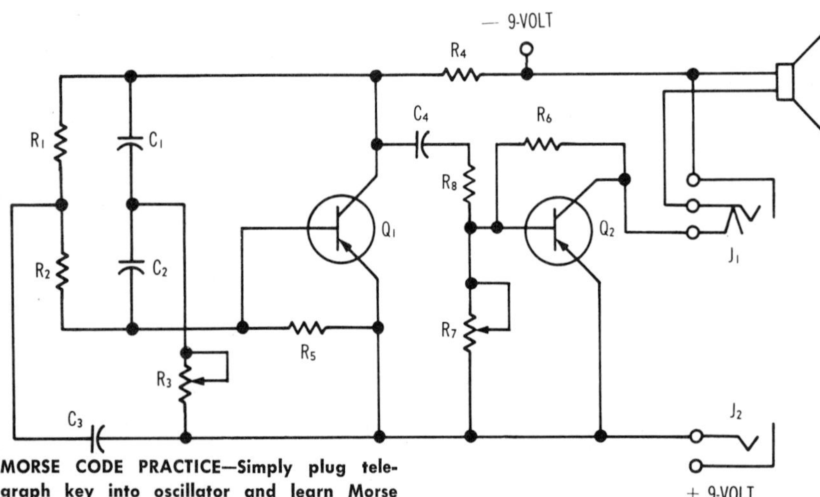

MORSE CODE PRACTICE—Simply plug telegraph key into oscillator and learn Morse code, either privately using headphones or in groups using speaker. Article gives construction details. Parts values are: R1-R2 62K; R3 5K; R4 5.6K; R5 6.8K; R6 100K; R7 50K; R8 15K; C1-C2 0.005 μF; C3 0.01 μF; C4 0.1 μF; Q1 HEP254; Q2 HEP253; speaker 100 ohms.—"Solid State Projects Manual," Motorola, Phoenix, Ariz., 1968, p 21–26.

BOOSTING S/N RATIO—Input signals above predetermined threshold level make amplifier gain increase suddenly, to give effect of stretching signal amplitude. Used to improve signal-to-noise ratio of keyed c-w signal. Maximum gain is 25 and minimum less than 1. Rise in gain results from sudden decrease in reverse resistance of zener diode when voltage across it passes critical level.—J. Holland, Zener Diodes Control Amplitude Stretching, *Electronics*, July 10, 1967, p 83.

CHAPTER 15
Comparator Circuits

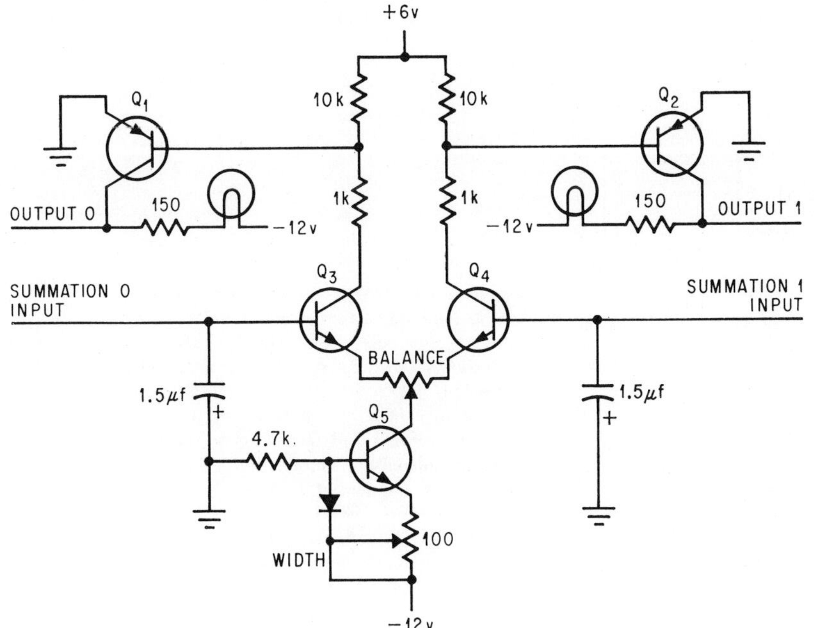

TERNARY DECISION UNIT—Compares voltage levels on the two input lines and gives 0 or 1 output depending on which input has more positive voltage. Input difference as small as 0.05 V will generate solid 0 or 1 output. Used in pattern recognizer developed by IBM for spoken words or graphic inputs. Transistor and diode types are not critical.—G. L. Clapper, Machine Looks, Listens, Learns, *Electronics*, Oct. 30, 1967, p 91–102.

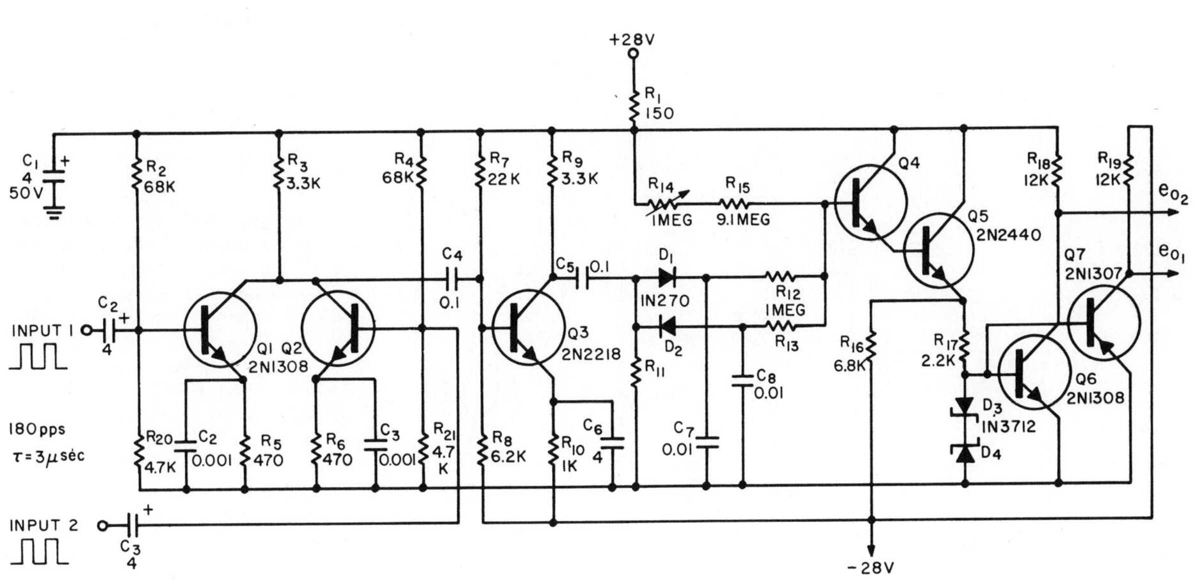

ALGEBRAIC COMPARATOR—Input stage Q1-Q2 adds pulses at inputs 1 and 2 algebraically, and feeds inverse of algebraic sum to amplifier Q3. Time constants of positive-negative rectifier circuit D1-D2-R11-R12-R13 can be adjusted to accommodate various input pulse frequencies and widths. Voltage at emitter of Q5 in Darlington pair is adjusted to zero (without input) by R14 to compensate for drift, leakage, or transistor changes. D3-D4 are Goto pair. Last stage has two outputs, one for positive algebraic sum and other for negative.—A. J. Burdi, Pulse Comparator Combines Versatility, Low Cost, *Electronic Design*, March 2, 1964, p 60 and 62.

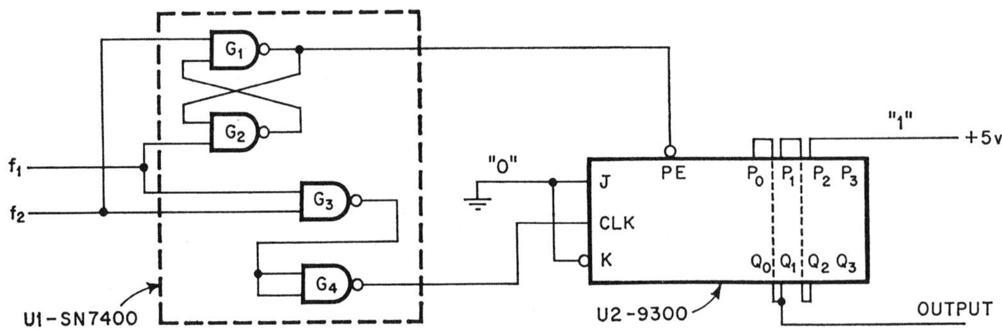

VARIABLE-FREQUENCY PHASE COMPARATOR—Produces output pulse pattern with duty cycle proportional to relative phase of two trains of input pulses having same frequency, but no outputs if other frequency ratios are present. Logic state of output Q1 is 0 as long as pulses arrive at f1 input or majority of pulses are f1. When f2 pulses predominate, output becomes constant logic 1.—I. Breikss, Shift Register Simplifies Design of Phase Comparator, *Electronics*, Jan. 19, 1970, p 93.

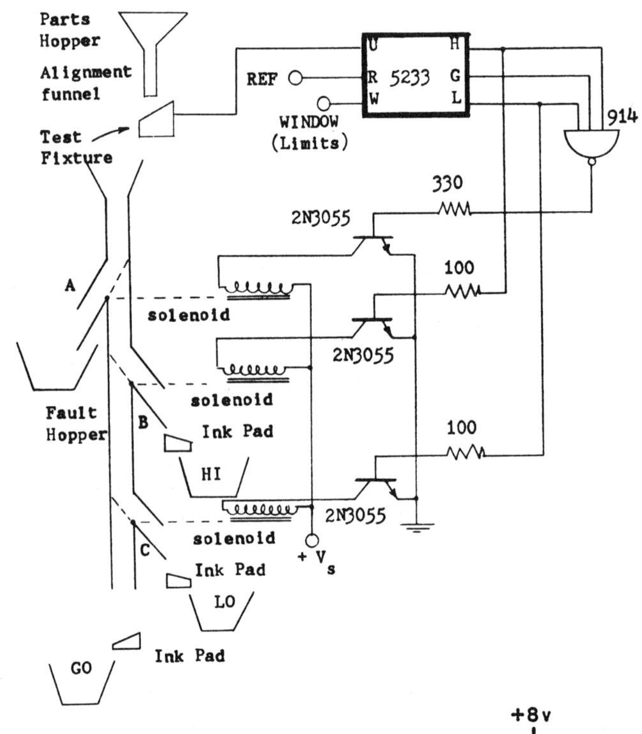

GO-NO-GO IC TESTER WITH HOPPER SORT—OEI Model 5233 IC comparator provides three outputs, depending on whether electrical characteristics of product under test are above, below, or within preset limits. Parts drop one by one into test fixture designed for automatic contact and measurement, with IC actuating solenoid of flapper that guides part into correct hopper after test. If part is within tolerance limits, it drops straight through into GO hopper. Ink pad at each hopper provides automatic color coding. If part fails all three tests, it is guided into fault or junk hopper. Test fixture may provide reset command signal for dropping next part after receiving signal indicating that part has fallen into appropriate hopper.—Using a Comparator for Production Selecting, Optical Electronics, Tucson, Ariz., No. 10102.

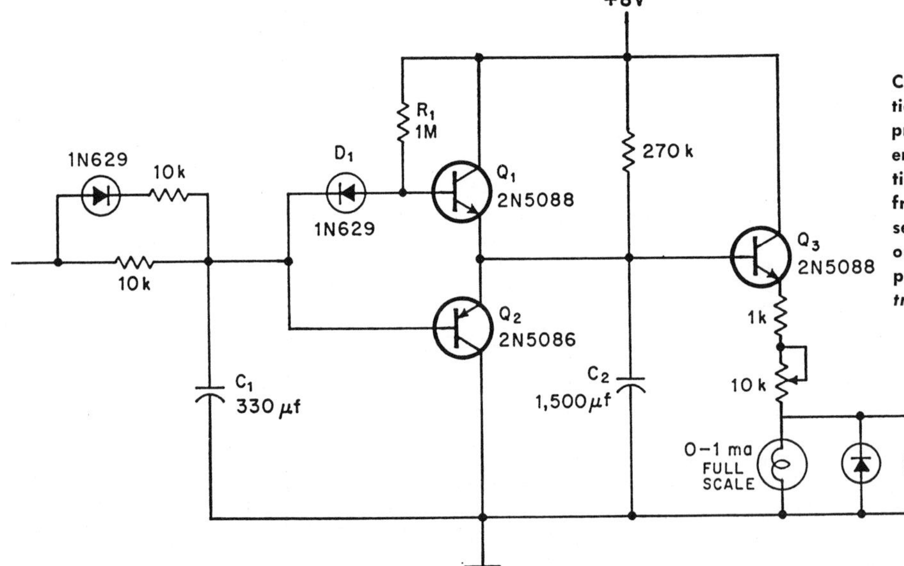

COMPARATOR IMPROVES RATE METER—Addition of comparator Q1-Q2 to rate meter improves measurement response time. Output emitter-follower Q3 delivers voltage proportional to repetition rate of input pulse train from preceding mono mvbr, with comparator serving to prevent input ripple from affecting output.—D. Wasserman and G. Parker, Comparator Increases Rate Meter's Response, *Electronics*, May 11, 1970, p 100.

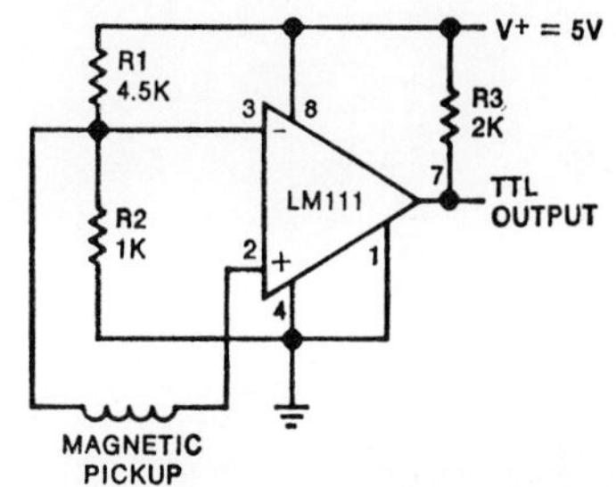

IC FOR MAGNETIC PICKUP—Universal IC voltage comparator will drive logic circuits, lamps, or relays up to 50 V at 50 mA, under control of pulses from magnetic pickup or other pulse source.—Detector for Magnetic Transducer (National Semiconductor ad), *Electronic News*, June 8, 1970, p 11.

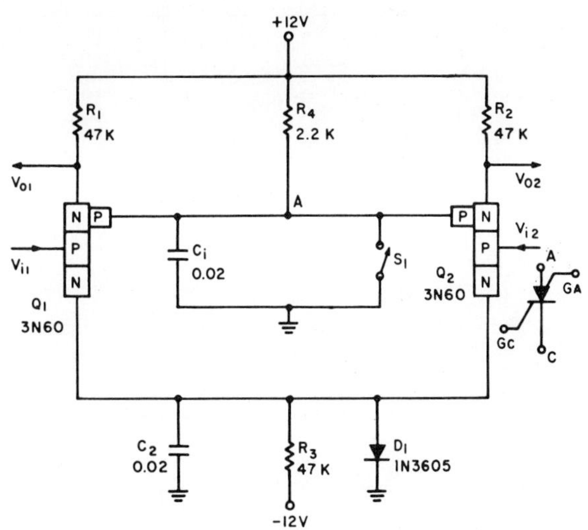

SCS STORES HIGHER OF TWO VOLTAGES—Silicon controlled switches (scs) Q1 and Q2, connected as differential amplifier and regenerative switch, sense channel having higher instantaneous voltage and store result. Threshold sensitivity is about 5 mV. Common-mode voltages can be up to 1 V in either polarity. Article describes operation in detail and suggests modifications for other applications.—T. P. Sylvan, SCS Linear Amplifier Gives Threshold Switching, *Electronic Design*, Jan. 20, 1964, p 78–79.

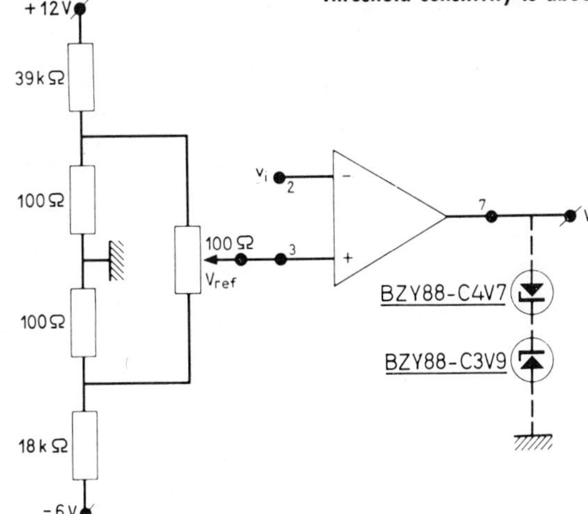

ZERO DETECTOR—Uses Philips TAA241 difference amplifier as comparator or zero detector. If input voltage Vi is greater than reference voltage, output is about −5 V; if input is below reference, output is +10 V. If zero reference is required, ground input terminal temporarily and adjust pot to compensate for offset voltage. If optional zeners are connected as shown, output voltages will be symmetrical at +5 V and −5 V.—J. Cohen and J. Oosterling, Applications of a Practical D. C. Difference Amplifier, Philips, Pub. Dept., Elcoma Div., Eindhoven, The Netherlands, No. 321, 1968.

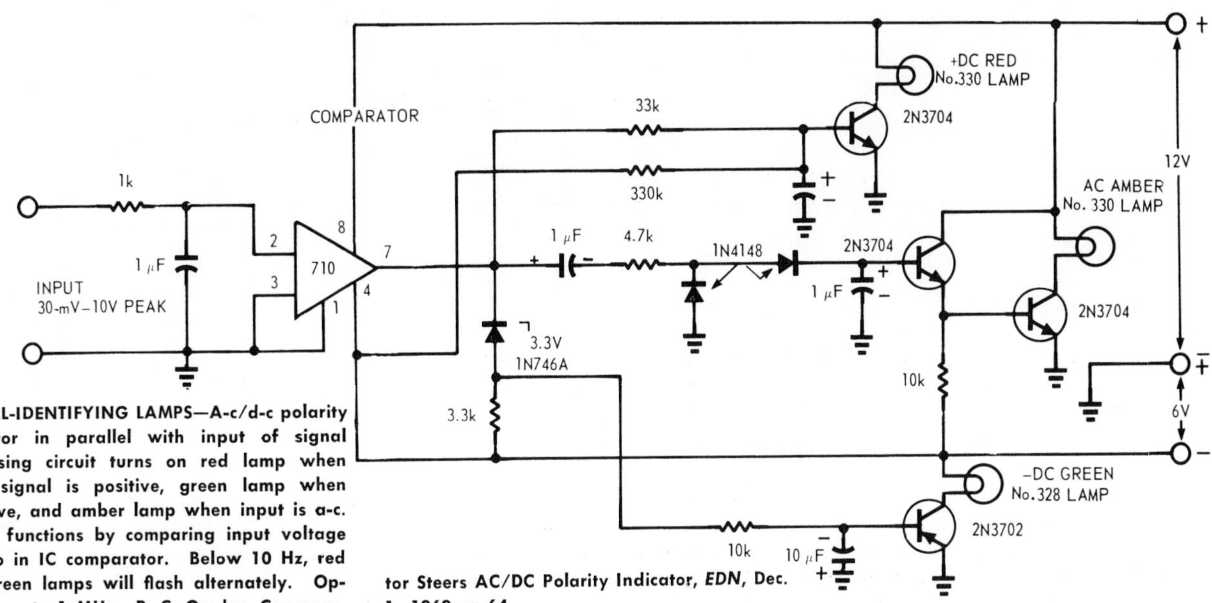

SIGNAL-IDENTIFYING LAMPS—A-c/d-c polarity indicator in parallel with input of signal processing circuit turns on red lamp when input signal is positive, green lamp when negative, and amber lamp when input is a-c. Circuit functions by comparing input voltage to zero in IC comparator. Below 10 Hz, red and green lamps will flash alternately. Operates up to 1 MHz.—R. C. Gerdes, Comparator Steers AC/DC Polarity Indicator, *EDN*, Dec. 1, 1969, p 64.

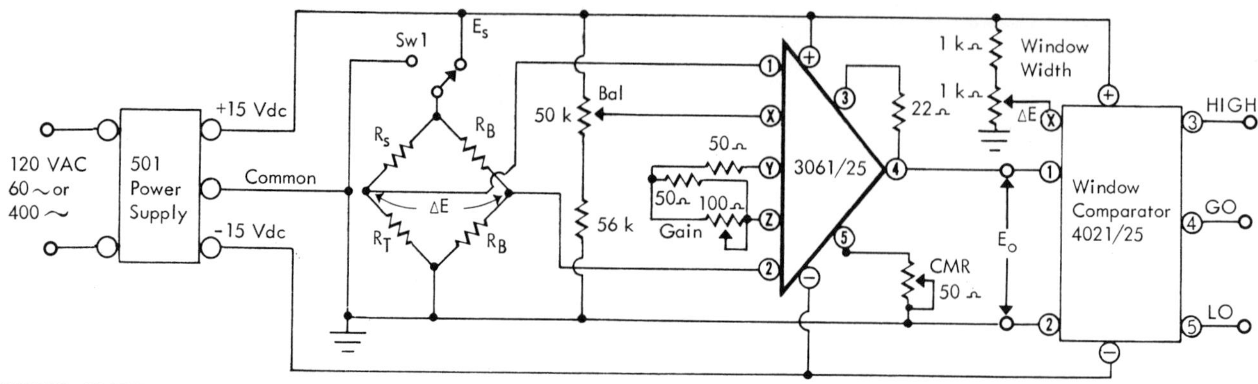

RESISTOR GRADER—Uses Burr-Brown 4021/25 window comparator fed by 3061/25 differential-input instrumentation amplifier and Wheatstone bridge containing unknown resistor. Pulse outputs of comparator provide convenient way of obtaining low, in-tolerance, or high indications for resistor under test. Used for matching pairs of resistors to within 1% accuracy. Article discusses operating procedures for matching to within 0.01%.—"Instrument Amplifiers," Burr-Brown Research, Tucson, Ariz., PDS-207C, 1969, p 24.

TRIGGER CHOOSES HIGHER OF TWO VOLTAGES—When used as comparator, circuit can decide which of two voltages in range from 0 to 12 V has the greater numerical value when one is positive and the other negative. When positive voltage is greater, Q3 is cut off and Q4 is saturated. When negative is greater, trigger Q3-Q4 flips over so Q4 is cut off and Q3 is saturated. Differing output voltages will then indicate which input is greater. By adding potentiometer to positive input terminal, as shown by dashed lines, circuit will act as Schmitt trigger in which trip point is equal to voltage-level setting of pot. —S. Stuhr, Wide-Range Trigger Compares Absolute Values, *Electronic Design*, Jan. 6, 1964, p 85–86.

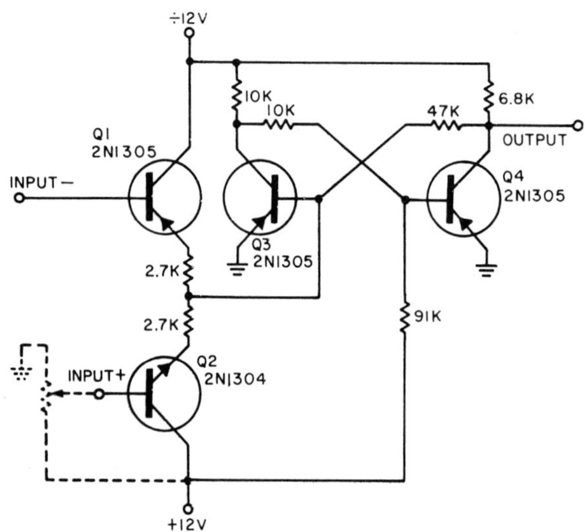

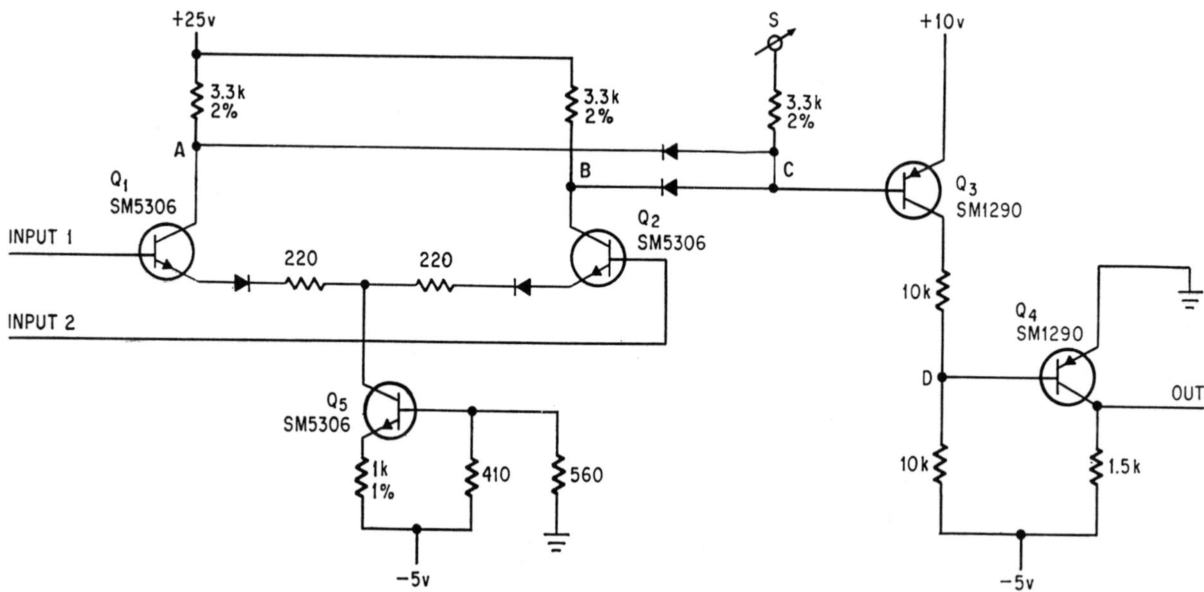

ADJUSTABLE-SENSITIVITY ANALOG COMPARATOR—Adjusting voltage S gives sensitivity range of 0.2 to 2 V. Binary 1 output occurs when the two inputs are equal within sensitivity margin. Used in Paramatrix system for preprocessing analog information, chiefly photos and graphs, while converting to digital signals under computer control.—W. J. Poppelbaum, M. Faiman, and E. Carr, Paramatrix Puts Digital Computer in Analog Picture, and Vice Versa, *Electronics*, Sept. 4, 1967, p 99–108.

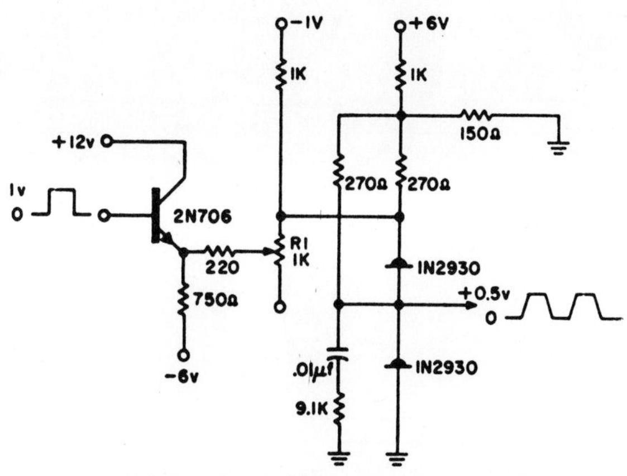

VOLTAGE COMPARATOR FOR 2 MHZ—Highly sensitive tunnel-diode comparator detects 5-mV change from on to off state. Tunnel diodes are biased as flip-flop, with bias chosen so 0.8 mA is required to make them switch. If output is required when input is above 1 V, R1 is adjusted to make diodes switch at this point.—N. Marchese, Voltage Comparator Uses Tunnel Diode Flip-Flop, "400 Ideas for Design Selected from Electronic Design," Hayden Book Co., N.Y., 1964, p 163.

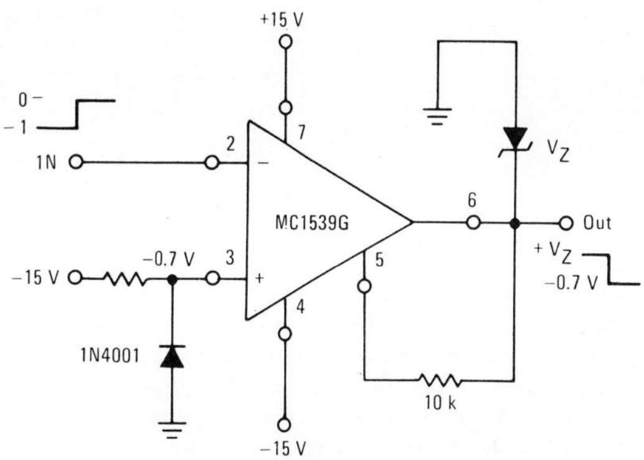

SINGLE-OPAMP VOLTAGE COMPARATOR—By interchanging inputs, can be made inverting or noninverting. Open-loop operation assures fast response. Tying zener between output and ground limits output level to that acceptable to saturated logic families.—K. Huehne, The Continuing Dominance of the Operational Amplifier, "State-of-the-Art—Linears in Action," Motorola, Phoenix, Ariz., 1969, p 5–13.

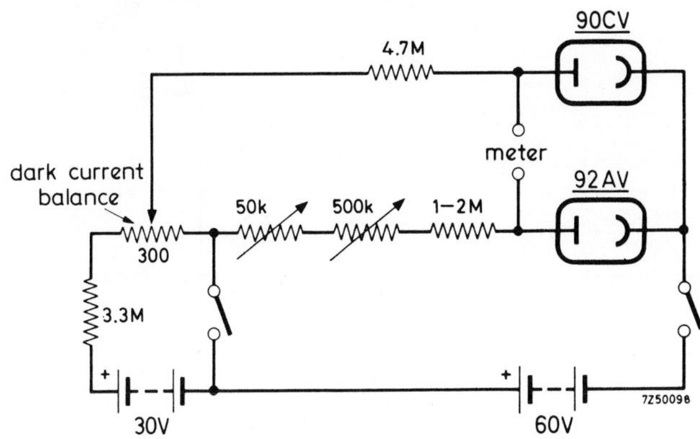

LAMP CALIBRATOR—Two photocells, 90CV red-sensitive and 92AV blue-sensitive, form part of bridge circuit in which electronic voltmeter serves as null detector. Used to compare color temperature of service lamp against that of standard calibration lamp mounted side by side in image-converter-tube tester. Report gives calibration and measurement procedures.—G. P. Brouwer and A. G. Geurts, An Instrument for Measuring the Sensitivity of Photocathodes, Philips, Pub. Dept., Elcoma Div., Eindhoven, The Netherlands, No. 323, 1966.

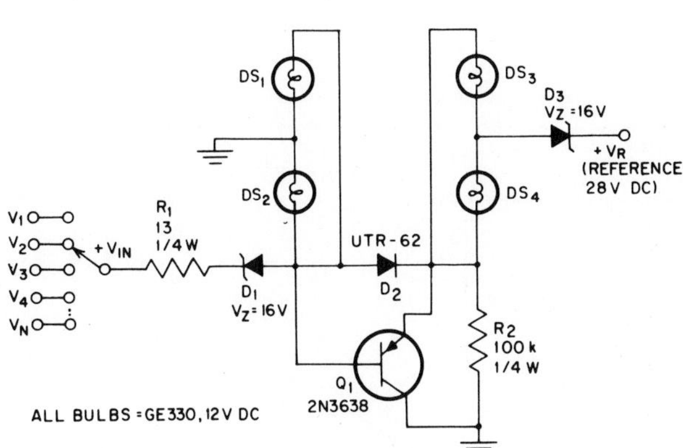

GO-NO-GO WITH READOUT—Compares monitored voltages with reference voltage and energizes lamps DS1-DS2 to indicate continuity. For open circuit, DS3-DS4 are on. Lamps are paired for redundancy, so circuit gives unambiguous indication even if one lamp fails.—W. A. Magee, Voltage Comparator with Visual Readout, *EEE*, May 1969, p 118 and 120.

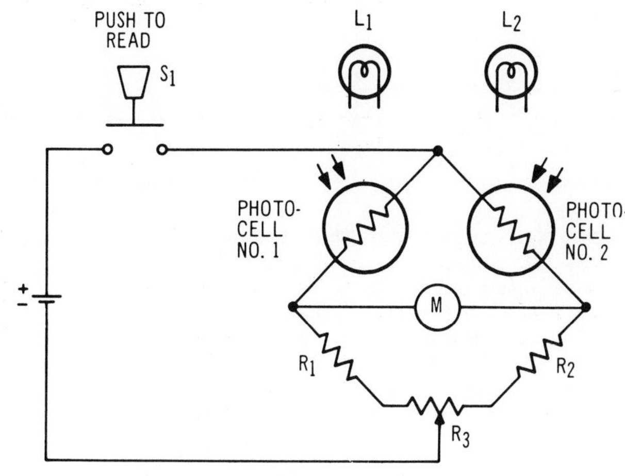

LIGHT COMPARATOR—Permits matching of two unknown light sources or one unknown with standard. Circuit is initially nulled with R3. Photocells are SQ2508; R1-R2 15K; R3 25K; meter 50—0—50 μA 2K; battery 1.4 V.—"Solid State Photosensitive Devices," RCA, Harrison, N.J., p 24.

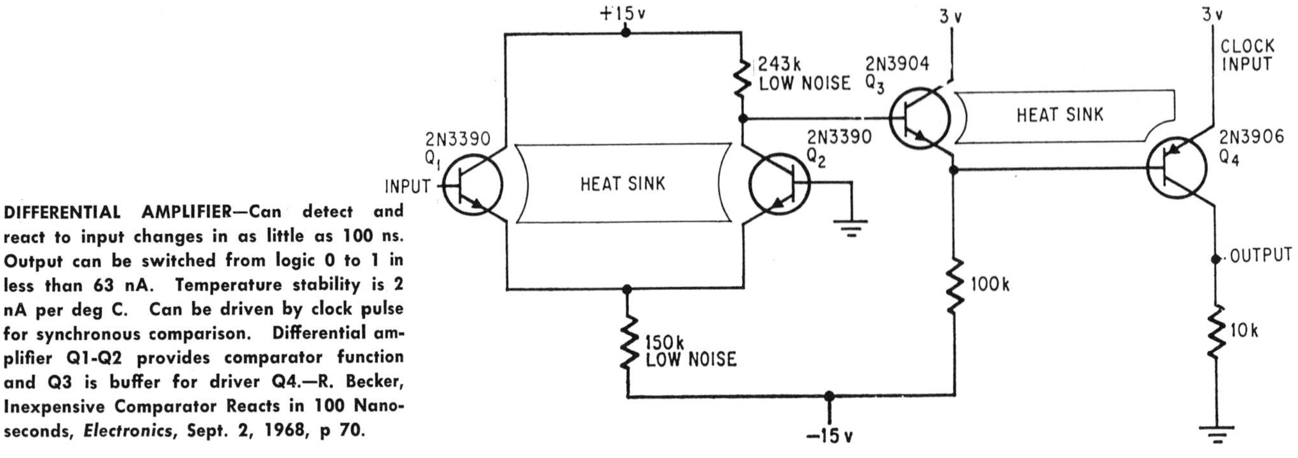

DIFFERENTIAL AMPLIFIER—Can detect and react to input changes in as little as 100 ns. Output can be switched from logic 0 to 1 in less than 63 nA. Temperature stability is 2 nA per deg C. Can be driven by clock pulse for synchronous comparison. Differential amplifier Q1-Q2 provides comparator function and Q3 is buffer for driver Q4.—R. Becker, Inexpensive Comparator Reacts in 100 Nanoseconds, *Electronics*, Sept. 2, 1968, p 70.

SIGNAL AMPLITUDE REGULATOR—Holds signal amplitude constant within 0.1 dB when input signal of telecommunications system is fluctuating plus or minus 10 dB. This regulation is maintained over temperature range of −10 to 60 deg C despite use of unselected components. Q1 is output stage of amplifier being regulated and Q6 is its input. Q3-Q4 form voltage comparator. Q5 drives lamp that varies resistance of photocell and thereby controls gain of amplifier being regulated.—A. E. Lofting, Stable Amplitude Regulator for Wide Temperature Range, *Electronics*, Feb. 6, 1967, p 71–72.

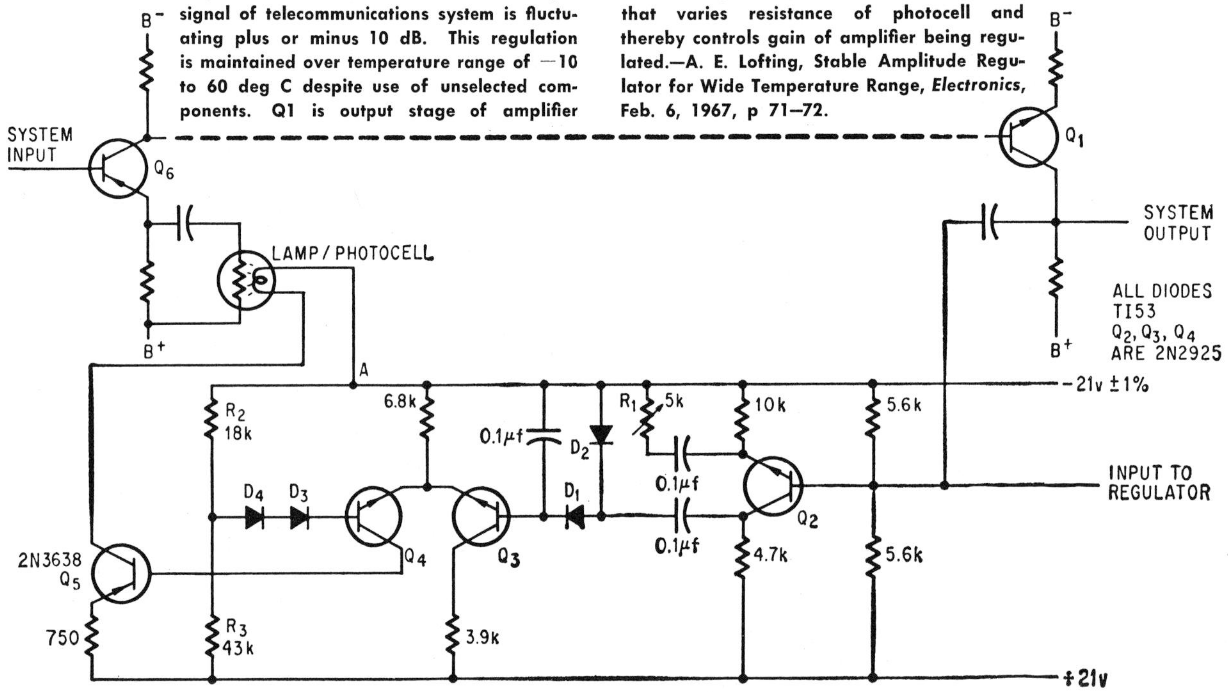

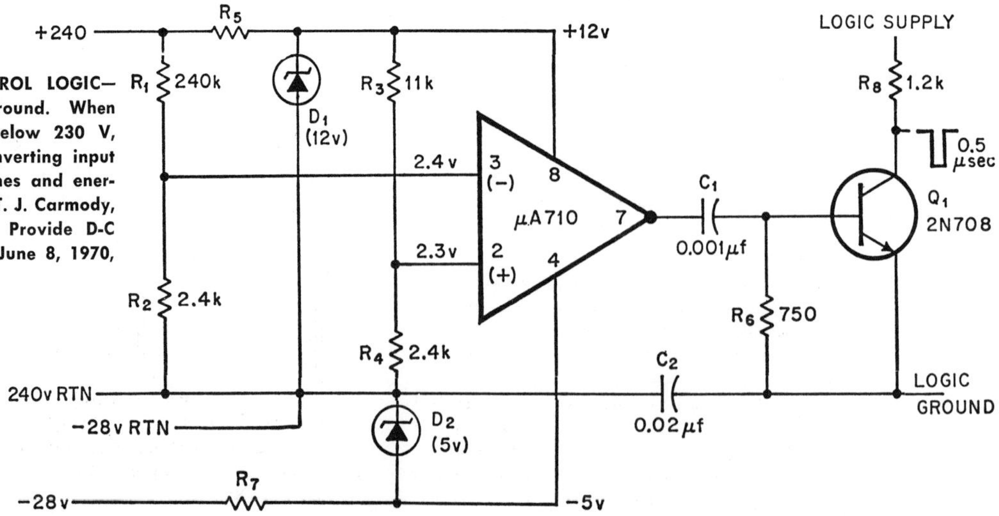

D-C TRANSFORMER FOR CONTROL LOGIC—Operates without common ground. When 240-V supply voltage drops below 230 V, less than 2.3 V is applied to inverting input of IC comparator, and it switches and energizes output logic through Q1.—T. J. Carmody, Comparator and A-C Coupling Provide D-C Transformer Action, *Electronics*, June 8, 1970, p 98.

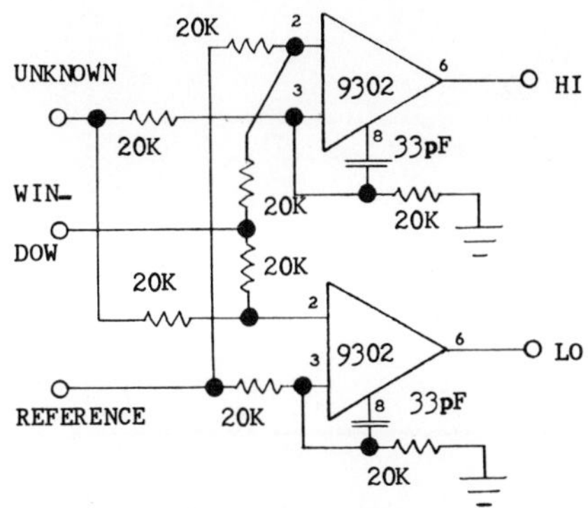

FULL COMPARATOR—Combination of two 9302 OEI opamps indicates whether unknown input is more positive than reference by giving HI output, less positive by giving LO output, or equal by giving LO output from both opamps. HI is +10 V and LO is −10 V. Window input accepts positive voltages and generates tolerance equal to window input. If unknown is within window voltage of reference, both outputs are −10 V corresponding to equal condition.—Applying the Model 9302 Monolithic Operational Amplifier, Optical Electronics, Tucson, Ariz., No. 10135.

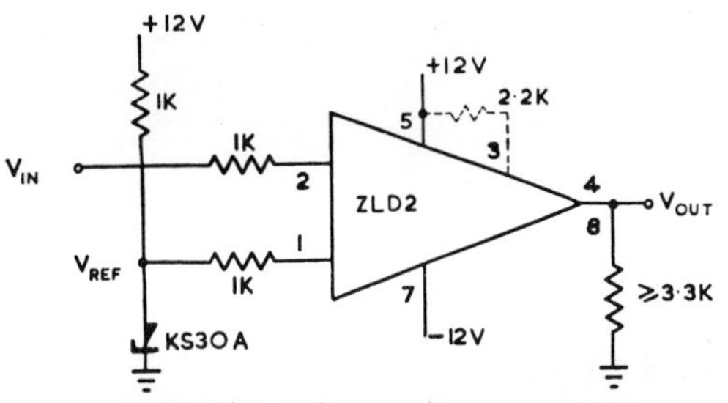

D-C VOLTAGE COMPARATOR—Signal voltage applied to terminal 2 of Ferranti ZLD2 IC differential-input d-c amplifier is compared with voltage of reference diode at other input. Output voltage will be either maximum negative or maximum positive, depending on whether signal voltage is greater or less than reference voltage.—Microlin Amplifiers ZLD2S and ZLD2T, Ferranti Ltd., Oldham, Lancs., England, No. 11, 1967, p 12.

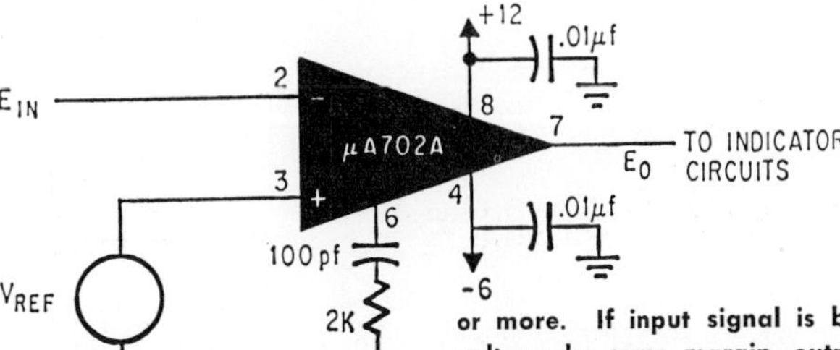

2-MV SENSITIVITY—Fairchild μA702A IC opamp amplifies difference between unknown signal and reference voltage, and delivers 5 V output if signal exceeds reference by 2 mV or more. If input signal is below reference voltage by same margin, output to indicator is −5 V. Article contains thirteen other IC opamp application circuits.—J. F. Gifford and M. Markkula, Linear IC's: Part 5, Ins and Outs of Op Amps, *Electronics*, Nov. 27, 1967, p 84–93.

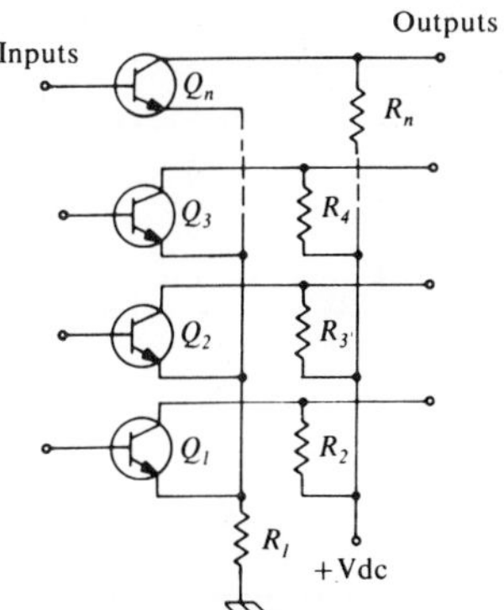

VOLTAGE COMPARATOR—Can be directly coupled to binary encoder for detection of highest input voltage. Has advantages over diode comparator gates. Operates from 20 V d-c supply, for inputs of zero to 10 V d-c and outputs of 20 or 10 V d-c. All transistors are 2N780, R1 is 100 ohms, and all other resistors 100K.—"Selected Electronic Circuitry," NASA SP-5046, 1966, Government Printing Office, Washington, D.C., p 80.

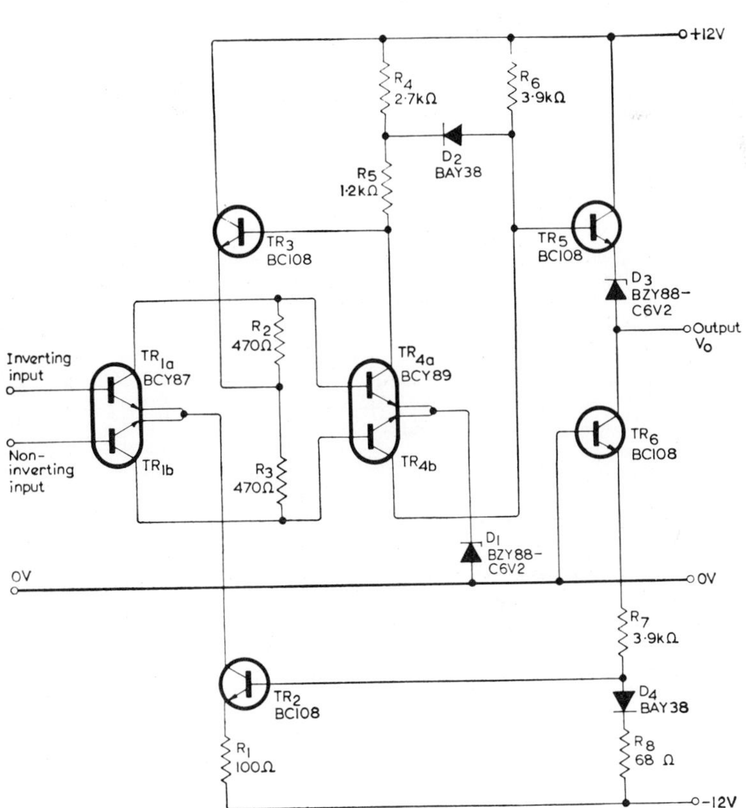

STABLE VOLTAGE COMPARATOR—Uses transistor pairs in differential stages, with constant-current transistor source for holding input stage emitter currents constant. Output voltage is limited to 0.7 V and 3 V, for driving wide variety of logic circuits.—"Circuits Using Low-Drift Transistor Pairs," Philips, Pub. Dept., Elcoma Div., Eindhoven, The Netherlands, 1968, p 26.

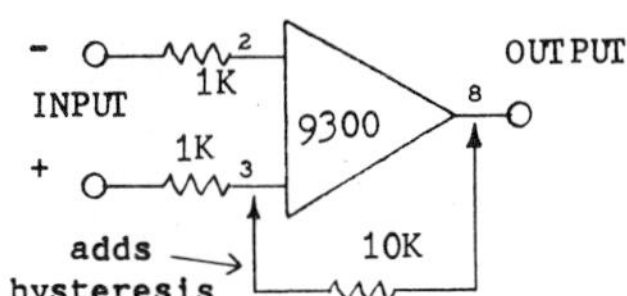

SIMPLE COMPARATOR—With only three external resistors, OEI 9300 opamp serves as voltage comparator with full performance to 2 MHz and reduced comparison accuracy at higher frequencies. Output level is compatible with DTL and RTL logic.—Applying the Model 9300 Monolithic Operational Amplifier, Optical Electronics, Tuscon, Ariz., No. 10134.

CHAPTER 16
Control Circuits

UJT PHASE-CONTROL FOR INDUCTIVE LOADS—Phase reference for ujt is derived from supply voltage instead of from bilateral scr. Gate drive for scr continues from point of triggering to end of half-cycle. Circuit provides symmetrical waveforms and positive triggering even when load current rises slowly.—E. K. Howell, Bilateral SCR Lets Designers Economize on Circuitry, *Electronic Design*, Jan. 20, 1964, p 74–77.

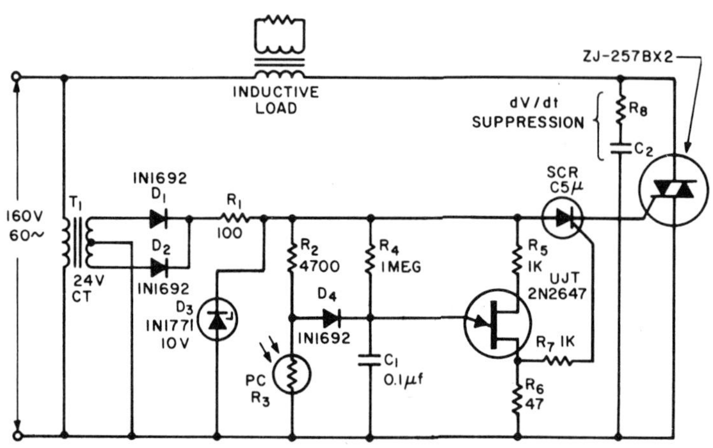

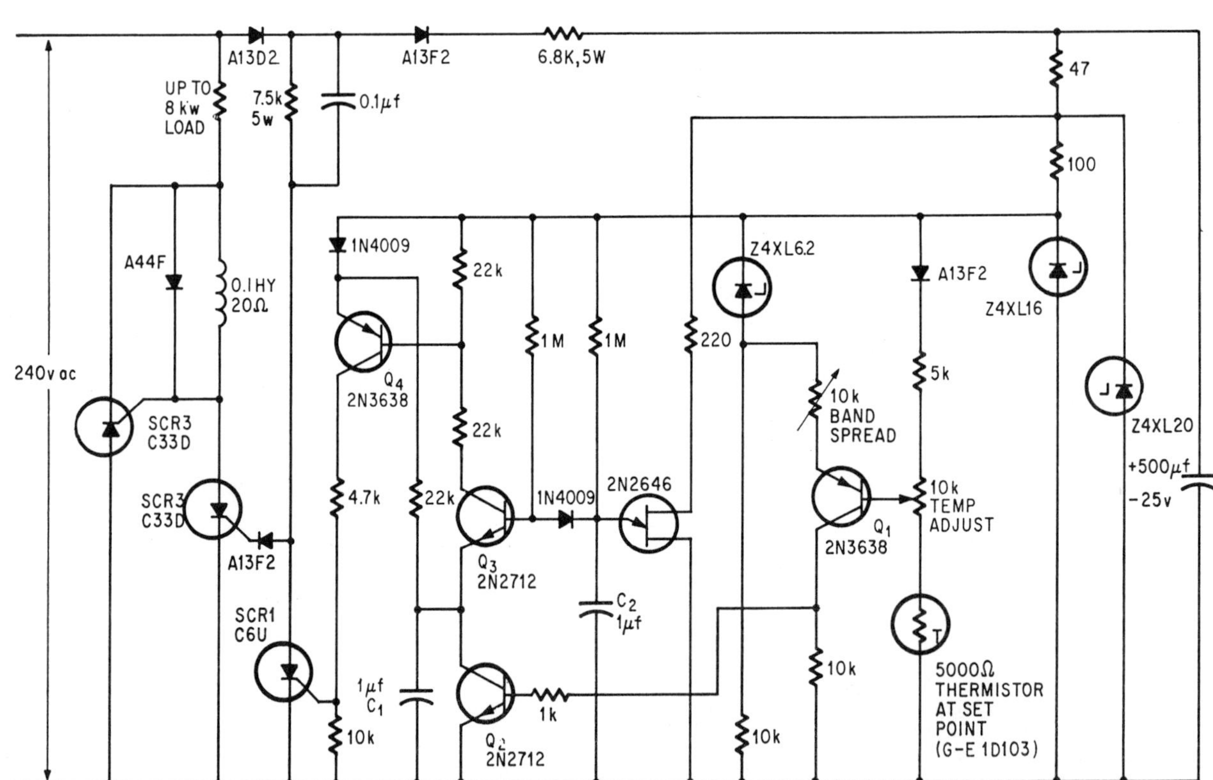

POWER CONTROL WITH DISCRETE COMPONENTS—Will control up to 8 kW through resistive load, though requiring over 40 components as compared to half a dozen if one is General Electric's PA424 IC described in same article.—F. W. Gutzwiller and J. H. Galloway, Power Grab by Linear IC's, *Electronics*, Aug. 21, 1967, p 81–86.

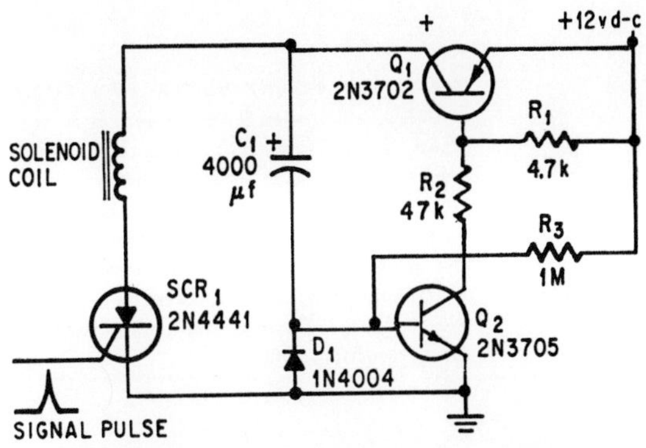

RAISING SATELLITE ANTENNA—Signal pulse from earth triggers SCR1, so C1 discharges through solenoid to provide powerful stroke for pushing out antenna or providing other required mechanical motion. Q1 then pulls capacitor-recharging current to low level to allow scr to turn off and thereby reduce recycling time of solenoid. When C1 is charged to 12 V, Q2 turns off and stops Q1. —J. J. Klinikowski, Transistor Speeds Up Charging Circuit, *Electronics*, Aug. 5, 1968, p 105.

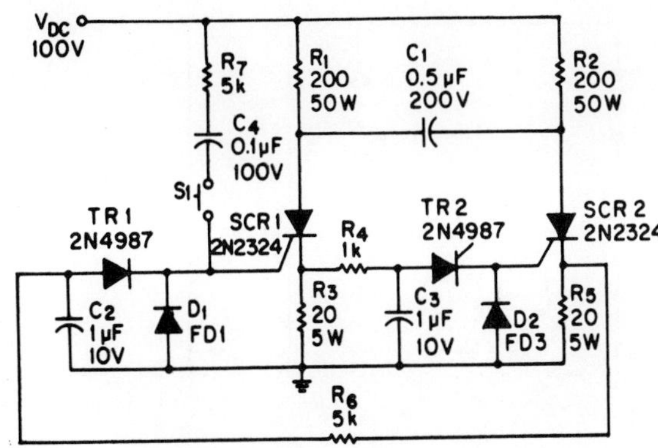

SEQUENTIAL CONTROL—Momentary closing of S1 initiates switching sequence, with each scr stage having independently adjustable operating time. Conduction of SCR1 is determined by R4, C3, drop across R3, and operating voltage of trigger diode TR1. Values shown are for 0.5-A load current. Additional controlled stages may be added.—E. Kiburis, Sequential Control with Silicon Controlled Rectifiers, *EEE*, March 1970, p 100–103.

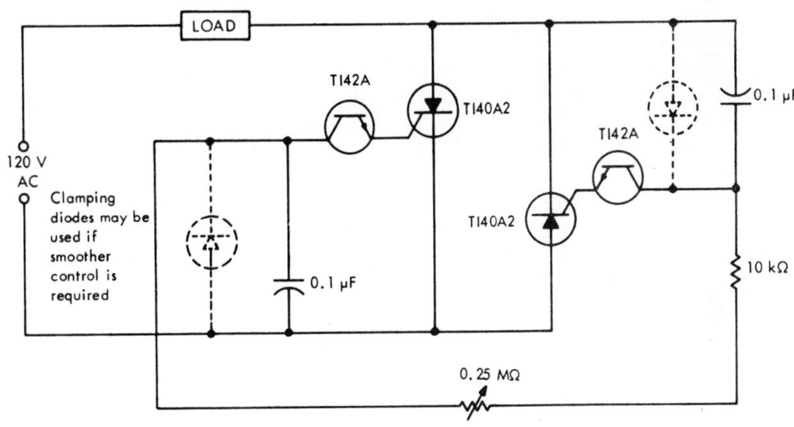

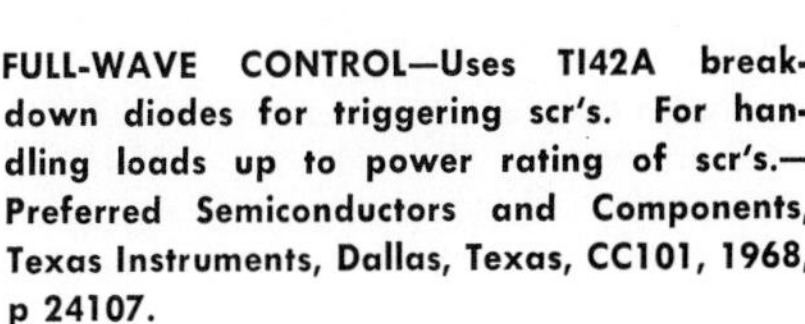

FULL-WAVE CONTROL—Uses TI42A breakdown diodes for triggering scr's. For handling loads up to power rating of scr's.—Preferred Semiconductors and Components, Texas Instruments, Dallas, Texas, CC101, 1968, p 24107.

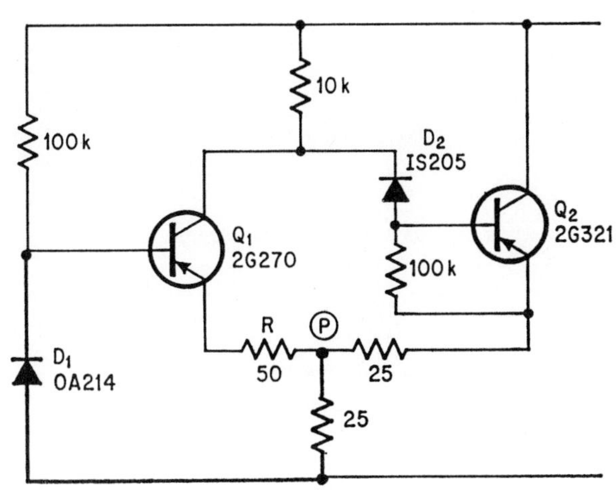

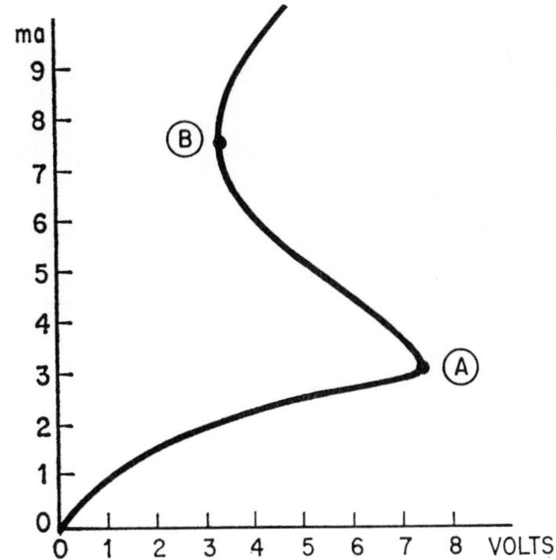

CURRENT-CONTROLLED NEGATIVE RESISTANCE—For currents up to 3 mA between circuit terminals, voltage drop across circuit increases almost linearly because only Q1 is conducting. For higher currents, up to about 7.5 mA, both transistors conduct and voltage decreases (negative slope, corresponding to negative resistance). Above 7.5 mA, only Q2 conducts and voltage again increases with current. Can be used as flip-flop.—F. Brochtoniolo, A Negative-Resistance Circuit Doubles for V or I Control, *Electronics*, April 28, 1969, p 78–79.

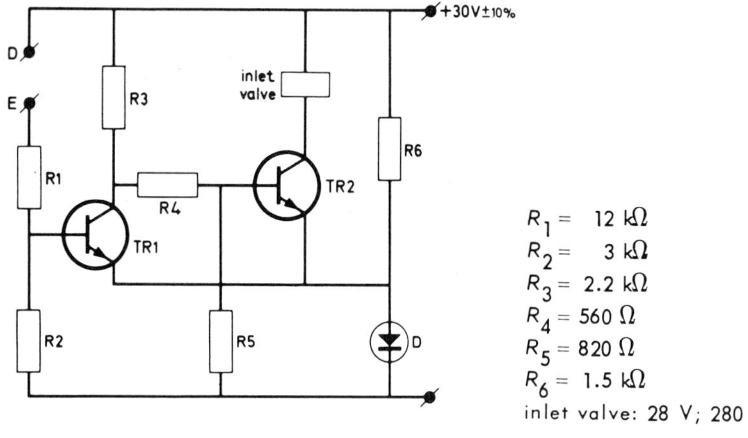

R_1 = 12 kΩ
R_2 = 3 kΩ
R_3 = 2.2 kΩ
R_4 = 560 Ω
R_5 = 820 Ω
R_6 = 1.5 kΩ
inlet valve: 28 V; 280 mA

TR_1 = BC147
TR_2 = BFY55
D = BA148

WASHING-MACHINE WATER-LEVEL CONTROL—Simple electrodes D and E sealed in wall of open vertical tube sense change in resistance when water level reaches both electrodes, then energize inlet valve through transistors to shut off water. Operates from same 30-V d-c supply used for other sensors in washing machine.—Transistorized Level Sensor, Philips, Pub. Dept., Elcoma Div., Eindhoven, The Netherlands, 1968.

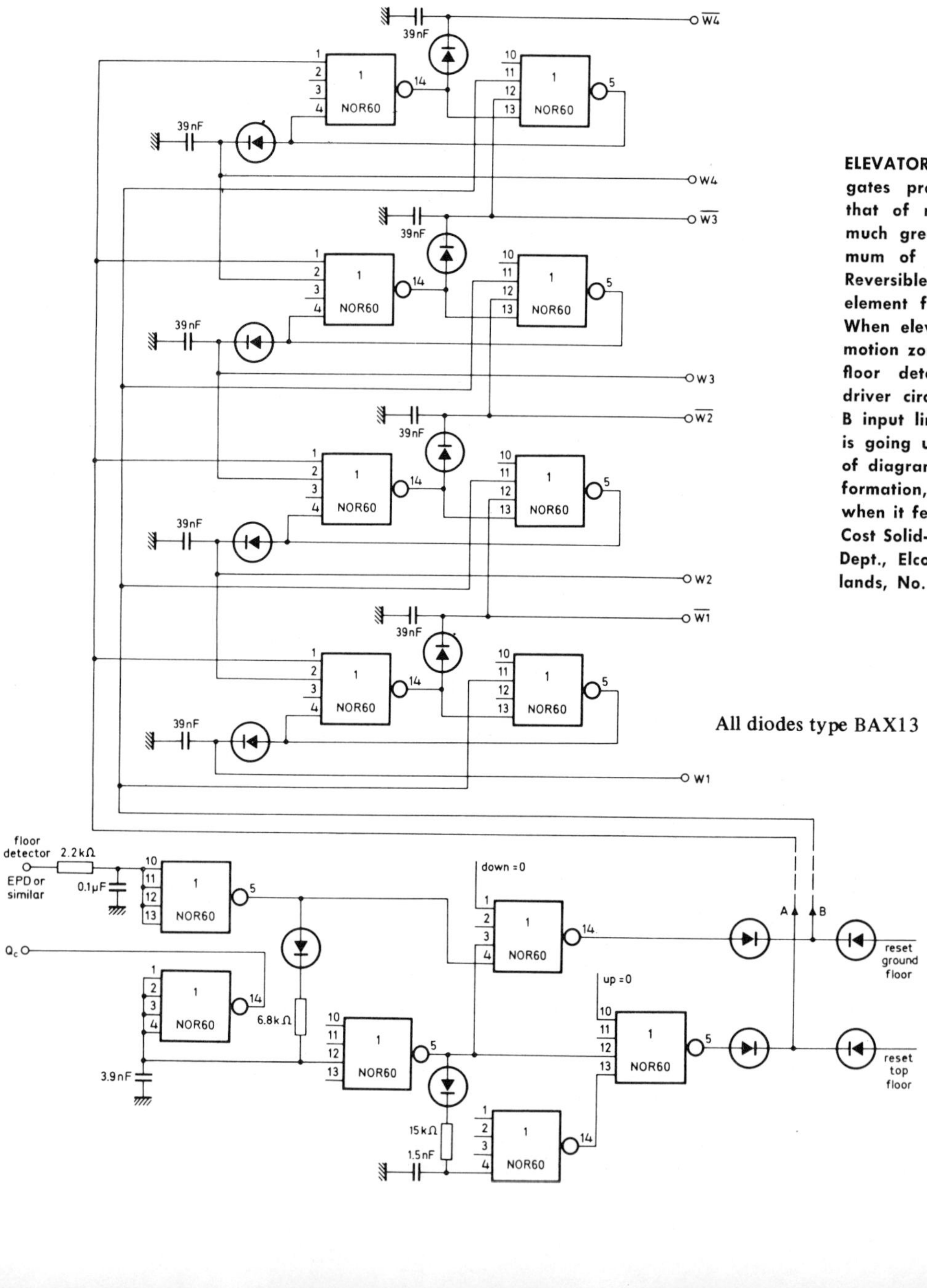

All diodes type BAX13

ELEVATOR POSITION REGISTER—Philips IC gates provide performance comparable to that of relay system, with same cost but much greater reliability. Can handle maximum of six floors in apartment building. Reversible column-type counter has memory element for all but top and bottom floors. When elevator passes lowest point of slow-motion zone at each floor, signal is fed from floor detector through pulse stretcher in driver circuit (bottom of diagram) to A or B input line, depending on whether elevator is going up or down. Pulse register at top of diagram stores and delivers positional information, except for top or bottom floor when it feeds reset signal.—J. P. Exalto, Low-Cost Solid-State Elevator Control, Philips, Pub. Dept., Elcoma Div., Eindhoven, The Netherlands, No. 69.

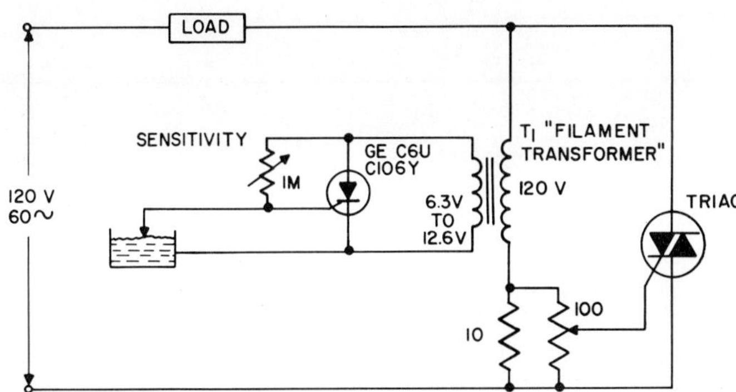

SENSING WATER LEVEL—Applies power to load through appropriately rated triac until water level touches probe and bypasses gate current from low-current C6U scr. This gives isolated low-voltage probe for meeting safety requirements.—J. H. Galloway, Using the Triac for Control of AC Power, General Electric, Syracuse, N.Y., No. 200.35, 1966, p 14.

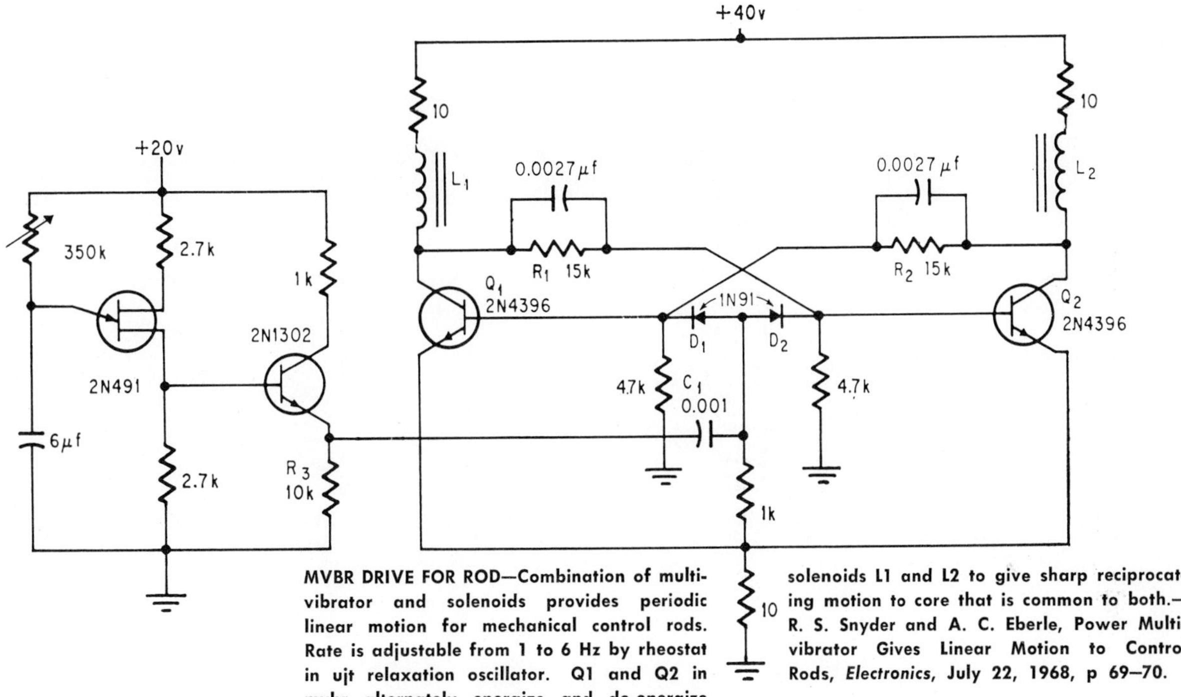

MVBR DRIVE FOR ROD—Combination of multivibrator and solenoids provides periodic linear motion for mechanical control rods. Rate is adjustable from 1 to 6 Hz by rheostat in ujt relaxation oscillator. Q1 and Q2 in mvbr alternately energize and de-energize solenoids L1 and L2 to give sharp reciprocating motion to core that is common to both.—R. S. Snyder and A. C. Eberle, Power Multivibrator Gives Linear Motion to Control Rods, *Electronics*, July 22, 1968, p 69–70.

ELEVATOR FLOOR CONTROL—Arrangement shown provides signal to floor indicator lamp of elevator control system and enabling signal for up and down command gates. General reset signal R, produced at top and bottom floors, is applied to upper left-hand memory.—J. P. Exalto, Low-Cost Solid-State Elevator Control, Philips, Pub. Dept., Elcoma Div., Eindhoven, The Netherlands, No. 69.

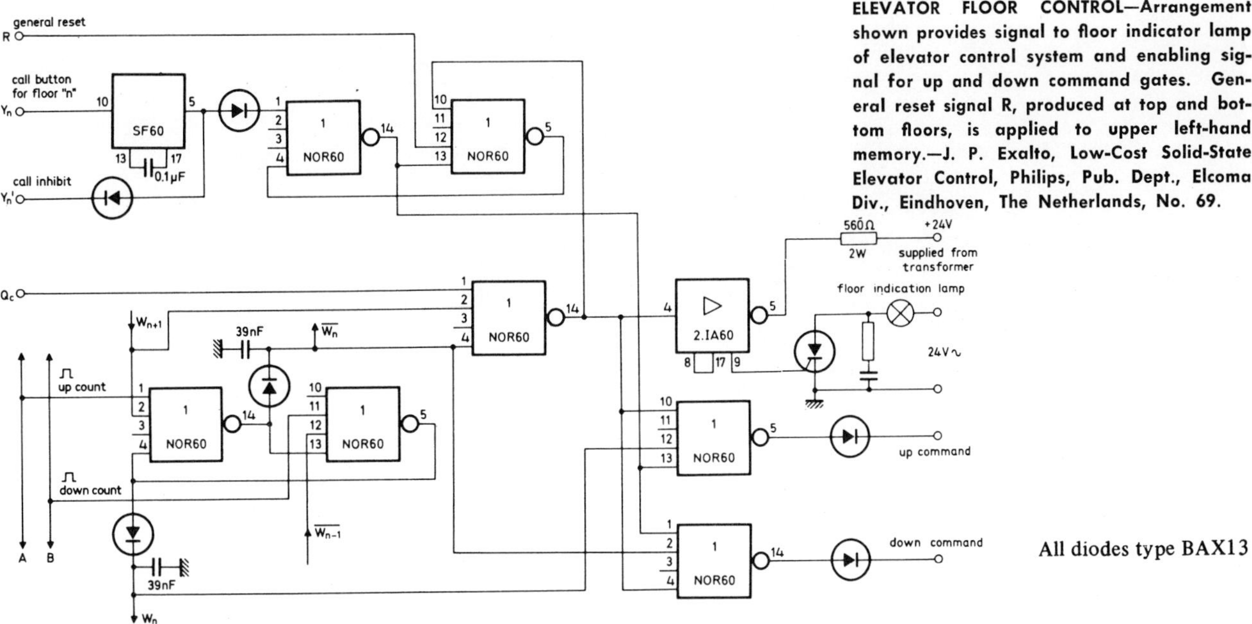

All diodes type BAX13

HALF-WAVE CONTROL—Uses TI42A breakdown diode for triggering scr at point in half-cycle determined by setting of rheostat. Load capacity depends on rating of scr.—Preferred Semiconductors and Components, Texas Instruments, Dallas, Texas, CC101, 1968, p 24107.

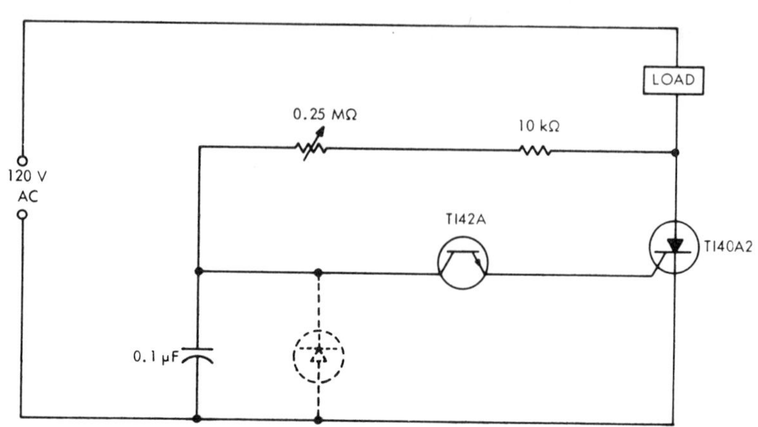

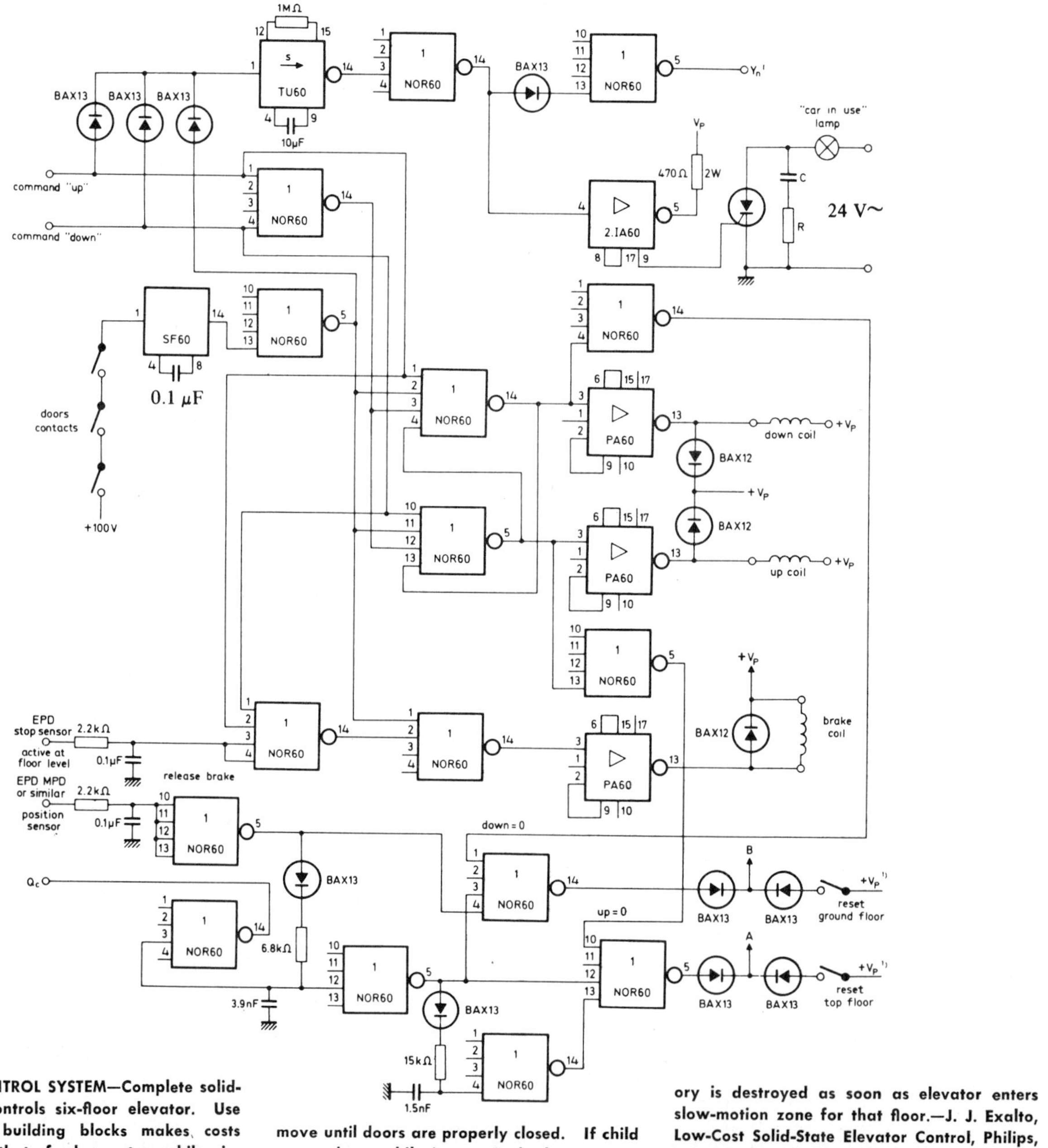

ELEVATOR CONTROL SYSTEM—Complete solid-state system controls six-floor elevator. Use of Philips IC building blocks makes costs comparable to that of relay system while giving much greater reliability. Elevator cannot move until doors are properly closed. If child opens doors while in transit, brakes are applied. Call information stored in floor memory is destroyed as soon as elevator enters slow-motion zone for that floor.—J. J. Exalto, Low-Cost Solid-State Elevator Control, Philips, Pub. Dept., Elcoma Div., Eindhoven, The Netherlands, No. 69.

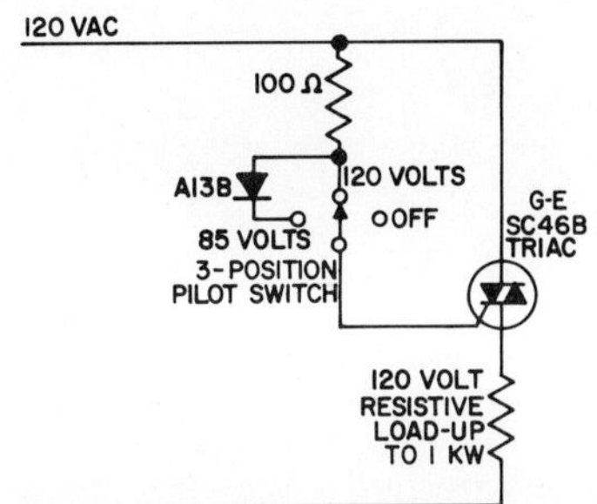

TRIAC POWER CONTROL—Three-position switch gives full or reduced power for load. At reduced power, rectifier changes triggering point of triac. Switch can be low-current type. Good for applications requiring cyclic switching without noise of circuit breakers, and for remote control.—F. W. Gutzwiller and E. K. Howell, Economy Power Semiconductor Applications, General Electric, Syracuse, N.Y., No. 671.1, 1965, p 7.

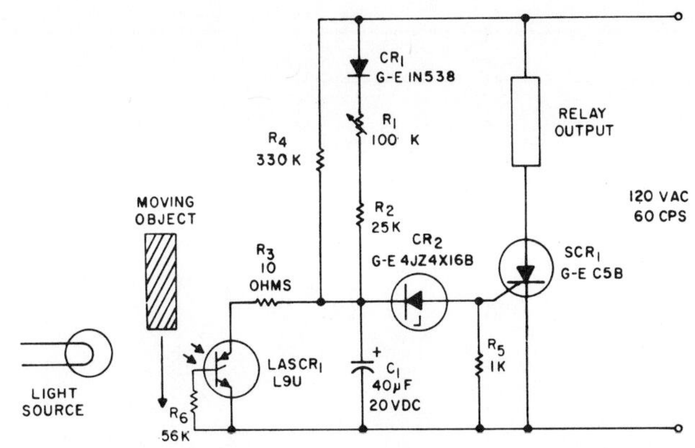

CONVEYOR-JAM MONITOR—Lascr and light source on opposite sides of conveyor or chute act with delay and scr to overlook or pass small self-clearing pile-ups but shut down line quickly for impending catastrophic jam. With light on, lascr conducts and prevents voltage buildup across C1. Each interruption of beam turns off lascr and starts charging of C1. Interruptions of only a few ms do not charge C1 enough to fire zener and scr. R1 adjusts delay before scr fires, up to several seconds.—E. K. Howell, The Light Activated SCR, General Electric, Syracuse, N.Y., No. 200.34, 1965.

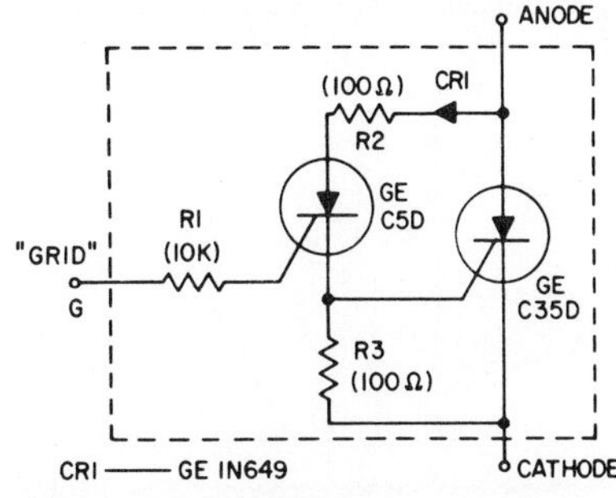

THYRATRON SUBSTITUTE—Combination of small scr as trigger and large scr for power-handling gives performance characteristics of thyratron gas tube, including very high signal input impedance. Maximum forward blocking voltage with single C5 trigger is 400 V. Maximum load current of circuit is 25 A rms. —"SCR Manual," 4th Edition, General Electric, 1967, p 169–170.

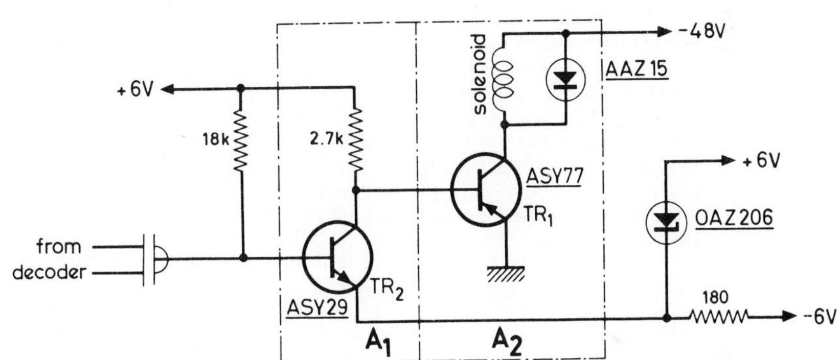

TYPEWRITER SOLENOID DRIVERS—Used to actuate printing keys of electric typewriter under control of electrical signals from computer or calculator. Each key has armature that is pulled down magnetically by solenoid. Since only one character can be printed at given moment, only one output transistor TR1 must conduct at given moment, with all other output transistors (for other keys) cut off.—Output Unit for an Electric Typewriter, Philips, Pub. Dept., Elcoma Div., Eindhoven, The Netherlands, No. 832, 1966.

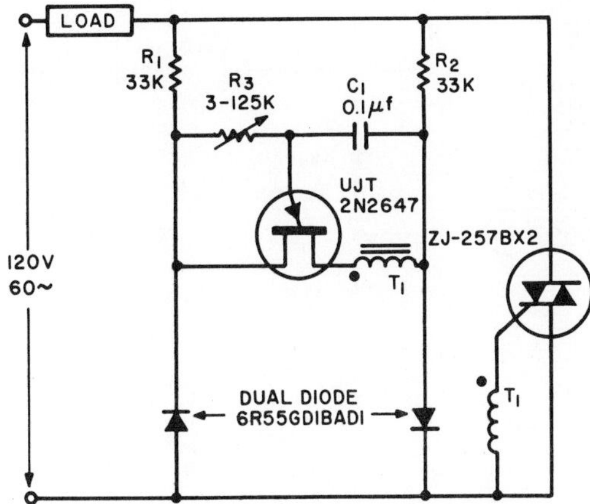

UJT PHASE CONTROL WITHOUT HYSTERESIS—Operation is independent of variations in supply voltage. Easily adapted for automatic feedback control systems by introducing transducer in one leg of bridge.—E. K. Howell, Bilateral SCR Lets Designers Economize on Circuitry, *Electronic Design*, Jan. 20, 1964, p 74–77.

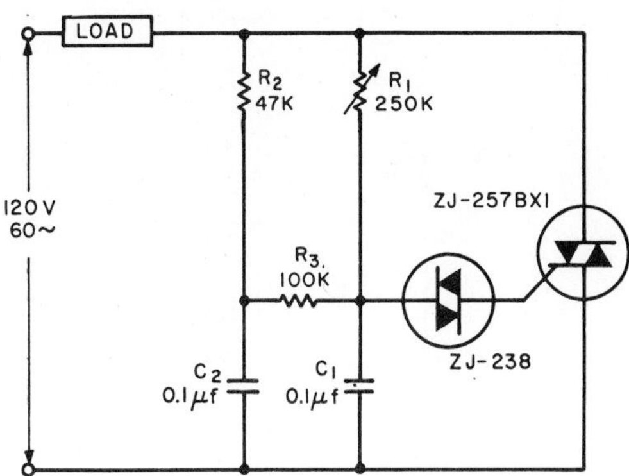

DUAL-RC BILATERAL SCR—Additional phase-shift network provides control over range of 5% to 95% load and reduces hysteresis. Suitable for lamps, heaters, and fan speed controls.—E. K. Howell, Bilateral SCR Lets Designers Economize on Circuitry, *Electronic Design*, Jan. 20, 1964, p 74–77.

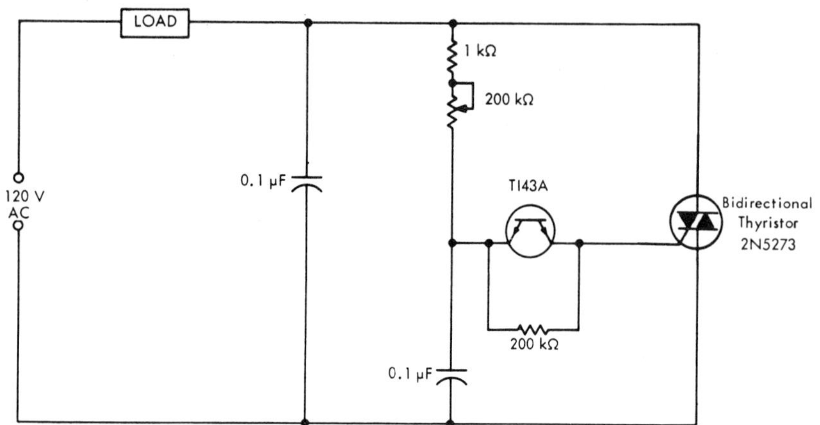

FULL-WAVE WITH THYRISTOR—Breakdown diode provides triggering of bidirectional thyristor on both half-cycles, at point in cycle determined by setting of pot. Load capacity depends on rating of thyristor.—Preferred Semiconductors and Components, Texas Instruments, Dallas, Texas, CC101, 1968, p 24108.

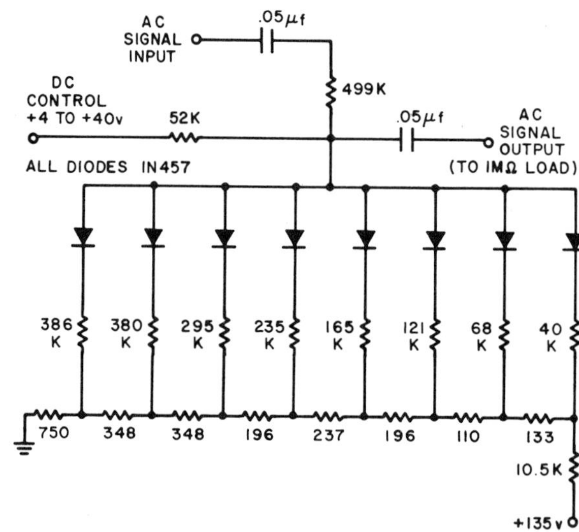

VOLTAGE-CONTROLLED GAIN CHANGER—Provides 4:1 gain change of 400-Hz square-wave carrier signal that is up to 25 V p-p at input. Diodes are used to switch additional parallel paths sequentially in simple voltage-divider circuit. Increasing d-c control voltage makes diodes conduct in sequence because of increasing back-bias applied to successive paths. Gain is maximum at lowest control voltage, when no diodes are conducting.—R. B. Mossman, Diode Divider Circuit Provides A-C Gain Control, *Electronic Design*, April 26, 1965, p 46–48.

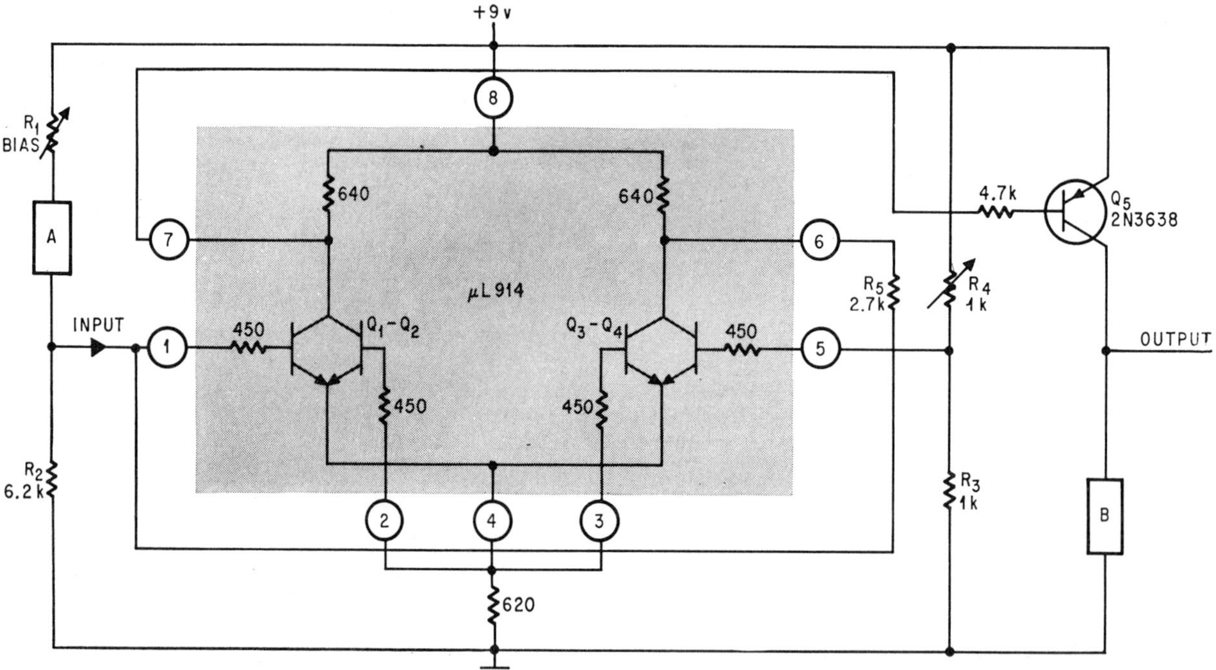

DIGITAL IC AS CONTROL SWITCH—Q5 serves as output stage for Fairchild dual-gate IC to give versatile circuit at total cost under $2. With resistors at A and B and R5 open, linear amplifier is obtained. Snap-action temperature control switch is obtained with R5 in, 1,000-ohm thermistor at A, and 6-V 100-mA relay at B. With FPM100 phototransistor at A and 330-ohm load resistor at B, circuit becomes light-sensing preamp with digital readout.—R. Ricks, Low-Cost Digital IC Performs Linear Functions, *Electronics*, July 24, 1967, p 86–87.

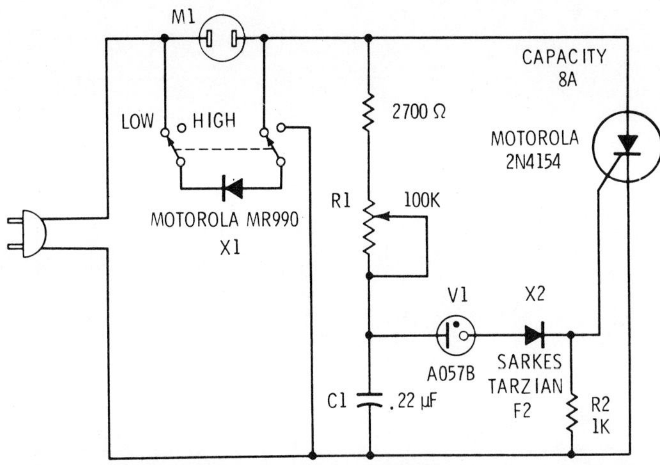

330-DEG SCR CONTROL—Turn-on pulse for scr X3 is generated when neon fires. Point at which it fires in positive half of a-c line cycle is determined by R1, to give 330-deg range for load control in each cycle.—W. G. Miller, "Using and Understanding Miniature Neon Lamps," H. W. Sams & Co., Indianapolis, Ind., 1969, p 62.

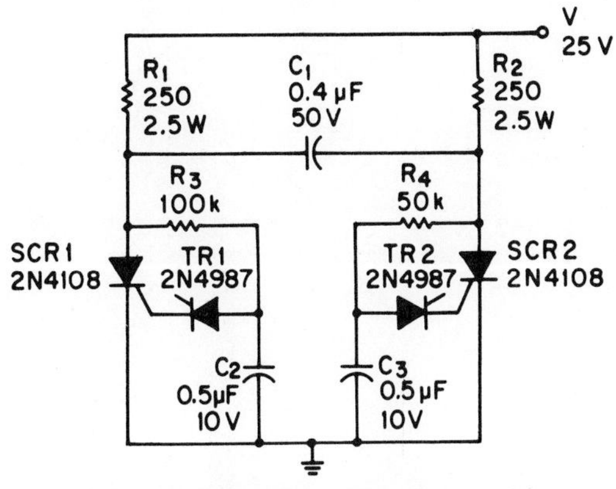

TWO-STATE SEQUENTIAL—Sequential control for only two loads gives high overall efficiency and is self-starting. Operating time of each 100-mA load is independently adjustable.—E. Kiburis, Sequential Control with Silicon Controlled Rectifiers, *EEE*, March 1970, p 100–103.

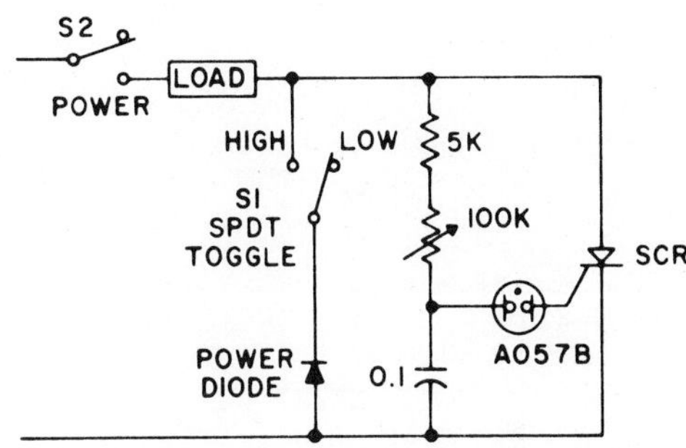

360-DEG PHASE SHIFTER—Neon-triggered scr regulates power delivered to load on both half-cycles. Full power is delivered when S1 is in HIGH position. Scr is TI-40A2.—E. Bauman, "Applications of Neon Lamps and Gas Discharge Tubes," Signalite, Neptune, N.J., p 121.

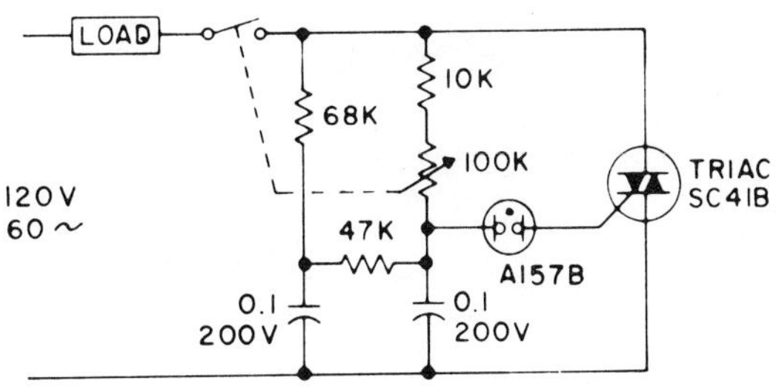

600-W TRIAC—Provides full-wave proportional control, using triac triggered by neon lamp whose breakdown voltage is same in both directions.—E. Bauman, "Applications of Neon Lamps and Gas Discharge Tubes," Signalite, Neptune, N.J., p 125.

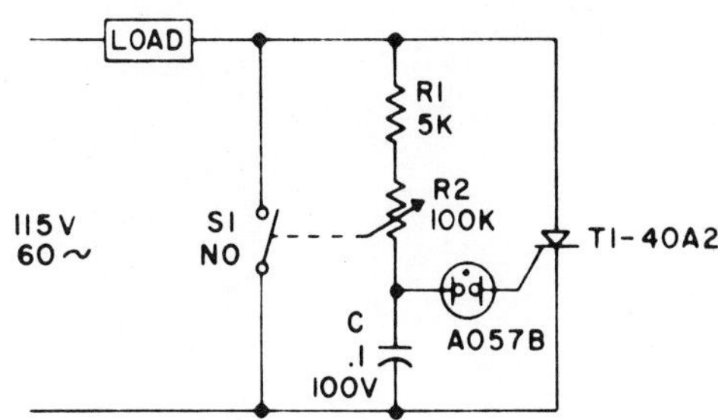

110-DEG PHASE SHIFTER—During each positive half-cycle of sine-wave voltage, 24% to 95% of available power (depending on setting of R2) is supplied to load via scr triggered by neon lamp. Full clockwise rotation of R2 applies full power to load through S1 ganged to R2.—E. Bauman, "Applications of Neon Lamps and Gas Discharge Tubes," Signalite, Neptune, N.J., p 120.

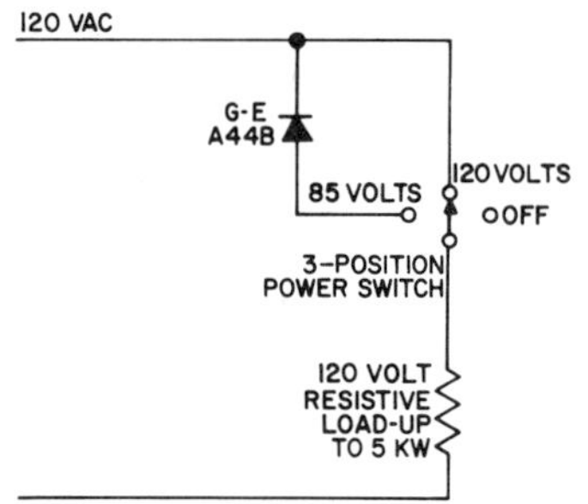

3-POSITION POWER CONTROL—Rectifier reduces load power by cutting line voltage to 85 V rms.—F. W. Gutzwiller and E. K. Howell, Economy Power Semiconductor Applications, General Electric, Syracuse, N.Y., No. 671.1, 1965, p 7.

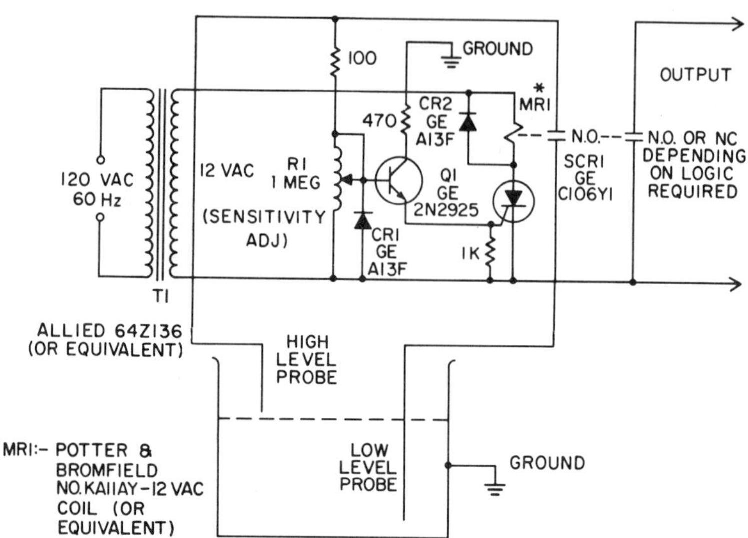

LIQUID-LEVEL CONTROL—Maintains liquid level between two previously established limits, determined by positioning two metal probes, in any reasonably well grounded container. Energization of probes with a-c eliminates electrolytic corrosion. Output can be pump, solenoid valve, or other device for changing liquid level. Operation from 12-V secondary of filament transformer contributes to safety.—D. R. Grafham, Automatic Liquid Level Control, General Electric, Syracuse, N.Y., No. 201.14, 1966.

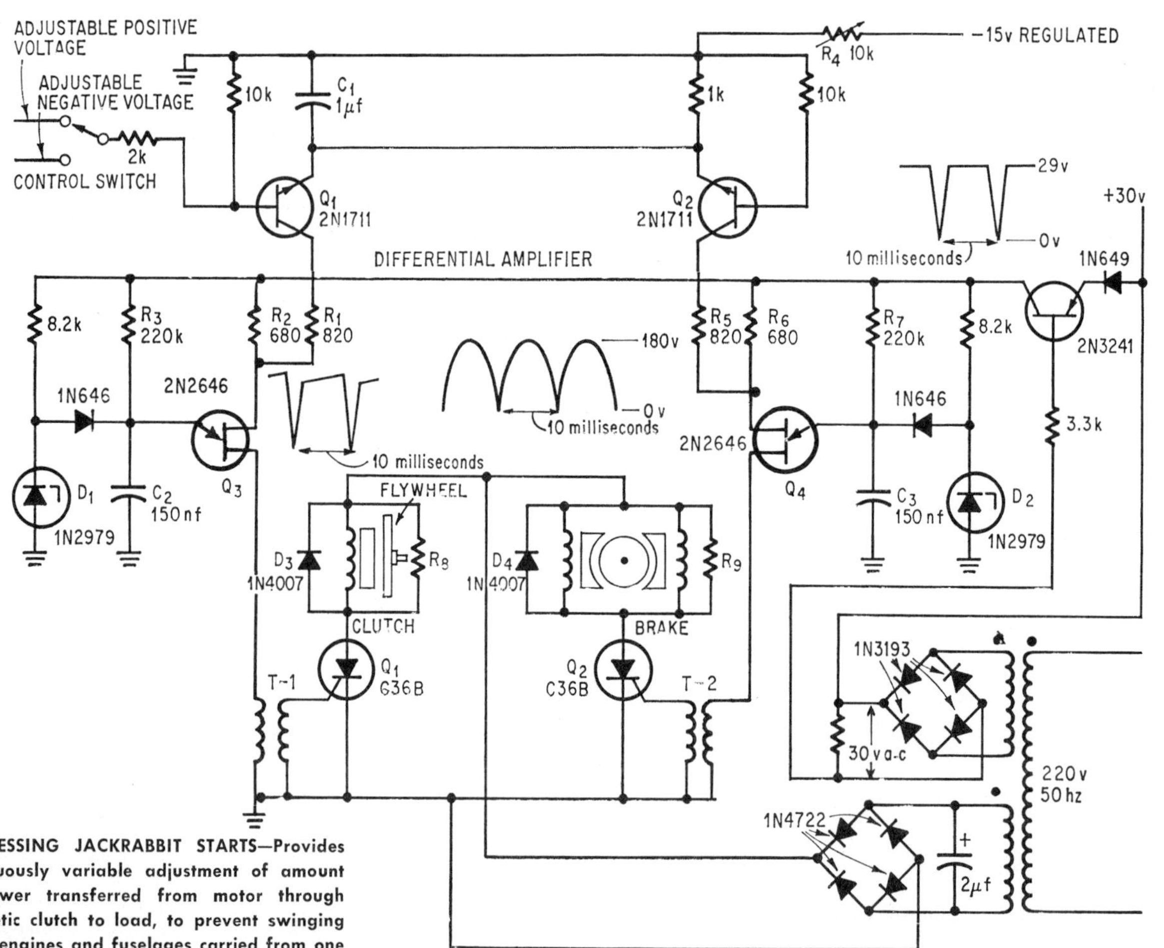

SUPPRESSING JACKRABBIT STARTS—Provides continuously variable adjustment of amount of power transferred from motor through magnetic clutch to load, to prevent swinging of jet engines and fuselages carried from one work station to next by overhead trolley. Same circuit acts on magnetic brakes to prevent jerky stops. Uses differential amplifier added to conventional ujt's Q3 and Q4 in brake and clutch control circuits. Control R4 serves both for startup and braking, since these can never occur simultaneously.—P. J. Kaskinen, Differential Amplifier Governs Magnetic Brakes And Clutches, *Electronics*, May 13, 1968, p 75–76.

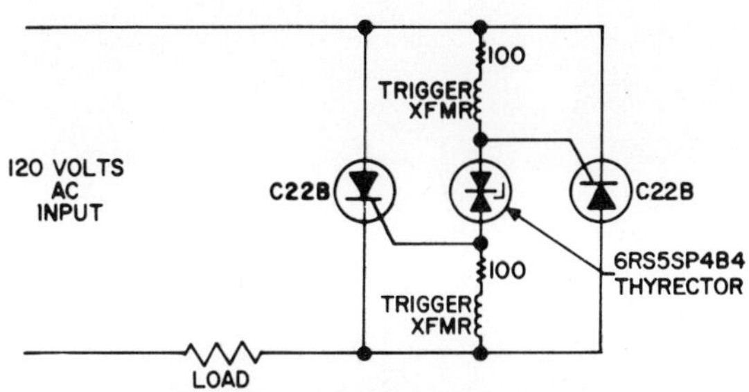

TRANSIENT SUPPRESSION WITH THYRECTOR—With thyrector connected in gate circuits of scr's, portion of transient energy triggers forward-biased scr into conduction, thereby protecting reverse-biased scr from damage. Arrangement permits use of smaller and lower-cost thyrector for given degree of protective effectiveness in an scr control circuit.—F. W. Gutzwiller and E. K. Howell, Economy Power Semiconductor Applications, General Electric, Syracuse, N.Y., No. 671.1, 1965, p 18.

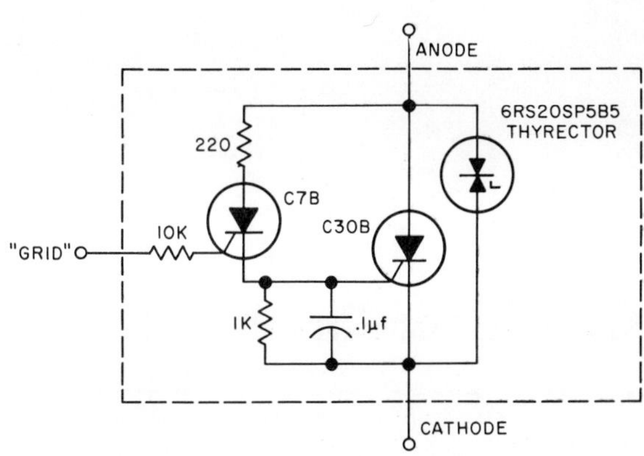

SCR REPLACEMENT FOR THYRATRON—Circuit shown is suitable for direct replacement of C3J thyratron in many 120-V a-c applications. Thyrector provides transient voltage protection for C30B scr.—D. R. Grafham, Using Low Current SCR's, General Electric, Syracuse, N.Y., No. 200.19, 1967, p 35.

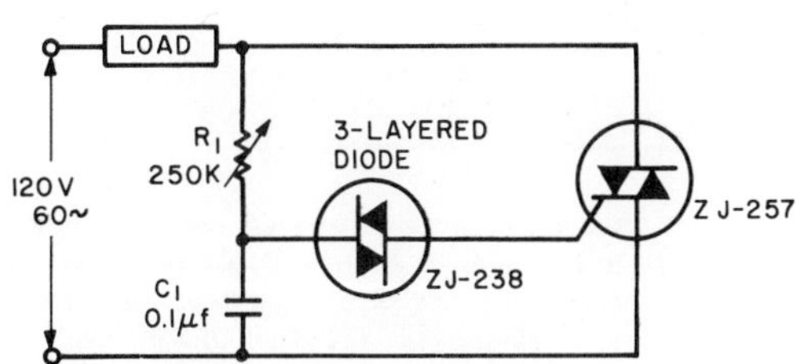

PHASE-CONTROLLED BILATERAL SCR—Requires only four components, though has limited control range and large hysteresis at low output. When voltage across triggering diode reaches 35 V, C1 discharges through diode into gate of bilateral scr.—E. K. Howell, Bilateral SCR Lets Designers Economize on Circuitry, *Electronic Design*, Jan. 20, 1964, p 74–77.

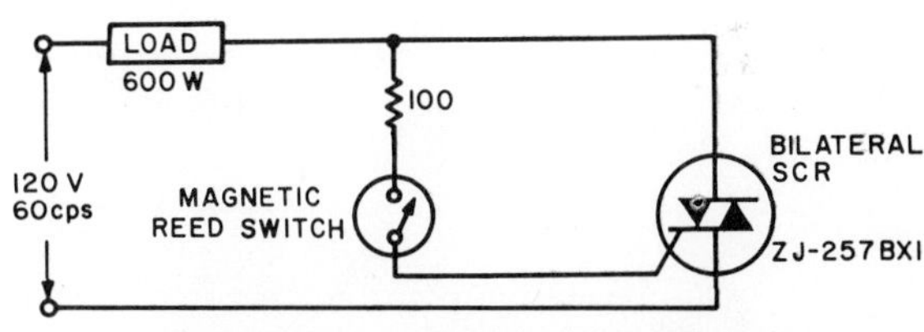

MECHANICALLY ACTUATED SCR—Only three components are needed with bilateral scr for full-wave control of a-c load, as compared to nine components and two conventional scr's in conventional circuit. Any other type of switch may be used.—E. K. Howell, Bilateral SCR Lets Designers Economize on Circuitry, *Electronic Design*, Jan. 20, 1964, p 74–77.

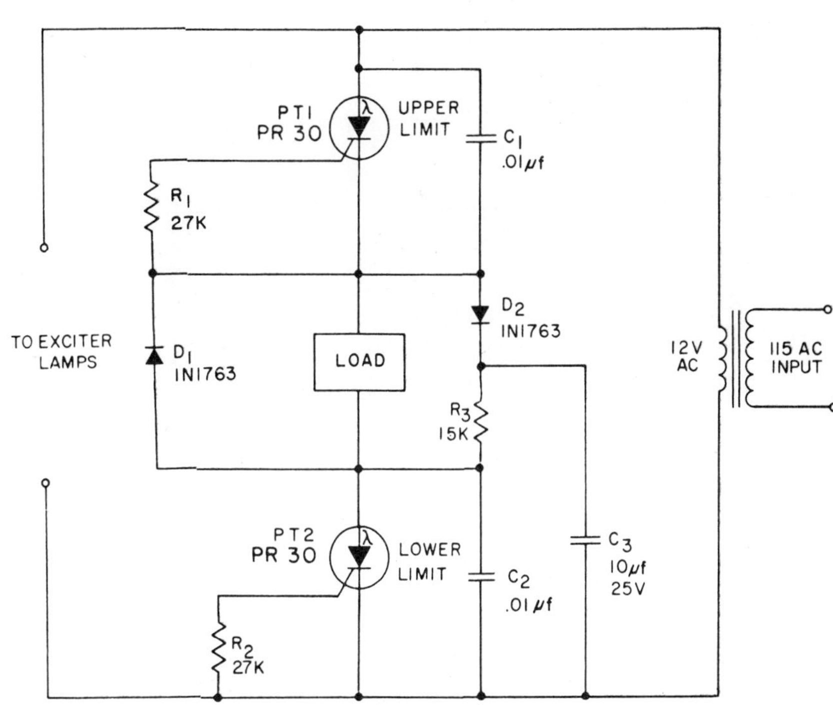

BIN LEVEL CONTROL—Uses two SSPI PR30 light-sensitive scr's with light sources, mounted at upper and lower control limits of material in bin. With level above upper limit, both photoscr's are dark and off. When level falls below upper limit, PT1 switches on and C3 charges to peak positive a-c supply voltage. When level falls below lower limit, PT2 is triggered on, making half-wave rectified a-c energize load and refill bin. When level rises above lower control limit, C3 voltage holds PT2 on. When level reaches upper limit, PT1 turns off and load is deenergized, stopping charging of C3 so PT2 also turns off.—Automatic Bin Feed Control, Solid State Products, Salem, Mass., No. 12.

CHAPTER 17

Converter Circuits—D-C to D-C

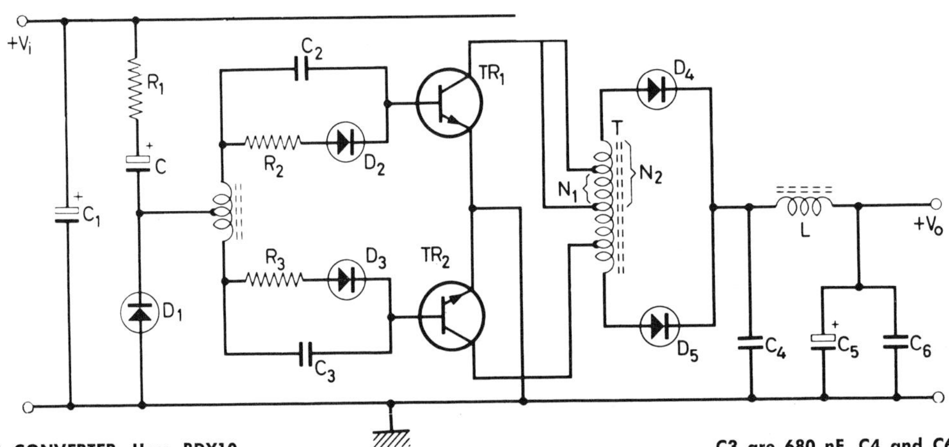

20-KHZ 30-W D-C CONVERTER—Uses BDY10 transistors in autotransformer connection that permits adding 13.8-V d-c input voltage to 26-V rectified output of converter to give required 40-V d-c output for mobile transmitter applications. Report gives all winding data. D1 is BYZ13, D2 and D3 are BYX10, and D4 and D5 are BY118. R1 is 68, and R2 and R3 are 10. C and C1 are 100 µF, C2 and C3 are 680 nF, C4 and C6 are 1 µF, and C5 is 8 µF.—A. H. Hilbers, D. C. Converters Operating at 20 KHZ, Philips, Pub. Dept., Elcoma Div., Eindhoven, The Netherlands, No. 436, 1966.

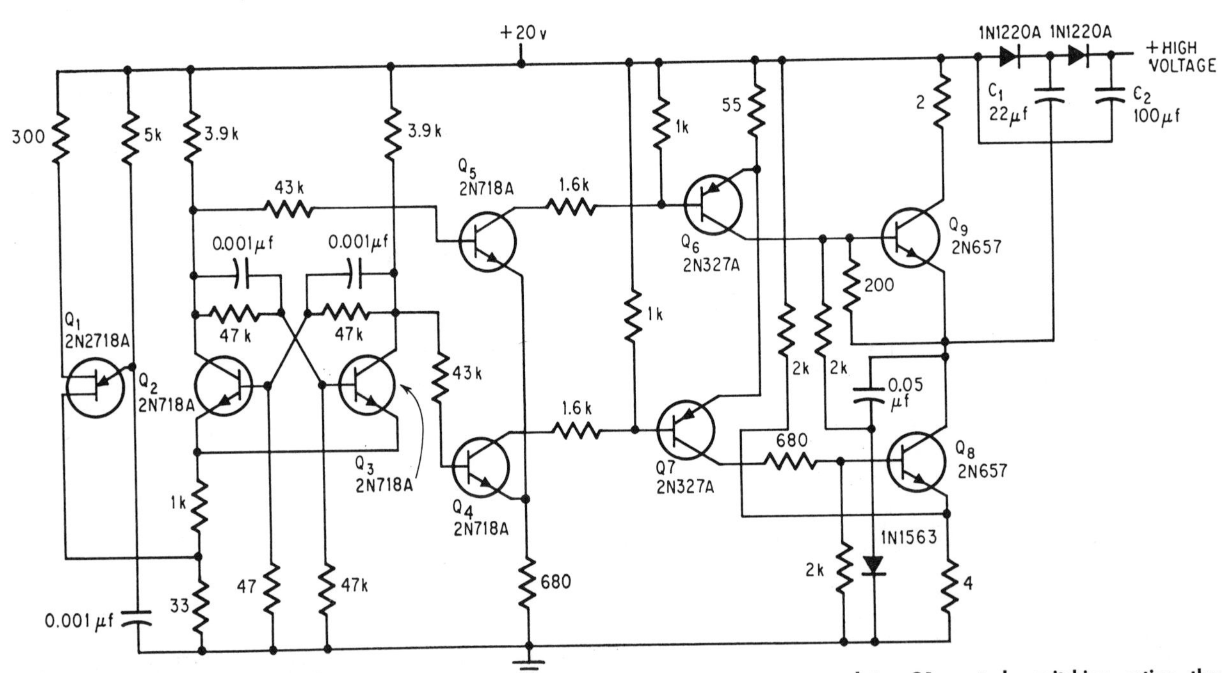

D-C STEPUP AUTOTRANSFORMER—Steps up supply voltage for solid-state circuit by using transistors Q8 and Q9 to charge C1 and then discharge it into C2 repeatedly. With 20-V input, output of circuit is 35.5 V at 80 mA, with efficiency of 60%. Ujt relaxation oscillator Q1 controls switching action through flip-flop Q2-Q3.—C. D. Brock and L. E. Johnston, Push-pull Capacitors Multiply Input Voltage, *Electronics*, Nov. 13, 1967, p 101–102.

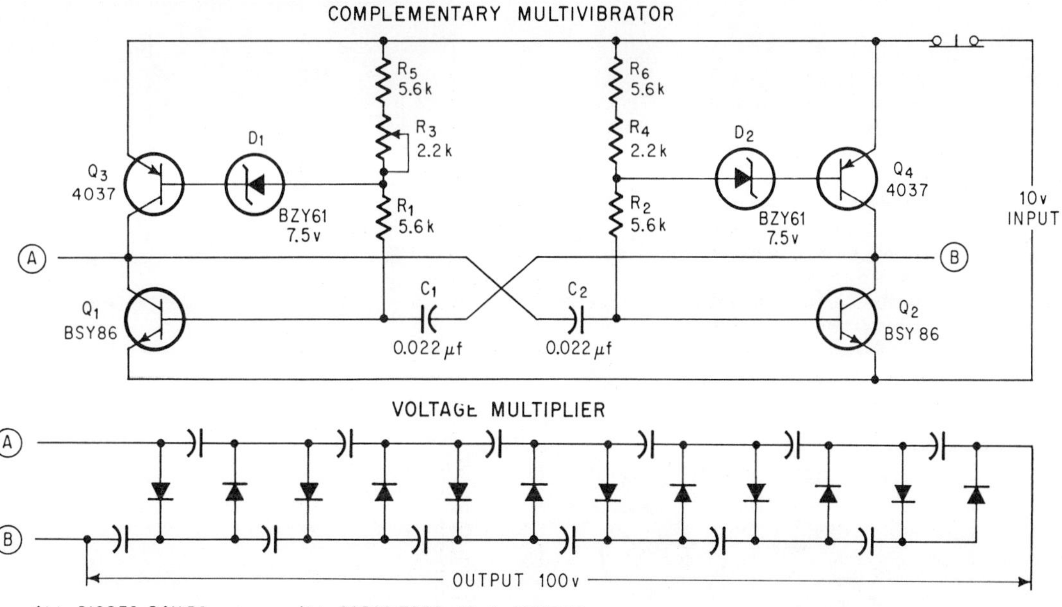

D-C VOLTAGE CONVERTER—Uses 10-kHz complementary mvbr to change 10-V input to 100-V output with 280 mW power. Efficiency is 70%. Square-wave output of mvbr is fed into diode-capacitor network below, for rectification and multiplying of amplitude according to number of multiplier stages. Reversing connections of diodes and capacitors changes output polarity. Mvbr does not restart itself, so starting switch is placed in d-c input line.—K. Van der Geer, Transformerless D-c Voltage Converter is 70% Efficient, *Electronics*, April 14, 1969, p 95.

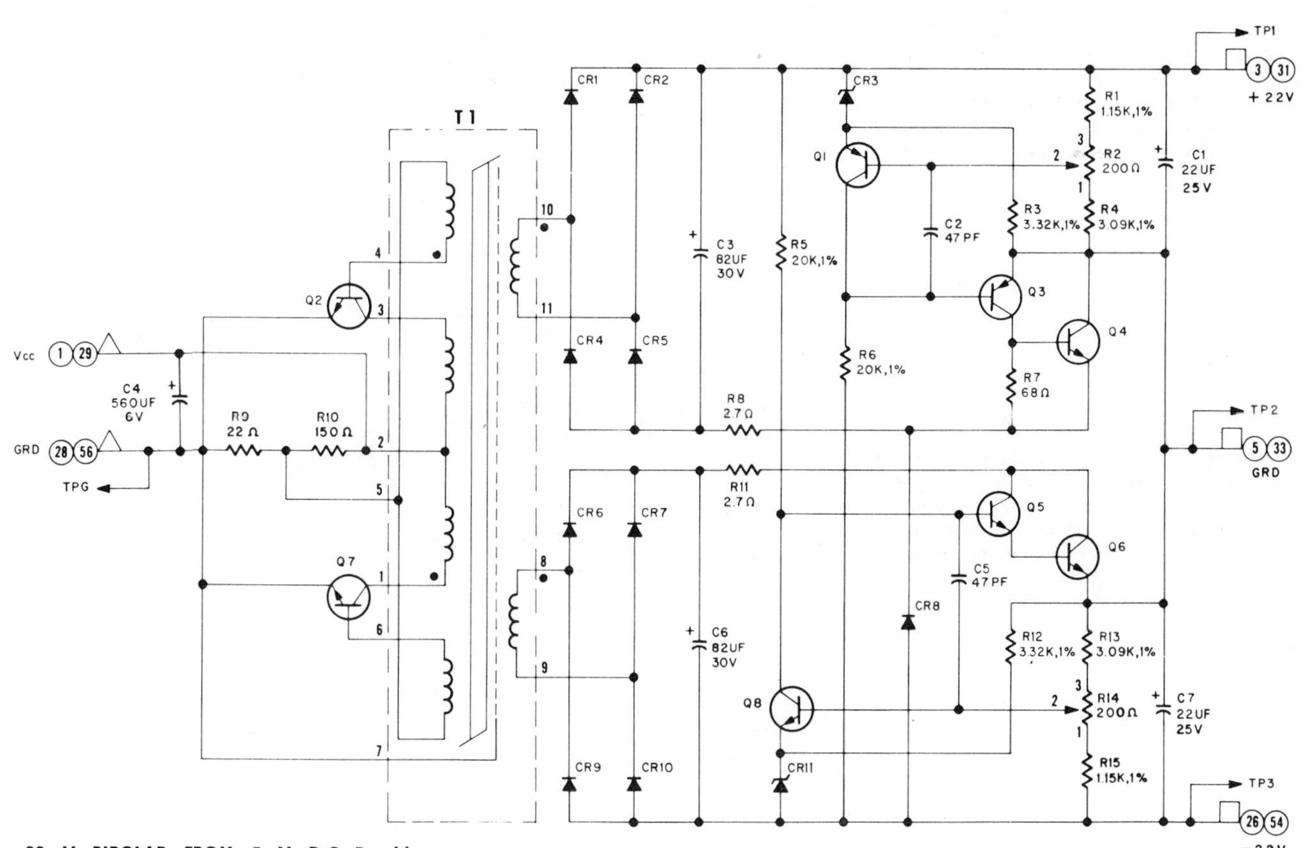

22 V BIPOLAR FROM 5 V D-C—Provides supply voltages required by analog cards, with load and line regulation better than 0.15% at 360 mA output current. Input is from standard 5-V d-c digital power source. Consists of d-c to a-c converter, rectifier, filter assembly, and regulator. Q1 & Q3 are 2N3906; Q4 & Q6 are 2N1485; Q2 & Q7 are 2N5190; Q5 & Q8 are 2N3904. CR3 & CR11 are IN5232B 5.6-V zener; all other diodes are MR310. T1 is Topa PNA8144. Available commercially as D-4085 plug-in module. Circled numbers are etched board connector pins.—Integrated Circuit Logic Cards, Electronic Engineering Co., Santa Ana, Cal., 1969, p DS77.

33 V FROM 12 V—Transistors act as switches for charging capacitors in parallel and discharging in series to obtain inexpensive transformerless voltage multiplication of square-wave pulses when required pulse amplitude is greater than available supply voltage. To obtain positive output pulses, use negative supply, reverse diodes, and change to pnp transistors. Values shown handle repetition rates up to 6 kHz into 2K load.—P. Yanczer, Eliminate Pulse Transformer with a Voltage Multiplier, *Electronic Design*, Aug. 15, 1968, p 234.

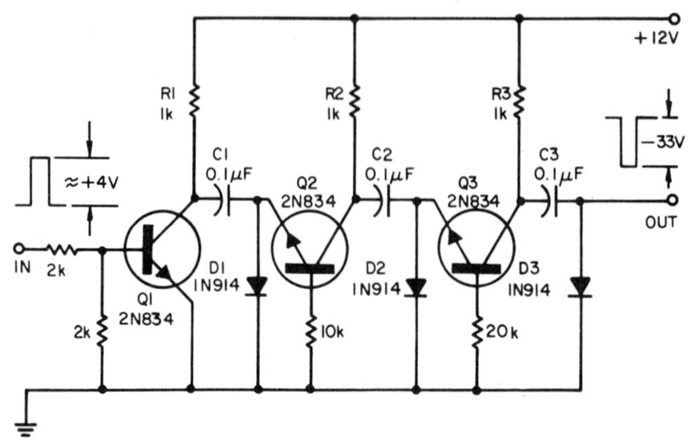

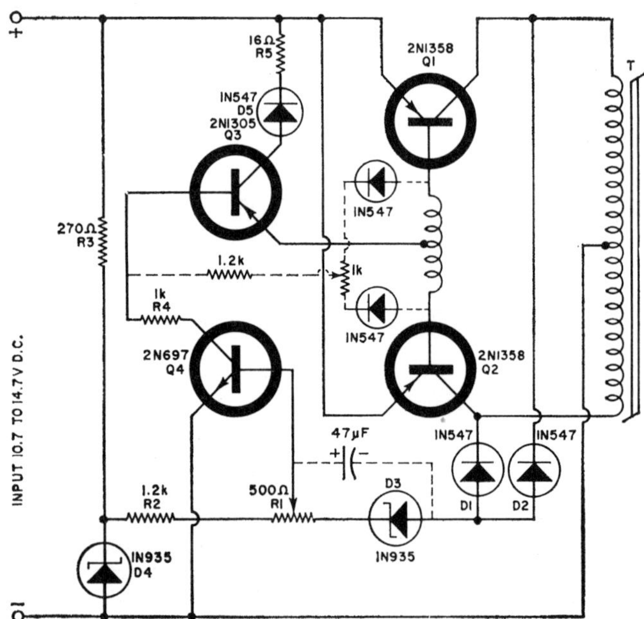

REGVERTER—Uses solid-state d-c converter as series regulator to obtain high efficiency as mobile supply operating from 12-V battery and delivering 25 W at 115 V and 400 Hz. Operated over 3 years in space orbit application. Output transformer (secondary not shown) uses Magnetics Inc. core 50425-4A with 556-turn secondary. Article gives transformer design data.—S. Levy and W. L. Blair, High-Efficiency D.C.-D.C. Converter, *Electronics World*, Feb. 1969, p 35–37 and 59.

100 W IN 12 OUNCES—Gives 85% efficiency at 50 kHz operating frequency, in converting 28 V d-c to 250 V d-c at 400 mA. Maximum ripple in output is 0.5%.—T. B. Mills, Designing Smaller, Lighter Dc-to-Dc Converters, *EEE*, March 1969, p 76–80.

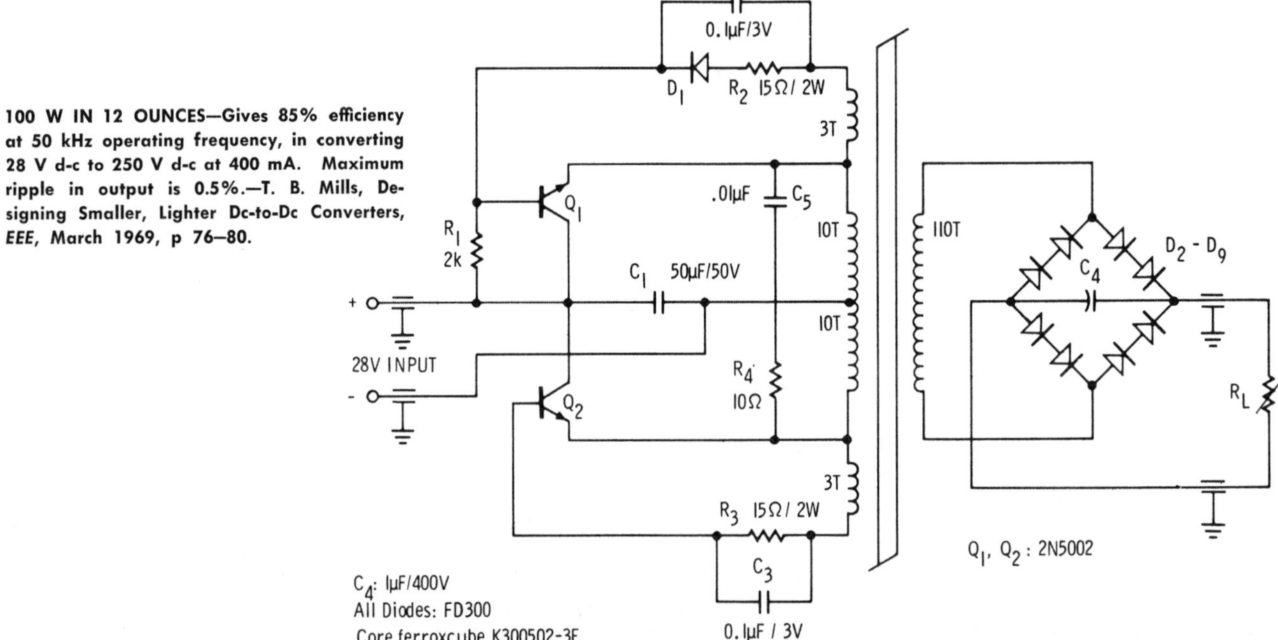

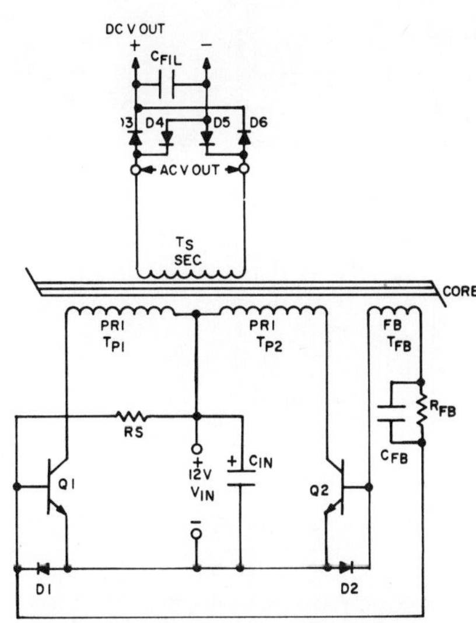

Q1, Q2	D27C3 HEATSINK	CORE: FERROXCUBE
D1, D2	A14F	#2616P-3E POT CORE
R_S	4.7 K Ω	T_{P1}, T_{P2} 7T #25 WIRE
R_{FB}	100Ω, 10 W	T_{FB} 10 T # 25 WIRE
C_{FB}	.0068 50V	T_S 160T # 32 WIRE
C_{IN}	100 μf	
C_{FIL}	1 μf 400V	
D3, 4, 5, 6	IN5056	

280 V D-C AT 20 W FROM 12 V D-C—Arrangement is compact low-cost means of obtaining high-voltage d-c supply from batteries. Can be used as d-c/a-c inverter by removing bridge rectifier, in which case output is 280 V a-c at 16 kHz. Article gives design criteria and detailed instructions for designing and winding pot-core transformer.—R. A. Yodlowski, Designing A 12 Volt DC to High Voltage DC Converter, General Electric, Syracuse, N.Y., No. 90.75, 1969.

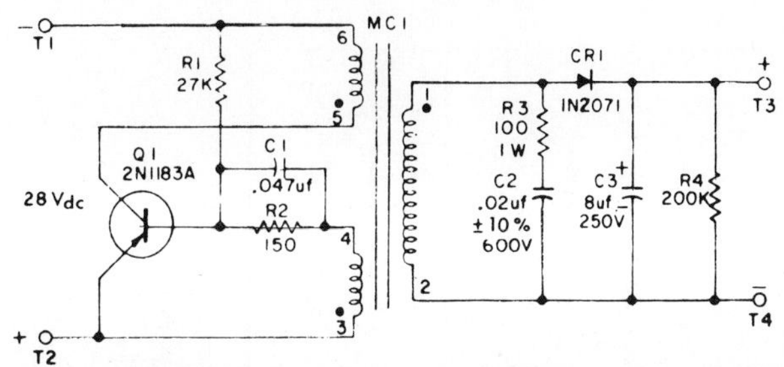

28–170 V D-C/D-C CONVERTER—Burroughs VC28-170-1 module was developed for operating Nixie tubes, driver modules, and other applications where required high-level d-c voltage is not available. Conversion of d-c voltage level is achieved with oscillator Q1, transformer, and rectifier. Maximum output current is 30 mA, with 4-V p-p ripple at full load.—DC-DC Converter, Burroughs, Plainfield, N.J., No. 1087A, 1967.

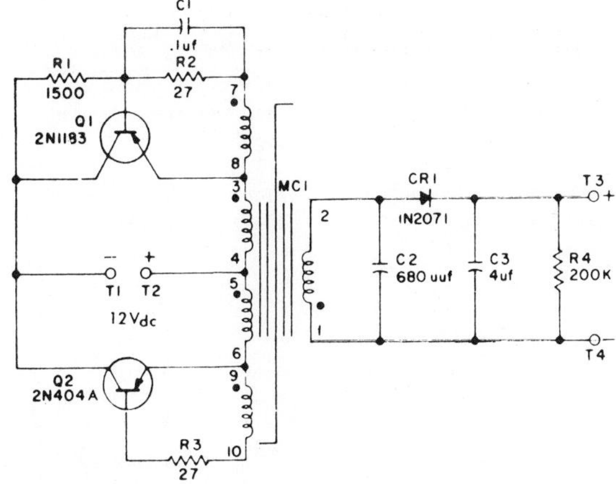

12–170 V D-C/D-C CONVERTER—Burroughs VC12-170-1 module can be used where high-level d-c voltage is not available, as for operating Nixies and driver modules. Step-up of d-c voltage is achieved by transistor oscillator Q1-Q2, transformer, and rectifier. Maximum output current is 30 mA, with 4-V p-p ripple at full load.—DC-DC Converter, Burroughs, Plainfield, N.J., No. 1087A, 1967.

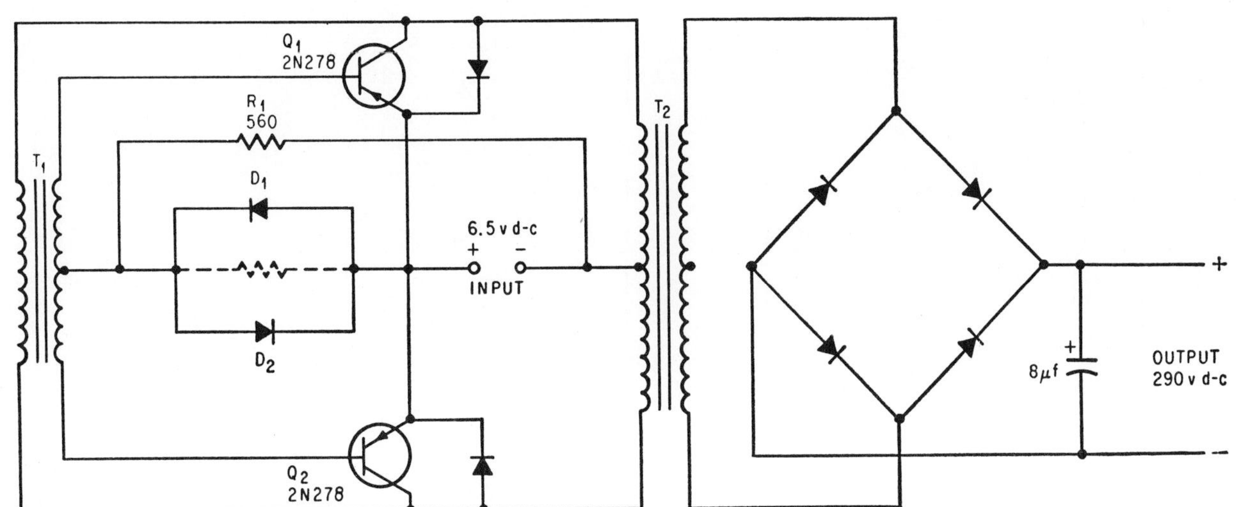

CUTTING START-UP POWER—Base return resistor in conventional d-c/d-c converter (shown dotted and normally 30 ohms) is replaced by back-to-back diodes D1-D2, to reduce large currents needed to develop starting voltage for switching transistors Q1-Q2 and thereby reduce power consumption.—R. M. Glorioso, Converter Cuts Start-Up Power, Offers Good Regulation, *Electronics*, Feb. 6, 1967, p 72–73.

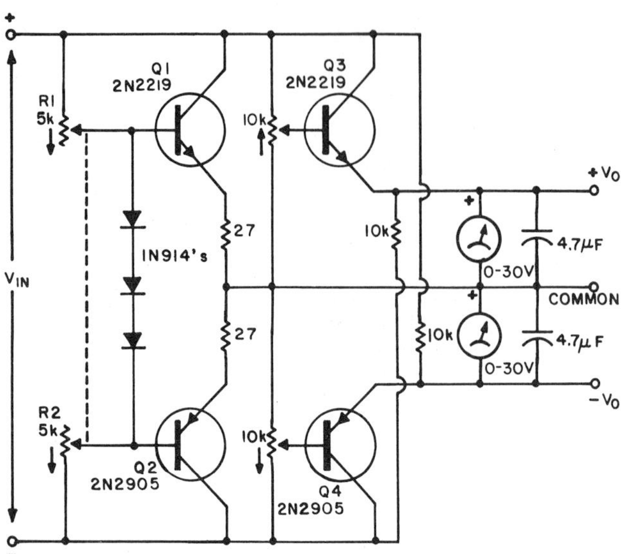

BOTH POLARITIES FROM ONE—When connected to single ungrounded power supply up to 40 V d-c, circuit provides both positive and negative voltages that are independently adjustable and can furnish up to 50 mA. Ideal for supplementing costly bench power supplies in circuit development laboratories. —C. Sewell, Jr., One Power Supply Does the Work of Two, *Electronic Design*, April 26, 1967, p 241–242.

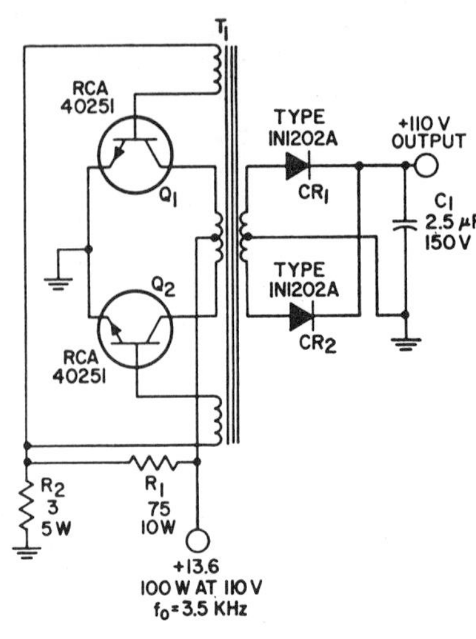

13.6 V D-C TO 3.5 KHZ TO 110 V D-C—Delivers d-c power output of 100 W. Book gives detailed procedure for selecting optimum transistors and component values for achieving efficiency above 75% at rated load. —"Silicon Power Circuits Manual," RCA, Harrison, N.J., SP-51, p 183.

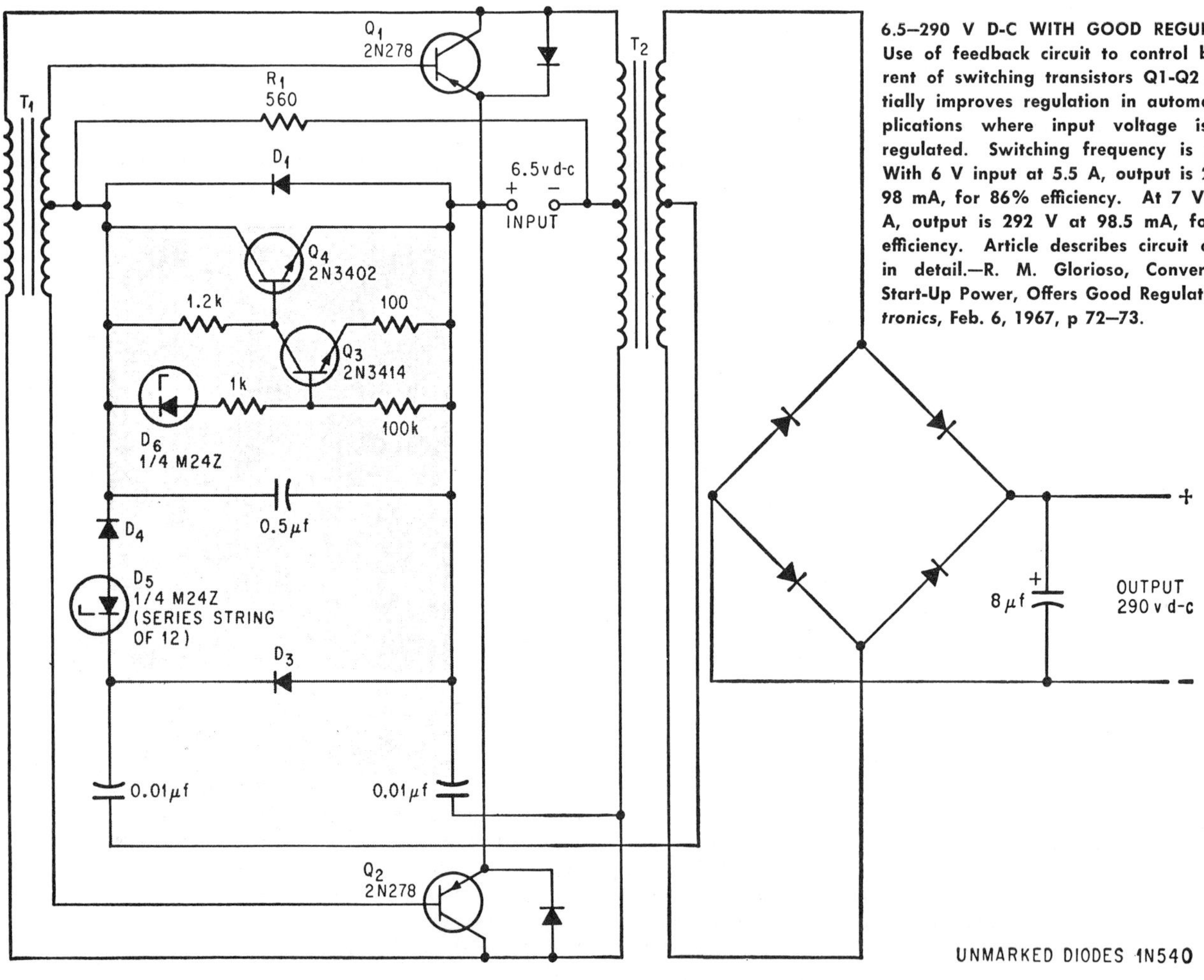

6.5–290 V D-C WITH GOOD REGULATION—Use of feedback circuit to control base current of switching transistors Q1-Q2 substantially improves regulation in automotive applications where input voltage is poorly regulated. Switching frequency is 1.2 kHz. With 6 V input at 5.5 A, output is 290 V at 98 mA, for 86% efficiency. At 7 V and 5.8 A, output is 292 V at 98.5 mA, for 70.7% efficiency. Article describes circuit operation in detail.—R. M. Glorioso, Converter Cuts Start-Up Power, Offers Good Regulation, *Electronics*, Feb. 6, 1967, p 72–73.

UNMARKED DIODES 1N540

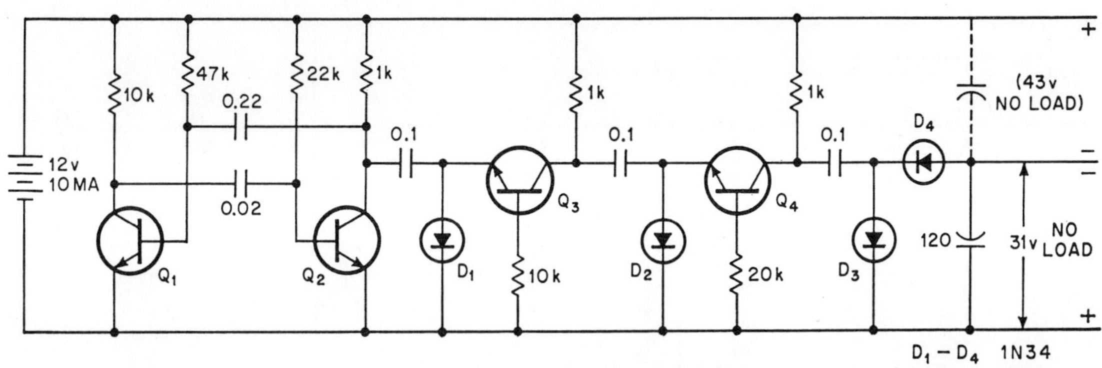

TRANSISTOR-SWITCHED SERIES-PARALLEL CAPACITORS—When Q2 is off, all three 0.1-μF capacitors charge to supply voltage less drops in diodes and 1K resistors. Q2 is part of free-running mvbr (about 1.35 kHz) that initiates switching action. When Q2 comes on for next half-cycle, Q3 and Q4 are forward-biased into conduction through capacitors to place all three 0.1-μF capacitors in series-aiding for transferring their charge through D4 to 120-μF output capacitor. Dashed line shows how extra stage of voltage multiplication can be obtained by connecting output capacitor to positive supply.—H. R. Mallory, Capacitors Add Up In Voltage Multiplier, *Electronics*, March 2, 1970, p 104.

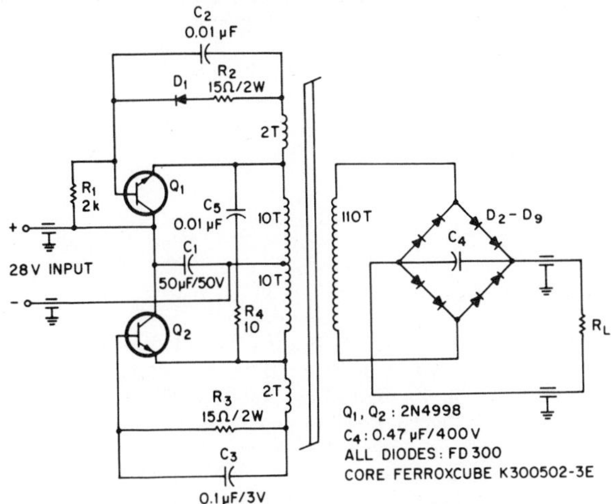

40 W USING HIGH-FREQUENCY TRANSISTORS—Article gives nomograms for output power and transformer design calculations, with 40-W circuit as example of design procedure. Inverter frequency is 46.5 kHz.—C. W. Young, Nomograms Simplify Design of DC-To-DC Converters, *EEE*, June 1970, p 46–47.

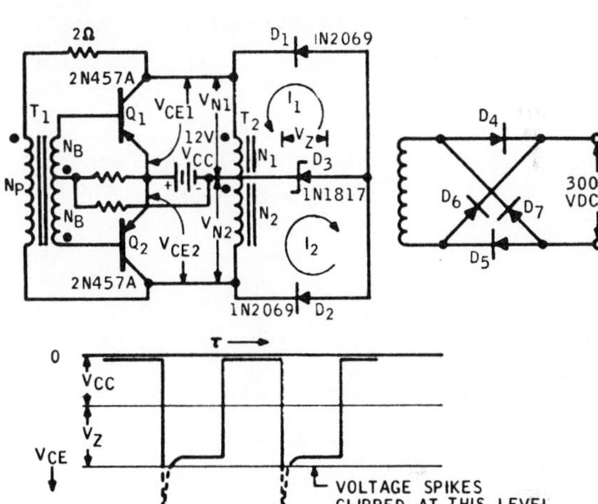

SPIKE-CLIPPING ZENER—Single zener D3 protects transistors in d-c converter from spikes that may be several times supply voltage, occurring when transistor current switches off through leakage inductance of power transformer.—P. Vergez, Transient Clipper For DC Converters, "400 Ideas for Design Selected from Electronic Design," Hayden Book Co., N.Y., 1964, p 208.

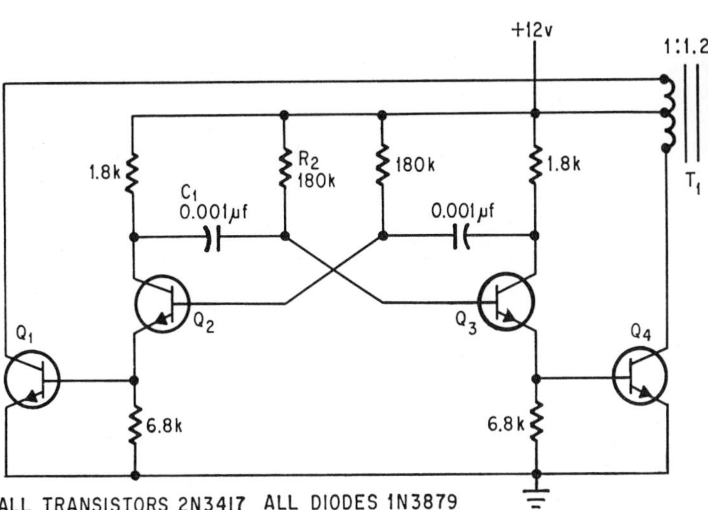

SQUARE WAVES FOR D-C CONVERTER—Astable mvbr Q2-Q3 generates square waves with 15% higher operating efficiency than saturable reactor sometimes used in d-c converters, and reduces cost and size. Frequency is 4 kHz, and rise and fall times are both less than 0.3 μs.—G. Marosi and F. Ludding, Multivibrator Replaces Reactor in D-C Converter, *Electronics*, July 10, 1967, p 81–82.

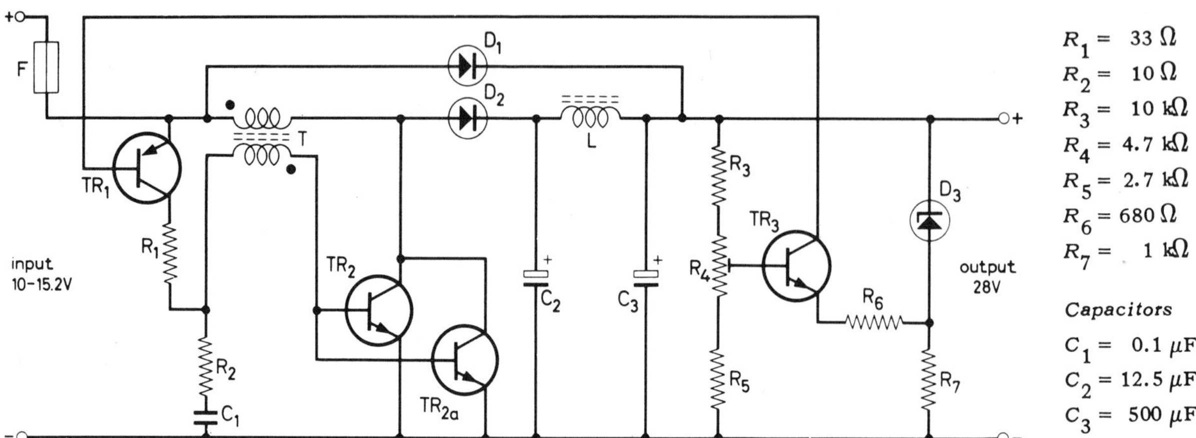

12 V D-C TO 28 V D-C STABILIZED—Delivers up to 800 mA with 80% efficiency, and will operate with supply voltages from 11 to 15 V. Oscillator frequency of 20 kHz gives noiseless operation and economically small design. Report gives winding data for transformer and choke. TR1 is BCY38, TR3 is BC108, and other transistors are BD121. D1 is BY126, D2 is BYX30/200R, and D3 is BZY94-C22.—J. M. Siemensma, A 23 W Voltage-Stabilized D. C. Converter, Philips, Pub. Dept., Elcoma Div., Eindhoven, The Netherlands, No. 439, 1967.

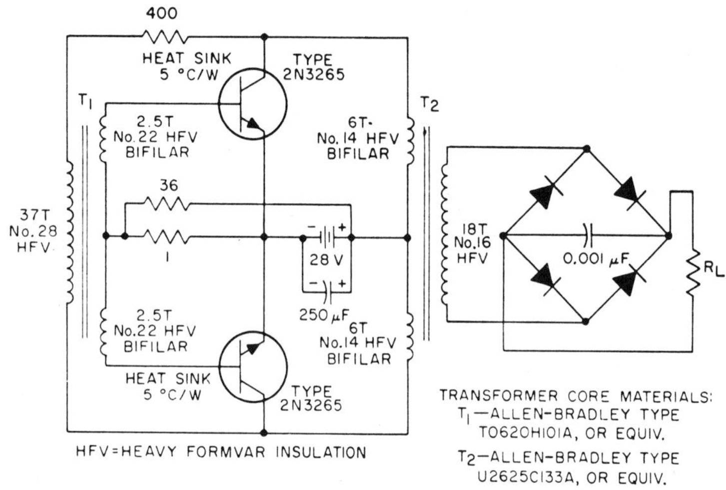

250-W 50-KHZ D-C/D-C—Sample circuit shown is used to explain procedure for designing practical high-speed two-transformer push-pull converter. Operates from 28-V d-c supply and delivers 80 to 90 V d-c depending on load.—"Silicon Power Circuits Manual," RCA, Harrison, N.J., SP-51, p 194.

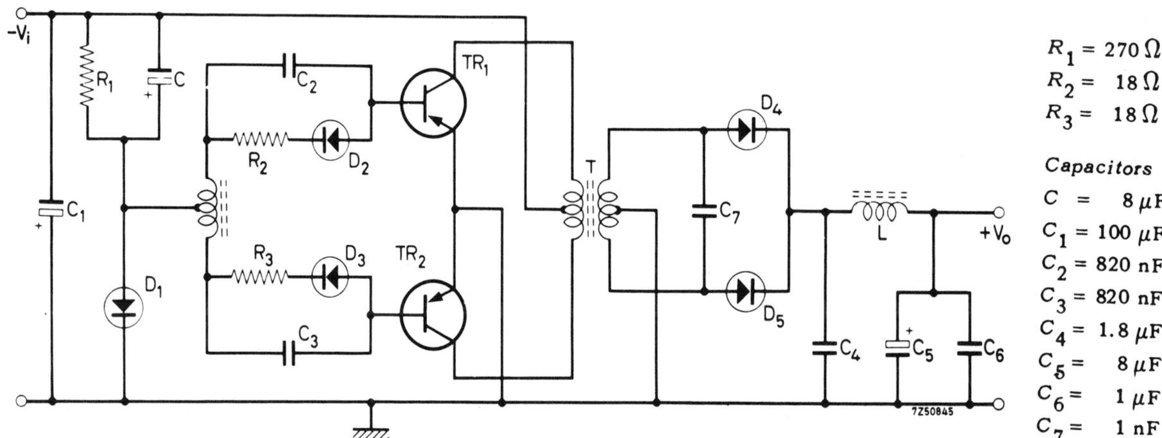

20-KHZ 60-W D-C CONVERTER—Use of transistors having high cutoff frequencies and power diodes with shorter switching times permits operation at 20 kHz where transformer noise is outside audible range, and gives reduction in size of transformer and filter components. Transistors are AU103 on heat sinks. D1 is BYZ13, D2 and D3 are BYX10, and D4 and D5 are BY118. Report gives winding data. Output is 60 W, at about 75% efficiency. Nominal input is 13.8 V d-c and output is 40 V d-c.—A. H. Hilbers, D. C. Converters Operating at 20 KHZ, Philips, Pub. Dept., Elcoma Div., Eindhoven, The Netherlands, No. 436, 1966.

CHAPTER 18
Converter Circuits—General

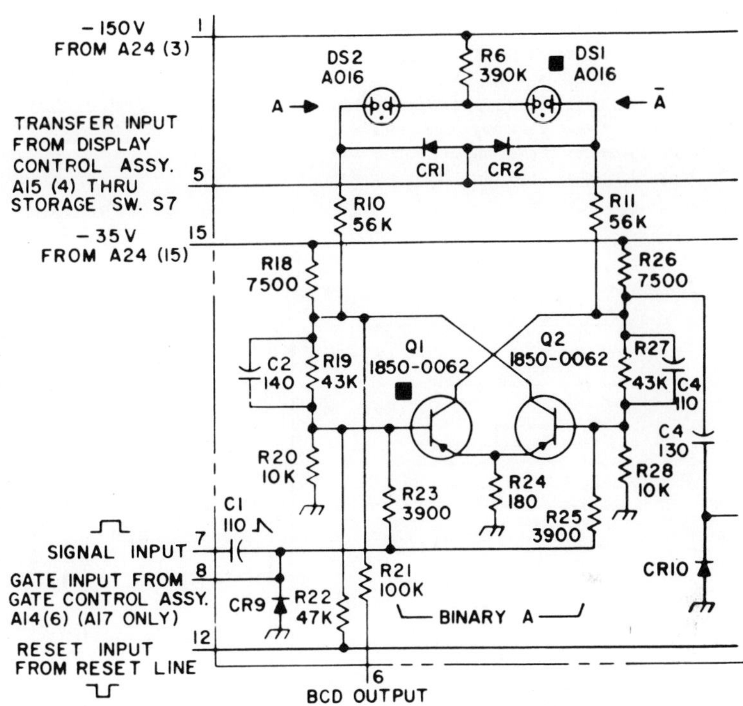

NEON BINARY-DECIMAL—Circuit shows one stage of binary counter developed by Hewlett-Packard, in which neon glow lamps and solid-state photoconductor elements perform decoding logic and necessary gain for driving decimal indicators. Light from neons falls on group of photocells to provide current path for operation of visual decimal display. (Book shows and describes photocell display matrix). Diodes CR1 and CR2 enable information to be stored while another counting operation proceeds. Circuit cycles in 10 counts instead of normal 16, and drives decimal display.—E. Bauman, "Applications of Neon Lamps and Gas Discharge Tubes," Signalite, Neptune, N.J., p 130–135.

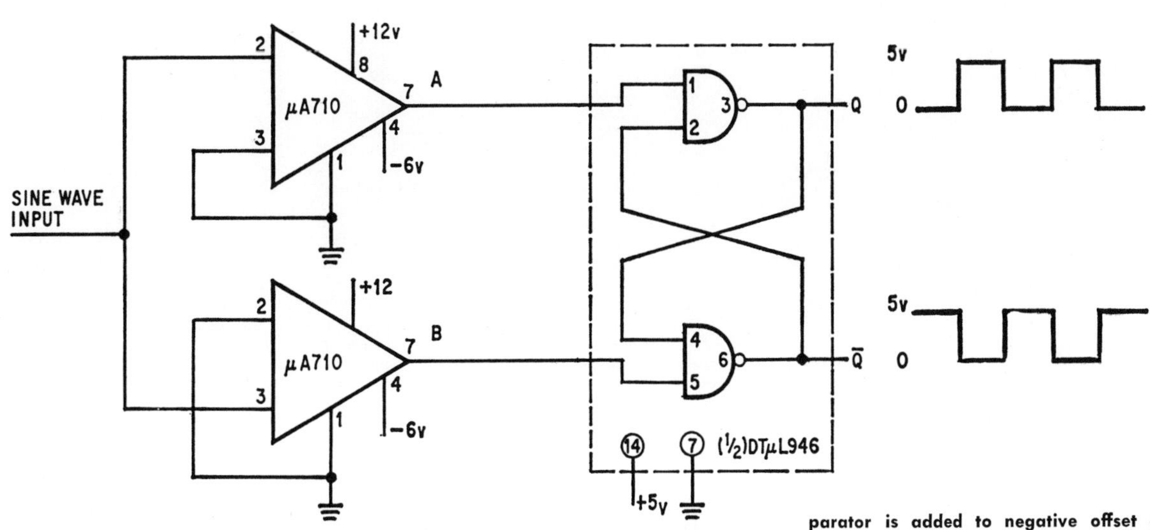

SINE-SQUARE CONVERTER—Two IC comparators convert sine waves to symmetrical square waves while operating in noise with wide temperature and amplitude variations. Outputs of comparators trigger R-S flip-flop on their edges. Positive offset from one comparator is added to negative offset of the other to maintain symmetry.—G. S. Oshiro, Two IC Comparators Improve Threshold Converter, *Electronics*, Dec. 23, 1968, p 59.

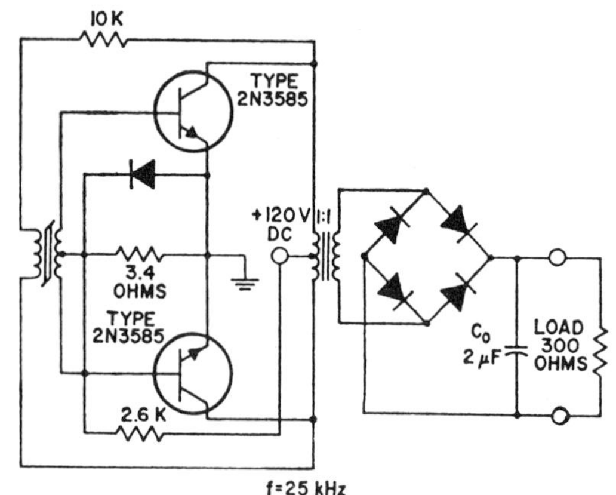

100-W 25-KHZ CONVERTER—Uses pulse switching techniques and two transformers to provide high d-c output voltage and high-speed operation. Book discusses load lines for optimum performance.—"Silicon Power Circuits Manual," RCA, Harrison, N.J., SP-51, p 98.

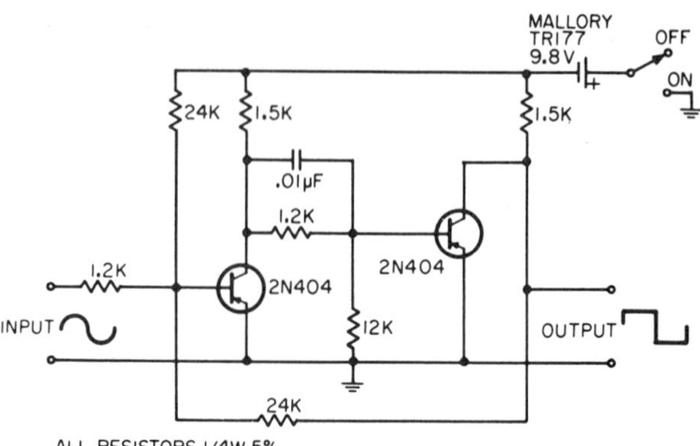

SINE-SQUARE CONVERTER—Schmitt trigger converts output of 600-ohm sine-wave signal generator to square waves required for testing digital equipment.—J. Shagena and A. Mall, Plug-In Squaring-Unit for Signal Generator, *EEE*, Oct. 1966, p 138.

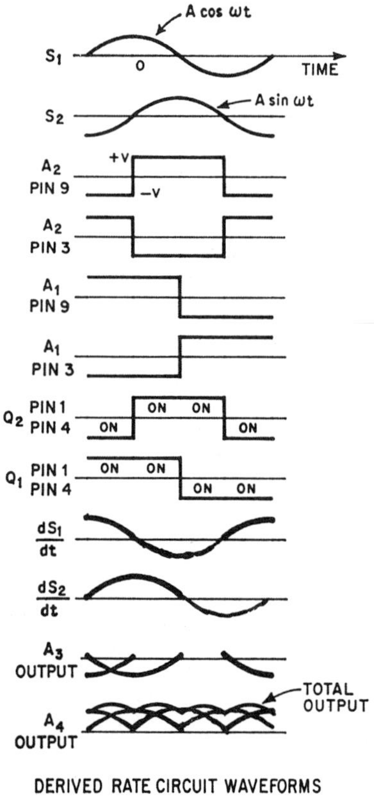

DERIVED RATE CIRCUIT WAVEFORMS

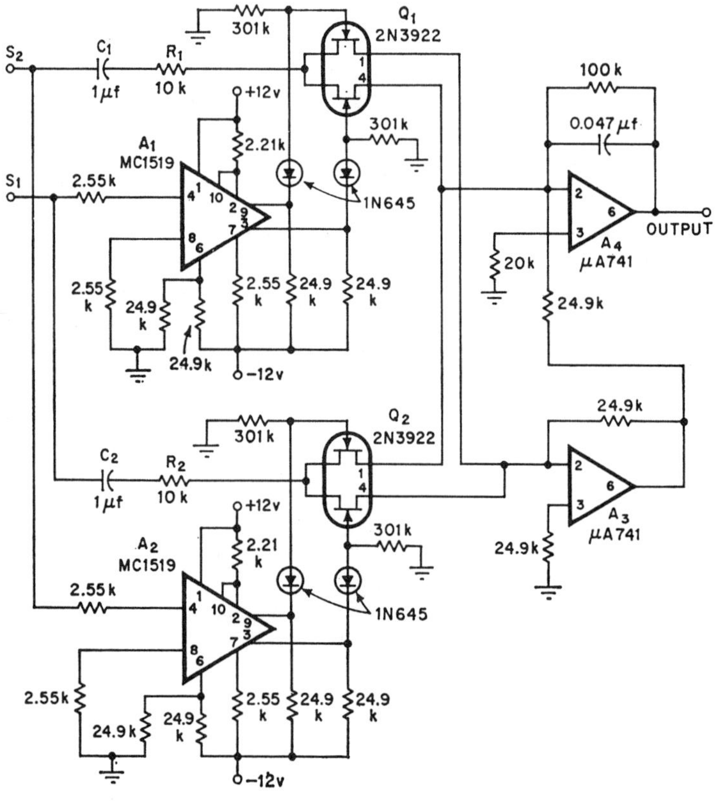

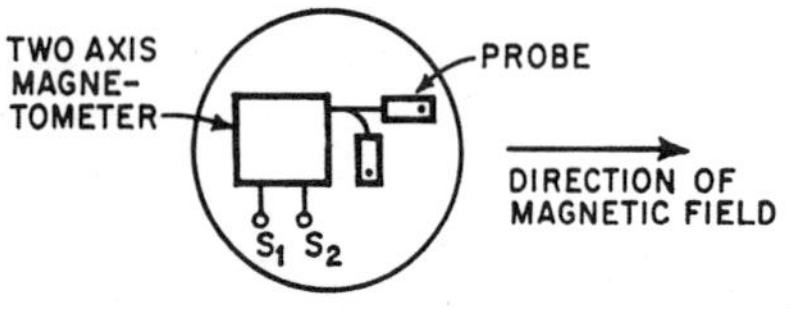

MAGNETOMETER ORIENTATION

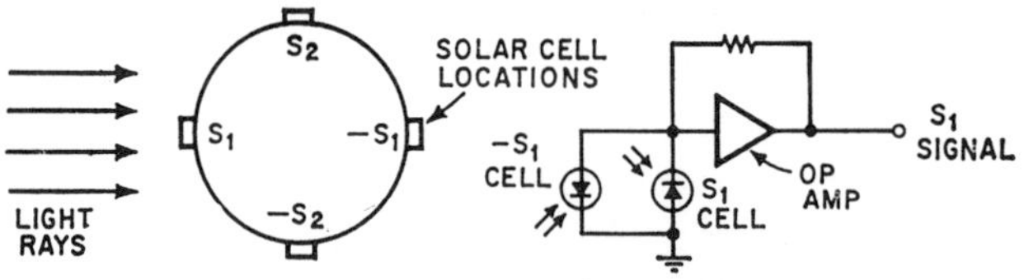

SOLAR CELL ORIENTATION AND CIRCUIT

ROLL RATE TO D-C VOLTAGE—Sensors on periphery of rocket or space vehicle generate sinusoidal inputs at S1 and S2 in quadrature, with frequency proportional to roll rate of vehicle. Inputs are differentiated to produce new signals whose amplitudes are proportional to angular frequency. Negative half-cycles are inverted by amplifier and summed with positive half-cycles to produce d-c output proportional to roll rate.—W. A. Cooke, IC's Gate FET's for Roll Rate Data, *Electronics*, Feb. 16, 1970, p 105–106.

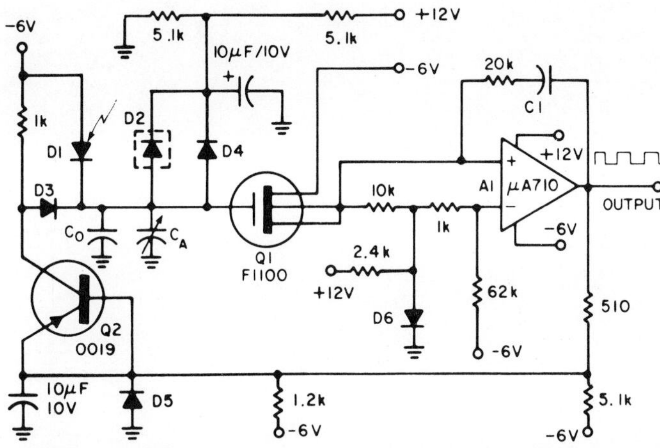

LIGHT-TO-FREQUENCY CONVERTER—Input impedance of mosfet Q1 is 10 teraohms, as required for obtaining linear relationship between light input on photodiode D1 and square-wave output frequency. Opamp functions as one-shot for generating 0.1-µs reset pulses. Used in exposure control for photolithographic equipment, in which output pulses are fed into counter that turns off light source at predetermined count. Can be calibrated so each pulse corresponds to exposure of 0.1 mW-s.—H. Murphy, Count Your Foot-Candles with Photodiodes, *Electronic Design*, Aug. 15, 1968, p 206–207.

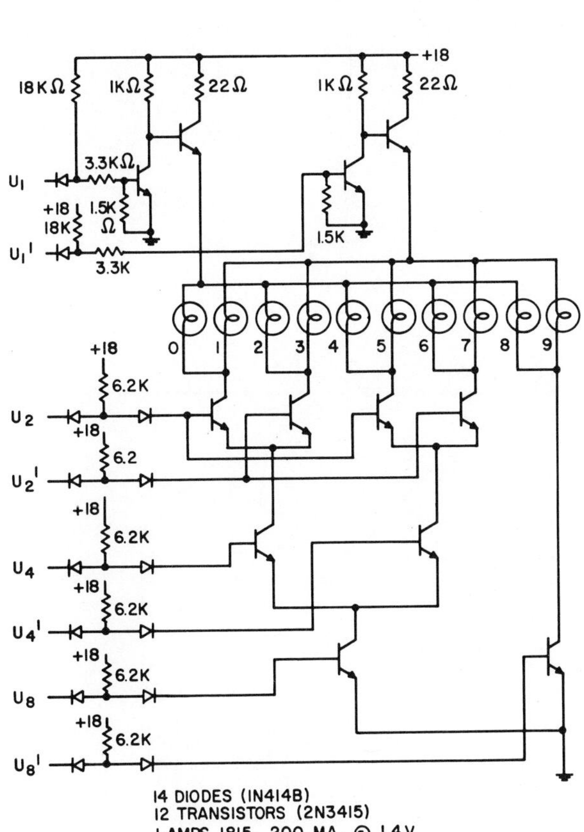

BINARY-TO-DECIMAL DECODER DRIVERS—Transistor matrix provides both logic and amplification for lighting appropriate one of ten indicator lamps for decimal display when input signal is in 8-4-2-1 code.—R. M. Muth, Digital Circuits with Visual Readouts, General Electric, Syracuse, N.Y., No. 671.3, 1966, p 11.

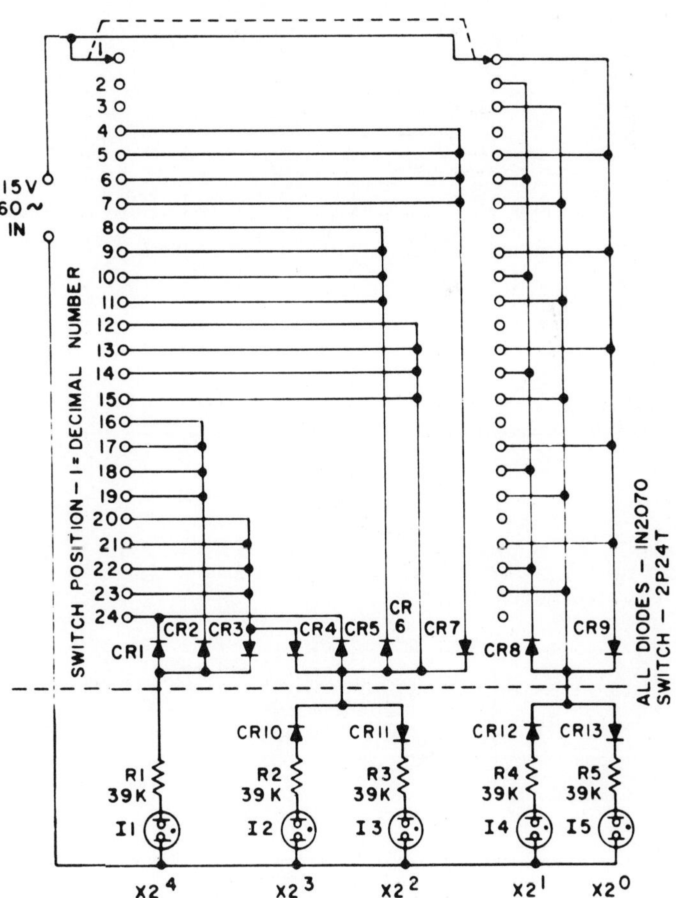

NEON DECIMAL-BINARY—Demonstrates binary arithmetic, using A072 neon lamps in simple circuit. Rotary switch permits 24 bits of information to be transmitted to remote visual display.—E. Bauman, "Applications of Neon Lamps and Gas Discharge Tubes," Signalite, Neptune, N.J., p 136.

UNIPOLAR TO BIPOLAR—Converts positive pulses to positive and negative (bipolar) pulses, as required in many business machines and data transmission sets. Article explains circuit operation wherein Q1 causes negative output when it stops conducting. Input of +8 V gives output of 12 V peak-to-peak.—W. D. Waddle, Switching Amplifier Converts Unipolar to Bipolar Pulses, *Electronics*, Oct. 3, 1966, p 103–104.

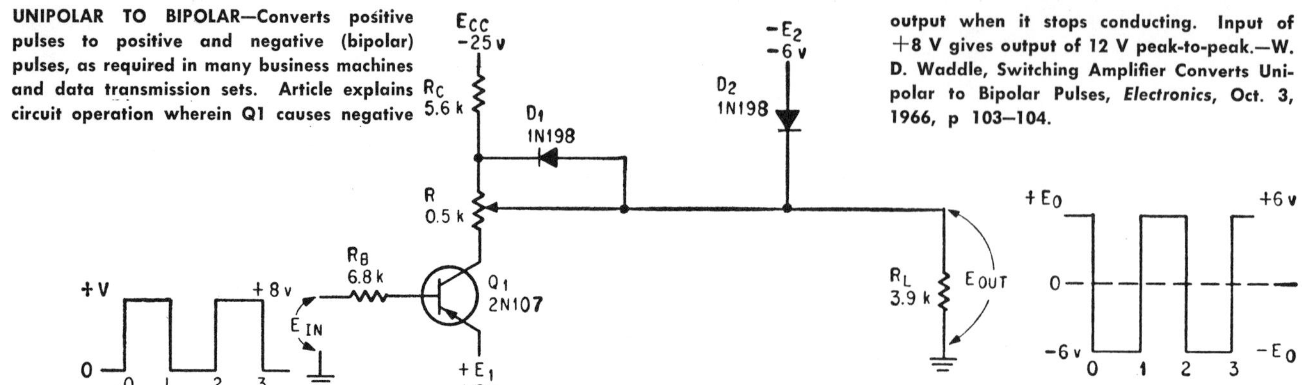

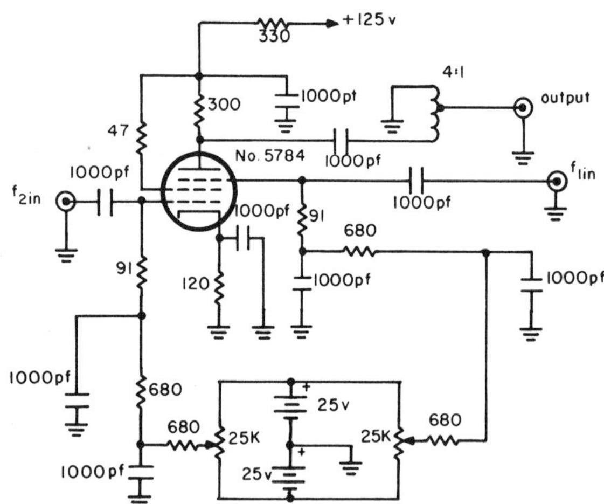

PENTODE MIXER—Developed for use in binary combination of oscillators and mixers for generating large number of discrete frequencies for phased (electronic scanning) radar. With 105 MHz at 0.7 rms applied to control grid and 40 MHz at same level applied to suppressor grid, second harmonic of 40-MHz signal is down 34 dB and all other harmonics are more than 50 dB below desired output signal.—G. F. Ross, Binary Generation of Frequencies Saves on Hardware, *Electronic Design*, Nov. 23, 1964, p 38–42 and 44–47.

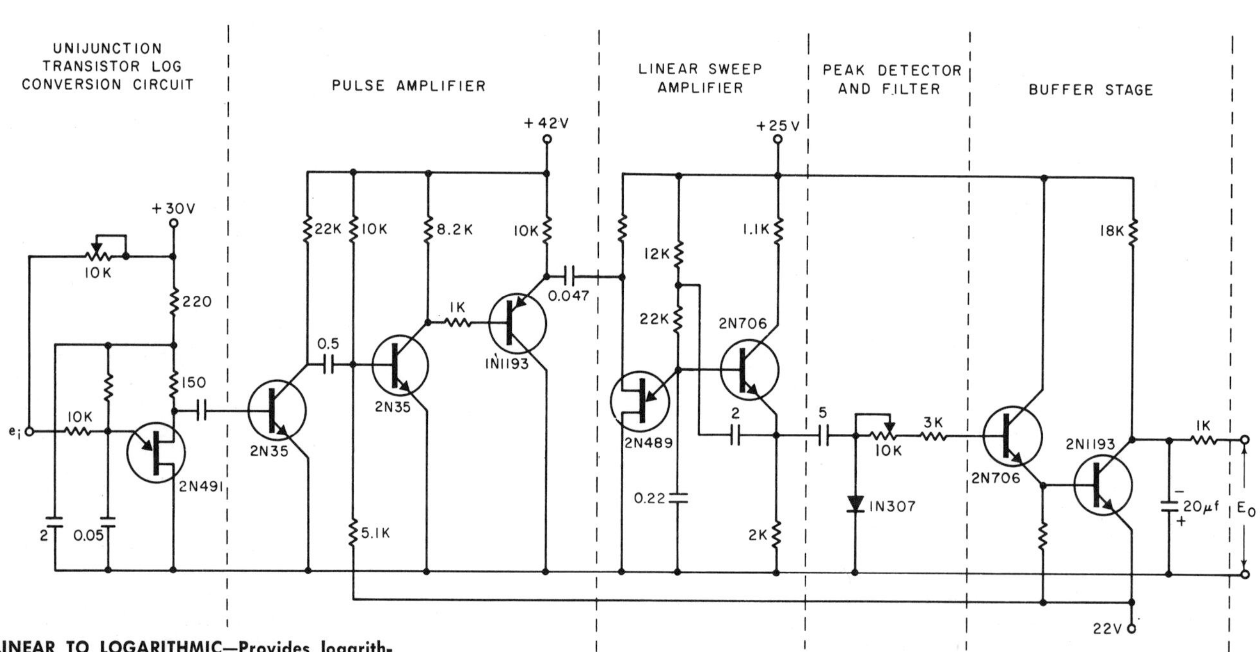

LINEAR TO LOGARITHMIC—Provides logarithmic d-c output for linear d-c input, using ujt in R-C relaxation oscillator network. Output pulses of ujt are amplified and used to synchronize linear sweep generator-amplifier. Resulting sawtooth pulses go through peak detector and filter to buffer amplifier that delivers desired d-c voltage, proportional to period of sync pulses and therefore proportional to natural logarithm of input voltage.—J. Sheehy, Device Provides DC Linear To Logarithmic Conversion, *Electronic Design*, July 6, 1964, p 50–51.

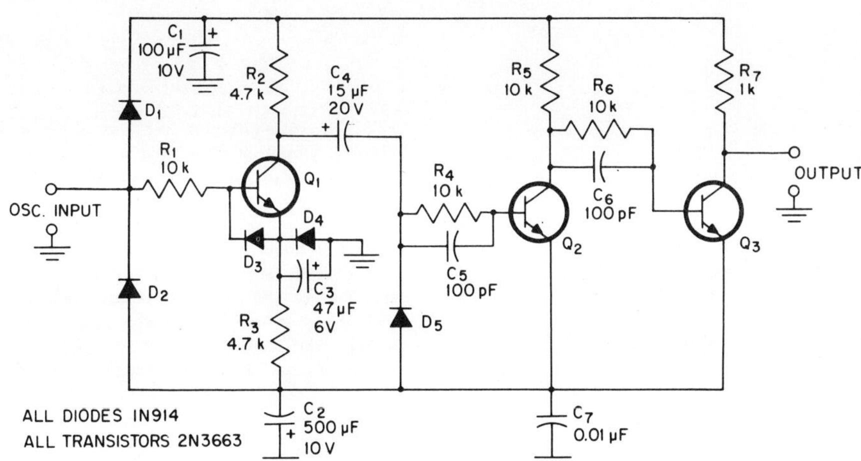

SIGNAL-POWERED SINE-SQUARE—Delivers square-wave output in range of 2 to 16 V p-p at frequency of 600-ohm oscillator feeding input, in range of 5 Hz to 600 kHz. Circuit derives its own positive and negative supply voltages by rectification of input signal in D1 and D2. Output waveform is essentially independent of frequency, with 20-ns rise time and 30-ns fall time.—D. R. Morgan, Signal-Powered Sine-To-Square Wave Converter, *EEE*, Nov. 1969, p 107–108.

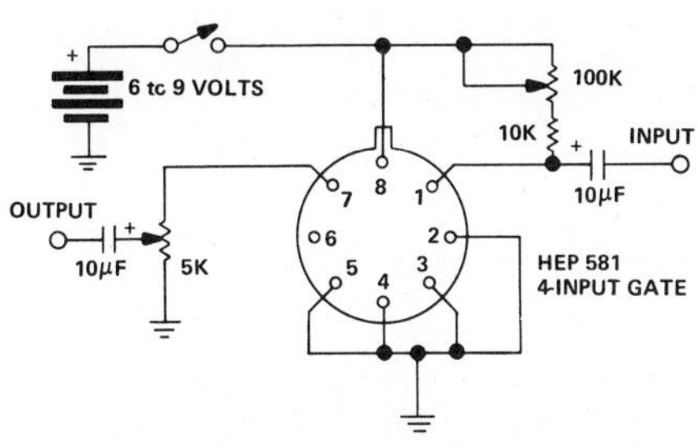

SINE TO SQUARE-WAVE IC—Converts any audio signal generator with at least 2 V p-p output to high-quality square-wave generator. —"Tips on Using IC's," HMA-32, Motorola, Phoenix, Ariz., 1968.

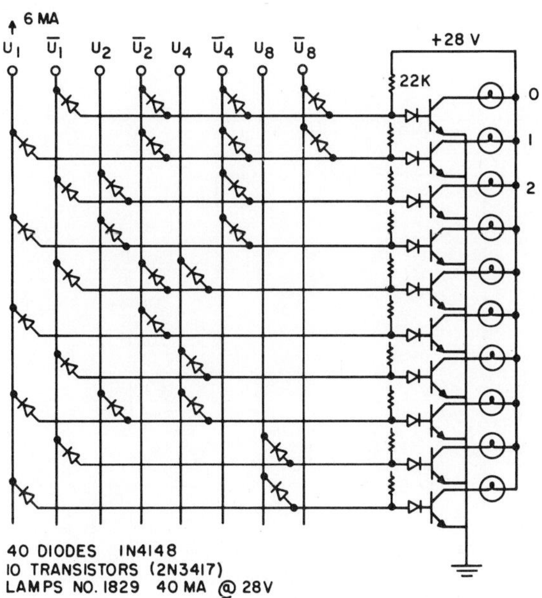

BINARY-TO-DECIMAL CONVERTER—Binary signal in 8-4-2-1 code is converted by diode matrix to decimal code which lights one of ten lamps, each having a transistor driver.—R. M. Muth, Digital Circuits with Visual Readouts, General Electric, Syracuse, N.Y., No. 671.3, 1966, p 11.

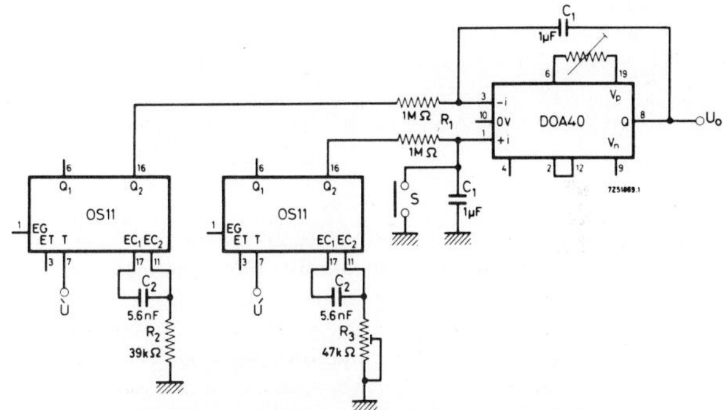

DIGITAL CONTROL OF VOLTAGE—Two parallel trains of information pulses are applied to balanced input terminals of Philips DOA40 IC opamp through two OS11 IC monostable mvbrs. With DOA40 externally connected as difference amplifier and integrator, output voltage Uo is proportional to difference between number of input pulses arriving per unit of time. This voltage is held even when no further pulses are delivered.—Electronic Potentiometer With 40- and 10-Series Circuit Blocks, Philips, Pub. Dept., Elcoma Div., Eindhoven, The Netherlands.

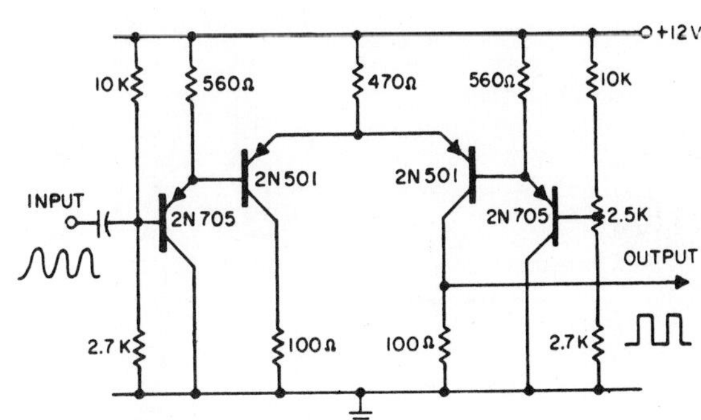

SINE-SQUARE CONVERTER—For 5-MHz sine-wave input at 2 V p-p, output is 2-V p-p square wave having rise time of about 20 ns. Circuit uses emitter-coupled limiter in which rise time is limited only by switching times of transistors.—H. Hahn, Emitter-Coupled Limiter Produces HF Square Waves, "400 Ideas for Design Selected from Electronic Design," Hayden Book Co., N.Y., 1964, p 66.

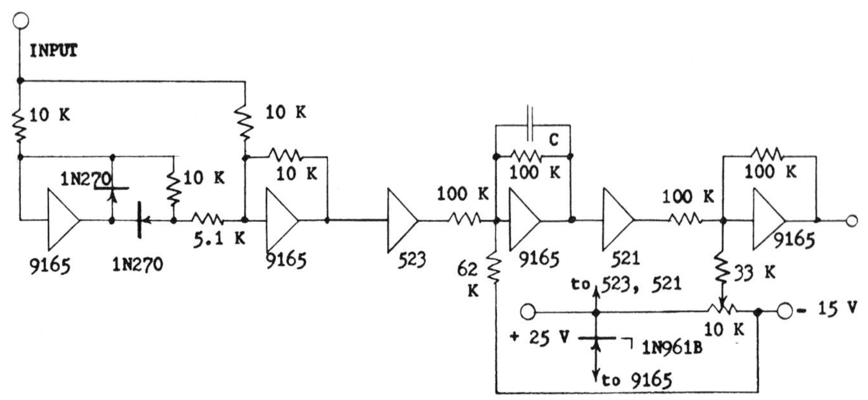

RMS TO D-C—Provides d-c output voltage directly proportional to rms value of input voltage. Input passes through a-c/d-c converter, polar squaring, integrating, and square-root operations. Input levels are limited to about 5 V peak or 3.5 V rms. Requires both 15-V bipolar d-c and 25 V d-c supplies for OEI IC units. Upper frequency limit is about 10 kHz and accuracy is 3%.—A True RMS To DC Converter, Optical Electronics, Tucson, Ariz., No. 10058.

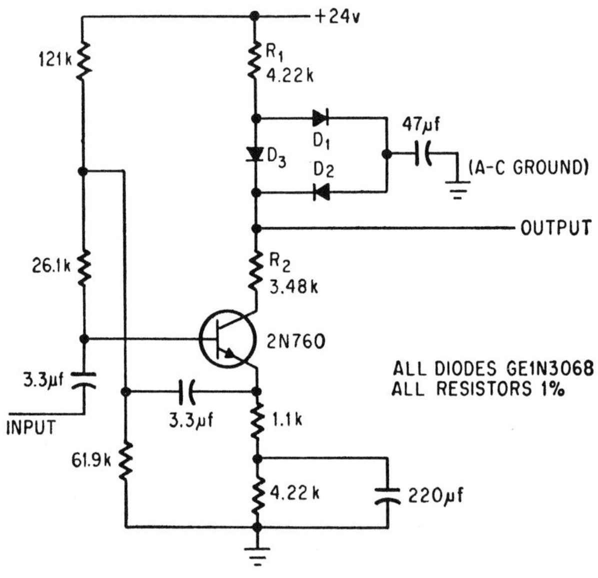

DIODE BIAS SUPPLY—Data-compressing converter delivers output voltage proportional to logarithm of a-c input over 36-dB range. Bias voltage is provided by single diode, instead of with separate batteries usually required.—R. K. Nisbett, Diode Bias Replaces Batteries in Logarithmic Converter, *Electronics*, Nov. 14, 1966, p 123–124.

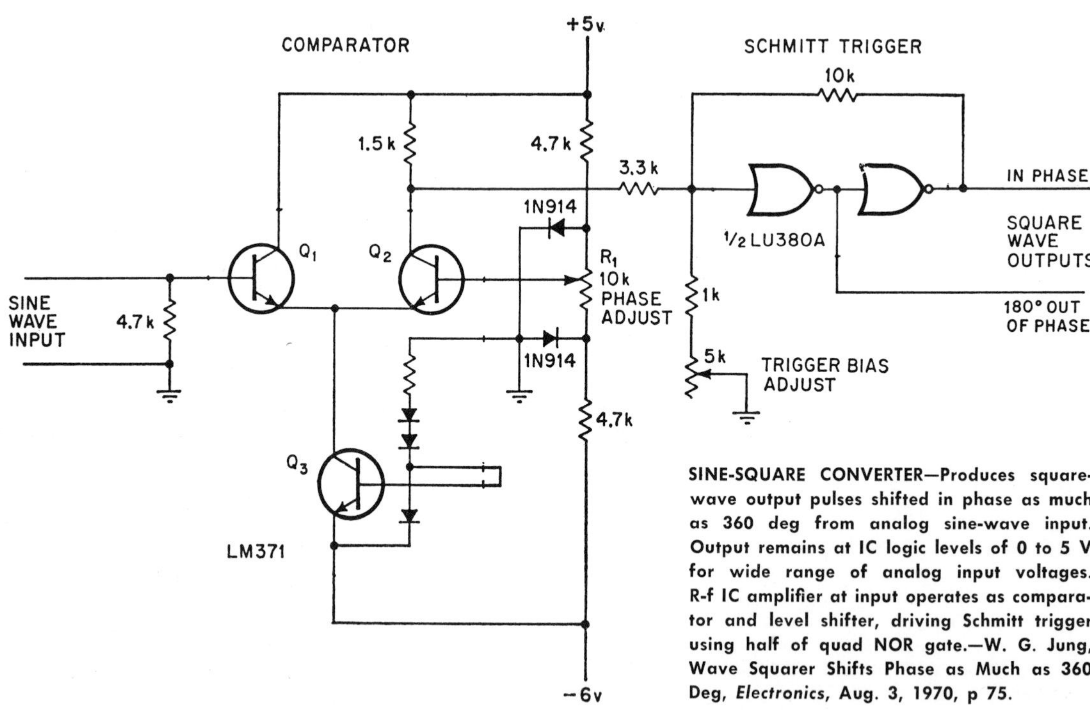

SINE-SQUARE CONVERTER—Produces square-wave output pulses shifted in phase as much as 360 deg from analog sine-wave input. Output remains at IC logic levels of 0 to 5 V for wide range of analog input voltages. R-f IC amplifier at input operates as comparator and level shifter, driving Schmitt trigger using half of quad NOR gate.—W. G. Jung, Wave Squarer Shifts Phase as Much as 360 Deg, *Electronics*, Aug. 3, 1970, p 75.

CHAPTER 19
Converter Circuits—Radio

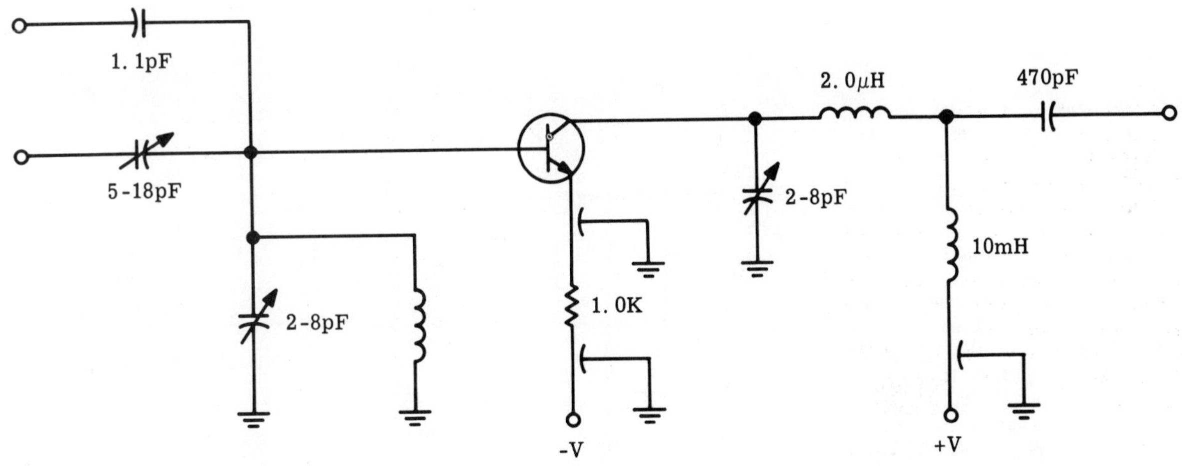

25 DB CONVERSION GAIN—With 300-MHz local oscillator signal (fed through 1.1 pF) and 250-MHz r-f signal injected into base of MM1941 transistor, output is 50 MHz. Report gives design procedure.—E. Klein, Transistor Mixer Design Using Admittance Parameters, Motorola, Phoenix, Ariz., AN-238, 1967.

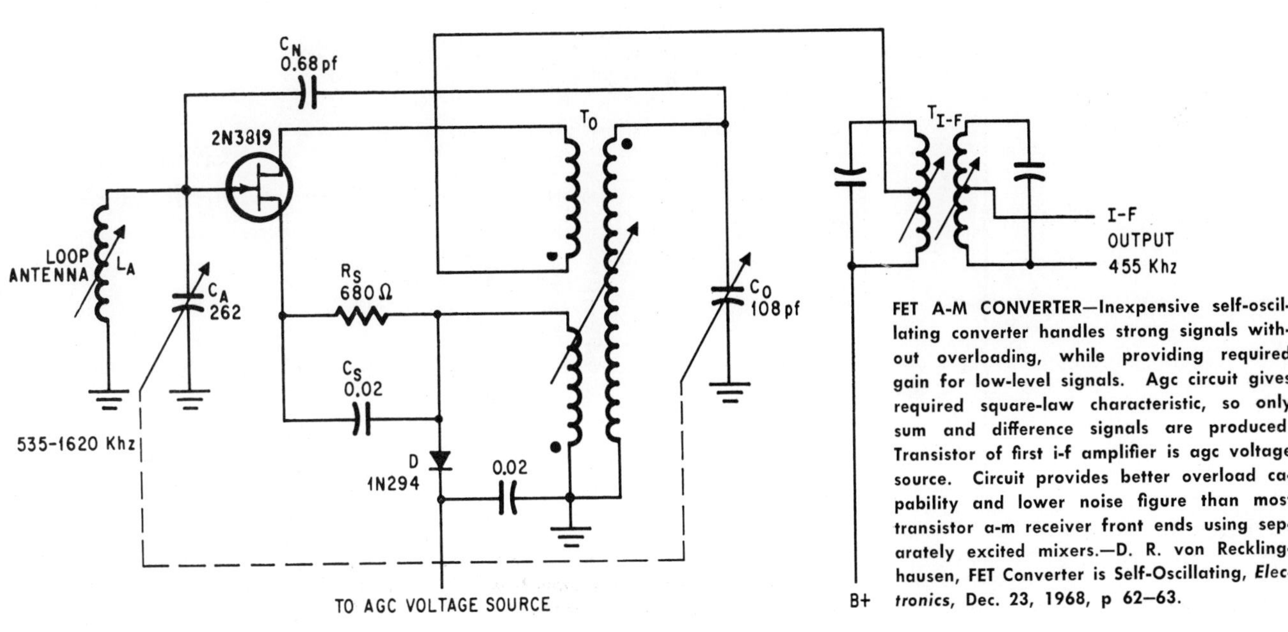

FET A-M CONVERTER—Inexpensive self-oscillating converter handles strong signals without overloading, while providing required gain for low-level signals. Agc circuit gives required square-law characteristic, so only sum and difference signals are produced. Transistor of first i-f amplifier is agc voltage source. Circuit provides better overload capability and lower noise figure than most transistor a-m receiver front ends using separately excited mixers.—D. R. von Recklinghausen, FET Converter is Self-Oscillating, *Electronics*, Dec. 23, 1968, p 62–63.

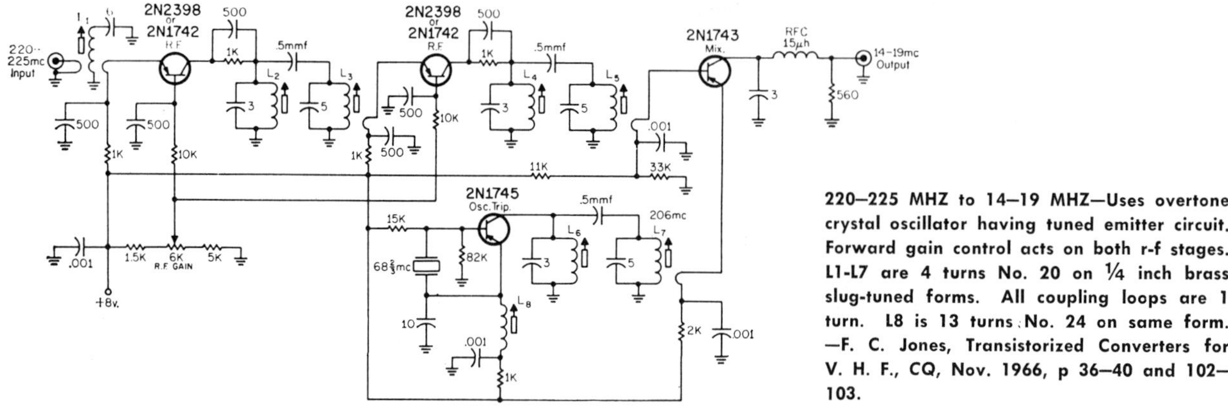

220–225 MHZ to 14–19 MHZ—Uses overtone crystal oscillator having tuned emitter circuit. Forward gain control acts on both r-f stages. L1-L7 are 4 turns No. 20 on 1/4 inch brass slug-tuned forms. All coupling loops are 1 turn. L8 is 13 turns No. 24 on same form. —F. C. Jones, Transistorized Converters for V. H. F., CQ, Nov. 1966, p 36–40 and 102–103.

6-METER CONVERTER—If connected between antenna and antenna terminals of receiver that can be tuned to 7 MHz, permits reception of 50–54 MHz amateur band. Gives overall gain of 30 dB, with sensitivity of 1 μV for 10 dB s/n ratio at receiver audio output with 30% modulated signal. Article gives construction and alignment details. Crystal is 43-MHz third-overtone. Coil-winding data is given. Parts values are: R1 5.1K; R2 8.2K; R3 1.2K; R4 11K; R5 10K; R6 2K; R7 12K; R8 2.2K; R9 470; R10 1K; C1 0.003 μF; C2, C6 5-80 pF trimmer; C3, C7 0.1 μF; C4 0.01 μF; C5 18 pF; C8 0.001 μF; C9 5 pF; C10 0.05 μF; C11 25-380 pF trimmer; C12, C13, C16, C17, C18 0.02 μF; C14 12 pF; C15 82 pF; Q1, Q3 HEP3; Q2 HEP2; RFC1 18 μH; XTAL 43-MHz third-overtone.—"Solid State Projects Manual," Motorola, Phoenix, Ariz., 1968, p 57–62.

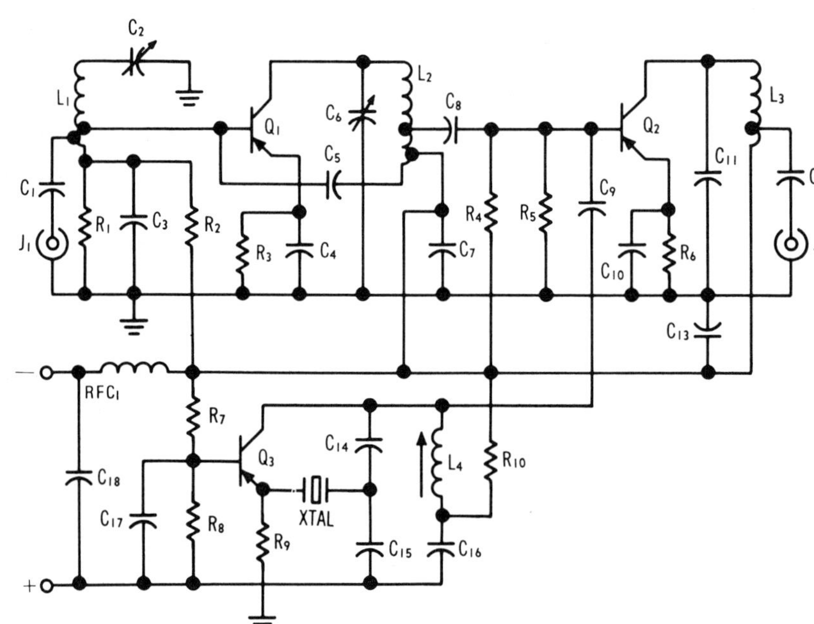

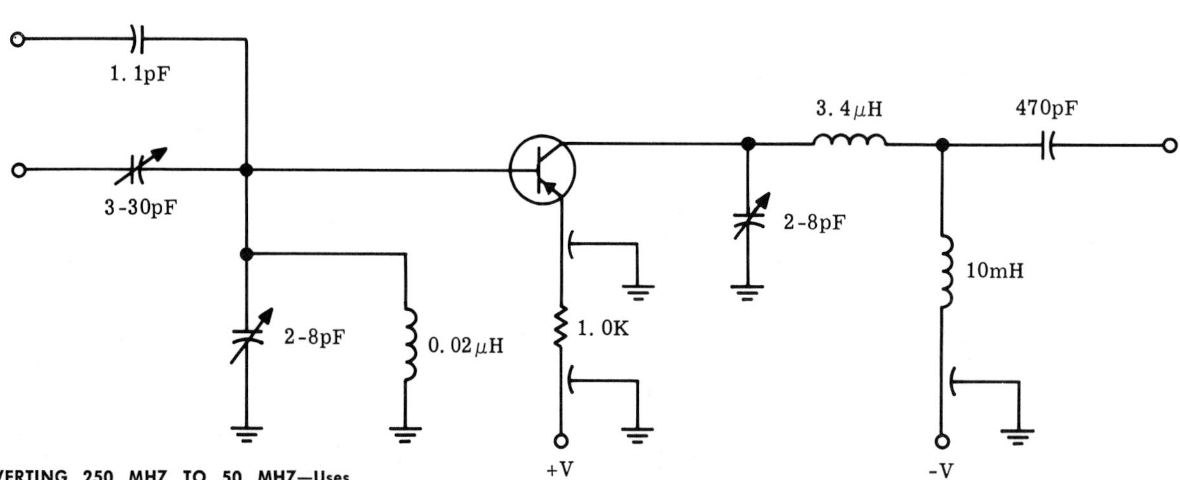

CONVERTING 250 MHZ TO 50 MHZ—Uses 2N3308 transistor, with base injection for both 250-MHz r-f signal and 300-MHz local oscillator signal fed through 1.1 pF. Report gives complete design procedure. Conversion gain is about 25 dB for 1 V input from local oscillator and 1.8 mV r-f input.—E. Klein, Transistor Mixer Design Using Admittance Parameters, Motorola, Phoenix, Ariz., AN-238, 1967.

+15 Vdc
0.001
0.15 μH
5.5-18 pF
50Ω
IF
60 MHz
L1
4:1
0.5-8 pF
50Ω
RF
200 MHz
0.5-8 pF
2N3823
470 pF
50Ω
LO - 260 MHz
L2
0.5-
18 pF
1.0 μH
0.5-8 pF
3.9 μH
RFC
0.001
-VGO
L1 = 36 TURNS #24 ENAMELED WIRE CLOSE WOUND ON 1/4" ID FORM WITH SLUG. TAP AT APPROXIMATELY 1/4 OF TOTAL LENGTH FROM ONE END.
L2 = 1-1/2 TURNS #18 SOFT DRAWN WIRE ON 3/10 INCH ID, 0.3 INCH LENGTH.
ALL OTHER COILS ARE STANDARD MOLDED CHOKES.

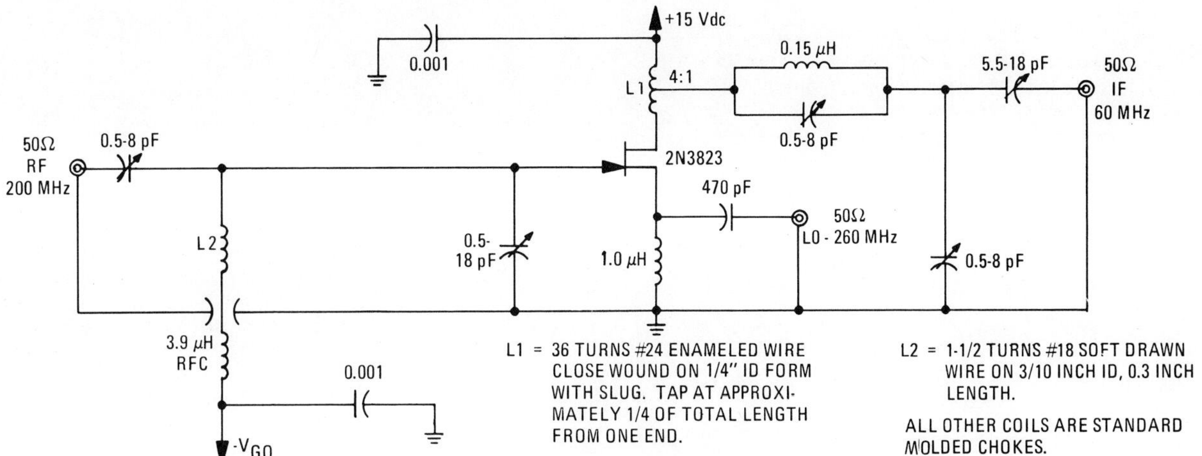

PARALLEL-TRAP MIXER—Trap removes 260-MHz local oscillator signal in 200-MHz common-source source-injection fet mixer. Autotransformer provides high-impedance matching at output. Conversion gain is 10 dB, noise figure 6.8 dB, and bandwidth 2.2 MHz.—S. P. Kwok, A Unified Approach to Optimum FET Mixer Design, Motorola, Phoenix, Ariz., AN-410, 1967.

50Ω
LO
250 MHz
C1
0.5-8 pF
+15 Vdc
0.001
L1 = 36 TURNS #24 ENAMELED WIRE, CLOSE WOUND ON 1/4 INCH I.D. FORM.
L2 = 2 TURNS #18 TINNED WIRE 3/10 INCH I.D., 0.3 INCH LONG.
ALL OTHER COILS ARE STANDARD MOLDED CHOKES.
RFC
3.9 μH
L3 0.15 μH
L1
C7
50Ω
IF
50 MHz
2N3823
5-30 pF
50Ω
RF
200 MHz
C2
0.5-8 pF
C5 0.5-8 pF
L2
C3
0.5-8 pF
C4
0.5-8 pF
C6
0.5-8 pF
RFC
3.9 μH
0.001
-VGO

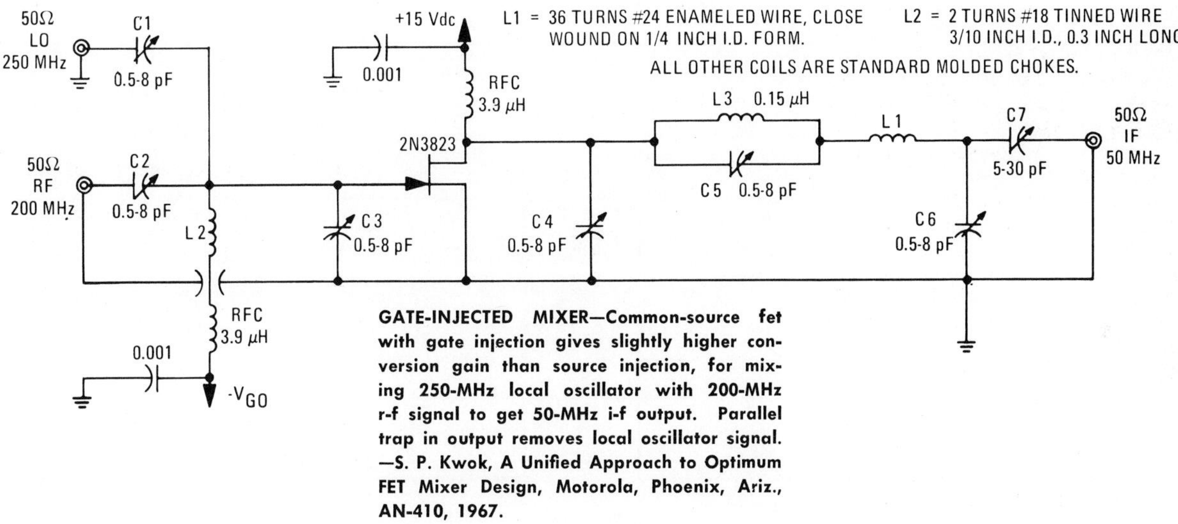

GATE-INJECTED MIXER—Common-source fet with gate injection gives slightly higher conversion gain than source injection, for mixing 250-MHz local oscillator with 200-MHz r-f signal to get 50-MHz i-f output. Parallel trap in output removes local oscillator signal. —S. P. Kwok, A Unified Approach to Optimum FET Mixer Design, Motorola, Phoenix, Ariz., AN-410, 1967.

SOURCE-INJECTION MIXER—Common-source fet mixer combines 200-MHz r-f input signal with 260-MHz local oscillator signal to give 60-MHz output with 11 dB conversion gain. Choke and two capacitors serve for both input and output matching networks.—S. P. Kwok, A Unified Approach to Optimum FET Mixer Design, Motorola, Phoenix, Ariz., AN-410, 1967.

VDS = 15 Vdc
0.05
RFC
10 μH
0.001
50Ω
60 MHz
L2
135 nH
L1
44 nH
2N3823
50Ω
200MHz
0.001
260 MHz
50Ω
C3
3 pF
C4
53 pF
RFC
2.7 μH
C1
55 pF
C2
15 pF
L3
1 μH
0.001
0.001
VGS = -0.8 VP
L1 = 5 TURNS TINNED #20 WIRE, ID = 0.15 INCHES, LENGTH = 0.6 INCHES. ALL OTHER INDUCTORS ARE STANDARD MOLDED CHOKES.

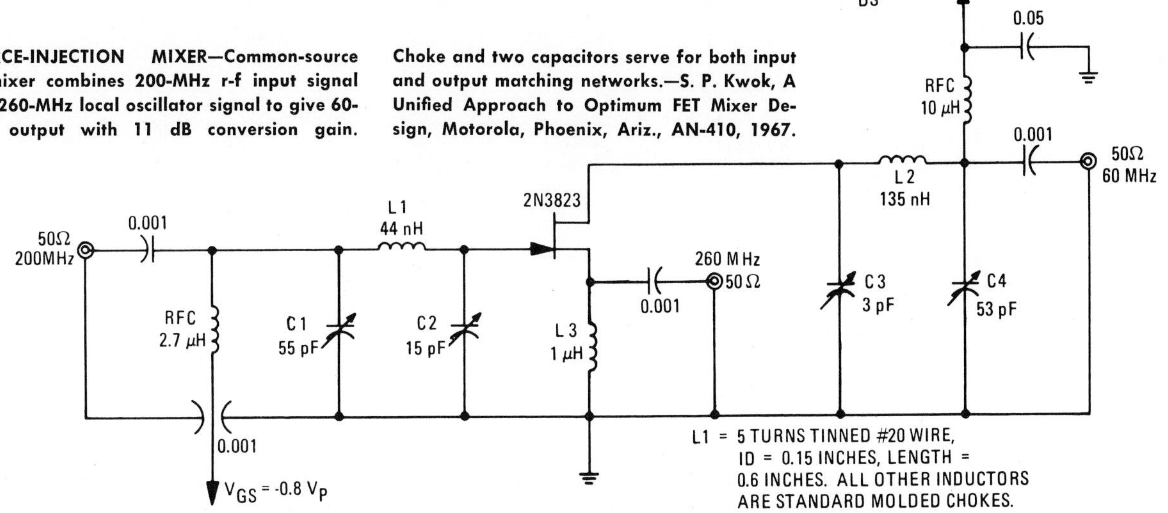

HALF-WAVE CARRIER SWITCH—Addition of two diodes (from CA3019 diode IC array) to conventional balanced mixer effectively doubles desired output voltage and halves undesired oscillator signal at output. Improvement in conversion gain cannot be realized above 20 MHz, because of capacitances associated with IC diodes.—"Linear Integrated Circuits," RCA, Harrison, N.J., IC-41, p 305.

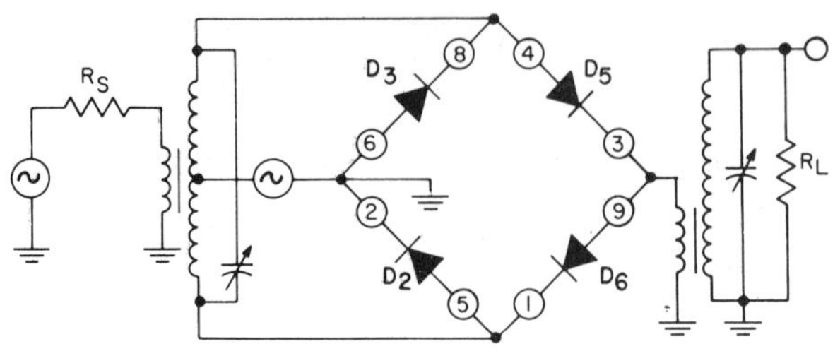

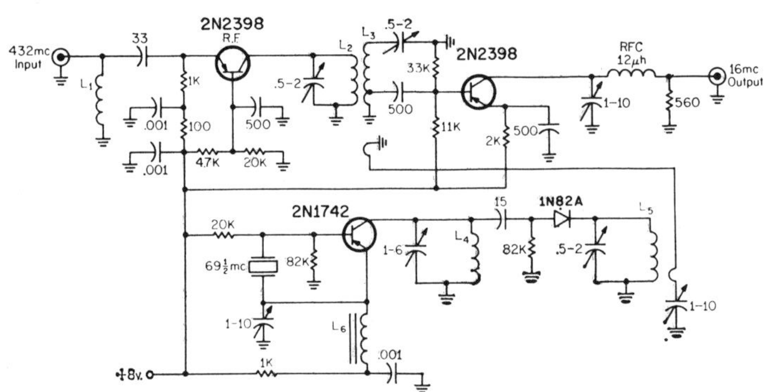

432 MHZ TO 16 MHZ—Overtone crystal shown is used for 16-MHz i-f; for 14-MHz i-f, use 69⅔ MHz crystal. Oscillator output is doubled in frequency by 1N82A diode. Article gives winding data for all coils.—F. C. Jones, Transistorized Converters for V. H. F., CQ, Nov. 1966, p 36–40 and 102–103.

ALL-BAND—High-Q toroidal antenna coil tunes from 7 to 28 MHz without bandswitching. L1 is 12-μH tube-type antenna coil in reverse. Use 10.5 MHz for Y1 and 1.5 μH for L2 to cover 7-MHz band, 17.5 MHz and 0.9 μH for 14 MHz, 24.5 MHz and 0.6 μH for 21 MHz, and 31.5 MHz and 0.5 μH for 28 MHz.—R. Jayaraman, A Deluxe 40673 Converter, CQ, Feb. 1970, p 46–48.

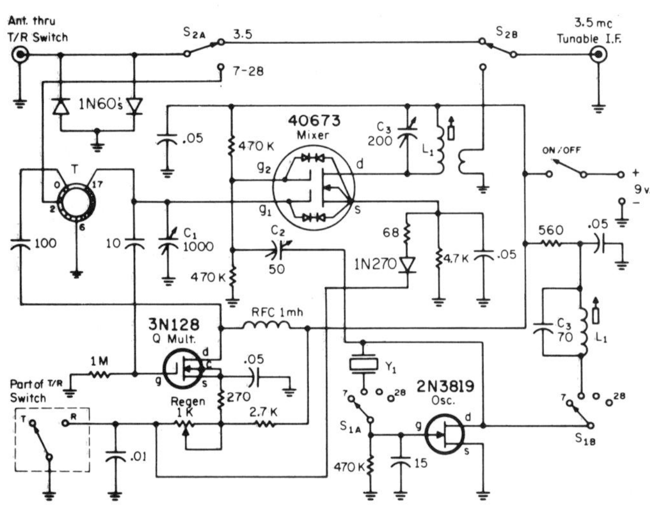

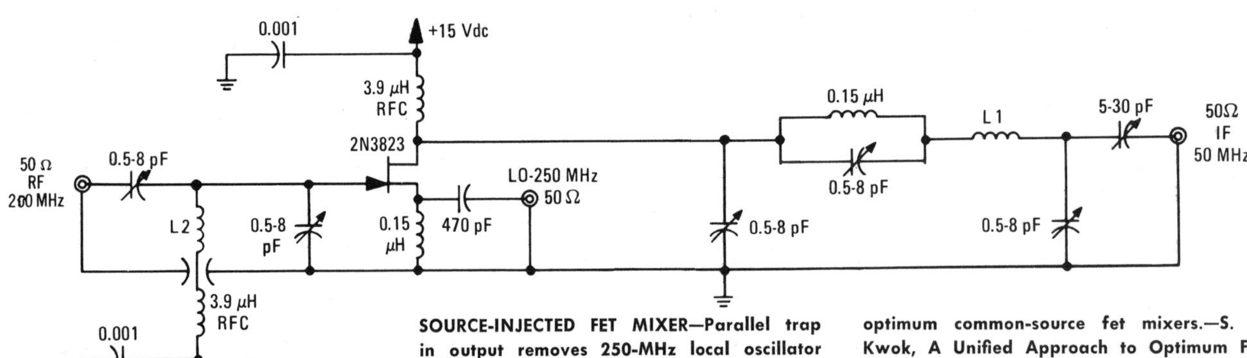

SOURCE-INJECTED FET MIXER—Parallel trap in output removes 250-MHz local oscillator signal which is injected into source through 470-pF capacitor. Report covers design of optimum common-source fet mixers.—S. P. Kwok, A Unified Approach to Optimum FET Mixer Design, Motorola, Phoenix, Ariz., AN-410, 1967.

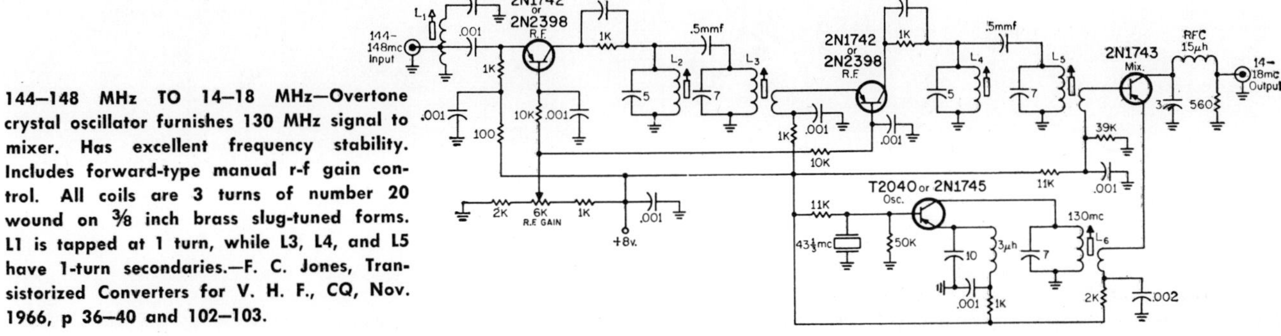

144–148 MHz TO 14–18 MHz—Overtone crystal oscillator furnishes 130 MHz signal to mixer. Has excellent frequency stability. Includes forward-type manual r-f gain control. All coils are 3 turns of number 20 wound on 3/8 inch brass slug-tuned forms. L1 is tapped at 1 turn, while L3, L4, and L5 have 1-turn secondaries.—F. C. Jones, Transistorized Converters for V. H. F., CQ, Nov. 1966, p 36–40 and 102–103.

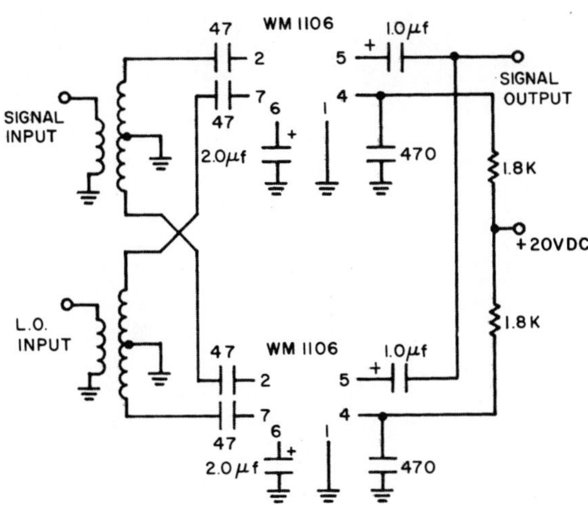

1 MHZ FROM 60 MHZ—Provides 20-dB suppression of 60-MHz i-f input signal and local oscillator signal in output, yet employs only simple fixed-tuned circuits using IC video amplifiers. Conversion gain is 5 dB. Uses double-balanced down converter.—S. G. Shepherd and A. E. Seman, Design With Integrated Circuits at 60 Mc, *Electronic Design*, Aug. 2, 1965, p 30–33.

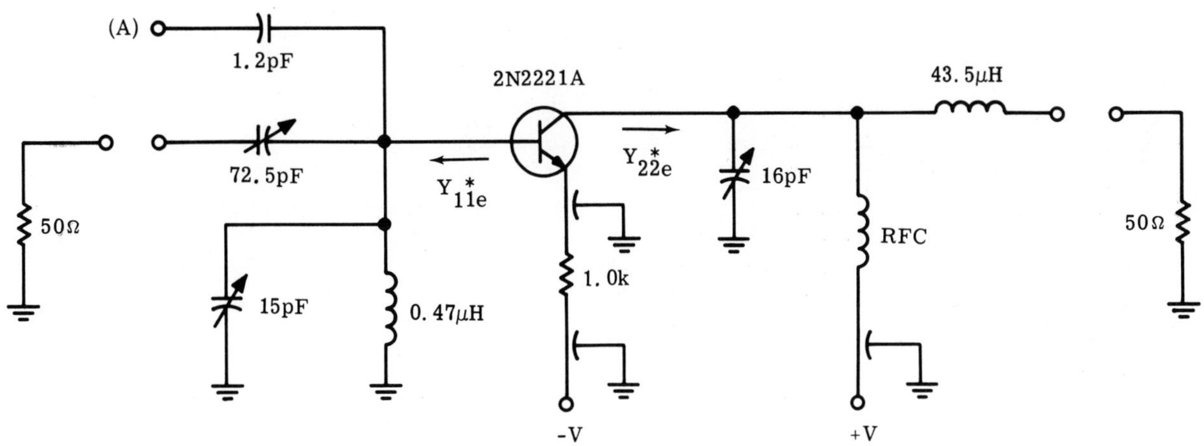

CONVERTING 30 MHZ TO 5 MHZ—Report gives complete design procedure. 35-MHz local oscillator signal is injected at terminal A, for base injection into transistor along with 30-MHz r-f signal, to give 5-MHz i-f signal at output. Conversion gain is above 30 dB for 1 V input from local oscillator.—E. Klein, Transistor Mixer Design Using Admittance Parameters, Motorola, Phoenix, Ariz., AN-238, 1967.

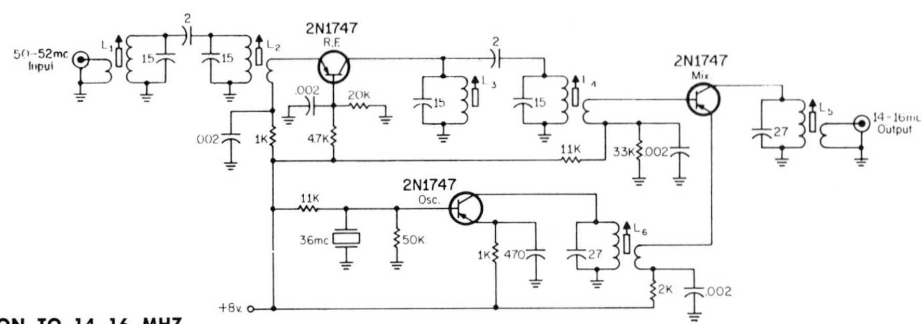

50–52 MHZ CONVERSION TO 14–16 MHZ—Four tuned circuits give good image suppression and i-f signal rejection. Can be used with either tube or transistor receiver that tunes to output frequency.—F. C. Jones, Transistorized Converters for V. H. F., CQ, Nov. 1966, p 36–40 and 102–103.

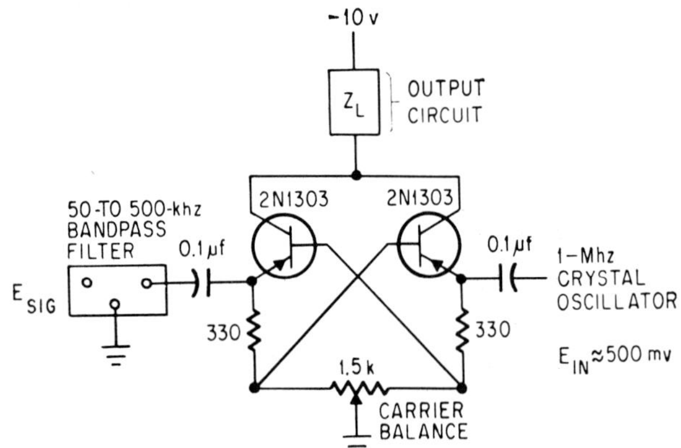

LOW-COST MIXER FOR 1-MHZ CARRIER—Two-transistor mixer eliminates costly transformer required by diode quad, and also provides conversion gain. Circuit cancels fundamental frequency and produces two sidebands across output load—for even-order harmonics of input and carrier. Crystal input amplitude is ten times 60-mV input signal amplitude.—L. E. Geisler, Cross-Coupled Transistors Form Balanced Mixer, *Electronics*, Oct. 17, 1966, p 91.

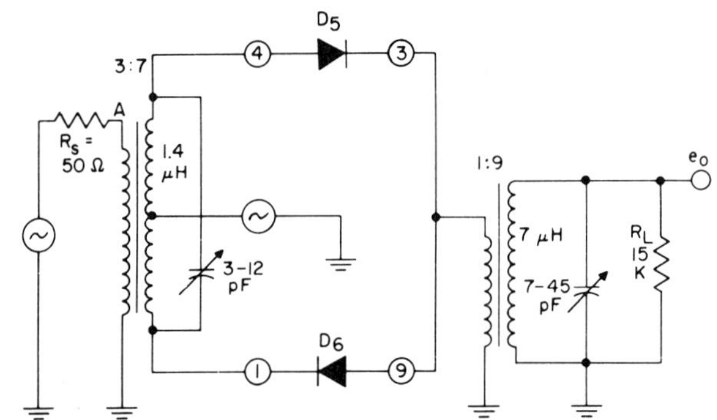

BALANCED MIXER—Uses two diodes in CA3019 diode IC array. Conversion gain for 45-MHz input signal and 55-MHz oscillator signal varies from −6 to −15 dB depending on oscillator voltage amplitude, and is −6 dB for 0.7 V.—"Linear Integrated Circuits," RCA, Harrison, N.J., IC-41, p 305.

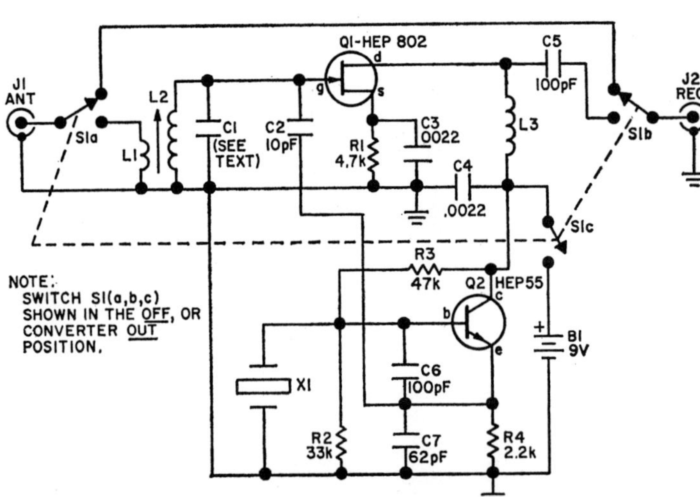

AUTO POLICE-BAND CONVERTER—Uses single fet Q1 as mixer for receiving any 1-MHz band between 25 and 55 MHz on any auto or portable radio. Article gives instructions for calculating crystal frequency for oscillator Q2 to receive desired band. F-m signals in emergency and business bands are received by tuning auto radio off to one side, to take advantage of slope detection. Value of C1 is 33 pF for 25 to 35 MHz, 15 pF for 35 to 45 MHz, and 10 pF for 45 to 55 MHz. Construction details are given.—Edward A. Morris, Build SimCon, *Elementary Electronics*, Mar.–Apr. 1970, p 57–62.

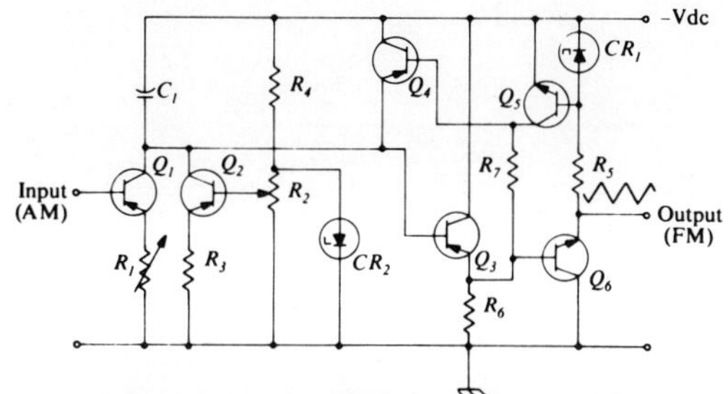

A-M TO F-M CONVERTER—Converts amplitude-modulated information to frequency-modulated information, with output frequency proportional to amplitude of input signal. R1 controls percentage of modulation or maximum number of cycles that signal will deviate from carrier position. Uses form of relaxation oscillator for conversion, with sawtooth output formed by charge and discharge of C1.—"Selected Electronic Circuitry," NASA SP-5046, Government Printing Office, Washington, D.C., p 16.

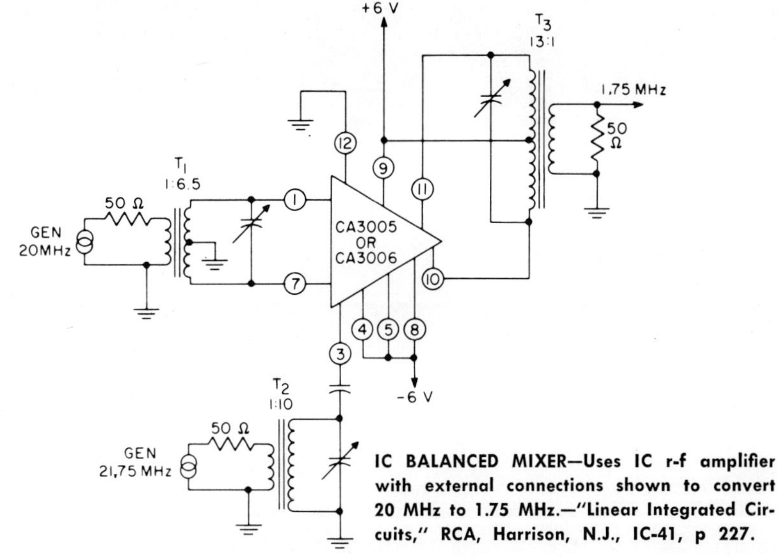

IC BALANCED MIXER—Uses IC r-f amplifier with external connections shown to convert 20 MHz to 1.75 MHz.—"Linear Integrated Circuits," RCA, Harrison, N.J., IC-41, p 227.

NOTE: To locate additional circuits in the category of this chapter, use the index at the back of this book. Check also the author's "Sourcebook of Electronic Circuits," published by McGraw-Hill in 1968.

CHAPTER 20
Counter Circuits

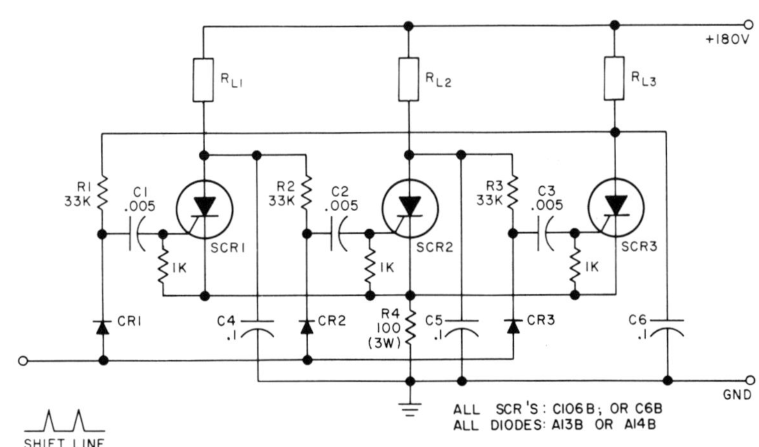

CATHODE-COUPLED SCR RING—Will drive high-voltage loads requiring currents up to 50 mA. Chief advantage is that square waves across each load are undistorted and free from commutation transients. Chief drawback is limitation placed on circuit speed by large values of commutating capacitors C4, C5, and C6.—D. R. Grafham, Using Low Current SCR's, General Electric, Syracuse, N.Y., No. 200.19, 1967, p 26.

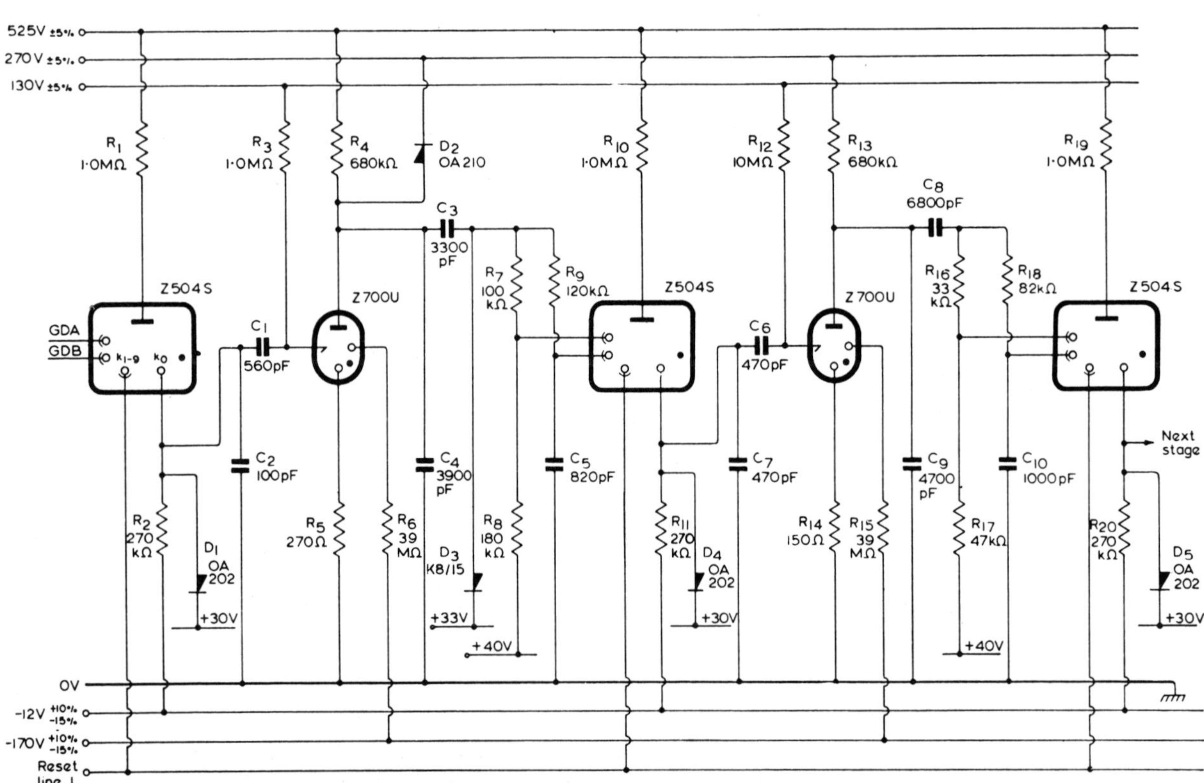

4-KHZ COUNTER CHAIN—Uses three gas-filled decade counter tubes, for counting units, tens, and hundreds at maximum speed of 4 kHz. First two tubes are coupled by 400-Hz cold-cathode trigger tube circuits, and last two tubes are coupled by 40-Hz circuit. Chain can be continued with 40-Hz coupling circuits.—G. F. Jeynes and S. Zilkha, Trigger Tube Coupling Circuits for the Z504S Stepping Tube, Philips, Pub. Dept., Elcoma Div., Eindhoven, The Netherlands, No. 15, 1965, p 16–25.

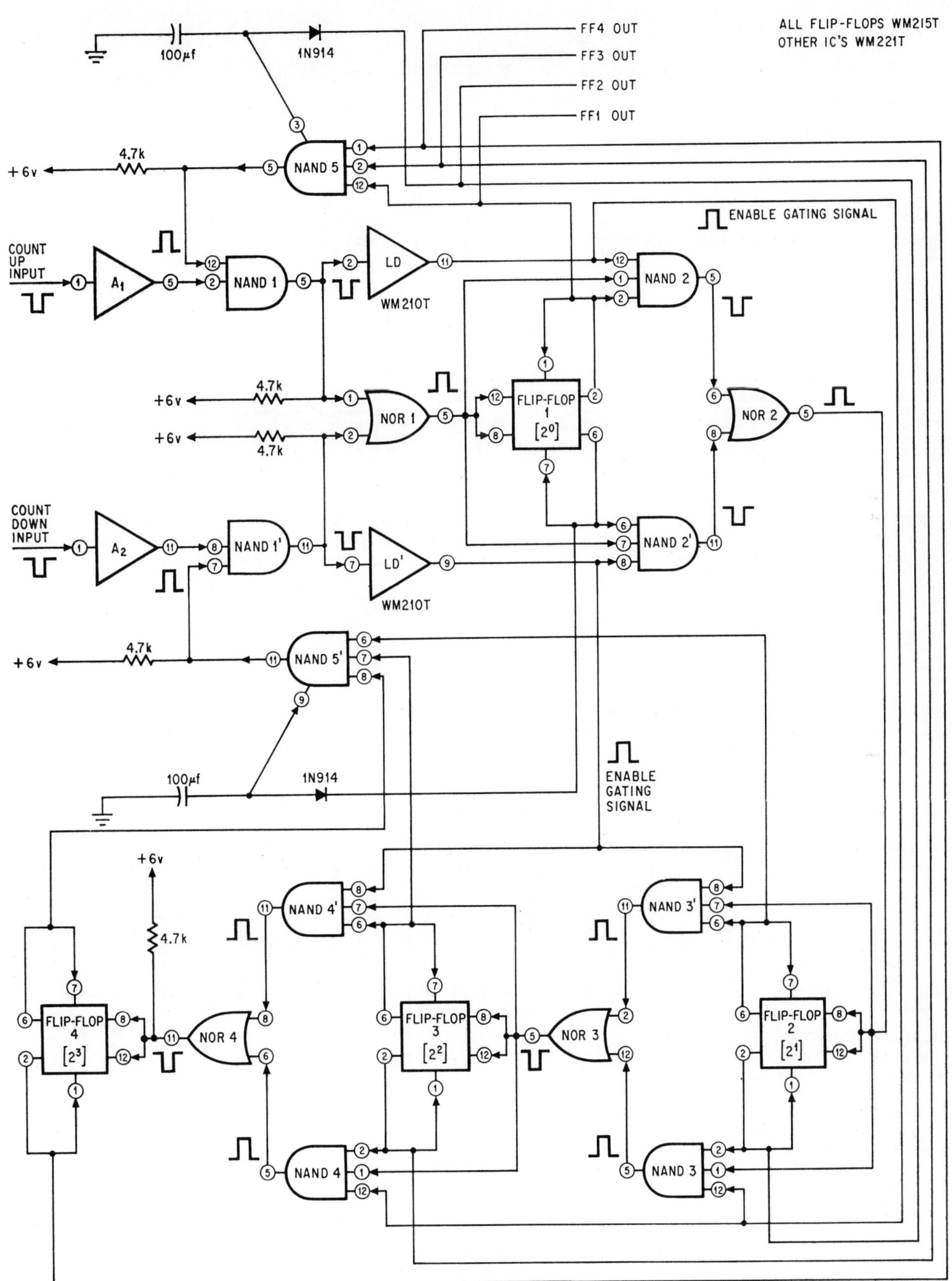

REVERSIBLE COUNTER WITH IC'S—Four stages are shown, to give general solution involving use of NAND gates and other digital IC's. Two identical serial counters share single set of flip-flops but reset in opposite directions. Article gives step-by-step description of counter operation. Switching speed is 150 ns.—L. J. Brocato, Digital IC's Shrink Reversible Counter, *Electronics*, Oct. 16, 1967, p 96–98.

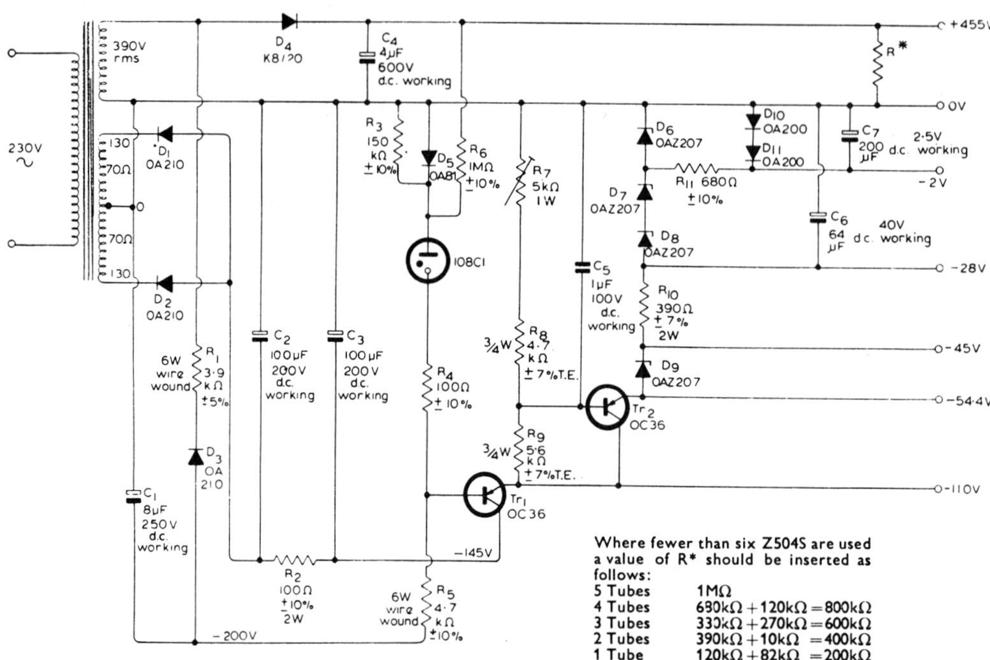

SIX-DECADE SCALER POWER SUPPLY—Provides all voltages required for six-decade scaler using Z504S decade stepping tube, with either photoelectric or triggered blocking-oscillator input.—G. C. Chappell and G. F. Jeynes, Transistor Coupling Circuits for the Z504S Stepping Tube, Philips, Pub. Dept., Elcoma Div., Eindhoven, The Netherlands, No. 15, 1965, p 26–38.

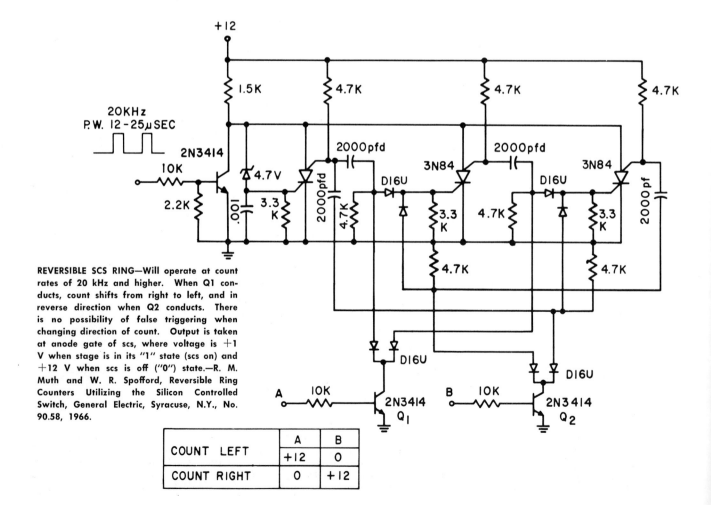

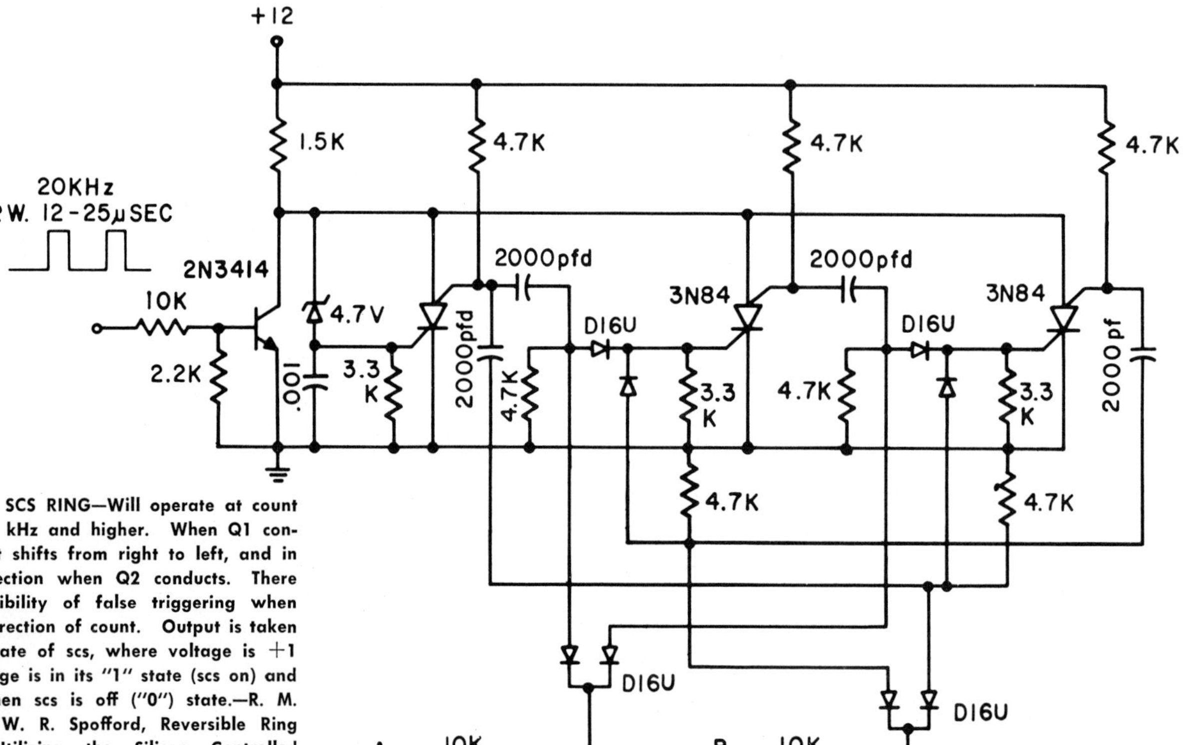

REVERSIBLE SCS RING—Will operate at count rates of 20 kHz and higher. When Q1 conducts, count shifts from right to left, and in reverse direction when Q2 conducts. There is no possibility of false triggering when changing direction of count. Output is taken at anode gate of scs, where voltage is +1 V when stage is in its "1" state (scs on) and +12 V when scs is off ("0") state.—R. M. Muth and W. R. Spofford, Reversible Ring Counters Utilizing the Silicon Controlled Switch, General Electric, Syracuse, N.Y., No. 90.58, 1966.

	A	B
COUNT LEFT	+12	0
COUNT RIGHT	0	+12

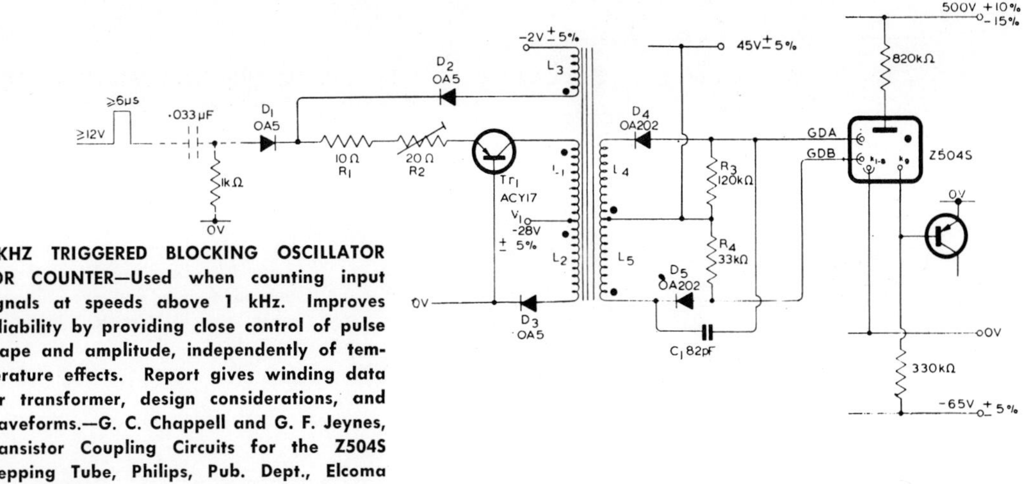

4-KHZ TRIGGERED BLOCKING OSCILLATOR FOR COUNTER—Used when counting input signals at speeds above 1 kHz. Improves reliability by providing close control of pulse shape and amplitude, independently of temperature effects. Report gives winding data for transformer, design considerations, and waveforms.—G. C. Chappell and G. F. Jeynes, Transistor Coupling Circuits for the Z504S Stepping Tube, Philips, Pub. Dept., Elcoma Div., Eindhoven, The Netherlands, No. 15, 1965, p 26–38.

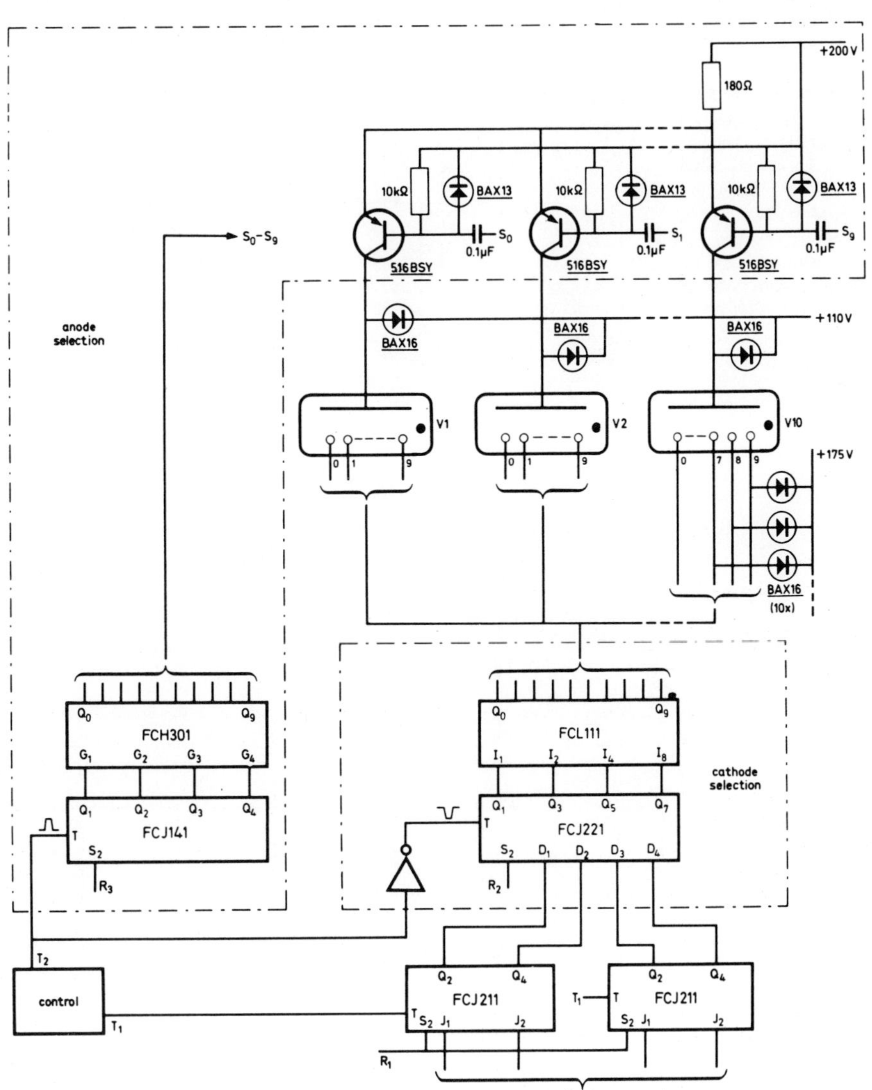

DYNAMIC DRIVE FOR INDICATORS—Handles ten numerical indicator tubes, of which three are shown. R1, R2, and R3 are reset terminals. Counter function is provided by Philips FCJ141 IC four-stage asynchronous decade counter producing NBCD-coded outputs. FCJ221 is Philips quadruple-latch flip-flop, FCJ211 is 4-bit shift register, and FCL-111 is decoder-driver. Numerical indicator tubes can be ZM1000.—Ph. de Weger, Numerical Indicator Tube Drive Using the FC Family of Integrated Circuits, Philips, Pub. Dept., Elcoma Div., Eindhoven, The Netherlands, No. 58, 1969.

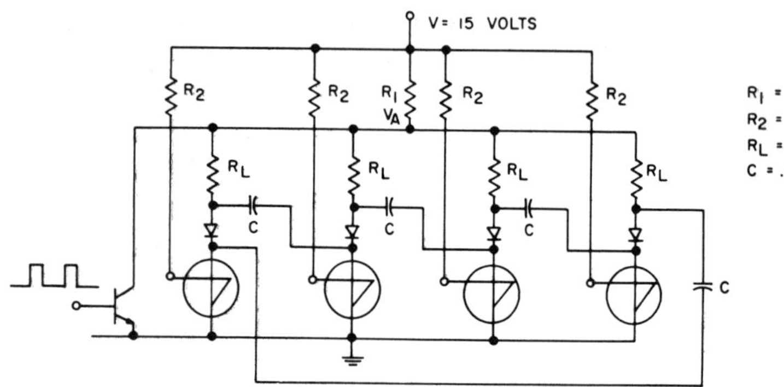

SUS RING WITH RATE-EFFECT RESISTOR—Uses resistor from supply to each gate lead to suppress rate effect. Will operate up to 10 kHz with type D13P1 sus and resistive loads such as lamps. Uses common-cathode connection. When supply voltage is applied, sus with lowest switching voltage comes on first, and succeeding pulses step count along.—W. R. Spofford, Jr., Applications of the New Silicon Bilateral Switch and the Silicon Unilateral Switch, General Electric, Syracuse, N.Y., No. 671.3, 1966, p 7.

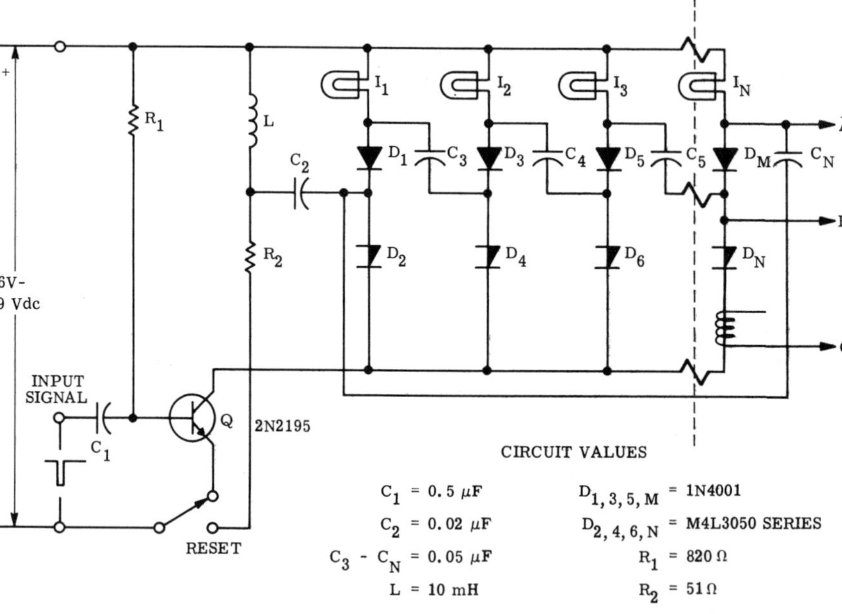

RING COUNTER WITH LAMPS—Sequentially transfers power to series of loads in response to pulse-train input signal. Any number of stages may be used. Output signals may be picked up as negative pulses at A or B, by current sensing at C, or by light sensing if lamps are used as loads. Input signal must be 6-mA negative current pulse lasting about 500 μs. Reset switch must be pressed and released after power is applied, to start operation.—J. Bliss and D. Zinder, 4-Layer and Current-Limiter Diodes Reduce Circuit Cost and Complexity, Motorola, Phoenix, Ariz., AN-221, 1966.

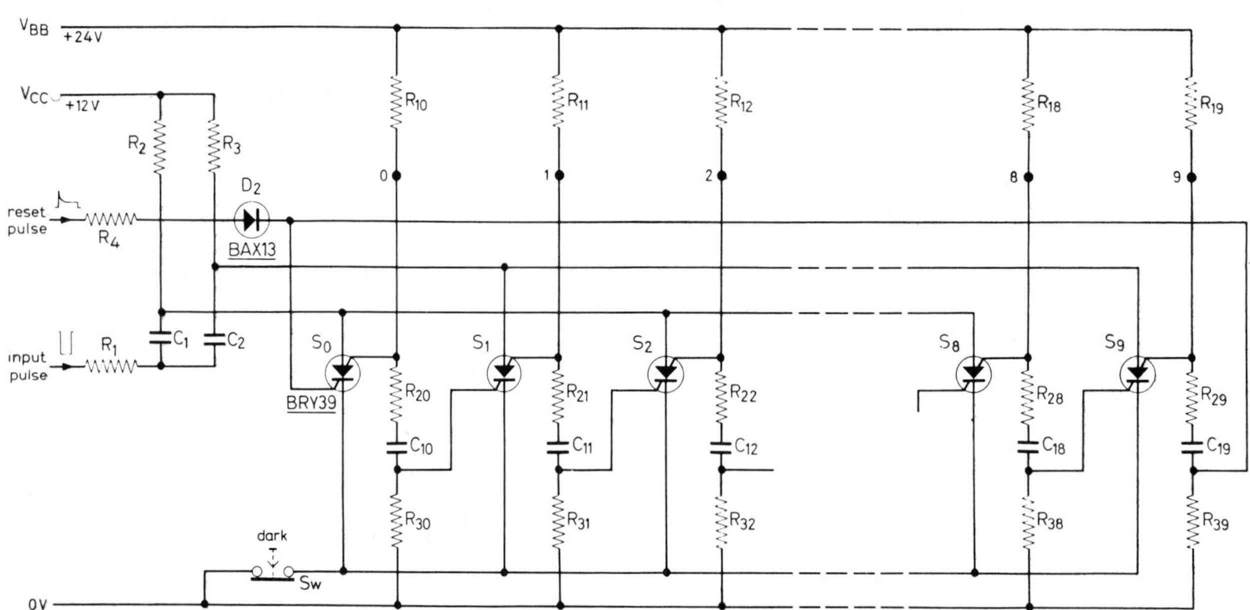

RING COUNTER WITHOUT DISPLAY—May be used to drive control circuit for numerical printout device, with negative-going output pulses taken from terminal points 0, 1, 2, . . ., 8, and 9. Values are: R1 820; R2, R3, 4.3K; R4, R10-R19 2.2K; R20-R29 3.9K; R30-R39 1K; C1, C2 5.6 nF; C10-C19 1 nF.—D. J. G. Janssen, Circuit Logic with Silicon Controlled Switches, *Electronic Applications*, Philips, Pub. Dept., Elcoma Div., Eindhoven, The Netherlands, Vol. 27, No. 1, 1966–1967, p 1–11.

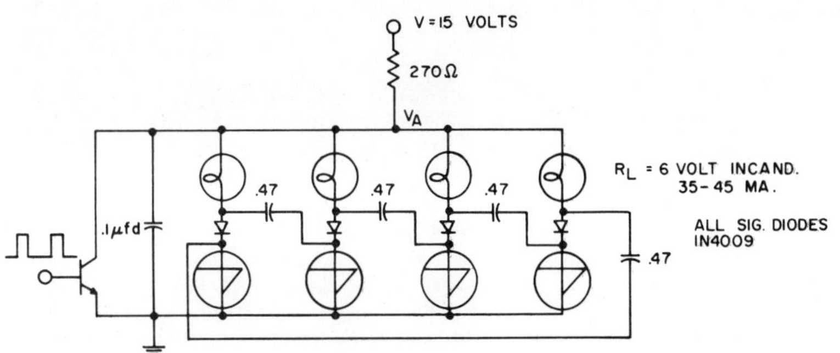

SUS LAMP-DRIVING RING COUNTER—Will operate up to 10 kHz. When supply voltage is applied, sus with lowest switching voltage comes on first. Succeeding count pulses applied to base of drive transistor step count along from stage to stage. Circuit is common-cathode type. Uses D13P1 sus.—W. R. Spofford, Jr., Applications of the New Silicon Bilateral Switch and the Silicon Unilateral Switch, General Electric, Syracuse, N.Y., No. 671.3, 1966, p 7.

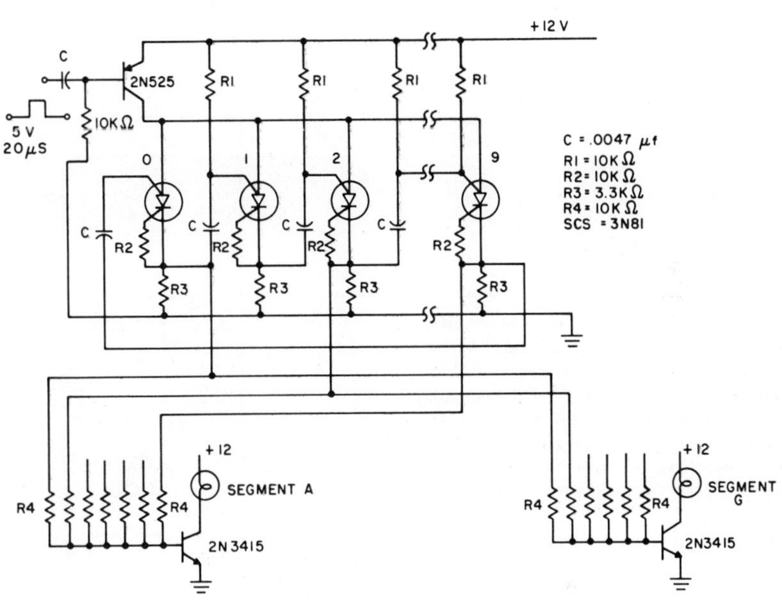

SEGMENT DECODING—Decoding circuit is OR gate formed by resistor group driving into transistor. This transistor provides threshold for gate and gain for driving lamp. Input to decoder is decimal-type signal from ring counter, portion of which is shown. Counter signal is referenced to ground, for compatibility with OR gates in decoding matrix.—R. M. Muth, Digital Circuits with Visual Readouts, General Electric, Syracuse, N.Y., No. 671.3, 1966, p 14.

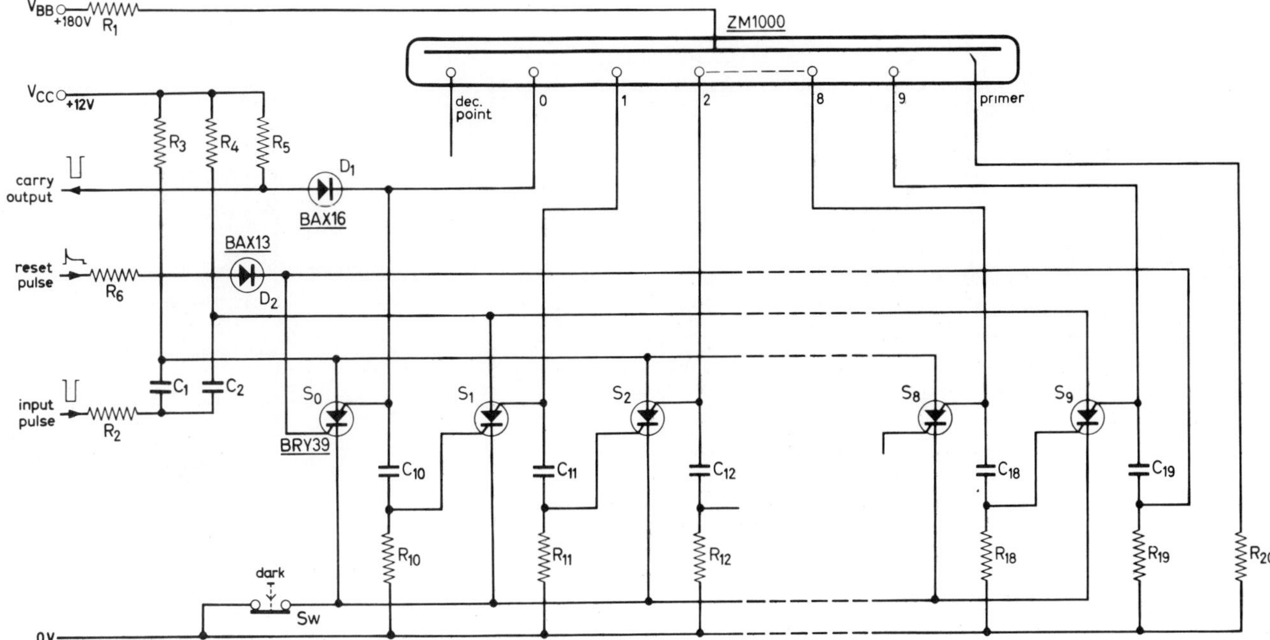

SCS RING COUNTER—Drives ZM1000 0-9 numerical indicator tube. Circuit design is simpler and less expensive than those using flip-flops. Input pulse amplitudes and durations are not critical, and can be about 12 V negative-going. Values are: R1 15K; R2, R10-R19 1K; R3-R4 5.1K; R5 10K; R6 2.2K; R20 10 meg; C1-C2 4.7 nF; C10-C19 390 pF.—D. J. G. Janssen, Circuit Logic with Silicon Controlled Switches, *Electronic Applications*, Philips, Pub. Dept., Elcoma Div., Eindhoven, The Netherlands, Vol. 27, No. 1, 1966–1967, p 1–11.

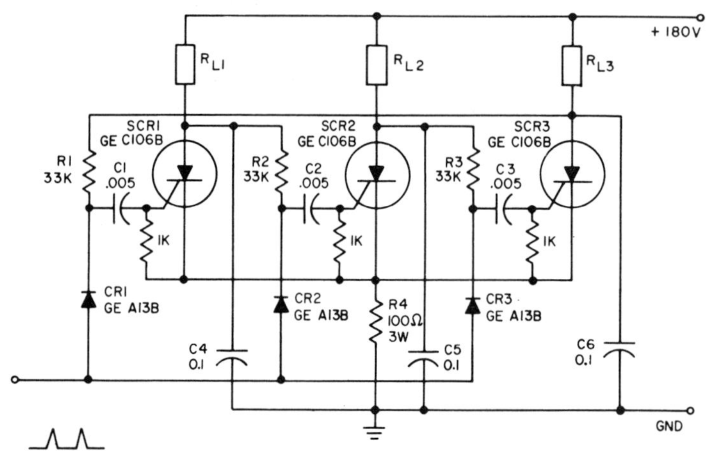

SCR RING COUNTER—Three-stage cathode-coupled ring counter can drive high-voltage loads up to 50 mA. Additional stages may be added. Useful in digital applications. Transfer along string always proceeds in same direction, with each transfer initiated by pulsing common input line. Gives undistorted square waves, free from commutation transients, across each load.—"SCR Manual," 4th Edition, General Electric, 1967, p 161–162.

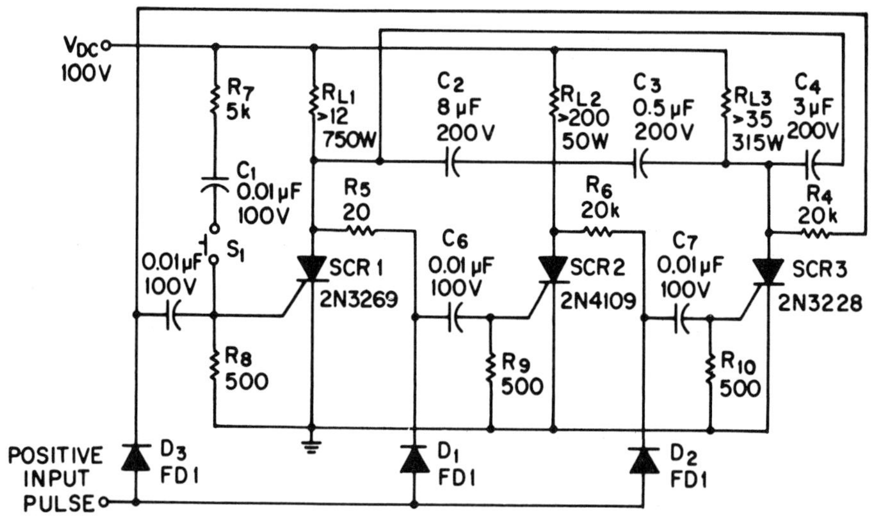

SCR HIGH-LEVEL SWITCHING—Scr's are both practical and economical for high-level switching within counting sequence in basic three-stage ring counter, despite popularity of IC modules for low-level switching. Article covers design procedure.—E. Kiburis, Sequential Control with Silicon Controlled Rectifiers, *EEE*, March 1970, p 100–103.

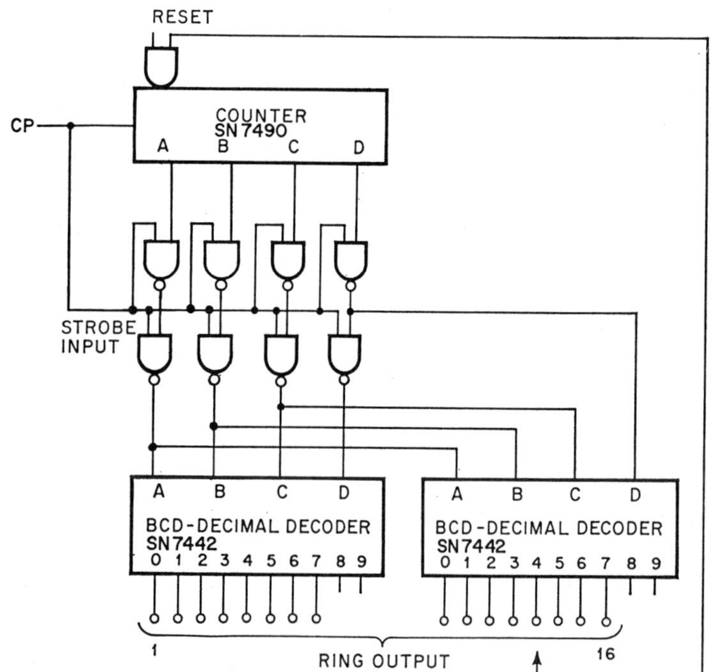

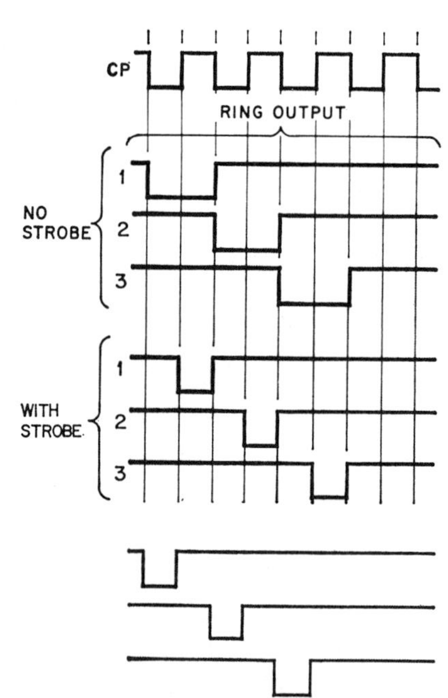

MSI RING COUNTER—Can be assembled with minimum number of IC connections. Straight-binary ripple-carry counter is driven by clock pulses and in turn drives two decoders, one for outputs 0 to 7 and the other for 8 to 15. Decoding networks allow only one output, so only one pulse can go around ring even if false triggering occurs.—W. Nadler, Build Ring Counters with Standard MSI, *Electronics*, June 8, 1970, p 96.

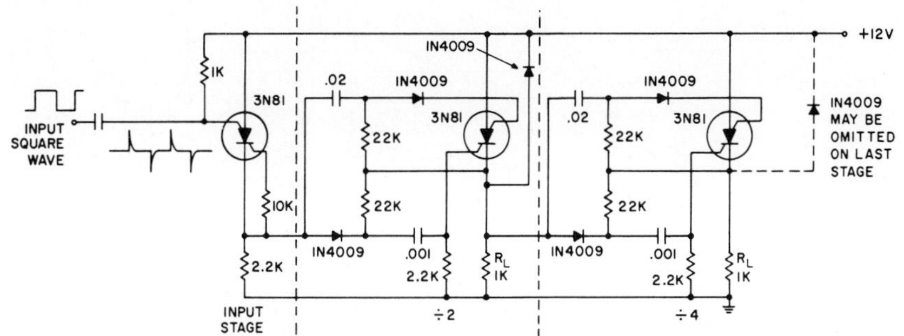

SCS BINARY—Stages are triggered by positive-going edge of input pulse, after sharpening by 3N81 scs input stage. Anode-cathode diode 1N4009 suppresses positive transients while scs is recovering. Each scs is turned on at cathode gate and turned off at anode gate.—Planar Silicon Controlled Switch 3N81/3N82, General Electric, Syracuse, N.Y., No. 65.16, 1964.

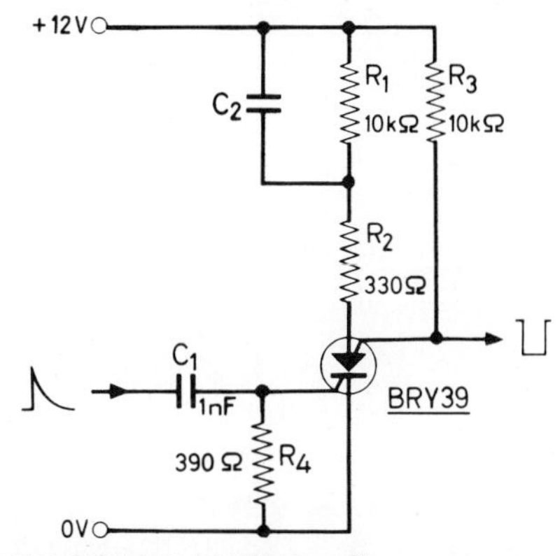

PULSE-SHAPING DRIVE—Supplies square-wave input signals to scs ring counter when positive-going pulses are fed to base of BRY39 scs.—D. J. G. Janssen, Circuit Logic with Silicon Controlled Switches, *Electronic Applications*, Philips, Pub. Dept., Elcoma Div., Eindhoven, The Netherlands, Vol. 27, No. 1, 1966–1967, p 1–11.

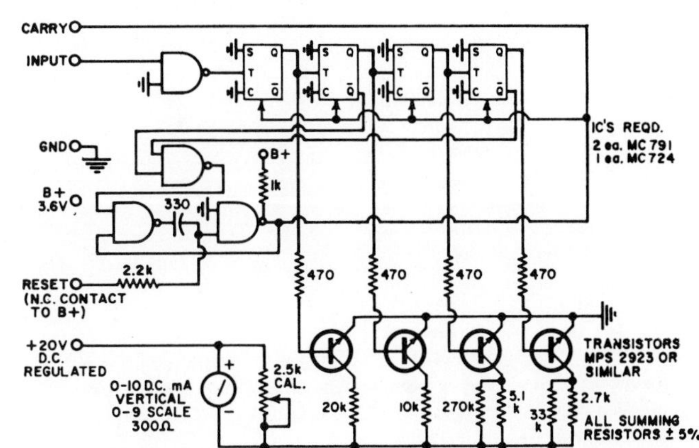

CURRENT SUMMING—Combines four integrated-circuit JK flip-flops in counter for use with meter or other analog readout. Sum of all currents will equal count stored with 1-2-4-8 counter. NAND gates at left are required for preclearing.—D. E. Lancaster, IC Decimal Counting Techniques, *Electronics World*, Sept. 1968, p 40–43 and 70.

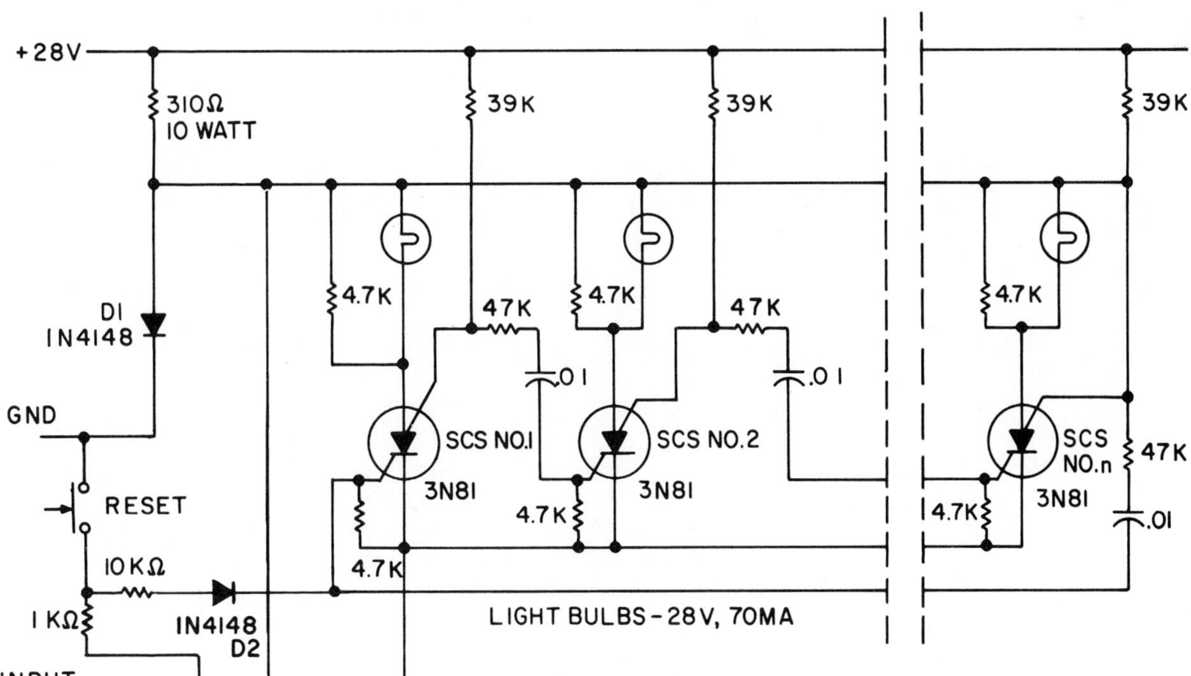

SCS LAMP-DRIVING RING COUNTER—Designed to handle large initial current drawn by incandescent lamp when cold. When power is first applied, any number of stages may turn on; these are turned off by turning on Q1 with reset button. When reset button is released, first scs stays on and the rest stay off. Each input pulse then moves turned-on stage one position to right.—R. M. Muth, A Ring Counter for Driving Incandescent Bulbs, General Electric, Syracuse, N.Y., No. 90.24, 1965.

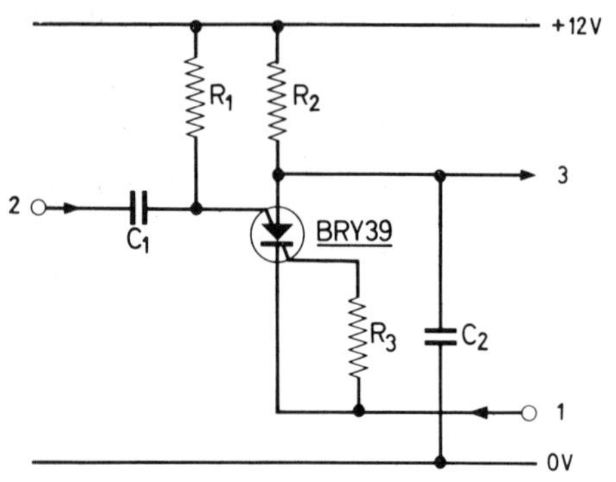

SYNCHRONOUS AND GATE—Scs gate is used with scs ring counter to carry out switching and logic functions that are to be coordinated by a train of clock pulses. Gate responds only when negative-going clock pulse is applied to terminal 1 in synchronism with negative-going input pulse of about 12 V at terminal 2, and then produces negative-going square-wave output pulse at terminal 3 lasting for duration of clock pulse. This output is used for driving counter. Values: R1 10K; R2, R3 1K; C1, C2 180 pF.—D. J. G. Janssen, Circuit Logic with Silicon Controlled Switches, *Electronic Applications*, Philips, Pub. Dept., Elcoma Div., Eindhoven, The Netherlands, Vol. 27, No. 1, 1966–1967, p 1–11.

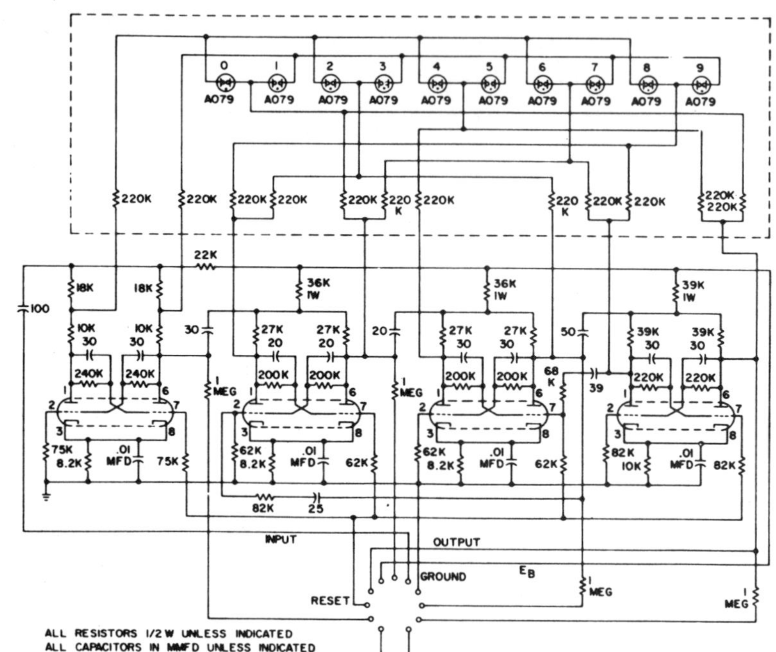

BINARY COUNTER—Neons provide high brightness and quick reaction time necessary for display. Good up to 1.2 MHz.—E. Bauman, "Applications of Neon Lamps and Gas Discharge Tubes," Signalite, Neptune, N.J., p 141.

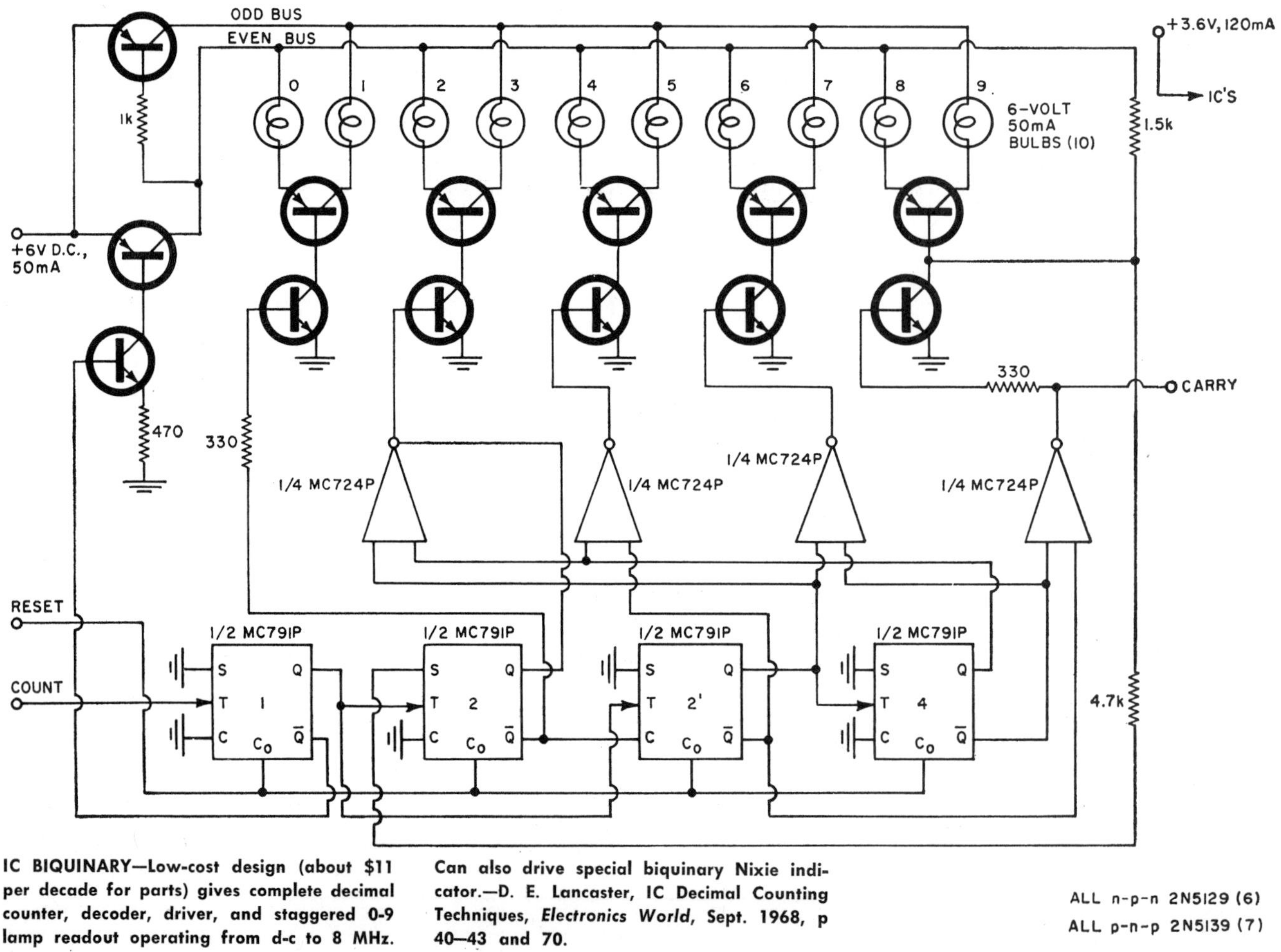

ALL n-p-n 2N5129 (6)
ALL p-n-p 2N5139 (7)

IC BIQUINARY—Low-cost design (about $11 per decade for parts) gives complete decimal counter, decoder, driver, and staggered 0-9 lamp readout operating from d-c to 8 MHz. Can also drive special biquinary Nixie indicator.—D. E. Lancaster, IC Decimal Counting Techniques, *Electronics World*, Sept. 1968, p 40–43 and 70.

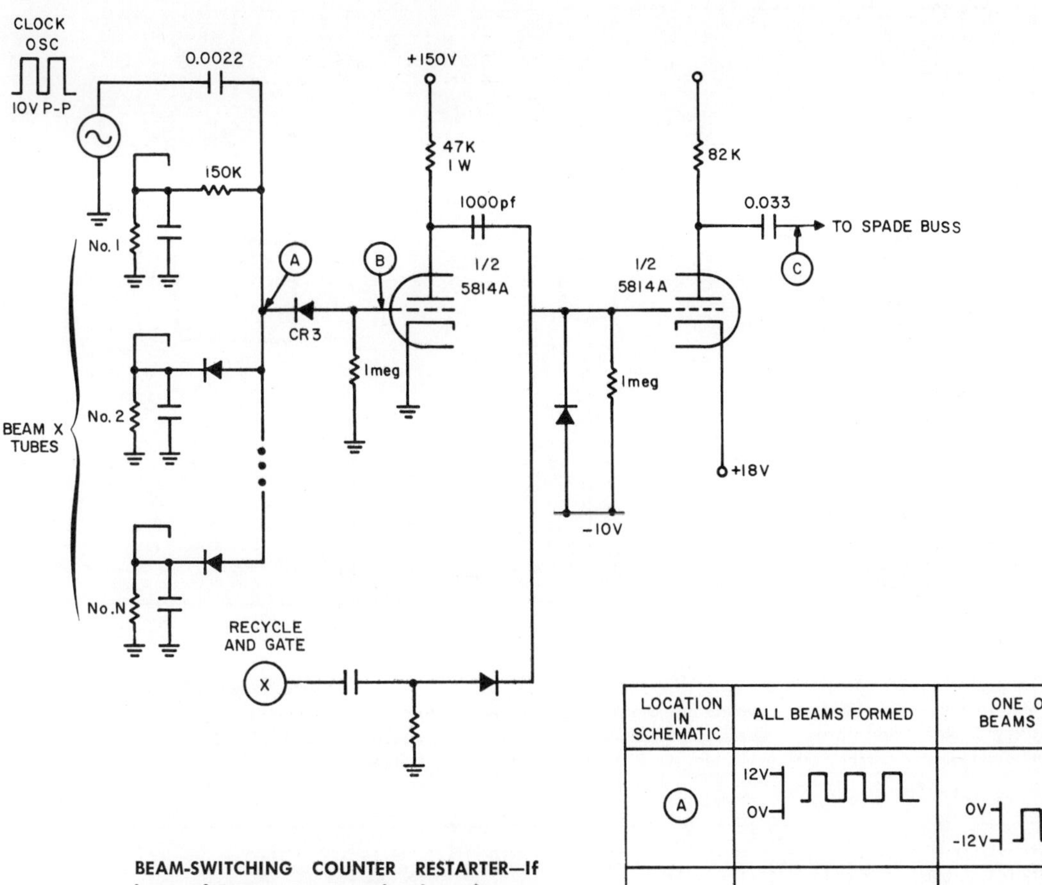

LOCATION IN SCHEMATIC	ALL BEAMS FORMED	ONE OR MORE BEAMS CLEARED
A	12V, 0V	0V, -12V
B	0V	0V, -12V
C	ESS	ESS, 0V

BEAM-SWITCHING COUNTER RESTARTER—If beam of Beam-x counter tube clears for any reason during operation, circuit shown will start tube again automatically. Circuit will operate on as little as 3 V from clock oscillator.—W. C. Whitworth, Simple Circuit Starts Beam Tubes Automatically, *Electronic Design*, Jan. 18, 1965, p 44 and 46.

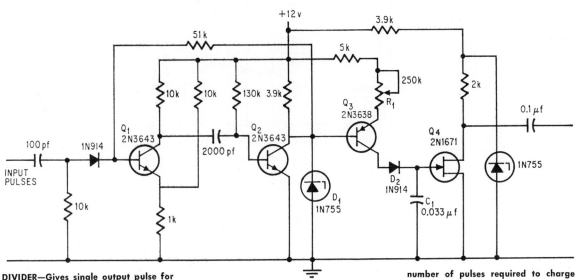

PULSE DIVIDER—Gives single output pulse for any desired number of input pulses in range from 2 to 90, without binary counter or decoder. Input pulses trigger one-shot mvbr Q1-Q2, which delivers 150-μs pulse that is clamped at 6 V by D1 and applied to base of constant-current source Q3 for charging C1. Setting of 10-turn precision pot R1 determines number of pulses required to charge C1 to point at which Q4 fires and delivers one output pulse.—S. Domanski, Circuit Divides Pulses Without Binary Counters, *Electronics*, Sept. 30, 1968, p 81–82.

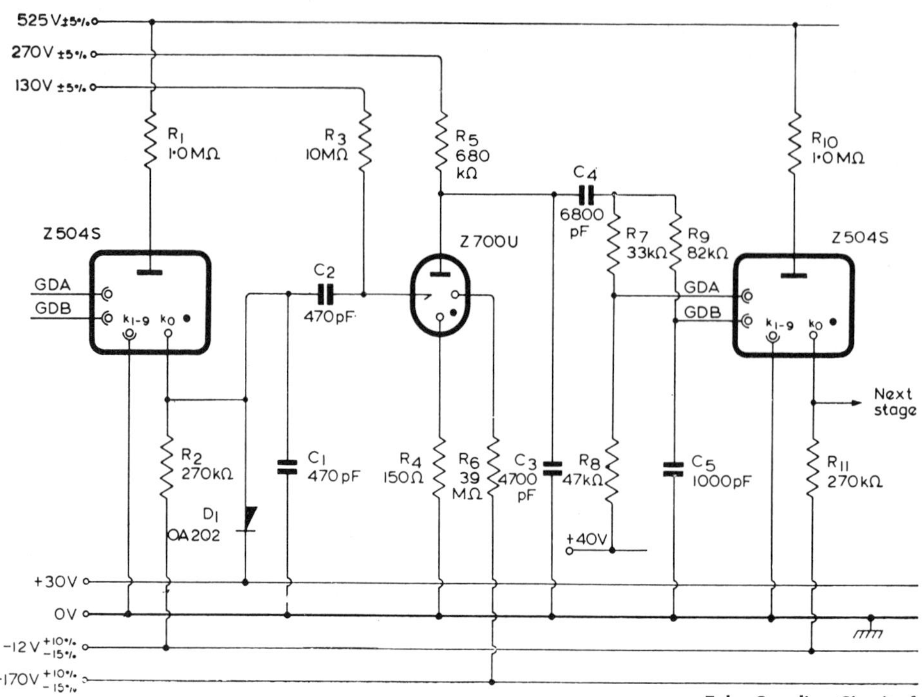

40-HZ COLD-CATHODE COUPLING—Circuit shows method of using Z700U cold-cathode trigger tube in self-extinguishing circuit to provide economical and reliable coupling between gas-filled decade counter tubes in counter chain.—G. F. Jeynes and S. Zilkha, Trigger Tube Coupling Circuits for the Z504S Stepping Tube, Philips, Pub. Dept., Elcoma Div., Eindhoven, The Netherlands, No. 15, 1965, p 16–25.

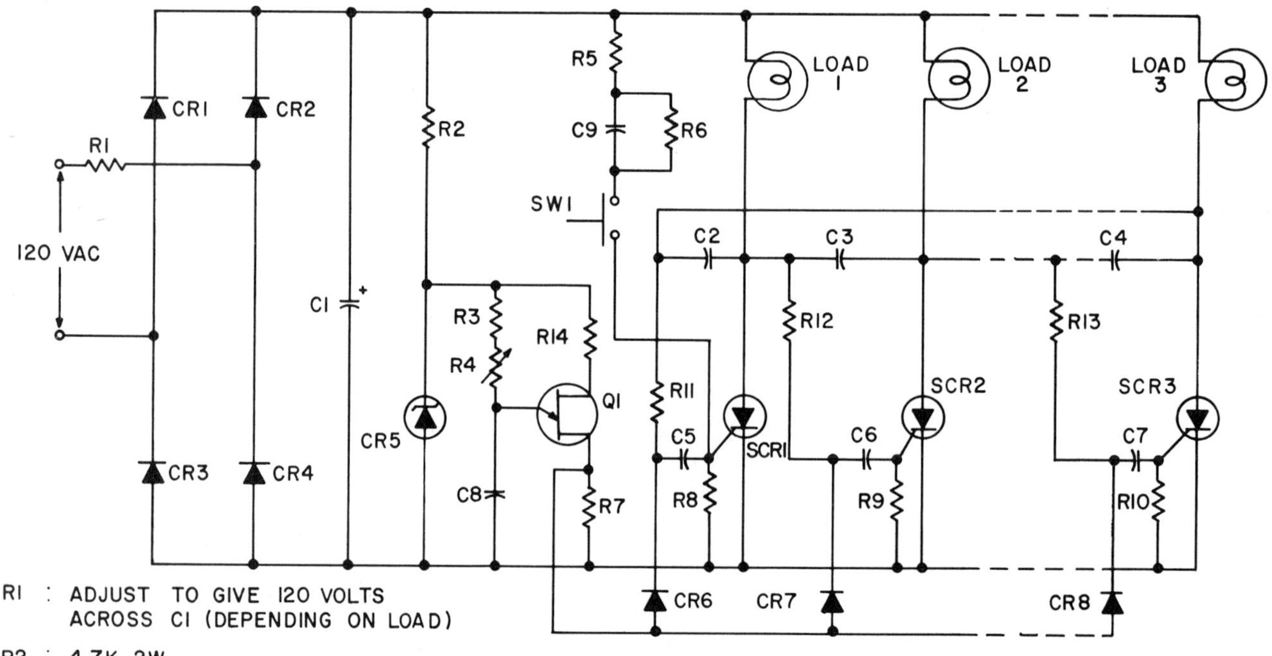

R1 : ADJUST TO GIVE 120 VOLTS ACROSS C1 (DEPENDING ON LOAD)
R2 : 4.7K 2W
R3 : 10K 1/2 W
R4 : 500K LINEAR POT
R5 : 100Ω 1/2 W
R6 : 1 MEG 1/2 W
R7 : 47Ω 1/2 W
R8, R9, R10 : 1K 1/2 W
R11, R12, R13 : 33K 1/2 W
R14 : 330 , 1/2 W

C1 : 100 μF, 200 V
C2, C3, C4 : 5 μF, 200 V
C5, C6, C7 : .01 μF
C8 : 1 μF, 25 V
C9 : .1 μF 200 V
CR1 - CR4 : GE A10B
CR5 : GE Z4XL18 ZENER
CR6 - CR8 : GE A13F

Q1 : GE 2N2646 UJT
SCR1, SCR2, SCR3 : GE C20B

LOADS : 100 W

ADDITIONAL STAGES MAY BE ADDED BETWEEN DASHED LINES.

THREE-STAGE SCR RING COUNTER—Each stage can handle lamp or other resistive load up to 100 W. Developed for counting applications, but can be used also for turning on string of lights sequentially as for advertising signs.—A. A. Adem, Flashers, Ring Counters and Chasers, General Electric, Syracuse, N.Y., No. 200.48, 1966, p 5.

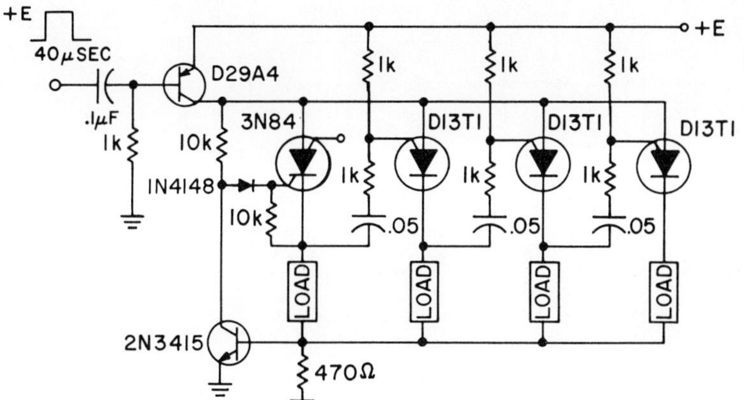

LOW-COST UJT RING COUNTER—Uses 3N84 scs ahead of D13T1 programmable ujt counting stages. When power is applied, only scs turns on. Next input pulse turns off D29A4 transistor momentarily, thereby turning off scs and turning on first D13T1 when power is restored after momentary interruption. Next pulse turns off first ujt and turns on next, with similar action.—W. R. Spofford, Jr., The D13T—A Programmable Unijunction Transistor, General Electric, Syracuse, N.Y., No. 90.70, 1967, p 13.

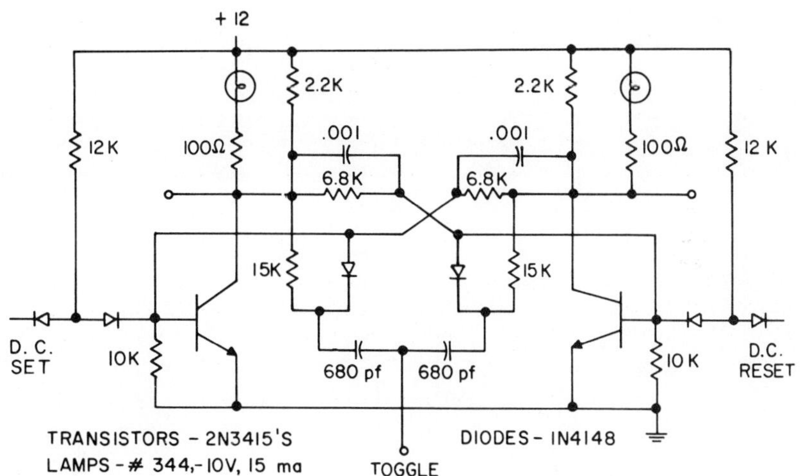

BINARY COUNTER WITH LAMP READOUT—High-gain transistors and low-current lamps eliminate need for separate driver stages. Continues to work when either or both lamps are burned out. Can drive other identical circuits to form binary counter chain.—R. M. Muth, Digital Circuits with Visual Readouts, General Electric, Syracuse, N.Y., No. 671.3, 1966, p 9.

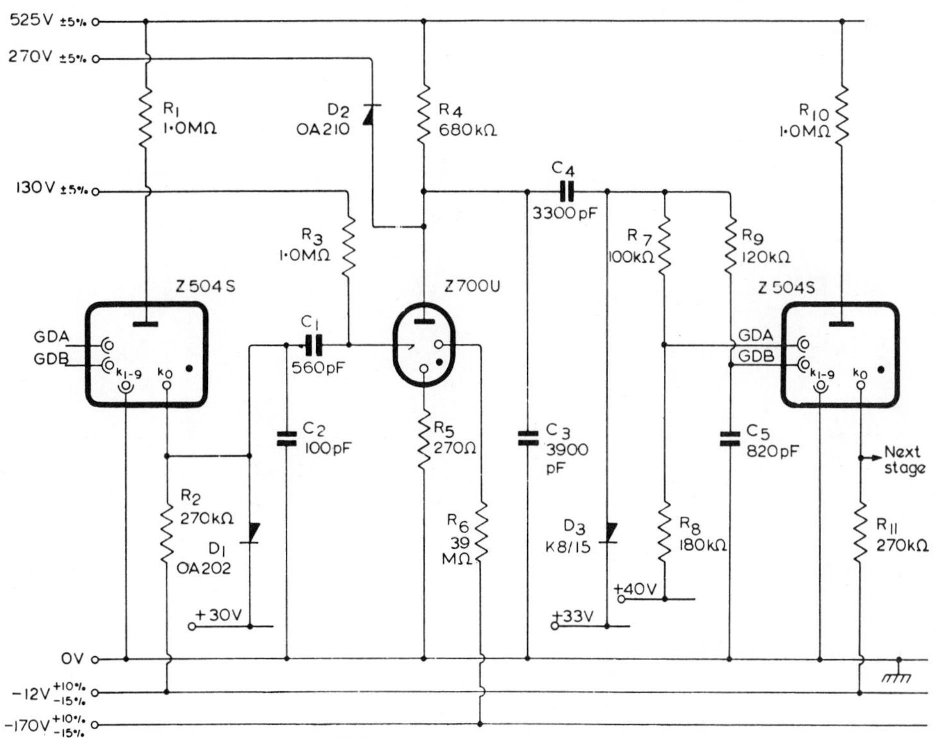

400-HZ COLD-CATHODE COUPLING—Cold-cathode Z700U trigger tube provides reliable coupling between gas-filled decade counter tubes in counter chain. Circuit components are carefully chosen to provide sufficient time for recovery of trigger tube after firing, without false triggering. D-c restoring diode D3 ensures that C4 discharges completely after each pulse.—G. F. Jeynes and S. Zilkha, Trigger Tube Coupling Circuits for the Z504S Stepping Tube, Philips, Pub. Dept., Elcoma Div., Eindhoven, The Netherlands, No. 15, 1965, p 16–25.

400-HZ PULSE-SHAPING COUPLER—Three-transistor coupling for gas-filled decade counter tubes will transfer pulses at speeds up to 400 Hz by producing new pulses of defined shape and amplitude for driving next Z504S stepping tube. TR1 is current amplifier, feeding cascode connection of TR2 and TR3 using inexpensive ACY17 low-voltage transistors instead of one high-cost high-voltage transistor. Input can be from external source through network CIN-RIN, or from cathode of previous stepping tube V1.—G. C. Chappell and G. F. Jeynes, Transistor Coupling Circuits for the Z540S Stepping Tube, Philips, Pub. Dept., Elcoma Div., Eindhoven, The Netherlands, No. 15, 1965, p 26–38.

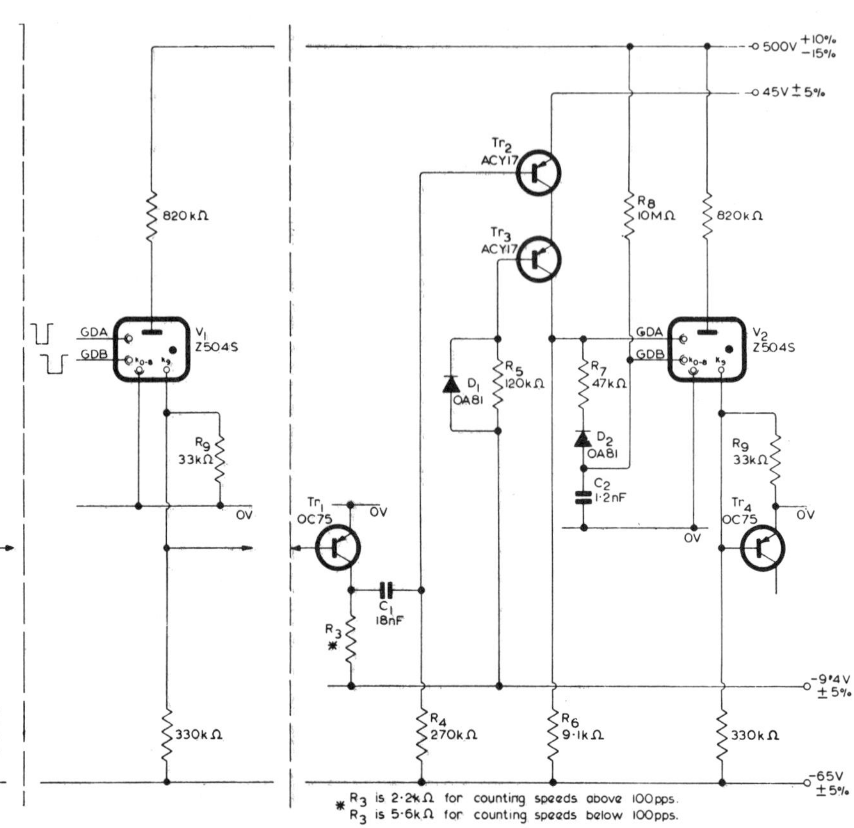

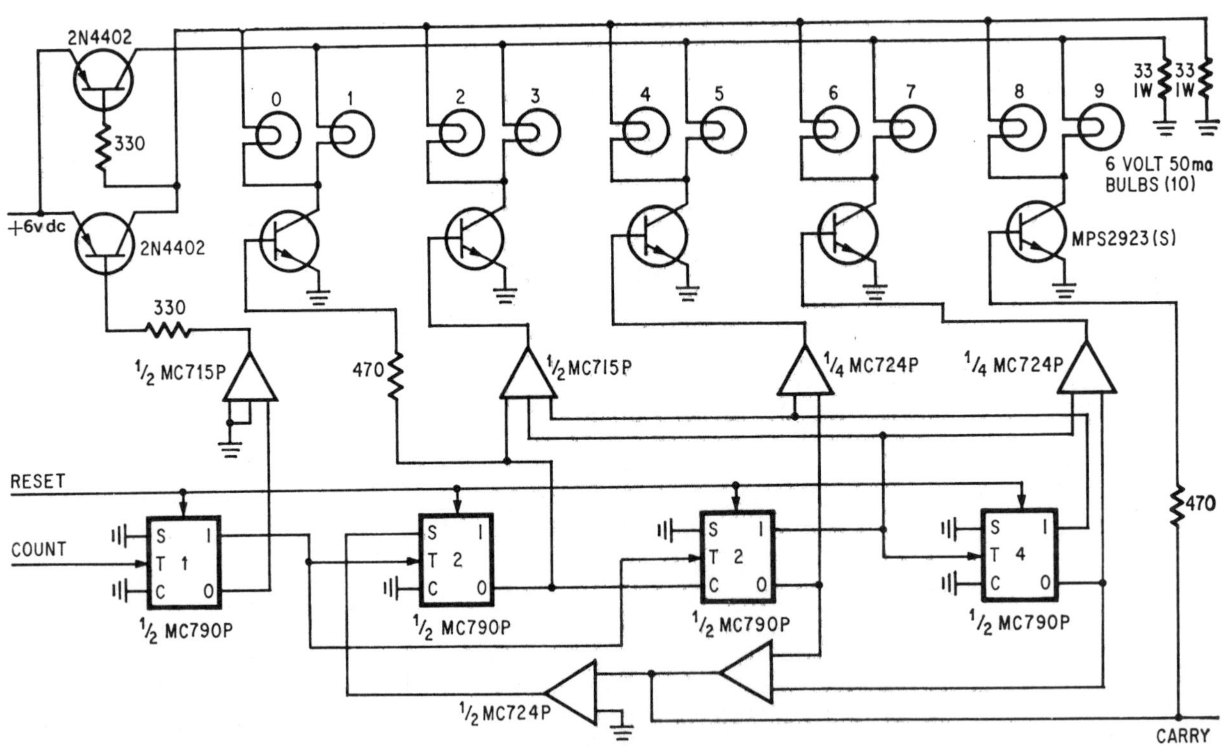

LOW-COST INCANDESCENT READOUT—Uses only seven switches to control ten bulbs. Sneak current paths keep all bulbs on all the time, but dimly. Effect is minimized by balancing resistors, to apply full supply voltage only to ON bulb, with one-third of supply voltage across OFF bulbs.—D. E. Lancaster, For Low Cost, Count on RTL, *Electronics*, Jan. 22, 1968, p 74–76.

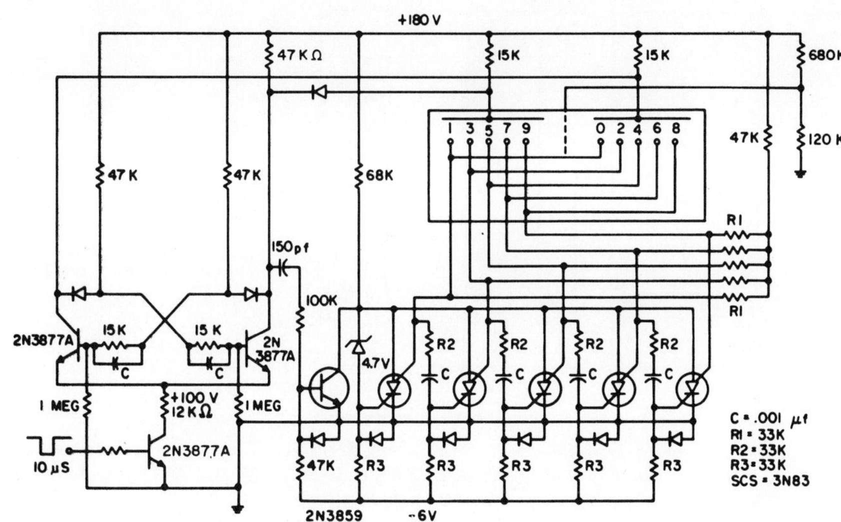

BIQUINARY COUNTER WITH READOUT—Consists of binary flip-flop driving five-stage (quinary) counter. Two high-voltage transistors perform both memory and driving functions in binary stage. Automatic reset of ring counter is provided by 4.7-V zener. Operating limit is 5 kHz.—R. M. Muth, Digital Circuits with Visual Readouts, General Electric, Syracuse, N.Y., No. 671.3, 1966, p 14.

LAMP-DRIVING RING COUNTER—When source voltage is applied, one stage will be dominant and its transistor pair will turn on first. Click pulse turns off this stage and turns on next stage in ring. To obtain indication of state of counter, 560-ohm resistor may be replaced by 8-V 0.1-A lamp in series with 47-ohm resistor, or additional transistor may be driven from tap on 560-ohm resistor to control brighter 12-V 2.2-W lamp. With transistor drive, counter continues to operate if lamp fails.—"E-Line Transistor Applications," Ferranti Ltd., Oldham, Lancs., England, 1969, p 18.

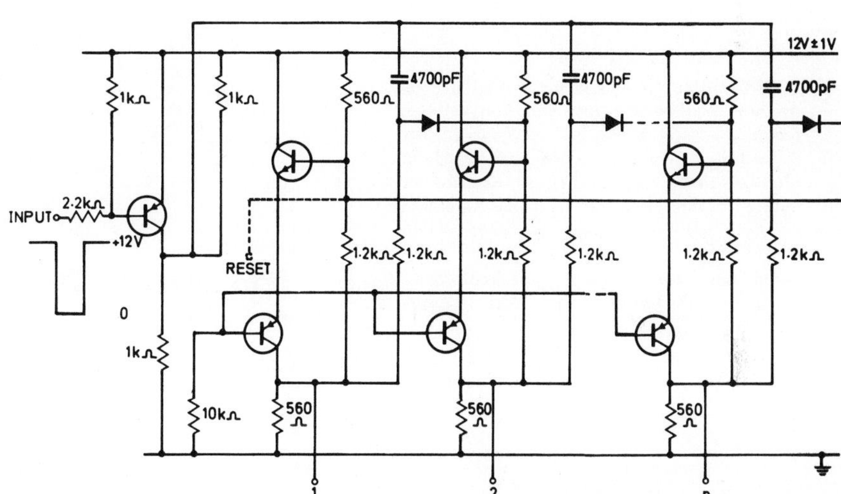

All n-p-n transistors, type ZTX300 (BCW10).
All p-n-p transistors, type ZTX500 (BCW11).
All diodes, type ZS140.

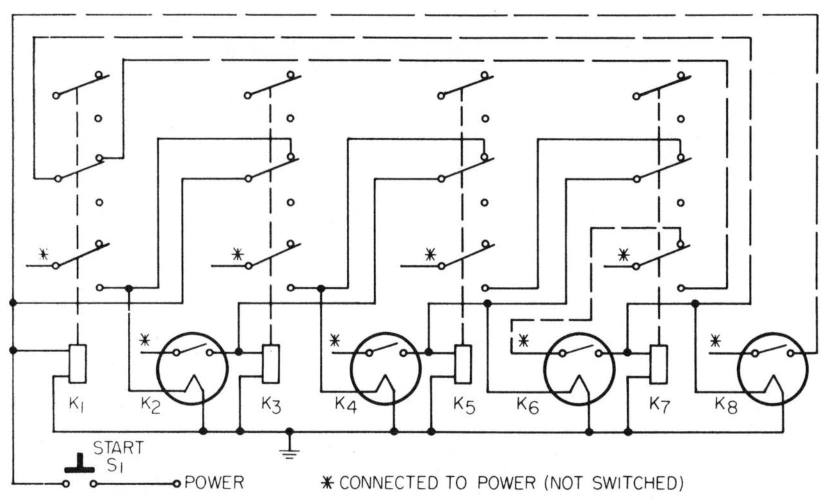

RING COUNTER WITH RELAYS—Low-cost combination of thermal delay relays gives adequate performance for low-speed counting applications, involving cycle times from 2 s to 3 min. If chain is closed, as indicated by dashed lines, counter runs continuously. Outputs are taken from third set of contacts on relays. If start switch is momentarily closed, circuit runs through one complete program and stops.—G. Richwell, Free-Running Ring Counter Uses Relays, *EEE*, Feb. 1967, p 144–145.

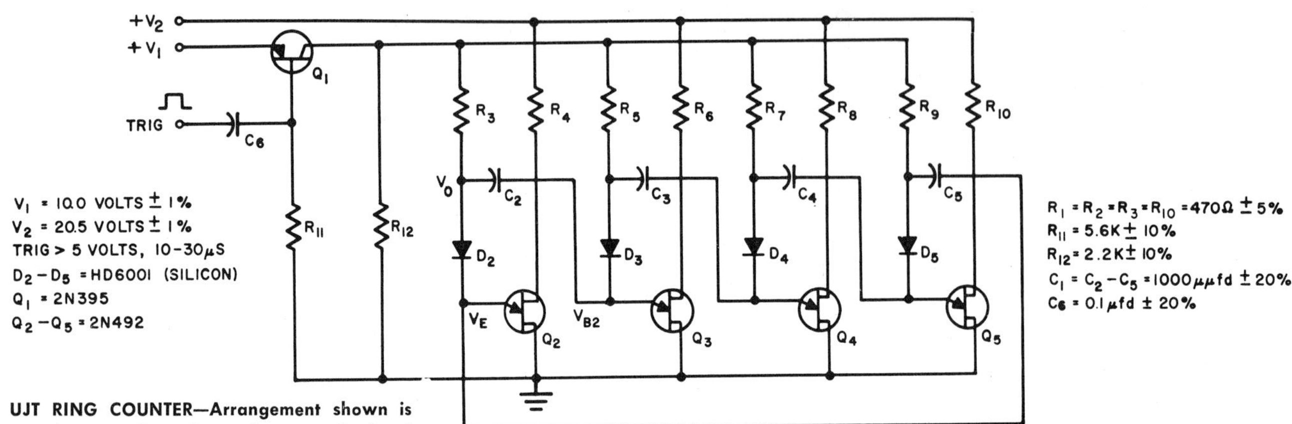

UJT RING COUNTER—Arrangement shown is superior to other ujt versions, on basis of design margins, flexibility, and overall performance. Any number of stages may be used. Each input trigger pulse advances "on" state one stage to right, then back from Q5 to Q2. Trigger width can vary over wide range.—T. P. Sylvan, The Unijunction Transistor Characteristics and Applications, General Electric, Syracuse, N.Y., No. 90.10, 1965, p 68.

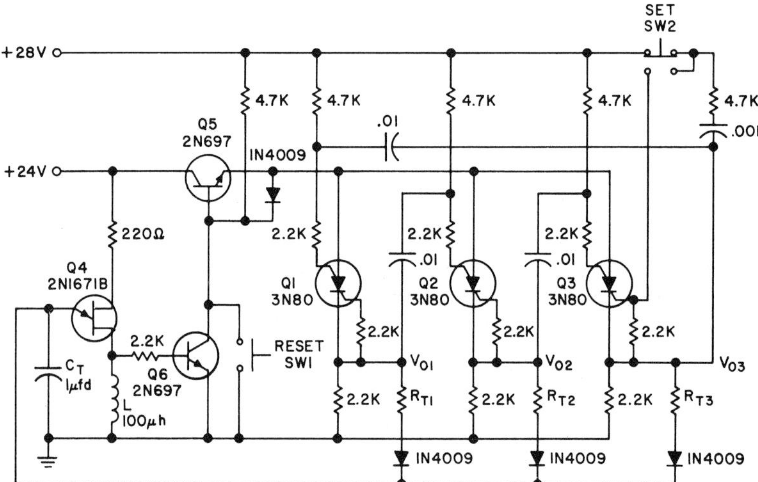

VARIABLE-TIMING SCS RING COUNTER—Will perform reliably over wide range of voltage, temperature, loading, and frequency. For telemetering, transducers can be used in place of timing resistors RT, so duration of output is indication of measured quantity. For visual indication, connect low-current lamp between each output (V) and ground. Additional stages can be added as desired.—"Unijunction Circuit Hints," General Electric, Syracuse, N.Y., Fig. 12.

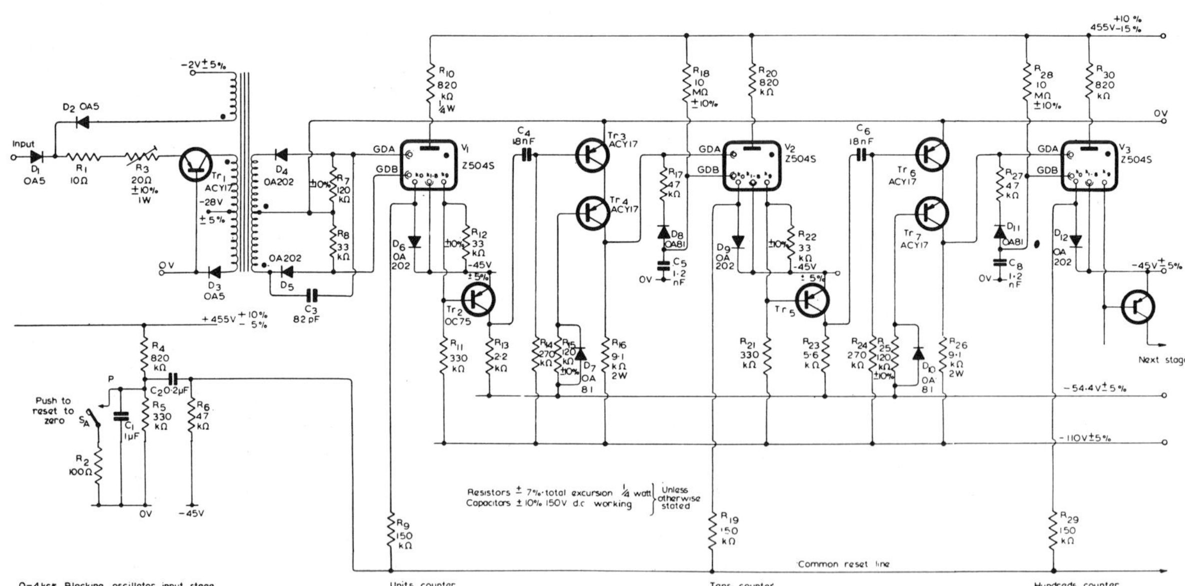

4-KHZ SIX-DECADE SCALER—Uses 4-kHz triggered blocking oscillator to drive first cold-cathode stepping tube in counter chain. Power supply is designed to handle up to three additional decade steppers with associated three-transistor pulse-shaping couplers. Includes reset circuit for setting all counters back to zero.—G. C. Chappell and G. F. Jeynes, Transistor Coupling Circuits for the Z504S Stepping Tube, Philips, Pub. Dept., Elcoma Div., Eindhoven, The Netherlands, No. 15, 1965, p 26–38.

SUS BINARY DIVIDER CHAIN—Silicon unilateral switch reduces number of components, as compared to transistor flip-flops. Output at point B is free from transients. 2N4987 sus may also be used.—Silicon Unilateral Switch 2N4983/2N4986, General Electric, Syracuse, N.Y., No. 65.25, 1967.

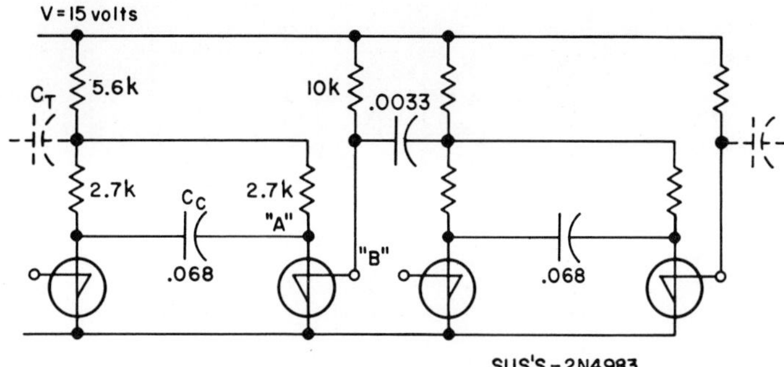

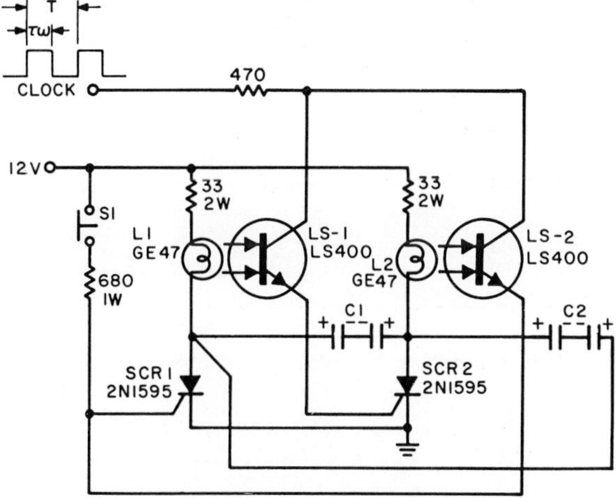

FOUR-STAGE RING—Time constant of lamps limits upper counting frequency to about 20 Hz in simple arrangement for counting clock pulses having widths between 2 and 10 ms. Count can be stopped mechanically by blocking light beam between lamp and corresponding light-sensitive silicon controlled rectifier.—R. Carvajal, Light-Sensing SCRs Make Simple Ring Counter, *Electronic Design*, Feb. 3, 1964, p 50—51.

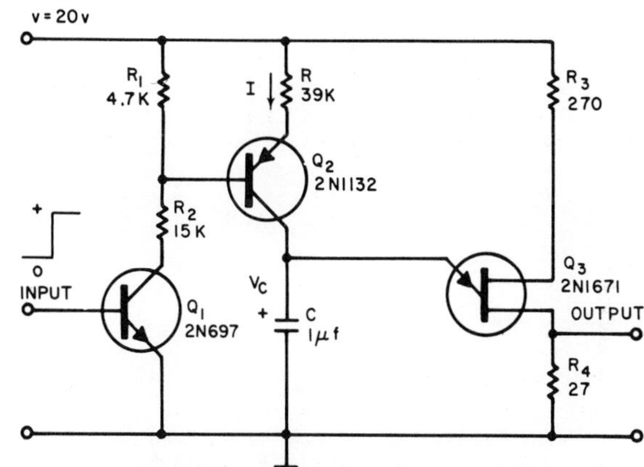

UJT COUNTER—Gives 100:1 count-down for 10-kHz input, to give one output pulse after 100 input pulses. Capacitor C charges through constant-current source Q2 each time Q1 is saturated by an input pulse. Circuit values are chosen from design equations given, so voltage across C will fire ujt Q3 and discharge C through R4 at 100th pulse. —R. A. Wilson, High-Ratio Pulse Counter Utilizes UJT Switch, *Electronic Design*, March 15, 1965, p 58—59.

NIXIE WITH AUTOMATIC RESET—Silicon controlled switches combine functions of memory element and high-voltage driver for ring counter. Feedback from last stage to first is accomplished by breakdown of 4.7-V zener, causing all stages to turn off. First stage comes on automatically when power is applied. If any other stage also comes on, it will be automatically cleared out by succeeding input pulses.—R. M. Muth, Digital Circuits with Visual Readouts, General Electric, Syracuse, N.Y., No. 671.3, 1966, p 13.

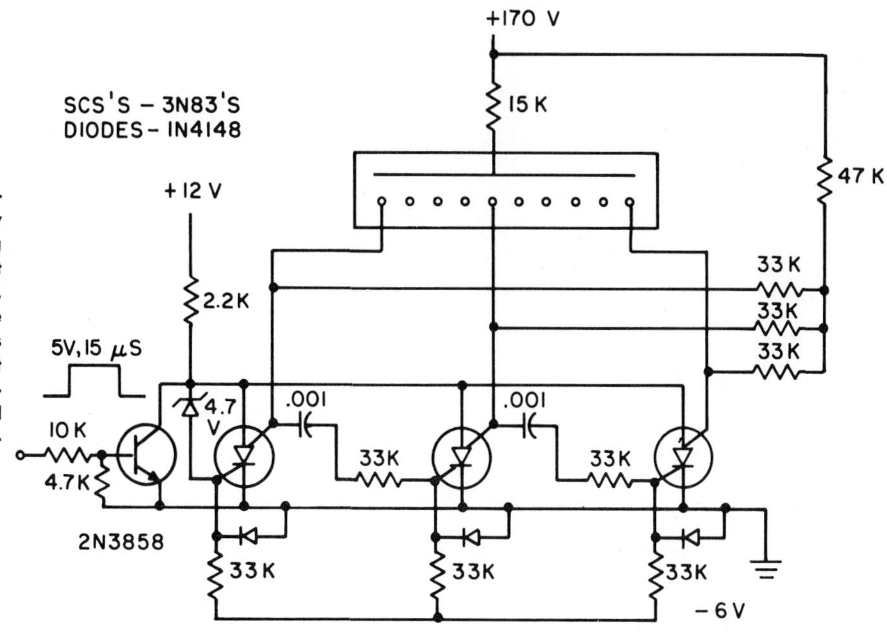

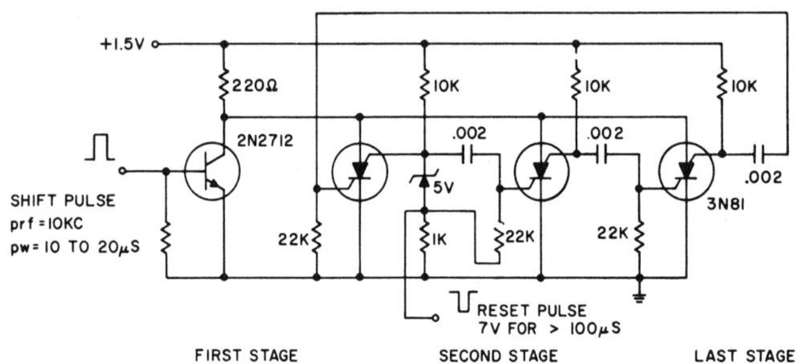

LOW-POWER RING—Requires only 6 mW at 1.5 V, with shift pulses of 1 to 6 V. Trailing edge of reset pulse turns on first stage. Maximum shift pulse width increases with voltage, approaching 70 μs for 6-V supply.—Planar Silicon Controlled Switch 3N81/3N82, General Electric, Syracuse, N.Y., No. 65.16, 1964.

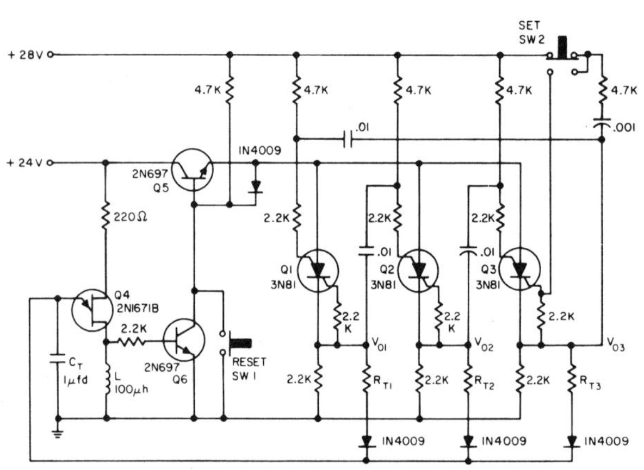

VARIABLE-TIMING RING—Intervals between ujt-generated shift pulses are controlled by values of RT and CT, which can be different for each stage.—Planar Silicon Controlled Switch 3N81/3N82, General Electric, Syracuse, N.Y., No. 65.16, 1964.

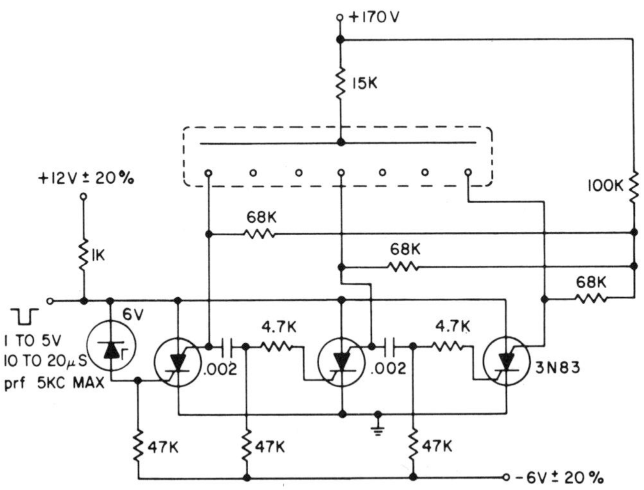

PLANAR PNPN SWITCHES DRIVE NIXIE—Uses one 3N83 switch for each Nixie electrode. Chief advantage is freedom from triggering by line transients.—Planar Neon Driver Silicon Controlled Switch 3N83, General Electric, Syracuse, N.Y., No. 65.17, 1964.

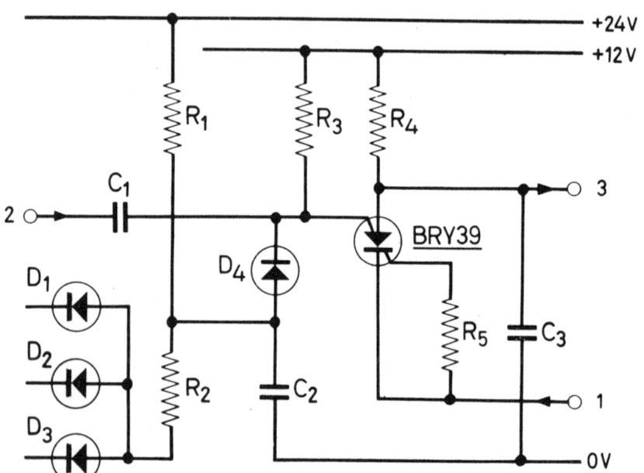

AND GATE WITH DELAYED OR—Used with scs ring counter to carry out switching and logic functions in synchronism with clock pulses applied to terminal 1. Negative-going 12-V input pulse at terminal 2 produces square-wave output pulse for as long as clock pulse is on 1, provided at least one of D1-D2-D3 OR inputs is at zero level. If all OR diodes are at positive 12 V level, input pulse has no effect. R2-C2 introduces delay to insure that change of d-c level has no effect until next clock pulse arrives. Values: R1 22K; R2 6.8K; R3 10K; R4, R5 1K; C1, C3 180 pF; C2 1 nF.—D. J. G. Janssen, Circuit Logic with Silicon Controlled Switches, *Electronic Applications*, Philips, Pub. Dept., Elcoma Div., Eindhoven, The Netherlands, Vol. 27, No. 1, 1966–1967, p 1–11.

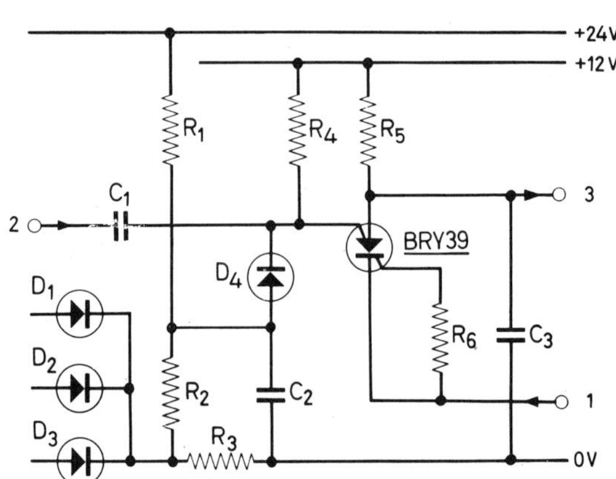

GATE WITH TWO DELAYS—Used with scs ring counter to carry out switching, logic, and delay functions as controlled by clock pulses. Diodes D1, D2, and D3 provide AND function, wherein negative-going input pulses at terminal 2 initiate square-wave output only if all d-c inputs to diodes have zero potential and no input is at +12 V or higher. Values: R1 22K; R2 6.8K; R3, R4, 10K; R5, R6 1K; C1, C3 180 pF; C2 1 nF.—D. J. G. Janssen, Circuit Logic with Silicon Controlled Switches, *Electronic Applications*, Philips, Pub. Dept., Elcoma Div., Eindhoven, The Netherlands, Vol. 27, No. 1, 1966–1967, p 1–11.

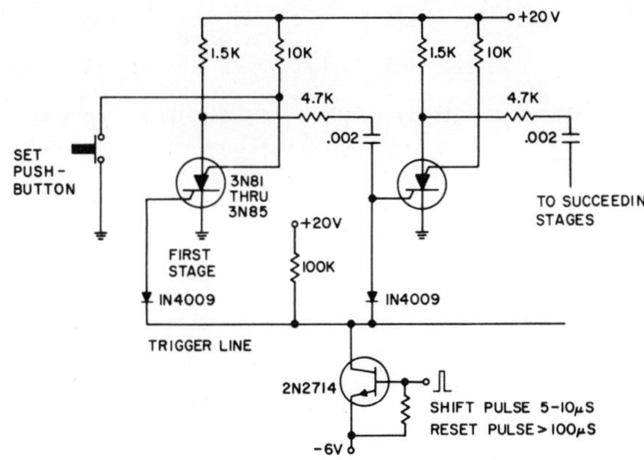

20-KHZ SCS RING—Shift pulse turns off conducting scs by reverse-biasing cathode gate. Charge stored on coupling capacitor then triggers next stage. Long shift pulse is used to turn off all stages by charging all capacitors. Grounding anode gate of stage will set it.—Planar Silicon Controlled Switch 3N81/3N82, General Electric, Syracuse, N.Y., No. 65.16, 1964.

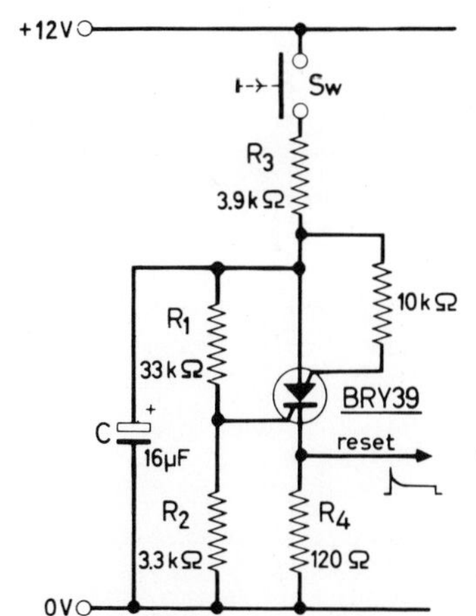

RESET PULSE GENERATOR—Closing of switch produces single pulse for simultaneously resetting scs ring counter to zero after numerical indicator tube has been darkened.—D. J. G. Janssen, Circuit Logic with Silicon Controlled Switches, *Electronic Applications*, Philips, Pub. Dept., Elcoma Div., Eindhoven, The Netherlands, Vol. 27, No. 1, 1966–1967, p 1–11.

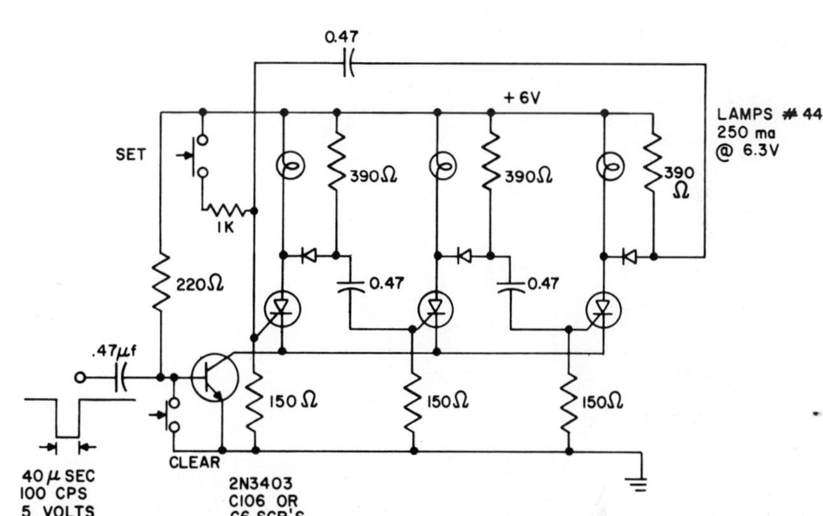

HIGH-CURRENT RING COUNTER—Operates at up to 2 kHz and will count either with or without lamps. Combines both memory and driving functions, with decimal readout by lamps.—R. M. Muth, Digital Circuits with Visual Readouts, General Electric, Syracuse, N.Y., No. 671.3, 1966, p 12.

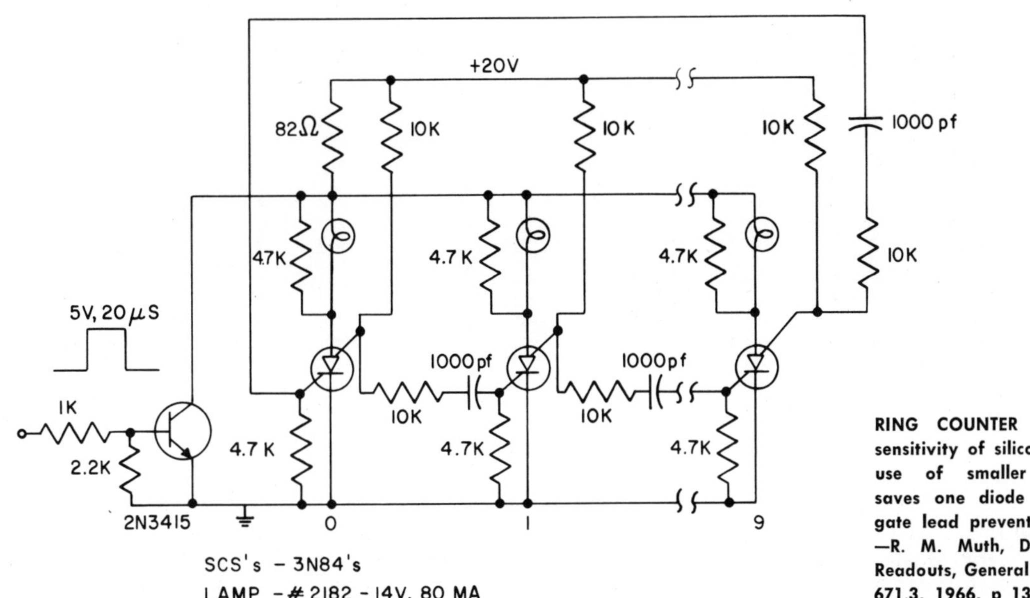

RING COUNTER FOR SMALL LAMPS—High sensitivity of silicon controlled switch permits use of smaller capacitors. Arrangement saves one diode per stage because anode gate lead prevents triggering by rate effect.—R. M. Muth, Digital Circuits with Visual Readouts, General Electric, Syracuse, N.Y., No. 671.3, 1966, p 13.

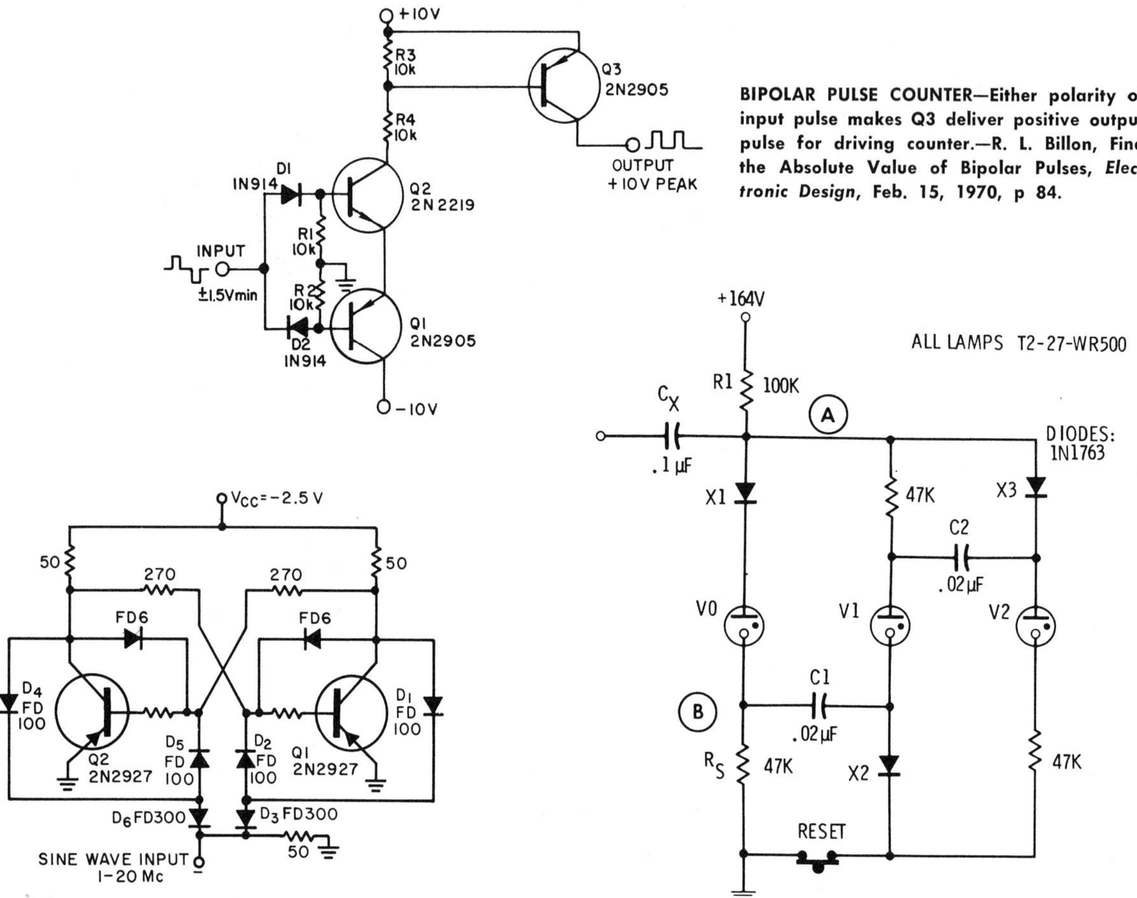

BIPOLAR PULSE COUNTER—Either polarity of input pulse makes Q3 deliver positive output pulse for driving counter.—R. L. Billon, Find the Absolute Value of Bipolar Pulses, *Electronic Design*, Feb. 15, 1970, p 84.

COUNTING PULSES AT 1 TO 20 MHZ—Flip-flop uses additional fast diodes to provide switching times under 10 ns. FD100's are for pulse steering, FD6's prevent collector saturation, and long-storage FD300's complete triggering action.—20 MC Counter Flip Flop, *Electronic Design*, March 2, 1964, p 58.

DECIMAL RING COUNTER—Can count up to 999 without need for buffer amplifier, at rates up to 500 Hz. Each stage has neon glow lamp, which can be used for visual readout (circuit shows only first three stages of decade). Pressing reset button fires V0 to indicate count of zero. First input pulse turns off V0 and turns on V1, with count advancing one stage for each succeeding pulse. Resistor and supply values are not critical. Known as Manley-Buckley ring counter.—W. G. Miller, "Using and Understanding Miniature Neon Lamps," H. W. Sams & Co., Indianapolis, Ind., 1969, p 55.

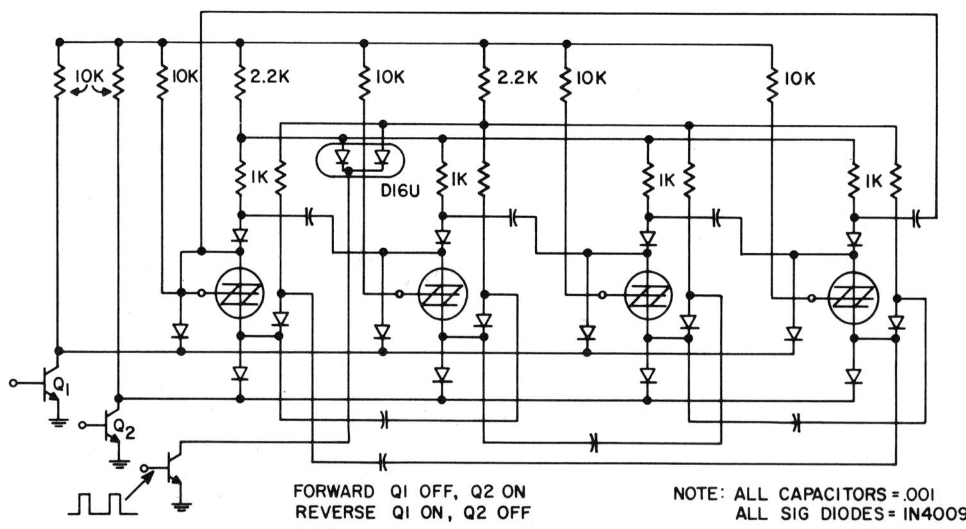

SBS REVERSIBLE RING COUNTER—Type D13Q1 silicon bilateral switches permit changing direction of stepping of stages simply by switching states of transistors Q1 and Q2. Operation can be about 10 kHz. During switch from forward to reverse count, stored charge in bottom p-n region of sbs serves to remember which stage was on.—W. R. Spofford, Jr., Applications of the New Silicon Bilateral Switch and the Silicon Unilateral Switch, General Electric, Syracuse, N.Y., No. 671.3, 1966, p 8.

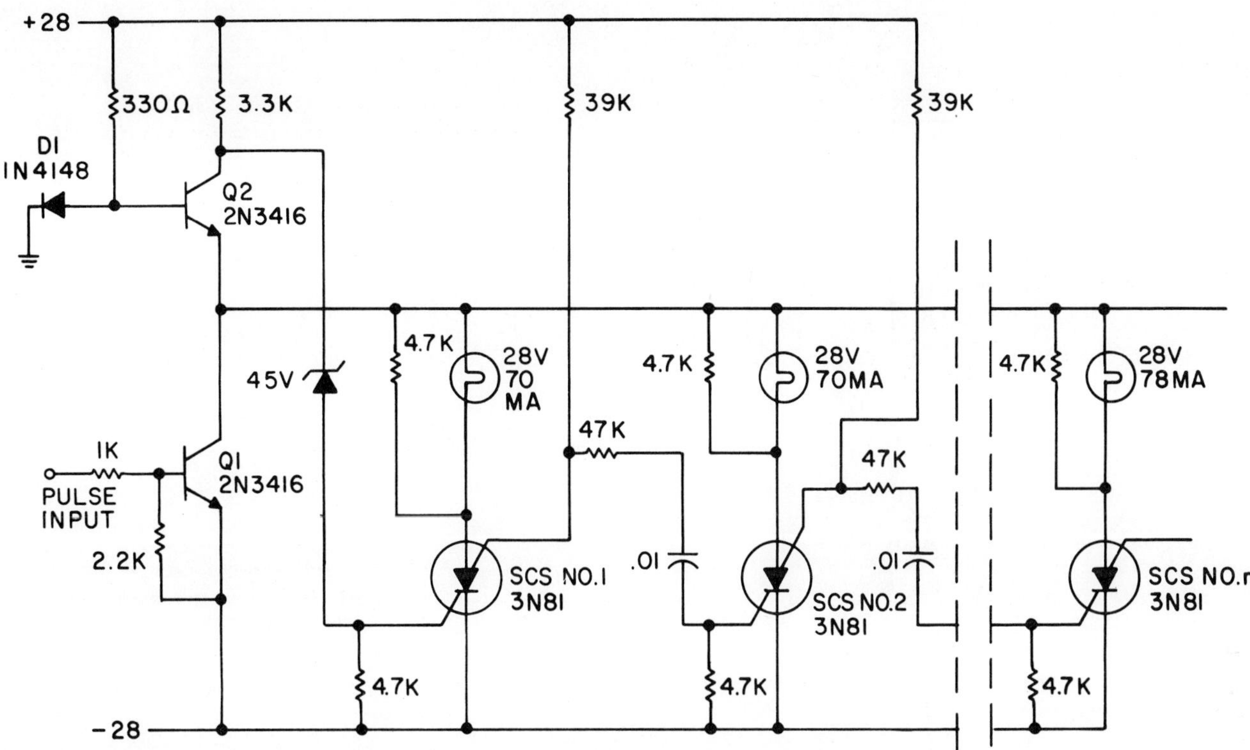

AUTOMATIC RESET—In this variation of lamp-driving scs ring counter, breakdown diode is used to couple last stage to first. First stage then turns on only if all other stages are off. —R. M. Muth, A Ring Counter for Driving Incandescent Bulbs, General Electric, Syracuse, N.Y., No. 90.24, 1965.

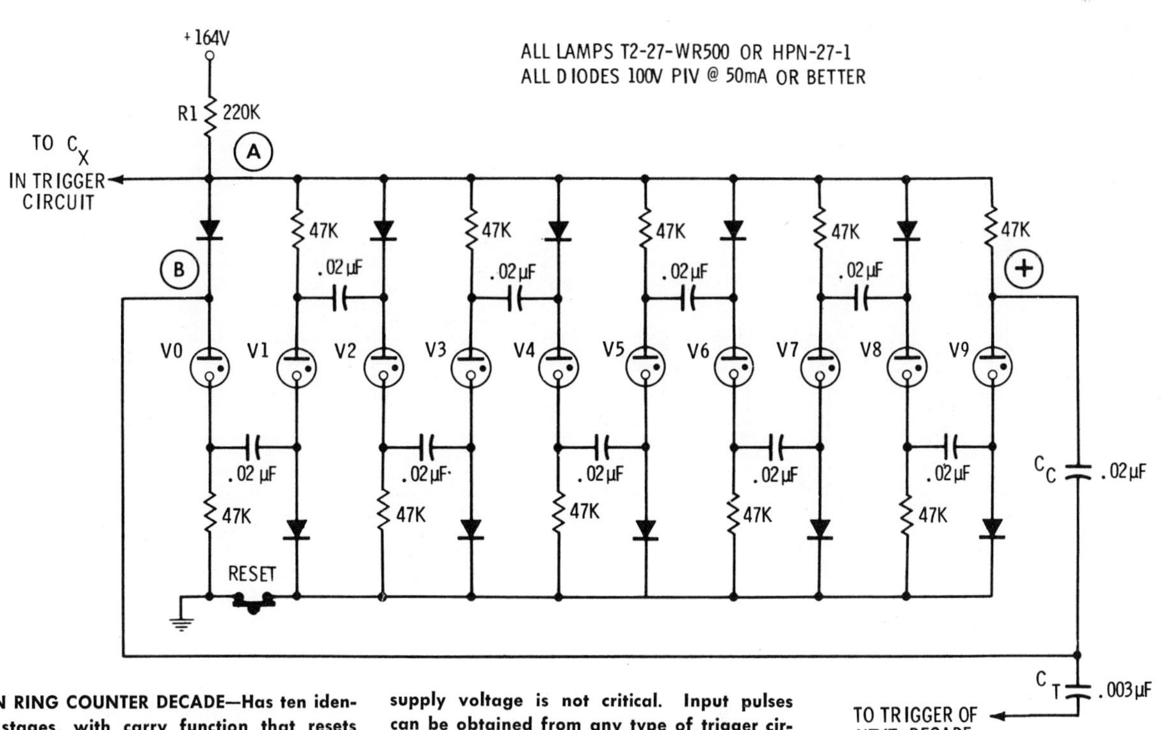

NEON RING COUNTER DECADE—Has ten identical stages, with carry function that resets decade to zero and actuates trigger stage of next decade. Power supply can be two Z82R10 miniature neon regulators in series; supply voltage is not critical. Input pulses can be obtained from any type of trigger circuit.—W. G. Miller, "Using and Understanding Miniature Neon Lamps," H. W. Sams & Co., Indianapolis, Ind., 1969, p 58.

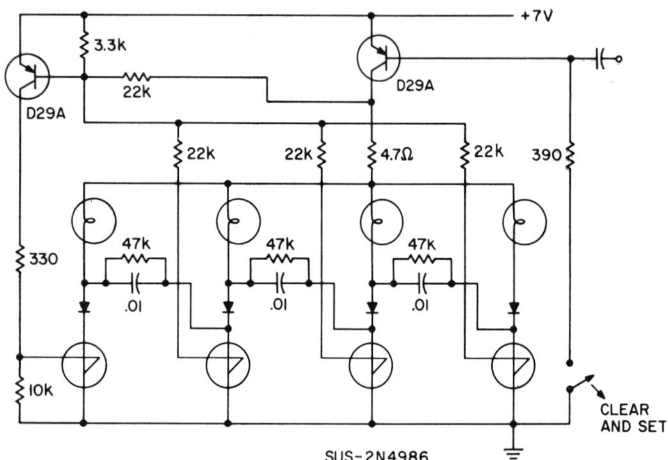

LAMP-DRIVING RING COUNTER—Uses 2N4986 (or 2N4990) silicon unilateral switches to drive incandescent lamps of ring counter.—Silicon Unilateral Switch 2N4983/2N4986, General Electric, Syracuse, N.Y., No. 65.25, 1967.

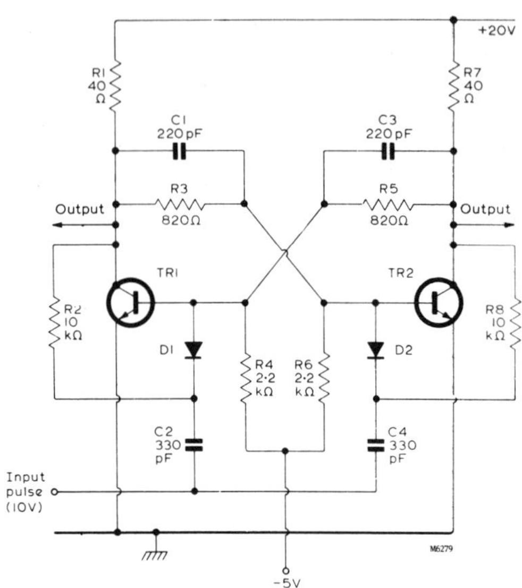

100-KHZ HIGH-CURRENT ECCLES-JORDAN—Transistors are BFY50 and diodes AAZ12. Input trigger pulses are negative.—Applications of the BFY50, BFY51 and BFY52, Philips, Pub. Dept., Elcoma Div., Eindhoven, The Netherlands, No. 428, 1965.

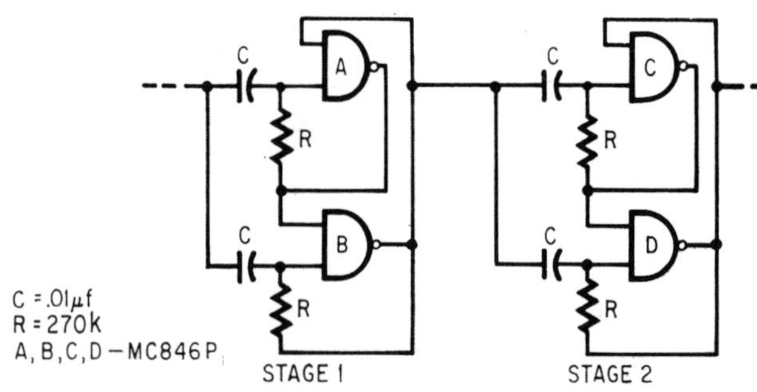

RIPPLE COUNTER—Two 0.01-μF capacitors and two 270K resistors added to MC846P NAND gate make low-cost ripple counter for applications where high speed is not important.—S. Kass, NAND Gate Counter is Cheaper to Make, *Electronics*, Jan. 20, 1969, p 87.

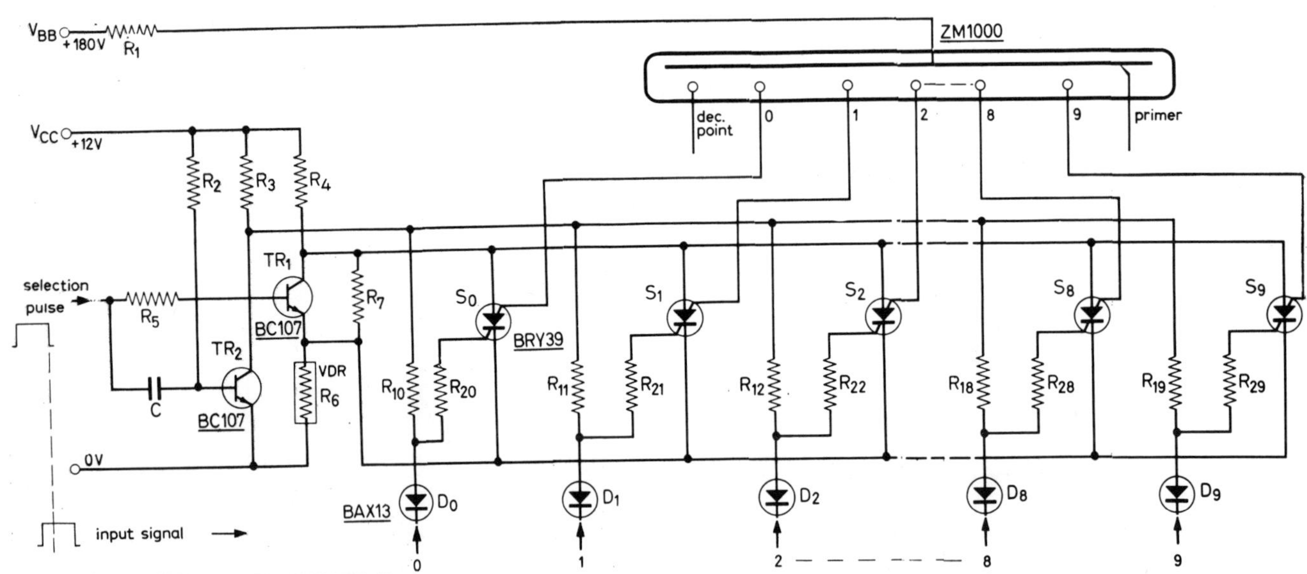

NUMERICAL DISPLAY WITH MEMORY—Used for controlling one numerical indicator tube in bank of such tubes used for displaying parallel digits representing information from computer or calculator. Scs associated with each digit acts as switch and memory, with digit remaining lit after input signal that selected it has ceased. Article describes operation in detail.—D. J. G. Janssen, Circuit Logic with Silicon Controlled Switches, *Electronic Applications*, Philips, Pub. Dept., Elcoma Div., Eindhoven, The Netherlands, Vol. 27, No. 1, 1966–1967, p 1–11.

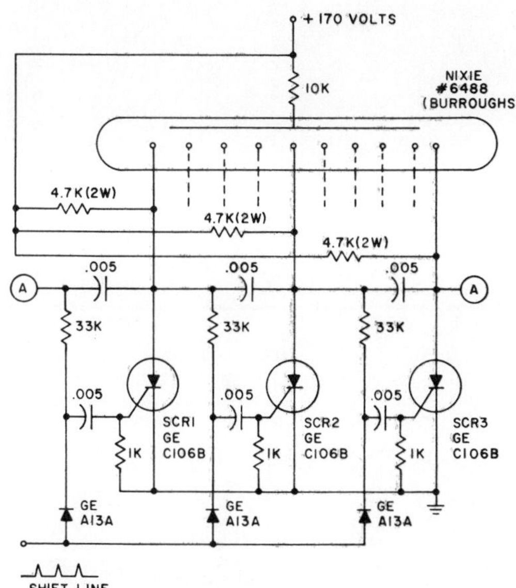

ANODE-COUPLED SCR RING COUNTER—Modification of basic cathode-coupled scr ring counter, as required for driving Nixie decade readout tube.—"SCR Manual," 4th Edition, General Electric, 1967, p 162.

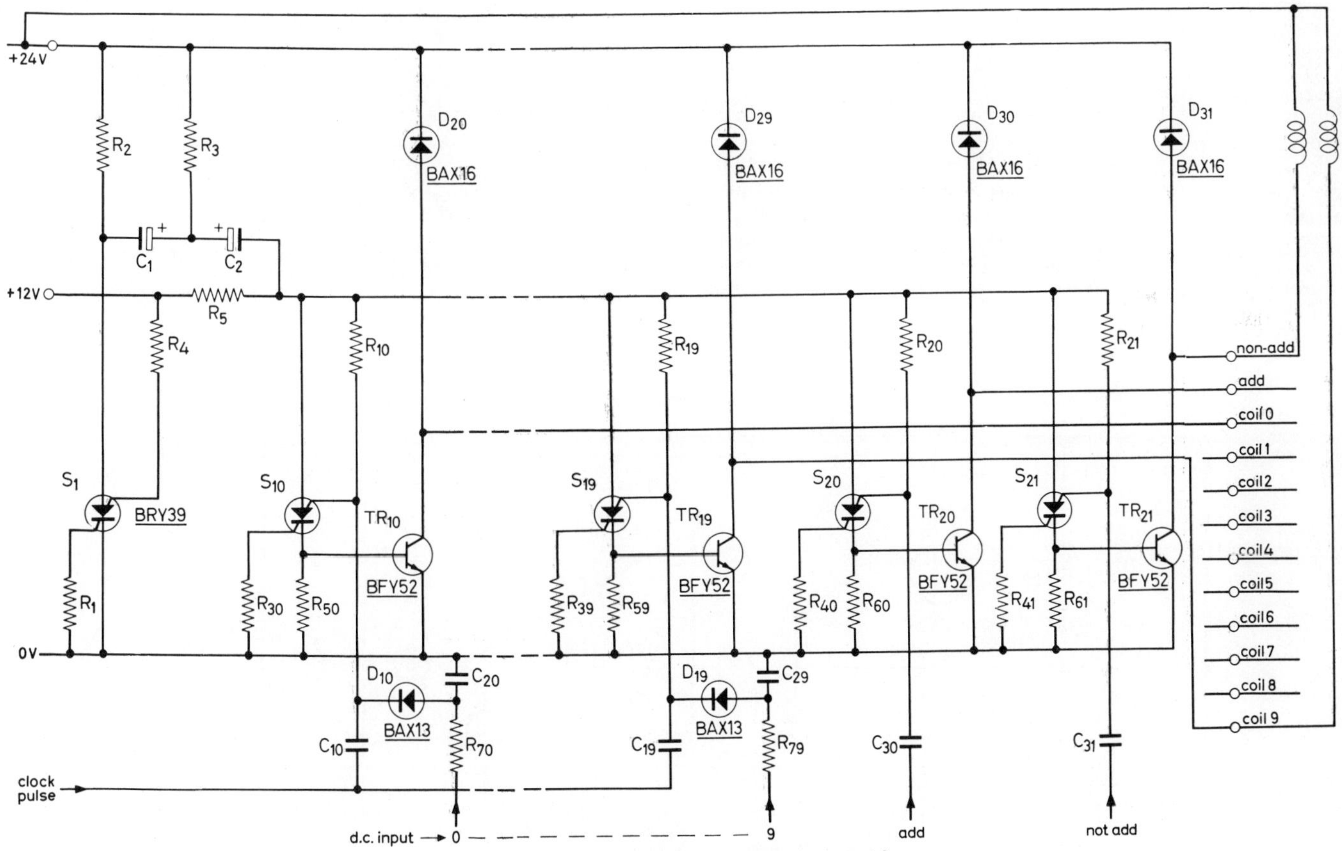

DRIVING NUMERICAL PRINTOUT—First and last stages for energizing coils of printout device are shown. Operation is similar to that of monostable mvbr, with normally-on scr S1 controlling period. Circuit produces 35-ms output pulses up to 300 mA. Article tells how to modify circuit for driving faster printout devices. Values are: R1 5.6K; R2 3.9K; R3 100K; R4, R10-R21, R30-R41, R50-R61 1K; R5 390; R70-R79 10K; C1-C2 10 μF; C10-C19, C30-C31, 180 pF; C20-C29 1 nF.—D. J. G. Janssen, Circuit Logic with Silicon Controlled Switches, *Electronic Applications*, Philips, Pub. Dept., Elcoma Div., Eindhoven, The Netherlands, Vol. 27, No. 1, 1966–1967, p 1–11.

NOTE: To locate additional circuits in the category of this chapter, use the index at the back of this book. Check also the author's "Sourcebook of Electronic Circuits," published by McGraw-Hill in 1968.

CHAPTER 21
Current Control Circuits

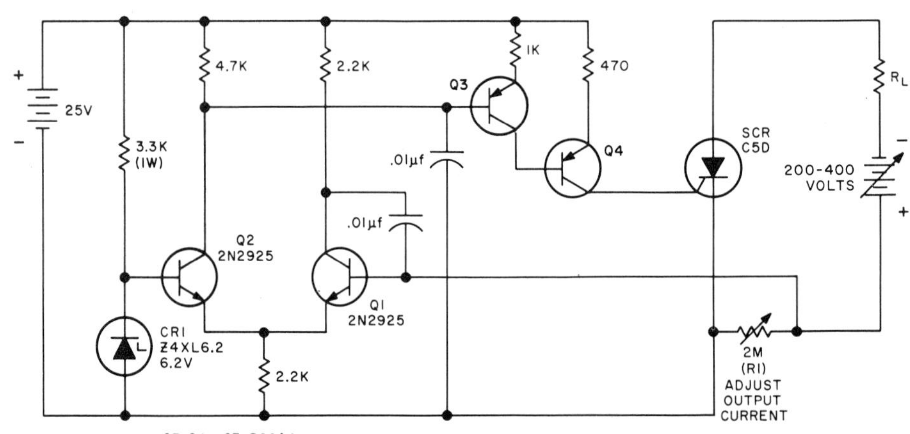

ADJUSTABLE CONSTANT-CURRENT SUPPLY—R1 gives range of 50 μA to 1 mA for output current of scr regulated supply. At 500 μA current is held constant within 0.1% when d-c supply voltage (at right) varies from 200–400 V. Load current is sensed by R1 and differential amplifier Q1-Q2. Zener CR1 provides reference input. Output error signal is applied to scr gate after amplification by Q3-Q4.—D. R. Grafham, Using Low Current SCR's, General Electric, Syracuse, N.Y., No. 200.19, 1967, p 40.

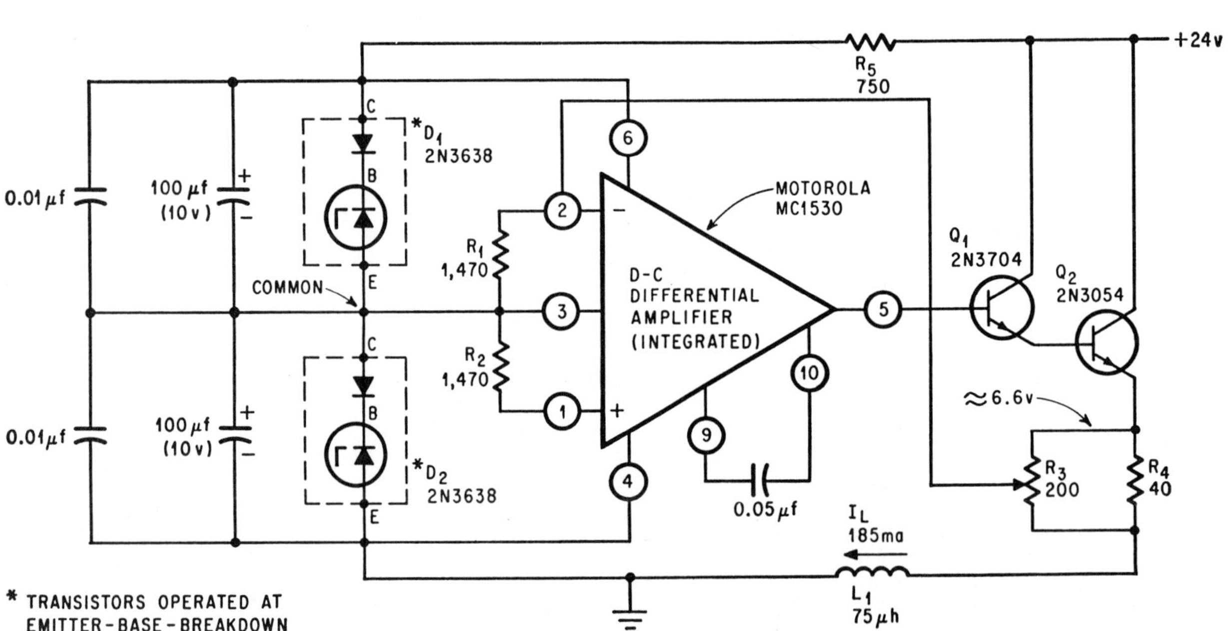

185-MA CURRENT STANDARD WITH IC—Can be built for about $40, has excellent regulation, and can serve as laboratory standard for calibrating magnetometers. Can generate several amperes of constant current if appropriate output transistors are added. Feedback loop goes from pin 2 of IC to R3. Passive components outside feedback loop must have low temperature coefficients.—C. S. Pepper, IC Amplifier Serves as Stable Current Source, *Electronics*, March 6, 1967, p 131–132.

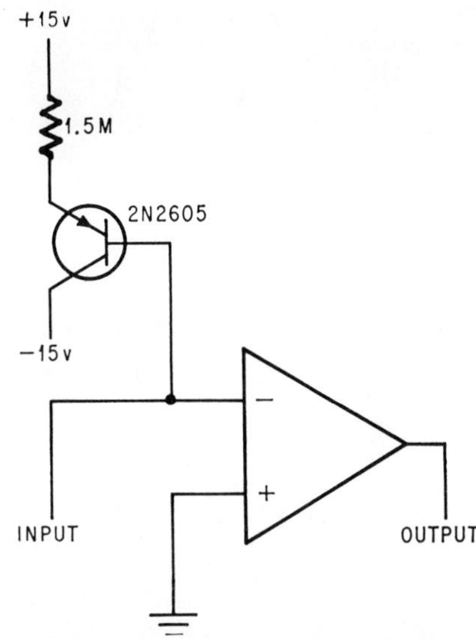

COMPENSATION NETWORK FOR SUMMING—Pnp transistor and 1.5-meg resistor compensate for bias current drift, independently of source impedance, for summing amplifier. Circuit is effective only over narrow range of positive supply voltages. Amount of temperature drift depends on how closely betas of IC and external transistors track.—R. J. Widlar, Linear IC's: Compensating For Drift, *Electronics*, Feb. 5, 1968, p 90–93.

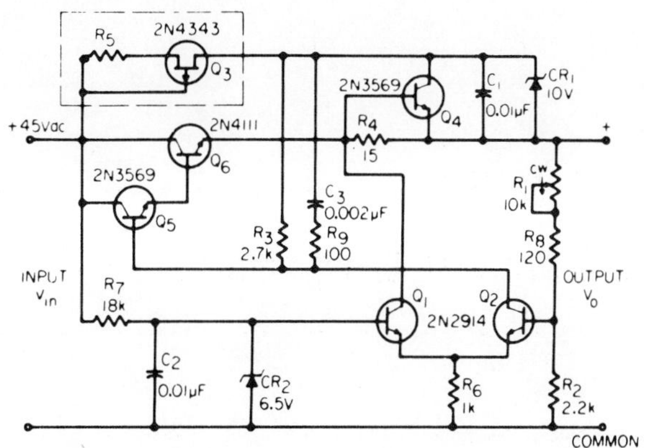

FET CONSTANT-CURRENT SOURCE—Q3 and R5 are added to conventional voltage regulator to improve regulation by making current through zener CR1 less dependent on input voltage and load current. Circuit also provides automatic current limiting. Choose value of R5 to bias fet at 4.5 mA drain current.—J. McPhail, FET Improves Voltage Regulation and Allows Current Limiting, *EEE*, July 1968, p 97–98.

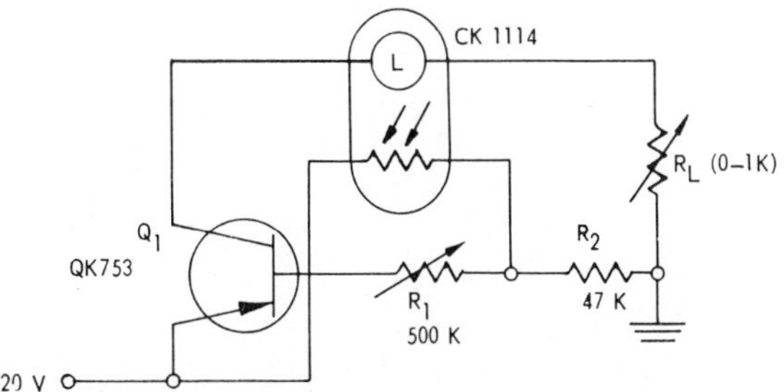

OPTOELECTRONIC CURRENT REGULATOR—Lamp of Raysistor senses current changes, and photocell in feedback circuit initiates compensation for change. R1 is set for desired load current. Regulation is within 10% for load range of 0 to 1,000 ohms.—Raysistor Optoelectronic Devices, Raytheon, Quincy, Mass., 1967, p 23.

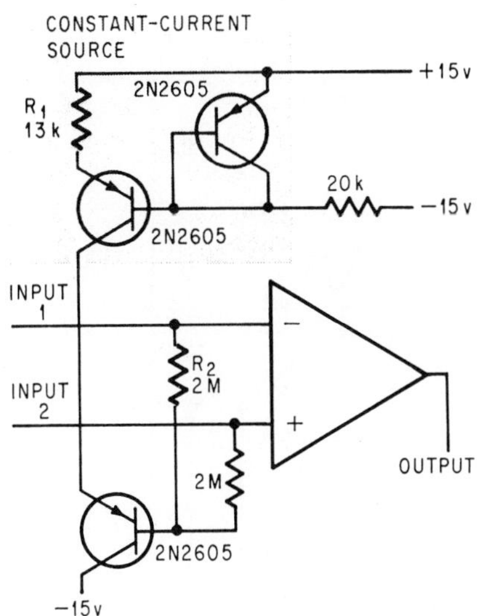

DRIFT-FREE DIFFERENTIAL INPUT—Three transistors and selected resistors R1 and R2 provide bias current compensation for differential-input IC amplifier, independently of source impedance for both inputs over entire common mode range.—R. J. Widlar, Linear IC's: Compensating For Drift, *Electronics*, Feb. 5, 1968, p 90–93.

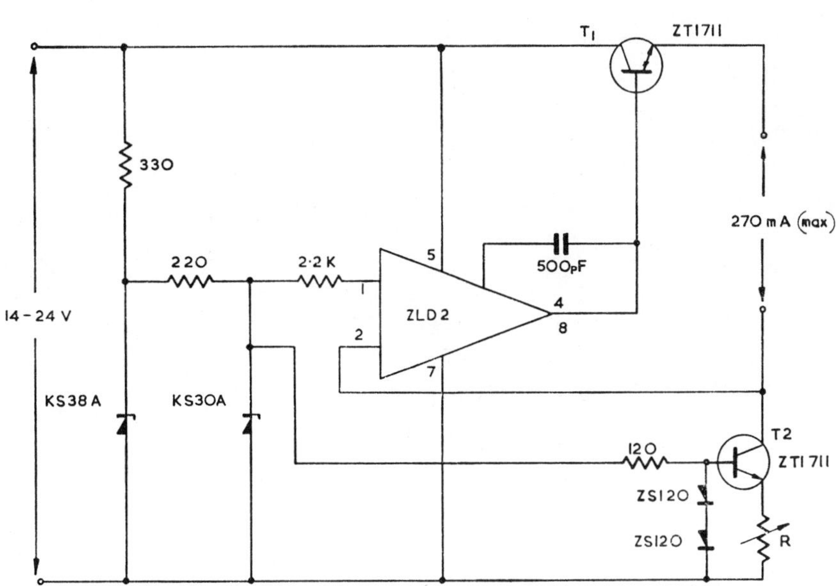

STABILIZED DIRECT CURRENT SUPPLY—Uses Ferranti ZLD2 as error signal amplifier, with d-c error signal being proportional to stabilized output current of d-c supply. Output current changes only about 0.03% per volt of change in d-c input voltage.—Microlin Amplifiers ZLD2S and ZLD2T, Ferranti Ltd., Oldham, Lancs., England, No. 11, 1967, p 15.

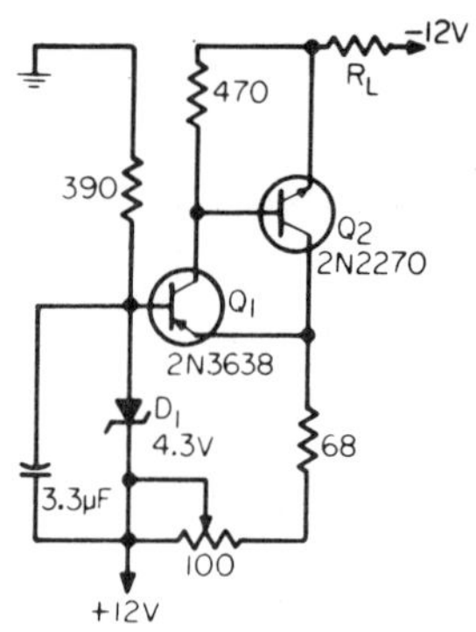

CONSTANT-CURRENT SOURCE—Addition of Q2 to conventional current source and careful adjustment of circuit values minimizes temperature drift and overcomes dissipation problem in Q1 when handling emitter currents above a few mA. With values shown, load current changes less than 0.5% over ambient temperature range of 0 to 70 C. Applications include differential amplifiers, timing generators, and fet stabilizers.—W. G. Jung, Temperature-Stabilized Constant-Current Source, *EEE*, Oct. 1968, p 126–127.

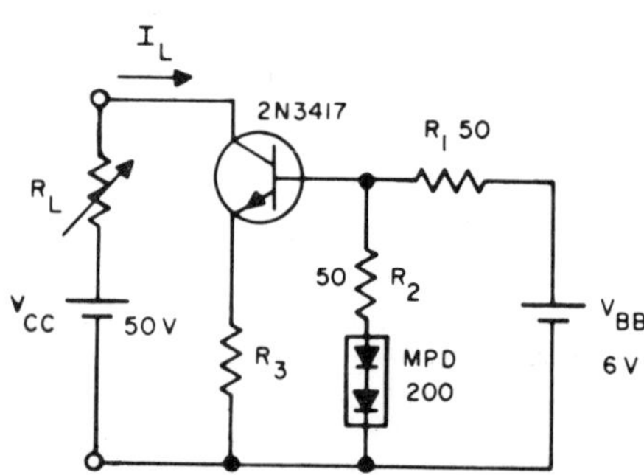

TEMPERATURE COMPENSATION WITH DIODE—Two-pellet diode in constant-current source compensates for variations in transistor base-emitter voltage due to temperature changes.—Silicon Multi-Pellet Diodes MPD200/MPD-300/MPD400, General Electric, Syracuse, N.Y., No. 75.42, 1966.

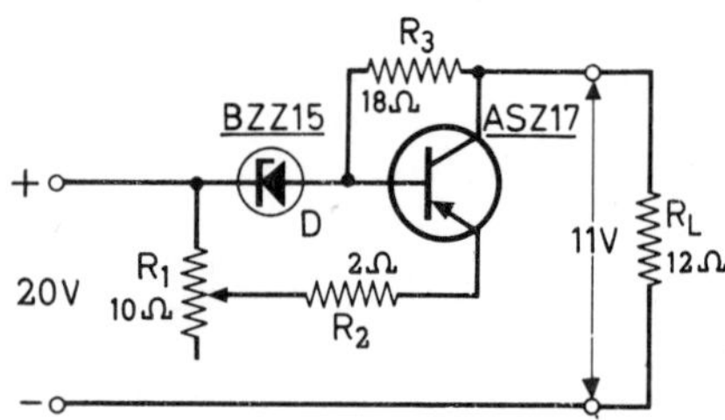

11-V CONSTANT-CURRENT SUPPLY—Any change in current through R3 modifies bias of power transistor, changing its differential impedance in such a way as to bring current through R3 and load back to original value. Uses power zener.—Zener Diodes and Their Applications, Philips, Publications Dept., Elcoma Division, Eindhoven, The Netherlands, Technical Information 17, 1966.

SSL REGULATOR—Two-transistor sink arrangement provides 4% current regulation for variations in supply voltage and 0.3% per deg C for thermal variations, for current-sensitive devices such as solid-state lamps. Suggested value for R2 is IL/10. Supply voltage can be as low as 3 V, with maximum value limited by transistor ratings.—L. M. Hertz, Solid State Lamps—Part II, General Electric, Cleveland, Ohio, No. 3-0121, 1970, p 27.

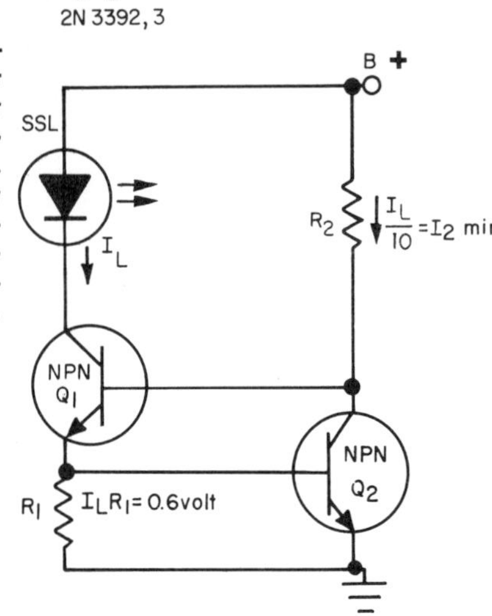

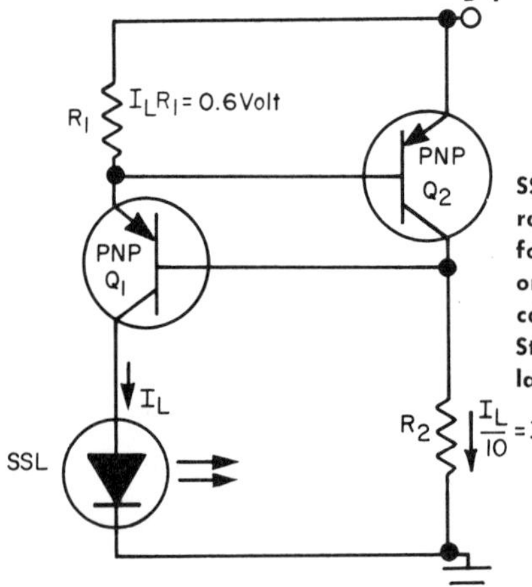

SSL REGULATOR—Two-transistor source arrangement provides 4% current regulation for solid-state lamp. Resistor values depend on current rating of lamp. Supply voltage can be as low as 3 V.—L. M. Hertz, Solid State Lamps—Part II, General Electric, Cleveland, Ohio, No. 3-0121, 1970, p 27.

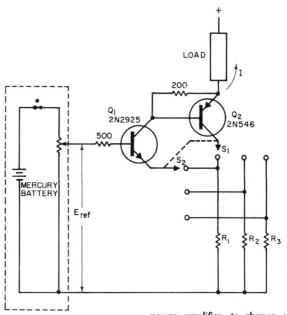

WIDE-RANGE CURRENT CONTROL—Uses variable reference voltage, obtained from mercury battery, with complementary-transistor power amplifier, to change current through load.—D. L. Boos, Complementary Transistors Expand Current Supply Range, *Electronic Design*, June 8, 1964, p 72–73.

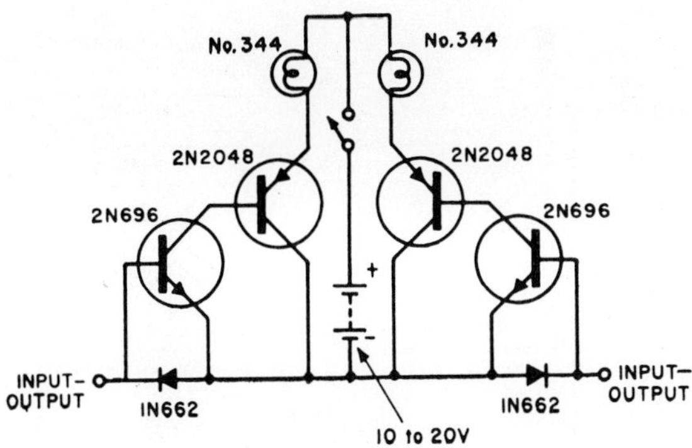

BIPOLAR CURRENT-LEVEL DETECTOR—Direct-coupled two-stage amplifiers drive two lamps to indicate when current between input-output terminals exceeds about 10 μA, with appropriate lamp lighting to indicate direction of current flow.—R. Gerdes, Sensitive Current Detector Indicates Direction of Flow, "400 Ideas for Design Selected from Electronic Design," Hayden Book Co., N.Y., 1964, p 150.

CURRENT REGULATOR—Circuit is basically grounded-base, with collector and emitter currents essentially equal because of high current gain of transistor. R3 must draw enough current through reference diode so its voltage drop will remain at 8 V as current regulator is loaded. Load current remains essentially constant until load resistance is increased to point where voltage drops across load and R3 become equal.—Current Regulator, Delco Radio, Kokomo, Ind., No. 4-B, May 1965.

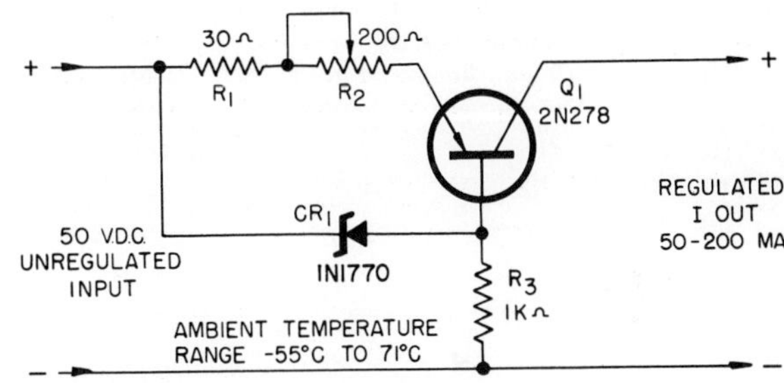

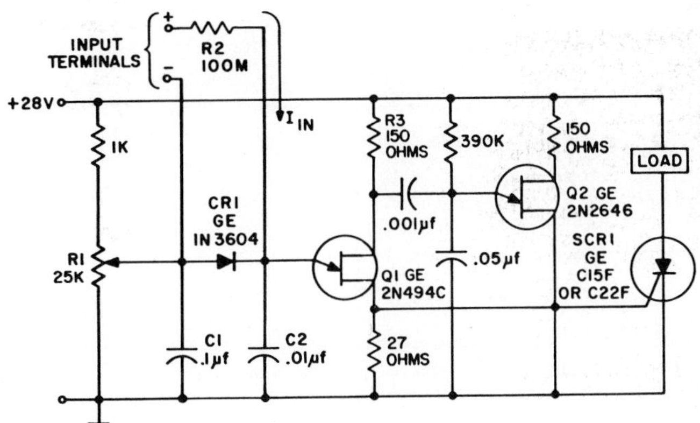

NANOAMPERE SENSING—May be used as sensitive current detector, or as voltage detector having high input impedance. Sampling technique gives input current sensitivity below 35 nA and input impedance above 100 meg. R1 is adjusted so circuit will not fire in absence of current input signal. Input signal then charges C2 through R2 toward emitter firing voltage of Q1. Relaxation oscillator Q2 supplies series of 0.75-V negative pulses to base 2 of Q1 to drop its firing voltage momentarily and permit firing even though R2 cannot furnish required peak point firing current of 2 μA.—"SCR Manual," 4th Edition, General Electric, 1967, p 166–167.

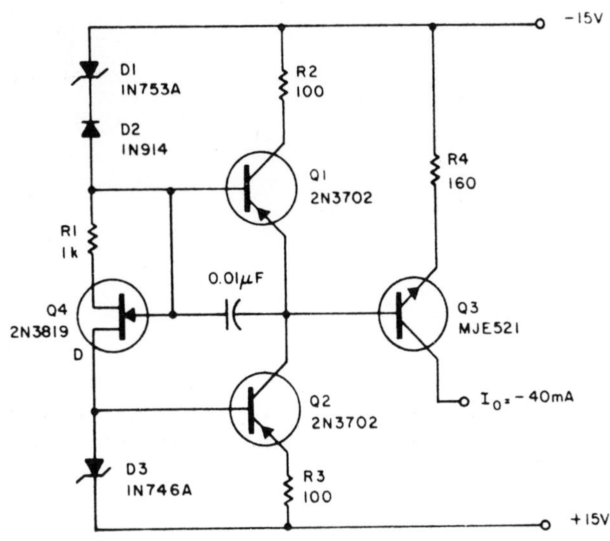

CONSTANT 40 MA WITH 0.1% REGULATION—Operates over wide range of supply voltages, temperatures, and loads yet cost of parts is only $5. Basic reference voltage, provided by zener D1 driven by constant current, is buffered by emitter-follower Q1 driven by constant-current source Q2.—R. C. Gerdes, Constant-Current Source is Stable and Inexpensive, *Electronic Design*, March 15, 1969, p 254.

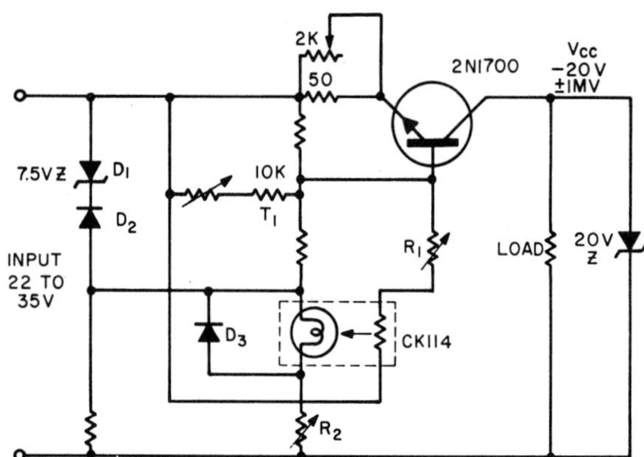

RAYSISTOR CONTROL OF 30 MA AT 20 V—Combination photoresistor and lamp (CK-114) provides electrically isolated compensation for input voltage changes from 22 to 35 V in constant-current generator. D3 simply protects lamp and helps offset positive temperature coefficient; type is not critical.—K. Myers, Raysistor Compensates Current Generator, *Electronic Design*, April 13, 1964, p 75–77.

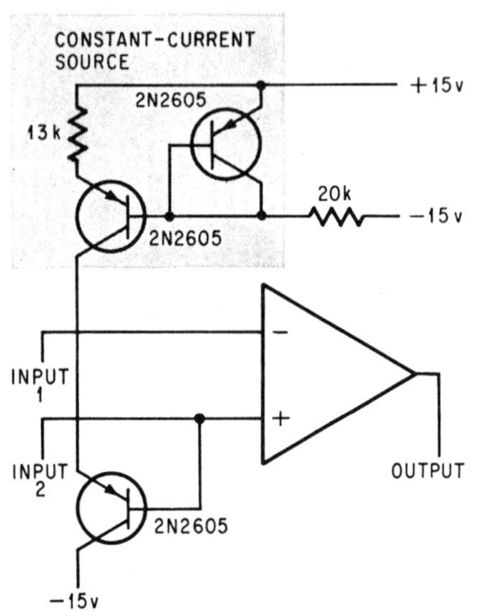

CONSTANT-CURRENT SOURCE—Three pnp transistors and selected 13K transistor serve as bias-current compensation network for noninverting IC amplifier requiring large common mode ranges. Circuit provides tight drift control but over limited temperature range. Feedback resistance of IC must be kept low.—R. J. Widlar, Linear IC's: Compensating For Drift, *Electronics*, Feb. 5, 1968, p 90–93.

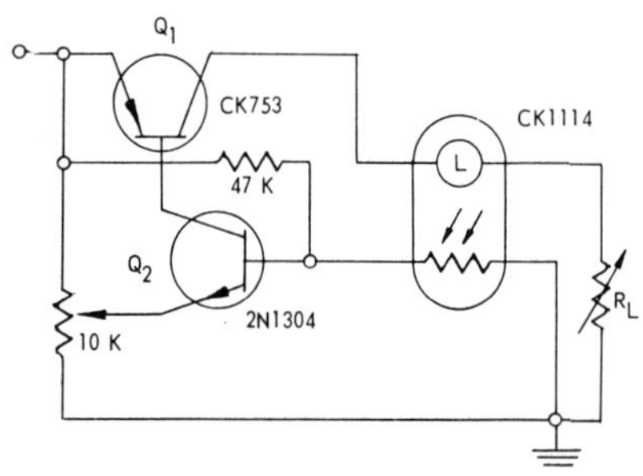

OPTOELECTRONIC REGULATOR—Additional transistor Q2 increases loop gain of optoelectronic constant-current regulator to provide improved regulation.—Raysistor Optoelectronic Devices, Raytheon, Quincy, Mass., 1967, p 24.

NOTE: To locate additional circuits in the category of this chapter, use the index at the back of this book. Check also the author's "Sourcebook of Electronic Circuits," published by McGraw-Hill in 1968.

CHAPTER 22
D-C Amplifier Circuits

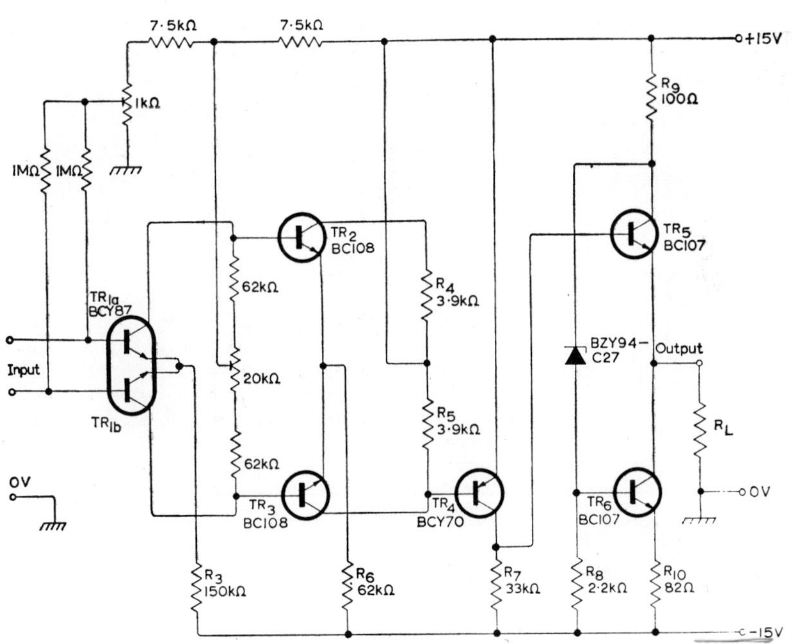

VOLTAGE GAIN 150,000—Input resistance is 240K and output resistance 10 ohms. Provides single-ended output of 10 V with either polarity at up to 20 mA. Output voltage is 0 V for zero input. Uses two differential amplifiers at input to keep differential voltage drift at required value of less than 12 μV per deg C.—"Circuits Using Low-Drift Transistor Pairs," Philips, Pub. Dept., Elcoma Div., Eindhoven, The Netherlands, 1968, p 11.

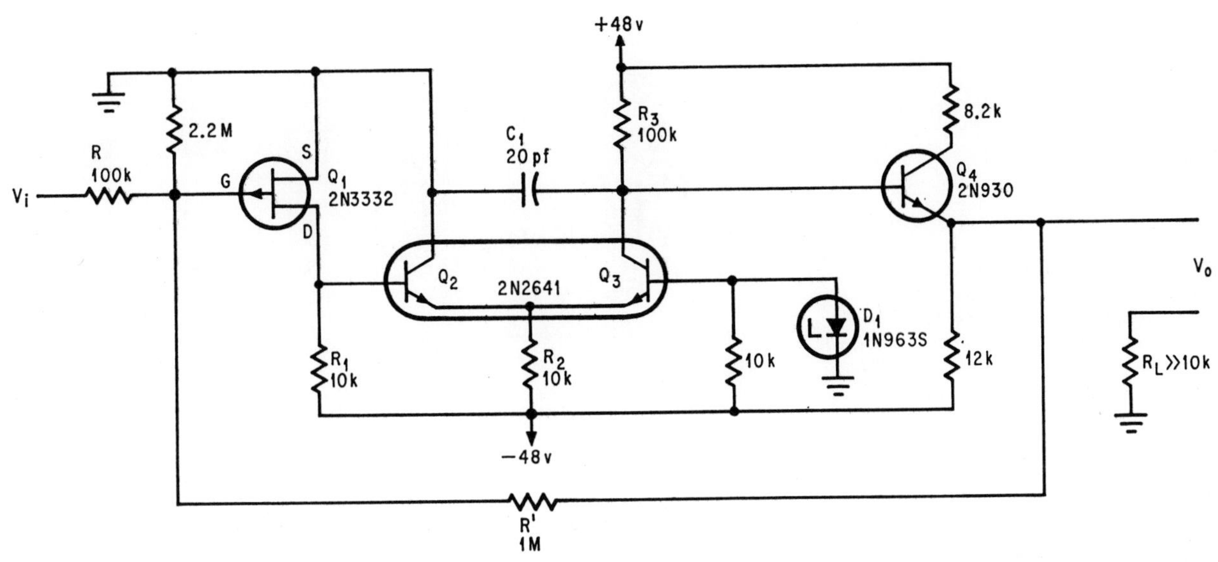

FET STABILIZATION—Addition of fet Q1 to d-c amplifier improves stability for wide range of temperatures and supply voltages, and gives high open-loop input impedance for operational amplifier applications. Article gives gain equations.—N. C. Voulgaris, FET Boosts Impedance of D-C Feedback Amplifier, *Electronics*, Oct. 16, 1967, p 98.

DIFFERENTIAL-INPUT IC WITH 90-DB CMR—Uses Ferranti ZLD2 IC low-power d-c amplifier having high common mode rejection, common mode range within 2 V of either supply voltage, and large output voltage swing.—Microlin Amplifiers ZLD2S and ZLD2T, Ferranti Ltd., Oldham, Lancs., England, No. 11, 1967, p 4.

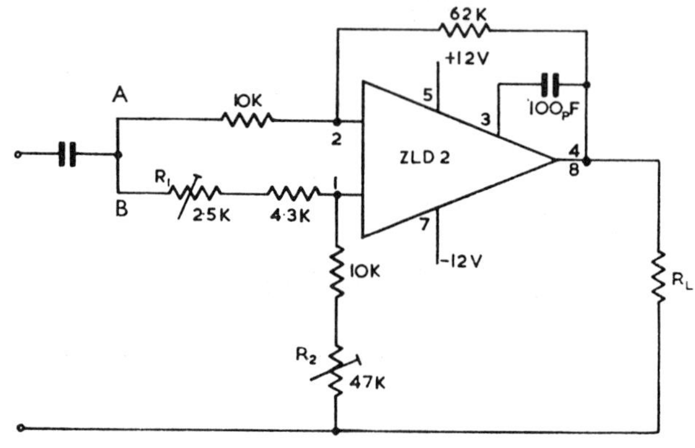

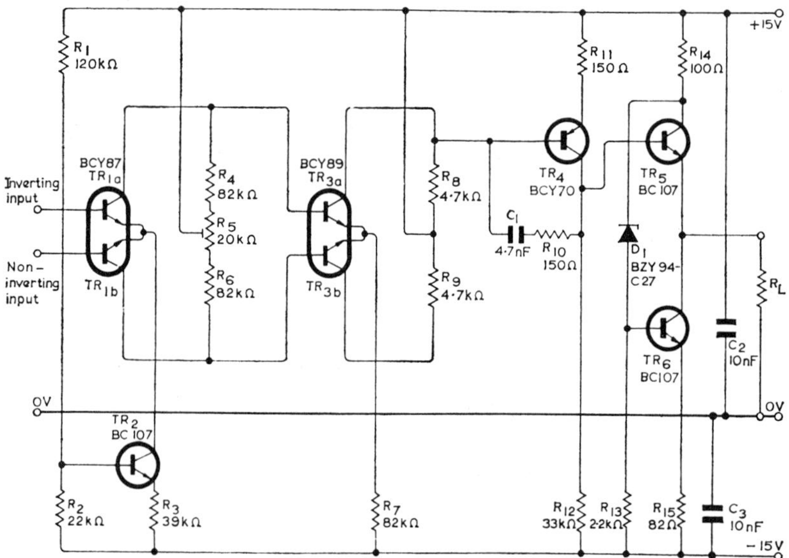

VOLTAGE GAIN 70,000—Four-stage d-c amplifier has differential input stage and single-ended output. Combined emitter currents of first stage are stabilized by constant-current source TR2. Nominal output voltage is 10 V at either polarity for up to 10 mA. Common-mode rejection ratio is 600. Differential voltage drift is 6 μV per deg C. Frequency response drops almost linearly from 96 dB at 10 Hz to 0 dB at 700 kHZ.—"Circuits Using Low-Drift Transistor Pairs," Philips, Pub. Dept., Elcoma Div., Eindhoven, The Netherlands, 1968, p 20.

VOLTAGE GAIN 100,000—Uses three differential stages and single-ended output, with TR2 serving as constant-current source for holding input stage emitter currents constant. Output stage uses long-tailed pair TR4-TR5 to drive TR6. Frequency response falls about 6 dB per octave from 100 dB voltage gain at 100 Hz down to 0 at 10 MHz. Output voltage is 10 V of either polarity at up to 2.5 mA. Differential voltage drift is 3 μV per deg C.—"Circuits Using Low-Drift Transistor Pairs," Philips, Pub. Dept., Elcoma Div., Eindhoven, The Netherlands, 1968, p 22.

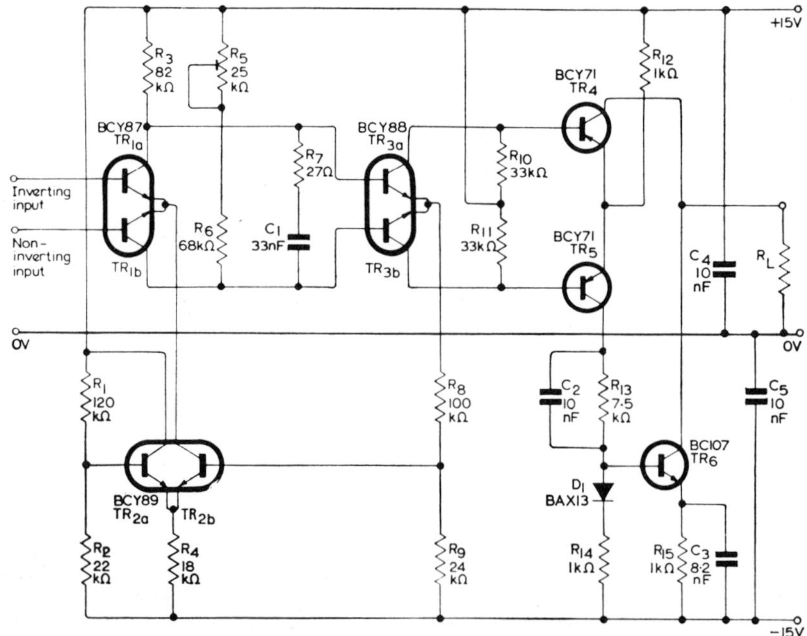

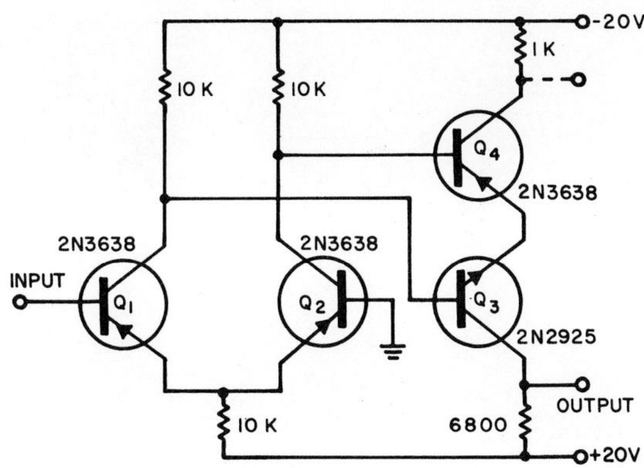

DUAL OUTPUT—Modified version of differential amplifier provides dual output along with higher gain and higher efficiency than conventional differential output stage. Dashed line indicates second output phase that is available, but d-c voltage excursion available is less desirable. Lowered current requirement makes this circuit highly desirable in analog systems using many amplifiers.—S. G. Freshour, Differential Amplifier Offers Efficient, Dual Outputs, *Electronic Design*, July 19, 1965, p 37–38.

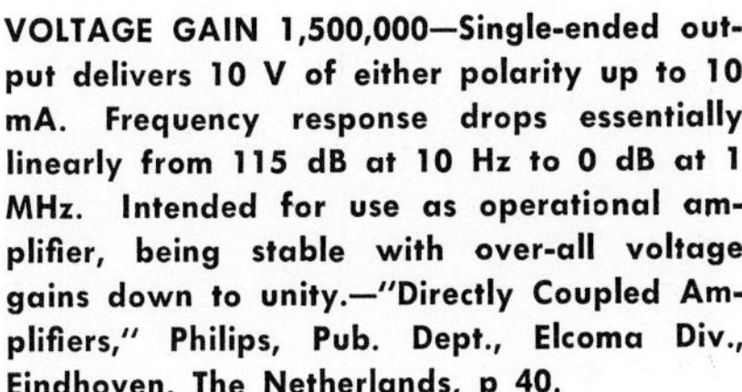
VOLTAGE GAIN 1,500,000—Single-ended output delivers 10 V of either polarity up to 10 mA. Frequency response drops essentially linearly from 115 dB at 10 Hz to 0 dB at 1 MHz. Intended for use as operational amplifier, being stable with over-all voltage gains down to unity.—"Directly Coupled Amplifiers," Philips, Pub. Dept., Elcoma Div., Eindhoven, The Netherlands, p 40.

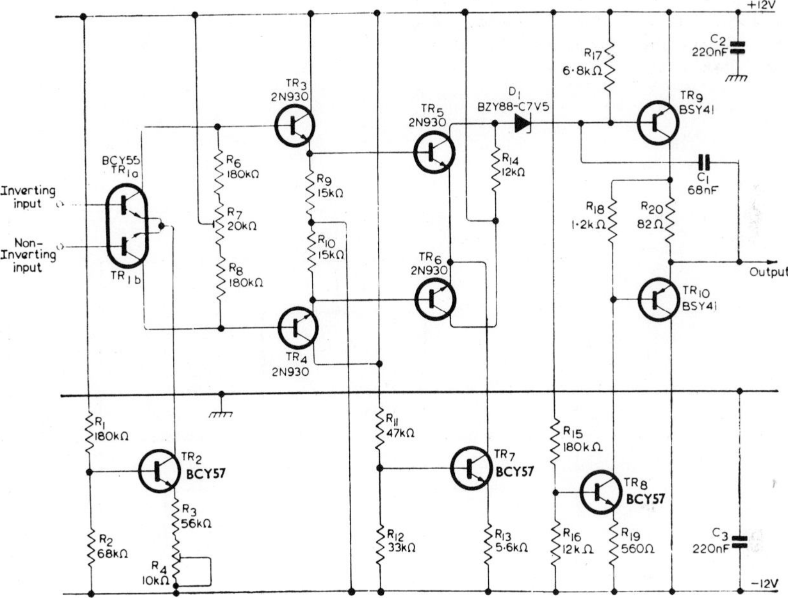

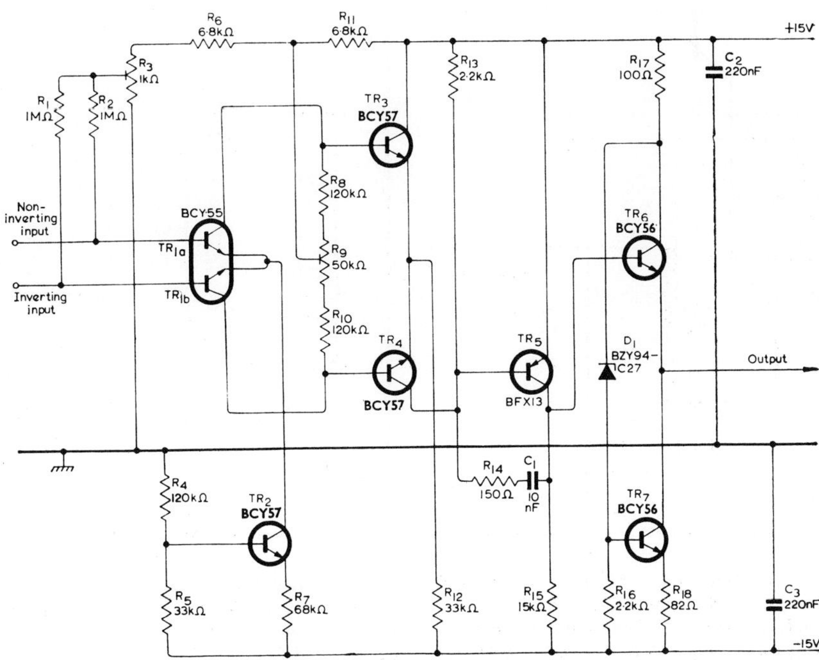

VOLTAGE GAIN 40,000—Differential input stage uses low-drift transistor pair, with constant-current source TR2 fixing combined emitter currents. Output is single-ended, delivering 10 V of either polarity at up to 20 mA. Frequency response drops about 6 dB per octave from 93 dB at 10 Hz to 0 dB at 2 MHz.—"Directly Coupled Amplifiers," Philips, Pub. Dept., Elcoma Div., Eindhoven, The Netherlands, p 34.

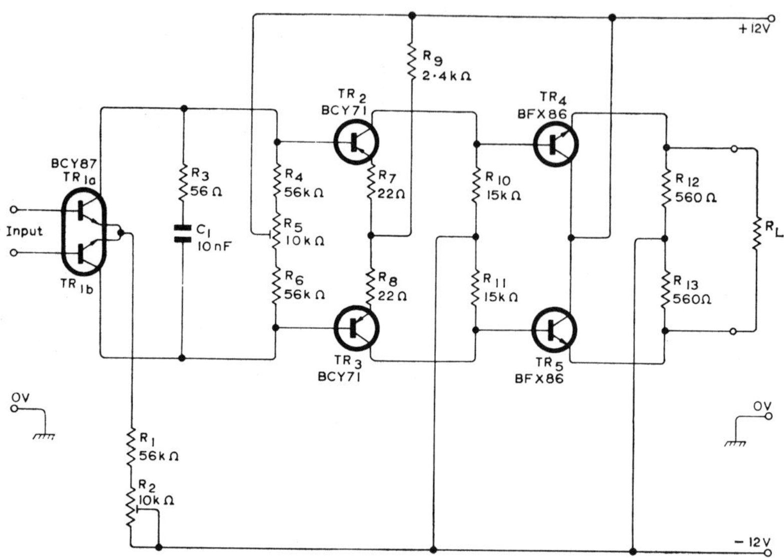

VOLTAGE GAIN 6,500—All three stages are push-pull. Differential-input first stage uses transistor pair, and second stage is long-tailed pair. Output is zero when there is no input signal, permitting use of over-all negative feedback without altering d-c conditions. Frequency response is intentionally shaped to fall about 6 dB per octave between 1 kHz and 10 MHz, from voltage gain of 76 dB below 1 kHz. Output voltage is 10 V of either polarity at 10 mA.—"Circuits Using Low-Drift Transistor Pairs," Philips, Pub. Dept., Elcoma Div., Eindhoven, The Netherlands, 1968, p 18.

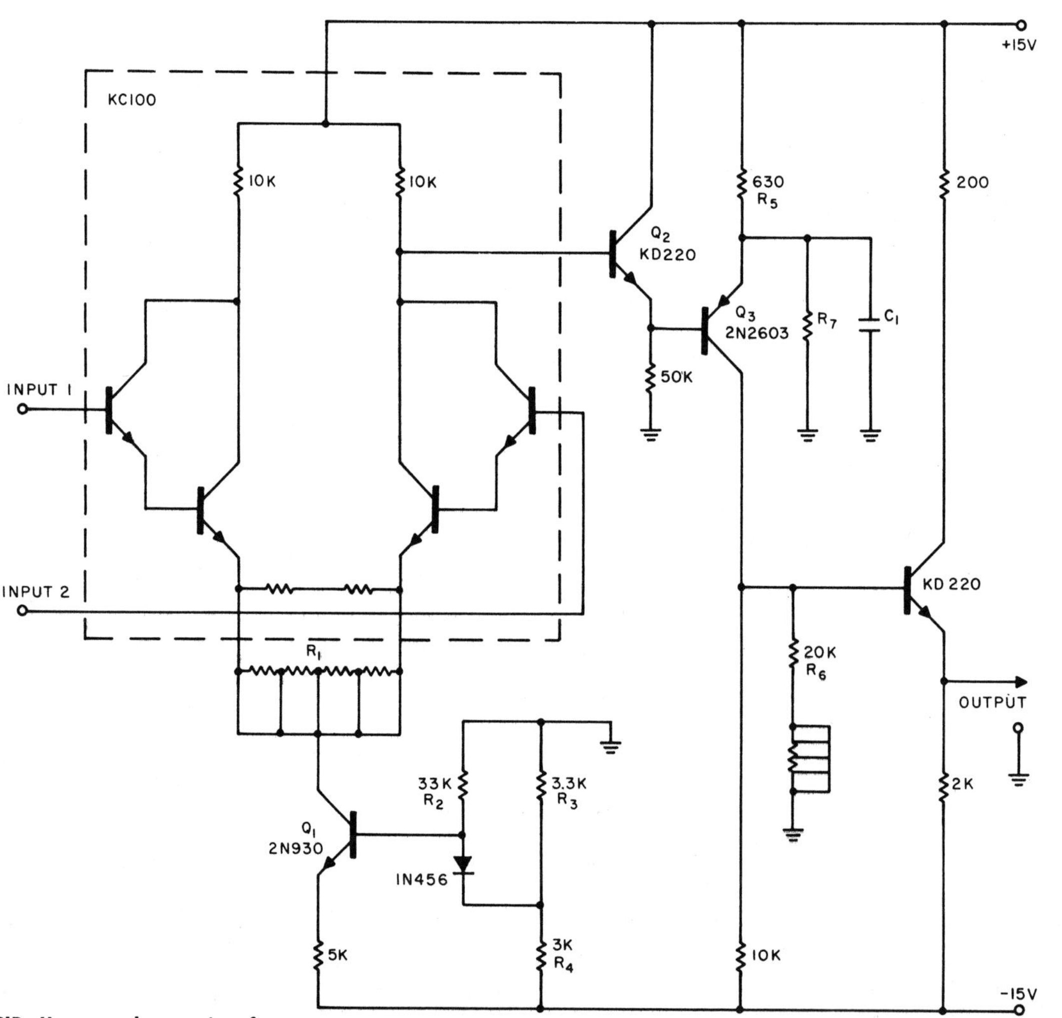

THIN-FILM HYBRID—Has open-loop gain of 500 and zero drift below 10 μV. With output capacitor, can be used as a-c amplifier for any gain between 1 and 500. Differential-pair input stage has 1-meg input resistance. Shorting bars on R1 are cut as required to correct for d-c unbalance, and on R6 to set open-loop gain. Dashed lines enclose IC which uses techniques described in article for reducing surface-area requirements of components.—A. Tuszynski, Skirting Thin-Film Design Problems, *Electronic Design*, Aug. 30, 1965, p 38–43.

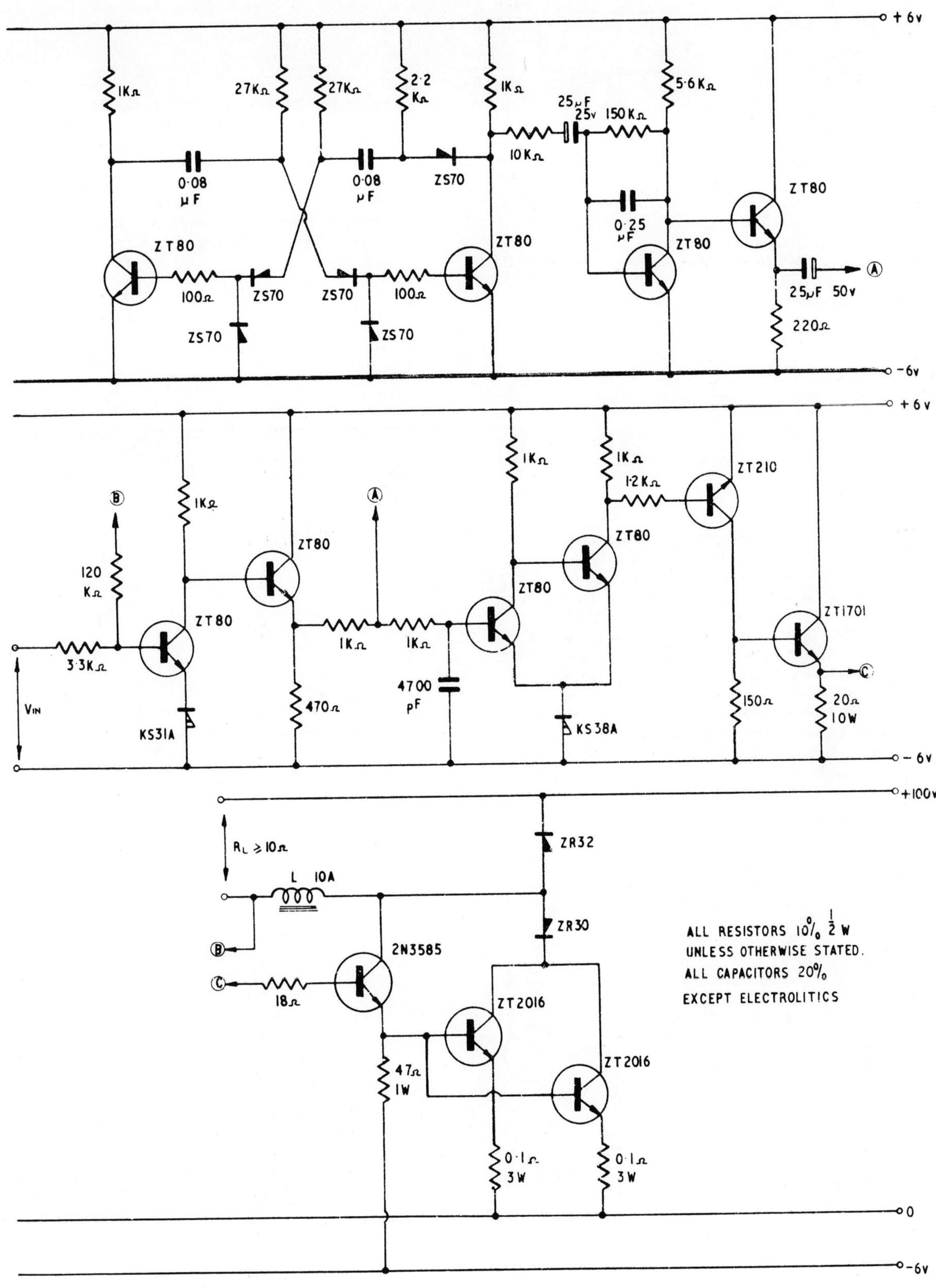

1-KW D-C AMPLIFIER FOR 10-OHM LOAD—Uses pulse-width modulation technique, with inductive filter in series with load to attenuate carrier. Output of 300-Hz mvbr is integrated to give linear sawtooth for adding to amplified d-c signal level to give constant-voltage sawtooth waveform whose level above zero is proportional to d-c input voltage. This is applied to Schmitt trigger that delivers rectangular pulses having mark-space ratio proportional to d-c level, for use in switching power transistor in series with filter and load. Output stage contains two 10-A 130-V ZT2016 transistors in parallel, driven by 2N3585. Input of 4 V gives full output, corresponding to power gain of 54 dB.—1-kW D.C. Amplifier, Ferranti, Oldham, Lancs., England, No. 32, 1966.

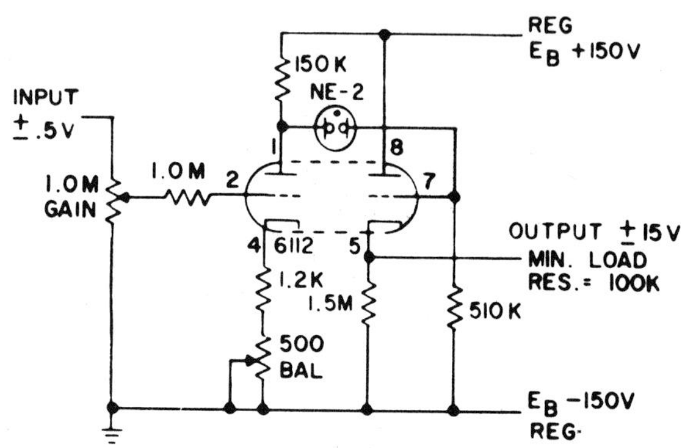

COUPLING BY MEMORY SWITCH—For d-c amplifiers, neon provides offset voltage to permit input and output voltages to operate about ground potential. Bottom of gain pot could be returned to output terminal for increased long-term stability.—E. Bauman, "Applications of Neon Lamps and Gas Discharge Tubes," Signalite, Neptune, N.J., p 75.

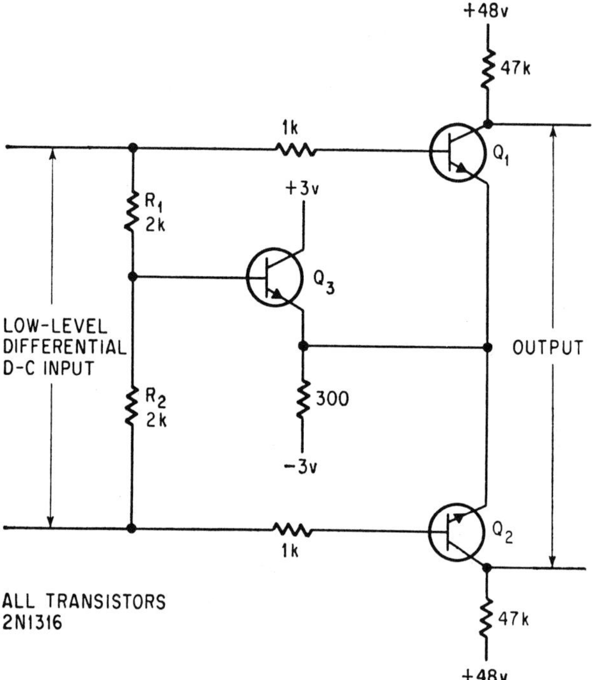

STABILIZED AT 2,000 GAIN—Common-mode noise and thermal drift are canceled in d-c differential amplifier by feeding input signal forward instead of using feedback. Technique gives gain of 2,000 with excellent stability, for delivering up to 2.5 A to servomotor in IBM 2310 disk storage drive. Circuit also provides locked-in temperature compensation, to prevent spurious triggering pulses from destroying bridge by turning on both sides at once.—F. J. Sordello, Forward Feed Stabilizes D-C Differential Amplifier, *Electronics*, Nov. 28, 1966, p 84.

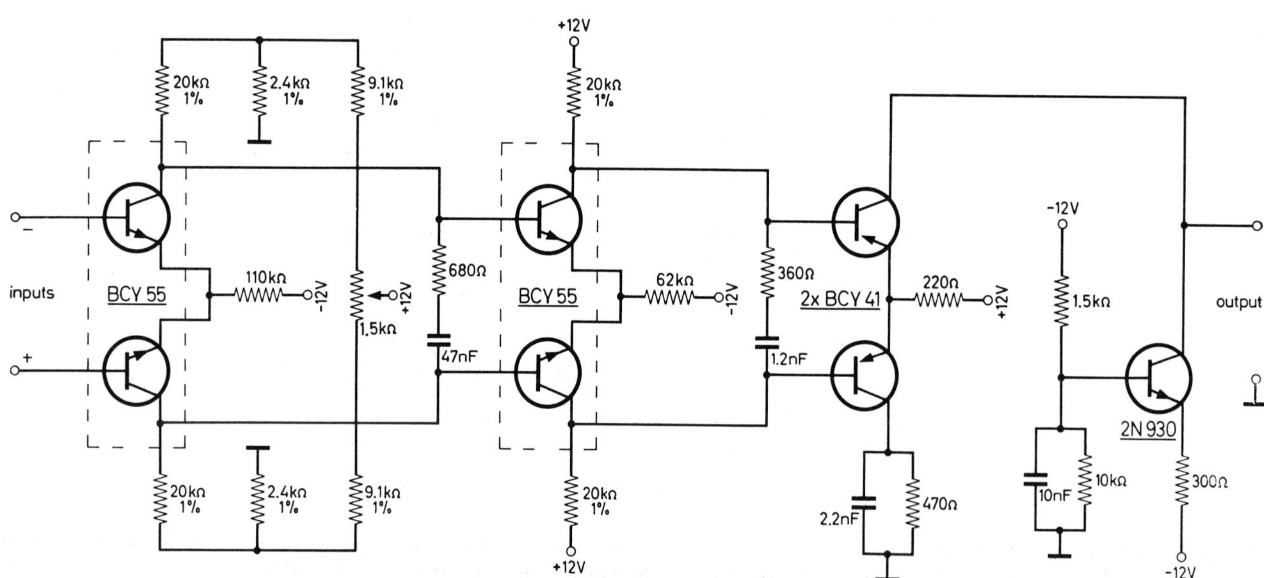

DIFFERENTIAL-TRANSISTOR AMPLIFIER—Use of silicon planar transistors encapsulated together and connected as differential pair gives highly stable opamp with open-loop gain of 60,000 and gain-bandwidth product of 10 MHz. Stability is better than 3 μV and 1 nA per deg C. Report gives circuit design procedure.—K. Hart, The Differential Transistor Pair BCY55 Employed in a D. C. Amplifier Having High Stability and Low Drift, Philips, Pub. Dept., Elcoma Div., Eindhoven, The Netherlands, No. 322, 1966.

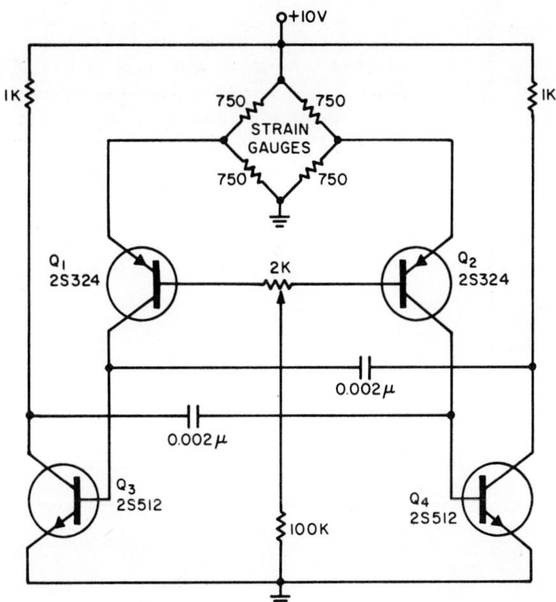

PULSE OUTPUT FROM STRAIN GAGE—Four transistors transform output signals of strain gage into modulated pulses. Q1 and Q2 form differential amplifier for amount of unbalance in strain-gage quad, and control mark-space output ratio of saturated-mode mvbr Q3-Q4. Resulting output may be measured by average-reading voltmeter connected between collectors of Q3 and Q4.—Strain Gage Output Amplifier Produces Modulated Pulse Signal, *Electronic Design*, May 24, 1965, p 52.

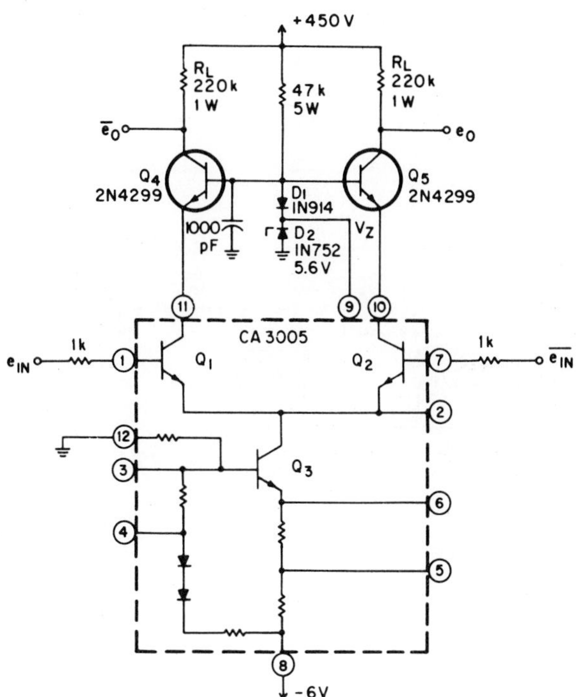

BOOSTING OUTPUT AND SPEED—Two-transistor circuit added to CA3005 IC differential amplifier permits operation from 450-V supply, as required for improving performance. —W. E. Peterson, Higher Speed, Gain, Output from IC Diff Amp, *EEE*, Jan. 1970, p 128.

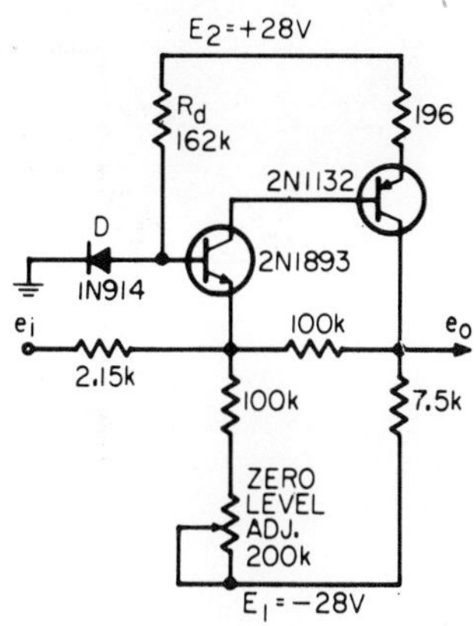

INVERTING WITH GAIN OF −30—Diode D brings input voltage close to zero to minimize dependence of output voltage on supply voltage. Article gives detailed design procedure.—T. Mollinga, Designing D-C Amplifiers, *EEE*, Feb. 1969, p 46–51.

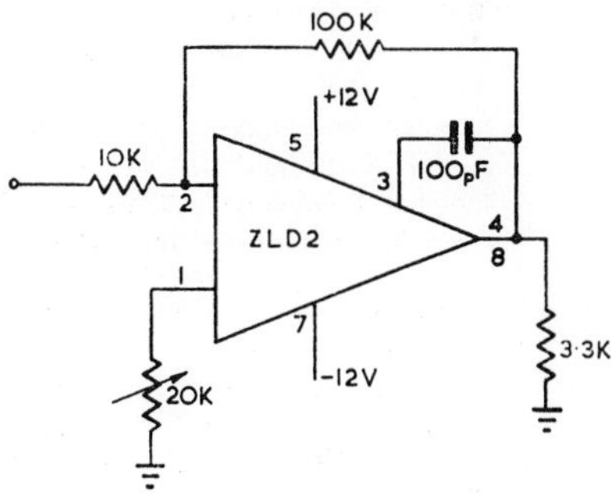

CANCELLING AMPLIFIER OFFSET VOLTAGE—Use of potentiometer as one of source resistances permits adjusting resistance value until differential voltage produced cancels out offset voltage of IC inverting d-c amplifier. Drawback of method is tendency to increase offset temperature drift.—Microlin Amplifiers ZLD2S and ZLD2T, Ferranti Ltd., Oldham, Lancs., England, No. 11, 1967, p 11.

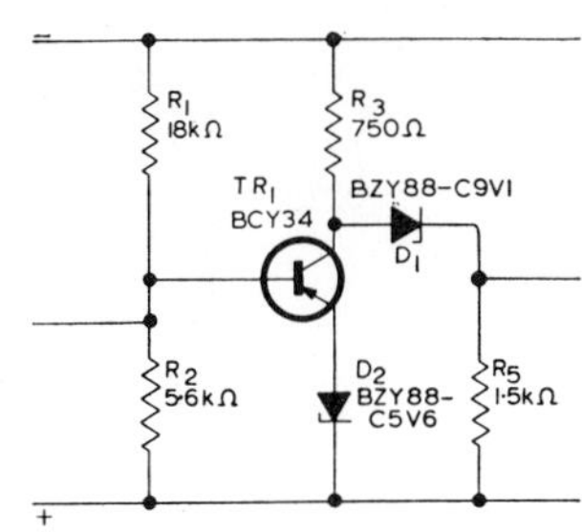

35 DB GAIN—Developed for use with 24-V d-c supply. Book gives design procedure for determining value of each component.—"Voltage Regulator (Zener) Diodes," Philips, Pub. Dept., Elcoma Div., Eindhoven, The Netherlands, p 53.

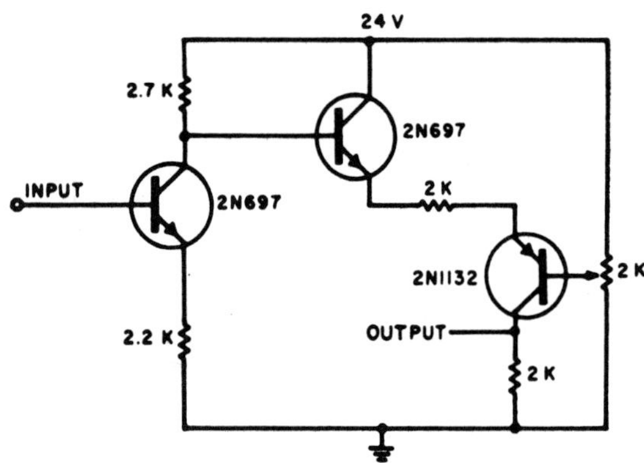

1:1 LEVEL CHANGER—With input of 0–9 V, output is 9–0 V with highly linear relationship. Temperature stability is good.—R. S. Hughes, Stable DC Amplifier Makes Good Level Changer, "400 Ideas for Design Selected from Electronic Design," Hayden Book Co., N.Y., 1964, p 19.

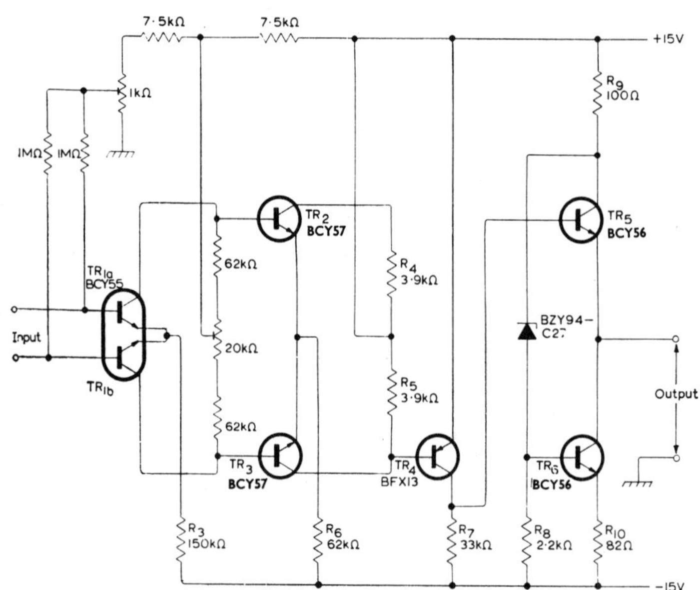

VOLTAGE GAIN 150,000—Low-drift transistor pair is used in differential input having resistance above 200K. Output voltage is 10 V with either polarity at up to 20 mA and output resistance is 20 ohms.—"Directly Coupled Amplifiers," Philips, Pub. Dept., Elcoma Div., Eindhoven, The Netherlands, p 31.

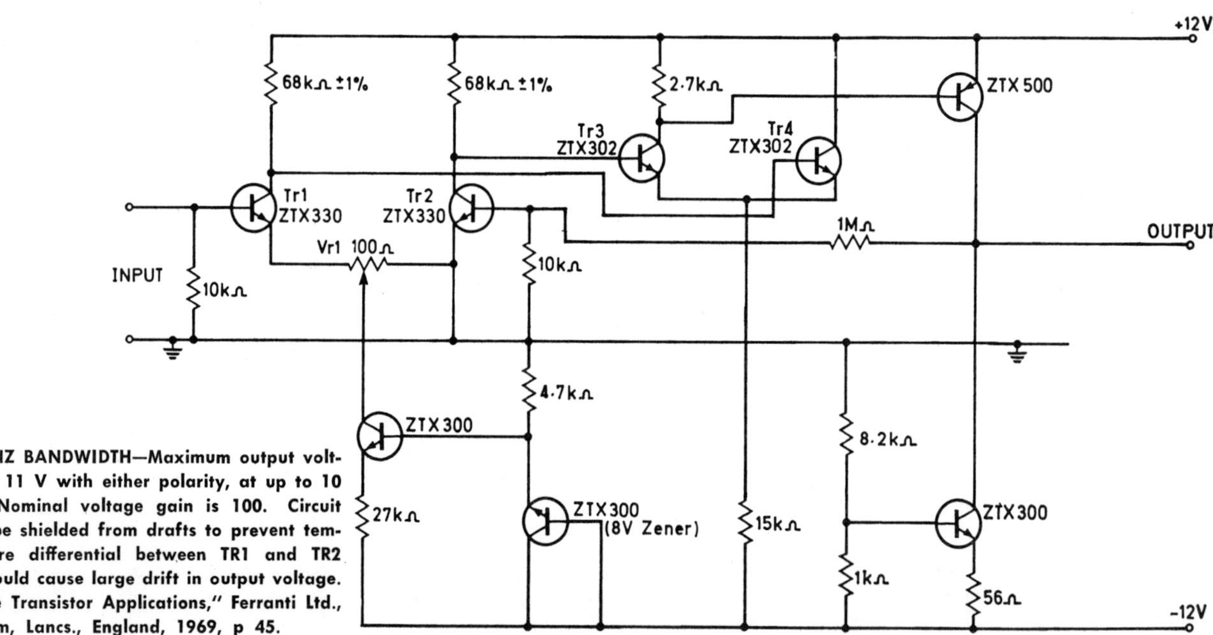

800-KHZ BANDWIDTH—Maximum output voltage is 11 V with either polarity, at up to 10 mA. Nominal voltage gain is 100. Circuit must be shielded from drafts to prevent temperature differential between TR1 and TR2 that could cause large drift in output voltage. "E-Line Transistor Applications," Ferranti Ltd., Oldham, Lancs., England, 1969, p 45.

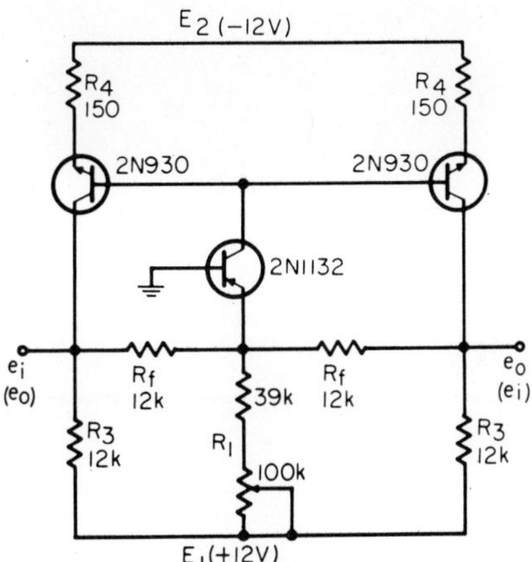

TWO-WAY INVERTING—Circuit is symmetrical, with output stage repeated at input side. Voltage gain is slightly less than unity. Article gives design equations.—T. Mollinga, Designing D-C Amplifiers, *EEE*, Feb. 1969, p 46–51.

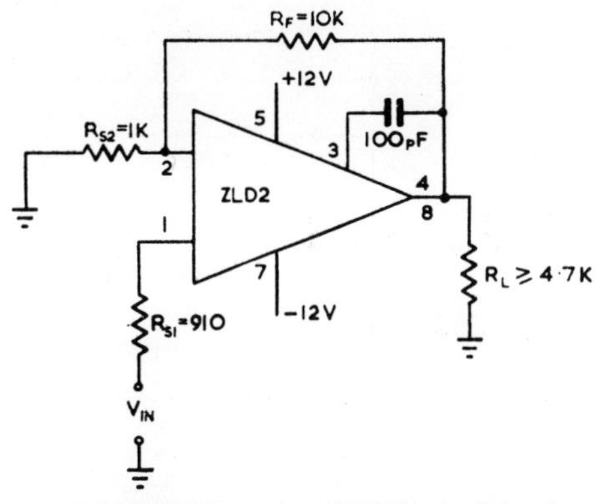

NONINVERTING D-C AMPLIFIER—Applying input between ground and terminal 1 of Ferranti ZLD2 IC differential-input d-c amplifier gives noninverting amplification of d-c input signal. Voltage gain is 10.—Microlin Amplifiers ZLD2S and ZLD2T, Ferranti Ltd., Oldham, Lancs., England, No. 11, 1967, p 11.

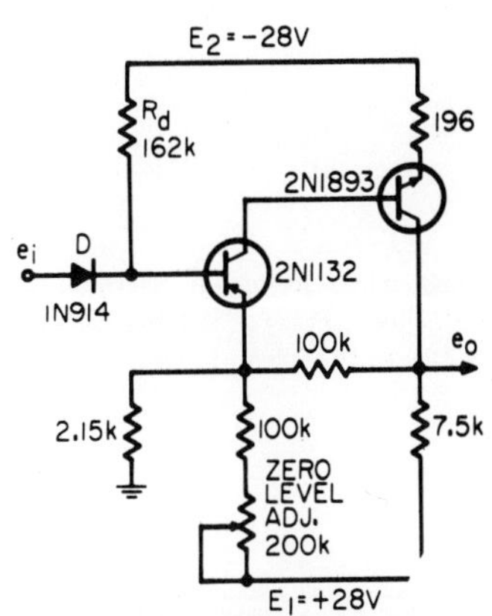

NONINVERTING WITH GAIN OF 30—Diode D brings input voltage close to zero, to minimize dependence of output voltage on +28 V supply voltage. Article gives detailed design procedure.—T. Mollinga, Designing D-C Amplifiers, *EEE*, Feb. 1969, p 46–51.

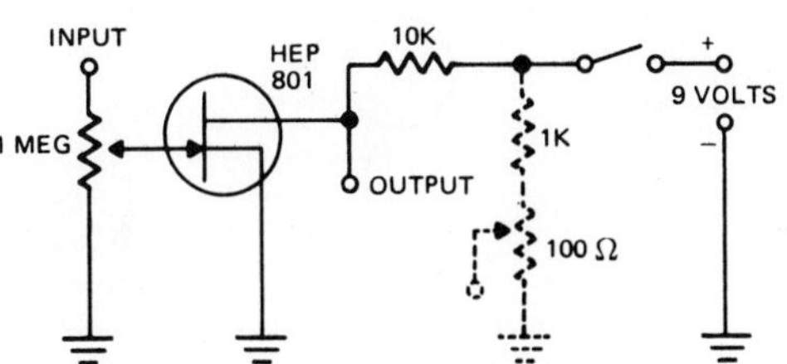

LOW-LEVEL FET—Gives output of 0.4 to 9 V on input of 0 to −1.5 V for scopes, vtvm, or as relay amplifier. To get output down to zero, add dashed circuit and use its terminal as ground for output. Adjust 100-ohm rheostat for zero output with input grounded.—"Tips on Using FET's," Motorola, Phoenix, Ariz., HMA-33, 1969.

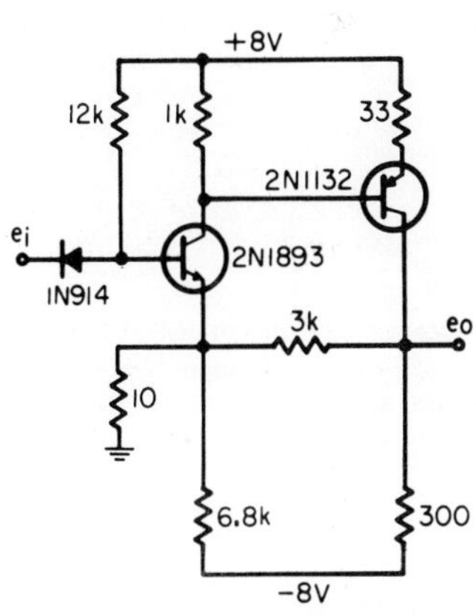

TO 1 MHZ WITH GAIN OF 100—Adding collector resistor (10 ohms) for 2N1893 increases bandwidth, to give essentially flat response from d-c up to 1 MHz.—T. Mollinga, Designing D-C Amplifiers, *EEE*, Feb. 1968, p 46–51.

NOTE: To locate additional circuits in the category of this chapter, use the index at the back of this book. Check also the author's "Sourcebook of Electronic Circuits," published by McGraw-Hill in 1968.

CHAPTER 23
Delay Circuits

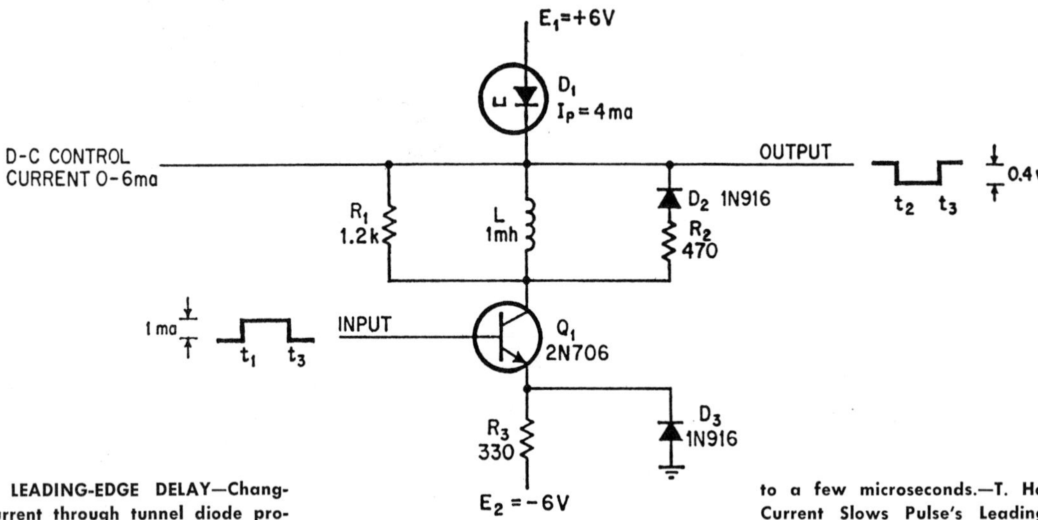

ADJUSTABLE LEADING-EDGE DELAY—Changing direct current through tunnel diode provides proportional change in delay between leading edges of output and input signals. Values shown give delay range from zero up to a few microseconds.—T. Hornak, Control Current Slows Pulse's Leading Edge, *Electronics*, Aug. 18, 1969, p 96.

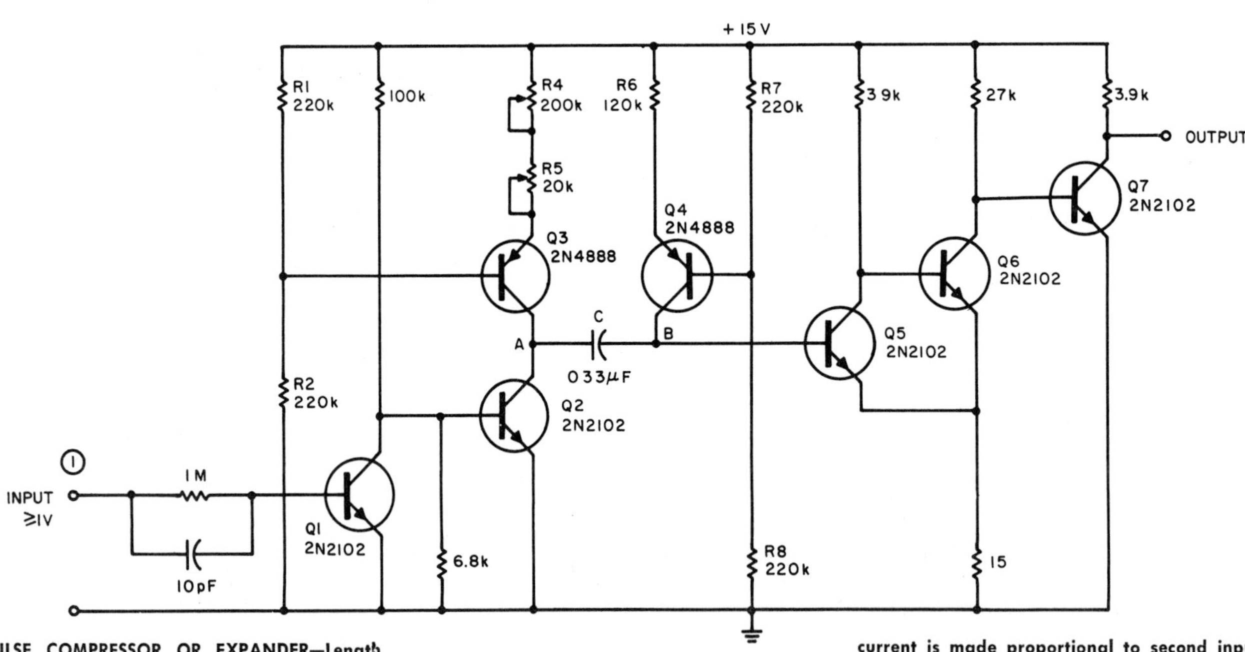

PULSE COMPRESSOR OR EXPANDER—Length of output pulse is proportional to length of input pulse, with output pulse being delayed for duration of input pulse. R4 and R5 provide wide adjustment range (0.1 to 10) for ratio of input to output pulse width. Can be used for pulse width modulation if Q2 current is made proportional to second input signal.—T. Weisz, Compress or Expand Pulses With A Simple Circuit, *Electronic Design*, Dec. 6, 1967, p 122 and 124.

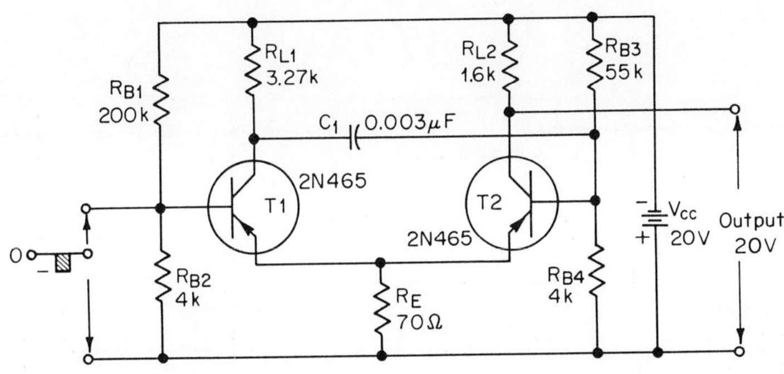

MONO FOR LAB USE—Remains in unstable state for length of time determined by reactive elements in circuit. Can be used for generating delay pulses and for standardizing pulses of random ON times. C1 helps determine duration of unstable state; reducing C1 reduces unstable time and therefore increases frequency.—A. C. Gillie, "Pulse and Logic Circuits," McGraw-Hill, N.Y., 1968, p 220.

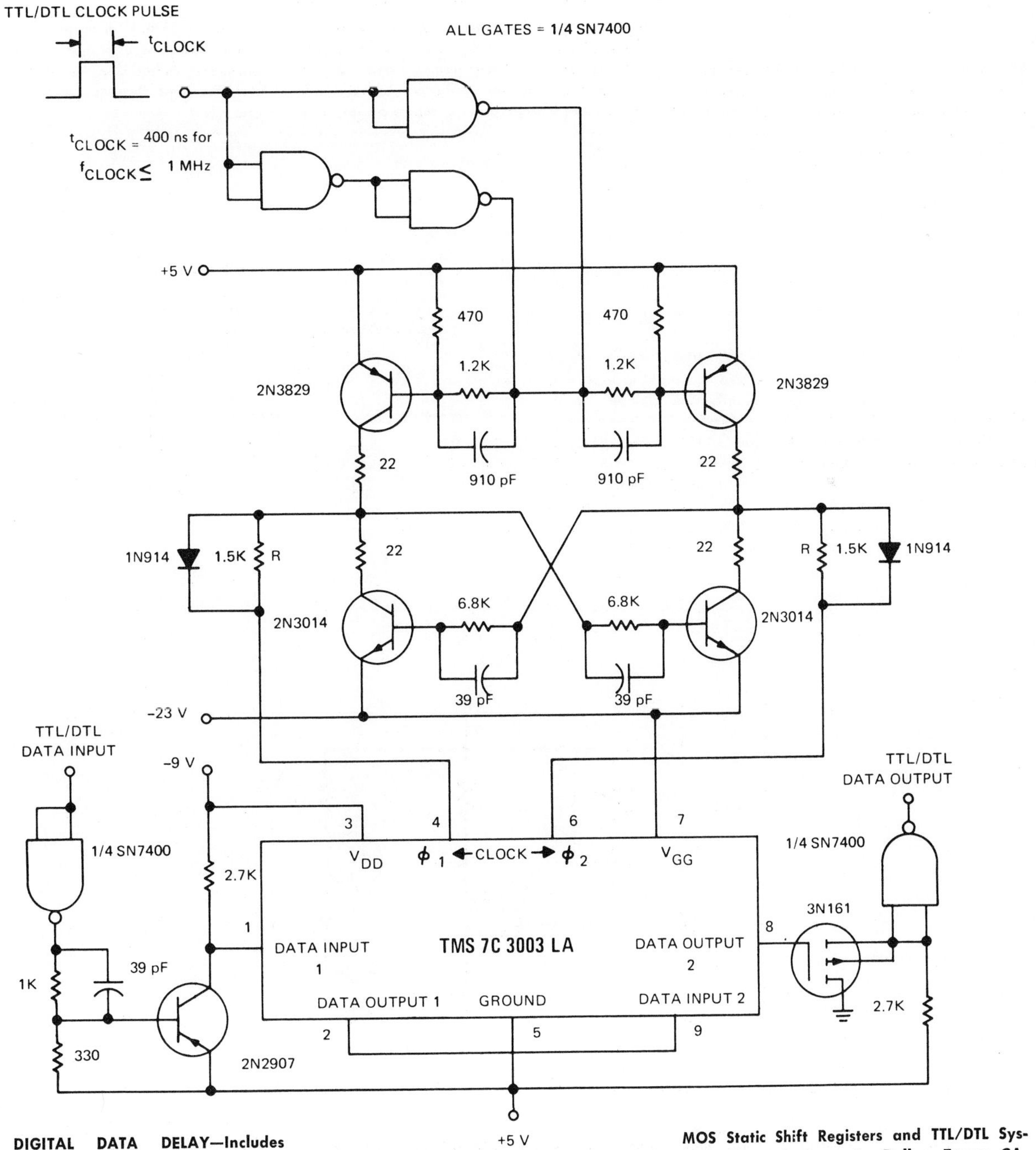

200-BIT DIGITAL DATA DELAY—Includes complete interface and clock driver circuitry for operation at rates from d-c to above 1 MHz. Report describes operation of each section of system in detail.—G. B. Hoffman, MOS Static Shift Registers and TTL/DTL Systems, Texas Instruments, Dallas, Texas, CA-114.

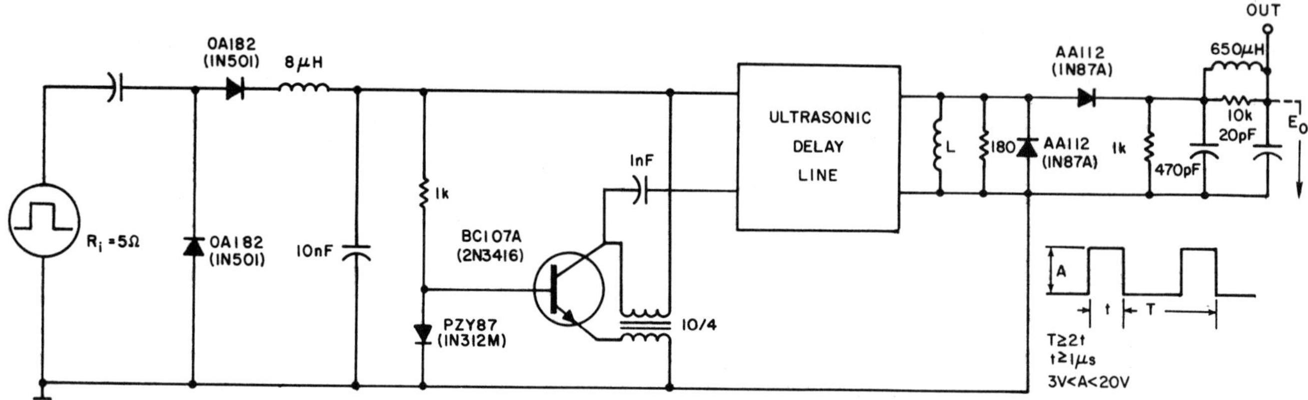

64-MICROSECOND PULSE DELAY—Self-powered circuit uses 7-inch glass rod driven by r-f oscillator as ultrasonic delay for single or repetitive positive pulses. Other lengths or types of delay lines can be used to obtain different delays. Input pulses provide supply voltage for transistor oscillator. Oscillator is amplitude-modulated with input pulses, and pulsed r-f signal at output of delay line is demodulated to filter out r-f.—P. Zamperoni, Ultrasonic Delay Line Needs No Power Supply, *Electronic Design*, Aug. 15, 1968, p 230 and 232.

MONO WITH POSITIVE-GOING EDGE DELAY—Uses Philips TAA293 general-purpose amplifier. Circuit has effect of delaying positive-going edge of rectangular input pulse. Delay time is about 100 μs when C is 10 nF. Times for other values of C are in direct proportion to C down to about 1 μs.—The TAA293 as a Schmitt Trigger and Multivibrator, Philips, Pub. Dept., Elcoma Div., Eindhoven, The Netherlands, No. 25, 1968.

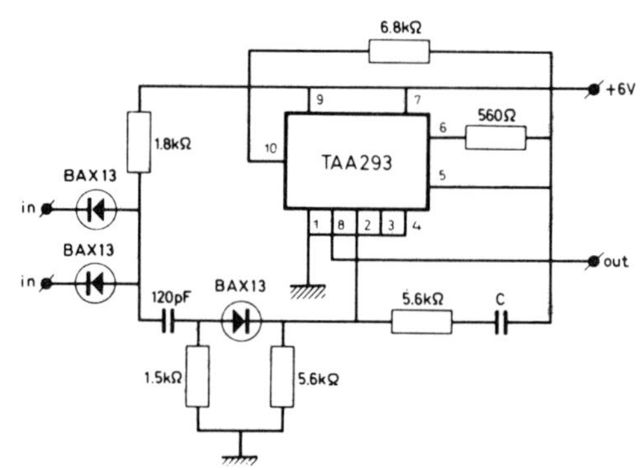

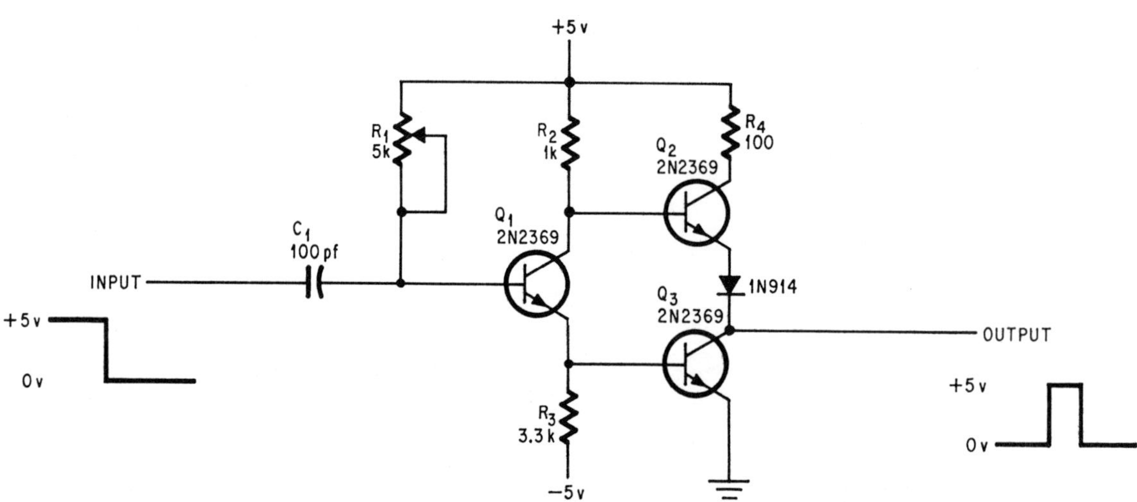

20-NS PULSE WITH DELAY—One-shot mvbr depends on fast removal of stored charge to give pulses as narrow as 20 ns with rise and fall times of only 10 ns. Pulse widths or delays up to 100 ns are determined by setting of R1. Stability is good for temperature and voltage changes.—L. V. Hendricks, Fast Discharge Reduces Multivibrator's Rise Time, *Electronics*, Nov. 25, 1968, p 82–83.

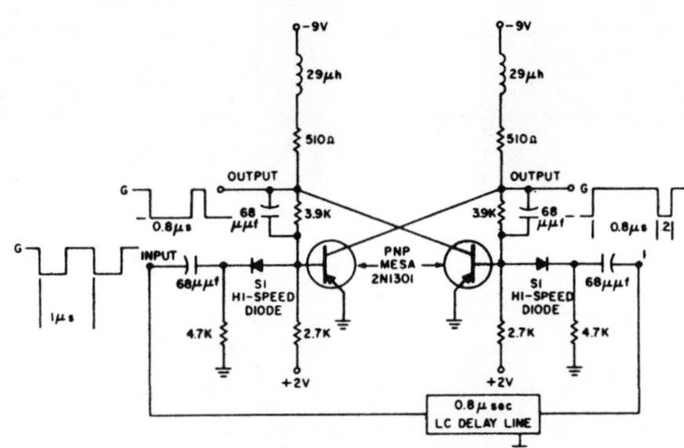

DELAY-LINE PULSE STRETCHER—Uses high-speed mesa-transistor flip-flop in which width of output pulse is accurately controlled by delay line, independently of input pulse width. Accuracy of output pulse width is the same as 1% accuracy in length of delay. With 1-MHz square-wave input, leading edge of pulse switches output of flip-flop and goes through delay line to reset flip-flop from other side, giving 0.8-μs output pulse when using 0.8-μs delay line. Remaining 0.2 μs is sufficient for flip-flop recovery.—J. Shirman, High-Speed Pulse-Stretcher Depends Upon Delay Line Time, "400 Ideas for Design Selected from Electronic Design," Hayden Book Co., N.Y., 1964, p 46.

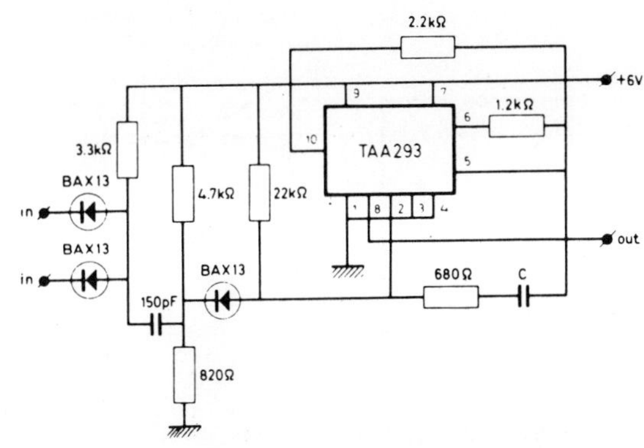

DELAY MONO FROM IC AMPLIFIER—Uses Philips TAA293 general-purpose amplifier. Output terminal rests in low state. Rectangular input pulse makes mvbr switch, driving output terminal to high state at 6 V. Circuit reverts to rest state after time delay, to give effect of delaying negative-going edge of input signal. Circuit cannot be retriggered until after recovery time nominally equal to delay time, both of which are about 100 μs when C is 10 nF. Times for other values of C are in direct proportion to C down to about 1 μs.—The TAA293 as a Schmitt Trigger and Multivibrator, Philips, Pub. Dept., Elcoma Div., Eindhoven, The Netherlands, No. 25, 1968.

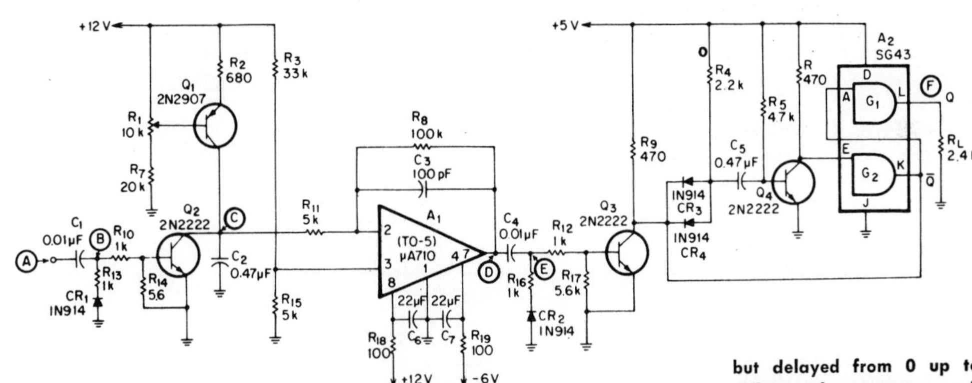

400-HZ VARIABLE APPARENT DELAY—Circuit senses positive excursion of 400-Hz input square wave and provides delay depending on value of control voltage or setting of R1. Delayed signal triggers 1.25-ms one-shot, to make output look like original square wave but delayed from 0 up to 2.5 ms. A1 is differential comparator, and one-shot A2 uses standard SUHL gates.—L. L. Pechi, Voltage or Pot-Variable 400-Hz Delay, *EEE*, Oct. 1969, p 112.

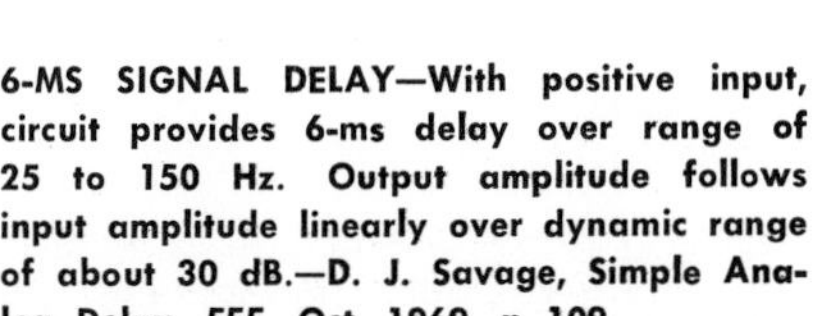

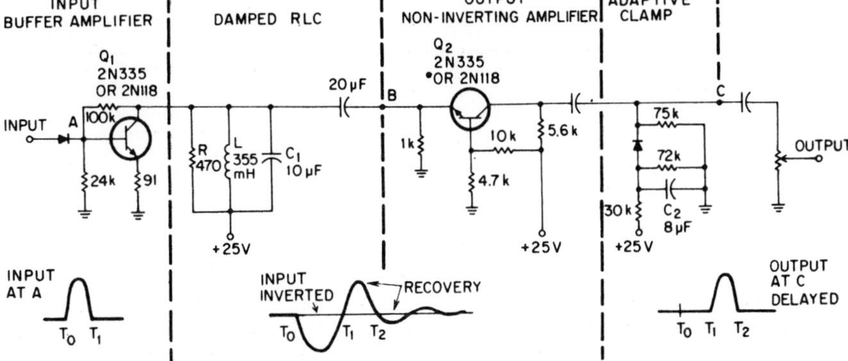

6-MS SIGNAL DELAY—With positive input, circuit provides 6-ms delay over range of 25 to 150 Hz. Output amplitude follows input amplitude linearly over dynamic range of about 30 dB.—D. J. Savage, Simple Analog Delay, *EEE*, Oct. 1969, p 109.

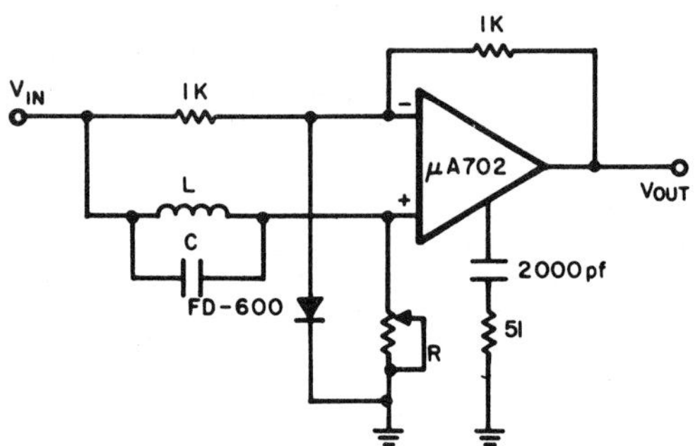

DELAY EQUALIZER—Uses Fairchild IC opamp as d-c amplifier to compensate for delay distortion in facsimile, high-speed telegraphy, and data-transmission carrier systems. Acts as all-pass circuit having amplitude characteristic that is independent of frequency over useful frequency range.—J. Toffler, The Integrated Operational Amplifier: A Versatile and Economical Circuit, "Microelectronic Design," Hayden Book Co., N.Y., 1966, p 189–194.

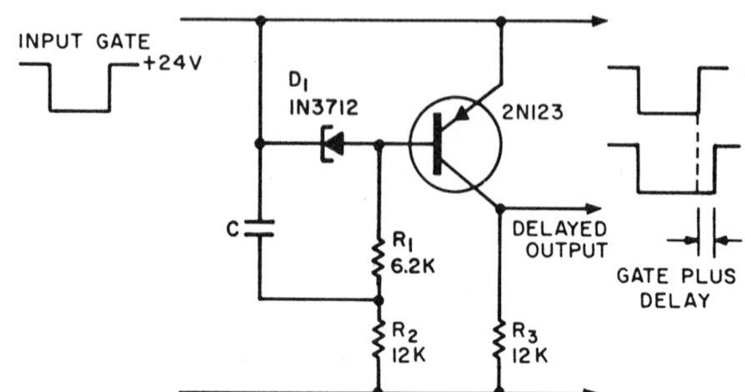

PULSE DELAY WITHOUT DISTORTION—Single transistor and tunnel diode generate delayed pulse or gate while maintaining or even improving sharp rise-time of input signal. With 0.002 μF for C, delay is 10 μs. Larger values of C give delays up to several seconds.—R. L. Shaum, Tunnel Diode Circuit Offers Non-Distorted Delayed Pulse, *Electronic Design*, May 10, 1965, p 46–47.

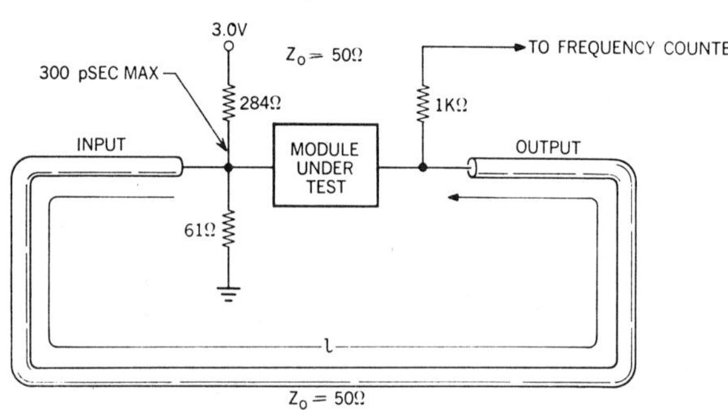

TESTING IC SWITCHING SPEED—Circulating loop test for ASLT modules permits rapid measurement of switching speed for each critical path in module. Unique test circuit drives input module from its own output, delayed in time by electrical length of cable in ns, to produce switching action. Counter then indicates number of switching actions during time period for test, from which switching speed is determined quickly and accurately.—R. F. Sechler, A. R. Strube, and J. R. Turnbull, ASLT Circuit Design, *IBM Journal*, Jan. 1967, p 74–85.

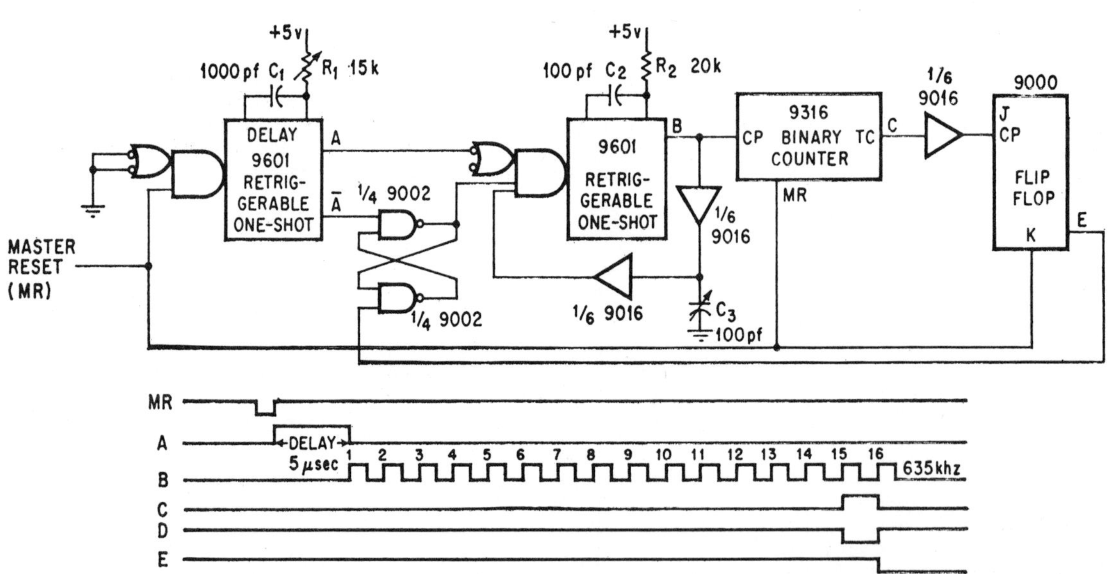

TRIGGERED DELAY FOR A/N DISPLAY—Used in alphanumeric cathode-ray display systems requiring that an oscillator start at preset time after arrival of trigger pulse, generate predetermined number of clock pulses, then shut down until next trigger arrives.—A. Liu, Retriggerable One-Shots Form Delayed-Key Oscillator, *Electronics*, Sept. 29, 1969, p 96.

CHAPTER 24
Detector Circuits

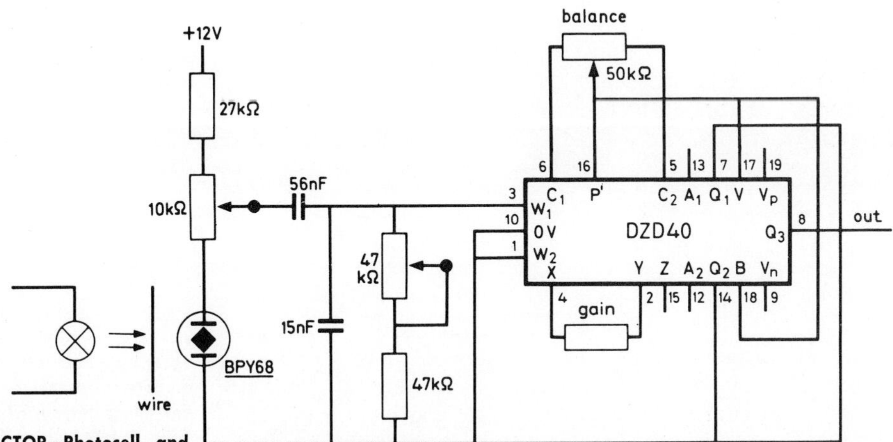

THREAD MOTION DETECTOR—Photocell and Philips DZD40 differential zero detector have sufficient sensitivity to detect shadow caused by moving wire or thread. Voltage peak produced across 56-nF capacitor by photocell trips DZD40 and makes its output switch to full supply voltage of 12 V. After wire has passed, sudden fall in photocell resistance makes DZD40 switch back to 0 V output. Slow changes in light on photocell have no effect.—Detection of Small Moving Objects Using the DZD40, Philips, Pub. Dept., Elcoma Div., Eindhoven, The Netherlands, No. 29.

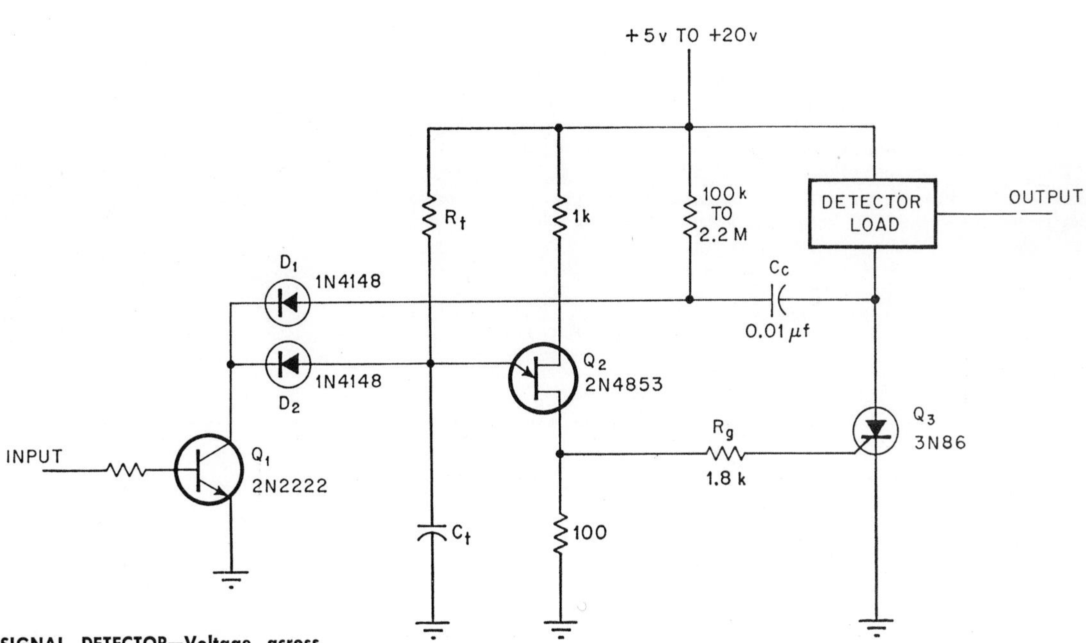

UJT-SCR SIGNAL DETECTOR—Voltage across load rises to indicate presence of input signal. When input signal terminates, ujt timing circuit is freed after time lapse determined by period of ujt circuit; if another input pulse arrives before Q2 is triggered, time lapse is restarted. Holding time can be anywhere between a few microseconds and several seconds, depending on values of Rt and Ct; 47K and 0.1 μF give 7ms, and 390K and 2.2 μF give 1.4 s.—D. K. Smith, Signal Detector Operates From 5-Volt Supply, *Electronics*, Mar. 30, 1970, p 95.

RAIN-GAGE RECORDER TURN-ON—Activator circuit turns on recorder only when it is raining. Hold feature prevents turn-off at drizzle rates. Used with system of tipping-bucket rain gages, each of which produces coded tone burst with arrival of each hundredth inch of precipitation. Each filled bucket produces 12-V 200-ms pulse at base of Q1 to turn it on and charge C1, which takes 20 ms. Circuit then pulls in relay that turns on recorder. With 100 meg switched in to gate of fet, C1 holds charge and keeps recorder on for 1.3 hours of drizzle.—J. Pike, Data-System Activator Has Hold Feature, *Electronic Design*, June 21, 1970, p 96 and 98.

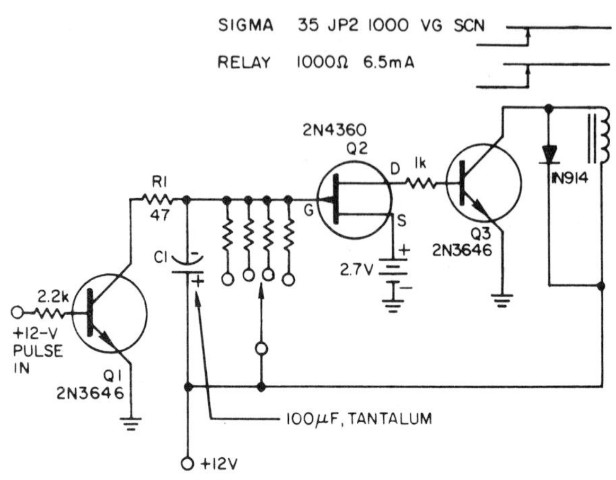

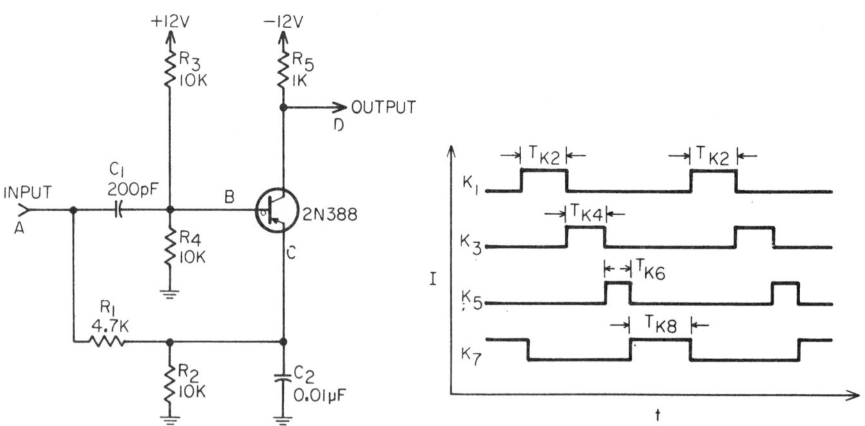

PULSE WIDTH SORTER—Simple bootstrap circuit delivers output pulse only when triggered by input pulse whose width is greater than predetermined value. Leading edge of positive-going output pulse coincides with trailing edge of input pulse. Useful as sync detector in pulse data systems.—C. Becklein and M. Yagud, Pulse-Width Sorter, *EEE*, Feb. 1967, p 146–147.

SCS PHASE SEQUENCE DETECTOR—Provides warning of incorrect phasing and detects reversal of three-phase motors. Scs is normally off. When opposite phase sequence occurs, with phase B lagging phase A by 120 deg, scs is triggered on for operating lamp, relay, or control actuator. With a-c anode supply, however, opposite condition occurs, with scs remaining on while phase B lags phase A. Will handle loads up to 250 mA. With AD107 scs, load can be 1.6 A.—Phase Sequence Detector for Three-Phase Systems, Solid State Products, Salem, Mass., No. 13.

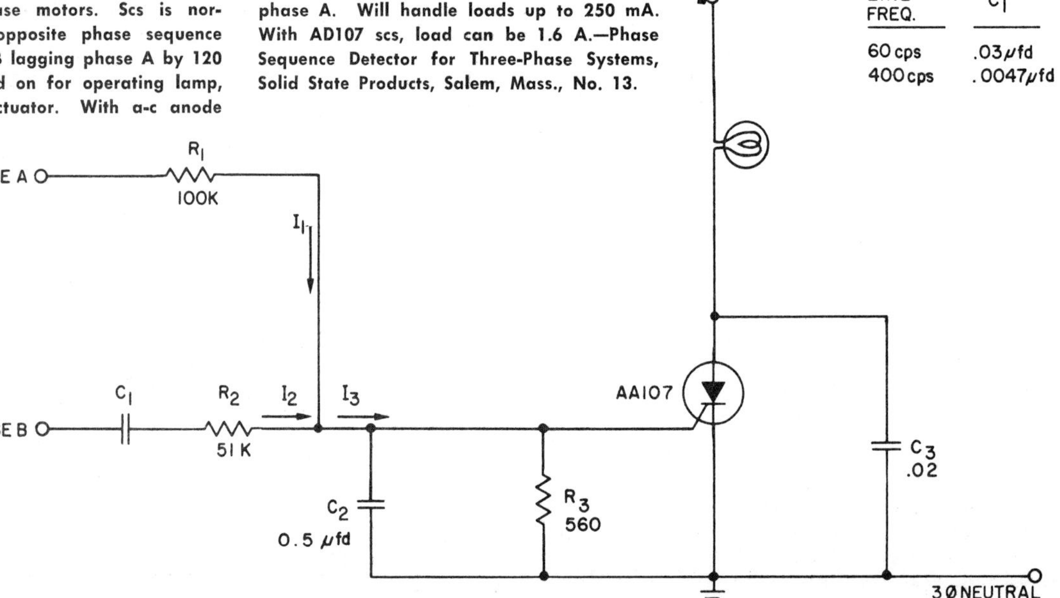

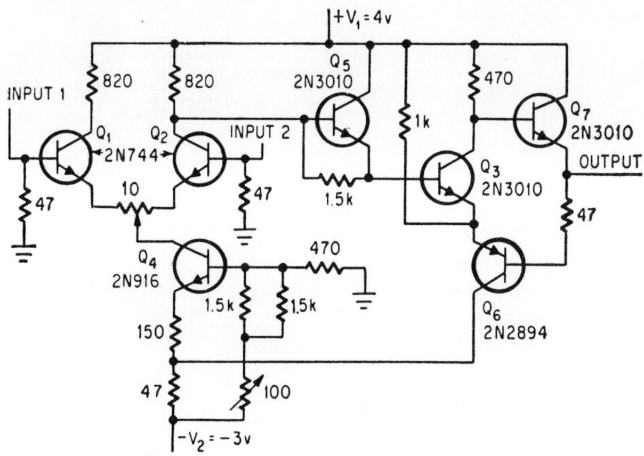

DIFFERENTIAL-INPUT WEAK-SIGNAL DETECTOR—Variation of paired Schmitt-trigger detector can detect absolute value of difference between two input signals riding on common-mode input signal of 0.5 V p-p at 14 MHz, for absolute difference values down to 15 mV. Dual input reduces hysteresis of detector one order of magnitude.—T. Weisz, Pairing Schmitt Triggers Produces Lower Hysteresis and Faster Switching, *Electronics*, Nov. 28, 1966, p 75–79.

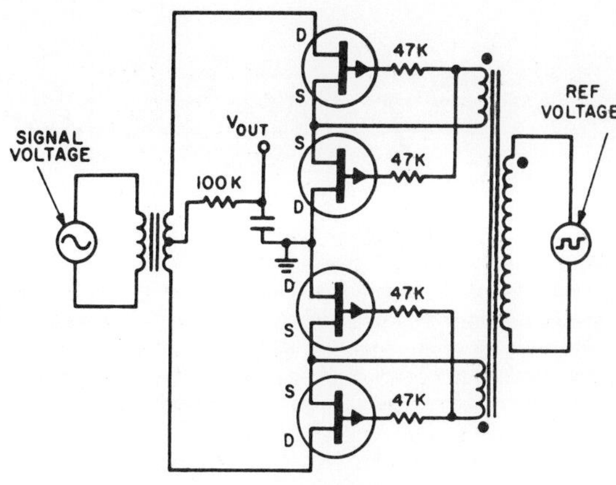

DETECTING SIGNALS BURIED IN NOISE—Amelco FG37 200-V field-effect transistors connected back-to-back provide detection of millivolt in-phase signals buried in noise having peak amplitudes several orders of magnitude greater. Reference voltage is 60-V p-p square-wave. May be operated at frequencies well up into higher audio range, with negligible switching time.—W. D. Hindson and T. Nishizaki, FET Makes High Level Phase-Sensitive Detector, "400 Ideas for Design Selected from Electronic Design," Hayden Book Co., N.Y., 1964, p 29.

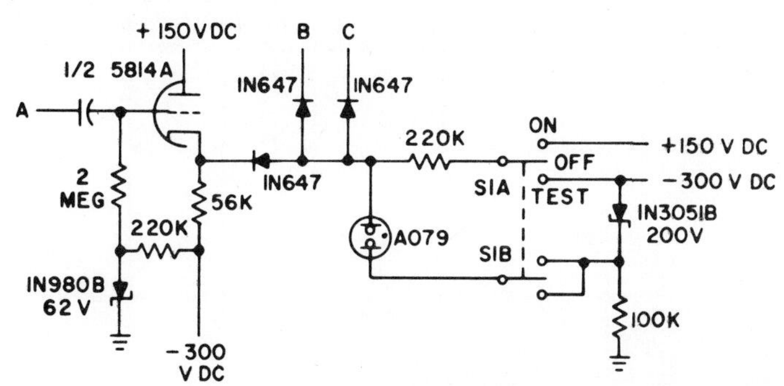

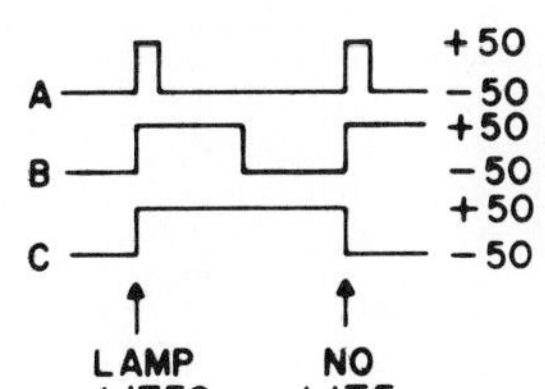

SIMULTANEOUS PULSES—With S1 in ON position, neon lamp lights only when all three 50-V positive pulses, at A, B, and C, occur at same time.—E. Bauman, "Applications of Neon Lamps and Gas Discharge Tubes," Signalite, Neptune, N.J., p 151.

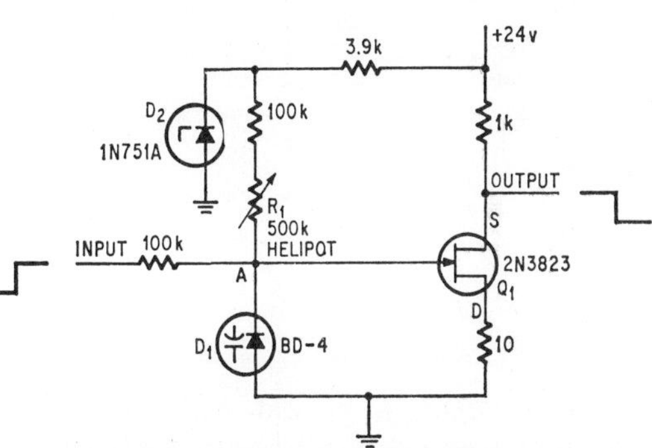

LOW-CURRENT DETECTOR—Will detect 1-μA currents with accuracy of 1%. When input signal exceeds preset threshold, sum of currents through backward diode D1 switches it to high-voltage state, generating pulse for amplification by fet output stage. Threshold jitter is negligible.—E. Elad, Backward Diode Plus FET Detects Low Currents, *Electronics*, Oct. 16, 1967, p 95–96.

MEASURING 2-MS PULSES—Provides output pulse whenever input pulse is less than minimum value or greater than maximum value. Can also be used as pulse-width error detector by providing error pulses of width equal to amount that input pulse width deviates from allowable limits. Developed for measuring 2-ms pulse widths within test window of 10%—I. Spector, Pulse-Width Discriminator, *EEE*, Sept. 1969, p 133–134.

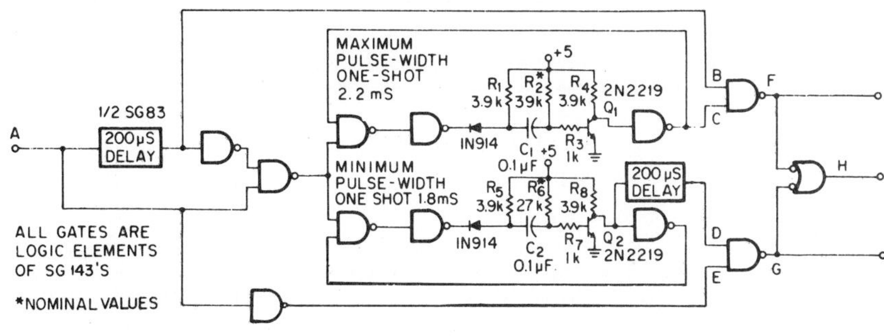

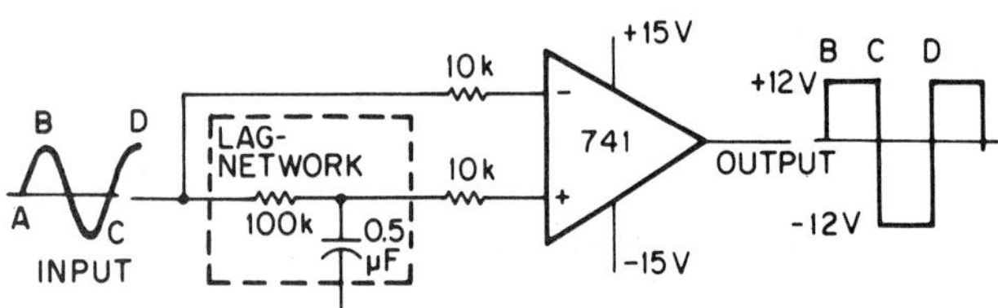

SLOPE CHANGE DETECTOR—Output is square wave in which high and low levels indicate changes in slope of input signal. Operation is independent of input level, and independent of distortion provided irregularities in distorted signal do not reverse slope at too high an amplitude. If distortion is severe, additional filtering is required in input line to make use of fundamental frequency. Lag network ahead of IC opamp has time constant of 50 ms and is useful from 0.1 to 10 Hz.—R. Antelman, Change-Of-Slope Detector, *EEE*, June 1970, p 94–95.

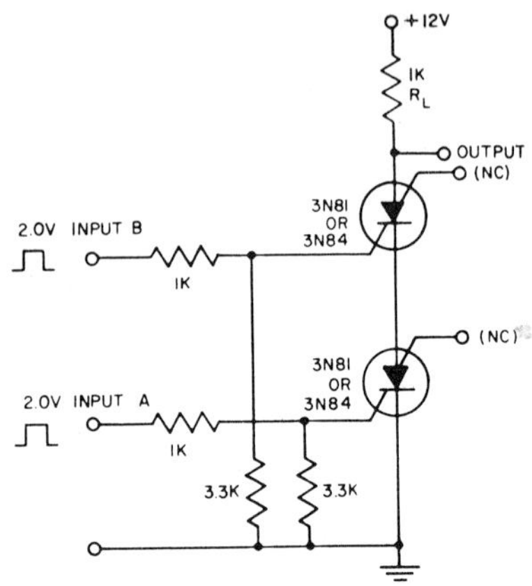

SCS PULSE COINCIDENCE DETECTOR—Voltage is developed across load RL only when inputs A and B occur simultaneously with amplitudes of 2 to 3 V. Pulse overlap of less than 1 μs is sufficient to give output. To detect coincidence of negative inputs, use scs units in complementary scr configuration, with detection by gates GA instead of GC. —Planar Silicon Controlled Switch 3N81/3N-82, General Electric, Syracuse, N.Y., No. 65.16, 1964.

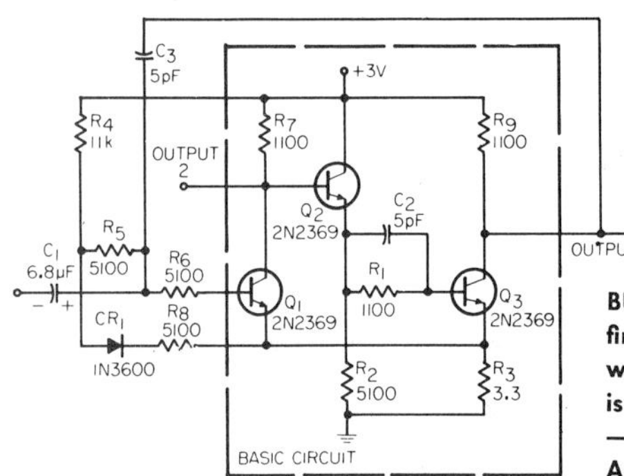

BUFFERED DETECTOR—Input of 1 mV p-p will fire circuit comparable to Schmitt trigger but with buffer Q2 in feedback path. Hysteresis is low for wide range of reference voltages. —R. H. Zimmerman, Buffered Detector, *EEE*, April 1967, p 138.

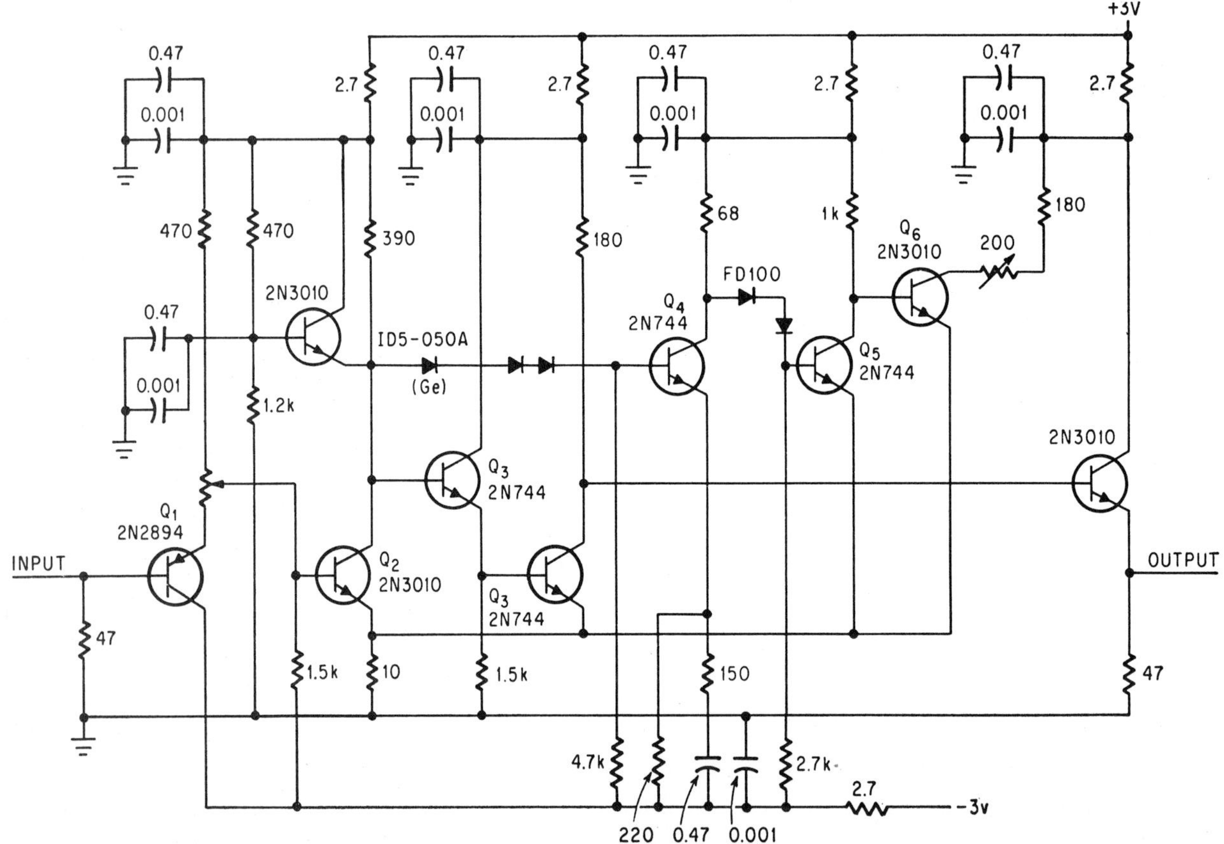

LOW-LEVEL SIGNAL DETECTOR—Pairs of Schmitt triggers provide high switching and cycling speeds with extremely low hysteresis, for detector of low-level signals at high frequencies. Can be used as sense amplifiers in high-speed computer memory systems. Article gives operating theory and limiting design equations. Circuit performed satisfactorily at 13 MHz, with hysteresis of only 2 mV.—T. Weisz, Pairing Schmitt Triggers Produces Lower Hysteresis and Faster Switching, *Electronics*, Nov. 28, 1966, p 75–79.

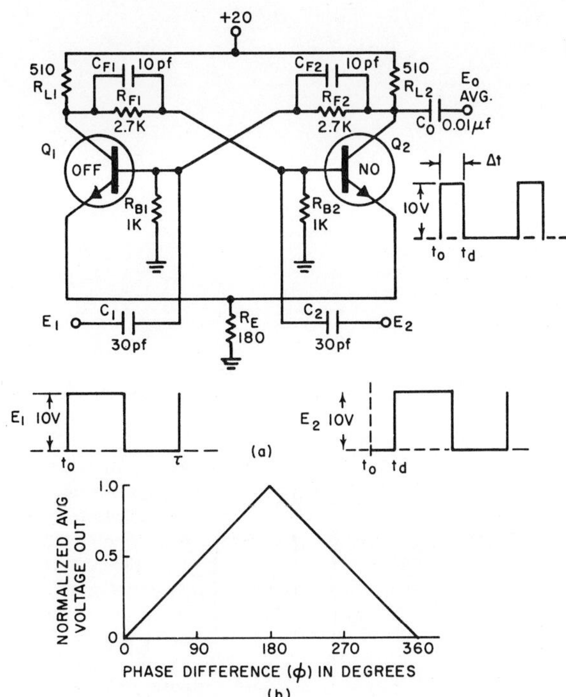

SQUARE-WAVE PHASE DETECTOR—Nonsaturating flip-flop provides linear average voltage output as function of phase difference between two 1-MHz square-wave signals. Average output voltage is zero when inputs E1 and E2 are in phase or 360 deg out-of-phase. Transistors are 2N2222.—J. F. Panicello, Flip-Flop Phase Detects RF Square Wave, *Electronic Design*, Nov. 9, 1964, p 71–72.

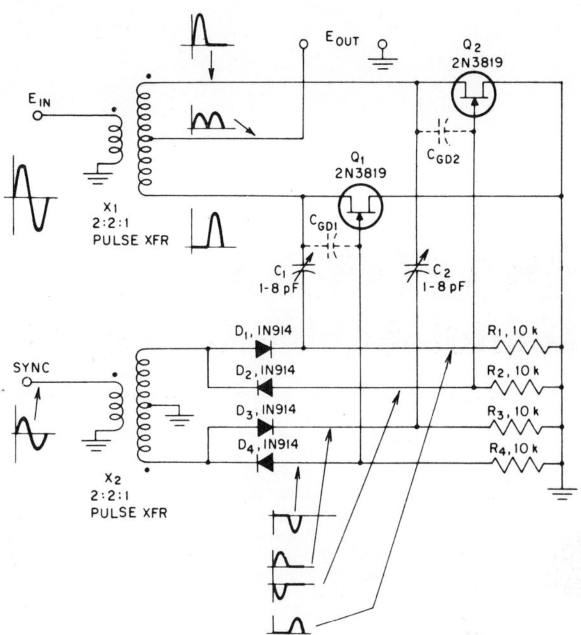

SYNCHRONOUS DETECTOR—Circuit shown overcomes capacitance problem in typical fet chopper by producing signal opposite in polarity to sync signal and feeding it to drain of fet through capacitance exactly equal to gate-drain capacitance. Dynamic range is 80 dB at 100 kHz.—R. P. Lackey, High-Speed Synchronous Detector, *EEE*, May 1970, p 103.

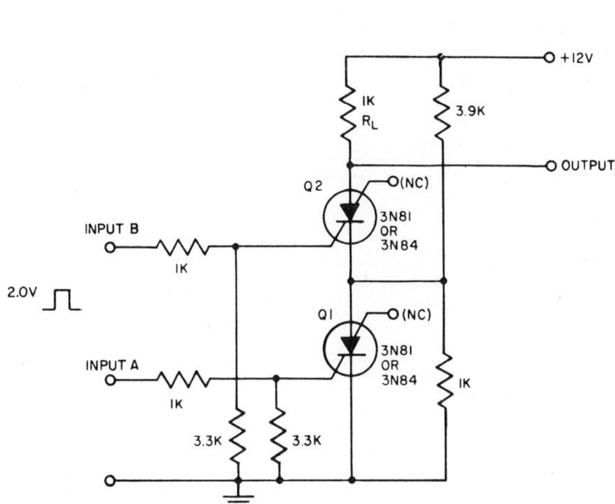

PULSE SEQUENCE DETECTOR—Resistor divider between Q1 and Q2 prevents input B from triggering Q2 unless Q1 is conducting. When pulse is applied in input A to make Q1 conducting, next pulse at input B triggers Q2 and sends current through load RL.—Planar Silicon Controlled Switch 3N81/3N82, General Electric, Syracuse, N.Y., No. 65.16, 1964.

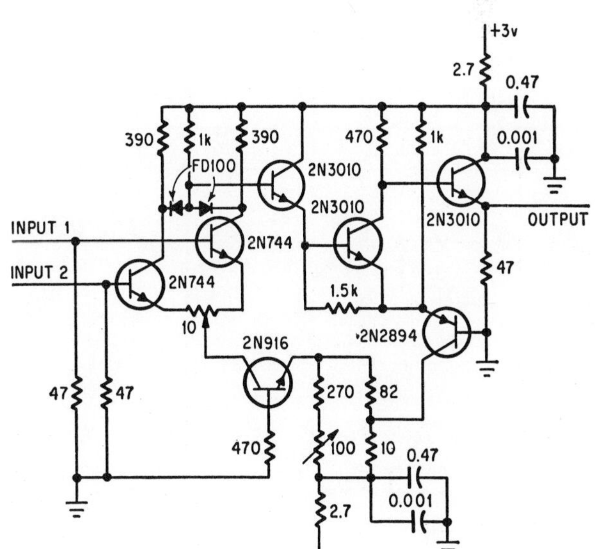

VOLTAGE BAND DETECTOR—Modification of paired Schmitt triggers produces output only when input 2 is within predetermined limits that are above voltage at input 1. Circuit thus detects absolute differences between two low-level input signals.—T. Weisz, Pairing Schmitt Triggers Produces Lower Hysteresis and Faster Switching, *Electronics*, Nov. 28, 1966, p 75–79.

CHAPTER 25
Digital-Analog Converter Circuits

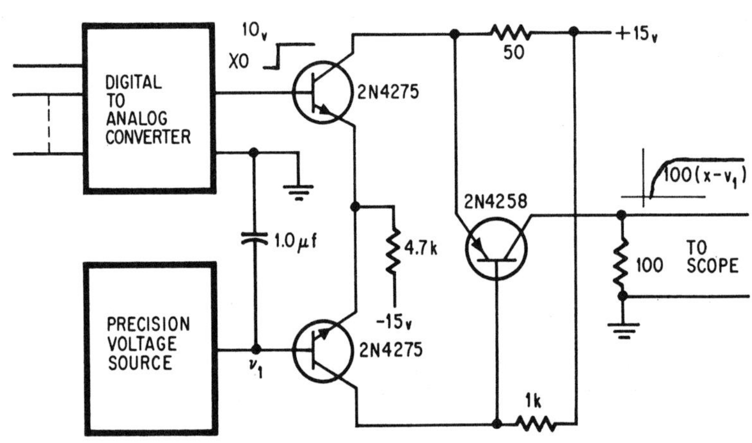

BOOSTER—Simple differential preamp ahead of cro provides necessary gain and sensitivity for measuring rise and settling times of d-a converter. Sufficient offset is provided by voltage source to look only at top of converter waveform.—J. J. Pastoriza, Know Your D-A Converter's Capability, *Electronics*, Nov. 10, 1969, p 129–130.

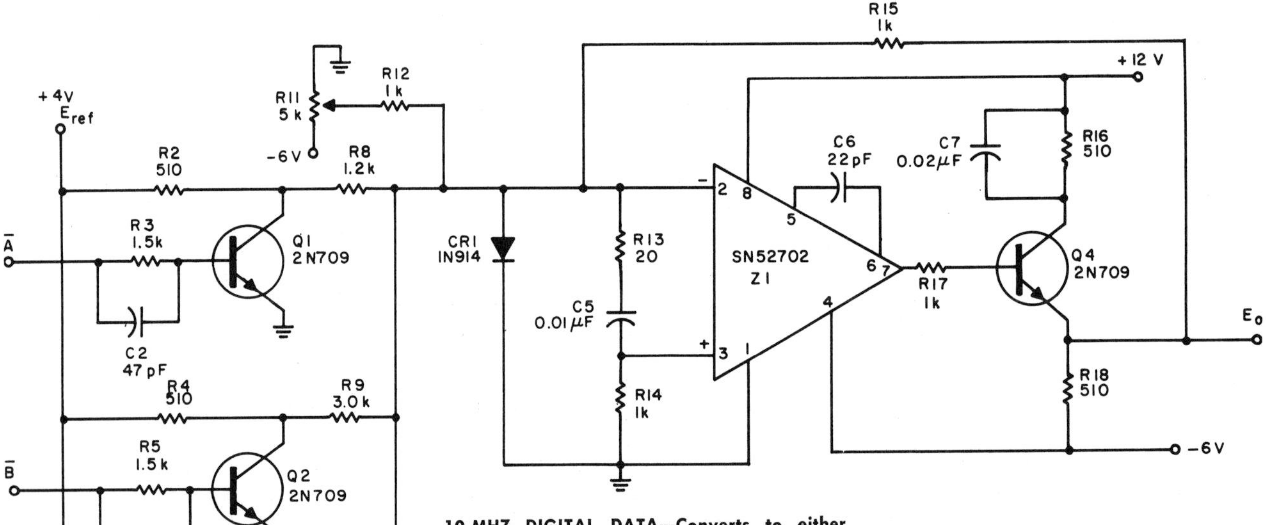

10-MHZ DIGITAL DATA—Converts to either positive or negative analog signal. Each bit of binary-coded input is applied to base of transistor switches Q1, Q2, and Q3, which are normally biased on. When bit turns off switch, 4-V reference voltage E-ref is summed through opamp. Values of input resistances R8 and R2 are chosen so each allows current flow proportional to weight or significance of its respective binary digit.—J. Mace and J. W. Bain, Digital-To-Analog Converter Is Fast and Simple, *Electronic Design*, June 6, 1968, p 118.

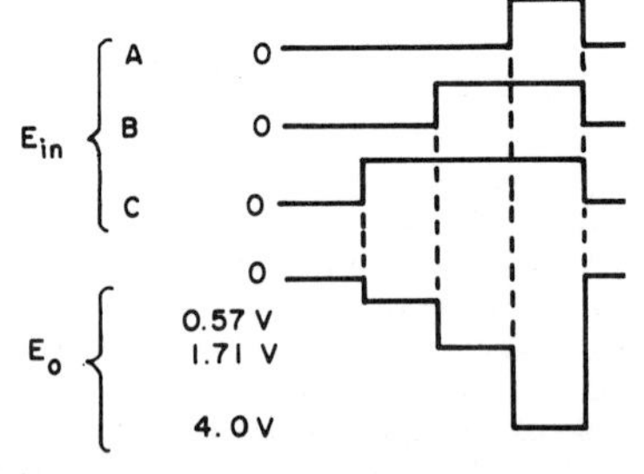

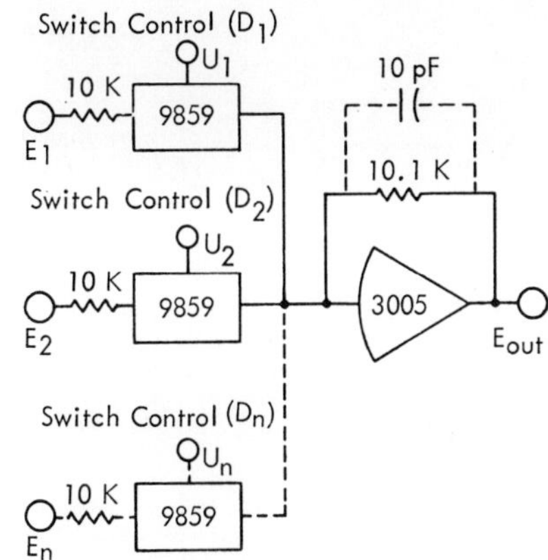

MULTIPLEXER—Any number of Burr-Brown 9859/15 integrate-hold electronic switch modules may be combined as shown for multiplexing at output of opamp if properly sequenced control pulses are fed to switches. With properly weighted input summing resistors, set of n switches may be used to construct n-bit digital-analog converter or n-bit multiplying digital-analog converter.—Integrate/Hold Electronic Switch, Burr-Brown Research, Tucson, Ariz., PDS189, 1967.

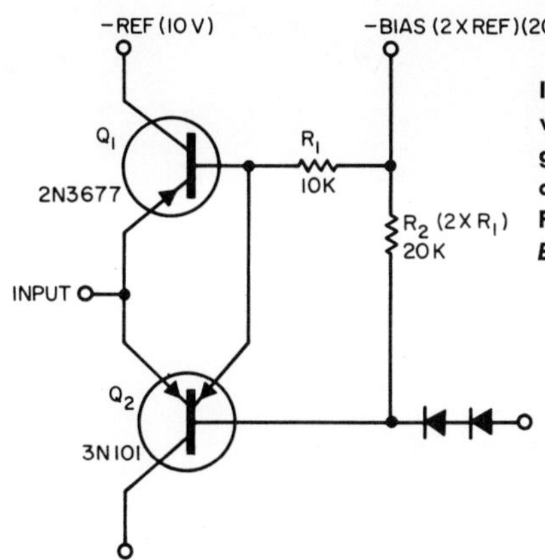

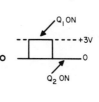

INTEGRATED CHOPPER—Digital-to-analog conversion is produced by spdt action of integrated chopper Q2, without complex drive circuitry.—J. M. Cohen, Integrated Chopper Forms Simple Digital-to-Analog Converter, *Electronic Design*, Nov. 22, 1965, p 60–61.

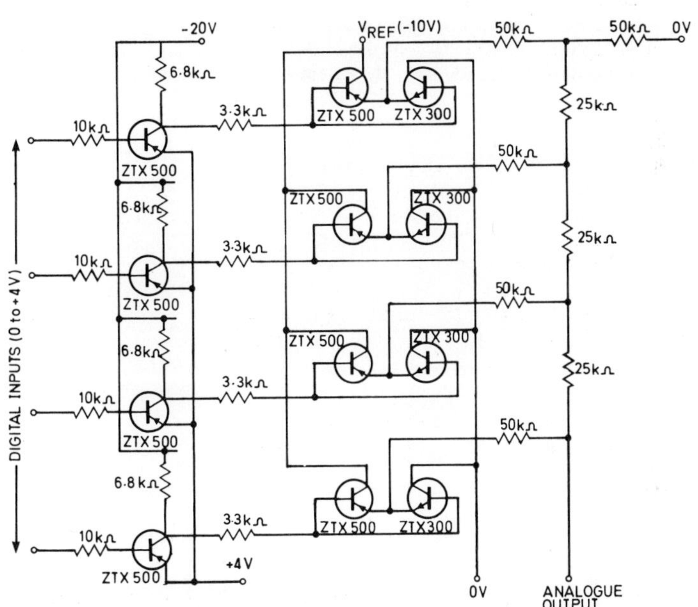

4-BIT DIGITAL-ANALOG—Uses complementary transistors as switches. Driver transistors at left operate from higher negative supply voltage to ensure that switching transistors will bottom satisfactorily. Ladder network, made up of close-tolerance resistors, is used for summing outputs.—"E-Line Transistor Applications," Ferranti Ltd., Oldham, Lancs., England, 1969, p 49.

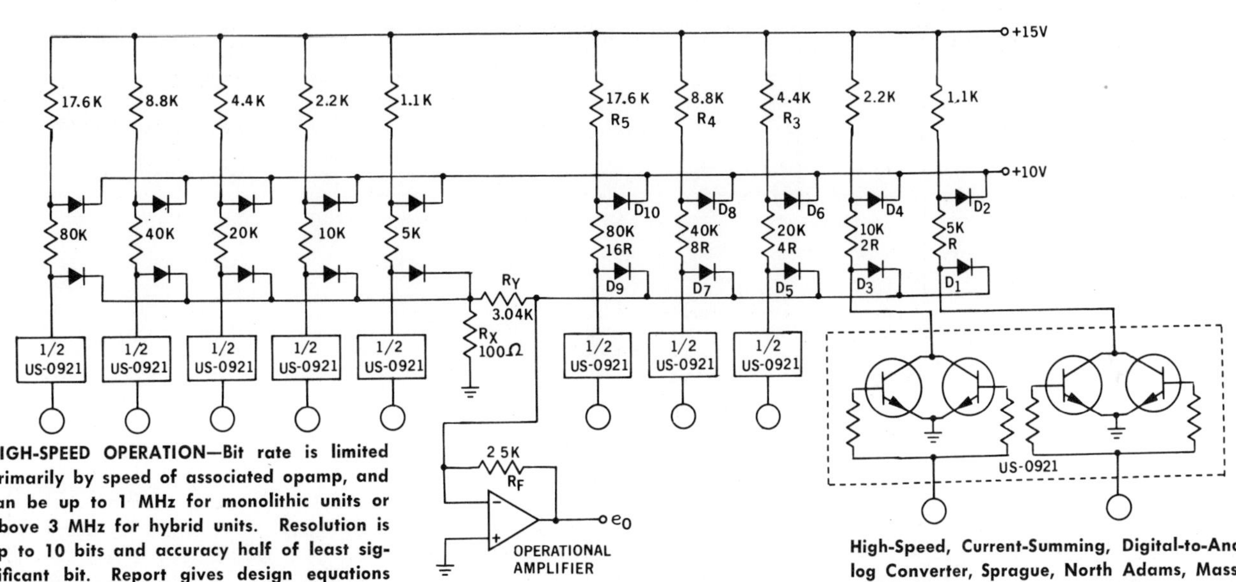

HIGH-SPEED OPERATION—Bit rate is limited primarily by speed of associated opamp, and can be up to 1 MHz for monolithic units or above 3 MHz for hybrid units. Resolution is up to 10 bits and accuracy half of least significant bit. Report gives design equations and application data.—N. S. Palazzini, A High-Speed, Current-Summing, Digital-to-Analog Converter, Sprague, North Adams, Mass., No. TP-68-9.

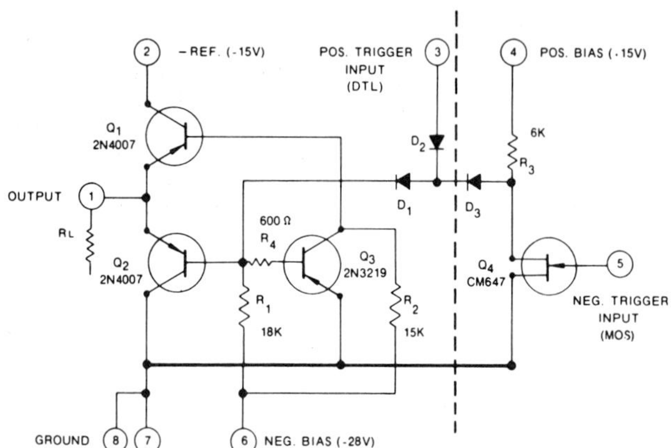

LADDER SWITCH—Crystalonics CDA1-2 packaged ladder switch for digital-analog converters accepts either 6-V positive or 24-V negative triggers directly from logic. Contains series-shunt switch and driver. Uses chips bonded directly to substrate.—Hybrid IC's, Crystalonics, Cambridge, Mass., 1969.

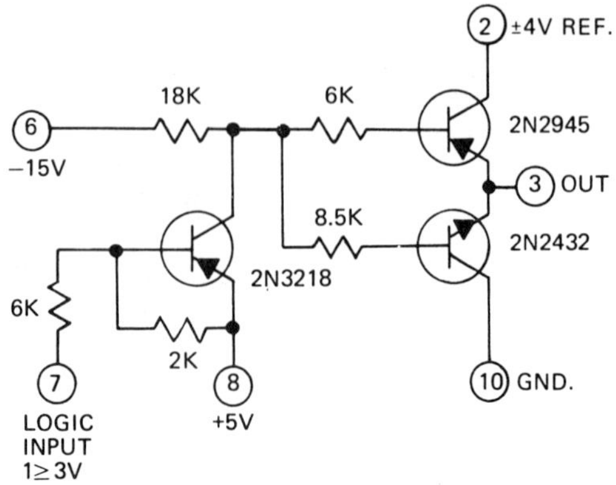

BIPOLAR-REFERENCE LADDER SWITCH—Crystalonics CDA5 hybrid package for digital-analog converters has maximum switching delay of only 3 μs, operating from either positive or negative 4-V reference.—Hybrid IC's, Crystalonics, Cambridge, Mass., 1969.

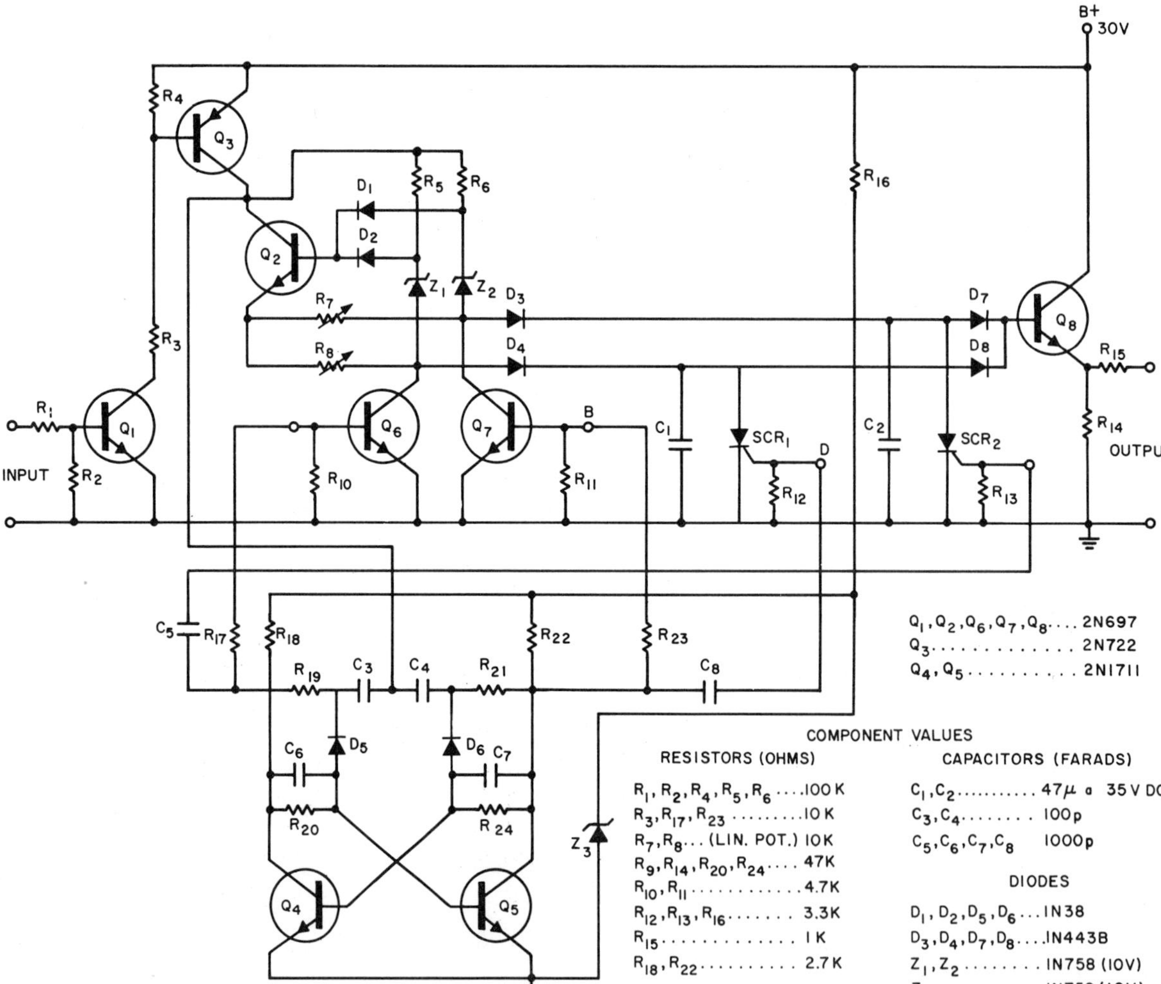

Q_1, Q_2, Q_6, Q_7, Q_8 . . . . 2N697
Q_3 . . . . 2N722
Q_4, Q_5 . . . . 2N1711

COMPONENT VALUES

RESISTORS (OHMS)

R_1, R_2, R_4, R_5, R_6 . . . . 100 K
R_3, R_{17}, R_{23} . . . . 10 K
R_7, R_8 . . . (LIN. POT.) 10 K
$R_9, R_{14}, R_{20}, R_{24}$ 47K
R_{10}, R_{11} 4.7K
R_{12}, R_{13}, R_{16} 3.3K
R_{15} . . . . 1 K
R_{18}, R_{22} . . . . 2.7 K

CAPACITORS (FARADS)

C_1, C_2 . . . . 47μ a 35 V DC
C_3, C_4 . . . . 100p
C_5, C_6, C_7, C_8 1000p

DIODES

D_1, D_2, D_5, D_6 . . . 1N38
D_3, D_4, D_7, D_8 . . . 1N443B
Z_1, Z_2 . . . . 1N758 (10V)
Z_3 . . . . 1N759 (12V)

CONVERTING PULSE WIDTH TO VOLTAGE—Can be used to convert voice-modulated variable-width pulses back to analog voltages over narrow-bandwidth space communication channels. Output is linearly proportional to pulse width. Operates over duty-cycle range from 0.06 to 60%, with pulse periods up to 500 ms. Requires only about 600 mW power. Can handle up to 10,000 pps.—A. L. Newcomb, Jr., Solid-State Integrator Combines Low Duty Cycle With Low Ripple, *Electronic Design*, April 12, 1965, p 42–45.

CLAMPED LOAD—Diode-resistor arrangement at right cuts cost of OFF level standardizer for driving flip-flop in digital-analog converter driven by counter or register. For 5-V logic level, output voltage error is less than 0.2 mV per degree C. Diodes can be unmatched but should be mounted close together to minimize temperature errors.—E. J. Rogers, Accurate Binary Levels In a Clamped Circuit, *Electronic Design*, April 27, 1964, p 91–92.

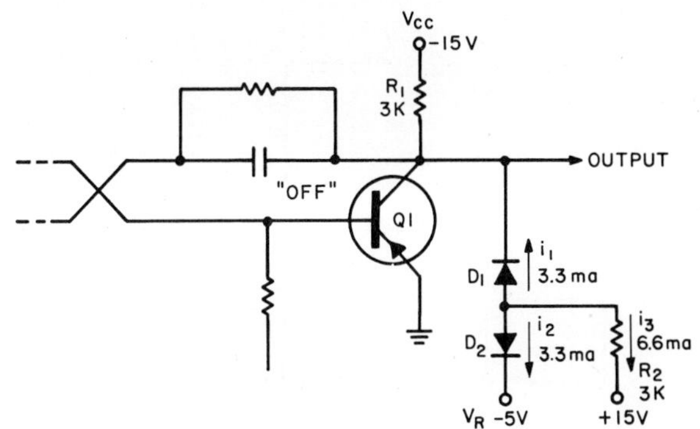

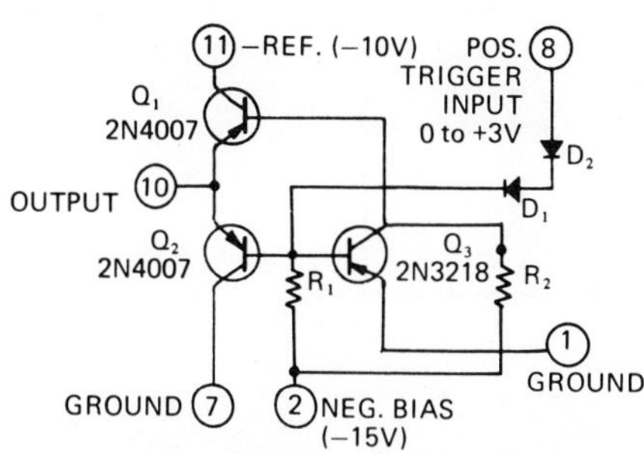

NEGATIVE-REFERENCE LADDER SWITCH—Crystalonics CMDA1 hybrid package for digital-analog converters gives 10-bit accuracy when used with 10K/20K ladder. Works directly from logic. Consists of series-shunt switch and driver.—Hybrid IC's, Crystalonics, Cambridge, Mass., 1969.

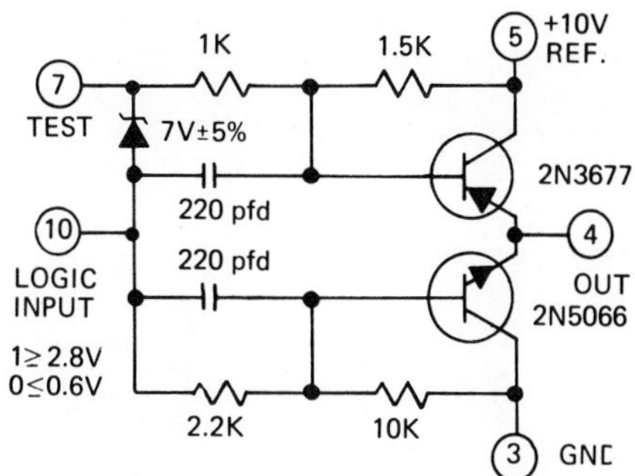

POSITIVE-REFERENCE LADDER SWITCH—Crystalonics CDA4A hybrid package for digital-analog converters gives 12-bit accuracy, works directly from logic, and uses positive 10-V reference.—Hybrid IC's, Crystalonics, Cambridge, Mass., 1969.

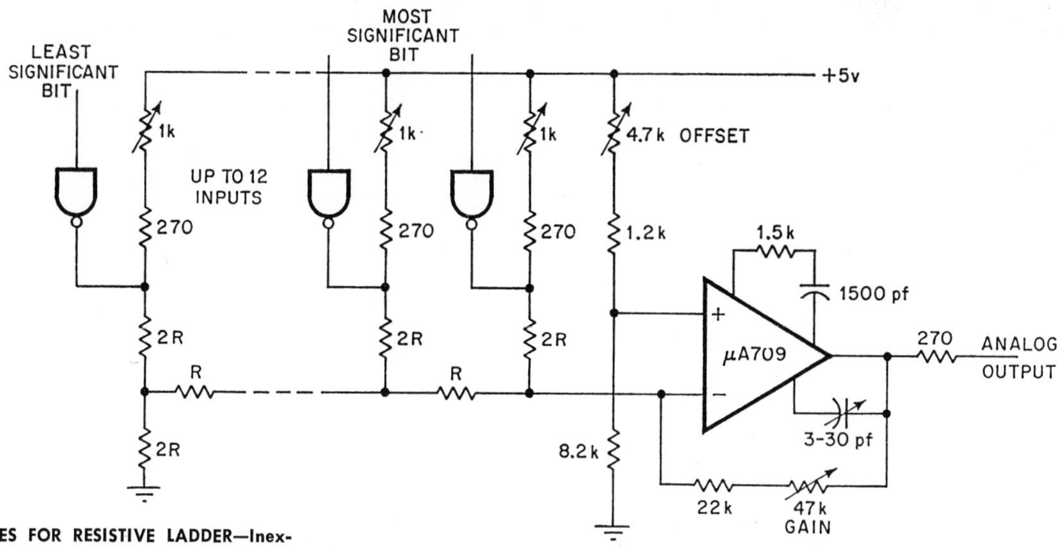

12 TTL GATES FOR RESISTIVE LADDER—Inexpensive, easily assembled d-a converter serves as low-cost drive for crt display terminals. TTL used must have open collector for external resistor and power supply, such as SN7401 quad NAND gate and SN7401 hex inverter. Current proportional to digital input is summed into one input of opamp. Resistive ladder network weights currents switched by logic gates according to significance of their input bits on binary scale. Value of R should be between 10K and 50K for best accuracy and settling time.—C. S. L. Keay and J. A. Kennewell, D-A Converter Switches Digital Inputs with TTL Gates, *Electronics*, Dec. 8, 1969, p 89.

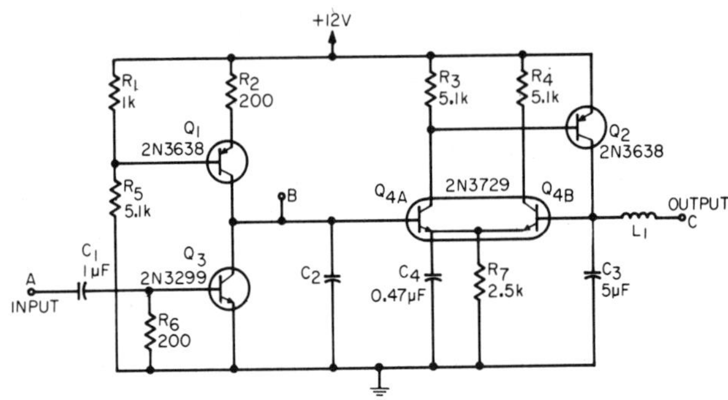

PWM TO VOLTAGE—Provides linear conversion from pulse width to analog output voltage, from input repetition frequencies of 1 kHZ to 1 MHz and duty cycles from 5 to 95%. Q1 generates linear ramp across C2, with duration and height controlled by input pulse width. Ramp voltage is applied to one input of differential amplifier Q4, and inverted output of amplifier Q2 is applied to other input. Feedback tends to maintain output voltage across C3.—O. Lykins, Simple Circuit Converts Pulse Duty Cycle Into Analog Voltage, *EEE*, July 1968, p 98–99.

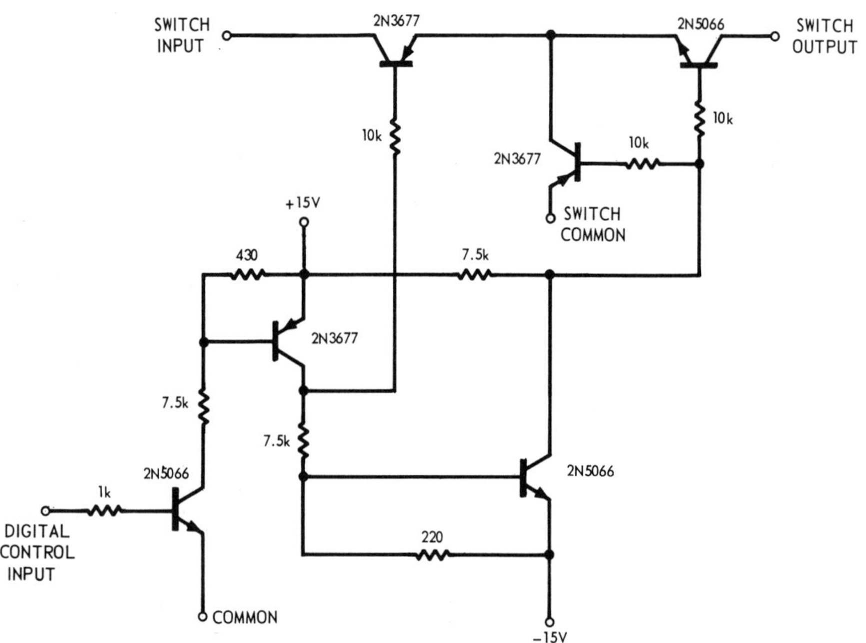

HIGH-LEVEL SIGNAL SWITCH—Controlled by standard TTL or DTL logic having ON-OFF time of about 200 ns. Complementary transistors isolate drive from signal current. Can be used for digital-analog conversion, video switching, and sample-and-hold. ON resistance is about 10 ohms.—R. C. Gerdes, High-Level Analog Switch, *EDN*, Sept. 1, 1969, p 73.

NOTE: To locate additional circuits in the category of this chapter, use the index at the back of this book. Check also the author's "Sourcebook of Electronic Circuits," published by McGraw-Hill in 1968.

CHAPTER 26
Display Circuits

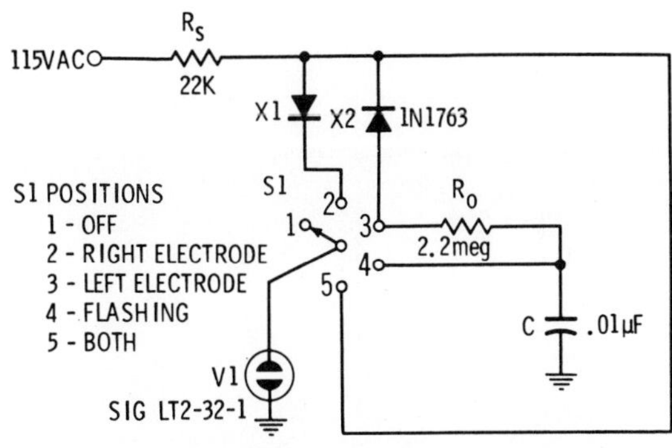

FIVE-CONDITION INDICATOR—Represents any of five states, using single neon lamp, by switching S1.—W. G. Miller, "Using and Understanding Miniature Neon Lamps," H. W. Sams & Co., Indianapolis, Ind., 1969, p 23.

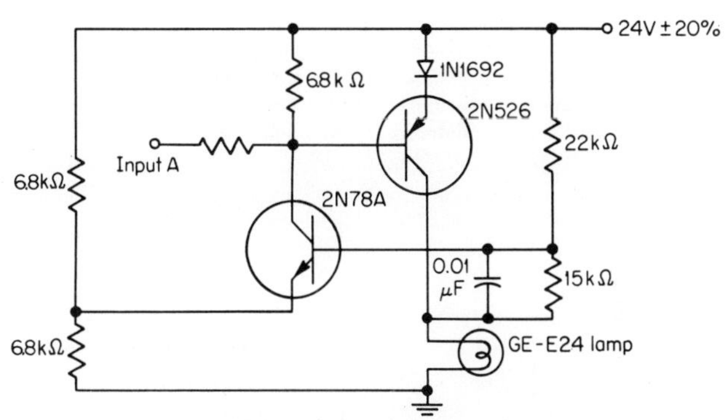

BISTABLE INDICATOR LAMP DRIVER—Lamp is turned on by short trigger pulse at input A and then remains on. Lamp is turned off by positive pulse at A and will remain off. Used with logical flip-flop.—A. C. Gillie, "Pulse and Logic Circuits," McGraw-Hill, N.Y., 1968, p 260.

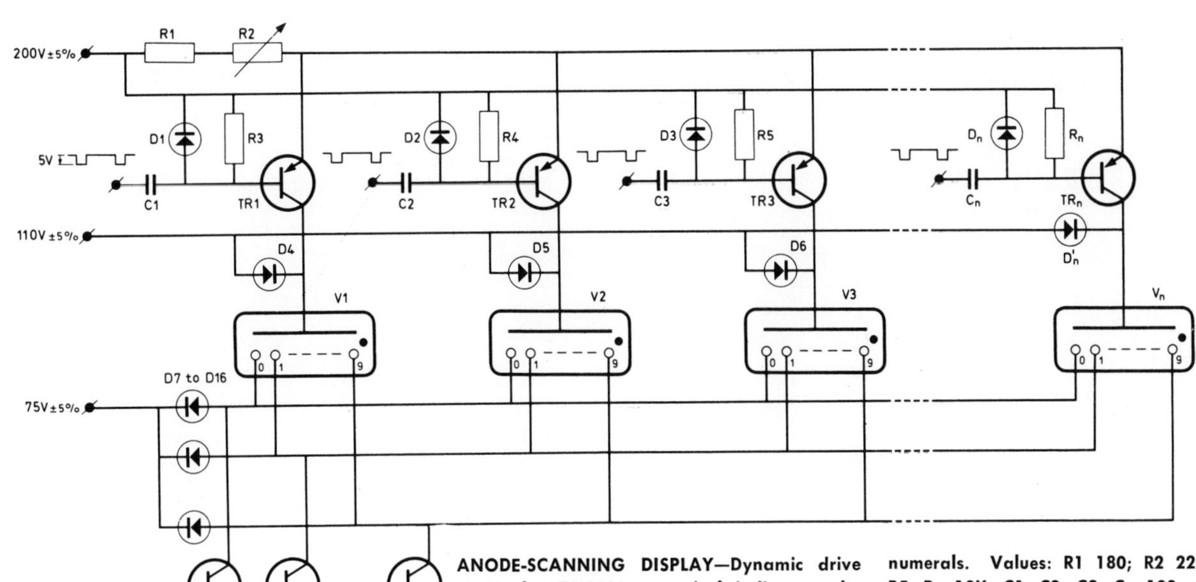

ANODE-SCANNING DISPLAY—Dynamic drive circuit for ZM1000 numerical indicator tube is externally excited by 5-V base drive pulses, mutually shifted in time, that make TR1 to TRn conduct in succession. Indicator tubes are thus sequentially selected for display, with cathode drive transistors made conductive at appropriate instant to show correct numerals. Values: R1 180; R2 220; R3, R4, R5, Rn 10K; C1, C2, C3, Cn 100 nF; D1, D2, D3, Dn BAX13; D4, D5, D6, Dn, BAX16; D7-D-16 BAX16; TR1-TRn 516BSY.—D. J. G. Janssen, A. G. Korteling, and P. H. G. van Vlodrop, Cold Cathode Numerical Indicator Tubes, Philips, Pub. Dept., Elcoma Div., Eindhoven, The Netherlands, No. 327, 1968.

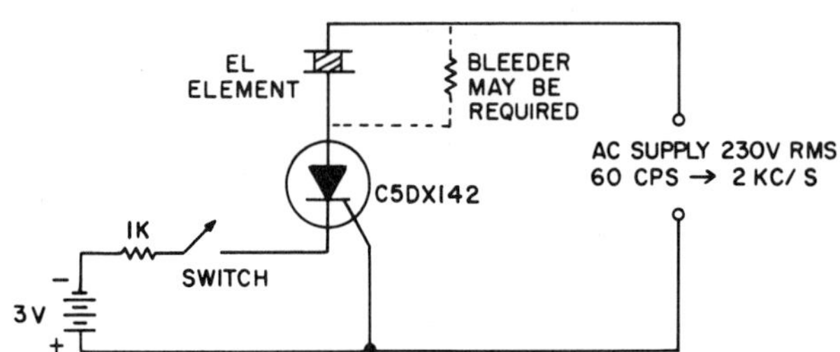

SERIES DRIVE FOR EL—Electroluminescent panel is off when switch is open. When switch is closed, scr gate is positive and scr conducts, with a-c load current flowing through scr, switch, 1K resistor, and control battery.—D. R. Grafham, Using Low Current SCR's, General Electric, Syracuse, N.Y., No. 200.19, 1967, p 40.

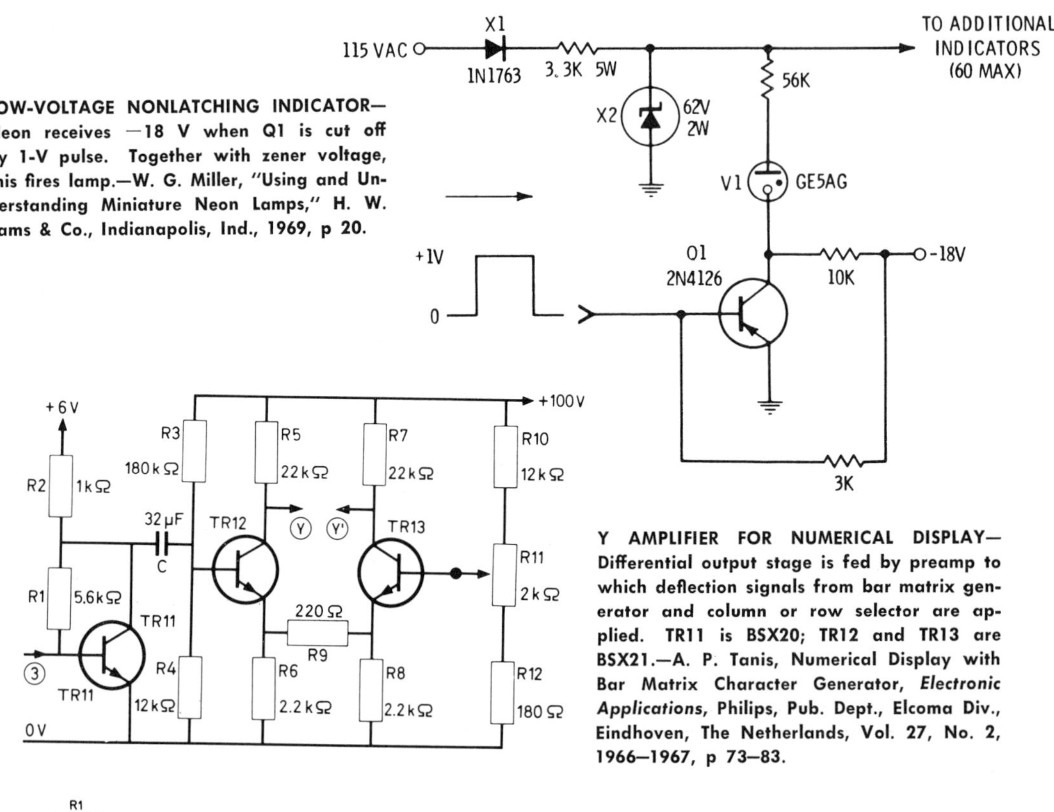

LOW-VOLTAGE NONLATCHING INDICATOR—Neon receives −18 V when Q1 is cut off by 1-V pulse. Together with zener voltage, this fires lamp.—W. G. Miller, "Using and Understanding Miniature Neon Lamps," H. W. Sams & Co., Indianapolis, Ind., 1969, p 20.

Y AMPLIFIER FOR NUMERICAL DISPLAY—Differential output stage is fed by preamp to which deflection signals from bar matrix generator and column or row selector are applied. TR11 is BSX20; TR12 and TR13 are BSX21.—A. P. Tanis, Numerical Display with Bar Matrix Character Generator, *Electronic Applications*, Philips, Pub. Dept., Elcoma Div., Eindhoven, The Netherlands, Vol. 27, No. 2, 1966–1967, p 73–83.

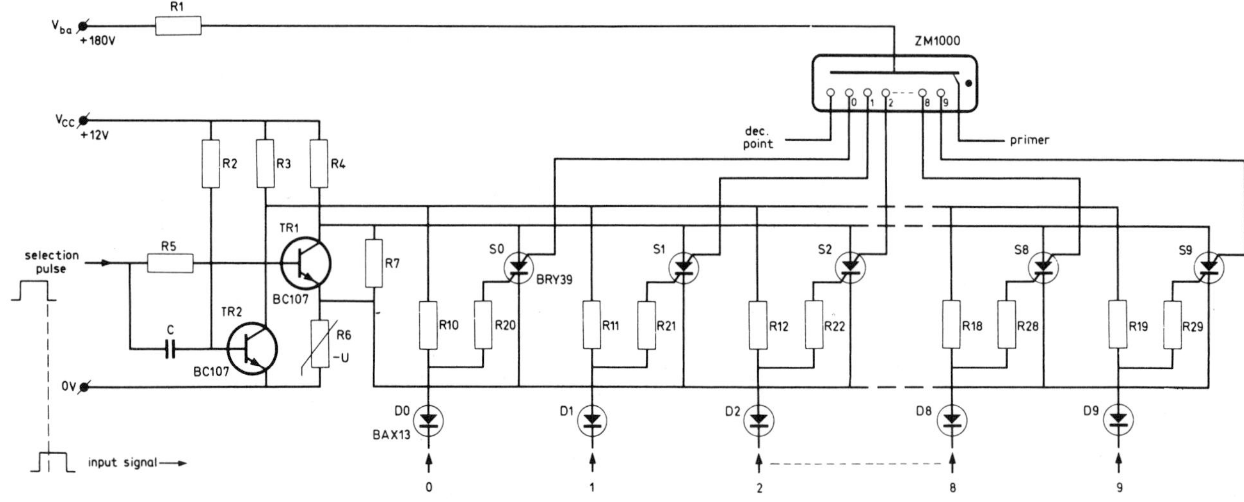

DISPLAY BANK WITH MEMORY—Circuit controls one numerical indicator tube in bank of such tubes, displaying parallel digits representing information from computer or calculator. Scs associated with each digit acts both as switch and memory so display is held after input signal has ceased. Display tubes are energized in sequence until entire numeral is visible. Display is blanked out by applying positive pulse to all selection pulse inputs, to turn off every conducting scs and extinguish all indicator tubes.—D. J. G. Janssen, A. G. Korteling, and P. H. G. van Vlodrop, Cold Cathode Numerical Indicator Tubes, Philips, Pub. Dept., Elcoma Div., Eindhoven, The Netherlands, No. 327, 1968.

R1 = 16 kΩ
R2 = 10 kΩ
R3 = 1.2 kΩ
R4 = 2.2 kΩ
R5, R6 = VDR

R7 = 8.2 kΩ
R10 to R19 = 8.2 kΩ
R20 to R29 = 3.3 kΩ
C = 2.7 nF
S0 to S9 = BRY39

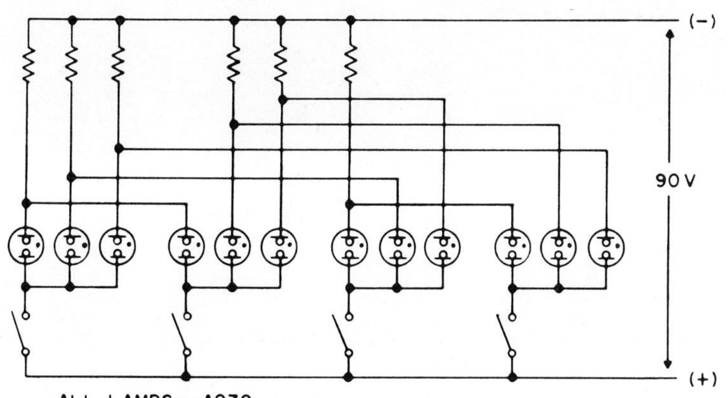

SWITCHED SEQUENCE—First microswitch to close causes three neon lamps to glow. Second switch lights only two lamps, third lights one, and fourth doesn't light any lamp.—E. Bauman, "Applications of Neon Lamps and Gas Discharge Tubes," Signalite, Neptune, N.J., p 143.

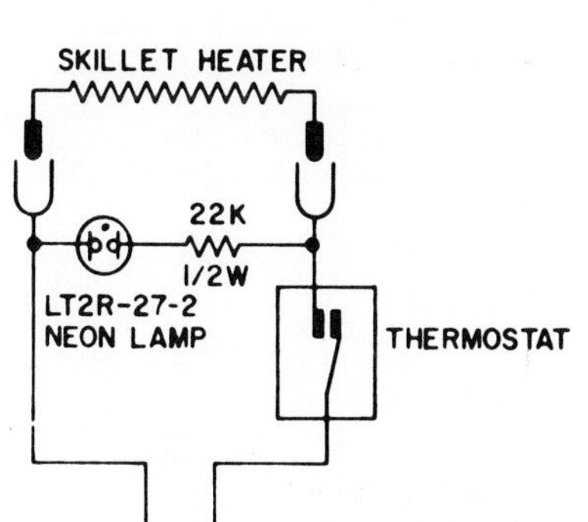

APPLIANCE ON INDICATOR—Neon lamp indicates when thermostatically controlled heating element is on.—E. Bauman, "Applications of Neon Lamps and Gas Discharge Tubes," Signalite, Neptune, N.J., p 138.

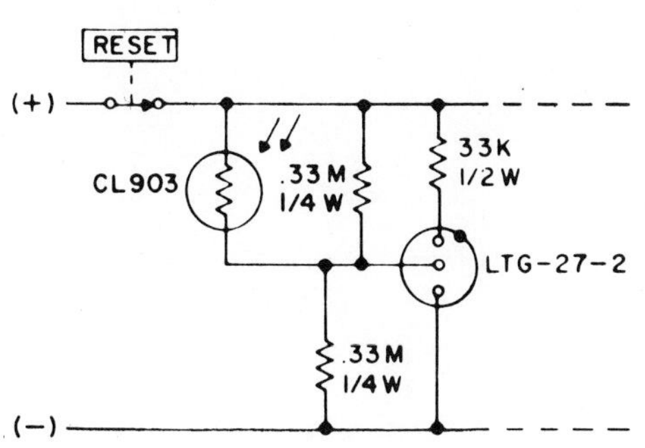

WRITE WITH FLASHLIGHT—Light excites one photocell in bank of 1,000, causing corresponding three-element neon lamp in bank of 1,000 to glow. Lamps remain on until reset button is pushed to turn all lamps off at once. Power source is 145 V.—E. Bauman, "Applications of Neon Lamps and Gas Discharge Tubes," Signalite, Neptune, N.J., p 116.

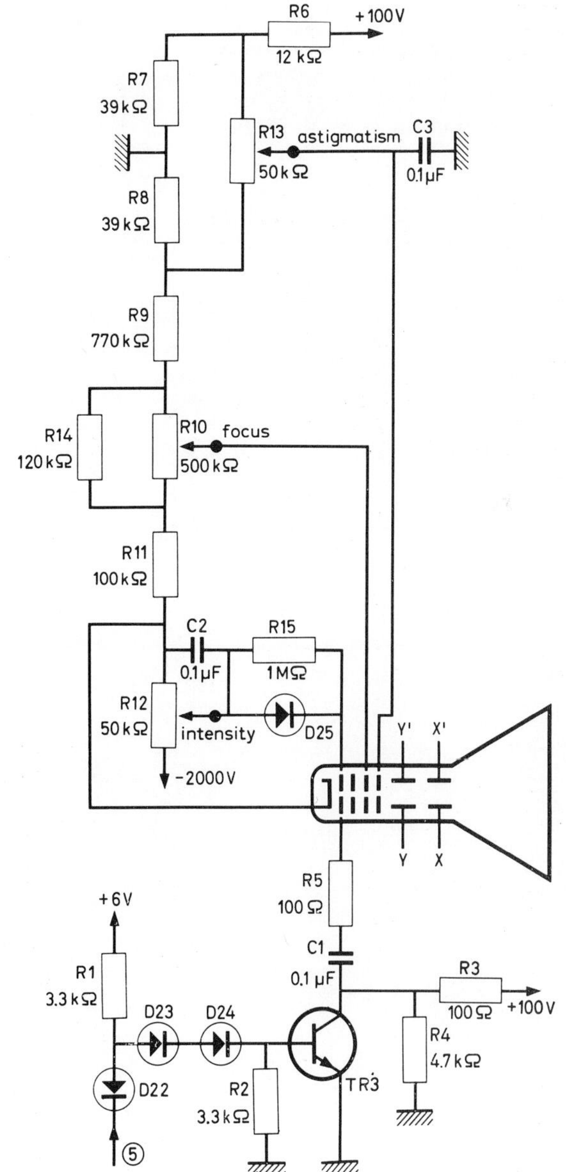

Z AMPLIFIER—Provides unblanking of crt at required instants in scan of figure-8 bars, under command of input register and decoder, for generating desired numeral on crt display. Transistor is BF177 and all diodes are BAX13.—A. P. Tanis, Numerical Display with Bar Matrix Character Generator, *Electronic Applications*, Philips, Pub. Dept., Elcoma Div., Eindhoven, The Netherlands, Vol. 27, No. 2, 1966–1967, p 73–83.

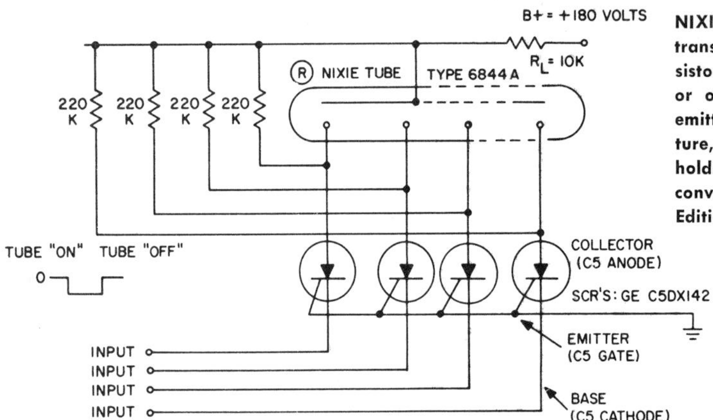

NIXIE DRIVER—Scr biased as remote-base transistor makes excellent high-voltage transistor for driving each element of Nixie, neon, or other type of digital display. Common-emitter current gain is 2. For memory feature, with display initiated by pulse and holding until reset externally, connect C5 conventionally as scr.—"SCR Manual," 4th Edition, General Electric, 1967, p 170–171.

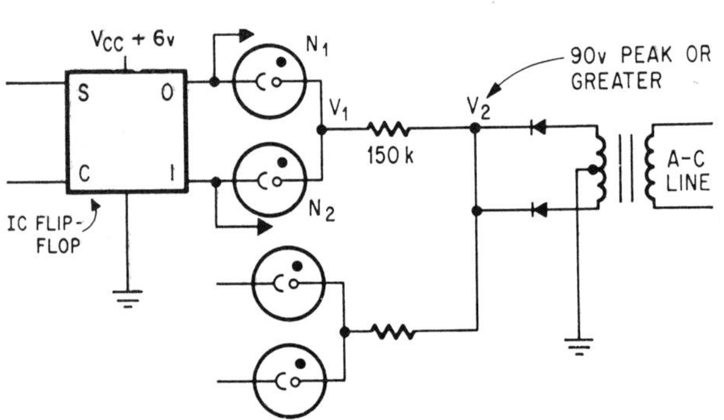

4 V TURNS ON NEONS—Low-voltage IC flip-flop turns neon glow-lamp indicators such as NE-23 on and off even though IC cannot handle 71-V breakdown of lamps. Pulsating d-c voltage at V2, obtained from a-c line, can turn lamps on and off with each cycle of a-c line. Only one lamp of a parallel pair can fire at a time. When lamp connected to "1" output of IC (4 V) turns on, V1 drops to maintaining voltage of 60 V and other lamp cannot turn on.—G. V. Wintriss, Integrated Circuit Drives Neons Directly, *Electronics*, Nov. 13, 1967, p 99.

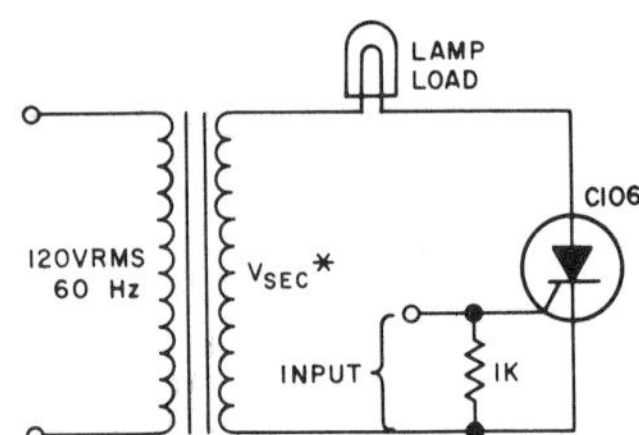

SCR DRIVER FOR LAMP—Designed for No. 24 24-V lamp requiring 34 V rms from transformer secondary for normal brilliance on half-wave.—D. R. Grafham, Using Low Current SCR's, General Electric, Syracuse, N.Y., No. 200.19, 1967, p 25.

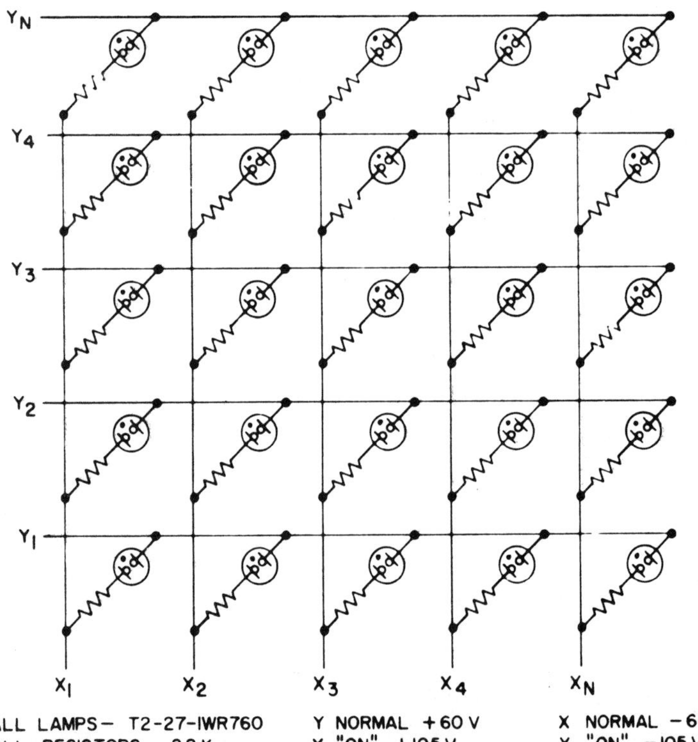

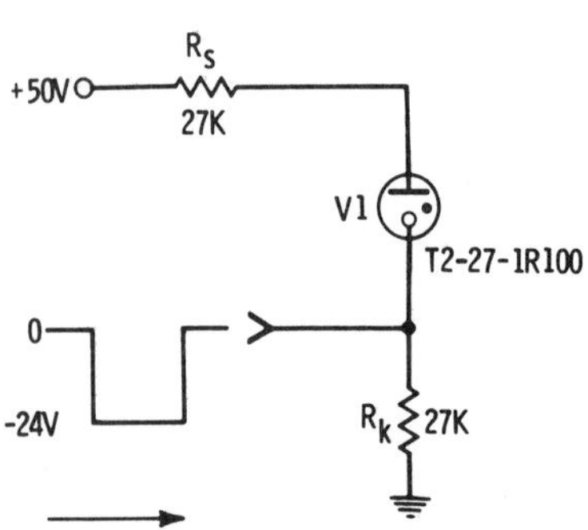

NONLATCHING INDICATOR—Neon glows only when negative pulse, which might come from transistor collector or other low-voltage source, is present.—W. G. Miller, "Using and Understanding Miniature Neon Lamps," H. W. Sams & Co., Indianapolis, Ind., 1969, p 20.

NEON X-Y MATRIX—Any one lamp lights only when both X and Y voltages on that line are increased to specified value. The matrix may be reset either by momentarily removing voltages or by reversing polarity along either axis so voltage across lamp is zero. Information may be fed in by X and Y ring counters. Readout may be visual or through photocells coupled to individual lamps and transistor circuitry.—E. Bauman, "Applications of Neon Lamps and Gas Discharge Tubes," Signalite, Neptune, N.J., p 76.

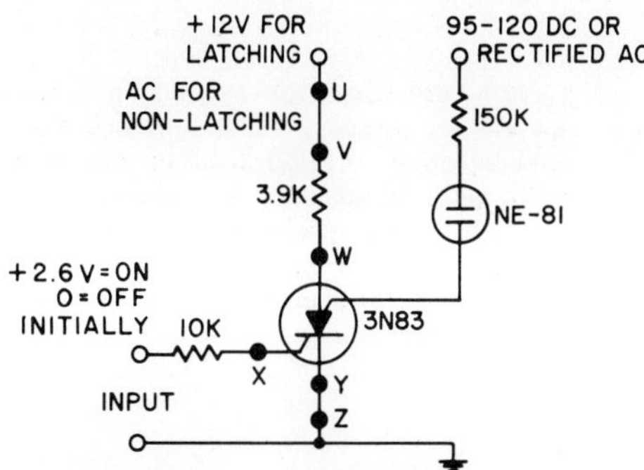

PLANAR PNPN SWITCH DRIVES NEON—Serves as low-cost latching-type driver for single neon indicator lamp, immune to triggering by line transients.—Planar Neon Driver Silicon Controlled Switch 3N83, General Electric, Syracuse, N.Y., No. 65.17, 1964.

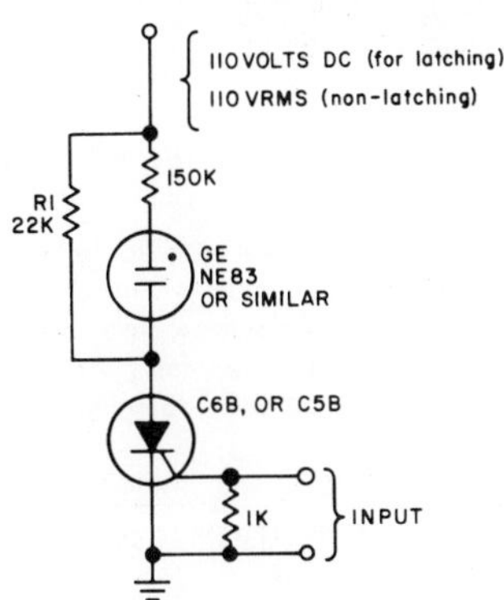

SCR DRIVER FOR NEON—Low-current scr has ample voltage capability for handling 110 V required for driving neons, Nixies, and other types of glow lamps. R1 provides holding current for scr.—D. R. Grafham, Using Low Current SCR's, General Electric, Syracuse, N.Y., No. 200.19, 1967, p 25.

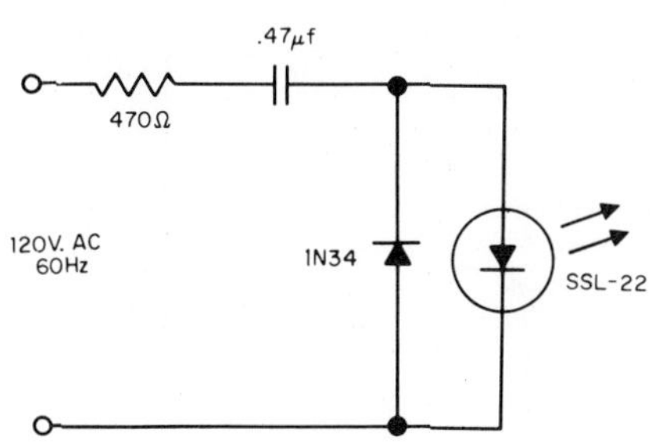

A-C LINE VOLTAGE INDICATOR—With solid-state lamp, power dissipation in circuit is less than 0.2 W. Surge-limiting resistor and surge-handling capability of diode and ssl make indicator self-protected from most line spikes or switching transients.—L. M. Hertz, Solid State Lamps—Part II, General Electric Co., Nela Park, Cleveland, Ohio, Applications Manual 3-0121, 1970, p 25.

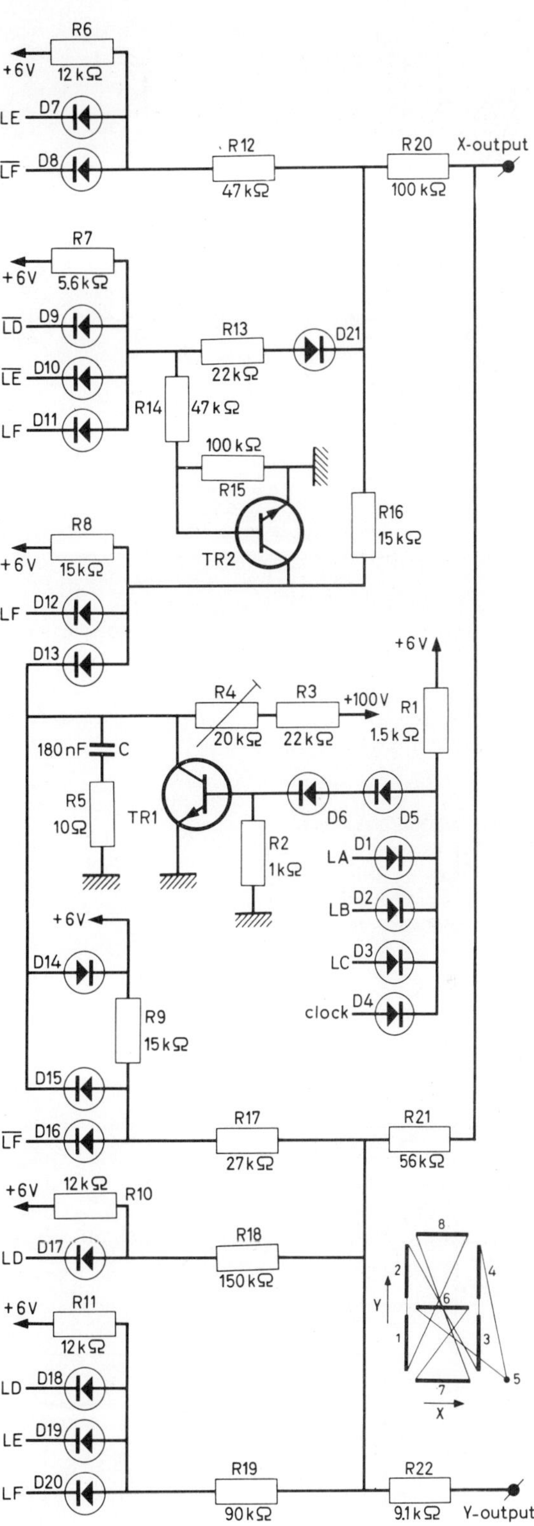

BAR MATRIX GENERATOR—Output of sawtooth generator (center) is selectively gated to X (top) and Y (bottom) deflection amplifiers of crt to repeatedly trace rectilinear figure 8 with decimal point slightly to its right, with beam being unblanked during sweep to display bars required to form desired numeral. All transistors are Philips BSX20 and diodes BAX13. Display shows four rows of 12 numerals each. Decimal point is formed by allowing beam to rest in fifth position of scan for period of 1 bar (32 μs). Field repetition frequency of 80 Hz eliminates flicker.—A. P. Tanis, Numerical Display with Bar Matrix Character Generator, *Electronic Applications*, Philips, Pub. Dept., Elcoma Div., Eindhoven, The Netherlands, Vol. 27, No. 2, 1966–1967, p 73–83.

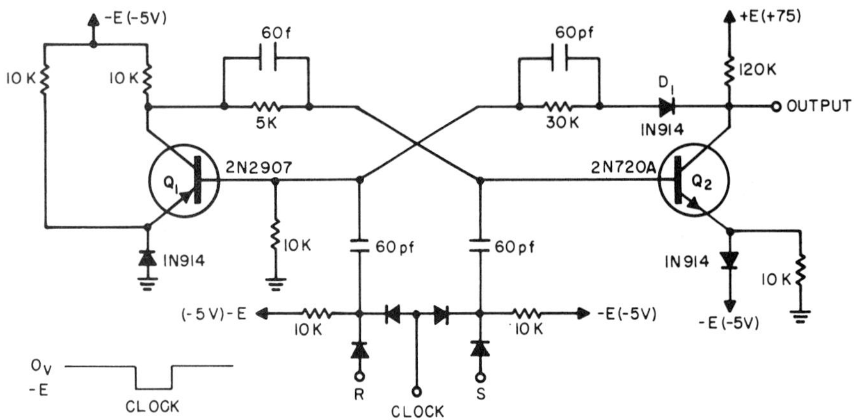

R-S FLIP-FLOP FOR NIXIE—When both transistors are on, output is −E (−5 V) and Nixie cathode is off. Circuits hold at this state until new information is received from external circuitry. Flip-flop thus serves both as driver and storage.—G. K. Kostopoulos, Nixie Driver Flip-Flop Also Stores Information, *Electronic Design*, Sept. 13, 1965, p 82.

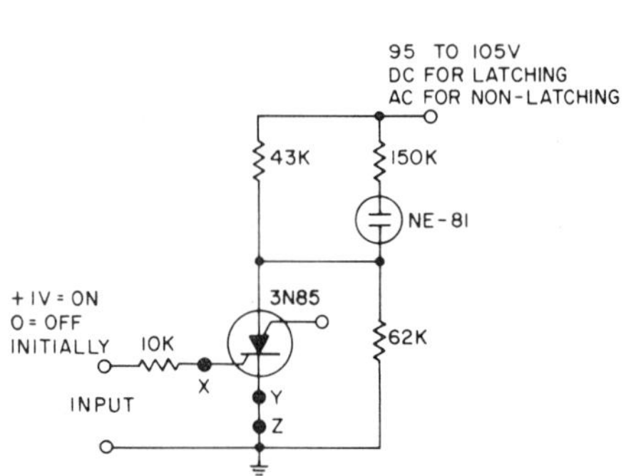

PLANAR SCS DRIVES NEON—Gives high reliability and uniformity of operation at low cost. Immune to voltage transients.—Planar Silicon Controlled Switch 3N84/3N85, General Electric, Syracuse, N.Y., No. 65.18, 1964.

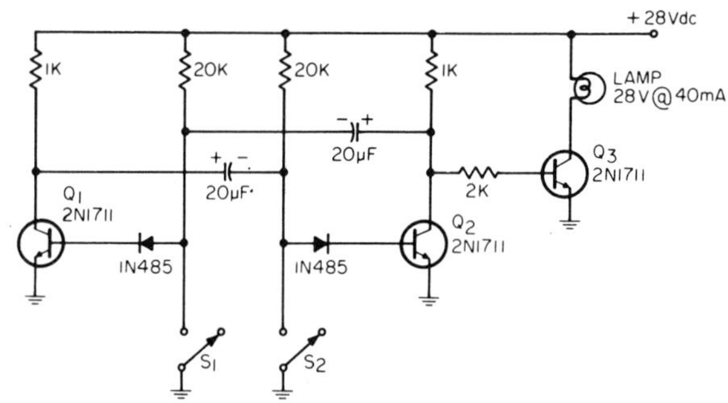

THREE-MODE INDICATOR LAMP—With both switches open, Q1-Q2 form part of astable mvbr that makes lamp blink once per second. With S1 open and S2 closed, lamp stays on. With S1 closed and S2 open, lamp goes out. Transistors or relays may be used in place of switches.—P. E. Dingwell, Three-State Indicator, *EEE*, March 1967, p 166.

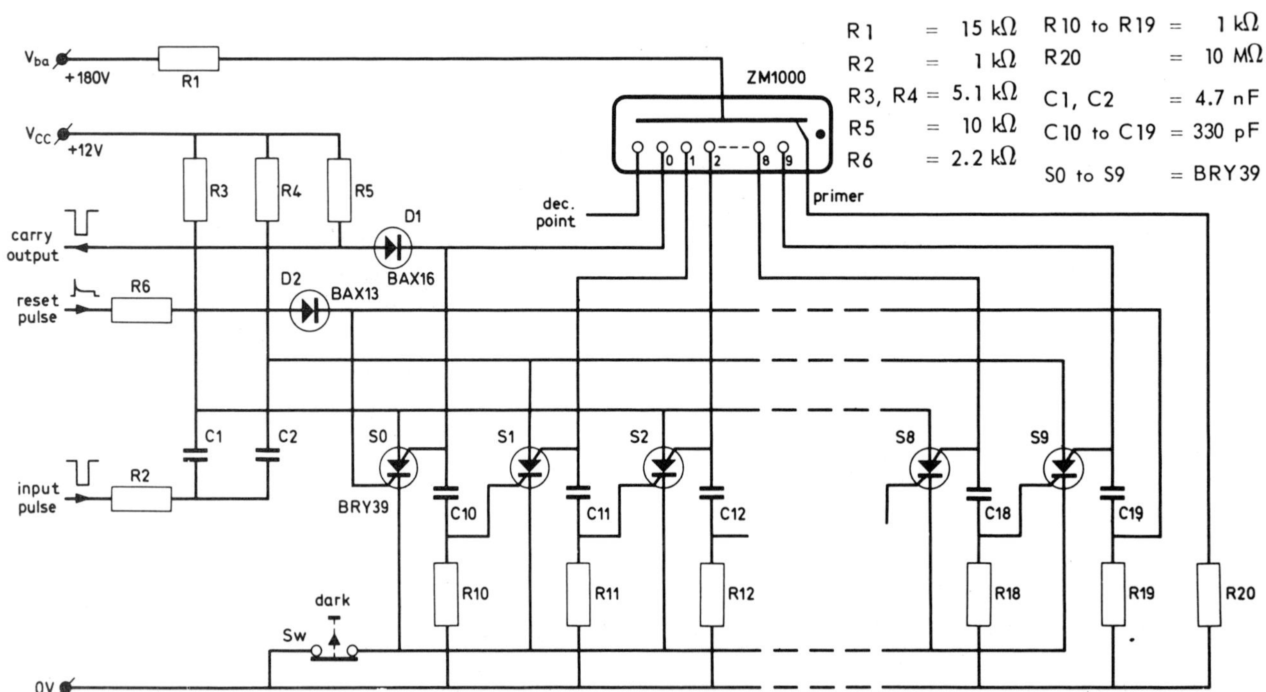

MULTI-DIGIT DISPLAY—Uses scs ring counter to provide static display on several numerical indicator tubes, with final count being held after train of counting pulses is terminated. When ring counter goes from position 9 back to 0, carry pulse is produced to drive identically designed succeeding display stage. Maximum count rate is 40 kHz.—D. J. G. Janssen, A. G. Korteling, and P. H. G. van Vlodrop, Cold Cathode Numerical Indicator Tubes, Philips, Pub. Dept., Elcoma Div., Eindhoven, The Netherlands, No. 327, 1968.

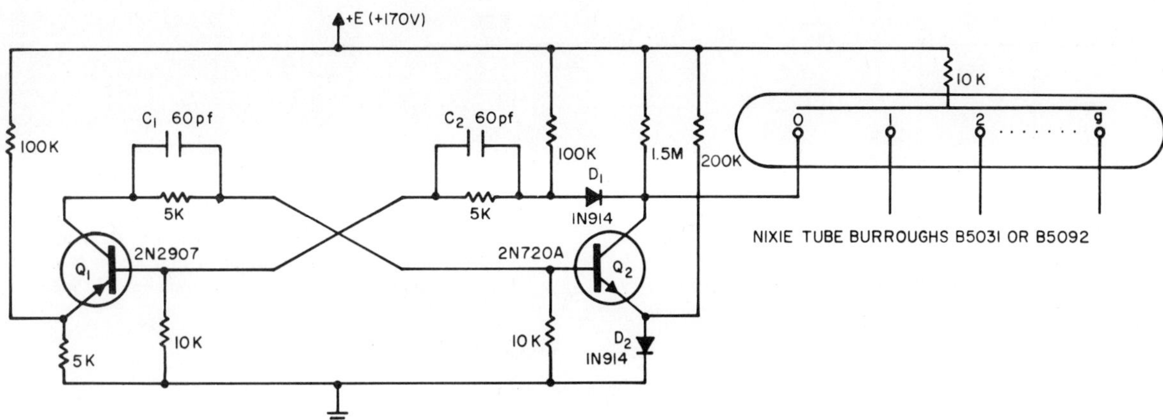

FLIP-FLOP STORAGE DRIVES NIXIE—Circuit shown drives one Nixie cathode and holds until new information is received from external circuitry. Power dissipation is very low. Both transistors are either on or off; when on, output voltage to cathode of Nixie is +1 V, and Nixie is on.—G. K. Kostopoulos, Nixie Driver Flip-Flop Also Stores Information, *Electronic Design*, Sept. 13, 1965, p 82.

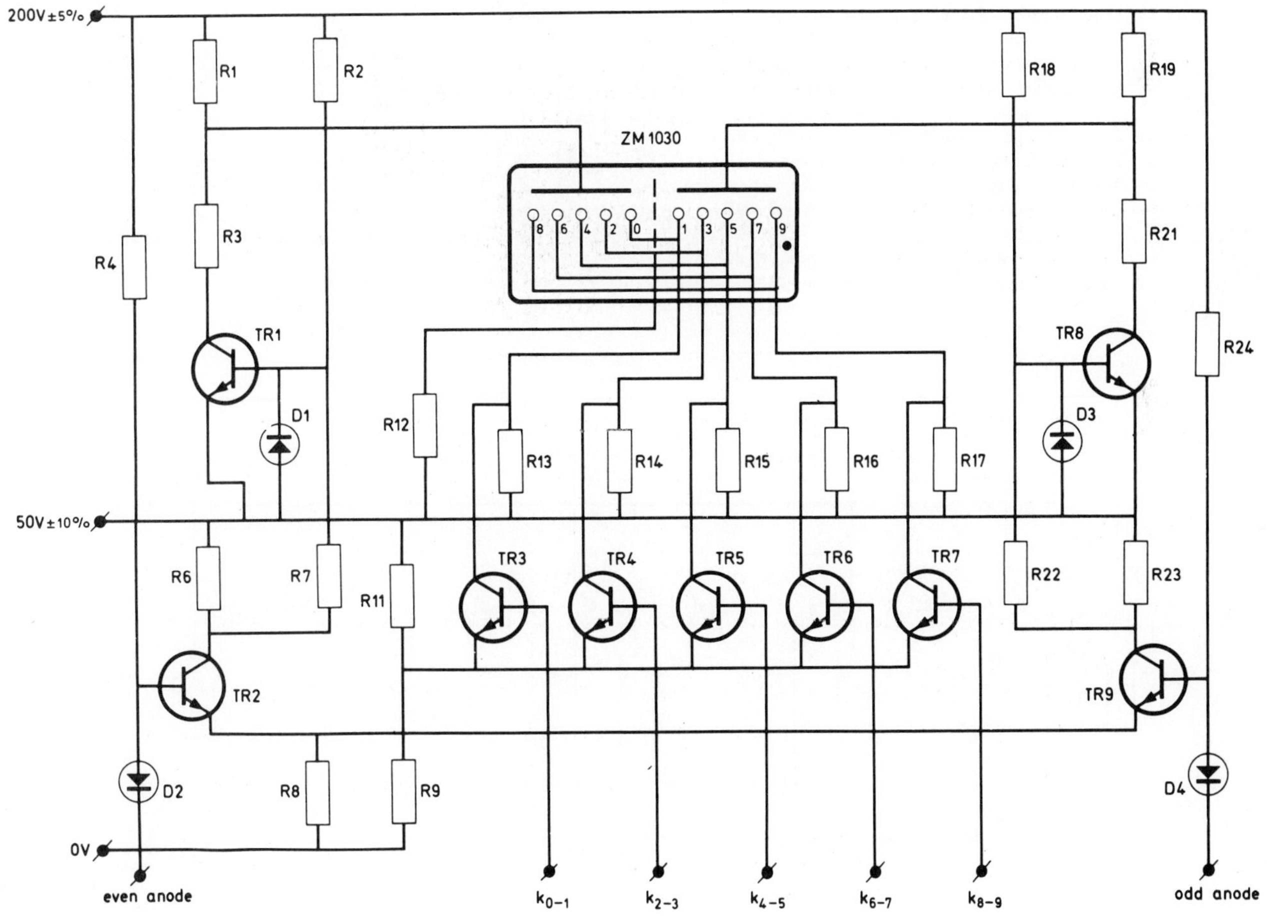

R1 = 15 kΩ		R12	= 10 kΩ
R2 = 270 kΩ		R13 to R17	= 100 kΩ
R3 = 6.8 kΩ		R18	= 270 kΩ
R4 = 750 kΩ		R19	= 15 kΩ
R6 = 15 kΩ		R21	= 6.8 kΩ
R7 = 47 kΩ		R22	= 47 kΩ
R8 = 330 kΩ		R23	= 15 kΩ
R11 = 470 kΩ		R24	= 750 kΩ

BIQUINARY INDICATOR DRIVE—Uses levels of 3 V for conducting anode and 0 V for nonconducting anode, corresponding to "1" and "0" signals respectively. With "1" at "even" anode terminal, TR2 will be bottomed and base of TR1 pulled negative to cut it off. Simultaneously, "0" is applied at "odd" anode input, to cut off TR9 and make TR8 conducting. Now, if one of the cathode switches TR3 to TR7 is made conducting, an "even" anode ignites and an "even" numeral is illuminated on display. R9 is VDR.—D. J. G. Janssen, A. G. Korteling, and P. H. G. van Vlodrop, Cold Cathode Numerical Indicator Tubes, Philips, Pub. Dept., Elcoma Div., Eindhoven, The Netherlands, No. 327, 1968.

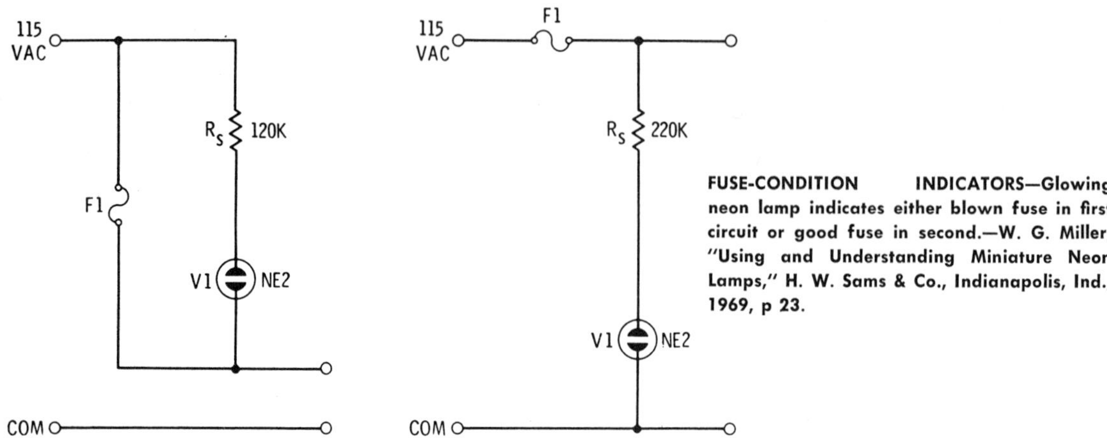

FUSE-CONDITION INDICATORS—Glowing neon lamp indicates either blown fuse in first circuit or good fuse in second.—W. G. Miller, "Using and Understanding Miniature Neon Lamps," H. W. Sams & Co., Indianapolis, Ind., 1969, p 23.

DIODES FOR NEON LAMP—Two inexpensive diodes replace costly high-voltage transistor for switching neon lamp on and off. Dashed connections show how additional lamps can be connected in parallel and operated from same supply. Diodes are part of logic circuit producing decimal readout for time and frequency meter. To hold lamp off, point A is connected directly to 25-V supply; lamp comes on when point A is grounded to raise lamp voltage above 75-V minimum for firing. While lighted, lamp turns on and off 120 times a second but flicker is not noticeable. In decimal readout, D1 is arm of AND gate, and D2 is arm of OR gate.—C. J. Ulrick, Diodes Reduce Cost of Switching Neon Lamps, *Electronics*, Feb. 6, 1967, p 70.

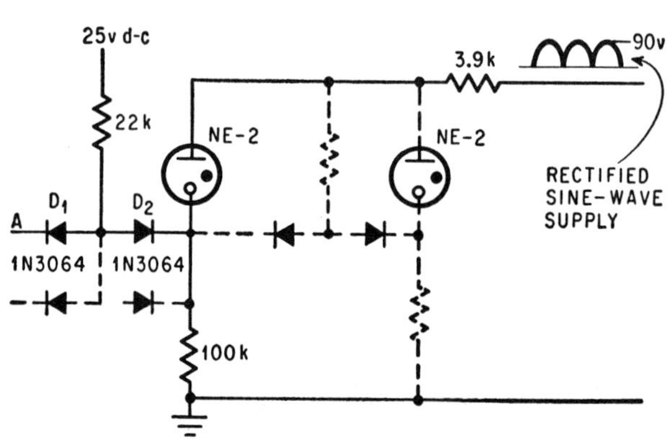

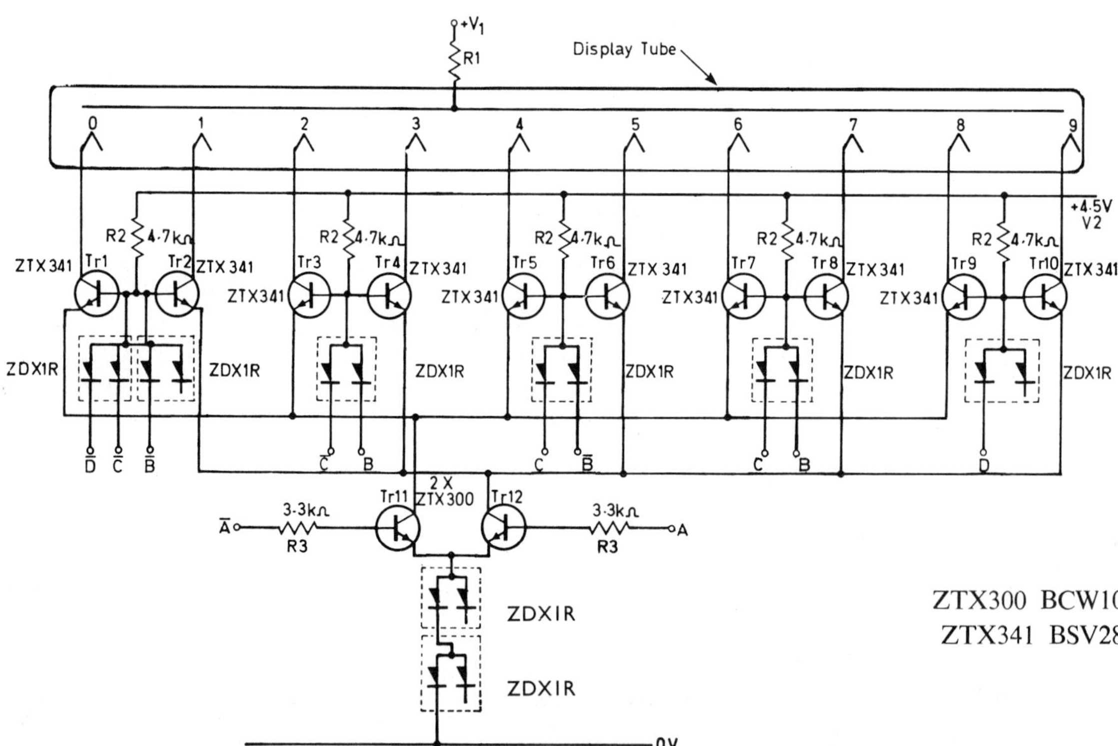

NIXIE DECODER AND DRIVER—Circuit accepts 8-line logical input in 8-4-2-1 binary coded decimal and decodes it to obtain decimal equivalent for energizing appropriate digit from 0 to 9 stacked together as cathodes of gas-filled indicator tube. Uses two stages of selection, based on fact that if least significant digit is eliminated, pairs of odd and even numbers share same logic. First selection stage decides into which of five pairs required number falls, and second stage decides whether number is odd or even. Only one output can satisfy both conditions.—"E-Line Transistor Applications," Ferranti Ltd., Oldham, Lancs., England, 1969, p 52.

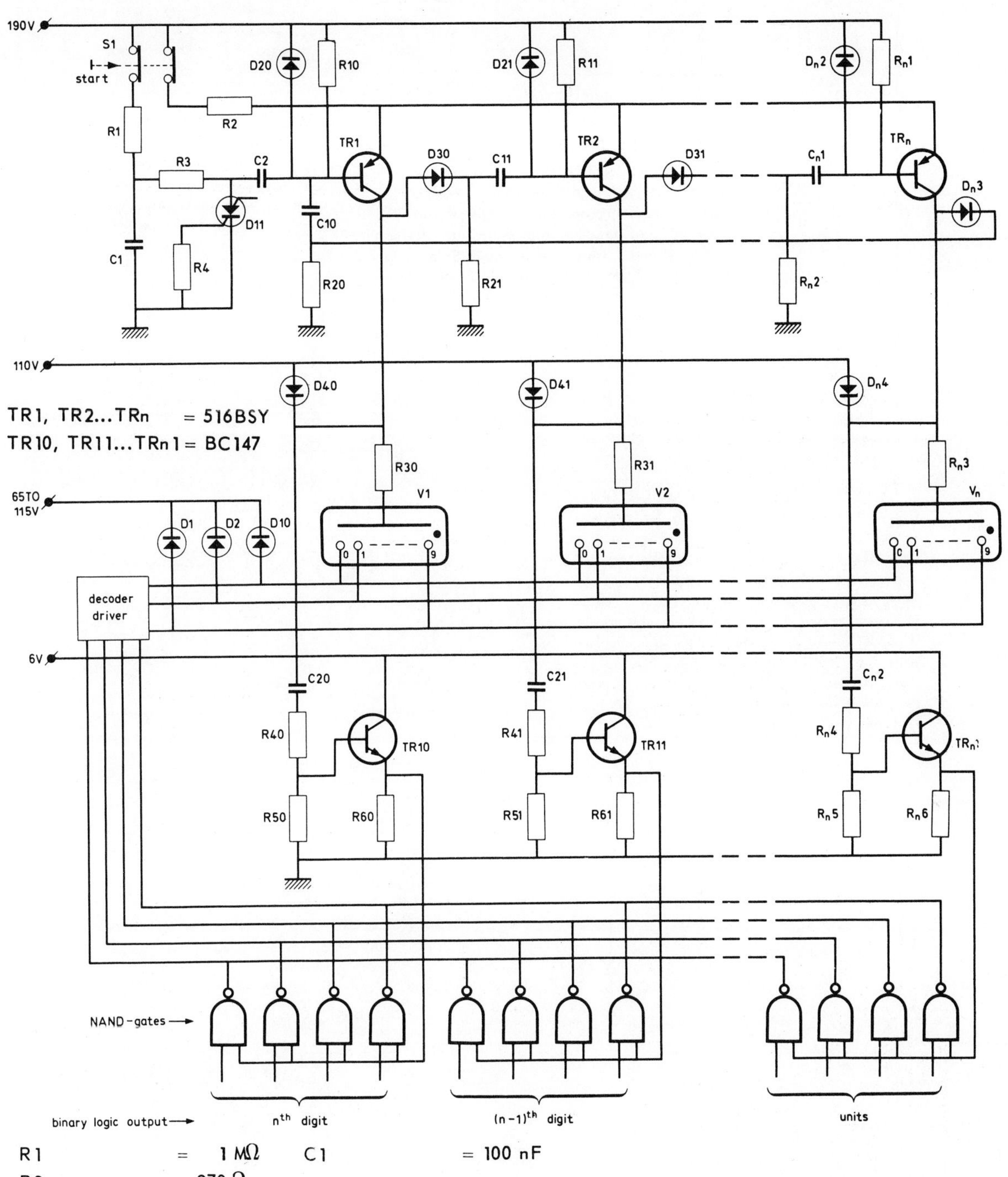

R1	= 1 MΩ	C1	= 100 nF
R2	= 270 Ω		
R3	= 270 Ω	C2	= 33 pF
R4	= 10 kΩ	C10, C11...Cn1	= 1 nF
R10, R11...Rn1	= 10 kΩ	C20, C21...Cn2	= 10 nF
R20, R21...Rn2	= 150 kΩ	D1, D2...D10	= BAX16
R30, R31...Rn3	= 3.3 kΩ	D11	BRY39
R40, R41...Rn4	= 100 kΩ	D20, D21...Dn2	= BAX16
R50, R51...Rn5	= 10 kΩ	D30, D30...Dn3	= BAX16
R60, R61...Rn6	= 100 Ω	D40, D41...Dn4	= BAX16

SELF-EXCITED DYNAMIC DRIVE FOR INDICATORS—Circuit is designed to display information presented to all digital inputs in parallel. After operation of start switch, anode switches TR1 through TRn are activated in turn in continuous cyclical order to provide scanning of binary information supplied to NAND gates.—D. J. G. Janssen, A. G. Korteling, and P. H. G. van Vlodrop, Cold Cathode Numerical Indicator Tubes, Philips, Pub. Dept., Elcoma Div., Eindhoven, The Netherlands, No. 327, 1968.

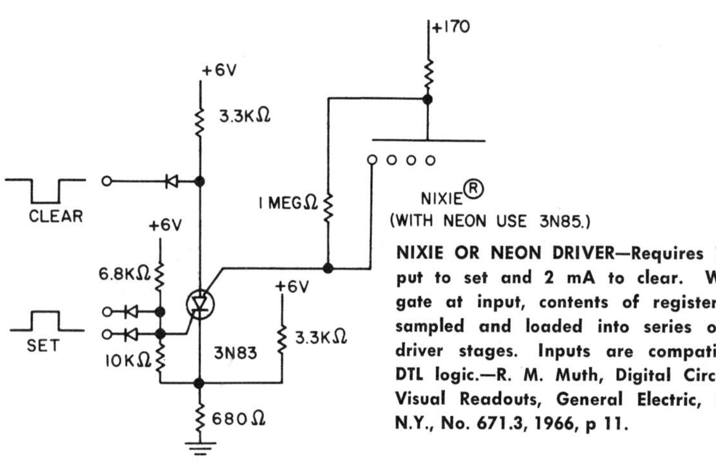

NIXIE OR NEON DRIVER—Requires 1 mA input to set and 2 mA to clear. With AND gate at input, contents of register can be sampled and loaded into series of similar driver stages. Inputs are compatible with DTL logic.—R. M. Muth, Digital Circuits with Visual Readouts, General Electric, Syracuse, N.Y., No. 671.3, 1966, p 11.

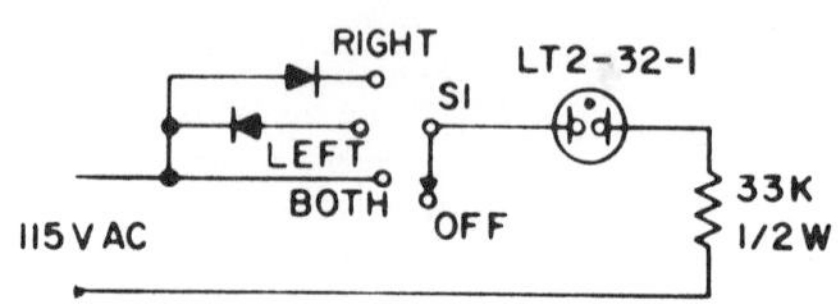

FOUR-CONDITION INDICATOR—Uses single neon lamp. By switching S1, either right, left, none, or both electrodes of lamp may be activated.—E. Bauman, "Applications of Neon Lamps and Gas Discharge Tubes," Signalite, Neptune, N.J., p 149.

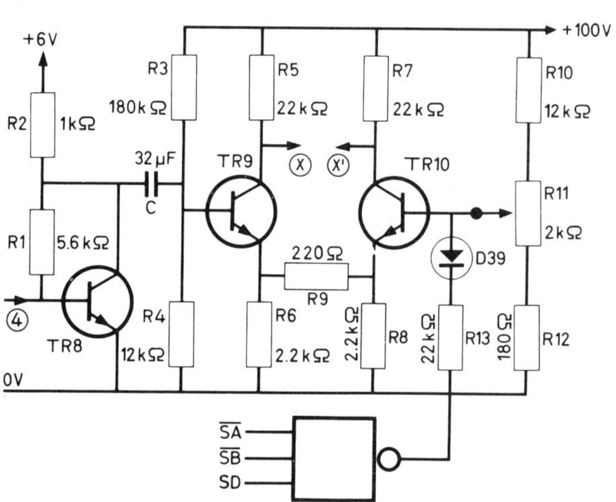

X AMPLIFIER FOR NUMERICAL DISPLAY—Differential output stage is fed by preamp to which deflection signals from bar matrix generator and column or row selector are applied. NAND gate connected to base of TR10 centers numeral 1 in its space. TR8 is BSX20, TR9 and TR10 are BSX21, and diode is BAX13.—A. P. Tanis, Numerical Display with Bar Matrix Character Generator, *Electronic Applications*, Philips, Pub. Dept., Elcoma Div., Eindhoven, The Netherlands, Vol. 27, No. 2, 1966–1967, p 73–83.

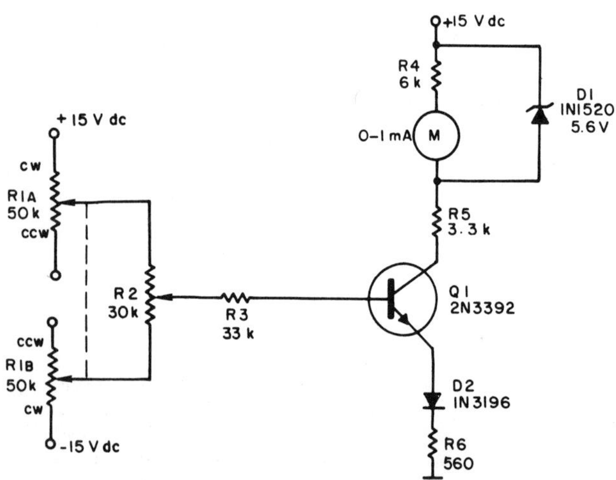

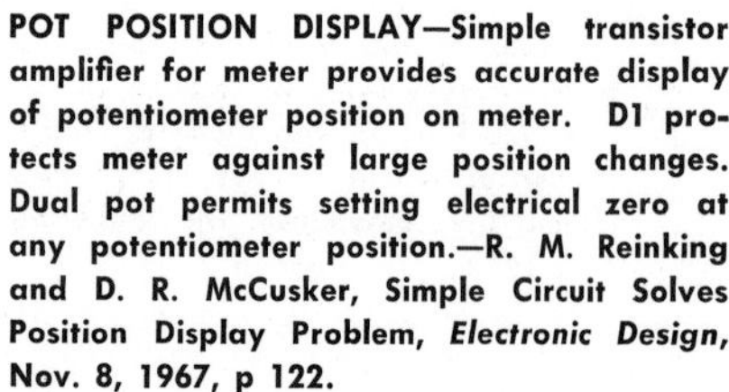

POT POSITION DISPLAY—Simple transistor amplifier for meter provides accurate display of potentiometer position on meter. D1 protects meter against large position changes. Dual pot permits setting electrical zero at any potentiometer position.—R. M. Reinking and D. R. McCusker, Simple Circuit Solves Position Display Problem, *Electronic Design*, Nov. 8, 1967, p 122.

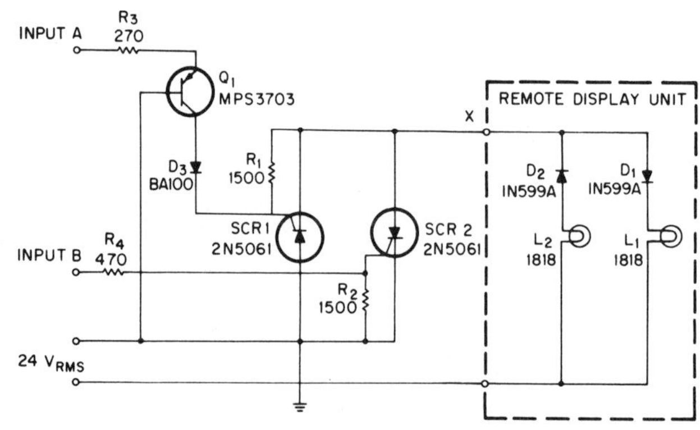

REMOTE LAMP DRIVER—Circuit minimizes number of lines to remote lamp displays. Diodes in series with lamps, connected with opposite polarity, and scr's similarly connected with opposite polarity at source cut number of lines to one for every two lamps, plus one common line. Inputs are compatible with Motorola MRTL logic. 24-V lamps are required for long life, because half-cycles from 24-V source heat filaments of 14.4-V lamps excessively and shorten life.—W. Lindenbach, Lamp Driver Minimizes Lines to Remote Display Unit, *EEE*, Dec. 1969, p 91–92.

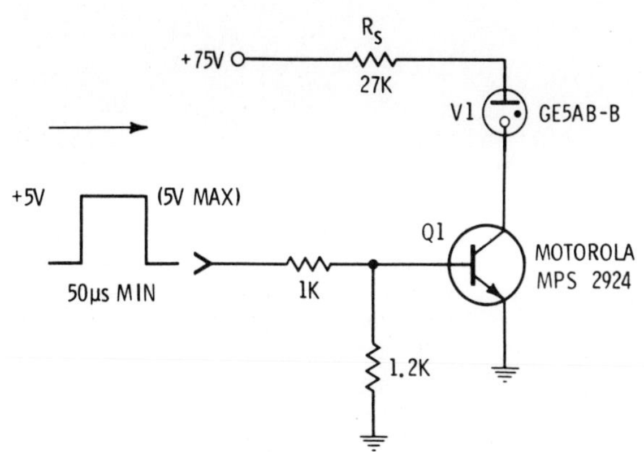

TRANSISTOR-OPERATED INDICATOR—Neon fires upon application of voltage pulse. 1.2K resistor prevents false starting by minimizing leakage effects.—W. G. Miller, "Using and Understanding Miniature Neon Lamps," H. W. Sams & Co., Indianapolis, Ind., 1969, p 22.

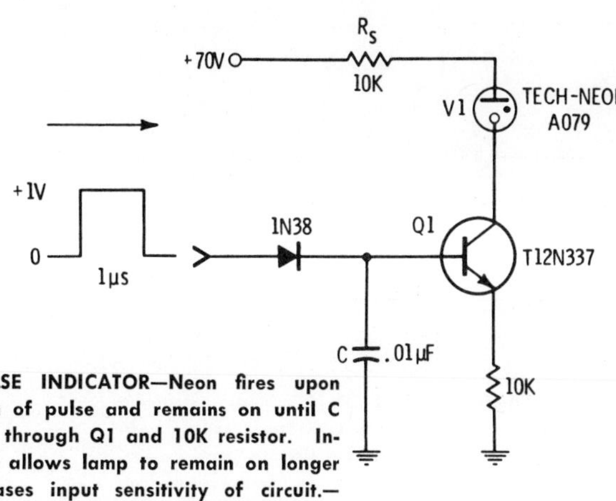

SHORT-PULSE INDICATOR—Neon fires upon application of pulse and remains on until C discharges through Q1 and 10K resistor. Increasing C allows lamp to remain on longer but decreases input sensitivity of circuit.—W. G. Miller, "Using and Understanding Miniature Neon Lamps," H. W. Sams & Co., Indianapolis, Ind., 1969, p 22.

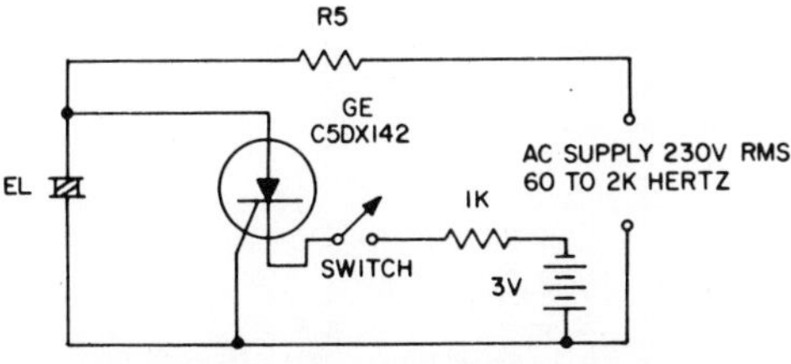

SHUNT DRIVE FOR EL PANEL—Electroluminescent display is on when switch is open (no 3-V control signal).—"SCR Manual," 4th Edition, General Electric, 1967, p 171.

115VAC

C .03µF

V1 C2A

ONE-MILLION-HOUR INDICATOR—Use where extremely long life and low power dissipation are required. Capacitor is used instead of resistor to limit current to half the design current, thereby increasing life of lamp by factor of 64.—W. G. Miller, "Using and Understanding Miniature Neon Lamps," H. W. Sams & Co., Indianapolis, Ind., 1969, p 24.

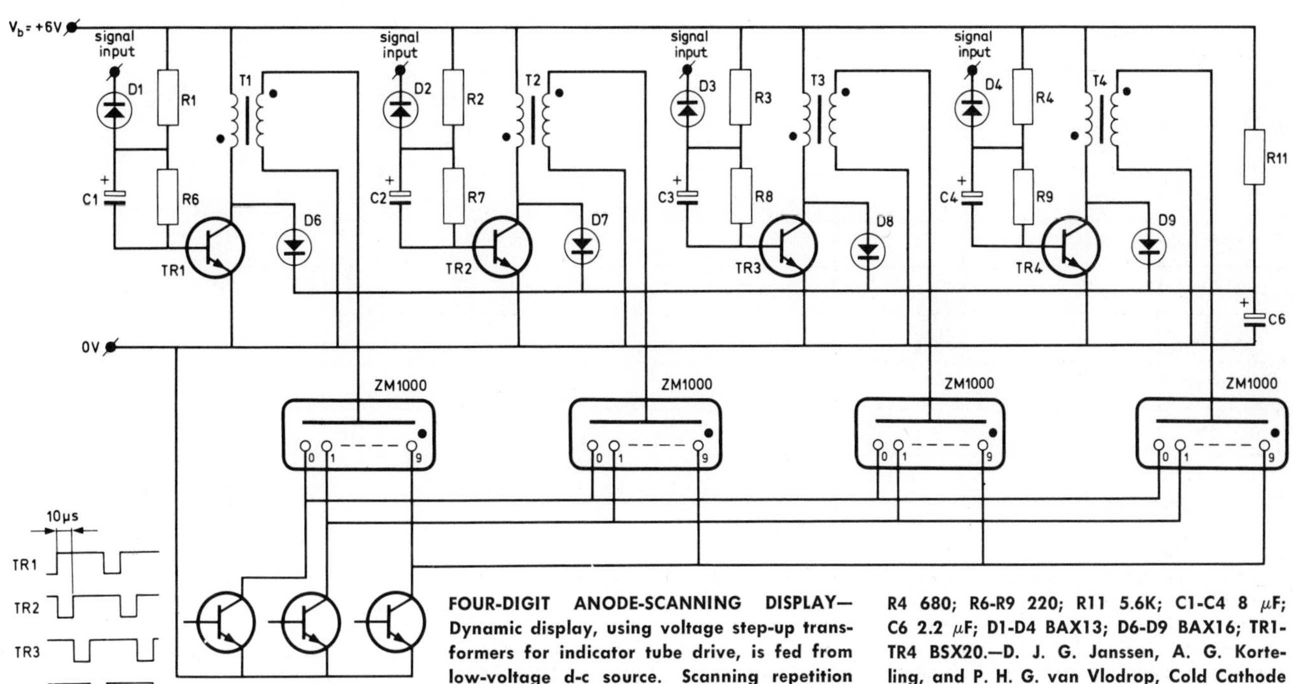

FOUR-DIGIT ANODE-SCANNING DISPLAY—Dynamic display, using voltage step-up transformers for indicator tube drive, is fed from low-voltage d-c source. Scanning repetition rate is 25 kHz. Transistor base drive signals are shifted simultaneously so numerical indicator tubes conduct in turn. Values: R1-R4 680; R6-R9 220; R11 5.6K; C1-C4 8 µF; C6 2.2 µF; D1-D4 BAX13; D6-D9 BAX16; TR1-TR4 BSX20.—D. J. G. Janssen, A. G. Korteling, and P. H. G. van Vlodrop, Cold Cathode Numerical Indicator Tubes, Philips, Pub. Dept., Elcoma Div., Eindhoven, The Netherlands, No. 327, 1968.

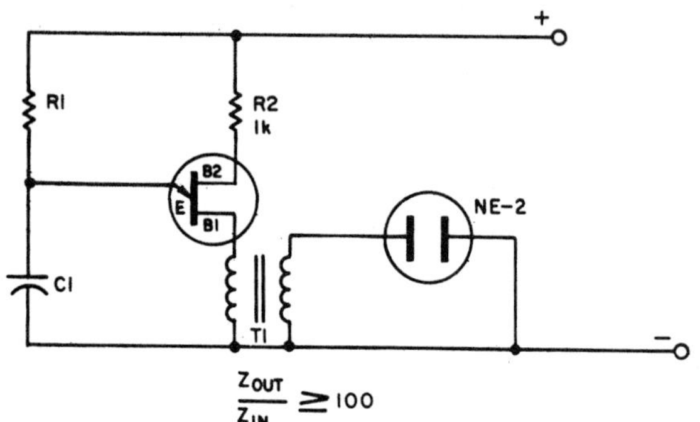

OPERATING NEON ON 1.5 V—Ujt oscillator and transformer step up battery supply voltage to that required for driving neon power-on indicator, for use in battery-operated equipment where power drawn by incandescent pilot lamp is more than that drawn by circuitry itself. By keeping frequency and duty cycle low to give flashing indication, power consumption is further reduced. Almost any ujt may be used for 6 to 40 V, but 2N2840 should be used if supply is single 1.5-V cell. Choose R1 and C1 to give desired frequency.—L. Toth, Circuit Powers Neon Lamps from Low-Voltage Sources, *Electronic Design*, May 10, 1969, p 136.

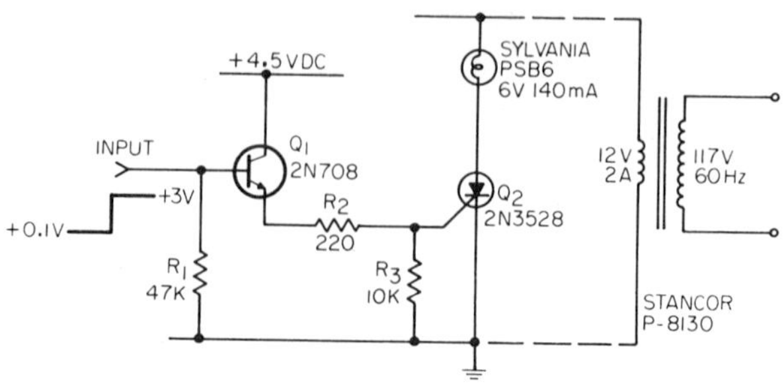

BINARY STATE INDICATOR—High input of 3 V for logical 1 makes scr conduct on each positive half-cycle of a-c line and keep lamp on for as long as input is at high level. Low input of 0.1 V for logical 0 will not trigger scr and lamp will not light. Low input current requirement of about 0.2 mA makes circuit excellent as readout for integrated circuits. Transformer specified can drive up to 14 identical readouts.—P. Galluzzi, Readout Circuit for Digital ICs, *EEE*, Jan. 1967, p 115.

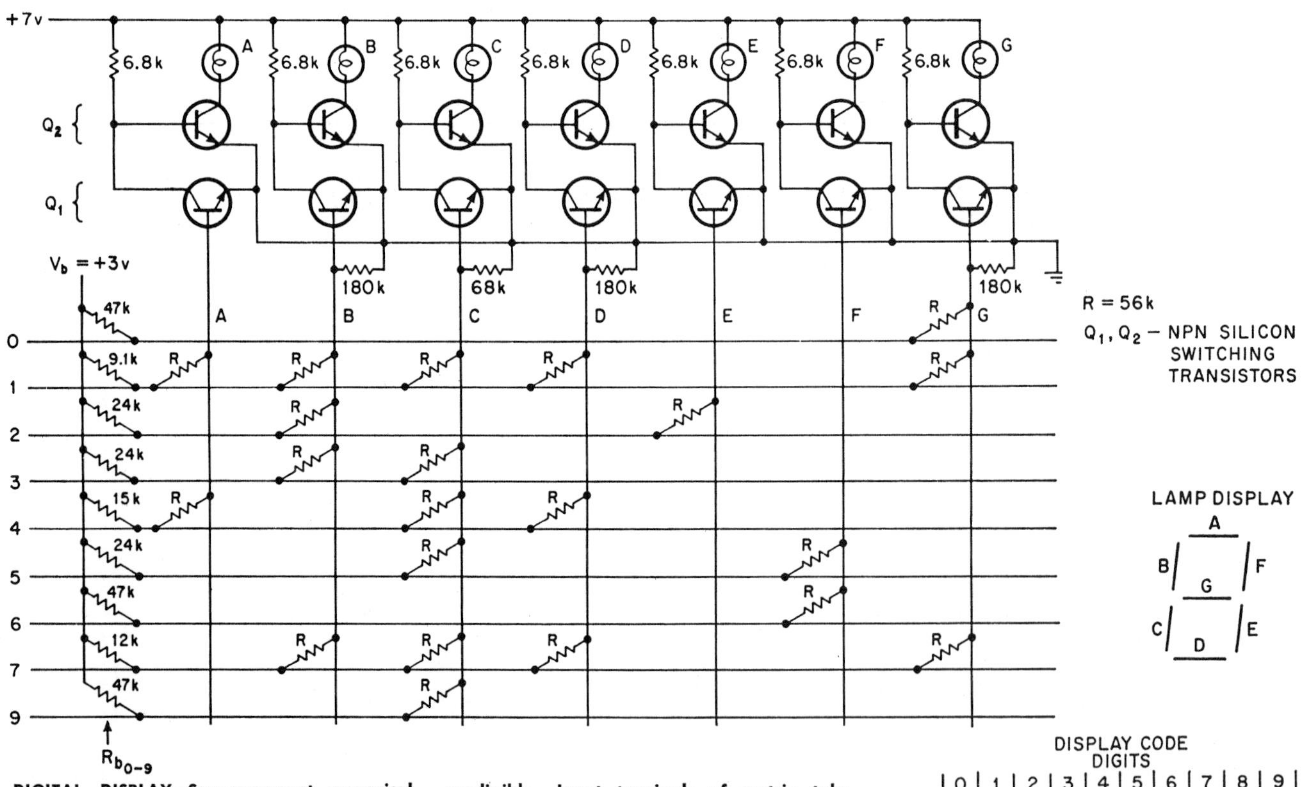

DISPLAY CODE

LAMPS

	DIGITS 0	1	2	3	4	5	6	7	8	9
A		X			X					
B		X	X	X				X		
C		X		X	X	X		X		X
D		X			X			X		
E			X							
F						X	X			
G	X	X						X		

DIGITAL DISPLAY—Seven-segment numerical display uses 21-resistor matrix and gives greater reliability than more costly 49-diode conventional matrix. All lamps glow when there is no input. Desired digit is obtained by turning off unwanted lamps. Use of high-value resistors makes current delivered to undesired transistors small enough to be negligible. Input terminals of matrix take signals from decoder that converts bcd output of binary counter into decimal numbers. Numeral 8 is formed when all lamps are on, so no input terminal is needed for it.—R. K. Sharma, Resistors Come to Light In Digital Display System, *Electronics*, Jan. 5, 1970, p 97–98.

CHAPTER 27

Electronic Music Circuits

PSYCHEDELIC DISPLAY—When connected to hi-fi speaker, circuit activates three sets of colored lamps in accordance with volume and frequency of sound, to give multicolored display changing in time to music. Uses No. 93 12-V 1-A automotive lamps permanently colored by manufacturer; blue is for low frequencies, red for mid-frequencies, and green for highs. Six additional No. 1488 colored lamps rated 12 V at 150 mA (not shown) are used at sides and corners of aluminum reflector behind translucent plastic panel. Used in Eico Model 3440 kit. Pots in inputs of two channels permit changing patterns as desired.—New Color-Organ Kit, *Electronics World*, May 1969, p 80.

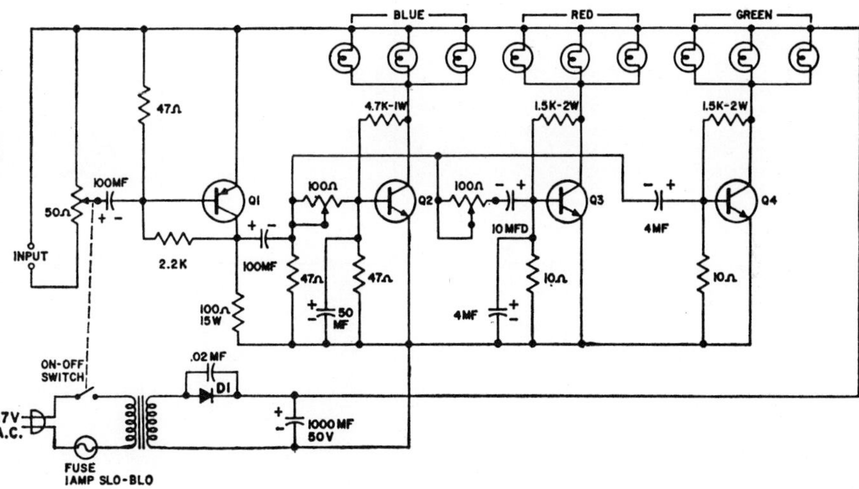

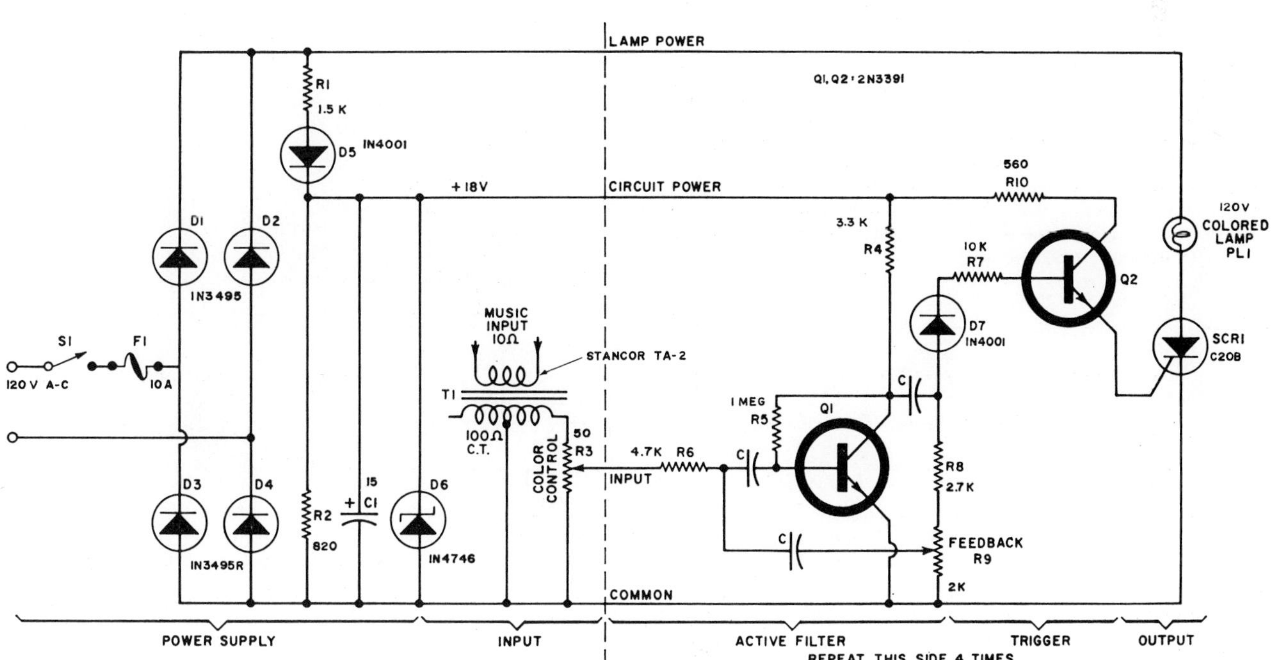

COLOR ORGAN—Music input is divided into four frequency bands by four active filters, each amplifying one frequency band much more than others. Each channel can drive up to 625-W lamp load, to give total of 2,500 W illumination in four different colors that change dynamically with musical tones even at low levels. Values of C in μF are 0.1 for green channel (lows), 0.047 for blue, 0.022 for red, and 0.01 for yellow (highs). R3 widens filter bandwidth to give effect of color blending.—J. M. Powell, A New Approach to Color-Organ Design, *Electronics World*, Jan. 1969, p 39 and 61.

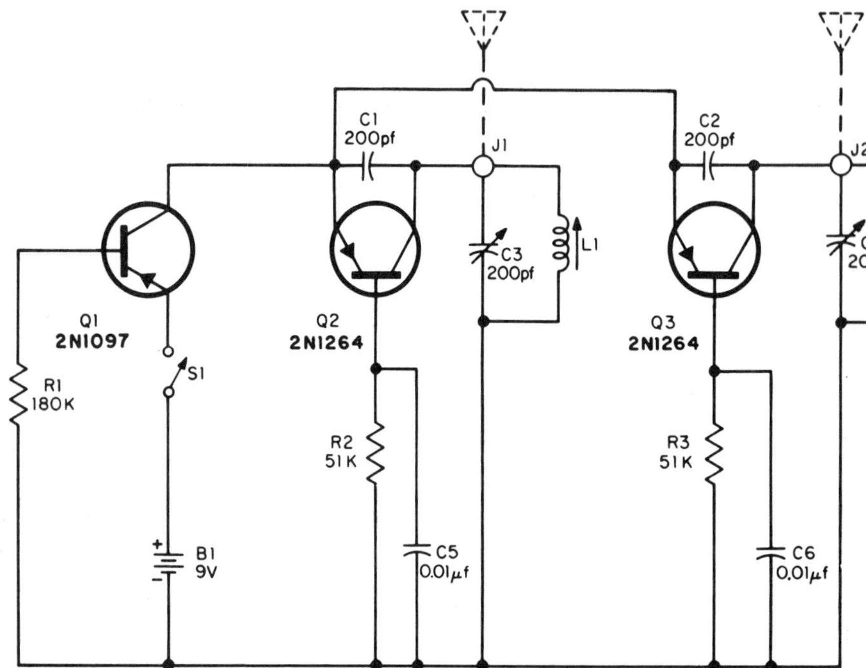

THEREMIN—Produces wailing sounds that change with frequency as hands are moved in air near 38-inch whip antennas inserted vertically in 5-way binding posts J1 and J2 mounted 7 inches apart. Place near back of a-m broadcast radio tuned to midband and adjust C3 until hissing sound is heard over radio, then adjust C4 for very loud whistle. Readjust C3 for lowest pitch, then play. L1 and L2 are vari-loopsticks. Book gives construction data.—"A Modern Transistor Workbook," Radio Shack, Boston, Mass., 1965, p 49.

SINGLE-VOICE ORGAN—Basic tones are formed by clock oscillator Q3-Q4, with output being frequency-modulated by applying very low frequency sine-wave output of Q1 to base of Q4 and collector of Q3. Values shown give tremolo of about 6 Hz. Series-connected resistors R19-R31 provide chromatic scale, and five series capacitors permit keying up or down two octaves from middle octave. Sawtooth output at terminal 9 and pulse output at terminal 7 are fed to external mixer for changing character of tones before feeding audio power amplifier.—"Hobby Circuits Manual," RCA, Harrison, N.J., HM-90, p. 106.

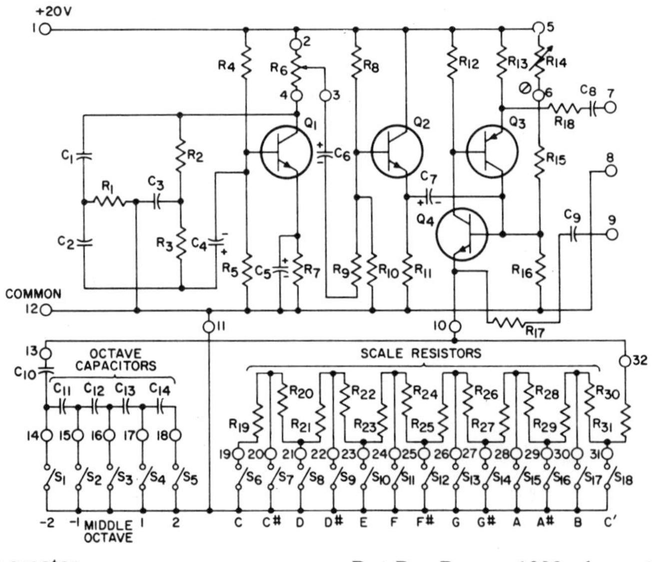

$C_1 C_2$ = 0.22 microfarad, 25 volts or greater, paper
$C_3 C_{10} C_{11}$ = 0.5 microfarad, 25 volts or greater, paper
C_4 = 50 microfarads, 15 volts, electrolytic
C_5 = 100 microfarads, 6 volts, electrolytic
$C_6 C_7$ = 4 microfarads, 25 volts, electrolytic
$C_8 C_9$ = 0.1 microfarad, 25 volts or greater
C_{12} = 0.25 microfarad, 25 volts or greater
C_{13} = 0.12 microfarad and 0.005 microfarad in parallel, 25 volts or greater
C_{14} = 0.056 microfarad and 0.0068 microfarad in parallel, 25 volts or greater
$Q_1 Q_2 Q_4$ = transistor, RCA SK3020
Q_3 = transistor, RCA SK3005
R_1 = 33,000 ohms, 1/2 watt, 10%
$R_2 R_3$ = 220,000 ohms, 1/2 watt, 10%
$R_4 R_8$ = 330,000 ohms, 1/2 watt, 10%
$R_5 R_{18}$ = 100,000 ohms, 1/2 watt, 10%
R_6 = potentiometer, 10,000 ohms, linear taper
R_7 = 3300 ohms, 1/2 watt 10%
R_9 = 270,000 ohms, 1/2 watt, 10%
R_{10} = 180,000 ohms, 1/2 watt, 10%
$R_{11} R_{21} R_{22}$ = 1000 ohms, 1/2 watt, 10%
R_{12} = 1500 ohms, 1/2 watt, 10%
R_{13} = 180 ohms, 1/2 watt, 10%
R_{14} = potentiometer, 1000 ohms, linear taper
R_{15} = 1200 ohms, 1/2 watt, 10%
R_{16} = 470 ohms, 1/2 watt, 10%
R_{17} = 2.2 megohms, 1/2 watt, 10%
$R_{19} R_{20}$ = 1100 ohms, 1/2 watt, 5%
$R_{23} R_{24}$ = 910 ohms, 1/2 watt, 5%
$R_{25} R_{26}$ = 820 ohms, 1/2 watt, 10%
R_{27} = 750 ohms, 1/2 watt, 5%
$R_{28} R_{29}$ = 680 ohms, 1/2 watt, 10%
R_{30} = 620 ohms, 1/2 watt, 10%
R_{31} = 10,000 ohms, 1/2 watt, 10%

UJT CHROMATIC-SCALE ORGAN—Gives full octave of sharp sawtooth tones that can be shaped or voiced at output, under control of 13 keys. Octave can be moved up or down with R2 from 130.81 Hz (C below middle C) to 1,046.05 Hz (C above middle C). Values in ohms of RT2 through RT13 for chromatic scale are 1,500 (B), 1,500, 1,650, 1,800, 1,800, 2,000, 2,200, 2,247, 2,470, 2,470, and 3,000 (C). R1 serves for initial calibration. For 8-key diatonic scale, omit sharps (♯) and use for remaining resistors 1,500, 3,150, 3,300, 4,200, 2,200, 4,700, and 5,400.—"Hobby Manual," General Electric, Owensboro, Ky., 1965, p 92.

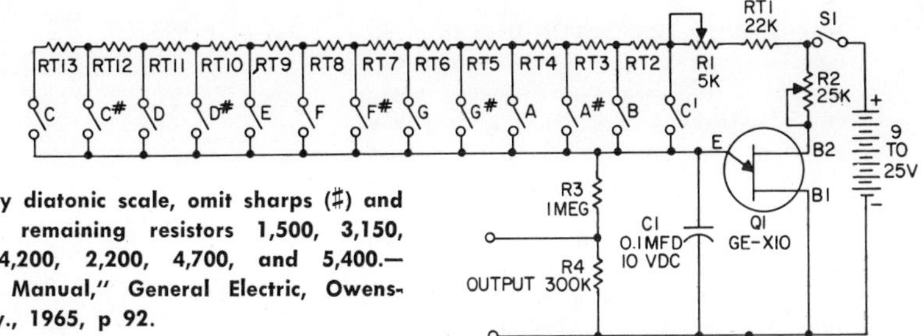

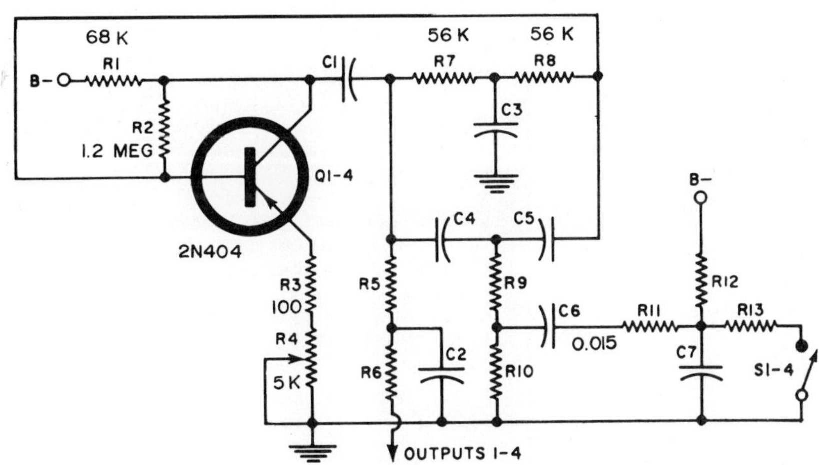

	DRUM	TOM-TOM	BONGO	BLOCKS
R5—	22,000	82,000	82,000	330,000
R6—	10,000	82,000	82,000	(Not used)
R9—	2700	6800	6800	6800
R10—	2200	2200	2200	2200
R11—	82,000	22,000	27,000	(Not used)
R12—	1 meg	0.56 meg	1 meg	1 meg
R13—	2700	2700	2700	6800
(Note: All resistors are ½ watt, 10%.)				
C1—	.1	.047	.047	.047
C2—	.1	.01	.01	(Not used)
C3—	.1	.047	.033	.01
C4—	.1	.027	.015	.0033
C5—	.1	.027	.015	.0033
C7—	.1	.1	.01	.1

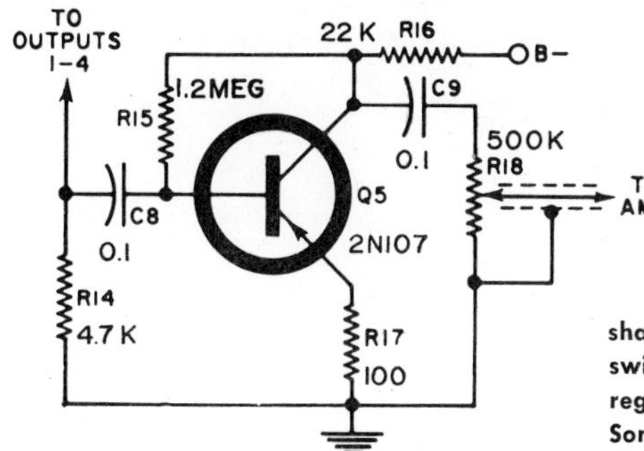

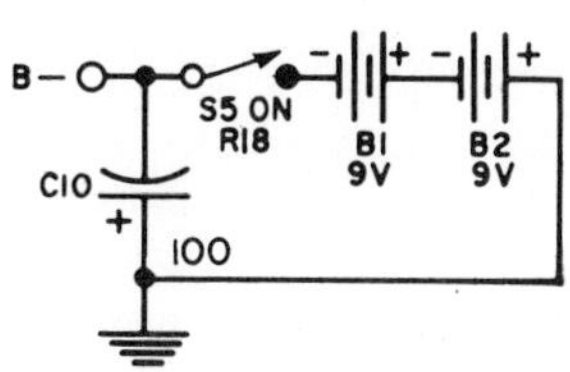

DRUM, TOM-TOM, BONGO, BLOCKS—Uses four identical one-shot twin-T oscillators, each with its own frequency-determining and shaping circuit (Q1-Q4). Pressing pushbutton switch for desired instrument gives one beat regardless of how long button is held down. Some or all buttons can be pressed simultaneously. Preamp Q5 permits use of instrument with almost any audio system.—C. Muller, Electronic Percussion Instruments, *Electronics World,* Feb. 1967, p 36–37.

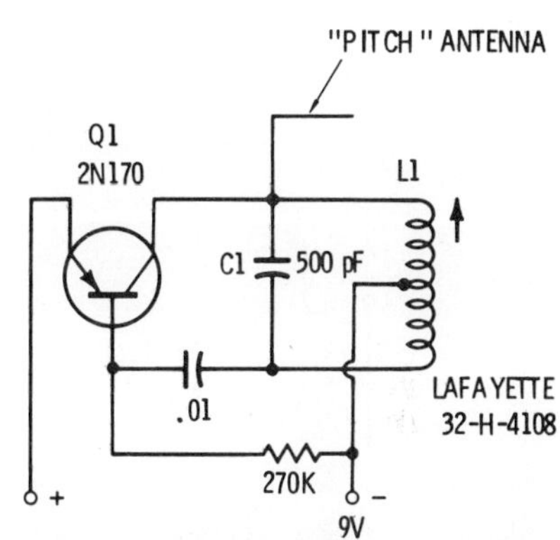

SIMPLEST THEREMIN—Makes use of ordinary broadcast receiver to supply fixed-frequency oscillator and mixer for Theremin. Place Theremin a few inches from back of receiver and tune to fairly strong station around 900 kHz, then adjust slug of L1 until most pleasing whistle tone is obtained. Moving hand near pitch antenna then makes tone change. Metal plate about 10 inches square may be used as antenna.—J. P. Shields, "Novel Electronic Circuits," H. W. Sams & Co., Indianapolis, Ind., 1968, p 76.

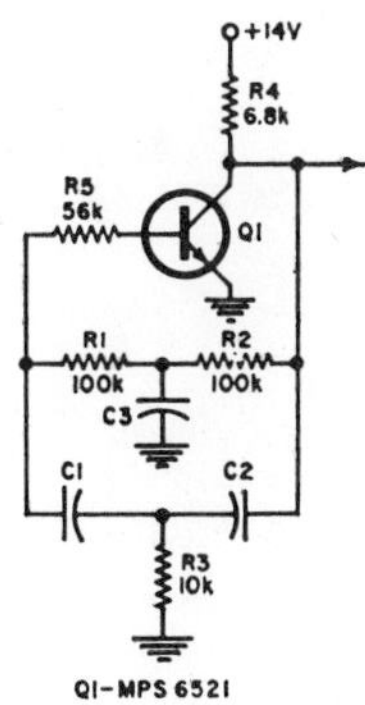

TWIN-T AUDIO—Basic circuit using Motorola high-gain silicon transistor with R-C networks is basic oscillator for many electronic music applications requiring up to 10 kHz. Article gives nomogram and design procedures for choosing capacitor values. C1 should always equal C2, in range from 0.0003 to 0.1 μF, and C3 should be twice as large as either.—F. B. Maynard, Twin T's: Designs & Applications, *Electronics World,* Aug. 1968, p 35–37 and 64.

7-HZ VIBRATO FOR ORGAN—Used to modulate frequency of each of 12 master tone generators in six-octave electronic organ. Provides wavering variation of pitch without affecting loudness. Triode in R-C phase-shifting network generates 7-Hz signal for driving pentode operating as cathode follower to match output to impedance of vibrato control potentiometer. R1 is voltage-dependent resistor.—Electronic Organ with Cold-Cathode Tube Frequency Dividers, Philips, Pub. Dept., Elcoma Div., Eindhoven, The Netherlands, No. 112, 1966.

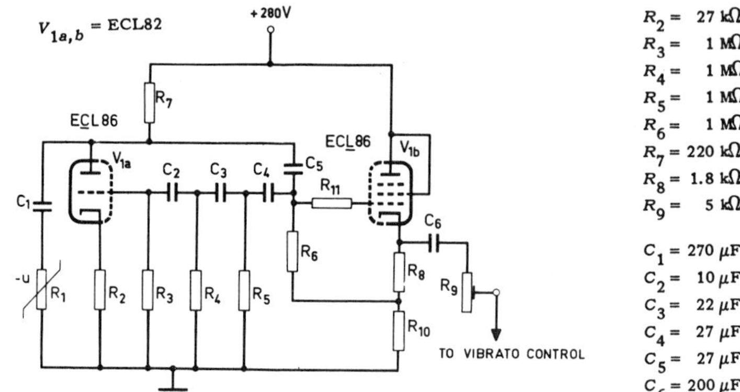

R_2 = 27 kΩ
R_3 = 1 MΩ
R_4 = 1 MΩ
R_5 = 1 MΩ
R_6 = 1 MΩ
R_7 = 220 kΩ
R_8 = 1.8 kΩ
R_9 = 5 kΩ

C_1 = 270 μF
C_2 = 10 μF
C_3 = 22 μF
C_4 = 27 μF
C_5 = 27 μF
C_6 = 200 μF

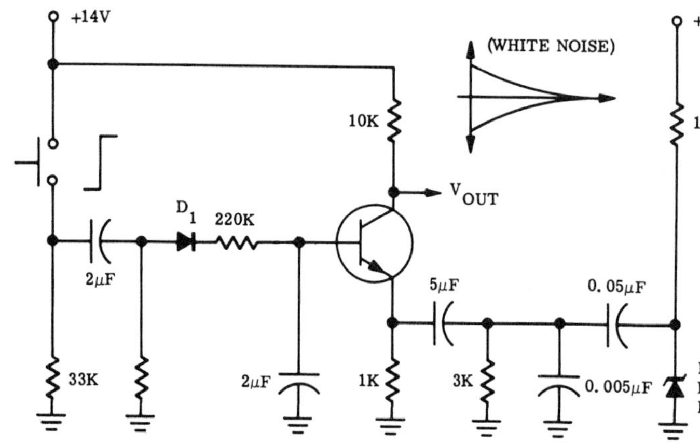

CYMBAL AFTERBEAT EFFECT—Special zener noise diode is combined with sustain control generator for use in electronic organ to create a desired noise effect. Transistor and D1 types are not critical.—"Zener Diode Handbook," Motorola, Phoenix, Ariz., 1967, p 9–5.

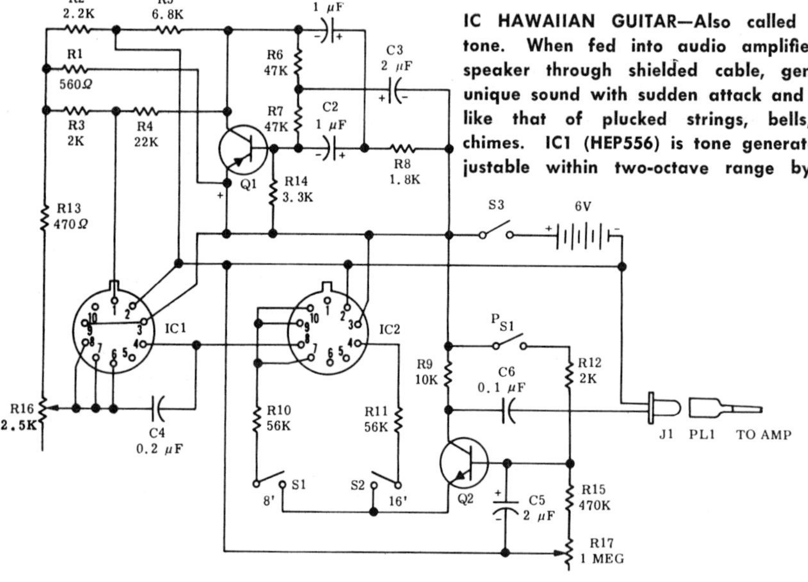

IC HAWAIIAN GUITAR—Also called Glidetone. When fed into audio amplifier and speaker through shielded cable, generates unique sound with sudden attack and decay like that of plucked strings, bells, and chimes. IC1 (HEP556) is tone generator adjustable within two-octave range by R16. This frequency is divided by IC2 (HEP558) to create tone exactly one octave lower. Stops S1 and S2 feed these tones singly or together to Q2 (HEP50) which provides sustain effect. Q1 (HEP251) provides 6-Hz vibrato. Circuit is thus similar to small portion of an electronic organ. Article gives construction details.—"Integrated Circuit Projects," Motorola, Phoenix, Ariz., 1966, p 70–79.

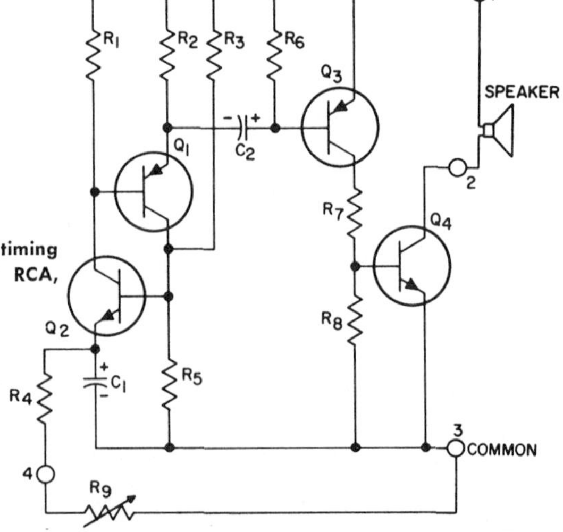

METRONOME—Produces audible beeps at rate determined by setting of R9, for metering musical cadence. If beep rate is set at 1 per second, may be used in darkroom for timing exposures.—"Hobby Circuits Manual," RCA, Harrison, N.J., HM-90, p 103.

$C_1 C_2$ = 20 microfarads, 12 volts, electrolytic
$Q_1 Q_3$ = transistor, RCA SK3005
$Q_2 Q_4$ = transistor, RCA SK3020
$R_1 R_3$ = 1000 ohms, 1/2 watt, 10%
R_2 = 68 ohms, 1/2 watt, 10%
R_4 = 3900, 1/2 watt, 10%
R_5 = 470 ohms, 1/2 watt, 10%
$R_6 R_8$ = 150 ohms, 1/2 watt, 10%
R_7 = 120 ohms, 1/2 watt, 10%
R_9 = potentiometer, 50,000 ohms, linear taper
Speaker = 3.2 ohms

ORGAN TONE GENERATOR—Inexpensive, stable, and highly reliable circuit covers six octaves, using basic triode master oscillator and five bistable neon oscillators as frequency dividers, each cutting previous frequency in half. Capacitive voltage divider in each stage prevents output tone from coupling back into previous stage and causing audible distortion. Values of unmarked resistors, which depend on leakage resistance of neon lamps, are not critical if type AO78 lamps are used. Output 5 is 523.3 Hz (C above middle C).—E. Bauman, "Applications of Neon Lamps and Gas Discharge Tubes," Signalite, Neptune, N.J., p 40–43.

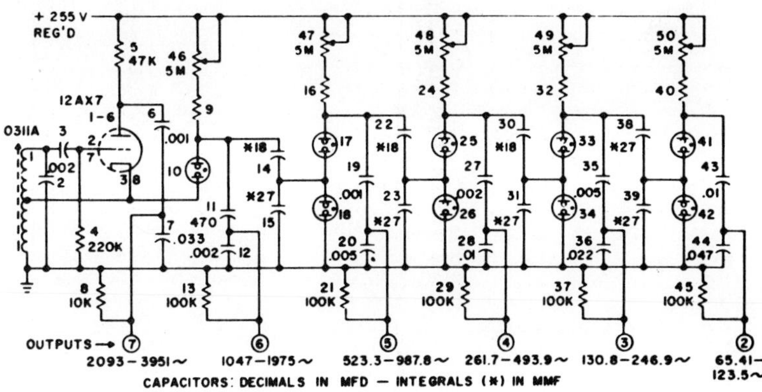

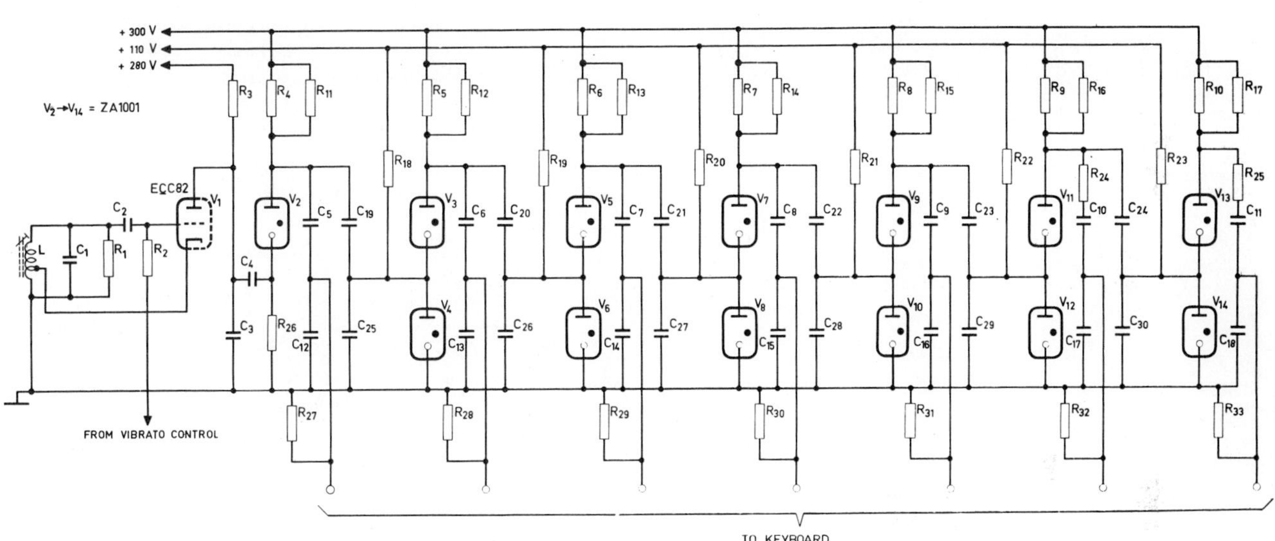

	Note:	C	B	A#	A	G#	G	F#	F	E	D#	D	C#	
	Frequency	8372	7902	7459	7040	6645	6272	5920	5588	5274	4978	4699	4435	Hz
C_1 polystyrene	125 V	8.2	8.2	10	12	12	15	15	18	22	22	27	27	nF
C_2 polyester	125 V	2200	2200	2200	2200	2200	2200	2200	2200	2200	2200	2200	2200	pF
C_3 polyester	400 V	1.8	1.8	1.8	2.2	2.2	2.2	2.7	2.7	2.7	3.3	3.3	3.3	nF
C_4 ceramic	350 V	0.68	0.68	0.82	0.82	0.82	1.0	1.0	1.2	1.2	1.2	1.5	1.5	nF
C_5 polyester	400 V	330	330	330	390	390	390	470	470	470	560	560	560	pF
C_6 polyester	400 V	390	390	390	390	470	470	470	470	560	560	560	560	pF
C_7 polyester	400 V	0.82	0.82	0.82	0.82	1.0	1.0	1.0	1.0	1.2	1.2	1.2	1.2	nF
C_8 polyester	400 V	1.8	1.8	1.8	1.8	2.2	2.2	2.2	2.2	2.7	2.7	2.7	2.7	nF
C_9 polyester	400 V	3.9	3.9	3.9	3.9	4.7	4.7	4.7	4.7	5.6	5.6	5.6	5.6	nF
C_{10} polyester	400 V	8.2	8.2	8.2	8.2	10	10	10	10	12	12	12	12	nF
C_{11} polyester	400 V	15	–	–	–	–	–	–	–	–	–	–	–	nF
C_{12} polyester	125 V	1.8	1.8	1.8	2.2	2.2	2.2	2.7	2.7	2.7	3.3	3.3	3.3	nF
C_{13} polyester	125 V	3.9	3.9	3.9	3.9	4.7	4.7	4.7	4.7	5.6	5.6	5.6	5.6	nF
C_{14} polyester	125 V	8.2	8.2	8.2	8.2	10	10	10	10	12	12	12	12	nF
C_{15} polyester	125 V	18	18	18	18	22	22	22	22	27	27	27	27	nF
C_{16} polyester	125 V	39	39	39	39	47	47	47	47	56	56	56	56	nF
C_{17} polyester	125 V	82	82	82	82	100	100	100	100	120	120	120	120	nF
C_{18} polyester	125 V	150	–	–	–	–	–	–	–	–	–	–	–	nF
C_{19} ceramic	350 V	10	10	10	10	10	10	10	10	10	10	10	10	pF
C_{20} ceramic	350 V	10	10	10	10	10	10	10	10	10	10	10	10	pF
C_{21} ceramic	350 V	10	10	10	10	10	10	10	10	10	10	10	10	pF
C_{22} ceramic	350 V	22	22	22	22	22	22	22	22	22	22	22	22	pF
C_{23} ceramic	350 V	47	47	47	47	47	47	47	47	47	47	47	47	pF
C_{24} ceramic	350 V	100	–	–	–	–	–	–	–	–	–	–	–	pF
C_{25} ceramic	350 V	10	10	10	10	10	10	10	10	10	10	10	10	pF
C_{26} ceramic	350 V	10	10	10	10	10	10	10	10	10	10	10	10	pF
C_{27} ceramic	350 V	10	10	10	10	10	10	10	10	10	10	10	10	pF
C_{28} ceramic	350 V	22	22	22	22	22	22	22	22	22	22	22	22	pF
C_{29} ceramic	350 V	47	47	47	47	47	47	47	47	47	47	47	47	pF
C_{30} ceramic	350 V	100	–	–	–	–	–	–	–	–	–	–	–	pF
R_1		22	22	27	27	27	33	33	39	39	39	47	47	kΩ

ORGAN TONE GENERATOR—Circuit shown (for C natural) is one of 12 master tone generators in electronic organ for homes or small public rooms. All notes comprising six-octave range of instrument are derived by ZA1001 cold-cathode relaxation oscillators operating in cascade as successive frequency dividers. Final stage, including V13 and V14, is omitted from tone generators for other notes. V1 is half of ECC82 double-triode. Resistors are identical for all 12 tone generators except for R11-R17 whose values must be selected for vibrato and frequency adjustment, and R1 whose values are given in table along with capacitor values. Values are: R2 47K; R3 22K; R4-R10 4.7 meg; R11-R17 1.8 to 22 meg; R18-R23 10 meg; R24, R25 4.7K; R26 15K; R27-R33 220K; L is 45 mH with core K30024 and 850 turns wild-wound, tapped at 210 turns. Report gives complete design and construction data for entire organ.—Electronic Organ with Cold-Cathode Tube Frequency Dividers, Philips, Pub. Dept., Elcoma Div., Eindhoven, The Netherlands, No. 122, 1966.

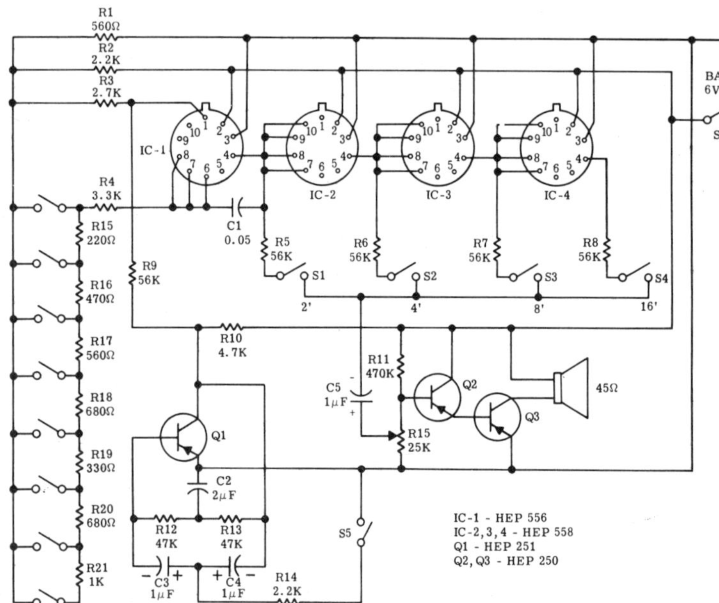

IC SINGLE-OSCILLATOR ORGAN—Linear amplifier IC-1 and eight switched-in resistors R15-R21 serve as oscillator for generating eight notes of diatonic scale—do, re, mi, fa, sol, la, ti, do, though not necessarily with perfect tuning to international musical scale unless resistor values are slightly changed. Other three IC's are J-K flip-flops that generate suboctaves by exact frequency division. Q1 is 6-Hz vibrato generator. Stop switches S1-S4, each providing different sound, are used singly or in combinations to provide voicing. Q2-Q3 serve as audio amplifier. Article gives construction details.—"Integrated Circuit Projects," Motorola, Phoenix, Ariz., 1966, p 32–45.

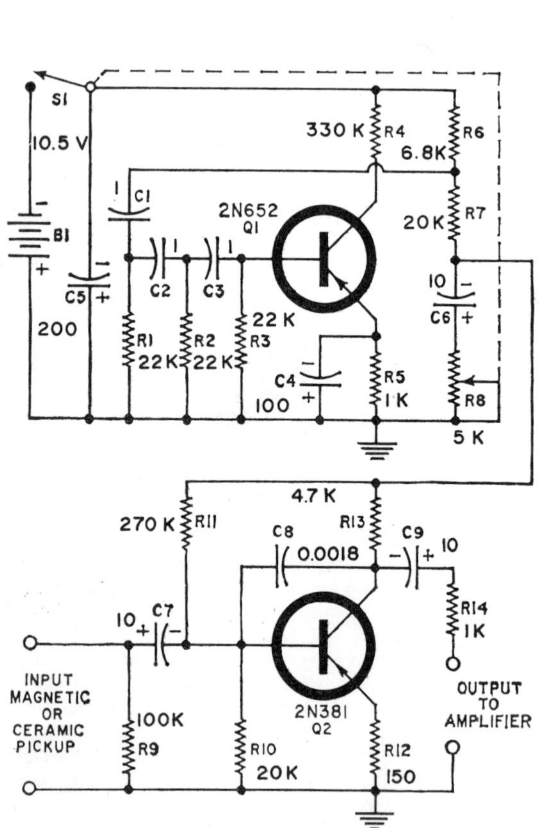

TREMOLO FOR GUITAR—Q1 is 6-Hz phase-shift oscillator acting on voltage amplifier Q2 to vary input signal strength and provide added depth to any musical instrument using pickup.—W. R. Shippee, Simplified Tremolo, *Electronics World*, Oct. 1966, p 89.

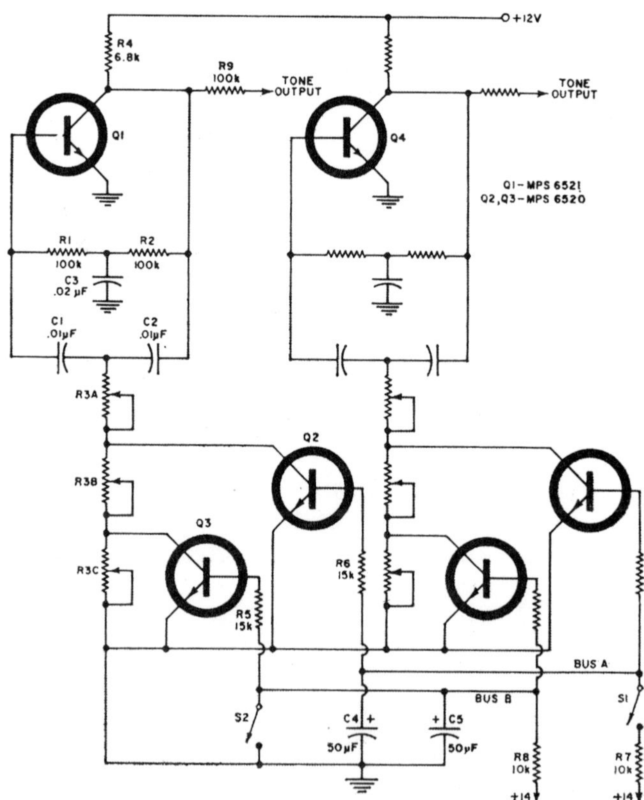

TWIN-T GLIDING-TONE—Used in experimental musical instruments to provide shifts and glides at any intervals within 1.5-octave frequency ranges of multiplicity of twin-T oscillators employed. Only part of circuit is shown, with values given for first oscillator Q1. Article gives design details for achieving desired musical effects.—F. B. Maynard, Twin T's: Designs & Applications, *Electronics World*, Aug. 1968, p 35–37 and 64.

BONGO—Provides ringing function for simulating musical instruments when R3 in basic twin-T oscillator is adjusted until circuit just becomes quiescent. If this is close to cutoff, duration of ringing can be up to 30 sine waves. Can be triggered by positive square waves or by touching indicated terminals. At around 100 Hz, effect sounds like bass drums. Middle frequencies simulate tom-toms and bongos. Above 1 kHz sounds of gongs, resonant wood blocks, and claves are generated. Can also be used for doorbells and signaling devices.—F. B. Maynard, Twin T's: Designs & Applications, *Electronics World*, Aug. 1968, p 35–37 and 64.

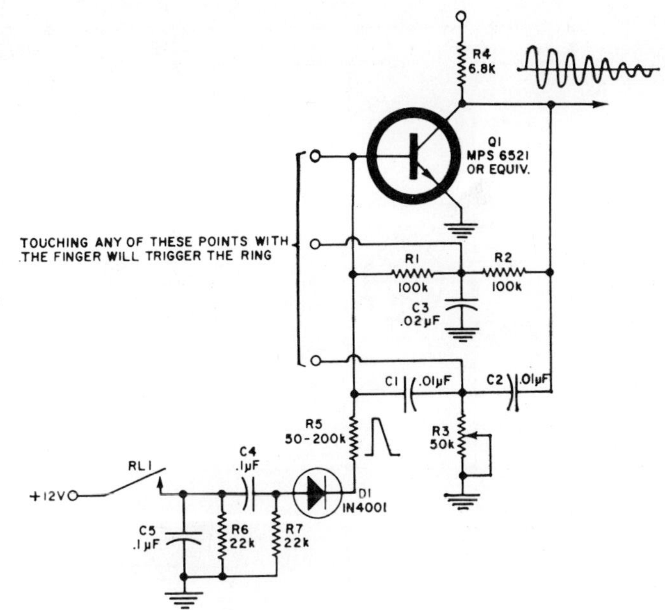

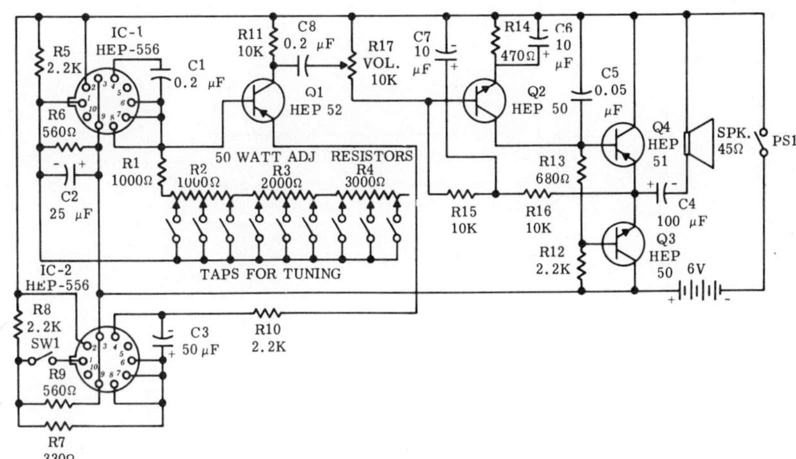

GUITAR—Uses two IC R-C oscillators, one tapped to provide notes over two-octave scale (250 to 1,100 Hz). Other gives fixed-frequency output around 12 Hz which may be turned on and off by SW1, adding a rapid string-plucking sound to instrument. Article gives construction details. Amplifier delivers 200 mW to speaker.—"Integrated Circuit Projects," Motorola, Phoenix, Ariz., 1966, p 80.

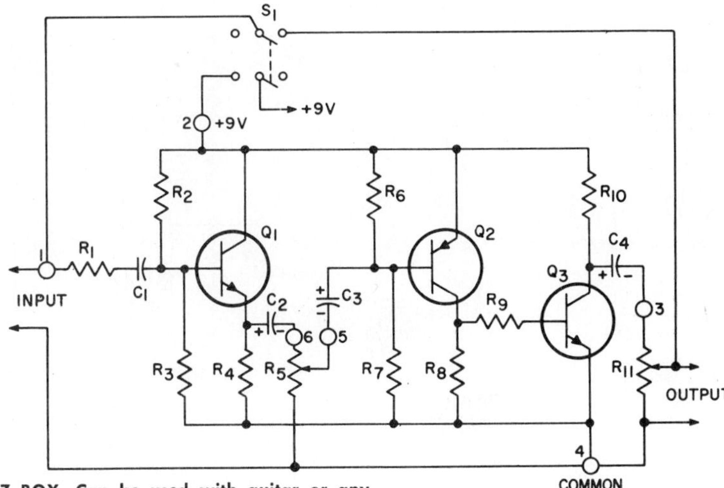

FUZZ BOX—Can be used with guitar or any other instrument whose musical output is amplified. Will change character of sound produced, to give variety of sounds not otherwise available from the instrument. Q2 is biased almost to cutoff and therefore amplifies only half of input signal. R5 changes level of signal at input to Q2 and therefore controls amount of fuzz. Q3 is biased to clip top of signal input and further change character of sound. Circuit requires 1 V input.—"Hobby Circuits Manual," RCA, Harrison, N.J., HM-90, p 91.

C_1 = 0.01 microfarad, 25 volts or greater
$C_2C_3C_4$ = 5 microfarads, 15 volts, electrolytic
Q_1Q_3 = transistor, RCA SK3020
Q_2 = transistor, RCA SK3005
$R_1R_2R_3R_7$ = 100,000 ohms, 1/2 watt, 10%
R_4 = 3300 ohms, 1/2 watt, 10%
R_5 = potentiometer, 5000 ohms, linear taper
R_6 = 15,000 ohms, 1/2 watt, 10%
R_8R_{10} = 2700 ohms, 1/2 watt, 10%
R_9 = 47,000 ohms, 1/2 watt, 10%
R_{11} = potentiometer, 10,000 ohms, linear taper
S_1 = switch, double-pole, double-throw

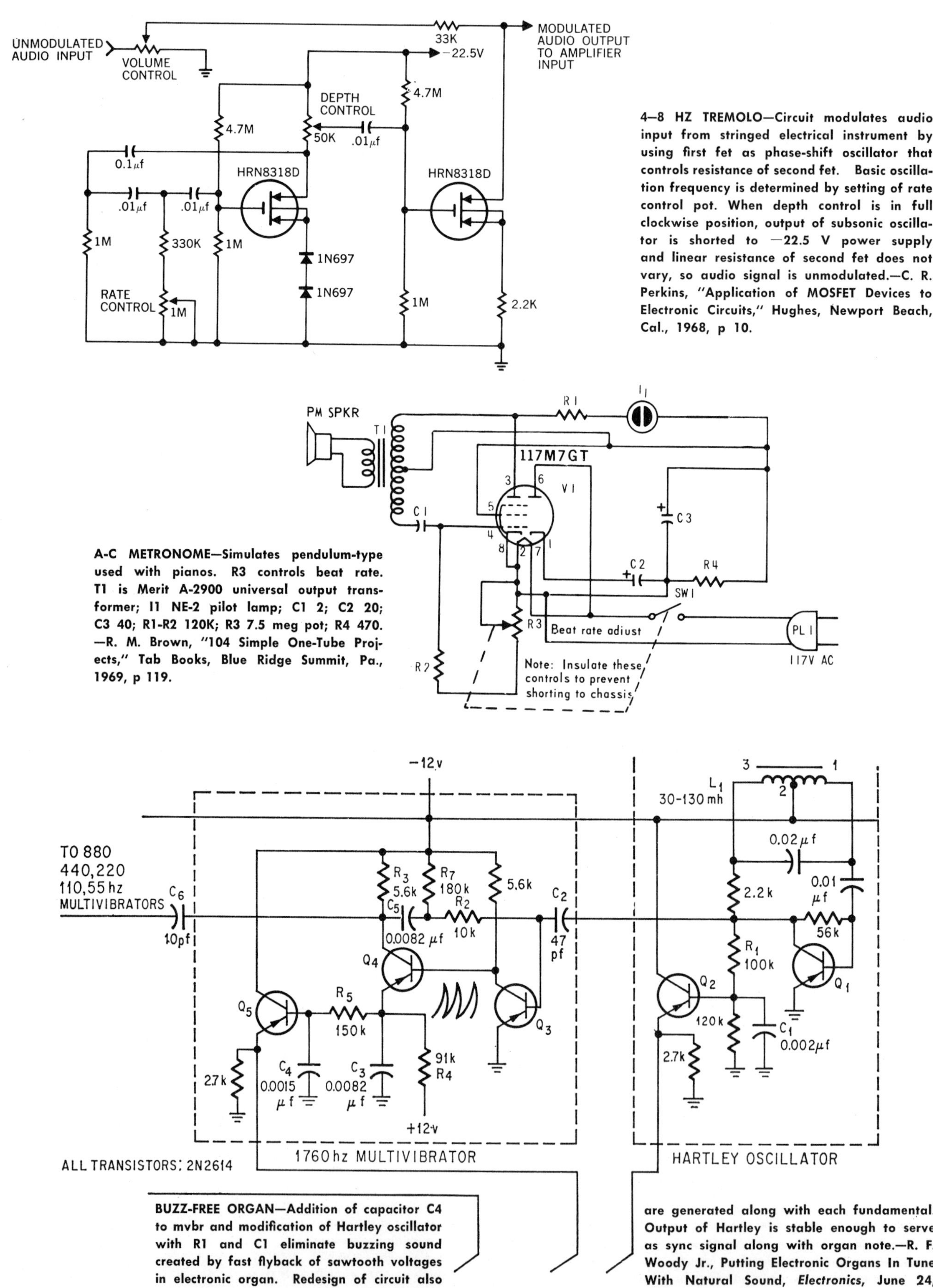

4–8 HZ TREMOLO—Circuit modulates audio input from stringed electrical instrument by using first fet as phase-shift oscillator that controls resistance of second fet. Basic oscillation frequency is determined by setting of rate control pot. When depth control is in full clockwise position, output of subsonic oscillator is shorted to −22.5 V power supply and linear resistance of second fet does not vary, so audio signal is unmodulated.—C. R. Perkins, "Application of MOSFET Devices to Electronic Circuits," Hughes, Newport Beach, Cal., 1968, p 10.

A-C METRONOME—Simulates pendulum-type used with pianos. R3 controls beat rate. T1 is Merit A-2900 universal output transformer; I1 NE-2 pilot lamp; C1 2; C2 20; C3 40; R1-R2 120K; R3 7.5 meg pot; R4 470.—R. M. Brown, "104 Simple One-Tube Projects," Tab Books, Blue Ridge Summit, Pa., 1969, p 119.

BUZZ-FREE ORGAN—Addition of capacitor C4 to mvbr and modification of Hartley oscillator with R1 and C1 eliminate buzzing sound created by fast flyback of sawtooth voltages in electronic organ. Redesign of circuit also adds richness to music, because all harmonics are generated along with each fundamental. Output of Hartley is stable enough to serve as sync signal along with organ note.—R. F. Woody Jr., Putting Electronic Organs In Tune With Natural Sound, *Electronics*, June 24, 1968, p 100–102.

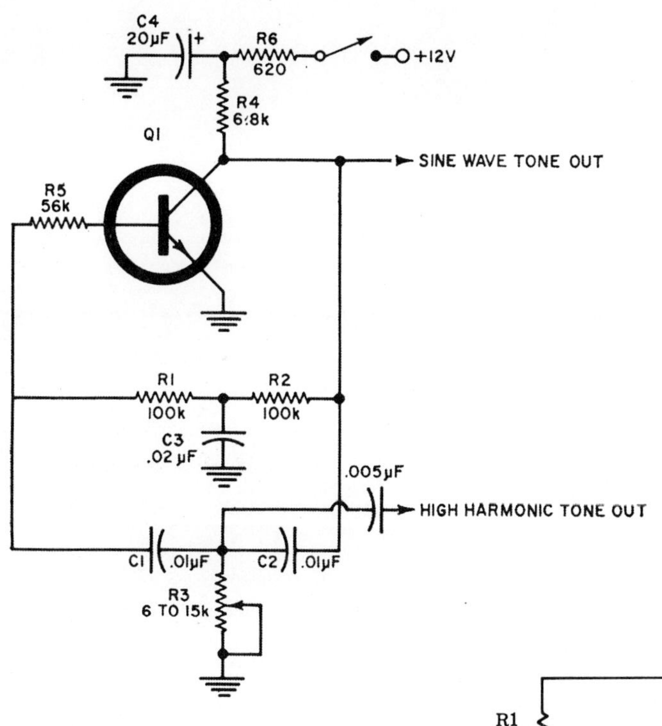

"SUSTAIN" EFFECT—Twin-T oscillator provides effect heard in pianos, bells, and string instruments, in which tone decreases gradually in intensity. Article has nomogram for choosing twin-T component values to give desired frequency. Voltage stability is sufficiently good that maximum deviation from constant frequency cannot be detected by most persons. Q1 is Motorola MPS6521.—F. B. Maynard, Twin T's: Designs & Applications, *Electronics World*, Aug. 1968, p. 35–37 and 64.

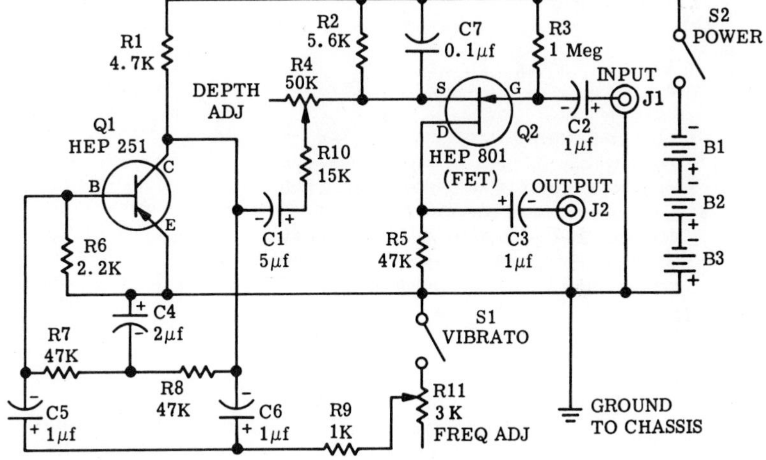

FET VIBRATO—Gives tremolo or other special effects to guitars, accordions, and reed-type electric chord organs. Connect high-impedance pickup or microphone to input jack J1, and connect output jack J2 to high-impedance input of any audio amplifier system. Twin-tee oscillator Q1 produces 6-Hz sine-wave output, adjustable by R11. Article gives construction and adjustment details.—"Field Effect Transistor Projects," Motorola, Phoenix, Ariz., 1966, p 15–25.

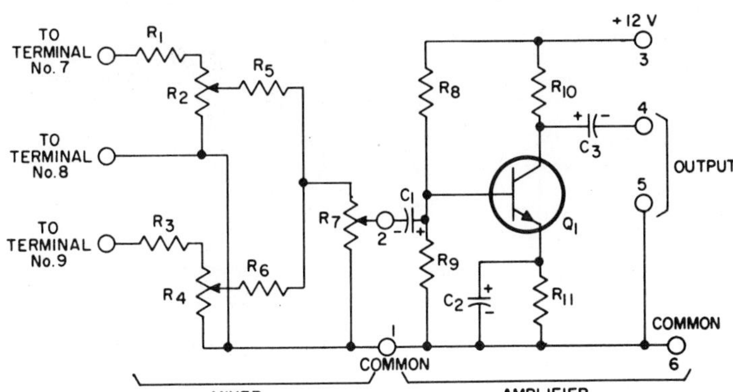

ORGAN MIXER-AMPLIFIER—Sawtooth input to R3 and pulse input to R1 from single-voice electronic organ are mixed to change character of tone before feeding into audio amplifier stage. Output at terminals 4 and 5 may be fed into hi-fi audio amplifier.—"Hobby Circuits Manual," RCA, Harrison, N.J., HM-90, p 107.

C_1 = 15 microfarads, 10 volts, electrolytic
C_2 = 100 microfarads, 6 volts, electrolytic
C_3 = 50 microfarads, 15 volts, electrolytic
Q_1 = transistor, RCA SK3020
R_1 R_5 R_6 R_9 = 100,000 ohms, 1/2 watt, 10%
R_2 = potentiometer, 5000 ohms, linear taper
R_3 = 2.2 megohms, 1/2 watt, 10%
R_4 = potentiometer, 250,000 ohms, linear taper
R_7 = potentiometer, 10,000 ohms, linear taper
R_8 = 330,000 ohms, 1/2 watt, 10%
R_{10} = 12,000 ohms, 1/2 watt, 10%
R_{11} = 3300 ohms, 1/2 watt, 10%

CHAPTER 28

Filter Circuits—Active

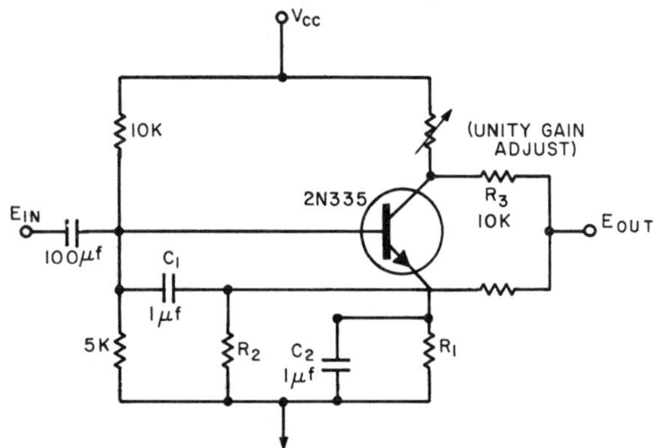

3–20 DB BANDWIDTH NOTCH FILTER—Adjusting values of R1 and R2 alters bandwidth without affecting notch attenuation. With 1,375 ohms for both, notch bandwidth is much narrower than when R1 is 310 ohms and R2 is 10K. Article gives response curves and phase characteristic for operating range of 100 to 150 Hz.—H. E. Butler, Variable Bandwidth From a Notch Filter, *Electronic Design,* April 27, 1964, p 90.

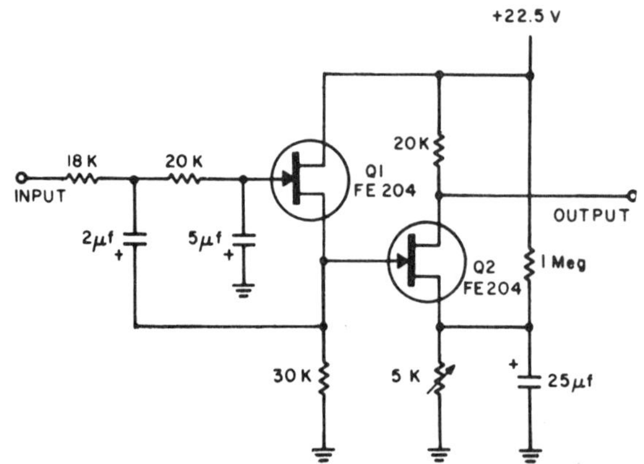

0–1 HZ ACTIVE FILTER—Low-pass filter with voltage gain to 2.5 has rolloff of 12 dB per decade of frequency and noise (referred to input) of only 15 μV per root cycle, as compared to 140 with ordinary low-noise transistor.—T. F. Prosser, Field Effect Transistor Improves Low Pass Filter Action, "400 Ideas for Design Selected from Electronic Design," Hayden Book Co., N.Y., 1964, p 15.

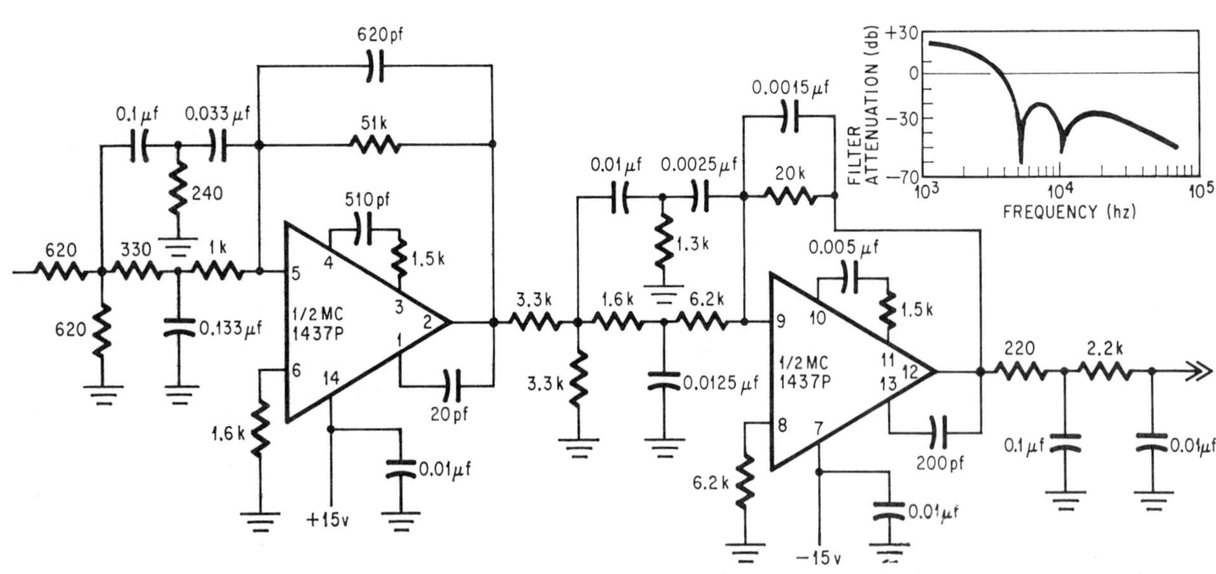

PHASE-LOCKED LOOP—Two-section active filter using opamps was developed for frequency synthesizer requiring d-c voltage gain of 15 V/V, 5-kHz reference frequency at least 70 dB down from d-c gain, 10-kHz second harmonic 60 dB down, and all other harmonics at least 50 dB down. Phase shift at 1 kHz must be less than 50 deg. Article gives design equations.—B. Welling, Active Filters: The Op Amp Saves Time and Money, *Electronics,* Feb. 3, 1969, p 82–90.

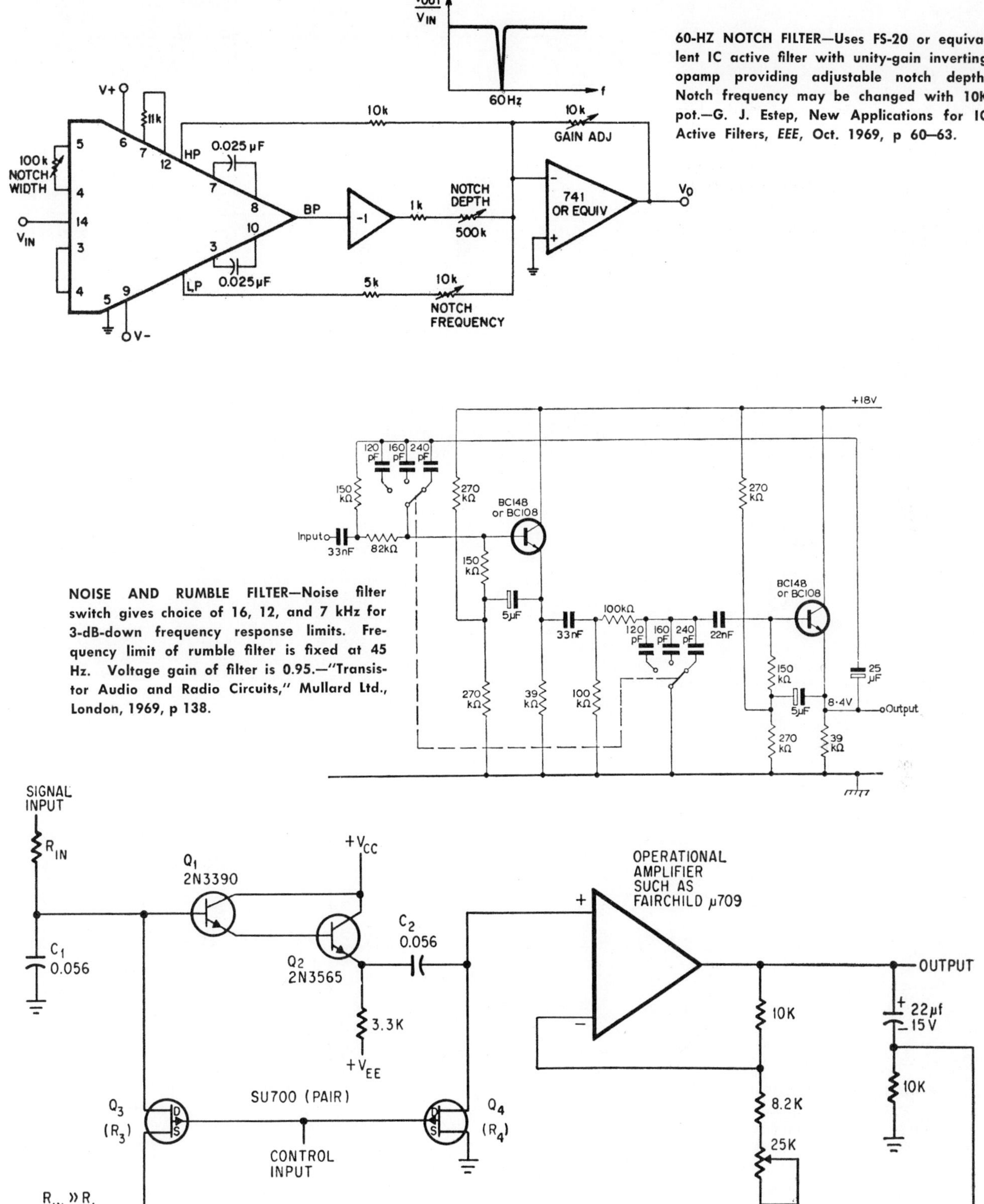

60-HZ NOTCH FILTER—Uses FS-20 or equivalent IC active filter with unity-gain inverting opamp providing adjustable notch depth. Notch frequency may be changed with 10K pot.—G. J. Estep, New Applications for IC Active Filters, *EEE*, Oct. 1969, p 60–63.

NOISE AND RUMBLE FILTER—Noise filter switch gives choice of 16, 12, and 7 kHz for 3-dB-down frequency response limits. Frequency limit of rumble filter is fixed at 45 Hz. Voltage gain of filter is 0.95.—"Transistor Audio and Radio Circuits," Mullard Ltd., London, 1969, p 138.

ACTIVE TUNABLE BANDPASS—Uses pair of fet's as tuning element to save money and space. Developed by Philco-Ford for speech bandwidth compression system needed by NASA to reduce transmission power for voice communication from Mars and deep space. Permits transmission of narrow band of encoded information that can be converted into intelligible synthetic speech on earth. Filter frequency is linearly related to control voltage for 20:1 frequency range. Article covers design of low, high, and bandpass filters using active filters with Q up to 100 for frequencies up to several hundred kHz. Bandpass version shown has overall gain of 2.—J. M. Loe, FET's Call The Tune In Active Filter Design, *Electronics*, Oct. 3, 1966, p 98–101.

OPTOELECTRONIC CONTROL OF NOTCH FILTER—D-c control voltage applied to lamp of CK1102 Raysistor makes active notch filter track from 800 to 1,200 Hz. To make tracking filter automatically follow applied signal frequency, in same range, use Schmitt trigger, differentiating circuit, and d-c amplifier to provide d-c control voltage of 0 to 1 V whose value varies with applied frequency.—Raysistor Optoelectronic Devices, Raytheon, Quincy, Mass., 1967, p 19.

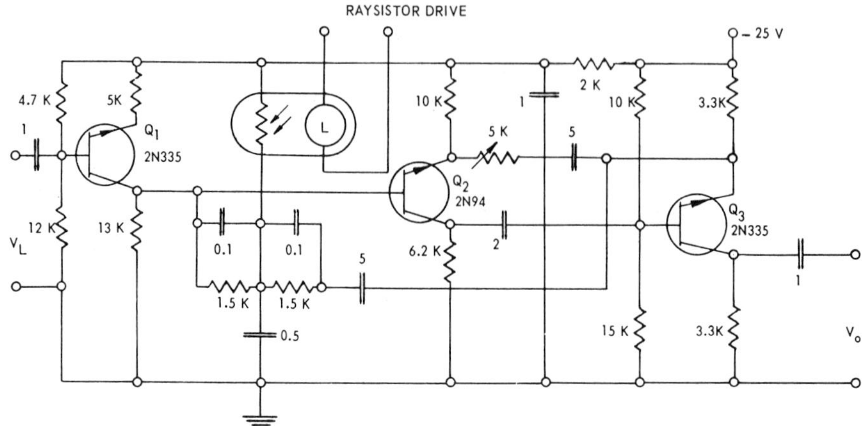

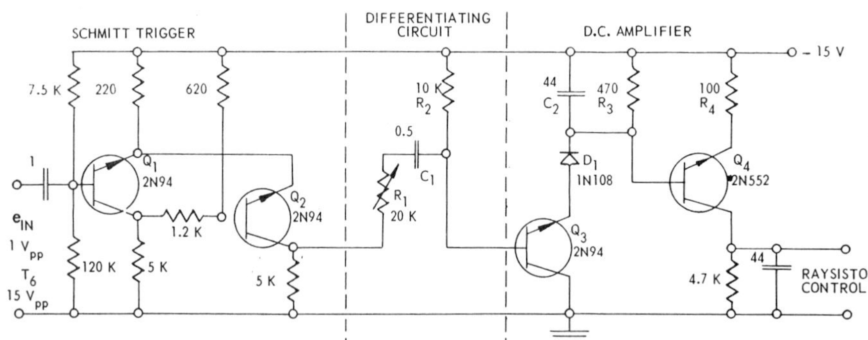

OPTOELECTRONIC TRACKING FILTER CONTROL—Converts input frequency in range of 800 to 1,200 Hz to proportional d-c output voltage from 0 to 1 V for lamp of Raysistor in active notch filter providing automatic tracking in same frequency range.—Raysistor Optoelectronic Devices, Raytheon, Quincy, Mass., 1967, p 20.

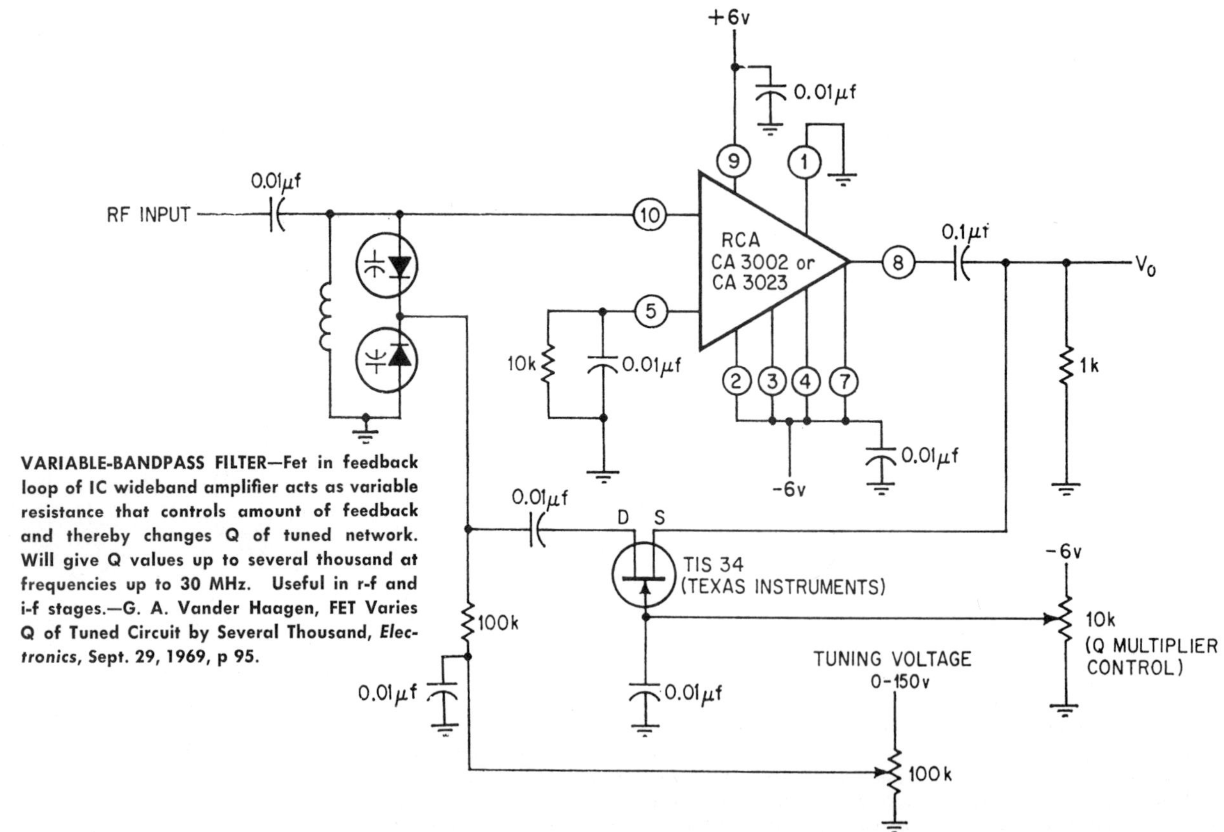

VARIABLE-BANDPASS FILTER—Fet in feedback loop of IC wideband amplifier acts as variable resistance that controls amount of feedback and thereby changes Q of tuned network. Will give Q values up to several thousand at frequencies up to 30 MHz. Useful in r-f and i-f stages.—G. A. Vander Haagen, FET Varies Q of Tuned Circuit by Several Thousand, *Electronics*, Sept. 29, 1969, p 95.

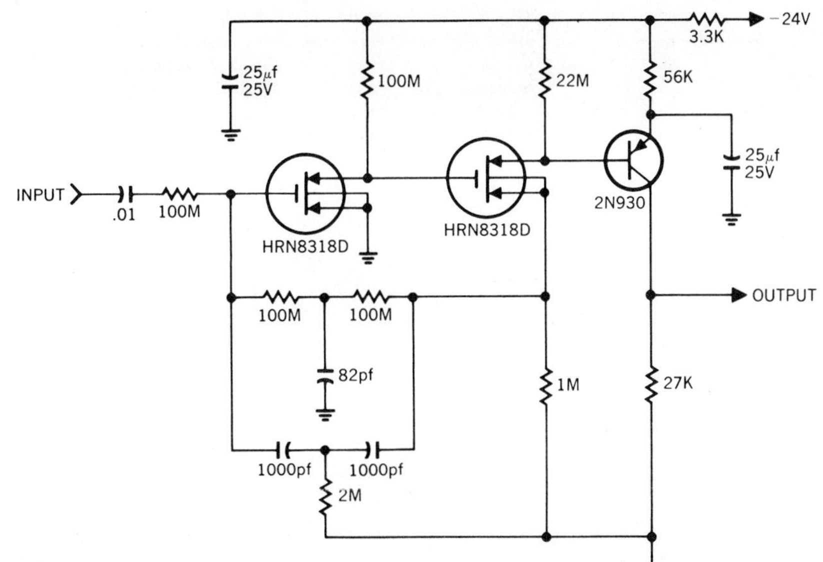

8-HZ TWIN-T IN MOSFET AMPLIFIER—Filter network in negative feedback loop of two-stage mosfet amplifier gives bandpass with 8-Hz center frequency. Output transistor provides additional gain and relatively low output impedance. Basic circuit can be adapted for detecting large number of discrete audio tones, for power analysis of audio spectrum, or for synthetic reconstruction of speech or music.—C. R. Perkins, "Application of MOSFET Devices to Electronic Circuits," Hughes, Newport Beach, Cal., 1968, p 15.

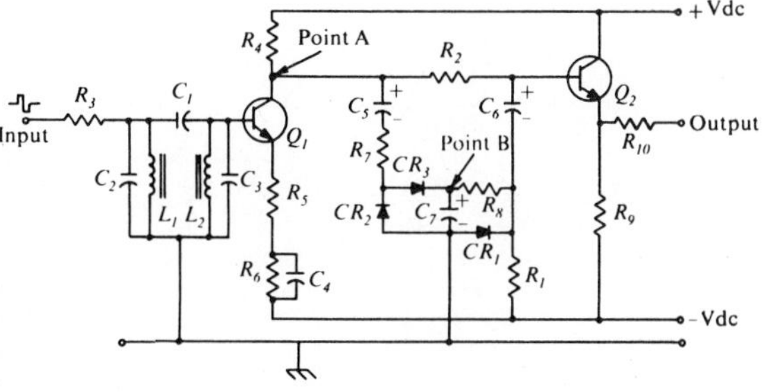

Supplies	+ 6 V dc, – 6 V dc
Q_1	2N336
Q_2	2N333
CR_1	1N137A
CR_2	1N629
CR_3	1N629
R_1	360K
R_2	68K
R_3	82K
R_4	5.6K
R_5	820 Ω
R_6	9.1K
R_7	6.8K
R_8	39K
R_9	16K
C_1	.008 μF
C_2	.093 μF
C_3	.113μF
C_4	2.2 μF, 20 V dc
C_5	1 μF, 20 V dc
C_6	1 μF, 20 V dc
C_7	1 μF, 20 V dc
L_1	1 H
L_2	1 H

SHARPENING FILTER—Electronic switch and discriminator serve as frequency-sensitive means of sharpening slopes of filter response curve. Can be used to eliminate interference caused by overmodulation of f-m transmitter in subcarrier telemetry systems. Square-wave input from frequency-modulated subcarrier oscillator is converted to sine wave by LC input bandpass filter, amplified by Q1, then converted to positive d-c voltage at point B, proportional to amplitude of signal voltage at point A. When input frequency goes beyond cutoff point of LC filter, voltage at B drops and no longer holds CR1 open; resulting low-impedance path from base of Q2 to ground causes signal voltage to be dropped almost entirely across R2 to give electronic equivalent of narrower filter.—"Selected Electronic Circuitry," NASA SP-5046, 1966, Government Printing Office, Washington, D.C., p 51.

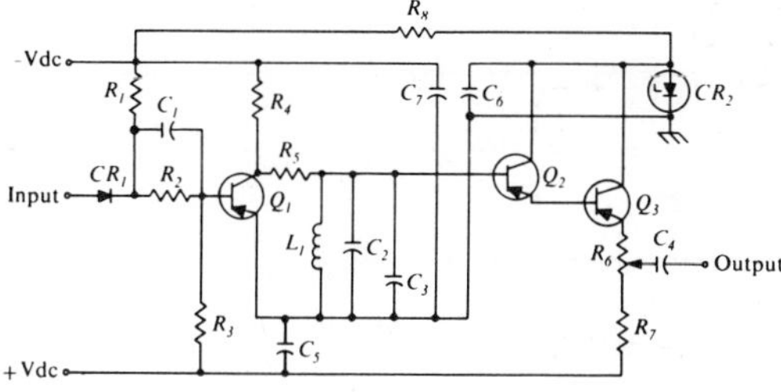

Supplies	– 18 V dc + 12 V dc
Q_1	2N1132
Q_2	2N1132
Q_3	2N1132
CR_1	1N695
Zener CR_2	–
R_6	1K
R_7	500 Ω
R_8	220 Ω
C_1	150 pF
C_4	0.47 μF, 50 V dc
C_5	0.068 μF
C_6	0.068 μF
C_7	0.068 μF

Comp.	1 Kc Filter	10 Kc Filter	100 Kc Filter
R_1	6.8K	6.8K	3.9K
R_2	2.2K	2.2K	8.2K
R_3	22K	22K	39K
R_4	1.2K	1.2K	3.9K
R_5	39K	39K	24K
R_9	10K	—	—
C_2	0.068 μF (2)*	0.033 μF	820 pF
L_1	0.25 H (2)*	8 mH	2.5 mH

*1 Kc Filter, Two Filter Stages.

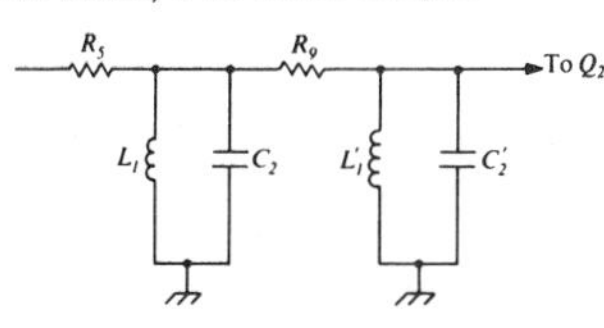

PULSE CONVERSION FILTER—Converts rectangular input signal to highly stable sine-wave output. Q1 applies amplified input signal to filter whose values are given for three different center frequencies. In each case, tuning of tank circuit to desired frequency is done by changing value of C3. Amplitude of sine-wave signal at output of Darlington emitter-follower Q2-Q3 varies with duty cycle of rectangular input waveform; 50% duty cycle gives optimum operation. Circuit can provide coordinated timing signals for several locations.—"Selected Electronic Circuitry," NASA SP-5046, 1966, Government Printing Office, Washington, D.C., p 54.

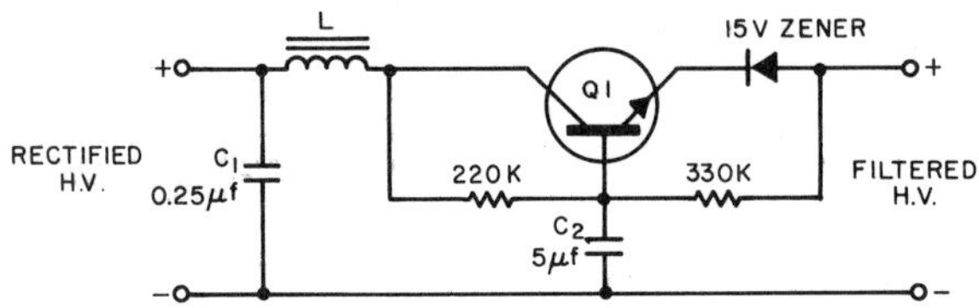

RIPPLE SUPPRESSION FOR HIGH-VOLTAGE SUPPLY—Capacitance multiplier circuit keeps anode voltage very low for high-voltage photomultiplier. Gives output of 2 kV at 2 mA. Transistor type is not critical.—G. P. Epstein, Photo-Multiplier Filter Adaptable Over Wide Range, *Electronic Design*, April 13, 1964, p 73.

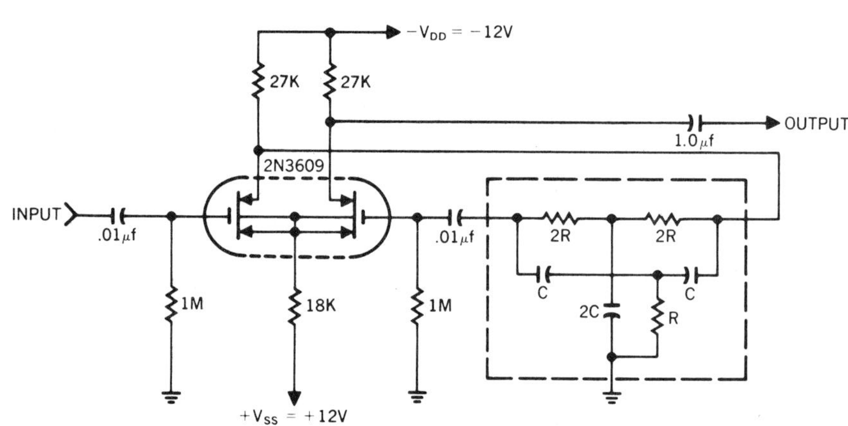

TWIN-T MOSFET—Fet pair acts as differential amplifier with extremely high input impedance. One side of differential amplifier is connected to twin-T filter to give notch filter at frequency determined by values used for R and C. Overall impedance of twin-T network should be above 100K for proper circuit operation.—C. R. Perkins, "Application of MOSFET Devices to Electronic Circuits," Hughes, Newport Beach, Cal., 1968, p 17.

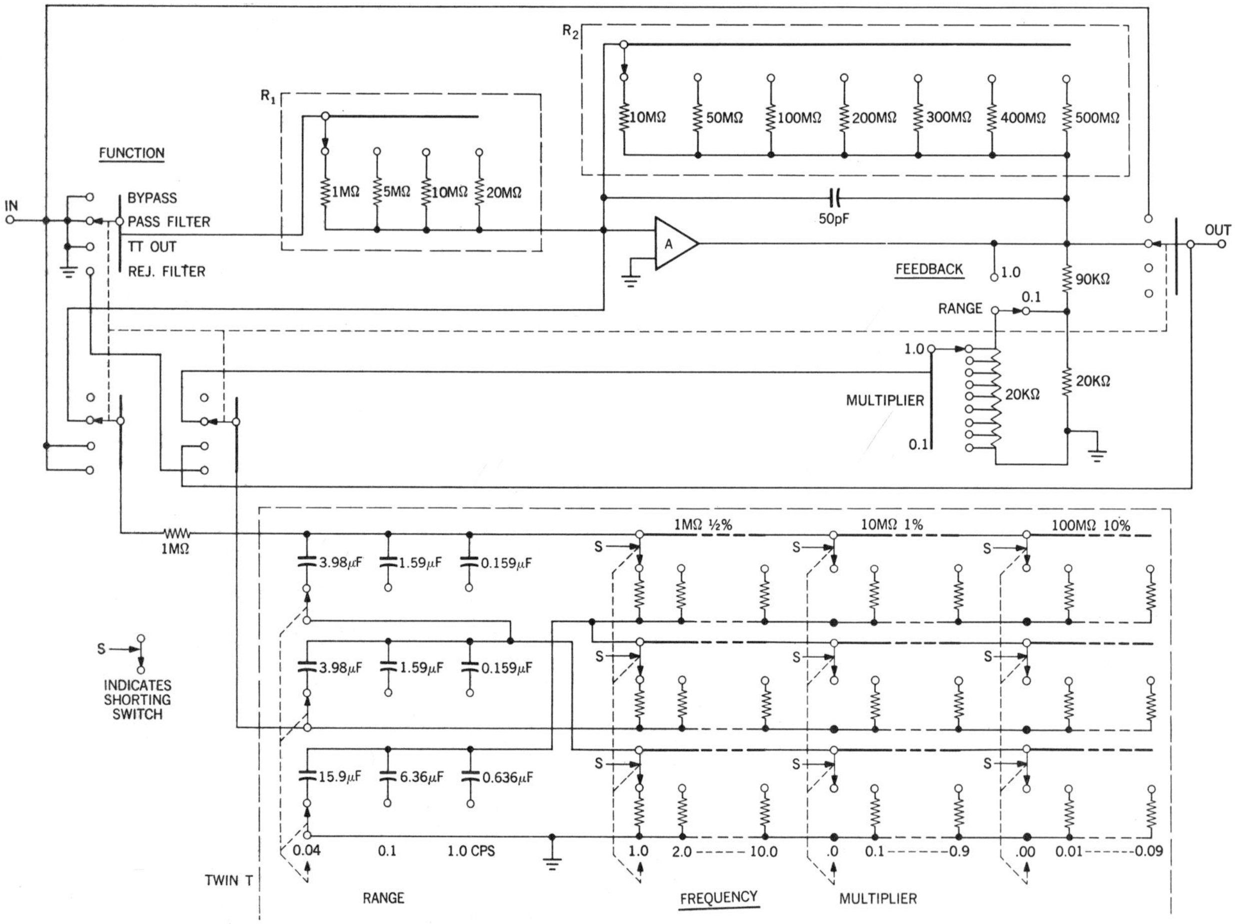

0.04–10.99 HZ TUNABLE TWIN-T—Used in measuring transverse dHS effect in bismuth at liquid helium temperatures. Switching matched sets of fixed capacitors gives three ranges having minimum values of 0.04, 0.1, and 1 Hz. Multiplication by factors between 1.0 and 10.99 in steps of 0.01 is achieved by varying elements of three equal resistance arms. Can be used in feedback line of opamp as pass filter or in input line as rejection filter. Article describes performance and gives details of measurement procedure. Opamp is Philbrick USA-3.—R. D. Brown III, New Methods for De Haas-Shubnikov Measurements, *IBM Journal*, Nov. 1966, p 462–471.

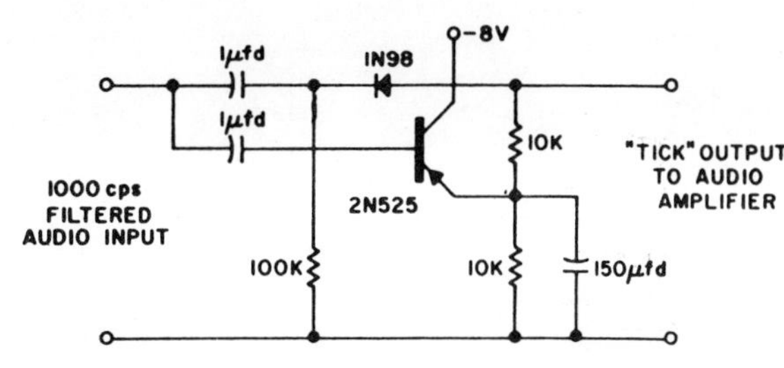

WWV 1-KHZ TICK-PASSING FILTER—Diode and transistor form biased-base clipper in circuit that passes 1,000-Hz seconds-tick tone in time signals from WWV while rejecting 440 and 600 Hz tones also transmitted. Each tick consists of 5 ms of 1,000-Hz tone. Undesired tones last longer than 5 ms and create back bias on diode, so do not appear in output.—T. E. Fay, Biased Base Clipper Isolates WWV Tick Tone, "400 Ideas for Design Selected from Electronic Design," Hayden Book Co., N.Y., 1964, p 137.

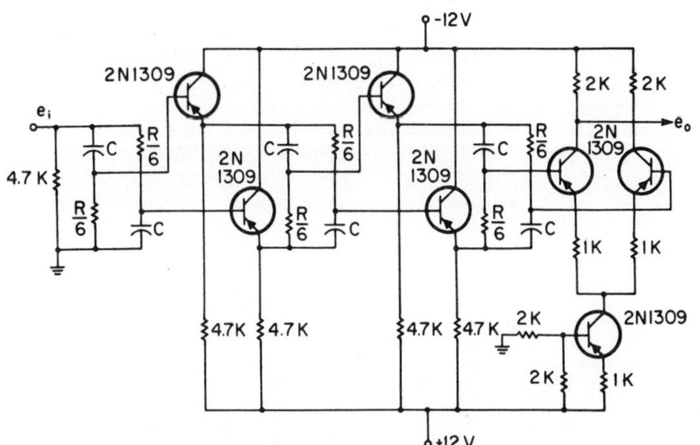

THREE-SECTION ALL-PASS—With 0.01 μF for C and 10K for R (1.67K for R/6), time delay of filter is 100 μs. Article gives design equations and examples of values for other time delays.—T. Mollinga, All-Pass Networks, *EEE*, Oct. 1966, p 84–88.

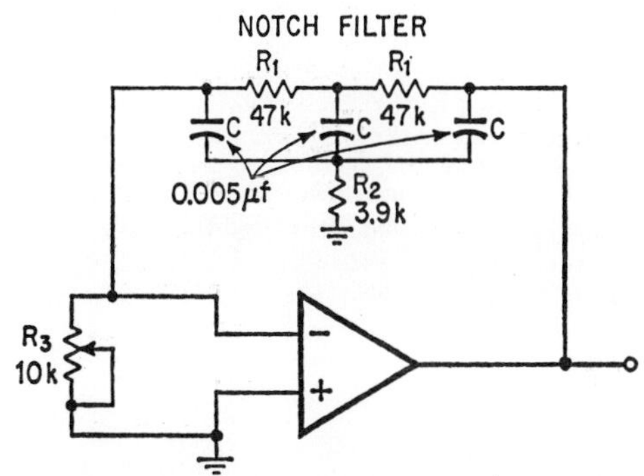

SHARP-BANDSTOP NOTCH FILTER—Notch filter alone is useful at low frequencies when bulky inductors are undesirable. Addition of opamp in active network, with R3 adjusted to make amplifier unstable, gives simple oscillator whose frequency corresponds to center frequency of filter (about 10 kHz). Article gives design nomograph for notch filter.—P. V. Wanek, Nomograph Charts a Fast Way to Build a Notch Filter, *Electronics*, September 15, 1969, p 119.

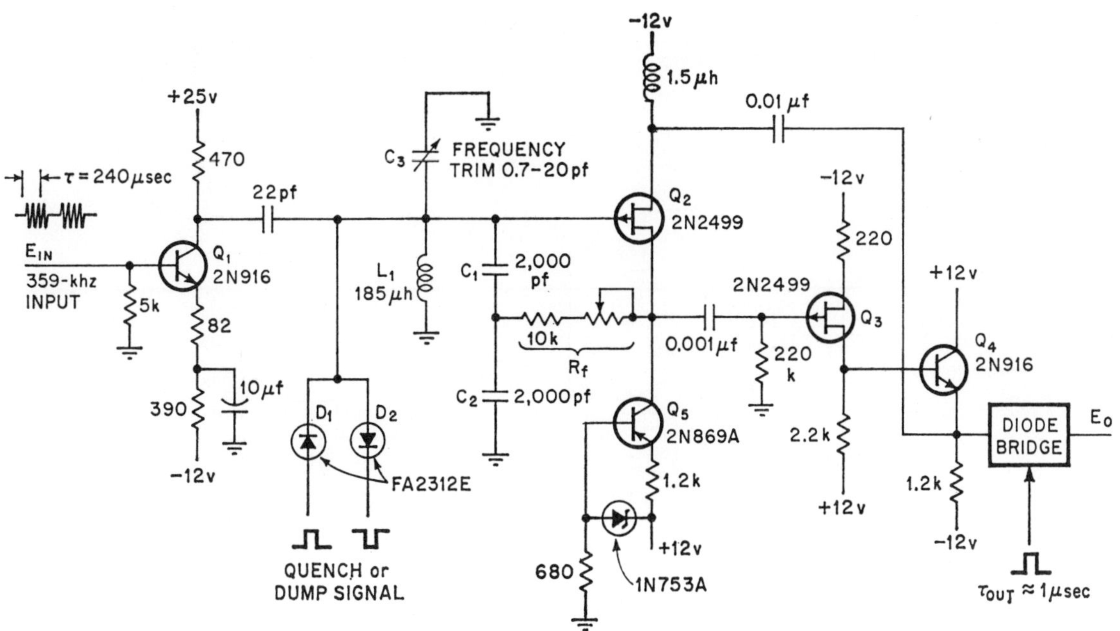

359-KHZ ACTIVE BANDPASS—Gated Q multiplier integrates, stores, filters, and analyzes audio tones that may be separated by as little as 80 Hz in phase-modulated communication system. High-Q tank circuit provides loaded Q's greater than 3,000 for integration. Tones are sequentially analyzed by filter, with only the one tone that is tuned to the 359-kHz center frequency providing positive integral during integration period.—R. J. Turner, Q-Multiplier Analyzes Audio-Frequency Tones, *Electronics*, May 25, 1970, p 94.

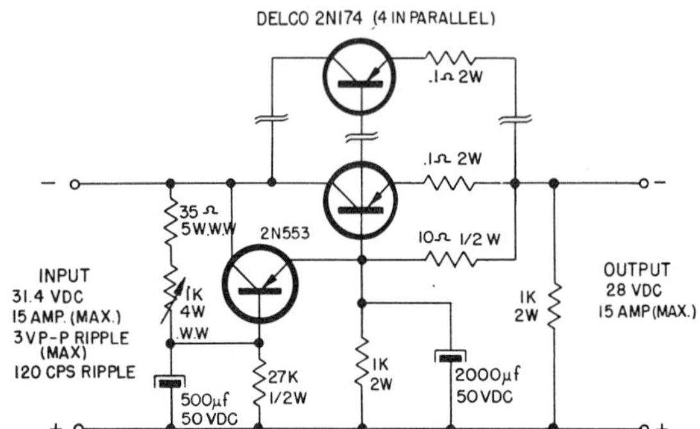

250:1 ELECTRONIC RIPPLE FILTER—Supplements conventional LC filter after that has reduced ripple to a value below 3V p-p, to reduce ripple electronically to 1/250th of that at input. Uses paralleled transistors to dissipate heat. Report gives theory of operation and design considerations.—Electronic Ripple Filter, Delco Radio, Kokomo, Ind., No. 28, 1965.

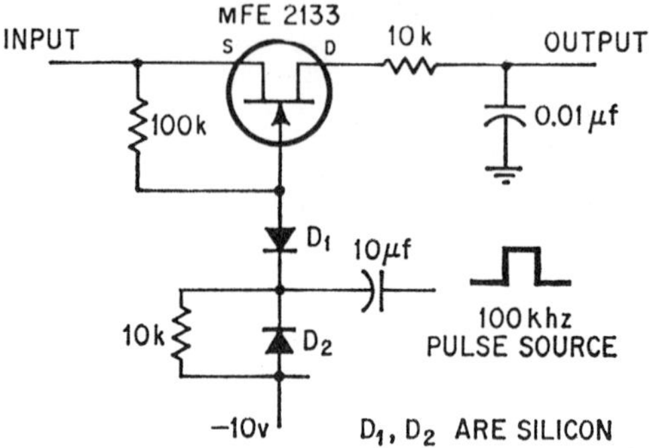

FET CONTROLS R-C FILTER—Switching of fet by pulse width modulated source varies circuit resistance, thereby controlling corner frequency (frequency selectivity) of R-C filter. As duty factor of pulse source is varied from 1 to 0 in circuit shown, effective resistance varies from 10,000 ohms to infinity.—L. L. Hamilton, Pulse-Train Duty Factor Controls RC Filter, *Electronics*, Aug. 4, 1969, p 93.

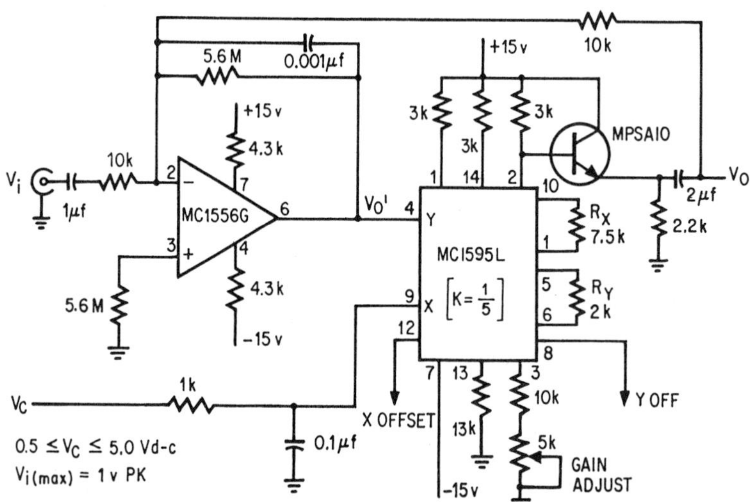

IC ACTIVE LOW-PASS—Gives transfer function of single-pole low-pass filter whose pole location can be controlled linearly by external d-c voltage Vc. Can be used as adaptive audio filter or voltage-tunable low-pass network. Gives one full decade of control in audio frequency range by varying Vc between 0.5 and 5 V.—E. Renschler and D. Weiss, Try the Monolithic Multiplier as a Versatile A-C Design Tool, *Electronics*, June 8, 1970, p 100–105.

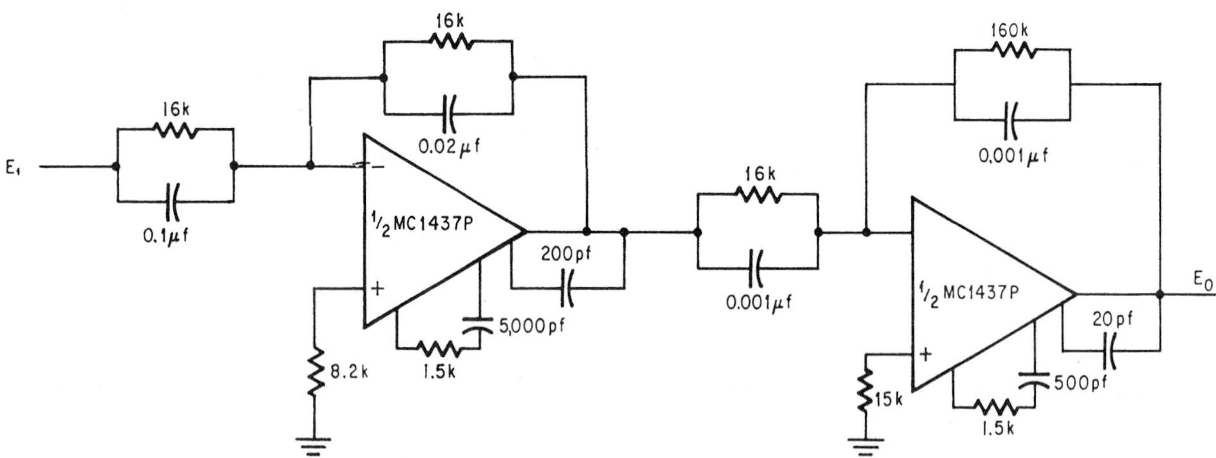

DUAL-OPAMP ACTIVE FILTER—Use of dual IC operational amplifier as active filter takes advantage of isolation between amplifiers to simplify calculations for obtaining desired transfer function. Article gives design equations. Compensating networks are added to both amplifiers to avoid instability with different d-c gains. First-stage gain is unity and second is 10, so amplifier is compensated for gain of 10.—B. Welling, Active Filters: The Op Amp Saves Time and Money, *Electronics*, Feb. 3, 1969, p 82–90.

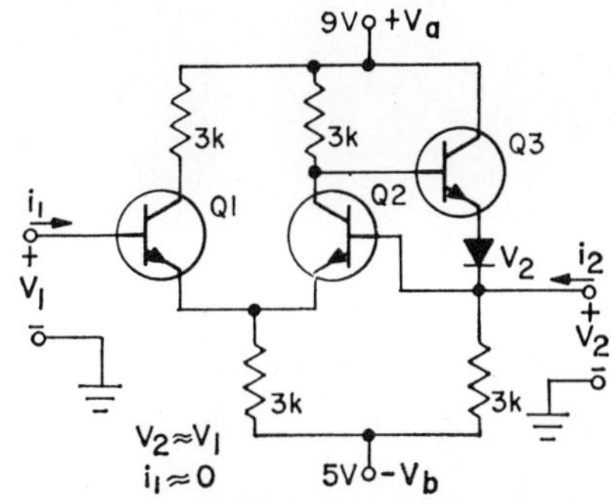

UNITY GAIN—Basic circuit fulfills standard conditions for active very low frequency filter, wherein V2 = V1 and input current is zero. Zener diode V2 serves only for biasing.—J. L. Hogin, Active Filters, *Electronics World*, April 1969, p 58–60.

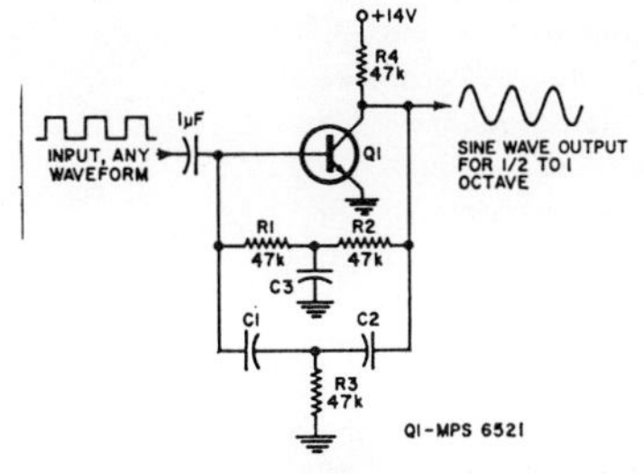

TWIN-T ACTIVE FILTER—Circuit is adjusted well into active region by choice of resistor values, to serve as active bandpass network. Useful for wave-shaping, as when producing flute or tibia voices from square waves in electronic organ. Bandpass is equivalent to about 1 octave of frequency. Article gives nomogram for selecting filter elements for any center frequency.—F. B. Maynard, Twin T's: Designs & Applications, *Electronics World*, Aug. 1968, p 35–37 and 64.

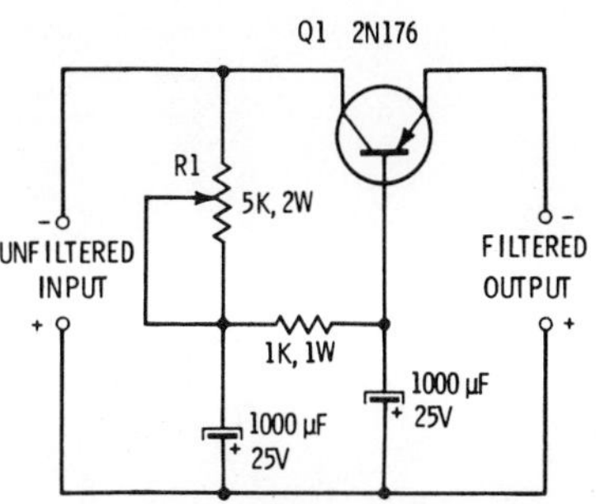

ELECTRONIC FILTER—Filtering action is comparable to that of 10,000-μF capacitor, reducing ripple in transistor power supply d-c output of 25 V to only a few millivolts. Current rating is 0.5 A.—J. P. Shields, "Novel Electronic Circuits," H. W. Sams & Co., Indianapolis, Ind., 1968, p 8.

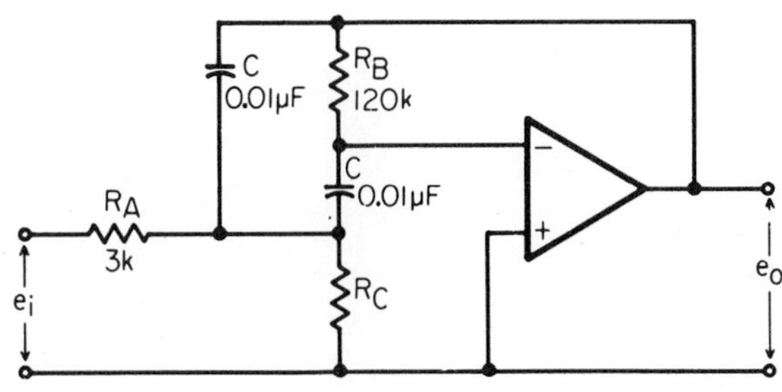

ACTIVE ADJUSTABLE BANDPASS—Requires only low-cost opamp and five discrete components. Values of Rc from 1,100 to 406 ohms give center frequency range of 1.6 to 2.4 kHz, without changing gain of 26 dB or bandwidth of 260 Hz for 3 dB down. Article gives procedure for designing filter for other parameters.—L. Robinson, Active Bandpass Filter with Adjustable Center Frequency and Constant Bandwith, *EEE*, Feb. 1968, p 124.

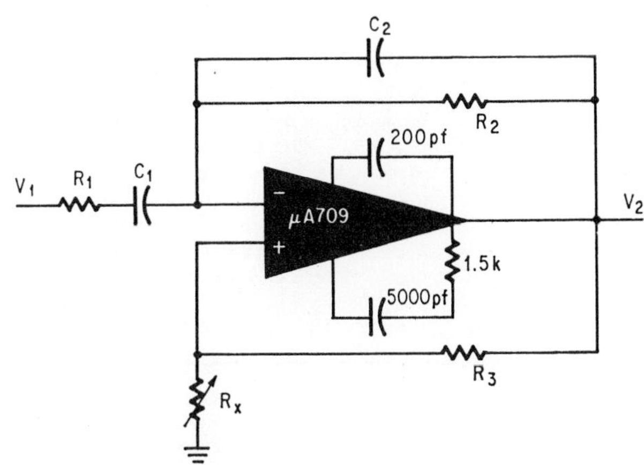

IC BANDPASS FILTER—Fairchild μA709 opamp provides both gain and frequency selectivity without use of inductors. Rx varies Q of circuit independently of center frequency determined by values of R-C inductor-synthesizing feedback elements. Filter is useful for f-m recording in range from 1 to 1,000 Hz and other applications where bulk and weight of inductor would create problems. For Q of 20, voltage gain is 7. Article gives transfer function equation.—J. F. Gifford and M. Markkula, Linear IC's: Part 5, Ins and Outs of Op Amps, *Electronics*, Nov. 27, 1967, p 84–93.

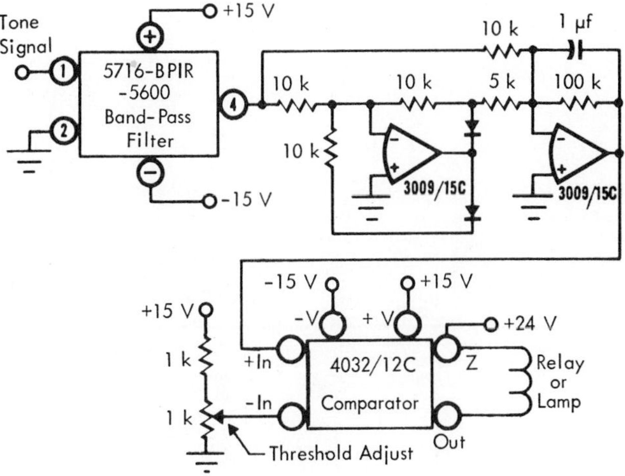

TONE SIGNALING SYSTEM—Uses Burr-Brown active bandpass filter module to detect and indicate presence of 560-Hz signal tone at 0.1 V rms. Precision rectifier with gain of 10 and time constant of 0.1 s converts desired a-c signal into d-c signal for comparison with reference voltage. Relay or lamp is actuated whenever d-c signal exceeds preset input threshold.—Burr-Brown Computer Designed Active Filters, Burr-Brown Research, PDS-203A, 1968, p 10.

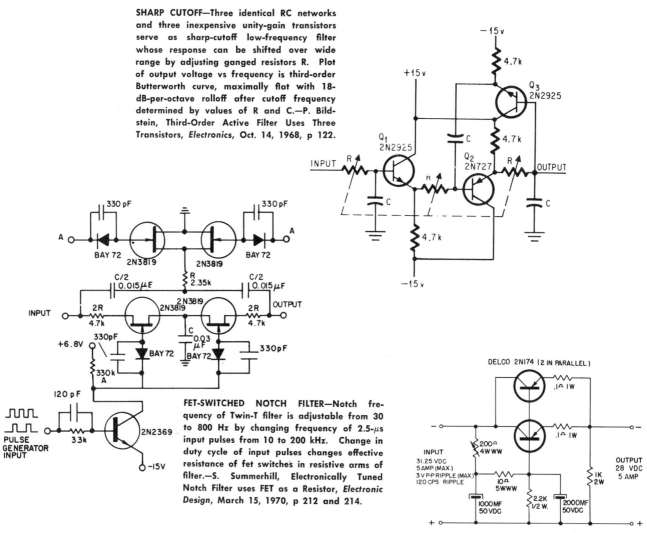

SHARP CUTOFF—Three identical RC networks and three inexpensive unity-gain transistors serve as sharp-cutoff low-frequency filter whose response can be shifted over wide range by adjusting ganged resistors R. Plot of output voltage vs frequency is third-order Butterworth curve, maximally flat with 18-dB-per-octave rolloff after cutoff frequency determined by values of R and C.—P. Bildstein, Third-Order Active Filter Uses Three Transistors, *Electronics,* Oct. 14, 1968, p 122.

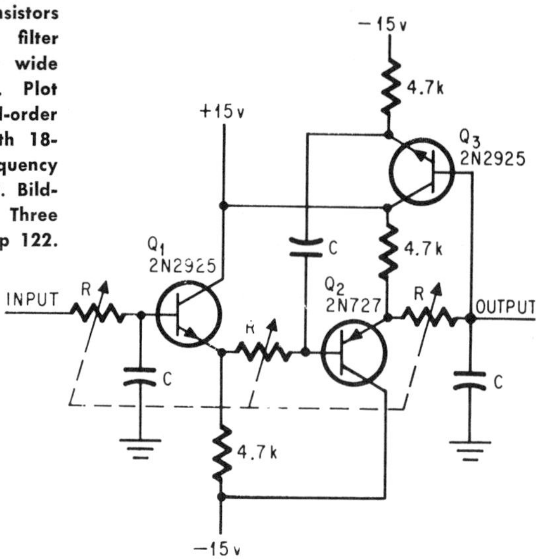

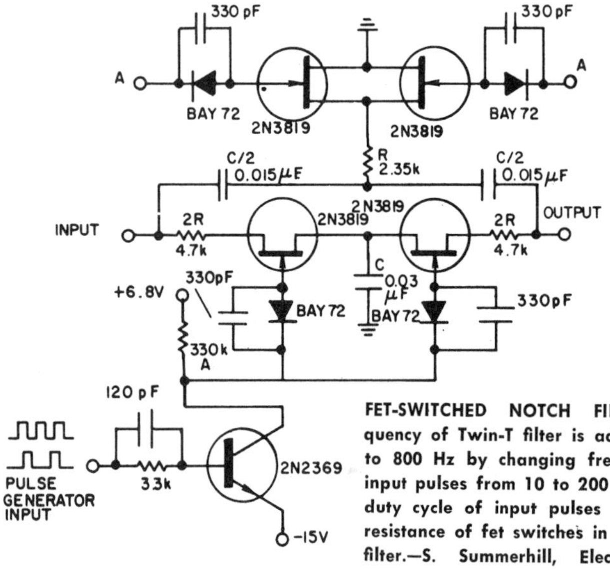

FET-SWITCHED NOTCH FILTER—Notch frequency of Twin-T filter is adjustable from 30 to 800 Hz by changing frequency of 2.5-μs input pulses from 10 to 200 kHz. Change in duty cycle of input pulses changes effective resistance of fet switches in resistive arms of filter.—S. Summerhill, Electronically Tuned Notch Filter uses FET as a Resistor, *Electronic Design,* March 15, 1970, p 212 and 214.

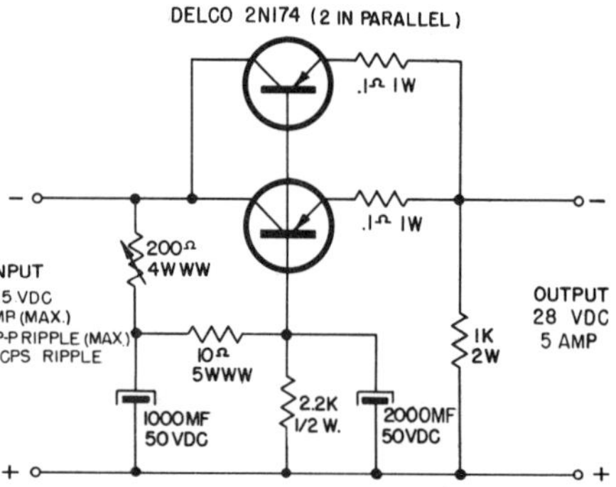

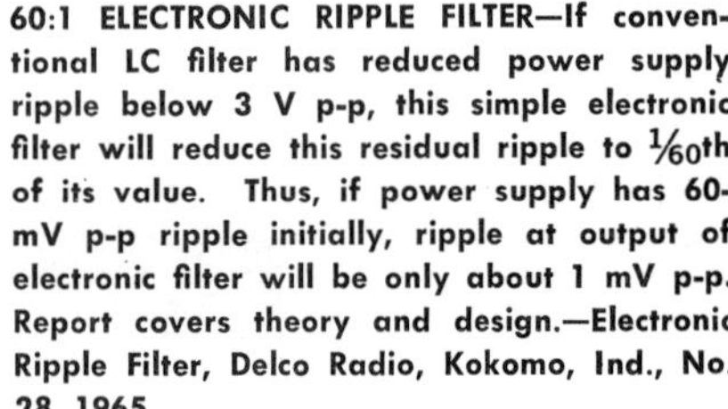

60:1 ELECTRONIC RIPPLE FILTER—If conventional LC filter has reduced power supply ripple below 3 V p-p, this simple electronic filter will reduce this residual ripple to 1/60th of its value. Thus, if power supply has 60-mV p-p ripple initially, ripple at output of electronic filter will be only about 1 mV p-p. Report covers theory and design.—Electronic Ripple Filter, Delco Radio, Kokomo, Ind., No. 28, 1965.

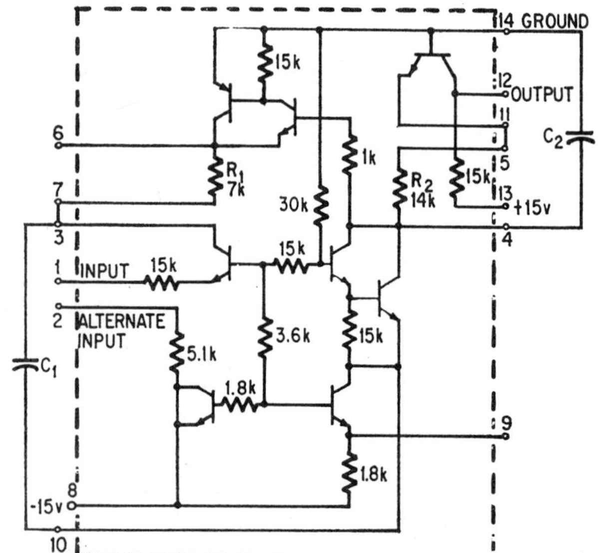

OPTIMUM ACTIVE FILTER—IC version, presented as example of detailed design procedures given for 24 different active filter designs, uses biasing arrangement that minimizes sensitivity to thermal and supply voltage variations. Can be tuned from d-c through 40 kHz, with any Q up to about 2,000, with no tendency to oscillate. Frequency response curve corresponds to that of ideal R-L-C- filter.—J. W. Mullaney, Active Filters: Part II—Varying the Approach, *Electronics,* July 21, 1969, p 86–93.

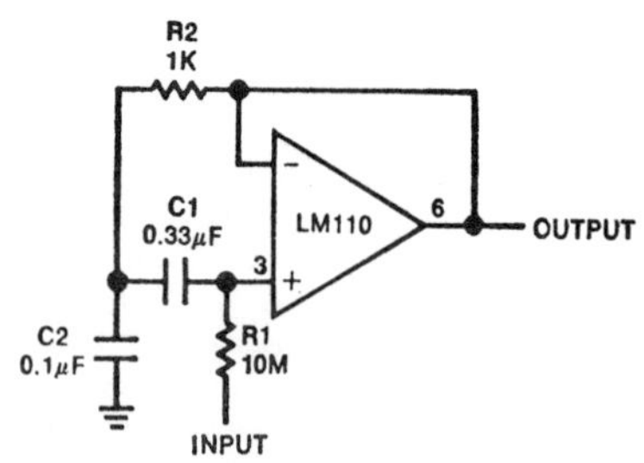

20-MHZ BANDWIDTH—IC uses super-gain transistors in follower requiring 10-nA bias current and giving 30-μs slew.—Bandpass Filter (National Semiconductor ad), *Electronic News,* June 8, 1970, p 11.

CHAPTER 29
Filter Circuits—Passive

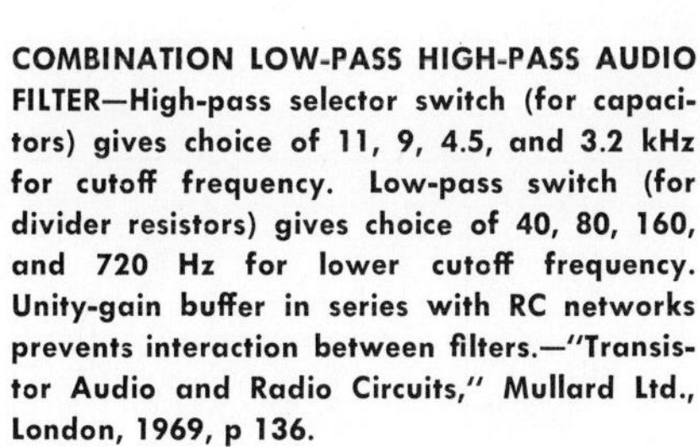

COMBINATION LOW-PASS HIGH-PASS AUDIO FILTER—High-pass selector switch (for capacitors) gives choice of 11, 9, 4.5, and 3.2 kHz for cutoff frequency. Low-pass switch (for divider resistors) gives choice of 40, 80, 160, and 720 Hz for lower cutoff frequency. Unity-gain buffer in series with RC networks prevents interaction between filters.—"Transistor Audio and Radio Circuits," Mullard Ltd., London, 1969, p 136.

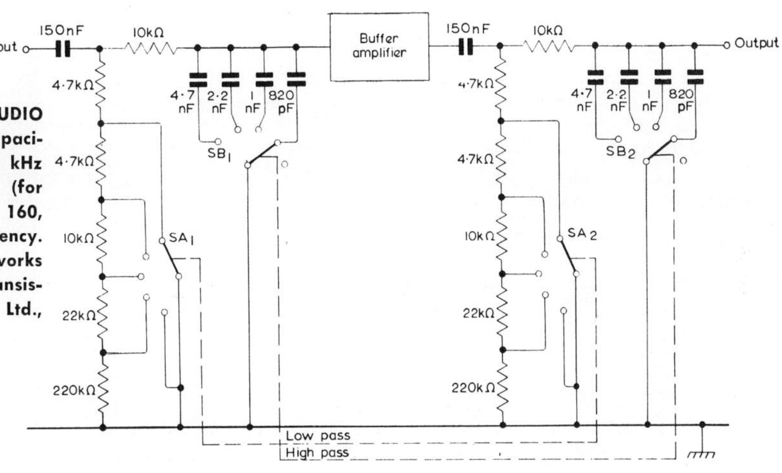

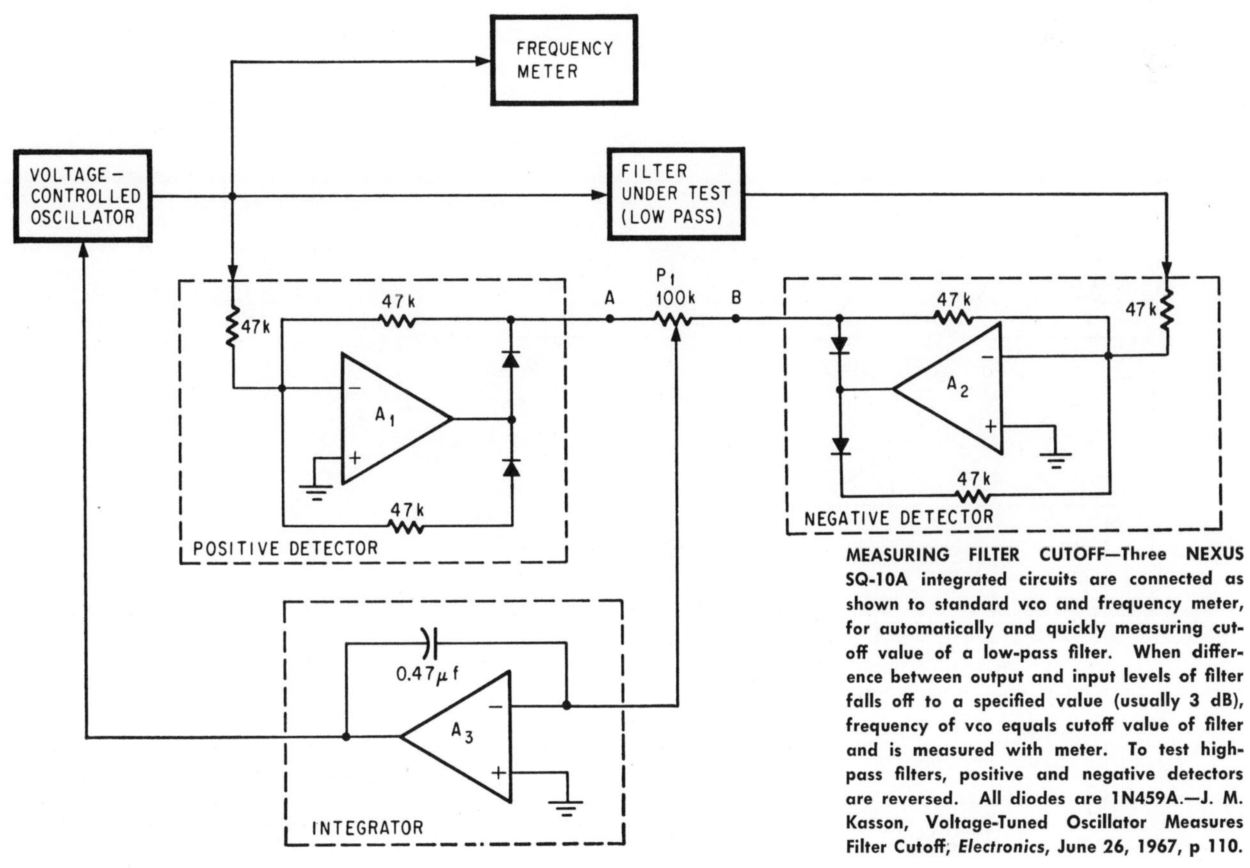

MEASURING FILTER CUTOFF—Three NEXUS SQ-10A integrated circuits are connected as shown to standard vco and frequency meter, for automatically and quickly measuring cutoff value of a low-pass filter. When difference between output and input levels of filter falls off to a specified value (usually 3 dB), frequency of vco equals cutoff value of filter and is measured with meter. To test high-pass filters, positive and negative detectors are reversed. All diodes are 1N459A.—J. M. Kasson, Voltage-Tuned Oscillator Measures Filter Cutoff, *Electronics*, June 26, 1967, p 110.

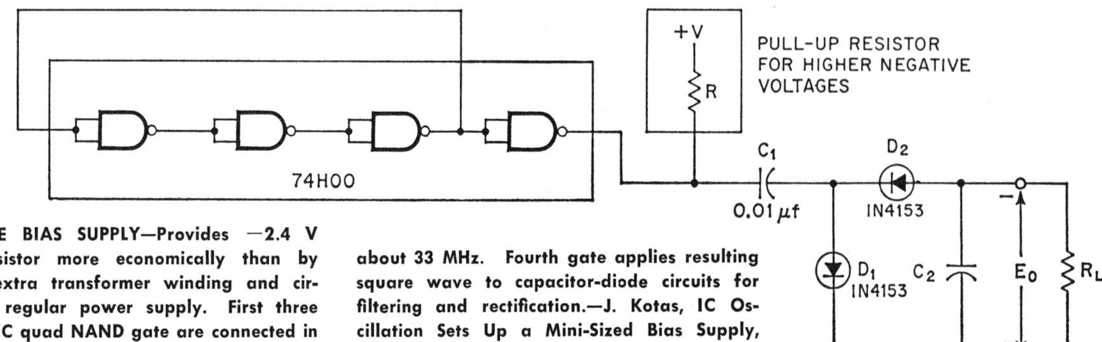

NEGATIVE BIAS SUPPLY—Provides −2.4 V for transistor more economically than by placing extra transformer winding and circuitry in regular power supply. First three gates in IC quad NAND gate are connected in loop to form astable mvbr that oscillates at about 33 MHz. Fourth gate applies resulting square wave to capacitor-diode circuits for filtering and rectification.—J. Kotas, IC Oscillation Sets Up a Mini-Sized Bias Supply, *Electronics*, July 6, 1970, p 76.

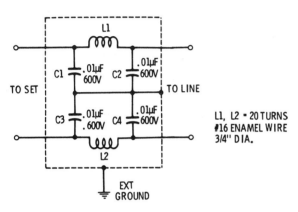

L1
C1 .01μF 600V
C2 .01μF 600V
TO SET
TO LINE
C3 .01μF .600V
C4 .01μF 600V
L2
EXT GROUND

L1, L2 = 20 TURNS #16 ENAMEL WIRE 3/4" DIA.

POWER-LINE INTERFERENCE FILTER—Used in a-c line to tv or radio receiver to suppress interference traveling over power line from nearby fluorescent lamp, electronic mixer, neon sign, or other source of rfi. Metal housing of filter should be grounded. For tv set, wind coils with No. 14 enamel wire. Use line cord at line side, and outlet for set.—J. P. Shields, "Novel Electronic Circuits," H. W. Sams & Co., Indianapolis, Ind., 1968, p 59.

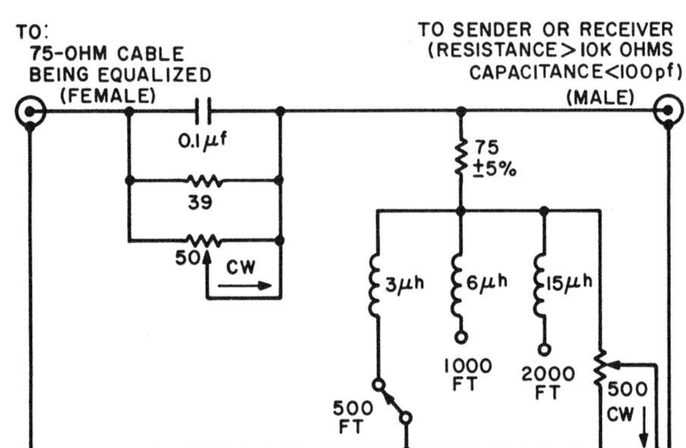

75-OHM COAX EQUALIZER—Passive filter network compensates for amplitude attenuation and phase retardation at video frequencies in four different lengths of cable. When used at both ends, provides 5 dB gain at 5 kHz and slight loss below 200 kHz. If used only at one end, other end must be terminated in resistance within 25% of 75-ohm nominal cable impedance.—A. H. Turner, Equalizer for 75-Ohm Cables Reduces Phase Retardation, *Electronic Design*, March 30, 1964, p 71.

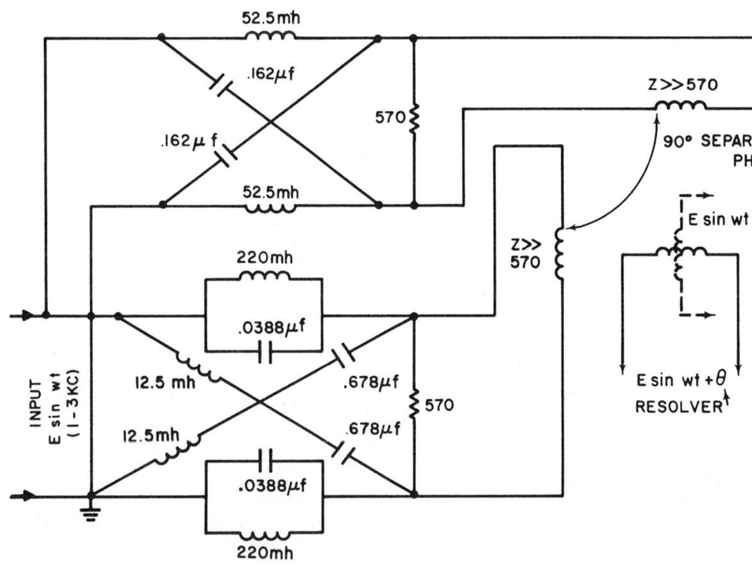

PHASE SPLITTER—Combines simple unipole all-pass network with duopole filter to give outputs separated by 90 deg, operating from 1 to 3 kHz, with tolerance of 5 deg. Article gives design equations for each type of filter and procedures for combining them for use with two-phase resolvers, single-sideband systems, and phase modulation applications. —C. C. Routh, All-Pass Filters Accurately Split the Phase, *Electronic Design*, Jan. 18, 1965, p 38–43.

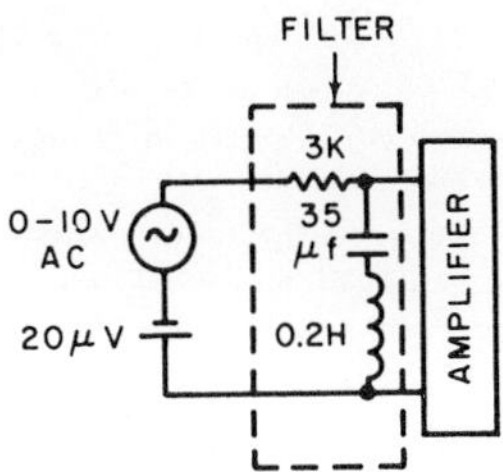

SUPPRESSING 60-HZ PICKUP—Simple LC filter improves performance of sensitive d-c amplifiers for microvolt d-c signals in the presence of 60-Hz power-line pickup up to 10 V. —R. L. Nuttall and D. C. Ginnings, Is 60-Cycle Pickup Degrading the Performance of your DC Amplifiers? *Electronic Design*, Dec. 20, 1965, p 34–35.

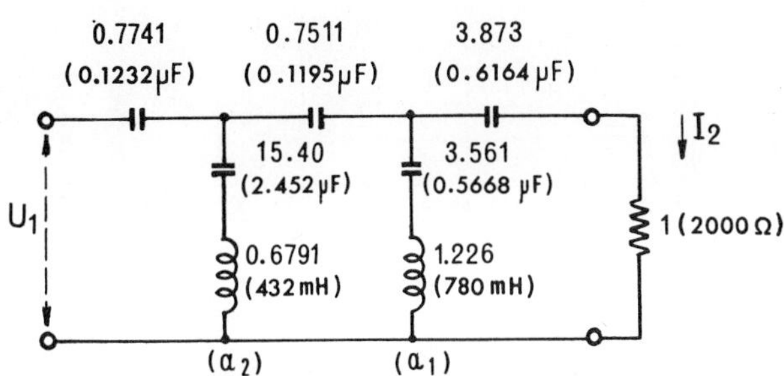

HIGH-PASS RLC—Provides attenuation of 52 dB below 245 Hz and only 0.044 dB above 500 Hz when inserted between voltage generator and 2,000-ohm resistance. Article gives design procedure.—P. Allemandou, Transfer Functions of RLC Filters, *IEEE Transactions on Circuit Theory*, Dec. 1968, p 483–485.

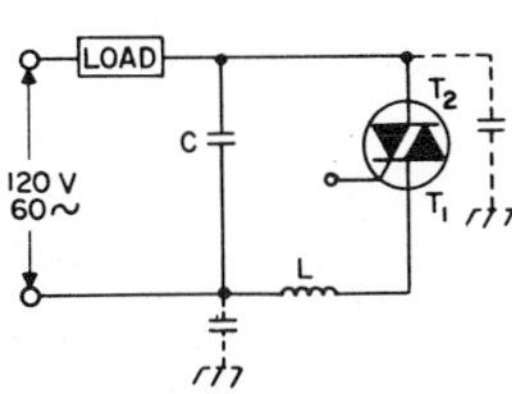

SUPPRESSING SCR AND TRIAC RFI—Single L-C low-pass filter having resonant frequency of 50 kHz gives about 40 dB of noise suppression at low end of broadcast band, for suppressing conducted rfi generated each time triac T2 (or scr) fires in resistive circuit such as lamp dimmer. At each firing, occurring 120 times per second with full-wave phase control, load current jumps from zero in fraction of microsecond and generates almost infinite spectrum of energy. For loads between 150 and 1,000 W, L can be 100 μH and C 0.1 μF.—J. H. Galloway, RF Filter Considerations for Triac and SCR Circuits, General Electric, Syracuse, N.Y., No. 201.19, 1966.

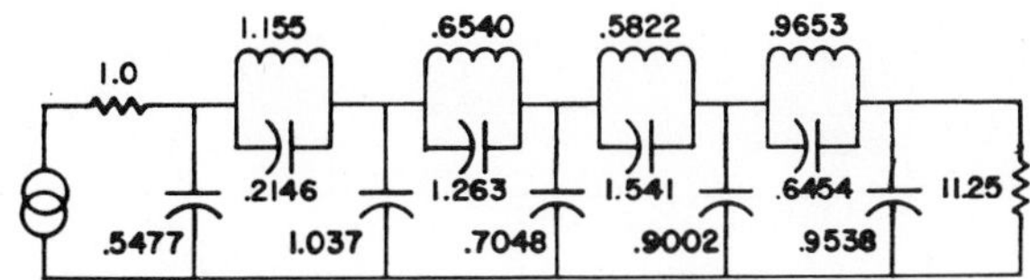

NINTH-ORDER LOW-PASS—When predistorted for average dissipation factor of 0.005, passband loss varies between 5.23 and 5.5 dB over passband of 0 to 1.0 frequencies.—W. N. Tuttle, Simplified Procedures for Approximation and Predistortion in Filter Synthesis by Digital Computer, *IEEE Transactions on Circuit Theory*, Dec. 1968, p 488–492.

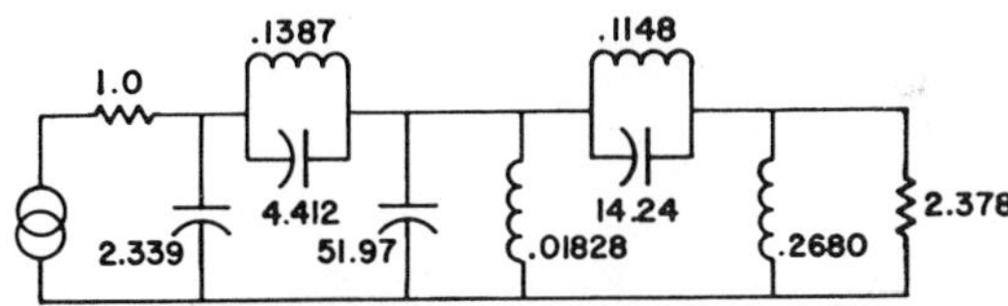

COMPUTER-DESIGNED BANDPASS—Values shown are for sixth-order symmetrical bandpass filter predistorted for average dissipation factor of 0.02. Attenuation is 7.45 dB for bandwidth of 10% above and 9% below center frequency.—W. N. Tuttle, Simplified Procedures for Approximation and Predistortion in Filter Synthesis by Digital Computer, *IEEE Transactions on Circuit Theory*, Dec. 1968, p 488–492.

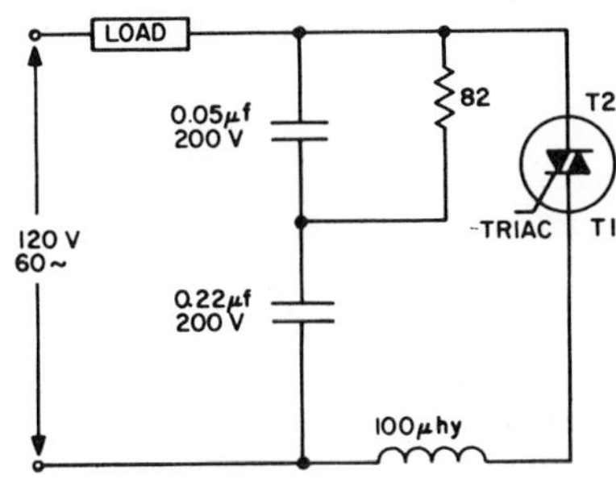

DAMPED R-F FILTER—Suppresses broadcast-band conducted rfi created by step-function action of triac. Upper resistor and capacitor provide damping required for proper operation under light load conditions, as for 60-W lamp dimmer.—"SCR Manual," 4th Edition, General Electric, 1967, p 334–335.

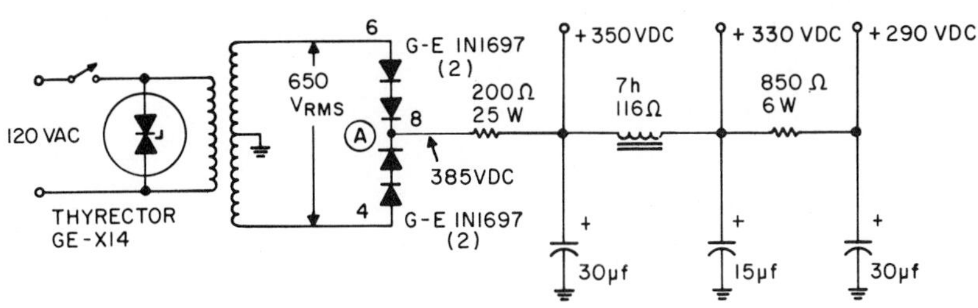

SILICON RECTIFIERS FOR TUBES—Gives procedures for substituting silicon rectifiers for vacuum, gas, or mercury rectifier tube. Arrangement shown is for 5U4GB. Only other change is addition of thyrector across primary to absorb line transients. Silicon rectifiers will give about 10% higher output voltage, which is usually not objectionable. To reduce supply voltage, place resistor (around 200 ohms at 25 W) in series with each pair of rectifiers.—"Hobby Manual," General Electric, Owensboro, Ky., 1965, p 192.

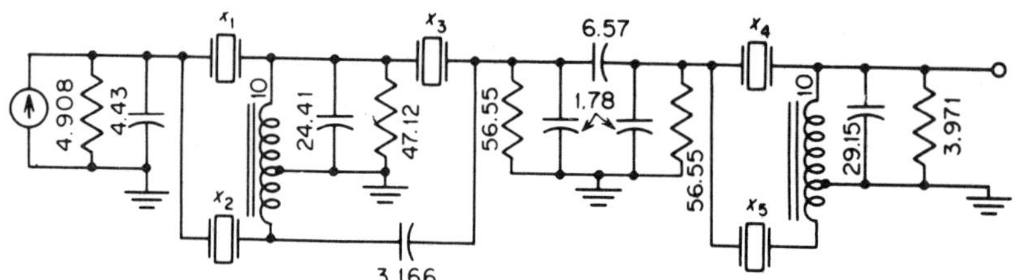

10-MHZ FIVE-CRYSTAL NARROW-BAND—Bandwidth for 3 dB down is 20 kHz, using AT-cut crystals and autotransformers having 10-μH inductance, Q of 150, and unity coupling. Article gives design equations for Chebyshev-type response and 1-dB passband ripple.—D. S. Humpherys, Network Synthesis of Narrow-Band Crystal Filters, *Electro-Technology*, Nov. 1965, p 36–43.

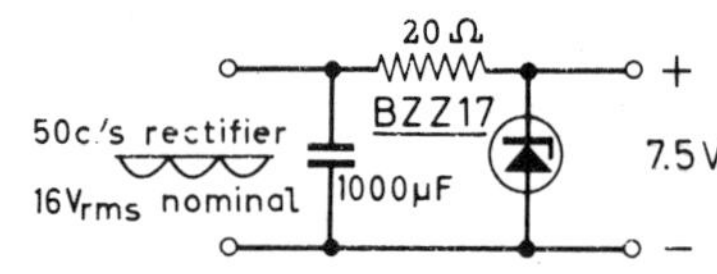

ZENER REPLACES CAPACITOR—Use of zener in place of output capacitor in smoothing filter gives smoothing comparable to that of 1,000-μF capacitor. Load current may vary from 0 to 300 mA.—Zener Diodes and Their Applications, Philips, Pub. Dept., Elcoma Div., Eindhoven, The Netherlands, No. 17, 1966.

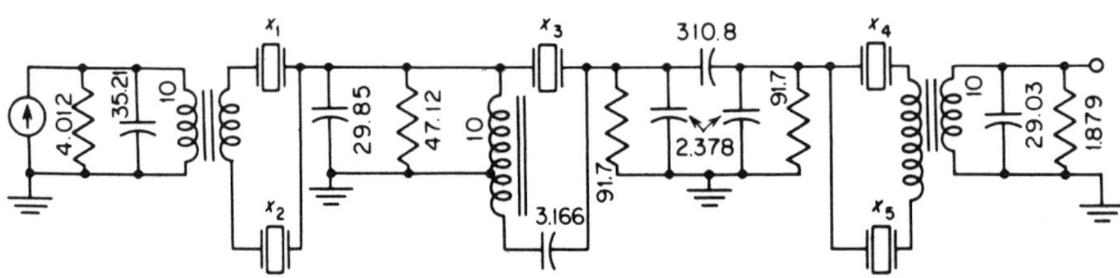

10-MHZ CRYSTAL FILTER—Design is based on left-half-plane reflection zeros, with hybrid transformers at each end for impedance transformations. Bandwidth is 20 kHz for 3 dB down, using AT-cut crystals and autotransformers having 10-μH inductance.—D. S. Humpherys, Network Synthesis of Narrow-Band Crystal Filters, *Electro-Technology*, Nov. 1965, p 36–43.

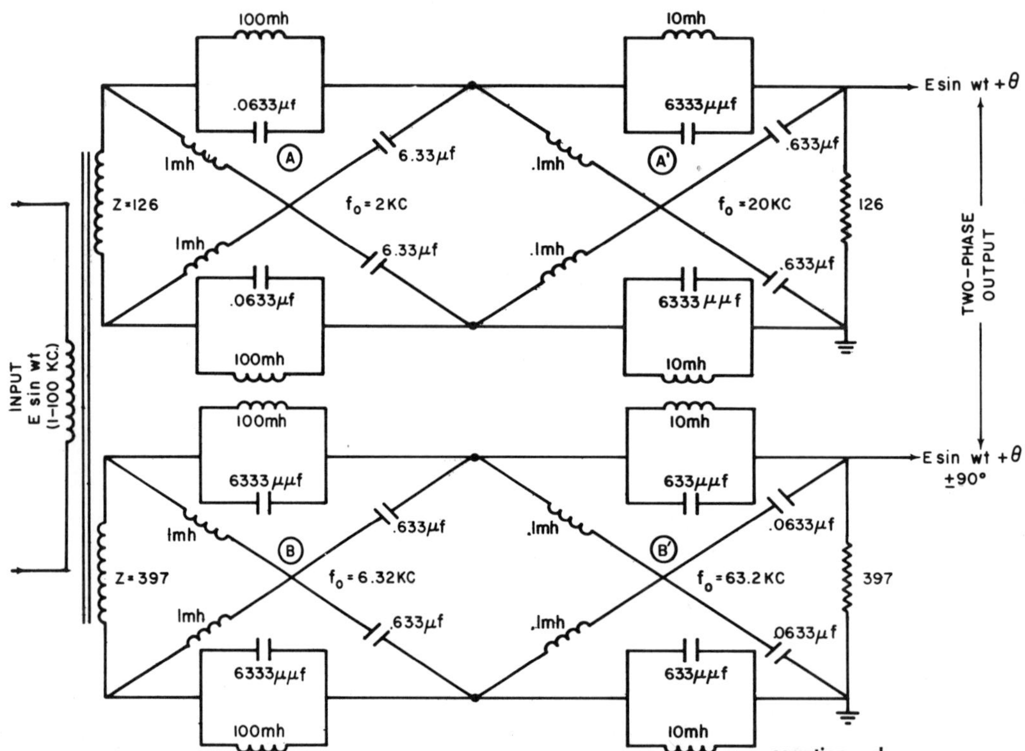

CASCADED PHASE-SPLITTER—Wideband operation from 1 to 100 kHz is obtained by cascading all-pass filters in both channels. Outputs are separated by 90 deg, as required for use with resolvers, ssb systems, and phase modulation systems. Article gives design equations, phase response graphs, and logical design procedures.—C. C. Routh, All-Pass Filters Accurately Split the Phase, *Electronic Design*, Jan. 18, 1965, p 38–43.

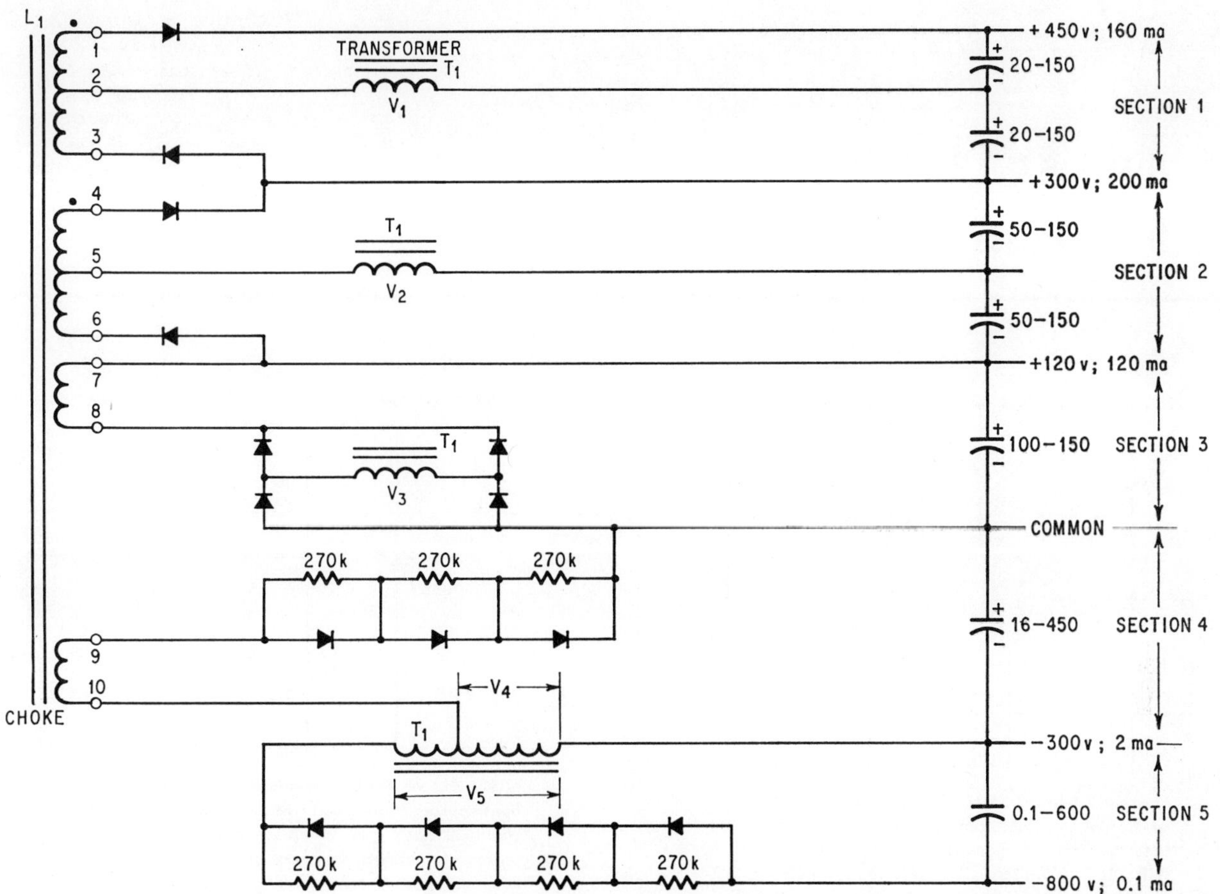

FIVE D-C OUTPUTS WITH ONE CHOKE—Weight-reducing design requires only one multiple-winding choke. Primary winding of transformer T1 (not shown) connects to a-c line, and secondary windings T1 supply required a-c voltages for the five choke-input rectifier sections. Article gives detailed procedures for calculating and winding sections of choke to give desired d-c output voltages and current.—A. G. Lloyd, Choking Up On LC Filters, *Electronics*, Aug. 21, 1967, p 93–97.

NOTE: To locate additional circuits in the category of this chapter, use the index at the back of this book. Check also the author's "Sourcebook of Electronic Circuits," published by McGraw-Hill in 1968.

CHAPTER 30
Flash Circuits

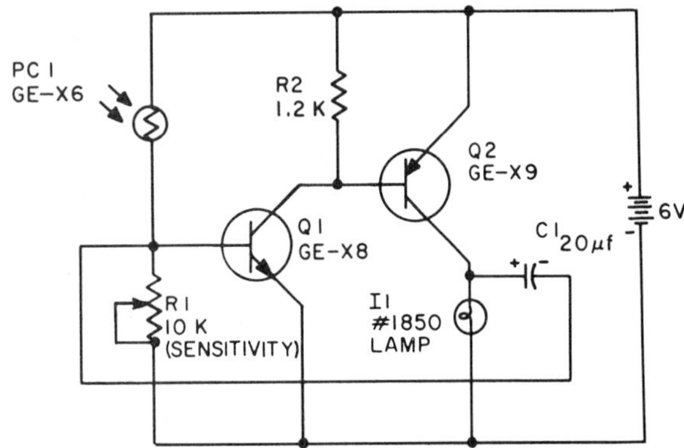

PHOTOCELL-CONTROLLED FLASH—Can be used as target for light gun, to give flash each time light-source gun is accurately aimed. Will flash continuously for steady light. Sensitivity control should be adjusted until flashing justs stops when not illuminated by desired light source.—"Hobby Manual," General Electric, Owensboro, Ky., 1965, p 78.

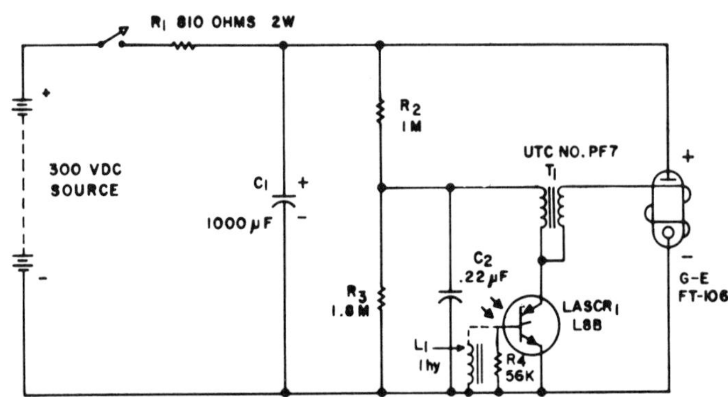

LASCR SLAVE FLASH—Developed for multiple-light-source high-speed photography. Uses standard flash gun, modified to use lascr in place of camera contacts or trip switch. Response is few ms, giving perfect sync between master and slave. For high ambient light levels that could trip lascr, 1-H choke L1 is added to serve as low impedance to ambient light but high impedance to flash.—E. K. Howell, The Light Activated SCR, General Electric, Syracuse, N.Y., No. 200.34, 1965.

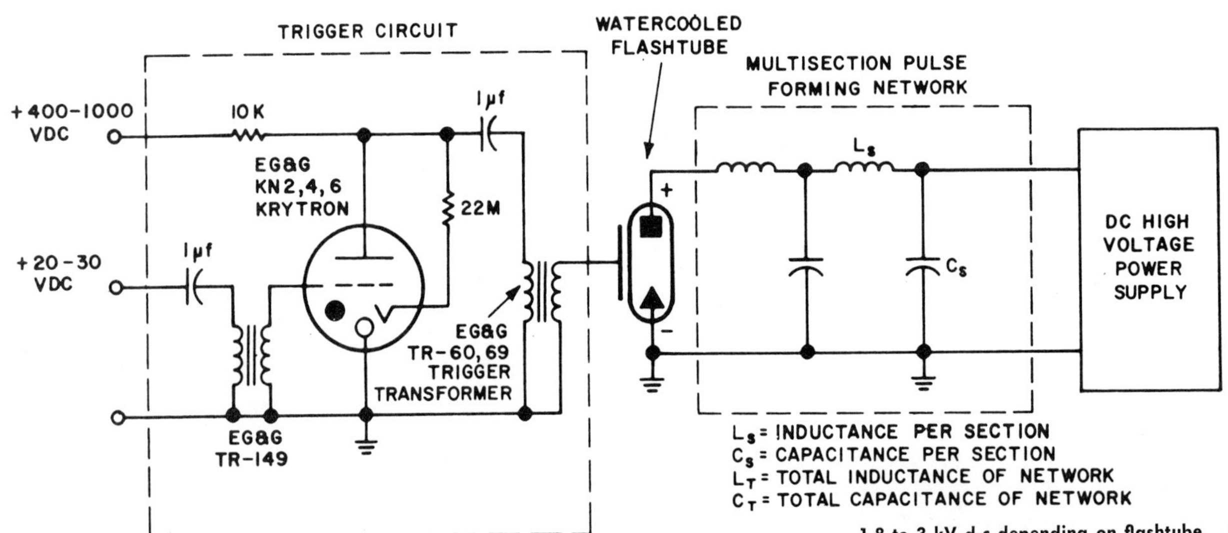

EXTERNAL TRIGGERING OF WATER-COOLED FLASHTUBE—Application of 20 to 30 V d-c to trigger circuit using Krytron four-element gas-filled cold-cathode switch tube generates 10-μs pulse at 5,000 V d-c and 2,500 A peak current (for KN-4) for primary of trigger transformer, to trigger water-cooled flashtube by applying 25 to 30 kV to external electrode. Operating voltage of flashtube, applied through pulse-forming network, ranges from 1.8 to 3 kV d-c depending on flashtube. Can be used for optical pumping of high-energy lasers, photography, and other applications requiring high-energy sources.—Linear Water-Cooled Xenon Flashtubes, EG&G, Boston, Mass., No. 1004, 1968.

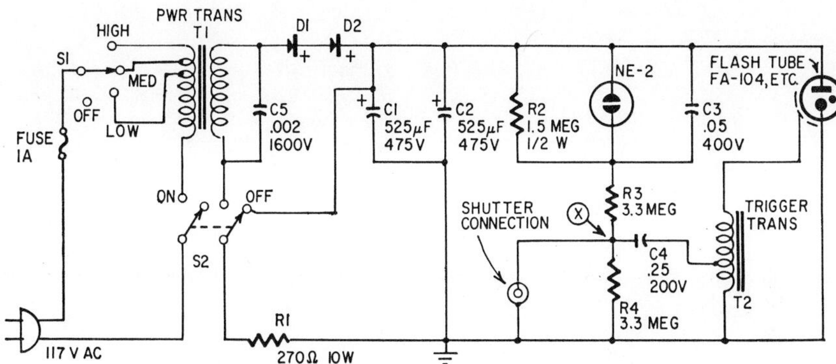

A-C FLASHTUBE SUPPLY—Circuit is typical of most small and low-cost electronic photoflash units, in which shutter of camera closes firing or triggering circuit that discharges capacitor through step-up transformer to produce single high-voltage pulse that ignites flashtube. One serious drawback is that discharge of C4 may soon burn out shutter contacts and give user harmless but unpleasant shock that may cause him to drop expensive camera.—L. E. Greenlee, SCR Trigger for Your Photoflash, *Radio-Electronics*, Nov. 1965, p 40–41.

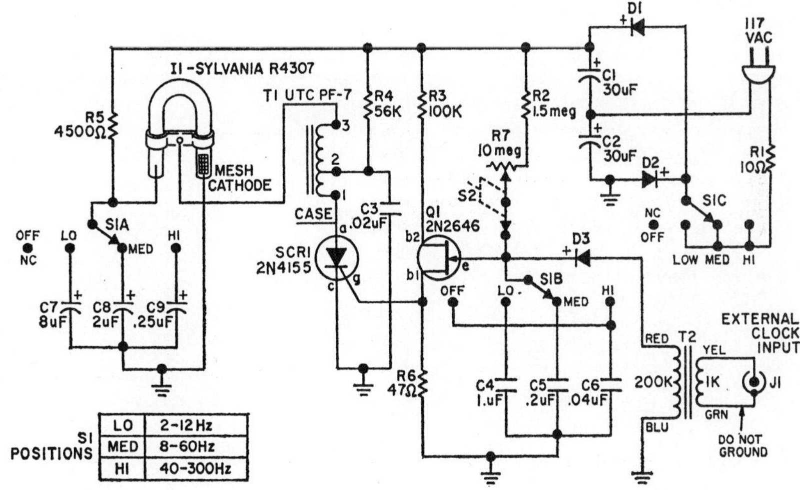

S1 POSITIONS	
LO	2-12Hz
MED	8-60Hz
HI	40-300Hz

LOW-COST STROBE—Uses ujt relaxation oscillator as clock for driving high-voltage trigger and xenon flashtube discharge circuit, with conventional 300-V voltage-doubling power supply. Switch S1 gives choice of three flash ranges: 2-12 Hz, 8-60 Hz, and 4-300 Hz. R7 adjusts flash rate within each range. Article gives construction details, calibration procedure, and suggestions for use.—S. Tennen, Pennypincher's Stroboscope, *Elementary Electronics*, Mar.–Apr. 1970, p 29–33 and 99.

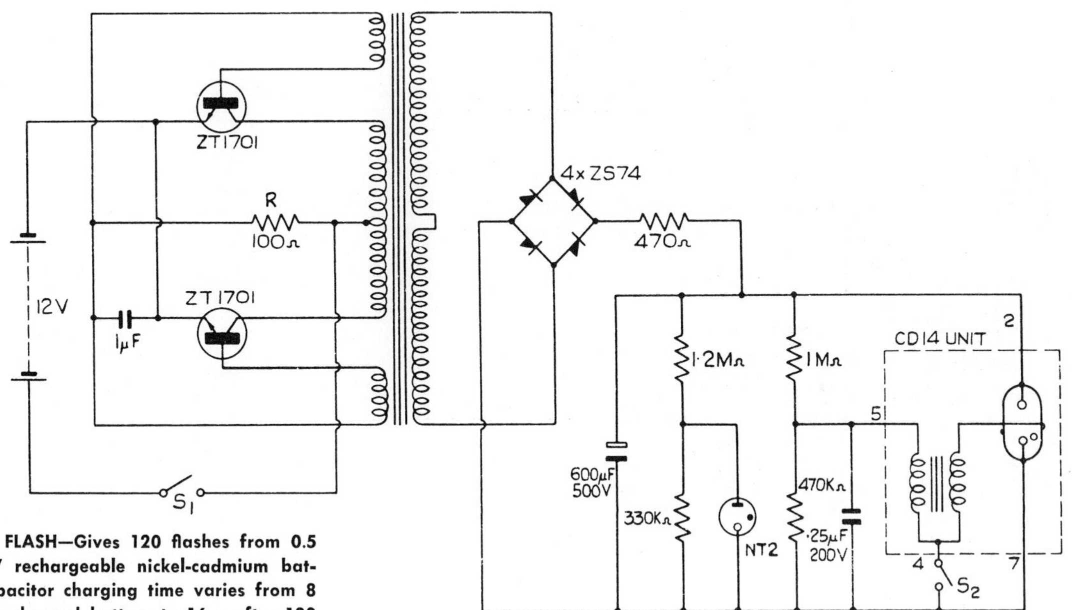

50-JOULE FLASH—Gives 120 flashes from 0.5 A-hr 12-V rechargeable nickel-cadmium battery. Capacitor charging time varies from 8 s for fully charged battery to 16 s after 120 flashes. Battery drives two-transistor inverter operating at about 1.5 kHz, with oscillation accomplished by saturating transformer. Secondary voltage is rectified for charging 600-μF capacitor to about 400 V. Neon then glows to indicate that unit is ready for use. Closing camera flash contacts S2 discharges 0.25-μF capacitor through pulse transformer, and resulting high-voltage pulse makes CD14 flash unit turn on so large capacitor discharges through it. Guide number is 40 for Kodachrome II. Report gives design equations and transformer winding data.—A 50-Joule Photographic Flash Unit Using Silicon Transistors, Ferranti Ltd., Oldham, Lancs., England, No. 21, 1965.

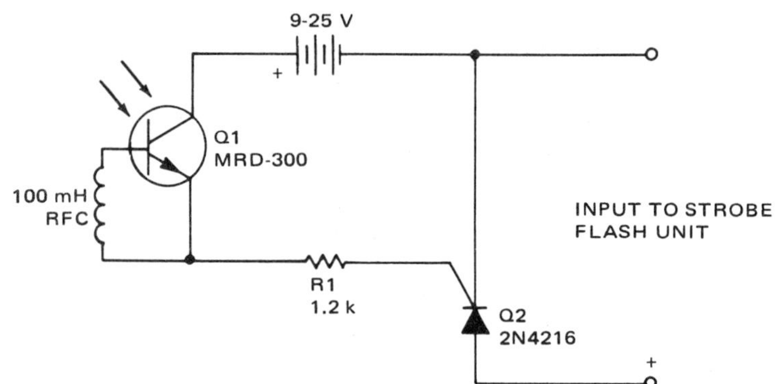

STROBELIGHT SLAVE—Serves as switch for triggering additional electronic strobe without using interconnecting wires. Unaffected by ambient light. Will trigger reliably up to about 20 ft from master strobe. Range can be increased by using lens or parabolic reflector to concentrate light on phototransistor. —"Semiconductor Power Circuits Handbook," Motorola, Phoenix, Ariz., 1968, p 6–42.

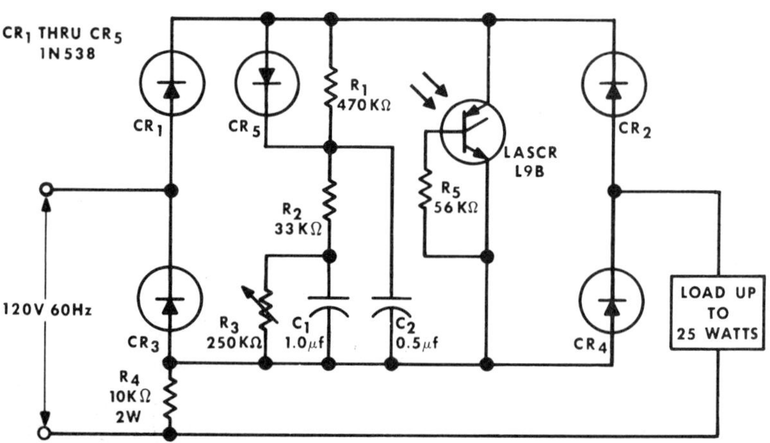

FLASH-ACTUATED SWITCH—Random flash of light fires lascr, turning on load. C1 and C2 then begin discharging. Setting of R3 determines how long flash-actuated switch remains on. Switch can turn on at any phase angle, but will turn off only at current zero, so rfi is negligible.—L. M. Hertz, Solid State Lamps—Part II, General Electric, Cleveland, Ohio, No. 3-0121, 1970, p 19.

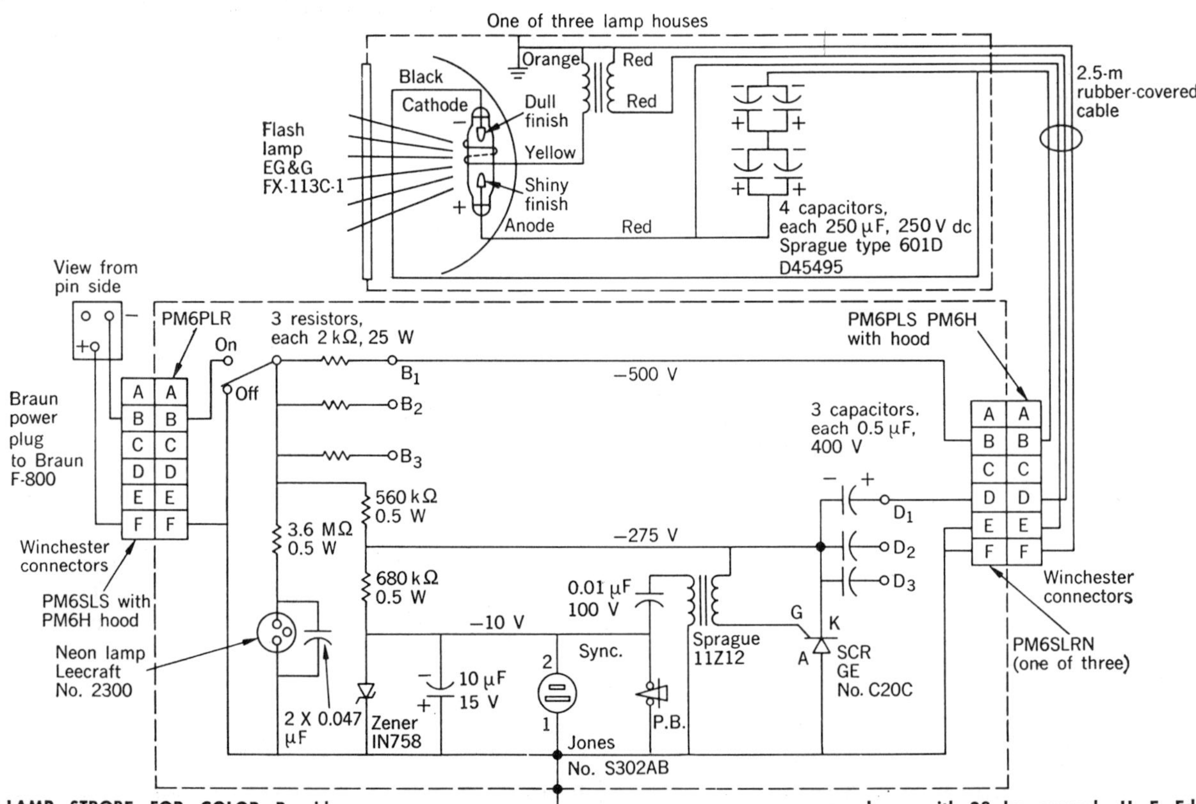

THREE-LAMP STROBE FOR COLOR—Provides 65-μs flashes, as required for photographing wing tips of hummingbirds in color without blur. Circuit is powered by Braun F800 unit. Stored energy is 31 joules per lamp, with light output of 1,500 beam candela seconds per lamp with 28-deg spread.—H. E. Edgerton, V. E. MacRoberts, and M. Khanna, Improvements in Electronics for Nature Photography, *IEEE Spectrum*, July 1969, p 89–94.

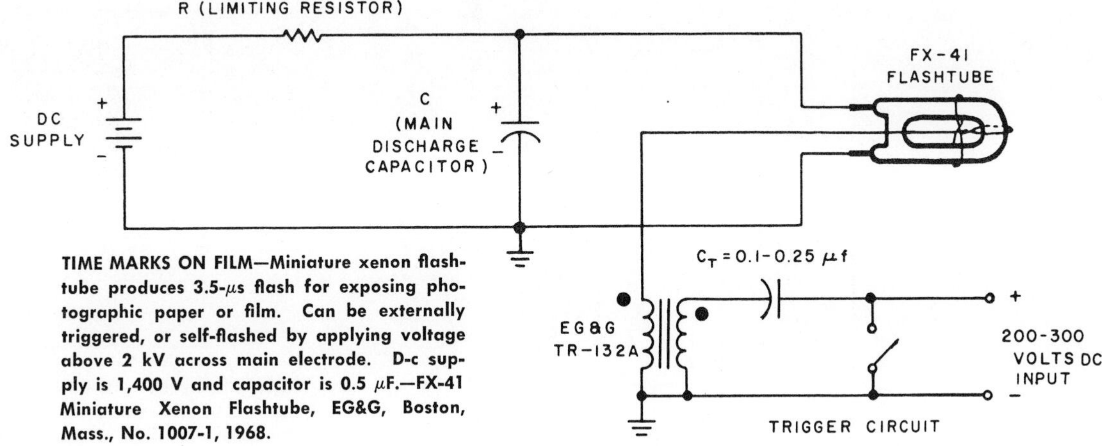

TIME MARKS ON FILM—Miniature xenon flashtube produces 3.5-μs flash for exposing photographic paper or film. Can be externally triggered, or self-flashed by applying voltage above 2 kV across main electrode. D-c supply is 1,400 V and capacitor is 0.5 μF.—FX-41 Miniature Xenon Flashtube, EG&G, Boston, Mass., No. 1007-1, 1968.

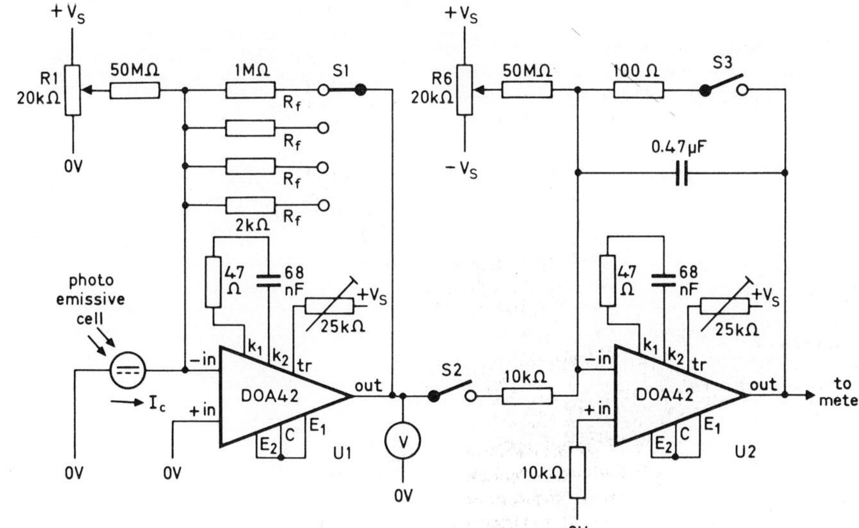

MEASURING FLASH ENERGY—With S2 open, Philips DOA42 IC opamp at left measures photocell current in four ranges, keeping voltage across photocell lower than a few millivolts so relationship between current flow and light intensity is linear. To measure total light energy, as from flash lamps, S2 is closed and S3 open, for integrating output of first amplifier. Supply voltages are +15 and −15 V.—J. Ph. Korthals Altes, Measurement of Light Intensity, Philips, Pub. Dept., Elcoma Div., Eindhoven, The Netherlands, No. 85.

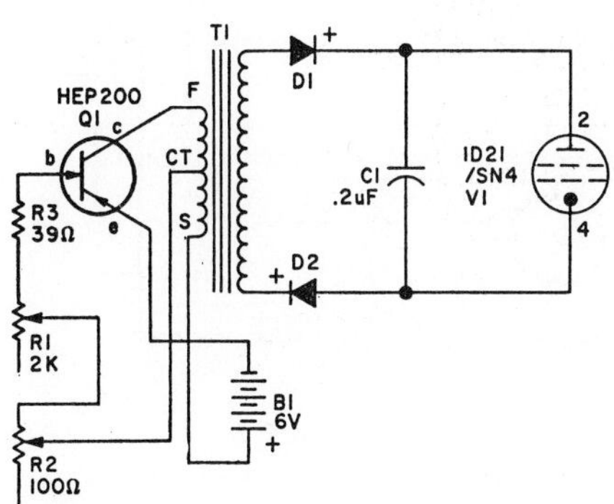

STROBOSCOPE—Audio oscillator Q1 generates variable-frequency output whose frequency is determined by settings of R1 and R2. T1 is power transformer used in reverse, with 6.3-V secondary in oscillator circuit, so step-up ratio of oscillator output is about 18.5:1. Diodes rectify stepped-up voltage to charge C1 to point where it fires Strobotron V1. Article gives construction details. Used for studying rotating objects, by adjusting flash rate until motion appears to be stopped.—S. Daniels, Stop Light Stroboscope, *Science and Electronics*, Jan. 1970, p 37–39.

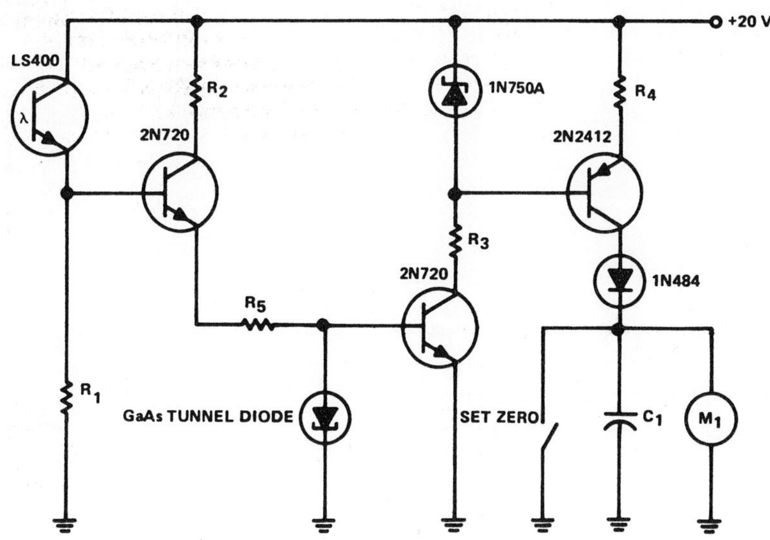

TIMING DURATION OF LIGHT PULSES—Uses LS400 npn planar silicon photocell for sensing flash of light. Duration of flash in seconds is equal to one-tenth of reading of vtvm M1 in volts. Range of measurable light pulse widths is 1 μs to 1 s. Values are: C1 100 μF Mylar; R1 4.7K; R2 1K; R3 1.5K; R4 3.6K; R5 500.—Preferred Semiconductors and Components, Texas Instruments, Dallas, Texas, CC101, 1968, p 27402.

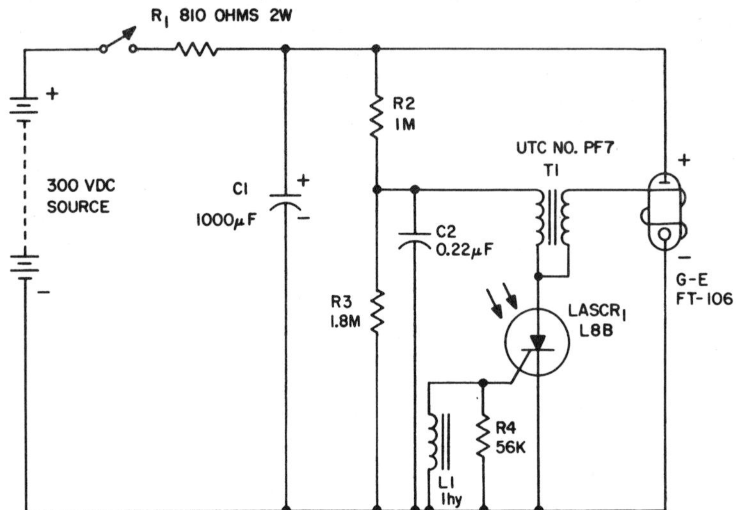

LASCR SLAVE FLASH—With S1 closed, C1 charges to 300 V and C2 charges to 200 V. When master flashgun is fired by contacts on camera, its light output triggers light-activated scr, which then discharges C2 into primary of T1 to trigger slave and discharge C1. Resonant action between C2 and T1 reverse-biases lascr for positive turnoff. Response time is few microsec, giving perfect master-slave sync. Choke L1 prevents triggering by high ambient light.—"SCR Manual," 4th Edition, General Electric, 1967, p 299–300.

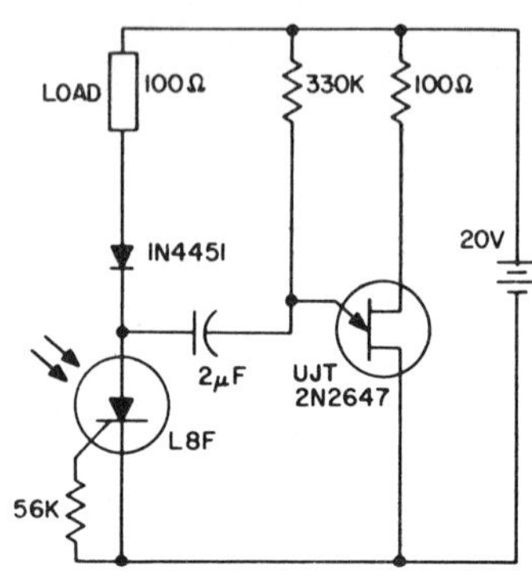

LIGHT-TRIGGERED ONE-SHOT—Ujt triggers about 0.6 s after pulse of light turns on type L8F lascr. If pulse of light is then ended, lascr turns off. If light is still on, ujt operates as relaxation oscillator but will turn lascr off the first time it fires after light is removed. High resistance of dark lascr then prevents ujt from oscillating.—"SCR Manual," 4th Edition, General Electric, 1967, p 297.

SCR-TRIGGERED PHOTOFLASH—Improved circuit uses scr to give more reliable triggering of flashtube without discharging C4 through shutter contacts. Maximum current through contacts is less than 1 mA, which practically eliminates pitting. Voltmeter indicates actual voltage across storage capacitors with far greater accuracy than neon flasher. Article gives construction details.—L. E. Greenlee, SCR Trigger for Your Photoflash, *Radio-Electronics*, Nov. 1965, p 40–41.

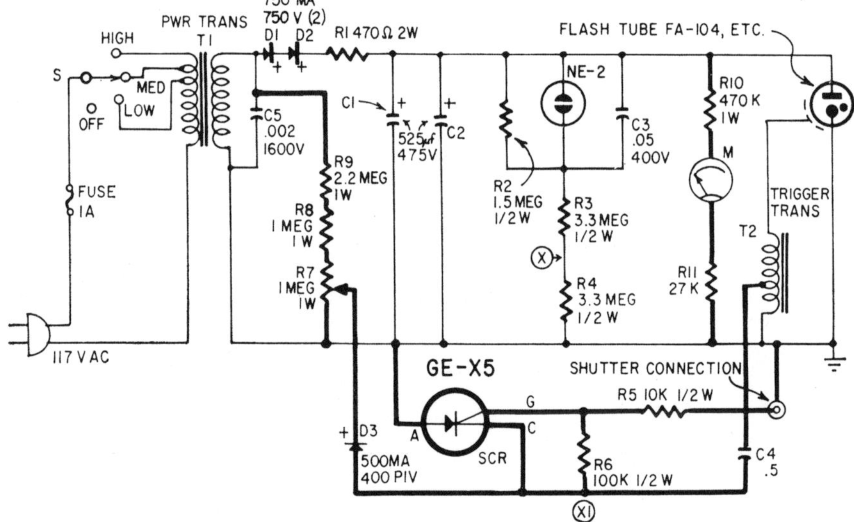

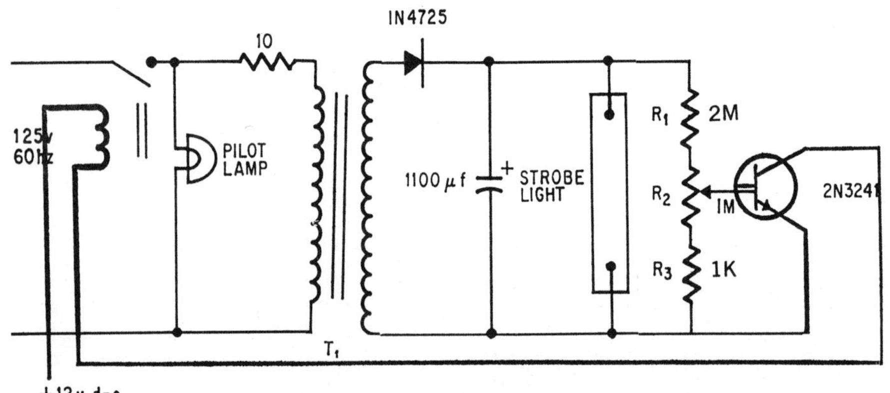

REGULATING PHOTOFLASH SUPPLY—Transistor and relay keep electrolytic capacitor voltage at correct charging level of 300 V, to prevent overcharging that shortens capacitor life. When voltage drops to about 290 V, relay drops out and charging starts again.—T. Lamb, Transistor and Relay Regulate High Voltages, *Electronics*, July 22, 1968, p 70.

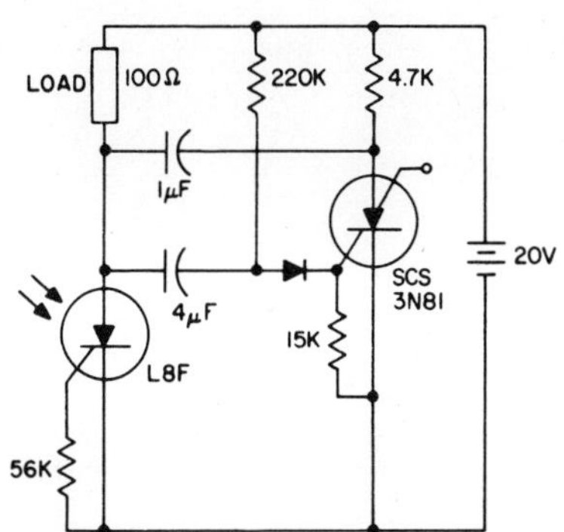

FLASH-DURATION SENSOR—With no light, scs conducts. When flash of light turns on lascr, scs goes off and 4-μF capacitor is charged. After about 0.6 s, scs turns on. If lascr is now dark, it goes off. If flash lasts longer than 0.6 s, lascr remains in conducting state. —"SCR Manual," 4th Edition, General Electric, 1967, p 298.

SIMPLE SCR PHOTOFLASH—Closing S1 discharges C2 through primary of trigger transformer when scr fires, to produce required high voltage across secondary for firing photographic flashtube.—Electronic Photoflash, *Popular Electronics*, April 1970, p 92.

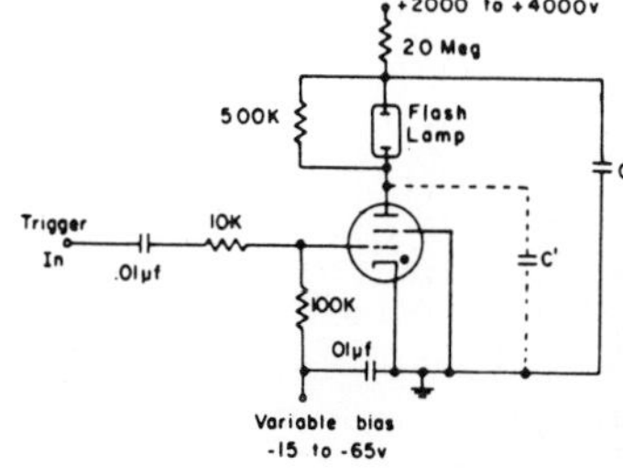

THYRATRON TRIGGER—2D21 thyratron triggers EG&G flashtube when input trigger is applied to control grid. 20-meg resistor in power supply lead ensures that both flashtube and thyratron are cut off after firing.—D. N. Bailey and D. M. Hercules, Flash Photolysis—A Technique for Studying Fast Reactions, *Journal of Chemical Education*, Feb. 1965.

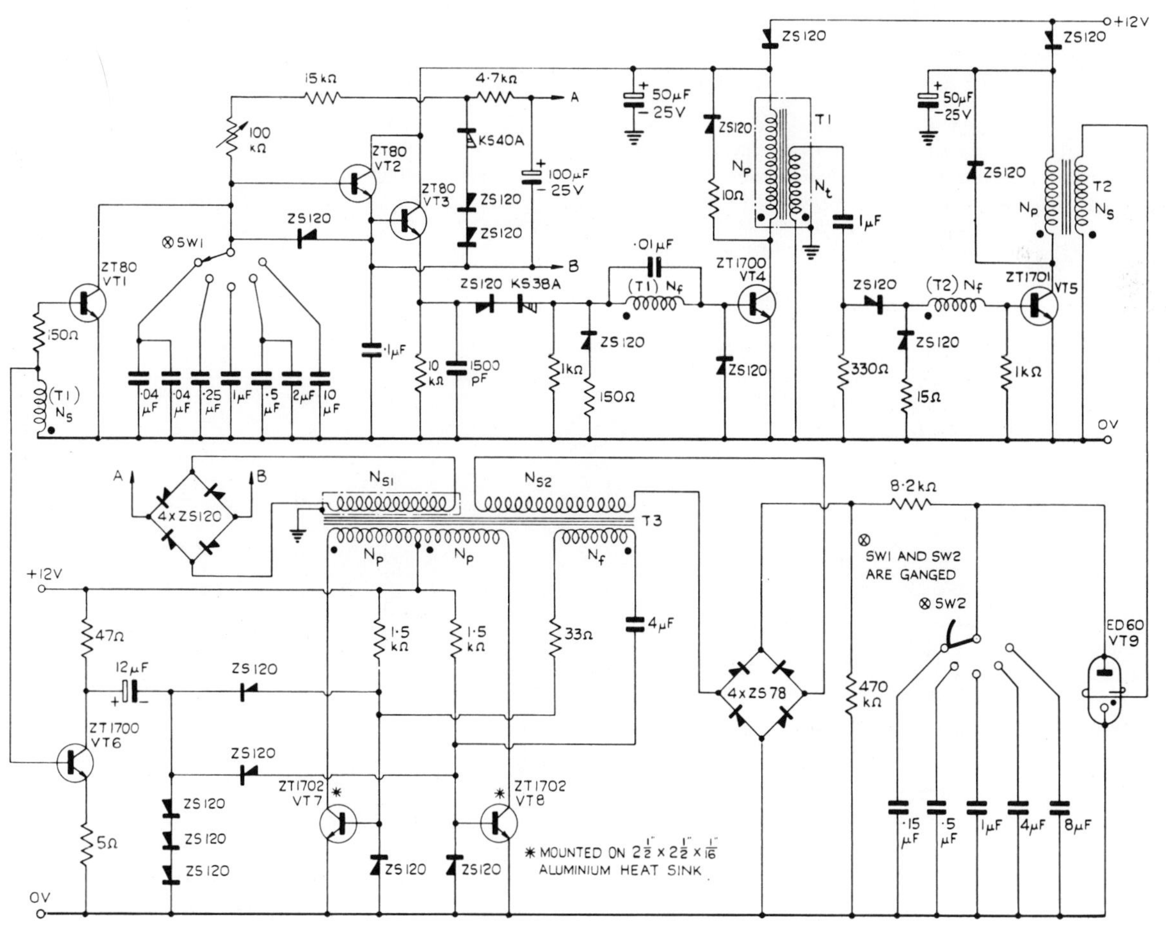

WIDE-RANGE PORTABLE STROBE—Switch gives choice of five repetition rates per second: 1–5, 3–15, 10–50, 30–150, 150–500. Draws maximum of 1.5 A from 12-V battery. Timing circuit VT1-VT4 drives flash tube trigger VT5 which produces 4-kV pulse at transformer secondary. Blocking oscillator VT1 also drives VT6 for switching off inverter VT7-VT8, to prevent self-retriggering of flash tube before gas deionizes on fastest range. Report gives winding data for all transformers.—A Wide Range Stroboscope Using Silicon Transistors, Ferranti Ltd., Oldham, Lancs., England, No. 27, 1964.

CHAPTER 31
Flasher Circuits

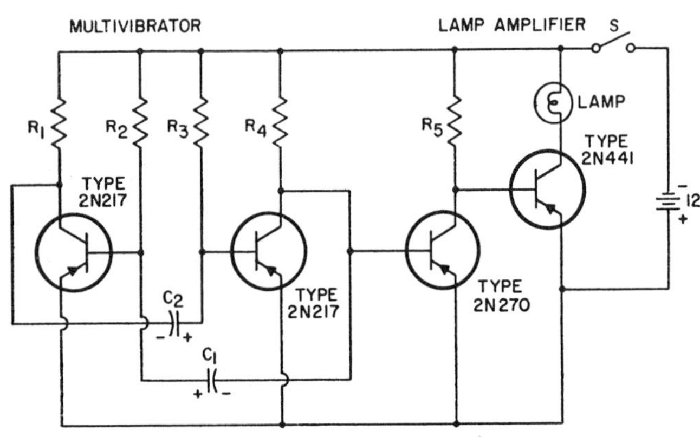

ONCE-PER-SECOND FLASHER—Will handle lamps up to 1 A at 12 V. Ideal for portable use. Lamp flashes at frequency of mvbr using pair of 2N217 transistors. Values: C1 25 μF; C2 100 μF; lamp 12 V at 1 A; R1, R4 2K; R2, R3 100K; R5 120.—"Transistor Manual," RCA, Harrison, N.J., SC-13, p 535.

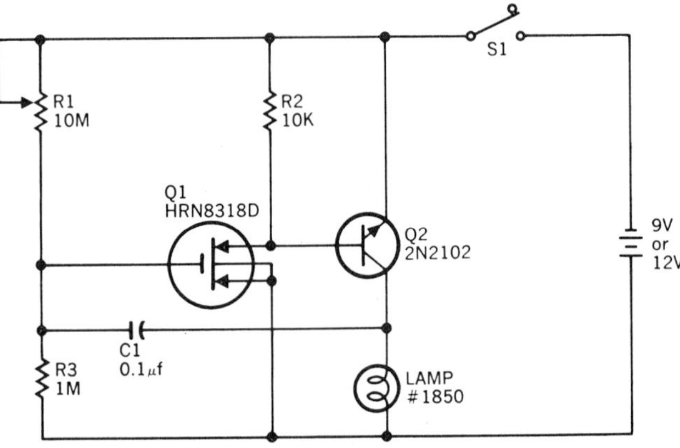

MOSFET FLASHER—Combination of npn transistor and p-channel mosfet gives extremely long duty cycles for flasher, reducing average power dissipation and increasing battery life. Time constant is determined by C1, R1, and R3. If common junction of these three timing components is connected to photocell, flasher will operate only when photocell is dark.—C. R. Perkins, "Application of MOSFET Devices to Electronic Circuits," Hughes, Newport Beach, Cal., 1968, p 45.

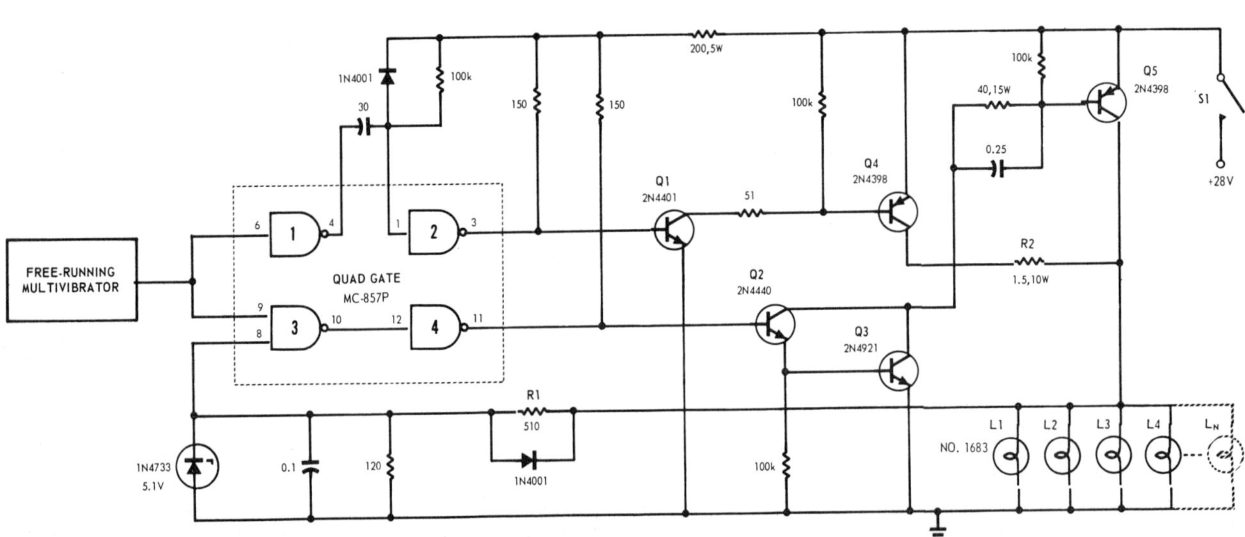

LONG-LIFE FLASHER—Circuit senses load current, withholding full load current until lamp filaments are warm or shorts are removed. Circuit automatically resets when defects are corrected. Maximum pulse current is limited to about 20 A by R2. Normal flashing cycle is 1 s.—R. A. Phillips, Lamp Flasher Outwits Shorts and Surges, *EDN*, Feb. 1, 1970, p 54–55.

1-KW BLINKER—Ujt Q1 operates as relaxation oscillator at frequency determined by R1, which may be potentiometer. Each ujt output pulse energizes relay through amplifier stage Q2, to apply power to lamp through relay contacts. Gives about one flash per second with values shown.—J. P. Shields, "Novel Electronic Circuits," H. W. Sams & Co., Indianapolis, Ind., 1968, p 90.

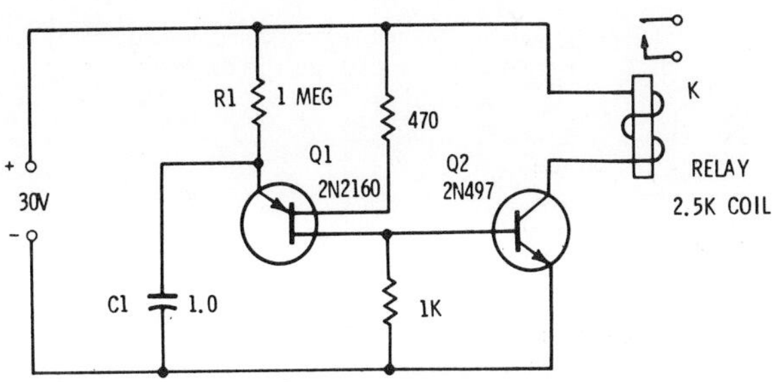

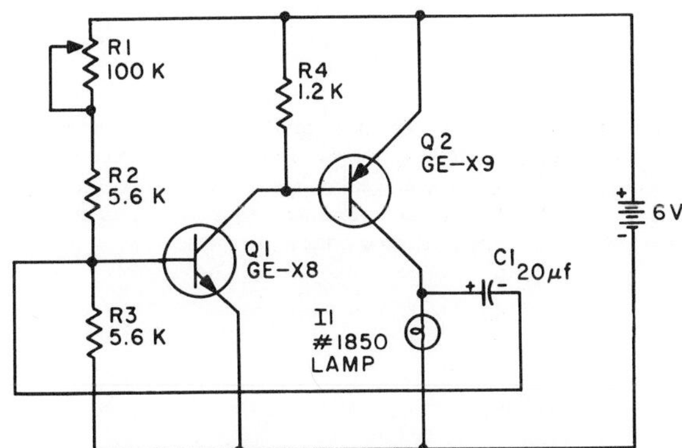

BICYCLE FLASHER—Two-stage direct-coupled flasher is connected as free-running mvbr operating from 600-V dry-cell pack. Can readily be mounted on bicycle for night safety. R1 controls both duration of flash and interval between flashes. Can also be used for identifying car at night in large parking lot, or identifying house for guests arriving after dark.—"Hobby Manual," General Electric, Owensboro, Ky., 1965, p 78.

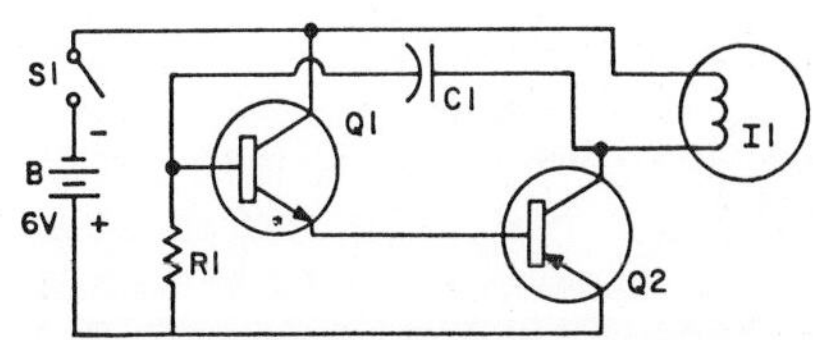

AUTO BREAKDOWN FLASHER—Will flash 6-V automotive lamp to full brilliance for use as warning light when breakdown occurs on turnpike. Operates from 6-V lantern battery. Uses relaxation oscillator, in which Q1 is 2N170, Q2 is 2N155, C1 is 50 μF, and R1 is 47K.—High Powered Flasher, *Elementary Electronics*, Jan.–Feb. 1968, p 14.

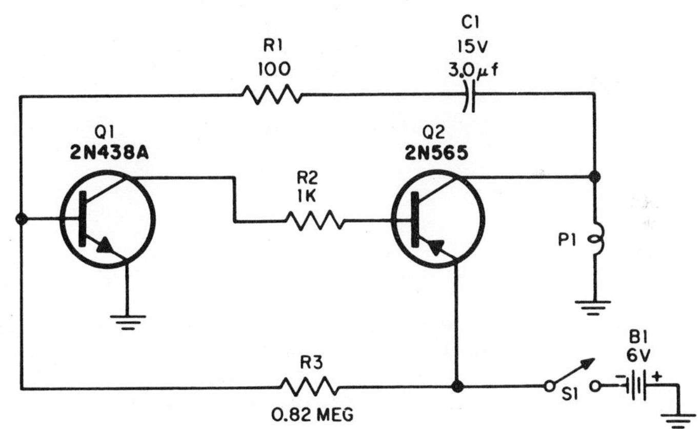

TINY FLASHER—No. 47 lamp at P1 flashes about once a second. Increase size of C1 to get brighter flash.—"A Modern Transistor Workbook," Radio Shack, Boston, Mass., 1965, p 64.

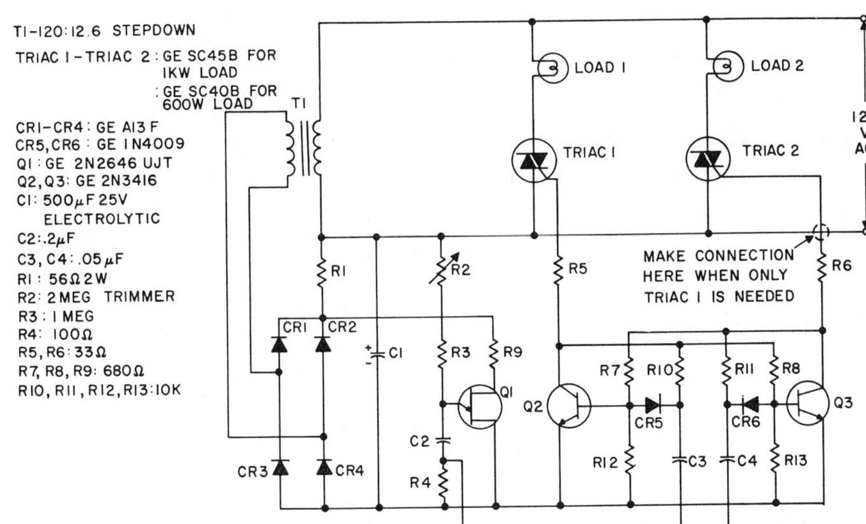

BASIC A-C TWO-LAMP FLASHER—Free-running ujt oscillator Q1 triggers flip-flop Q2-Q3 that alternately fires two triacs each capable of handling 1-kW lamp load. For on-off flashing of one lamp, omit second triac and make connection as indicated. A-c flasher is more popular than d-c version when handling hundreds of watts of power. R2 determines frequency of Q1. Synchronization of flashing with Q1 minimizes rfi.—A. A. Adem, Flashers, Ring Counters and Chasers, General Electric, Syracuse, N.Y., No. 200.48, 1966, p 2.

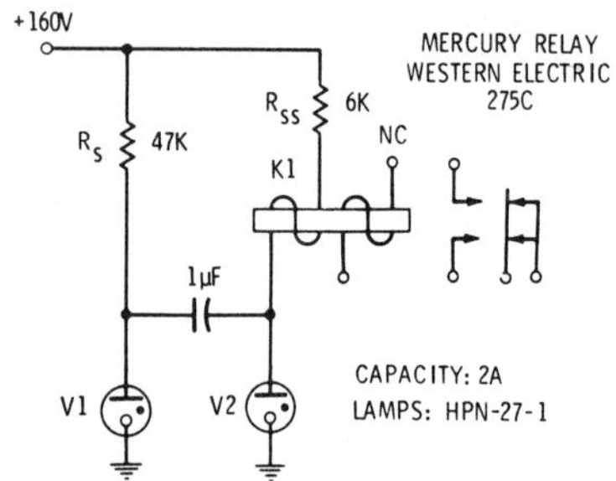

RELAY CONTROL FOR 3-HZ FLASHER—Neon-lamp mvbr is here used to keep mercury relay de-energized five times longer than it is energized, to give flash rate of 3 Hz for lamp connected to relay contacts.—W. G. Miller, "Using and Understanding Miniature Neon Lamps," H. W. Sams & Co., Indianapolis, Ind., 1969, p 65.

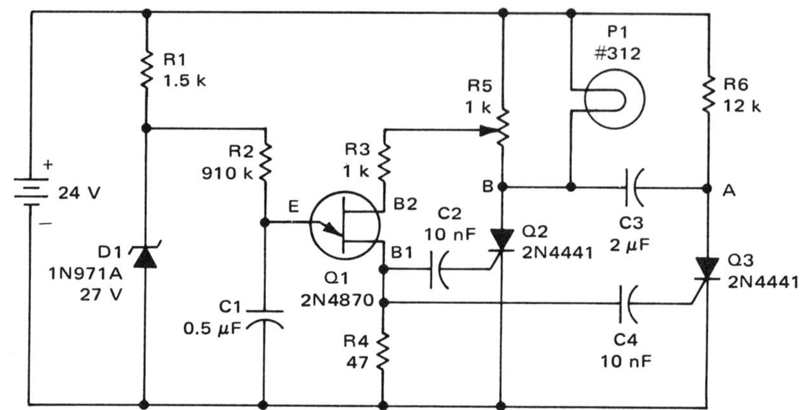

HIGH-RELIABILITY FLASHER—Basic flip-flop is modified so only one scr can come on at any time, to prevent circuit latchup. Duration of flash is adjustable from 10% to 50% of duty cycle; about 30% gives maximum visibility along with 40% saving in power over maximum duty cycle. Developed for boats, aircraft, and emergency vehicles.—"Semiconductor Power Circuits Handbook," Motorola, Phoenix, Ariz., 1968, p 6–35.

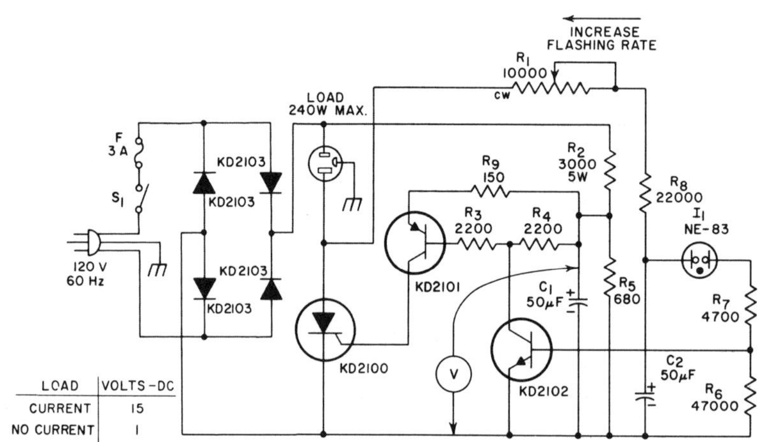

LOAD	VOLTS-DC
CURRENT	15
NO CURRENT	1

240-W WITH 0.5-S FLASHES—R1 adjusts intervals between flashes having fixed duration. For warning signals, typical adjustment is 40 flashes per minute, each lasting about 0.5 s and with 1-s OFF time. With buzzer as load, can serve as metronome.—"Silicon Controlled Rectifier Experimenter's Manual," RCA, Harrison, N.J., 1967, p 69.

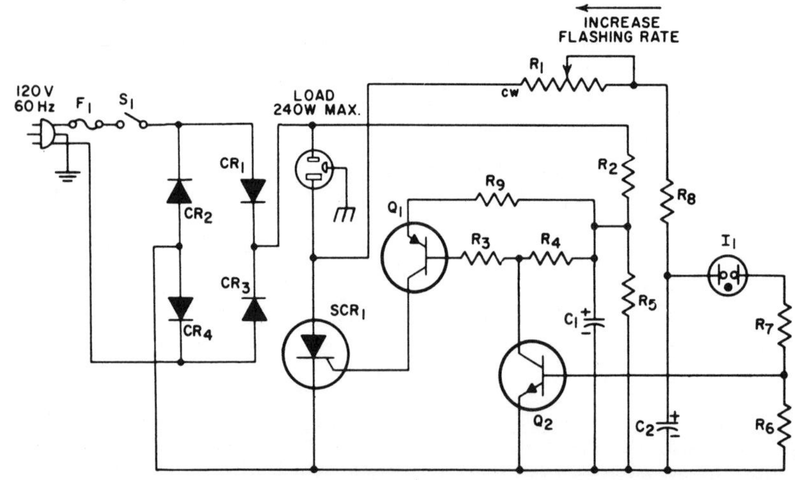

240-W FLASHER—Time of each ON pulse is fixed at about 0.5 s, and duration of OFF time is adjustable with R1 to provide desired number of flashes per minute. Can be used for Christmas-tree lights, advertising signs, warning signals, or for driving alarm bell having clapper hitting gong. Values: C1, C2 50 μF; diodes SK3016; F1 3A; I1 NE-83; Q1 SK3005; Q2 SK3020; R1 10K; R2 3K; R3, R4 2.2K; R5 680; R6 47K; R7 4.7K; R8 22K; R9 150; SCR1 KD2100.—"Hobby Circuits Manual," RCA, Harrison, N.J., HM-90, p 159.

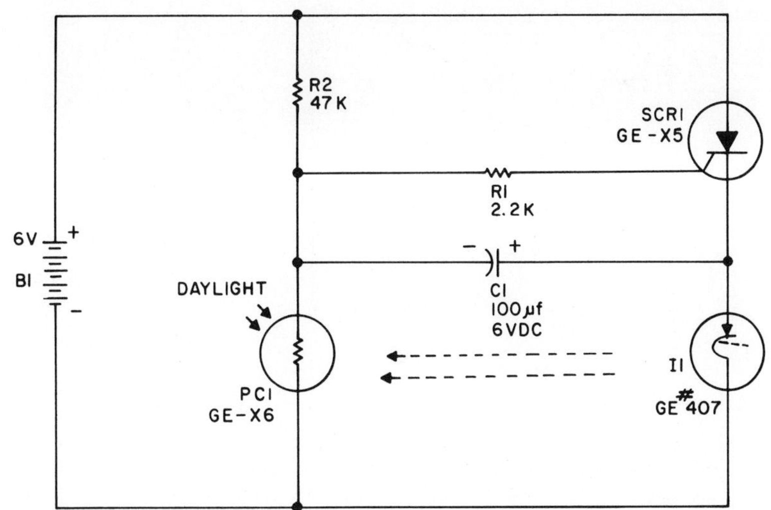

DAYLIGHT-OFF FLASHER FOR BUOYS—Photoelectric switch turns on 6-V single-lamp scr flasher at night and shuts it off at dawn, to conserve battery power and lamp light. For use in isolated locations at which a-c line power is not available. Gives about 12 flashes per minute. Mount photocell to receive as much light from flashing lamp as possible without interfering with visibility of lamp, so flashes lower resistance of photocell. Uses flasher-type lamp having built-in bimetallic switch that opens when lamp heats up (1 or 2 s) and closes again after 0.5 s of lamp cooling.—"Hobby Manual," General Electric, Owensboro, Ky., 1965, p 84.

1-KW DAYLIGHT-CONTROLLED FLASHER—Operates from a-c line, for use as warning light on tower, pier, or construction hazard, as well as for advertising signs. Photocell starts flasher at sunset and turns it off at dawn.—"Hobby Manual," General Electric, Owensboro, Ky., 1965, p 88.

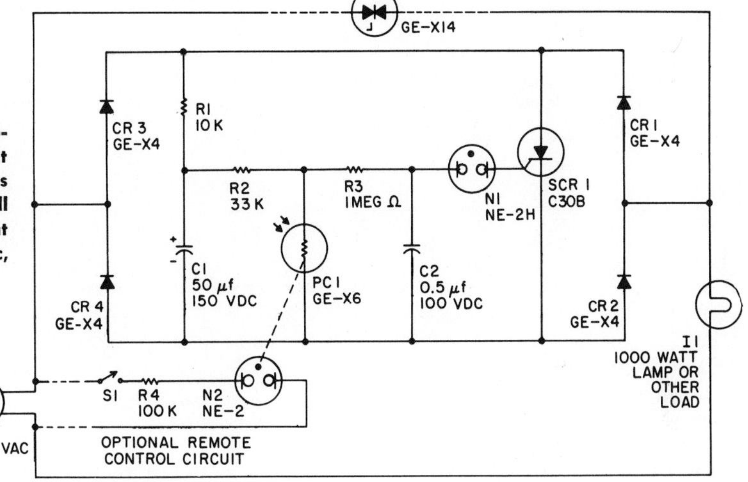

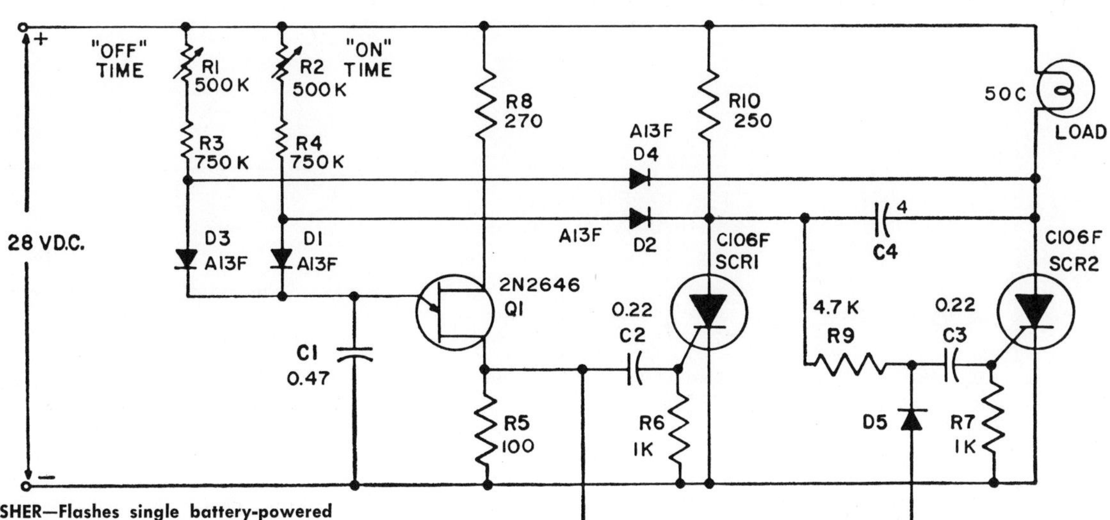

D-C FLASHER—Flashes single battery-powered lamp at adjustable on and off times, for automotive or portable traffic hazard warnings. Uses capacitor-commutated scr flip-flop. SCR2 should be selected so lamp current is within its rating, but SCR1 can be lower rating. Network R9-C3-D5 insures that only SCR1 will be turned on when power is first applied.—A. A. Adem, Solid-State Flashers for Light Displays, *Electronics World*, Aug. 1967, p 83–84.

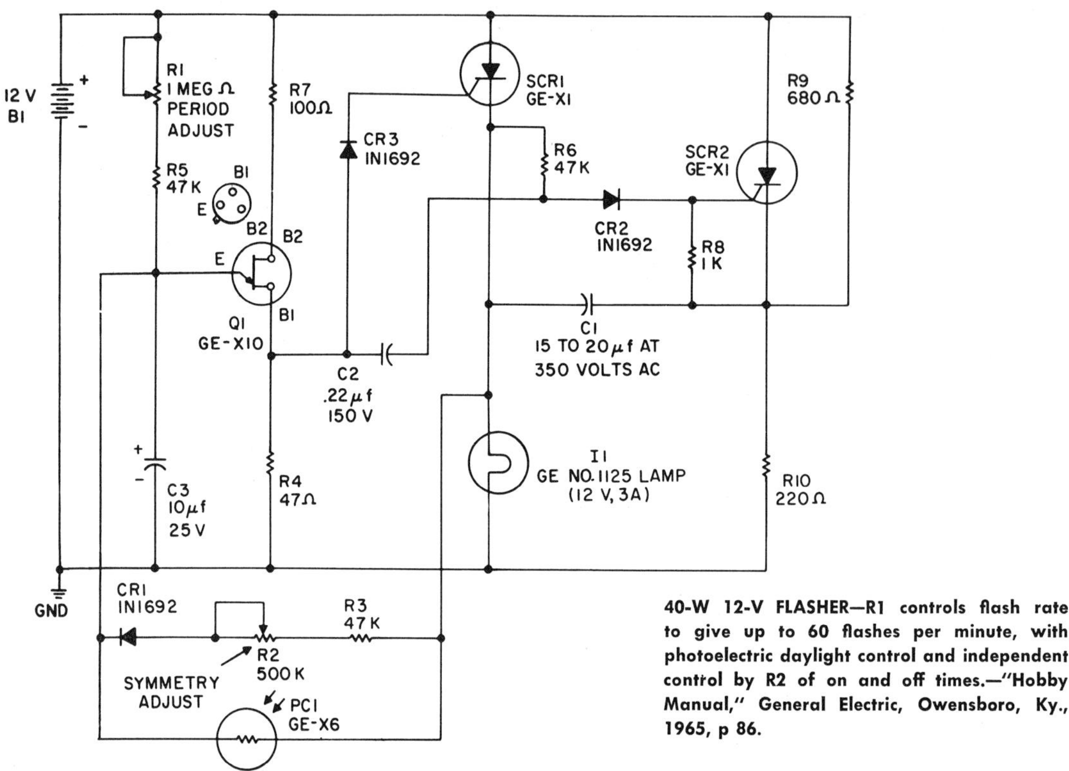

40-W 12-V FLASHER—R1 controls flash rate to give up to 60 flashes per minute, with photoelectric daylight control and independent control by R2 of on and off times.—"Hobby Manual," General Electric, Owensboro, Ky., 1965, p 86.

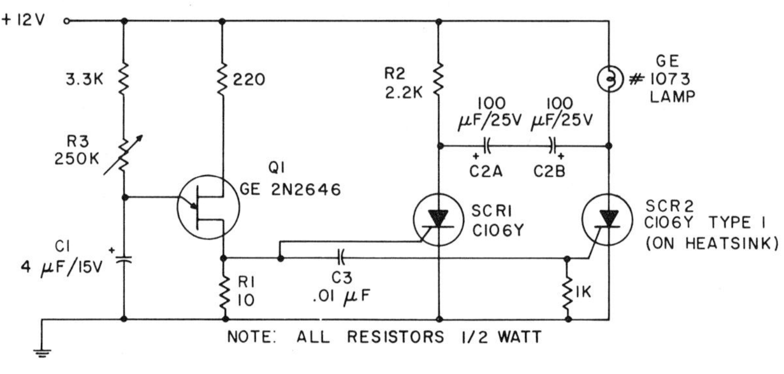

BARRICADE FLASHER—Uses two scr's to drive single lamp at flash rate adjustable by R3 in range of 36 to 160 flashes per minute. Circuit is self-starting when power from 12-V battery is applied, and operates reliably even for fluctuating (noisy) battery supplies. May also be used in autos and boats.—D. R. Grafham, Using Low Current SCR's, General Electric, Syracuse, N.Y., No. 200.19, 1967, p 38.

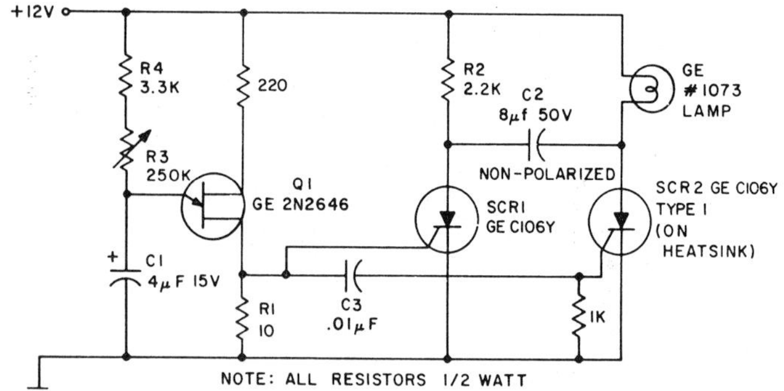

12-V SCR/UJT LOW-POWER FLASHER—Provides 36 to 160 flashes per minute, depending on setting of R3. Ujt Q1 operates as relaxation oscillator, delivering train of trigger pulses to two scr gates.—"SCR Manual," 4th Edition, General Electric, 1967, p 160.

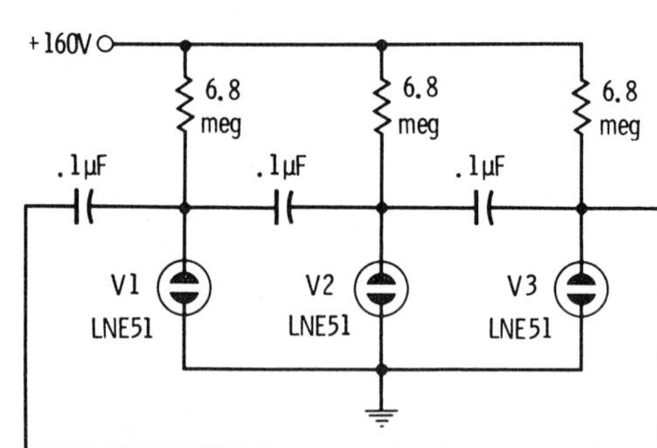

NEON SEQUENTIAL FLASHER—Flashing sequence will either be 1:2:3 or 3:2:1, but starting sequence is not predictable.—W. G. Miller, "Using and Understanding Miniature Neon Lamps," H. W. Sams & Co., Indianapolis, Ind., 1969, p 47.

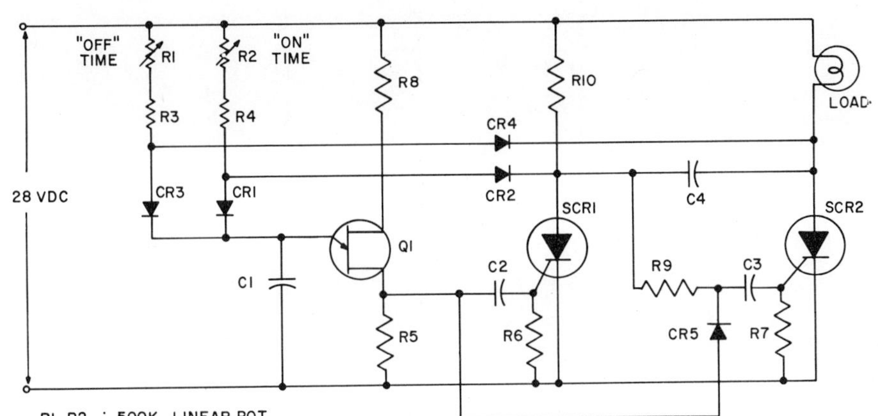

R1, R2	: 500K, LINEAR POT	C4	: 4 μF, 50 VOLTS NON-POLARIZED
R3, R4	: 750K 1/2 W	Q1	: GE 2N2646 UJT
R5	: 100Ω 1/2 W	SCR1, SCR2	: GE C106F
R6, R7	: 1K, 1/2 W	CR1 - CR5	: GE A13F
R8	: 270Ω 1/2 W	LOAD	: GE 50C 1.4A LAMP
R9	: 4.7K, 1/2 W		
R10	: 250Ω, 5W		
C1	: .47μF 50V		
C2, C3	: .22μF 50V		

SCR FLIP-FLOP D-C FLASHER—Has independent adjustments for on and off times of single lamp load. Circuit is capacitor-commutated scr flip-flop, with network R9-C3-CR5 added to ensure triggering of only one scr when power is first applied.—A. A. Adem, Flashers, Ring Counters and Chasers, General Electric, Syracuse, N.Y., No. 200.48, 1966, p 3.

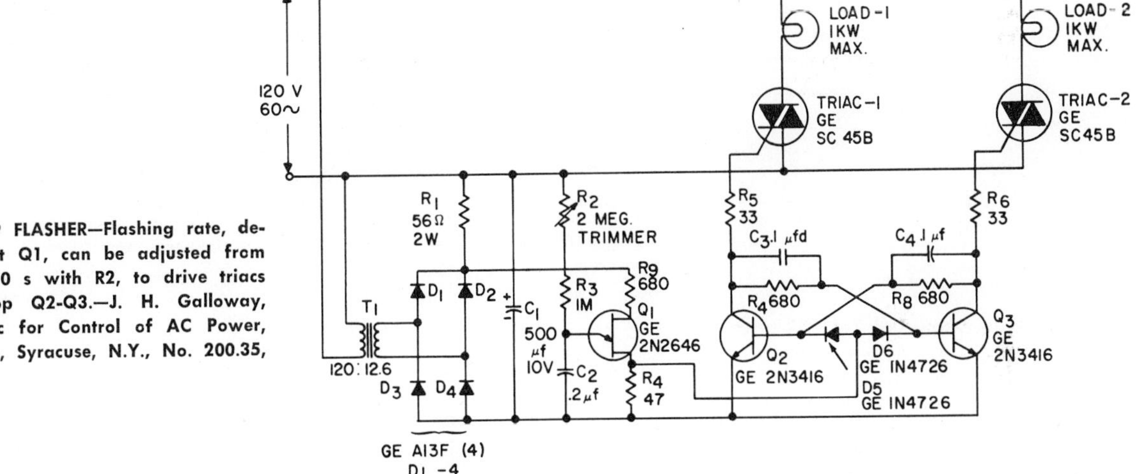

1-KW FLIP-FLOP FLASHER—Flashing rate, determined by ujt Q1, can be adjusted from about 0.1 to 10 s with R2, to drive triacs through flip-flop Q2-Q3.—J. H. Galloway, Using the Triac for Control of AC Power, General Electric, Syracuse, N.Y., No. 200.35, 1966, p 16.

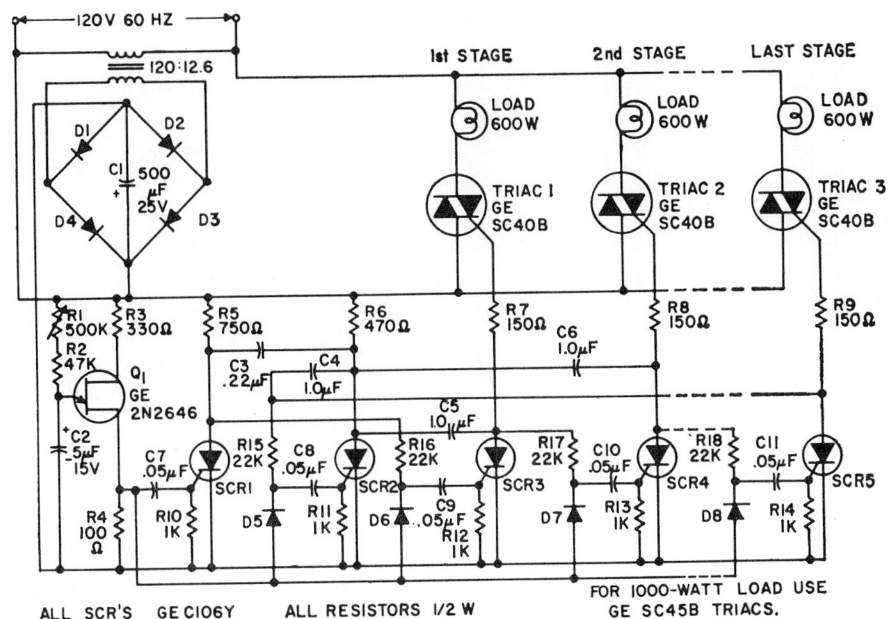

FOR 1000-WATT LOAD USE GE SC45B TRIACS.

ALL SCR'S GE C106Y
ALL DIODES GE A13 F
ALL RESISTORS 1/2 W
ADDITIONAL STAGES MAY BE INSERTED BETWEEN DOTTED LINES.

CHASER—Turns on lamps sequentially, at equal intervals, with each one staying on until all are on. Circuit then turns all of them off and starts again with first lamp. Used chiefly in advertising signs.—A. A. Adem, Solid-State Ring Counters and Chasers for Light Displays, *Electronics World*, Sept. 1967, p 84–85.

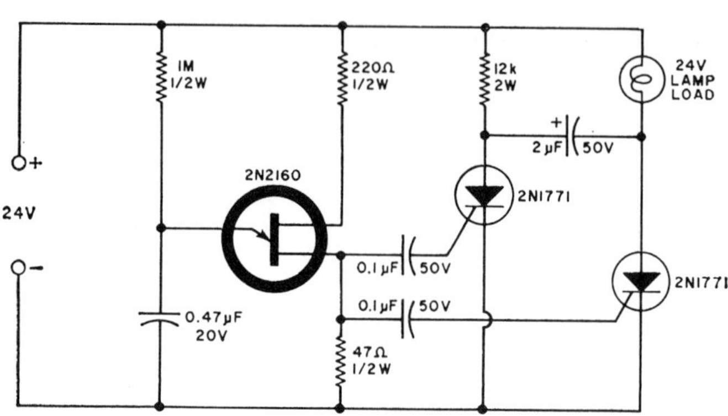

24-V LAMP FLASHER—With components shown, gives about 60 flashes per minute. To vary flashing rate, use 0.5-meg pot and 0.5-meg resistor in place of 1M resistor.—D. Cooper, SCR's and Triacs—the Revolution Continues, *Electronics World*, Aug. 1968, p 25–28.

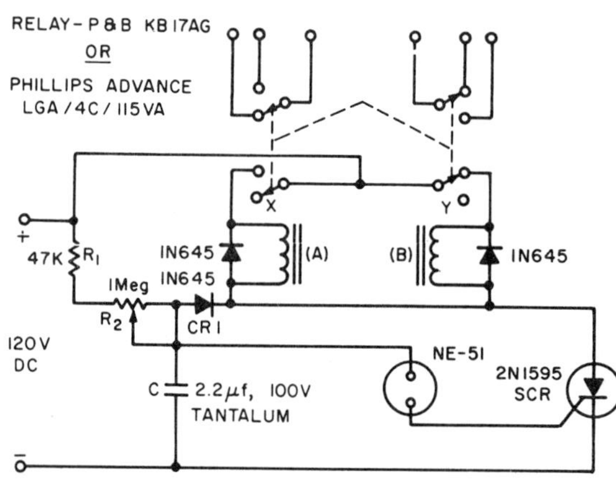

POWER FLIP-FLOP—Combination of scr and dual-coil latching relay provides variable-frequency on-off switching cycle. Extra contacts on relay can be used to drive warning flasher or, with unequal resistance paths for charging capacitor, provide asymmetrical flip-flop action. Values shown give operating frequency range of 12 to 180 cycles per minute. This range permits use as metronome or as interval timer.—V. P. Holec, SCR Relay Circuit Makes Flip-Flop or Interval Timer, *Electronic Design*, June 7, 1965, p 39–40.

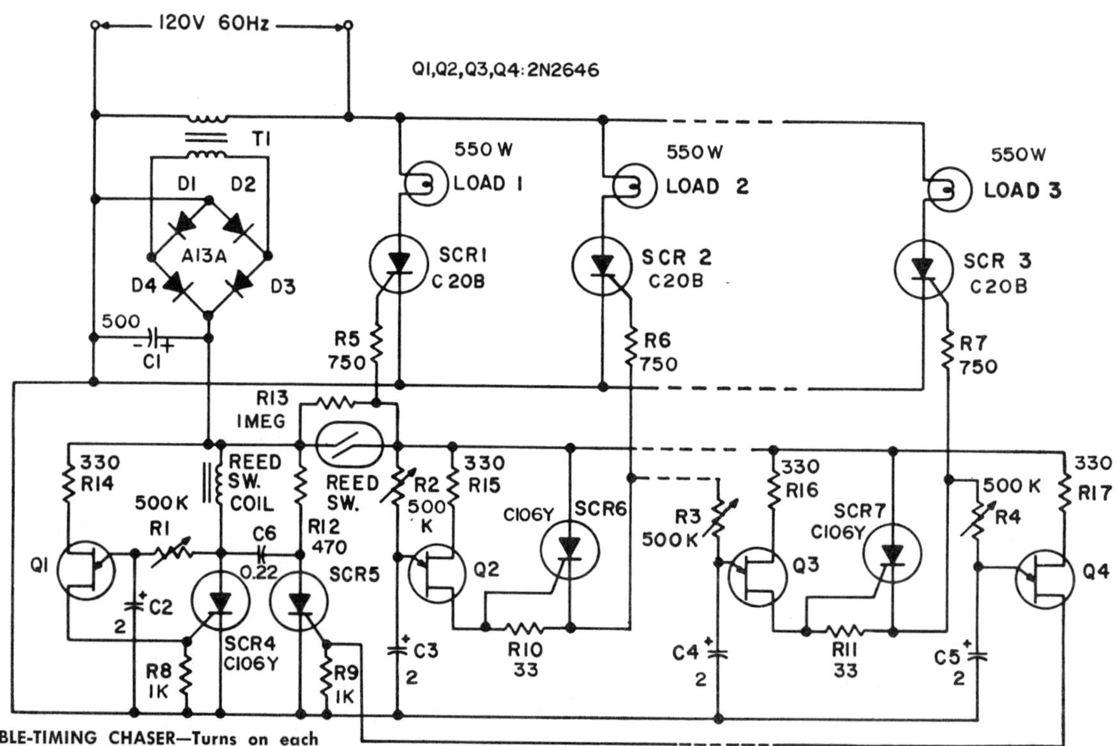

ADJUSTABLE-TIMING CHASER—Turns on each lamp in turn, with separately adjustable time delay in each lamp stage (R1, R2, R3, R4). All lamps stay on until end of sequence, when all go out and process repeats. Used chiefly in advertising signs. Any number of lamp stages can be used. Additional stages may be inserted between dashed lines.—A. A. Adem, Solid-State Ring Counters and Chasers for Light Displays, *Electronics World*, Sept. 1967, p 84–85.

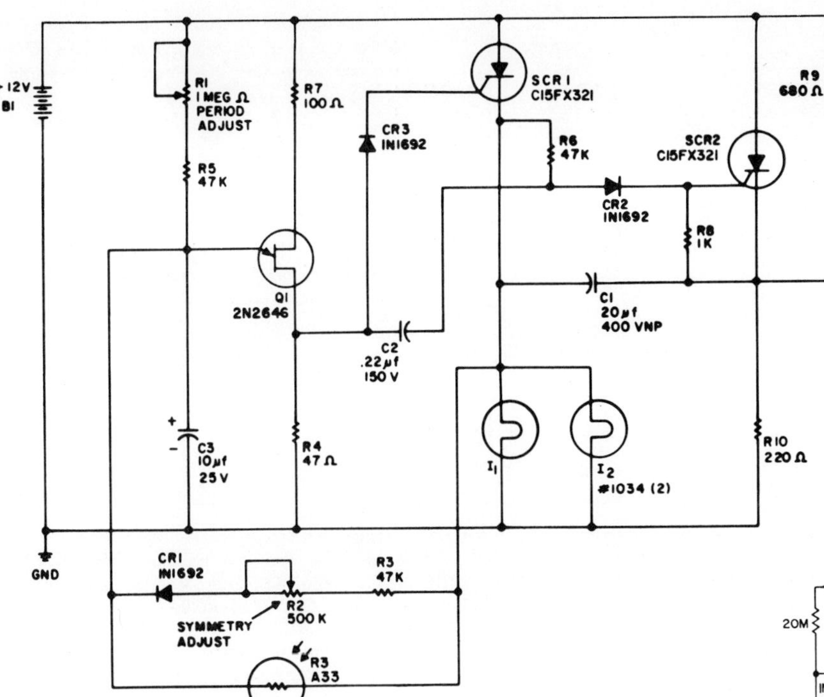

40 W WITH DAYLIGHT-OFF CONTROL—Operates from 12-V battery and gives up to 60 flashes per minute as determined by setting of R1. R2 gives independent control of on and off times. Photocell R3 shuts off flasher during daylight, increasing battery life.—F. W. Gutzwiller and E. K. Howell, Economy Power Semiconductor Applications, General Electric, Syracuse, N.Y., No. 671.1, 1965, p 5.

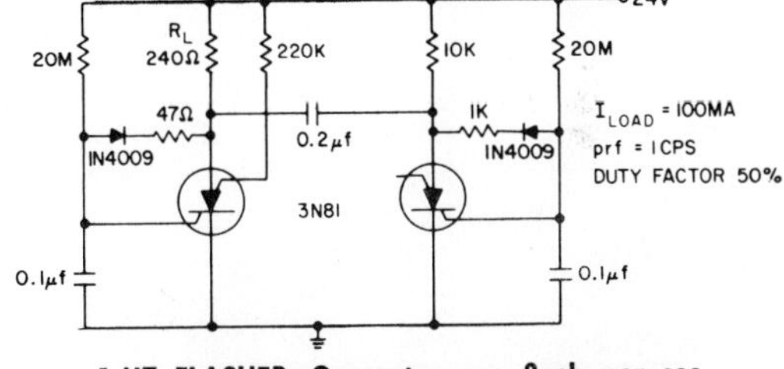

1-HZ FLASHER—Generates one flash per second with 100 mA through 240-ohm lamp load RL without need for electrolytics. When one scs triggers on, 0.2-µF commutating capacitor turns off other one and charges its gate capacitor to negative voltage through 20 meg until retriggering occurs. Circuit efficiency is 88%. 20-meg resistors can be made variable for changing frequency or duty factor.—Planar Silicon Controlled Switch 3N81/3N82, General Electric, Syracuse, N.Y., No. 65.16, 1964.

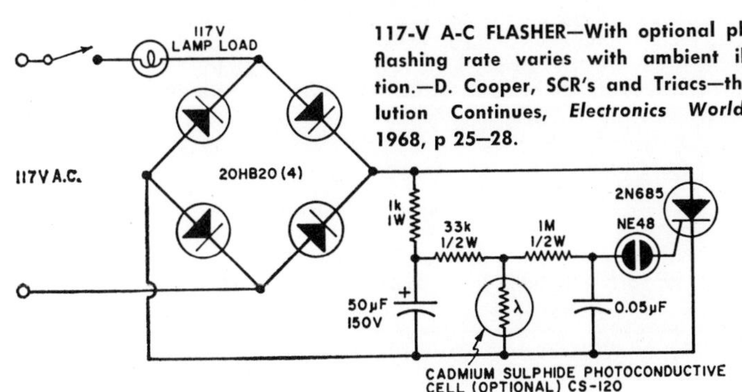

117-V A-C FLASHER—With optional photocell, flashing rate varies with ambient illumination.—D. Cooper, SCR's and Triacs—the Revolution Continues, *Electronics World*, Aug. 1968, p 25–28.

XENON TRIGGER—Two xenon flashtubes operating in 60-400 Hz range can provide pulses of light for triggering lascr's (light-activated scr's). Ujt relaxation oscillator provides alternate pulses for scr's, turning them on and making 0.22-µF capacitors discharge into primaries of high-voltage trigger transformers, to give 6-kV pulses for ionizing flashtubes to give pulses of light.—"SCR Manual," 4th Edition, General Electric, 1967, p 118–119.

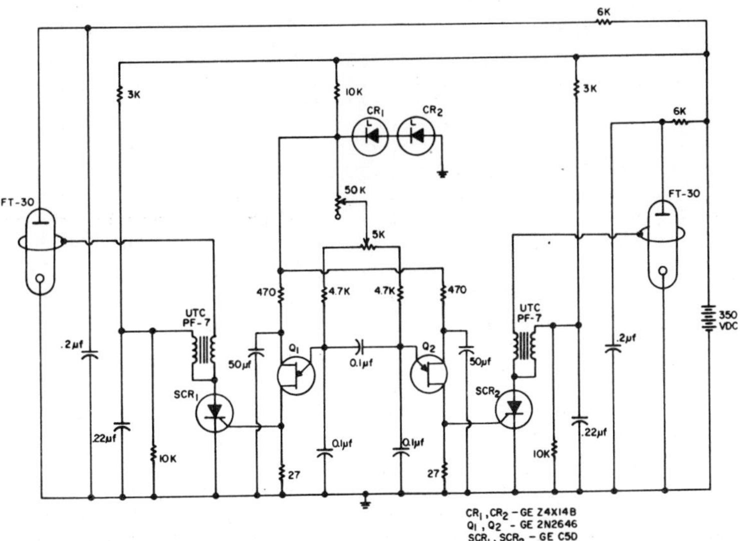

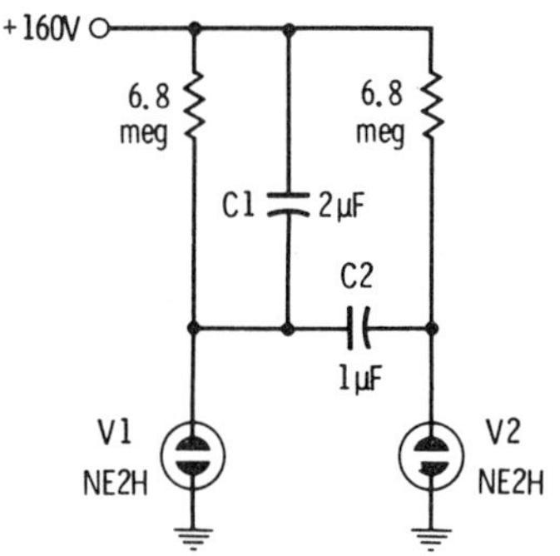

1:2:2:2:1:2:2:2 SEQUENTIAL NEON—Flashing sequence may be varied by changing capacitor values. Large capacitance values permit bright flash.—W. G. Miller, "Using and Understanding Miniature Neon Lamps," H. W. Sams & Co., Indianapolis, Ind., 1969, p 47.

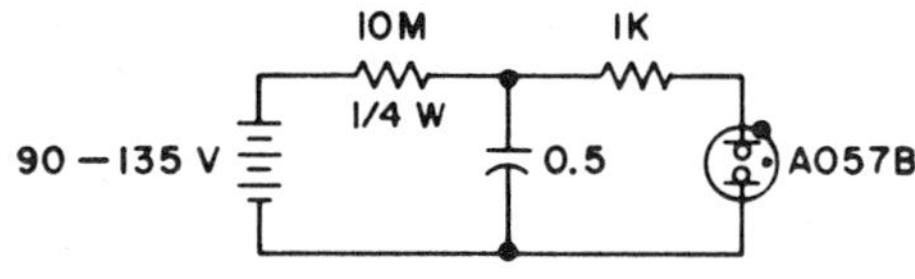

NEON BLINKER—Simple circuit flashes once every 5 s.—E. Bauman, "Applications of Neon Lamps and Gas Discharge Tubes," Signalite, Neptune, N.J., p 153.

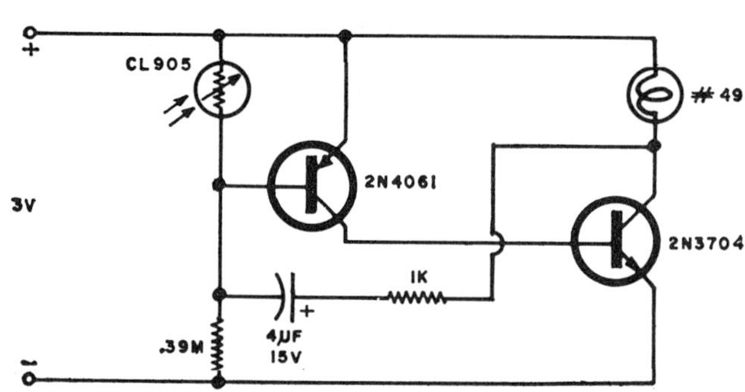

BLINKING NIGHT LIGHT—Gives about 50 flashes per minute when darkness falls, for drawing attention to hazards. Two type-D cells will operate flasher for several months, since battery drain is below 75 μA in daylight.—J. G. Rabinowitz, Photocells—Types, Characteristics, and Applications, *Electronics World*, Sept. 1968, p 23–26.

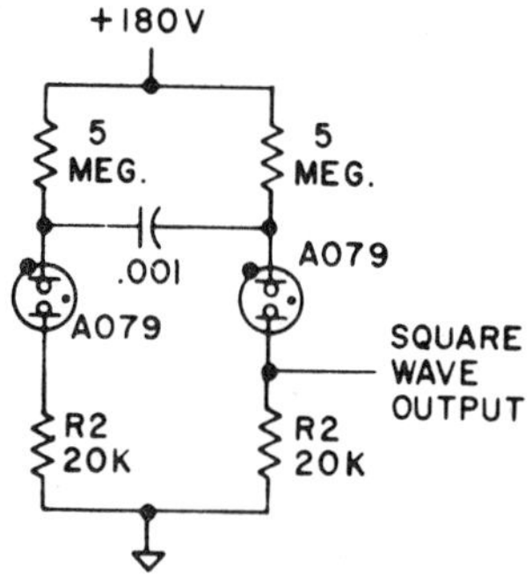

300-HZ FLASHER—Provides slightly imperfect square-wave output at approximately 300 Hz. One use is as sequence flasher.—E. Bauman, "Applications of Neon Lamps and Gas Discharge Tubes," Signalite, Neptune, N.J., p 36.

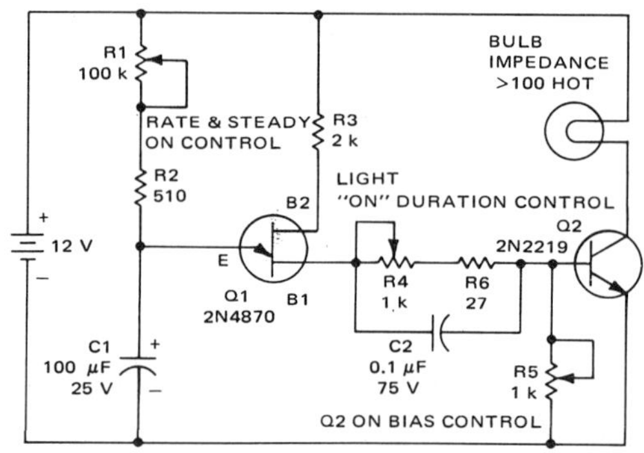

1-W 12-V FLASHER—Low-cost circuit gives 6 to 120 flashes per minute, each adjustable in duration from 40 ms to 0.5 s.—"Semiconductor Power Circuits Handbook," Motorola, Phoenix, Ariz., 1968, p 6–34.

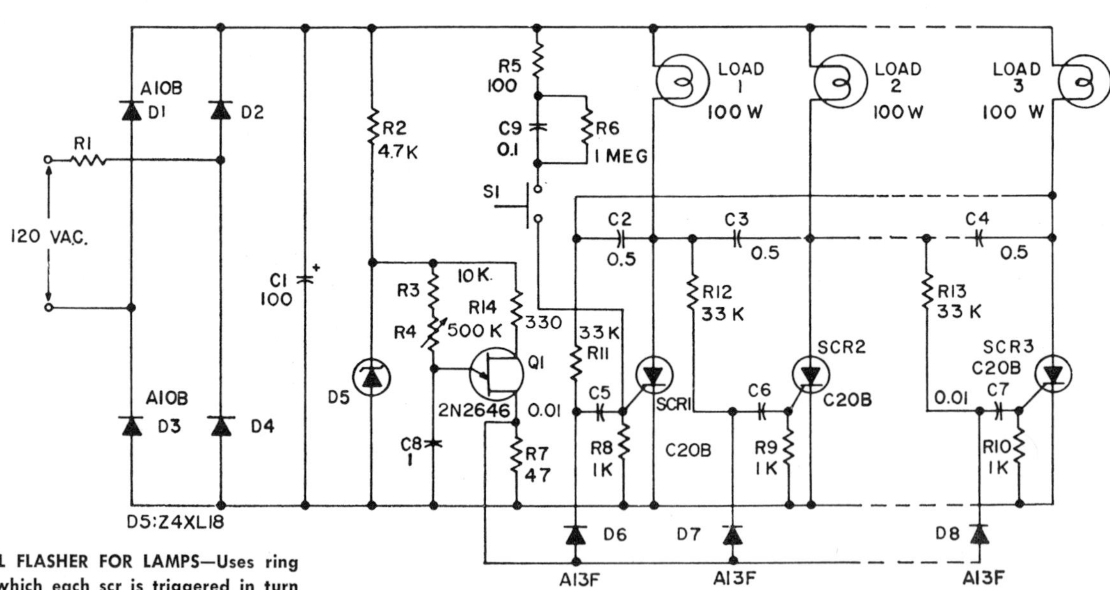

SEQUENTIAL FLASHER FOR LAMPS—Uses ring counter in which each scr is triggered in turn to operate its load. Can be used for displays, traffic warning lights, and advertising signs. Additional lamp stages can be added between the dotted lines. Article tells how to change components to handle higher-wattage lamps. Adjust R1 to give 120 V across C1.—A. A. Adem, Solid-State Ring Counters and Chasers for Light Displays, *Electronics World*, Sept. 1967, p 84–85.

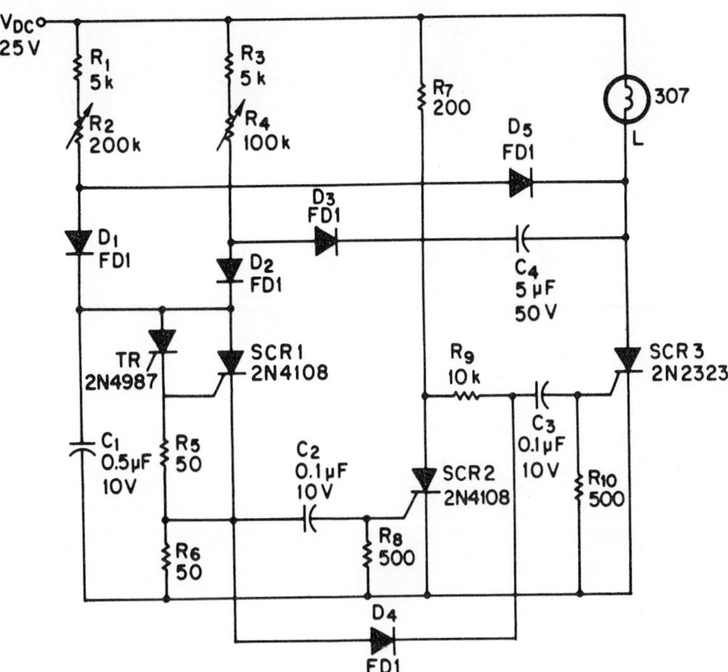

TWO-ADJUSTMENT FLASHER—On and off times are individually set by R2 and R4 in versatile lamp flasher. Any number of load-controlling scr's may be added, each with its own timed pulse spacing.—E. Kiburis, Sequential Control with Silicon Controlled Rectifiers, *EEE*, March 1970, p 100–103.

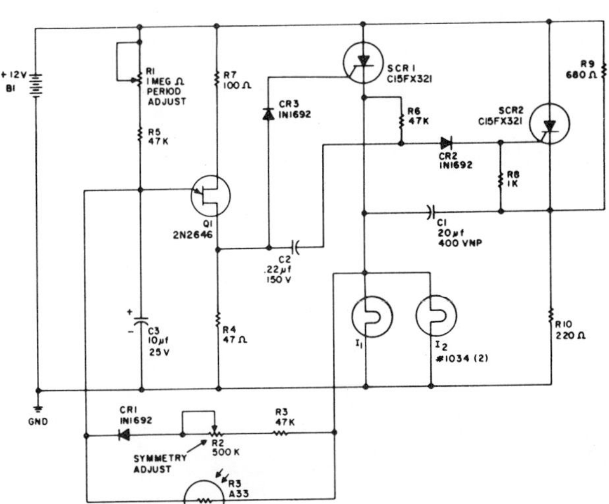

40-W NIGHT-ONLY FLASHER—Photoelectric daylight control turns flasher on at sunset and off at dawn to conserve battery light. Timing of scr flip-flop is controlled by ujt oscillator having variable control for flash rate and independent control of on and off times of flash.—High-Power, Battery-operated Flasher With Photoelectric Control, General Electric, Auburn, N.Y., No. 630.15.

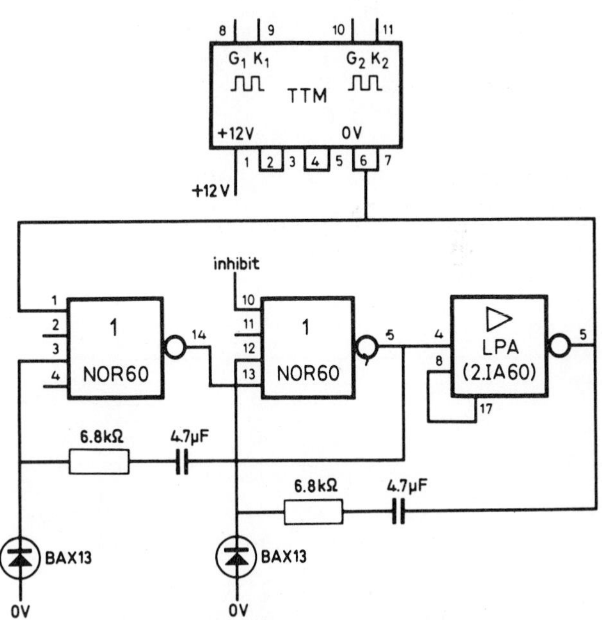

TRAFFIC LIGHT FLASHER—Combination of two Philips NORbit blocks and LPA amplifier serves as simple astable mvbr, used for driving TTM thyristor trigger module for switching one or two thyristors at given repetition rate as determined by values of capacitors used. With 12-V supply and values shown, flash rate is 1 Hz.—L. J. Lemmens, Multivibrator Circuit for Control of Thyristors, Philips, Pub. Dept., Elcoma Div., Eindhoven, The Netherlands, No. 61.

NOTE: To locate additional circuits in the category of this chapter, use the index at the back of this book. Check also the author's "Sourcebook of Electronic Circuits," published by McGraw-Hill in 1968.

CHAPTER 32
Flip-Flop Circuits

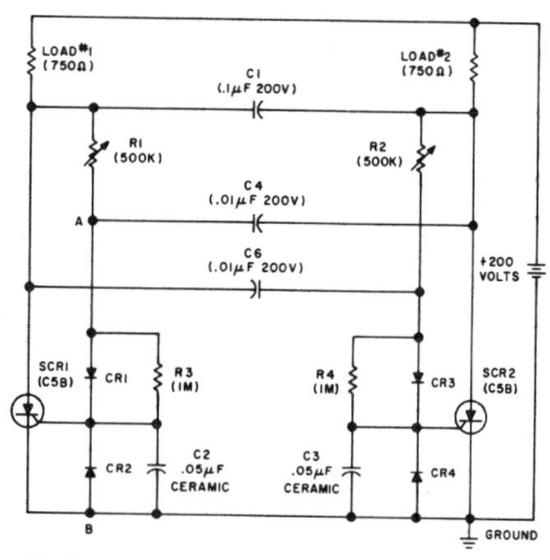

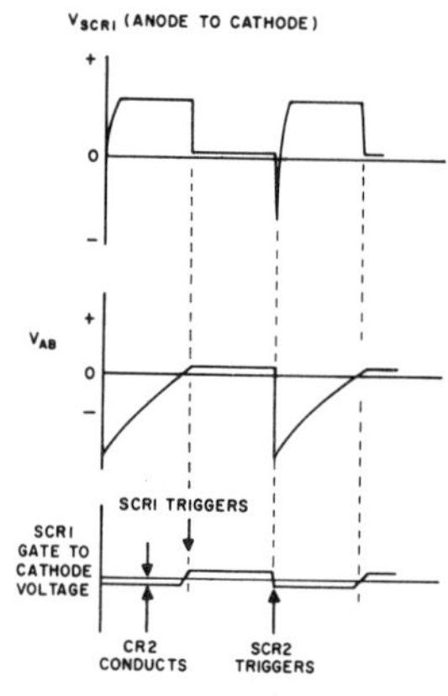

FREE-RUNNING HIGH-VOLTAGE SCR—Operates as low-frequency astable mvbr. By increasing sizes of timing capacitors C4 and C6, circuit can be made to operate at very low frequencies; it can then be used as high-voltage flasher driving lamp loads.—D. R. Grafham, Using Low Current SCR's, General Electric, Syracuse, N.Y., No. 200.19, 1967, p 27.

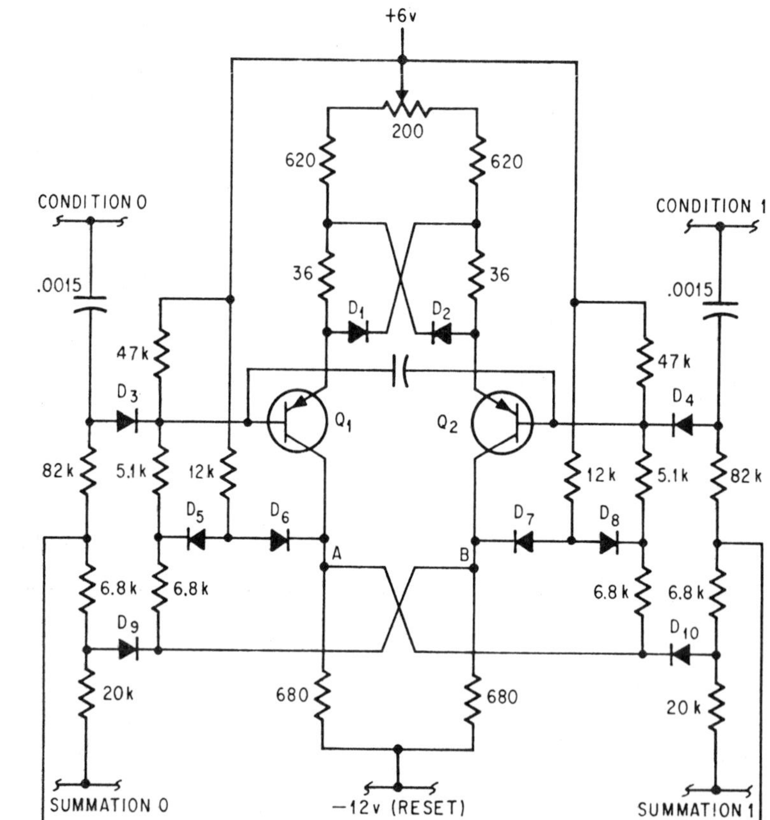

QUINARY TRIGGER—Six additional diodes (D1-D2 and D5-D8) in Eccles-Jordon flip-flop provide three additional stable states. Used as quinary memory in pattern recognizer developed by IBM for spoken words or graphic inputs. Transistor and diode types are not critical.—G. L. Clapper, Machine Looks, Listens, Learns, *Electronics*, Oct. 30, 1967, p 91–102.

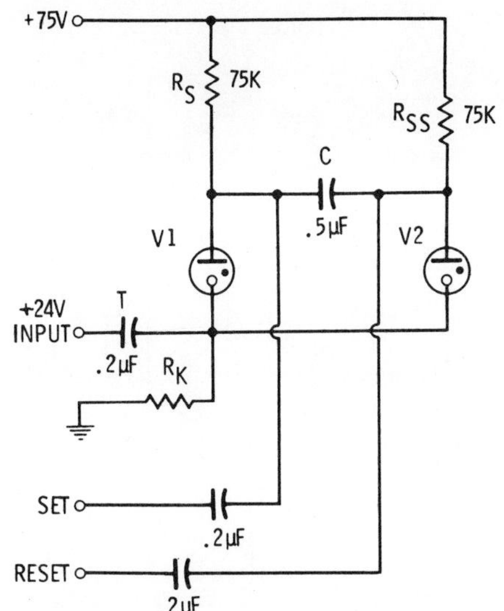

BINARY NEON—Zero potential applied at RESET terminal extinguishes V2 and permits V1 to ignite. Choose value for common cathode resistor RK such that V2 cannot fire. 24-V pulse at input, of duration depending on time constant of RK and 0.2-μF capacitor, causes flip-flop to switch, indicating count of ONE. Same lamp is lit once for every two input pulses. All lamps are 5AB-B.—W. G. Miller, "Using and Understanding Miniature Neon Lamps," H. W. Sams & Co., Indianapolis, Ind., 1969, p 50.

BASIC BISTABLE UJT—Circuit has two stable operating points, called the ON and OFF states. When OFF, only very small current flows through load and power dissipation in load is below 1 nW. When trigger is applied to input X or Y, or both (positive for X and negative for Y), load power dissipation becomes about 135 mW. Negative trigger at X will turn circuit OFF.—T. P. Sylvan, The Unijunction Transistor Characteristics and Applications, General Electric, Syracuse, N.Y., No. 90.10, 1965, p 59.

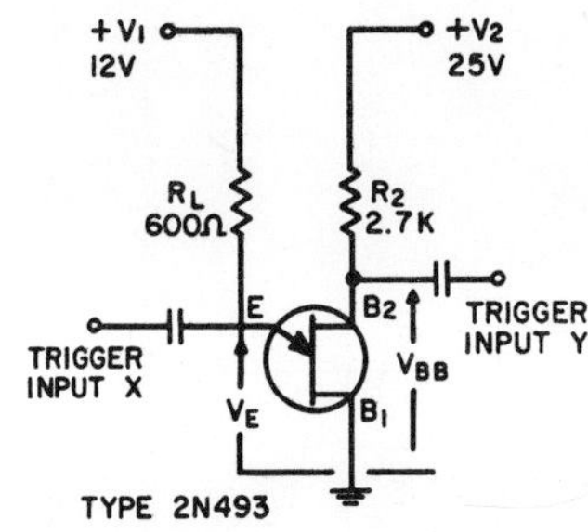

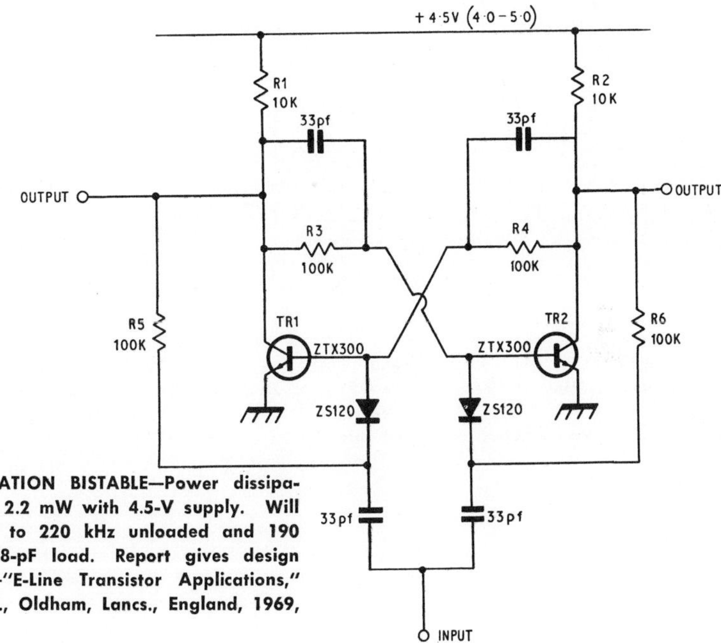

LOW-DISSIPATION BISTABLE—Power dissipation is only 2.2 mW with 4.5-V supply. Will operate up to 220 kHz unloaded and 190 kHz into 68-pF load. Report gives design procedure.—"E-Line Transistor Applications," Ferranti Ltd., Oldham, Lancs., England, 1969, p 13.

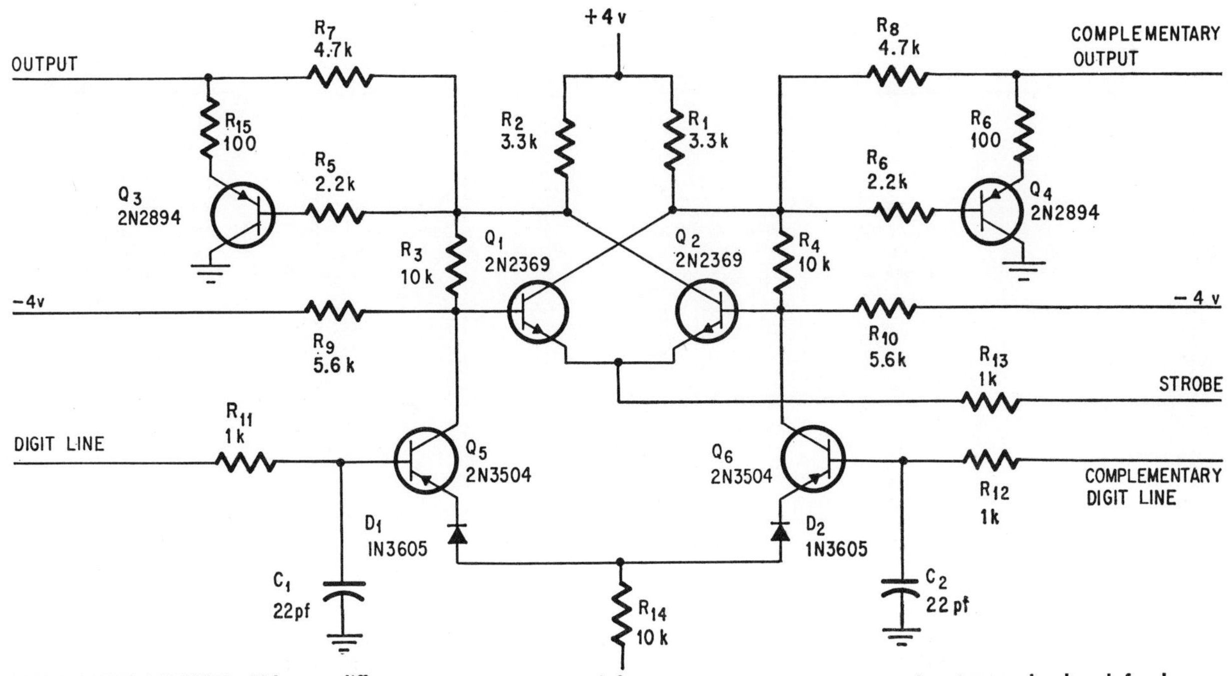

MEMORY SENSE AMPLIFIER—Picks up difference between currents in complementary digit lines, to bias flip-flop Q1-Q2 through differential amplifier Q5-Q6. Strobe read signal sets flip-flop to state toward which differential amplifier previously biased it, to generate appropriate complementary outputs. Used in computer storage developed for long space trips.—D. E. Brewer, S. Nissim, and G. V. Podraza, Suitcase-size Memory for Longer Space Trips, *Electronics*, Nov. 13, 1967, p 138–146.

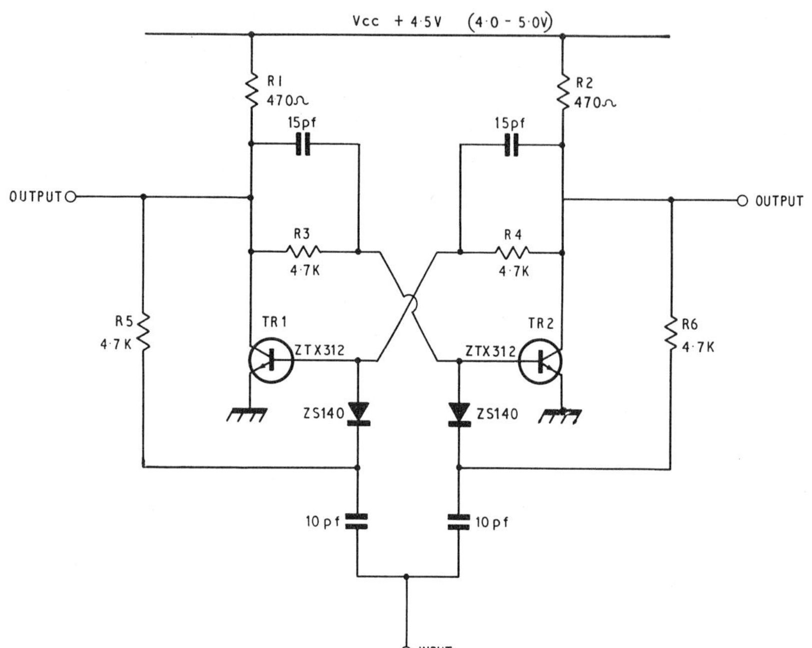

FAST FLIP-FLOP—Can be used as frequency divider up to 7.5 MHz. Requires only one 4.5-V supply. Used in Johnson decade counter. Report gives design procedure and equations, along with modification for increasing speed to 13 MHz.—"E-Line Transistor Applications," Ferranti Ltd., Oldham, Lancs., England, 1969, p 11.

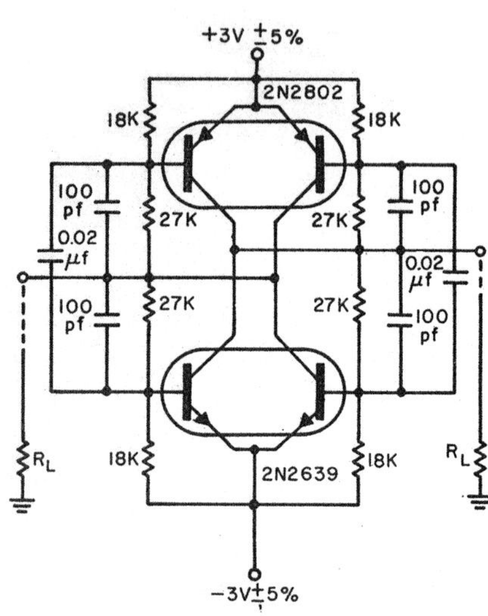

COMPLEMENTARY SILICON TRANSISTORS—Use of complementary transistor in place of collector load resistor in basic flip-flop gives higher operating efficiency, higher operating speed, and lower output impedance. Article gives design procedure for determining optimum values of components, for operation at temperatures from −55 to +150 C at 1-mA collector currents.—P. Ward, Complementary Flip-Flops Improve Bistable Performance, *Electronic Design*, May 11, 1964, p 50–55.

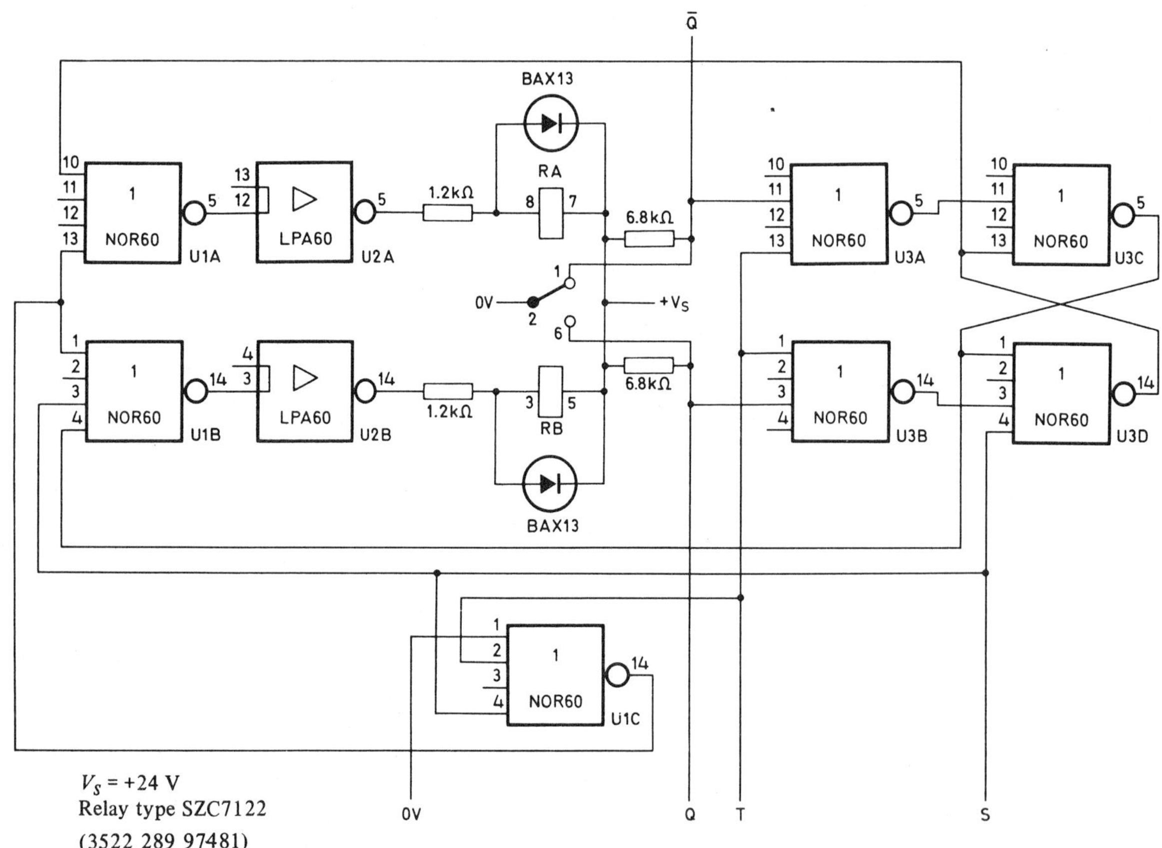

MEMORY FOR POWER FAILURE—Divide-by-two flip-flop uses bipolar relay to provide memory function so information is not lost if supply voltage is removed because of power failure or any other reason. Uses Philips amplifier and gate blocks. Terminal T is input. High level at terminal S stops flip-flop. Complementary outputs are taken from terminals Q.—L. J. Lemmens, A Non-Volatile Flip-Flop, Philips, Pub. Dept., Elcoma Div., Eindhoven, The Netherlands, No. 72.

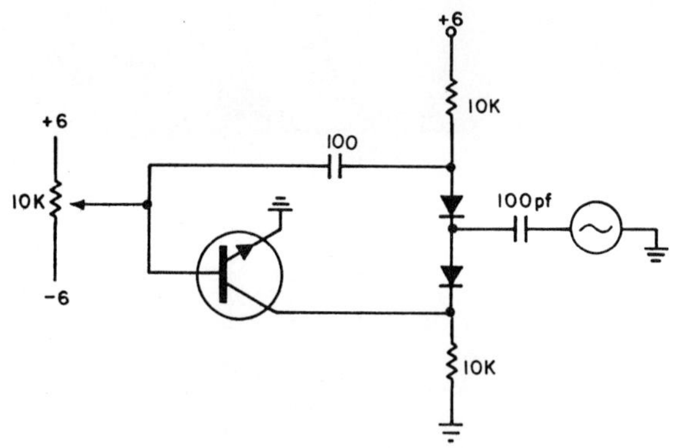

COLLECTOR-FOLLOWING EFFECT—Operation depends on driving base potential of single saturated common-emitter transistor rapidly toward cutoff. Collector voltage then follows base, if collector resistance is sufficiently high. Article gives theory of operation. No transformer is required. Will operate for collector resistances of 2K to 100K for variety of transistors ranging from 2N1613 to 2N706. Frequency of sine-wave source is not critical. Can be used as shift register, delay, and radiation detector.—R. E. Briley, One-Transistor Flip-Flop, *Electronic Design*, Aug. 17, 1964, p 132–134.

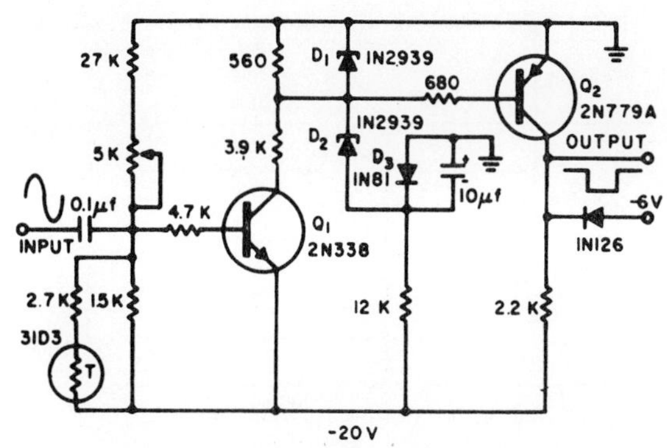

TUNNEL-DIODE FLIP-FLOP—Used in converting analog voltage waveform to digital logic levels. Provides faster rise time than conventional Schmitt trigger and maintains accurate zero-crossing information without phase distortion. Circuit requires only one supply voltage, plus lamp voltage if desired. Output is clean square wave at any frequency from 1 to 25 kHz for 1-V p-p input signal.—C. S. Miller, Fast Squaring Circuit Preserves Phase Information, "400 Ideas for Design Selected from Electronic Design," Hayden Book Co., N.Y., 1964, p 96.

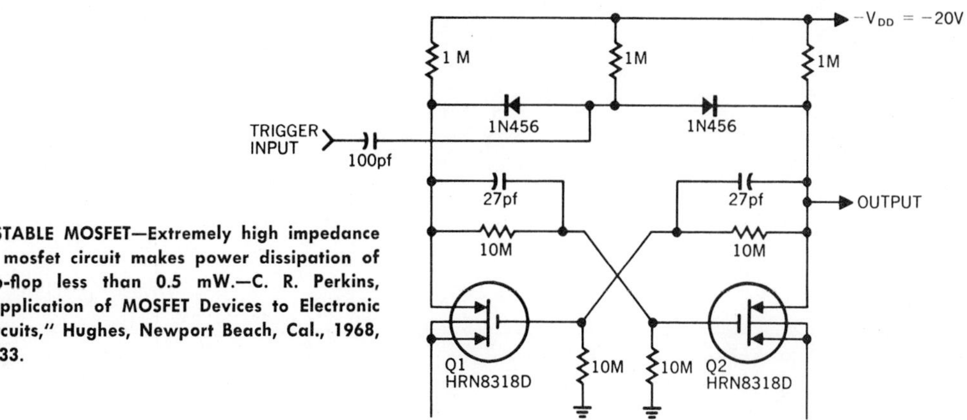

BISTABLE MOSFET—Extremely high impedance of mosfet circuit makes power dissipation of flip-flop less than 0.5 mW.—C. R. Perkins, "Application of MOSFET Devices to Electronic Circuits," Hughes, Newport Beach, Cal., 1968, p 33.

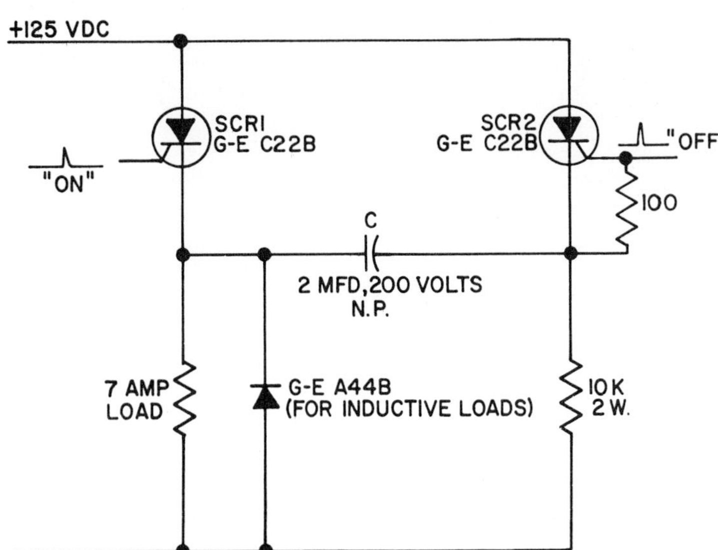

LATCHING STATIC SWITCH—Load current flows when pulse is applied to gate of SCR1, which then triggers and latches on. To turn off load, pulse is applied to SCR2 to turn it on and short out SCR1 momentarily through C to make SCR1 drop out. Can be used as flasher, heavy-duty relay, heater control, circuit breaker, power mvbr, etc.—F. W. Gutzwiller and E. K. Howell, Economy Power Semiconductor Applications, General Electric, Syracuse, N.Y., No. 671.1, 1965, p 4.

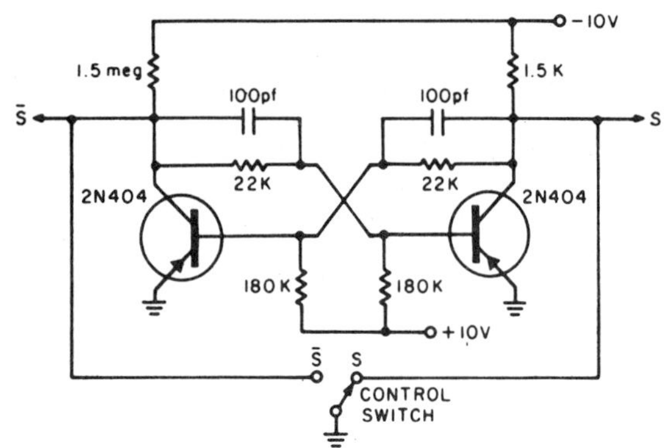

BOUNCE-FREE SWITCH—When logic signal is to be generated by manual switching of flip-flop, bounce at switch contacts can be eliminated by using spdt switch connected as shown, to short-circuit one transistor of flip-flop each time switch is operated to make flip-flop change its state.—B. Ross, Flip-Flop Switch Eliminates Contact Bounce, "400 Ideas for Design Selected from Electronic Design," Hayden Book Co., N.Y., 1964, p 232.

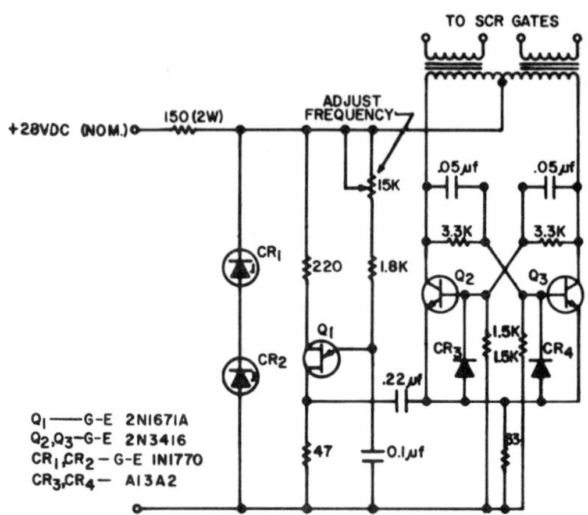

400-HZ TRIGGER—Delivers square-wave gate signals alternating from 7 V positive to 7 V negative through transformer for driving scr or triac gates. Current is up to 800 mA. Can be free-running, or driven by ujt for precise timing.—"SCR Manual," 4th Edition, General Electric, 1967, p 85–86.

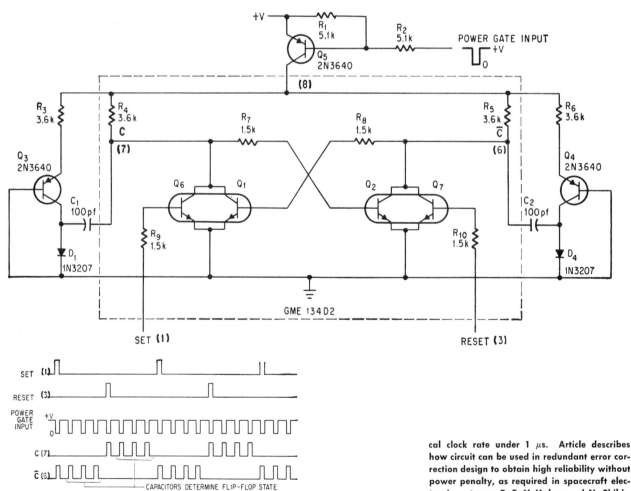

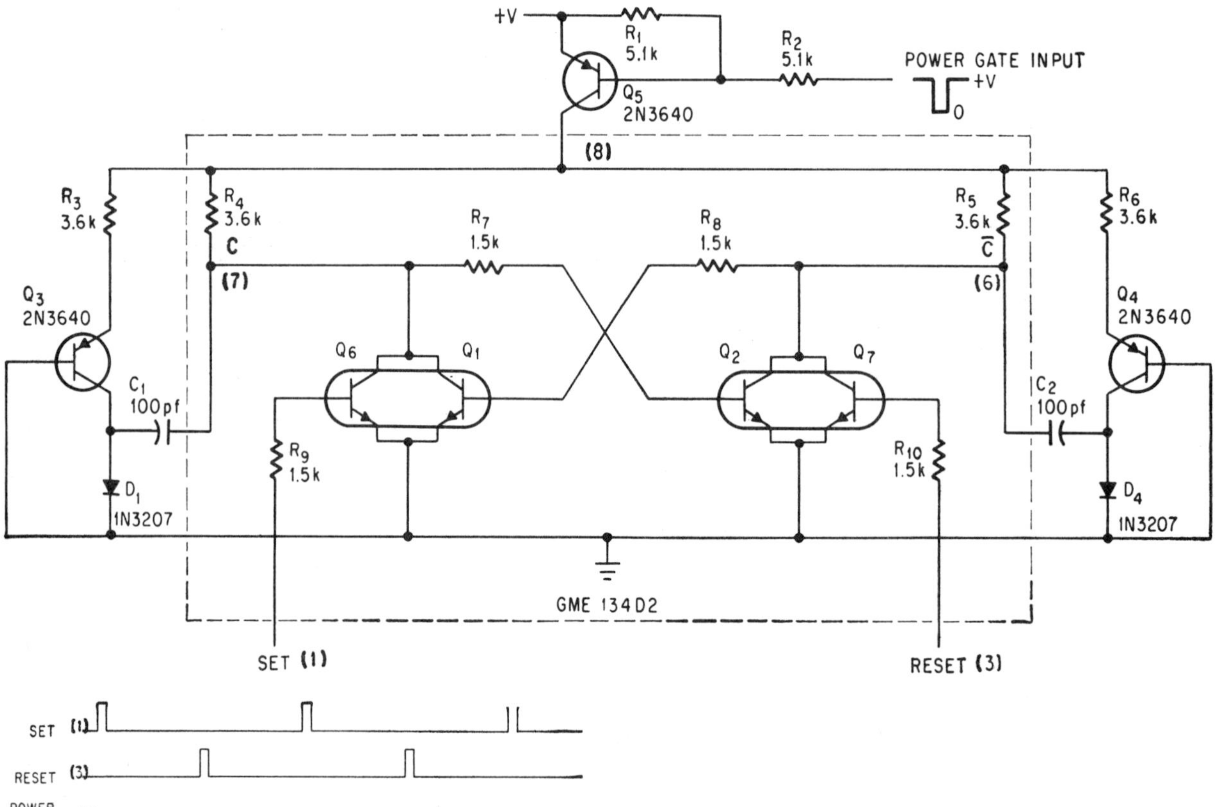

MICROPOWER FOR REDUNDANCY—Use of pulsed or gated power mode for Philco-Ford set-reset IC flip-flop cuts operating power to a few microwatts instead of the usual several milliwatts. Supply voltage is gated to digital elements only during clock interval, with typical clock rate under 1 μs. Article describes how circuit can be used in redundant error correction design to obtain high reliability without power penalty, as required in spacecraft electronic systems.—R. E. McMahon and N. Childs, Micropower Redundant Circuits Correct Errors Automatically, *Electronics*, Feb. 6, 1967, p 66–69.

COMPLEMENTARY GERMANIUM TRANSISTORS—Complementary arrangement with germanium transistors gives higher operating efficiency, higher operating speed, and lower output impedance. With circuit unbalanced to ground, only one supply voltage is needed. Circuit also illustrates use of commutative triggering from positive-going input. Article gives design procedure.—P. Ward, Complementary Flip-Flops Improve Bistable Performance, *Electronic Design*, May 11, 1964, p 50–55.

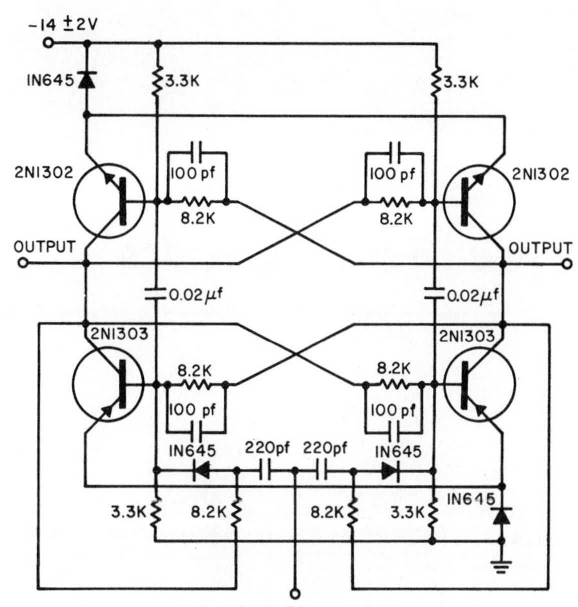

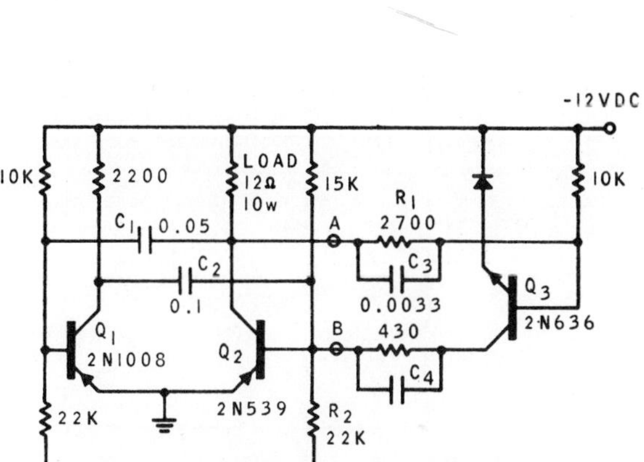

REGENERATIVE OUTPUT FOR FLIP-FLOP—Amplifier Q3 boosts peak power to 10 W for 12-ohm load. Circuit at left of points A-B is astable flip-flop, but technique can be applied to stable and monostable flip-flops as well.—R. A. Durand, Regenerative Stage Enhances Flip-Flop Power Output, "400 Ideas for Design Selected from Electronic Design," Hayden Book Co., N.Y., 1964, p 180–181.

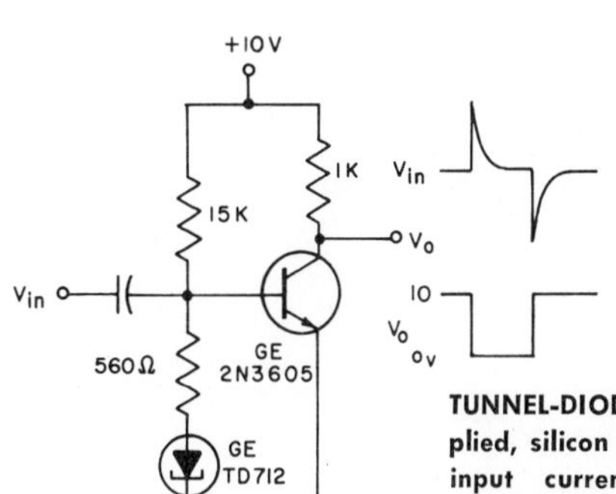

TUNNEL-DIODE HYBRID—When power is applied, silicon transistor stays off. Addition of input current through coupling capacitor switches tunnel diode to its high-voltage state, making transistor turn on. Applying negative pulse at input makes circuit switch back to low-voltage state, giving equivalent of flip-flop action.—W. R. Spofford, Jr., Applications For The New Low Cost TD 700 Series Tunnel Diodes, General Electric, Syracuse, N.Y., No. 90.66, 1967, p 8.

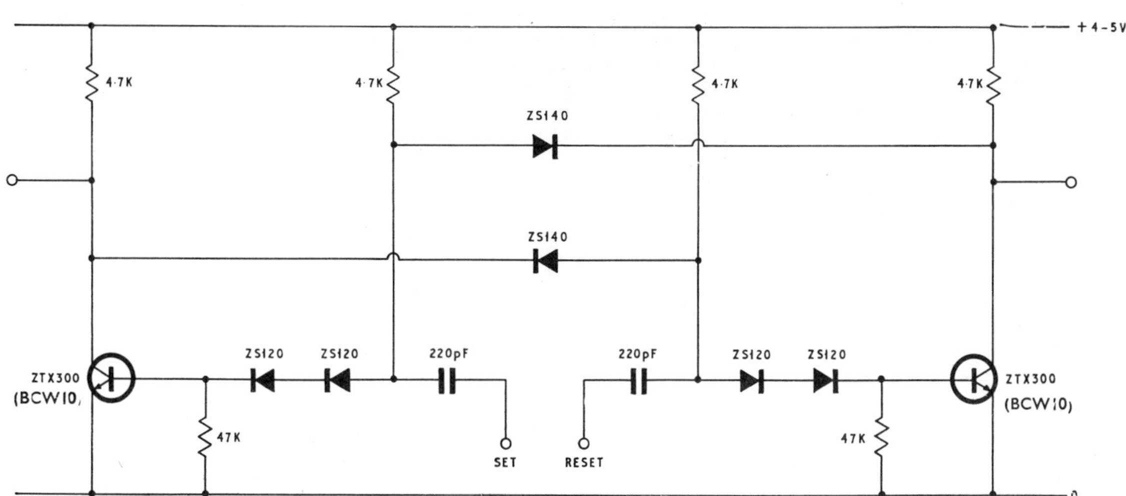

SET-RESET BISTABLE—Cross-coupling of two NOR gates gives logical flip-flop that is useful for control purposes where two separate signals are available to trigger bistable between its two states. Inputs are normally up, and triggering occurs when input is pulled to ground or below 1 V.—"E-Line Transistor Applications," Ferranti Ltd., Oldham, Lancs., England, 1969, p 10.

CHAPTER 33
Frequency Divider Circuits

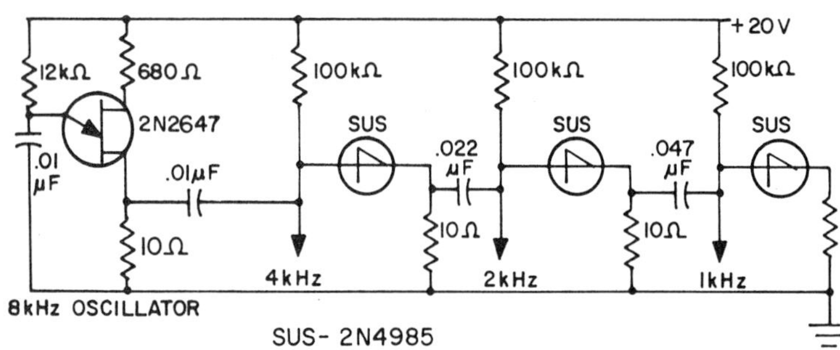

SIMPLIFIED 8 KHZ:1 KHZ DIVIDER—Sawtooth output of each silicon unilateral switch stage is half the frequency of preceding stage. May also be used with 2N4989 sus.—Silicon Unilateral Switch 2N4984/2N4985, General Electric, Syracuse, N.Y., No. 65.27, 1967.

DIVIDE-BY-12 MVBR—Provides precise division up to 12 with values shown, and up to 1,000 by adding self-controlled input gate and 1-MHz crystal clock feeding three circuits in cascade. Circuit in dashed area is added to generate neatly squared 1-ms pulses for synchronizing another divider stage. Use minimum value for C and adjust pot to give desired fixed division factor. Generated pulse can be stopped or started with any positive edge of clock pulse.—V. Mosca, One-Shot Multivibrator Yields Division up to 12, *Electronics*, April 14, 1969, p 96.

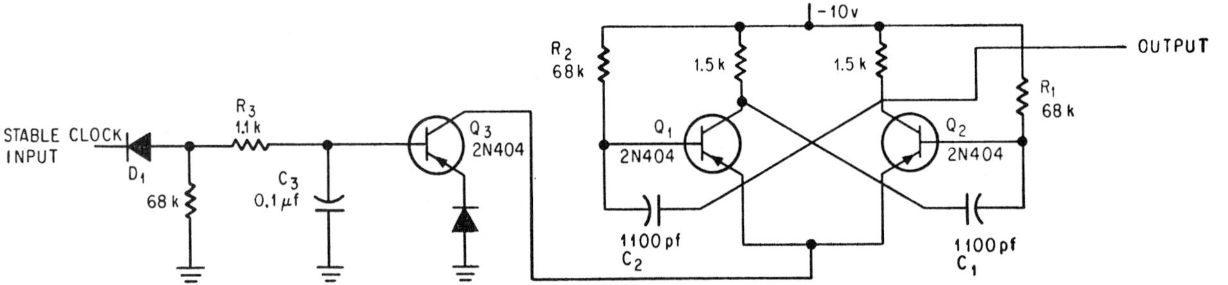

60:1 WITH ASTABLE MVBR—Circuit easily synchronizes to 92-V sinusoidal or square-wave clock input over frequency range of 10 to 600 kHz and gives either 10:1 or 60:1 frequency division. Components R3 and C3 are selected to offer ripple to base of Q3 at clock frequency; ripple is amplified by Q3 and fed to mvbr Q1-Q2 to lock it to clock. If clock fails, Q3 stops mvbr.—A. L. Plevy and E. N. Monacchio, Fail-safe Frequency Divider, *Electronics*, Sept. 19, 1966, p 127.

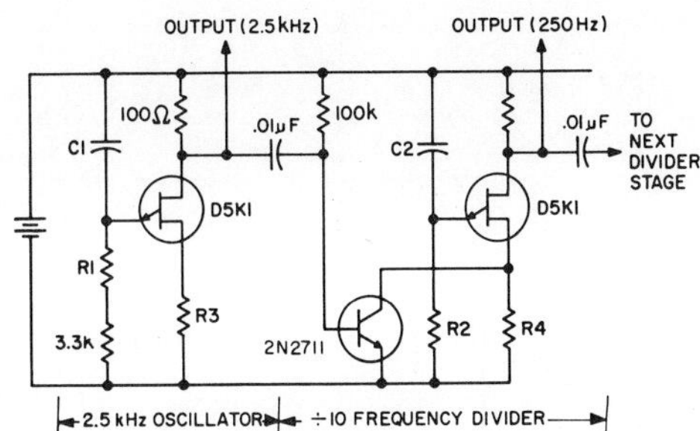

DECADE DIVIDER—Starts with 2.5-kHz ujt oscillator. Each following transistor-ujt stage divides frequency by 10. C1 and C2 are 0.0047, R1 is 100K, R2 is 1 meg, and R3 and R4 are around 1K, adjusted to match ujt's. For next stage, product of R2 and C2 should be ten times that of preceding stage, with R2 between 27K and 10 meg.—Silicon Complementary Unijunction Transistor D5K1, General Electric, Syracuse, N.Y., No. 60.15, 1967.

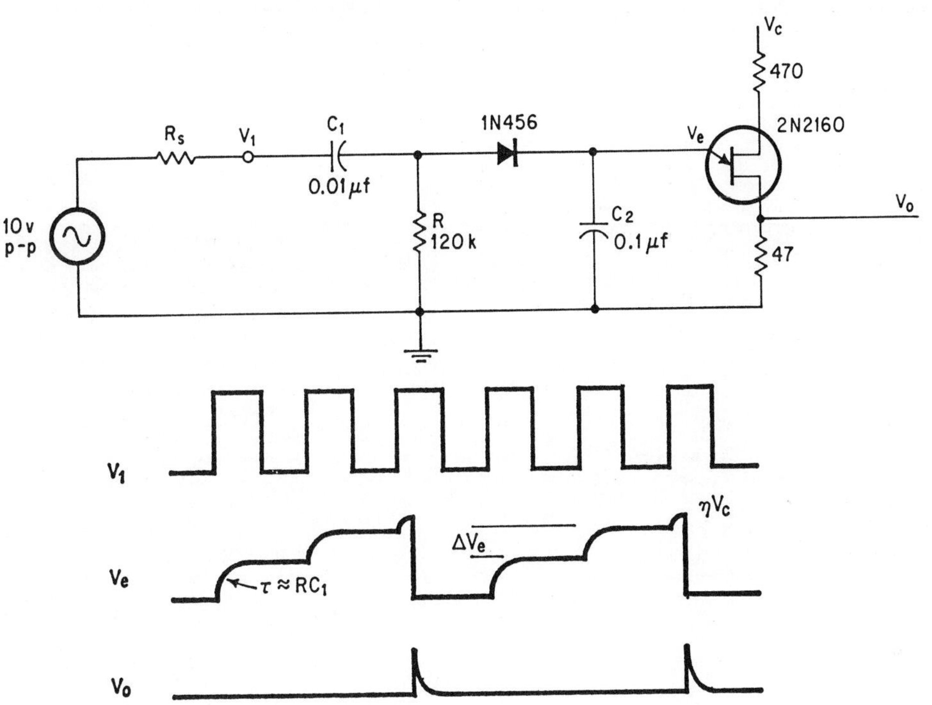

JITTER KILLER—Control voltage Vc of ujt determines frequency division ratio, in range of 2 to 20. For values shown, circuit operates over frequency range of 20 to 150 Hz. Characteristics of ujt make it tolerate large amounts of jitter in input.—J. P. Budlong, UJT Gives Frequency Divider an Immunity to Input Jitter, *Electronics*, July 7, 1969, p 105.

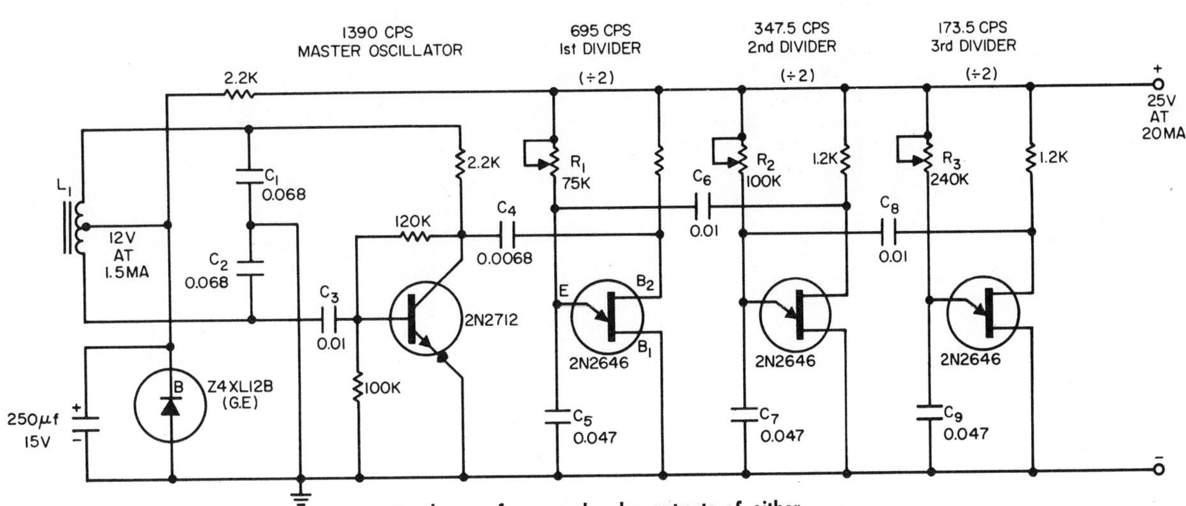

CASCADED UJT'S DIVIDE 1,390 HZ BY 8—Simple ujt relaxation oscillators are cascaded and synchronized from 1,390-Hz Hartley oscillator to give reliable frequency division. Sawtooth waveforms and pulse outputs of either polarity are available from each divider stage.—J. F. Cleary and D. V. Jones, Cascaded UJT Oscillators Form Stable Frequency Divider, *Electronic Design*, Nov. 8, 1965, p 52.

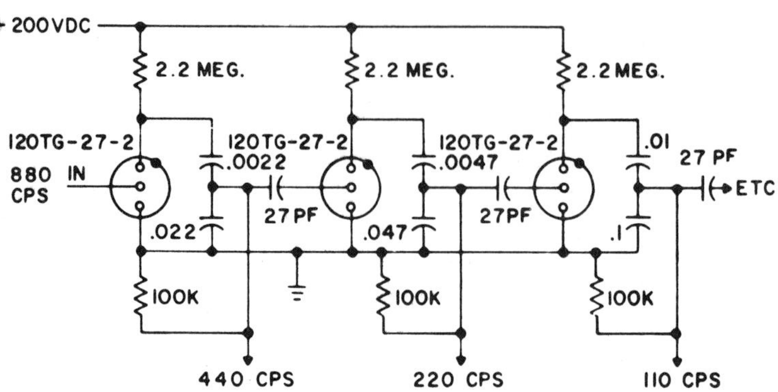

DIVIDE-BY-2—Uses 3-element neon lamps powered by a 200-V supply which also runs 880-Hz master oscillator. Output is 440-Hz linear sawtooth.—E. Bauman, "Applications of Neon Lamps and Gas Discharge Tubes," Signalite, Neptune, N.J., p 51.

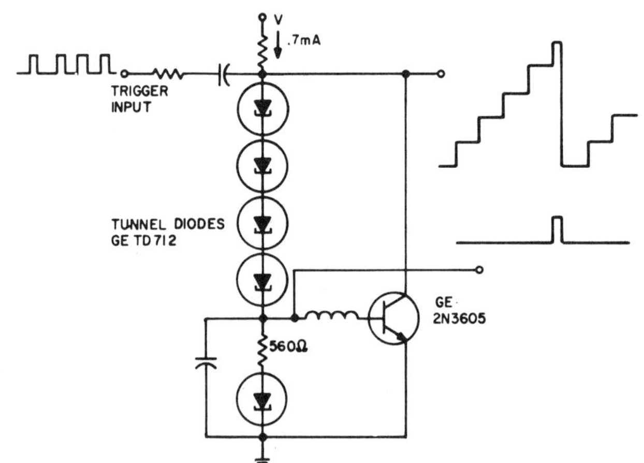

TUNNEL-DIODE DIVIDER—Lowest of five diodes in series string is chosen to have highest peak point current. First trigger pulse turns on diode having lowest peak point current, creating first voltage jump at output. Successive trigger pulses will in turn trigger other diodes one at a time, until finally the bottom diode is turned on. Voltage across entire string then drops to zero, turning off all diodes, and sequence begins again. Can be used as 5:1 pulse frequency divider or as staircase waveform generator.—W. R. Spofford, Jr., Applications For The New Low Cost TD 700 Series Tunnel Diodes, General Electric, Syracuse, N.Y., No. 90.66, 1967, p 10.

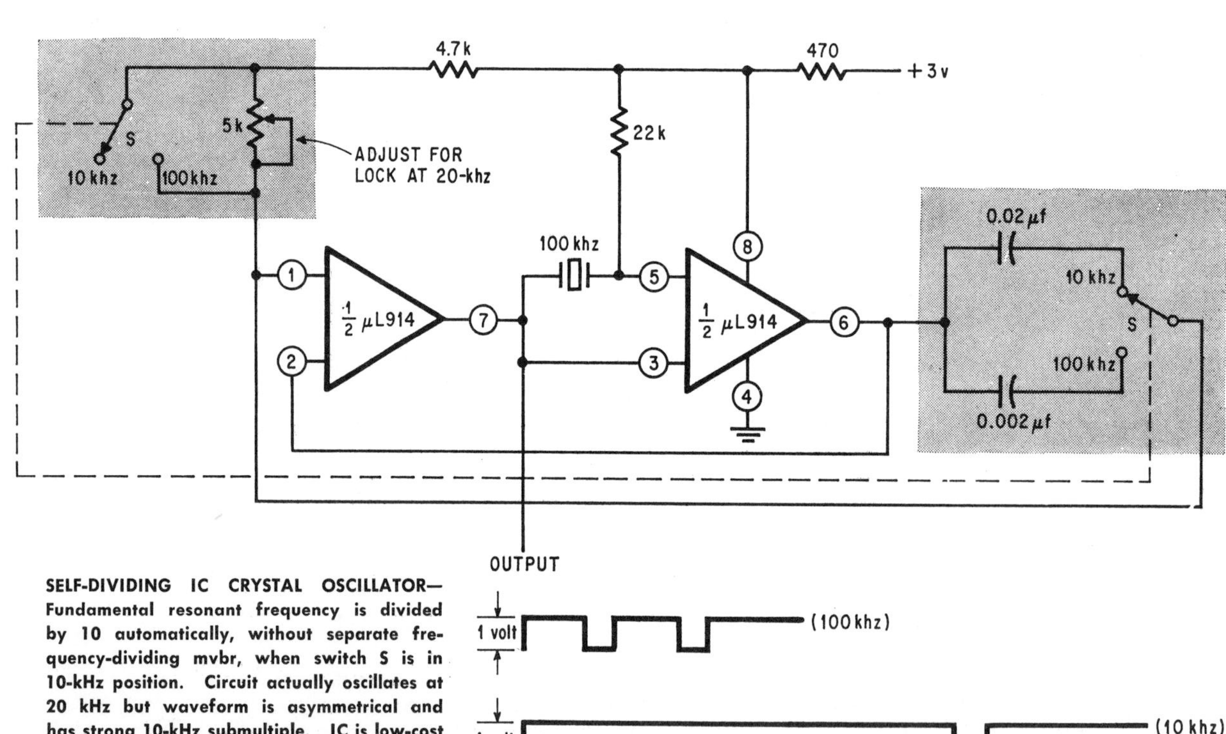

SELF-DIVIDING IC CRYSTAL OSCILLATOR—Fundamental resonant frequency is divided by 10 automatically, without separate frequency-dividing mvbr, when switch S is in 10-kHz position. Circuit actually oscillates at 20 kHz but waveform is asymmetrical and has strong 10-kHz submultiple. IC is low-cost Fairchild μL914 dual two-input gate.—J. Althouse, Dividing the Frequency of an Oscillator by 10, *Electronics*, December 11, 1967, p 98.

DIVIDE BY 2 OR 3—Transistor coupling between stages prevents audio signal of one stage from leaking back into previous one. A low-impedance sine-wave generator in series with I1 provides dividing signal. Circuit may be used as organ tone generator if second stage is adjusted to divide by 2.—E. Bauman, "Applications of Neon Lamps and Gas Discharge Tubes," Signalite, Neptune, N.J., p 50.

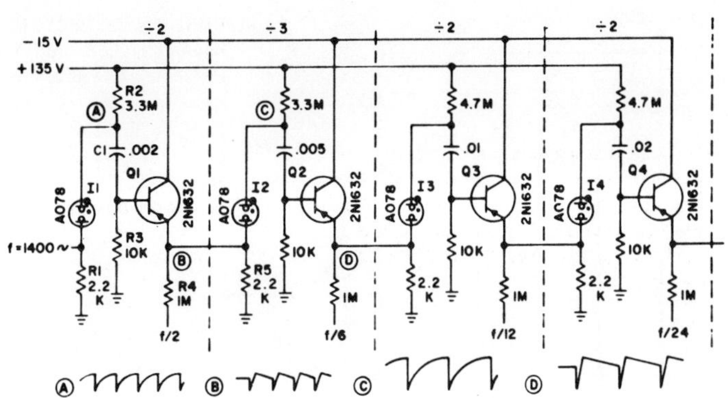

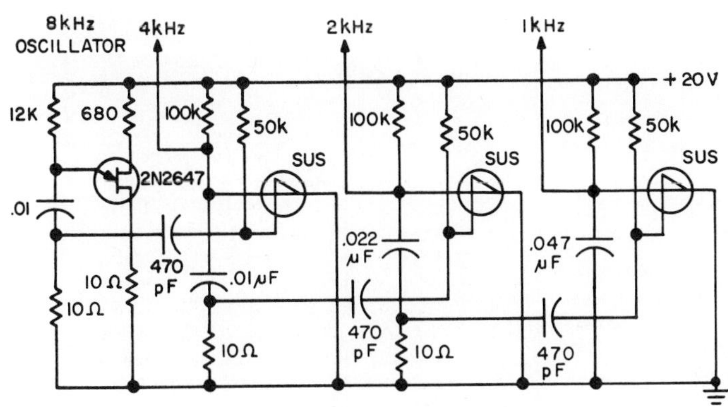

SUS - 2N4985

TRANSIENT-FREE SUS 8:1 DIVIDER—Spikes in center of sawtooth are eliminated in this silicon unilateral switch circuit by triggering at gate. May also be used with 2N4989 sus.—Silicon Unilateral Switch 2N4984/2N4985, General Electric, Syracuse, N.Y., No. 65.27, 1967.

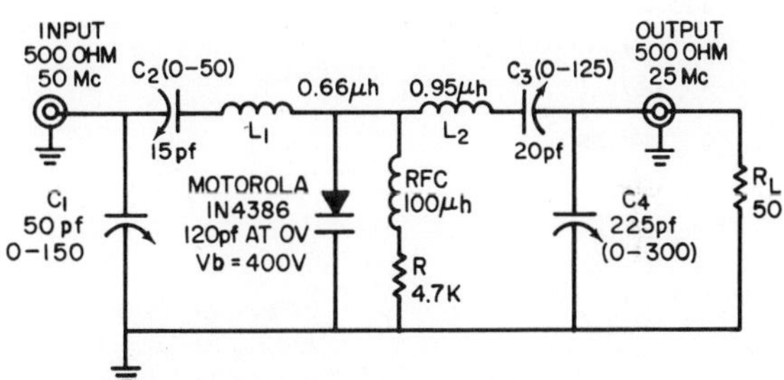

L_1: 5 1/2 T, 1 1/8" I.D., 1/8" DIA TUBE, COPPER, 1/8" TURN SPACING
L_2: 7 1/2 T, 5/8" I.D., #16 ENAM. WIRE, CLOSE WOUND

VARACTOR FREQUENCY-SPLITTER — Converts 50 MHz to 25 MHz with 80% efficiency. Spurious harmonic energy is 20 dB below 25-MHz output and input vswr below 1.2 for input power range of 7 to 125 W.—B. A. Ziegner, Varactor Achieves High Power Subharmonic Frequency Division, *Electronic Design*, Sept. 27, 1965, p 64–65.

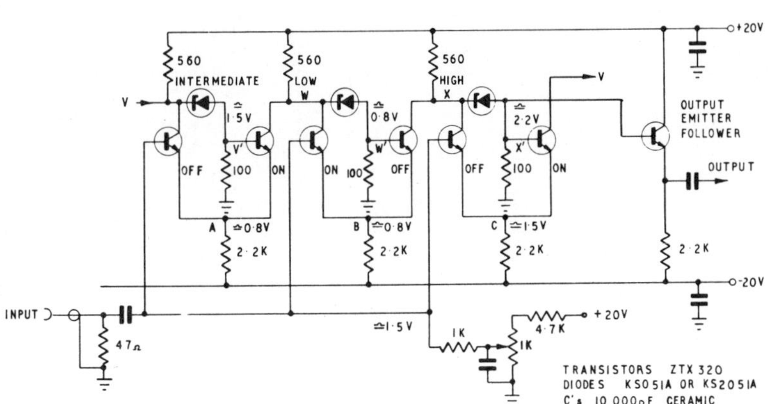

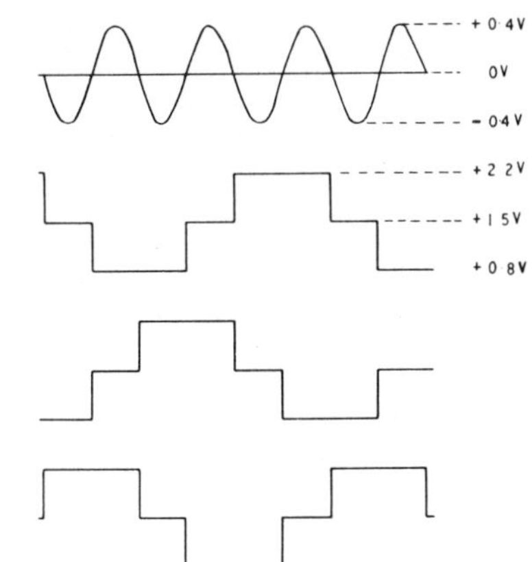

3-STAGE RING DIVIDER—Intended for feeding with sine-wave input. Can only have odd number of stages. Supply voltages are not critical, and can be as low as 10 V. When transistors are in states shown, the three pairs of collectors (V, W, and X) are at three different voltages levels—intermediate, low, and high. Intermediate level is unstable; in absence of input, this level moves around the ring and gives self-oscillation. Small input signal locks circuit to signal, so unstable state moves one stage for each input half-cycle. Can handle inputs above 300 MHz, if lead lengths are minimized.—A V.H.F. Ring Divider, Ferranti Ltd., Oldham, Lancs., England, No. 39, 1969.

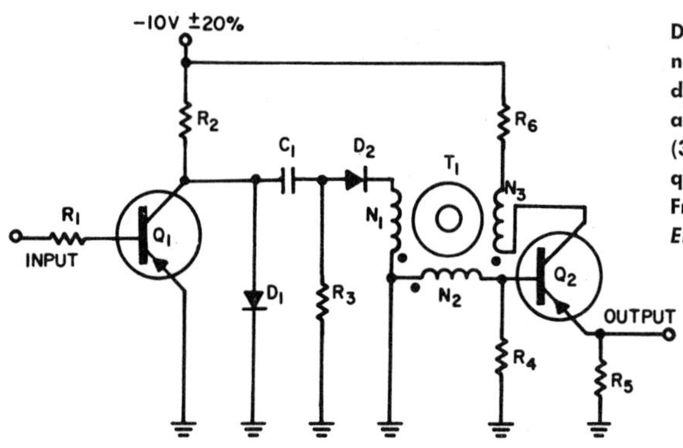

R1 - 150
R2 - 820
R3 - 180
R4 - 390
R5 - 3.9
R6 - 18
C1 - .068μf
Q1 - 2N2905
Q2 - 2N2905

T1 - 122D1000-18 (ARNOLD)
80505-1A-MA (MAGNETICS)
D1 - IN751A
D2 - IN3730
N1 - 31 TURNS
N2 - 60 TURNS
N3 - 30 TURNS

DIVISION FROM 1 TO 10—Adjusting C1 or number of turns on N1 of toroid core changes division. Circuit is largely immune to temperature changes. Output is sufficient across R5 (3 V) to drive another divider for further frequency division.—E. J. Willette, Magnetic Core Frequency Divider Uses Fewer Components, *Electronic Design*, Oct. 26, 1964, p 54–55.

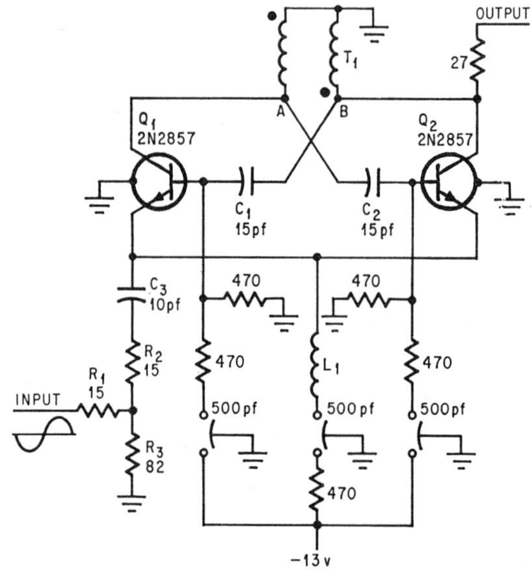

DIVIDE BY TWO IN 150–450 MHZ RANGE—Adding transformer T1 to astable mvbr speeds turn-on and turn-off of transistors, increases maximum oscillator frequency, and makes divide-by-two operation available over entire uhf range for sine, square, or pulse input. For 4:1 division, feed output to similar circuit in which input pad R1-R2-R3 is omitted.—D. E. Sanders, Adding a Transformer Halves Uhf Frequencies, *Electronics*, March 4, 1968, p 87–88.

T1 = FERROX-CUBE CORE 56-590-65-3B, 1 TURN NO. 36 BIFILAR WIRE, 2 TURNS TOTAL
L1 = FERROX-CUBE CORE 56-590-65-3B, 6 TURNS NO. 36

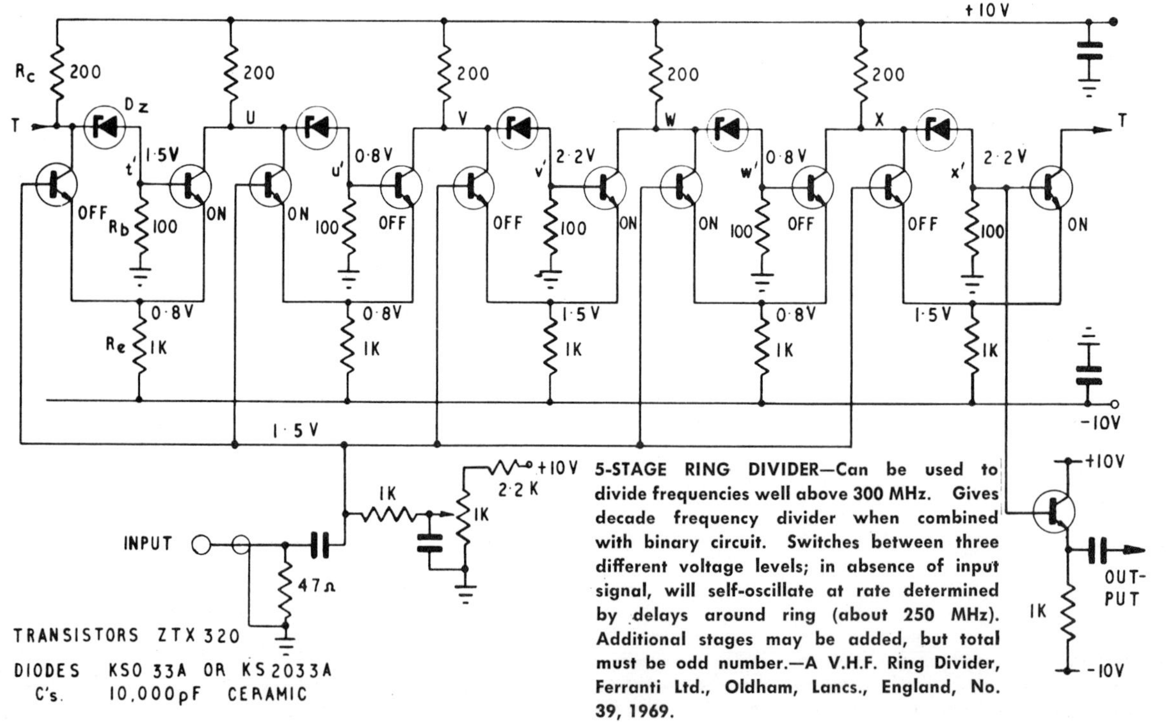

5-STAGE RING DIVIDER—Can be used to divide frequencies well above 300 MHz. Gives decade frequency divider when combined with binary circuit. Switches between three different voltage levels; in absence of input signal, will self-oscillate at rate determined by delays around ring (about 250 MHz). Additional stages may be added, but total must be odd number.—A V.H.F. Ring Divider, Ferranti Ltd., Oldham, Lancs., England, No. 39, 1969.

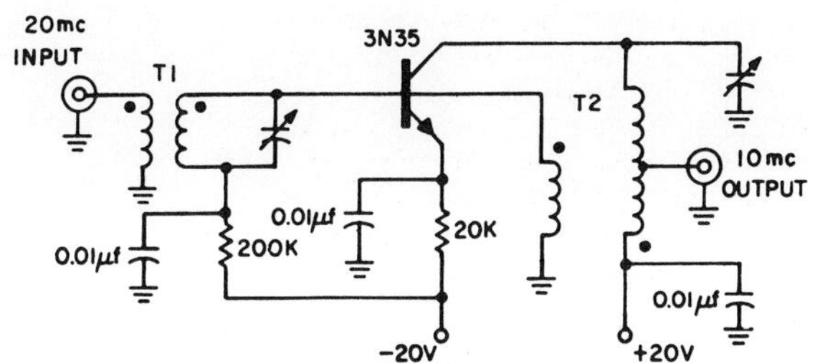

DIVIDING 20 MHZ—With input resonant circuit tuned to 20 MHz and output to 10 MHz, circuit performs well as frequency divider.—H. F. Verse, Jr., Simple Circuit Halves 20-Mc Supply Frequency, "400 Ideas for Design Selected from Electronic Design," Hayden Book Co., N.Y., 1964, p 174.

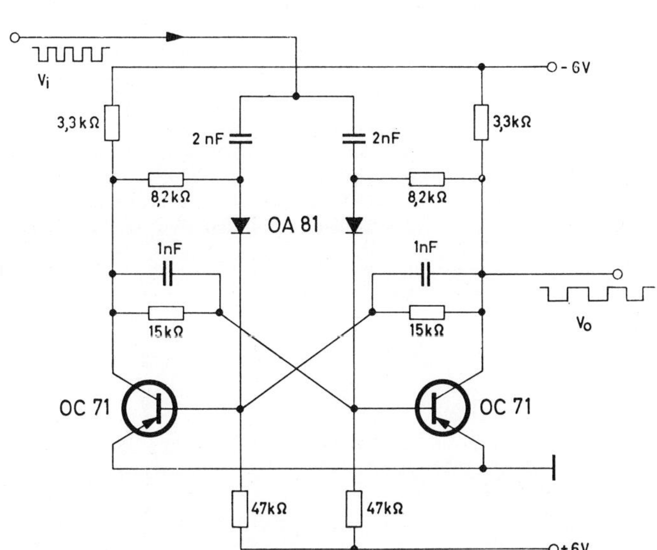

2:1 PULSE SCALER—Used when counting pulses at frequencies above reliable operating speed of counter, generally around 2,000 Hz. For higher count-down ratio, several such stages should be connected in series. Maximum input frequency for circuit is about 35 kHz.—"Counting Units for Programmed Control," Philips, Pub. Dept., Elcoma Div., Eindhoven, The Netherlands, 1964, p. 18.

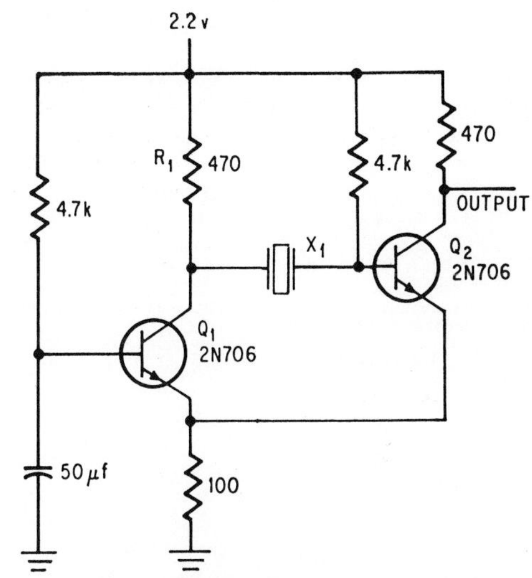

CRYSTAL DIVIDE-BY-10 MVBR—Emitter-coupled mvbr with crystal in place of timing capacitor makes excellent pulse generator for driving chain of synchronized divide-by-10 mvbr stages used in calibrating time bases of precision oscilloscopes.—G. W. Harrison, Crystal Gives Precision To a Stable Multivibrator, *Electronics*, Nov. 11, 1968, p 121.

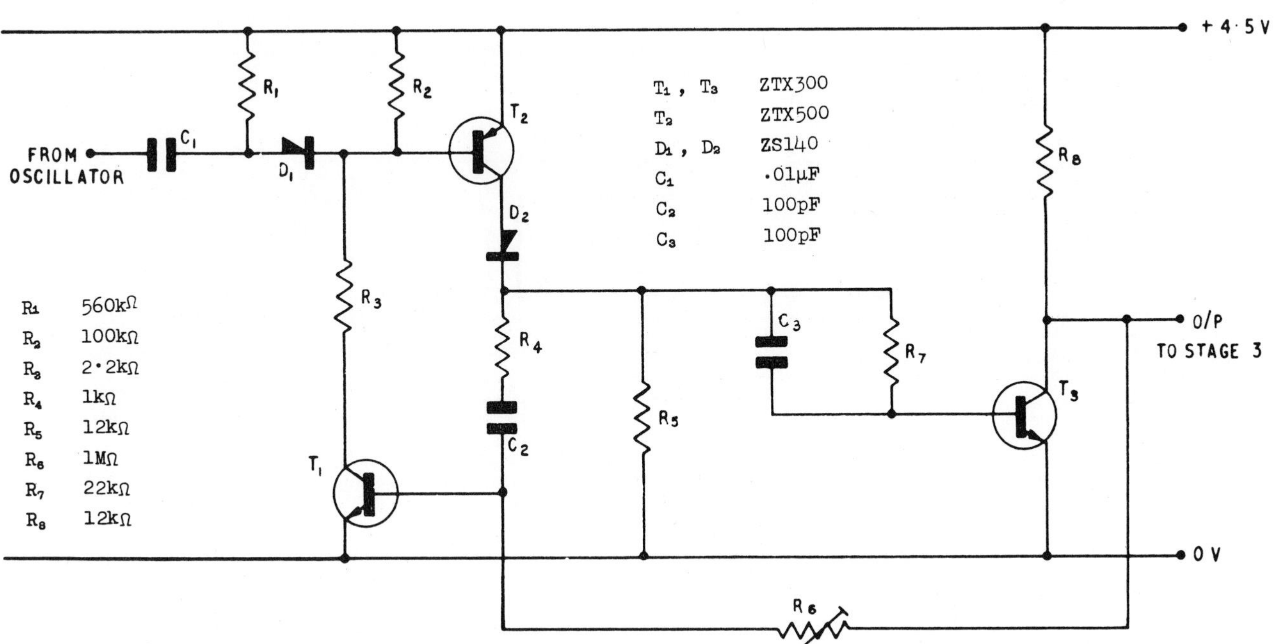

SINE-WAVE DIVIDE-BY-5—Used as first counting stage of battery-powered clock controlled by 100-kHz crystal oscillator. Circuit is free-running, as form of mvbr, with no input, but synchronizes to exact multiple of sine-wave input. R6 is adjusted to give required count of 5 for this stage of clock.—A Crystal Clock Using Plastic Transistors, Ferranti Ltd., Oldham, Lancs., England, No. 34, 1968.

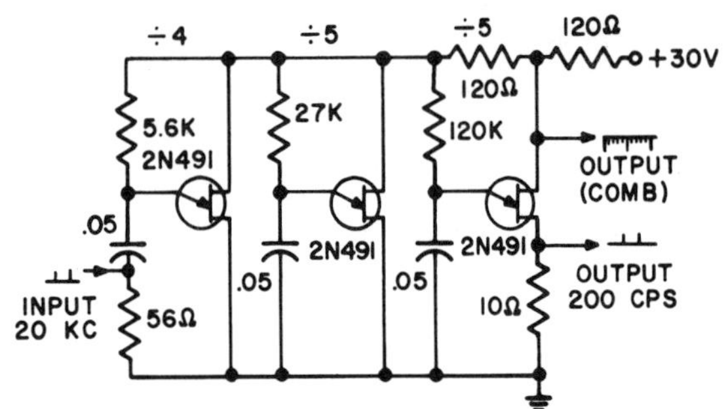

SIMPLE 100:1 DIVIDER—Requires only three ujt's to get 200 Hz output from 20,000 Hz input. With division ratios of 4 and 5, potentiometer adjustments will be required for the capacitor-charging resistors.—T. P. Sylvan, The Unijunction Transistor Characteristics and Applications, General Electric, Syracuse, N.Y., No. 90.10, 1965, p 73.

VARACTOR DIVIDER—With C1 and first coil resonating at 150-MHz input frequency, action of varactor makes L2-C2 resonate at 75 MHz, operating over 4% bandwidth. Cost is much less than that of IC designed for these frequencies.—M. Stevens and D. Steward, Varactor Diode is the Key to a Simple Frequency Divider, *Electronic Design*, Feb. 15, 1970, p 88.

AVALANCHE-MODE DIVIDER—Operation of transistor in avalanche mode gives simple relaxation oscillator that can be operated either as frequency divider or as low-output-impedance voltage generator. Capacitor is charged until breakdown voltage of transistor is reached, then discharged through transistor to give next output pulse. Period of divider can be adjusted by changing input amplitude and value of coupling resistor from preceding stage. Division ratio depends on values of R, C, and input amplitude, and is 5:1 for values shown.—A. Moiraghi, Single Transistor Divides Frequency in Avalanche Mode, *Electronics*, Sept. 29, 1969, p 96–97.

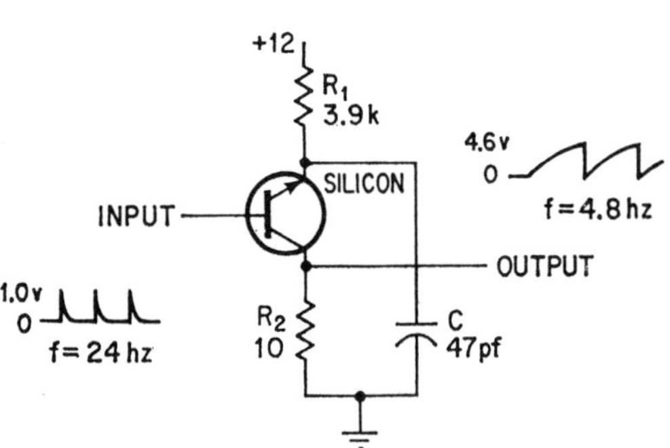

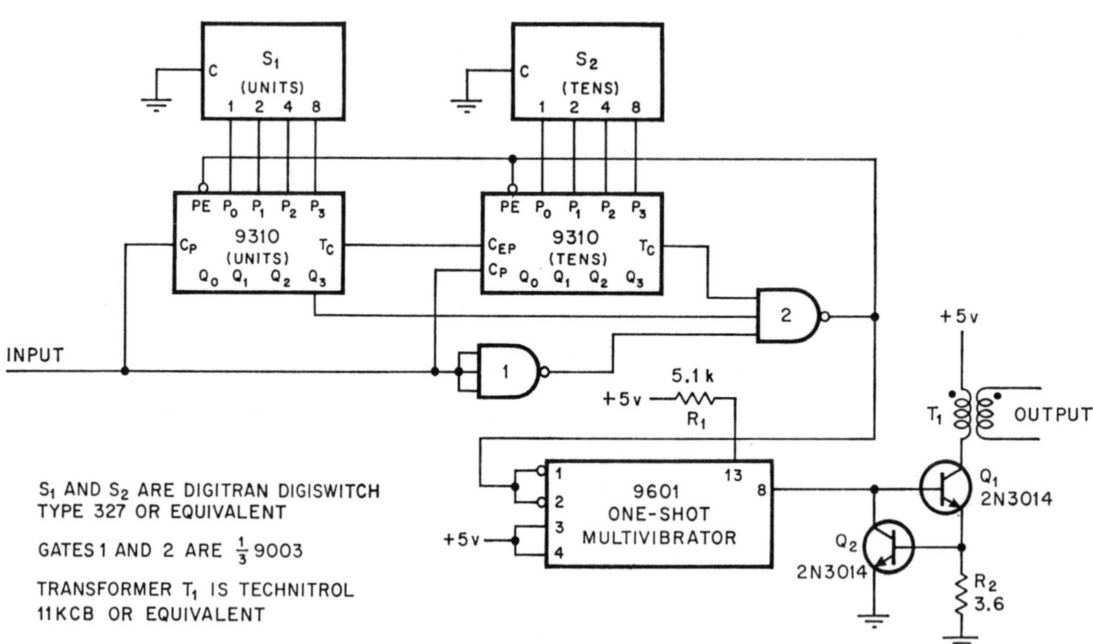

UP TO 99:1—Two thumbwheel switches, S1 and S2, can be set to provide any division ratio from 1 to 99 for programmable pulse frequency divider. Will handle frequencies exceeding 10 MHz. Uses two IC decade counters and IC one-shot to drive pulse transformer.—K. Erickson, Divider Splits Frequency into Any Ratio from 1 to 99, *Electronics*, April 13, 1970, p 107–108.

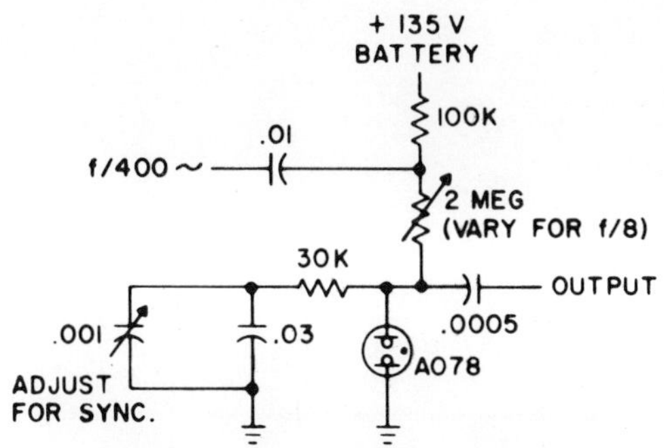

SCALE-OF-8—Simple battery-operated neon circuit produces one pulse every 8 Hz of 400-Hz source.—E. Bauman, "Applications of Neon Lamps and Gas Discharge Tubes," Signalite, Neptune, N.J., p 50.

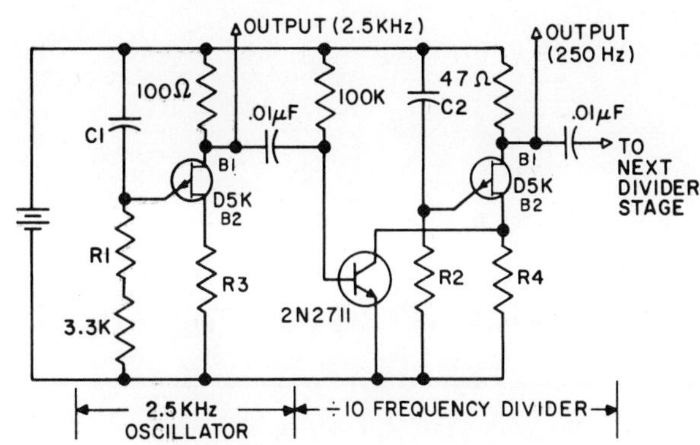

10:1 DIVIDER—Complementary ujt D5K, with highly predictable voltage threshold, gives excellent performance in large-countdown frequency dividers such as are used in television color bar generators.—W. R. Spofford, Jr., Complementary Unijunction Transistor, General Electric, Syracuse, N.Y., No. 90.72, 1968, p 13.

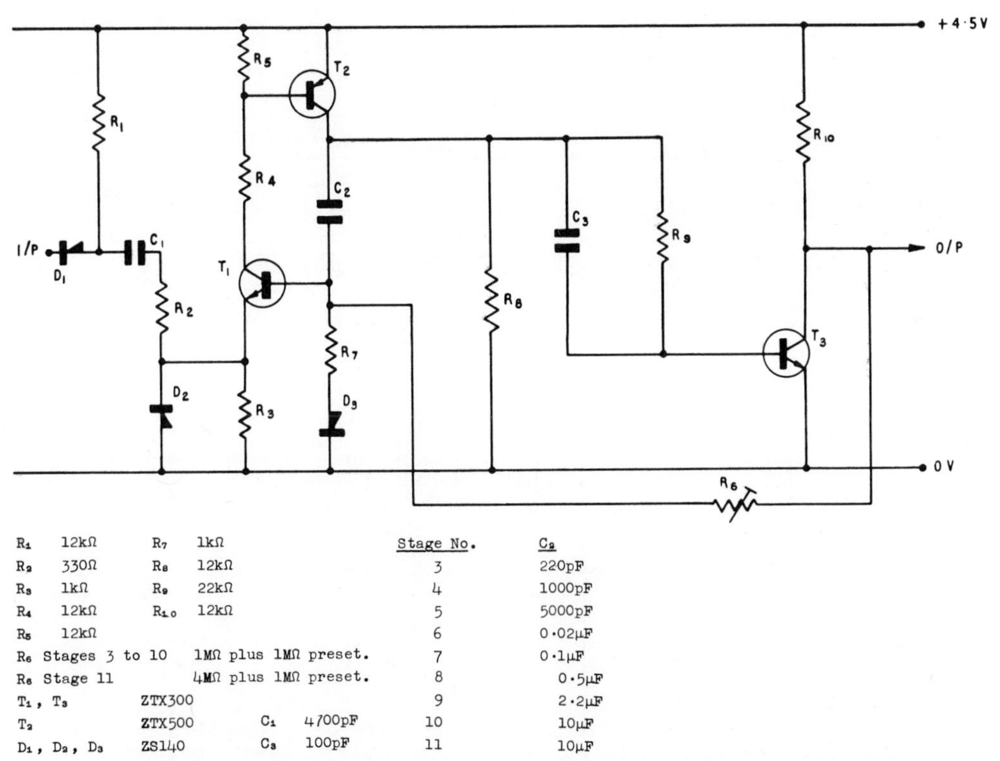

R_1	12kΩ	R_7	1kΩ
R_2	330Ω	R_8	12kΩ
R_3	1kΩ	R_9	22kΩ
R_4	12kΩ	R_{10}	12kΩ
R_5	12kΩ		
R_6 Stages 3 to 10	1MΩ plus 1MΩ preset.		
R_6 Stage 11	4MΩ plus 1MΩ preset.		
T_1, T_3	ZTX300		
T_2	ZTX500	C_1	4700pF
D_1, D_2, D_3	ZS140	C_3	100pF

Stage No.	C_2
3	220pF
4	1000pF
5	5000pF
6	0·02μF
7	0·1μF
8	0·5μF
9	2·2μF
10	10μF
11	10μF

DIVISION BY 5, 4, OR 3—Used in battery-powered 100-kHz quartz crystal clock to give one pulse every half-minute for driving ratchet mechanism that moves hands of clock half a minute per pulse. Circuit synchronizes on integral number of narrow trigger pulses from preceding stage, with number determined by setting of R6. Division ratios of stages 3-11 are 5, 4, 5, 5, 4, 5, 5, 4, and 3, following stage 2 which divides sine-wave output of crystal by 5. Accuracy of clock is about 1 sec per week.—A Crystal Clock Using Plastic Transistors, Ferranti Ltd., Oldham, Lancs., England, No. 34, 1968.

NOTE: To locate additional circuits in the category of this chapter, use the index at the back of this book. Check also the author's "Sourcebook of Electronic Circuits," published by McGraw-Hill in 1968.

CHAPTER 34
Frequency Measuring Circuits

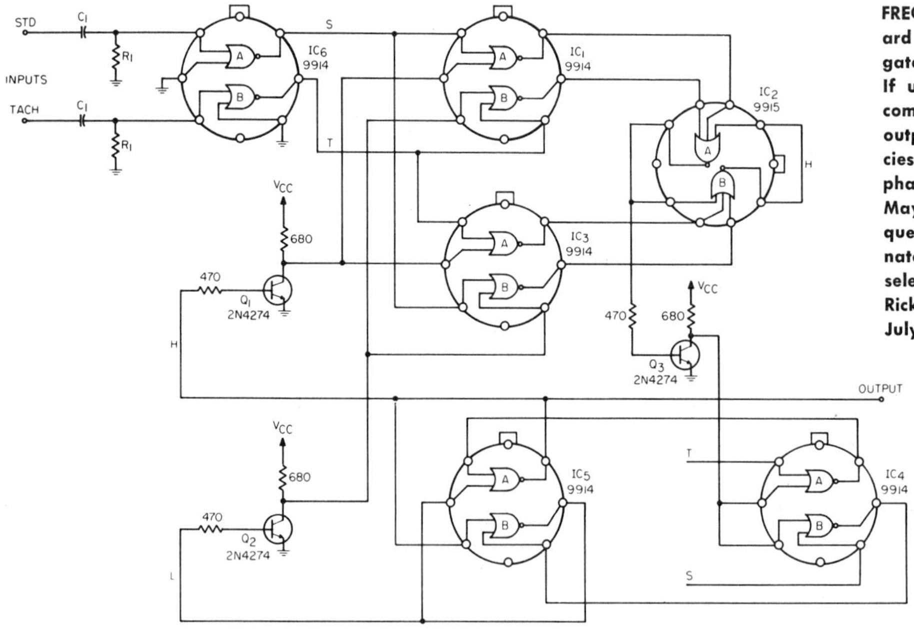

FREQUENCY COMPARATOR—Compares standard frequency at one input of dual NOR gate with unknown frequency at other input. If unknown is lower, d-c level at output of comparator is low. If unknown is higher, output d-c level is high. When input frequencies are equal, circuit functions as linear phase discriminator having no tuned circuits. May be used as vco control, go-no-go frequency comparator, or as frequency discriminator. Output may be either polarity by selecting appropriate terminal of IC5.—R. Ricks, Frequency Comparator Uses ICs, *EEE*, July 1967, p 128–129.

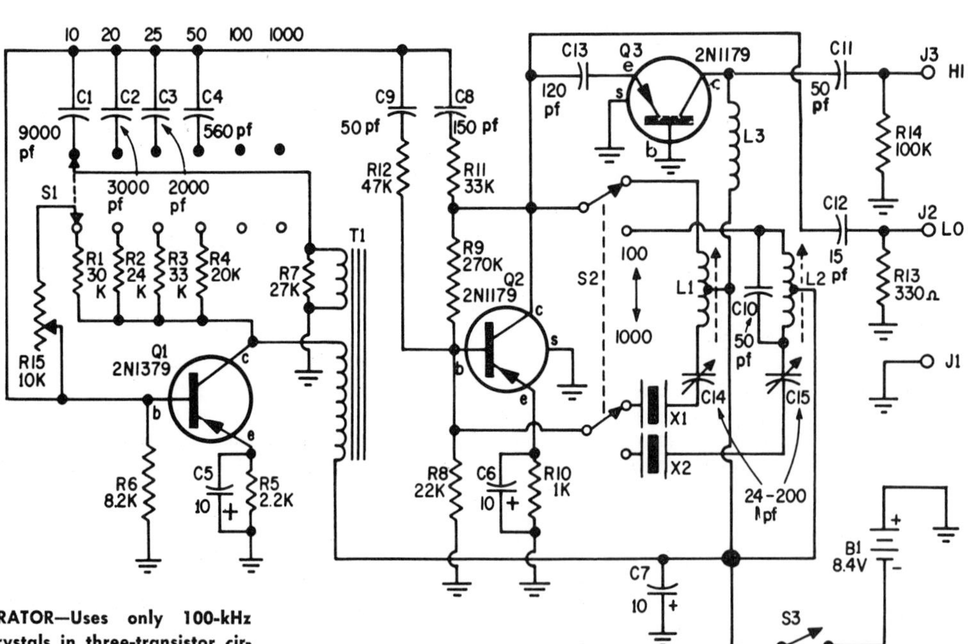

CRYSTAL CALIBRATOR—Uses only 100-kHz and 1,000-kHz crystals in three-transistor circuit to provide accurate calibrating signals at 10, 20, 25, 50, 100, and 1,000 kHz, with harmonics well beyond 34 MHz. Book gives construction details and tells how to check adjustments with WWV. Blocking oscillator transformer T1 is Stancor A-8111. L1 is 2.5-7 mH (J. W. Miller 6316), L2 is 35-300 μH (J. W. Miller 2002), and L3 is 2.5-mH r-f choke.—A. A. Mangieri, Solid-State Crystal Calibrator, "Bench-Tested Communications Projects," Hayden Book Co., N.Y., p 116–121.

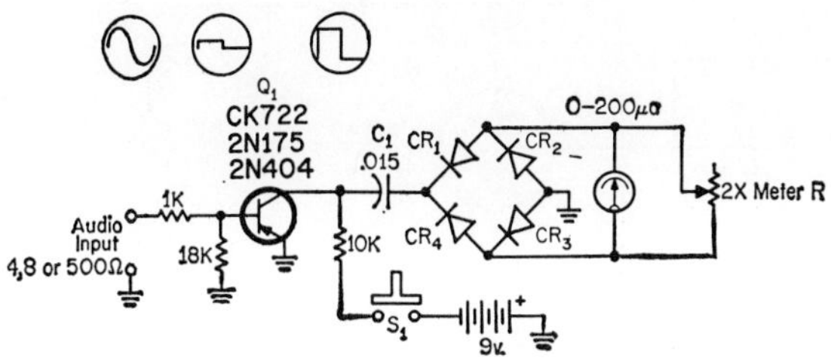

FREQUENCY METER—Full-scale range is 2 kHz, and accuracy is within 20 Hz at midscale. Accuracy is ample for ssb and radioteletype applications. Silicon rectifiers are not critical, if piv rating is above 100 V, as in Sarkes Tarzian K200 diodes.—J. Alan Biggs, The W3ZP Meter, *CQ*, July 1966, p 70–71.

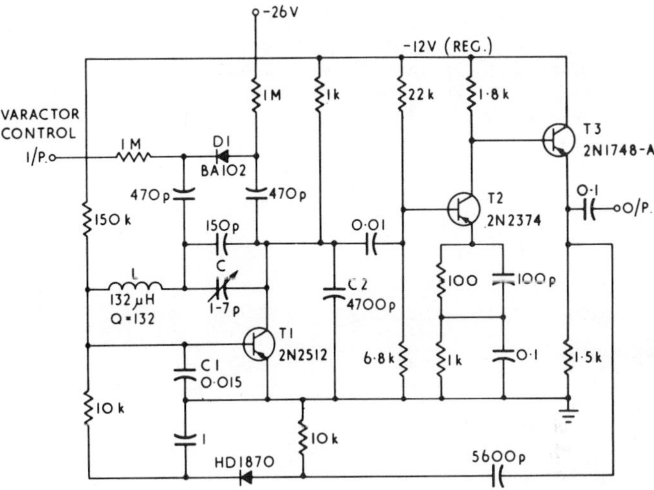

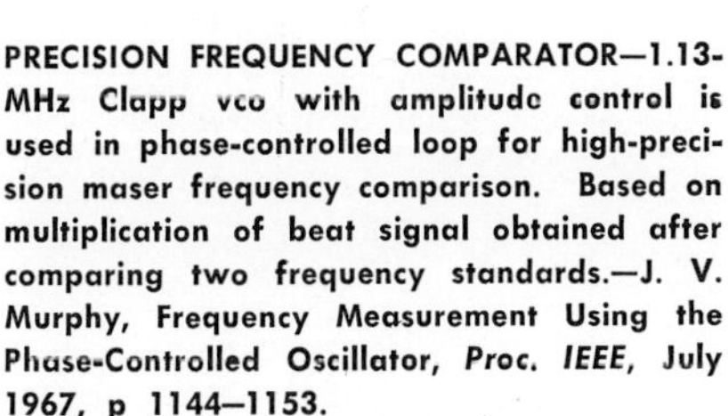

PRECISION FREQUENCY COMPARATOR—1.13-MHz Clapp vco with amplitude control is used in phase-controlled loop for high-precision maser frequency comparison. Based on multiplication of beat signal obtained after comparing two frequency standards.—J. V. Murphy, Frequency Measurement Using the Phase-Controlled Oscillator, *Proc. IEEE*, July 1967, p 1144–1153.

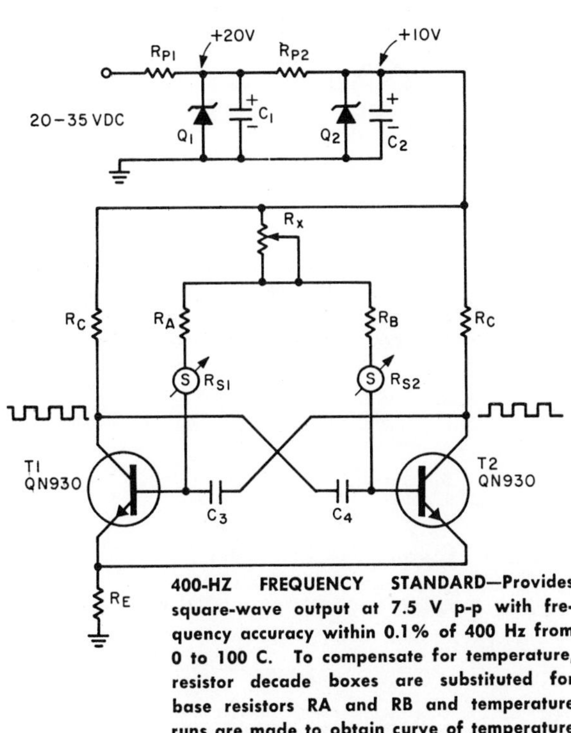

400-HZ FREQUENCY STANDARD—Provides square-wave output at 7.5 V p-p with frequency accuracy within 0.1% of 400 Hz from 0 to 100 C. To compensate for temperature, resistor decade boxes are substituted for base resistors RA and RB and temperature runs are made to obtain curve of temperature vs base resistance to yield symmetrical square wave at correct frequency. Two sensistors and two series resistors are then selected to track the curves obtained. Rx, about 1/100th of RA + RS1, is adjusted for fine-tuning to exact frequency. Other values are those of conventional mvbr and power supply.—E. B. Nelson, Multivibrator Adapted As Frequency Standard, *Electronic Design*, Feb. 17, 1964, p 94–95.

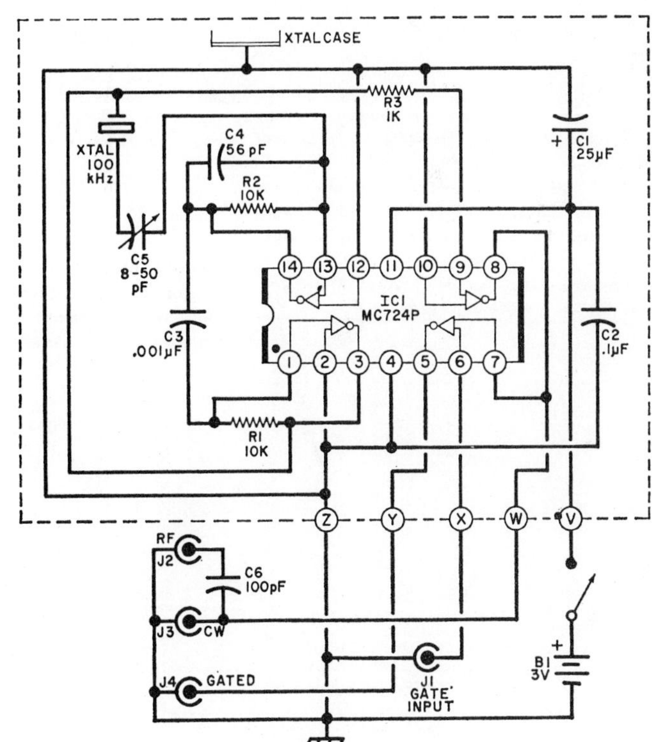

RECEIVER CALIBRATOR—Provides birdie every 100 kHz for calibrating short-wave and amateur radio receivers. For optimum accuracy, can be adjusted to zero-beat against WWV. Uses crystal and single IC in simple circuit operating from 3-V battery. Article gives construction and adjustment details.—D. Lancaster, Build the 100-kHz Standard, *Popular Electronics*, April 1970, p 56–58 and 105.

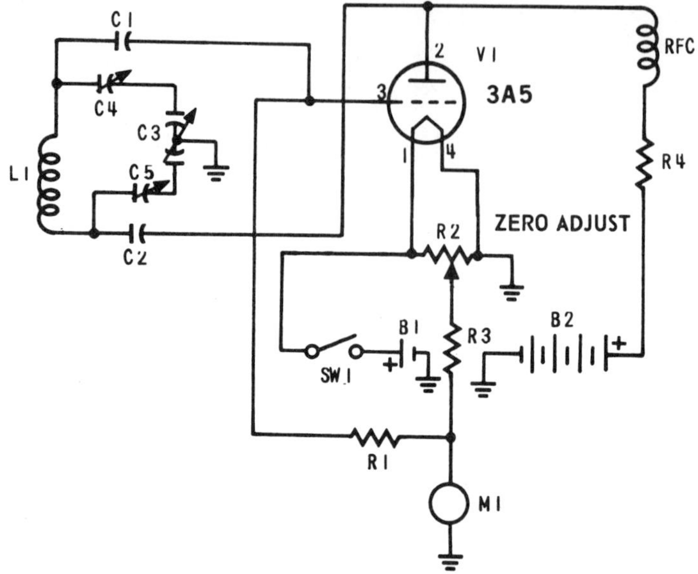

GRID DIP METER—1-mA d-c meter dips whenever circuit is brought near resonant circuit oscillating at same frequency. Once variable capacitors in tank of 3A5 oscillator are calibrated for frequency, circuit can be used to identify exact frequency at which transmitter is putting out signal. B1 is 1.5 V and B2 67.5 V. Values: R1 5.6K; R2 750; R3 1.1K; R4 15K; C1, C2 0.0025 μF; C3 100 pF per section; C4, C5 51 pF; RFC1 2.5 mH; L1 plug-in coil for desired range (winding data given in book).—R. M. Brown, "104 Simple One-Tube Projects," Tab Books, Blue Ridge Summit, Pa., 1969, p 149.

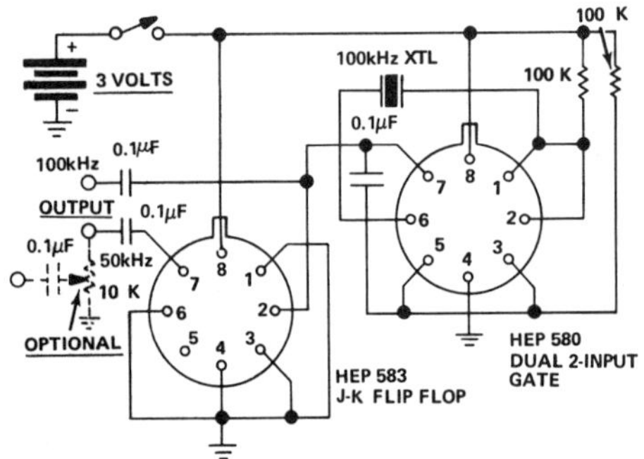

IC FREQUENCY STANDARD—Accurate, compact, and simple-to-operate 100-kHz crystal oscillator and flip-flop frequency divider for checking or aligning frequency settings of receivers. Has harmonic-rich square-wave outputs at 100 and 50 kHz, from which lower values can be obtained by adding various combinations of divide-by-2 and divide-by-5 IC flip-flops.—"Tips on Using IC's," Motorola, Phoenix, Ariz., HMA-32, 1968.

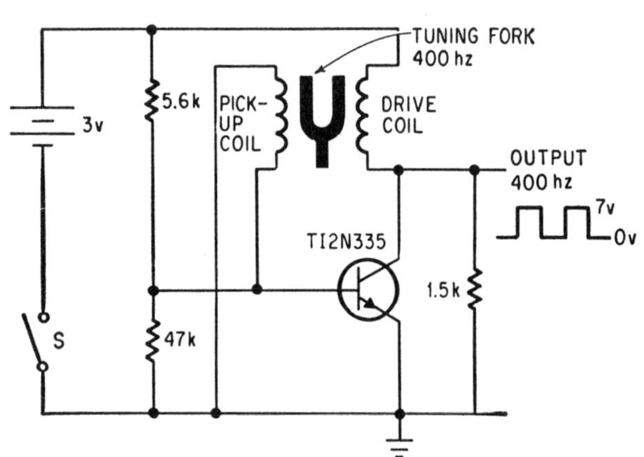

FORK-STABILIZED 400-HZ—Use of tuning fork in place of pulse transformer in blocking oscillator converts circuit to portable frequency standard with square-wave output. Circuit worked 39 hr on two AA cells, using Varo Model 6250L-400 fork.—S. V. Scheffel, Tuning Fork Drives Portable Frequency Standard, *Electronics*, Nov. 14, 1966, p 122–123.

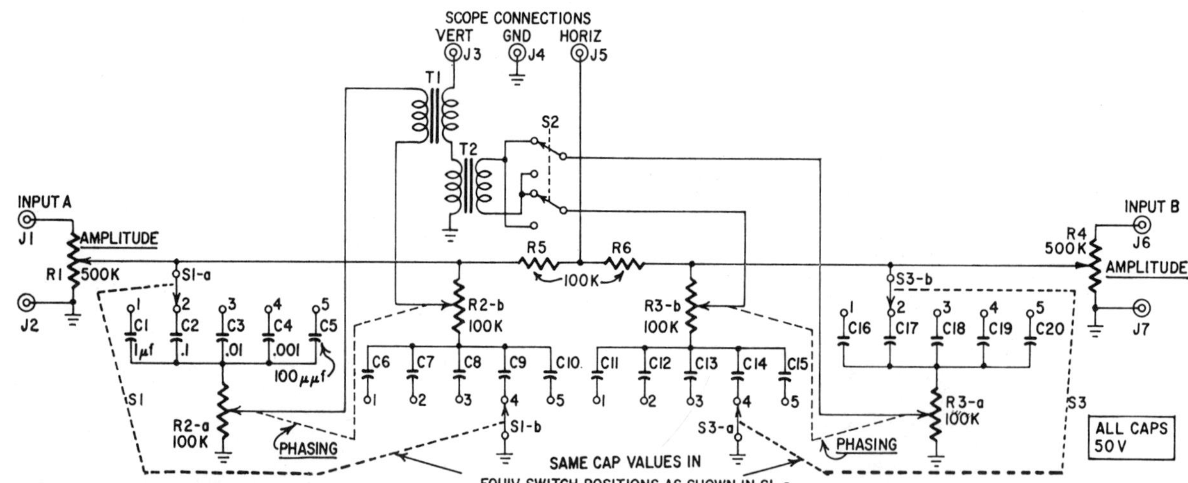

IMPROVED CYCLOID ADAPTER—Known and unknown frequencies are applied to inputs and R2 or R3 adjusted so phase difference is 90 deg. Shifting of phase does not affect magnitude of signal, so resulting cycloid patterns are much easier to read. Loops on cycloid are counted to give ratio of frequencies. May be used with practically any oscilloscope.—T. Jaski, Cycloids for Frequency Measurement, *Radio-Electronics*, July 1965, p 60–61.

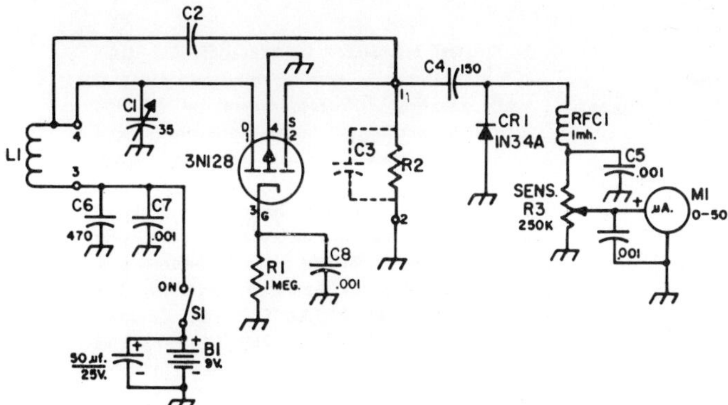

FET GRID-DIP METER—Performance is equivalent to tube-type circuit. Will work up to 150 MHz, using plug-in coils. Meter shows dip when unit is tuned to resonant frequency of coil to which it is coupled. Book gives construction details, including coil-winding data and calibration procedure.—L. G. McCoy, A Field-Effect Transistor Dipper, "The Mobile Manual for Radio Amateurs," ARRL, Newington, Conn., 1968, p 179–182.

FREQUENCY COUNTER FOR SCOPE—Designed for use with kits or less expensive scopes, to serve in place of calibrated time base found on more costly instruments, for accurate frequency measurements. Consists of Schmitt trigger Q1 and monostable multivibrator Q3, with Q2 common to both. Circuit triggers at about 2 V. Values of R2 (ohms) and C depend upon frequency range, as follows: 0–250 Hz—15,000 and 0.0072 μF; 0–2,500 Hz—8,000 and 0.001 μF; 0–2,500 Hz—1,000 and 300 pF; 0–250,000 Hz—200 and 150 pF.—R. L. Carroll, Simple Frequency Counter, *Electronics World*, July 1969, p 82.

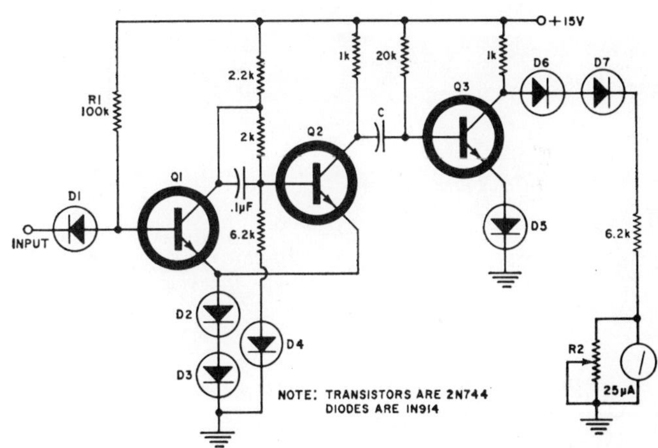

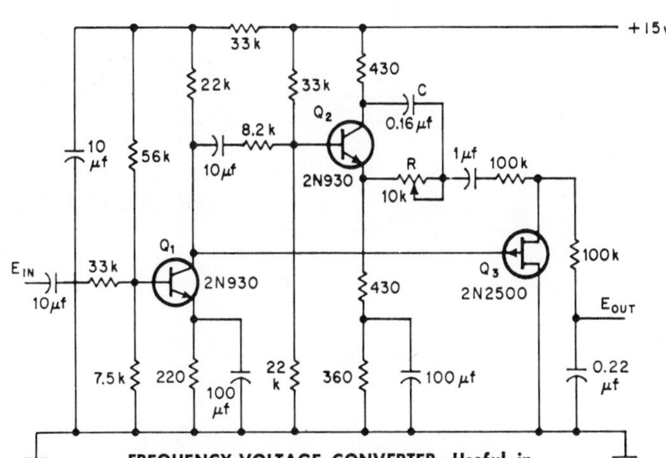

FREQUENCY-VOLTAGE CONVERTER—Useful in frequency meters and for measuring carrier frequency drift of r-f signals after demodulation. Will operate in audio range. Uses fet Q3 with phase-shifted inputs to gate and source, wherein amount of phase shift depends on frequency and on setting of pot R. With 90-deg phase shift, d-c output voltage of phase-sensitive detector is zero. At lower frequency, output is positive, while higher frequencies produce negative output.—J. Kalinski, FET Phase Detector Can Be Frequency-Voltage Converter, *Electronics*, July 20, 1970, p 87–88.

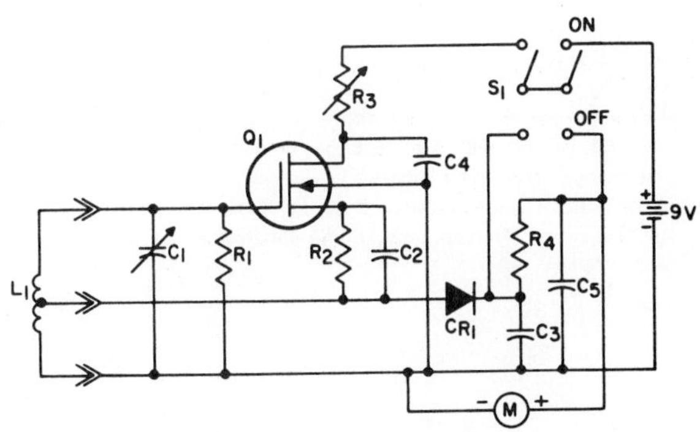

DIP/WAVE METER—Uses mosfet oscillator with set of seven plug-in coils to cover range of 1.16 to 110 MHz. With power switch off, circuit becomes absorption-type wavemeter that measures resonant frequency of energized r-f circuits. Needle of meter jumps upward slightly when frequency of oscillator in meter matches that of L-C circuit being measured. With power switch on, meter measures resonant frequency of unenergized r-f circuits. Book gives winding data for plug-in coils. Values: R1 47K; R2 1K; R3 10K; R4 6.8K; C1 50 pF; C2, C4, C5 0.01 μF; C3 0.001 μF; CR1 1N914; Q1 3N128; M 100 μA.—"Hobby Circuits Manual," RCA, Harrison, N.J., HM-90, p 141.

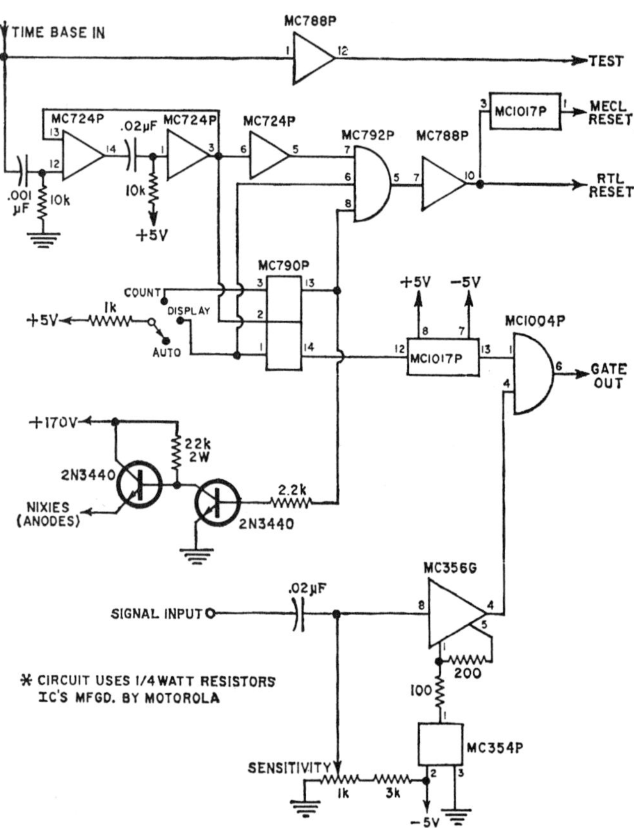

$400 UNIT MEASURES CB FREQUENCIES—Uses IC's and Nixies in special circuits to cut cost while meeting FCC requirement of 0.005% measuring accuracy. Combines Motorola and Fairchild logic units. Control circuits, signal-conditioning section, and main gate are shown. Schmitt trigger changes input signal to pulse train having one pulse for each cycle of signal input. Article gives IC interconnections and circuits of the three power supplies used.—F. E. Cody, A 50-mHz Digital Counter, *Electronics World*, March 1969, p 40–42 and 61.

CYCLOID ADAPTER FOR CRO—Based on use of two sine waves 90 deg out of phase, to produce cycloid patterns on screen from which ratio of unknown to known frequency can be seen at glance. Article gives 14 such patterns. Technique is comparable to that using Lissajous figures. One drawback of adapters shown is that changing of phase relationship with R1 or R2 will also change amplitude, distorting pattern and making frequency ratio more difficult to recognize.—T. Jaski, Cycloids for Frequency Measurement, *Radio-Electronics*, July 1965, p 60–61.

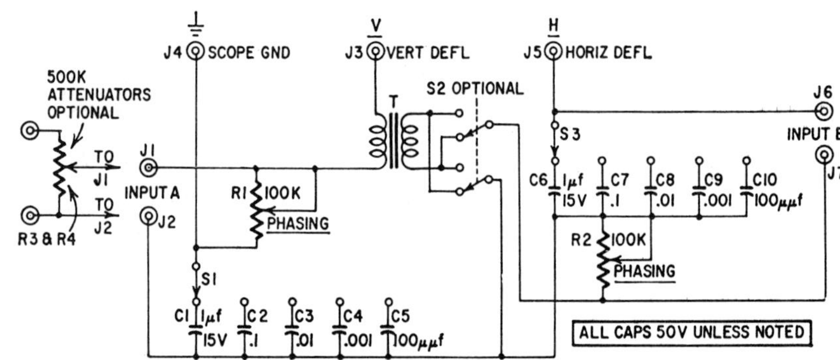

NOTE: To locate additional circuits in the category of this chapter, use the index at the back of this book. Check also the author's "Sourcebook of Electronic Circuits," published by McGraw-Hill in 1968.

CHAPTER 35
Frequency Modulation Circuits

R-F INPUT STAGE—For use in high-quality f-m broadcast receivers. Minimum noise figure is 2.2 dB at 100 MHz. Article discusses theory of circuit design.—G. Wolf, Recent Developments in Circuits and Transistors for Television Receivers, *Electronic Applications*, Philips, Pub. Dept., Elcoma Div., Eindhoven, The Netherlands, Vol. 26, No. 4, 1965–1966, p 145–165.

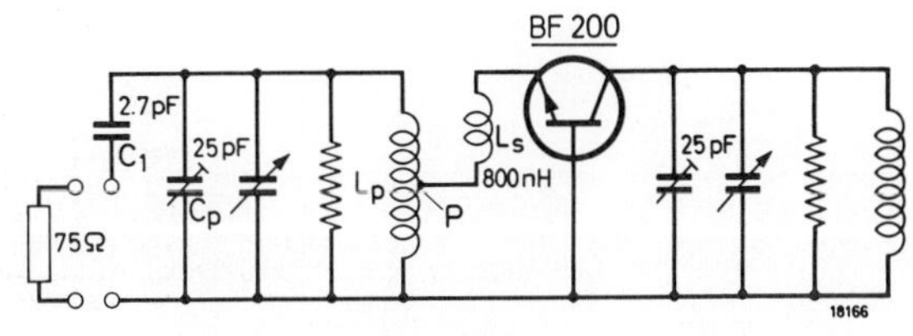

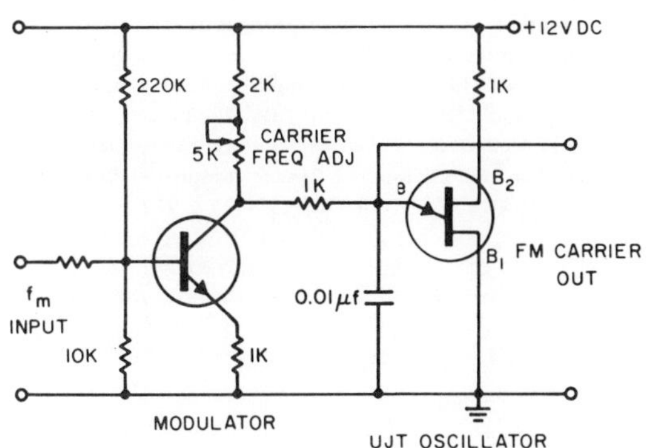

500-HZ DEVIATION OF 2 KHZ—Simple ujt relaxation oscillator is frequency-modulated by npn transistor, neither of which are critical as to type. Transistor input of 0.45 V at base sets center frequency at 2 kHz.—D. Learned, UJT Oscillator Makes Simple FM Modulator, *Electronic Design*, May 10, 1965, p 47–48.

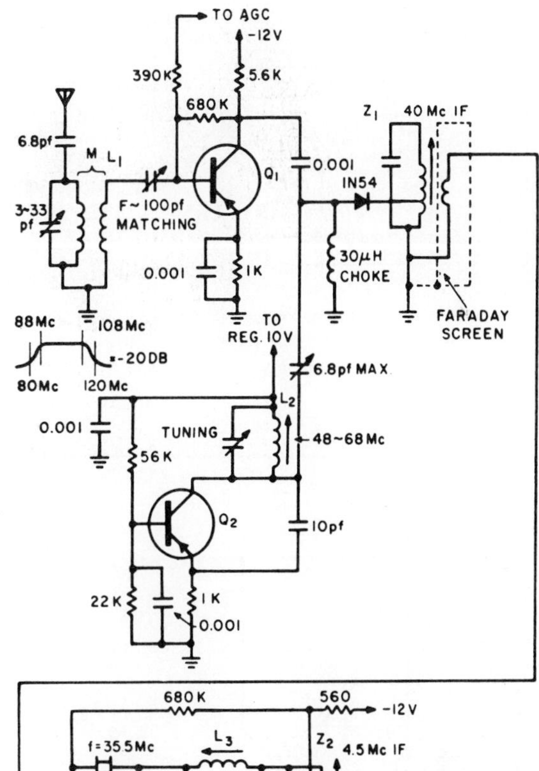

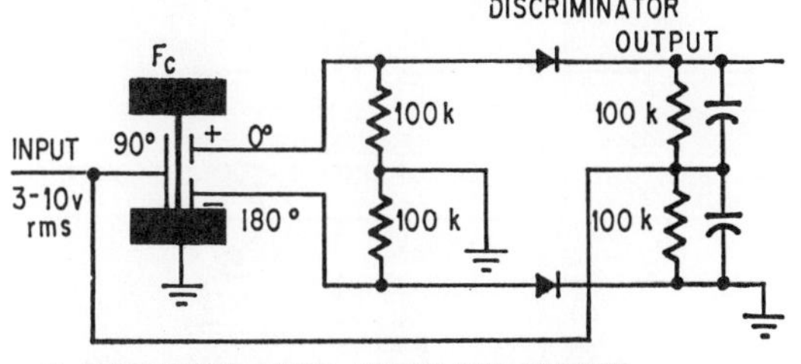

H RESONATOR GIVES LARGE F-M SWINGS—Twintron H-shaped piezoelectric resonator with Q of 4,000 acts with out-of-phase transducers to make f-m discriminator produce large change in output for small shift in frequency. Effect is that of ultra-narrow-band discriminator. Article gives other applications for Twintrons in tone communication systems.—H. Baker and J. R. Cressey, H-Shaped Resonators Signal Upturn in Tone Telemetering, *Electronics*, Oct. 2, 1967, p 99–106.

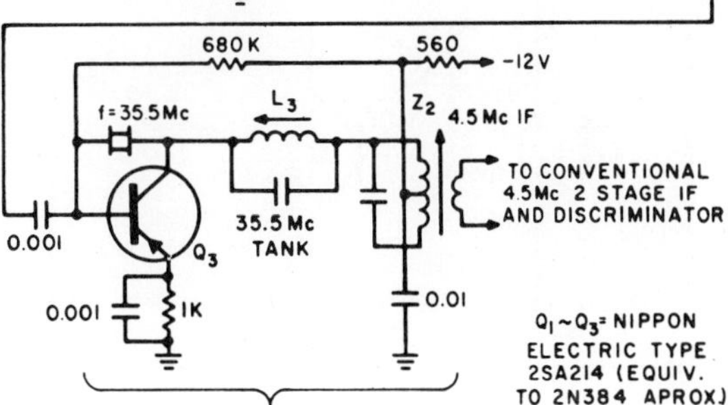

DOUBLE-CONVERSION RECEIVER—Crystal in overtone circuit converts 40-MHz first i-f down to 4.5 MHz. With crystal control, afc is not needed. Intended for use in areas having many f-m stations, where receiver must handle both powerful and weak signals without audio distortion caused by narrow i-f passband. Crystal can be low-cost CB unit.—L. E. Geisler, Double Conversion Improves Transistorized FM Receivers, "400 Ideas for Design Selected from Electronic Design," Hayden Book Co., N.Y., 1964, p 33–34.

10.7-MHZ TWO-IC I-F STRIP—Requires triple-tuned filter ahead of first IC to provide required selectivity. Available gain of strip is 65 dB, but limiting by second IC reduces this about 17 dB.—"Linear Integrated Circuits," RCA, Harrison, N.J., IC-41, p 283.

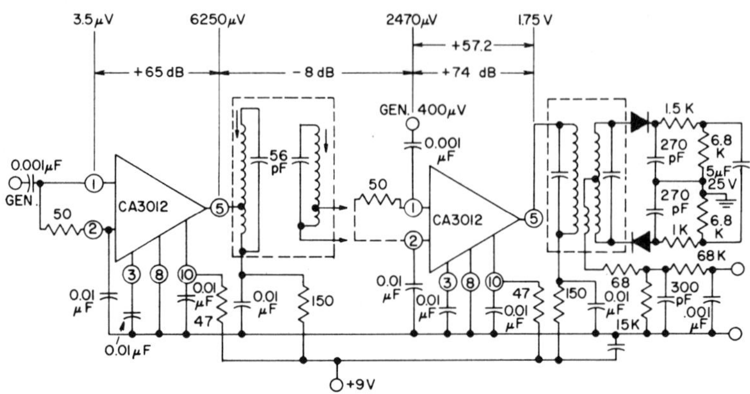

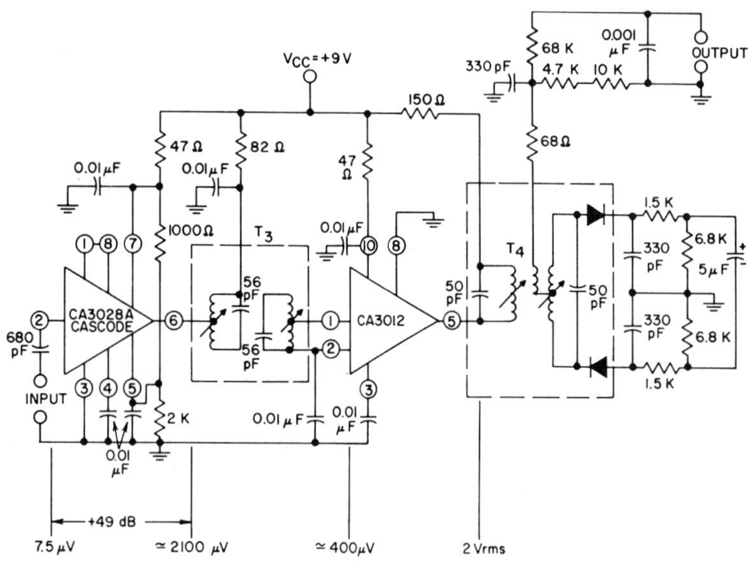

10.7-MHZ CASCODE I-F IC—CA3028A IC r-f amplifier is used in high-gain, high-performance cascode configuration in conjunction with CA3012 IC f-m i-f amplifier having sensitivity of 7.5 μV. T3 is TRW 22486 and T4 is TRW 22516. Provides 155 mV audio output for 140 μV input.—"Linear Integrated Circuits," RCA, Harrison, N.J., IC-41, p 217.

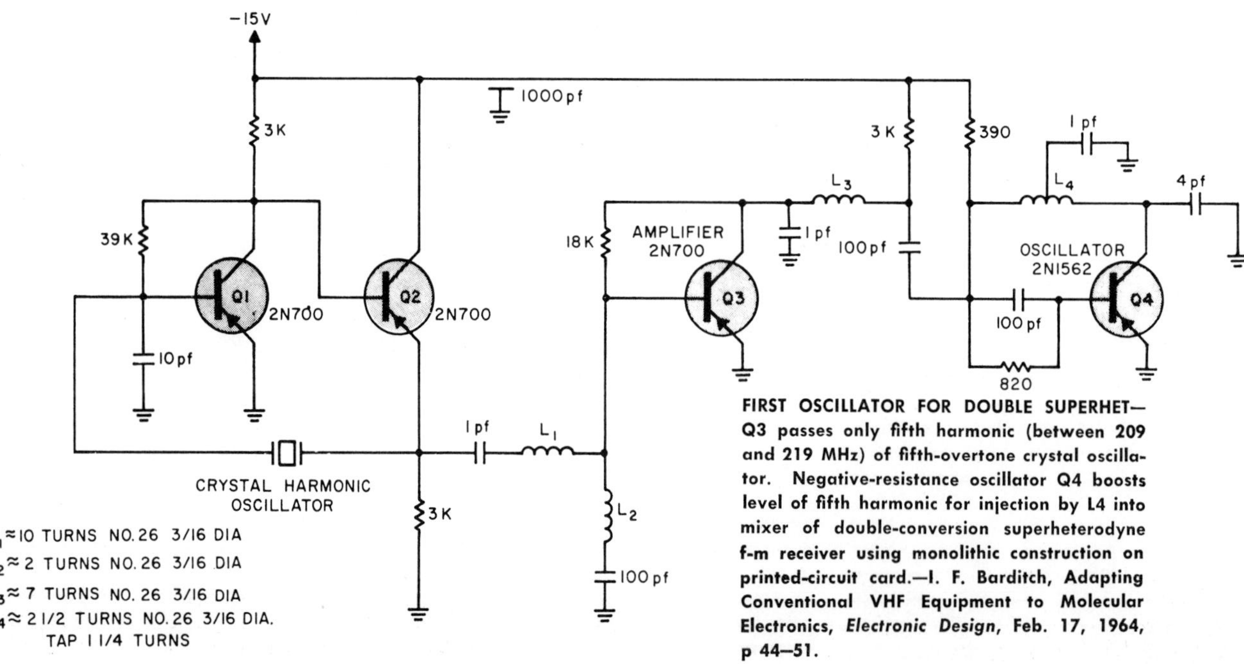

FIRST OSCILLATOR FOR DOUBLE SUPERHET—Q3 passes only fifth harmonic (between 209 and 219 MHz) of fifth-overtone crystal oscillator. Negative-resistance oscillator Q4 boosts level of fifth harmonic for injection by L4 into mixer of double-conversion superheterodyne f-m receiver using monolithic construction on printed-circuit card.—I. F. Barditch, Adapting Conventional VHF Equipment to Molecular Electronics, *Electronic Design*, Feb. 17, 1964, p 44–51.

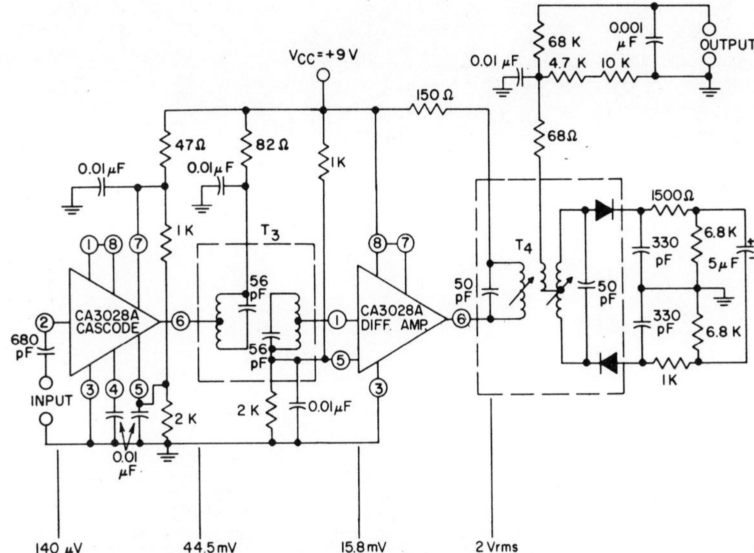

10.7-MHZ IC I-F STRIP—Uses two IC r-f amplifiers, one connected as cascode amplifier having 50 dB voltage gain, and the other as differential amplifier having 42 dB voltage gain.—"Linear Integrated Circuits," RCA, Harrison, N.J., IC-41, p 219.

T_3: Interstage transformer TRW #22486 or equiv.
T_4: Ratio detector TRW #22516 or equiv.

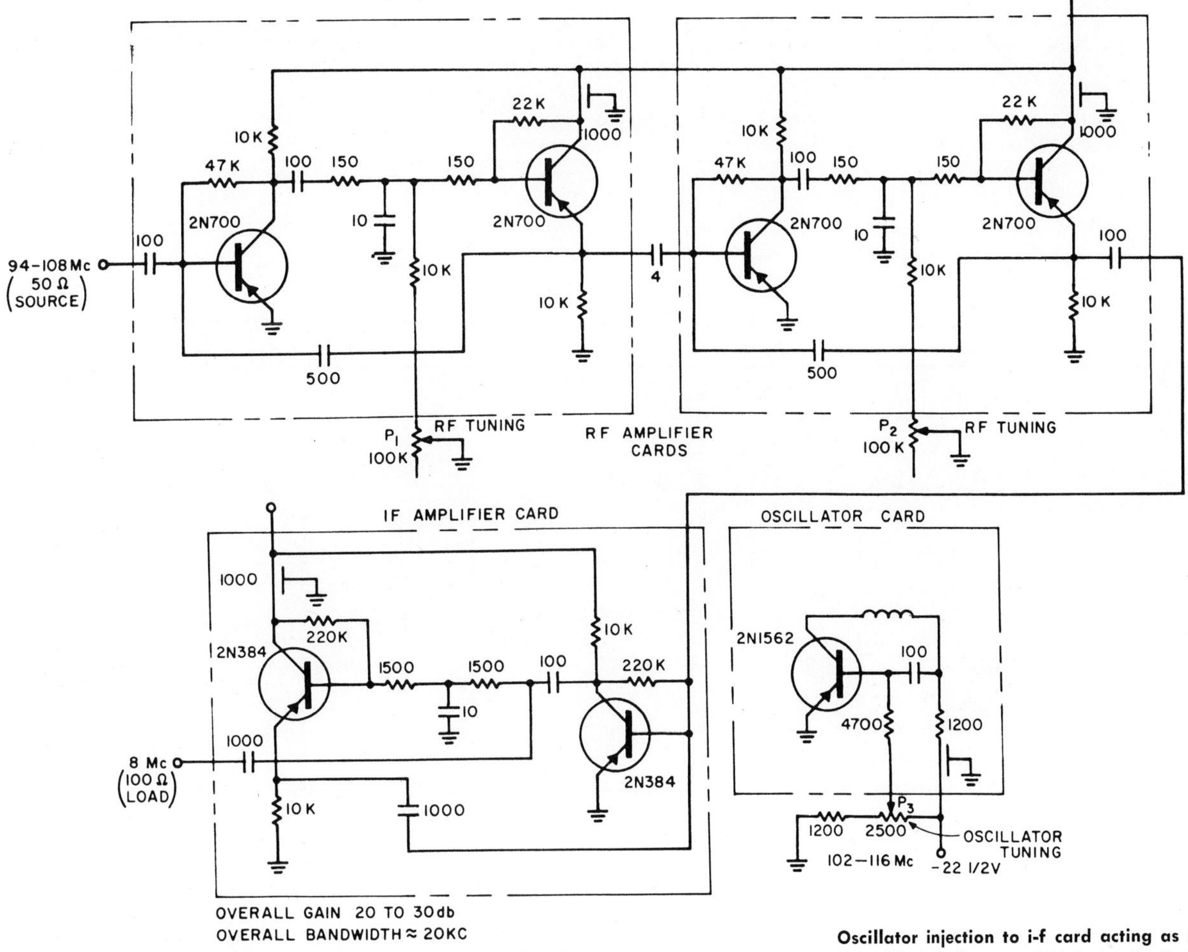

OVERALL GAIN 20 TO 30db
OVERALL BANDWIDTH ≈ 20KC

INDUCTORLESS 94–108 MHZ TUNER—Three 100-MHz R-C selective amplifiers using monolithic construction on printed-circuit cards are combined with distributed-inductance oscillator, with potentiometers used for tuning. Chief drawbacks are distortion and detuning for signal levels above 1 mV, and instability with small changes in source impedance. Oscillator injection to i-f card acting as mixer is achieved by proximity.—I. F. Barditch, Adapting Conventional VHF Equipment to Molecular Electronics, *Electronic Design*, Feb. 17, 1964, p 44–51.

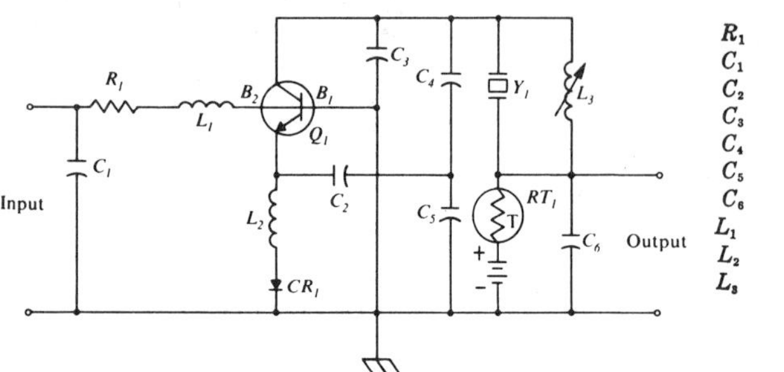

R_1	15K
C_1	0.01 μF
C_2	0.5 μF
C_3	82 pF
C_4	200 pF
C_5	220 pF
C_6	0.5 μF
L_1	2.5 mH
L_2	2.5 mH
L_3	480–800 μH

CURRENT-CONTROLLED F-M OSCILLATOR—Q1 is T1926 tetrode driving 455-kHz crystal Y1. Frequency is controlled by feeding input current to second base B2 of tetrode operated in reverse mode. Can be used in small f-m transmitters and vco applications. Supply voltage is 4 V. Choose CR1 to allow 0.5 mA. Thermistor is 10K Fenwal 4151.—"Selected Electronic Circuitry," NASA SP-5046, 1966, Government Printing Office, Washington, D.C., p 18.

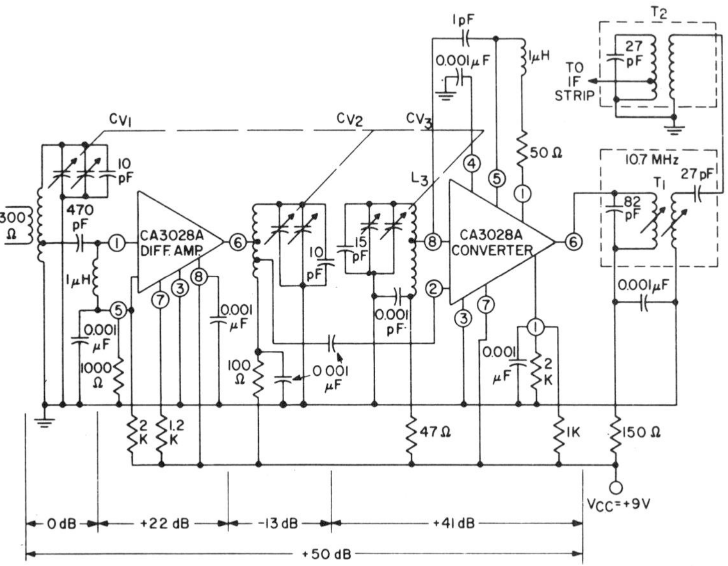

IC FRONT END—Pair of IC r-f amplifiers serves as complete tuner for 88–108 MHz f-m receiver. Book gives winding data for coils.—"Linear Integrated Circuits," RCA, Harrison, N.J., IC-41, p 221.

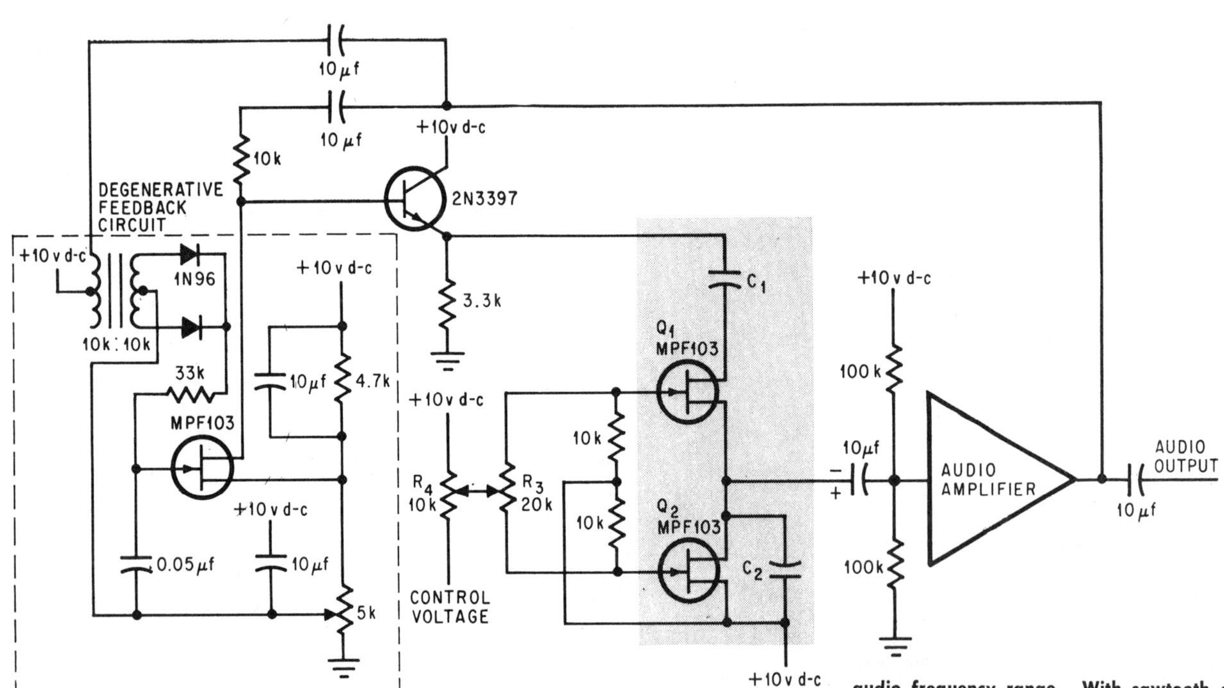

TALKING TO DOLPHINS—Circuit shown is modification of Wien-bridge oscillator in audio signal generator. Used to make audio output frequency vary with d-c control voltage derived from human amplitude-modulated speech. Resulting frequency-modulated human speech is then similar to whistle signal of dolphin and can be used to control his movements. Degenerative feedback circuit keeps output amplitude constant over wide audio frequency range. With sawtooth controlled voltage, can be used to sweep output across entire audio spectrum for checking frequency response of systems.—S. L. Moshier, FET Oscillator Helps Dolphins Understand People, *Electronics,* Feb. 5, 1968, p 85–86.

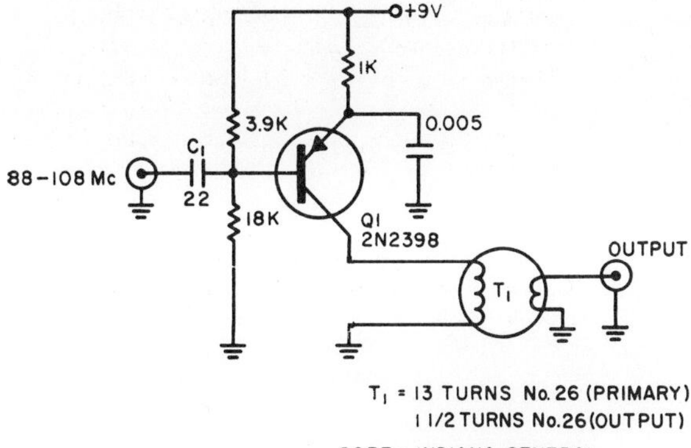

SIMPLE F-M PREAMP—Provides substantial gain across 88–108 MHz band, by taking advantage of low noise and high gain of transistor and wide-band properties of ferrite core in transformer. Gain is about 16 dB at center frequency and down only 3 dB at band limits.—G. Costa, FM Preamp Uses VHF Ferrite Transformer, *Electronic Design*, Feb. 3, 1964, p 51.

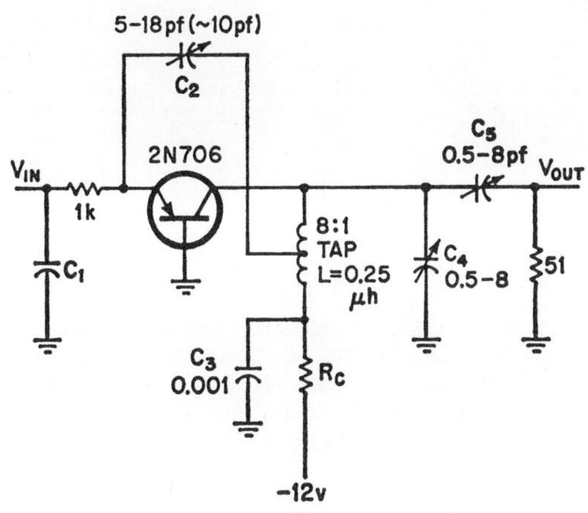

DUAL MODULATION—Modulating both emitter current and collector voltage of transistor in 100-MHz Hartley oscillator provides good linearity and stability when only small deviation is required. Deviation sensitivity is high, being up to 2.5 MHz per V. Modulation can be audio or video.—R. J. Turner, Stable F-M Oscillator Offers Sensitivity and Linearity, *Electronics*, Aug. 18, 1969, p 95.

F-M WITH VARACTOR DIODE—Frequency modulator gives deviation of 75 kHz above and below 52 MHz. Voltage input is limited to 200 mV. Article also describes other methods of using varactors in place of bulky tuning capacitors.—I. Carroll, Variable-Capacitance Diodes, *Electronics World*, July 1969, p 38–40.

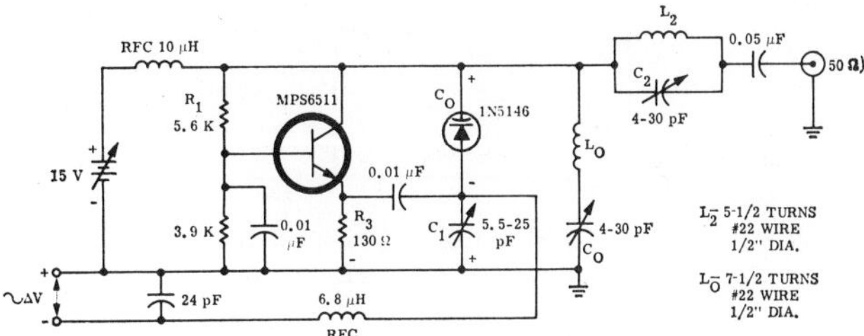

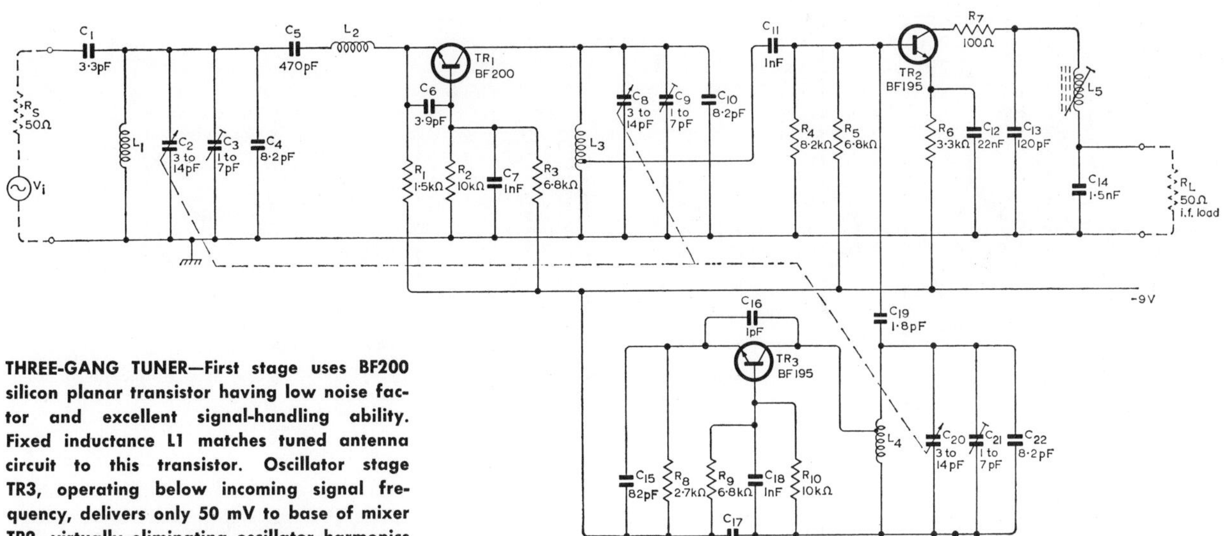

THREE-GANG TUNER—First stage uses BF200 silicon planar transistor having low noise factor and excellent signal-handling ability. Fixed inductance L1 matches tuned antenna circuit to this transistor. Oscillator stage TR3, operating below incoming signal frequency, delivers only 50 mV to base of mixer TR2, virtually eliminating oscillator harmonics at input of mixer without affecting conversion gain. Discussion in book covers repeat-spot suppression, double-beat suppression, continuous-beat suppression, spurious-response suppression, image rejection, and i-f rejection.—"Transistor Audio and Radio Circuits," Mullard Ltd., London, 1969, p 146.

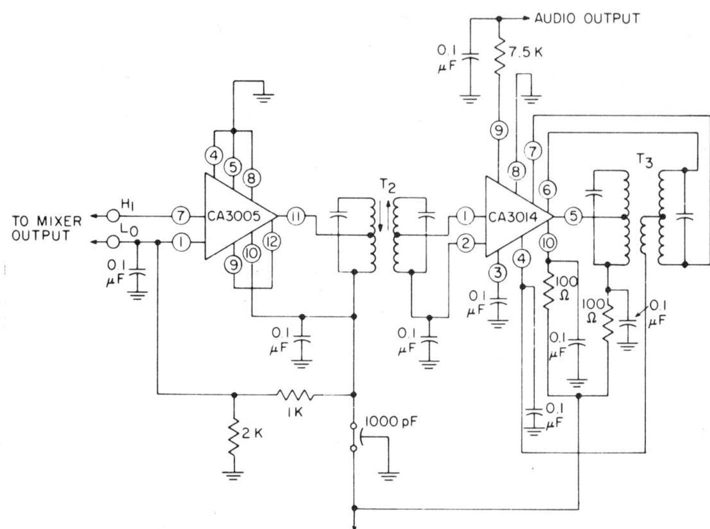

95 DB GAIN AT 10.7 MHZ—Two IC i-f amplifier stages feed discriminator. Input limiting knee for strip is 30 μV. T2 is TRW 21969 and T3 is 21590.—"Linear Integrated Circuits," RCA, Harrison, N.J., IC-41, p 291.

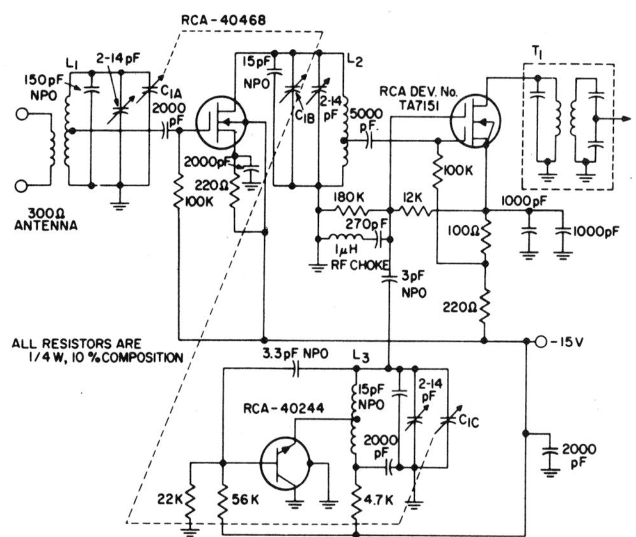

TUNER USING DUAL-GATE MOSFET MIXER—TA7151 mixer is preceded by single-gate mosfet r-f amplifier that provides 13 dB power gain at 5 mA. Total gain of tuner is 31 dB. Requires only three coils, with minimum shielding. Report gives coil data and complete design procedure.—H. M. Kleinman, Application of Dual-Gate MOS Field-Effect Transistors in Practical Radio Receivers, RCA, Somerville, N.J., ST-3486, 1967.

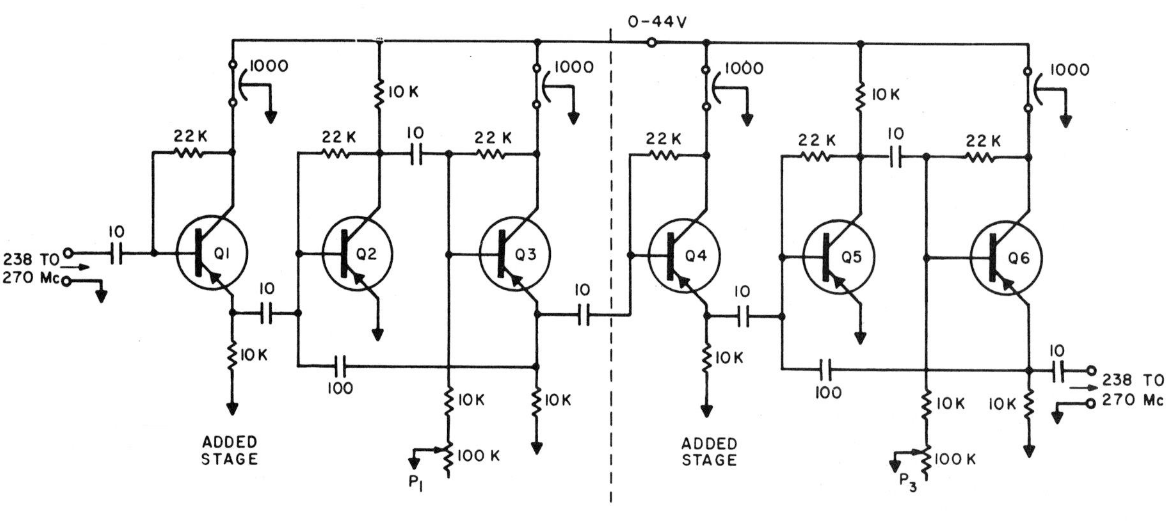

238–270 MHZ R-F AMPLIFIER—Used in experimental 243 MHz to 28 MHz R-C tuner-converter using potentiometers for tuning. All transistors are 2N700. Stability is fair, but gain falls rapidly at higher frequencies if fixed bias supply is used.—I. F. Barditch, Adapting Conventional VHF Equipment to Molecular Electronics, *Electronic Design*, Feb. 17, 1964, p 44–51.

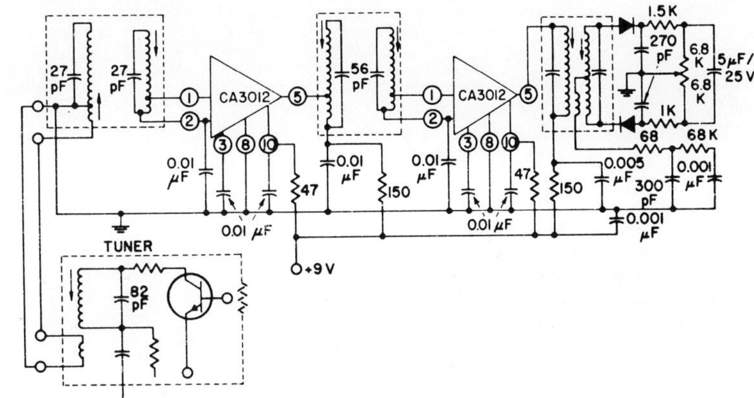

COMPLETE 10.7-MHZ I-F STRIP—Provides 155-mV audio signal at output of ratio detector. Capture ratio varies from 5 dB at 2 μV to 1.2 dB above 500 μV. Book gives performance curves.—"Linear Integrated Circuits," RCA, Harrison, N.J., IC-41, p 287.

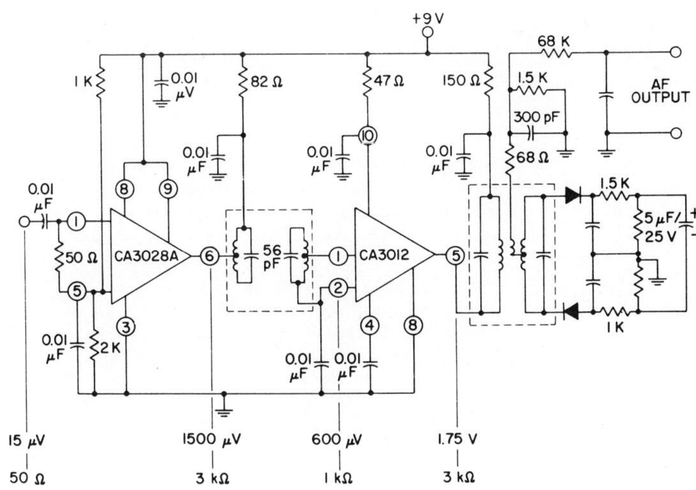

TWO-STAGE IC I-F STRIP—Combines high gain with single-stage-per-package approach. Both IC amplifiers are used in differential-mode connection. Gives i-f sensitivity of 15 μV.—"Linear Integrated Circuits," RCA, Harrison, N.J., IC-41, p 289.

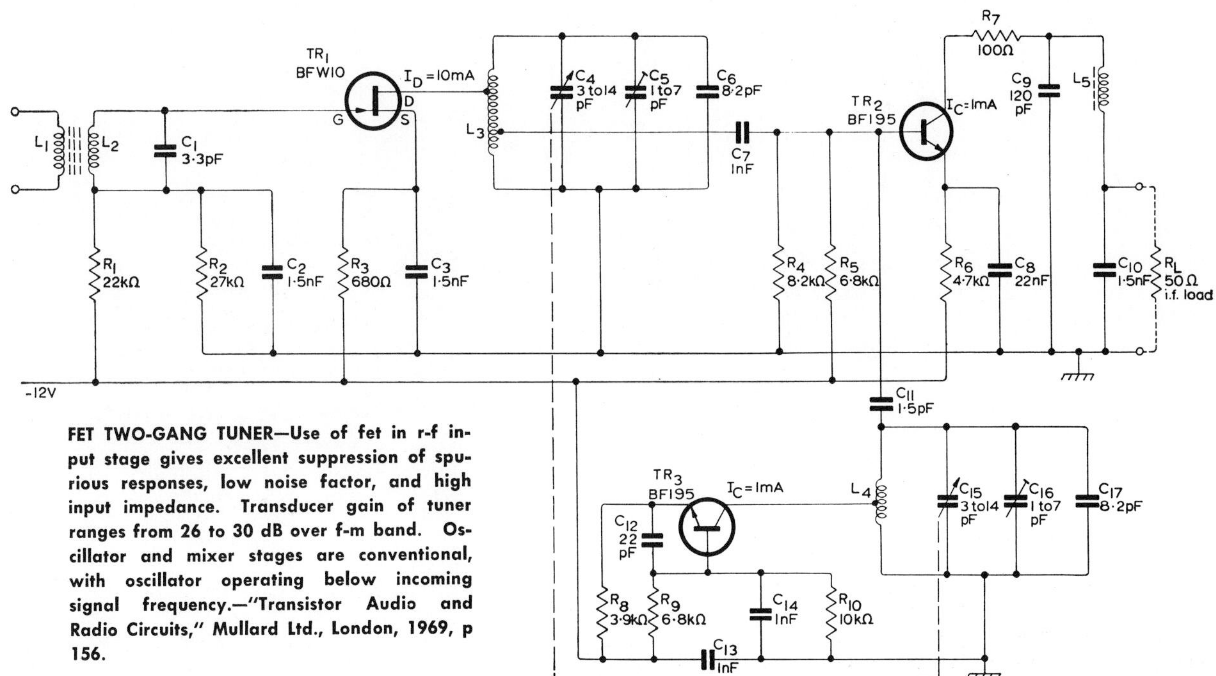

FET TWO-GANG TUNER—Use of fet in r-f input stage gives excellent suppression of spurious responses, low noise factor, and high input impedance. Transducer gain of tuner ranges from 26 to 30 dB over f-m band. Oscillator and mixer stages are conventional, with oscillator operating below incoming signal frequency.—"Transistor Audio and Radio Circuits," Mullard Ltd., London, 1969, p 156.

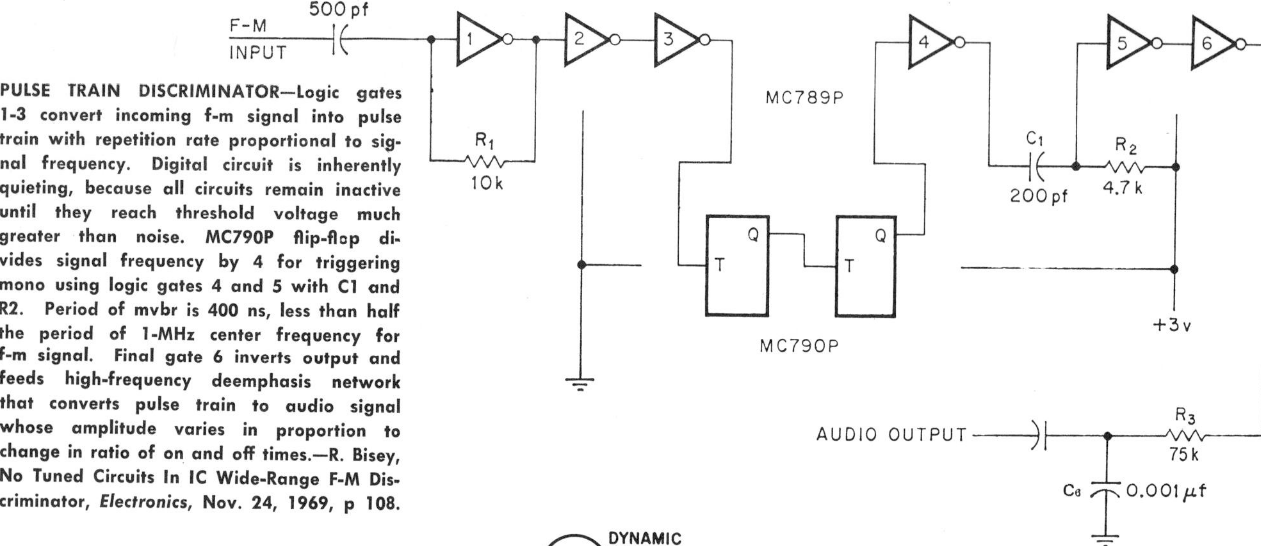

PULSE TRAIN DISCRIMINATOR—Logic gates 1-3 convert incoming f-m signal into pulse train with repetition rate proportional to signal frequency. Digital circuit is inherently quieting, because all circuits remain inactive until they reach threshold voltage much greater than noise. MC790P flip-flop divides signal frequency by 4 for triggering mono using logic gates 4 and 5 with C1 and R2. Period of mvbr is 400 ns, less than half the period of 1-MHz center frequency for f-m signal. Final gate 6 inverts output and feeds high-frequency deemphasis network that converts pulse train to audio signal whose amplitude varies in proportion to change in ratio of on and off times.—R. Bisey, No Tuned Circuits In IC Wide-Range F-M Discriminator, *Electronics*, Nov. 24, 1969, p 108.

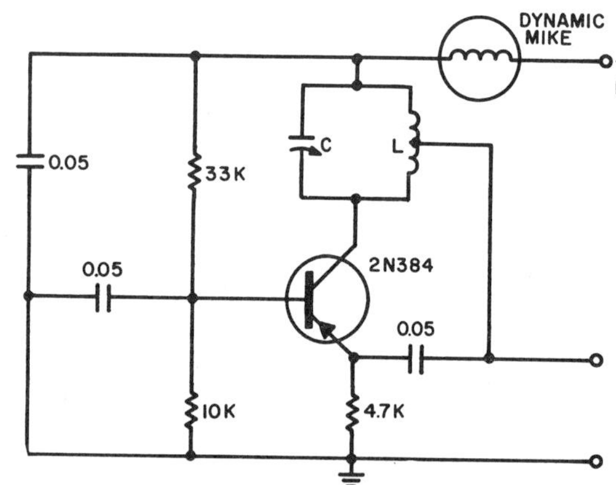

SIMPLE MODULATOR—Dynamic microphone, in series with negative supply lead of stable transistor oscillator, provides frequency modulation with deviation of 4 to 6 kHz. Carrier frequency is in range of 3 to 4 MHz, depending on values used for L and C in tank circuit. Operation depends on transistor interelectrode capacitance becoming part of tank having high L/C ratio.—R. E. Baird, Modulated Oscillator Makes Simple FM Source, *Electronic Design*, March 30, 1964, p 72.

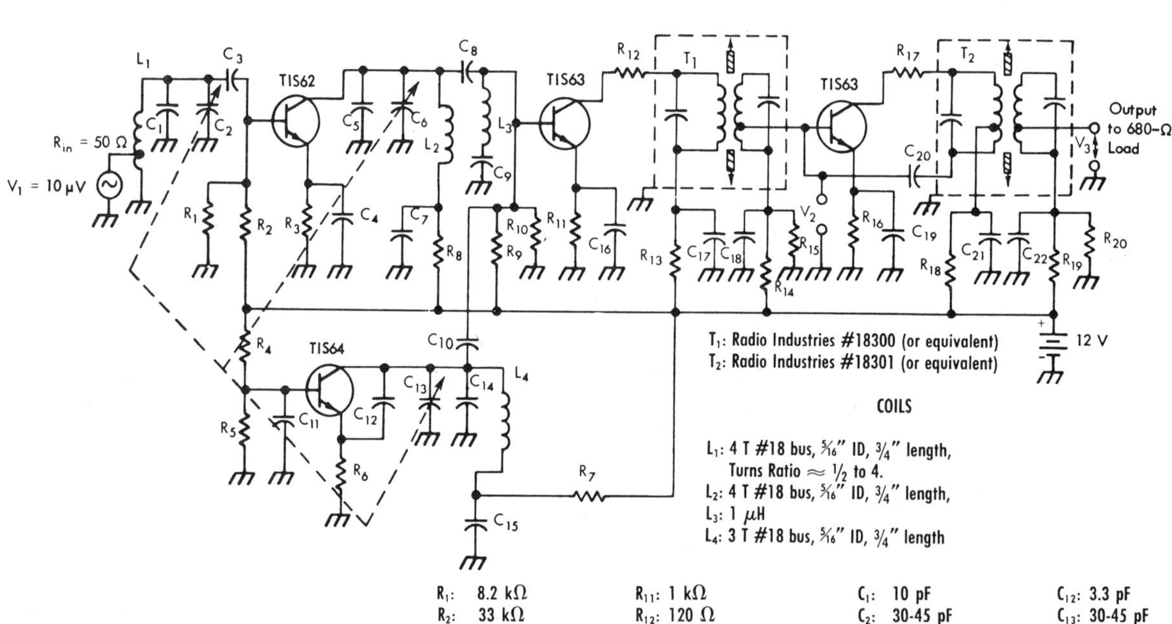

R_1:	8.2 kΩ	R_{11}:	1 kΩ	C_1:	10 pF	C_{12}:	3.3 pF
R_2:	33 kΩ	R_{12}:	120 Ω	C_2:	30-45 pF	C_{13}:	30-45 pF
R_3:	1 kΩ	R_{13}:	330 Ω	C_3:	3.3 pF	C_{14}:	10 pF
R_4:	12 kΩ	R_{14}:	10 kΩ	C_4:	0.001 µF	C_{15}:	0.001 µF
R_5:	2.7 kΩ	R_{15}:	3.9 kΩ	C_5:	10 pF	C_{16}:	0.01 µF
R_6:	1 kΩ	R_{16}:	1.2 kΩ	C_6:	30-45 pF	C_{17}:	0.01 µF
R_7:	330 Ω	R_{17}:	120 Ω	C_7:	0.001 µF	C_{18}:	0.01 µF
R_8:	330 Ω	R_{18}:	330 Ω	C_8:	3.3 pF	C_{19}:	0.01 µF
R_9:	15 kΩ	R_{19}:	10 kΩ	C_9:	240 pF	C_{20}:	2.2 pF
R_{10}:	2.7 kΩ	R_{20}:	3.9 kΩ	C_{10}:	0.82 pF	C_{21}:	0.01 µF
				C_{11}:	0.001 µF	C_{22}:	0.01 µF

All resistors 1/2 W, ten percent tolerance.

F-M TUNER WITH I-F STAGE—Uses four npn planar silicon transistors. Power gain is 54 dB. Image rejection at 98 MHz is 50 dB. I-f input voltage V2 is 1.5 mV and output V3 is 19 mV.—Preferred Semiconductors and Components, Texas Instruments, Dallas, Texas, CC101, 1968, p 1030.

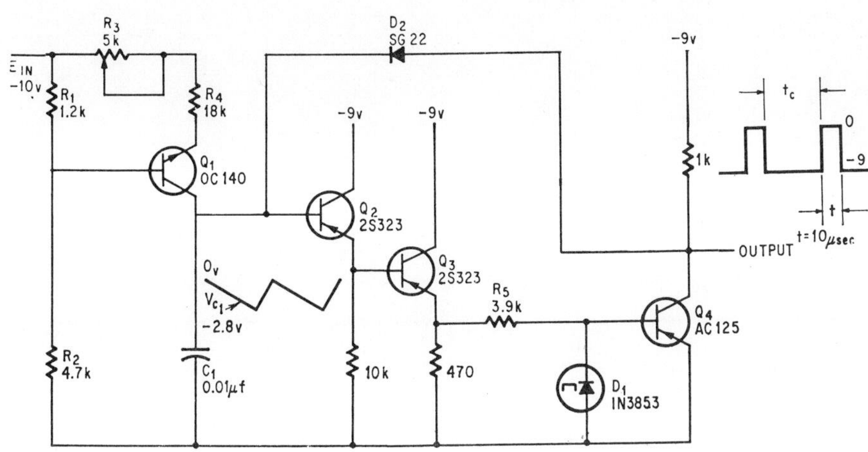

PULSE FREQUENCY MODULATOR—R3 varies repetition frequency of fast pulses linearly from 1,300 to 2,600 pps. Pulse width is 10 μs. D1 operates as fast switch that turns Q4 on and off to produce output pulses. Article gives design equation, performance curves, and detailed operation.—T. W. Sian, Tunnel Diode Speeds Pulse Frequency Modulation, *Electronics*, Jan. 22, 1968, p 73.

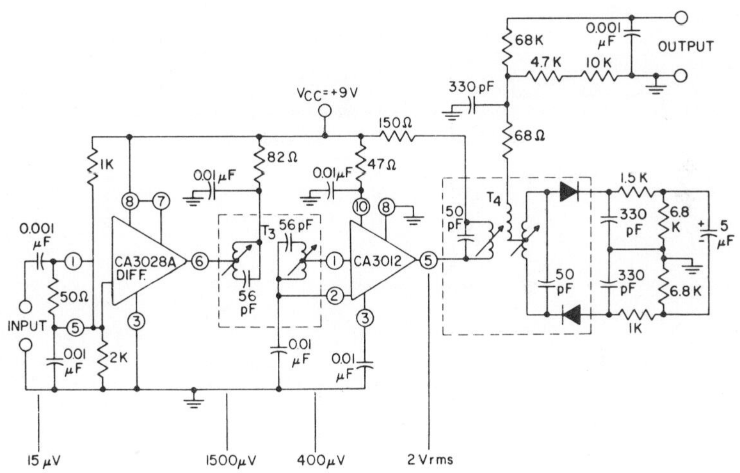

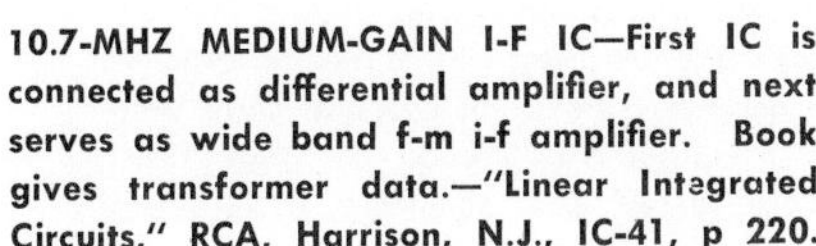
10.7-MHZ MEDIUM-GAIN I-F IC—First IC is connected as differential amplifier, and next serves as wide band f-m i-f amplifier. Book gives transformer data.—"Linear Integrated Circuits," RCA, Harrison, N.J., IC-41, p 220.

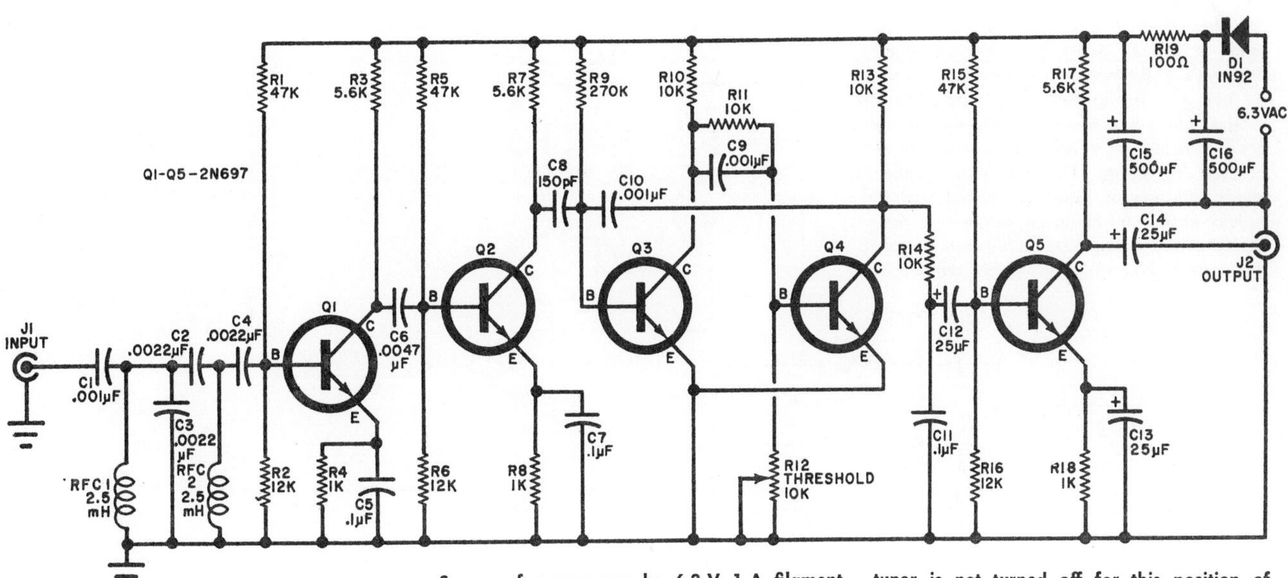

SCA BACKGROUND-MUSIC ADAPTER—Permits listening to continuous music uninterrupted by commercials or news, on f-m subcarrier that is offset from regular carrier frequency of f-m station by 67.5 kHz. Called SCA for Subsidiary Communications Authorization. Source of power can be 6.3-V 1-A filament transformer connected to terminals at upper right. Adapter is connected between detector and R-C deemphasis network of f-m receiver. Output of adapter may be fed either to separate amplifier and speaker or to auxiliary input jack at rear of set, provided f-m tuner is not turned off for this position of function switch of set. Input jack should be connected to set through isolation resistor of about 3,000 ohms, with exact value depending on receiver used.—W. F. Splichal, Jr., Simple SCA Adapter, *Popular Electronics*, June 1970, p 49–52.

CHAPTER 36
Gate Circuits

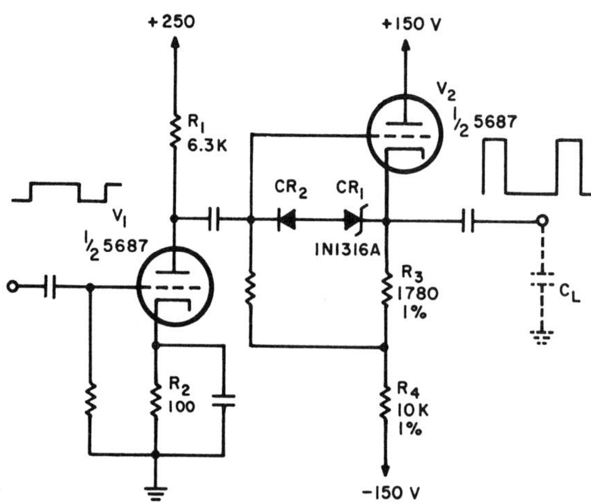

FASTER FALL TIME—Use of zener diode as switch gives low output impedance for both positive and negative excursions of gating pulse. This offsets shunt capacitance in load, to give fast transit times with conventional circuit and components. Article gives equation for fall times; for values shown, it is 0.9 μs, and 0.5 μs for rise time. Capacitor values are not critical.—B. I. Wolff, Gate Generator Arrangement Speeds Up Fall Time, *Electronic Design*, Oct. 26, 1964, p 53–54.

FET BLOCKS SPIKES—When control signal switches from 9 V to ground, drain resistance of fet Q3 drops from several meg to 90 ohms and cleanly transfers input signal to output. Arrangement eliminates differentiated spikes and other spurious signals normally arising in bidirectional analog gates during switching. C2 provides common-mode rejection of small differential pedestal spikes passed by Miller capacitance of Q3.—T. J. Davis, Analog Gate's Output Is Cleaned Up By FET, *Electronics*, Nov. 25, 1968, p 81.

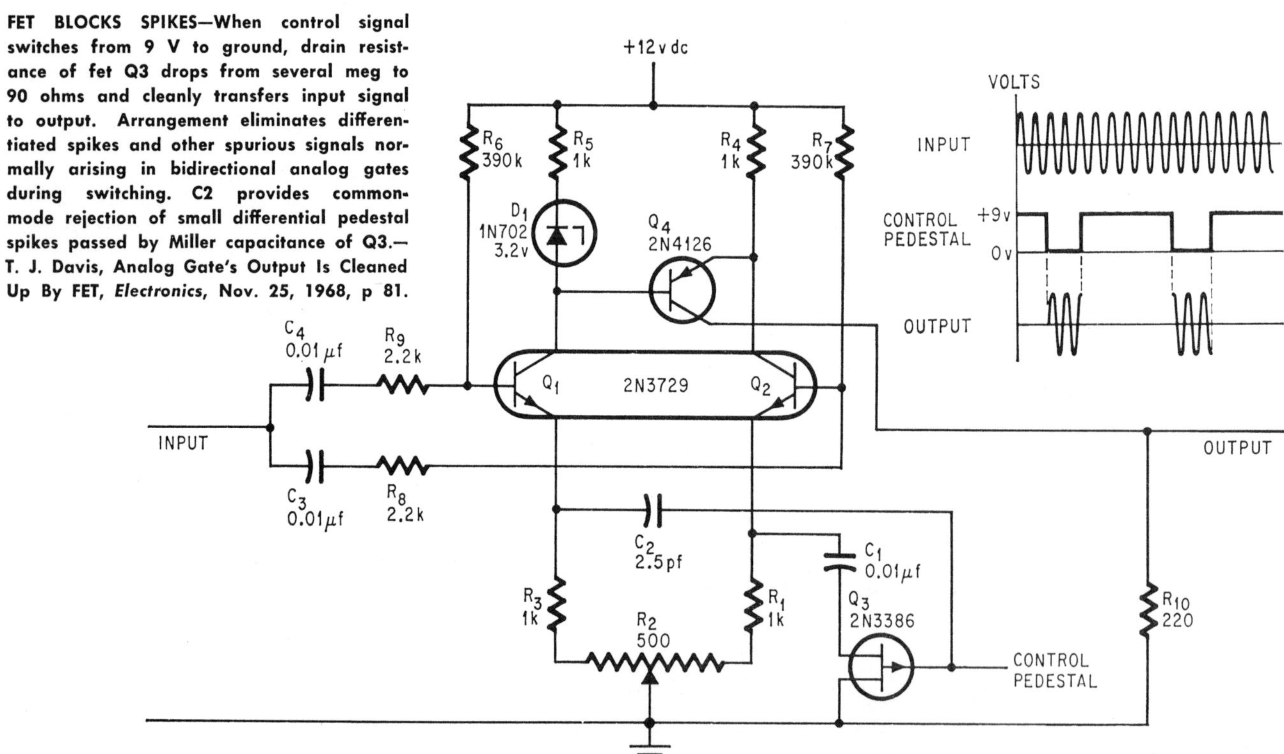

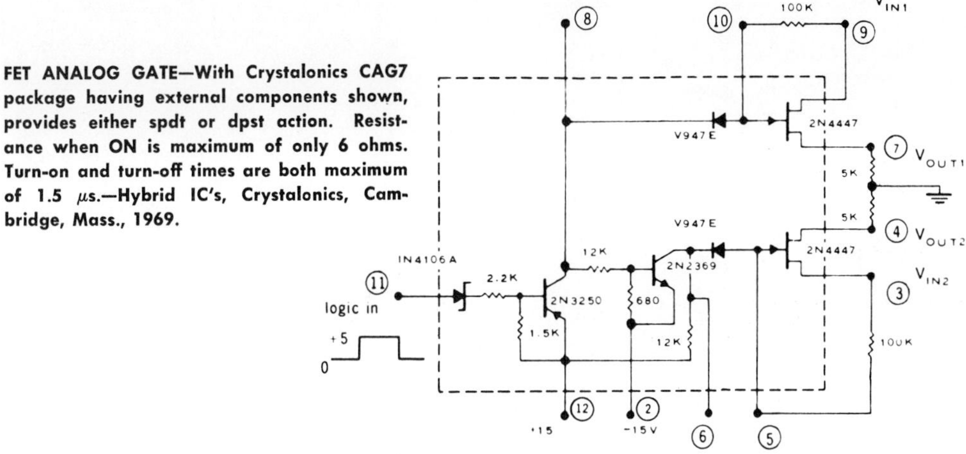

FET ANALOG GATE—With Crystalonics CAG7 package having external components shown, provides either spdt or dpst action. Resistance when ON is maximum of only 6 ohms. Turn-on and turn-off times are both maximum of 1.5 μs.—Hybrid IC's, Crystalonics, Cambridge, Mass., 1969.

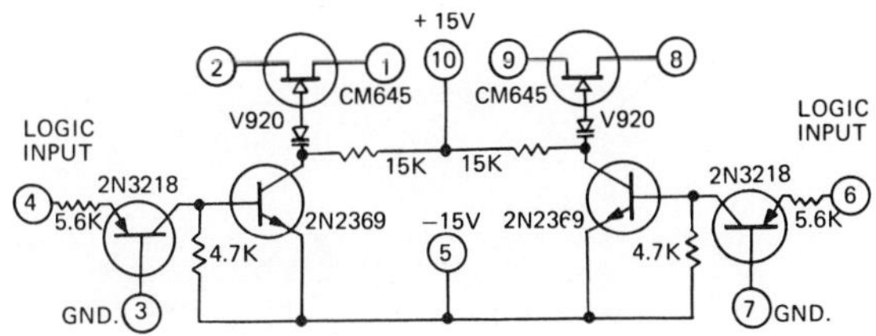

DUAL FET ANALOG GATE—Crystalonics CAG13 package provides spst action with 500-ns switching speed, break-before-make, and inherent zero offset voltage. Handles positive and negative 9-V signal levels directly from most logic circuits. Maximum ON resistance is 50 ohms at room temperature.—Hybrid IC's, Crystalonics, Cambridge, Mass., 1969.

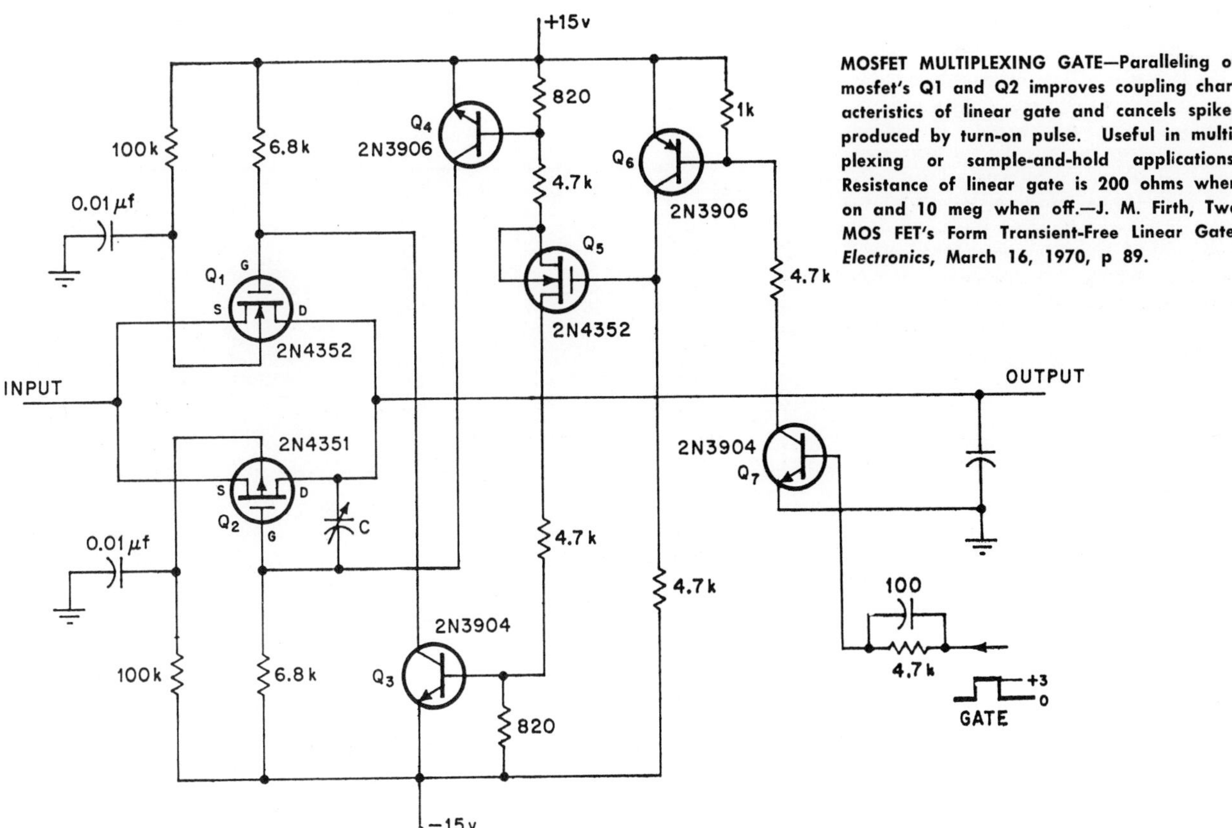

MOSFET MULTIPLEXING GATE—Paralleling of mosfet's Q1 and Q2 improves coupling characteristics of linear gate and cancels spikes produced by turn-on pulse. Useful in multiplexing or sample-and-hold applications. Resistance of linear gate is 200 ohms when on and 10 meg when off.—J. M. Firth, Two MOS FET's Form Transient-Free Linear Gate, *Electronics*, March 16, 1970, p 89.

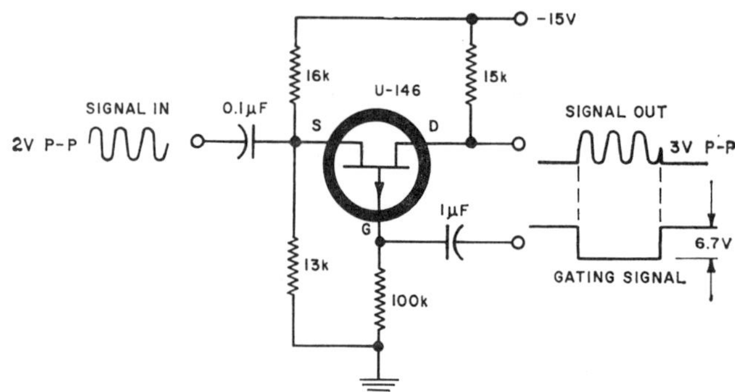

LINEAR FET GATE—Can also serve as electronic switch for amplitude modulator.—J. H. Wujek, Jr. and M. E. McGee, Field-Effect Transistor Circuits, *Electronics World*, May 1967, p 32–33 and 75.

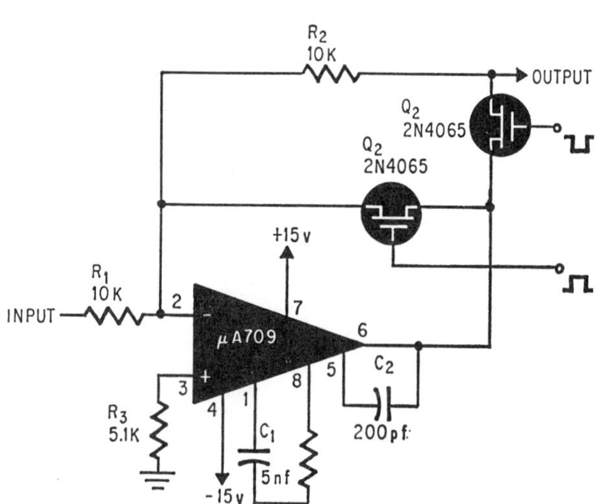

PRECISION ANALOG GATE—Uses Fairchild μA709 opamp with fet switches in feedback loop. Gate is opened and closed by alternately driving the two switches Q2 on and off. Circuit operates as unity-gain inverting amplifier having essentially zero on-gate resistance. Isolation between input signal and load is nearly perfect.—J. F. Gifford and M. Markkula, Linear IC's: Part 5, Ins and Outs of Op Amps, *Electronics*, Nov. 27, 1967, p 84–93.

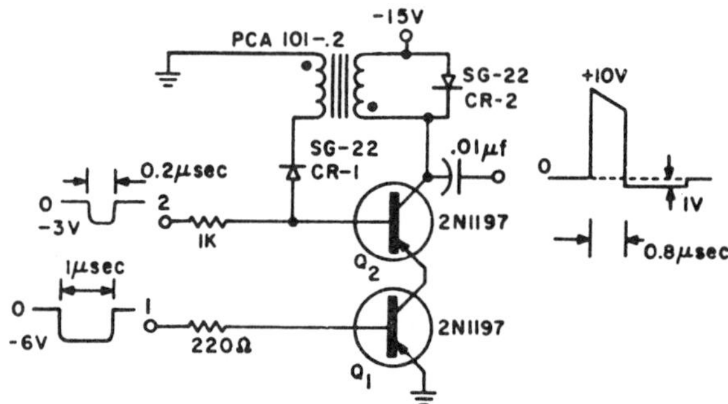

BLOCKING OSCILLATOR AND GATE—Produces standard output pulse only when input signals are applied simultaneously to both transistors. Gate at input 1 must be wider than 0.8-μs output pulse, in order to keep Q1 conducting until output pulse is terminated. Diode prevents trigger feedback from input 2 into transformer.—A. W. Zinn, Blocking Oscillator-And Gate Produces Standard Output Pulse, "400 Ideas for Design Selected from Electronic Design," Hayden Book Co., N.Y., 1964, p 77.

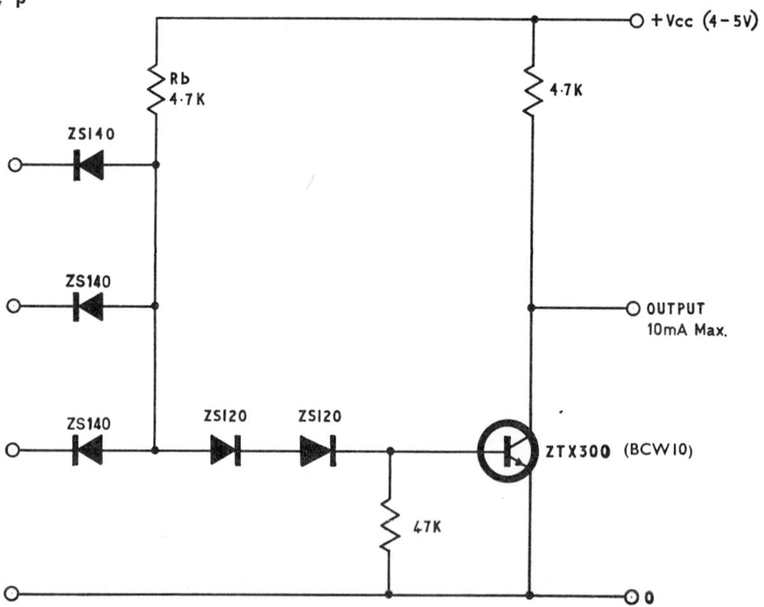

DTL NOR—Provides fan-out of 11 for low-voltage low-power noncritical diode-transistor logic applications.—"E-Line Transistor Applications," Ferranti Ltd., Oldham, Lancs., England, 1969, p 8.

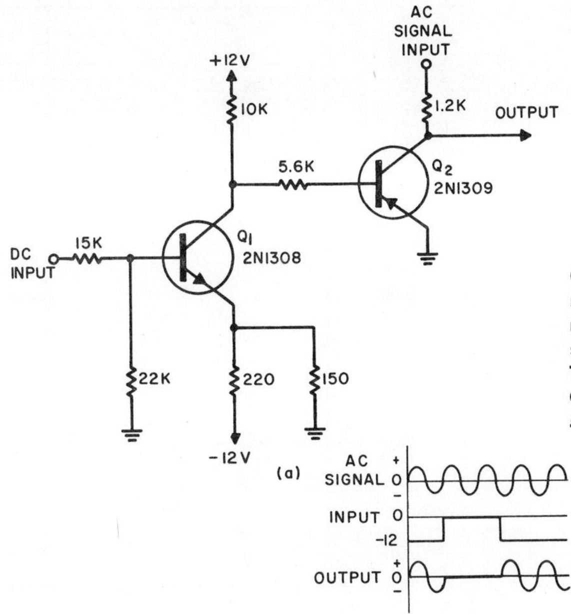

GATING A-C WITH D-C—Simple transistor arrangement achieves positive gating of 2-V rms a-c signal by 12-V d-c input. Blocked signal output is 46 dB down.—T. A. Radomski, Transistorized Switch Provides A-C Signal Gate, *Electronic Design*, Jan. 18, 1965, p 49–50.

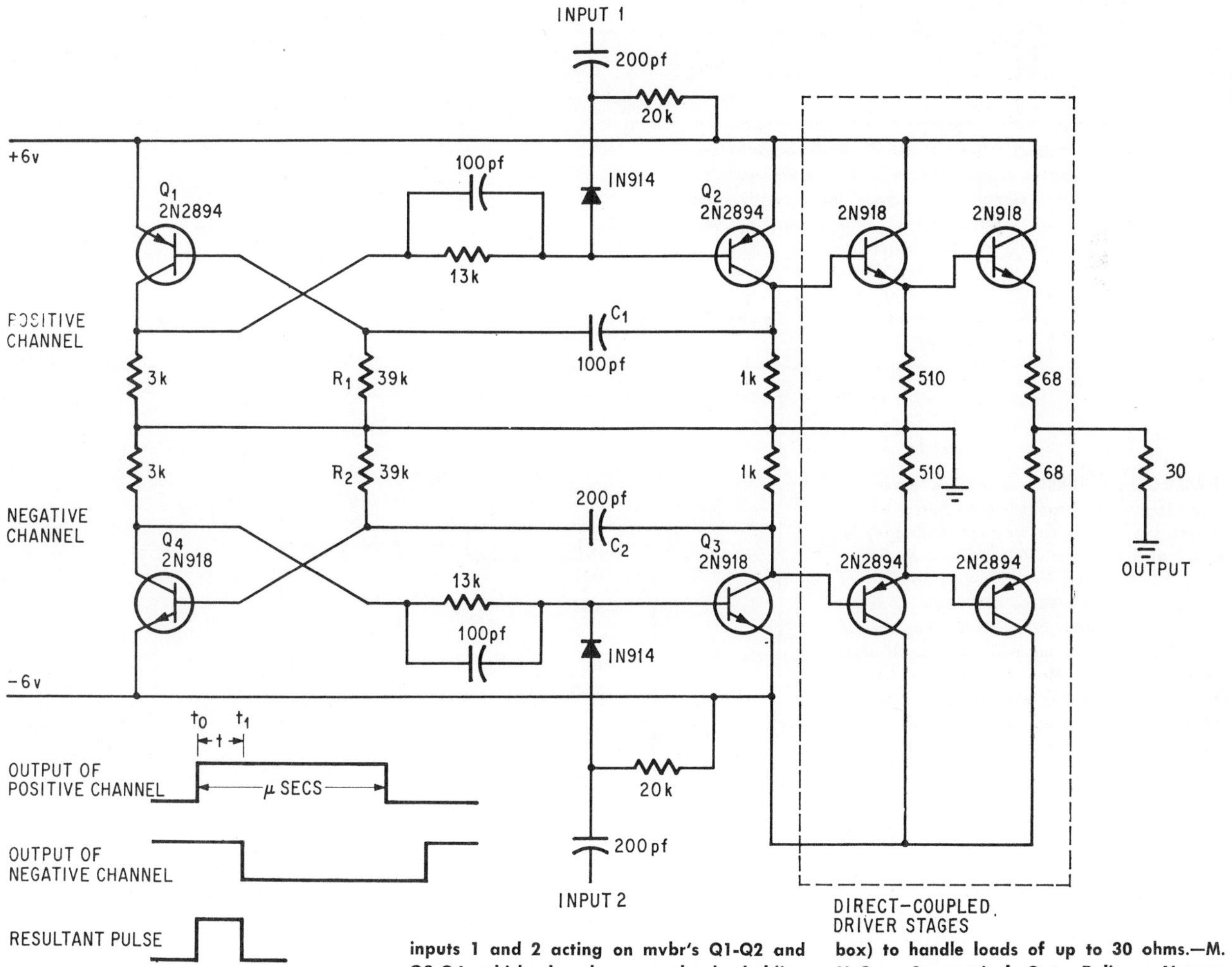

INPUT 1
200pf
20k
+6v
100pf
IN914
Q1
2N2894
Q2
2N2894
2N918
2N918
13k
POSITIVE
CHANNEL
C1
100pf
3k
R1 39k
1k
510
68
3k
R2 39k
1k
510
68
30
NEGATIVE
CHANNEL
200pf
Q4
2N918
C2
Q3
2N918
2N2894
2N2894
OUTPUT
13k
100pf
IN914
-6v
t0 t1
t
OUTPUT OF
POSITIVE CHANNEL
μ SECS
20k
OUTPUT OF
NEGATIVE CHANNEL
200pf
INPUT 2
DIRECT-COUPLED
DRIVER STAGES
RESULTANT PULSE

PULSE-SHARPENING GATE—Width of output pulse is determined by time interval between inputs 1 and 2 acting on mvbr's Q1-Q2 and Q3-Q4, which also sharpen pulse by holding rise and fall times to less than 5 ns. Two d-c amplifiers are used as drivers (dashed box) to handle loads of up to 30 ohms.—M. McGee, Symmetrical Gate Delivers Narrow Pulses to Fan-Out, *Electronics*, Dec. 11, 1967, p 99.

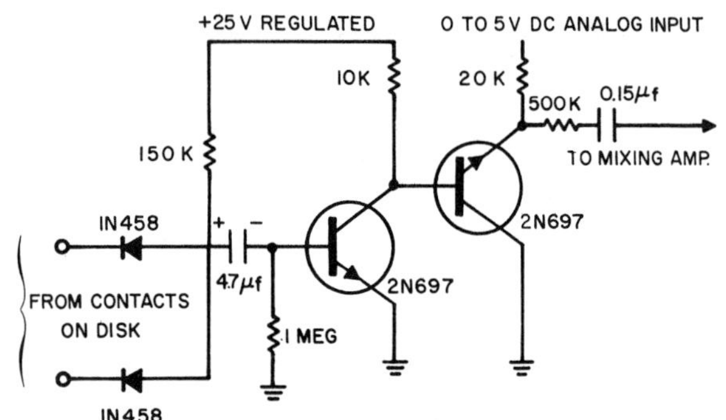

POSITIVE-ONLY GATE—Responds only to peaks above zero voltage level, to prevent frequency-doubling of signals picked off multiphase generating disk. Used with electronic commutator disk having 32 contacts around edge to provide gating for 32 channels.—J. P. Spacer, Jr., Pick Off Multiphase Signals From a Disk, *Electronic Design*, July 19, 1965, p 20–23.

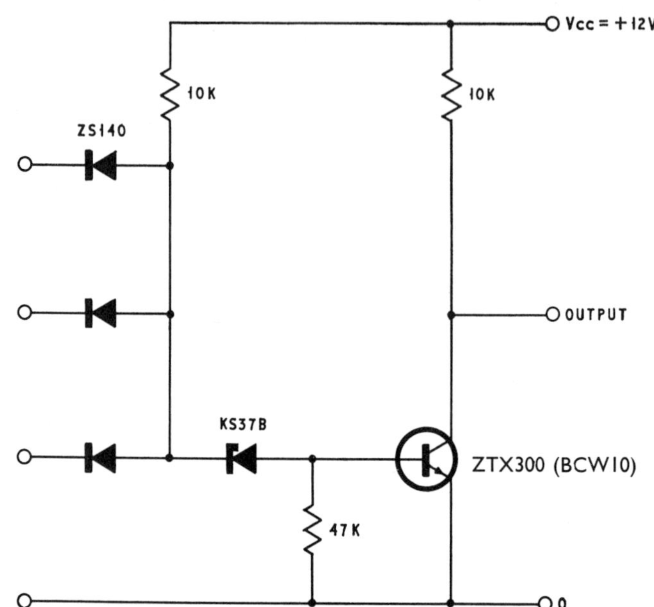

HIGH NOISE IMMUNITY—Provides d-c noise immunity of 4 V minimum, for applications having switching transients in a-c line and stray magnetic or electric fields. Intended for low-speed systems. Maximum fan-out is 10.—"E-Line Transistor Applications," Ferranti Ltd., Oldham, Lancs., England, 1969, p 10.

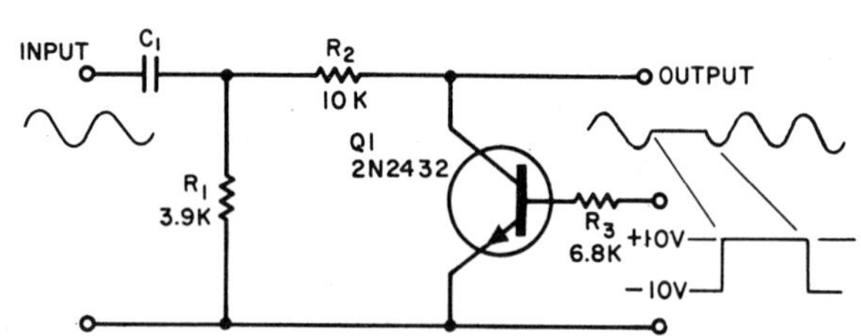

VIDEO CONTROL GATE—When base of transistor is made negative by square-wave control signal, gate passes both positive-going and negative-going video signals. When base is made positive, gate is closed. Attenuation of 20-kHz signal then exceeds 45 dB.—R. Vokoun, Bipolar Video Gate Needs No Balancing Circuit, *Electronic Design*, May 11, 1964, p 86–87.

PHASE-LOCKED BURSTS—Delay-line generator circuit is used to produce pulse bursts whose phases are locked to start of gating cycle. Bursts of from 1 to 10 pulses, each 25 ns wide, are obtained by increasing spacing of gating pulses from 40 to 490 ns in 50-ns increments. Q2 and R1 control time interval of oscillations. Circuit will work at 20-MHz repetition rate. May be used to trigger time base of sampling oscilloscope.—J. Kalisz, Simple Gating Yields Phase-Locked Pulse Bursts, *Electronics*, Jan. 6, 1969, p 96.

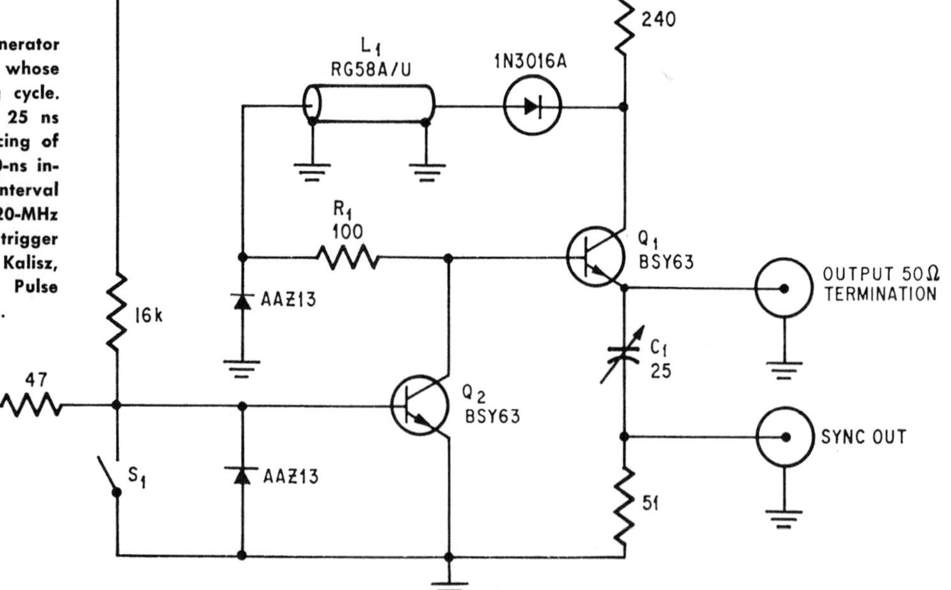

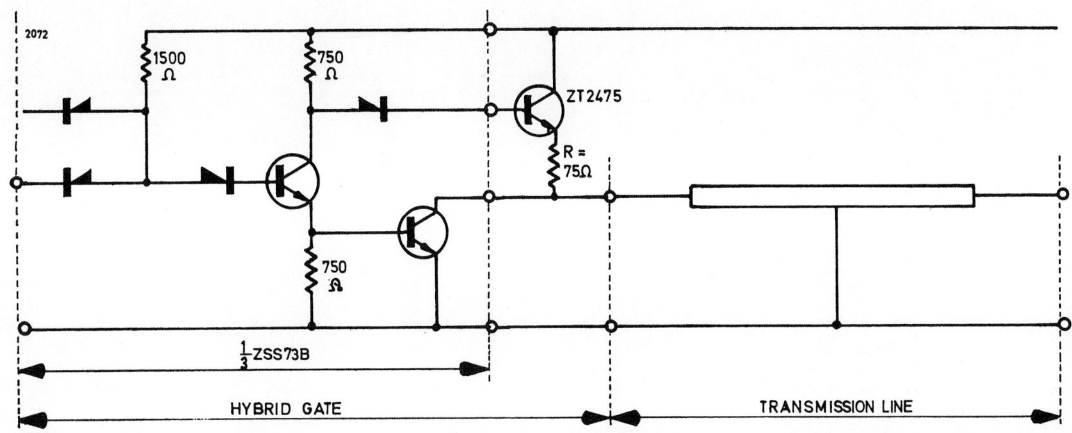

TRANSMISSION-LINE DRIVE—Uses third of Ferranti ZSS73B hybrid gate with single external transistor and one resistor to drive 150-ohm transmission line.—The Micronor II Range of Silicon Integrated Circuits, Ferranti Ltd., Oldham, Lancs., England, 1967, p 64.

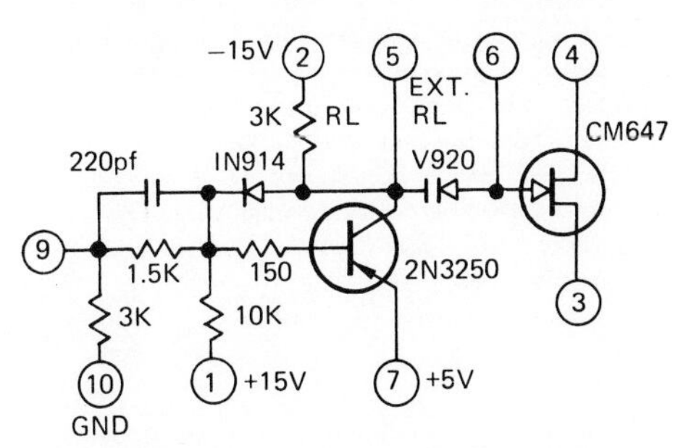

HIGH-SPEED FET ANALOG GATE—Crystalonics CAG10 package provides spst action with switching speeds of 50 ns working directly from logic. Maximum ON resistance is about 50 ohms.—Hybrid IC's, Crystalonics, Cambridge, Mass., 1969.

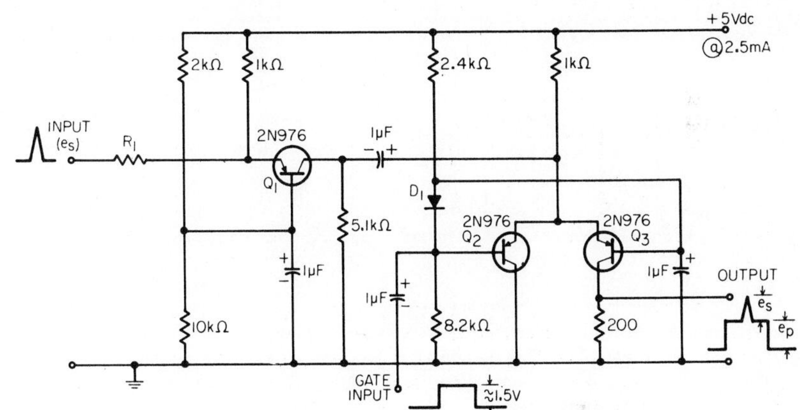

FAST-PULSE TRANSMISSION GATE—Operates in current-switching mode to provide reliable isolation of signal input from output when gate is turned off. Positive pulse of about 1.5 V at gate input cuts off Q2, to turn on Q3 for transmitting input signal to output. Gate rejection is 100:1 for 1.5-ns pulses.—J. D. Nickell, High-Speed Pulse Transmission Gate, *EEE*, July 1967, p 130.

HIGH-VOLTAGE SWITCHING—Fet pair inserted at virtual ground input of opamp permits handling signal voltages limited only by maximum signal swing of opamp and its slew rate. Up to ten pairs of these fet switches may be stacked to give ten-input commutator for ten input signals. Will operate at switching rates up to 100 kHz.—F. J. Honey, DTL/TTL Controls Large Signals in Commutator, *Electronics*, March 16, 1970, p 90.

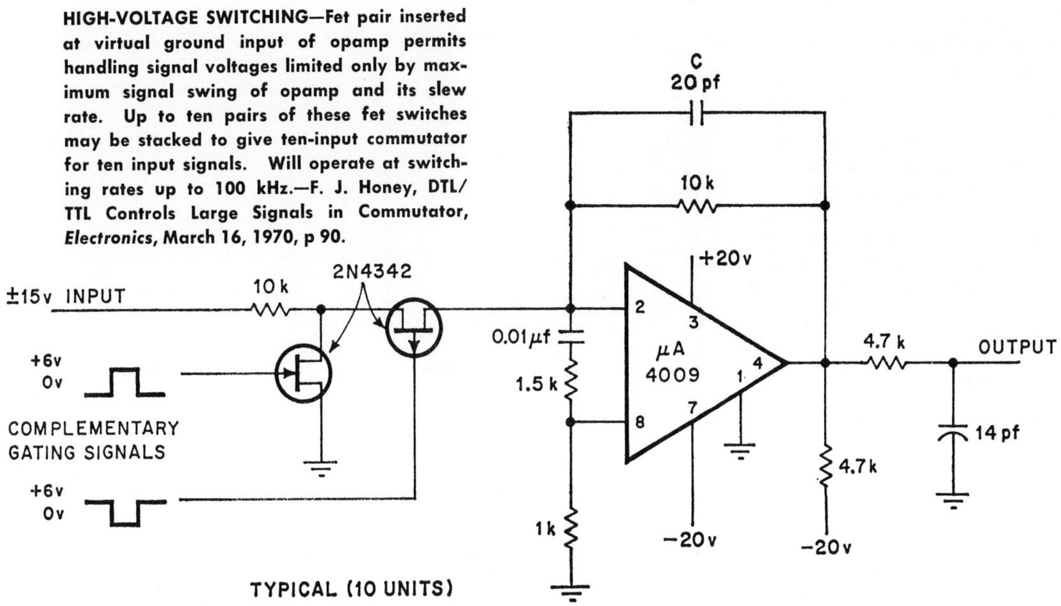

CHAPTER 37
High-Voltage Circuits

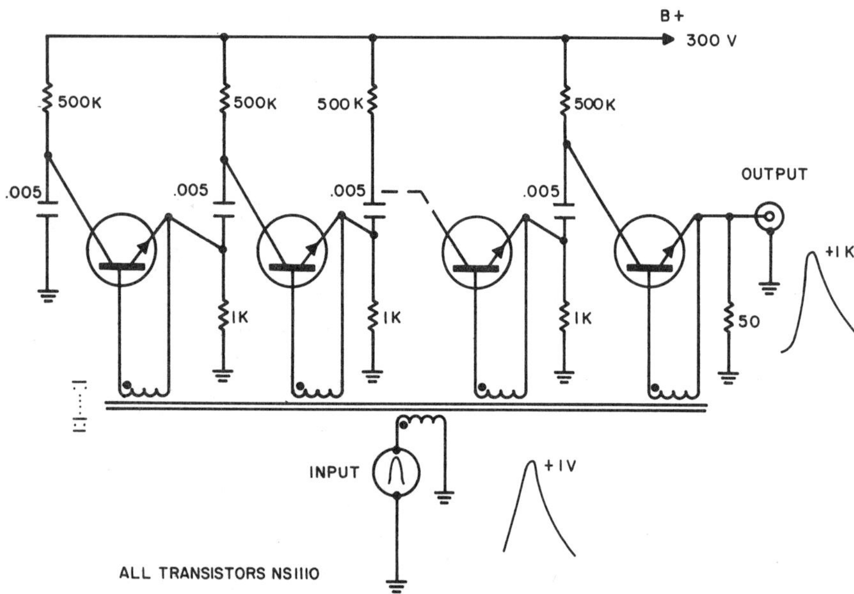

1,000-V PULSES—Combining of avalanche transistors as shown, for charging capacitors in parallel and discharging them into load in series, permits use of lower-voltage transistors for high-level pulse output stages. Load can be placed at either end of circuit, to give choice of polarity.—E. J. Snyder and A. Whetstone, Series-Parallel Connection Produces High-Level Pulses, *Electronic Design*, Dec. 6, 1965, p 52.

WIDE-RANGE INDICATOR—Neon gives visual indication of presence of voltages from 90 to 4,000 V. At about 500 V, circuit becomes relaxation oscillator and lamp will flash brightly.—W. G. Miller, "Using and Understanding Miniature Neon Lamps," H. W. Sams & Co., Indianapolis, Ind., 1969, p 19.

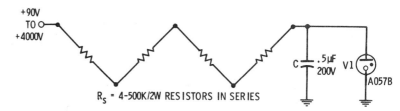

+90V TO +4000V

C .5µF 200V

V1 A057B

R_S = 4-500K/2W RESISTORS IN SERIES

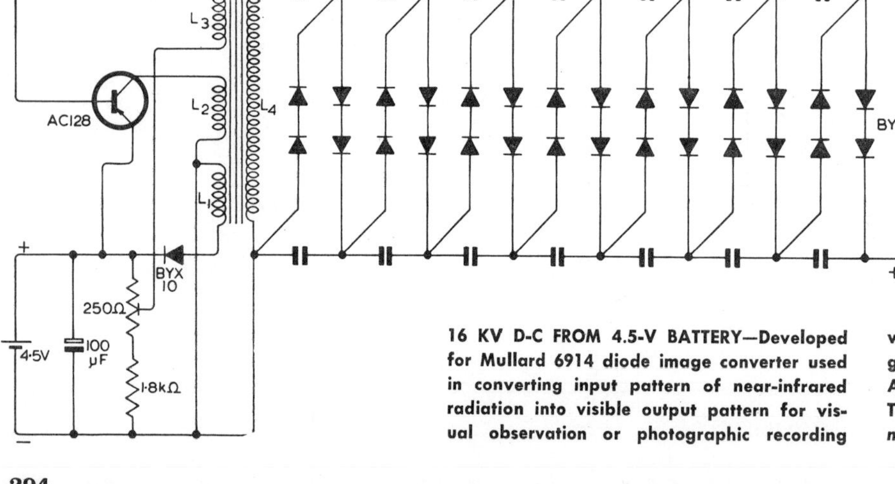

16 KV D-C FROM 4.5-V BATTERY—Developed for Mullard 6914 diode image converter used in converting input pattern of near-infrared radiation into visible output pattern for visual observation or photographic recording without light source. One application is forgery detection. Power output is 320 µW.—K. A. Cook, Diode Image Converter Tubes and Their Applications, *Mullard Technical Communications*, Sept. 1967, p 256–260.

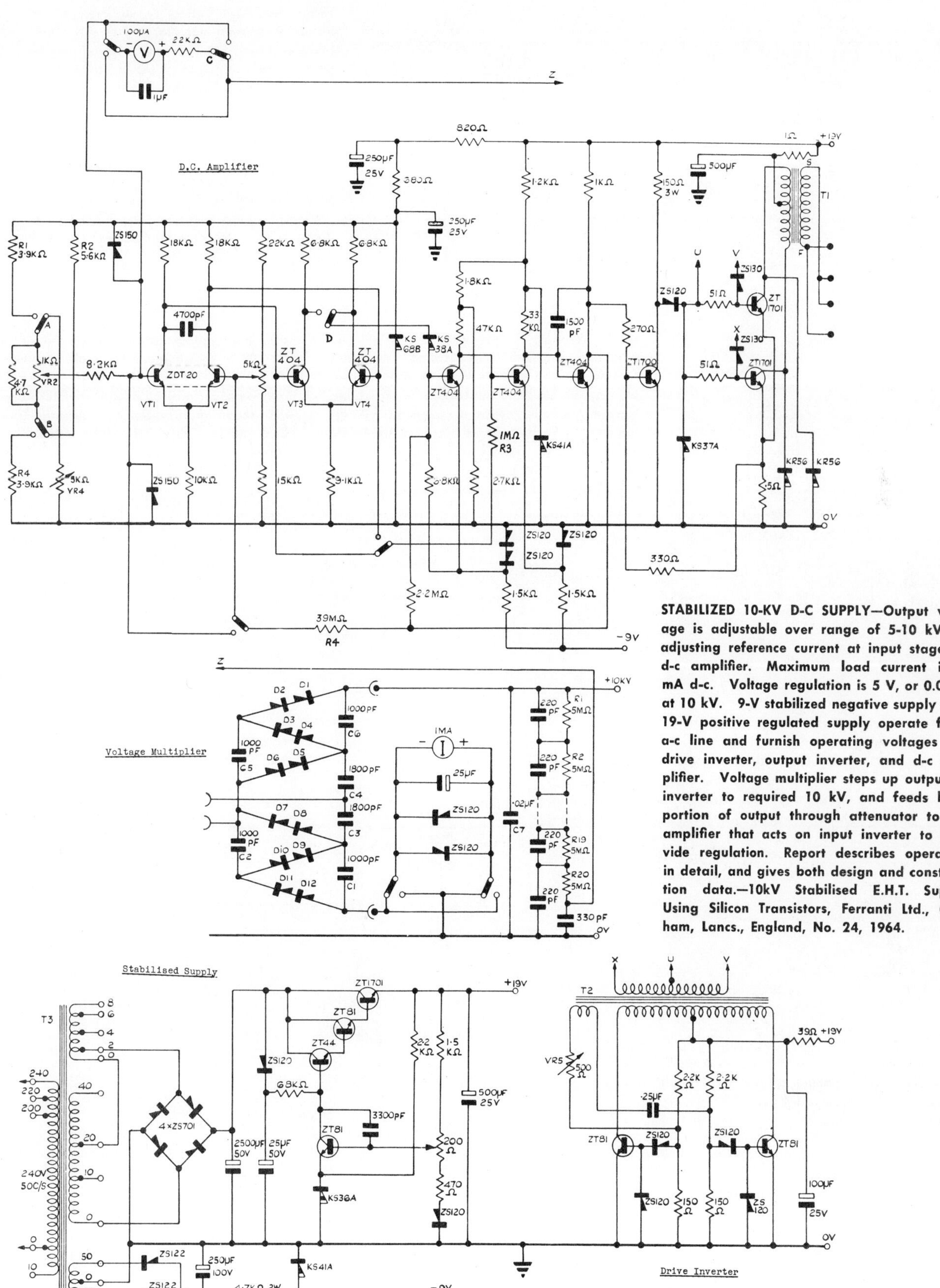

STABILIZED 10-KV D-C SUPPLY—Output voltage is adjustable over range of 5-10 kV by adjusting reference current at input stage of d-c amplifier. Maximum load current is 1 mA d-c. Voltage regulation is 5 V, or 0.05% at 10 kV. 9-V stabilized negative supply and 19-V positive regulated supply operate from a-c line and furnish operating voltages for drive inverter, output inverter, and d-c amplifier. Voltage multiplier steps up output of inverter to required 10 kV, and feeds back portion of output through attenuator to d-c amplifier that acts on input inverter to provide regulation. Report describes operation in detail, and gives both design and construction data.—10kV Stabilised E.H.T. Supply Using Silicon Transistors, Ferranti Ltd., Oldham, Lancs., England, No. 24, 1964.

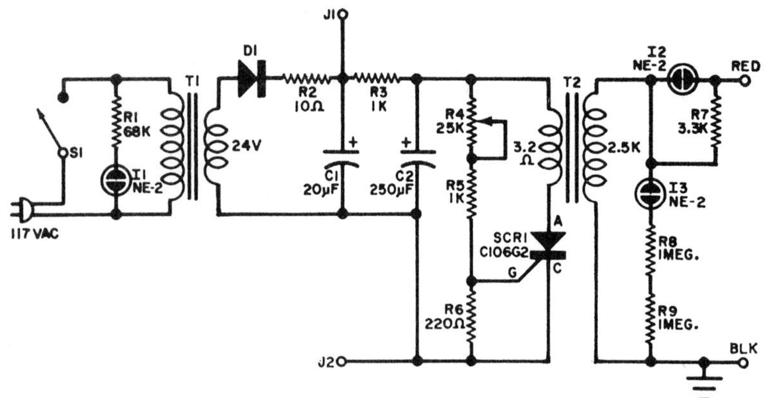

FENCE CHARGER—Solid-state circuit operates either from 45-V battery or a-c line. In addition to conventional charging of single-wire fence enclosing horse or cow pasture, may be used to keep dogs out of metal garbage can insulated from ground by dry wood or plastic. Delivers disturbing but harmless electrical sting to any person or animal touching charged metal, and should therefore be turned off on garbage collection day. If soil is very dry, moisture may be required for good ground contact.—L. E. Greenlee, Electric Fence, "Electronic Experimenter's Handbook," Ziff-Davis, N.Y., 1969 Spring Edition, p 15–18.

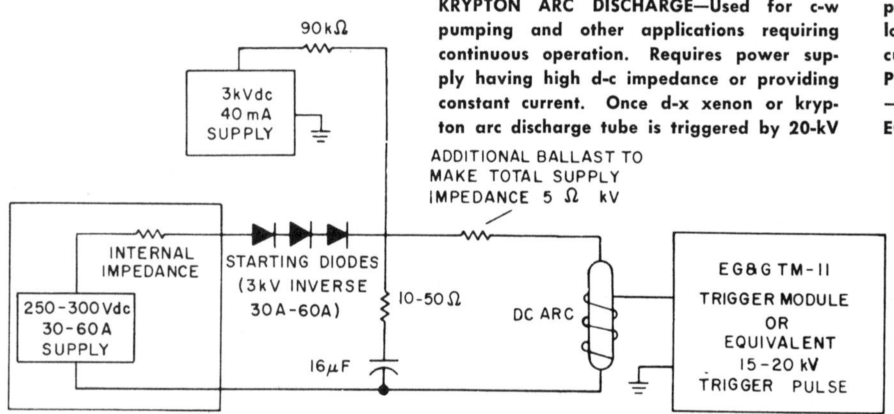

KRYPTON ARC DISCHARGE—Used for c-w pumping and other applications requiring continuous operation. Requires power supply having high d-c impedance or providing constant current. Once d-x xenon or krypton arc discharge tube is triggered by 20-kV pulse, high voltage across arc lamp drops below 200 V d-c so diodes in main supply circuit conduct and operate lamp continuously. Provides both infrared and ultraviolet output. —DC Xenon and Krypton Arc Discharge Tubes, EG&G, Boston, Mass., No. 1008, 1968.

KRYTRON-TRIGGERED SPARK GAP—Four-element cold-cathode gas-filled switch tube produces high peak current for short duration through trigger transformer, for developing 20 to 30 kV pulse for triggering spark gap or xenon flashtube.—Krytrons—Cold Cathode Switch Tubes, EG&G, Boston, Mass., KR-100, 1968.

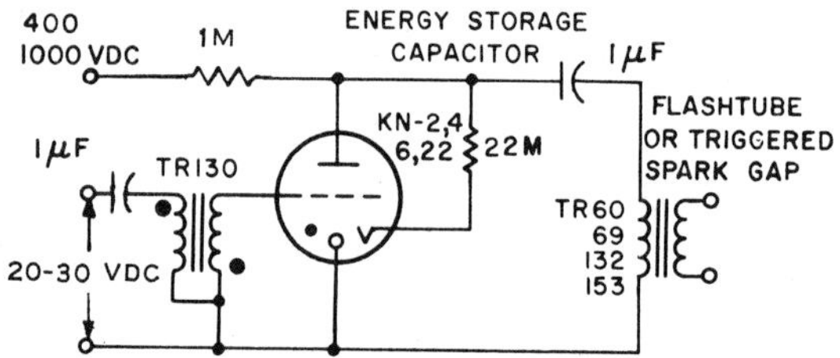

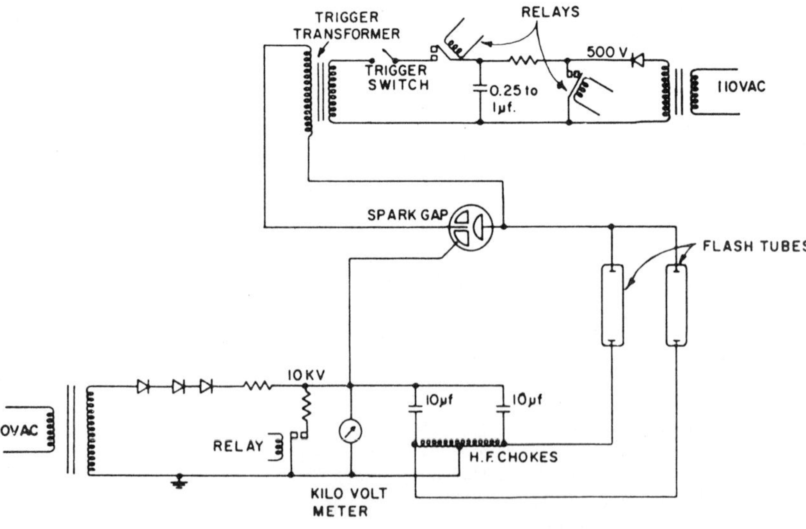

SPARK-GAP SWITCH—High-voltage trigger transformer turns on spark gap with 5 to 25 kV pulse when capacitor discharges through primary. When gap is triggered, full 10 kV of main storage capacitors is applied to two flashtubes, making them fire. Storage capacitors then begin charging automatically for next flash. Protective relays short storage and trigger capacitors through appropriate resistors when power is off, while relay in primary of trigger transformer prevents accidental firing of lamps. Used in studying excited-state processes in organic molecules. —D. N. Bailey and D. M. Hercules, Flash Photolysis—A Technique for Studying Fast Reactions, *Journal of Chemical Education*, Feb. 1965.

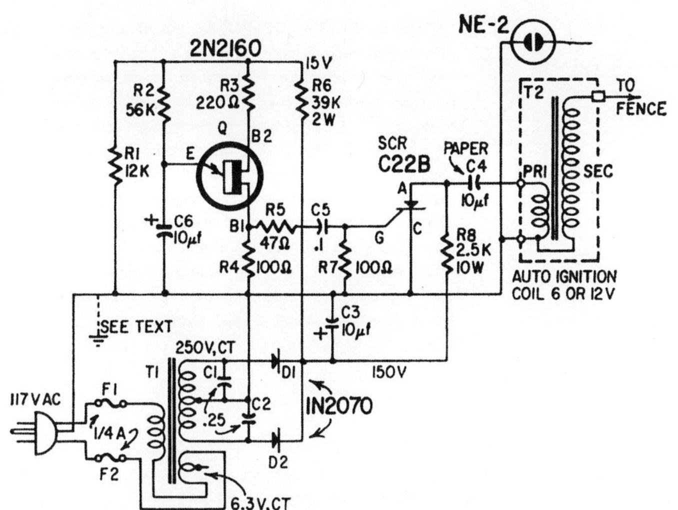

SCR ELECTRIC FENCE CHARGER—Generates 1-ms pulse once per second, with short-circuit current and total energy limited to safe value by characteristics of capacitor and automotive ignition coil used. Power transformer isolates a-c line from fence circuit. Will easily handle quarter-mile of fence. Power consumption is about 20 W. Grounding of line by sunflowers or other plants will not damage charger but will cause rfi and reduce strength of voltage pulses. Direct short will blow fuse in primary of transformer. Neon flashes once per second to indicate charger is working.—E. T. Hansen, SCR Electric Fence Charger, *Radio-Electronics*, July 1965, p 35–37.

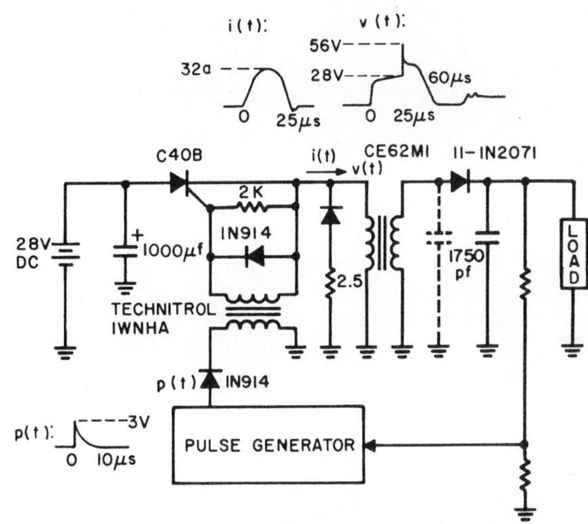

28 V TO 3,500 V—Only one scr is needed, because resonance of transformer primary forces scr to turn off. Pulse generator for triggering scr can be operated at up to 3 kHz. Load capacitor can be capacitance of pulse-forming network if load is thyratron for switching energy from network to 200-ohm load. With fixed resistive load, feedback from load to pulse generator for changing frequency can be used to regulate load voltage.—W. B. McCartney and E. O. Uhrig, Inverter Uses Only One Silicon-Controlled Rectifier, *Electronic Design*, Nov. 23, 1964, p 61–62.

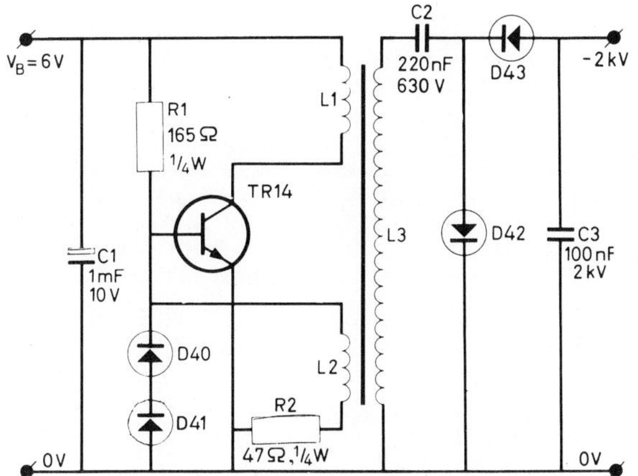

2-KV SUPPLY FOR CRT NUMERICAL DISPLAY—Uses d-c converter operating at 20 kHz with transistor BD121 to step up 6-V d-c supply to 2-kV accelerating voltage required by crt for figure-8 numerical character generator. Diodes D40 and D41 are BAY39 and other diodes are BY153.—A. P. Tanis, Numerical Display with Bar Matrix Character Generator, *Electronic Applications*, Philips, Pub. Dept., Elcoma Div., Eindhoven, The Netherlands, Vol. 27, No. 2, 1966–1967, p 73–83.

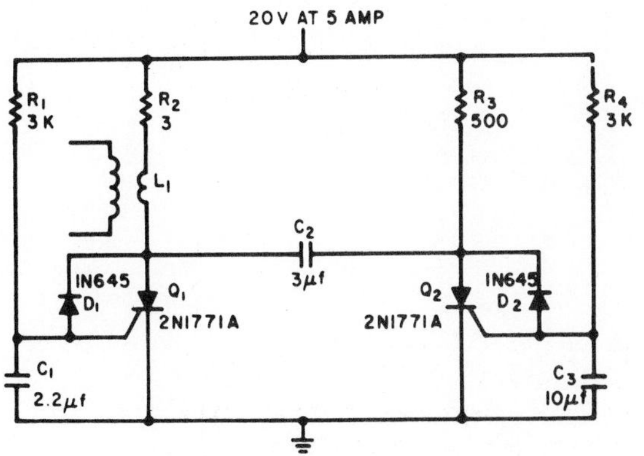

ARC-LAMP STARTER—Simple scr power supply boosts 20-V d-c input to 20 kV a-c for starting arc lamp having 2-cm gap. Inexpensive standard auto ignition coil, modified to give required 200:1 ratio, was used for L1. Duty cycle is less than 10%, permitting use of less expensive scr's than those shown.—D. Duffy, Low-Cost SCR Multivibrator Yields 20 Kv from 20-V Input, "400 Ideas for Design Selected from Electronic Design," Hayden Book Co., N.Y., 1964, p 214.

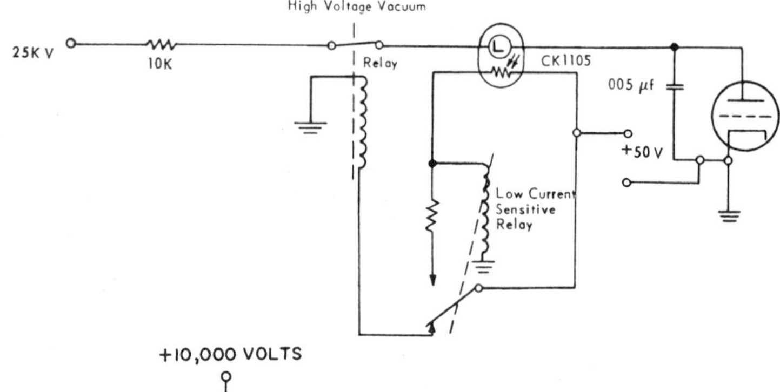

OPTOELECTRONIC OVERLOAD PROTECTION—Intermittent short-circuit in tube, or other overload that causes increase in average current through neon lamp of Raysistor, reduces resistance of its photocell, to energize low-current relay which in turn pulls in high-voltage vacuum relay to open circuit and prevent damage to components. Response time is rapid because current flows continuously through lamp circuit. For higher load current, change to CK1108 having filamentary lamp.—Raysistor Optoelectronic Devices, Raytheon, Quincy, Mass., 1967, p 15.

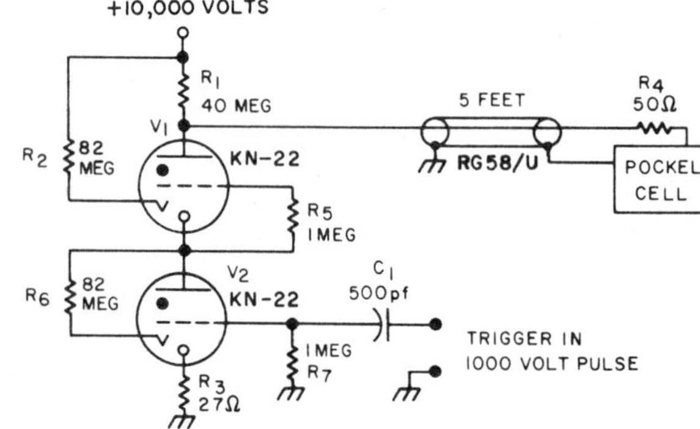

POCKEL CELL PULSER—Two EG&G Krytron gas-filled switch tubes generate up to 10-kV pulses at repetition rates from 50 to 750 pps for switching pockel cell crystals. Output coax serves as energy storage capacitor in series with R1, to permit locating pulser several feet away from cell.—Krytron Pockel Cell Pulser, EG&G, Boston, Mass., No. KN-22, 1968.

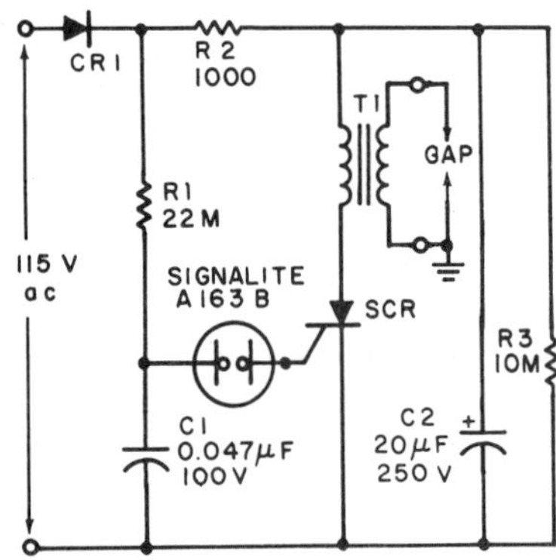

GAS IGNITION—Timing circuit, switching circuit, and high-voltage transformer, in unit called Electronic Match, produce 18,000-V spark at gap once per second, as substitute for pilot flame in gas appliances.—F. Egan, Whether It's Cold or Whether It's Hot . . . , *Electronic Design*, April 12, 1967, p 17–22.

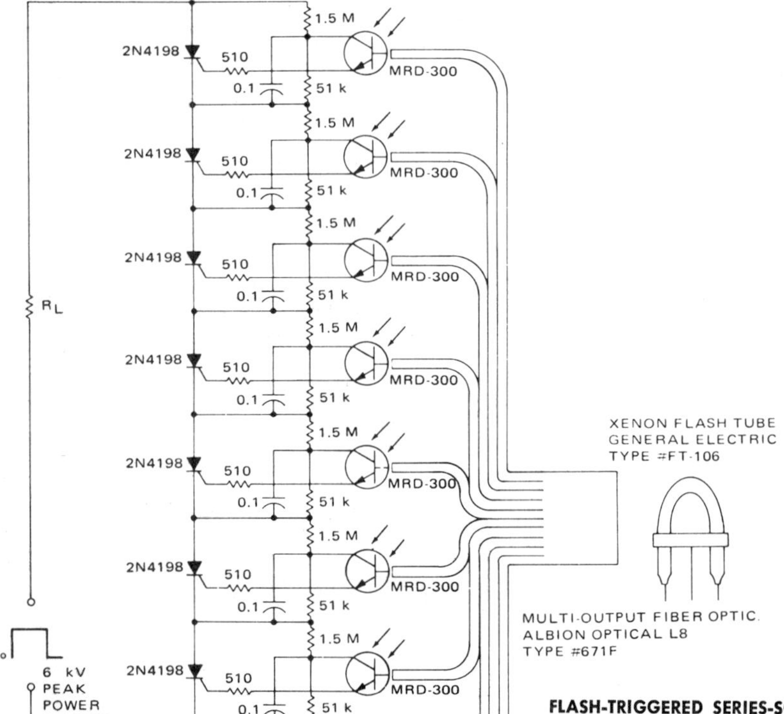

FLASH-TRIGGERED SERIES-SCR HIGH-VOLTAGE SWITCH—Xenon flash acting on ten phototransistors through fiber optics provides simultaneous triggering of ten scr's in series, for applying 6,000-V power pulse to load. Triggering with light gives simultaneous firing, without inductive delays occurring with conventional wiring, and also eliminates need for costly special trigger transformers to handle high voltages involved. Used in high-voltage crowbars and pulse-forming networks.—"Semiconductor Power Circuits Handbook," Motorola, Phoenix, Ariz., 1968, p 6–23.

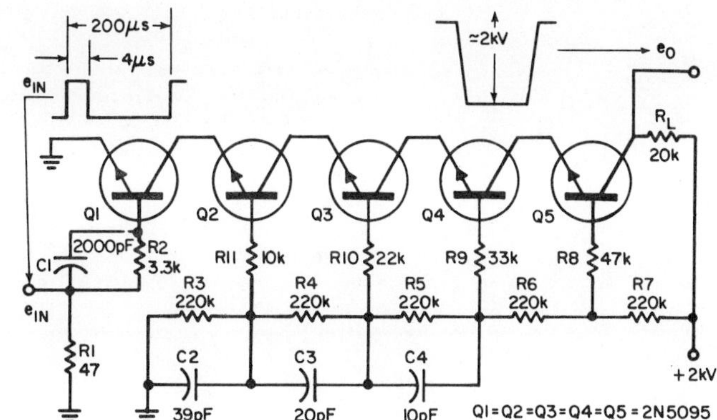

2-KV PULSE-GENERATING SWITCH—When 5-V pulse is applied to input to turn on Q1, remaining four mesa transistors (connected in series and operating in avalanche mode) are turned on to serve as economical high-voltage switch for generating 2-kV negative-going output pulse.—S. A. Ritterman, A 2-KV 0.1-A Switch Uses Mesa Transistors, *Electronic Design*, Oct. 11, 1967, p 102.

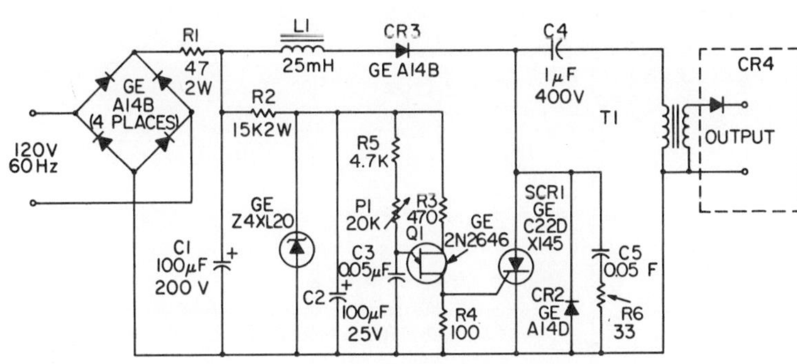

HIGH VOLTAGE FOR NEON SIGNS—Cost, size, and weight are all much less than for conventional 60-Hz stepup transformer. Rectified 60-Hz line voltage is converted to 1,000 Hz with scr inverter, and ferrite-core transformer T1 then used to step voltage up to desired value at 1,000 Hz. If d-c output is required, selenium rectifier stack CR4 should be selected according to current and voltage requirements. For 7,500 V d-c and capacitive load up to 4 mA d-c in half-wave circuit, CR4 can be General Electric 6RS9PH250PHB1. Can also be used for electrostatic precipitators and copying machines.—A. Adem, High Voltage Power Supply for Low Current Applications, General Electric, Syracuse, N.Y., No. 201.18, 1966.

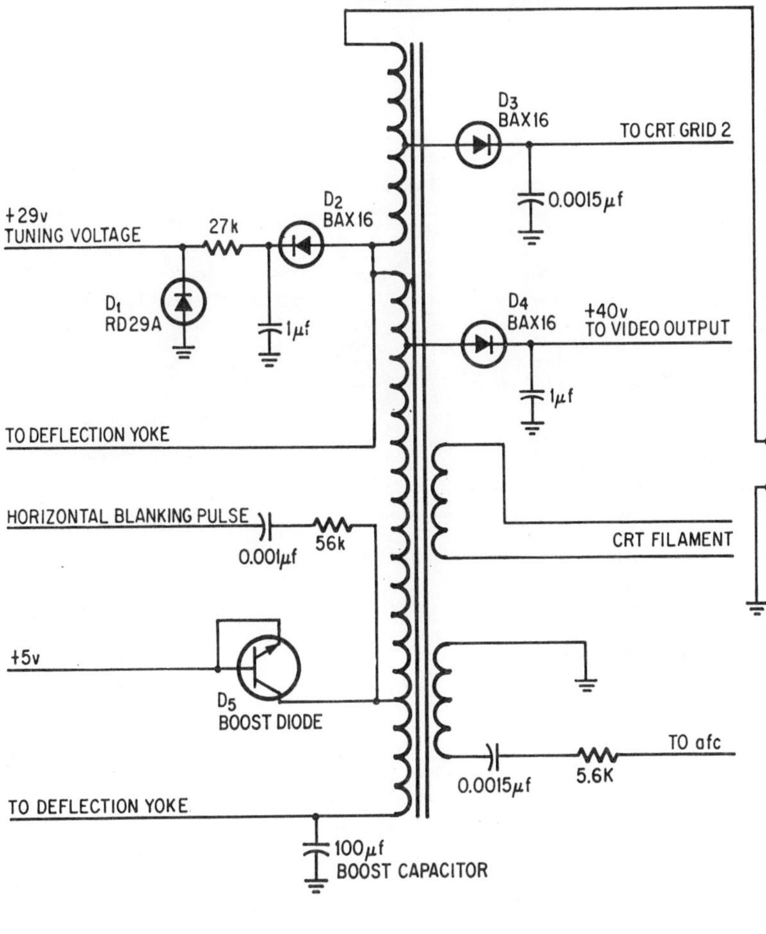

5 KV FROM PENLIGHTS—Used in Matsushita 1.5-inch-diagonal tv operating from 5-V penlight batteries. Pot-type flyback transformer core prevents induction of high-voltage pulses into other circuits. Voltage multiplication consists of progressive sharing and transfer of charge from larger input capacitors to smaller output capacitors.—R. Sasaki and K. Uno, Low-Power Design is Heart of Penlight-Powered Mini-Tv, *Electronics*, June 8, 1970, p 106–113.

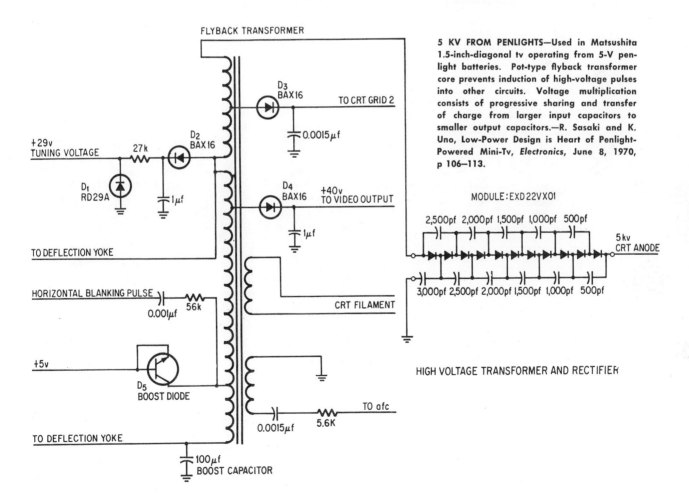

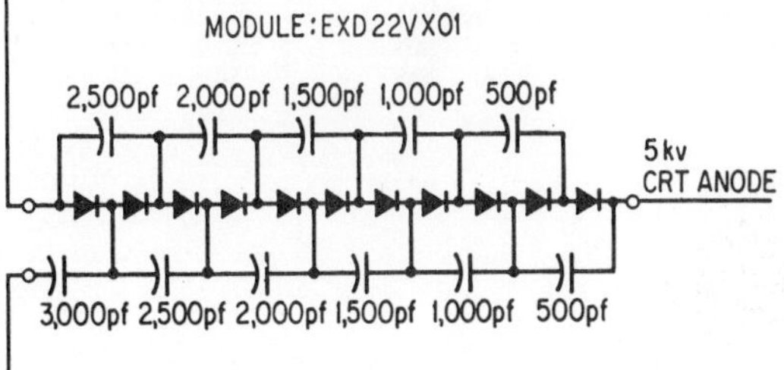

HIGH VOLTAGE TRANSFORMER AND RECTIFIER

CHAPTER 38
Hobby Circuits

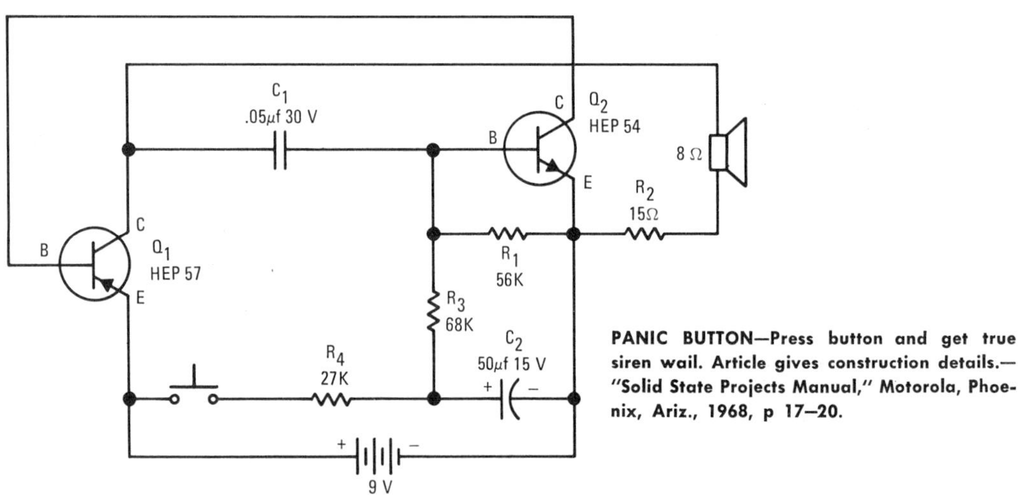

PANIC BUTTON—Press button and get true siren wail. Article gives construction details.—"Solid State Projects Manual," Motorola, Phoenix, Ariz., 1968, p 17–20.

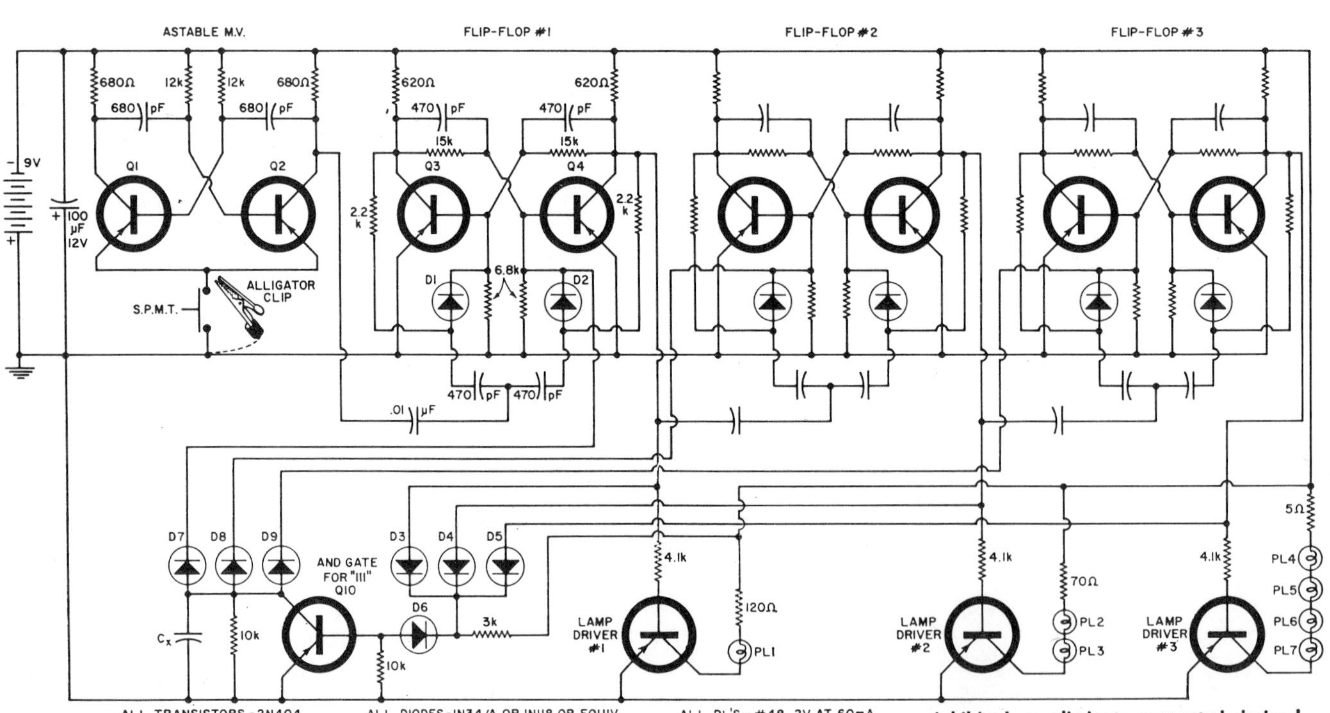

CRAPS—Three-stage binary counter drives seven pilot lamps arranged like dots on dice. Counter is driven by free-running multivibrator (above 60 kHz) that is started and stopped by single-pole momentary-throw switch or by touching alligator clip to terminal. Breaking circuit makes counter stop at one of its six possible states, in true random fashion corresponding to rolling of hand-thrown dice in crap game. First and eighth states of counter are inhibited, to eliminate unwanted decimal numbers 0 and 7. For actual game, switch can be actuated twice to simulate rolling two dice, or two identical circuits can be built.—A. L. Plevy, Electronic Dice, *Electronics World*, Oct. 1968, p 82–84.

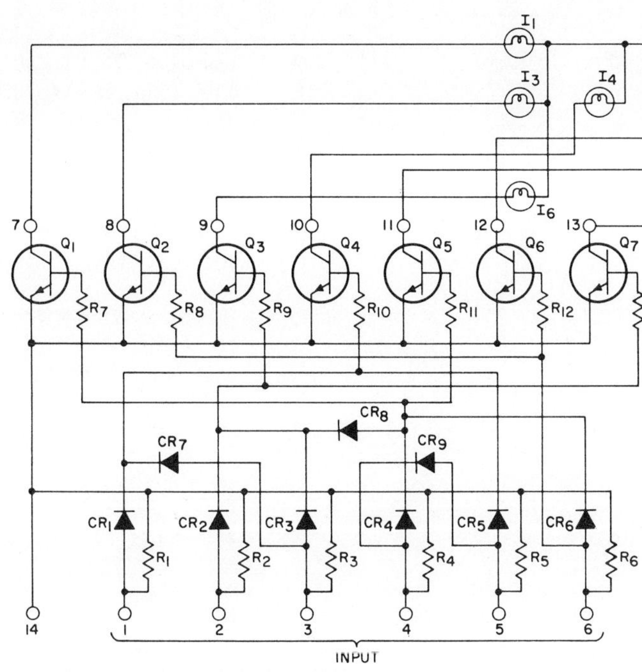

CRAP GAME—Gate and driver circuits shown are used to drive seven lamps at upper right that flash randomly for few seconds and then stop at pattern corresponding to numbers from 1 to 6 on dice. Eliminates problem of loaded dice. Book gives construction details. —"Hobby Circuits Manual," RCA, Harrison, N.J., HM-90, p 131.

CR_1 through CR_9 = silicon rectifier, type 1N270
I_1 through I_7 = any 12-volt lamp drawing 150 milliamperes or less
Q_1 through Q_7 = transistor, RCA SK3020
R_1 through R_6 = 1200 ohms, 1/2 watt, 10%
R_7 through R_{13} = 680 ohms, 1/2 watt, 10%

OBNOXIOUS NOISEMAKER—Q1-Q2 start with loud low-pitch wail that increases in frequency to very high shriek, then suddenly drops back to low tone and starts over again. Q3-Q4 provides sufficient amplification for speaker to disturb entire apartment building. May be used either to break lease or collect hospitalization for broken nose.—S. Breskend, "The Lease-Breaker" and "The Drip," *Popular Electronics*, Feb. 1968, p 33–35.

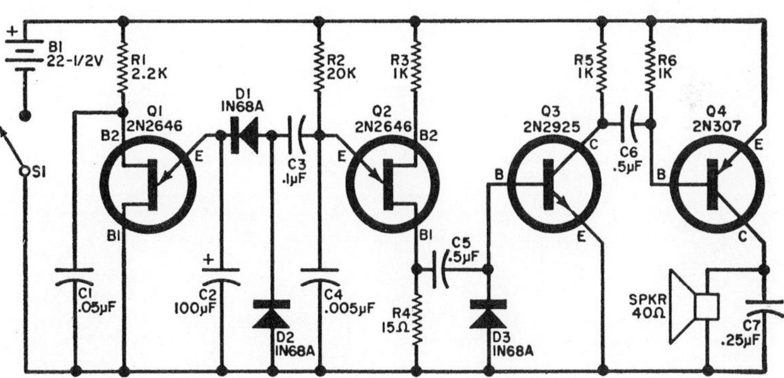

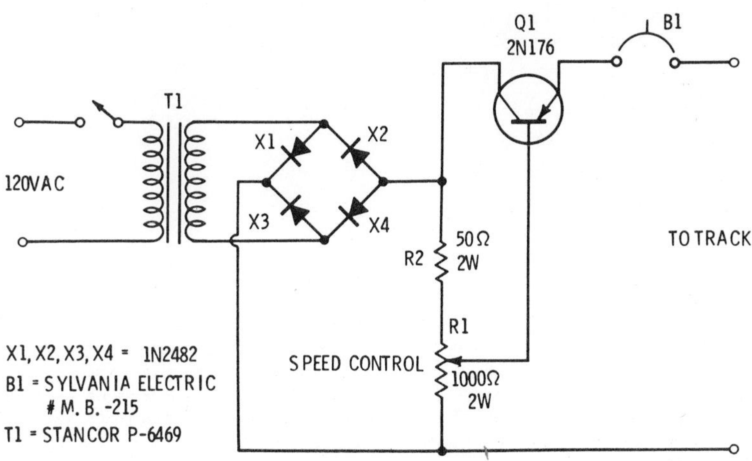

MODEL TRAIN CONTROL—Provides smoother control of speed than conventional wire-wound rheostat. D-c output of about 25 V is applied to tracks through miniature self-resetting circuit breaker B1.—J. P. Shields, "Novel Electronic Circuits," H. W. Sams & Co., Inc., Indianapolis, Ind., 1968, p 15.

RUNNING OSCILLATOR FOR SLOT MACHINE—Electronic slot machine uses three vertical columns of lights instead of spinning wheels. Oscillator circuit shown is used in two versions, as running oscillator producing pulses at rapid rate when power is applied, and for three stop oscillators each producing a pulse about once every 4 s but at different rates for as long as power is on. Book tells how to connect oscillators with flip-flops, NAND gates, shift registers, and lamps for completely random scoring action.—"Hobby Circuits Manual," RCA, Harrison, N.J., HM-90, p 121.

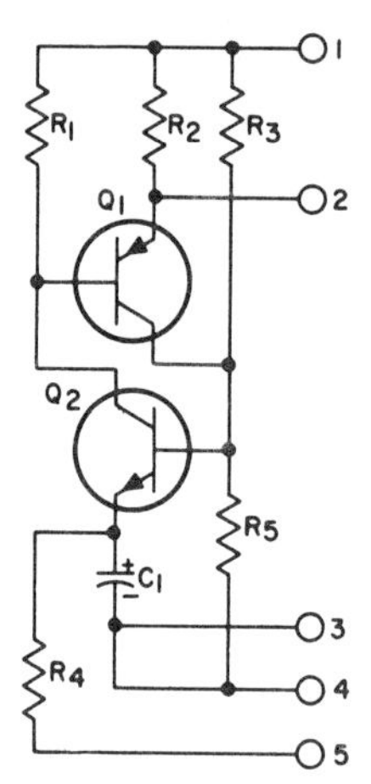

Running Oscillator (1 req'd)

C_1 = 2 microfarads, 15 volts, electrolytic
Q_1 = transistor, RCA SK3005
Q_2 = transistor, RCA SK3020
R_1 = 1500 ohms, 1/2 watt, 10%
R_2 = 47 ohms, 1/2 watt, 10%
R_3 = 1000 ohms, 1/2 watt, 10%
R_4 = 15,000 ohms, 1/2 watt, 10%
R_5 = 4700 ohms, 1/2 watt, 10%

Stop Oscillator (3 req'd)

C_1 = 100 microfarads, 15 volts, electrolytic
Q_1 = transistor, RCA SK3005
Q_2 = transistor, RCA SK3020
R_1 = 1000 ohms, 1/2 watt, 10%
R_2 = 68 ohms, 1/2 watt, 10%
R_3 = 1000 ohms, 1/2 watt, 10%
R_4 = 27,000 ohms, 33,000 ohms, 39,000 ohms, one in each of 3 oscillators
R_5 = 470 ohms, 1/2 watt, 10%

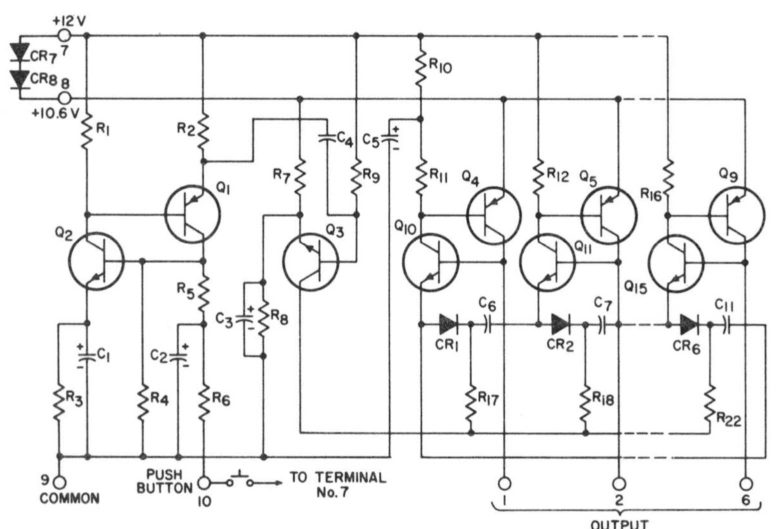

CRAP GAME—Digital pulser and six-stage shift register are used in circuit for actuating arrangement of seven lamps that flash randomly for few seconds and then stop at pattern corresponding to numbers from 1 to 6 on dice. Book gives construction details.—"Hobby Circuits Manual," RCA, Harrison, N.J., HM-90, p 132.

C_1 = 1 microfarad, 25 volts, electrolytic
C_2 = 500 microfarads, 25 volts, electrolytic
C_3 = 100 microfarads, 6 volts, electrolytic
C_4 C_6 through C_{11} = 0.05 microfarad, 25 volts or greater, ceramic
C_5 = 10 microfarads, 25 volts, electrolytic
CR_1 through CR_6 = silicon rectifier, type 1N270
CR_7 CR_8 = silicon rectifier, RCA SK3030
Q_1 Q_4 through Q_9 = transistors, RCA SK3005
Q_2 = transistor, RCA SK3020
Q_3 Q_{10} through Q_{15} = transistor, RCA SK3010
R_1 = 1500 ohms, 1/2 watt, 10%
R_2 R_8 = 47 ohms, 1/2 watt, 10%
R_3 = 27,000 ohms, 1/2 watt, 10%
R_4 R_7 R_{12} through R_{16} = 1000 ohms, 1/2 watt, 10%
R_5 = 3300 ohms, 1/2 watt, 10%
R_6 = 15 ohms, 1/2 watt, 10%
R_9 = 5600 ohms, 1/2 watt, 10%
R_{10} R_{11} = 470 ohms, 1/2 watt, 10%
R_{17} through R_{22} = 270 ohms, 1/2 watt, 10%

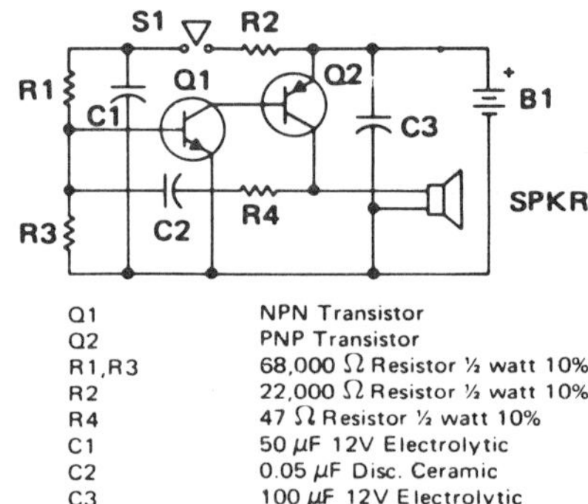

Q1	NPN Transistor
Q2	PNP Transistor
R1,R3	68,000 Ω Resistor ½ watt 10%
R2	22,000 Ω Resistor ½ watt 10%
R4	47 Ω Resistor ½ watt 10%
C1	50 µF 12V Electrolytic
C2	0.05 µF Disc. Ceramic
C3	100 µF 12V Electrolytic

SIREN—Operates from 9-V transistor radio battery, driving speaker to produce piercing wail that rises and falls. Can be used as home or garage burglar alarm, auto theft alarm, or for enlivening dull party.—Calectro Handbook, GC Electronics, Rockford, Ill., FR-69-C, p 42.

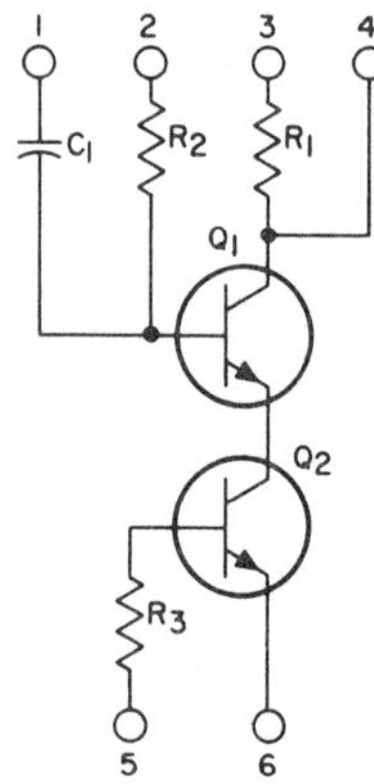

ELECTRONIC SLOT MACHINE—Circuit is one of three identical NAND gates used with other digital circuits to simulate random action of spinning-wheel slot machine, with three columns of lamps indicating score. Book gives construction data. Values: R1 1K; R2-R3 10K; C1 0.1 µF; Q1-Q2 SK3020.—"Hobby Circuits Manual," RCA, Harrison, N.J., HM-90, p 122.

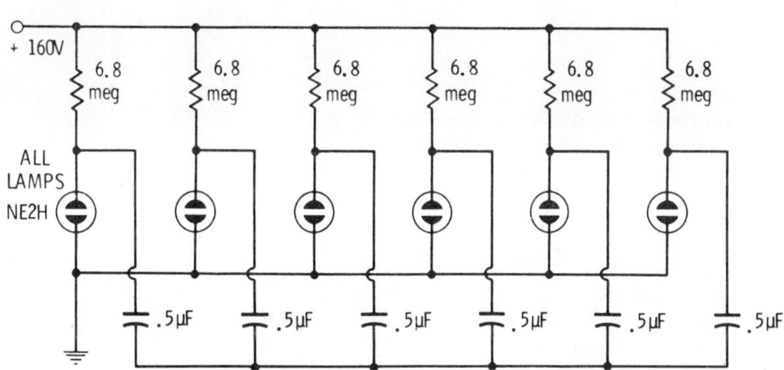

RANDOM NEON—Flashing sequence is totally unpredictable.—W. G. Miller, "Using and Understanding Miniature Neon Lamps," H. W. Sams & Co., Indianapolis, Ind., 1969, p 48.

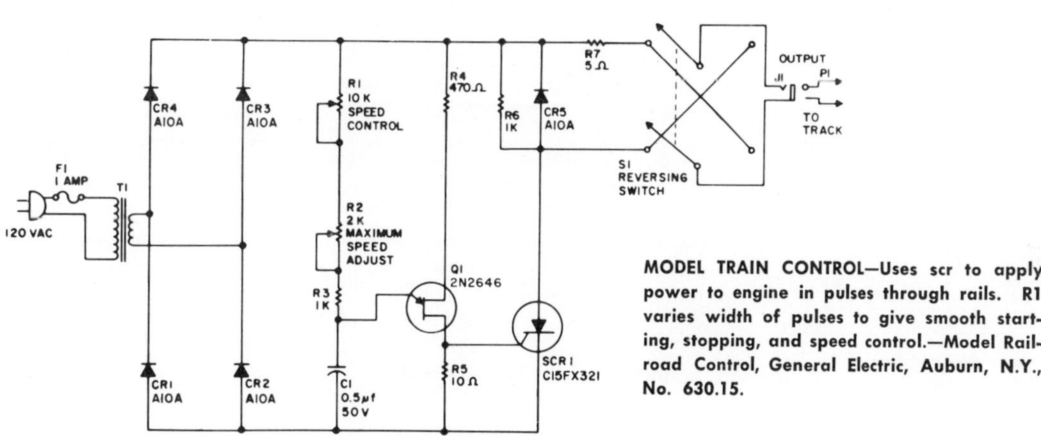

MODEL TRAIN CONTROL—Uses scr to apply power to engine in pulses through rails. R1 varies width of pulses to give smooth starting, stopping, and speed control.—Model Railroad Control, General Electric, Auburn, N.Y., No. 630.15.

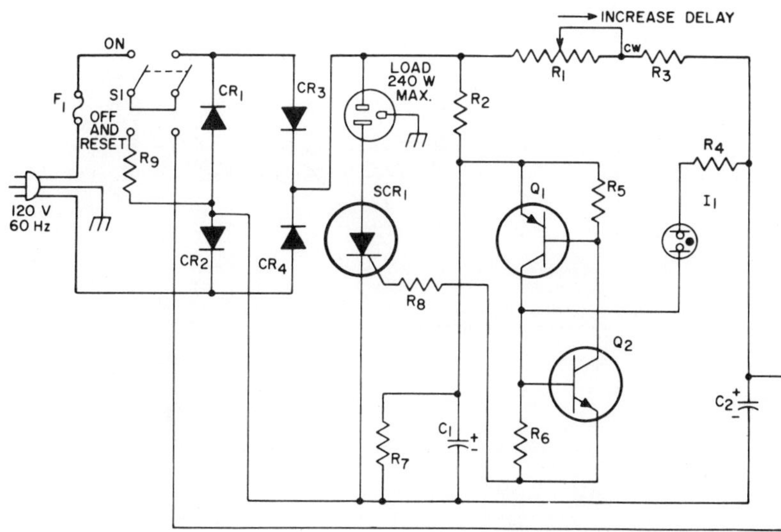

CHESS-PLAYER TIMER—Signals end of predetermined interval agreed upon as thinking time for chess or card players. May also be used to provide electronic delay that allows photographer to get into picture before camera clicks. With values shown for R1, R3, and C2, delay range is 5—120 s. Will handle loads up to 2 A or 240 W.—"Hobby Circuits Manual," RCA, Harrison, N.J., HM-90, p 162.

C_1 = 50 microfarads, 15 volts, electrolytic
C_2 = 50 microfarads, 150 volts, electrolytic
$CR_1CR_2CR_3CR_4$* = diode, RCA SK3016 mounted in fuse clip for heat sinking
F_1 = fuse, 125 volts, 3 amperes
I_1 = lamp, neon, NE-83 or equivalent
Q_1 = transistor, RCA SK3004
Q_2 = transistor, RCA SK3020
R_1 = potentiometer, 1 megohm, 2 watts, linear taper
R_2 = 3000 ohms, 5 watts, 10%
R_3 = 47,000 ohms, 1/2 watt, 10%
R_4 = 10,000 ohms, 1/2 watt, 10%
R_5 = 150 ohms, 1/2 watt, 10%
R_6 = 470 ohms, 1/2 watt, 10%
R_7 = 180 ohms, 1/2 watt, 10%
R_8 = 100 ohms, 1/2 watt, 10%
R_9 = 33 ohms, 1/2 watt, 10%
S_1 = switch, 125 volts, 3 amperes, double-pole, double-throw, toggle
SCR_1* = silicon controlled rectifier, RCA KD2100

*These components are available in SCR Silicon Controlled Rectifier Experimenter's Kit KD2105.

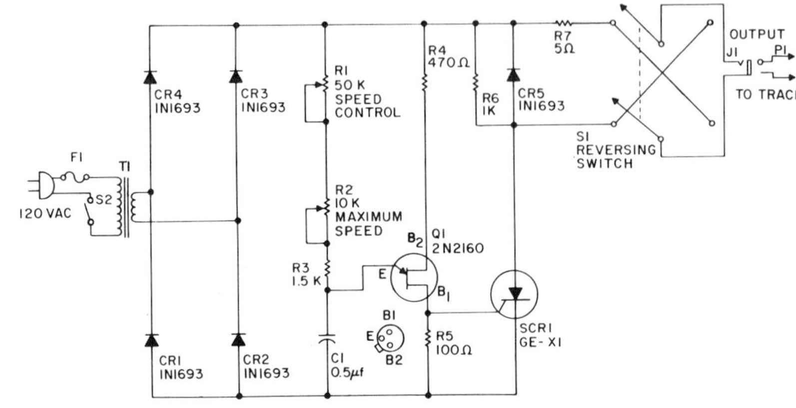

SCR CONTROL FOR MODEL TRAIN—Applies power to engine through rails in controllable-width pulses to give smooth starting and stopping along with reversing. Will handle up to 1.2 A continuously. Transformer is Stancor P-6469 having 25-V secondary.—Hobby Manual, General Electric Co., Owensboro, Ky., 1965, p 98.

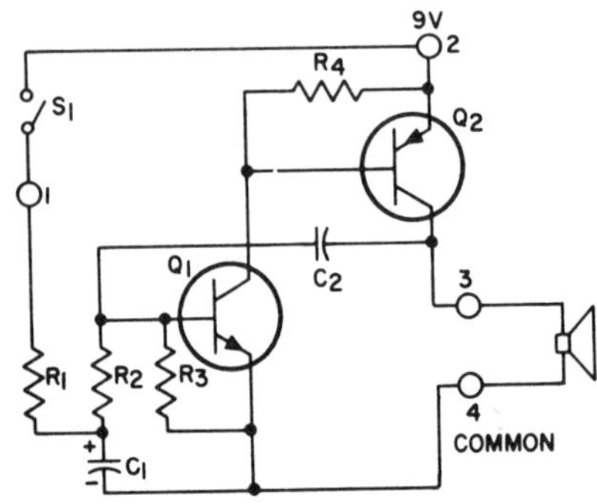

C_1 = 50 microfarads, 12 volts, electrolytic
C_2 = 0.018 microfarad, 25 volts or greater
Q_1 = transistor, RCA SK3020
Q_2 = transistor, RCA SK3005
R_1 = 27,000 ohms, 1/2 watt, 10%
R_2 = 68,000 ohms, 1/2 watt, 10%
R_3 = 56,000 ohms, 1/2 watt, 10%
R_4 = 470 ohms, 1/2 watt, 10%
S_1 = switch, any single-pole push-button type
Speaker = 3.2-ohms or 8-ohms

POLICE SIREN—Pressing S1 produces wailing sound that slowly increases in frequency. When switch is released, sound slowly decreases in frequency. Increasing value of R1 or C1 lengthens rate at which frequency of oscillation increases. Battery drain is only 400 μA with S1 open, so power switch is not normally necessary.—"Hobby Circuits Manual," RCA, Harrison, N.J., HM-90, p 117.

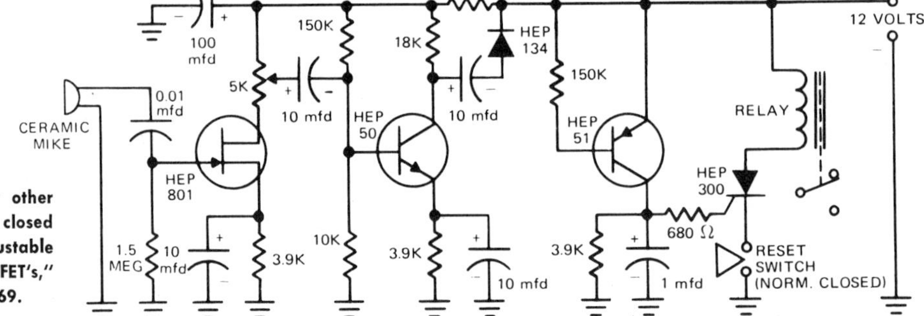

SOUND-ACTIVATED—Clap of hands or other sharp sound closes relay, which remains closed until manually reset. Sensitivity is adjustable with 5K potentiometer.—"Tips on Using FET's," Motorola, Phoenix, Ariz., HMA-33, 1969.

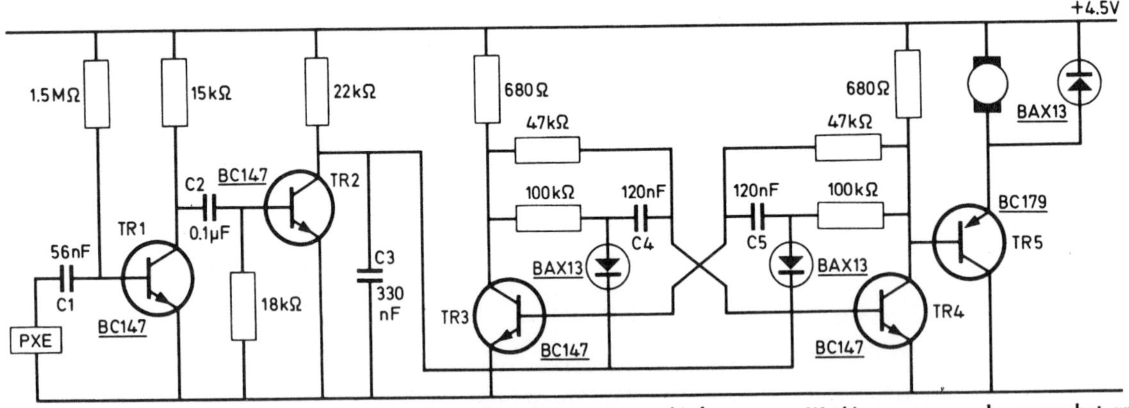

WHISTLE CONTROL—PXE (piezoxide) ceramic material in detector serves for converting sound waves of ordinary whistle into audio signals for controlling motor-driven toy. If first whistle note makes TR4 conducting in mvbr, TR5 will also conduct and motor will get full supply voltage. Next whistle command will make bistable mvbr switch over and stop motor. Frequency of whistle should match that of PXE detector, in which case output of PXE detector will be about 50 mV when whistle is blown firmly about 20 feet away. Working range can be somewhat greater because mvbr will switch over for input signal of about 25 mV.—PXE Detector, Philips, Pub. Dept., Elcoma Div., Eindhoven, The Netherlands, No. 43, 1969.

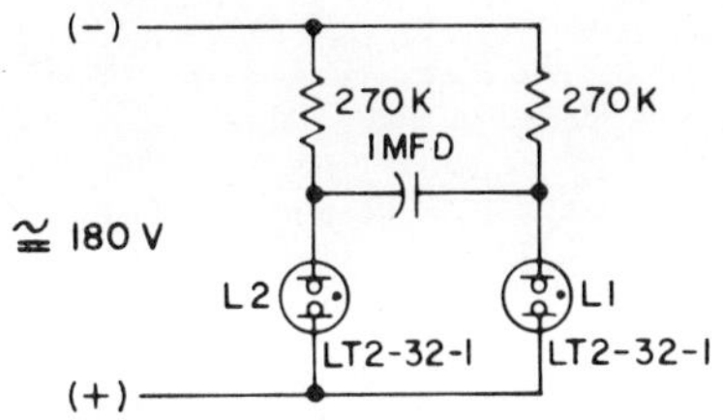

FLICKERING-NEON FLASHER—Uses two neon lamps which light alternately, with light flickering from electrode to electrode on each to get attention.—E. Bauman, "Applications of Neon Lamps and Gas Discharge Tubes," Signalite, Neptune, N.J., p 154.

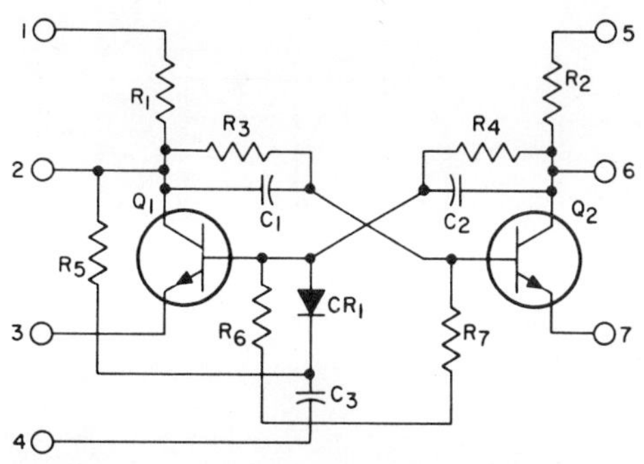

ELECTRONIC SLOT MACHINE—Three identical flip-flops are used with other digital circuits to simulate random action of spinning-wheel slot machine, but with three columns of lamps for indicating score. Book gives detailed

C_1 C_2 = 560 picofarads, 25 volts or greater
C_3 = 0.01 microfarad, 25 volts or greater
CR_1 = silicon rectifier, type 1N270
Q_1 Q_2 = transistor, RCA SK3020
R_1 R_2 = 1500 ohms, 1/2 watt, 10%
R_3 R_4 R_5 = 10,000 ohms, 1/2 watt, 10%
R_6 R_7 = 6800 ohms, 1/2 watt, 10%

construction data.—"Hobby Circuits Manual," RCA, Harrison, N.J., HM-90, p 122.

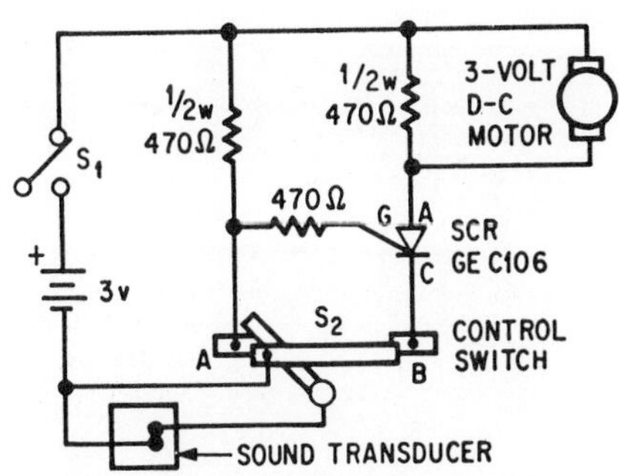

SOUND-CONTROLLED TURTLE—Inexpensive scr is turned on and off alternately by loud shouts of "Go!" and "Stop!", to drive or stop small d-c motor inside toy turtle. Sound picked up by transducer momentarily breaks ground on scr gate, turning on scr to energize motor. When motor starts, it trips shaft that moves lever of make-before-break switch S2 from A to B. Next shout then turns off motor and resets switch lever to A. Requires two D cells for 40 hours operation.—Toying With SCR's, *Electronics*, Sept. 18, 1967, p 46 and 48.

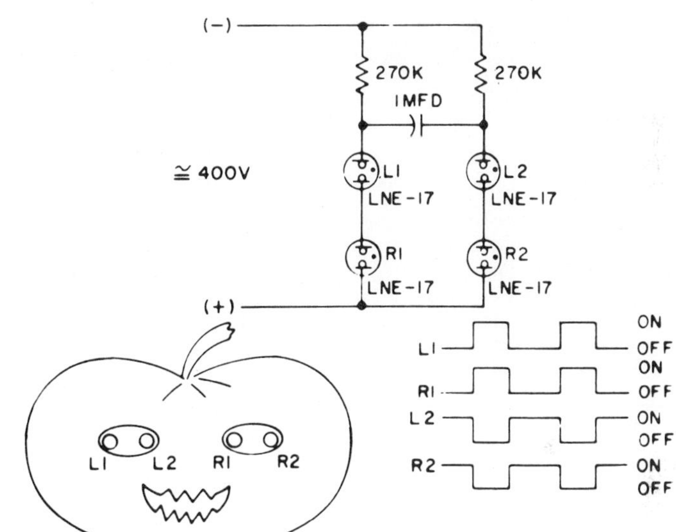

PUMPKIN BLINKER—When neon lamps are installed as shown, the lights blink from side to side.—E. Bauman, "Applications of Neon Lamps and Gas Discharge Tubes," Signalite, Neptune, N.J., p 154.

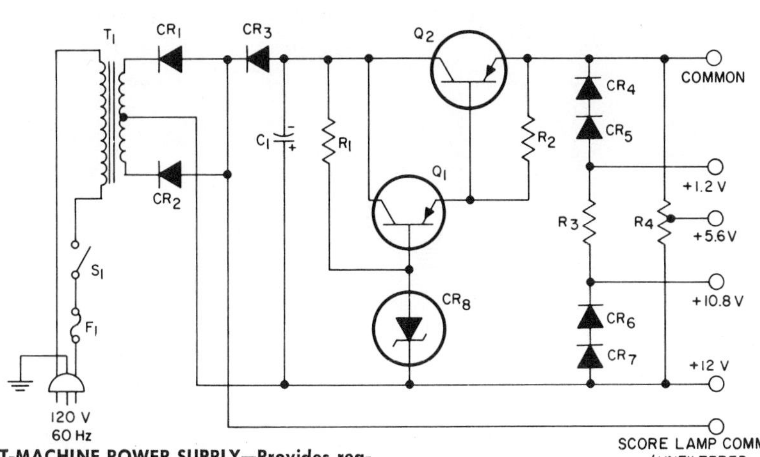

SLOT-MACHINE POWER SUPPLY—Provides regulated voltages required by digital circuits used to simulate random action of spinning-wheel slot machine, with three columns of lamps indicating score. Book gives construction data.—"Hobby Circuits Manual," RCA, Harrison, N.J., HM-90, p 123.

C_1 = 2000 microfarads, 15 volts, electrolytic
CR_1 through CR_7 = silicon rectifier, RCA SK3030
CR_8 = zener diode, 13 volts, 1 watt
F_1 = fuse, 1 ampere, 3AG
Q_1 = transistor, RCA SK3005
Q_2 = transistor, RCA SK3009
R_1 = 1800 ohms, 1/2 watt, 10%
R_2 = 68 ohms, 1/2 watt, 10%
R_3 = 470 ohms, 1/2 watt, 10%
R_4 = 100 ohms, 25 watts, adjustable
S_1 = toggle switch, single-pole single-throw
T_1 = transformer, primary 117 volts, secondary 25 volts at 1 ampere, Stancor No. P6469 or equivalent

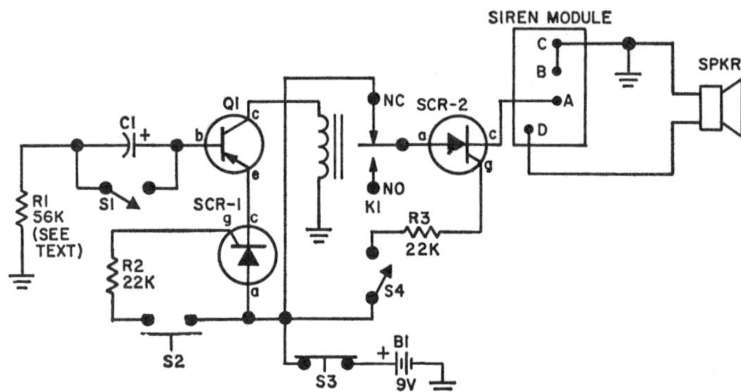

SIREN IN BOX—Solid-state electronic timer is combined with electronic siren. Once a curious person turns it on, either instantly by flipping S4 or after 40-s delay if he flips S2 first, siren can be stopped only by pushing concealed switch S3 through hole in perfboard case. Will enliven dull party or conference, but should be recovered and turned off before someone throws it out window. Siren module is Lafayette 19E55053 or equivalent. Speaker is 8 ohms and 2½ inches. C1 is 100 μF, 6 V. Value shown for R1 gives timing delay of about 40 s for Q1-C1-R1-K1 delay circuit. Q1 is HEP250 and scr's are GE 10EY1.—S. Daniels, Interval Screamer, *Elementary Electronics*, Mar.—Apr. 1970, p 62–65 and 102.

MODEL-TRAIN SPEED CONTROL—Single scr provides smooth full-wave control of speed, along with regulation, over complete range from zero to full speed, for model trains or track-guided model race cars requiring up to 12 V d-c.—"Silicon Controlled Rectifier Experimenter's Manual," RCA, Harrison, N.J., 1967, p 84.

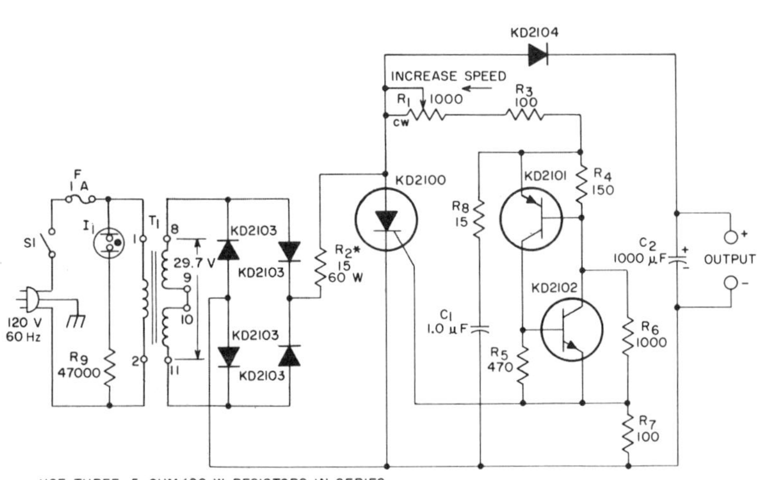

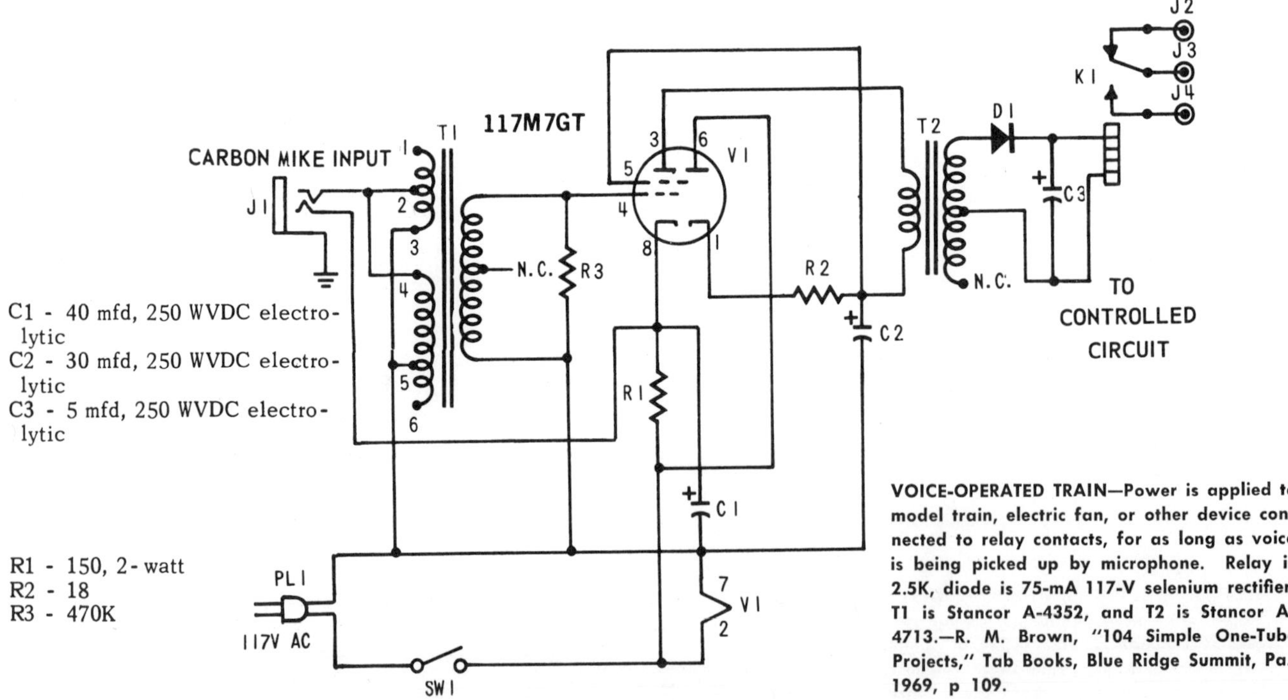

VOICE-OPERATED TRAIN—Power is applied to model train, electric fan, or other device connected to relay contacts, for as long as voice is being picked up by microphone. Relay is 2.5K, diode is 75-mA 117-V selenium rectifier, T1 is Stancor A-4352, and T2 is Stancor A-4713.—R. M. Brown, "104 Simple One-Tube Projects," Tab Books, Blue Ridge Summit, Pa., 1969, p 109.

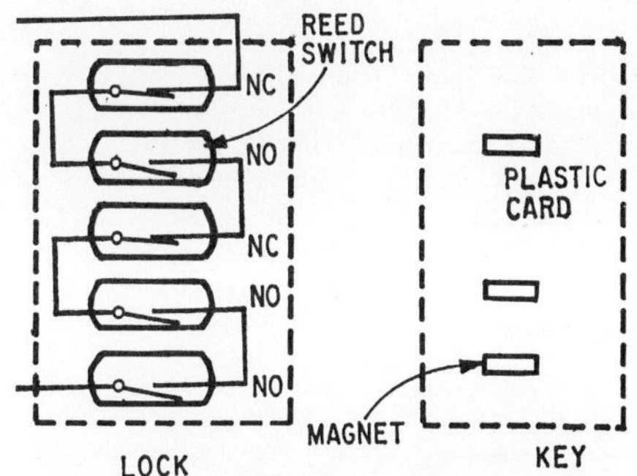

MAGNETIC COMBINATION LOCK—Combination of normally open and normally closed magnetic reed switches can be activated only by correct pattern of small permanent magnets on card. Security factor increases with number of switches used. Normally closed switches are used to prevent operation with single large magnetic field.. Switches should be concealed by nonmagnetic material. Can be used with electric door latch or as auto ignition switch.—R. M. Zilberstein, Reed Switches Form a Nonmechanical Lock, *Electronics*, Oct. 28, 1968, p 92.

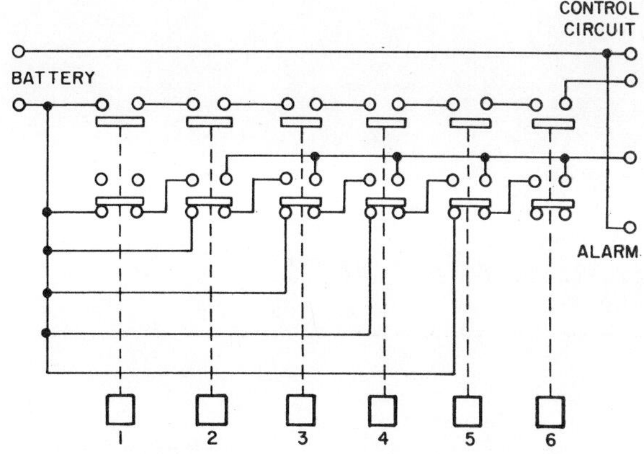

ELECTRIC COMBINATION LOCK—Power is applied to control circuit only if toggle, lever, or self-latching pushbutton switches are closed in one correct sequence. For all other sequences, alarm circuit goes off. Additional switches can be used to increase difficulty of finding correct combination even if alarm is somehow disabled. Manual or other means should be provided for releasing all switches.—K. C. Herrick, Circuit Determines Correct Operating Sequence, *Electronic Design*, Nov. 23, 1964, p 62.

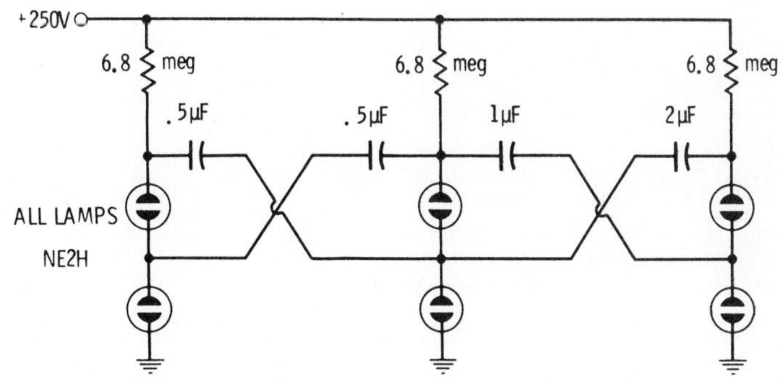

SIX-LAMP RANDOM—Gives interesting and unpredictable pattern of blinking neon lights, using few parts.—W. G. Miller, "Using and Understanding Miniature Neon Lamps," H. W. Sams & Co., Indianapolis, Ind., 1969, p 48.

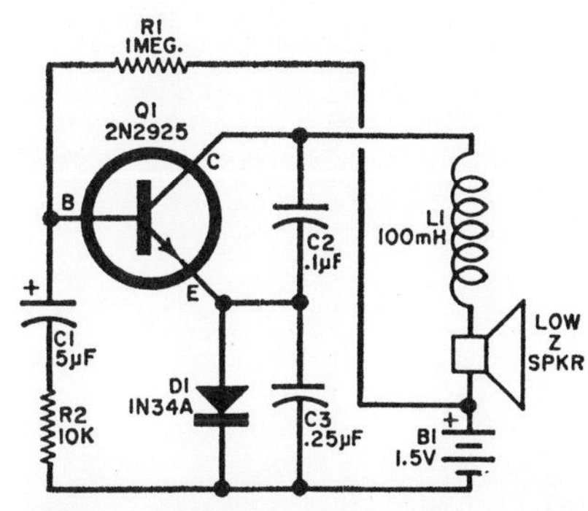

INSANITY GENERATOR — Produces gentle-sounding chirp about once per second, for annoying next-door neighbors without incurring risk of having lease broken. Sound is comparable to Chinese torture in which water drips slowly on forehead of victim strapped to floor. Use either small speaker or low-impedance earphone.—S. Breskend, "The Lease-Breaker" and "The Drip", *Popular Electronics*, Feb. 1968, p 33–35.

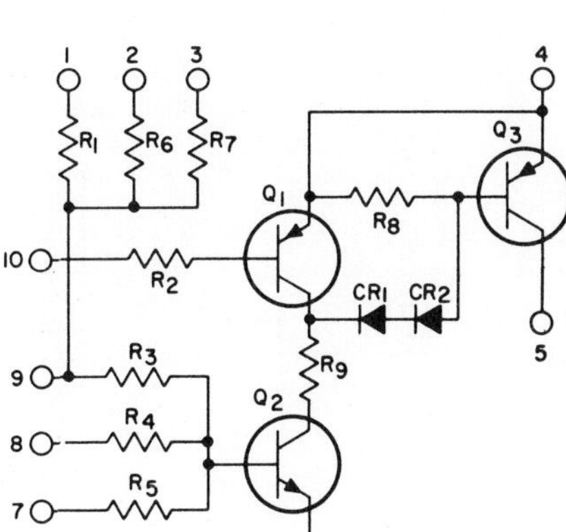

NOR GATE FOR SLOT MACHINE—Circuit is one of scoring gates used with other digital circuits to simulate random action of spinning-wheel slot machine, with three columns of lamps indicating score. Book gives construction data. Values: R1-R6 4.7K; R7 3.9K; R8-R9 180; CR1-CR2 SK3030; Q1, Q3 SK3005; Q2 SK3010.—"Hobby Circuits Manual," RCA, Harrison, N.J., HM-90, p 122.

NOTE: To locate additional circuits in the category of this chapter, use the index at the back of this book. Check also the author's "Sourcebook of Electronic Circuits," published by McGraw-Hill in 1968.

CHAPTER 39
I-F Amplifier Circuits

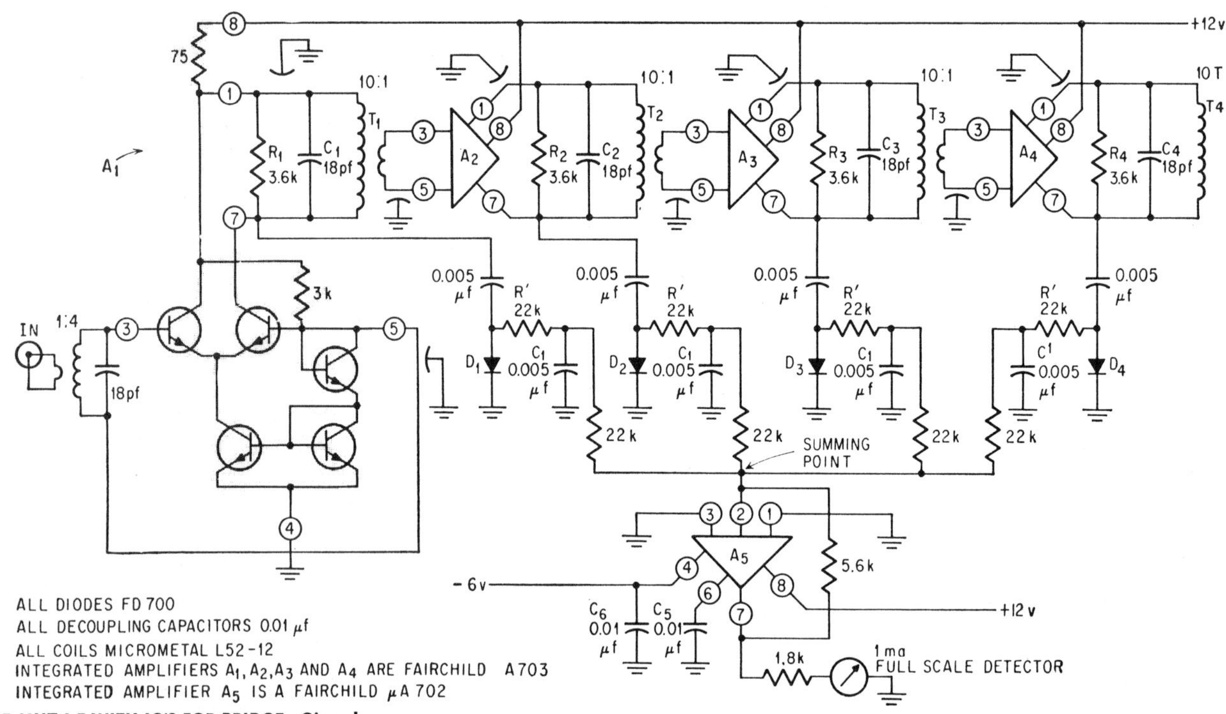

45-MHZ I-F WITH IC'S FOR BRIDGE—Gives low-cost detector for bridge network. Logarithmic transfer characteristic is generated by sampling outputs of cascaded IC amplifiers A1, A2, A3, and A4 and combining samples in video summing amplifier A5. Large input signal forces successive stages to limit in sequence, dropping slope of transfer characteristic 20 dB. Circuit is highly stable, but slow logging makes it unsuitable for radar.—R. Q. Lane, Low-Cost IC's Improve 45-MHz I-f Amplifier, *Electronics*, March 20, 1967, p 88–89.

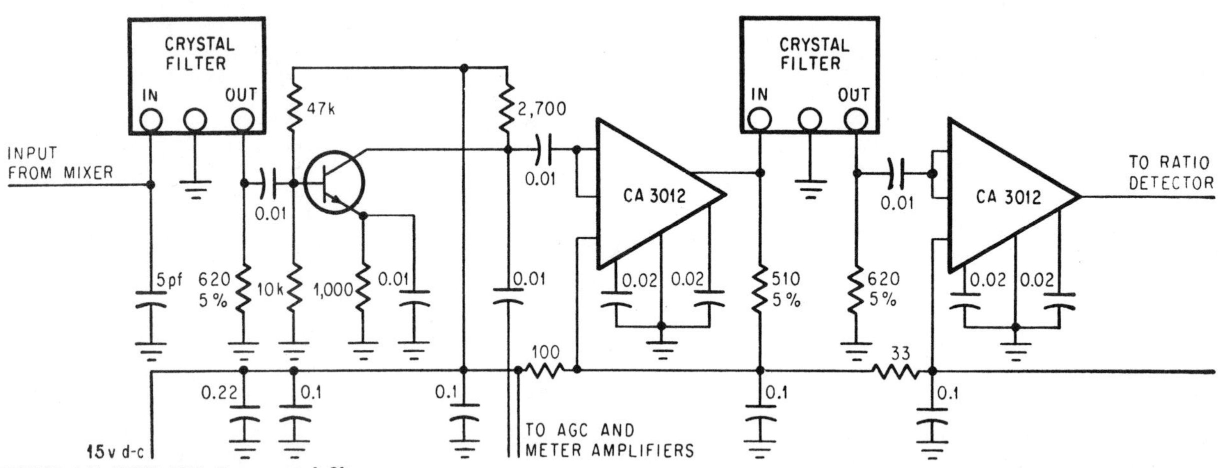

HEATHKIT F-M WITH IC'S—Two crystal filters and two RCA wideband high-gain amplifier-limiters improve performance of f-m i-f. Overall gain is 120 dB, capture ratio is reduced to 1.8 dB, and adjacent-channel selectivity is 70 dB. Four-pole lattice-design quartz crystal filters together give selectivity comparable to that of eight single-tuned transformer-coupled circuits.—IC's Sound Better, *Electronics*, January 23, 1967, p 41–42.

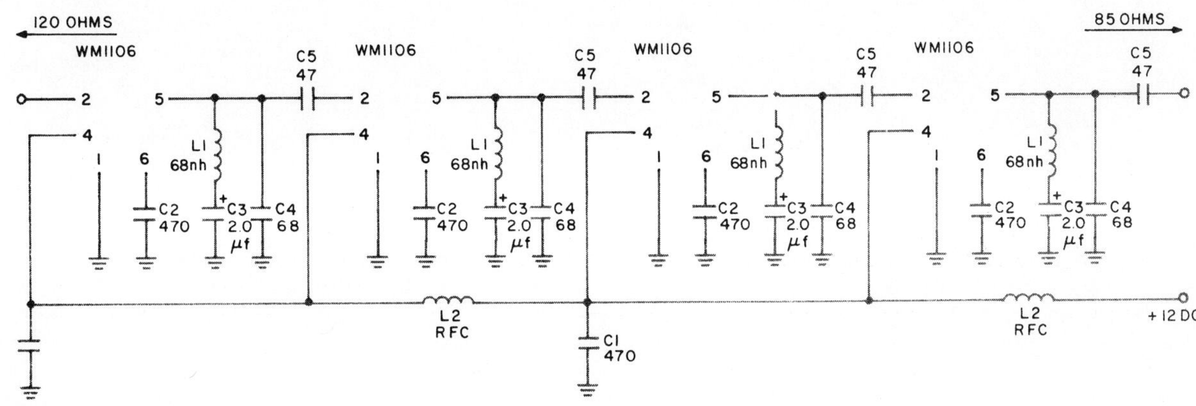

60 MHZ WITH FOUR IC STAGES—Four stages provide total gain up to 43 dB, depending on IC used, with bandwidth of 8.4 MHz overall. —S. G. Shepherd and A. E. Seman, Design With Integrated Circuits at 60 Mc, *Electronic Design*, July 19, 1965, p 32–35.

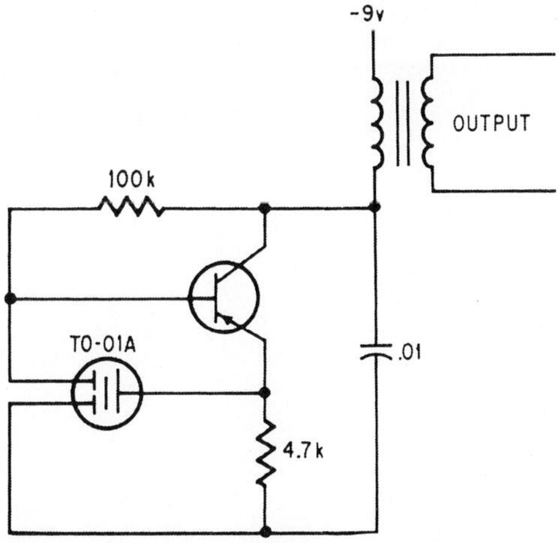

TRANSFILTER—Ceramic transfilter serves in place of transformer as coupling element, and also forms oscillating element in 455-kHz i-f system. Frequency stability is 0.1% from 20 to 60 C. Transistor can be either pnp or npn, depending on power supply, but should have beta of 50 to 100 and cutoff of 10 MHz. —C. Hartley, Oscillator Has a Transfilter As The Resonant Device, *Electronics*, Feb. 3, 1969, p 78.

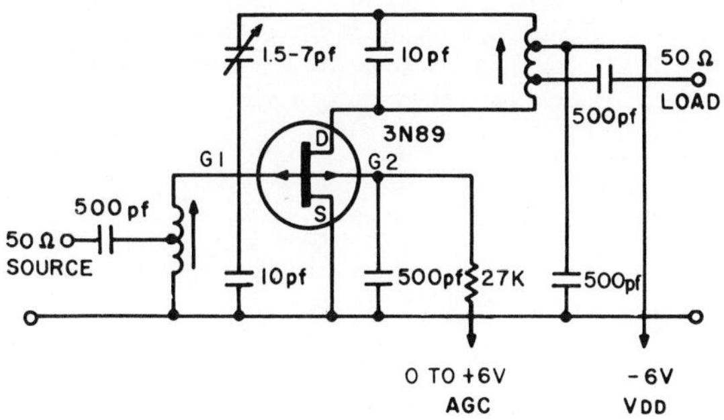

TETRODE FET WITH 40-DB AGC—Power gain is 15 dB in 45-MHz single stage shown. Can also be used as video amplifier having linear gain control.—J. S. Sherwin, Need High Z and Low C? Turn to the Tetrode FET for HF Design, *Electronic Design*, June 7, 1965, p 20–25.

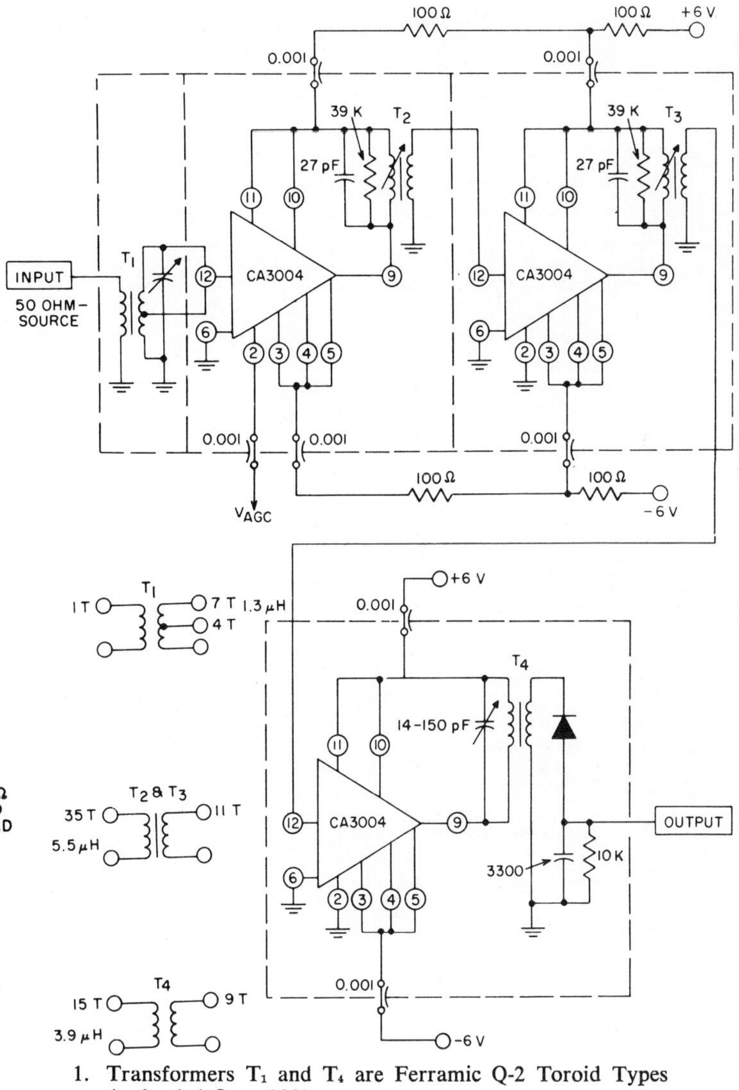

Notes:
1. Transformers T_1 and T_4 are Ferramic Q-2 Toroid Types (unloaded Q = 200).
2. Transformers T_2 and T_3 are slug-tuned with carbonyl IT-71 material (unloaded Q = 70).

12-MHZ GAIN-CONTROLLED A-M I-F—Uses three IC r-f amplifiers in cascade to provide 25 dB gain per stage. Agc range for first stage is 60 dB and 3-dB bandwidth is 160 kHz.—"Linear Integrated Circuits," RCA, Harrison, N.J., IC-41, p 214.

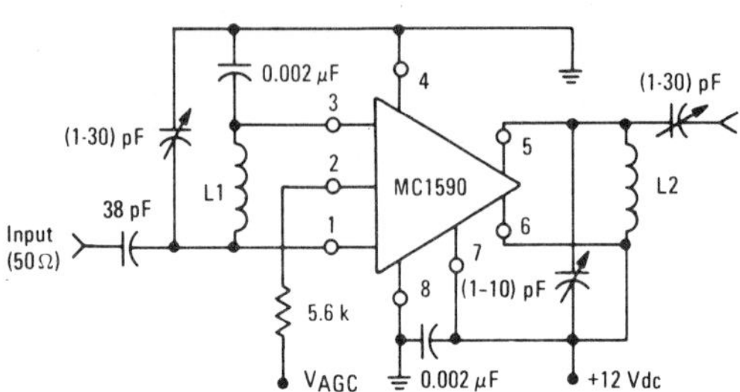

L1 = 12 Turns #22 AWG Wire on a Toroid Core, (T37-6 Micro Metal or Equiv)
L2 = 17 Turns #20 AWG Wire on a Toroid Core, (T44-6 Micro Metal or Equiv)

30-MHz IC—Single-ended coupling at input and output eliminates transformers. Power gain is 50 dB. Uses Motorola direct-coupled high-gain IC amplifier.—R. Hejhall and B. Trout, Integrated Circuits for the World of High Frequency, "State-of-the-Art—Linears in Action," Motorola, Phoenix, Ariz., 1969, p 21–26.

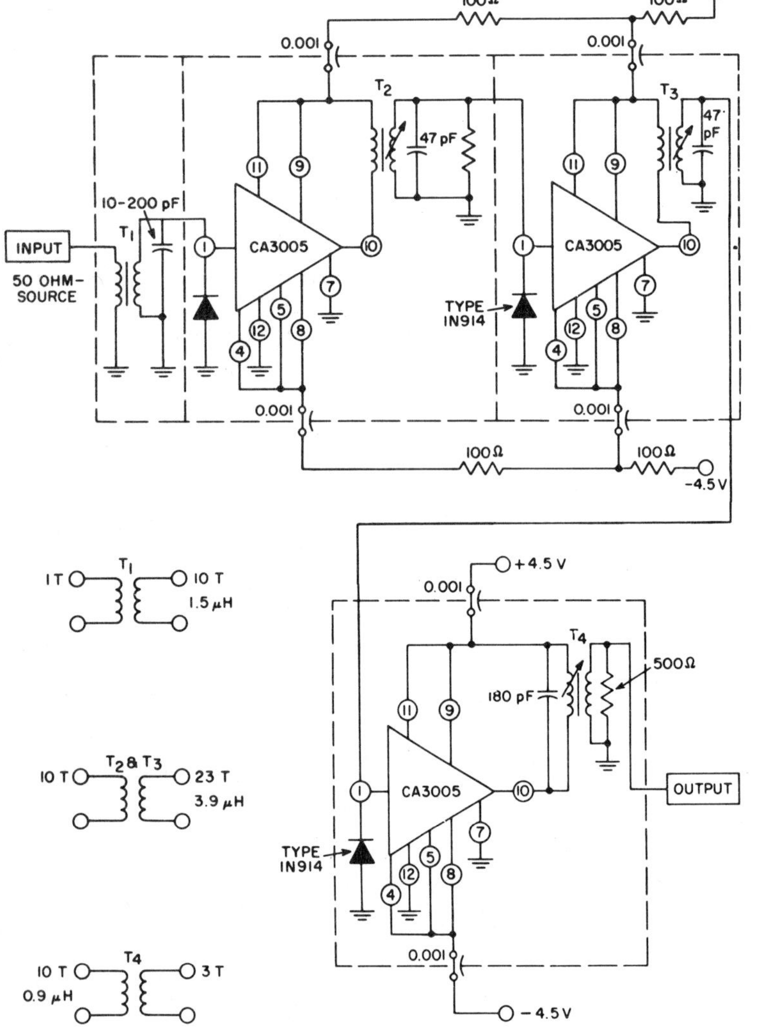

Notes: 1. Transformer T_1 is a Ferramic Q-2 Type (unloaded Q = 200).
2. Transformers T_2, T_3, and T_4 are slug-tuned with carbonyl IT-75 material (unloaded Q = 75).

12-MHZ LIMITING I-F AMPLIFIER—Uses three IC r-f amplifiers in cascade to provide 26 dB gain per stage for f-m use. Limiting action begins at about 30 µV.—"Linear Integrated Circuits," RCA, Harrison, N.J., IC-41, p 213.

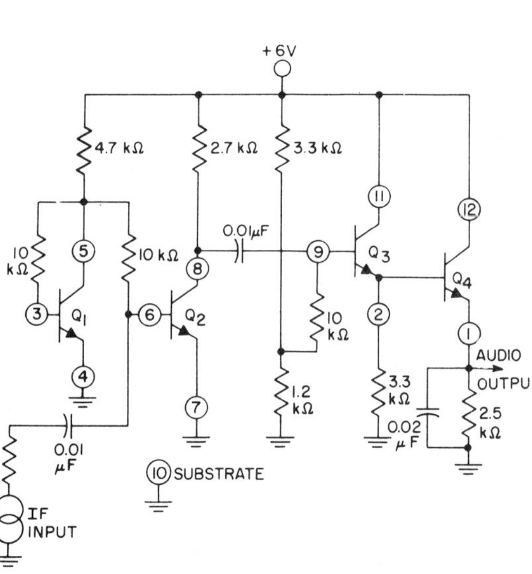

30 DB AT 1 MHZ—Uses RCA CA3018 IC transistor array as final i-f amplifier stage and cascaded emitter-follower Q3-Q4 as second detector.—"Linear Integrated Circuits," RCA, Harrison, N.J., IC-41, p 314.

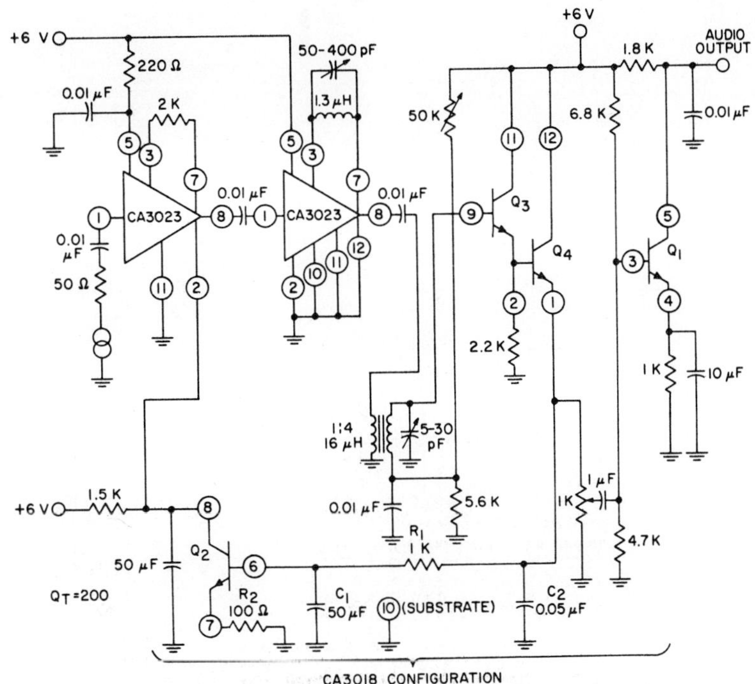

10-MHZ TWO-STAGE IC I-F—Uses two IC video amplifiers and CA3018 IC transistor array to provide required 86-dB i-f voltage gain at 10 MHz along with detection, audio amplification, and d-c amplification.—"Linear Integrated Circuits," RCA, Harrison, N.J., IC-41, p 177.

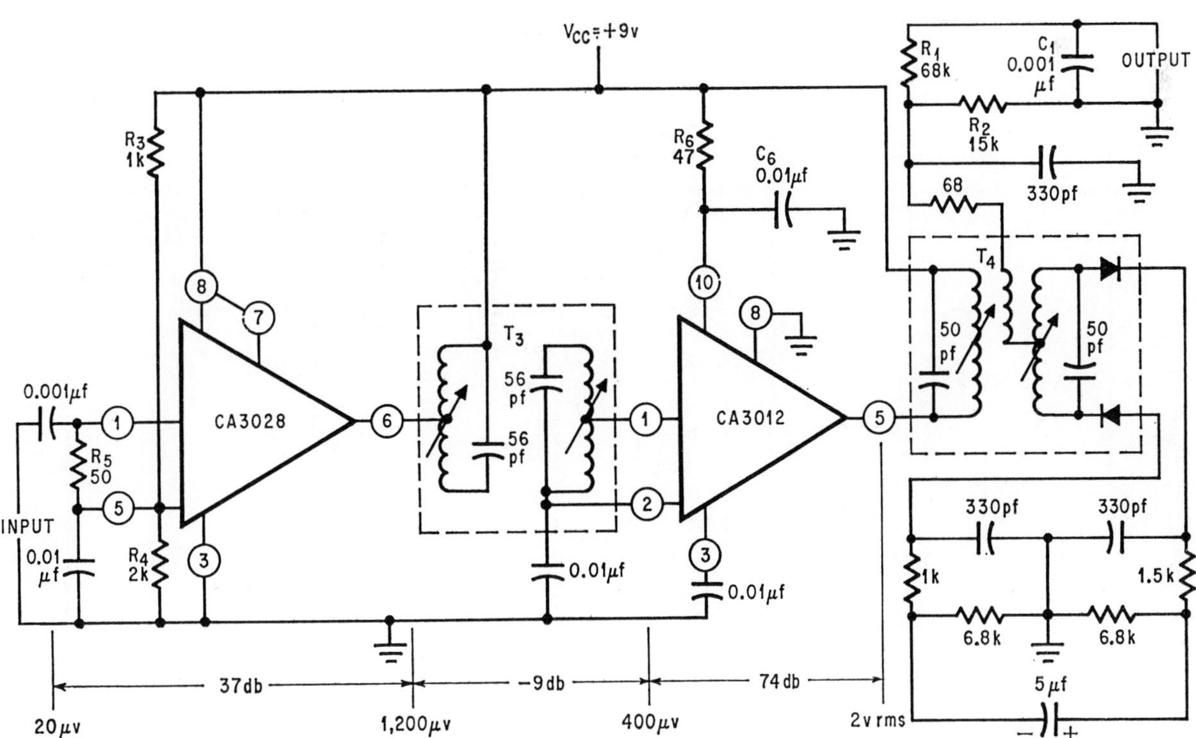

10.7-MHZ I-F WITH TWO IC'S—Two RCA IC's provide 100 dB of gain for complete i-f strip. First IC is differential amplifier, and second provides limiting action along with gain.—J. P. Keller, Linear IC's: Part 3—Differential Amplifiers At Work, *Electronics*, Sept. 18, 1967, p 96–104.

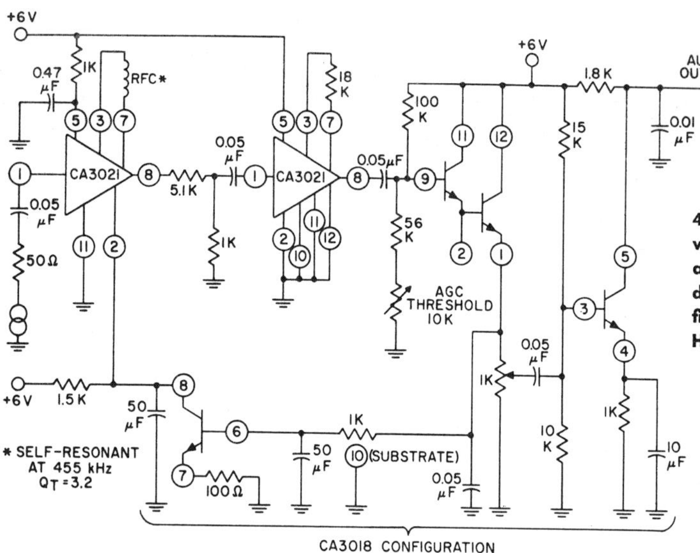

455-KHZ TWO-STAGE IC I-F—Uses two IC video amplifiers and CA3018 IC transistor array to provide required i-f gain along with detection, audio amplification, and d-c amplification.—"Linear Integrated Circuits," RCA, Harrison, N.J., IC-41, p 178.

FET AMPLIFIER OR OSCILLATOR—Choose i-f transformers for 50 kHz, 455 kHz, or 10.7 MHz. Add link coupling to convert to stable oscillator; use 6 turns of wire at each end.—"Tips on Using FET's," Motorola, Phoenix, Ariz., HMA-33, 1969.

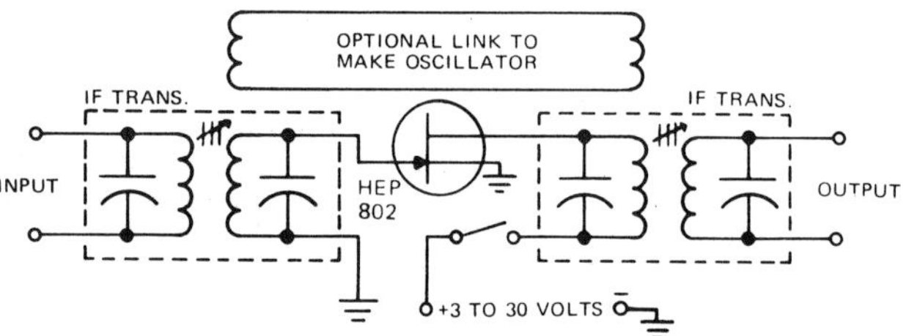

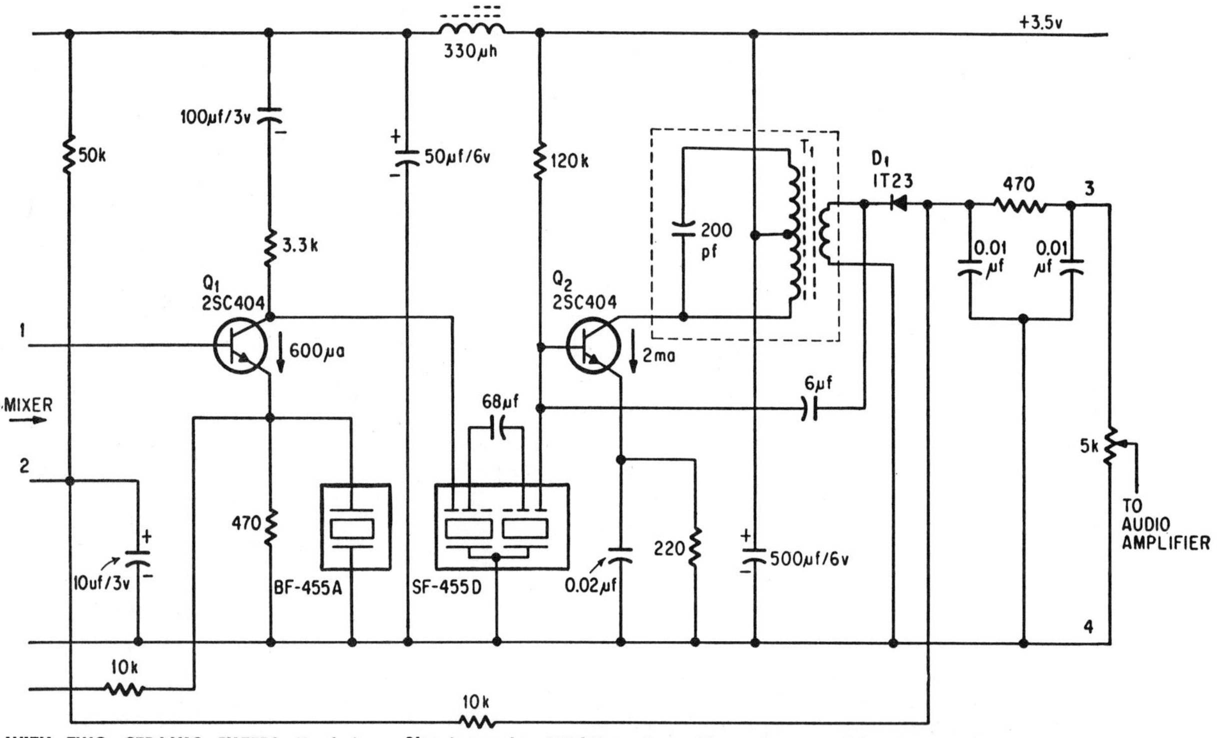

I-F WITH TWO CERAMIC FILTERS—Used in Sony model TR-1000 ten-transistor multiband portable radio to reduce number of components, simplify production and cut costs. First filter is tuned to 455 kHz and provides emitter-to-ground bypassing for first i-f transistor Q1. Other filter is double-tuned to 455 kHz, and provides interstage coupling.—Ceramic Filters Edge Out Costly I-F Transformers, *Electronics*, Nov. 14, 1966, p 160–163.

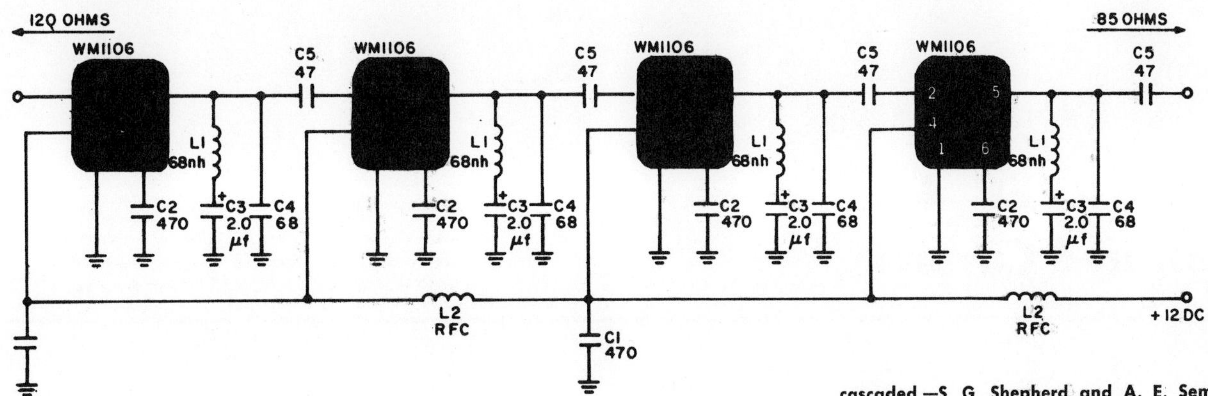

60-MHZ FOUR-IC WITH 43 DB GAIN—Bandwidth is 8.4 MHz and power gain 13.1 dB for four-stage amplifier. Article presents empirical approach, involving d-c measurements, for selecting external components that will not cause oscillation when four stages are cascaded.—S. G. Shepherd and A. E. Seman, Design with Integrated Circuits at 60 Mc, "Microelectronic Design," Hayden Book Co., N.Y., 1966, p 90–97.

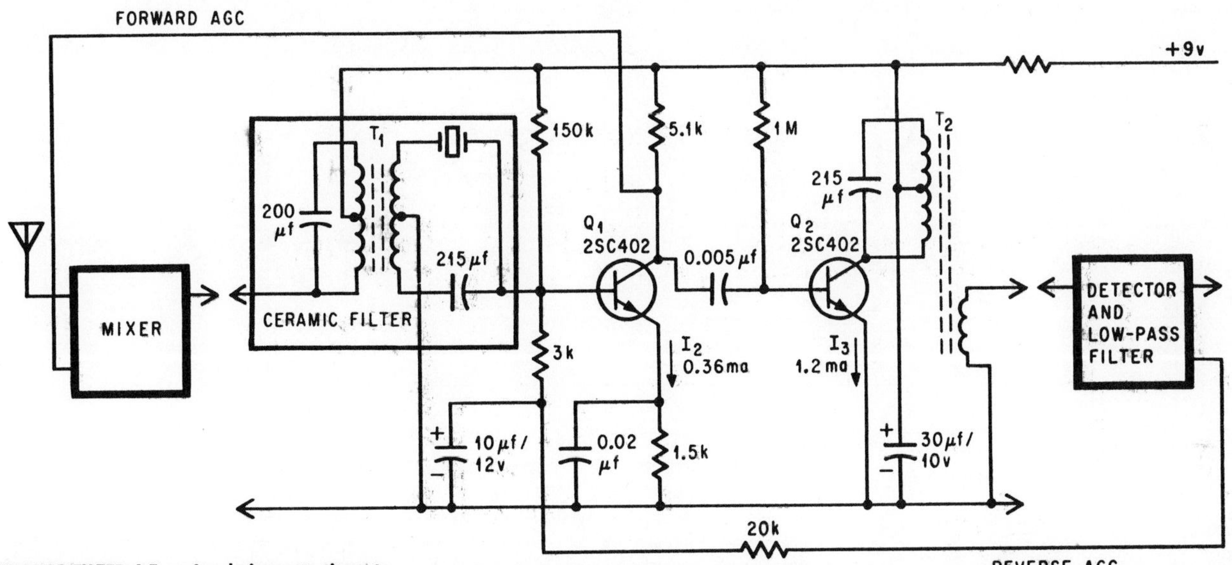

CERAMIC-FILTER I-F — Lead-zirconate-titanate piezoelectric ceramic filter in i-f stage of low-cost a-m portable radio provides selectivity comparable to that of three single-tuned transformer stages, eliminates need for alignment during production, and cuts number of components. Used in Sony model 2R-27 radio.—Ceramic Filters Edge Out Costly I-F Transformers, *Electronics*, Nov. 14, 1966, p 160–163.

NOTE: To locate additional circuits in the category of this chapter, use the index at the back of this book. Check also the author's "Sourcebook of Electronic Circuits," published by McGraw-Hill in 1968.

CHAPTER 40
Infrared Circuits

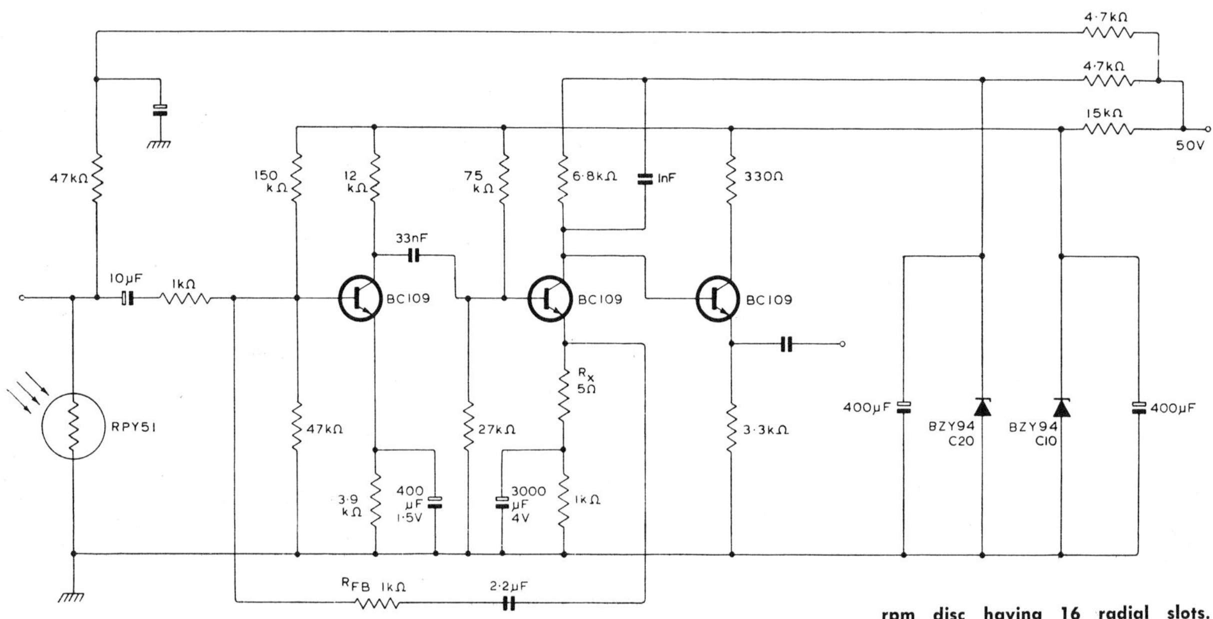

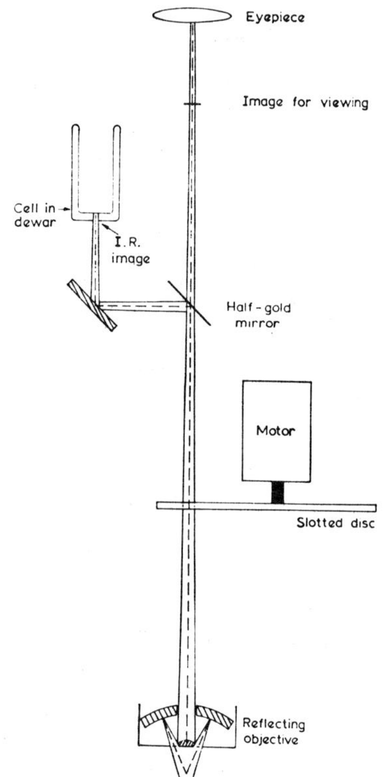

IC TEMPERATURE DISTRIBUTION—Infrared microscope uses Mullard RPY51 indium antimonide detector cooled by liquid nitrogen for measuring temperature of extremely small area, such as portion of integrated-circuit chip. Motor-driven chopper converts radiation from target to about 800 Hz with 3,000-rpm disc having 16 radial slots. Circuit features low noise and high gain stability. Article gives design equations and other circuits required for complete thermal microscope system.—T. J. Jarratt, Infrared Microscope for Temperature Measurement of Small Areas, *Mullard Technical Communications*, May 1968, p 101–107.

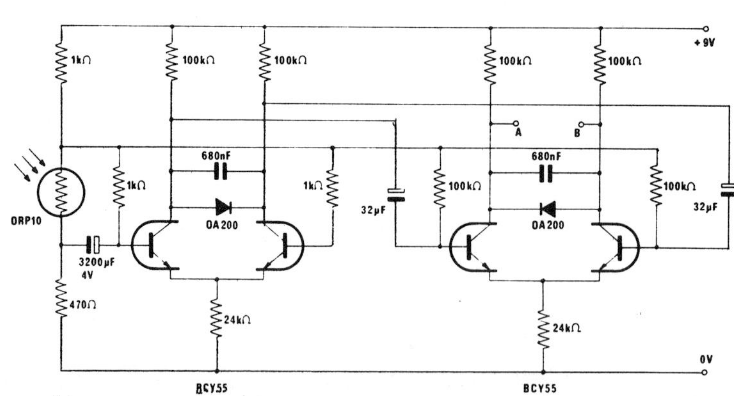

IR INTRUSION ALARM—Uses Mullard ORP10 uncooled indium antimonide photocell in unchopped system to detect objects with temperatures above 10 deg C moving across field of view against steady background at room temperature. Detector is a-c coupled to low-drift differential amplifier driving alarm circuit. Responds to minimum angular speed of about 1 milliradian per second by intruder.—R. A. Lockett, Passive Intruder Alarm Using Infrared Detector, *Mullard Technical Communications*, May 1968, p 88–90.

INTRUSION ALARM—When R2 is adjusted just below maximum ambient illumination, slight increase in light falling on photocell makes scr oscillate and produce loud clicking sounds in speaker. Frequency of clicks increases with illumination. Will respond to flashlight of intruder or to turning on of room lights in vacant office or home. Uses GE-X6 cadmium sulfide photoconductor. For infrared detection or fire alarm, use cadmium selenide cell.—"Hobby Manual," General Electric, Owensboro, Ky., 1965, p 124.

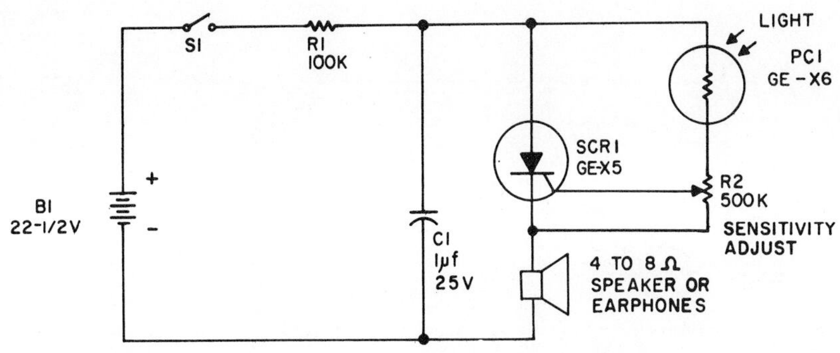

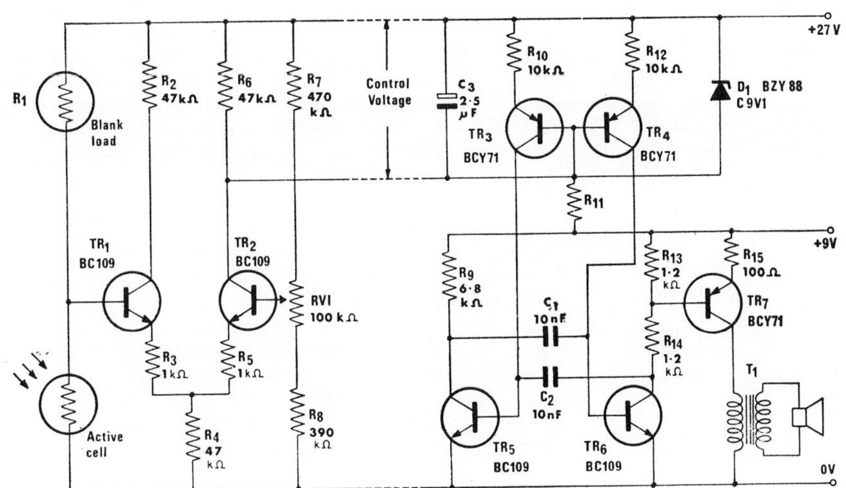

LOCATING FIRE IN SMOKE—Uses uncooled lead sulfide cell with lens to pick up source of fire or heat when visibility is completely obscured by smoke, dust, or fumes. Cell is Mullard developmental type 119CPY. Additional cell R1 is blacked out and serves as temperature-compensating load for active cell, which drives adjustable-gain preamp that controls base currents of square-wave relaxation oscillator TR5-TR6. Emitter-follower TR7 provides necessary current gain for driving speaker which gives low note of about 100 Hz for no fire and increasing pitch up to 10 kHz for increasing infrared radiation from fire. Unit is portable and battery-operated, to permit use by firemen in aiming hose.—P. R. D. Coleby, Simple Heat Locator Using Infrared Detector, *Mullard Technical Communications*, May 1968, p 86–88.

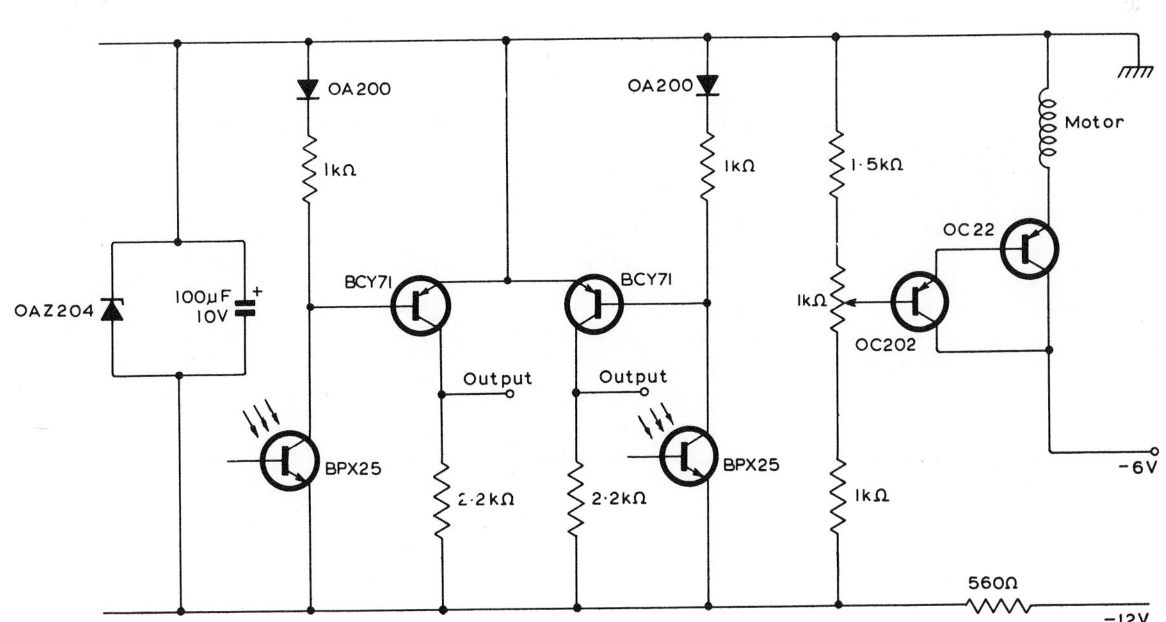

IR CAMERA PULSE AMPLIFIER—Uses pair of BPX25 silicon phototransistors receiving light pulses through rotating 30-hole Nipkow scanning disc on which infrared image is focused. One phototransistor receives sync pulses from uniformly spaced holes on disc, and other receives pulses from scanning spiral of holes. Resulting electrical pulses are squared, amplified, and applied to time bases of camera feeding standard oscilloscope. Motor drive circuit at right, for disc, applies constant voltage to motor, with 1K pot providing 10% range of speed control. Used for examining patients for cancerous growths, locating hot spots on circuit boards, and detecting flaws in glass furnace walls.—M. H. Jervis, Closed Circuit Infrared Television System, Mullard Ltd., London, TP950, 1967.

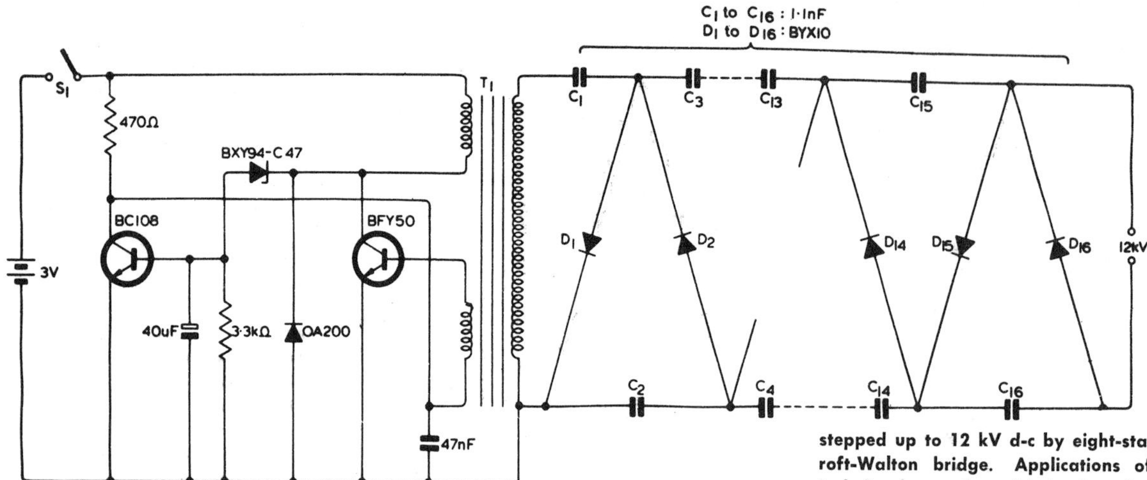

12 KV D-C—Used with Mullard 6929-1 image converter tube for converting near-infrared radiation to visible yellow-green emitted radiation. Uses simple blocking oscillator operating from 3-V battery to drive high-ratio transformer giving 1.5-kV pulses. These are stepped up to 12 kV d-c by eight-stage Cockroft-Walton bridge. Applications of system include observation of behavior of people in the dark, animals at night, scatter from laser beams, and hot-spots on defective high-voltage insulators.—Infrared Image Converter, Mullard Ltd., London, TP898, 1967.

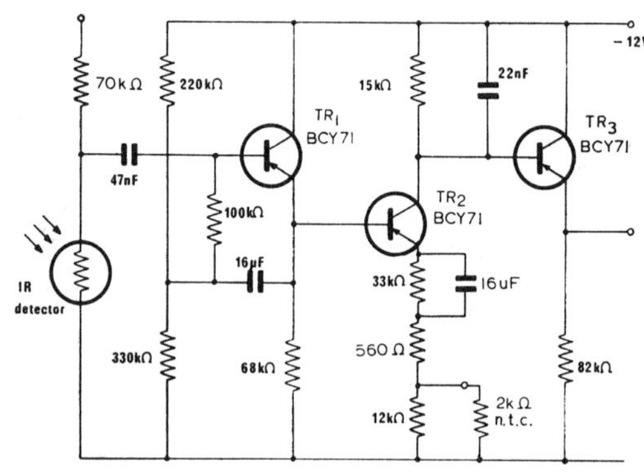

RADIATION THERMOMETER—Covers 100 to 500 C in five ranges, using linear amplification. Detector is Mullard 61SV lead sulfide cell having high infrared sensitivity at room temperature, for measuring radiant energy from surface of target. Energy from target is conducted to chopper wheel by light pipe, for a-c input to head amplifier that provides necessary transformation from high to low impedance and compensates for decrease in cell sensitivity with increasing ambient temperature.—P. R. D. Coleby, Radiation Thermometer for Temperatures Greater than 100 deg C, *Mullard Technical Communications*, May 1968, p 91–98.

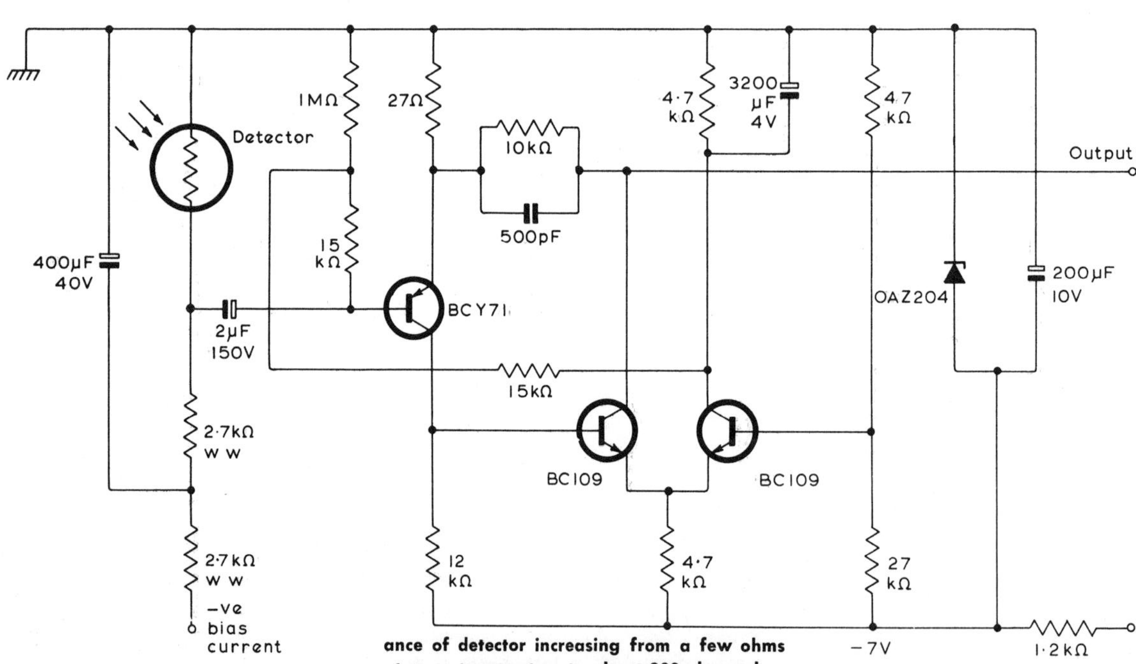

INDIUM ANTIMONIDE DETECTOR PREAMP—Will detect temperature changes from room temperature down to 77 deg K, with impedance of detector increasing from a few ohms at room temperature to about 200 ohms when back of detector is cooled by liquid nitrogen drip-feed system. Used in industrial and medical thermal scanning systems employing 30-hole Nipkow scanning disc.—M. H. Jervis, Closed Circuit Infrared Television System, Mullard Ltd., London, TP950, 1967.

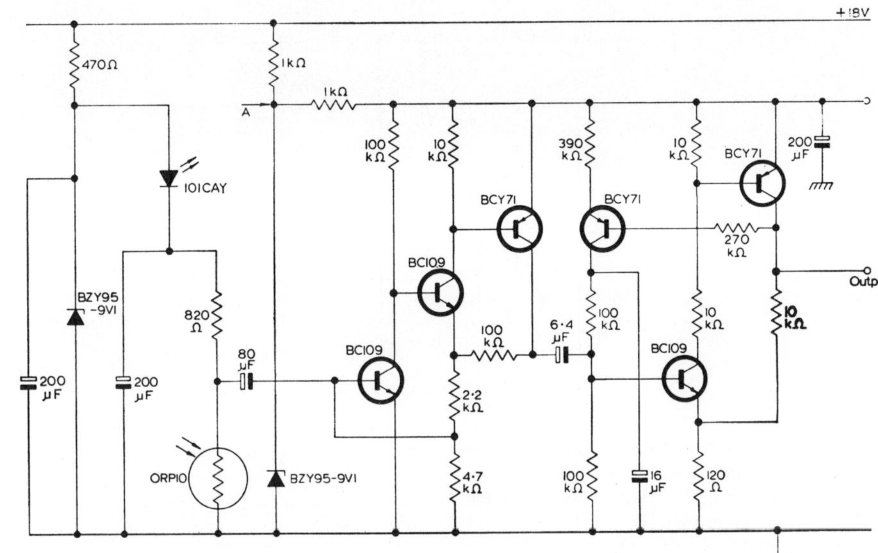

IR CLINICAL THERMOMETER—Covers range of 30 to 40 C, for measuring temperature of external auditory canal. Closely approximates oral measurements. Uses Mullard ORP10 uncooled indium antimonide cell for which radiation is interrupted at about 600 Hz by motor-driven chopper. Resulting a-c signal is amplified by flat-response wideband amplifier, mixed with signal corresponding to room temperature, then fed to phase-sensitive rectifier that derives its reference signal from interruption of secondary beam of radiation (between 101CAY emitter and BPX25 detector) by same chopper blade. Direct current from rectifier drives indicating meter. Article gives all circuits.—R. A. Lockett, Room Temperature Radiation Thermometer, *Mullard Technical Communications*, May 1968, p 98–101.

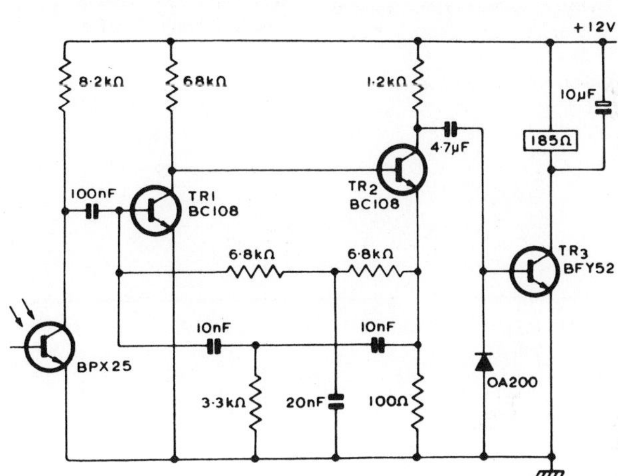

CODED-LIGHT DETECTOR—Tuned amplifier following phototransistor has twin-T network that greatly attenuates all signals more than 1 Hz off from 2.7 kHz. Only light within this narrow passband will turn on TR3 and energize load. One application is in photoelectric safety devices, where stray light might negate interruption of safety beam.—Applications of Silicon Planar Phototransistor BPX25, Philips, Pub. Dept., Elcoma Div., Eindhoven, The Netherlands, No. 316, 1967.

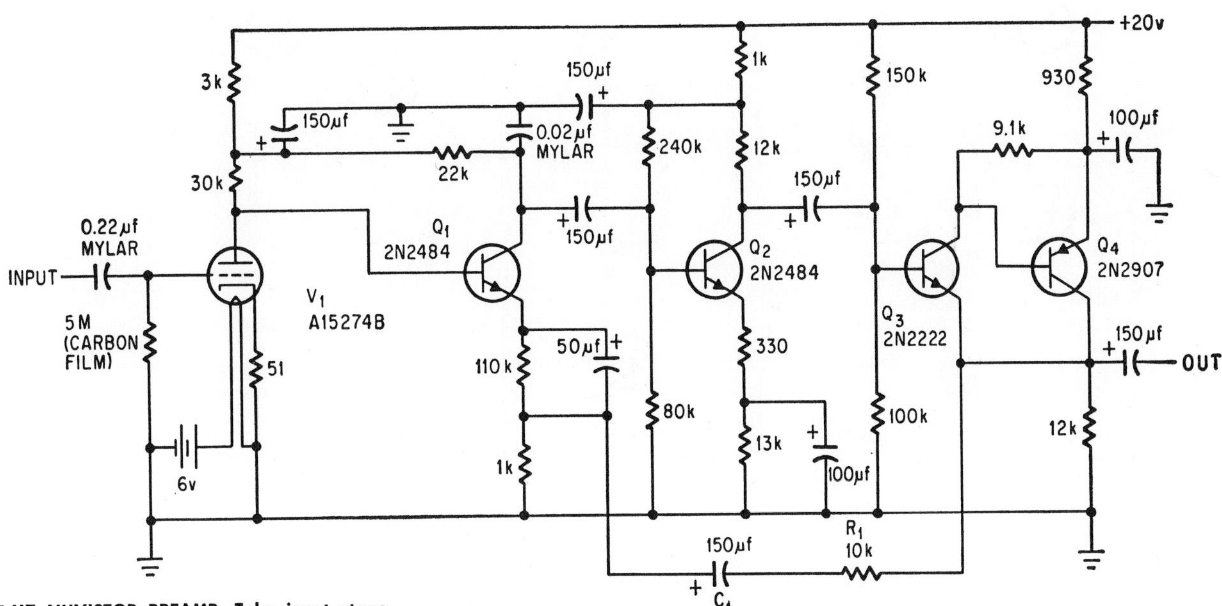

15-HZ NUVISTOR PREAMP—Tube input stage has much lower internal noise than bipolar transistor, and provides sufficient amplification to overcome noise of following transistor stages. Used in narrow-band signal processor for infrared radiometer. Gain overall is 40 dB, with less than 0.1 dB variation from −40 C to 60 C.—G. C. Kuipers, Front-End Nuvistor Lowers Transistor Amplifier Noise, *Electronics*, Oct. 31, 1966, p 71–72.

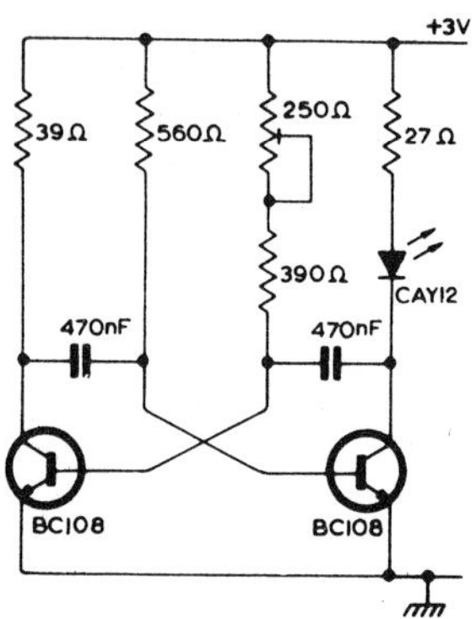

CODED INFRARED SOURCE—Used when unmodulated visible or infrared beam may be subject to interference from nearby stray light sources. Gallium arsenide light-emitting diode is energized by mvbr whose frequency is adjusted to match that of coded infrared source. Although mvbr modulator gives square-wave output, typically at 2.7 kHz, coded-beam detector responds to fundamental frequency.—Applications of Silicon Planar Phototransistor BPX25, Philips, Pub. Dept., Elcoma Div., Eindhoven, The Netherlands, No. 316, 1967.

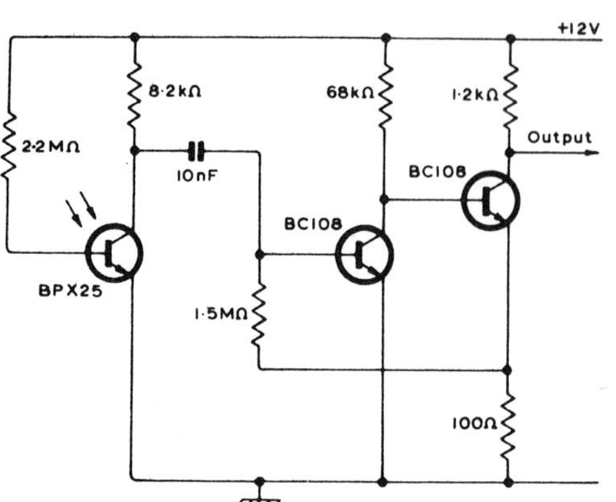

INFRARED DETECTOR—Uses BPX25 phototransistor which has good sensitivity to near infrared wavelengths. With two amplifier stages, peak input of 1 lux will produce peak output of 400 mV. Response at 4 kHz is 3 dB below that at 1 kHz. Provides compact communication system giving secrecy and freedom from interference at ranges up to 100 ft when using either f:2 collimating lenses or parabolical reflectors at light source and at phototransistor. For near infrared, ordinary glass lenses are satisfactory.—Applications of Silicon Planar Phototransistor BPX25, Philips, Pub. Dept., Elcoma Div., Eindhoven, Netherlands, No. 316, 1967.

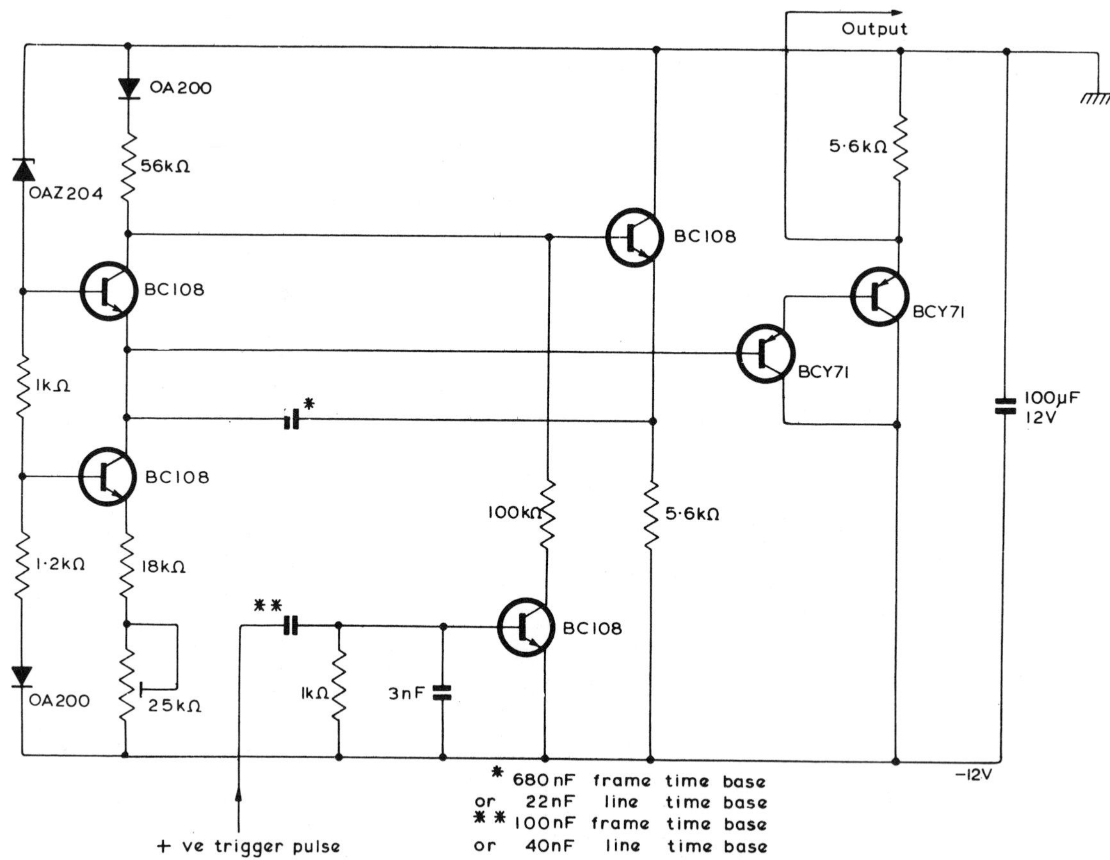

IR CAMERA TIME BASES—Circuits for X and Y inputs of display cro for infrared Nipkow-disc scanning camera are identical sawtooth generators except for timing capacitor changes indicated below diagram. Trigger pulses are obtained from pulse amplifier fed by phototransistor. Used in medical and industrial infrared applications.—M. H. Jervis, Closed Circuit Infrared Television System, Mullard Ltd., London, TP950, 1967.

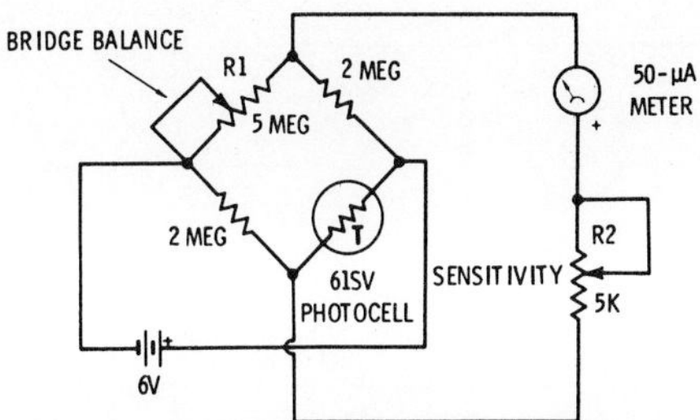

NONCONTACTING TEMPERATURE SENSOR—Simple resistance bridge having Amperex 61SV infrared photocell in one leg permits measuring temperature of furnace, flat iron, or other heated objects from distance of several feet. When bridge is balanced, meter will read upscale when cell resistance is decreased by exposure to infrared radiation. —J. P. Shields, "Novel Electronic Circuits," H. W. Sams & Co., Indianapolis, Ind., 1968, p 11.

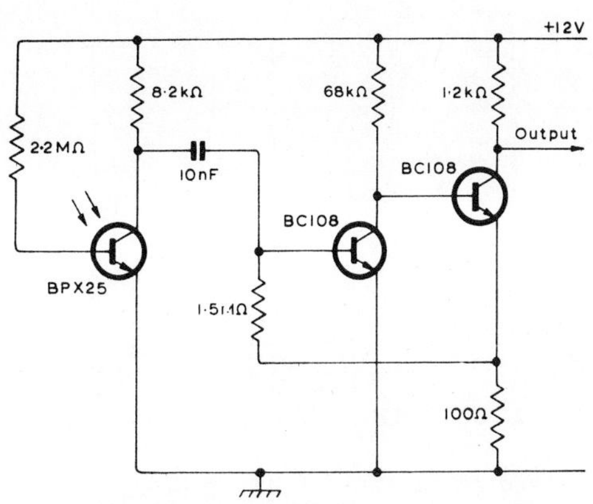

IR COMMUNICATION DETECTOR—Uses BPX25 phototransistor followed by two amplifying stages to pick up modulated infrared radiation in communication system. Range is over 100 ft when using modulated gallium arsenide diode as light source.—Silicon Planar Phototransistors, Mullard Ltd., London, TP1000, 1968.

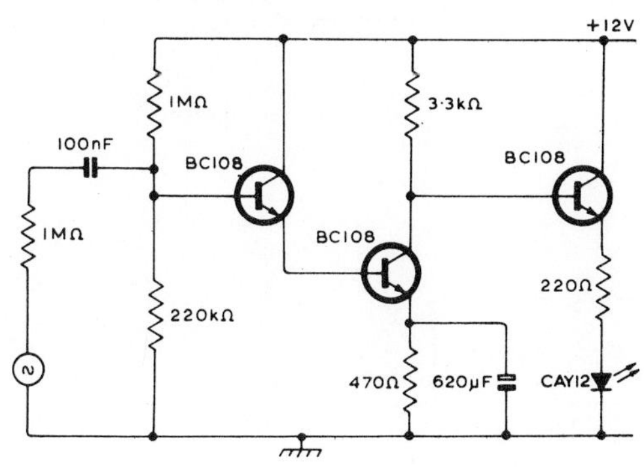

IR COMMUNICATION SOURCE—Gallium arsenide light-emitting diode is fed by microphone or other signal source driving three-stage amplifier. Response at 80 kHz is 3 dB below that at 1 kHz. Range is up to about 100 ft when using BPX25 phototransistor at receiving end.—Silicon Planar Phototransistors, Mullard Ltd., London, TP1000, 1968.

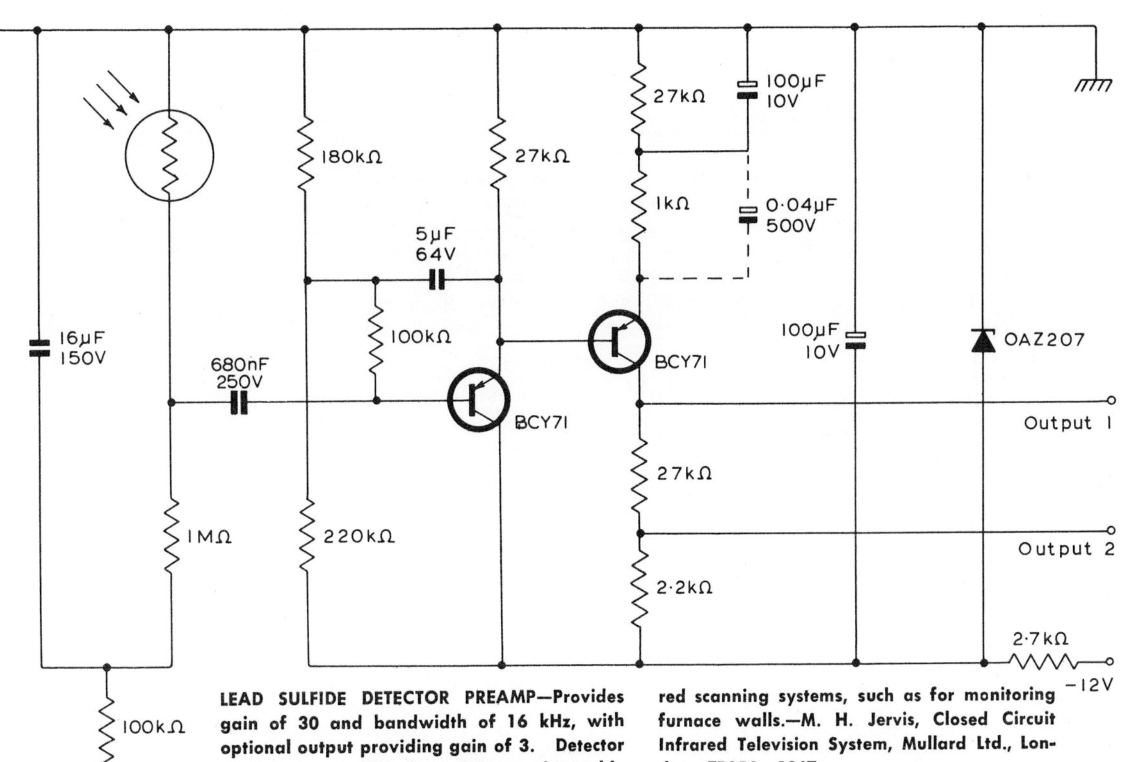

LEAD SULFIDE DETECTOR PREAMP—Provides gain of 30 and bandwidth of 16 kHz, with optional output providing gain of 3. Detector requires no cooling, but minimum detectable temperature is 120 C. Used in industrial infrared scanning systems, such as for monitoring furnace walls.—M. H. Jervis, Closed Circuit Infrared Television System, Mullard Ltd., London, TR950, 1967.

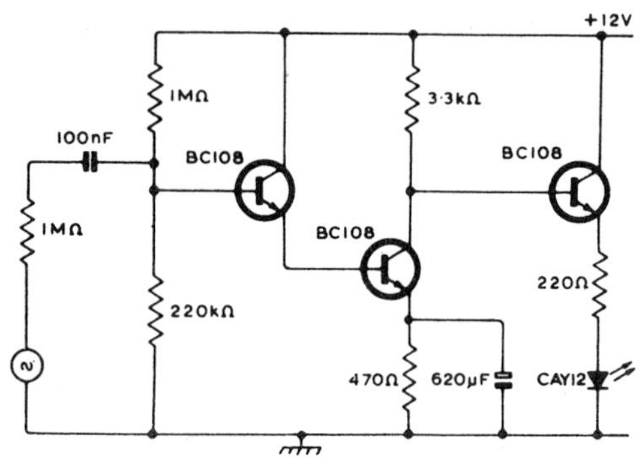

INFRARED MODULATOR—Serves as transmitter for short-range communication system using modulated infrared radiation. Light source at output of audio amplifier is CAY12 gallium arsenide diode. Can be used well above audio range, because response at 80 kHz is only 3 dB below that at 1 kHz. Peak diode current at 10 mA is obtained with input of 150 mV peak from microphone or other source.—Applications of Silicon Planar Phototransistor BPX25, Philips, Pub. Dept., Elcoma Div., Eindhoven, The Netherlands, No. 316, 1967.

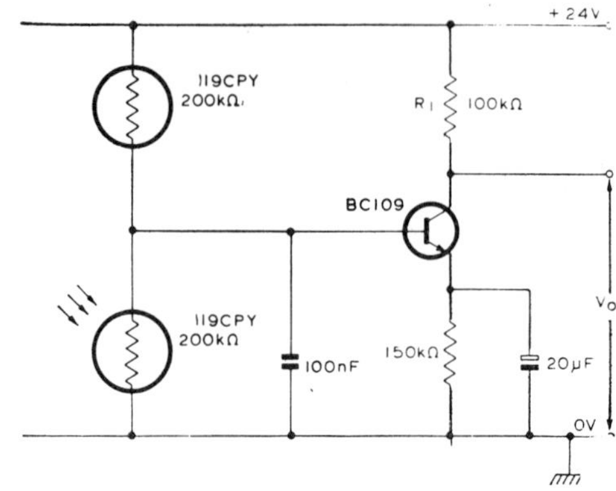

FIRE ALARM—Infrared flame detector produces voltage for actuating alarm as soon as flame occurs in field of view of Mullard 61SV lead sulfide detector which contains two 119CPY cells. Upper cell is covered, and serves to provide tracking with temperature changes. Circuit feeds bistable circuit (shown in article) that drives audible alarm such as Mallory Sonalert.—P. R. D. Coleby, Fire Alarm System Using Infrared Flame Detector, *Mullard Technical Communications,* May 1968, p 82–86.

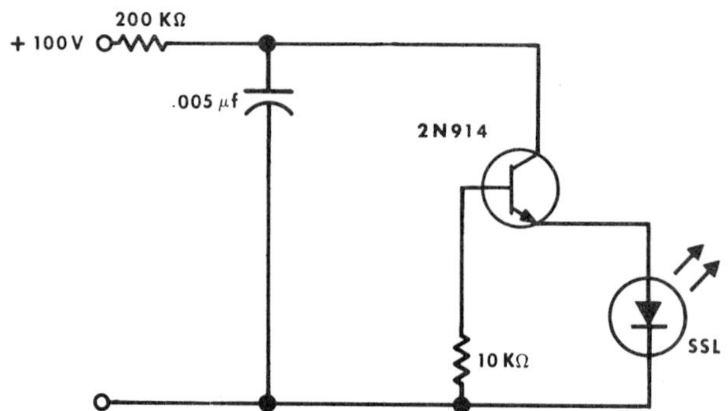

SSL OSCILLATOR—Gallium arsenide solid-state lamp in avalanche-transistor oscillator produces IR pulse durations in nanosecond range, with infrared power output of a few mW and pulse repetition rates of several kHz.—L. M. Hertz, Solid State Lamps—Part II, General Electric, Cleveland, Ohio, No. 3-0121, 1970, p 7.

NOTE: To locate additional circuits in the category of this chapter, use the index at the back of this book. Check also the author's "Sourcebook of Electronic Circuits," published by McGraw-Hill in 1968.

CHAPTER 41
Integrated Circuits

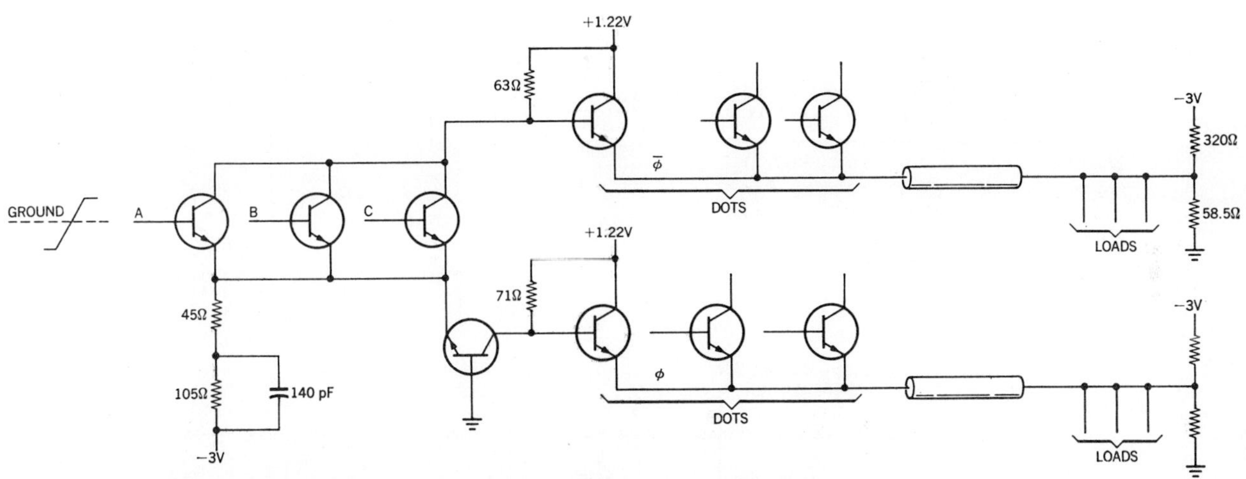

ASLT IC FOR IBM 360/91—Double-level logic block with high fan power, predictable delays, and 5-ns propagation time utilizes full switching-speed potential of high-performance 1-GHz transistors by incorporating phase-compensating network in emitter current source. Article covers design procedure for module.—R. F. Sechler, A. R. Strube, and J. R. Turnbull, ASLT Circuit Design, *IBM Journal*, Jan. 1967, p 74–85.

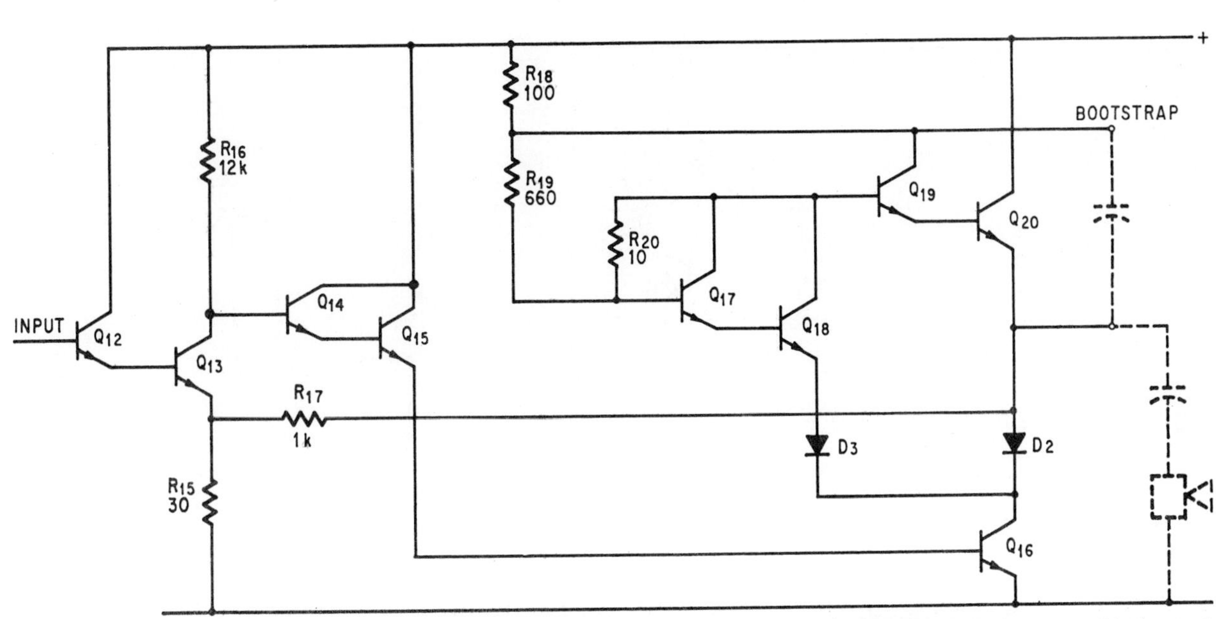

AUDIO AMPLIFIER—Circuit shown is portion of single 20-pin IC containing all circuits for 3-W British car radio except i-f filter and r-f tuner. Handles up to 1.5 A to produce 3-W output. Operation is similar to push-pull circuit but without phase splitter and output transformer. Uses large negative feedback for good linearity. Crossover distortion is negligible.—M. J. Gay, J. A. Skingley, and M. C. Sucker, Lots of Radio on Just One IC, *Electronics*, Aug. 5, 1968, p 124–129.

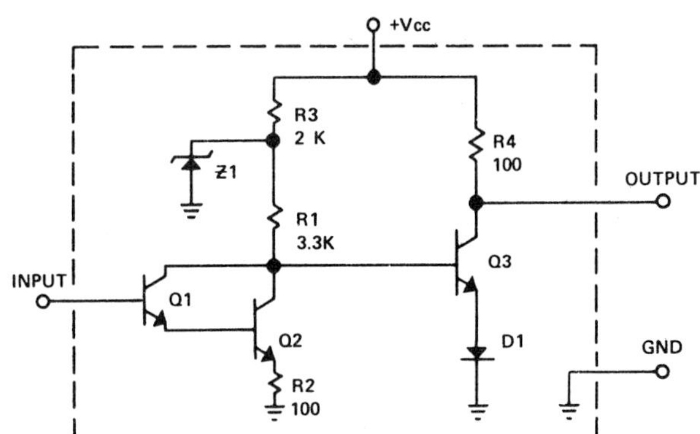

MIC0201 AUDIO DRIVER—Designed to drive single-ended pnp germanium power output transistors. Consists of Darlington input stage Q1-Q2 providing high input impedance with both voltage and current gain, feeding common-emitter amplifier Q3. Requires 12 V d-c supply.—M. L. Deschler, Integrated Circuit Audio Driver Amplifier, Mallory, Indianapolis, Ind., APPN-1, 1968.

MC1539 OPAMP—Motorola IC features open-loop gain of 120,000, high slew rate of 34 V per μs, input diode limiting for overvoltage protection, and output current-limiting protection.—K. Huehne, The Continuing Dominance of the Operational Amplifier, "State-of-the-Art—Linears in Action," Motorola, Phoenix, Ariz., 1969, p 5—13.

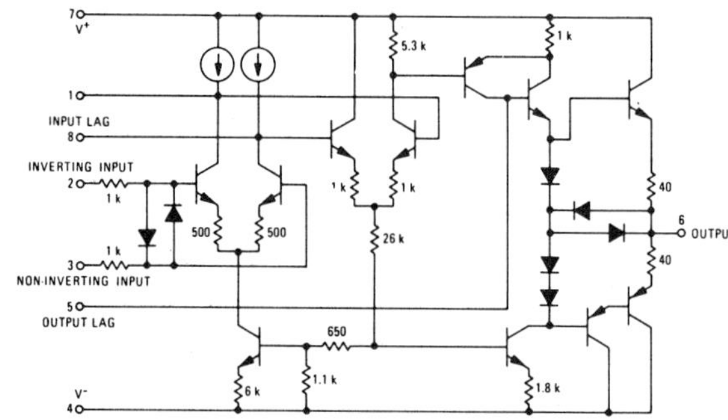

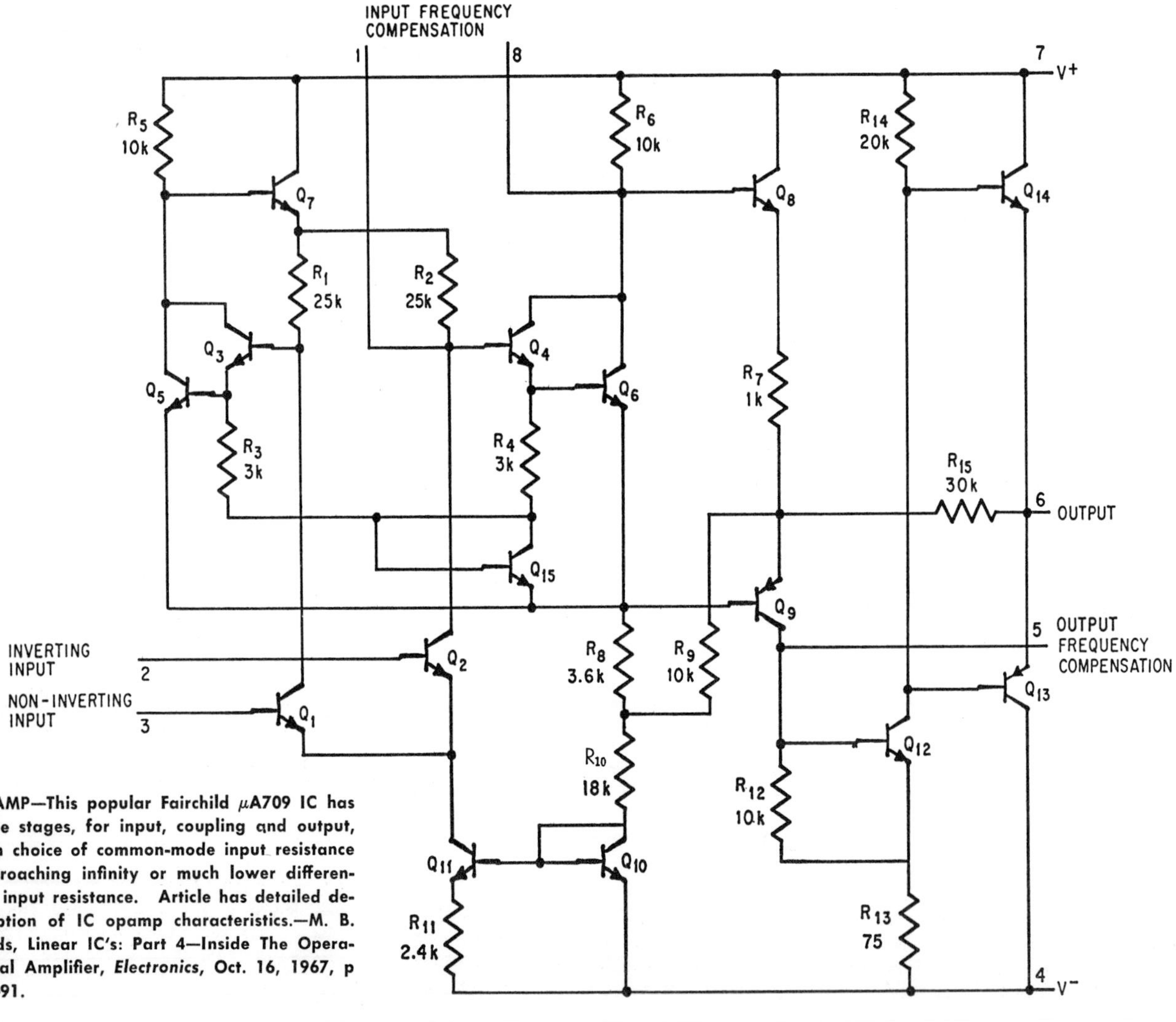

OPAMP—This popular Fairchild μA709 IC has three stages, for input, coupling and output, with choice of common-mode input resistance approaching infinity or much lower differential input resistance. Article has detailed description of IC opamp characteristics.—M. B. Leeds, Linear IC's: Part 4—Inside The Operational Amplifier, *Electronics*, Oct. 16, 1967, p 86–91.

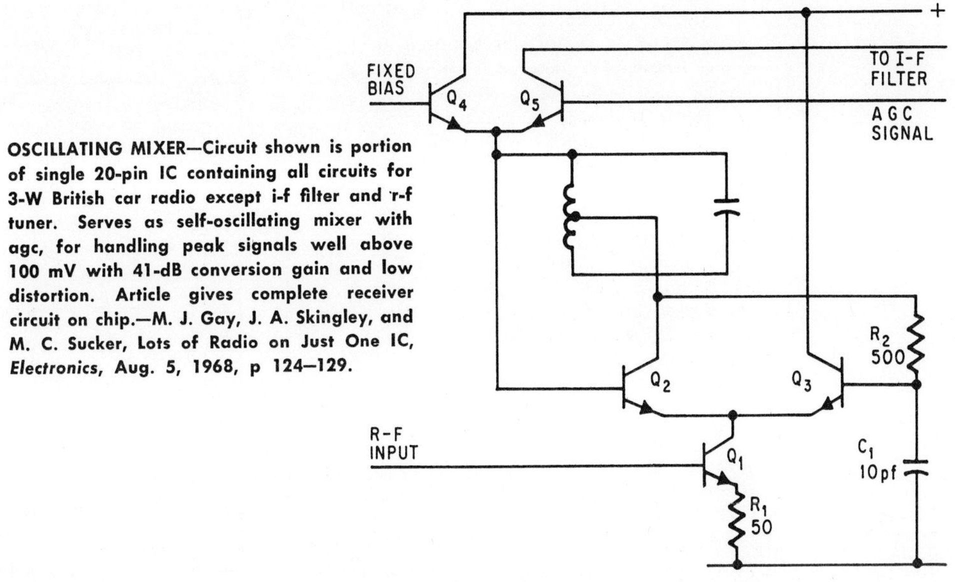

OSCILLATING MIXER—Circuit shown is portion of single 20-pin IC containing all circuits for 3-W British car radio except i-f filter and r-f tuner. Serves as self-oscillating mixer with agc, for handling peak signals well above 100 mV with 41-dB conversion gain and low distortion. Article gives complete receiver circuit on chip.—M. J. Gay, J. A. Skingley, and M. C. Sucker, Lots of Radio on Just One IC, *Electronics*, Aug. 5, 1968, p 124–129.

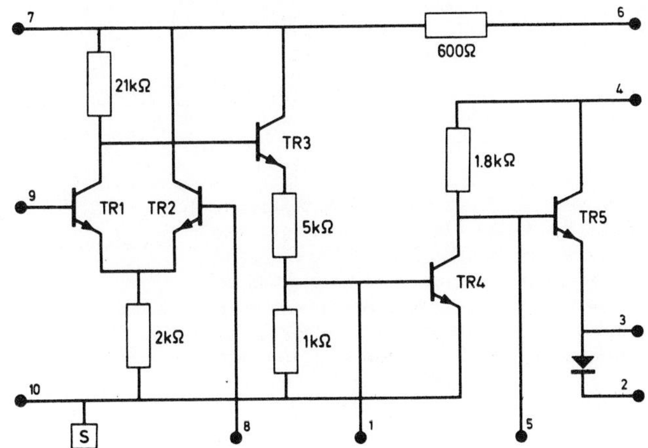

TAA435 A-F DRIVER—Philips TAA435 IC audio amplifier is intended for driving complementary output stages in medium-power audio amplifiers. TR1 and TR2 form differential amplifier permitting both a-c and d-c feedback to be applied. Input impedance is above 70K. Supply voltage can be 10 to 18 V.—Complementary Output Stages Driven by the TAA435, Philips, Pub. Dept., Elcoma Div., Eindhoven, The Netherlands, No. 18, 1968.

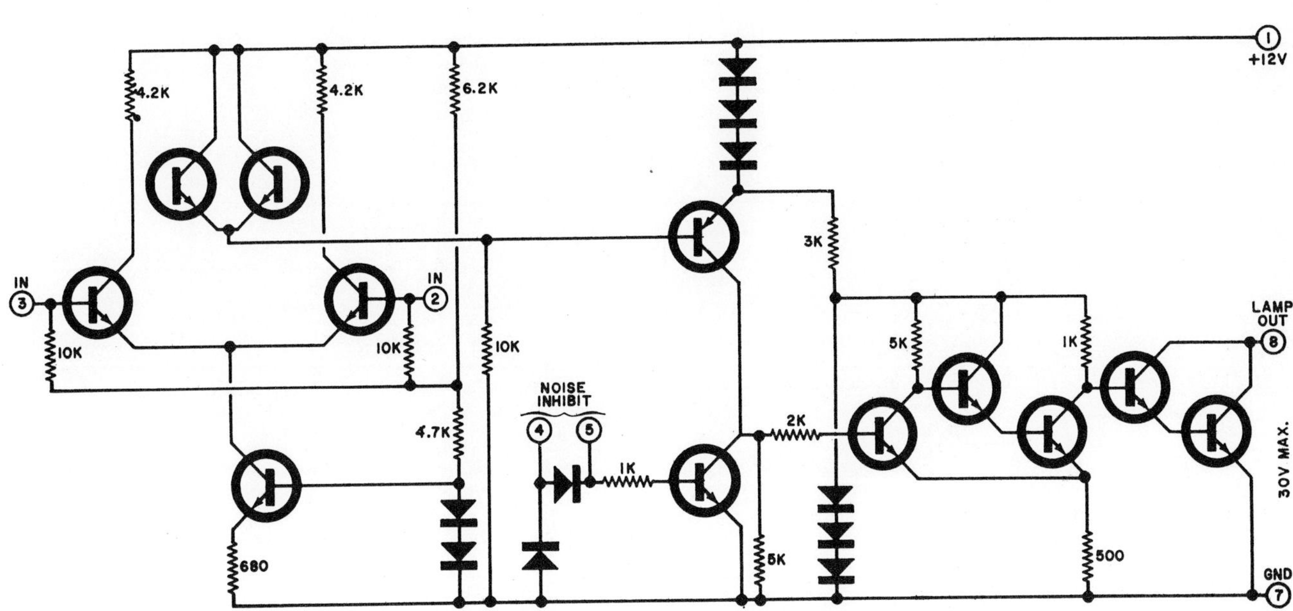

PERFECT TUNE LAMP DRIVE—Single IC chip serves as computer-type comparator circuit that turns on "Perfect Tune" lamp when set is tuned to exact center point for f-m station. Interstation noise is filtered, amplified, and rectified to turn off light between stations. IC-304 chip was made by Motorola for H. H. Scott hi-fi f-m receiver.—L. W. Fish, Jr. and K. J. Peter, New Concepts in Hi-Fi Receiver Design, *Electronics World*, Feb. 1969, p 32–34 and 69–70.

THERMAL STABILITY IN IC PREAMP—Used to determine frequency response of experimental IC preamp near lower limiting frequency of 4 Hz. Effects of thermal feedback were excluded as far as possible by making measurements with load resistance RL of output transistor increased to 10K so collector dissipation here is negligible. Article deals with methods of improving thermal stability.—H. Schmidt, Thermal Feedback in Integrated Circuits, *Electronic Applications*, Philips, Pub. Dept., Elcoma Div., Eindhoven, The Netherlands, Vol. 28, No. 1, 1968, p 29–39.

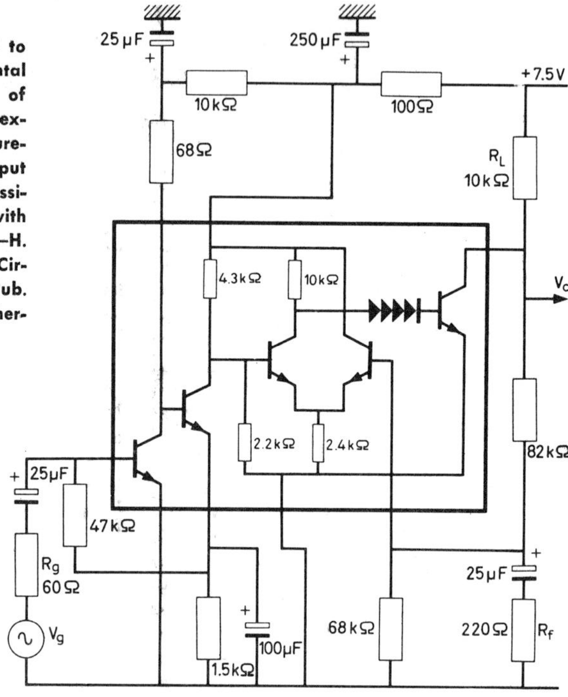

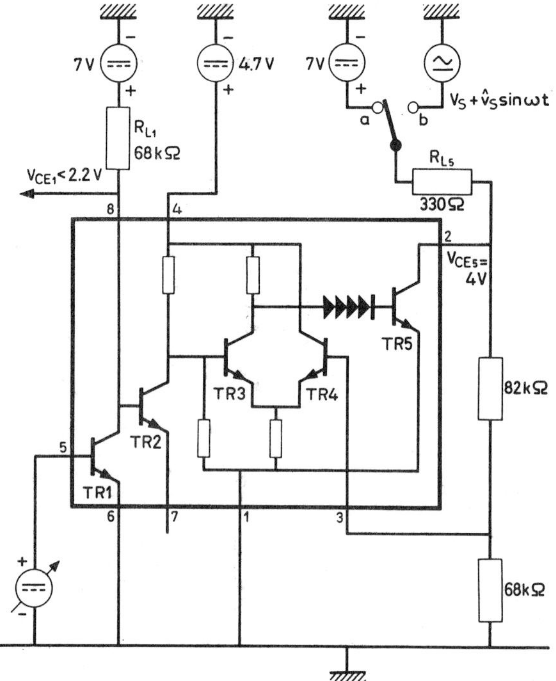

THERMAL FEEDBACK IN IC PREAMP—Experimental multistage IC preamplifier was developed to investigate transmission properties of heat path from output transistor TR5 to input transistor TR1. With switch in position a, TR5 has constant collector dissipation, for investigating thermal switching-on transient. With switch in position b, sinusoidal heat wave is generated in TR5 at frequencies ranging from 3 to 400 Hz, and propagation and phase shift of wave are analyzed. Article presents methods of improving thermal stability in integrated circuits.—H. Schmidt, Thermal Feedback in Integrated Circuits, *Electronic Applications*, Philips, Pub. Dept., Elcoma Div., Eindhoven, The Netherlands, Vol. 28, No. 1, 1968, p 29–39.

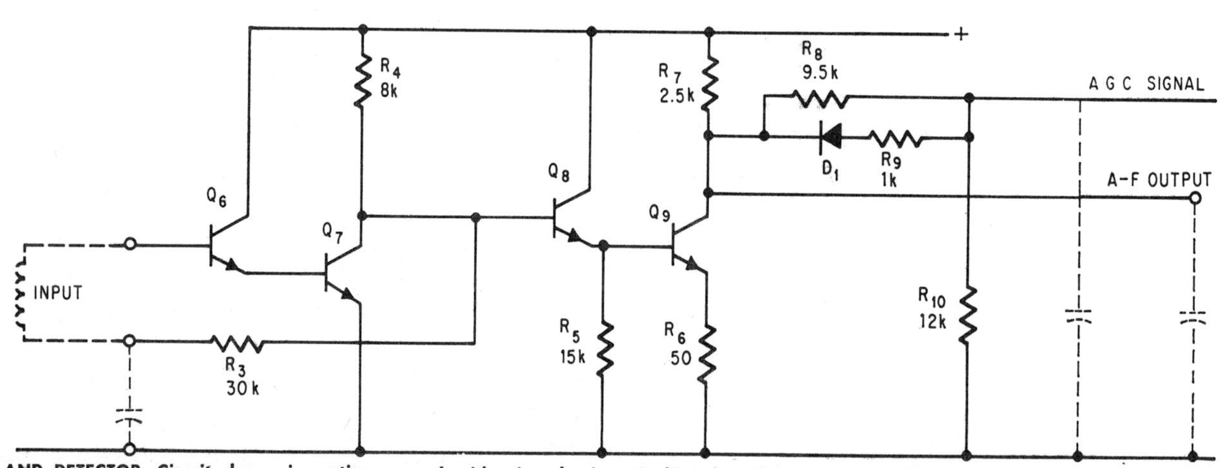

I-F AND DETECTOR—Circuit shown is portion of single 20-pin IC containing all circuits for 3-W British car radio except i-f filter and r-f tuner. Provides only 40 dB gain because used with mixer having 40 dB gain. Detector is directly coupled to final i-f. Input from mixer is about 200 mV rms. Article gives complete receiver circuit on chip.—M. J. Gay, J. A. Skingley, and M. C. Sucker, Lots of Radio on Just One IC, *Electronics*, Aug. 5, 1968, p 124–129.

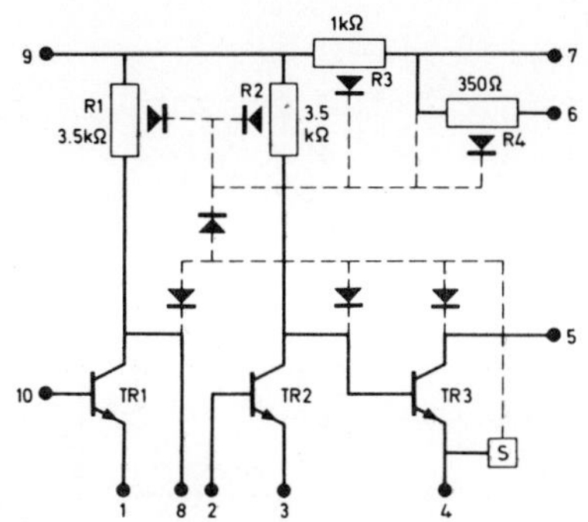

TAA293 AMPLIFIER—Contains three transistors and four resistors, which can be connected to minimum of external components for use as voltage-operated or current-operated Schmitt trigger, astable mvbr, or mono mvbr.—The TAA293 as a Schmitt Trigger and Multivibrator, Philips, Pub. Dept., Elcoma Div., Eindhoven, The Netherlands, No. 25, 1968.

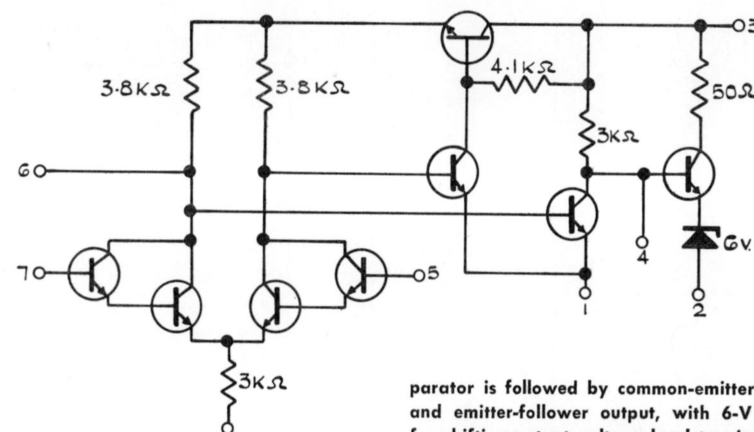

SL701 D-C AMPLIFIER—Uses precision comparator front end with Darlington compound pairs in long-tailed pair configuration. Comparator is followed by common-emitter stage and emitter-follower output, with 6-V zener for shifting output voltage level to give symmetrical swing about ground with bipolar 12-V supply.—R. C. Foss and B. J. Green, The SL700 Series and Applications, Plessey, Swindon, England, No. 7.

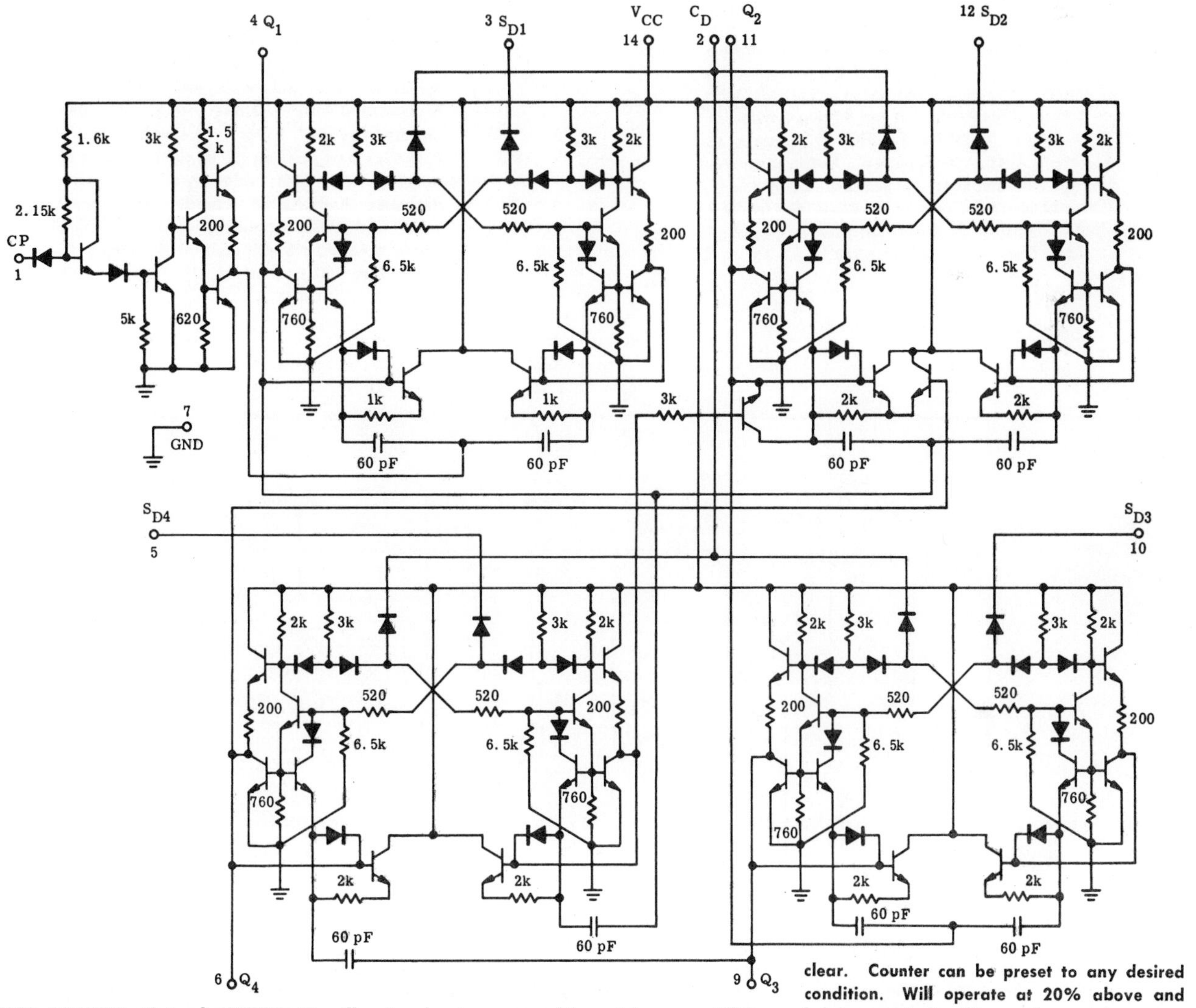

DECADE COUNTER—Motorola MC938F IC will operate at counting frequencies up to 20 MHz. Uses active pull-up devices in outputs to increase capacitive drive capabilities. Outputs correspond to standard 8-4-2-1 bcd, with individual direct sets and common direct clear. Counter can be preset to any desired condition. Will operate at 20% above and below nominal 5-V supply requirement.—MDTL Decade Counter, Motorola, Phoenix, Ariz., PS65, 1967.

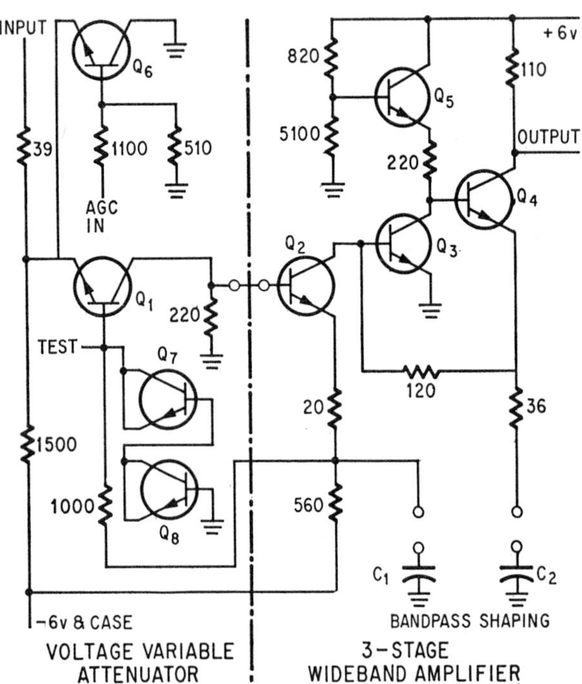

PHILCO-FORD PA7601—Uses voltage-variable attenuator for gain control to preserve frequency response, and input transistor with emitter degeneration in amplifying portion of IC to give broad bandwidth. Bandpass is 45 to 130 MHz at 3-dB points. Article gives 70-MHz i-f amplifier application.—D. W. Ford, M. M. Gutman, and W. F. Allen, Jr., It's Not How Much an IC Costs—But How Much It Can Save, *Electronics*, Oct. 30, 1967, p 66–68.

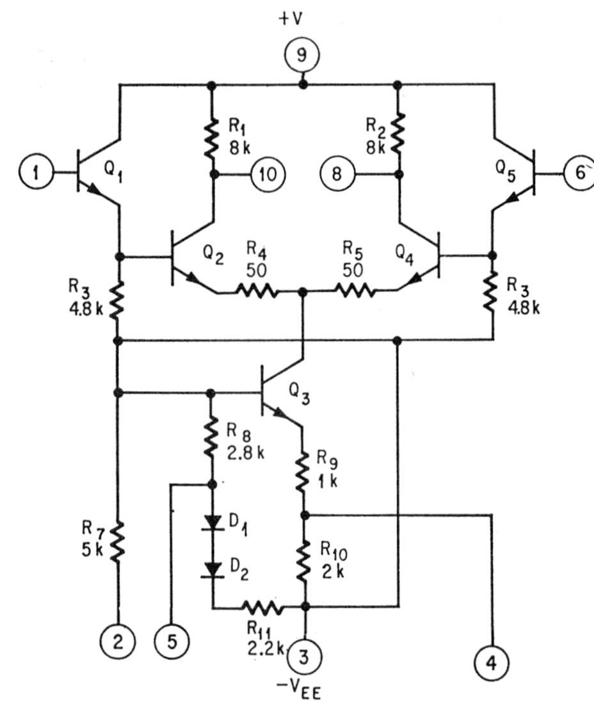

RCA CA3000 VIDEO AMP—Video-type differential amplifier has flat gain-versus-frequency response from d-c well into vhf region (around 300 MHz). Offers both single-ended or double-ended output. Presence of diffused resistors R1 and R2 in collector legs of amplifier identifies video-type IC. Article describes methods of adapting to narrow band and other applications.—J. P. Keller, Linear IC's: Part 3—Differential Amplifiers At Work, *Electronics*, Sept. 18, 1967, p 96–104.

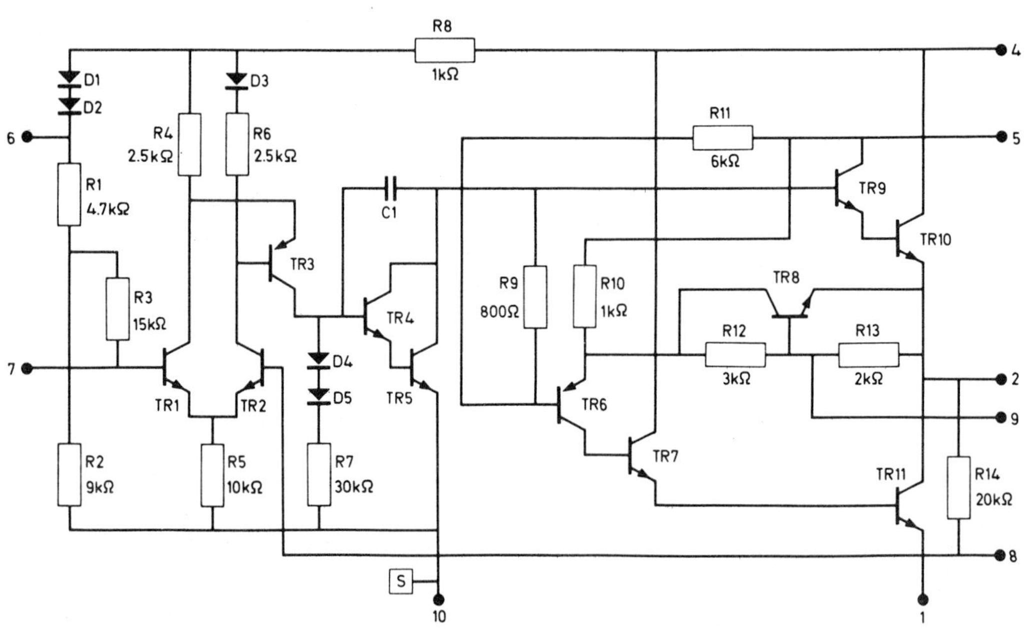

TAA300 AUDIO AMPLIFIER—Delivers 1 W audio power to 8-ohm load when operating from 9-V battery, at 10% distortion. Consists of differential-amplifier input stage TR1-TR2 having 15,000 ohms input impedance, driver stage with TR3 providing d-c coupling to TR4 and TR5 in cascade, and direct-coupled single-ended push-pull output stage using remaining transistors.—A. M. Peters, TAA300 Integrated 1 W Class B A. F. Amplifier, Philips, Pub. Dept., Elcoma Div., Eindhoven, The Netherlands, No. 136, 1969.

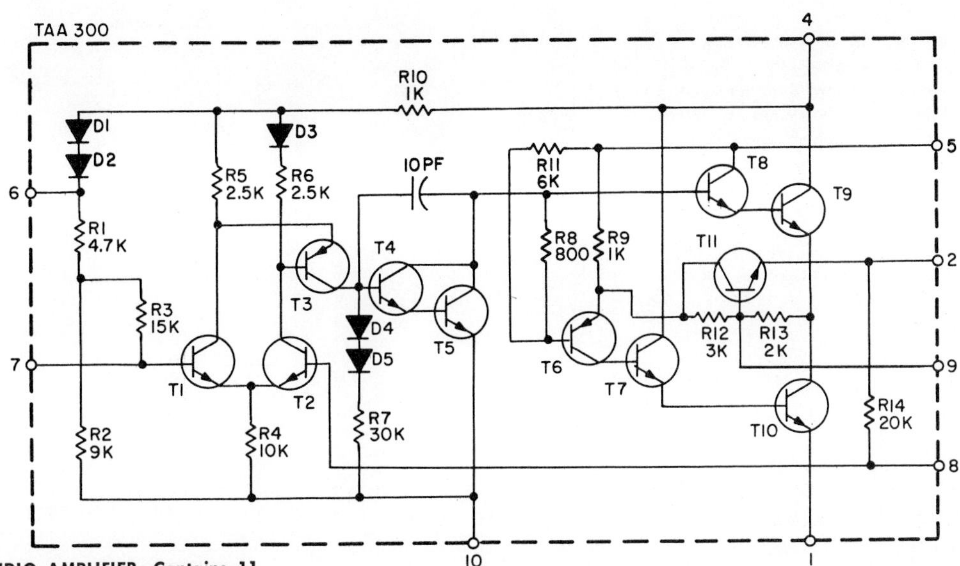

TAA300 1-W AUDIO AMPLIFIER—Contains 11 transistors and 5 diodes mounted on 2-mm silicon chip with 14 resistors and 1 capacitor. —The Amperex TAA 300 Monolithic Integrated Circuits Used as a Complete Audio Amplifier, Amperex, Slatersville, R.I., S-138, 1968.

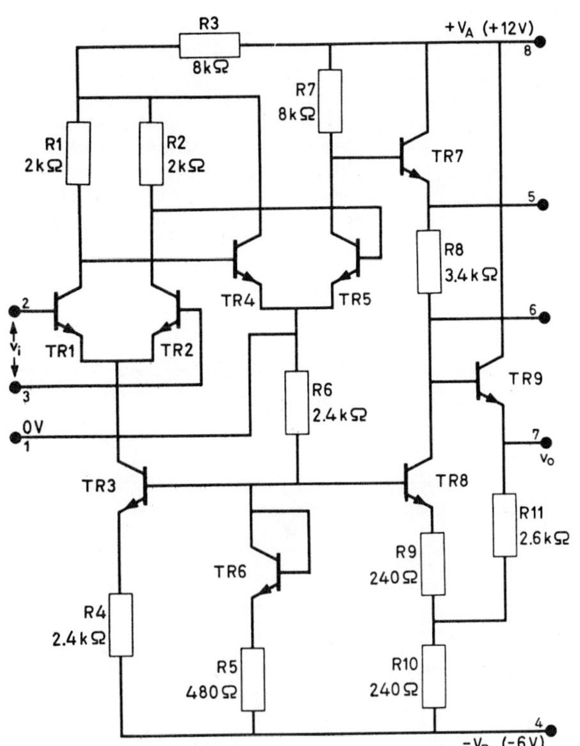

TAA241 DIFFERENCE AMPLIFIER—Input stage TR1-TR2 is difference amplifier, with TR3 in common emitter branch to insure high common-mode rejection ratio. TR7, TR8, and TR9 together form output stage, giving zero output when there is no input signal. Output impedance is about 200 ohms. Open-loop voltage gain can be as high as 6,000. —J. Cohen and J. Oosterling, Applications of a Practical D. C. Difference Amplifier, Philips, Pub. Dept., Elcoma Div., Eindhoven, The Netherlands, No. 321, 1968.

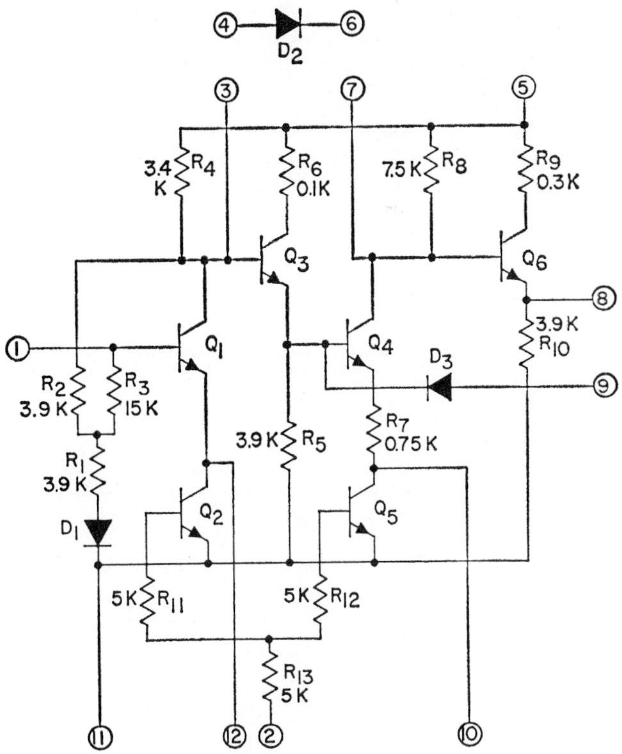

WIDEBAND AMPLIFIER—Circuit shown is that of RCA CA3023 IC, specifically designed as multistage i-f amplifier providing up to 60 dB of gain up to 10 MHz. Emitter-follower Q3 provides impedance matching and level shifting between voltage amplifiers Q1 and Q4. Emitter-follower Q6 provides low-impedance output, while Q2 and Q5 provide agc.—H. M. Kleinman, IC R.F. and I.F. Amplifiers, *Electronics World*, July 1968, p 45–48.

LM108 SUPER-BETA OPAMP—Design goals for National Semiconductor IC included lowest possible input currents and minimum power consumption. Output swings to within 1 V of supply voltages which may be as low as 2 V. Requires external compensation.—Op-Amp ICs With Super-Gain Transistors, *EEE*, Nov. 1969, p 16, 19–20, 22, and 24.

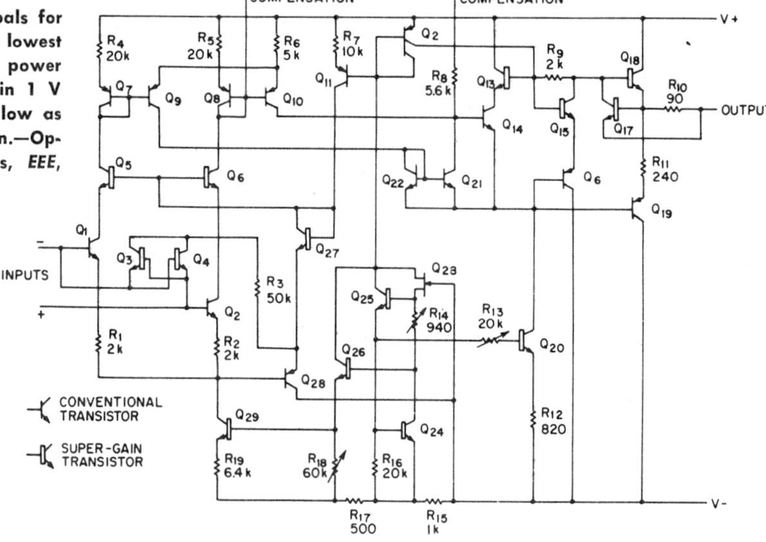

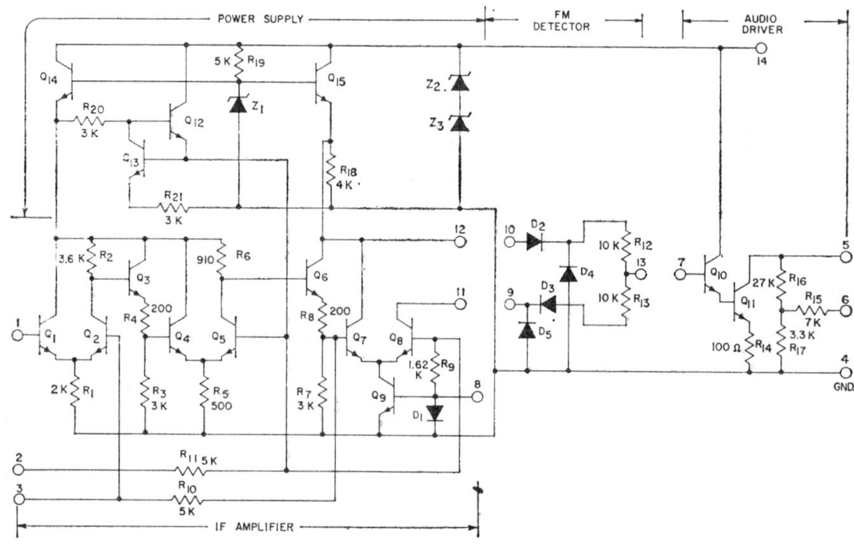

TV SOUND I-F—RCA CA3041 integrated circuit provides 70 dB gain as i-f amplifier-limiter, matched diodes for f-m detector, and audio driver, yet is priced under $2 in quantities of 11 or more.—H. M. Kleinman, IC R. F. and I.F. Amplifiers, *Electronics World*, July 1968, p 45–48.

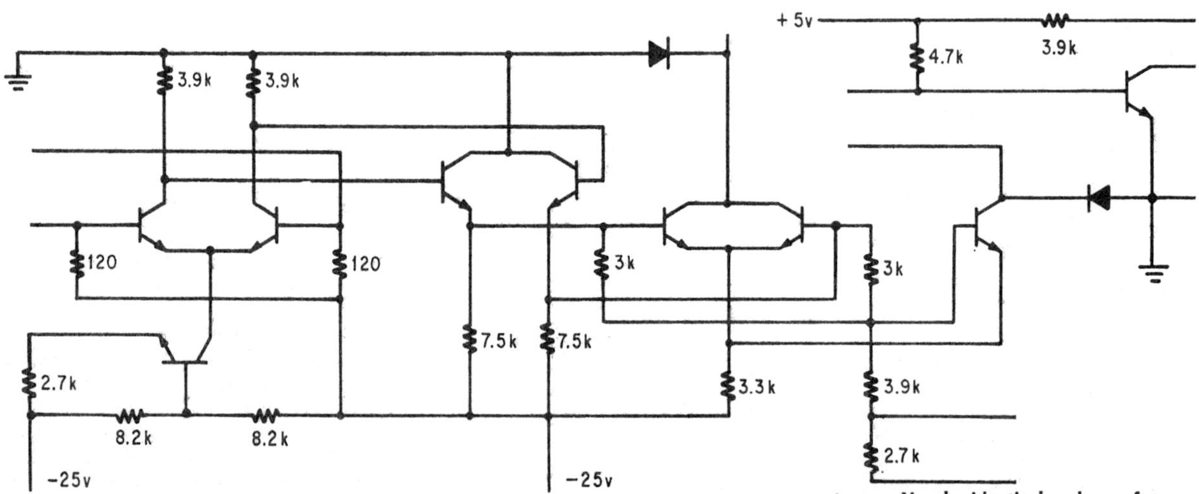

COMPUTER SENSE AMPLIFIER—Includes balanced differential amplifier fed by active constant-current source, pair of emitter-followers, common-emitter pair, three-resistor network, and output amplifier stage, as used in Sylvania MSP-24 IC. Author presents this as example of good IC design, that meets specs and has no unusual problems for manufacturer. Nearly identical values of two components are easier to produce than specified absolute values.—H. I. Cohen, Avoiding IC System Design Pitfalls, *Electronics*, Aug. 5, 1968, p 110–116.

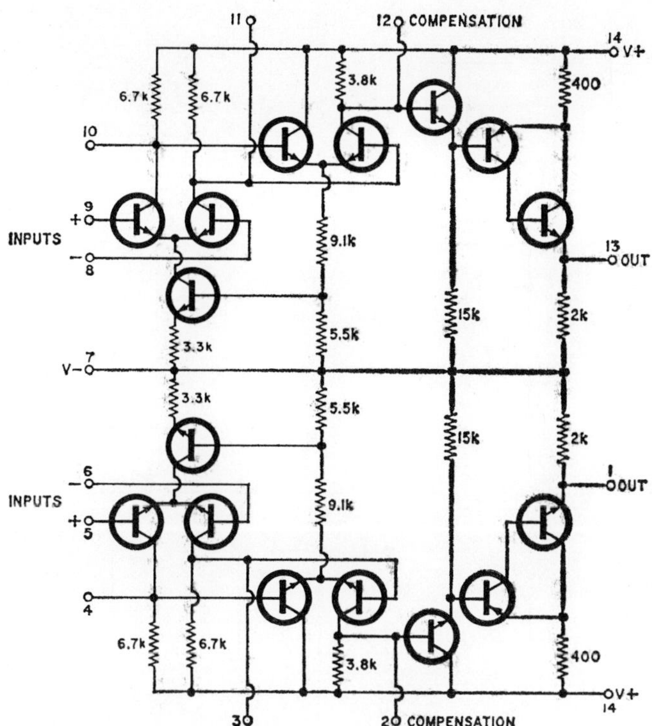

DUAL OPAMP—Used as equalized preamp section of H. H. Scott Series 2500 a-m/f-m compact stereo system. Input transistors for the two channels are connected as emitter-coupled differential amplifiers.—D. R. von Recklinghausen, IC Op-Amp Hi-Fi Preamplifier, *Electronics World*, June 1968, p 44–45.

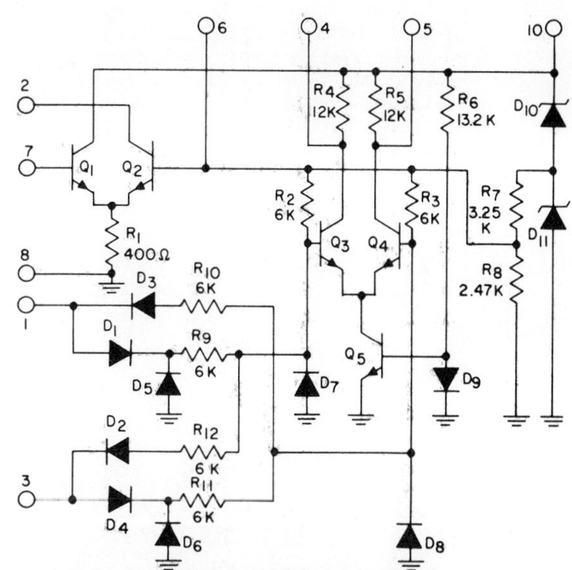

DIODES D5 AND D6 ACT AS CAPACITORS AND ARE USED TO BALANCE THE DETECTOR SUBSTRATE CAPACITANCES.

COLOR AFT—Special-function IC was developed for automatic frequency control applications in color tv. Includes zener-regulated power supply that improves performance and reduces system cost. Consists of 45-MHz limiter-amplifier Q1-Q2, four-diode matrix D1-D4 forming balanced detector that converts output of phase transformer to filtered d-c signal, constant-current driven differential amplifier Q3-Q4-Q5 providing sufficient sensitivity and power to permit use of low-cost tuning element, and zener regulator D10-D11 operating from d-c supply of 15 to 30 V.—W. M. Austin, H. M. Kleinman, and J. Sundburg, Application of the RCA-CA3044 and CA3044V1 Integrated Circuits in Automatic-Fine-Tuning Systems, RCA, Harrison, N.J., ICAN-5831, 1968.

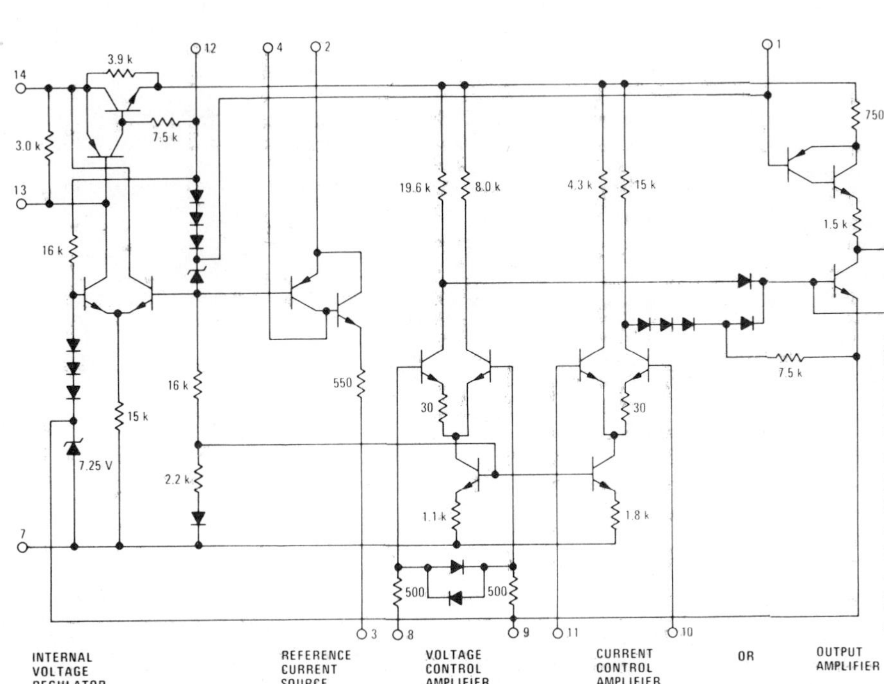

MC1566 VOLTAGE REGULATOR—Motorola IC is designed to float on output voltage, so total output voltage is limited only by external series-pass transistor voltage breakdown and safe operating area. Control amplifier samples output voltage directly. Separate differential amplifier samples output current and produces limiting so sharp that it is constant within 1% plus or minus 1 mA. —D. Kesner, Voltage Regulators—Old and New, "State-of-the-Art—Linears in Action," Motorola, Phoenix, Ariz., 1969, p 14–20.

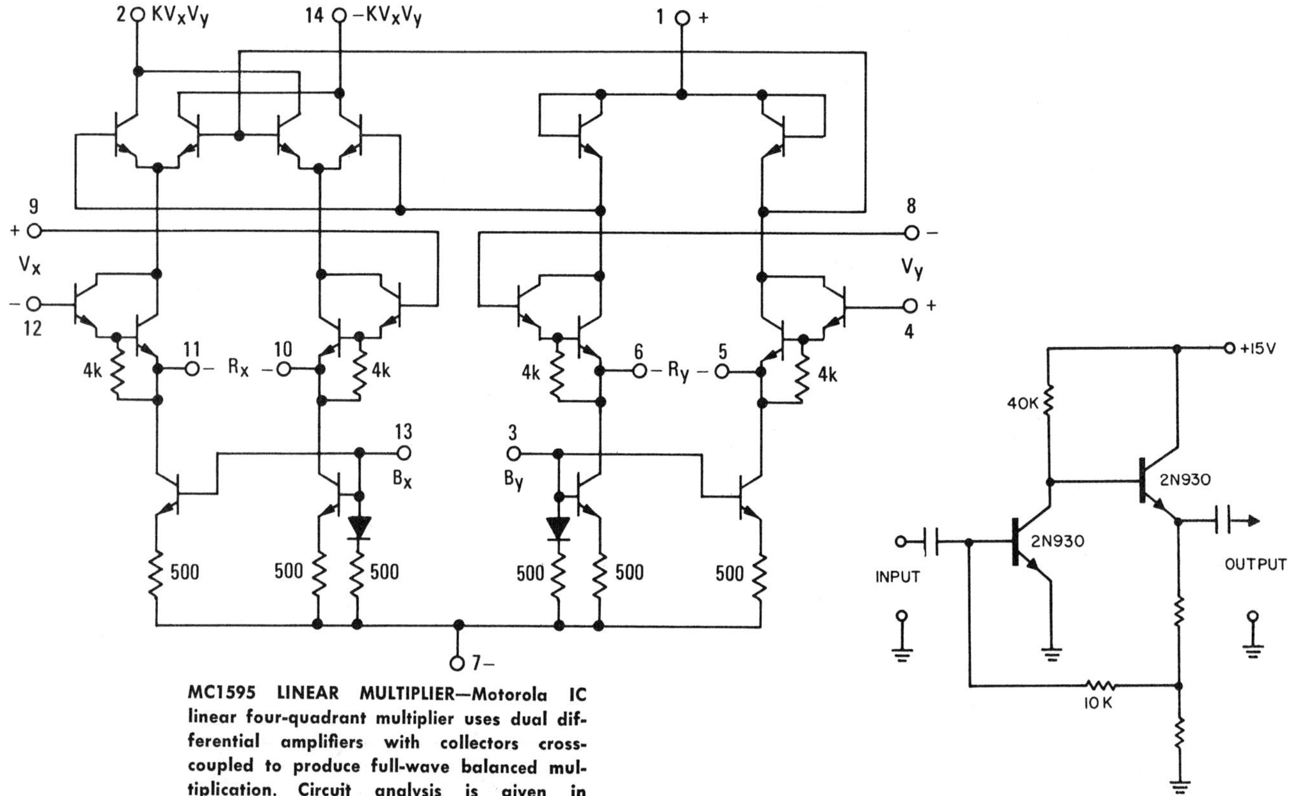

MC1595 LINEAR MULTIPLIER—Motorola IC linear four-quadrant multiplier uses dual differential amplifiers with collectors cross-coupled to produce full-wave balanced multiplication. Circuit analysis is given in Motorola Application Notes AN-489 and AN-490.—E. Renschler, The Monolithic Multiplier Breakthrough, "State-of-the-Art—Linears in Action," Motorola, Phoenix, Ariz., 1969, p 27–36.

MILLER-FEEDBACK BIASING—Eliminates need for large-value emitter bypass capacitor in IC amplifier. Article also covers techniques for reducing resistor surface-area requirements in various IC circuits.—A. Tuszynski, Skirting Thin-Film Design Problems, *Electronic Design*, Aug. 30, 1965, p 38–43.

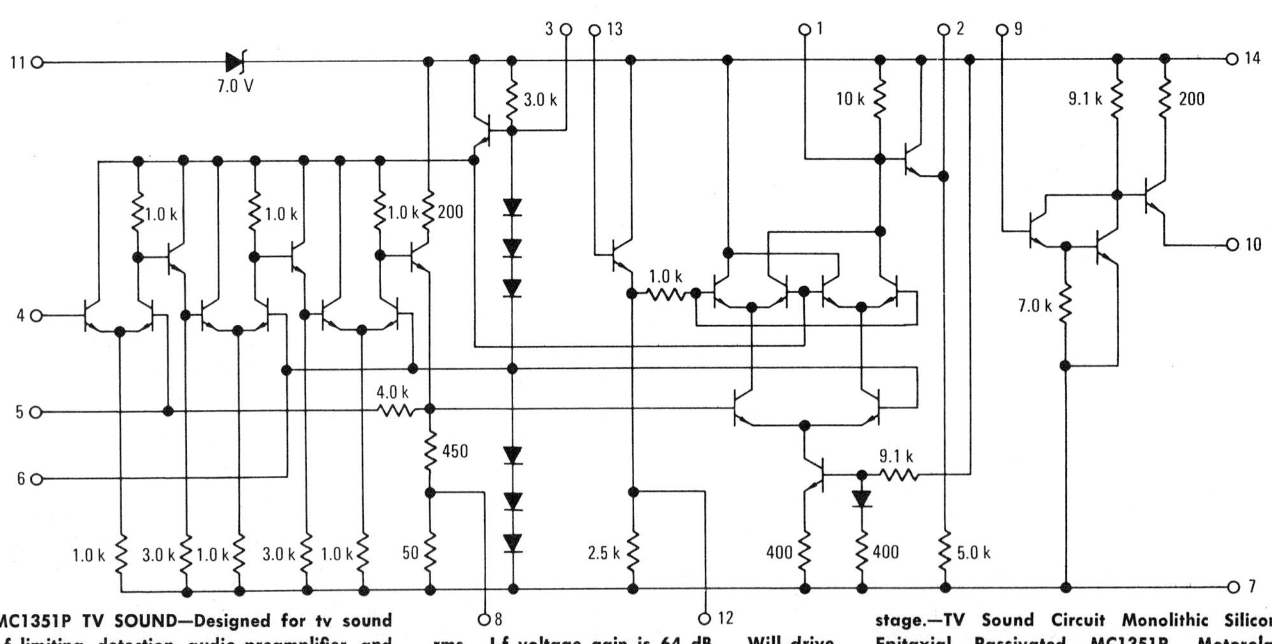

MC1351P TV SOUND—Designed for tv sound i-f limiting, detection, audio preamplifier, and driver. Output voltage swing is up to 3 V rms. I-f voltage gain is 64 dB. Will drive single external transistor serving as output stage.—TV Sound Circuit Monolithic Silicon Epitaxial Passivated MC1351P, Motorola, Phoenix, Ariz., DS9126, 1969.

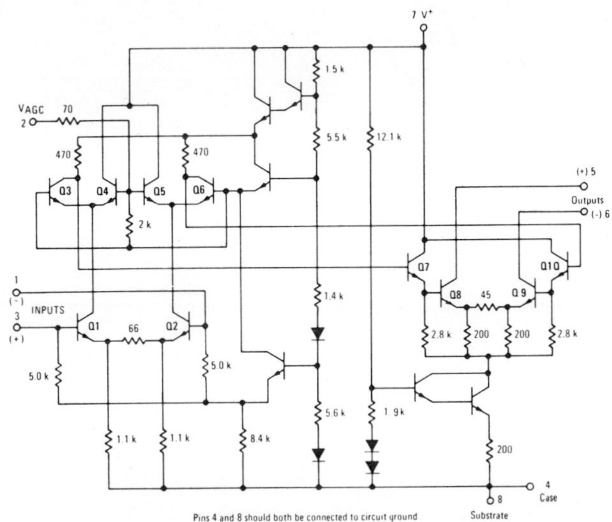

MC1590 I-F AMPLIFIER—Motorola IC is direct-coupled high-gain amplifier intended primarily for i-f applications up to 150 MHz. Wide-range agc characteristic makes it suitable for many video amplifier applications. May be used either single-ended or differentially coupled at input and at output.—R. Hejhall and B. Trout, Integrated Circuits for the World of High Frequency, "State-of-the-Art—Linears in Action," Motorola, Phoenix, Ariz., 1969, p 21–26.

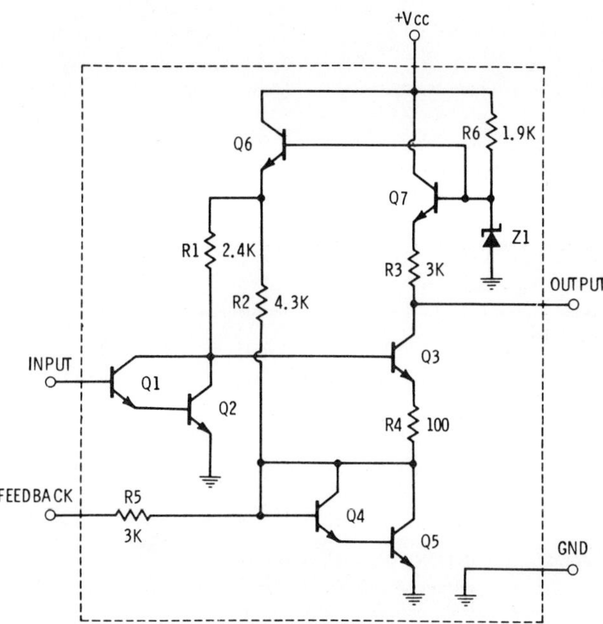

MIC0101 AUDIO-VIDEO PREAMP—Ideal for tape playback and other low-level applications where input signals are 1 mV or less. Frequency response extends well beyond radio frequencies, to about 700 kHz for 3 dB down. Consists of common-emitter Darlington directly coupled to amplifier Q3 for combined gain of about 60 dB. Series regulator circuit Q6-Q7 provides power supply filtering, while Q4 and Q5 serve as constant 1.4-V d-c bias source. Companion MIC0103 has two identical MIC0101 chips in same package for stereo applications.—M. L. Deschler, Integrated Circuit Preamplifiers, Mallory, Indianapolis, Ind., APPN-2, 1968.

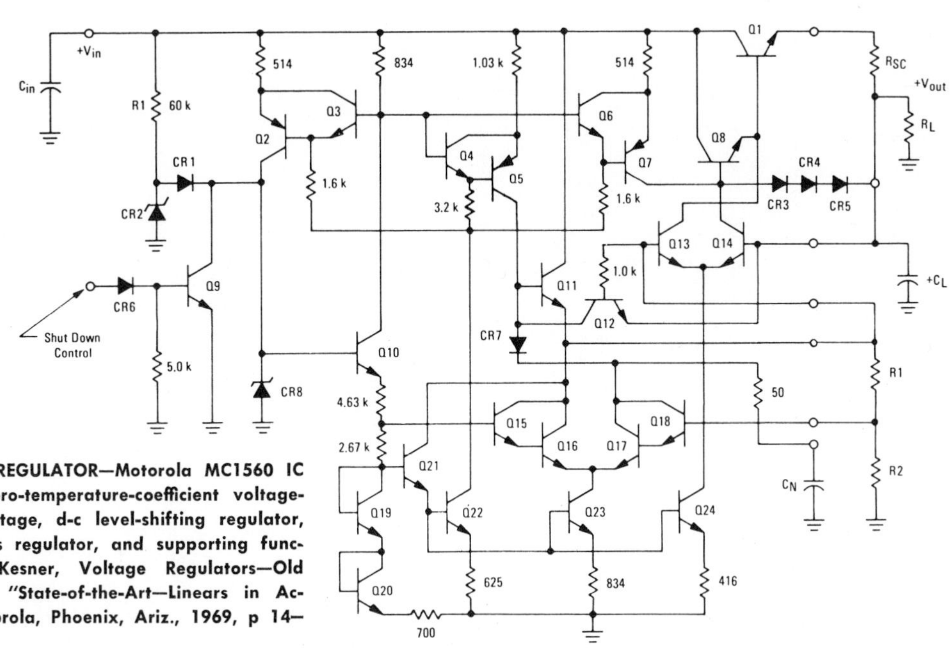

VOLTAGE REGULATOR—Motorola MC1560 IC includes zero-temperature-coefficient voltage-reference stage, d-c level-shifting regulator, main series regulator, and supporting functions.—D. Kesner, Voltage Regulators—Old and New, "State-of-the-Art—Linears in Action," Motorola, Phoenix, Ariz., 1969, p 14–20.

CHAPTER 42
Inverter Circuits

IMPROVED JENSEN—Saturable core in conventional two-transistor Jensen inverter limits switching speed, reducing efficiency at high frequencies. Improved circuit shown, using cross-coupled IC gates to form 20-kHz free-running mvbr, has 90% efficiency and good voltage regulation. Frequency is independent of load current. Maximum output is 1 kW, and power-weight ratio is better than 100 W per lb.—P. K. Edwards, New Line-Operated Inverter Offers Fast Switching and High Efficiency, *EEE*, Feb. 1969, p 115–116.

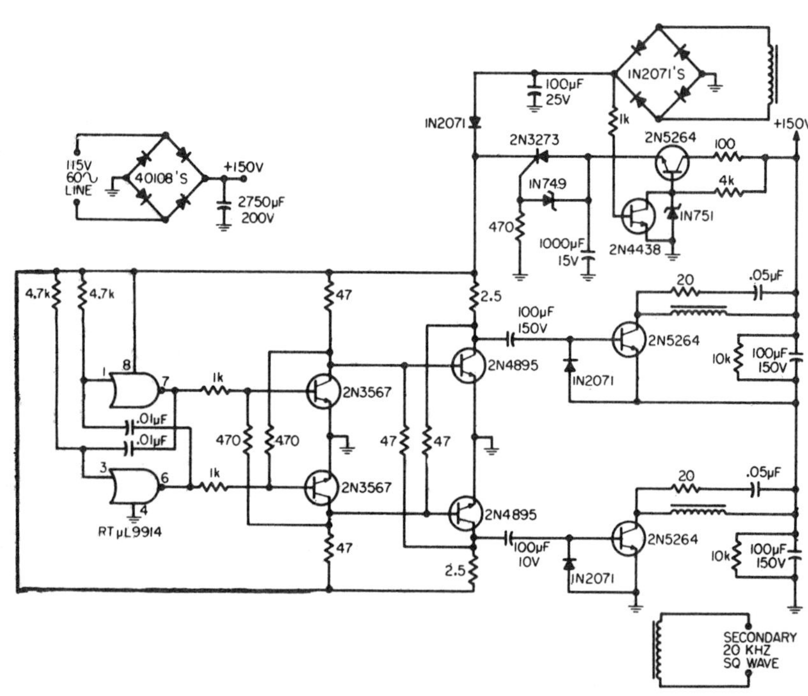

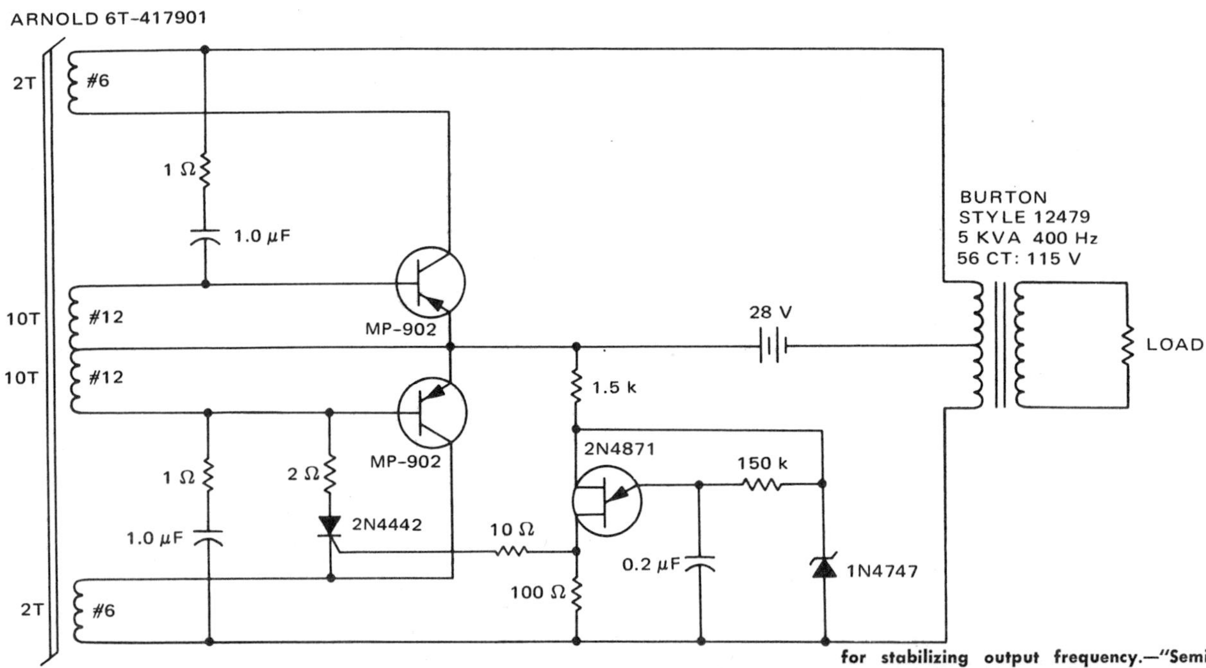

120-V A-C AT 2 KW AND 580 HZ FROM 28 V D-C—High-power inverter produces square-wave output at efficiencies of 80–90% depending on load. Circuit has no provisions for stabilizing output frequency.—"Semiconductor Power Circuits Handbook," Motorola, Phoenix, Ariz., 1968, p 2–47.

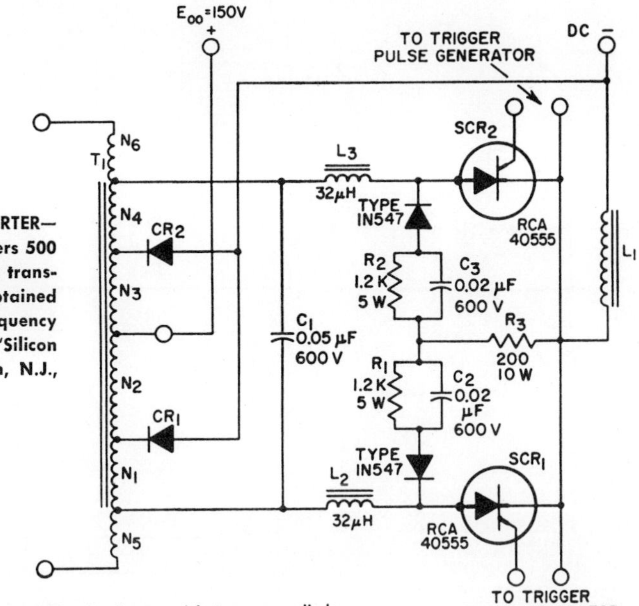

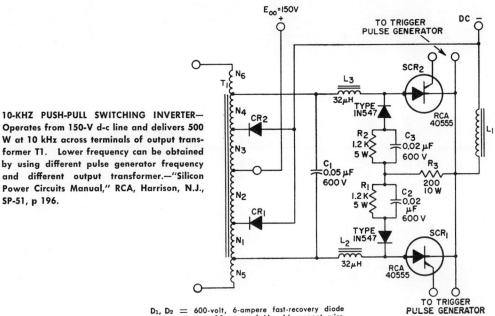

10-KHZ PUSH-PULL SWITCHING INVERTER—Operates from 150-V d-c line and delivers 500 W at 10 kHz across terminals of output transformer T1. Lower frequency can be obtained by using different pulse generator frequency and different output transformer.—"Silicon Power Circuits Manual," RCA, Harrison, N.J., SP-51, p 196.

D_1, D_2 = 600-volt, 6-ampere fast-recovery diode
L_1 = Inductor, 95 turns of No. 16 magnet wire wound on Arnold Engineering Type A4-17172 (or equiv.) core
T_1 = Output transformer: N_1 = N_4 = 9 turns of No. 18 magnet wire, two strands; N_2 = N_3 = 36 turns of No. 18 magnet wire; N_5 = N_6 = 21 turns of No. 18 magnet wire; core, two sets of Siemens Type 266215-A0000-R026 (or equiv.) with 4-mil air gap

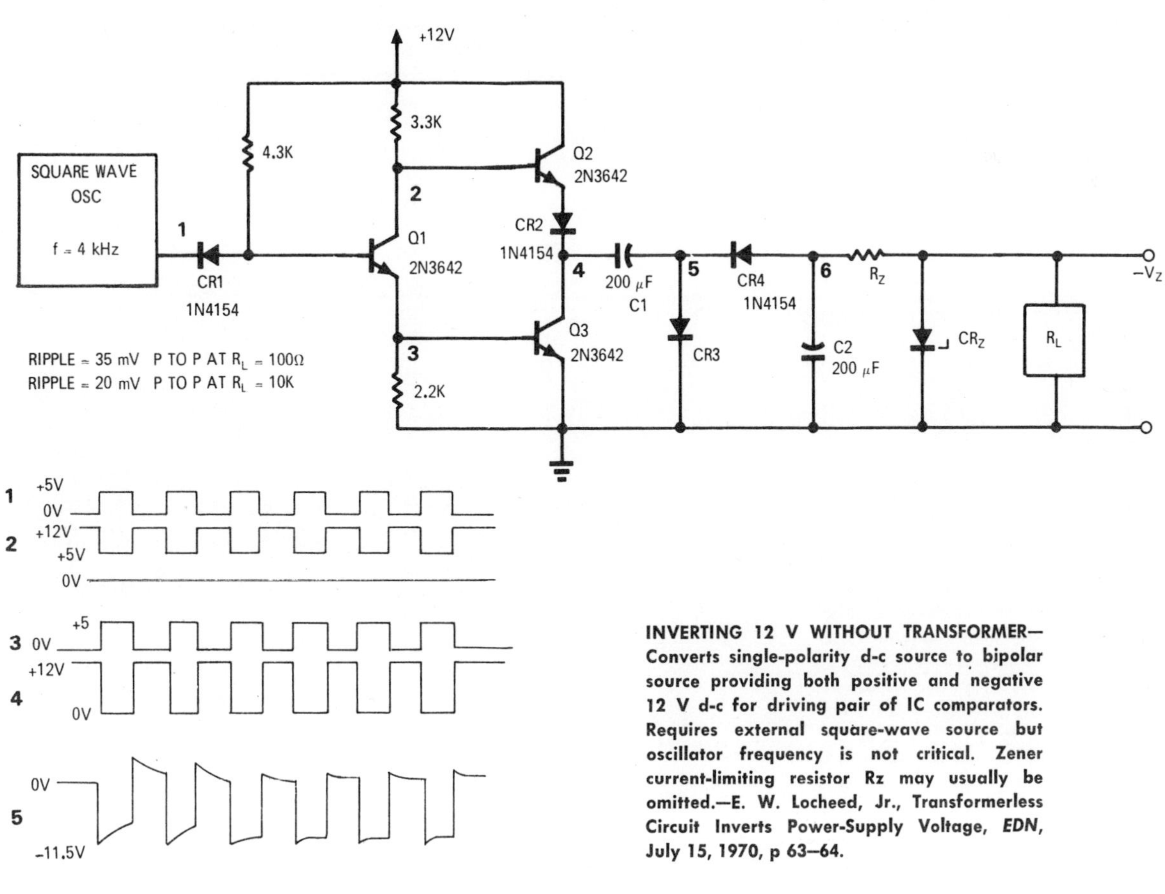

INVERTING 12 V WITHOUT TRANSFORMER—Converts single-polarity d-c source to bipolar source providing both positive and negative 12 V d-c for driving pair of IC comparators. Requires external square-wave source but oscillator frequency is not critical. Zener current-limiting resistor Rz may usually be omitted.—E. W. Locheed, Jr., Transformerless Circuit Inverts Power-Supply Voltage, *EDN*, July 15, 1970, p 63–64.

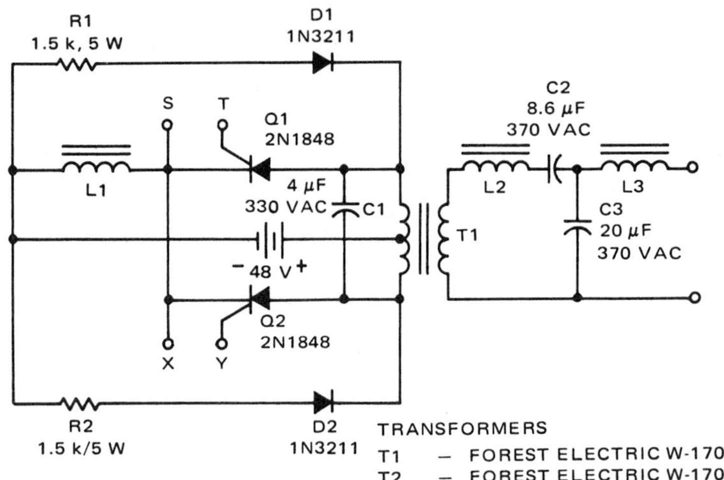

120-V A-C AT 100 W AND 60 HZ FROM 48 V D-C—Sine-wave output frequency is highly stable for both input and load voltage variations because drive circuit is frequency-controlled inverter having two secondary windings, for feeding terminals S, T, X, and Y of output inverter. Combination is commercially available as Felco Model W-1694 Inverter.—"Semiconductor Power Circuits Handbook," Motorola, Phoenix, Ariz., 1968, p 2–38.

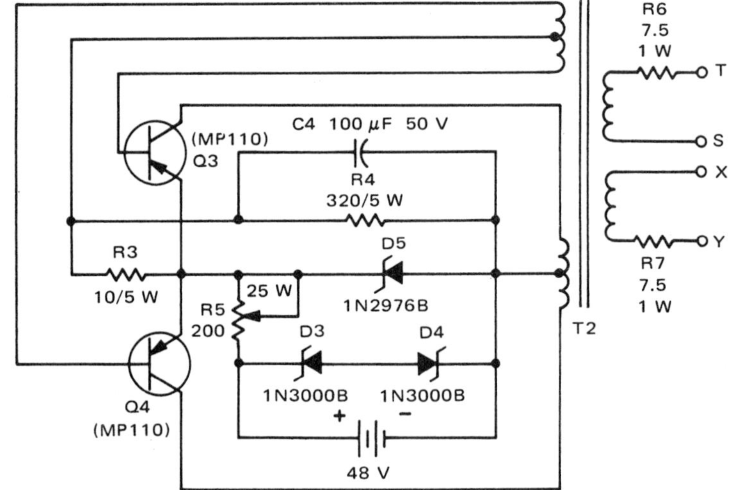

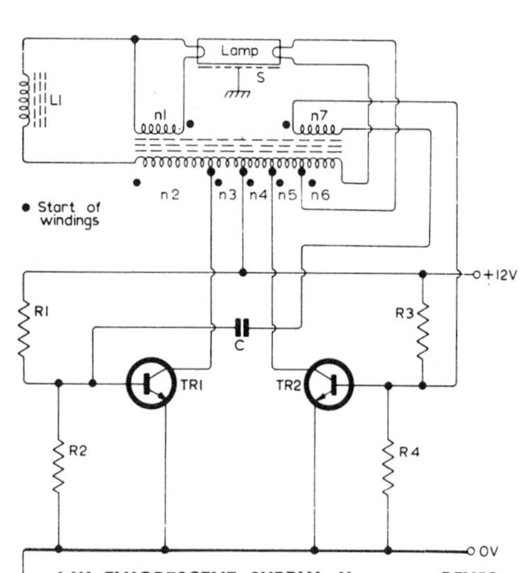

4-W FLUORESCENT SUPPLY—Uses two BFY50 transistors operating as square-wave push-pull oscillator driving lamp through transformer. Operating frequency is about 20 kHz. R1 and R3 are 180, R2 and R4 are 15, and C is 1 μF. Report gives choke and transformer winding data for both 4-W and 6-W circuits.—Applications of the BFY50, BFY51 and BFY52, Philips, Pub. Dept., Elcoma Div., Eindhoven, The Netherlands, No. 428, 1965.

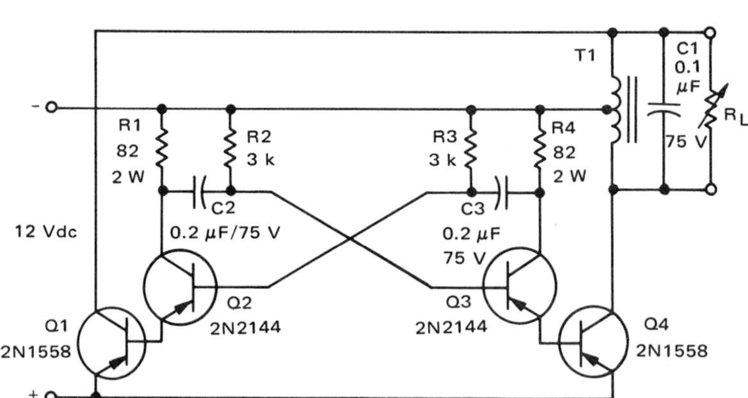

20-V A-C AT 50 W AND 1 KHZ FROM 12 V D-C—Inverter driven by free-running mvbr provides excellent frequency regulation for variations in both load and input voltages. Output is square wave at 20 V rms. Switching of output power transistors Q1 and Q4 is done by mvbr Q2-Q3 rather than by feedback from output transformer. Useful for precision systems requiring carefully controlled frequency and waveform.—"Semiconductor Power Circuits Handbook," Motorola, Phoenix, Ariz., 1968, p 2–61.

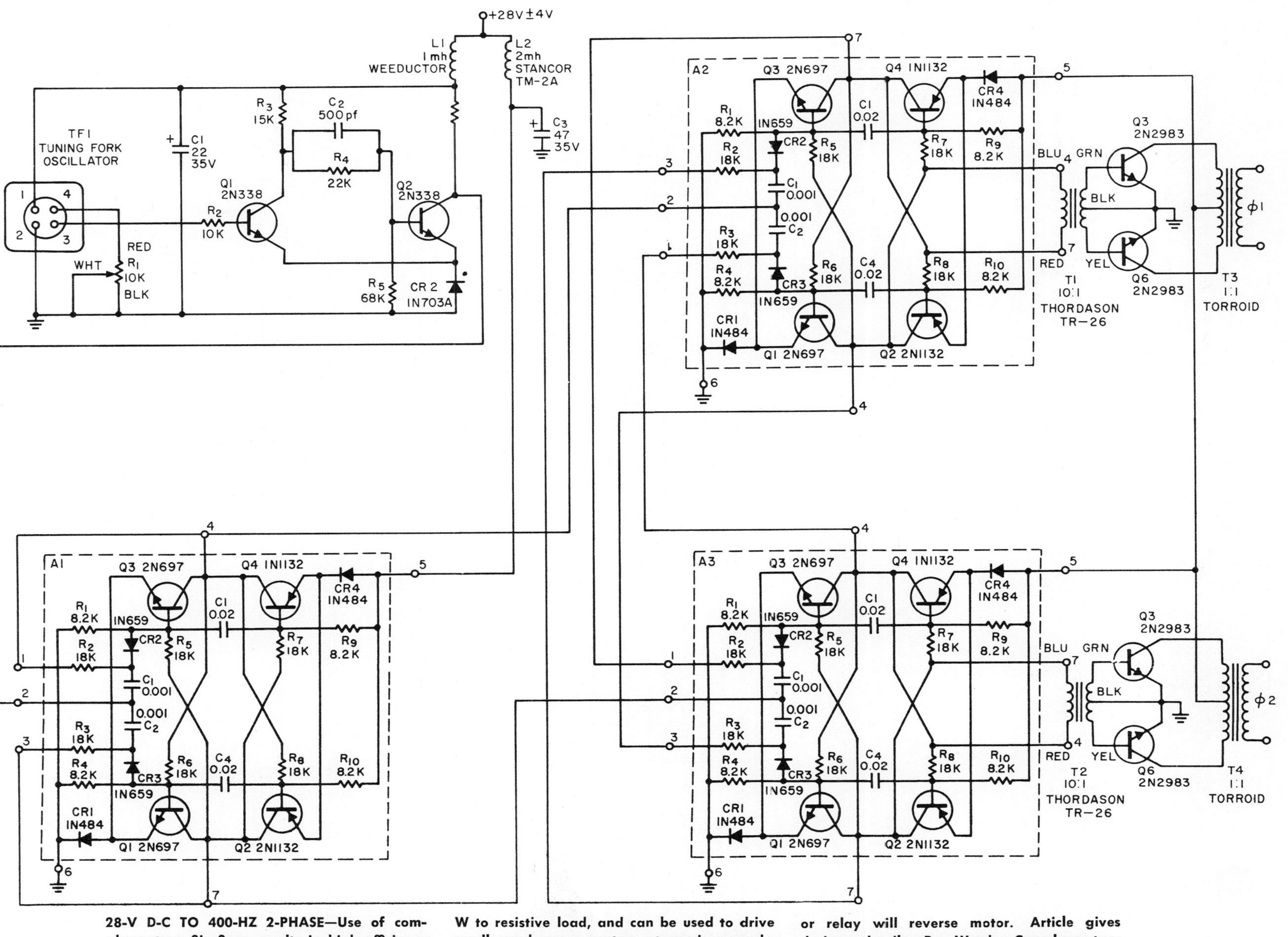

28-V D-C TO 400-HZ 2-PHASE—Use of complementary flip-flops results in high efficiency for inverter synchronized from 1,600-Hz single-phase tuning-fork oscillator. Can deliver 50 W to resistive load, and can be used to drive small synchronous motors at precise speeds. No-load standby power is less than 2 W. Reversal of one output phase leg with switch or relay will reverse motor. Article gives design details.—P. Ward, Complementary Flip-Flops Improve Bistable Performance, *Electronic Design*, May 11, 1964, p 50–55.

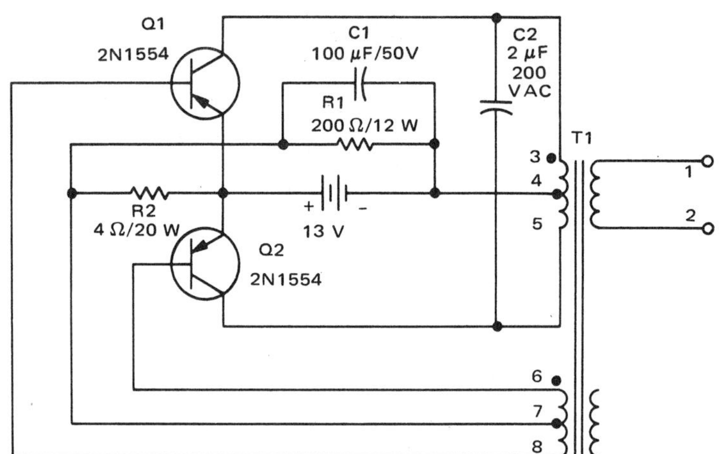

120-V A-C AT 120 W AND 60 HZ FROM 12 V D-C—Used to operate a-c equipment in automobiles. Output is square wave whose magnitude varies with load and input voltage. Regulation from no load to full load is about 30%, which means that 6-W increase in load decreases output voltage 1 V. Efficiency is 75% at full load, which is excellent for single-transformer inverter.—"Semiconductor Power Circuits Handbook," Motorola, Phoenix, Ariz., 1968, p 2–52.

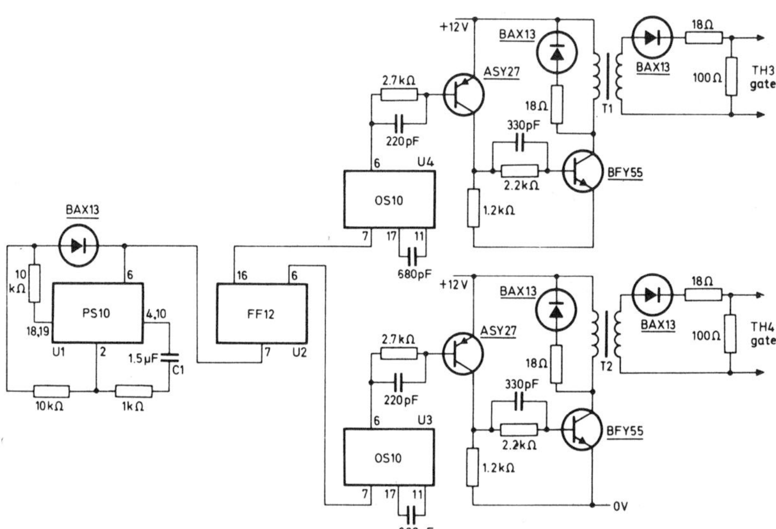

TRIGGER FOR 1-KW INVERTER—U1 generates 50-Hz square wave that is fed into IC flip-flop U2, whose outputs are 180 deg out of phase and feed monostable mvbr's U3 and U4 having same phase difference between their output pulses. After amplification, these pulses are fed to thyristors in stand-by inverters served by trigger. Transformers each have 150-turn primary and 75-turn secondary. Trigger can be permanently connected to its battery supply because current drain is negligible.—N. Bergstra and R. v. d. Linden, Stand-By Inverter for Emergency Mains Supply, Philips, Pub. Dept., Elcoma Div., Eindhoven, The Netherlands, No. 96, 1970.

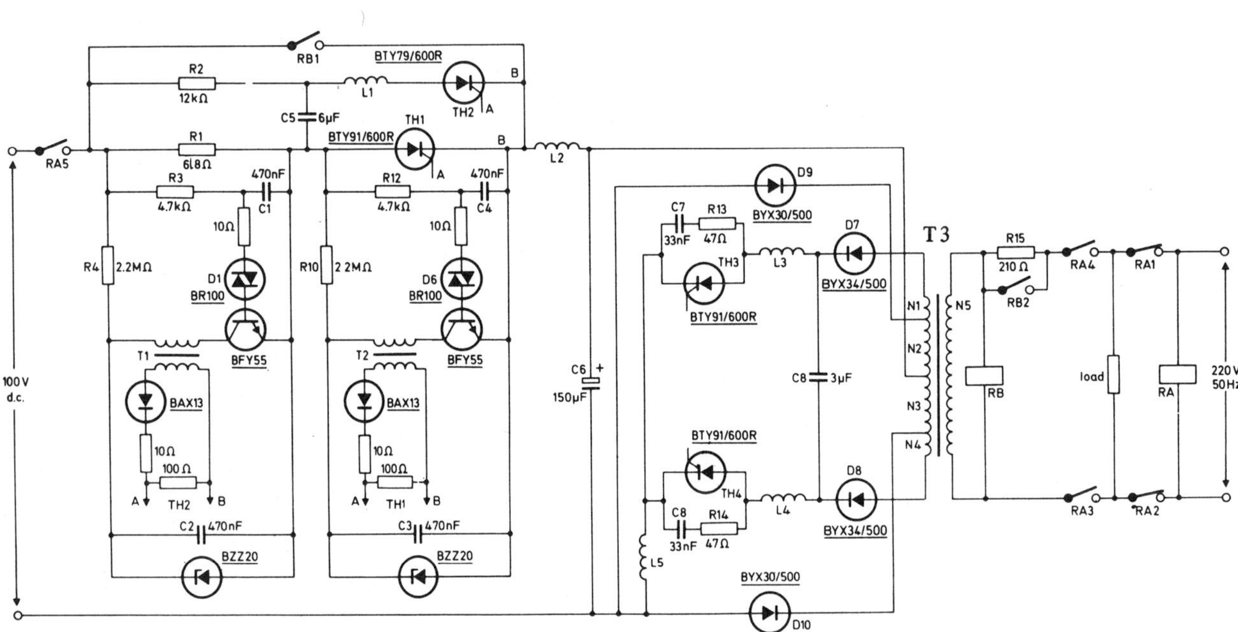

1-KW INVERTER FOR A-C LINE FAILURE—Protects critical production operation from interruption of a-c supply for more than a few cycles. McMurray Bedford inverter circuit is used to obtain good regulation, with special starting circuit to prevent short-circuit at startup if half of output transformer primary was saturated at previous shutdown. Both relays are 10 A at 220 V, 50 Hz. Gates of thyristors are fed by trigger pulses produced by separate trigger generator operating from 12-V battery.—N. Bergstra and R. v. d. Linden, Stand-By Inverter for Emergency Mains Supply, Philips, Pub. Dept., Elcoma Div., Eindhoven, The Netherlands, No. 96, 1970.

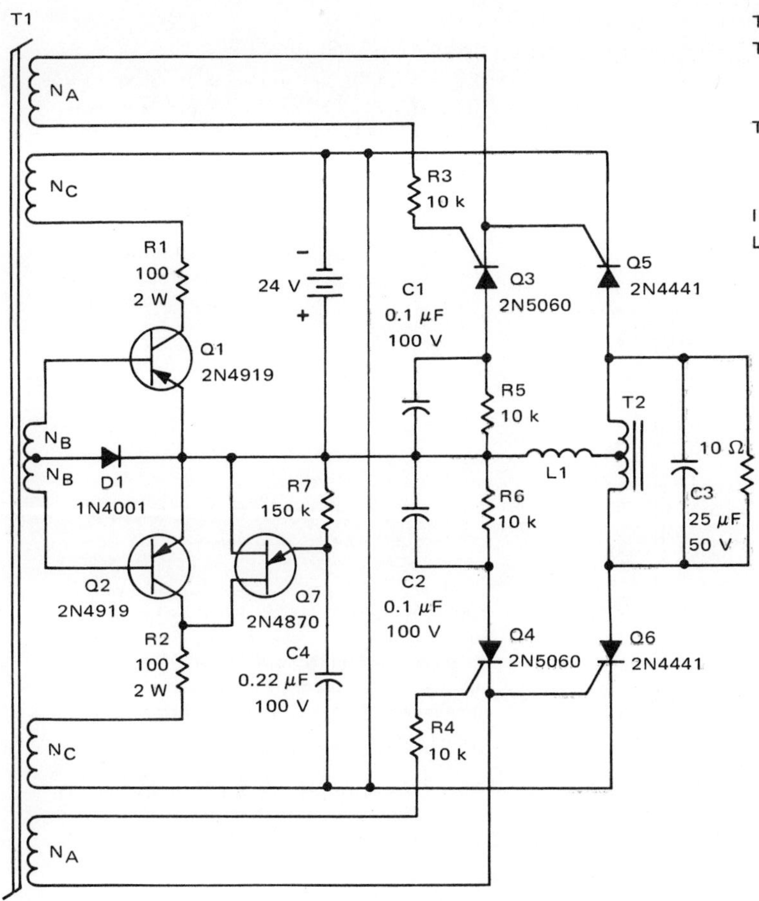

TRANSFORMERS

T1 — ARNOLD CORE 6T-5340-D1
$N_A + N_B$ 83 TURNS EACH #30 WIRE
N_C 8 TURNS #26 WIRE

T2 — PHOENIX TRANSFORMER PX2677
350 V, 1 kVA, 1 kHz

INDUCTOR

L1 — PHOENIX TRANSFORMER PX1710 2 mH, 30 A

45-V SQUARE WAVE AT 150 W WITH INVERTER-DRIVEN INVERTER—Will operate from 10–28 V d-c and deliver 45-V a-c 400 Hz which is independent of load and has high stability for input voltage variations. Efficiency is 70%. Drive circuit is current-feedback inverter Q1-Q2 with ujt Q7 in starting network. Windings on timing transformer drive pair of sensitive-gate scr's (Q3-Q4) which in turn drive main parallel-commutated inverter Q5-Q6 that supplies power to 10-ohm load across T2.—"Semiconductor Power Circuits Handbook," Motorola, Phoenix, Ariz., 1968, p 2–36.

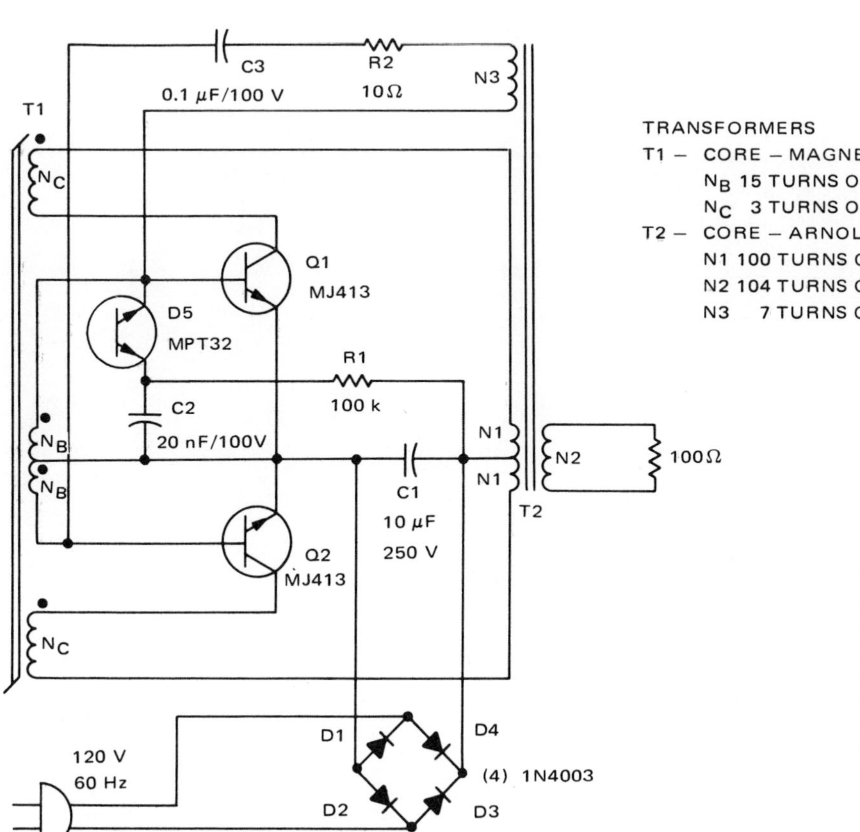

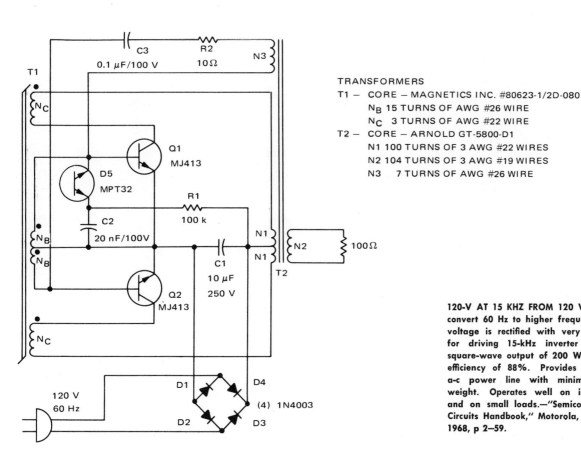

TRANSFORMERS

T1 — CORE — MAGNETICS INC. #80623-1/2D-080
N_B 15 TURNS OF AWG #26 WIRE
N_C 3 TURNS OF AWG #22 WIRE

T2 — CORE — ARNOLD GT-5800-D1
N1 100 TURNS OF 3 AWG #22 WIRES
N2 104 TURNS OF 3 AWG #19 WIRES
N3 7 TURNS OF AWG #26 WIRE

120-V AT 15 KHZ FROM 120 V A-C—Used to convert 60 Hz to higher frequency. A-c line voltage is rectified with very little filtering, for driving 15-kHz inverter that delivers square-wave output of 200 W with full-load efficiency of 88%. Provides isolation from a-c power line with minimum size and weight. Operates well on inductive loads and on small loads.—"Semiconductor Power Circuits Handbook," Motorola, Phoenix, Ariz., 1968, p 2–59.

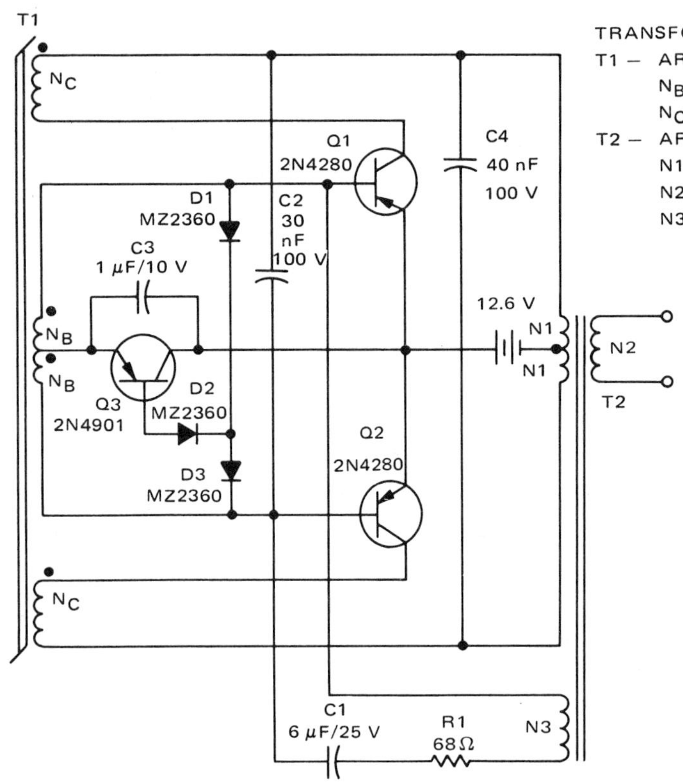

TRANSFORMERS

T1 — ARNOLD CORE 6T 7699D1
N_B 54 TURNS #20 WIRE
N_C 3 TURNS TWO #12 WIRES IN PARALLEL

T2 — ARNOLD CORE 3T 6464-L4
N1 12 TURNS TWO #12 WIRES IN PARALLEL
N2 120 TURNS #16 WIRE
N3 7 TURNS #20 WIRE

120-V A-C AT 400 HZ FROM 12 V D-C—Hybrid-feedback inverter gives square-wave output of 400 W at efficiency above 85% for full range of output power. Can be used with fluorescent lamps, 400-Hz 90-W motor, and other inductive as well as resistive loads. Feedback winding N3 ensures starting without load.—"Semiconductor Power Circuits Handbook," Motorola, Phoenix, Ariz., 1968, p 2–57.

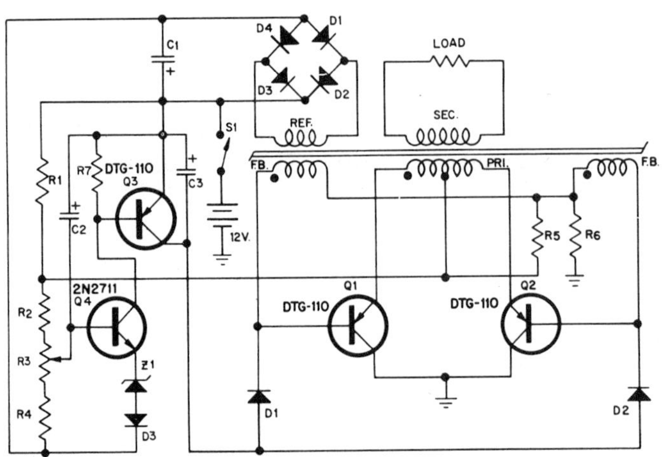

115-V A-C AT 10 W FROM 12-V BATTERY—Q1-Q2 and transformer oscillate at 400 Hz when S1 is closed, with startup assured by forward bias developed across R5-R6. Series regulator Q3-Q4 senses output of full-wave bridge, which is proportional to a-c load voltage, and controls base drive of output transistors Q1-Q2 to regulate both output voltage and frequency. Developed as low-cost regulated a-c power source for mobile applications.—Regulated Inverter, Delco Radio, Kokomo, Ind., No. 37, 1966.

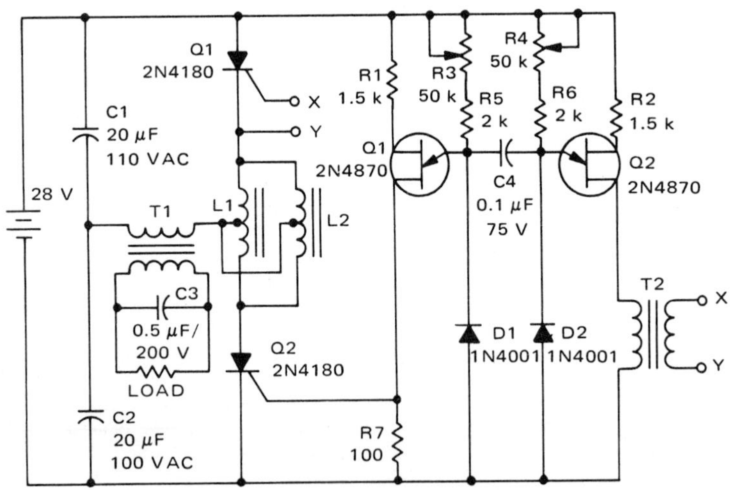

L1 and L2 — TRIAD C-49 V 32 mH CT, 5A
T1 — TRIAD F-22A 120/6.3 V 20 A
T2 — SPRAGUE 11Z13

120-V A-C AT 40 W AND 400 HZ FROM 28 V D-C—Gives pure sine-wave output with 10% voltage regulation for both input and load voltages. Can be operated indefinitely with open or shorted load. Output voltage increases from about 30 to 130 V rms as load is applied; load resistance must therefore be limited to certain range if voltage variations are undesirable. Efficiency is about 40% for 250-ohm load.—"Semiconductor Power Circuits Handbook," Motorola, Phoenix, Ariz., 1968, p 2–33.

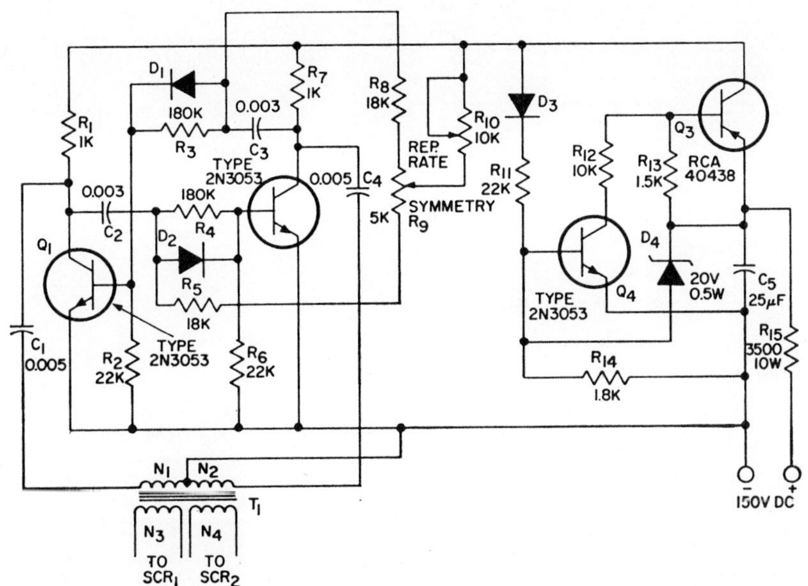

D4 = Zener diode, 20-volt, ½-watt
T1 = Pulse transformer; center-tapped primary: N1 = N2 = 150 turns of No. 36 wire; split secondaries: N3 = N4 = 100 turns of No. 36 wire; core material: Indiana General Type No. CF902, or equiv.

TRIGGER GENERATOR FOR INVERTER—Used for triggering pair of thyristors, SCR1 and SCR2, in 10-kHz push-pull switching inverter. Transients that might exceed maximum rating of scr's are suppressed by network consisting of R1, R2, R3, C2, C3, and two 1N547 diodes, D1 and D2.—"Silicon Power Circuits Manual," RCA, Harrison, N.J., SP-51, p 197.

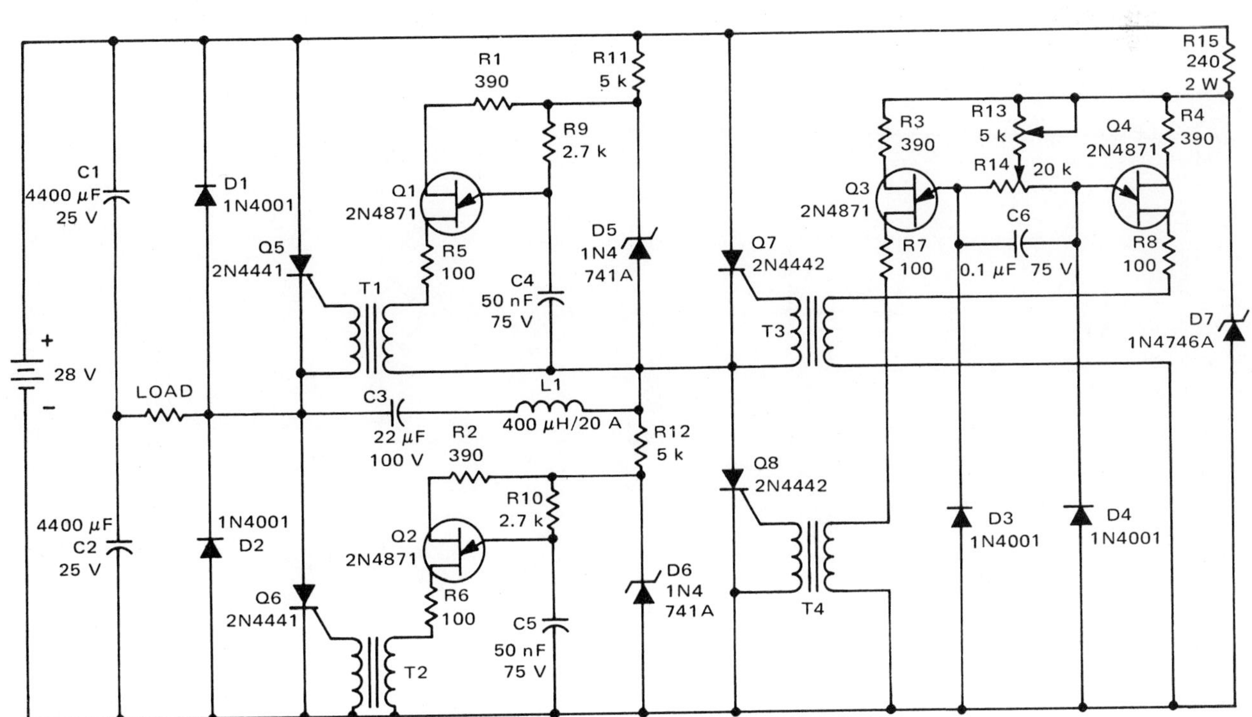

T1 − T4 − SPRAGUE 11Z12

12-V A-C AT 60 W AND 465 HZ FROM 28 V D-C—Uses impulse-commutated scr inverter to generate well-regulated square-wave output that can be used to drive 400-Hz transformer. Efficiency is about 65% at full load.—"Semiconductor Power Circuits Handbook," Motorola, Phoenix, Ariz., 1968, p 2–41.

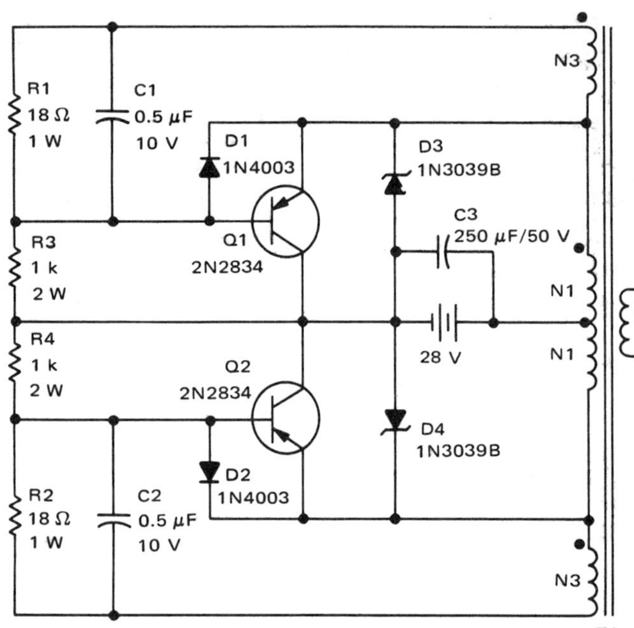

T1 – ARNOLD CORE GT-5502-D500
N1 26 TURNS OF AWG #14 WIRE
N2 52 TURNS OF AWG #14 WIRE
N3 3 TURNS OF AWG #22 WIRE

52-V A-C AT 100 W AND 15 KHZ FROM 28 V D-C—High-frequency inverter provides square-wave output with efficiency of 85% at full load. Frequency stability is excellent, being dependent only on input voltage and not load. Excellent for applications requiring minimum size and weight.—"Semiconductor Power Circuits Handbook," Motorola, Phoenix, Ariz., 1968, p 2–54.

SELF-STARTER—Combination of low-cost plastic-encapsulated ujt and scr provides almost instantaneous saturation of Q1 in inverter circuit, for reliable startup at 400 Hz. Once inverter is operating, starting circuit stays turned off and hence consumes negligible power. Output to load is 200 W at 115 V. —R. A. Phillips, Starting Network for Transistor Inverters, *EEE*, Feb. 1969, p 114–115.

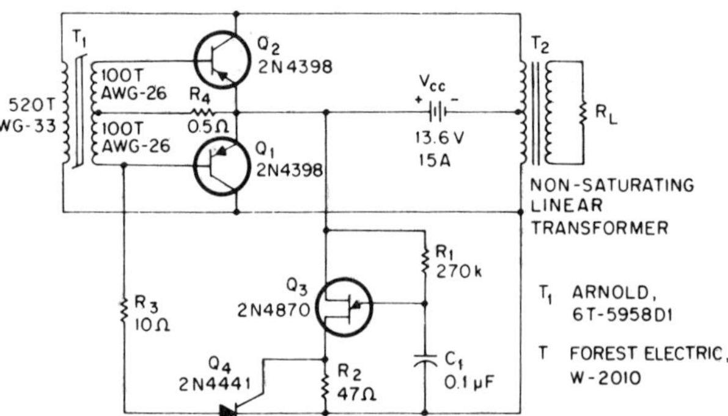

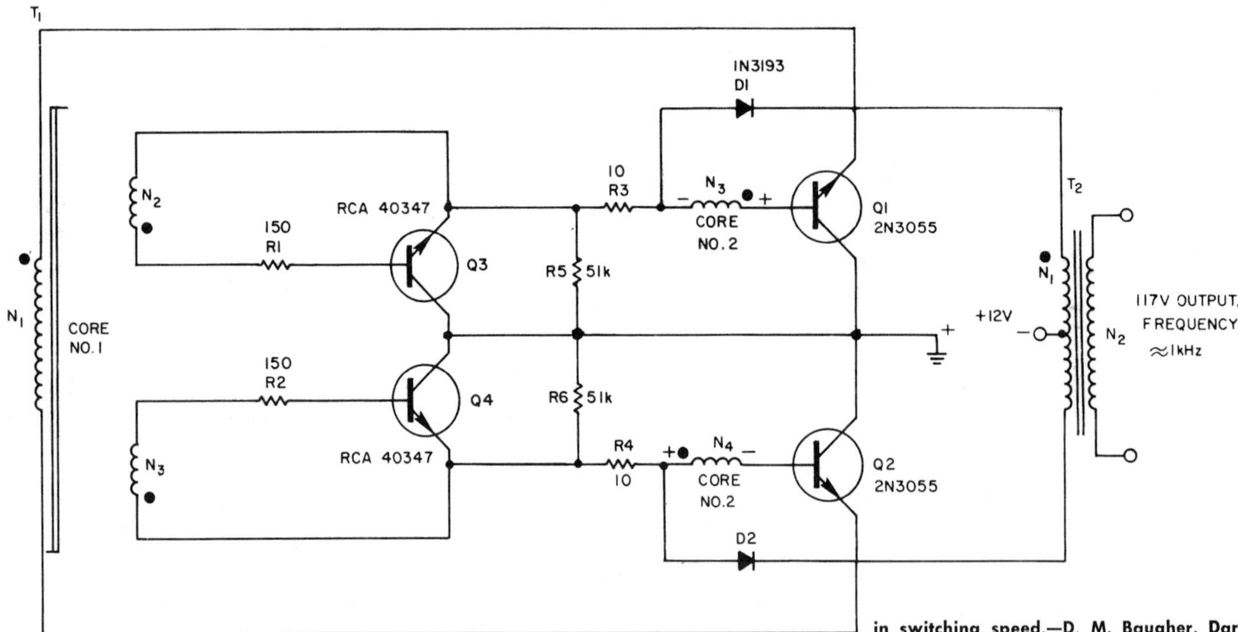

CUTTING TRANSFORMER COST—Extra windings N3 and N4 on output transformer, plus addition of D1 and D2 to Darlington inverter, reduce transformer size and cost without having excessive dissipation of conventional Darlington approach. Circuit also gives increase in switching speed.—D. M. Baugher, Darlington Inverter Features Turn-Off Drive and Low V-ce(sat), *Electronic Design*, July 5, 1969, p 86.

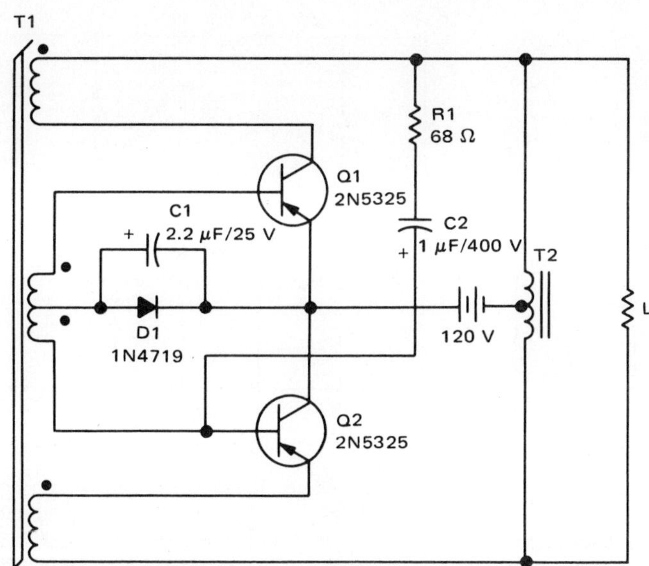

T1 — ARNOLD CORE 6T 4168S1
46T OF #23 FOR EACH BASE WINDING
5T OF 3 #18 FOR EACH COLLECTOR WINDING
T2 — PHOENIX TRANSFORMER PX-2677

240-V A-C AT 1 KW AND 1,200 HZ FROM 120 V D-C—Square-wave output is produced at efficiency of 92% for full load, with excellent frequency stability. Will operate over input voltage range of 20 to 160 V d-c. Circuit will fail-safe if either input voltage or load is removed, even though self-excited. Has no starting limitations.—"Semiconductor Power Circuits Handbook," Motorola, Phoenix, Ariz., 1968, p 2–50.

22-W AUTOMOTIVE—Uses inexpensive Bendix plastic-encased power transistors to convert 12-V storage-battery power to any desired higher a-c voltage determined by turns ratio of transformer, or to d-c voltage if output rectifier and filter are added.—D. E. Lancaster, Plastic Power Transistors—Advantages and Applications, *Electronics World*, Feb. 1968, p 50–52.

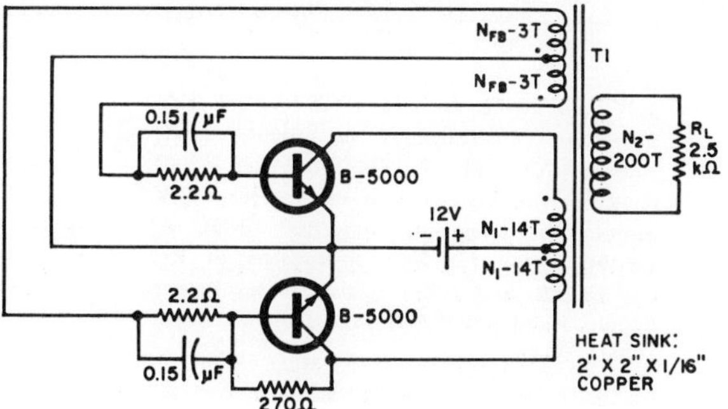

TI-WESTINGHOUSE C CORE, CATALOG #H425, WINDING #20 WIRE
(B) 22-WATT INVERTER

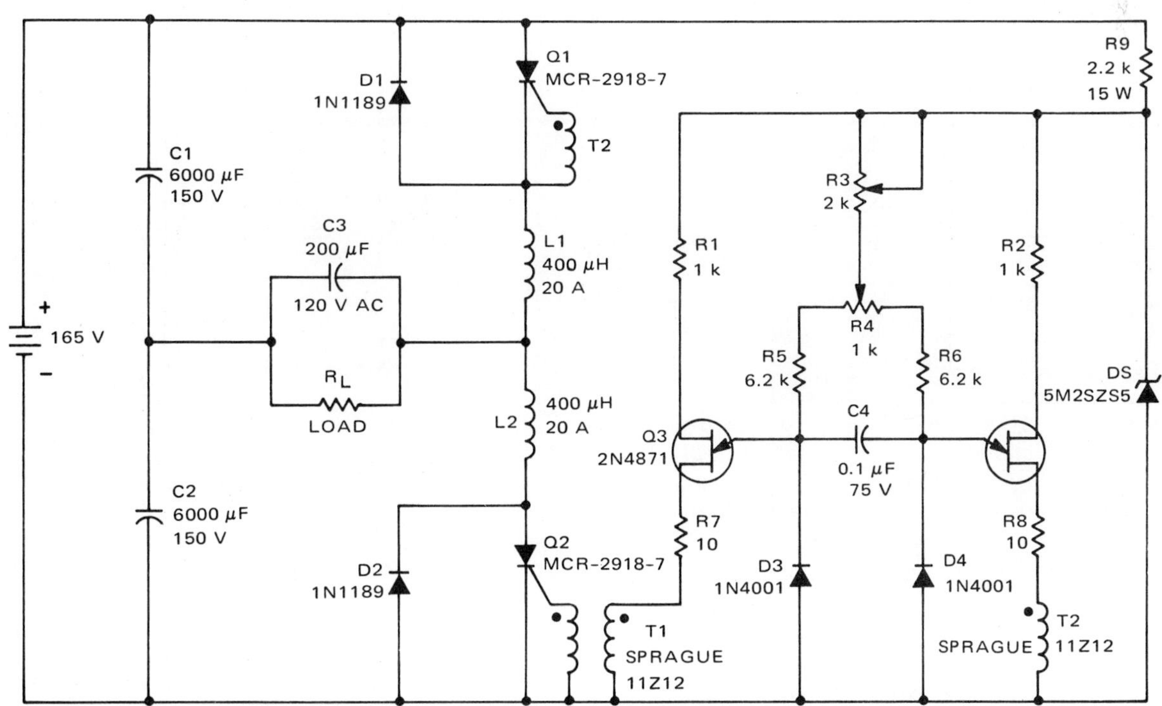

120-V A-C AT 800 W AND 400 HZ FROM 165 V D-C—Considered to be best sine-wave inverter in use today. Output voltage is well regulated for load changes, frequency is independent of normal input and load variations, and efficiency is 60% at rated output.—"Semiconductor Power Circuits Handbook," Motorola, Phoenix, Ariz., 1968, p 2–31.

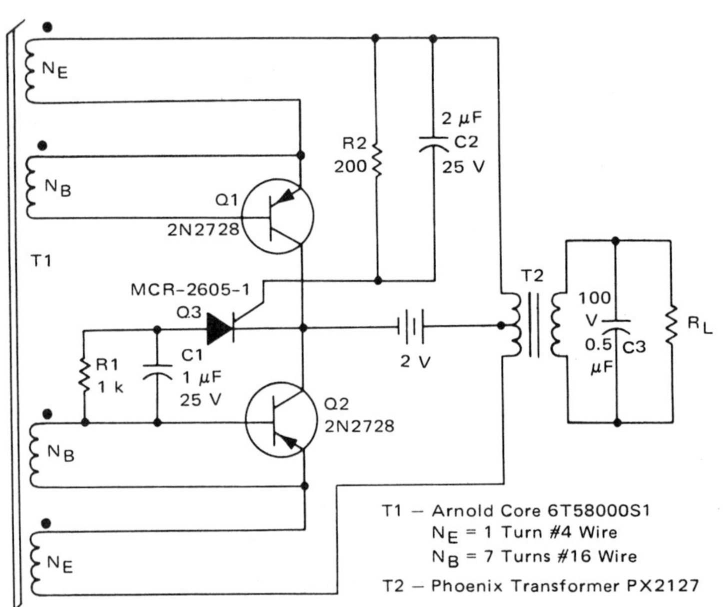

35-V A-C AT 80 W AND 1 KHZ FROM 2 V D-C—Current-feedback inverter provides maximum efficiency of 87% for 30-W load and 70% for full load. Input current from 2-V battery has allowable range of 10–50 A. Starting circuit for inverter consists of R1, C1, R2, C2, and Q3.—"Semiconductor Power Circuits Handbook," Motorola, Phoenix, Ariz., 1968, p 2–45.

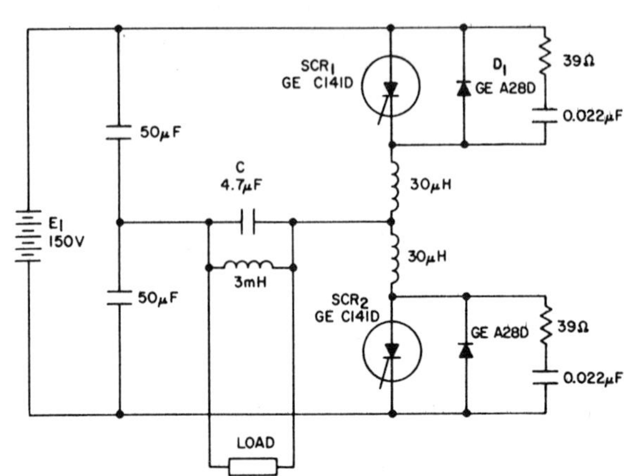

CLASS A INVERTER—Circuit is self-commutated by resonating load, for transforming d-c to a-c. Is most suitable for operation at about 1,000 Hz, because L-C resonant circuit carries full load current. Scr current is nearly sinusoidal. When SCR1 is triggered, C is charged to voltage approaching 300 V (twice supply voltage). Current then reverses and flows back to supply through D1 while C discharges. SCR2 is triggered next, with cycle repeating at about 1,000 Hz to provide 120 V a-c for load.—"SCR Manual," 4th Edition, General Electric, 1967, p 228.

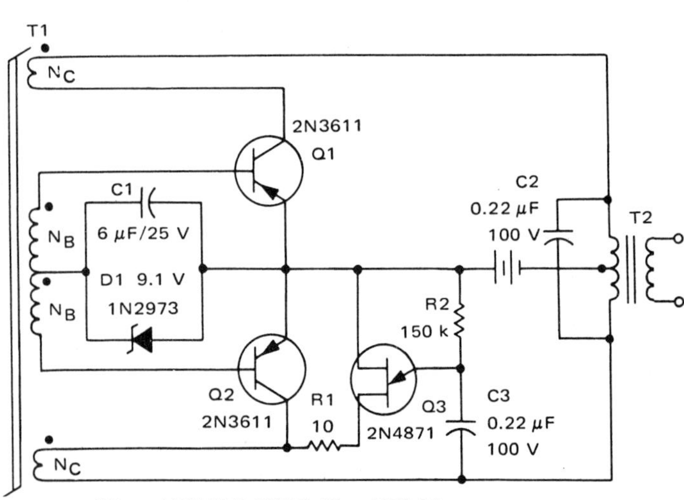

120-V A-C AT 40 W AND 400 HZ FROM 12 V D-C—Gives frequency-stable square-wave output. Efficiency is about 80%.—"Semiconductor Power Circuits Handbook," Motorola, Phoenix, Ariz., 1968, p 2–43.

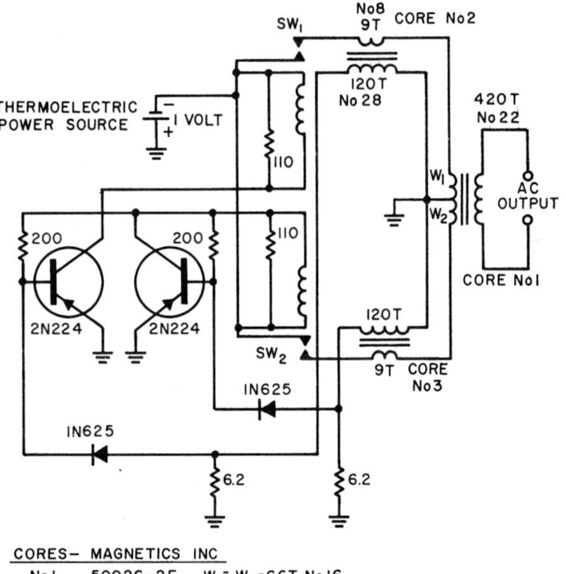

REED-SWITCH INVERTER—Converts 1-V d-c output of thermoelectric generator to 10 V a-c. Low-power transistor flip-flop drives reed switch coils, to eliminate contact bounce problems. Operating frequency of 100 Hz gives 1,000-hour reed switch life for 1 W delivered to load, with efficiency of 65%.—J. M. Loe, Reed Switches Reduce Power Converter Cost, *Electronic Design*, May 11, 1964, p 80–81.

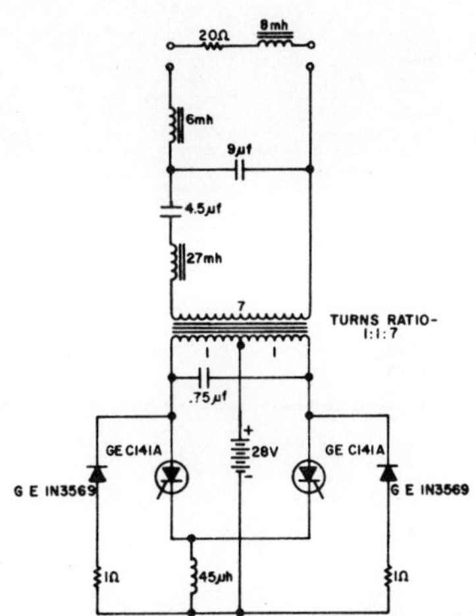

400-HZ INVERTER—Class C inverter with Ott filter converts 28 V d-c to 120 V a-c at 400 Hz with 360 W output power into 28-ohm inductive load having 20 ohms resistance. Input power is 424 W, for 85% efficiency. Article gives design equations.—"SCR Manual," 4th Edition, General Electric, 1967, p 235–237.

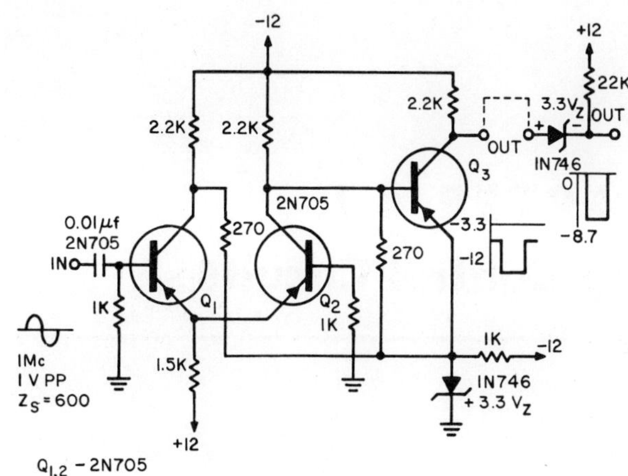

SQUARER—Uses transient-free current-mode inverter Q1-Q2, followed by saturating inverter Q3, to convert sine waves to square waves for driving switching circuits. Thermal stability and noise immunity are excellent and sensitivity is high.—M. Neidich, Squaring Circuit Improves Symmetry and Thermal Stability, *Electronic Design*, Aug. 31, 1964, p 48.

NOTE: To locate additional circuits in the category of this chapter, use the index at the back of this book. Check also the author's "Sourcebook of Electronic Circuits," published by McGraw-Hill in 1968.

CHAPTER 43
Lamp Control Circuits

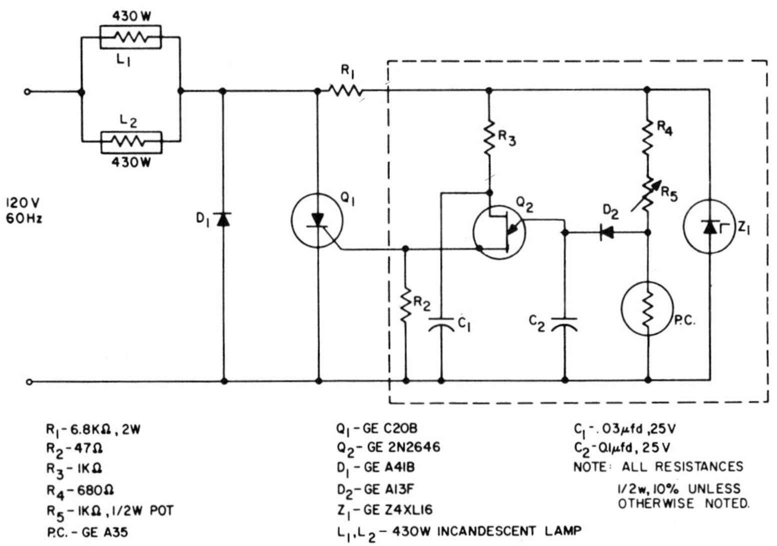

860-W LAMP CONTROL—Uses controlled-half-plus-fixed-half-wave phase control to regulate 860-W lamp from half to full power. Light output range is then 30% to 100% of maximum, regulated within 1% for 10% change in supply voltage. Not suitable for transformer-fed loads, because this method of phase control gives unsymmetrical wave having d-c components. Photocell serves as feedback element in closed loop.—"SCR Manual," 4th Edition, General Electric, 1967, p 285.

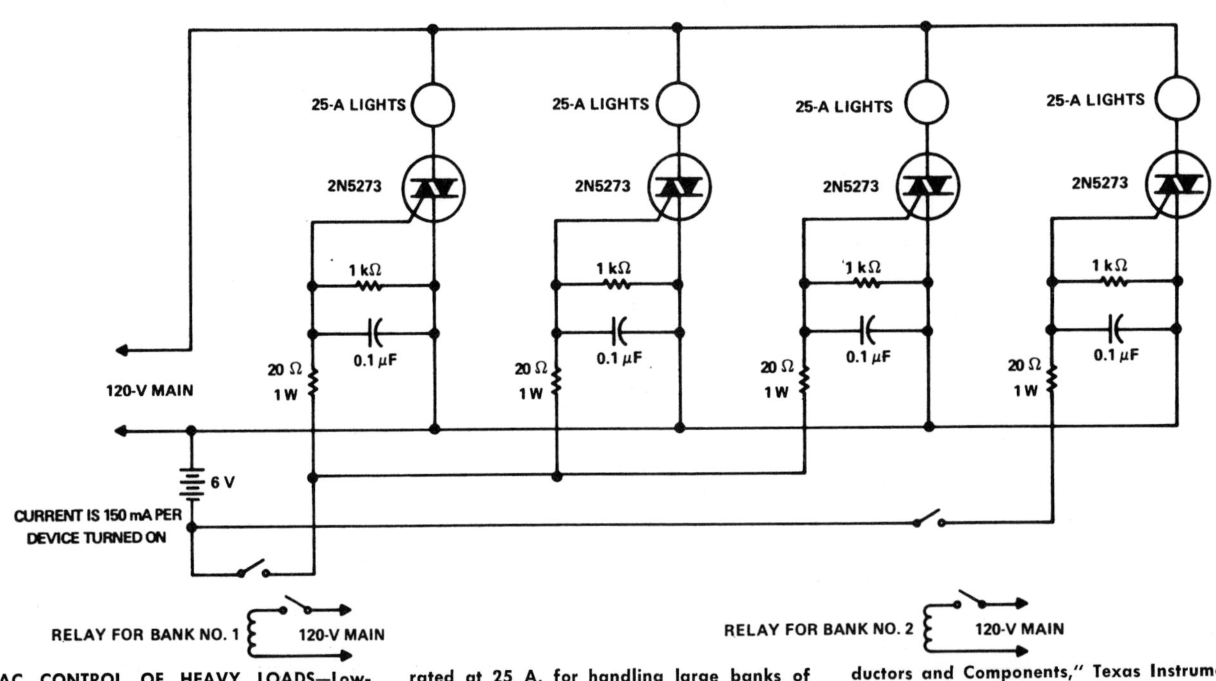

TRIAC CONTROL OF HEAVY LOADS—Low-power control arrangement turns on triacs rated at 25 A, for handling large banks of lights or other loads.—"Preferred Semiconductors and Components," Texas Instruments, Dallas, Texas, CC101, 1968, p 24608A.

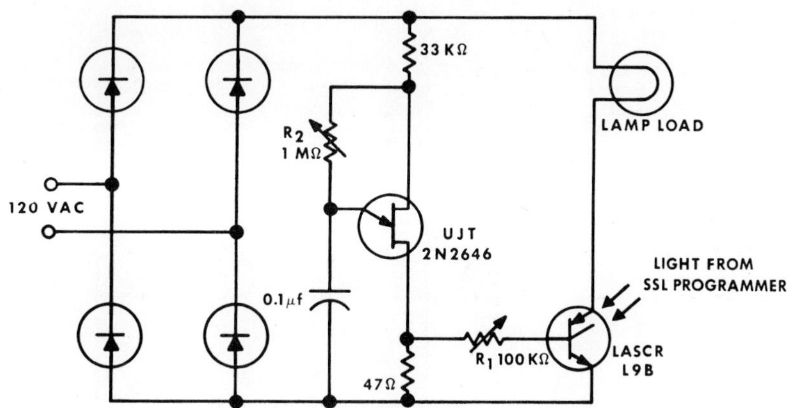

PREHEATER—Ujt provides preheating of repetitively programmed incandescent lamps by triggering lascr late in each half-cycle, with setting of R2 determining current that maintains filament temperature just below visible level. R1 adjusts sensitivity of lascr to light, to give reliable turn-on of lamp load under control of solid-state lamp in programmer.—L. M. Hertz, Solid State Lamps—Part II, General Electric, Cleveland, Ohio, No. 3-0121, 1970, p 17.

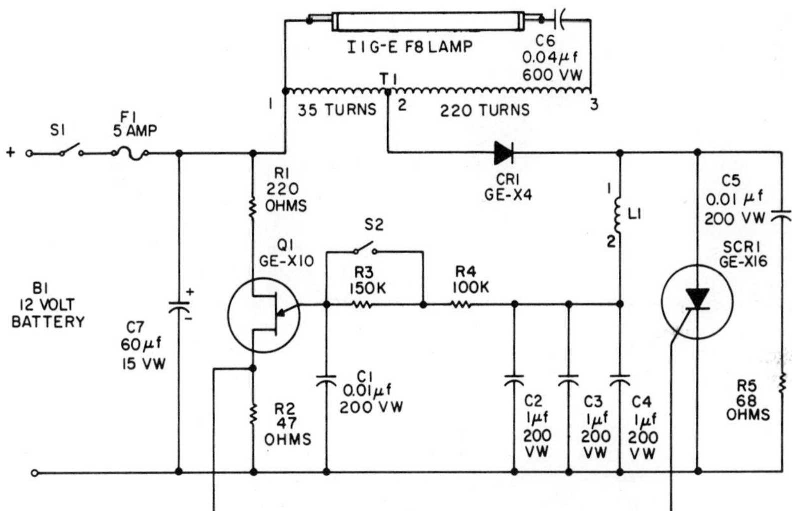

BATTERY-OPERATED FLUORESCENT—Will operate 12-inch F8 fluorescent from 12-V battery for portable use, or from 12-V auto, boat, or trailer storage battery. Remove ballast and starter from lamp fixture and replace with autotransformer for which book gives winding instructions. Inverter circuit used is high enough in frequency to give flicker-free illumination.—"Hobby Manual," General Electric, Owensboro, Ky., 1965, p 138.

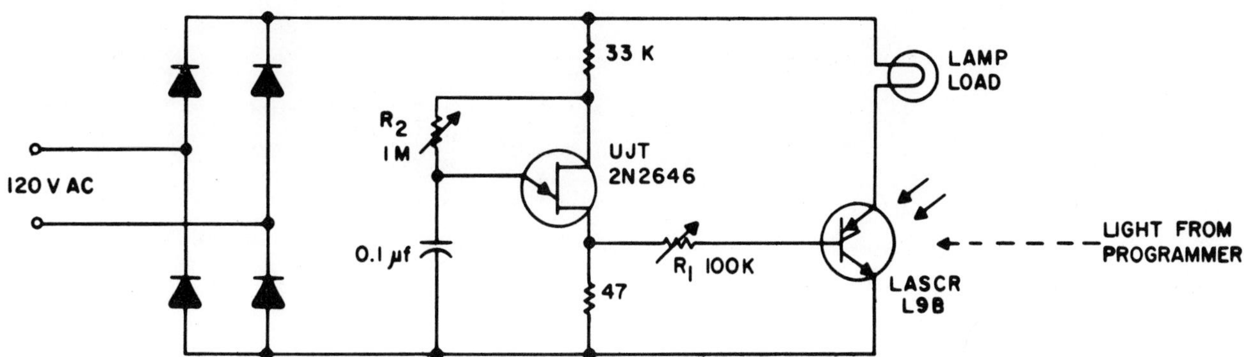

PREHEATING FOR PROGRAMMED LAMPS—Prevents thermal stresses on lamps that are optically programmed on and off for long periods of time. Ujt provides preheating by triggering lascr late in each half-cycle when programmed off. This keeps lamp current at minimum (adjusted with R2) required to maintain filament temperature just below visible level. R1 controls lascr sensitivity to light. Single ujt can serve several lascr-lamp circuits if separate gate resistor R1 is used for each lascr.—E. K. Howell, The Light Activated SCR, General Electric, Syracuse, N.Y., No. 200.34, 1965.

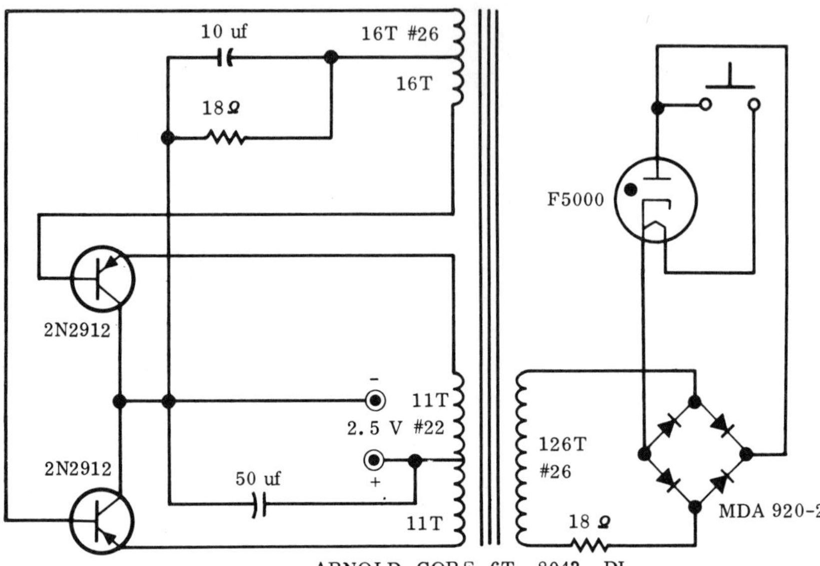

PORTABLE ULTRAVIOLET SOURCE—Converter circuit operates from 2.5-V rechargeable battery and supplies 400 mA at 26 V d-c for F5000 ultraviolet lamp. Frequency of inverter is 8 kHz.—"Circuits Manual," Motorola, Phoenix, Ariz., 1965, p 7–1–7.

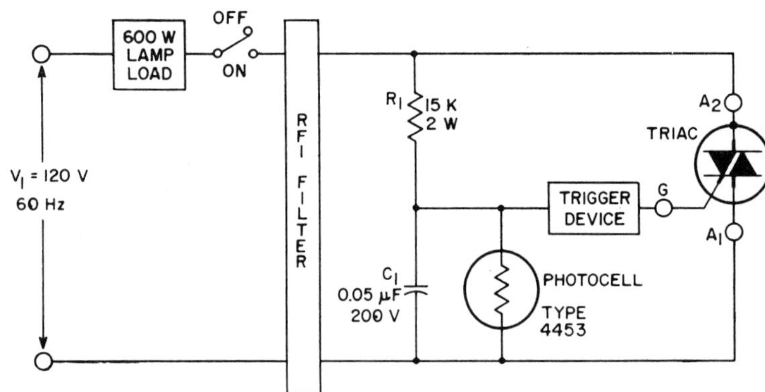

LAMPS ON AT NIGHT—Lamp load is turned on by triac when drop in illumination on photocell increases its impedance enough to make trigger diode turn on. Can be used for outdoor lighting controls.—"Silicon Power Circuits Manual," RCA, Harrison, N.J., SP-51, p 259.

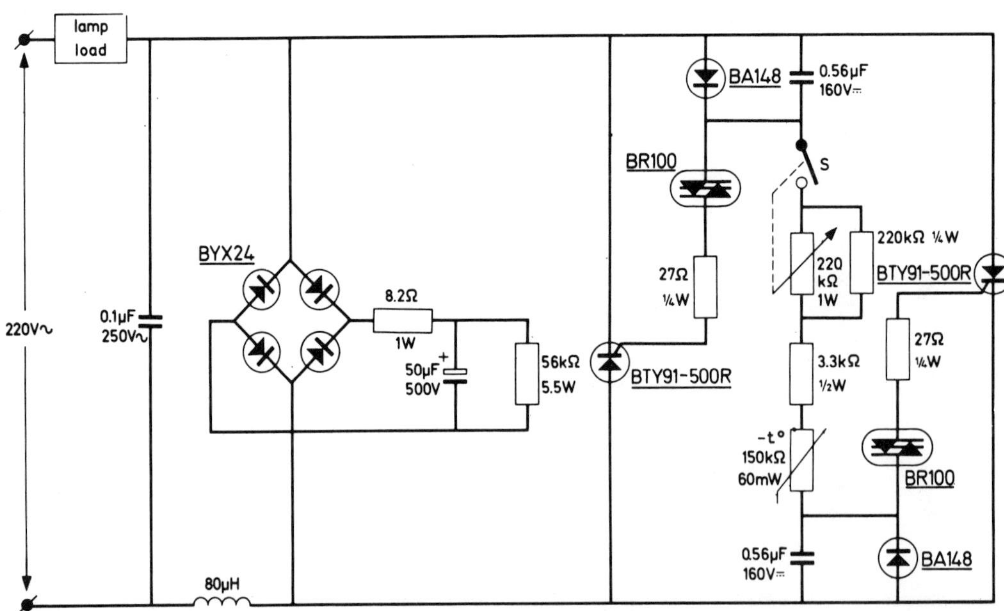

3-KW ANTIPARALLEL-THYRISTOR CONTROL—Will handle starting surges for lamp loads up to 3 kW, and up to 7 kW if there are no starting surges. Thermistor in R-C network limits amplitude and duration of initial current surge for incandescent lamps. Steepness of current transients is limited by 80-µH choke consisting of 50 turns wound on Ferroxcube 50-mm rod 10 mm in diameter.—Lamp Dimmer, Philips, Pub. Dept., Elcoma Div., Eindhoven, The Netherlands, No. 2, 1967.

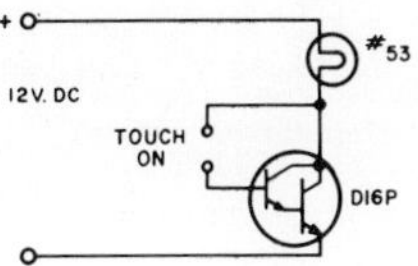

DARLINGTON TOUCH SWITCH—Lamp is turned on only while finger is touching both collector and base terminals of D16P Darlington transistor. Works well with slightly moist skin, but may not work for dry-skin touch.—E. K. Howell, Small Scale Integration in Low Cost Control Circuits, General Electric, Syracuse, N.Y., No. 671.9, 1968, p 19.

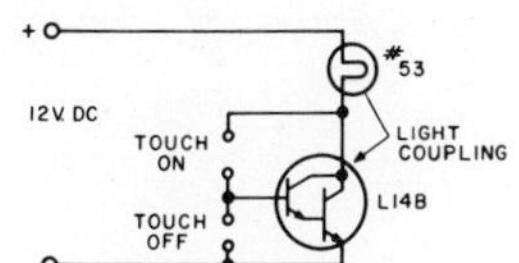

LATCHING TOUCH SWITCH—Touching finger to both collector and base of L14B Darlington transistor turns on lamp, and light coupling between lamp and L14B latches lamp on. Lamp is turned off by touching base and emitter terminals, bypassing light-generated internal base current. Works well with slightly moist skin, but may not work for dry-skin touch.—E. K. Howell, Small Scale Integration in Low Cost Control Circuits, General Electric, Syracuse, N.Y., No. 671.9, 1968, p 19.

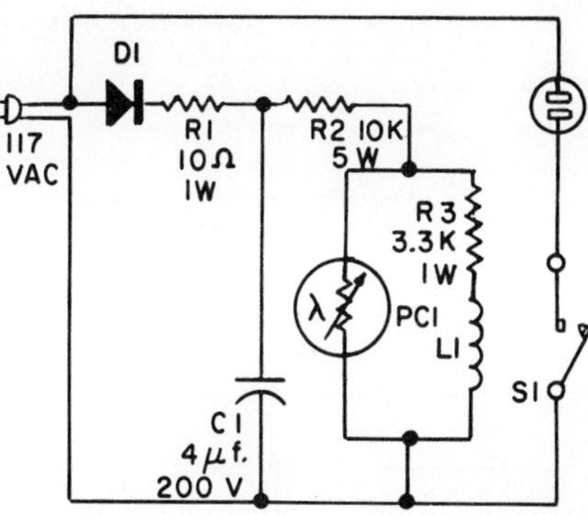

NIGHT LIGHT—Automatically turns 15-W light on at sunset and turns it off at sunrise. Uses GE-X7 magnetic reed switch for S1. Lamp plugs into outlet in series with switch. Diode D1 is GE-504. PC1 is GE-X6 or equivalent photocell.—"Hobby Manual," General Electric, Owensboro, Ky., 1965, p 120.

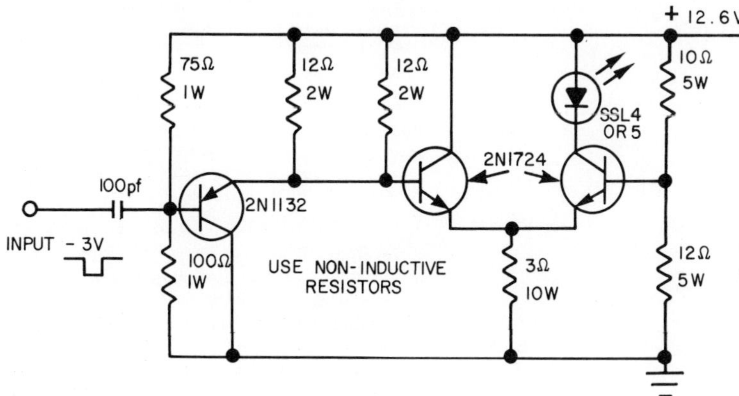

SWITCH FOR SOLID-STATE LAMP—Used in pulsed-light communication, with current-mode switch driving solid-state lamp with peak currents of 2 A at 50-ns rise and fall times.—L. M. Hertz, Solid State Lamps—Part II, General Electric, Cleveland, Ohio, No. 3-0121, 1970, p 21.

SOLID-STATE LAMP PULSER—Pulsing of ssl at 500 mA for 20% duty cycle increases light output up to five times. Asymmetrical flip-flop produces current drive for Q3 for 20% of period, which acts as low-current switch for constant-current source Q1-Q2 that pulses solid-state lamp. Period of flip-flop is about 350 μs.—L. M. Hertz, Solid State Lamps—Part II, General Electric, Cleveland, Ohio, No. 3-0121, 1970, p 26.

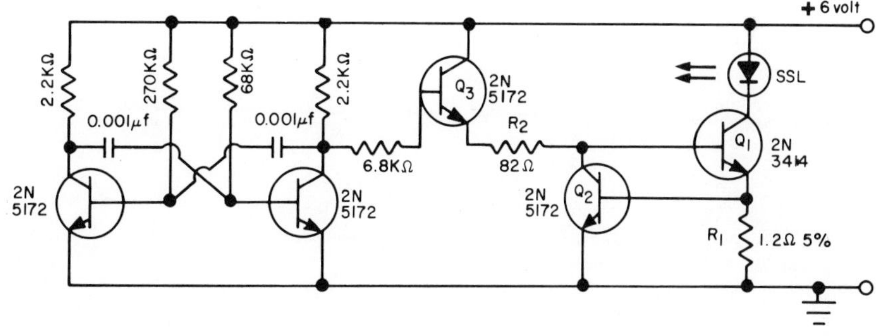

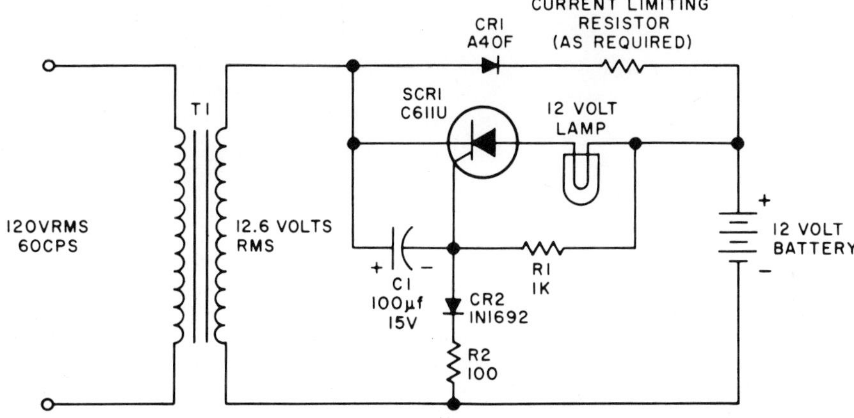

EMERGENCY-LIGHTING SWITCH—Provides battery-operated emergency lighting instantaneously and automatically when 120-V a-c line power fails. When a-c power is restored, emergency lamp is turned off and battery recharged. Suitable for restaurants, shops, corridors, elevators, and other places where loss of illumination is undesirable or intolerable.—D. R. Grafham, Using Low Current SCR's, General Electric, Syracuse, N.Y., No. 200.19, 1967, p 33.

EMERGENCY LIGHT—Turns on battery-powered lamp instantly when a-c power service fails. Emergency light turns off when line power is restored, and battery then recharges from a-c line. Requires no maintenance.—"Silicon Controlled Rectifier," General Electric, Syracuse, N.Y., No. 150.9, 1969.

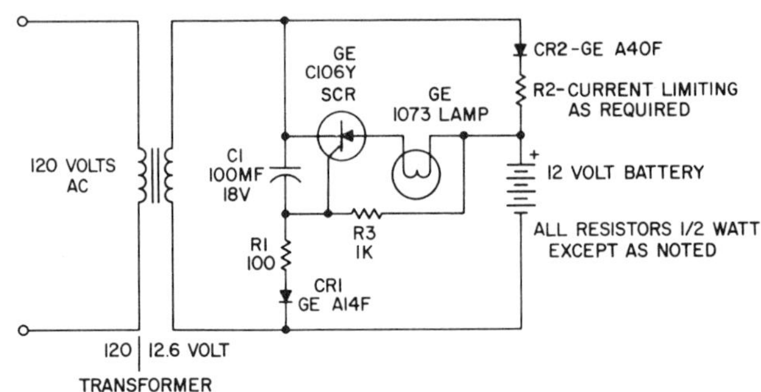

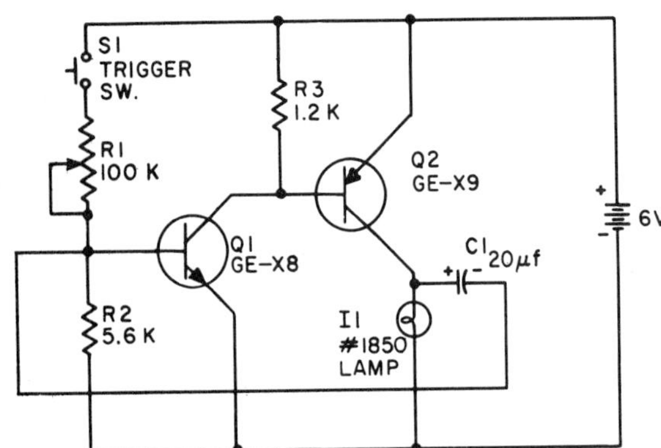

TRIGGERED LIGHT SOURCE—Can be used with appropriate focusing lens in light-source gun, for shooting alleys where target rifles are not permissible. Intended for use with photoelectric target that flashes when hit by light beam.—"Hobby Manual," General Electric, Owensboro, Ky., 1965, p 79.

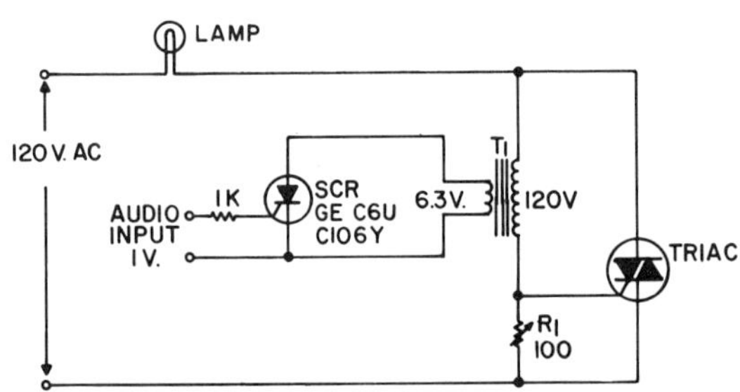

NOTE: T_1 IS A 6.3 V, 1 A. "FILAMENT" TRANSFORMER. ADJUST R_1 FOR MAXIMUM RESISTANCE THAT WILL NOT TURN ON LAMP WITH ZERO INPUT.

AUDIO-CONTROLLED LAMP—Low audio input voltage (1 V) provides on-off control of 120-V 500-W lamp. Switching action of scr-triac combination is very rapid compared to response times of lamp and human eye, so effect produced with audio input is similar to proportional control circuit. If input to scr consists of phase-controlled pulses, full-wave control of lamp load is obtained.—J. H. Galloway, Using the Triac for Control of AC Power, General Electric, Syracuse, N.Y., No. 200.35, 1966, p 14.

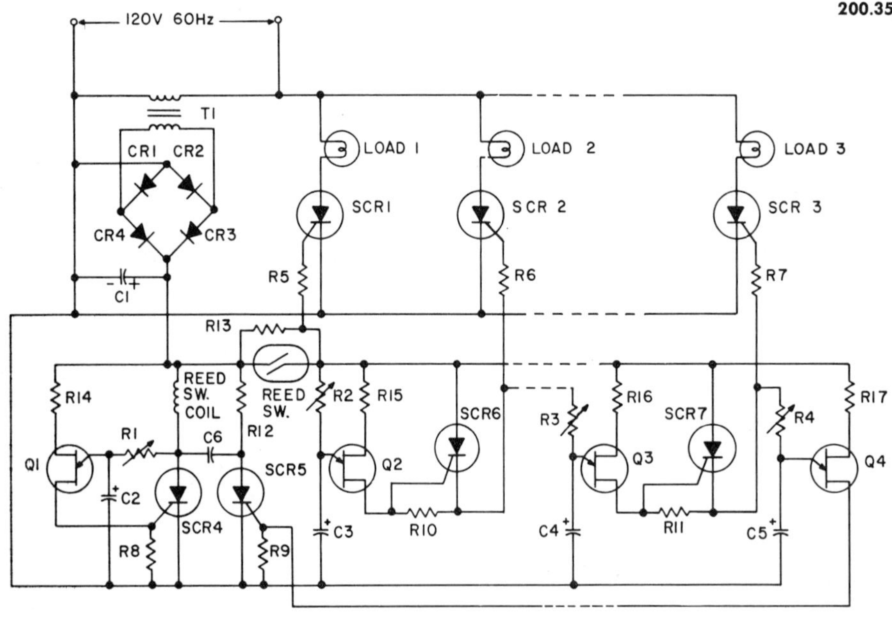

HALF-WAVE CHASER—Used for turning on string of lights sequentially to give effect of moving sign. Each stage has individual timing adjustment. When power is applied, all scr's are off; Q1 starts timing and, after delay set by R1, fires SCR4 which energizes reed switch. This turns SCR1 and first lamp on, and initiates timing of Q2 for delayed firing of SCR6 and SCR2. Process continues until Q4 fires, turning on SCR5 and turning off SCR4. Reed switch then drops out, turning off all scr's except SCR5 and resetting circuit for next sequential flashing cycle.—A. A. Adem, Flashers, Ring Counters and Chasers, General Electric, Syracuse, N.Y., No. 200.48, 1966, p 7.

R1, R2, R3, R4 : 500K POTS
R5, R6, R7, : 750Ω 1/2 W
R8, R9 : 1K 1/2 W
R10, R11 : 33Ω 1/2 W
R12 470Ω 1/2 W
R13 : 1 MEG 1/2 W
R14, R15, R16, R17 : 330Ω 1/2 W

C1 : 500μF 25 V
C2, C3, C4, C5 : 2μF, 10V
C6 : .22μF 100V
T1 : 120 : 12.6 STEPDOWN
REED SW : GE 2DR15 (1 AMP)
GE 2DR30 (3 AMP)
REED SW COIL : 10,000 T #39 WIRE 825Ω
CR1 - CR4 : (4) GE A13A

Q1 - Q4 : (4) GE 2N2646 UJT
SCR1 - SCR3 (3) GE C20B
SCR4 - SCR7 (4) GE C106Y
LOADS : 550 WATTS EACH

ADDITIONAL STAGES MAY BE ADDED BETWEEN DASHED LINES.

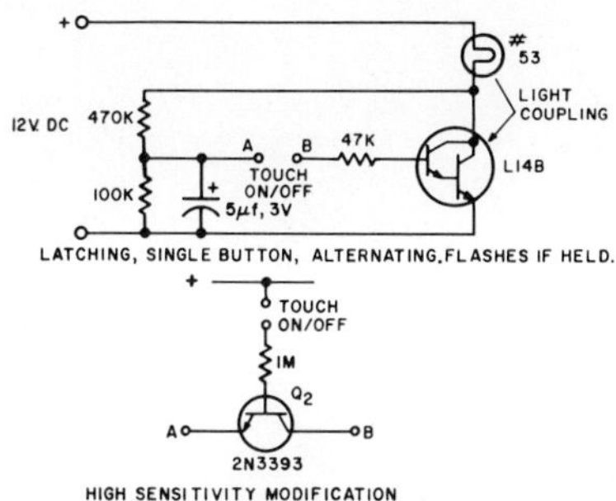

SINGLE-BUTTON ON-OFF TOUCH SWITCH—Touching single pair of contacts alternately turns lamp on and off. Lamp flashes if finger is held on button. Latching is provided by light coupling between lamp and L14B Darlington transistor. Works well with slightly moist skin, but may not work for dry-skin touch. High-sensitivity modification ensures dry-skin operation.—E. K. Howell, Small Scale Integration in Low Cost Control Circuits, General Electric, Syracuse, N.Y., No. 671.9, 1968, p 19.

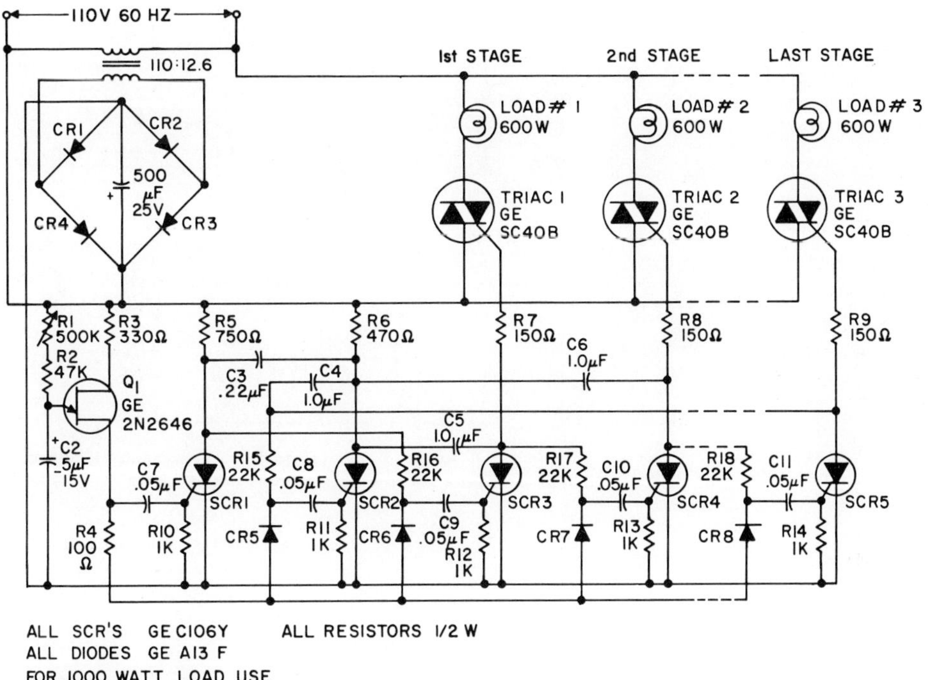

A-C CHASER—Modification of ring counter is used for turning on string of lights sequentially to give effect of moving sign. When power is first turned on, all scr's are off and ujt oscillator is energized by bridge rectifier. At end of delay determined by setting of R1, ujt fires and turns on SCR1. Next firing of ujt turns on SCR3 and fires triac 1. Next two pulses turn on SCR4 and SCR5 in turn and fire triacs 2 and 3 in turn. Following pulse fires SCR2 which commutates other four scr's off. Next pulse starts cycle over again by turning SCR1 on and SCR2 off. OFF time thus takes two pulses and ON time one pulse, which makes performance more appealing to the eye. If ujt frequency is 1 Hz, each lamp is on 1 s and off 2 s.—A. A. Adem, Flashers, Ring Counters and Chasers, General Electric, Syracuse, N.Y., No. 200.48, 1966, p 6.

NOTE: To locate additional circuits in the category of this chapter, use the index at the back of this book. Check also the author's "Sourcebook of Electronic Circuits," published by McGraw-Hill in 1968.

CHAPTER 44
Lamp Dimmer Circuits

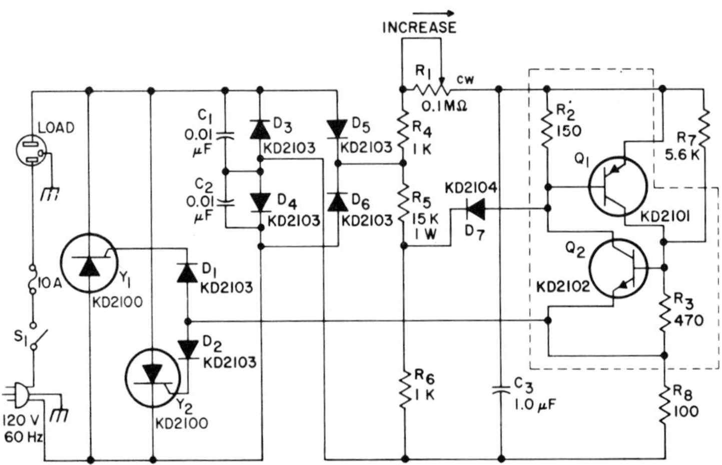

DUAL-SCR DIMMER—Can handle 500-W incandescent-lamp load, heater, or universal motor, providing full range of control and high reliability.—"Silicon Controlled Rectifier Experimenter's Manual," RCA, Harrison, N.J., 1967, p 49.

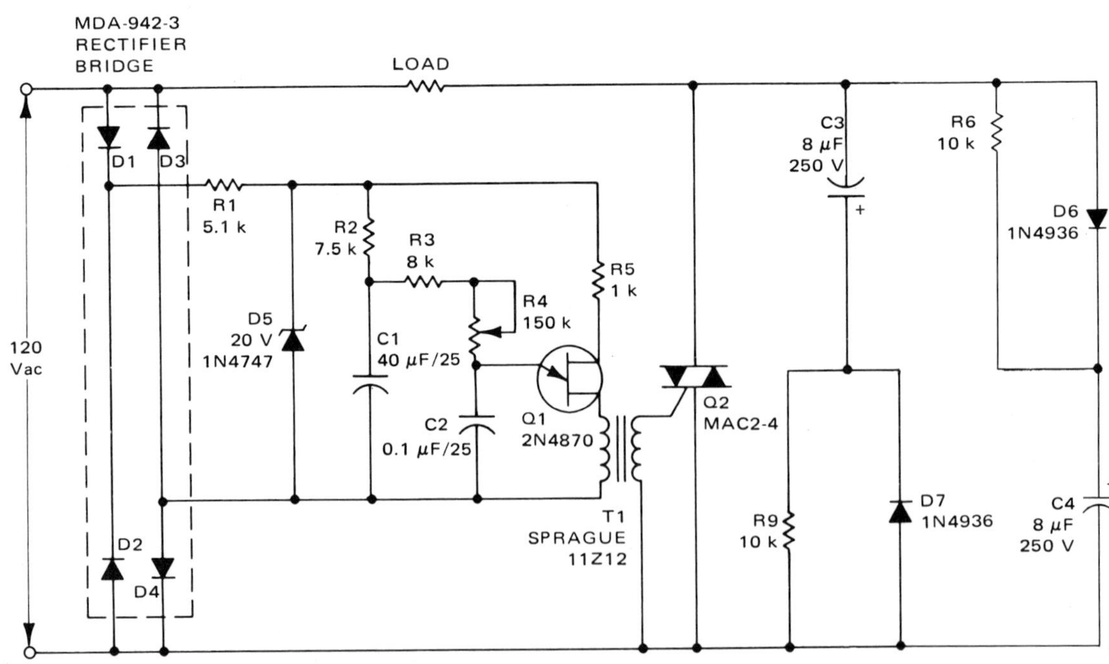

800-W SOFT-START DIMMER—Combining soft-start feature with dimmer control R4 prevents high inrush currents to cold filaments of incandescent lamps, thereby extending lamp life. Accidental turnon is prevented by special dv/dt network including capacitors C3 and C4.—"Semiconductor Power Circuits Handbook," Motorola, Phoenix, Ariz., 1968, p 6–14.

20-MINUTE DIMMER—Time-dependent incandescent-lamp dimmer handles up to 600-W load with triac specified. High input impedance of Darlington Q1-Q2 permits very long charging and discharging times for C1, to give very slow turn-on or turn-off of lamp load, depending on setting of SW1. At maximum-resistance setting of R3, about 20 minutes is required for lights to dim automatically from full-on to full-off. Also called bachelor light.—F. W. Gutzwiller and E. K. Howell, Economy Power Semiconductor Applications, General Electric, Syracuse, N.Y., No. 671.1, 1965, p 14.

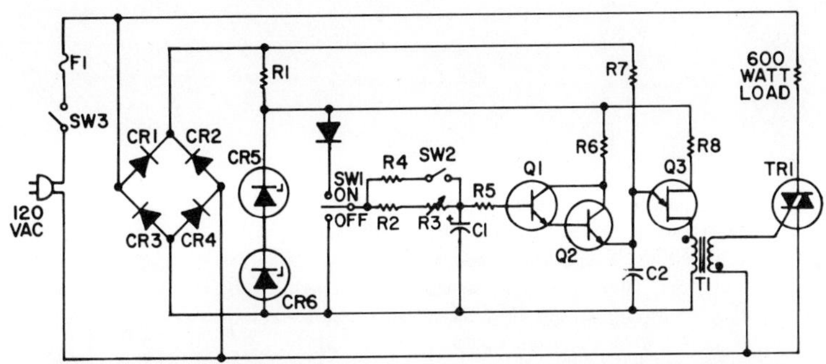

CRI THRU CR4 : G-E INI693 RECTIFIER DIODE
CR5, CR6 : G-E Z4XL7.5 ZENER DIODE
CR7 : G-E INI692 RECTIFIER DIODE
CI : 100 μf, 15 WVDC ELECTROLYTIC CAPACITOR (G-E QTI-22)
C2 : 0.1 μf, 15 WVDC CAPACITOR
QI, Q2 : G-E 2N2712 n-p-n TRANSISTOR
Q3 : G-E 2N2647 UNIJUNCTION TRANSISTOR
TRI : TRIAC SC41B
FI : 3 AMPERE FUSE
RI : 3.3 K OHM, 2 WATT RESISTOR
R2,R4 : 4.7K OHM, 1/2 WATT RESISTOR
R3 : 5 MEGOHM, 1 WATT POTENTIOMETER
R5,R7 : 1 MEGOHM, 1/2 WATT RESISTOR
R6 : 2.2 K OHM, 1/2 WATT RESISTOR
R8 : 470 OHM, 1/2 WATT RESISTOR
SWI : SPDT SWITCH
SW2 : SPST SWITCH
TI : SPRAGUE 35ZM923 PULSE TRANSFORMER

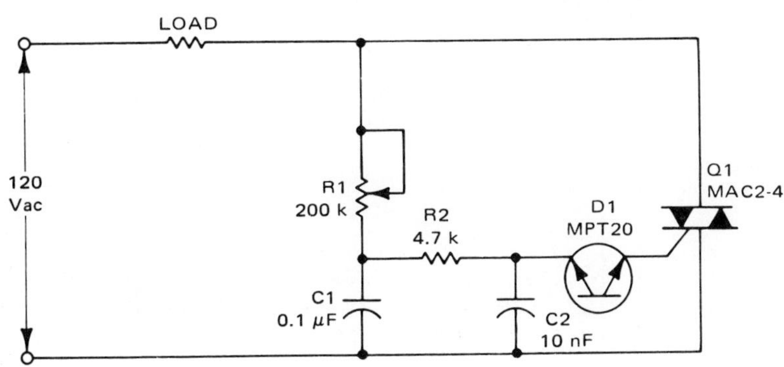

800-W TRIAC DIMMER—Simple control circuit controls conduction angle of triac from zero to about 170 degrees, providing better than 97% of full-power control. One possible problem is high starting current in lamps with cold filaments.—"Semiconductor Power Circuits Handbook," Motorola, Phoenix, Ariz., 1968, p 6–16.

FULL-RANGE DIMMER—Provides control from full brilliance to zero by switching out rectifier and half of potentiometer resistance at midpoint of dimming range.—"Circuits Manual," Motorola, Phoenix, Ariz., 1965, p 10–2–2.

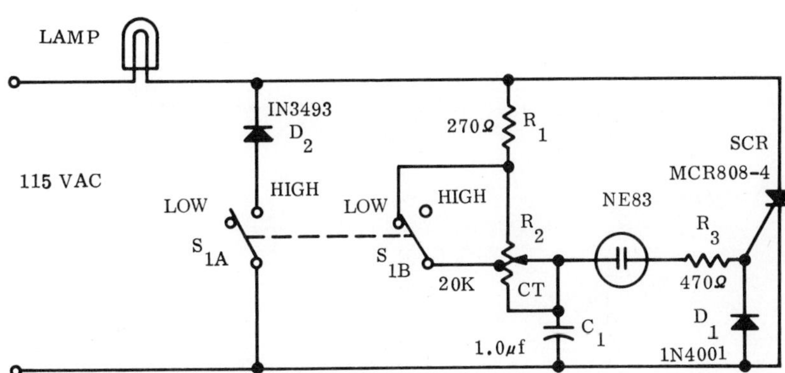

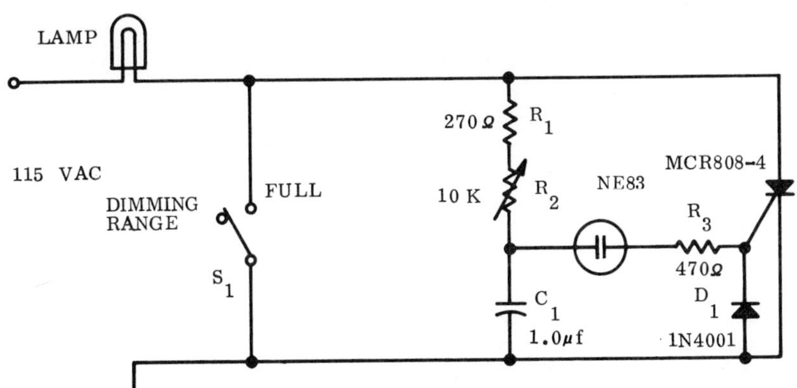

HALF-WAVE DIMMER—Provides from 70% of maximum brilliance down to zero. Switch bypasses control when full brilliance is desired. Rating of scr determines wattage of lamp.—"Circuits Manual," Motorola, Phoenix, Ariz., 1965, p 10–2–1.

CROSSFADER FOR SLIDE PROJECTORS—Tandem dimmer circuit can be used for such applications as fading between two slide projectors, two movie projectors, or two illuminated signs. Moving R3 to either side of center fires one triac earlier in each half-cycle and the other later, with total light output for both lamps staying about constant for all control positions. Choice of triac depends on lamp wattage.—J. H. Galloway, Using the Triac for Control of AC Power, General Electric, Syracuse, N.Y., No. 200.35, 1966, p 17.

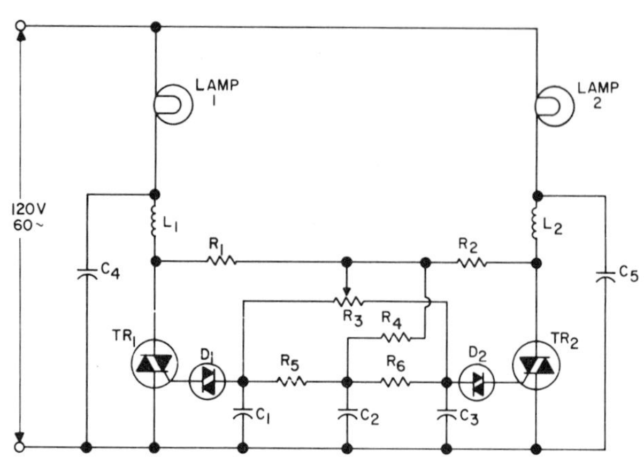

$R_1 = R_2 = 6800\Omega$, 1 WATT
$R_3 = 150K\ \Omega$ LINEAR POT. 1W
$R_5 = R_6 = 22K\Omega$, 1/2W.
$R_4 = 15K\Omega$, 1/2W.
$TR_1 = TR_2 =$ TRIAC
$D_1 = D_2 =$ GE ST-2 DIAC

$L_1 = L_2 = 60\mu hy$ (FERRITE CORE)
$C_1 = C_2 = C_3 = 0.1\mu f$ 50V
$C_4 = C_5 = 0.1\mu f$ 200 VOLTS

NOTE: TOTAL LIGHT LEVEL (SUM OF LAMPS 1+2) CONSTANT WITHIN 15%.

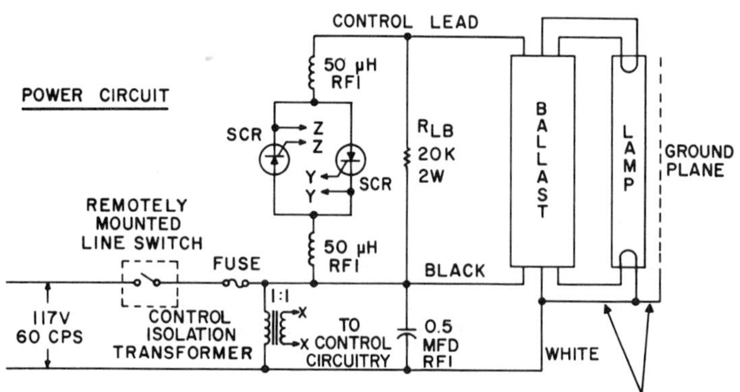

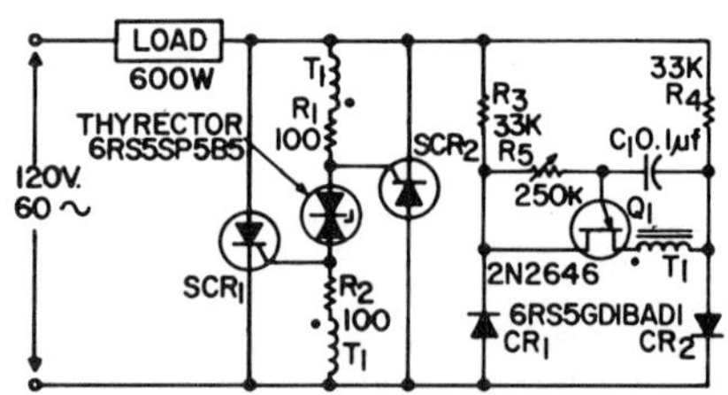

FULL-WAVE 600-W SCR CONTROL—Provides manual dimming of lamp load with R5, but over limited range. Can also be used for heater and fan control.—F. W. Gutzwiller and E. K. Howell, Economy Power Semiconductor Applications, General Electric, Syracuse, N.Y., No. 671.1, 1965, p 15.

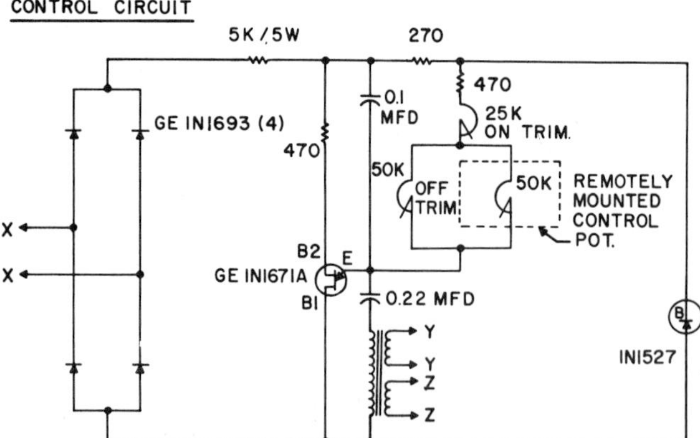

FLUORESCENT DIMMER—Uses scr's connected in inverse parallel with special G-E 89G718 dimming ballast for one F40T12 rapid-start fluorescent lamp. Includes rfi suppression. Excellent basic reference article on design requirements for fluorescent dimmers. Choice of scr depends on average value of current waveform; C11 and C15 types are adequate for all but largest installations. Ground plane, consisting of metal strip 1" from lamp and connected to common or white side of line, is necessary as starting aid for lowest setting of control.—E. E. Von Zastrow, Fluorescent Lamp Dimming with SCR's and Associated Semiconductors, General Electric, Syracuse, N.Y., No. 200.18, 1962.

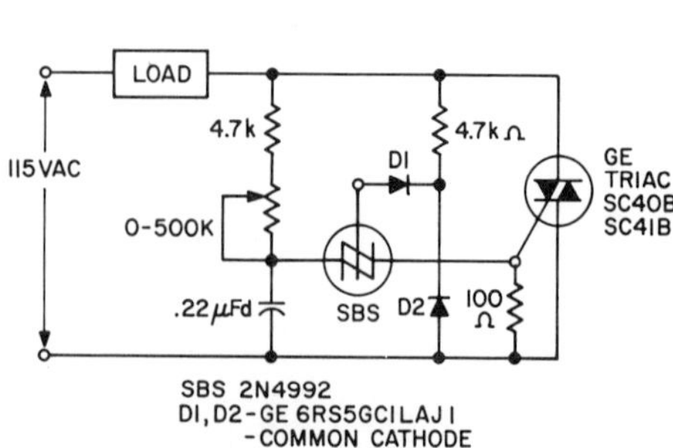

LAMP DIMMER—Silicon bilateral switch and triac give hysteresis-free phase control for lamp dimming and similar applications. 8-V switching voltage of sbs is stable over wide temperature range.—Silicon Economy Bilateral Switch 2N4992, General Electric, Syracuse, N.Y., No. 65.32, 1967.

$C_1\,C_2$ = 0.068 microfarad, 200 volts, 10%

F_1 = fuse, size suitable to load

I_1 = lamp, neon type NE-83

Q_1 = triac, RCA 40502 or RCA 40429 (the RCA 40429 may be used with the Wakefield No. NC401K or equivalent heat sink.)

R_1 = potentiometer, 50,000 ohms, 2 watts, linear taper

R_2 = 15,000 ohms, 1/2 watt, 10%, carbon

S_1 = switch, 120 volt, single-pole, single-throw, capable of handling expected load current

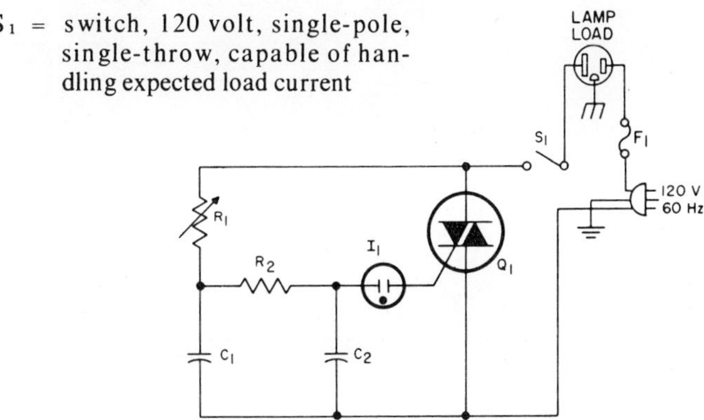

700-W DIMMER—Triac provides full-wave control from maximum brilliance down to zero illumination for incandescent lamp loads. Heat sink must be used with triac for loads above 300 W.—"Hobby Circuits Manual," RCA, Harrison, N.J., HM-90, p 81.

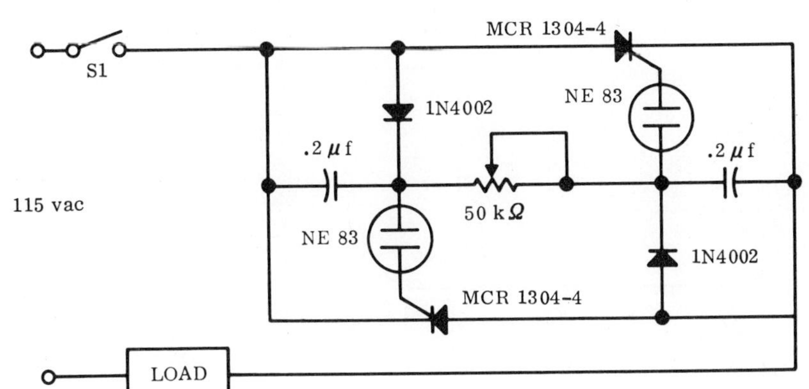

TWO-SCR DIMMER—Handles 300-W lamp and provides full range of brilliance control, using minimum number of low-cost components.—"Circuits Manual," Motorola, Phoenix, Ariz., 1965, p 10–2–3.

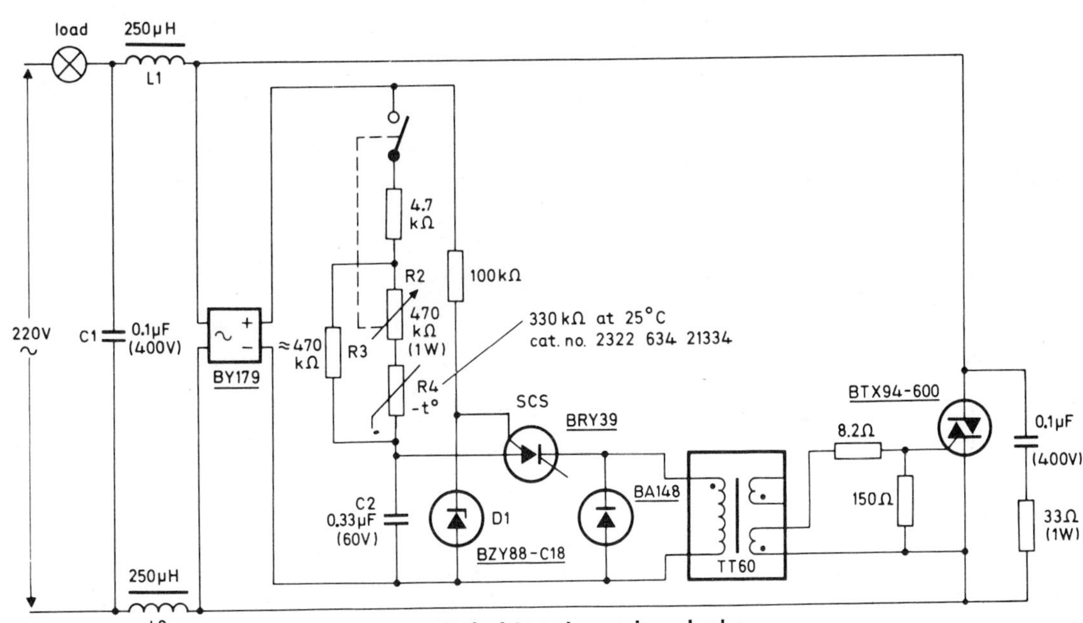

3,000-W LAMP DIMMER—Triac controlled by scs handles starting surges and gives smooth power control of incandescent lamp load up to 3 kW.—G. J. Derksen and G. J. Tobisch, Lamp Dimmer, Philips, Pub. Dept., Elcoma Div., Eindhoven, The Netherlands, No. 82, 1970.

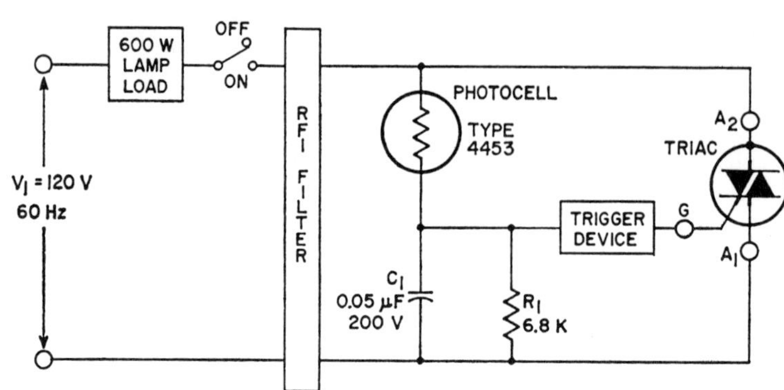

LIGHT TURNS ON LAMP GRADUALLY—Increase in light on photocell causes proportional reduction in cell resistance, to make trigger-triac increase lamp load voltage proportionally.—"Silicon Power Circuits Manual," RCA, Harrison, N.J., SP-51, p 259.

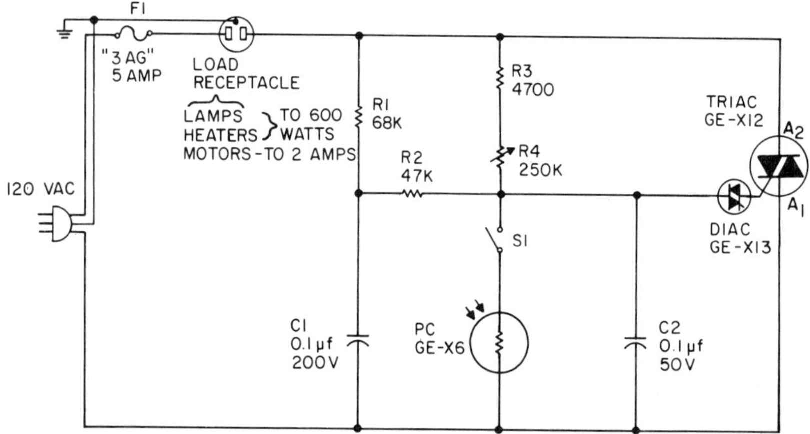

FULL-WAVE DIMMER AND MOTOR CONTROL—Gives full symmetrical control from zero to 100% of line voltage for lamp or motor plugged into load receptacle. Also includes cadmium sulfide photocell for turning lamp on automatically in home at dusk. With shaded-pole fan or blower motor, range of speed control is about 4 to 1. With motors, performance is improved by placing 100-ohm 1-W resistor in series with 0.1-μF capacitor across triac.—"Hobby Manual," General Electric, Owensboro, Ky., 1965, p 147.

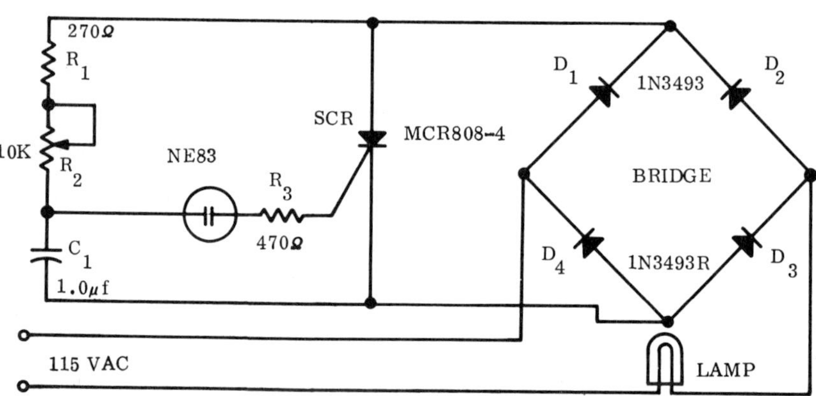

FULL-WAVE BRIDGE DIMMER—Gives full range of control from maximum brilliance to zero continuously with single scr that is phase-controlled over both halves of cycle.—"Circuits Manual," Motorola, Phoenix, Ariz., 1965, p 10–2–2.

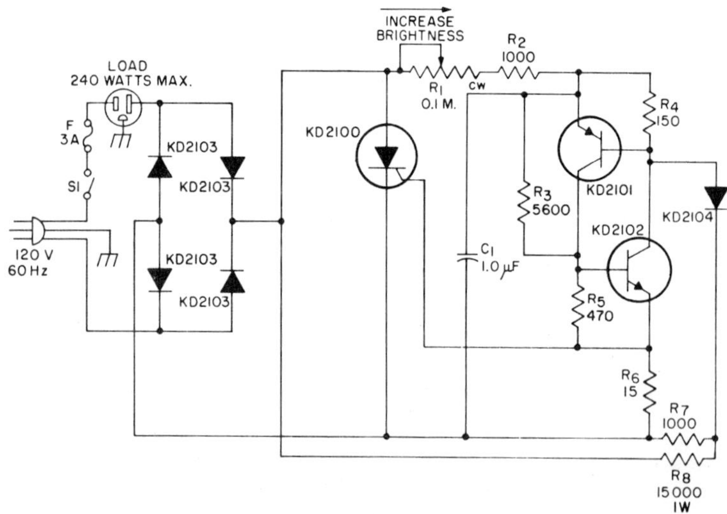

240-W DIMMER—R1 adjusts point in each half-cycle of a-c line at which scr is triggered for passing current through lamp load. Provides full range of brightness control. Produces some rfi, which can be reduced with L-filter consisting of 0.05-μF paper capacitor on which is wound 18 ft of No. 18E wire, with choke in series with load. Capacitor is connected between lamp-coil junction and other side of line.—"Silicon Controlled Rectifier Experimenter's Manual," RCA, Harrison, N.J., 1967, p 45.

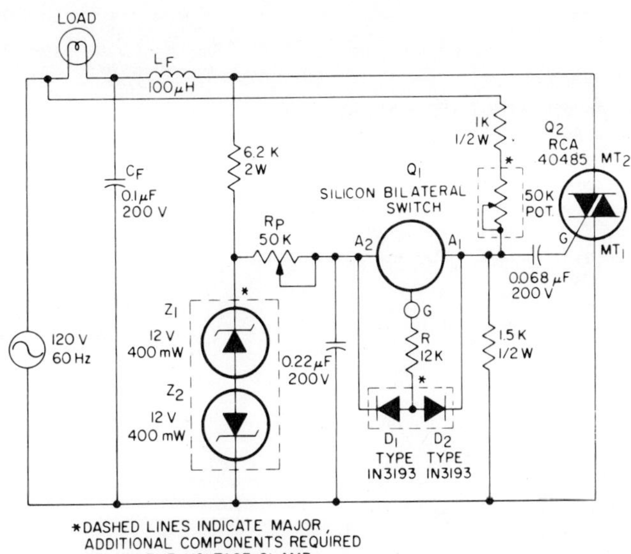

DIMMER WITH CLAMPING—Steering diodes D1 and D2 act with R to permit larger conduction angles and prevent circuit from misfiring at low light levels when subjected to dips in line voltage. Circuit also extends lamp life by holding line voltage rises to within 3% of 120 V.—G. J. Granieri, AC Voltage Regulators Using Thyristors, RCA, Harrison, N.J., AN-3886, 1969.

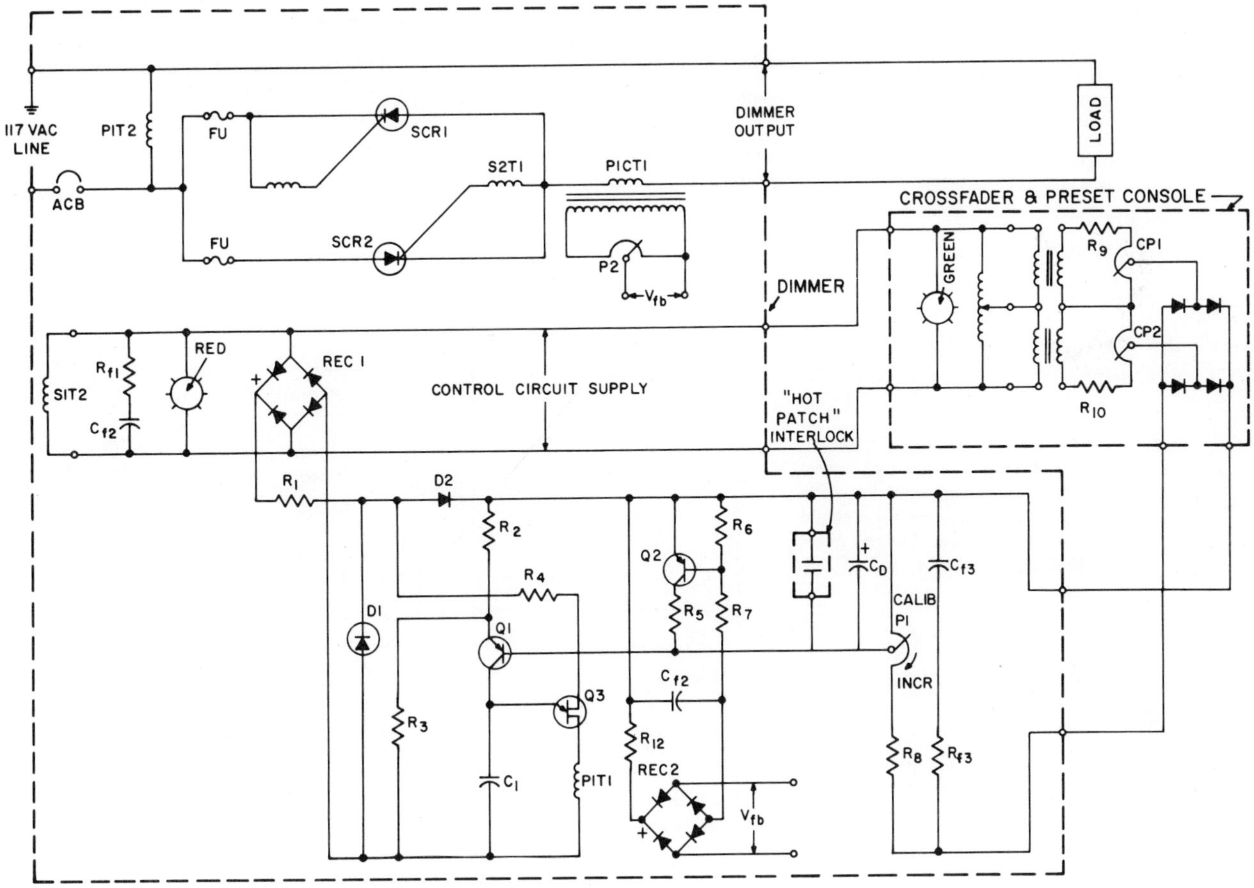

DIMMER WITH PRESET AND CROSSFADER—Solid-state incandescent-lamp dimmer may have any number of presets, although circuit shows only one load with two-scene preset for theatrical applications. When crossfader control is moved and voltage is taken away from one circuit of preset and applied to another, takeover circuit applies the larger of the two voltages acting on it to dimmer as input reference. Values are: P1 1K; R1 3K; R2 470; R3 22K; R4 220; R5 47; R6 330; R7 22K; R8-10 3.3K; C1 0.2 μF; CD 200 μF; REC-1-2 4 G-E 1N1695; D1 1N1527; Q1-2 2N525; Q3 2N1671A; D2 1N536; T1 UTC H51.—E. E. Von Zastrow, The Silicon Controlled Rectifier in Lamp Dimming and Heating Control Service, General Electric, Syracuse, N.Y., No. 200.14, 1965.

600-W DIMMER WITH SERIES GATE RESISTOR—Resistor R3, in series with trigger device (usually avalanche diode) limits discharge current from C2, to reduce instantaneous voltage drop across C2 and minimize both hysteresis and quick-turn-on effect.—"Silicon Power Circuits Manual," RCA, Harrison, N.J., SP-51, p 258.

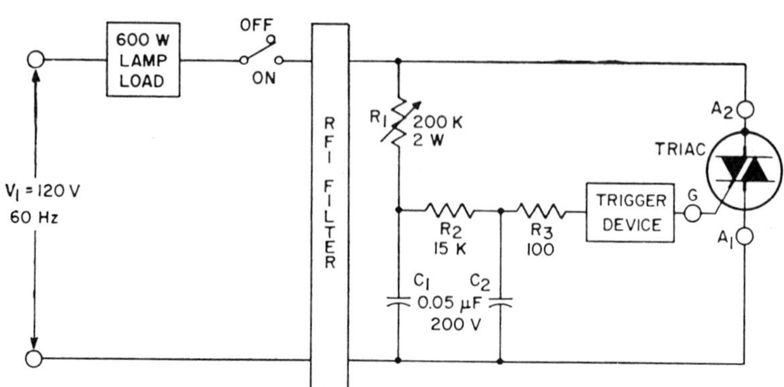

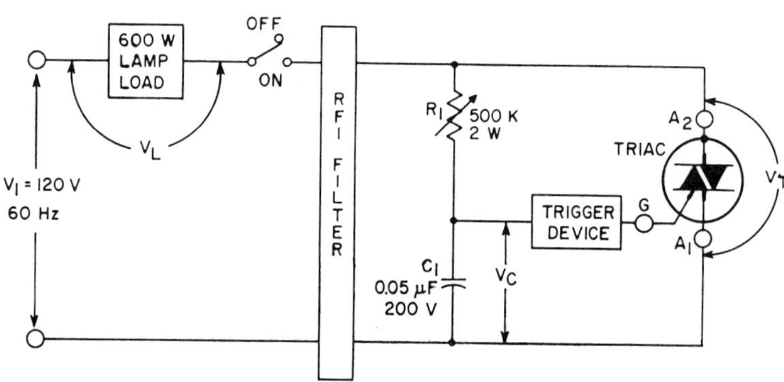

SINGLE-TIME-CONSTANT 600-W PHASE CONTROL—Used as dimmer. Has some hysteresis effect. Will turn on incandescent lamp with appreciable initial brilliance, for reasons explained in book.—"Silicon Power Circuits Manual," RCA, Harrison, N.J., SP-51, p 256.

DOUBLE-TIME-CONSTANT 600-W DIMMER—Gives lower initial load voltage and lower initial lamp brightness, along with less hysteresis, than phase control circuit having single time constant.—"Silicon Power Circuits Manual," RCA, Harrison, N.J., SP-51, p 257.

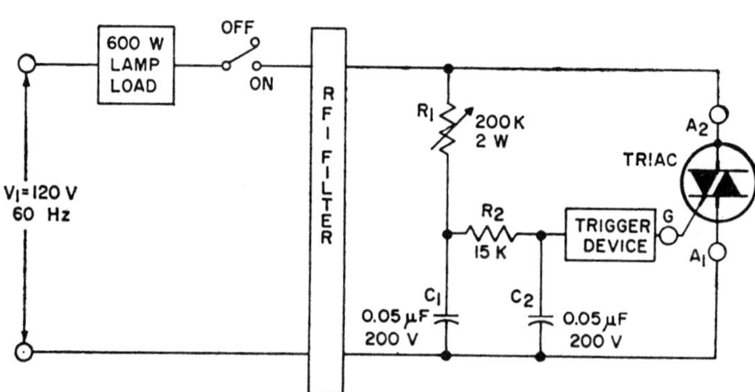

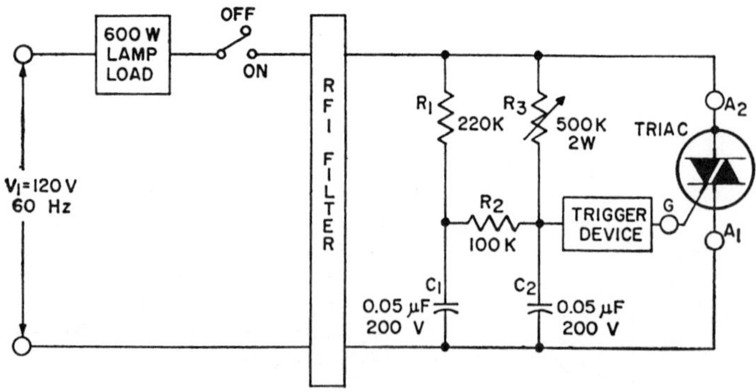

600-W WITH TRIAC BLEEDER CURRENT—Prevents triac from going completely out of conduction, thereby preventing hysteresis and preventing turn-on at undesirably high illumination level.—"Silicon Power Circuits Manual," RCA, Harrison, N.J., SP-51, p 258.

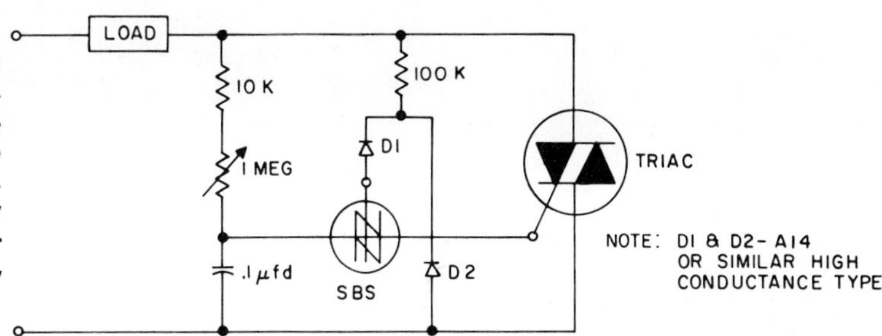

12-V A-C LAMP DIMMER—Full-wave triac phase control circuit uses D13Q1 silicon bilateral switch as trigger to achieve hysteresis-free operation for control of low-voltage load. Choice of triac depends on load power. —W. R. Spofford, Jr., Applications of the New Silicon Bilateral Switch and the Silicon Unilateral Switch, General Electric, Syracuse, N.Y., No. 671.3, 1966, p 8.

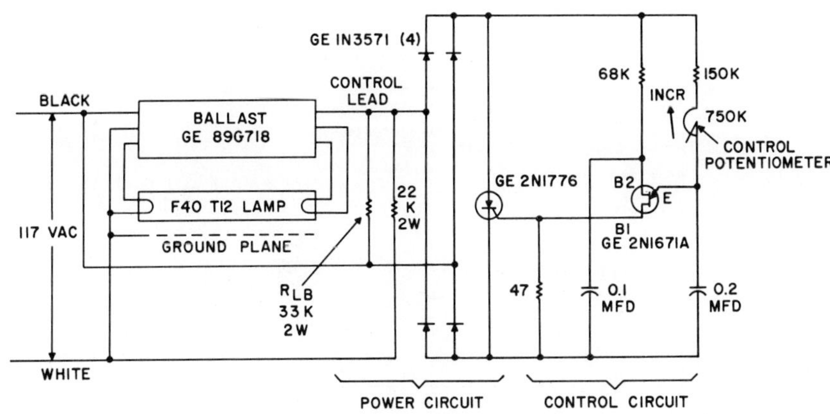

LOW-COST FLUORESCENT DIMMER—Uses rectified ballast voltage directly for control circuit, to reduce number of components while still giving satisfactorily smooth dimming. Does not include trim pot for making all lamps track when dimming large numbers in cove or valance lighting. Lamp requires ground plane (metal strip) 1" away as starting aid at low light levels. Excellent basic reference article on design requirements for fluorescent dimmers.—E. E. Von Zastrow, Fluorescent Lamp Dimming with SCR's and Associated Semiconductors, General Electric, Syracuse, N.Y., No. 200.18, 1962.

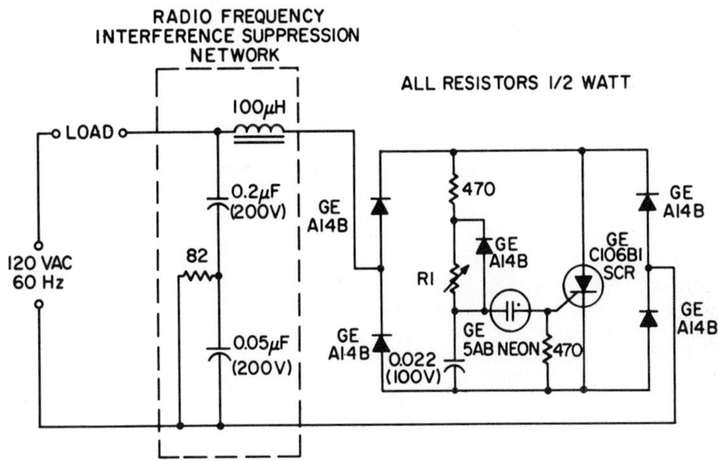

HIGH-INTENSITY LAMP DIMMER—Used to dim miniature low-voltage desk lamps operating from small transformer. Includes rfi filter that also serves to prevent transients from triggering scr. R1 should be 250K. Can also serve as speed control for 120-V a-c shaded-pole fan motors rated up to 1.5 A, if R1 is changed to 100K. Speed range is about 3:1. —D. R. Grafham, Fan Motor Speed Control—"Hi-Intensity" Lamp Dimmer, General Electric, Syracuse, N.Y., No. 201.16, 1966.

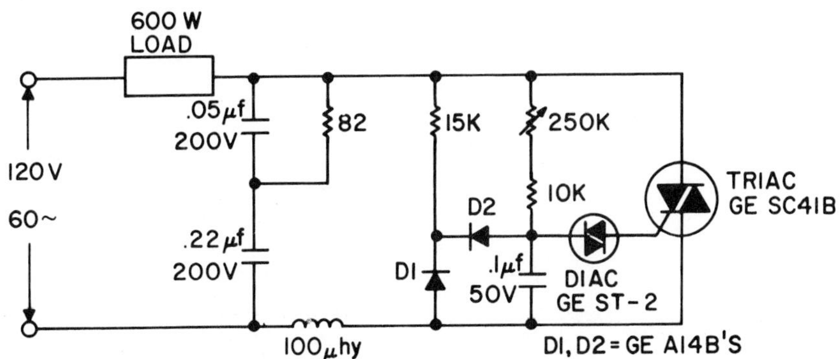

600-W TRIAC LAMP DIMMER—Includes built-in damping for L-C filter to maintain proper operation of triac during dimming action.—J. H. Galloway, Using the Triac for Control of AC Power, General Electric, Syracuse, N.Y., No. 200.35, 1966, p 10.

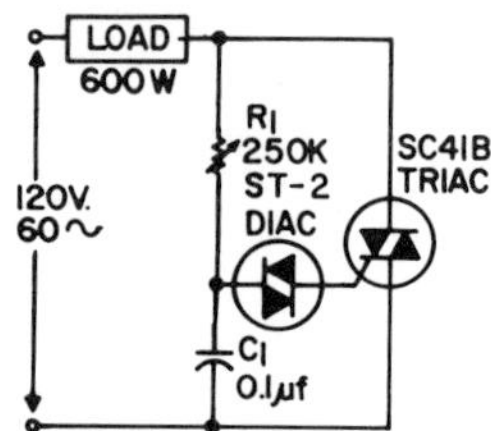

FULL-WAVE 600-W TRIAC—Provides manual dimming of lamp load with R1, but over limited range. For photoelectric control, replace R1 with cadmium sulfide photocell such as G-E B425. To reverse function of photoelectric control, place photocell in parallel with C1 and change R1 to 10K. Can also be used for heater and fan control.—F. W. Gutzwiller and E. K. Howell, Economy Power Semiconductor Applications, General Electric, Syracuse, N.Y., No. 671.1, 1965, p 15.

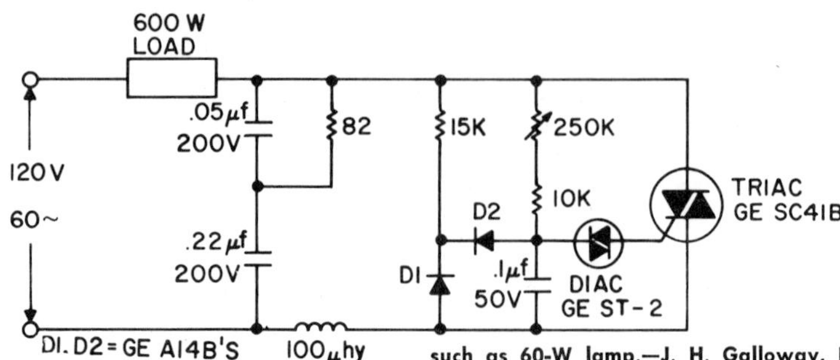

600-W DIAC-TRIAC DIMMER—Circuit includes damped r-f filter for suppression of rfi without affecting triggering of triac at small loads such as 60-W lamp.—J. H. Galloway, RF Filter Considerations for Triac and SCR Circuits, General Electric, Syracuse, N.Y., No. 201.19, 1966.

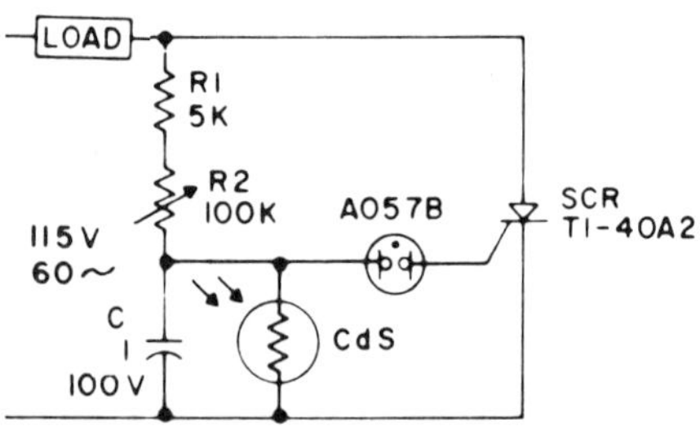

PHOTOCELL-CONTROLLED DIMMER—Initial light level is set with R2 when CdS cell is dark. As cell is exposed to light, neon lamp triggers scr and power to lamp load decreases. Choice of cadmium sulfide cell determines light sensitivity of circuit.—E. Bauman, "Applications of Neon Lamps and Gas Discharge Tubes," Signalite, Neptune, N.J., p 124.

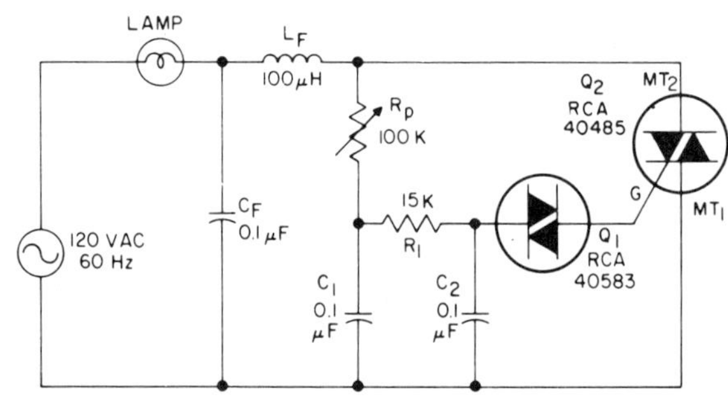

LOW-HYSTERESIS DIMMER—Provides continuous control up to maximum conduction angle. If Rp is set for high resistance (low illumination) and line voltage drops momentarily, high breakover voltage of diac Q1 combined with high resistance could cause circuit misfire, with lamp remaining extinguished until control is readjusted to higher light level.—G. J. Granieri, AC Voltage Regulators Using Thyristors, RCA, Harrison, N.J., AN-3886, 1969.

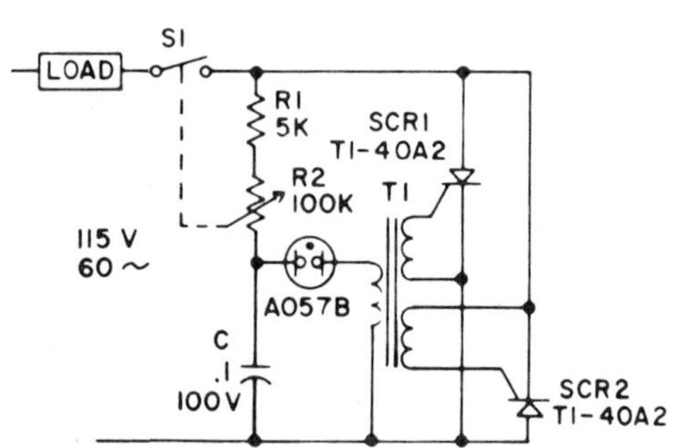

FLICKERLESS DIMMER—Since both scr's are fired by same timing circuit made up of neon lamp and pulse transformer, unsymmetrical firing problem is eliminated and there is no flickering of lamp load at low light levels. T1 may be Sprague 31Z286 or equivalent 1:1:1 with 40 turns per winding. S1 is ganged to R2 to disconnect load.—E. Bauman, "Applications of Neon Lamps and Gas Discharge Tubes," Signalite, Neptune, N.J., p 123.

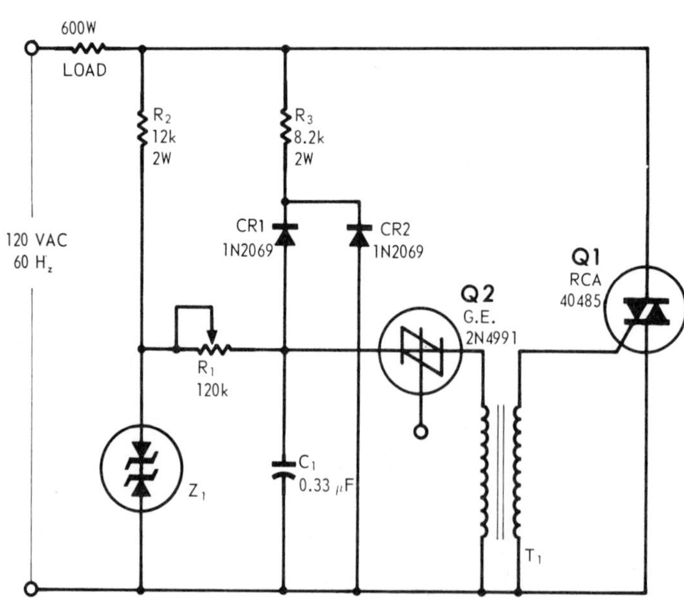

600-W A-C LOAD CONTROL—Provides smooth control of lamp or other load from 2% to 98% of full power, with R1 changing conduction angle for both halves of cycle.—J. J. Klinikowski, Cheap, Simple AC Power Control, *EDN*, Jan. 15, 1970, p 63.

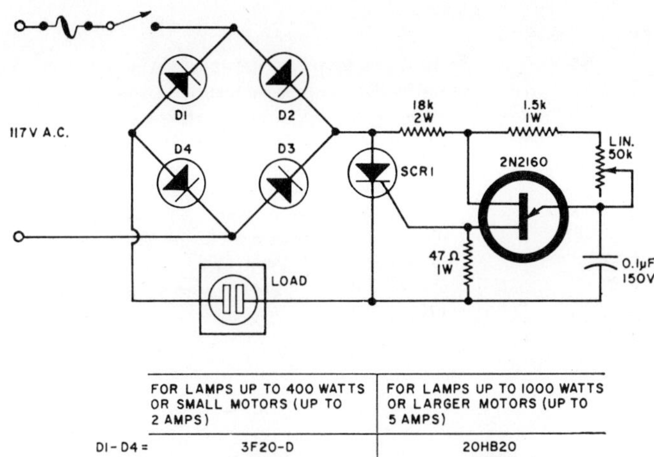

	FOR LAMPS UP TO 400 WATTS OR SMALL MOTORS (UP TO 2 AMPS)	FOR LAMPS UP TO 1000 WATTS OR LARGER MOTORS (UP TO 5 AMPS)
D1-D4 =	3F20-D	20HB20
SCR1 =	2N1774	2N685

LAMP DIMMER—With 2N1774 for SCR1 and 3F20-D diodes, circuit will handle lamps up to 400 W or motors drawing up to 2 A. With 2N685 for SCR1 and 20HB20 diodes, will handle up to 100 W lamp load or motors drawing up to 5 A.—D. Cooper, SCR's and Triacs—the Revolution Continues, *Electronics World,* Aug. 1968, p 25–28.

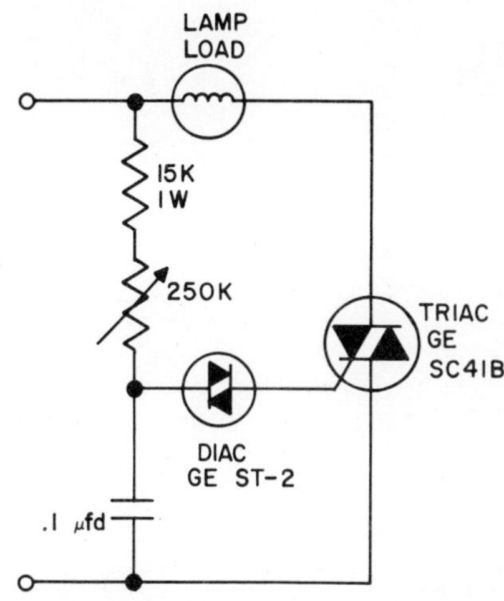

TABLE LAMP DIMMER—Designed for mounting inside lamp, where space is usually at a premium. Only drawback is slight hysteresis effect. Circuit takes advantage of availability of both sides of lamp load.—J. H. Galloway, Using the Triac for Control of AC Power, General Electric, Syracuse, N.Y., No. 200.35, 1966, p 19.

LIMITED-RANGE CONTROL—Provides control only over range from half to full power, which is sufficient for most illumination control applications. Rectifier supplies one half-cycle uncontrolled, with scr providing ramp-and-pedestal phase control for other half-cycle. Low-resistance photocell is used to give fast response time and eliminate hunting. —F. W. Gutzwiller and E. K. Howell, Economy Power Semiconductor Applications, General Electric, Syracuse, N.Y., No. 671.1, 1965, p 13.

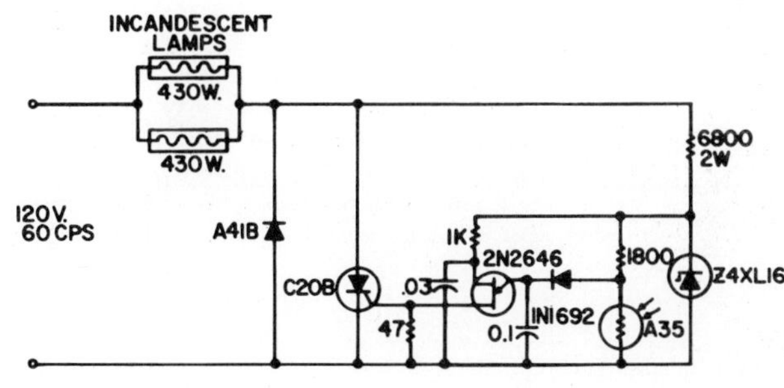

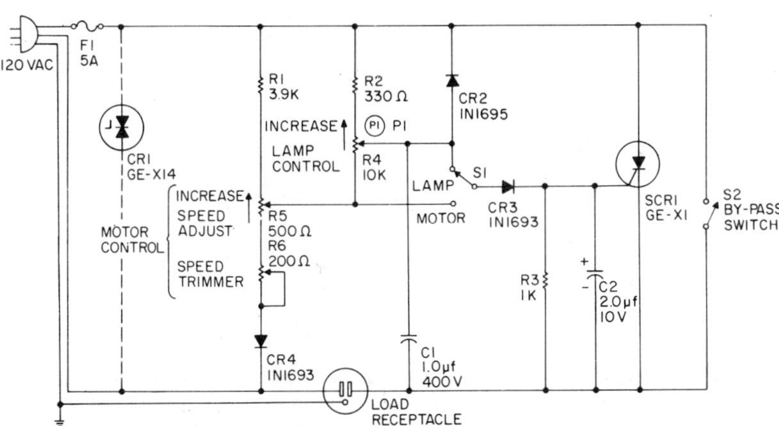

HALF-WAVE LAMP-MOTOR CONTROL—Dual-purpose single-scr control circuit varies output voltage from zero to about 70% of a-c line voltage (up to 84 V). When S1 is in LAMP position, incandescent lamp plugged into load outlet is controlled by P1 from zero brightness to about 30% of its normal visual light output. Closing bypass switch S2 bypasses scr to give full lamp brightness. With S1 in MOTOR position, control circuit includes feedback feature that tends to maintain constant speed for universal motor plugged into outlet. Use only on motors having commutator and brushes.—"Hobby Manual," General Electric, Owensboro, Ky., 1965, p 146.

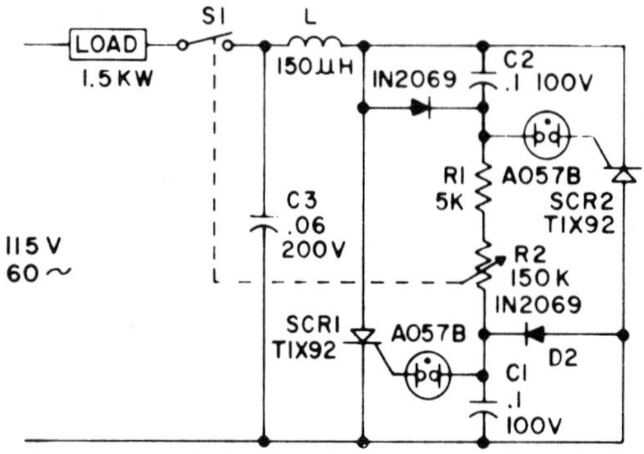

DUAL-SCR WITH NEONS—Supplies power over full cycle, using neon lamps to trigger scr's. Filter L-C3, used to reduce rfi caused by fast turn-on of scr's, is unnecessary with highly inductive loads such as universal motors. Full counterclockwise rotation of R2 opens S1, cutting off power to load. Can be used as dimmer for incandescent lamps.—E. Bauman, "Applications of Neon Lamps and Gas Discharge Tubes," Signalite, Neptune, N.J., p 126.

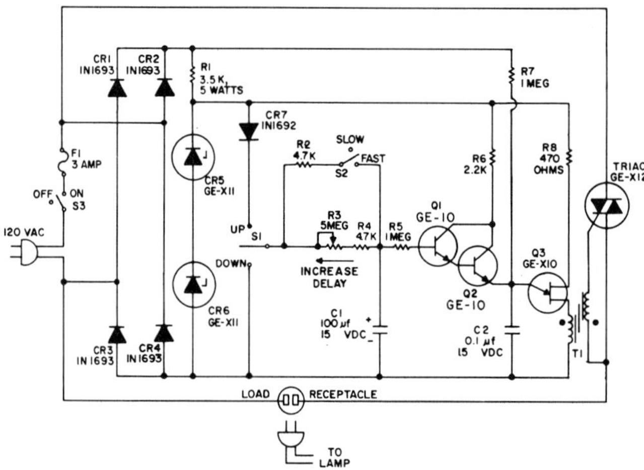

SOFT-OFF DIMMER—When switch is closed, lamp load up to 500 W plugged into load receptacle will be slowly dimmed over adjustable period of 15–20 min as determined by setting of R3, when S1 is in DOWN position. Ideal for control of room lights in bedroom after children have been put to bed. With S1 in UP position, room lights will be turned up slowly over same period, under control of clock timer, for those who must get up before sunrise. Combination of S2 and R4 gives option of fixed fast turn-on and turn-off.—"Hobby Manual," General Electric, Owensboro, Ky., 1965, p 134.

NOTE: To locate additional circuits in the category of this chapter, use the index at the back of this book. Check also the author's "Sourcebook of Electronic Circuits," published by McGraw-Hill in 1968.

CHAPTER 45
Laser Circuits

RAMP-TRIGGERED RECTANGULAR PULSE—Pulse-forming circuit senses when ramp voltage of time-expansion circuit in laser cloud height radar exceeds predetermined threshold value. Q4 is then cut off, cutting off Q5 and turning on Q6, to close electronic switch Q7 and start production of 10-V rectangular output pulse. Width of pulse is 1,000 times that of interval being measured, permitting observation on low-speed oscilloscope.—G. M. Ettinger, Chronometer Expands Pulses to Measure Nanosecond Intervals, *Electronics*, Jan. 23, 1967, p 108–112.

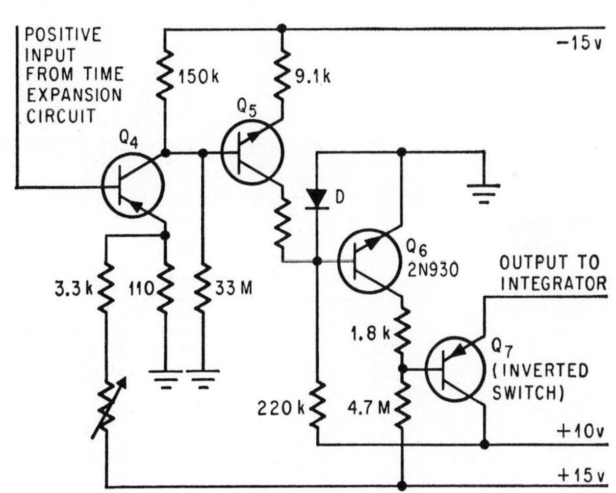

Q_4 — MULLARD LTD. TYPE BCY32 Q_7 — MULLARD LTD. TYPE OC2
Q_5 — MULLARD LTD. TYPE BCY43 D — MULLARD LTD. TYPE OA2

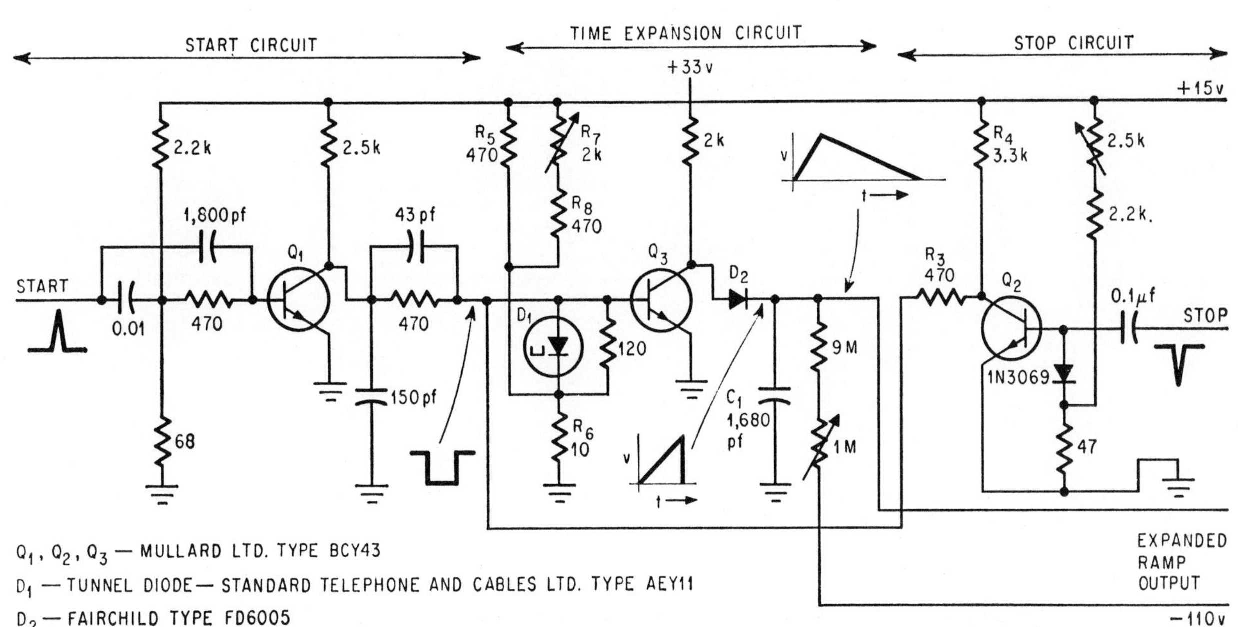

TIME-INTERVAL EXPANDER—Used in laser cloud height radar to resolve time intervals down to 10 ns and make it possible to display time interval data on low-speed scope. Converts input pulses to proportionately longer pulses from which range information can be derived. Value of C1 and 9-meg resistor are given for 8-μs range. Output is ramp waveform 1,000 times longer than time interval between start and stop pulses. Can also be used for very short range conventional radar and for detection of nuclear particles.—G. M. Ettinger, Chronometer Expands Pulses to Measure Nanosecond Intervals, *Electronics*, Jan. 23, 1967, p 108–112.

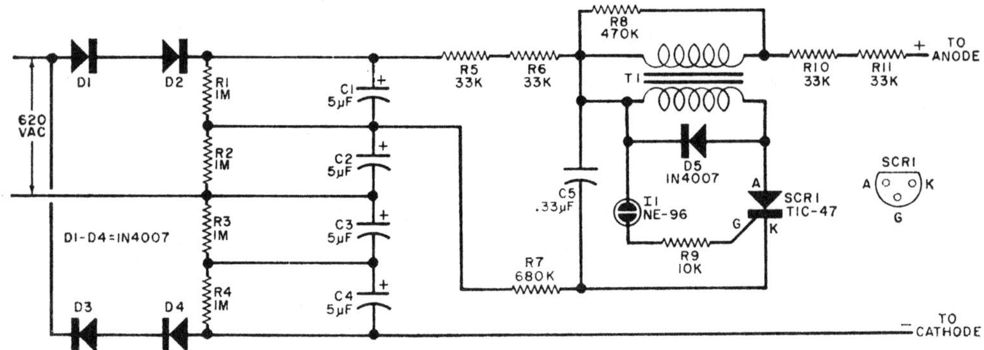

1,600-V AUTOMATIC-START LASER SUPPLY—Will fire laser automatically shortly after 620 V a-c is applied by means of step-up transformer connected to a-c line. T1 is 200:1 conventional auto ignition coil that is critically damped with resistor across secondary to produce single spike. Amglo MT-55 flashtube trigger transformer may be used instead. Caution: Circuit is dangerous when power is applied.—C. H. Knowles, Experimenters' Laser, *Popular Electronics*, Dec. 1969, p 27–32 and 110–111.

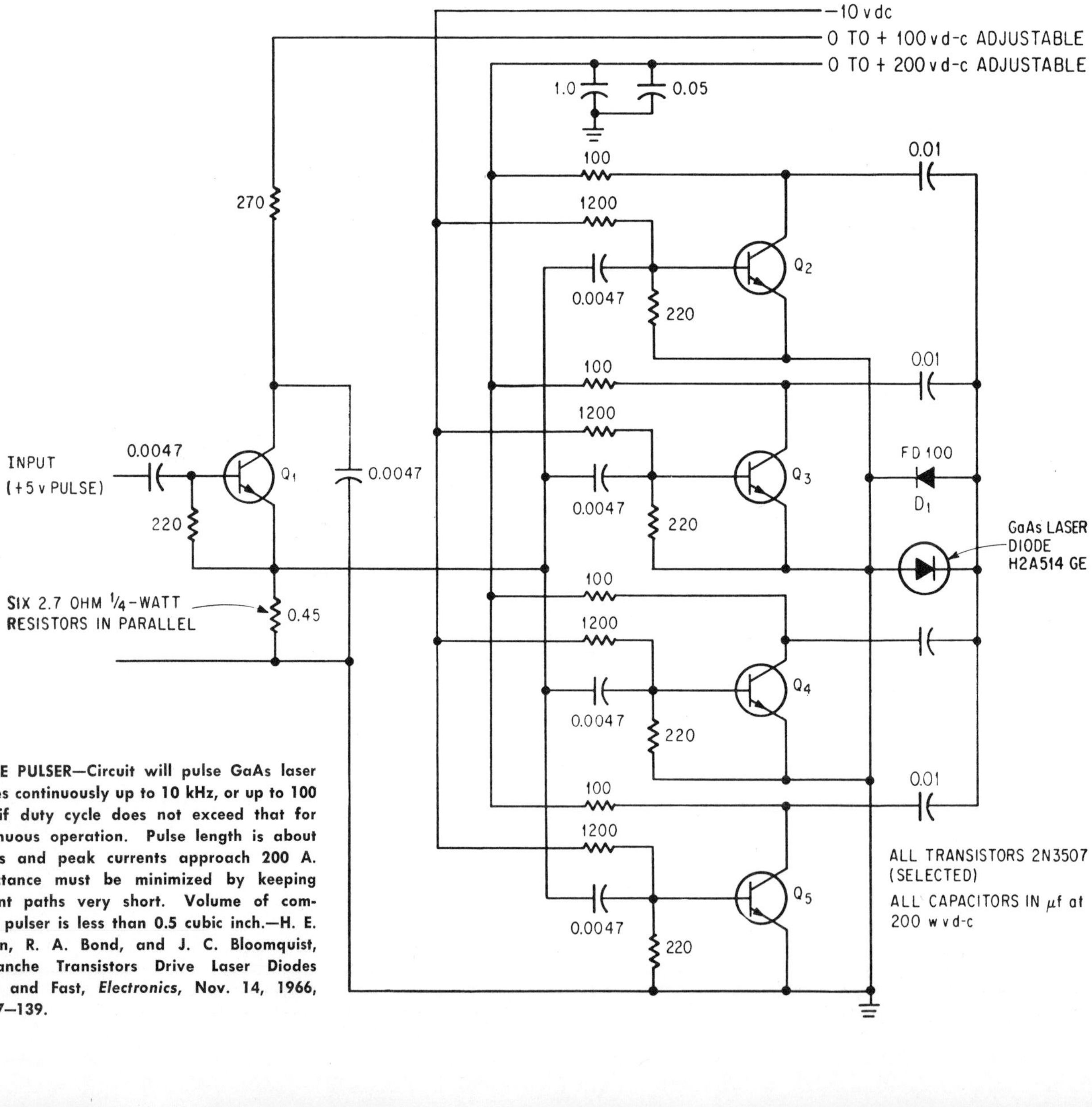

ALL TRANSISTORS 2N3507 (SELECTED)
ALL CAPACITORS IN μf at 200 wvd-c

DIODE PULSER—Circuit will pulse GaAs laser diodes continuously up to 10 kHz, or up to 100 kHz if duty cycle does not exceed that for continuous operation. Pulse length is about 60 ns and peak currents approach 200 A. Inductance must be minimized by keeping current paths very short. Volume of complete pulser is less than 0.5 cubic inch.—H. E. Brown, R. A. Bond, and J. C. Bloomquist, Avalanche Transistors Drive Laser Diodes Hard and Fast, *Electronics*, Nov. 14, 1966, p 137–139.

R12 1M
R13 1M
C6 8μF
C7 8μF
D6
D7
620 VAC
D6-D9=1N4007
D8
D9
C8 8μF
C9 8μF
C10 8μF
C11 8μF
R14 1M
R15 1M
R16 1M
R17 1M
R18 33K
R19 33K
R20 33K
R21 33K
S1
C12 1000pF
R22 2M
R23 2M
R24 2M
+ TO ANODE
– TO CATHODE

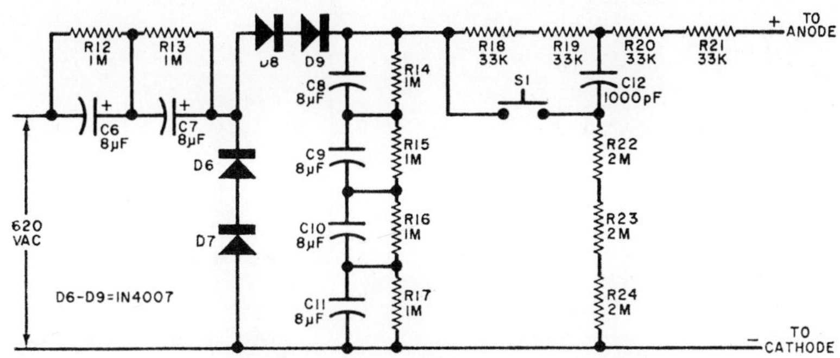

1,600-V MANUAL-START LASER SUPPLY—After 620-V a-c is applied by means of step-up transformer connected to a-c line, switch S1 must be closed to fire laser. Caution: Circuit is dangerous once power is applied.—C. H. Knowles, Experimenters' Laser, *Popular Electronics*, Dec. 1969, p 27–32 and 110–111.

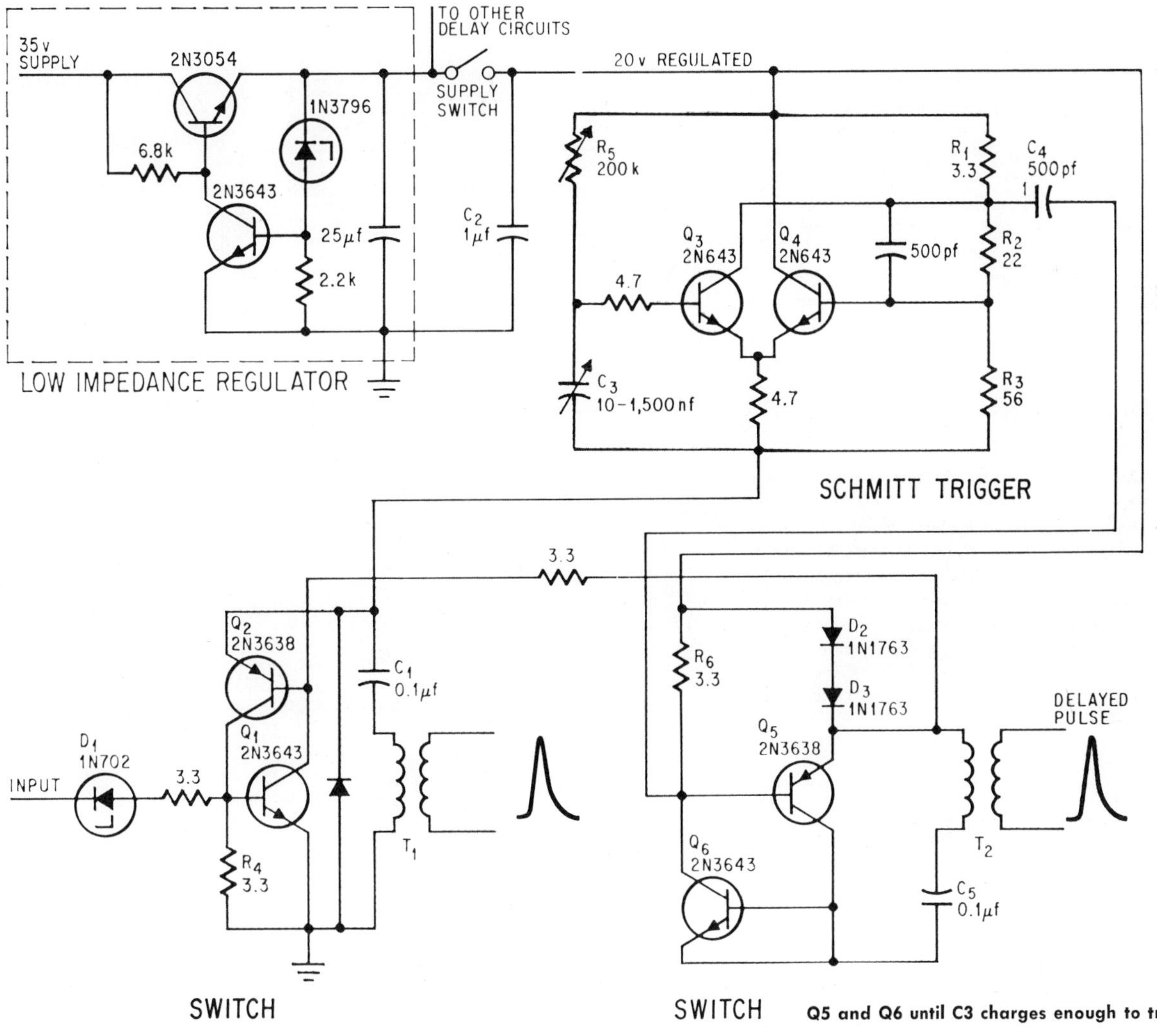

35 v SUPPLY
2N3054
6.8k
2N3643
1N3796
25μf
2.2k
LOW IMPEDANCE REGULATOR
TO OTHER DELAY CIRCUITS
SUPPLY SWITCH
C2 1μf
20 v REGULATED
R5 200 k
4.7
Q3 2N643
Q4 2N643
500 pf
R1 3.3
C4 500 pf
R2 22
R3 56
C3 10-1,500 nf
4.7
SCHMITT TRIGGER
3.3
Q2 2N3638
C1 0.1μf
Q1 2N3643
D1 1N702
INPUT
3.3
R4 3.3
T1
SWITCH
R6 3.3
D2 1N1763
D3 1N1763
Q5 2N3638
Q6 2N3643
DELAYED PULSE
T2
C5 0.1μf
SWITCH

FIRING PULSE CONTROL—Combination of Schmitt trigger with stable linear R-C charging keeps time intervals accurate within 1% for pulses that fire gas discharge lasers in ionization experiments. Input pulse makes Q1 and Q2 conduct, but has no effect on Q5 and Q6 until C3 charges enough to trigger Q3. Opening switch resets timer.—P. F. Howden, RC-Biased Schmitt Trigger Times Pulses Accurately, *Electronics*, April 1, 1968, p 64.

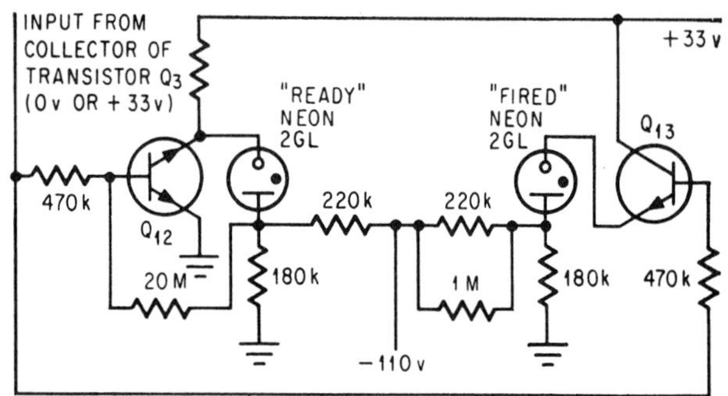

ECHO AMBIGUITY RESOLVER—Used in laser cloud height radar to eliminate ambiguity between echoes below 50 feet and extremely distant echoes (over 1 mile). Operates by sensing state of transistor switch in chronometer circuit after each laser firing pulse, and energizing one of two neon lamps to tell observer whether or not chronometer has been reset and is ready for next echo.—G. M. Ettinger, Chronometer Expands Pulses to Measure Nanosecond Intervals, *Electronics*, Jan. 23, 1967, p 108–112.

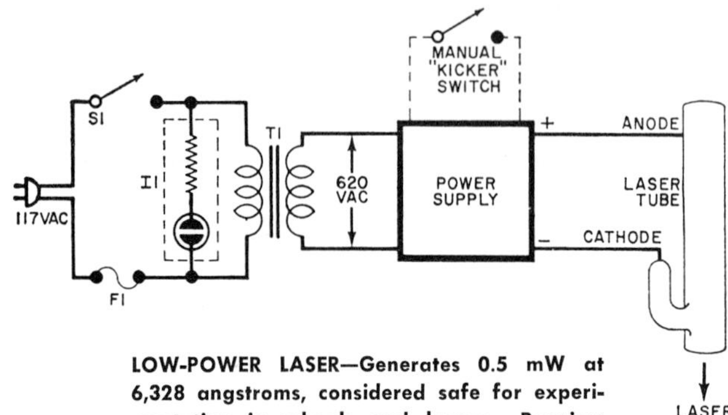

LOW-POWER LASER—Generates 0.5 mW at 6,328 angstroms, considered safe for experimentation in schools and homes. Requires 1,600-V d-c power supply, for which automatic and manual-start versions are given in article along with construction details and sources for laser and other special parts. Caution: do not aim at eyes; light is extremely bright and temporarily blinding.—C. H. Knowles, Experimenters' Laser, *Popular Electronics*, Dec. 1969, p 27–32 and 110–111.

LASER PUMP—Uses xenon annular flashtube developed primarily for optical pumping of laser crystals. Designed so crystal rod is surrounded by gas discharge plasma. Outer surface of flashtube can then be wrapped with aluminum or silver foil serving both as reflector and trigger electrode. Requires 25 to 30 kV trigger voltage from trigger transformer.—FX-53C-3, FX-53Z-3 Annular Xenon Flashtubes, EG&G Inc., Boston, Mass., No. 1007-3, 1968.

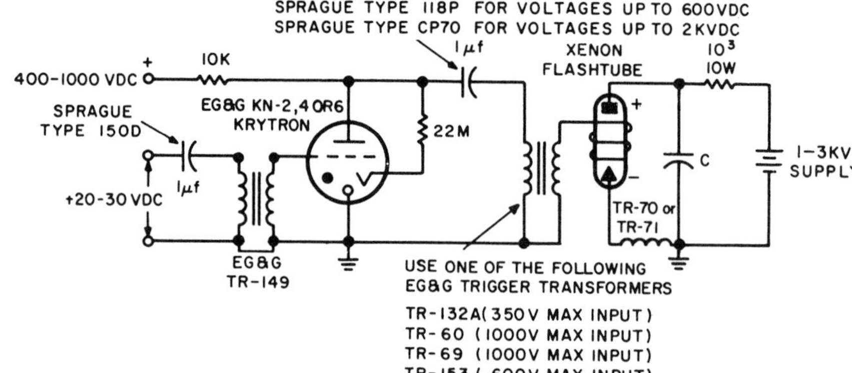

LASER ENERGY MONITOR—Circuit provides permanent record of total energy entering eye of patient each time pulsed ruby laser photocoagulator is fired. Dichroic beamsplitter reflects small fraction of laser beam to phototransistor that feeds monitor circuit. Output of monitor drives recorder. Circuit is calibrated by measuring total beam energy with thermopile.—E. J. Scribner, Circuit Monitors Energy of Laser Photocoagulator, *Electronics*, July 7, 1969, p 110–111.

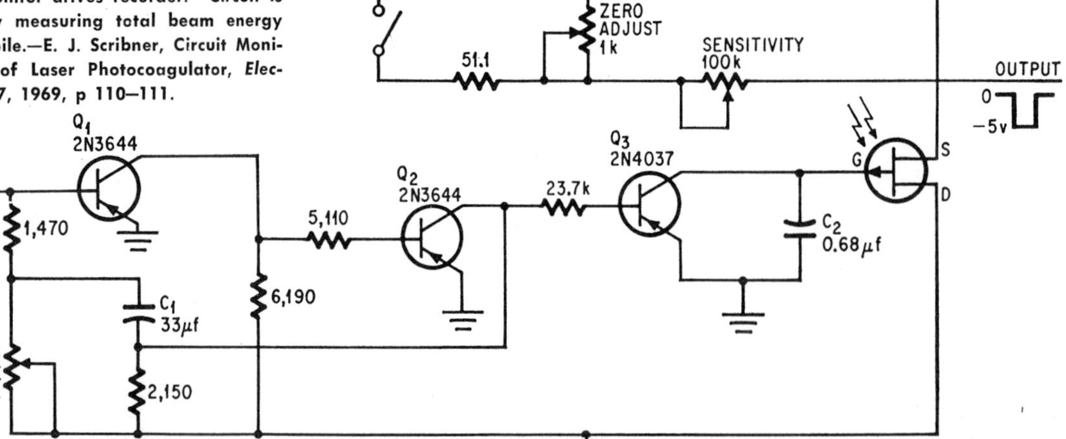

INJECTION LASER PULSE GENERATOR—EG&G Krytron pulser produces peak currents of several thousand amperes at repetition rates up to 500 pulses per second, for pulsing high-power injection lasers at room temperature. Outstanding features are simplicity, small size, and low cost. Capacitor C is charged from 510-V d-c source, then discharged through laser diode D and Krytron switch.—W. Koechner, Extremely Small and Simple Pulse Generator for Injection Lasers, *Review of Scientific Instruments*, Jan. 1967, p 17–20.

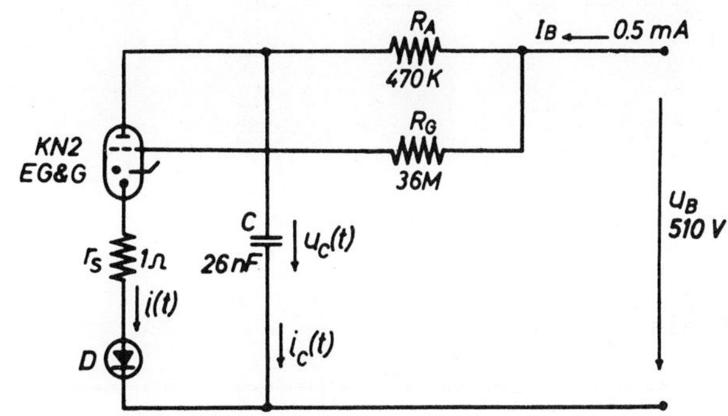

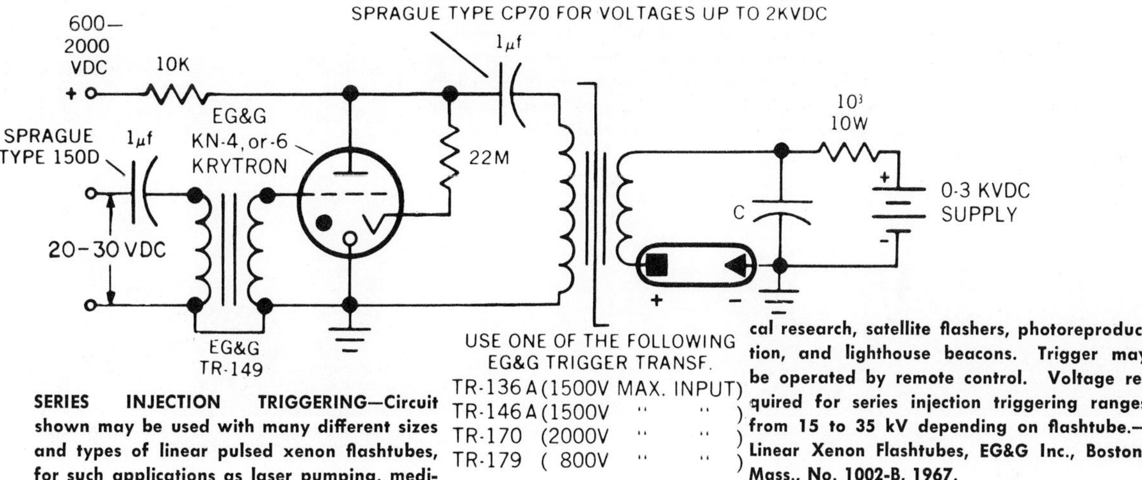

SERIES INJECTION TRIGGERING—Circuit shown may be used with many different sizes and types of linear pulsed xenon flashtubes, for such applications as laser pumping, medical research, satellite flashers, photoreproduction, and lighthouse beacons. Trigger may be operated by remote control. Voltage required for series injection triggering ranges from 15 to 35 kV depending on flashtube.—Linear Xenon Flashtubes, EG&G Inc., Boston, Mass., No. 1002-B, 1967.

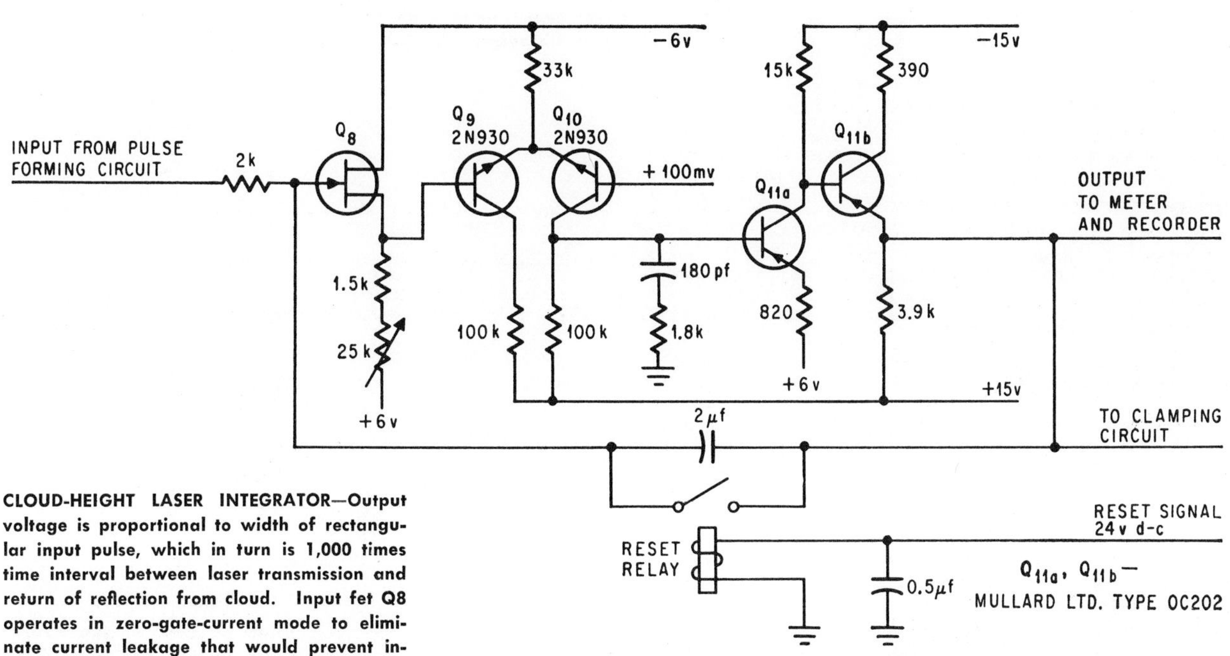

CLOUD-HEIGHT LASER INTEGRATOR—Output voltage is proportional to width of rectangular input pulse, which in turn is 1,000 times time interval between laser transmission and return of reflection from cloud. Input fet Q8 operates in zero-gate-current mode to eliminate current leakage that would prevent information from being stored in integrator without degradation between measurements. Relay shorts integrator capacitor to reset to zero.—G. M. Ettinger, Chronometer Expands Pulses to Measure Nanosecond Intervals, *Electronics*, Jan. 23, 1967, p 108–112.

CHAPTER 46
Latching Circuits

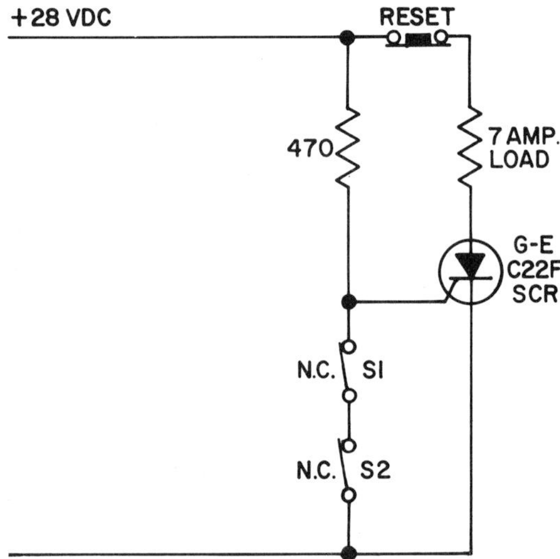

D-C LATCH FOR ALARM—Momentary opening of either switch triggers scr, which then latches and provides full load power until reset switch is pushed. Can be used for alarms, firing of explosive squibs, protection circuits, and display lamps.—F. W. Gutzwiller and E. K. Howell, Economy Power Semiconductor Applications, General Electric, Syracuse, N.Y., No. 671.1, 1965, p 3.

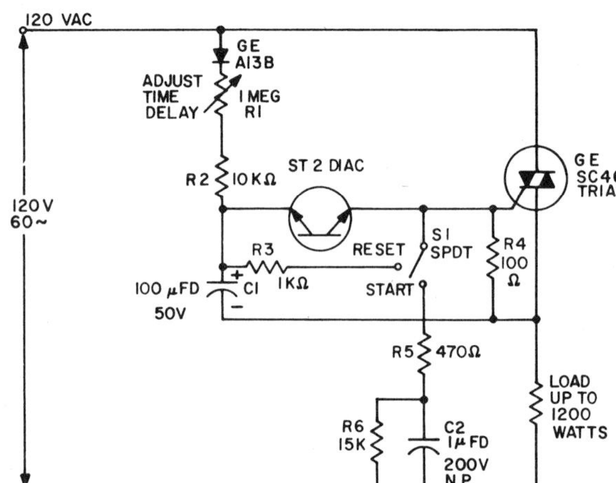

60-S LATCHING DELAY—When C1 charges to diac voltage, in 60 s for values shown, triac fires and energizes load until S1 is operated to discharge C1 through R3 and R4.—"SCR Manual," 4th Edition, General Electric, 1967, p 148.

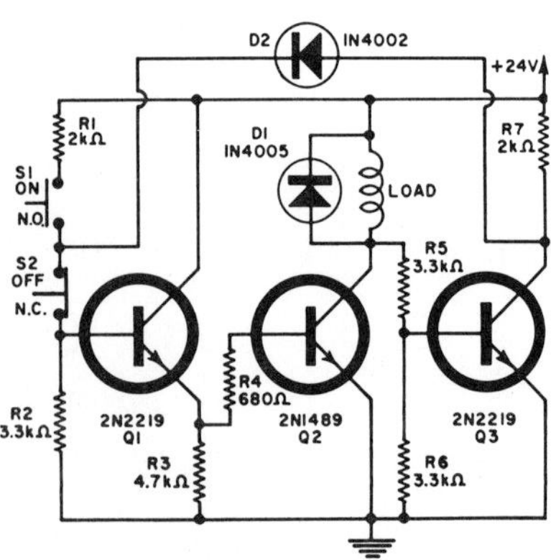

SOLENOID DRIVER WITH LATCH—Momentary closing of S1 energizes solenoid load, and circuit holds in this condition until S2 is momentarily opened. Load current can be up to 5 A.—A. Harris, Semiconductor Switching of Low-Power Circuits, *Electronics World,* June 1967, p 33–35.

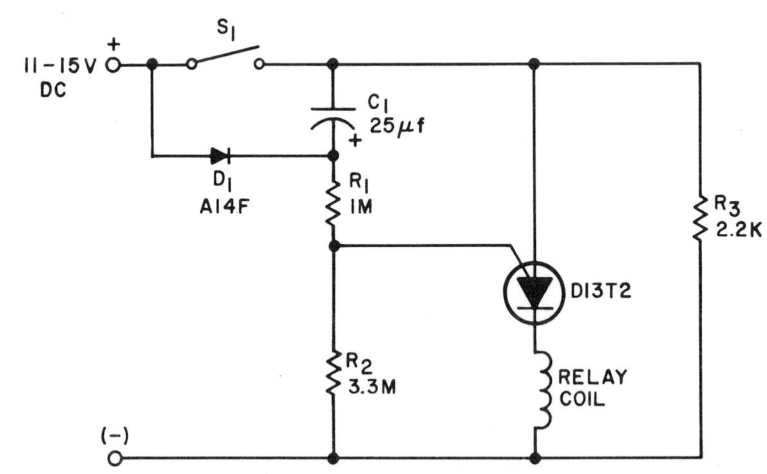

60-S DELAY WITH LATCHING—Uses D13T2 programmable ujt for both timing and latching of relay. High gate sensitivity makes long delays possible with reasonable resistor and capacitor sizes.—E. K. Howell, Small Scale Integration in Low Cost Control Circuits, General Electric, Syracuse, N.Y., No. 671.9, 1968, p 18.

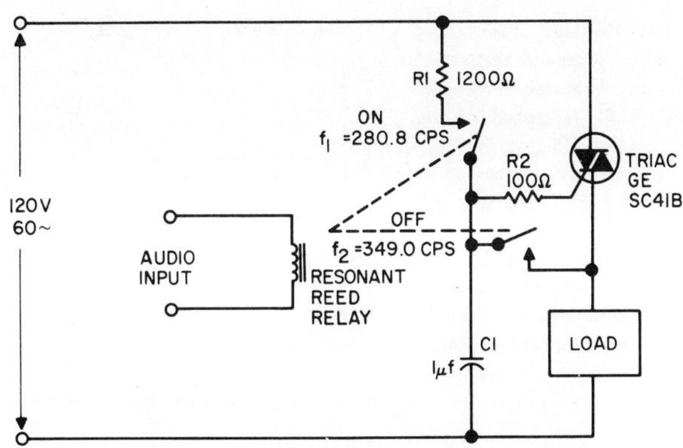

TRIAC TONE-ACTUATED SWITCH—Resonant reed relay is pulled in by 280.8-Hz audio tone, to apply trigger that turns on and latches triac, to apply a-c line voltage to load. Relay releases when tone stops, but latch action of triac keeps load energized. Only 349-Hz tone can make relay pull in the OFF armature and bypass trigger long enough for triac to open or block.—J. H. Galloway, Using the Triac for Control of AC Power, General Electric, Syracuse, N.Y., No. 200.35, 1966, p 6.

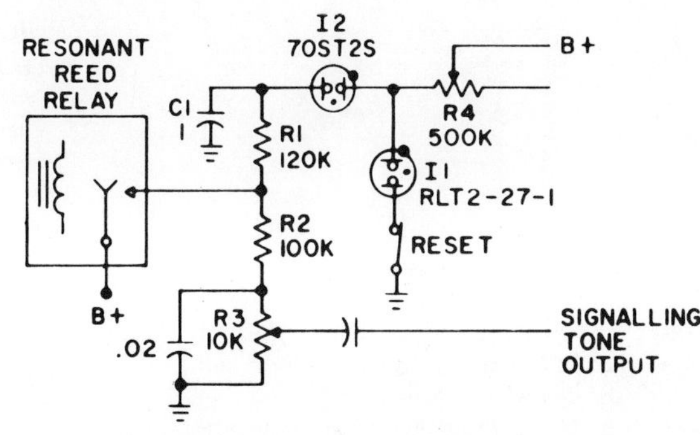

STATION CALL INDICATOR—Serves as memory device in selective calling of unattended two-way radios. Signalling tone from transmitter causes relay to apply total circuit voltage to "call" indicator neon I1, which lights. Circuit remains latched until operator returns and throws reset switch.—E. Bauman, "Applications of Neon Lamps and Gas Discharge Tubes," Signalite, Neptune, N.J., p 71.

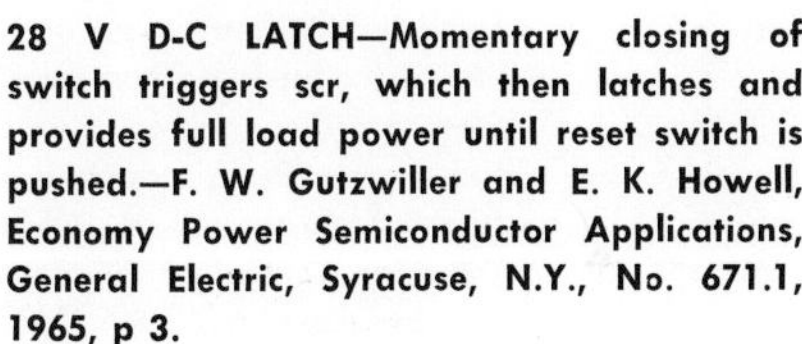

28 V D-C LATCH—Momentary closing of switch triggers scr, which then latches and provides full load power until reset switch is pushed.—F. W. Gutzwiller and E. K. Howell, Economy Power Semiconductor Applications, General Electric, Syracuse, N.Y., No. 671.1, 1965, p 3.

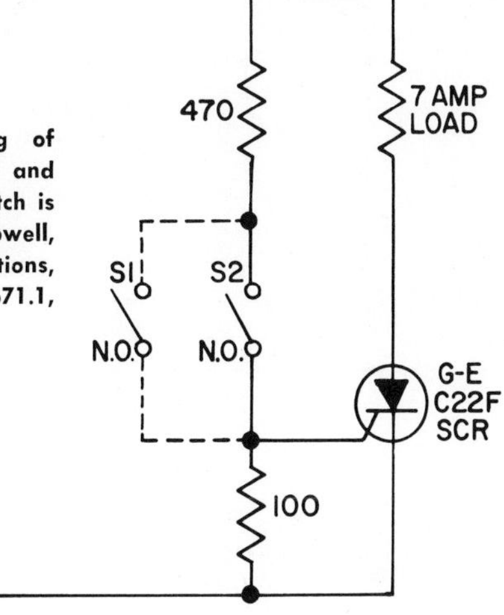

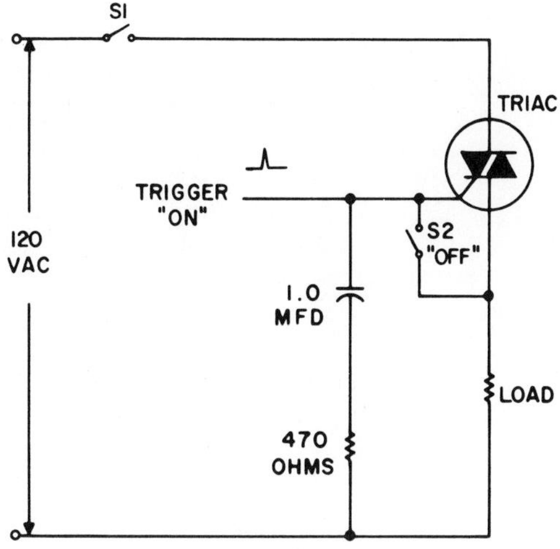

TRIAC A-C LATCH—When triac is triggered on by external pulse, voltage developed across capacitor by load voltage triggers triac on each succeeding cycle, until momentary closing of S2 discharges capacitor without triggering triac. Choose triac to meet load requirements.—F. W. Gutzwiller and E. K. Howell, Economy Power Semiconductor Applications, General Electric, Syracuse, N.Y., No. 671.1, 1965, p 8.

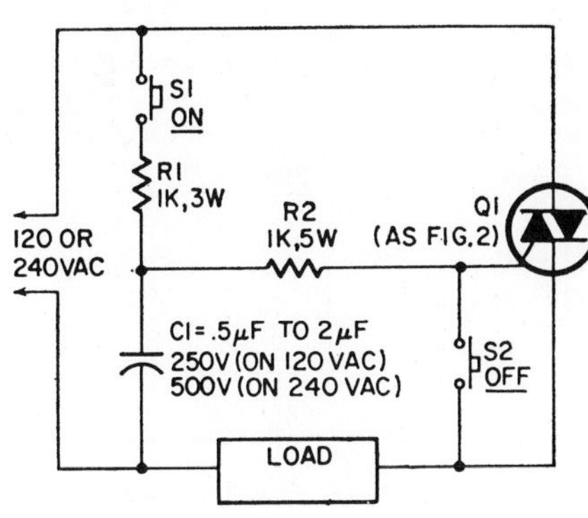

SELF-LATCHING TRIAC—Momentary closing of S1 makes triac stay on continuously until S2 is momentarily closed, to give latching control of current through 6-A load. Use RCA 40429 triac for 120 V and 40430 for 240 V.—R. M. Marston, 20 Triac Circuits, *Radio-Electronics*, June 1970, p 51–53 and 97.

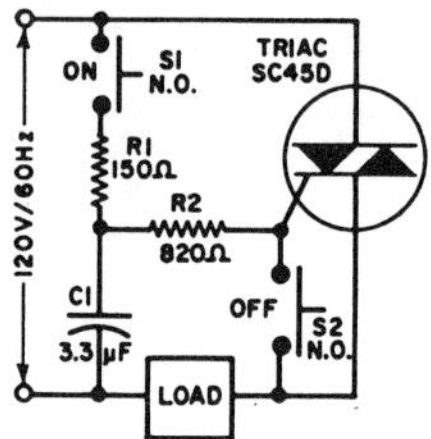

TRIAC LATCH—When S1 is closed, triac saturates and C1 charges. At end of first half-cycle, C1 discharges through gate and triggers triac into saturation for next half-cycle. Process continues, to give latching action, until S2 is closed. Triac then cuts off at next zero crossover and stays off.—A. Harris, Semiconductor Switching of Low-Power Circuits, *Electronics World*, June 1967, p 33–35.

REMOTE-CONTROL LATCH—Uses two scr's rated at 7.4 A, with momentary-contact switches that can be remotely located. When S1 is actuated, SCR2 is gated on by remote power supply voltage acting through R1, and load receives current. When S2 is actuated, SCR1 is gated on and acts through C1 to turn off SCR2 by lowering its anode voltage. The scr's thus operate in flip-flop action so when one is cut off, the other is conducting.—A. Harris, Semiconductor Switching of Low-Power Circuits, *Electronics World*, June 1967, p 33–35.

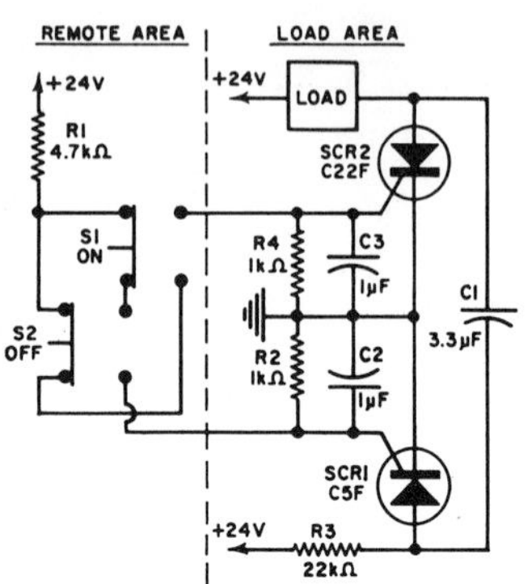

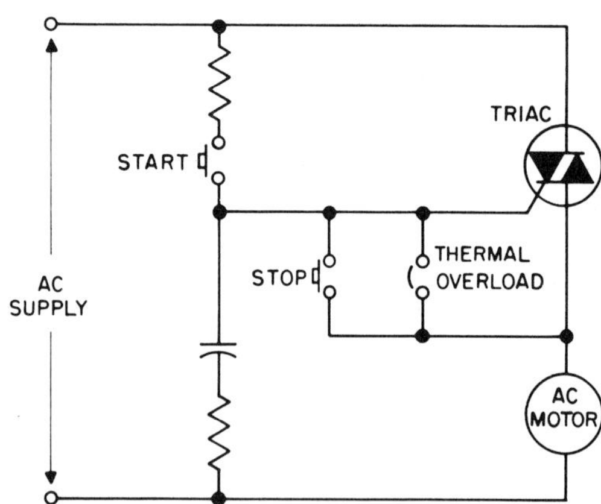

TRIAC A-C MOTOR STARTER—Serves as solid-state equivalent of magnetic a-c motor starter. Choice of triac depends on motor current rating and on a-c line voltage. Resistor and capacitor values in voltage divider are chosen to give trigger voltage required for triac chosen; capacitor is generally 0.1 μF. Triac latches when start button is pressed momentarily, and is then retriggered each half-cycle. Press stop button momentarily to turn off motor.—J. H. Galloway, Using the Triac for Control of AC Power, General Electric, Syracuse, N.Y., No. 200.35, 1966, p 6.

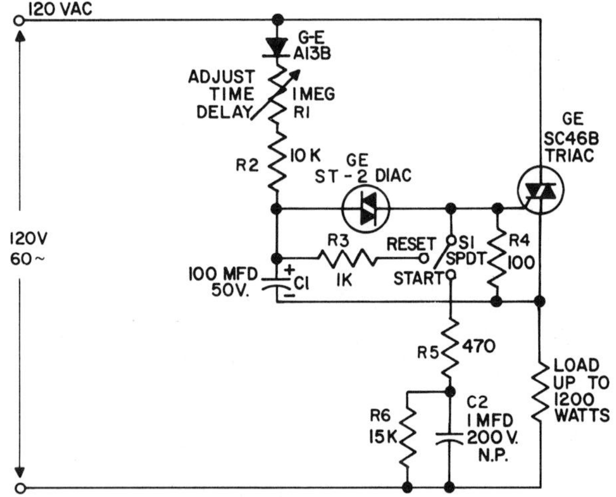

1,200-W TRIAC WITH DELAY—Adjustable delay applies trigger to triac at predetermined time after S1 is set at START, after which triac latches on and applies full line voltage to load. Moving switch to RESET opens triac and recharges capacitor for next operation. —J. H. Galloway, Using the Triac for Control of AC Power, General Electric, Syracuse, N.Y., No. 200.35, 1966, p 6.

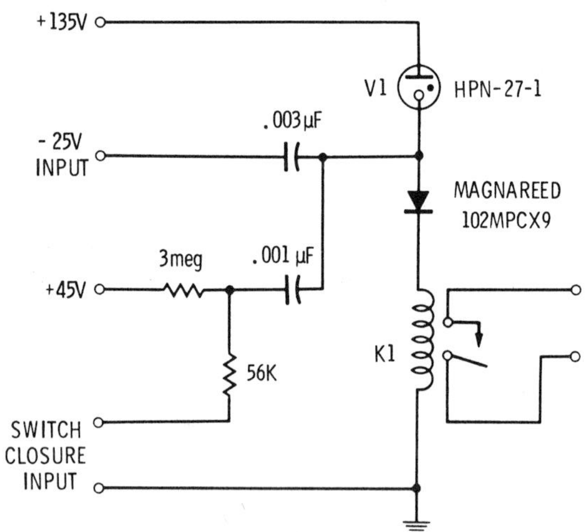

MEMORY FOR MOMENTARY CONTACT—Shorting of switch contacts discharges 0.001-μF capacitor through neon, firing it and holding relay closed until 135-V supply line is opened.—W. G. Miller, "Using and Understanding Miniature Neon Lamps," H. W. Sams & Co., Indianapolis, Ind., 1969, p 66.

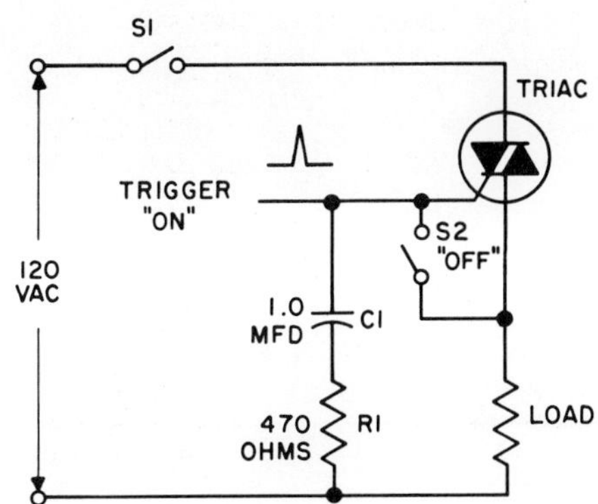

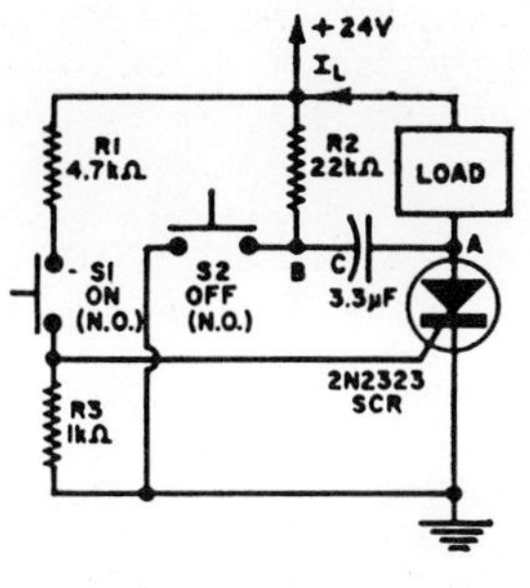

SCR LATCH—Closing S1 momentarily makes scr saturate, sending up to 1.6 A through load. Closing S2 momentarily causes commutating capacitor C to begin discharging, thereby turning off scr and keeping it off until another gate pulse is applied by S1.—A. Harris, Semiconductor Switching of Low-Power Circuits, *Electronics World*, June 1967, p 33–35.

BASIC TRIAC LATCH—Used as switch for applying power to load when trigger pulse reaches input terminal. Can be turned off either by interrupting power with S1 or bypassing trigger with S2. Triac is initially blocking when load is applied, and latches to conducting state because it is retriggered by a-c line each half-cycle after being turned on by external trigger. Triac used must be specially selected for triggering in III+ mode (third quadrant, positive gate current and voltage), at load current required. For 220-V line, change C1 to 0.5 μF.—J. H. Galloway, Using the Triac for Control of AC Power, General Electric, Syracuse, N.Y., No. 200.35, 1966, p 6.

LATCHING LAMP DRIVER—Uses single planar pnpn switch, equivalent to pnp-npn complementary transistor pair, as low-cost driver for Nixie tubes, alphanumeric display tubes, and neon lamps. Circuit is immune to triggering by line transients.—Planar Neon Driver Silicon Controlled Switch 3N83, General Electric, Syracuse, N.Y., No. 65.17, 1964.

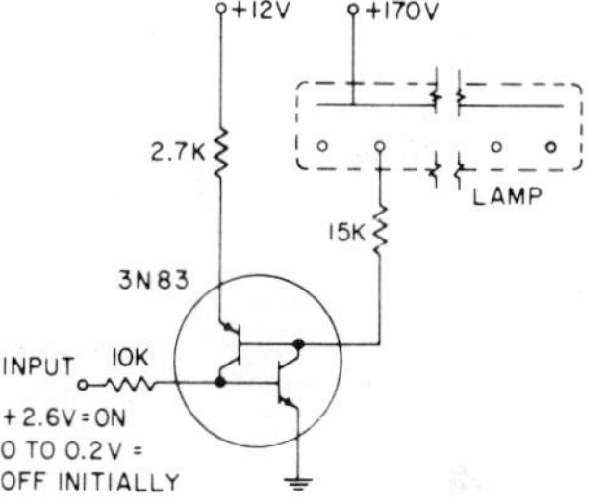

MAGNETIC-CORE READOUT—Provides high-level output through scr for solenoids, magnetic clutches or brakes, and squibs without intermediate amplifier stages. Once circuit is triggered on, it remains on until reset by opening d-c anode supply.—High Level Readout From Magnetic Cores, Solid State Products, Salem, Mass., No. 2.

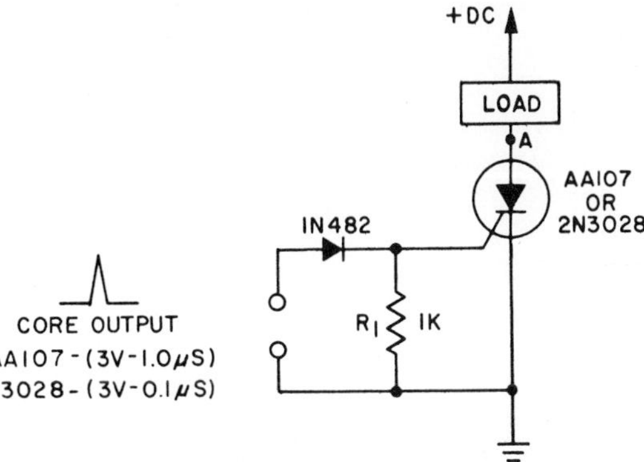

NOTE: To locate additional circuits in the category of this chapter, use the index at the back of this book. Check also the author's "Sourcebook of Electronic Circuits," published by McGraw-Hill in 1968.

CHAPTER 47
Logic Circuits

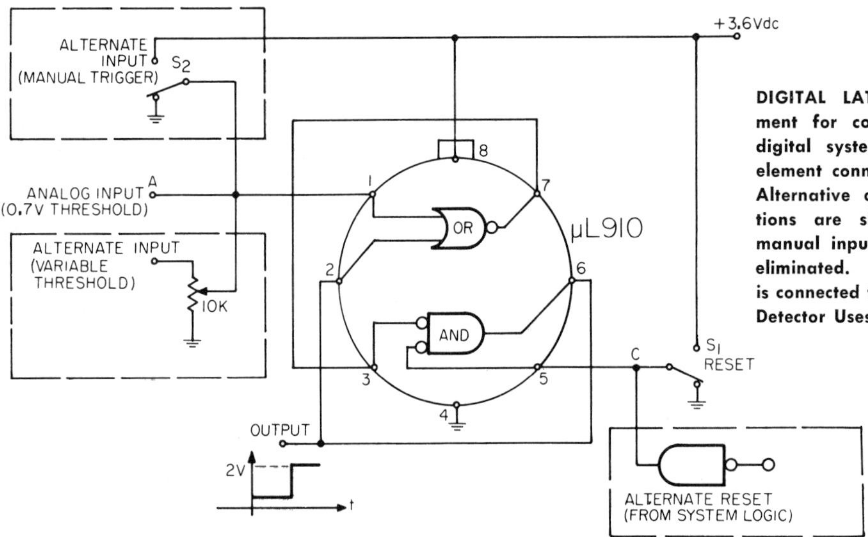

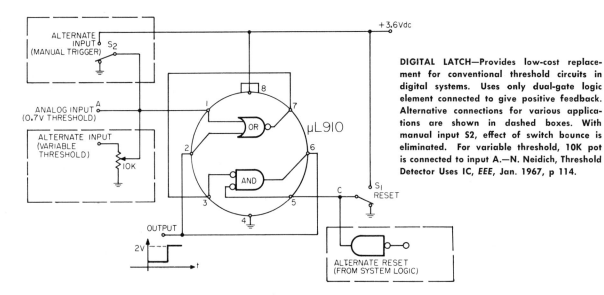

DIGITAL LATCH—Provides low-cost replacement for conventional threshold circuits in digital systems. Uses only dual-gate logic element connected to give positive feedback. Alternative connections for various applications are shown in dashed boxes. With manual input S2, effect of switch bounce is eliminated. For variable threshold, 10K pot is connected to input A.—N. Neidich, Threshold Detector Uses IC, *EEE*, Jan. 1967, p 114.

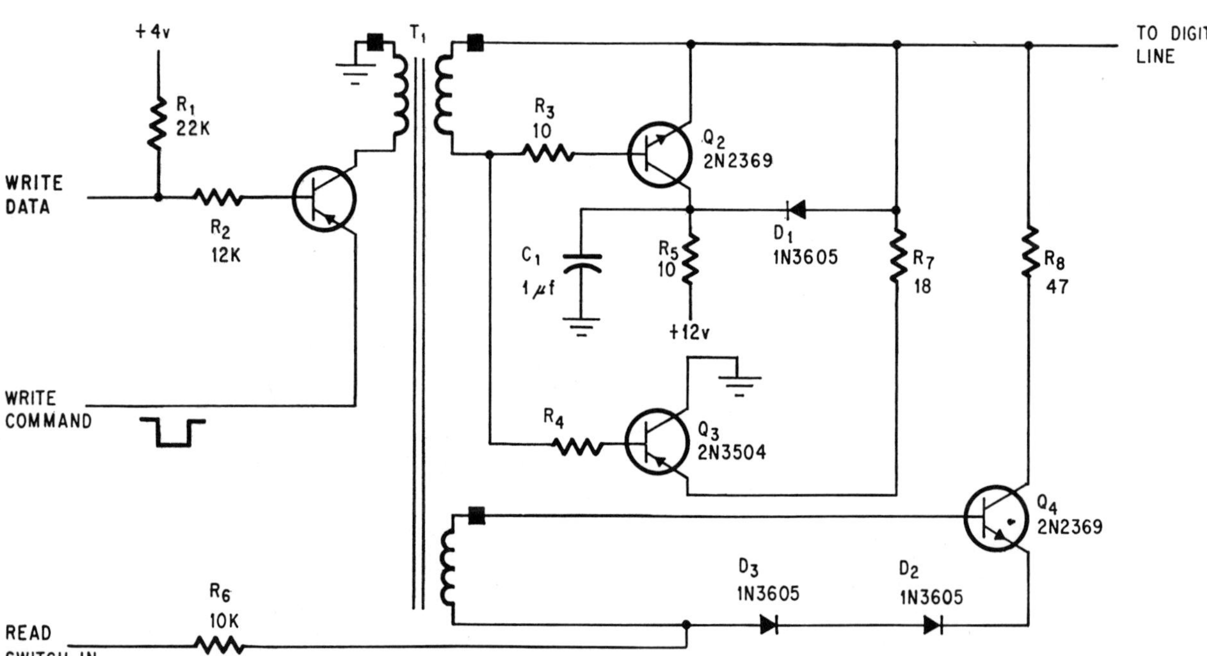

MEMORY WRITE DRIVER—Write-command signal and binary 1 on write data line together turn off Q4 and turn on Q2, to make 12-V signal appear on digit line. End of command pulse turns off Q2 and turns on Q3, for fast discharge of digit line, after which Q4 turns on again to ground line. Used in computer storage developed for long space trips.—D. E. Brewer, S. Nissim, and G. V. Podraza, Suitcase-size Memory for Longer Space Trips, *Electronics*, Nov. 13, 1967, p 138–146.

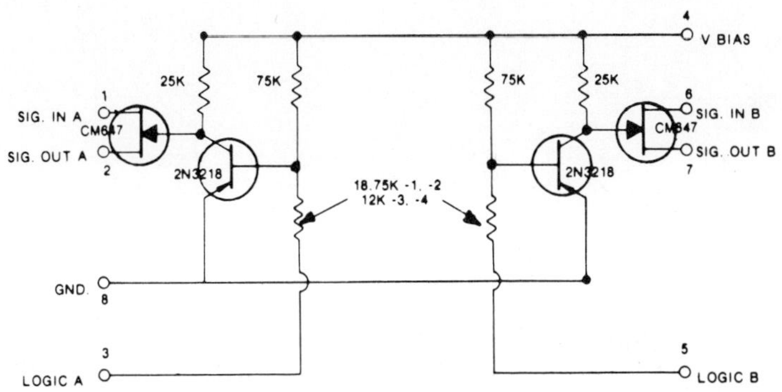

DUAL FET ANALOG SWITCH—Crystalonics CDA2 hybrid package contains pair of basic fet switches with integral drivers, working directly from logic. Intended for switching analog signals to ground or virtual ground only. Logic current drain and power consumption are kept low, by tradeoff with switching speed. Can also be used as integrator reset. —Hybrid IC's, Crystalonics, Cambridge, Mass., 1969.

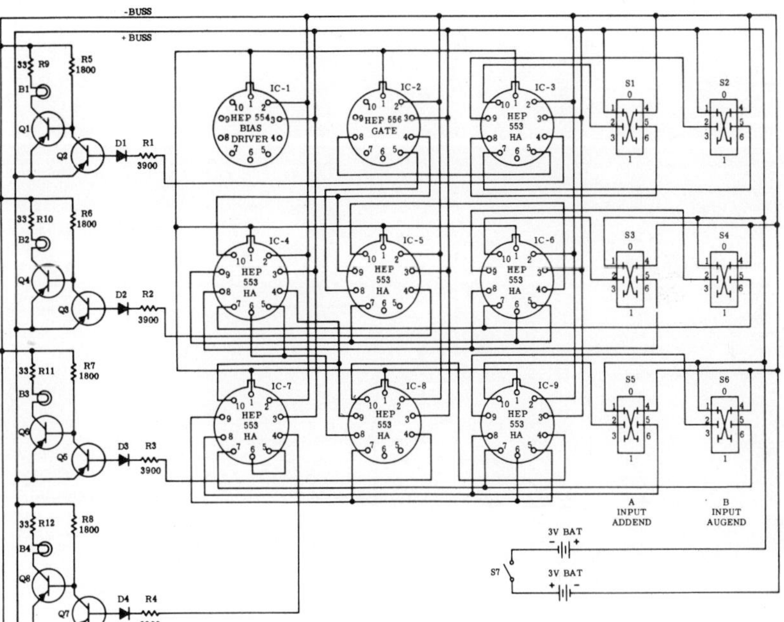

IC BINARY COMPUTER—Simple 3-bit adder is excellent for illustrating binary arithmetic. All transistors are Motorola HEP-51 and all diodes are HEP-154. S1-S6 are dpdt slide switches, and lamps B1-B4 are GE No. 48. Article gives construction details.—"Integrated Circuit Projects," Motorola, Phoenix, Ariz., 1966, p 19–31.

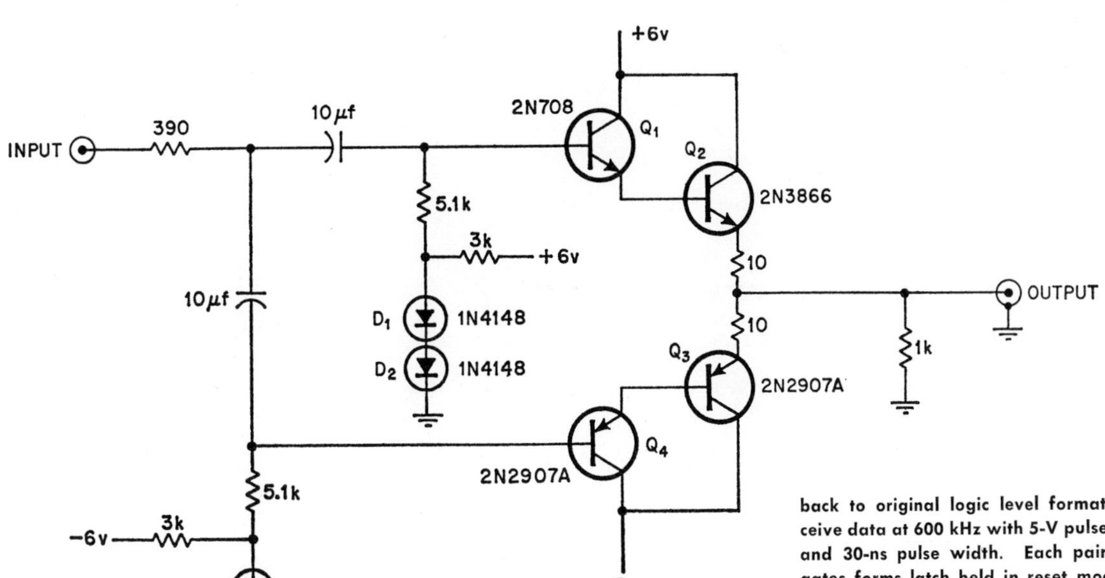

CONVERTING TRANSMITTED DIGITAL DATA TO LOGIC LEVELS—Accepts digital data transmitted long distances over four pairs of lines, with clock input from fifth line, and converts back to original logic level format. Will receive data at 600 kHz with 5-V pulse amplitude and 30-ns pulse width. Each pair of NAND gates forms latch held in reset mode prior to arrival of input clock pulse. Clock triggers 1-μs one-shot while incoming data pulses set appropriate latches made from NAND gates.—K. Erickson, EC Line-Receiver Converts Pulse to Logic Levels, *Electronics*, Jan. 19, 1970, p 94.

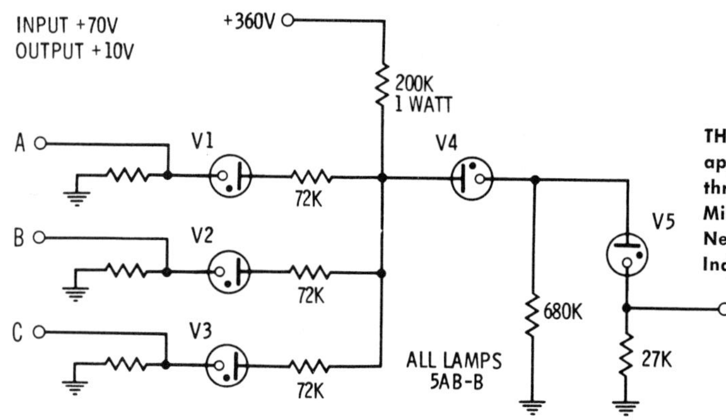

THREE-INPUT MAJORITY GATE—10-V output appears at X whenever at least two of the three lamps (V1, V2, V3) extinguish.—W. G. Miller, "Using and Understanding Miniature Neon Lamps," H. W. Sams & Co., Indianapolis, Ind., 1969, p 53.

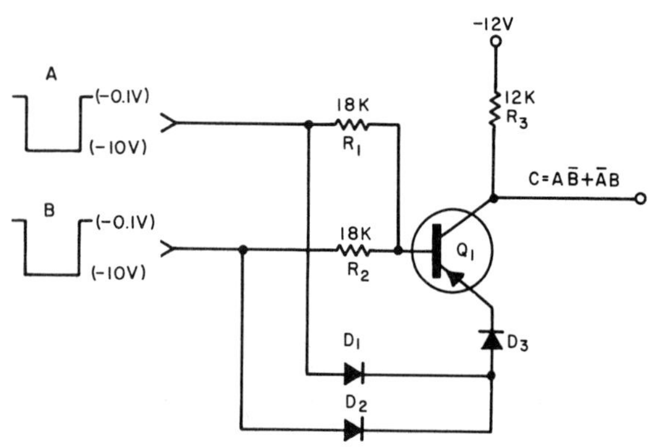

EXCLUSIVE-OR—Uses only one transistor and three diodes, none of which are critical as to type. Q1 is off when A and B are both at −0.1 V or when both are at −10 V. Q1 is on when A and B are at different levels. D3 may not be needed if binary data levels are maintained within a few tenths of a volt.—A. J. Franchi, Exclusive-Or Circuit Uses Fewer Components, *Electronic Design*, Sept. 14, 1964, p 74–75.

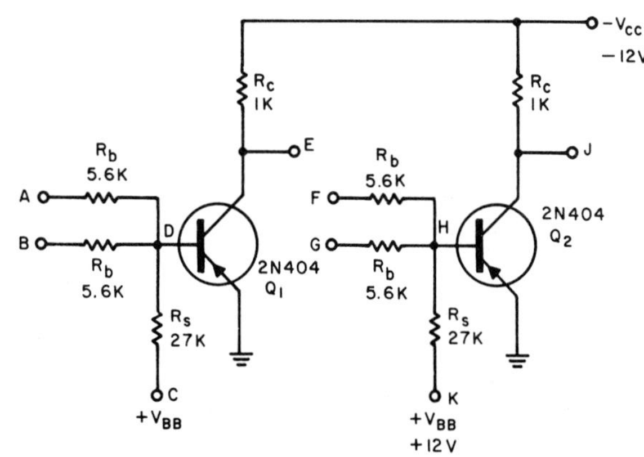

CONVERTING NOR LOGIC TO MVBR—Addition of timing capacitors to two transistor-resistor NOR logic circuits gives astable and monostable mvbr operations. Article gives equation for values of Rb and external C to give desired frequency. Flip-flop is obtained by adding R-C differentiator steering diode networks.—L. E. Frenzel, Jr., NOR Circuits Easily Convert to Multivibrators, *Electronic Design*, Feb. 15, 1965, p 76–77.

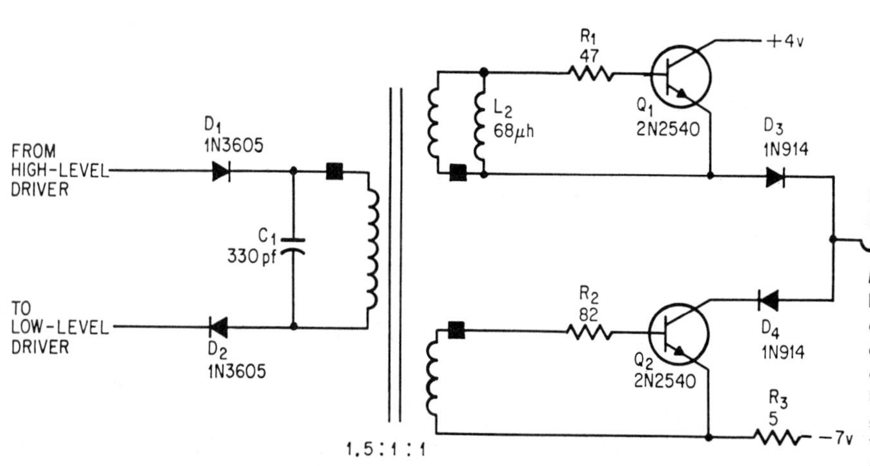

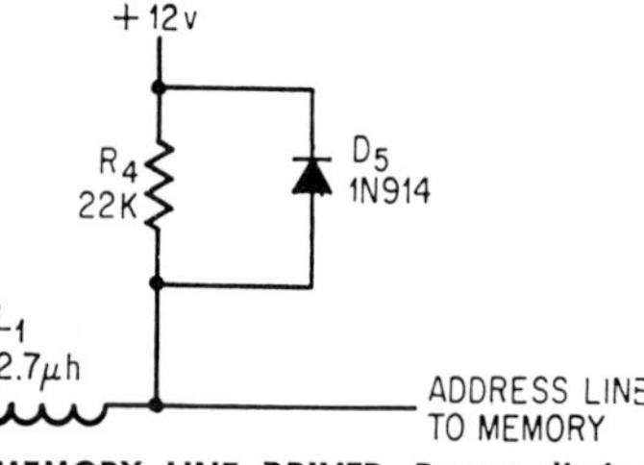

MEMORY LINE DRIVER—Power dissipation is held down to 0.8 W by making inductive output impedance form resonant circuit with distributed capacitance of line. Nonlinear characteristics of driver prevent ringing. Used in computer storage developed for long space trips.—D. E. Brewer, S. Nissim, and G. V. Podraza, Suitcase-size Memory for Longer Space Trips, *Electronics*, Nov. 13, 1967, p 138–146.

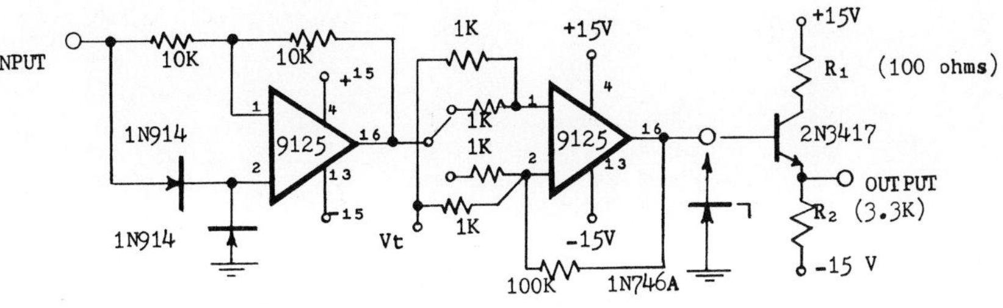

INTERFACE—Provides logic 1 output at required level such as +3 V for any logic 1 input. Uses OEI 9125 opamp. First opamp is absolute-value circuit, and second is small-hysteresis that provides sharp transition from one stage to the other. Output is bound by single zener. When switch is up as shown, zero input gives logic 1 output. With switch down, zero input gives logic 0 output.—A Universal Digital Interface, Optical Electronics, Tucson, Ariz., No. 10132.

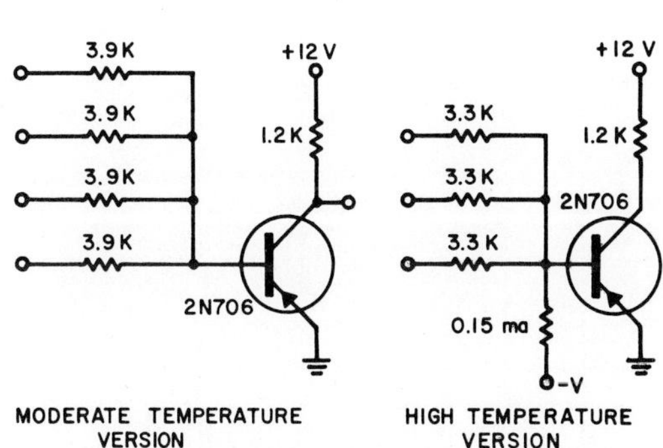

TEMPERATURE EFFECTS ON NOR—Circuit at left permits fan-in and fan-out ratio of 4 for temperatures from −55 C up to moderate temperatures. For higher temperatures, negative voltage supply is needed to compensate for leakage current of transistor, and fan-in, fan-out ratio is reduced to 3. Logic speed of both versions is up to 4 MHz, but can be doubled by using 2N2369.—Basic NOR Logic Circuit, *Electronic Design*, April 13, 1964, p 66.

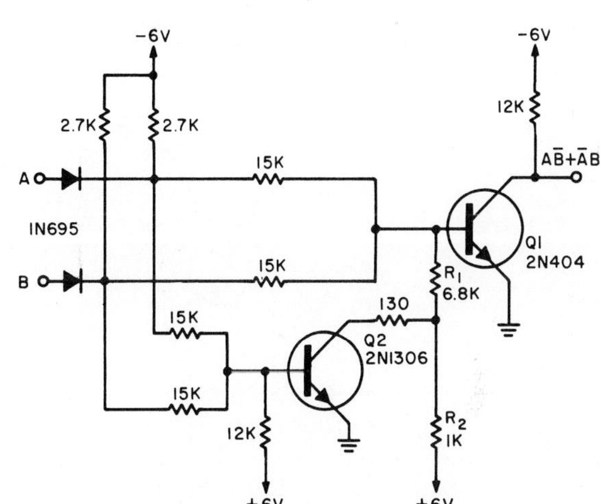

EXCLUSIVE-OR—Complementary transistors reduce cost and complexity. When inputs A and B are both logical zero (−6 V), output is logical zero. When either A or B is logical one (ground), output changes to logical one. When A and B are both logical one, output is logical zero.—J. L. Shagena, Complementary Transistors Reduce Exclusive-OR Size, *Electronic Design*, March 16, 1964, p 102.

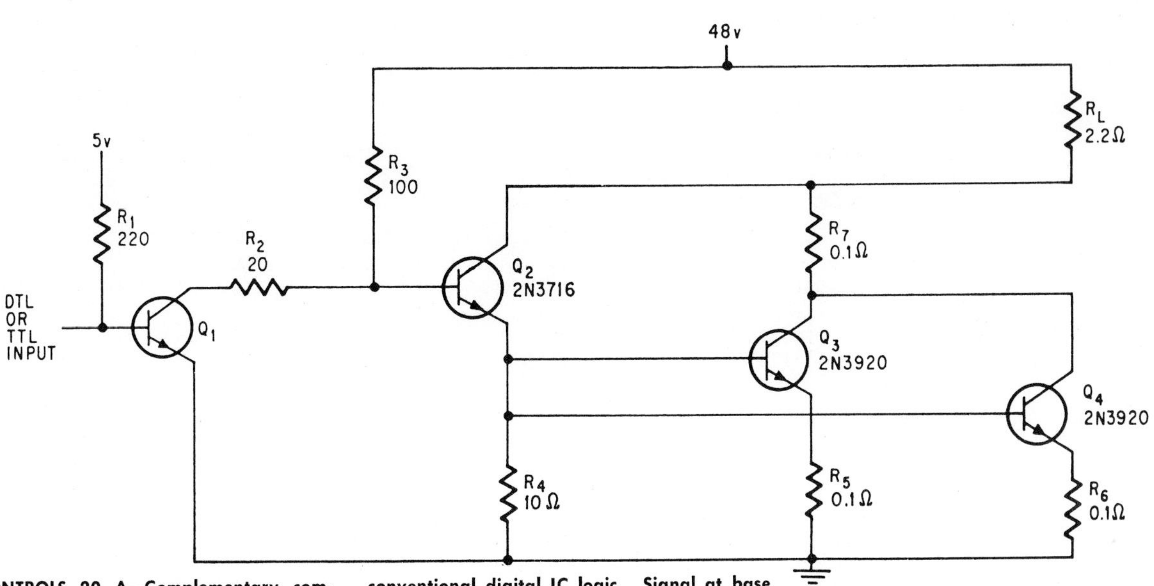

DTL CONTROLS 20 A—Complementary compound switch, operated by buffer transistor Q1, permits control of loads up to 20 A with conventional digital IC logic. Signal at base of Q1 saturates it, turning on Q2 and 10-A transistors Q3 and Q4.—L. S. Bell, High-Current Switch Is Driven by an IC, *Electronics*, Nov. 11, 1968, p 120.

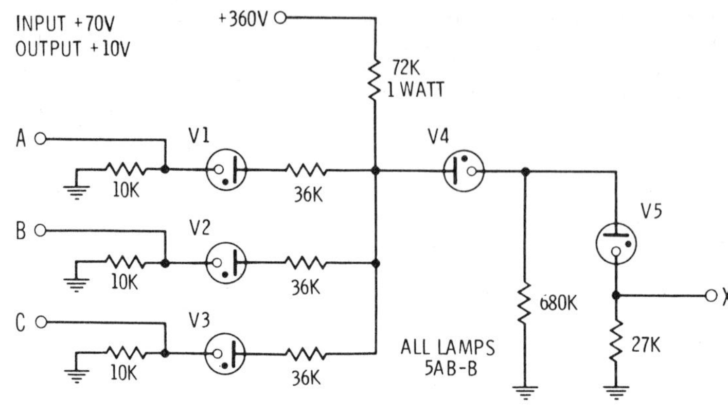

THREE-INPUT OR GATE—Converts high-level (70-V) logic to value useful in solid-state circuits (10 V). Point X is at 10 V if either V1 or V2 or V3 is extinguished by 70-V input. Output is taken from voltage developed across 27K resistor when V5 fires.—W. G. Miller, "Using and Understanding Miniature Neon Lamps," H. W. Sams & Co., Indianapolis, Ind., 1969, p 51.

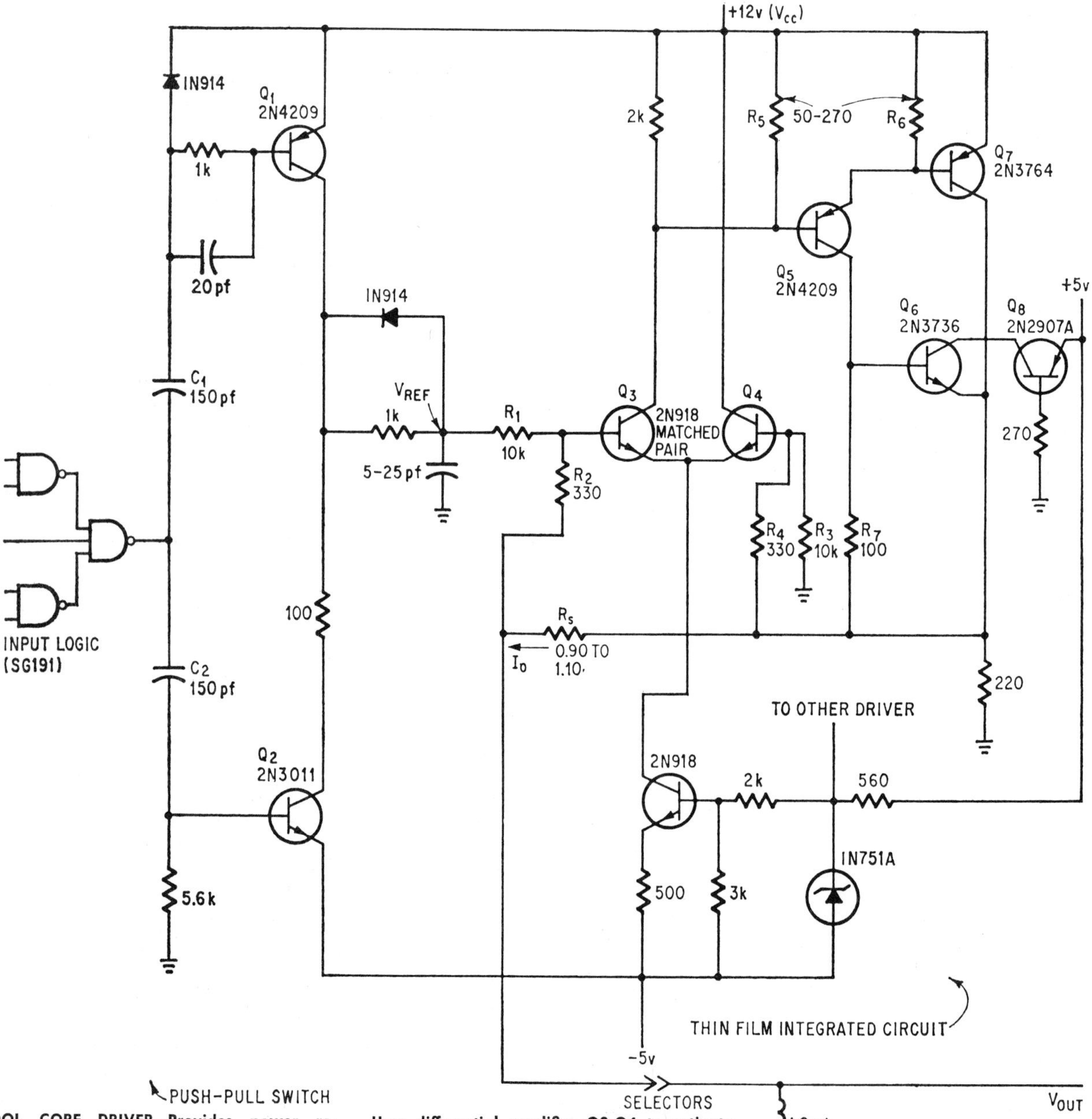

COOL CORE DRIVER—Provides power required to give fast rise time in core windings, then automatically switches to low-power constant-current source having low supply voltage, to reduce power dissipation in transistors and thereby improve circuit reliability. Uses differential amplifier Q3-Q4 to activate either 5-V or 12-V supply, when triggered by comparator that senses current flowing through core winding.—C. J. Ulrick, Core-Memory Driver Runs Cooler, *Electronics*, Oct. 13, 1969, p 102–103.

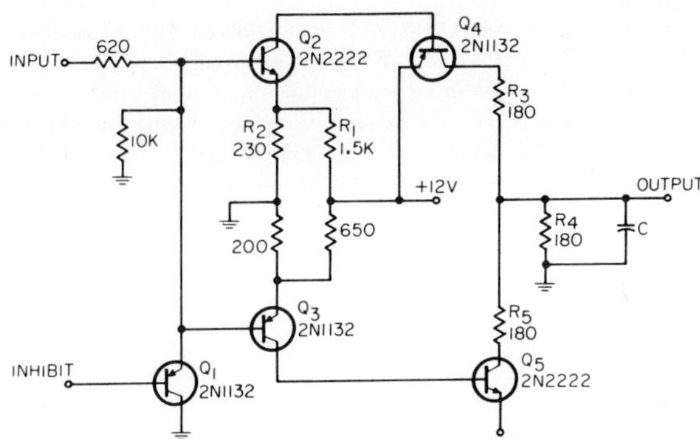

LEVEL-SHIFTER—Converts unbalanced input pulses (0 V and +4 V) to balanced output pulses (−6 V and +6 V). With values shown, output impedance is 90 ohms. If inhibit terminal is grounded, output is held at −6 V regardless of input voltage. Circuit was originally used to convert fast-rise pulses to slow-rise pulses for transmission over long lines.—W. J. Travis, Unbalanced to Balanced Level-Shifter, *EEE*, Nov. 1966, p 155–156.

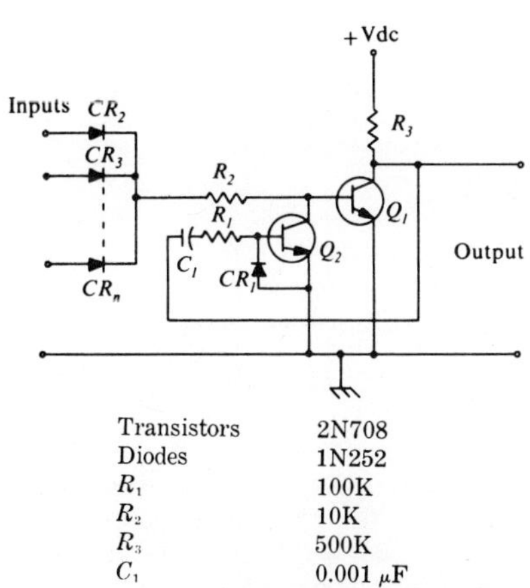

Transistors	2N708
Diodes	1N252
R_1	100K
R_2	10K
R_3	500K
C_1	0.001 μF

PULSE STRETCHER WITH NOR GATE—Provides output pulse having predetermined minimum duration of about 1 ms, as required in square-root computers and digital oscillators. With all inputs at ground, output is positive and current flow through C1-R1 turns on Q2 until C1 is charged. If inputs become positive while Q2 is still conducting, Q1 is not affected because its base is grounded by Q2. Inputs regain control when Q2 stops conducting.—"Selecting Electronic Circuitry," NASA SP-5046, 1966, Government Printing Office, Washington, D.C., p 78.

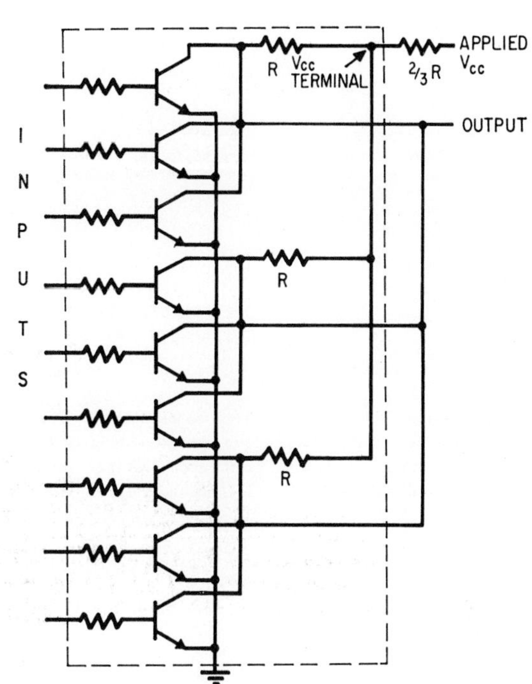

ADDING INPUTS TO NAND GATE—By changing value of Vcc and adding resistor, three triple-input gates in common package can be converted to single 9-input gate. Output is high only when negative voltage is applied to all inputs.—R. L. Frank, NAND Gate Inputs Expanded by Adding Resistor, *Electronics*, March 17, 1969, p 95–96.

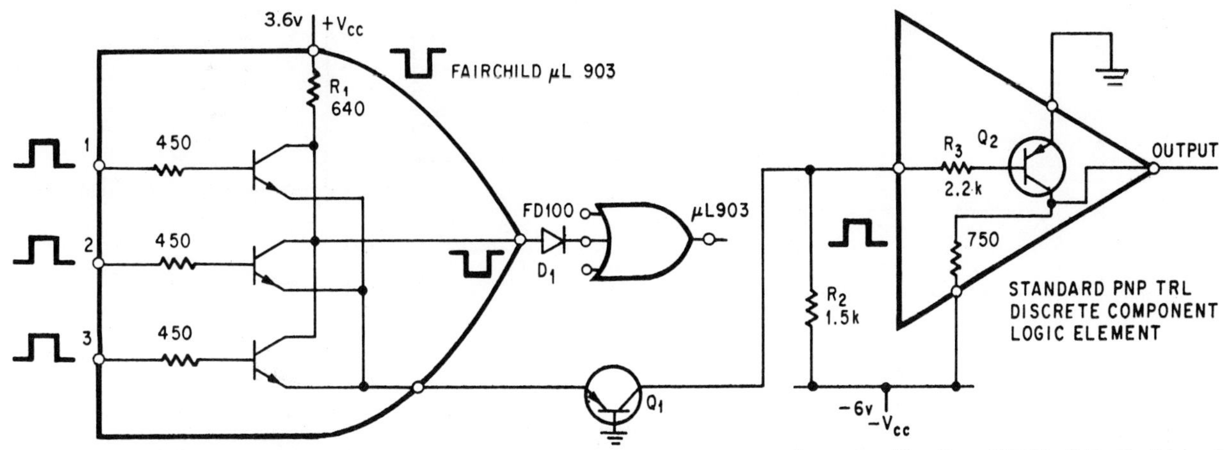

TRANSISTOR COUPLES NPN TO PNP—Germanium 2N1303 Q1 converts signals from npn IC to correct polarity and levels required by pnp discrete transistor at right. Arrangement also improves input noise rejection capability of IC at left.—G. D. Morant, Grounded-Base Amplifier Mates NPN To PNP, *Electronics*, Feb. 5, 1968, p 89.

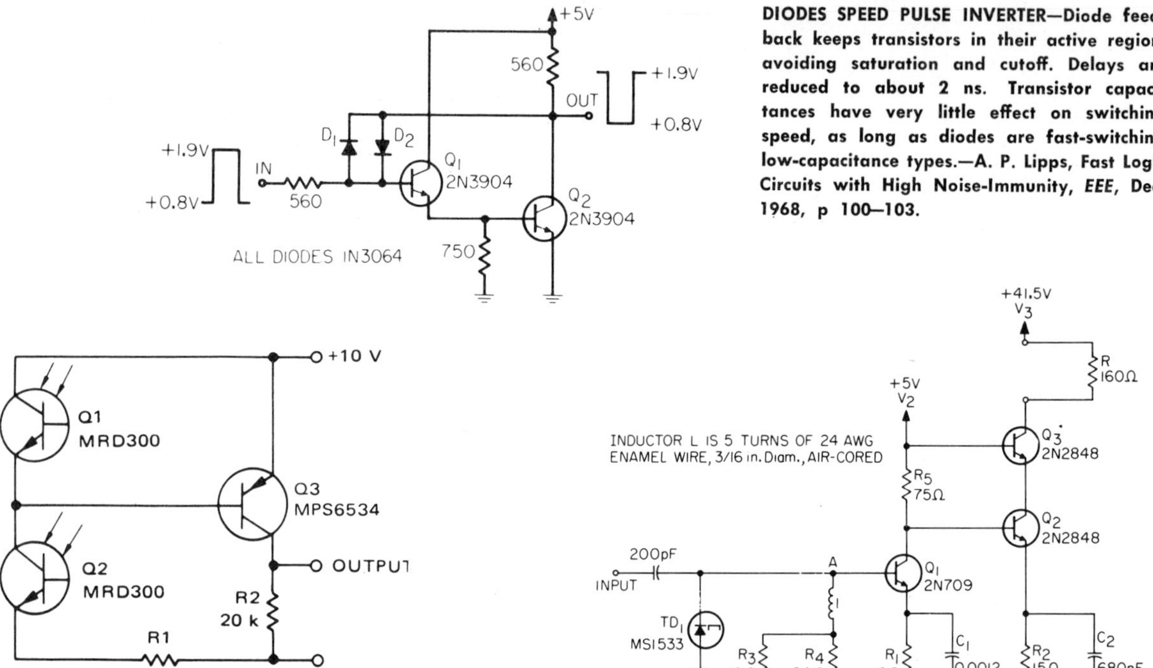

DIODES SPEED PULSE INVERTER—Diode feedback keeps transistors in their active region, avoiding saturation and cutoff. Delays are reduced to about 2 ns. Transistor capacitances have very little effect on switching speed, as long as diodes are fast-switching low-capacitance types.—A. P. Lipps, Fast Logic Circuits with High Noise-Immunity, *EEE*, Dec. 1968, p 100–103.

OPTICAL LOGIC DRIVER—Output is zero at all times except when Q2 is illuminated by about 220 foot-candles and Q1 is not. Q2 then saturates Q3 and gives positive output for driving 10-mA load. Can be used to furnish control signal for static switch.—"Semiconductor Power Circuits Handbook," Motorola, Phoenix, Ariz., 1968, p 4–21.

WORD-LINE DRIVER—Tunnel diode acts as one-shot to give fast switching speed and adjustable recovery time while delivering 220 mA to 160-ohm load. Delay time is 5 ns, while rise and fall times are 4 ns. Pulse width is adjustable from 15 to 22 ns.—W. W. Wu, Tunnel Diode Speeds Word-Line Driver, *EEE*, Jan. 1968, p 118 and 120.

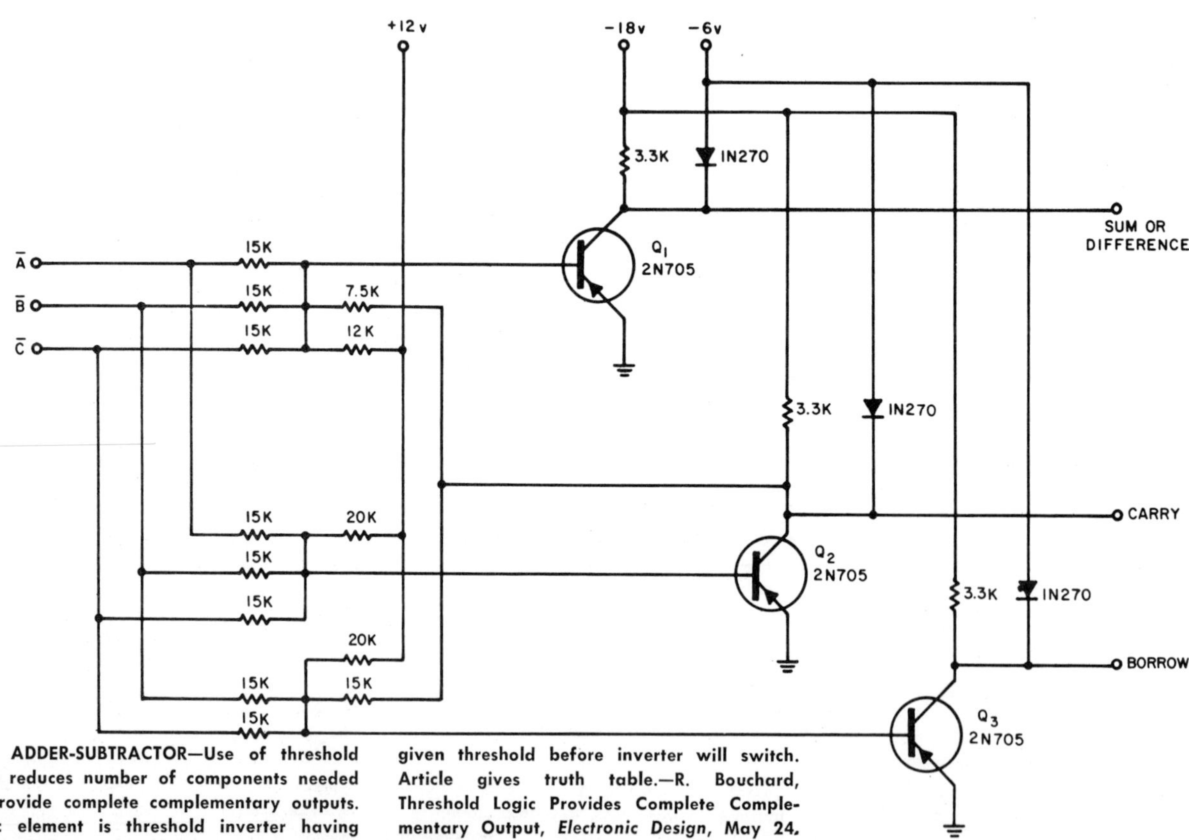

FULL ADDER-SUBTRACTOR—Use of threshold logic reduces number of components needed to provide complete complementary outputs. Basic element is threshold inverter having weighted inputs, some of which must exceed given threshold before inverter will switch. Article gives truth table.—R. Bouchard, Threshold Logic Provides Complete Complementary Output, *Electronic Design*, May 24, 1965, p 50.

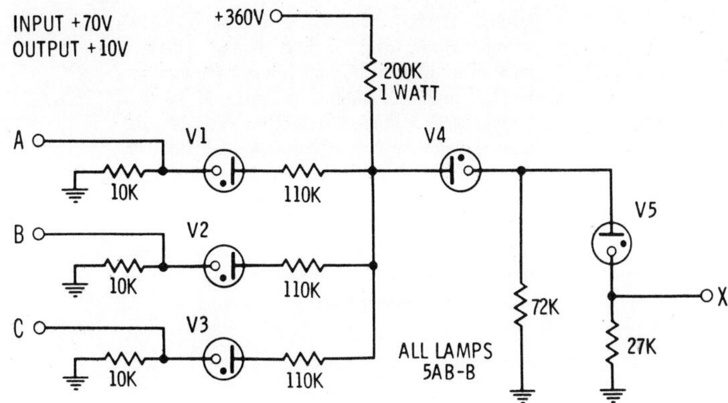

THREE-INPUT AND GATE—Converts high-level (70-V) logic to value useful in solid-state circuits (10 V). Output is taken from voltage developed across 27K resistor when V5 fires. This happens only when V1 and V2 and V3 are extinguished by 70-V inputs.—W. G. Miller, "Using and Understanding Miniature Neon Lamps," H. W. Sams & Co., Indianapolis, Ind., 1969, p 52.

LOGIC-LEVEL SHIFTER—Although more complex than single-transistor circuits used to shift voltage levels in digital systems requiring two or more driving voltages, three-transistor version provides much more accurate control of output level, has good thermal stability, and has high input impedance. Signals can be shifted over 18-V range. One desirable application is interfacing.—J. E. Walters, Adding Transistors Makes Voltage Shifter Adjustable, *Electronics*, Dec. 12, 1966, p 108–109.

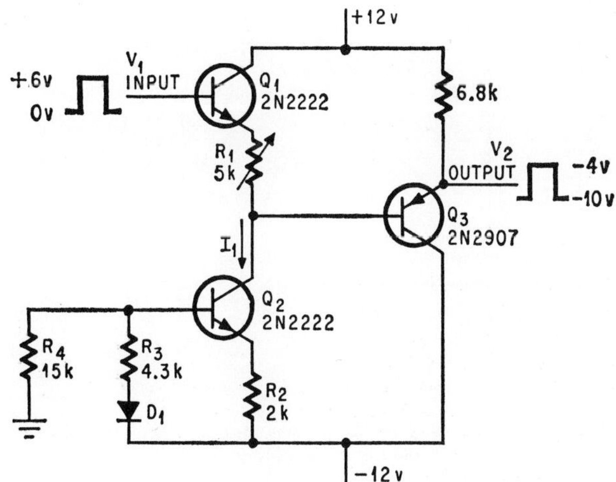

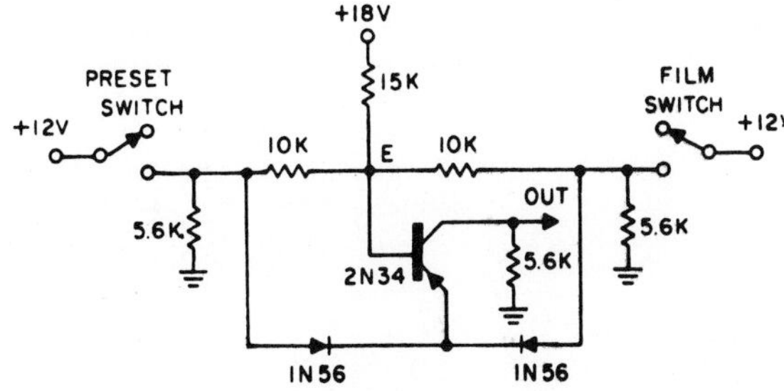

EXCLUSIVE-OR—Used to compare binary bits from film memory with binary numbers set on switches. If preset switch is open, output signal is high only if film switch is closed. With preset switch closed, output is high only if film switch is open. This gives exclusive-OR function. Both sets of conditions allow point E to drop below +12 V and turn on transistor.—F. Neu, Inverted Exclusive-OR Circuit Compares Binary Bits, "400 Ideas for Design Selected from Electronic Design," Hayden Book Co., N.Y., 1964, p 83.

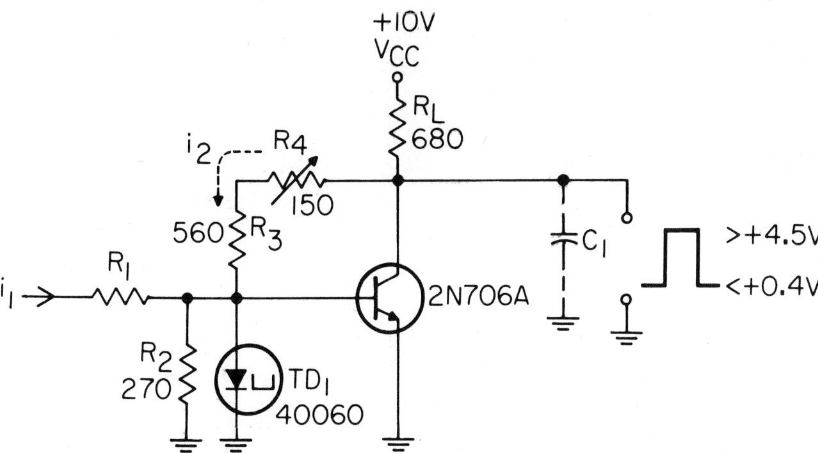

INTERFACE—Output levels of adjustable-hysteresis threshold circuit are compatible with TTL or DTL IC's. Tunnel diode switches to high-voltage state when input current is greater than peak current of diode, but does not switch back to low-voltage state until input current is less than sum of diode's valley current and transistor base current. Magnitude of I2 determines whether circuit hysteresis is positive, zero, or negative (unstable). Used for interfacing within digital computer.—O. A. Horna, Improved Tunnel-Diode Threshold Circuit Has Adjustable Hysteresis, *EEE*, Feb. 1968, p 125.

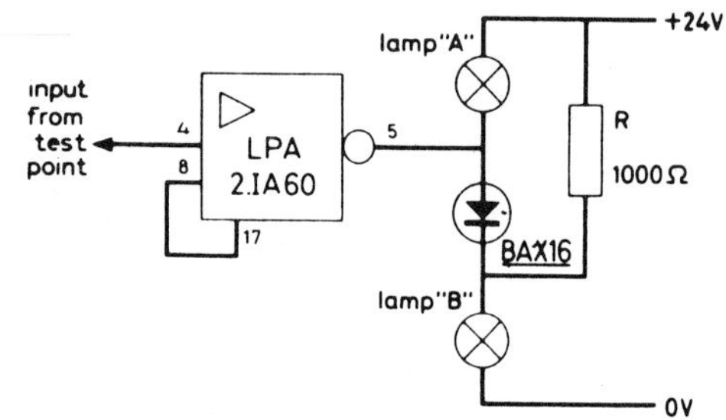

LOGIC LEVEL INDICATOR—Lamp A glows when output level of LPA Philips 60-series NORbit block is high, and lamp B glows when level is low. Display is fail-safe; if lamp A blows, lamp B immediately goes dim. Operation depends on use of lamps having different ratings; lamp A is 28 V and 0.1 A, while lamp B is 16 V and 40 mA. High level here is 11.4 to 30 V, and low level is 0 to 0.3 V.—Logic Level Indication By Two Lamps, Philips, Pub. Dept., Elcoma Div., Eindhoven, The Netherlands, Application Note.

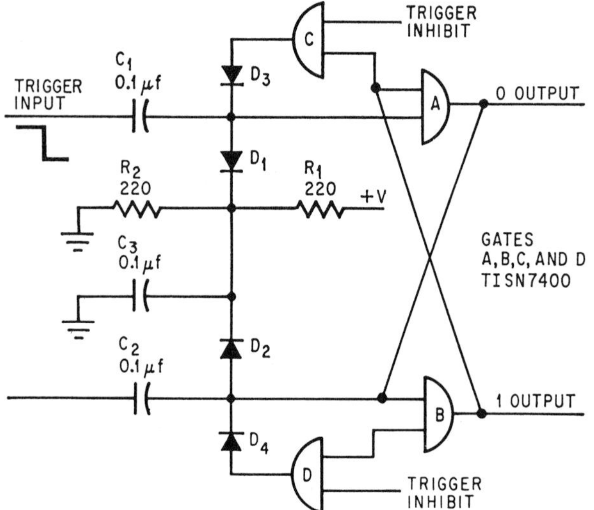

SET-RESET FLIP-FLOP—Use of four gates on single IC, connected as shown, is convenient low-cost method of obtaining common logic circuit not readily available in completely integrated form. Positive logic NAND gates A and B form d-c bistable flip-flop that changes state when trigger input to C1 goes to zero. To switch it back, trigger input to C1 must be returned to ONE state and negative input applied to gate B. Gates C and D provide fast recovery time. Will trigger on sine waves down to about 50 Hz and generate clean, symmetrical square waves.—R. Glasgal, Dual-Quad IC Gives Flip-Flop a Fast Recovery, *Electronics*, Feb. 5, 1968, p 86–87.

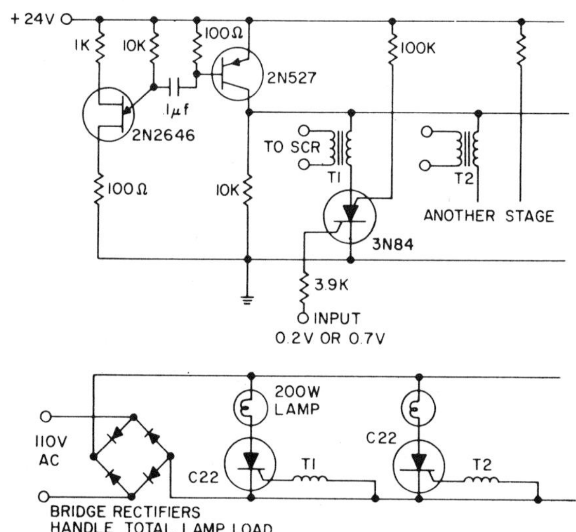

DRIVING LAMP WITH LOW-LEVEL LOGIC—Turns on 200-W lamp for 0.7-V upper logic level, giving normal brilliance, but does not turn on scs and lamp for 0.2-V lower logic level. 2N2646 oscillator turns on 2N527 for about 20 μs at 1-kHz rate; this pulse rate acts through transformer T1 to trigger scr C22 and give full brilliance of 110-V lamp.—Planar Silicon Controlled Switch 3N84/3N85, General Electric, Syracuse, N.Y., 65.18, 1964.

$10 PER DECADE—Resistor-transistor IC logic, although slower than DTL and TTL schemes, gives operating speeds from d-c to 8 MHz for counting decades, at about third of parts cost of more modern IC's. All IC's use 3.6 V d-c supply. Best code is 1-2-2-4 weighted biquinary, arranged as shown.—D. E. Lancaster, For Low Cost, Count On RTL, *Electronics*, Jan. 22, 1968, p 74–76.

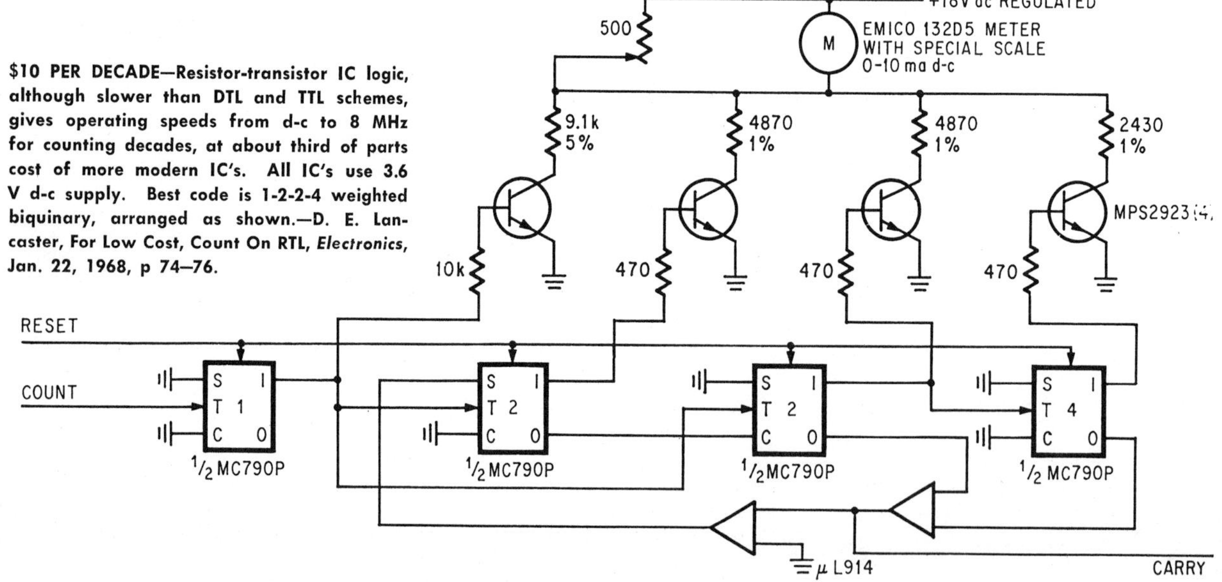

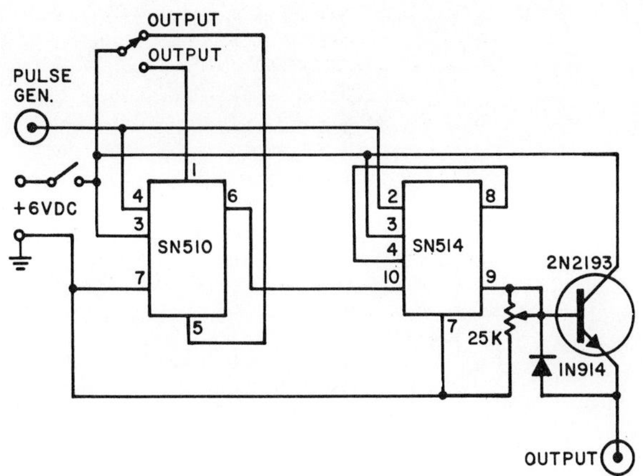

IC SWITCHING—R-S flip-flop IC SN510 acts as selector to provide switched output without interrupting pulse generator. Eliminates chatter caused by manual switch alone. When switch is in OUTPUT' position, +6 V is applied to reset line; output of flip-flop is then positive and no signal goes to SN514 dual NAND gate. In OUTPUT position, flip-flop is near ground and SN514 controls transistor driver that can furnish 4.5 V at up to 75 mA for several clock line pulses.—G. P. Carter, Circuit Prevents Pulse Interruption or Chatter, *Electronic Design*, March 16, 1964, p 106–107.

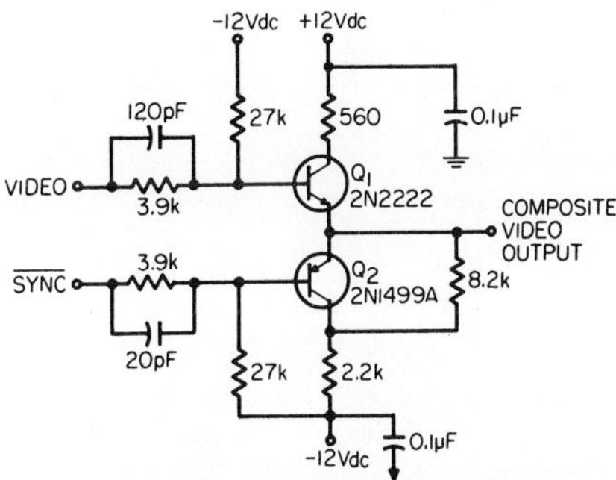

DIGITAL TV DISPLAY—Converts 5-V logic 1 and 0-V logic 0 signals to EIA standards for video (+1 V video, −0.1 V blanking, and 0.4 V sync) feeding into EIA standard 75-ohm load. Used for computer-generated digital television displays. Several crt monitors may be fed in parallel, with 70-ohm termination attached to last monitor. Frequency response is flat within 1 dB from d-c to 20 MHz.—T. A. Anderson, Inexpensive Video Distribution Amplifier Converts Logic Signals for TV Displays, *EEE*, Nov. 1967, p 124.

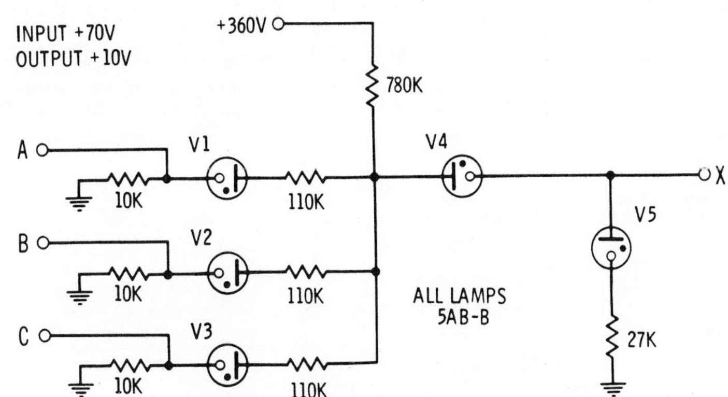

NEON AND GATE—Has 70-V input and same output for operating additional high-level logic circuits. V5 fires only when V1, V2, and V3 are extinguished.—W. G. Miller, "Using and Understanding Miniature Neon Lamps," H. W. Sams & Co., Indianapolis, Ind., 1969, p 53.

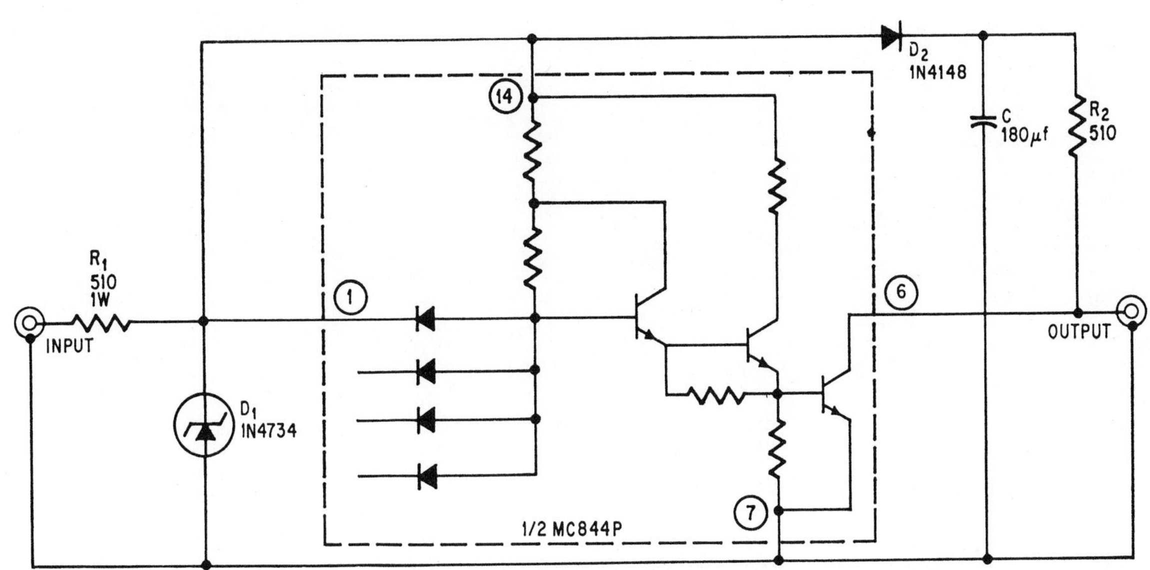

PROTECTING IC FROM NEGATIVE OVERDRIVE—Permits driving DTL, TTL, and other current-sinking logic with standard laboratory signal generators that produce output waveform symmetrical to ground and which therefore may exceed ratings of logic elements in negative direction. Voltage swings of 25 V negative will not damage IC. R1 and D1 clamp positive inputs to 5 V and negative to 0.7 V. —R. K. Underwood, Converted Generator Drives Heavy Logic Loads, *Electronics*, Feb. 17, 1969, p 97–98.

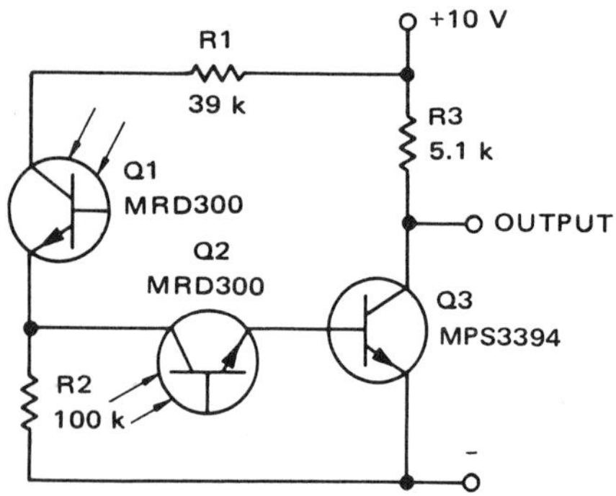

OPTICAL LOGIC DRIVER—Can be used for delivering control signal to static switch. Output is positive, providing 2 mA to load, at all times except when phototransistors Q1 and Q2 are both exposed to bright light of about 220 foot-candles.—"Semiconductor Power Circuits Handbook," Motorola, Phoenix, Ariz., 1968, p 4–20.

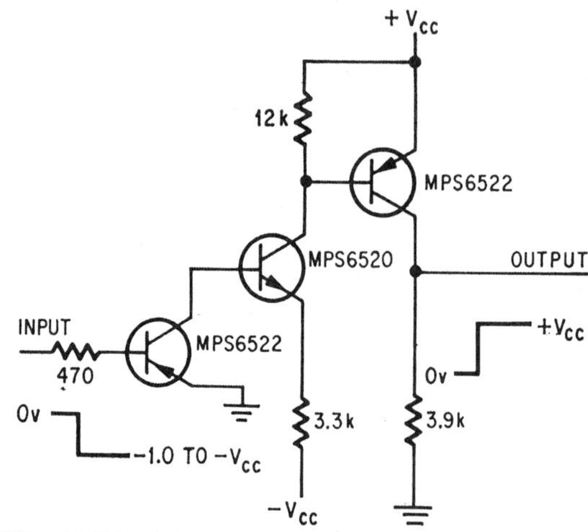

NEGATIVE-POSITIVE LOGIC CONVERTER—Transforms negative control signal into required positive logic for digital IC, at clock rates from d-c to above 2 MHz. Negative d-c voltage levels below zero are changed to positive logic level of system, in range of 3.6 to 7 V. When negative pulse reaches input, all three transistors are switched on, and inverted signal appears at output. Noise immunity is better that 400 mV for 0 to 100 C.—J. A. D'Cunha, Negative Signals Converted to Positive Logic, *Electronics*, March 17, 1969, p 97.

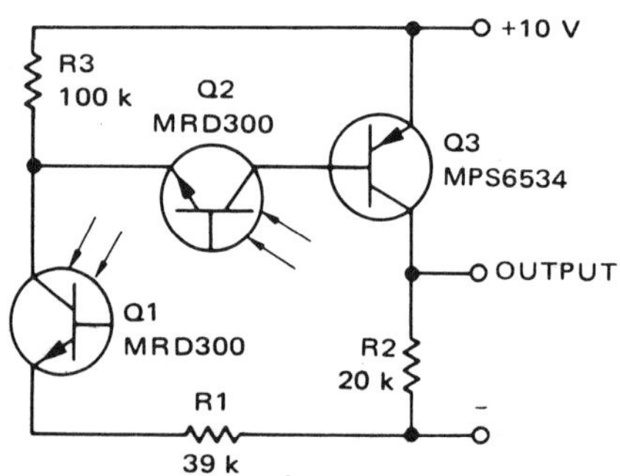

OPTICAL LOGIC DRIVER—Output is zero at all times except when both Q1 and Q2 are illuminated by about 220 foot-candles, in which case they saturate Q3 so it can provide at least 10 mA for static switch or other load. —"Semiconductor Power Circuits Handbook," Motorola, Phoenix, Ariz., 1968, p 4–20.

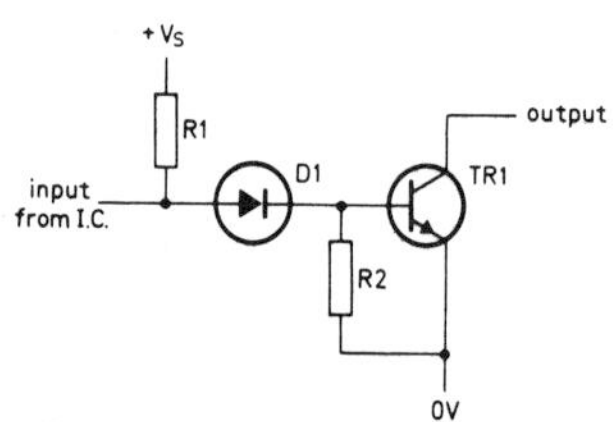

BOOSTING LOGIC OUTPUT—With input from IC and 6-V supply, low input gives 35 V maximum output at 5 μA, and high input gives 0.2 V maximum output at 100 mA. Diode is BAX13, R1 is 560 ohms, and R2 is 6.8K.—J. Deerson, FC Family of DTL Integrated Circuits, Philips, Pub. Dept., Elcoma Div., Eindhoven, The Netherlands, 1970, p 139.

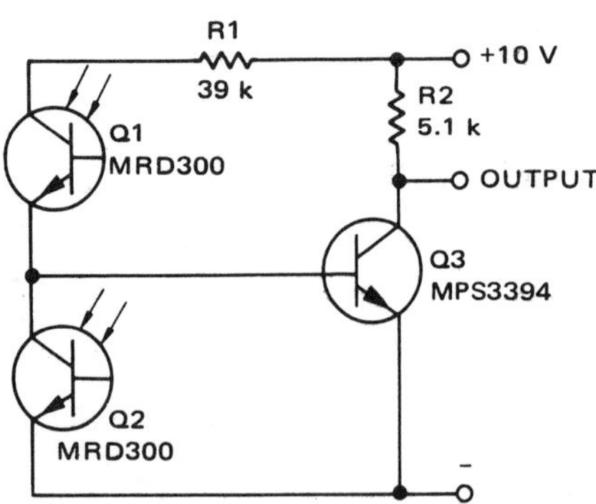

OPTICAL LOGIC DRIVER—Provides positive output voltage for all combinations of illumination on phototransistors Q1 and Q2 except that when light is on Q1 but not on Q2. Will furnish 2 mA to load. About 220 foot-candles from flashlight shining on Q1 will saturate Q3 and reduce output to zero.—"Semiconductor Power Circuits Handbook," Motorola, Phoenix, Ariz., 1968, p 4–20.

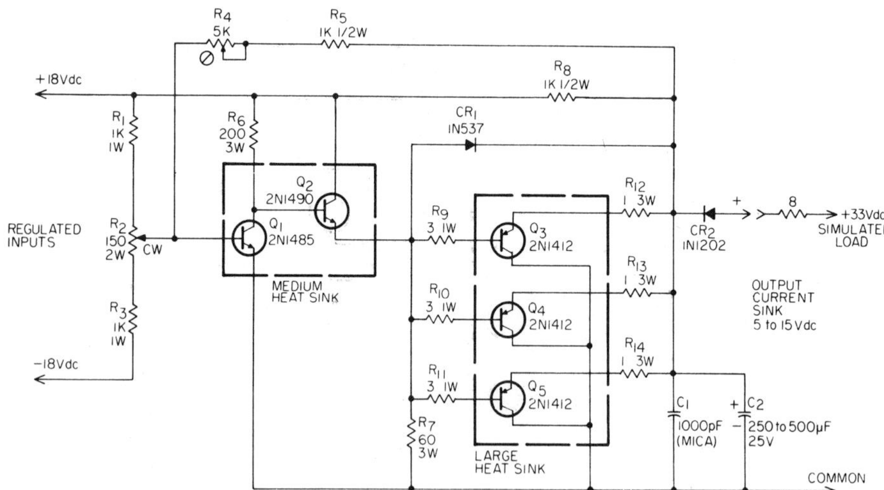

CONSTANT-VOLTAGE SINK FOR CLAMPED LOGIC—Gives any constant voltage from 5 to 15 V d-c and will sink up to 3 A of reverse current when serving as constant-voltage sink. Output voltage regulation is better than 2%. Circuit is similar to shunt-regulated power supply except for reversed load.—M. W. Raybin, Second Breakdown Gives Fast Pulses, *EEE*, March 1967, p 162 and 164.

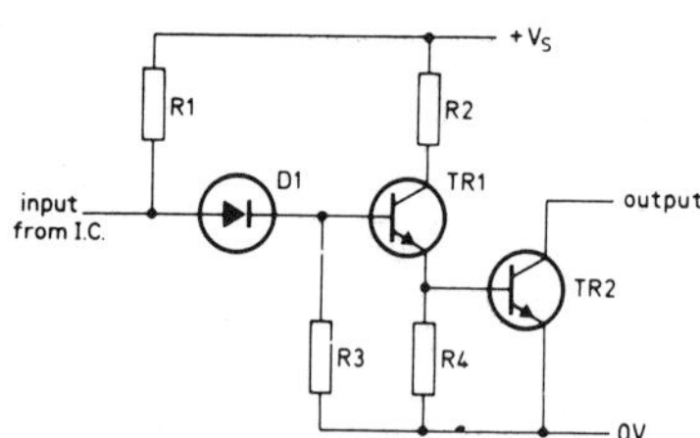

1-A LOW LOGIC—With input from IC logic unit and 6-V supply, low input gives 35 V maximum output at 5 μA and high input gives 1 V maximum output at 1 A. Values are: D1 BAX13; TR1 BFY51; TR2 BFY50 with heatsink; R1 560; R2 30; R3 6.8K; R4 470.—J. Deerson, FC Family of DTL Integrated Circuits, Philips, Pub. Dept., Elcoma Div., Eindhoven, The Netherlands, 1970, p 139.

CHAPTER 48
Magnetic Tape Circuits

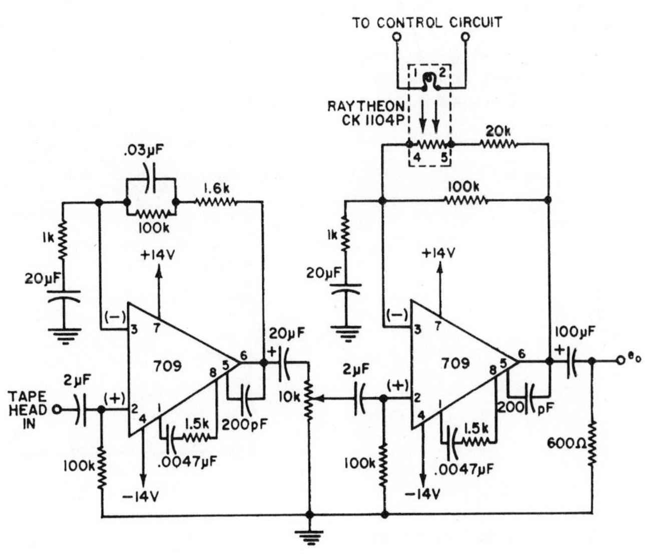

TAPE PREAMP—Output is flat within 1 dB from 20 to 20,000 Hz with NAB equalization. Gain is remotely controlled electro-optically; control circuit changes intensity of light source acting on photoresistor, altering effective feedback resistance. Technique provides completely noise-free control of gain. Uses Fairchild μA709 or National LM709 IC opamps.—S. L. Silver, IC Op Amps Boost Audio Circuit Performance, *Electronics World*, Sept. 1968, p 30–32.

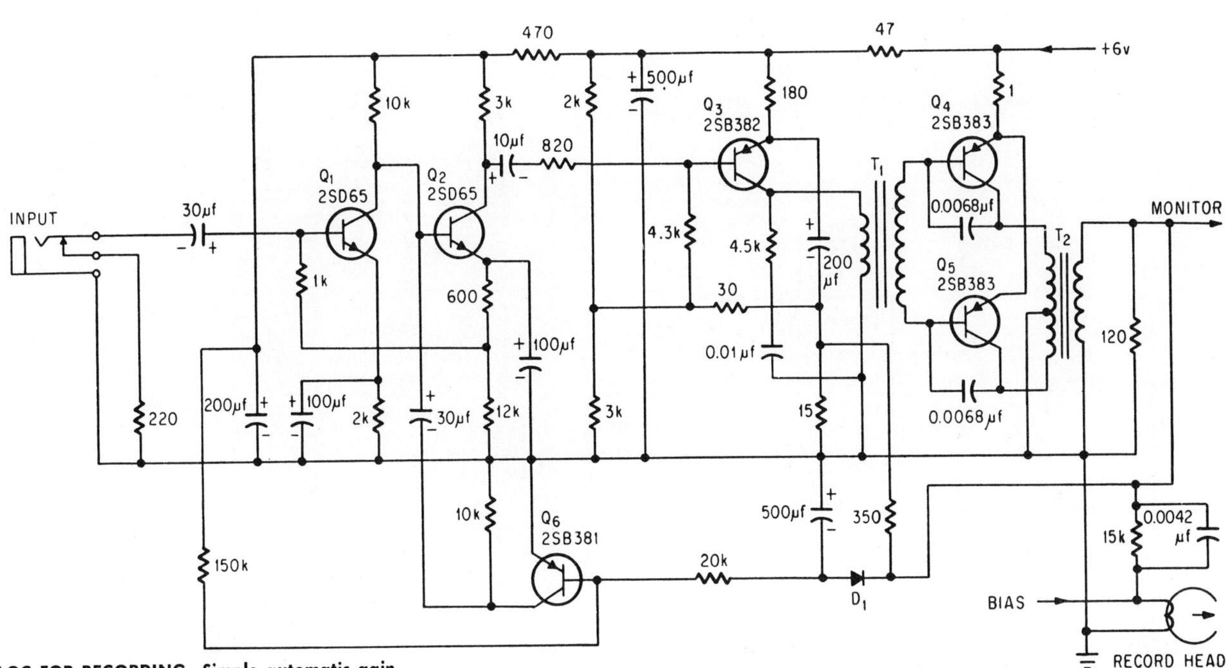

AGC FOR RECORDING—Simple automatic gain control amplifier, used in Sonymatic TC-900 tape recorder, maintains proper recording level automatically within 10 dB, for input level changes up to 30 dB. Agc control transistor Q6 acts as variable shunt impedance at output of amplifier Q1, to adjust overall gain.—Recorder Gain Control Eliminates Level Indicator, *Electronics*, Nov. 14, 1966, p 165–166.

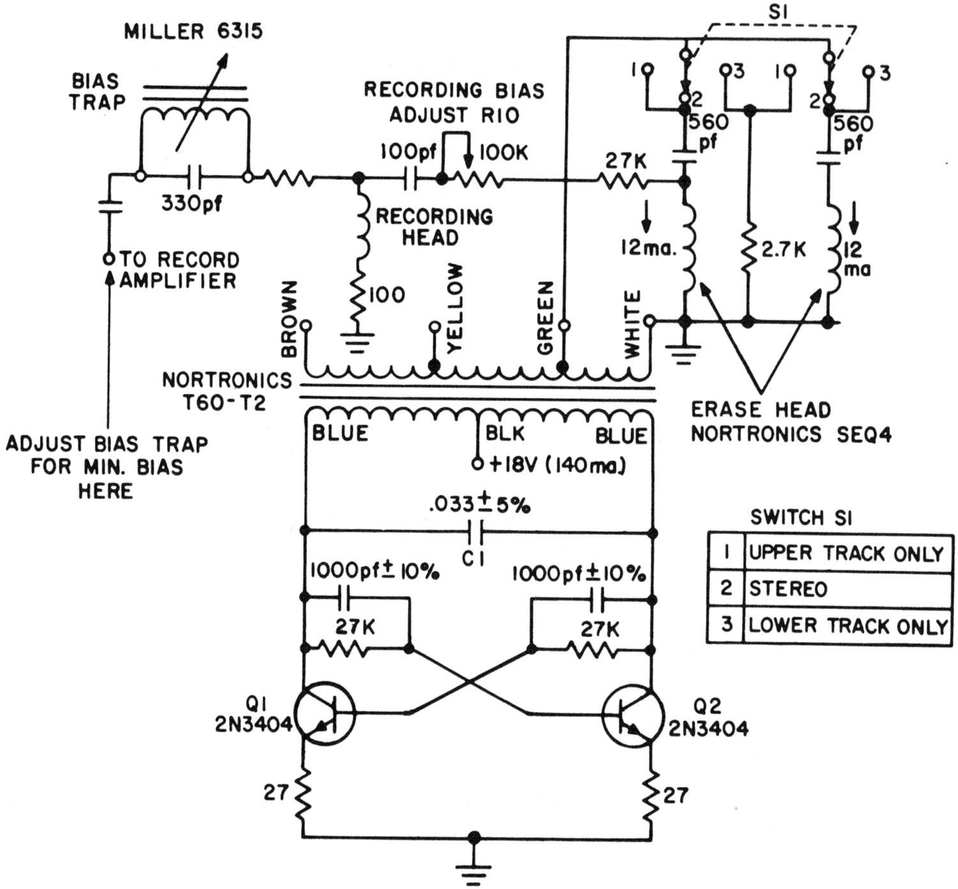

70-KHZ ERASE-BIAS OSCILLATOR—Uses low-cost silicon transistors requiring no heat sinks. Provides sufficient power (over 10 mA at 70 to 80 kHz) to give minimum of 60 dB erasure with stereo erase head. Total power output is 1.5 W, with 60% efficiency. Circuit is cross-coupled mvbr with tuned load.—D. V. Jones, Tape Erase and Bias Oscillator, General Electric, Syracuse, N.Y., No. 90.14, 1965.

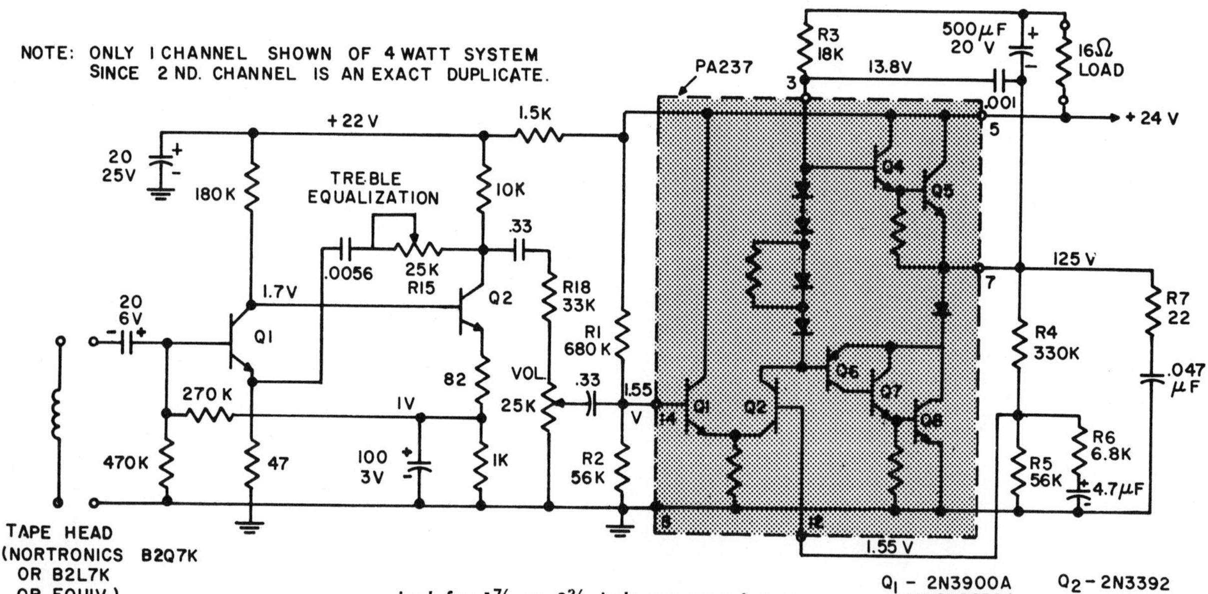

4-W IC STEREO TAPE CARTRIDGE SYSTEM—Uses GE PA-237 integrated circuit to drive 16-ohm load, with two-transistor preamp between tape head and IC. Preamp is equalized for 1⅞ or 3¾ inch per second tape speed. Treble equalization control is used to compensate for program material, tape head, speaker, or serve as ordinary tone control. Output is adequate for 8-track system.—Dwight V. Jones, Monolithic 2 Watt Integrated Amplifier—Characteristics and Applications, General Electric, Syracuse, N.Y., No. 90.73, 1968, p 13.

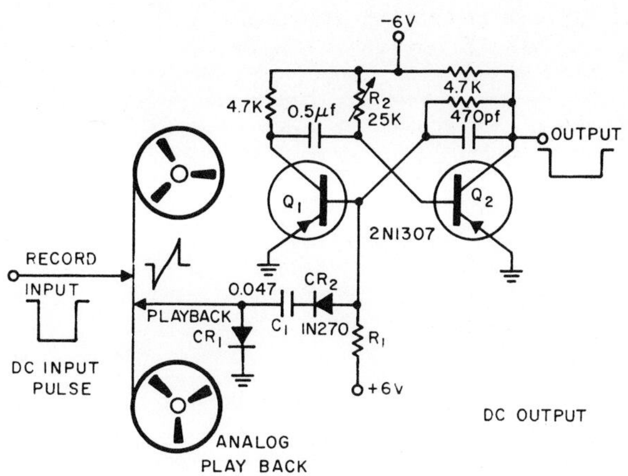

REGENERATING PULSES ON PLAYBACK—Simple one-shot mvbr regenerates d-c pulses recorded on analog tape. Pulse width, pulse amplitude, and time relationships of recorded waveform are thus preserved at output of channel. External voltage divider can be used to set output amplitude.—B. C. Tupper, Regenerator Restores Pulses Recorded on Analog Tape, *Electronic Design*, Nov. 23, 1964, p 61.

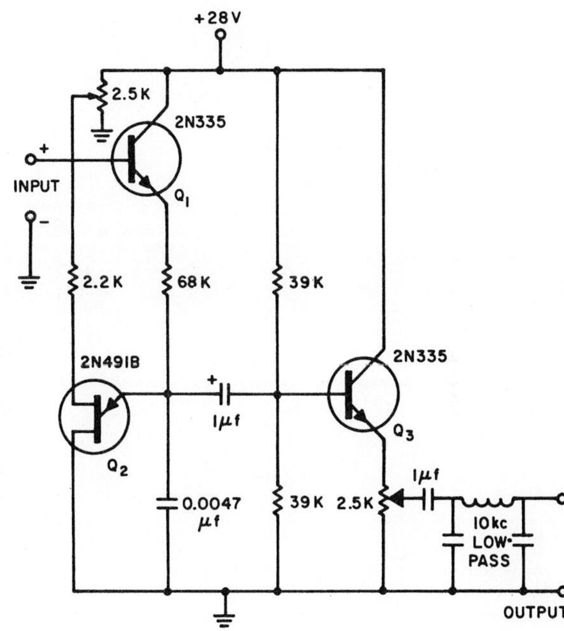

LINEAR LOW-FREQUENCY MODULATOR—Uses ujt to generate sawtooth whose period is controlled by input to give f-m signal for recording on magnetic tape. Low-pass filter at output attenuates sawtooth harmonics above audio frequencies to prevent them from heterodyning with bias oscillator of recorder. Original d-c signal can be restored by playing back into limiter, discriminator, and d-c amplifier.—J. H. Hammond, Inexpensive FM Modulator Has Good Linearity, *Electronic Design*, Nov. 9, 1964, p 72–75.

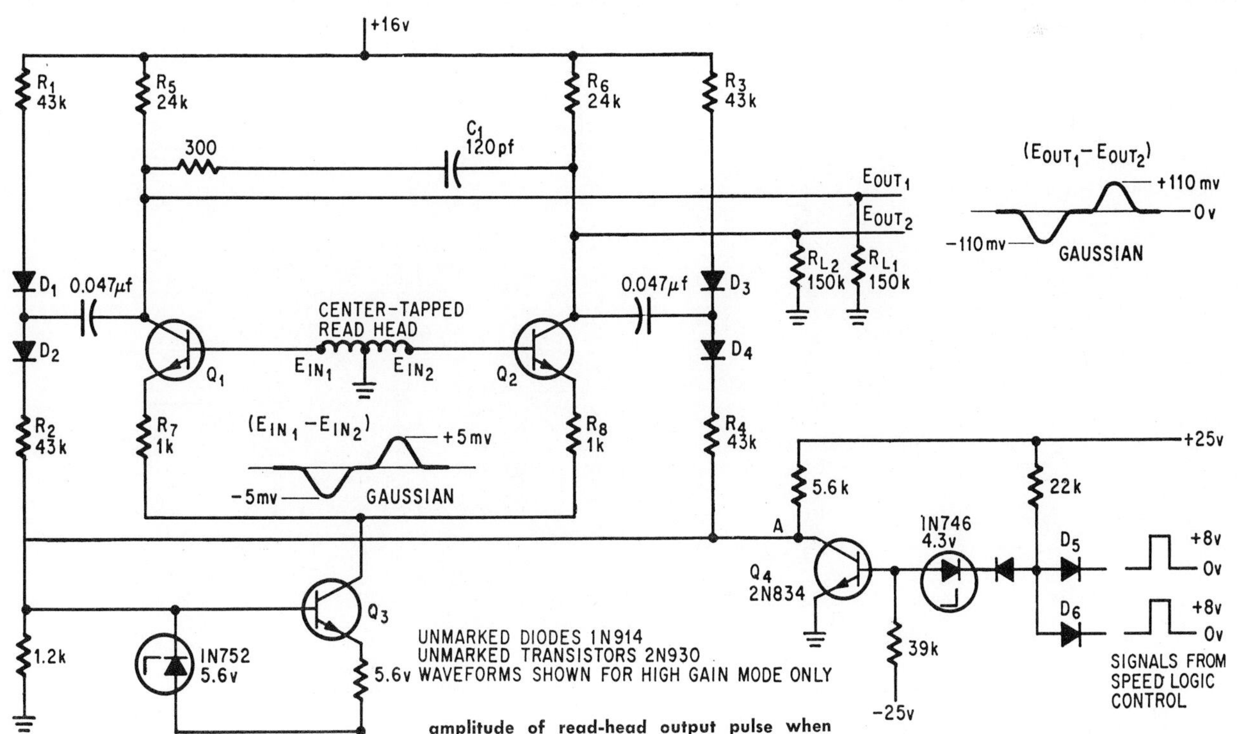

DIGITAL CONTROL—Two predetermined gain levels in preamplifier for digital magnetic tape transport are selected by digital command. Higher gain mode compensates for reduced amplitude of read-head output pulse when recorder is operated at slower of its two speeds. Speed-changing commands are derived automatically from speed control logic of recorder. Differential amplifier Q1-Q2 allows preamp to handle signals with peak-to-peak difference amplitudes as low as millivolts while rejecting common-mode noise.—I. W. Salmon, Digital Commands Control Differential Amplifier Gain, *Electronics*, July 24, 1967, p 85–86.

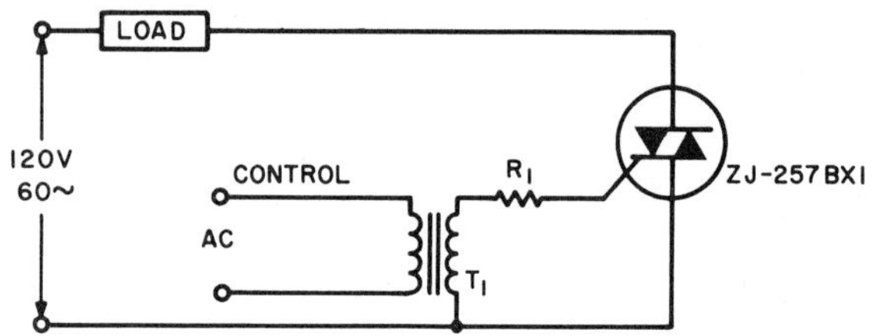

ELECTRICALLY ACTUATED SCR—Control signal for bilateral scr can be either properly phased 60-Hz or any signal above 600 Hz. If T1 is tuned, tones from tape recorder can be used to activate selectively two or more of these switches.—E. K. Howell, Bilateral SCR Lets Designers Economize on Circuitry, *Electronic Design*, Jan. 20, 1964, p 74–77.

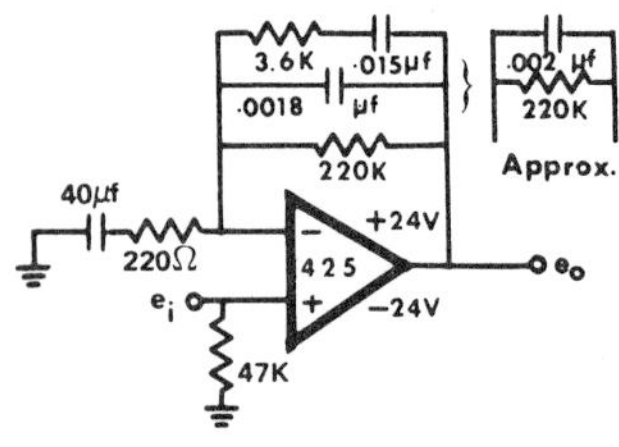

NAB EQUALIZATION—Uses Model 425 IC opamp in network giving standard equalization for magnetic tape. Simpler network at right will serve for less critical applications. —B. J. Losmandy, Operational Amplifier Application for Audio Systems, Opamp Labs, Los Angeles, Cal., 1968.

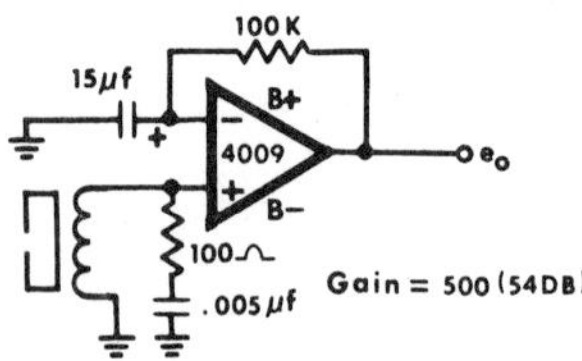

TAPE HEAD PREAMP—R-C network across winding of tape head suppresses oscillation in Model 4009 d-c opamp. Gain is 500 (54 dB).—B. J. Losmandy, Operational Amplifier Application for Audio Systems, Opamp Labs, Los Angeles, Cal., 1968.

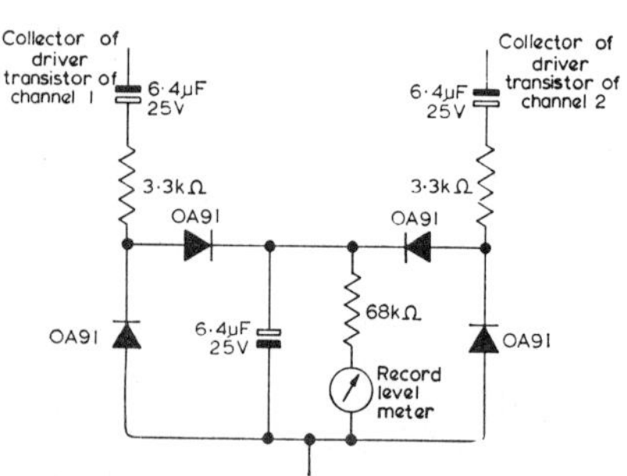

STEREO RECORDING LEVEL INDICATOR—Meter reading is proportional to peak-peak voltage at collector of driver transistor in channel having highest recording level. At input of 4 V rms, corresponding to point where distortion due to tape saturation becomes significant in typical recorder, direct current through meter is 95 µA.—"Transistor Audio and Radio Circuits," Mullard Ltd., London, 1969, p 79.

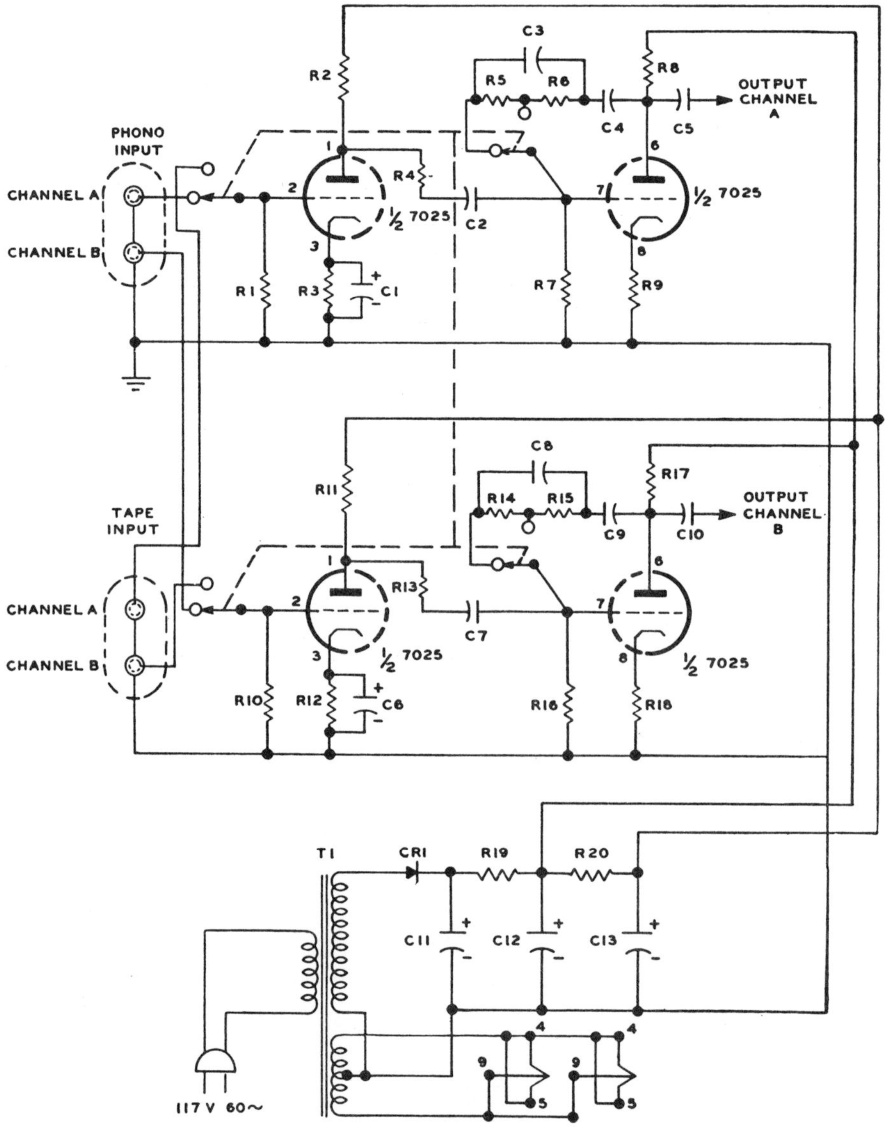

C_1 C_6—30 µf 25V
C_2 C_7—0.1 µf 400V
C_3 C_8—330 µµf
C_4 C_9—0.001 µf
C_5 C_{10}—0.047 µf 400V
C_{11}—50 µf 150V
C_{12} C_{13}—20 µf 150V
CR_1—Selenium Rectifier 15 Ma DC
R_1 R_{10}—47 K
R_2 R_{11}—270 K
R_3 R_{12}—5.1 K
R_4 R_{13}—51 K
R_5 R_{14}—160 K
R_6 R_{15}—75 K
R_7 R_{16}—1 Meg
R_8 R_{17}—100 K
R_9 R_{18}—1 K
R_{19}—10 K
R_{20}—22 K
T_1—Power Transformer: Sec—125V, 15Ma; 6.3V, 0.6A

PHONO-TAPE PREAMP—Developed for stereo magnetic phono cartridges and stereo tape heads. Ganged switch provides R1AA equalization at phono setting and NARTB equalization for tape setting.—"Essential Characteristics", General Electric, Owensboro, Ky., 13th Edition, 1969, p 363.

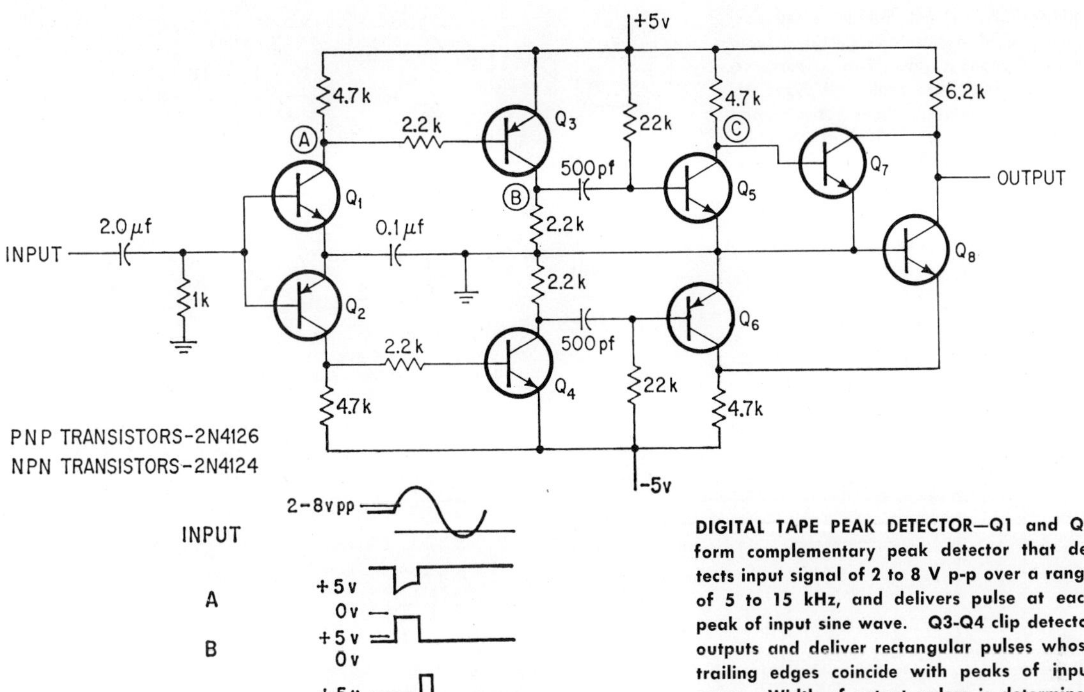

DIGITAL TAPE PEAK DETECTOR—Q1 and Q2 form complementary peak detector that detects input signal of 2 to 8 V p-p over a range of 5 to 15 kHz, and delivers pulse at each peak of input sine wave. Q3-Q4 clip detector outputs and deliver rectangular pulses whose trailing edges coincide with peaks of input wave. Width of output pulses is determined only by time constant of R-C networks at input to pulse amplifiers Q5-Q6. Circuit eliminates need for full-wave rectifier normally used to make bipolar pulses from tape head unipolar. —C. A. Herbst, Peak Detector Senses Bipolar Inputs, *Electronics*, July 21, 1969, p 81.

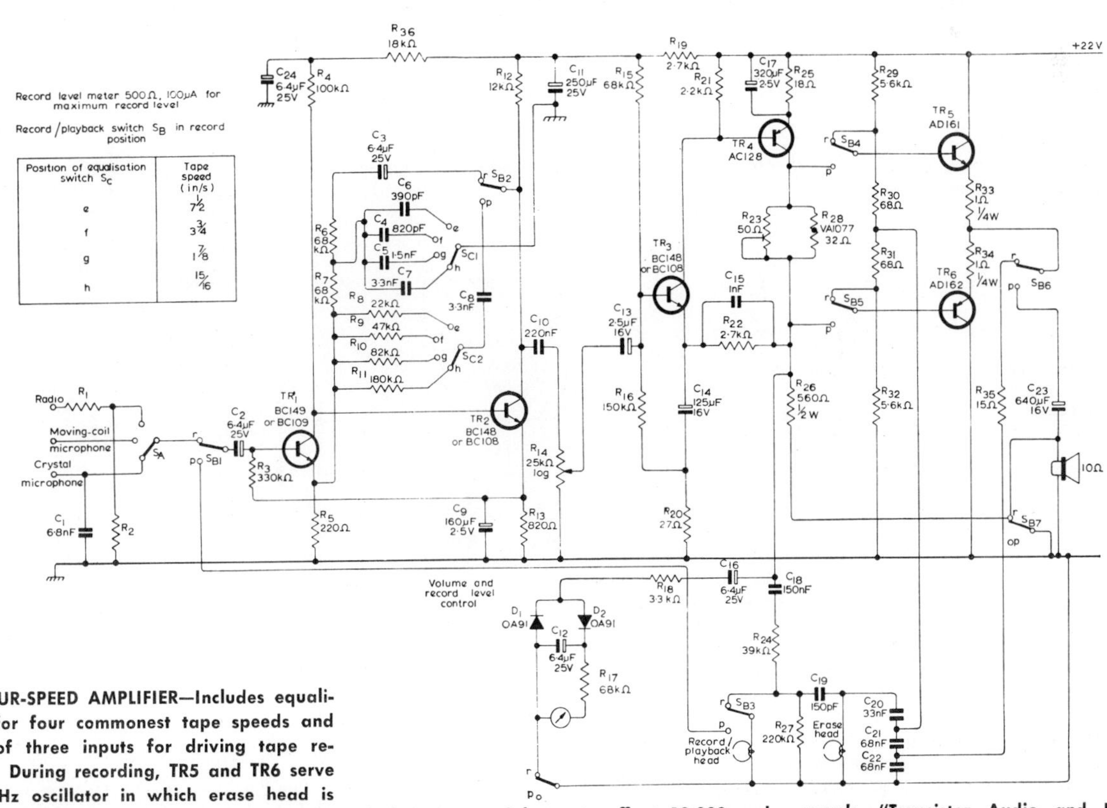

Position of equalisation switch S_C	Tape speed (in/s)
e	7½
f	3¾
g	1⅞
h	15/16

4-W FOUR-SPEED AMPLIFIER—Includes equalization for four commonest tape speeds and choice of three inputs for driving tape recorder. During recording, TR5 and TR6 serve as 50-kHz oscillator in which erase head is used as oscillator coil. Frequency response is flat within 3 dB from 55 to 20,000 Hz for 7.5-inch-per-s speed but cuts off at 12,000 and 6,000 Hz respectively for next two lower speeds.—"Transistor Audio and Radio Circuits," Mullard Ltd., London, 1969, p 70.

TAPE RECORDER MOTOR SUPPLY—Used for quick checking of batteries in portable tape recorders and phonographs. Two outputs, for 3 and 9 V, handle practically all types of motors used in these applications. 3-V supply is variable, for checking motors at specified operating voltages.—L. Chioma, Tape Recorder Repair, *G-E Techni-Talk*, Fall 1967, p 1.

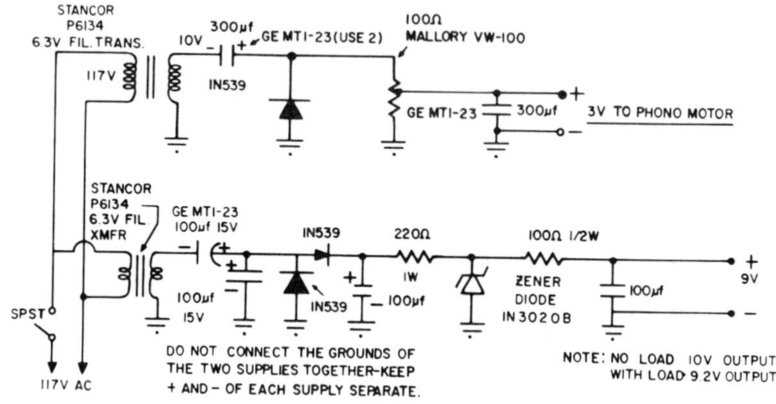

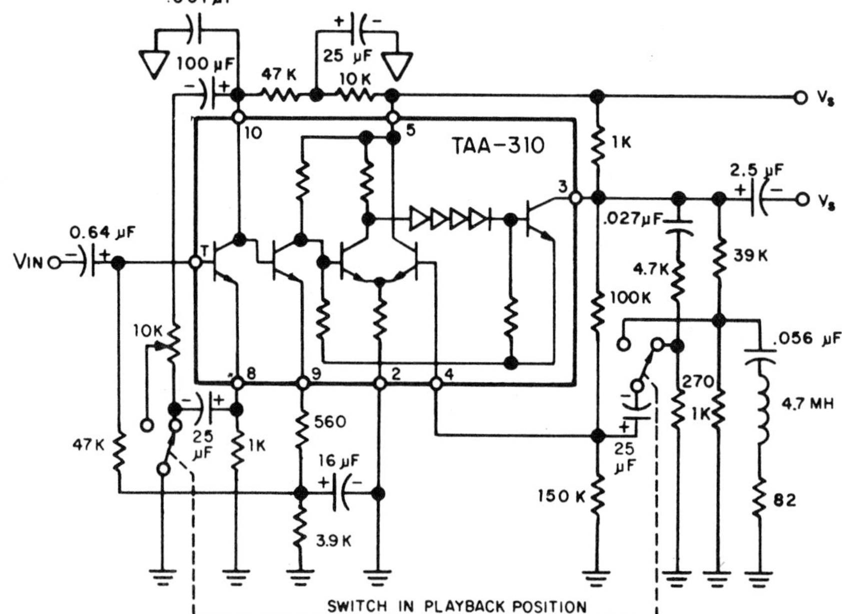

RECORD-PLAYBACK PREAMP—Uses TAA310 low-level linear IC amplifier having high input impedance, 90-dB voltage gain, and noise less than 4 dB. External components include frequency compensation networks and volume control. Designed to feed 1,000-ohm impedance. Report gives characteristic curves.—The Amperex TAA310 in Tape Recorder Preamplifiers, Amperex, Slatersville, R.I., S-132, 1967.

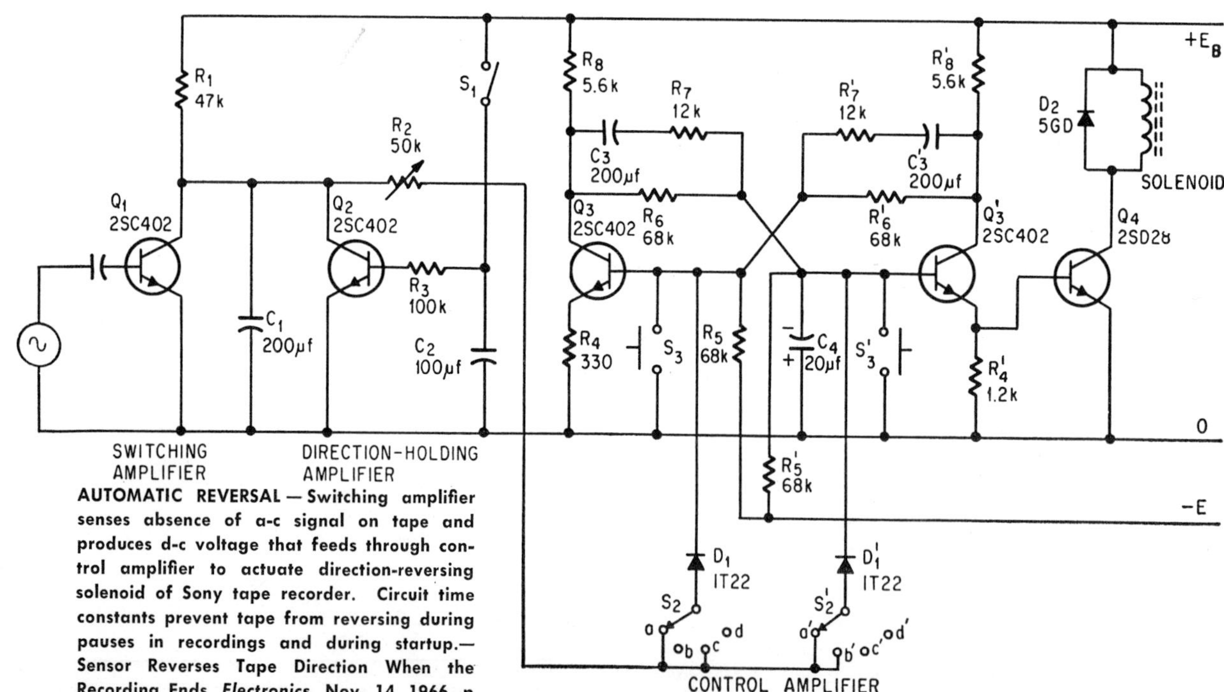

AUTOMATIC REVERSAL — Switching amplifier senses absence of a-c signal on tape and produces d-c voltage that feeds through control amplifier to actuate direction-reversing solenoid of Sony tape recorder. Circuit time constants prevent tape from reversing during pauses in recordings and during startup.—Sensor Reverses Tape Direction When the Recording Ends, *Electronics*, Nov. 14, 1966, p 163–165.

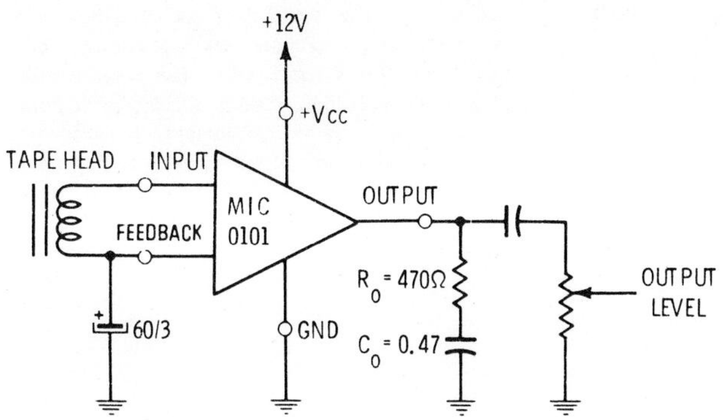

COMPENSATED PLAYBACK PREAMP—Uses Mallory MIC0101 IC audio preamp with R-C compensation network connected to output to compensate for increase in input signal with increasing recorded frequency. Gives essentially flat over-all response. Values of R and C should be selected to give flat response when NAB standard tape is played through head whose playback characteristics are known.—M. L. Deschler, Integrated Circuit Preamplifiers, Mallory, Indianapolis, Ind., APPN-2, 1968.

TAPE PREAMP—Uses audio integrated circuit with 7-V single-ended supply to provide 4-dB noise figure, 90-dB voltage gain, and uncompensated frequency limit of 15 kHz. Ideal for tape record-playback preamp. Values of unlabeled resistors should be chosen for optimum results.—D. E. Lancaster, Audio Integrated Circuits—What's Available?, *Electronics World*, Oct. 1967, p 34–36.

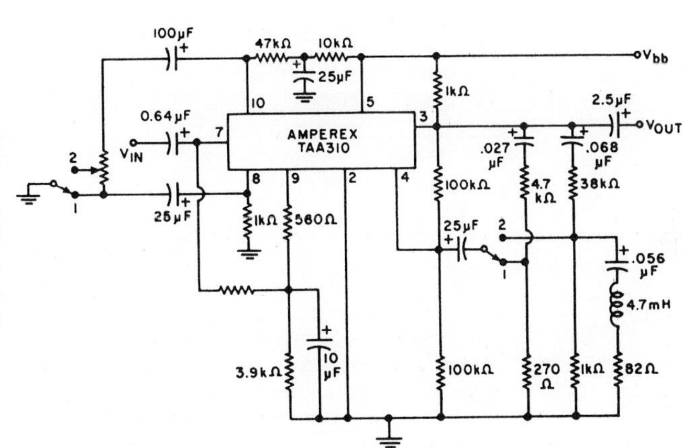

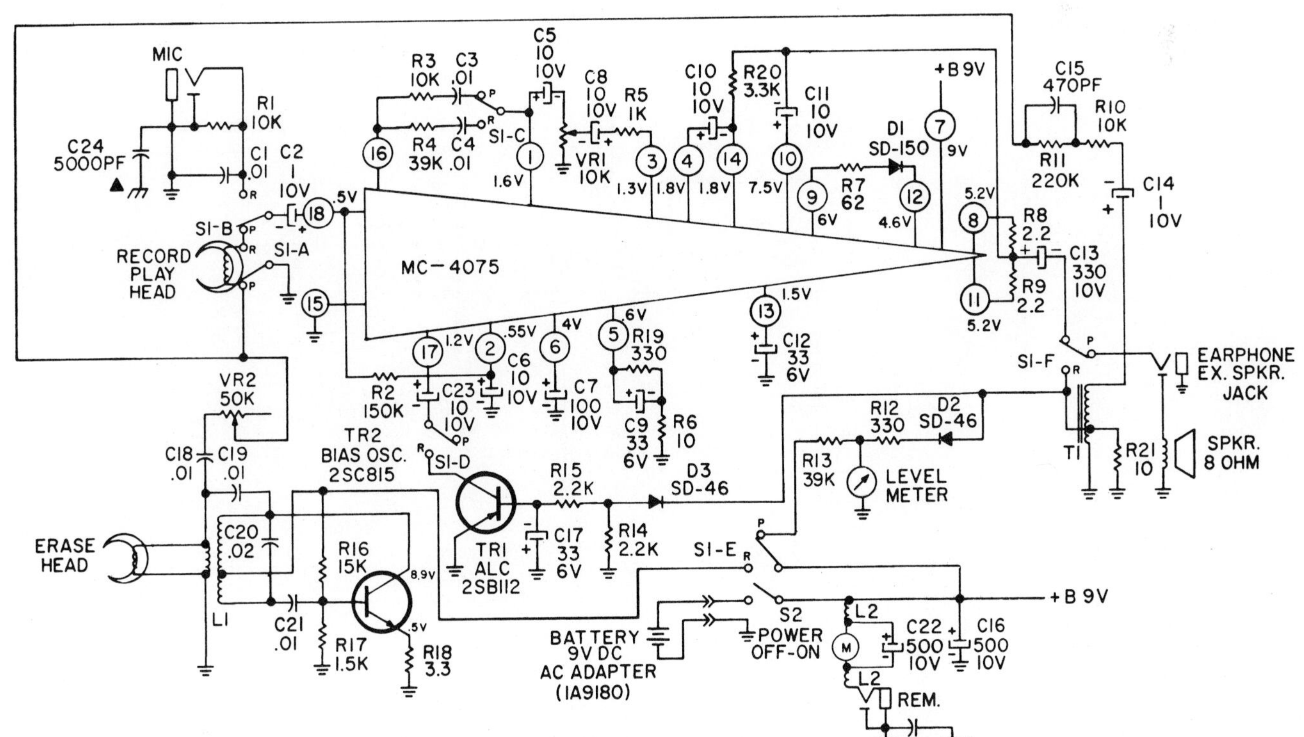

CASSETTE-RECORDER-PLAYER—Uses monaural two-track tape running at 1⅞ inches per second, and operating from either 9-V battery or equivalent a-c adapter. Special Magnavox IC requires only two additional transistors to provide required functions along with automatic level control and accidental-erasure prevention for prerecorded cassettes.—1V9019 Cassette Tape Recorder, Magnavox Service Manual 6293, Fort Wayne, Ind., 1969.

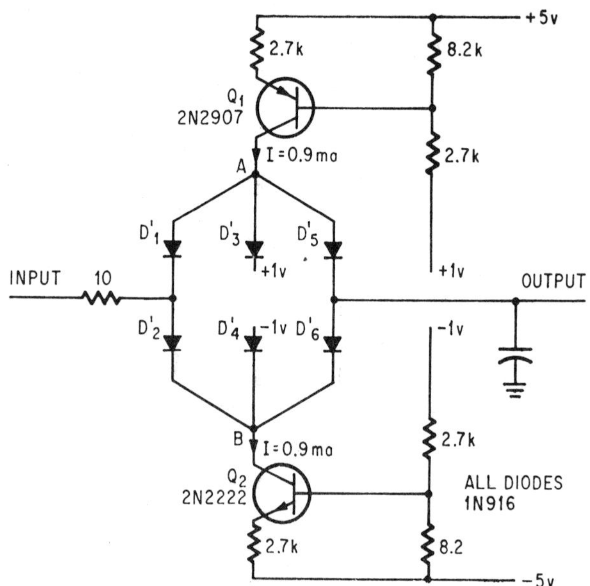

LOW-HEAT F-M RATE LIMITER—Constant-current transistors Q1 and Q2 replace resistors in diode-bridge rate limiter for instrumentation tape recording, to reduce undesirable heat dissipation. Use of complementary transistors gives constant-current operation.—D. F. Franklin, Diodes Prevent Overload by Limiting Input's Slope, *Electronics*, Jan. 22, 1968, p 69–70.

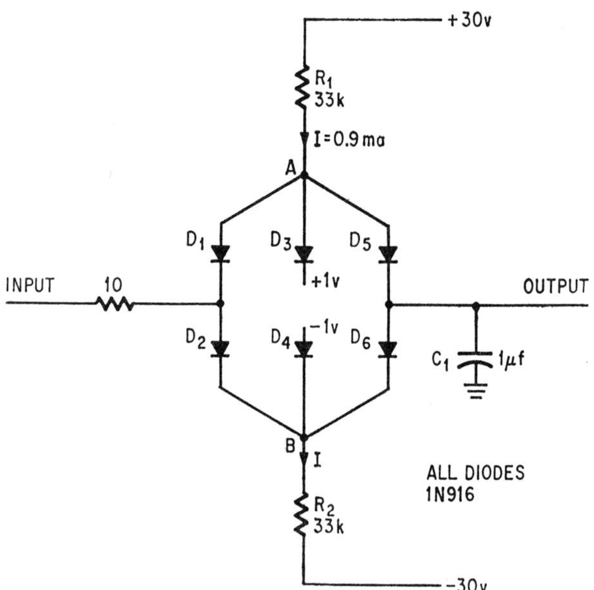

F-M RATE LIMITER—Prevents overloading caused by excessive rate of change and amplitude when recording random signals on magnetic tape for instrumentation, using wideband f-m. Slope of output signal is limited to rate of charge or discharge of C1 through D6. Has no effect on bandwidth. —D. F. Franklin, Diodes Prevent Overload by Limiting Input's Slope, *Electronics*, Jan. 22, 1968, p 69–70.

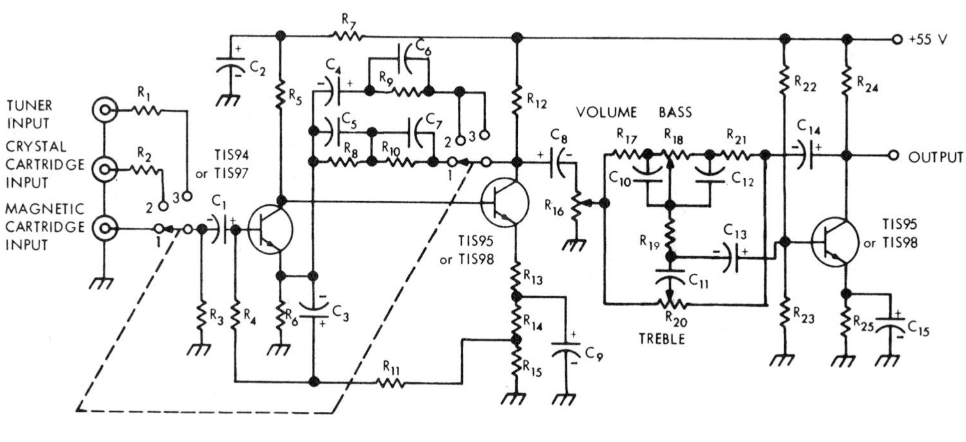

R_1: 1 MΩ	R_{10}: 56 kΩ	R_{18}: 0–1 MΩ	C_1: 10 μF, 3 V, electrolytic	C_9: 50 μF, 6 V, electrolytic
R_2: 2.7 MΩ	R_{11}: 100 kΩ	R_{19}: 47 kΩ	C_2: 2 μF, 50 V, electrolytic	C_{10}: 0.003 μF
R_3: 47 kΩ	R_{12}: 33 kΩ	R_{20}: 0–500 kΩ	C_3: 50 μF, 3 V, electrolytic	C_{11}: 470 pF
R_4: 100 kΩ	R_{13}: 270 Ω	R_{21}: 82 kΩ	C_4: 20 μF, 25 V, electrolytic	C_{12}: 0.003 μF
R_5: 150 kΩ	R_{14}: 2.2 kΩ	R_{22}: 470 kΩ	C_5: 0.0033 μF	C_{13}: 5 μF, 6 V, electrolytic
R_6: 330 Ω	R_{15}: 1 kΩ	R_{23}: 56 kΩ	C_6: 47 pF	C_{14}: 1 μF, 25 V, electrolytic
R_7: 15 kΩ	R_{16}: 0–100 kΩ	R_{24}: 39 kΩ	C_7: 1200 pF	C_{15}: 20 μF, 6 V, electrolytic
R_8: 1.2 MΩ	R_{17}: 82 kΩ	R_{25}: 4.7 kΩ	C_8: 1 μF, 50 V, electrolytic	
R_9: 75 kΩ				

RIAA-COMPENSATED PREAMP—Compensation, for magnetic input only, is within 1 dB of ideal curve from 20 to 20,000 Hz. Circuit uses npn epitaxial planar silicon transistors. Output is 1 V for 4-mV magnetic cartridge input, 220-mV crystal cartridge input, and 100-mV tuner input. Response is within 1 dB from 20 to 20,000 Hz, and total harmonic distortion below 0.14% for any input.—Preferred Semiconductors and Components, Texas Instruments, Dallas, Texas, CC101, 1968, p 1054.

$C_1 C_2 C_3 C_7$ = 0.1 microfarad, paper
C_4 = 10 microfarads, 12 volts, electrolytic
C_5 = 15 microfarads, 6 volts, electrolytic
C_6 = 5 microfarads, 25 volts, electrolytic
C_8 = 50 microfarads, 25 volts, electrolytic
CR_1 CR_2 = silicon rectifier, type 1N270
$Q_1 Q_2$ = MOS field-effect transistor, type 3N128
$Q_3 Q_4$ = transistor, RCA SK3020
$R_1 R_2 R_3 R_4 R_7$ = 100,000 ohms, 1/2 watt, 10%
R_5 = potentiometer, 10,000 ohms, audio taper
R_6 = 180,000 ohms, 1/2 watt, 10%
R_8 = potentiometer, 5000 ohms, straight taper
$R_9 R_{13}$ = 1 megohm, 1/2 watt, 10%
R_{10} = 15,000 ohms, 1/2 watt, 10%
R_{11} = 10,000 ohms, 1/2 watt, 10%
R_{12} = 1500 ohms, 1/2 watt, 10%

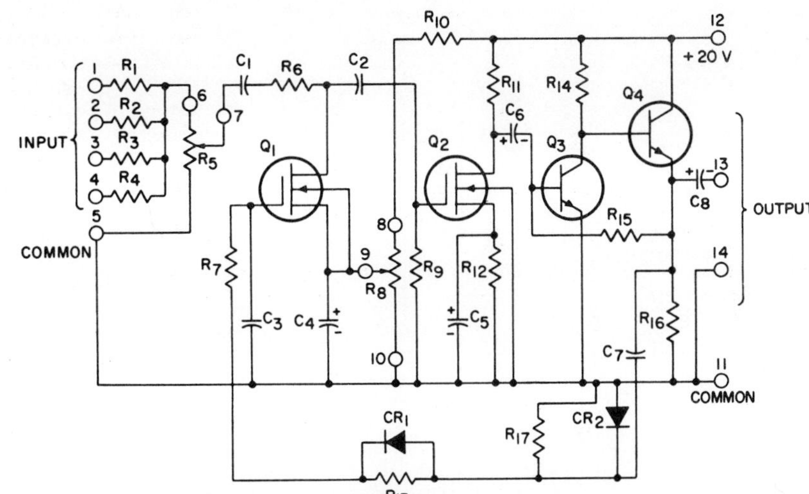

LINE AMPLIFIER WITH MIXER—Used to produce uniform audio levels required for high-quality tape recordings. Circuit also includes volume compression to prevent overload by loud passages of speech or music.—"Hobby Circuits Manual," RCA, Harrison, N.J., HM-90, p 72.

R_{14} = 1200 ohms, 1/2 watt, 10%
R_{15} = 100,000 ohms, 1/2 watt, 10%
R_{16} = 470 ohms, 1/2 watt, 10%
R_{17} = 2 megohms, 1/2 watt, 10%

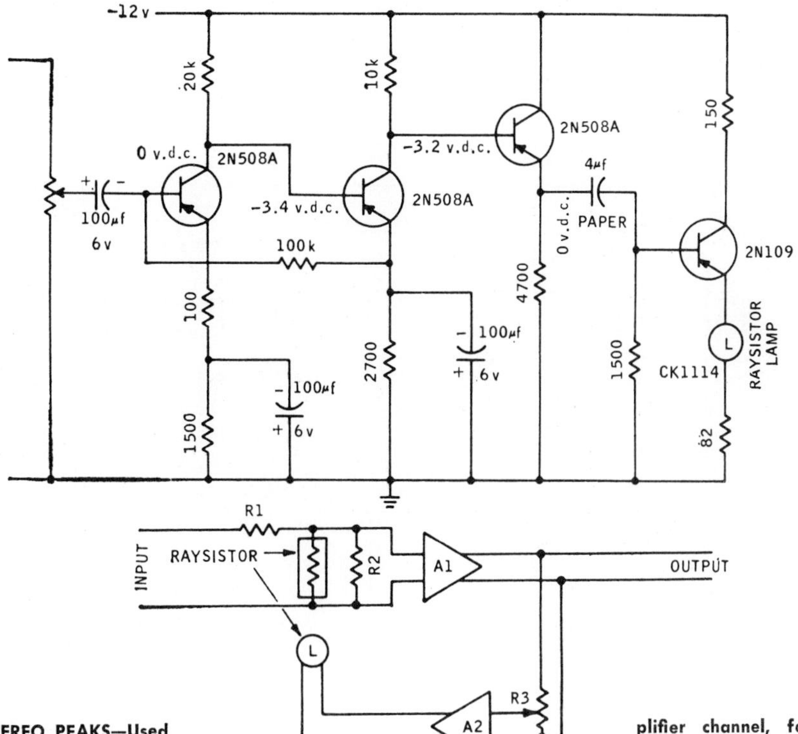

CLIPPING MOMENTARY STEREO PEAKS—Used in recording amateur performances on stereo magnetic tape, where dB output cannot always be accurately predicted in time for manual reduction of gain. Intended to catch only momentary peaks, rather than serve for automatic gain-riding. Requires separate limiter for each channel, but resulting wandering of stereo images is not as serious as momentary overloads that are prevented. Block diagram illustrates how input is taken from any convenient point following limiter in amplifier channel, for feeding side amplifier shown here which drives lamp in Raytheon Raysistor unit. Photocell of Raysistor varies shunt resistance across input of channel amplifier (A1) to give desired limiting.—J. Young and W. B. Denny, Solid State Limiter for Tape Recording, *Audio*, Sept. 1965.

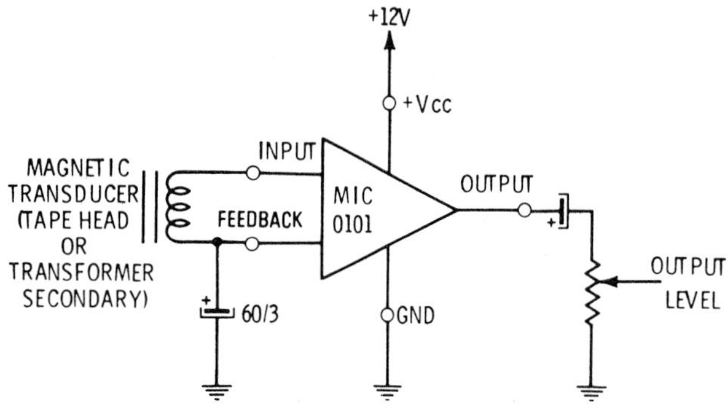

PLAYBACK PREAMP—Uses Mallory MIC0101 IC audio preamp with input terminals connected directly to tape playback head. Suitable for either audio or instrumentation applications. Uncompensated overall voltage gain of 57 to 63 dB can easily be obtained with 3-dB bandwidth of 10 Hz to 700 kHz and output of 3 V p-p with under 10% total harmonic distortion. —M. L. Deschler, Integrated Circuit Preamplifiers, Mallory, Indianapolis, Ind., APPN-2, 1968.

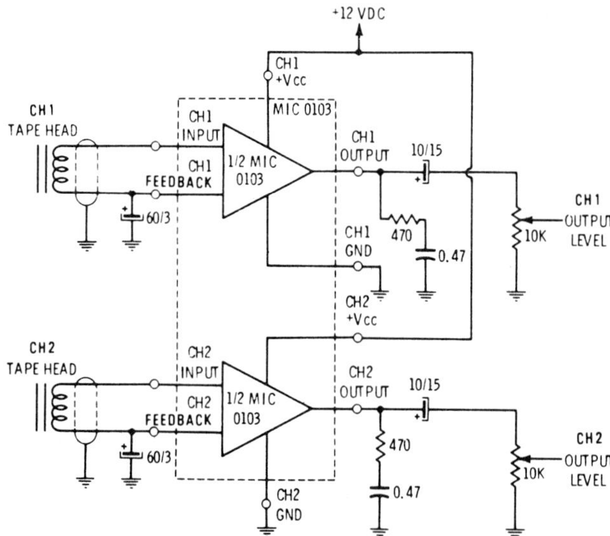

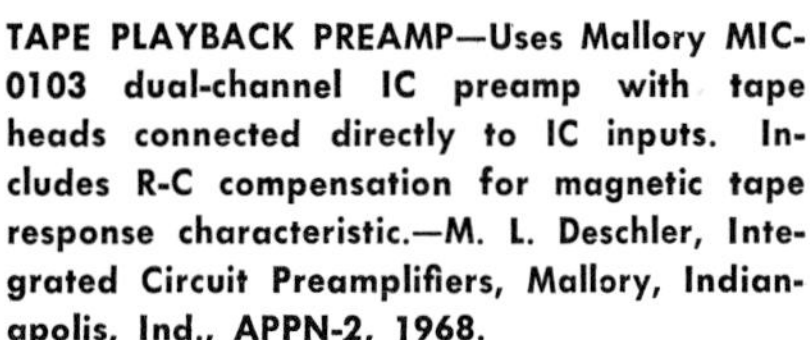
TAPE PLAYBACK PREAMP—Uses Mallory MIC-0103 dual-channel IC preamp with tape heads connected directly to IC inputs. Includes R-C compensation for magnetic tape response characteristic.—M. L. Deschler, Integrated Circuit Preamplifiers, Mallory, Indianapolis, Ind., APPN-2, 1968.

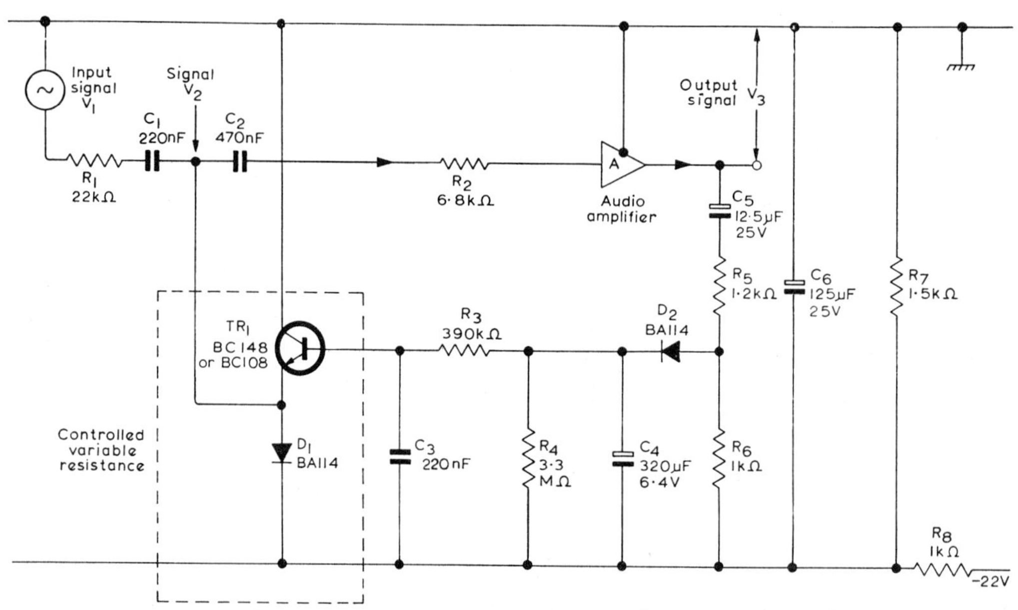

AGC FOR RECORDER—Automatically reduces gain of recording amplifier when optimum recording level is exceeded, to prevent severe distortion that occurs at tape saturation. Eliminates need for monitoring recording-head current with meter or magic eye and manually adjusting level. Circuit responds very rapidly to overload signal, producing attenuation of 40 dB within 50 ms, but has long recovery time to prevent volume compression wherein loud and soft musical passages would be recorded with equal loudness. Book describes operation of circuit in detail.—"Transistor Audio and Radio Circuits," Mullard Ltd., London, 1969, p 80.

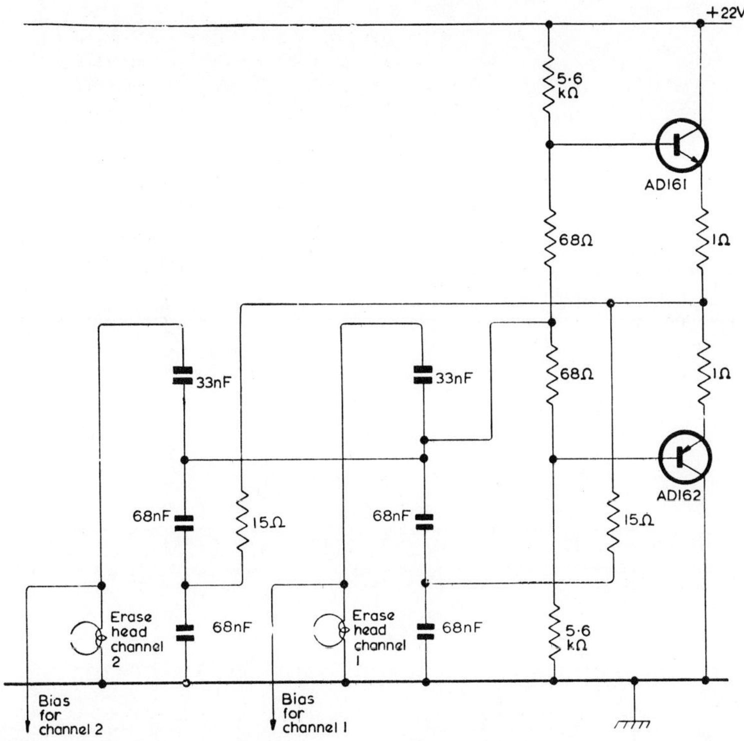

COMMON BIAS-ERASE OSCILLATOR FOR STEREO—Keeps bias and erase frequencies equal for stereo channels, to prevent production of audio beat frequencies. Tuned erase heads are connected in parallel to form load and feedback circuits for one of complementary pairs of transistors, but bias voltages for recording heads are still derived from erase voltages across individual erase heads. —"Transistor Audio and Radio Circuits," Mullard Ltd., London, 1969, p 77.

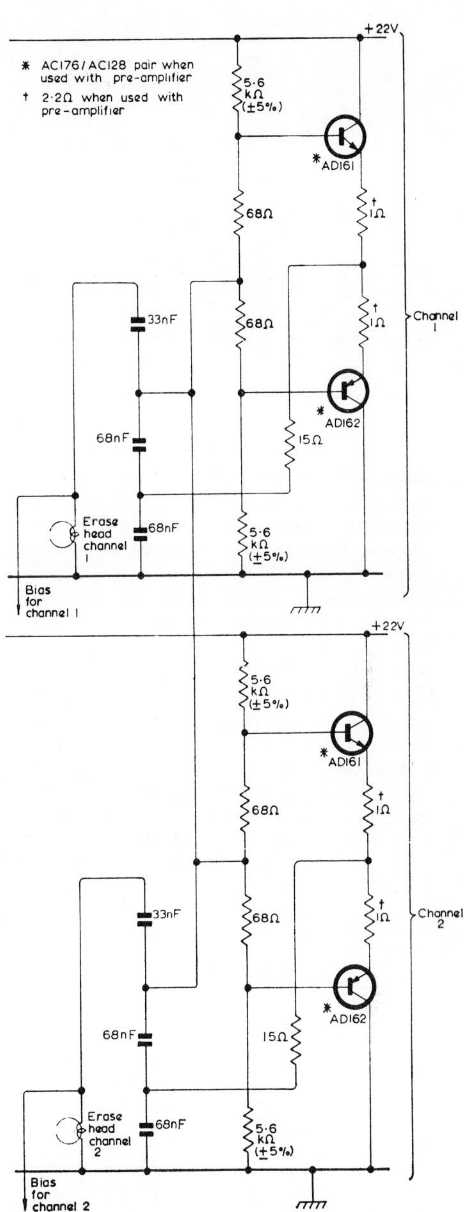

LOCKED BIAS-ERASE OSCILLATORS FOR STEREO—Feedback paths of individual oscillators are connected together to make bias and erase frequencies equal for both stereo channels, thereby preventing production of audio beat frequencies.—"Transistor Audio and Radio Circuits," Mullard Ltd., London, 1969, p 78.

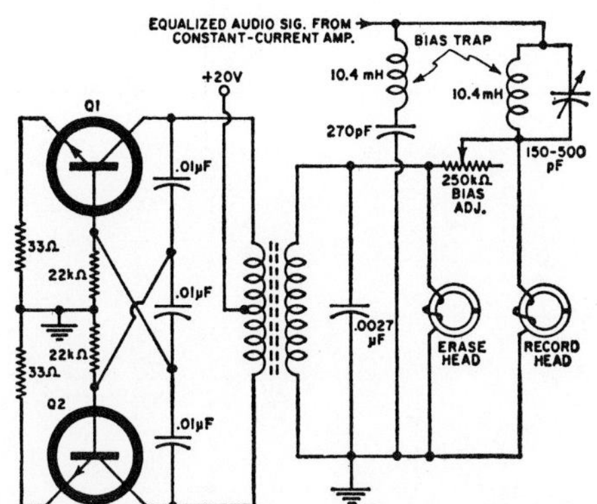

MAGNETIC TAPE BIAS OSCILLATOR—Basic transistor circuit for applying a-c bias uses common astable mvbr with center-tapped transformer, in place of normal collector resistors and capacitors, to complete parallel resonant circuit with transformer. This tuned circuit determines frequency of oscillation and makes signal sinusoidal. Transistors are not critical for bias frequency of 95 kHz. —J. G. McKnight, Biasing in Magnetic Tape Recording, *Electronics World*, Aug. 1967, p 34–36 and 75.

NOTE: To locate additional circuits in the category of this chapter, use the index at the back of this book. Check also the author's "Sourcebook of Electronic Circuits," published by McGraw-Hill in 1968.

CHAPTER 49
Measuring Circuits

MEASURING LIGHT INTENSITY—Uses high-gain opamp to hold voltage across photoemissive cell at almost zero voltage, to take advantage of linear relationship between current flow and light intensity at cell voltages below a few millivolts. Output voltage of opamp is then equal to product of cell current and feedback resistance Rf which is selected in steps by S1. Total light energy, as from flash lamps, can be measured by closing S2 and opening S3 to integrate output in second opamp.—J. Ph. Korthals Altes, Measurement of Light Intensity, Philips, Pub. Dept., Elcoma Div., Eindhoven, The Netherlands, No. 85, 1970.

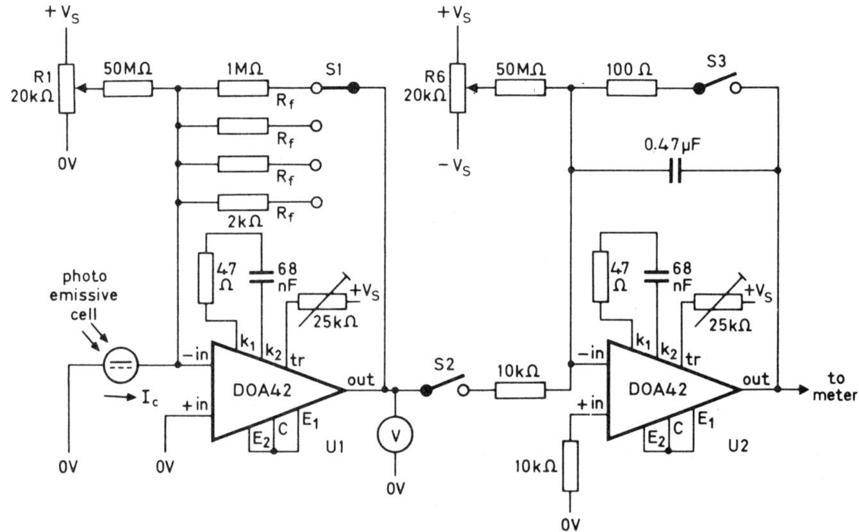

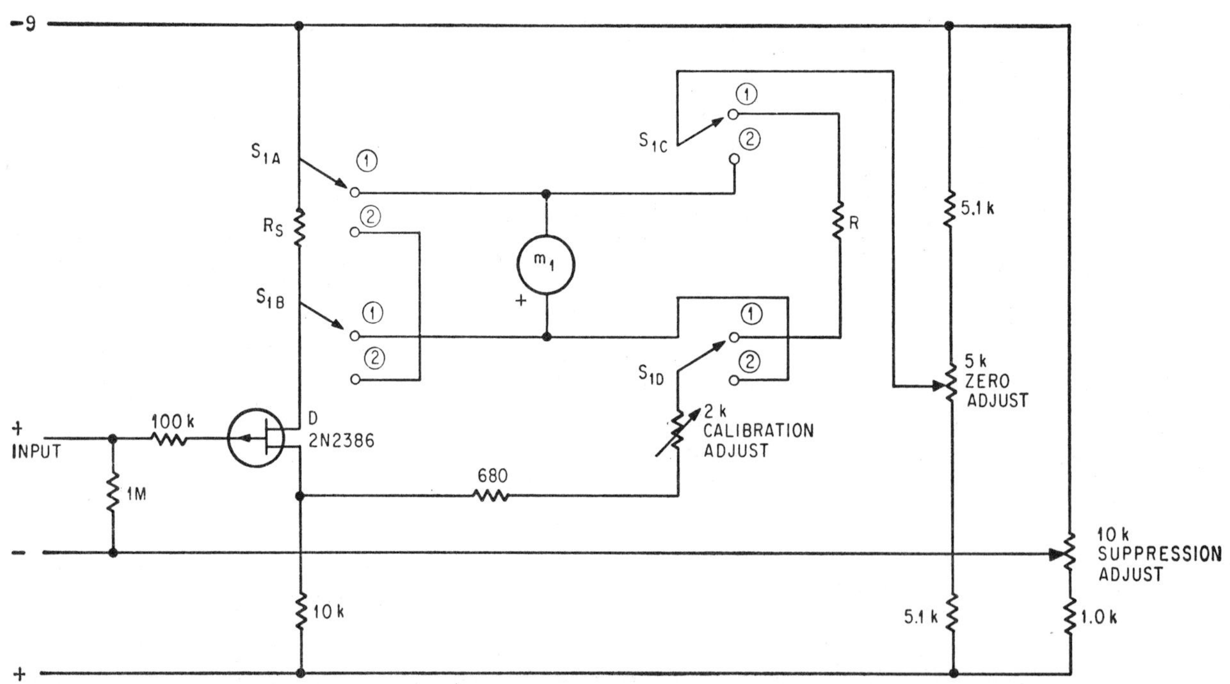

MOVABLE-RANGE D-C VOLTMETER—Full-scale range of 1 V may be positioned anywhere between 0 and 7 V d-c input, such as for reading 4 to 5 V. With switch at position 1, and input at low limit of voltage to be measured, drain current of fet is set at 350 μA with suppression-adjust pot. Switch is then moved to position 2, input voltage is increased 1 V above low limit, and calibration-adjust pot is set to give full-scale reading on 100-μA meter. Accuracy is 2%.—R. Traina, Multirange D-C Voltmeter, *Electronics*, Sept. 19, 1966, p 126.

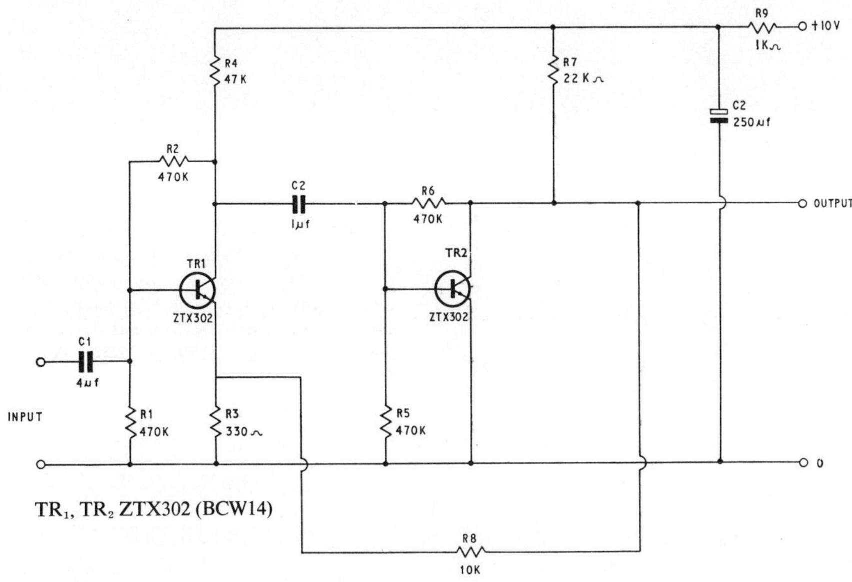

MILLIVOLTMETER PREAMP—Increases sensitivity of rectifier-type a-c millivoltmeter from 20 mV rms down to 1 mV rms for full-scale deflection. Bandwidth is 800 kHz, same as rectifier stage. Voltage gain is 22, and may be adjusted, while input impedance is 100K. Report gives design procedure.—"E-Line Transistor Applications," Ferranti Ltd., Oldham, Lancs., England, 1969, p 34.

TRANSISTOR STRAIN GAGE—Uses silicon npn planar piezoelectric transistor called Pitran (made by Stow Labs, Stow, Mass.), having emitter-base junction mechanically coupled to diaphragm in top of TO-46 can. Is sensitive enough to respond to feather touch. Voltage change per unit strain is over 10 times better than metal and other types of strain gages. Output is linearily proportional to mechanical input, and ranges up to 20% of d-c supply voltage.—R. M. Moore, Semiconductor Gages Make Sense in Most Transducer Applications, *Electronics*, March 18, 1968, p 109–116.

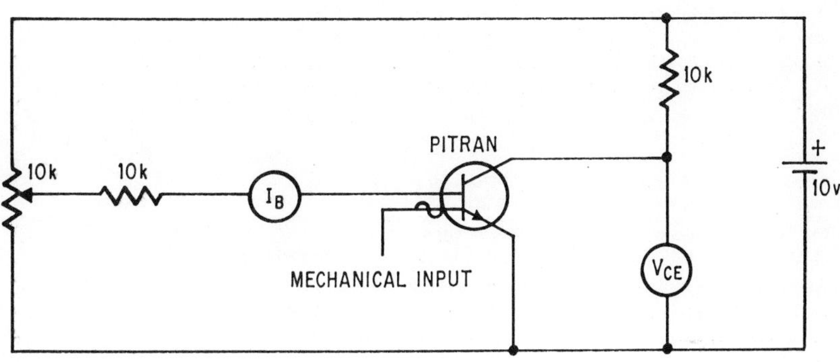

MEASURING TRANSISTOR-DESTROYING SPIKES—Uses voltage divider for accurately dividing spike voltage generated by inductive switching, then increases power content of resulting low voltage so it can be measured with ordinary microammeter. Used in development work to locate and eliminate transistor-destroying spikes without having to spend hours watching cro screen. Meter pointer holds its position as long as switch S1 is on HOLD as shown. RESET position returns needle to zero fast, and DELAY position makes needle return to zero slowly.—G. R. Phillips, FET Voltmeter Reads Transients, *Electronics*, June 10, 1968, p 109–110.

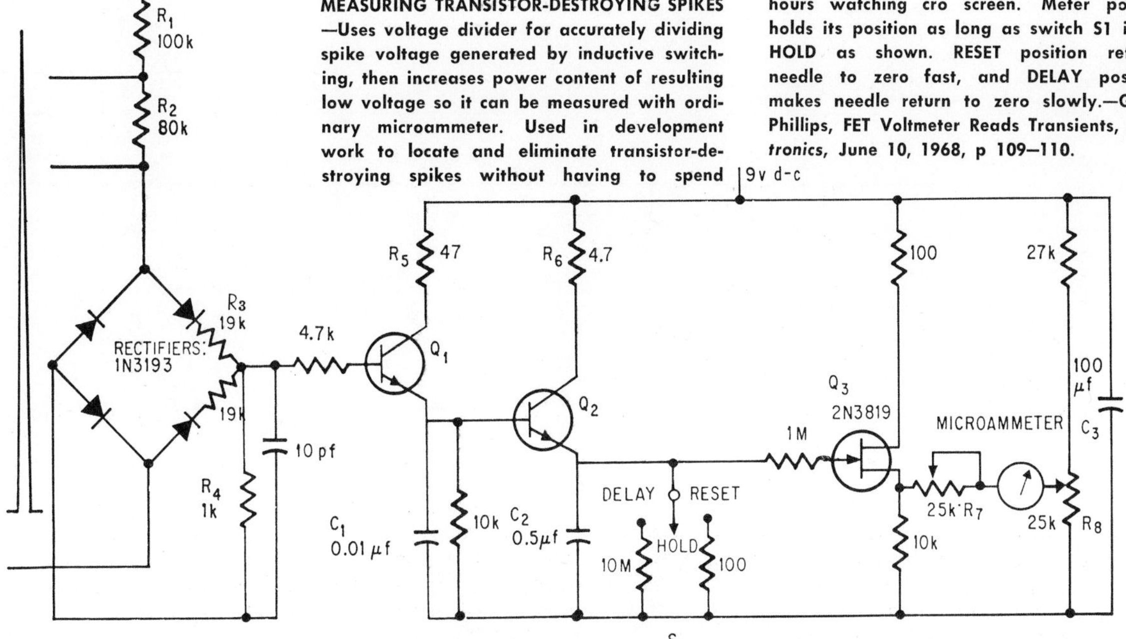

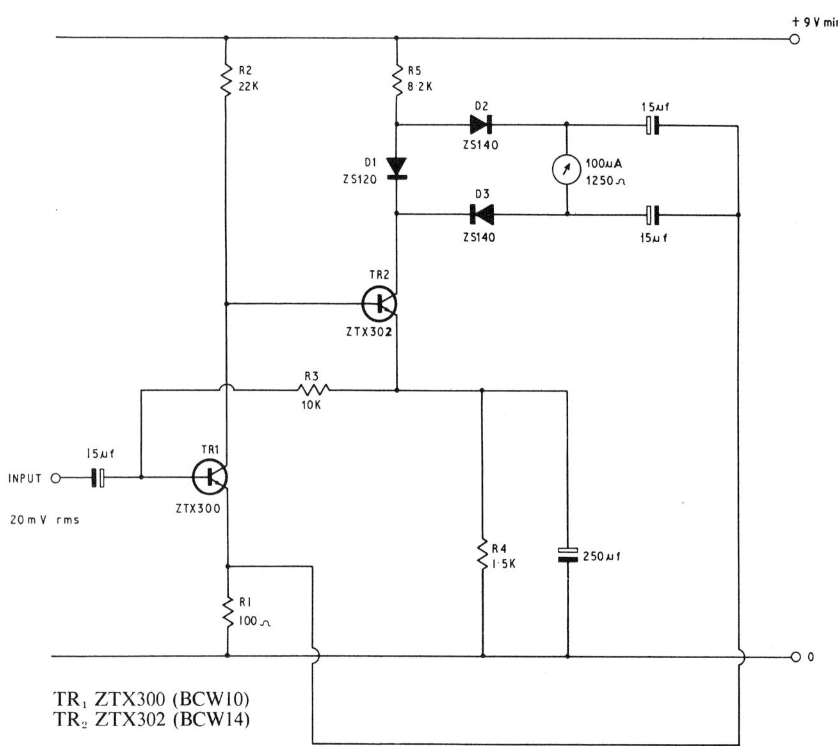

A-C MILLIVOLTMETER—Gives full-scale deflection on 100-µA linear-scale meter for input of about 20 mV rms over bandwidth of 800 kHz. Input impedance is 10K. Report gives design procedure.—"E-Line Transistor Applications," Ferranti Ltd., Oldham, Lancs., England, 1969, p 33.

VTVM ADAPTER FOR MULTIMETER—Uses only typical 60 to 100 µA meter of multimeter, for making low-voltage d-c measurements (1-V and 10-V scales) at high impedance. Adapter draws only 1 µA from measured circuit at full-scale deflection, which is equivalent to sensitivity of 1 meg per V. Uses silicon transistors in two-stage differential amplifier. Has no warm-up zero drift. Since standby battery drain is only fraction of µA, no on-off switch is required. Set multimeter to 60 (or 100) µA position and plug test leads of adapter into corresponding jack. Does not interfere with normal use of multimeter.—"Hobby Manual," General Electric, Owensboro, Ky., 1965, p 170.

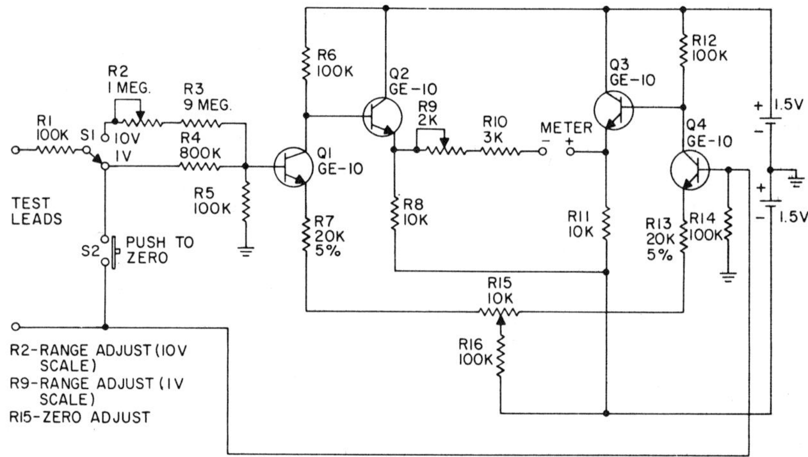

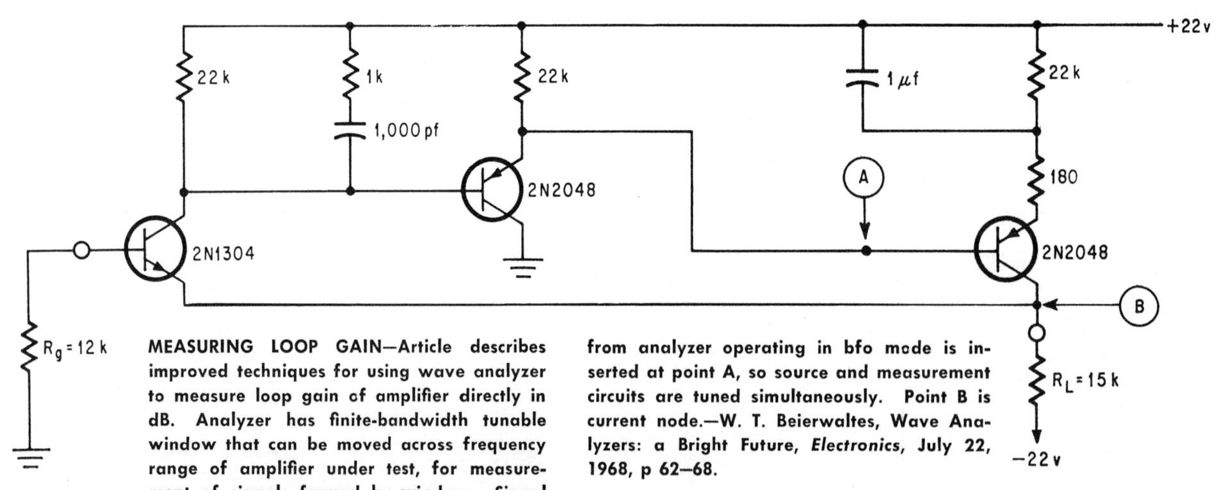

MEASURING LOOP GAIN—Article describes improved techniques for using wave analyzer to measure loop gain of amplifier directly in dB. Analyzer has finite-bandwidth tunable window that can be moved across frequency range of amplifier under test, for measurement of signals framed by window. Signal from analyzer operating in bfo mode is inserted at point A, so source and measurement circuits are tuned simultaneously. Point B is current node.—W. T. Beierwaltes, Wave Analyzers: a Bright Future, *Electronics*, July 22, 1968, p 62–68.

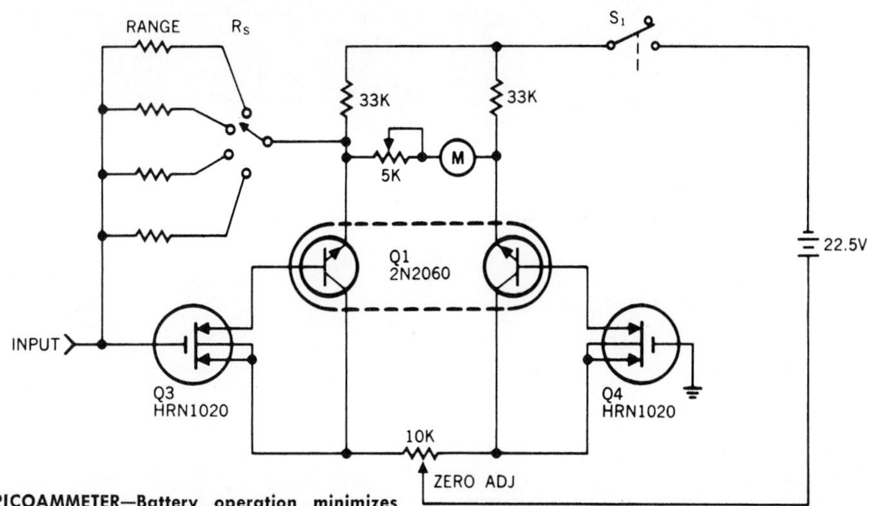

PICOAMMETER—Battery operation minimizes noise and allows excellent isolation between input and meter. Mosfet Q3 provides high impedance to minimize effect on circuit being measured. Q4 provides reference for balancing meter when input is short-circuited for calibration. Dual transistors are connected as emitter-followers to drive low-impedance meter movement. Will measure low d-c voltages as well as picoamperes.—C. R. Perkins, "Application of MOSFET Devices to Electronic Circuits," Hughes, Newport Beach, Cal., 1968, p 19.

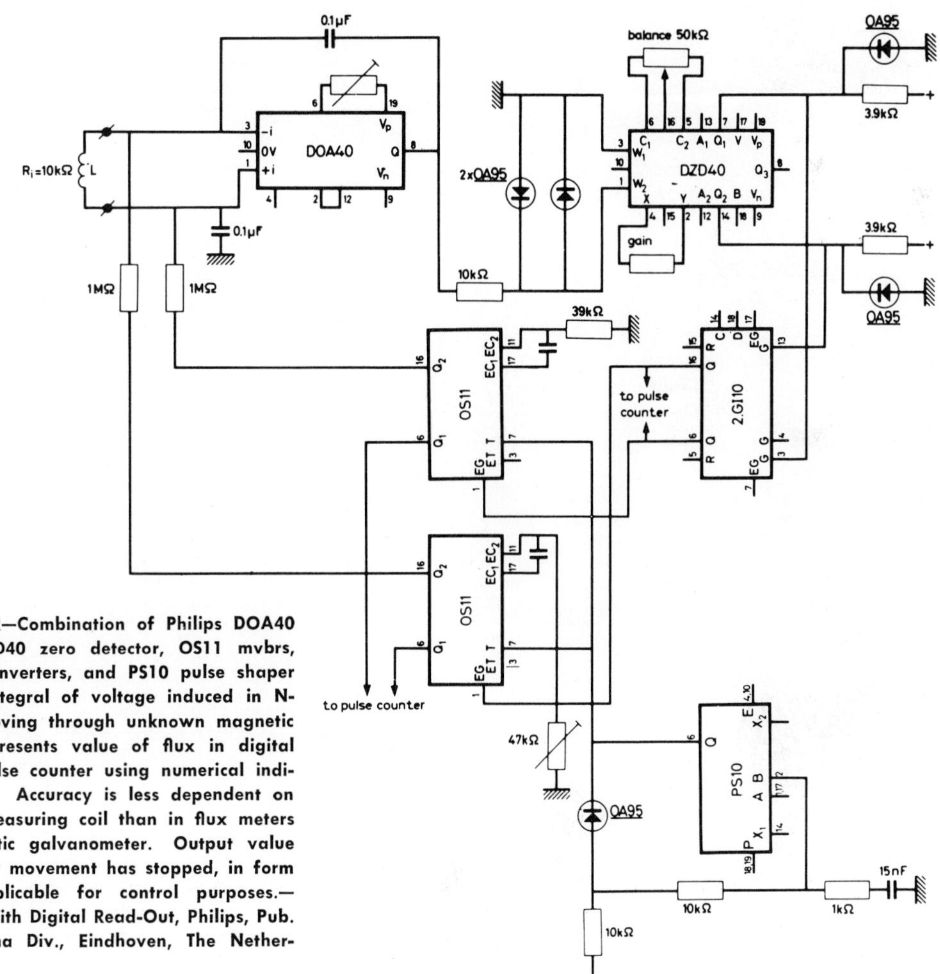

FLUX METER—Combination of Philips DOA40 opamp, DZD40 zero detector, OS11 mvbrs, GI10 gate inverters, and PS10 pulse shaper evaluates integral of voltage induced in N-turn coil moving through unknown magnetic flux, and presents value of flux in digital form on pulse counter using numerical indicator tubes. Accuracy is less dependent on speed of measuring coil than in flux meters using ballistic galvanometer. Output value is held after movement has stopped, in form directly applicable for control purposes.—Fluxmeter With Digital Read-Out, Philips, Pub. Dept., Elcoma Div., Eindhoven, The Netherlands.

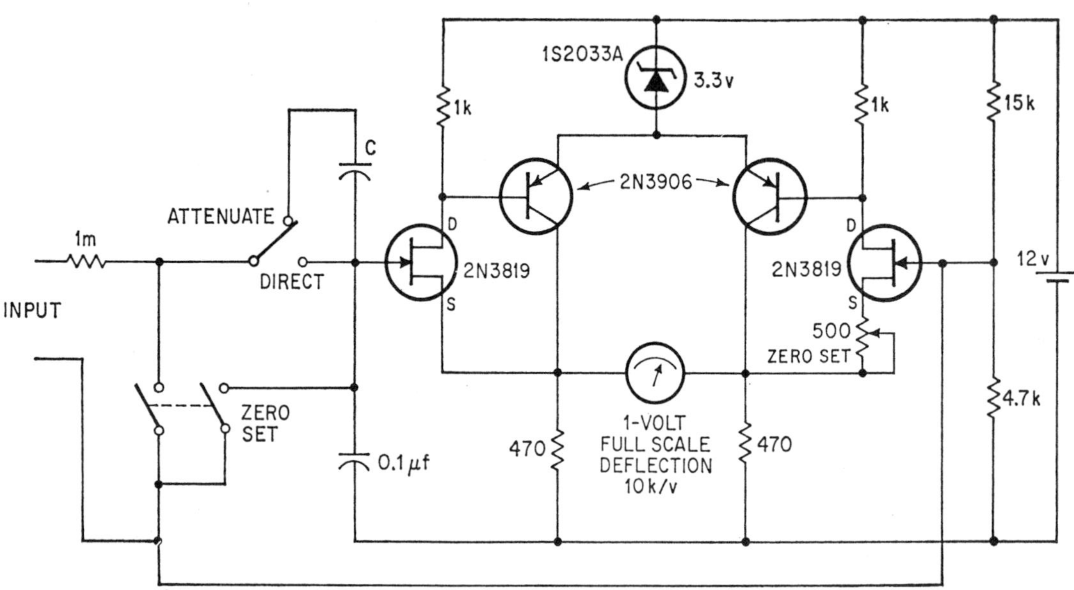

DRIFT-BALANCING VTVM—High-impedance voltmeter has current-measuring sensitivity of 1 nA. Two source-followers are connected to meter for cancellation of drift caused by temperature changes. Output to meter is 1 V at 100 μA. When current to be measured is sent through 1,000-meg shunt across input terminals, meter will read 1 nA full scale. Value of C depends on voltage range desired. —D. F. Wadsworth, Pair of Source Followers Keep a Voltmeter Steady, *Electronics*, June 23, 1969, p 103.

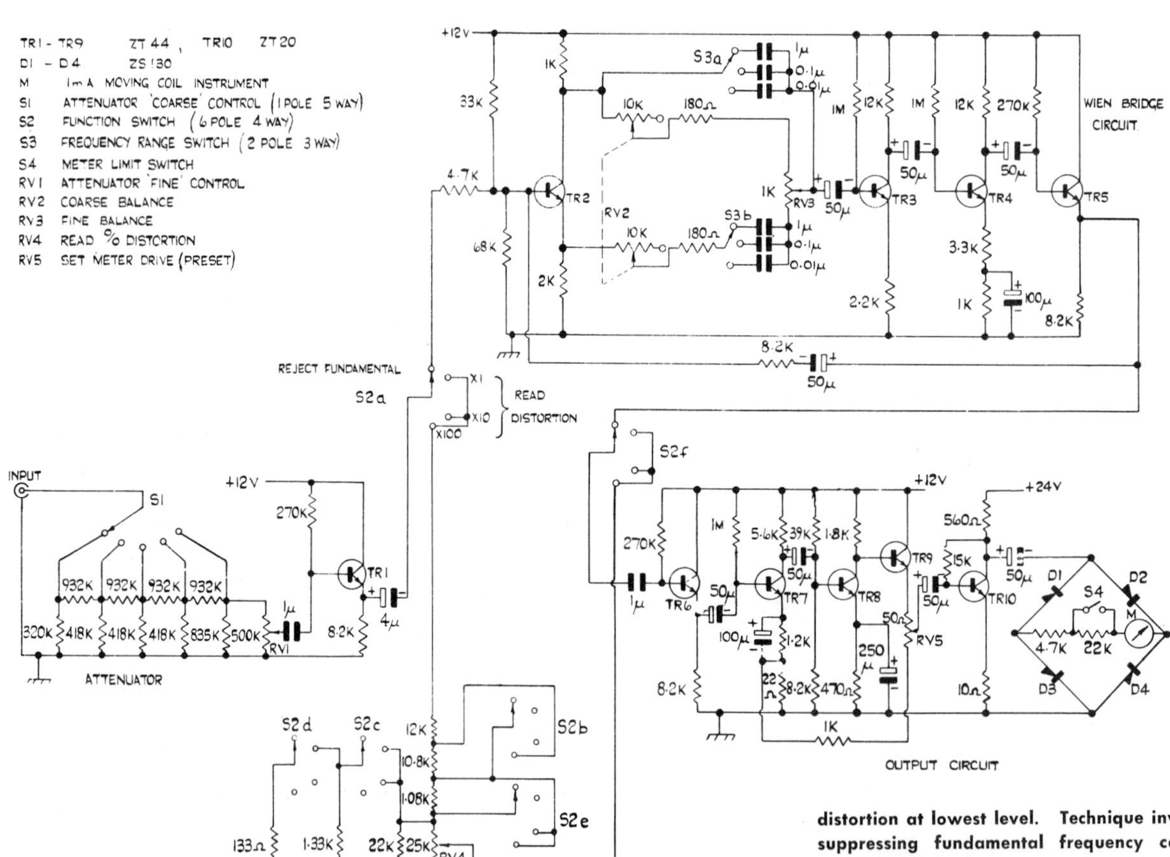

DISTORTION METER—Measures total distortion of audio signal in fundamental frequency range of 15 Hz to 20 kHz, including harmonic components up to fifth. Signal levels measured can range from 150 mV to 75 V rms, with sensitivity sufficient to measure 0.1% distortion at lowest level. Technique involves suppressing fundamental frequency component of signal, then comparing residual voltage with total signal voltage by means of full-wave rectifier meter.—Silicon Transistor A. F. Distortion Meter, Ferranti Ltd., Oldham, Lancs., England, No. 17, 1965.

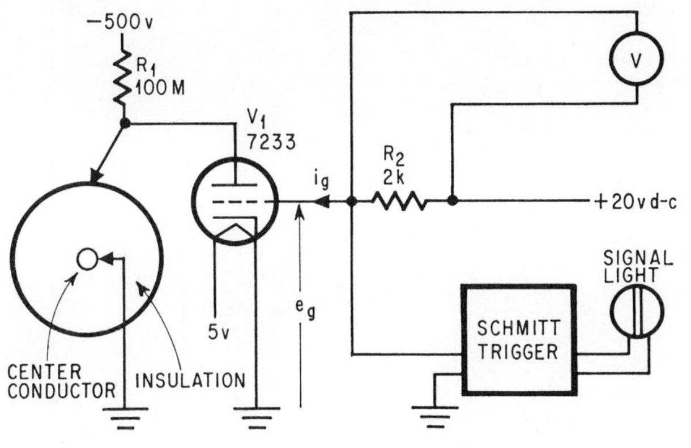

INFINITE-Z VOLTMETER—Used for measuring insulation on high-voltage conductors. Anode of triode is made negative with respect to cathode, to give infinite impedance. Insulation leak makes anode voltage drop, and resulting change in grid voltage turns on Schmitt trigger and signal light used as level detector. Voltage limit of tube is 600 V.—R. A. Parks, Reversed-Polarity Triode Measures Insulation, *Electronics*, Feb. 5, 1968, p 87–88.

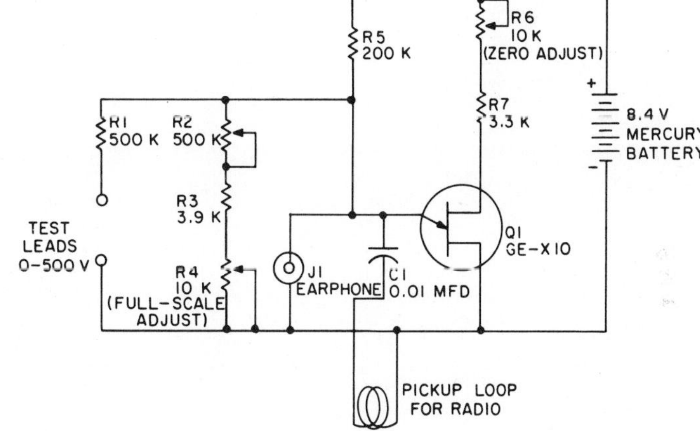

METERLESS D-C VOLTMETER—Covers range of 0–500 V d-c, with 0.5-meg input impedance minimizing risk of damage to components in tested circuit. With test leads in position for measurement, turn on voltmeter and rotate R2 until audio tone is just heard; dial then indicates d-c voltage, either in earphone or in nearby radio tuned to quiet spot at low-frequency end of a-m broadcast band. Loop should be close to antenna of radio. Radio picks up high-frequency harmonics of audio tone generated by ujt. Book gives calibration procedure.—"Hobby Manual," General Electric, Owensboro, Ky., 1965, p 178.

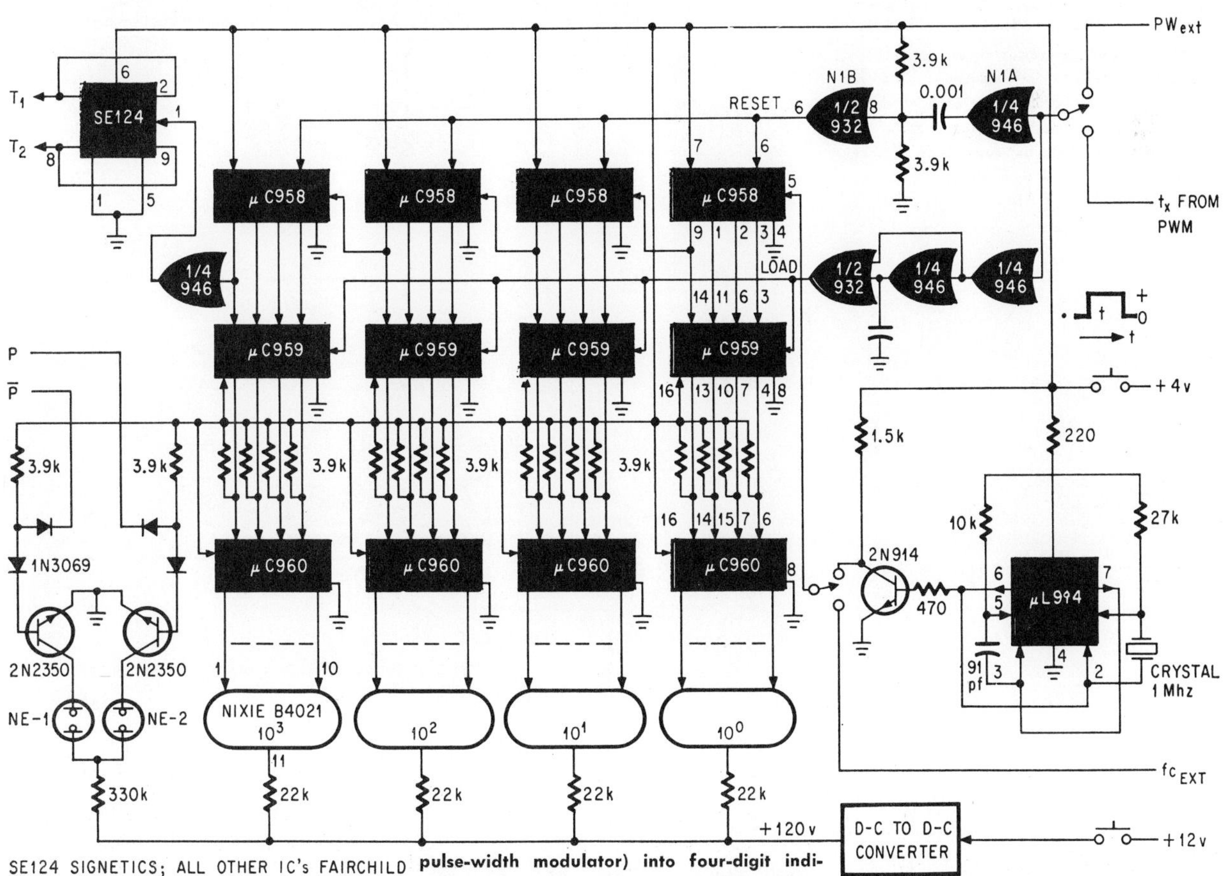

SE124 SIGNETICS; ALL OTHER IC's FAIRCHILD

IC DIGITAL VOLTMETER—Counter section of meter converts pulse width (obtained from pulse-width modulator) into four-digit indication of input voltage on Nixie tubes. Crystal oscillator using Fairchild μL914 IC generates accurate 1-MHz clock frequency for counter.—H. Schmid, Digital Meters for Under $100, *Electronics*, Nov. 28, 1966, p 88–94.

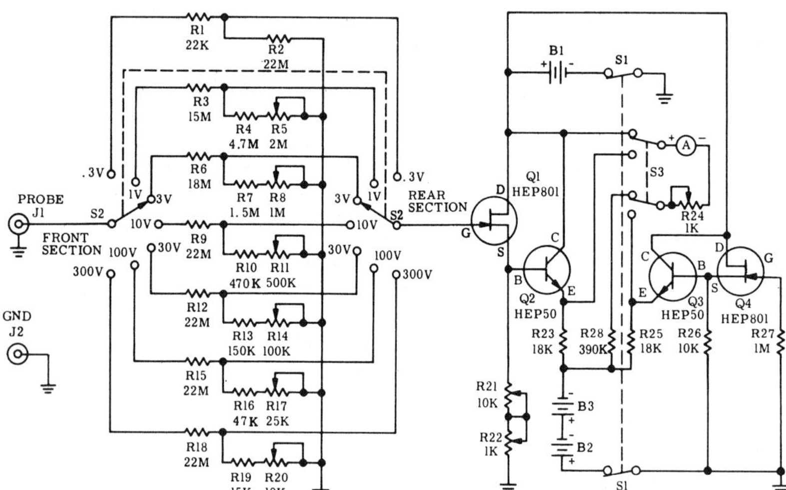

FET D-C VOLTMETER—Compact, inexpensive, and accurate meter features 22-meg input impedance on seven ranges, using three 9-V batteries for power. Article gives construction details.—"Field Effect Transistor Projects," Motorola, Phoenix, Ariz., 1966, p 75–90.

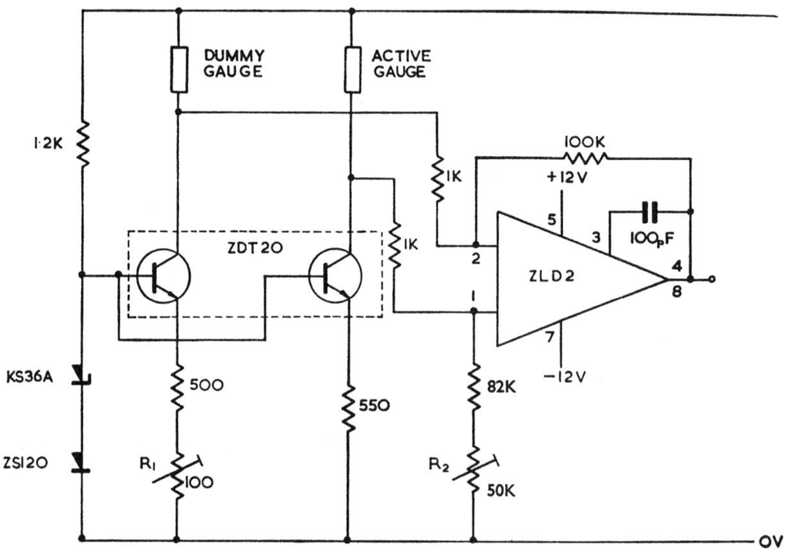

IC STRAIN-GAGE AMPLIFIER—Uses two constant-current generators feeding about 10 mA into active and dummy silicon strain gages. Differential output of gages is fed into Ferranti ZLD2 IC differential amplifier. R1 is adjusted until output of ZLD2 is zero, and R2 is adjusted for maximum common mode rejection of ZLD2.—Microlin Amplifiers ZLD2S and ZLD2T, Ferranti Ltd., Oldham, Lancs., England, No. 11, 5/67, p 18.

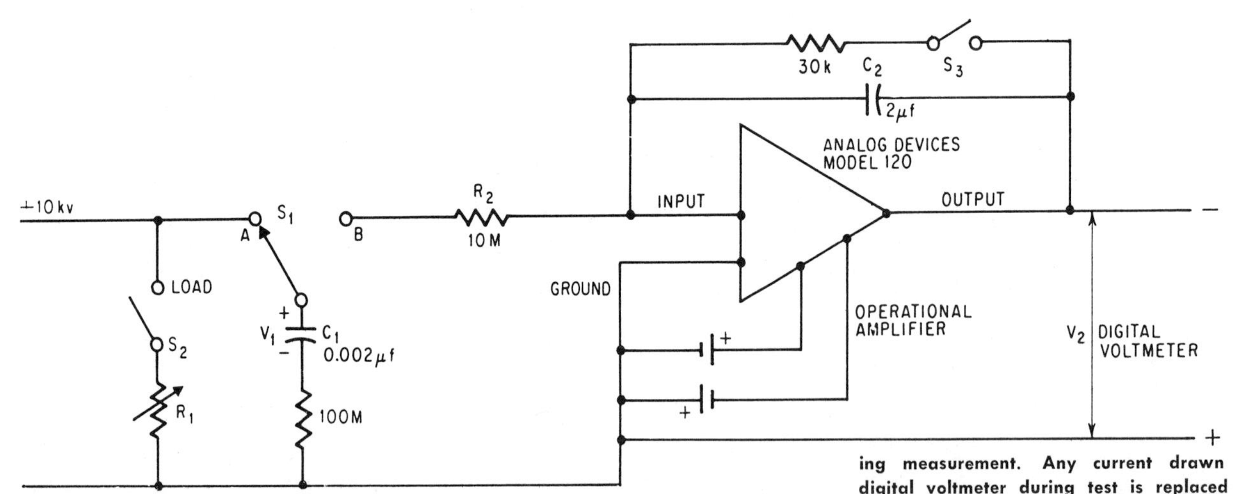

HIGH-ACCURACY ELECTROSTATIC VOLTMETER—Charge transfer circuit used with IC opamp ahead of digital voltmeter permits measuring voltages up to 10 kV to accuracy of 0.5%, as compared to 2% accuracy of conventional electrostatic voltmeter. Circuit precisely divides high voltage being measured and protects divided voltage from current drain during measurement. Any current drawn by digital voltmeter during test is replaced by opamp. Article gives measuring procedure.—T. P. Kohler and E. H. Hudspeth, Operational Amplifier Overcomes Voltmeter Loading, *Electronics*, Dec. 25, 1967, p 67–68.

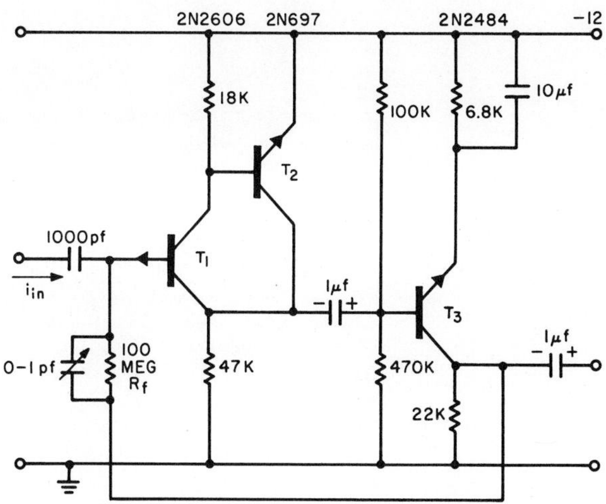

FET ELECTROMETER AMPLIFIER—Low-noise characteristic of fet T1 makes it possible to measure currents as low as 100 femtoamperes at room temperature in audio range, over 1-Hz bandwidth. Article gives design equations. Transistor types are given at top of diagram.—R. Munoz, Put FETs to Work in Electrometers, *Electronic Design*, May 11, 1964, p 56–61.

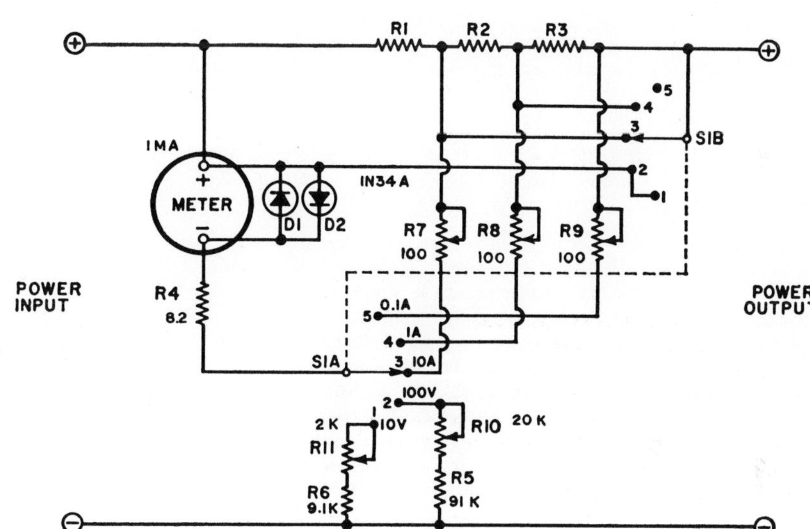

D-C VOLT-AMMETER—Design of current-range selection circuit minimizes effect of variations in range switch contact resistance. Accuracy is better than 3%, yet total cost of parts is under $30. Current ranges are 0.1, 1, and 10 A, and voltage ranges are 10 and 100 V. Article gives detailed construction and calibration procedures. R1 is 18″ of No. 16 enameled wire, R2 is 20″ of No. 26, and R3 is 48″ of No. 32, all wound on 2-W fixed resistors used as coil forms.—M. Chan and R. Brock, Shunt Switching Method Reduces Meter Errors, *Electronics World*, Oct. 1968, p 76–77.

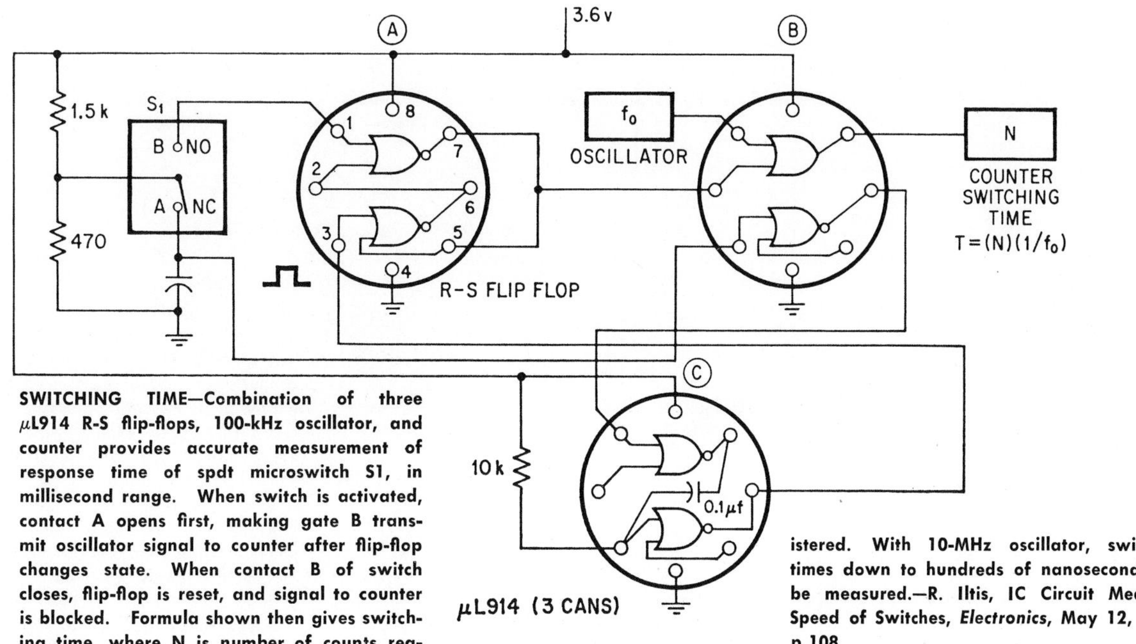

SWITCHING TIME—Combination of three μL914 R-S flip-flops, 100-kHz oscillator, and counter provides accurate measurement of response time of spdt microswitch S1, in millisecond range. When switch is activated, contact A opens first, making gate B transmit oscillator signal to counter after flip-flop changes state. When contact B of switch closes, flip-flop is reset, and signal to counter is blocked. Formula shown then gives switching time, where N is number of counts registered. With 10-MHz oscillator, switching times down to hundreds of nanoseconds can be measured.—R. Iltis, IC Circuit Measures Speed of Switches, *Electronics*, May 12, 1969, p 108.

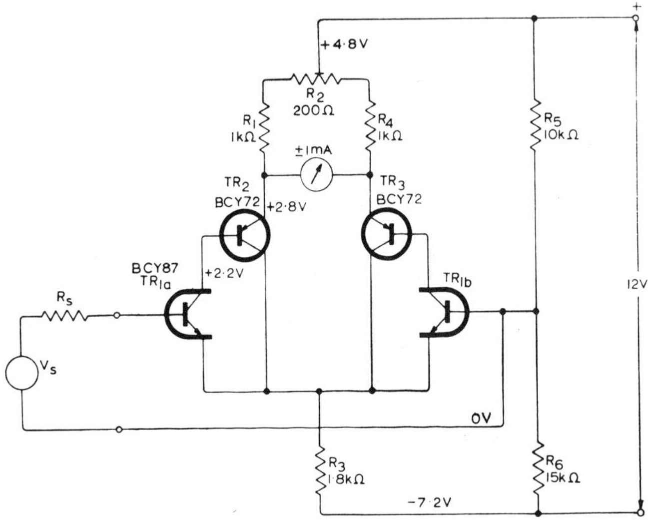

GALVANOMETER AMPLIFIER—Amplifies small direct current sufficiently to drive rugged zero-center 1-mA meter. Consists of long-tailed pair directly coupled to two emitter-followers connected to output meter. R2 permits adjusting meter current to zero for zero input voltage. With 10-ohm meter, 30-mV input gives full-scale deflection. Corresponding input value is 34 mV for 220-ohm meter. Input current for zero output is typically 65 nA, and 90 nA for full-scale deflection.—"Circuits Using Low-Drift Transistor Pairs," Philips, Pub. Dept., Elcoma Div., Eindhoven, The Netherlands, 1968, p 15.

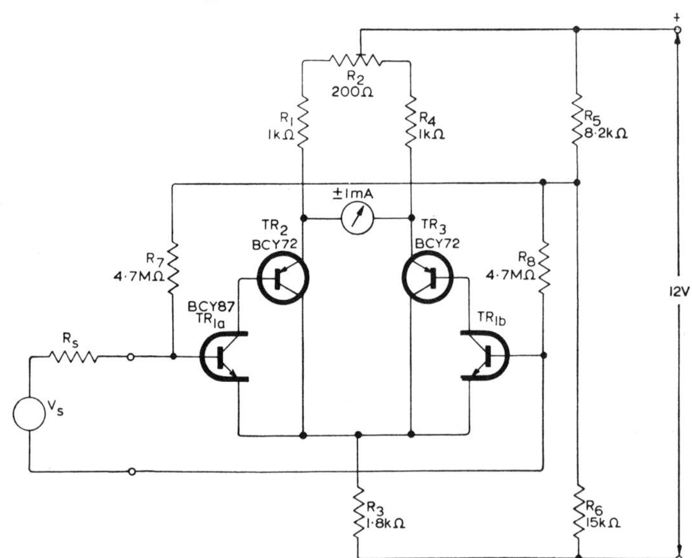

GALVANOMETER AMPLIFIER—Gives full-scale deflection of rugged zero-center 1-mA meter for input current of 35 nA. Maximum differential voltage drift is 7.5 μV per deg C, which is 2.5 times maximum voltage drift. Uses bias arrangement in which half the difference between input transistor base currents passes through signal source.—"Circuits Using Low-Drift Transistor Pairs," Philips, Pub. Dept., Elcoma Div., Eindhoven, The Netherlands, 1968, p 16.

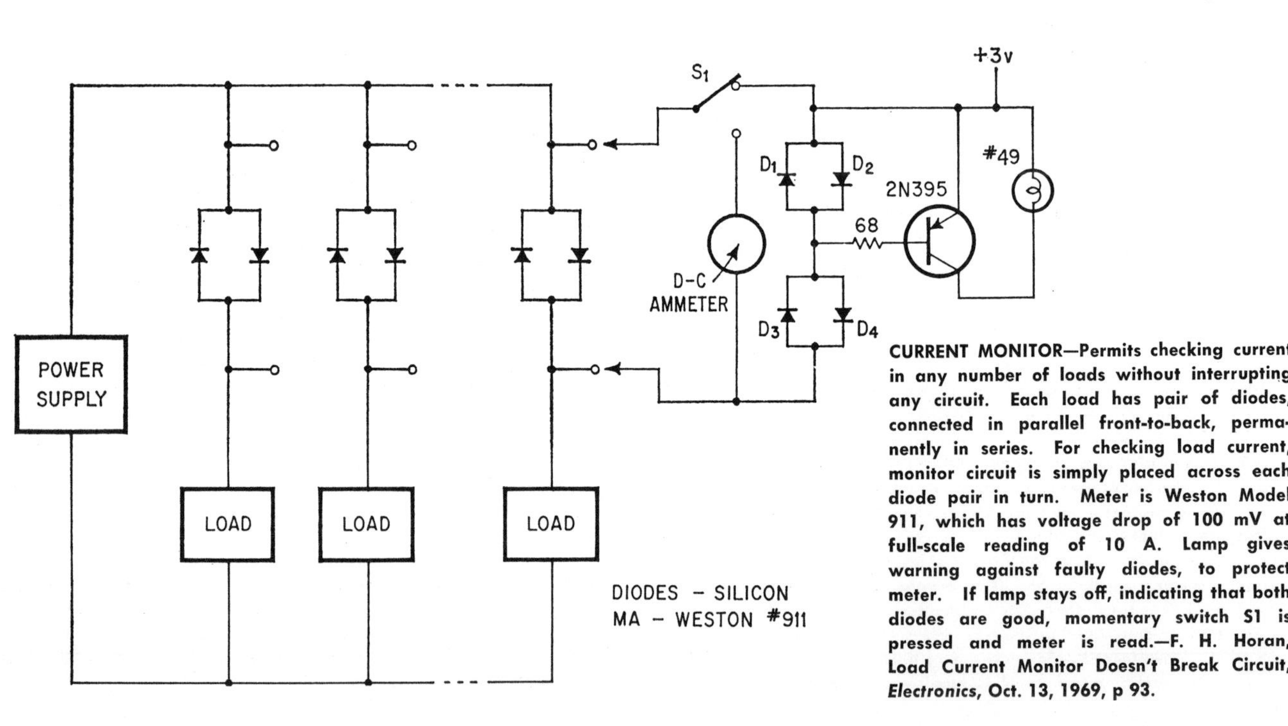

CURRENT MONITOR—Permits checking current in any number of loads without interrupting any circuit. Each load has pair of diodes, connected in parallel front-to-back, permanently in series. For checking load current, monitor circuit is simply placed across each diode pair in turn. Meter is Weston Model 911, which has voltage drop of 100 mV at full-scale reading of 10 A. Lamp gives warning against faulty diodes, to protect meter. If lamp stays off, indicating that both diodes are good, momentary switch S1 is pressed and meter is read.—F. H. Horan, Load Current Monitor Doesn't Break Circuit, *Electronics*, Oct. 13, 1969, p 93.

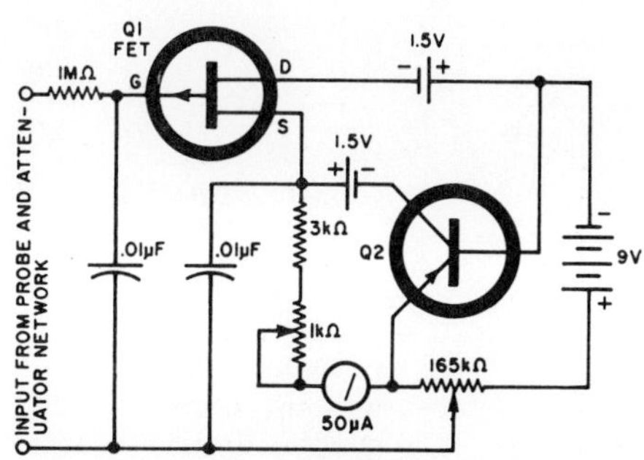

TRANSISTORIZED MULTIMETER—Use of fet with its high input impedance, in cascade with conventional transistor Q2 having low output impedance, gives advantages of vtvm. Circuit shown is simplified; complete circuit with transistor types and switching network is given in Triplett Model 600 service manual.—Triplett Model 600 Transistorized V.O.M., *Electronics World*, Aug. 1967, p 74.

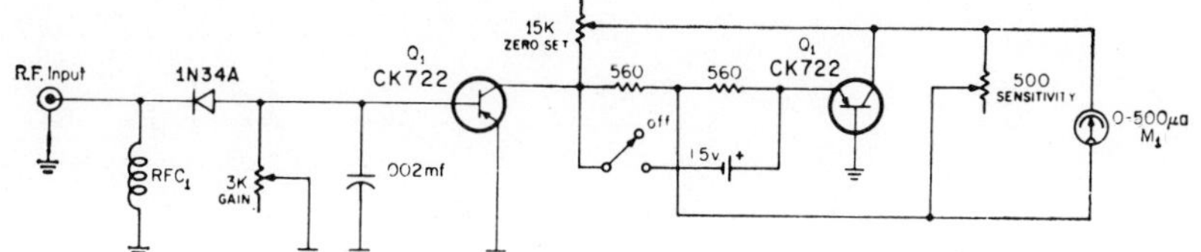

UNTUNED FIELD STRENGTH METER—Untuned choke input for diode eliminates need for tuning and plug-in coils, and high-gain two-transistor d-c amplifier provides required sensitivity. Any other high-gain transistors may be used.—"Electronic Circuits Handbook," Vol. II, Cowan Pub. Corp., Port Washington, N.Y., 1966, p 82.

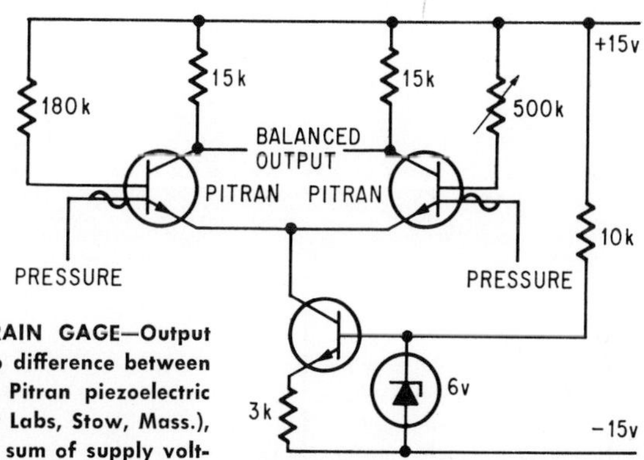
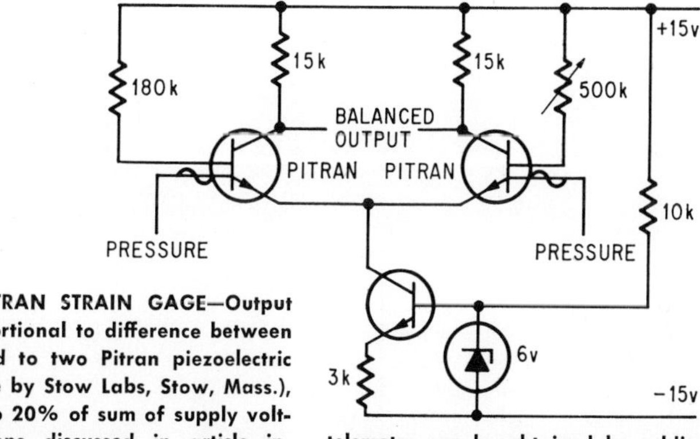

DIFFERENTIAL-PITRAN STRAIN GAGE—Output is linearly proportional to difference between pressures applied to two Pitran piezoelectric transistors (made by Stow Labs, Stow, Mass.), and can be up to 20% of sum of supply voltages. Applications discussed in article include seismic exploration, accelerometers, and wind-tunnel research. Transistor type is not critical. Pulse width modulation output for telemetry can be obtained by adding simple mvbr.—R. M. Moore, Semiconductor Gages Make Sense in Most Transducer Applications, *Electronics*, March 18, 1968, p 109–116.

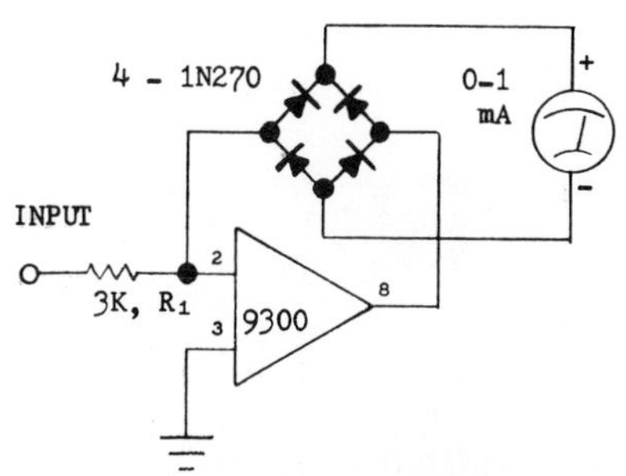

WIDEBAND METER DRIVER—OEI 9300 opamp with bridge rectifier in feedback path responds to average value of input regardless of whether it is d-c, sinusoidal, or any other waveform at frequencies up to 1 MHz. Serves as voltmeter.—Applying the Model 9300 Monolithic Operational Amplifier, Optical Electronics, Tucson, Ariz., No. 10134.

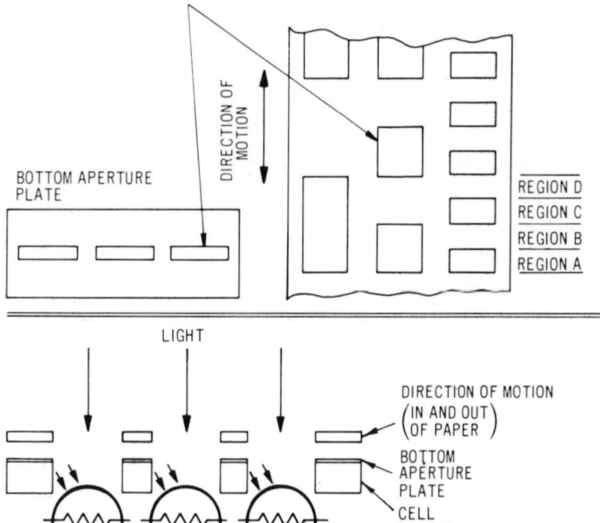

POSITION INDICATOR—Three photocells combined with fixed and moving aperture plates can be arranged to measure either linear or angular position with high degree of accuracy. Combinations of different aperture sizes give illumination on 1, 2, or 3 photocells, which with simple counting logic circuits can be converted into total number of smallest units of displacement.—"Solid State Photosensitive Devices," RCA, Harrison, N.J., p 25.

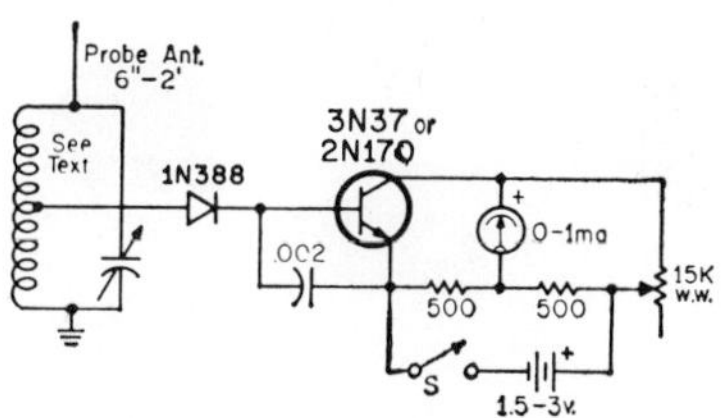

FIELD STRENGTH METER—Simple single-transistor circuit can be used for transmitter tune-up, adjustment of beam antennas, or as monitor if phones are connected in series with meter and collector of transistor. Use coil and tuning capacitor that will resonate at desired frequency; for 10 or 20 meters, coil can be six turns of No. 22 enamel spaced slightly on 1-inch form and tapped two turns from ground end. Any good npn transistor may be used.—"Electronic Circuits Handbook," Vol. II, Cowan Pub. Corp., Port Washington, N.Y., 1966, p 81.

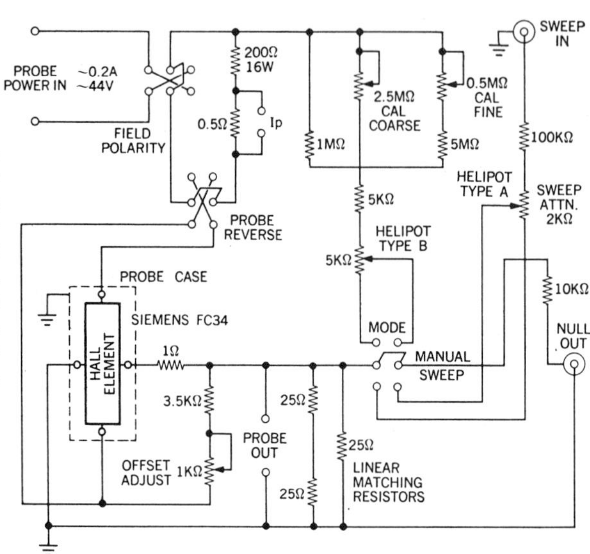

HALL PROBE FIELD CONTROL—Probe consists of Siemens FC-34 Hall element and circuitry needed to adjust for Hall arm offset, plus loading resistors for linearizing probe response. Output of Hall element is about 20 mV per kilogauss for input current of 0.2 A. Used in measuring transverse dHS effect in bismuth at liquid helium temperatures.—R. D. Brown III, New Methods for De Haas-Shubnikov Measurements, *IBM Journal*, Nov. 1966, p 462–471.

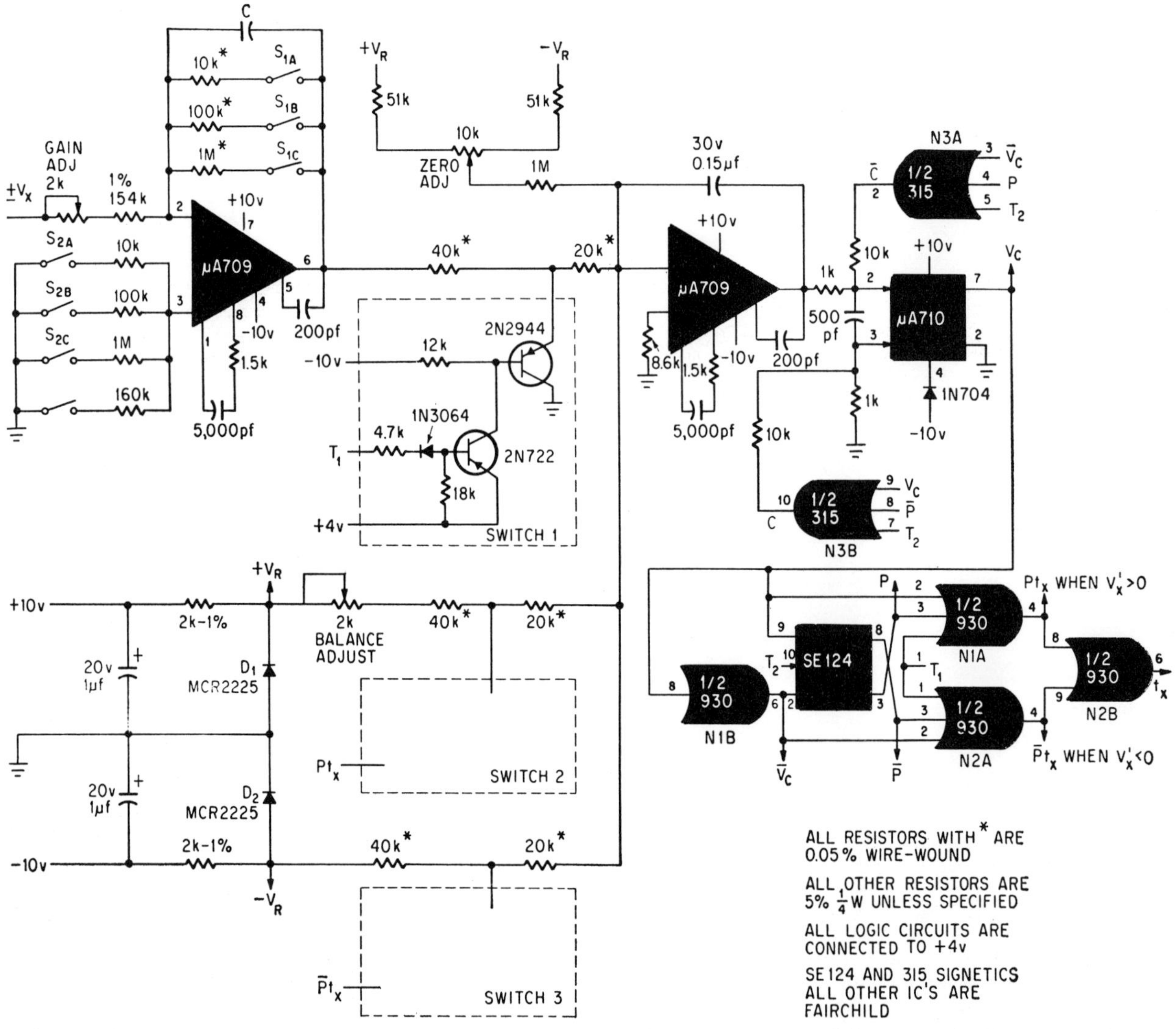

ALL RESISTORS WITH * ARE 0.05% WIRE-WOUND

ALL OTHER RESISTORS ARE 5% $\frac{1}{4}$W UNLESS SPECIFIED

ALL LOGIC CIRCUITS ARE CONNECTED TO +4v

SE124 AND 315 SIGNETICS ALL OTHER IC'S ARE FAIRCHILD

IC DIGITAL VOLTMETER—Use of low-cost IC linear amplifiers and IC logic chips minimizes cost of instrument comparable in performance to conventional four-digit voltmeters costing over $1,000. Uses up-down modulation to convert unknown analog voltage to digital pulse-width signal that is converted from bcd value in counter to decimal value for reading on Nixie tubes. Circuit shown is analog portion, for pulse-width modulator, which includes range selection, integrator, comparator, three solid-state shunt switches, output logic, and reference voltage.—H. Schmid, Digital Meters for Under $100, *Electronics*, Nov. 28, 1966, p 88–94.

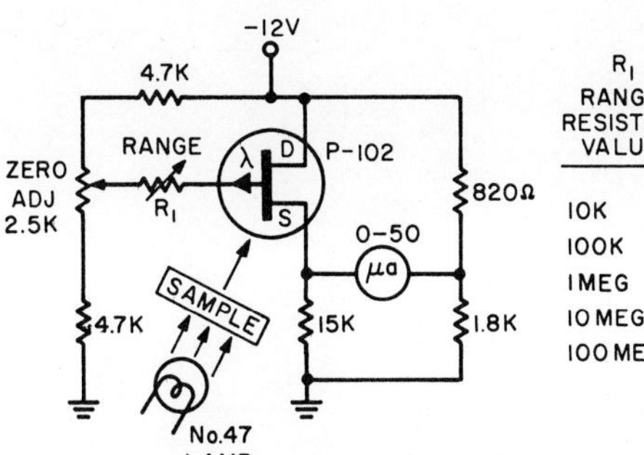

R_1 RANGE RESISTOR VALUE	FULL-SCALE OPTICAL DENSITY CALIBRATION
10K	0.0 (100% TRANS)
100K	1.0 (10% TRANS)
1MEG	2.0 (1% TRANS)
10 MEG	3.0 (0.1% TRANS)
100 MEG	4.0 (0.01% TRANS)

PHOTOMETER—Used to measure changes in optical density of translucent materials. Setting of R1 determines full-scale range. Minimum full-scale range, for 0.01% transmission or density of 4.0, is obtained with 100 meg.—M. Shipley, Using Photo Field-Effect Transistors, *Electronic Design*, Aug. 31, 1964, p 76.

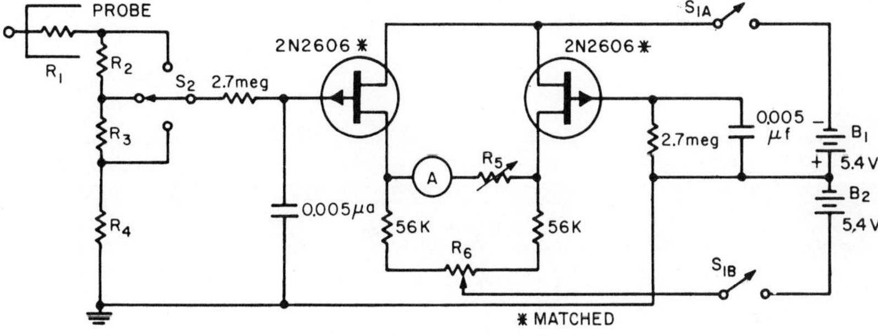

FET VTVM—Can be mounted directly on small meter. Input impedance is 30 meg. Ranges are 2, 10, and 20 V. Resistor values are: R1 15 meg; R2 12 meg; R3 1.5 meg; R4 1.5 meg; R5 10,000; R6 5,000.—Field Effect Voltmeter, *Electronic Design*, Jan. 6, 1964, p 78.

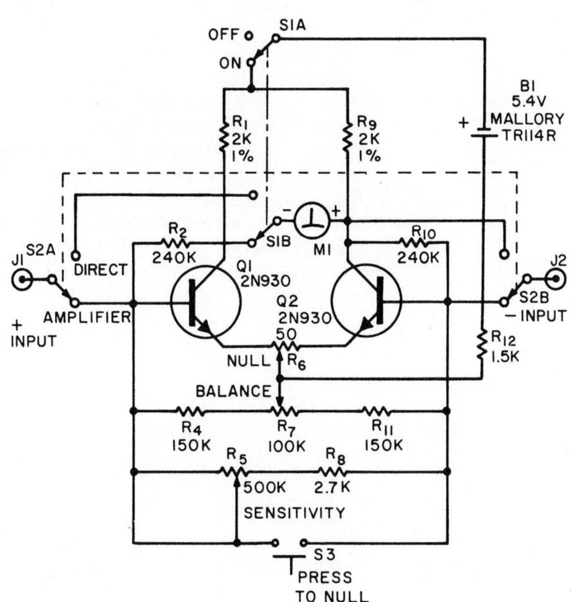

DIFFERENTIAL MICROAMMETER AMPLIFIER—Differential amplifier, using degenerative biasing and collector feed to 100-μA meter, gives excellent null stability and 2-μA instrument sensitivity.—J. P. Graham, Galvanometer Amplifier Has Greater Sensitivity, *Electronic Design*, Feb. 17, 1964, p 90–91.

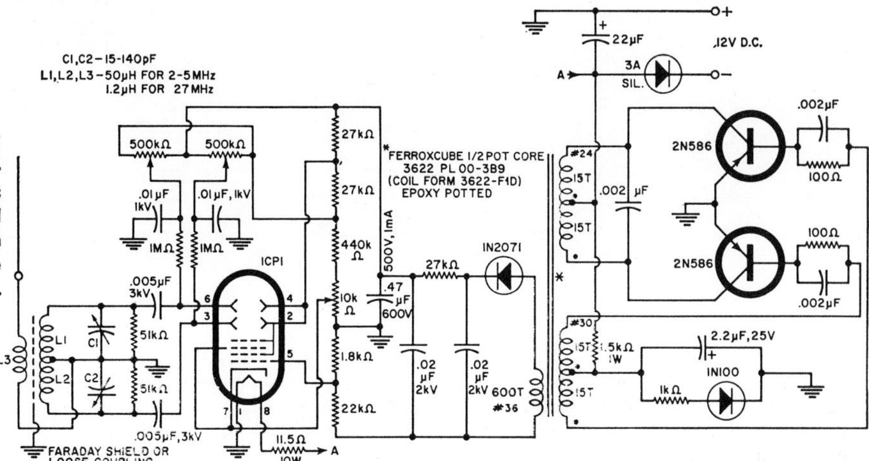

% MODULATION ON CRT—Operates off 12-V battery for measuring percentage of amplitude modulation of transmitter when no a-c power is available. Percentage is indicated as ratio of radii of two circles on 1-inch cathode-ray tube.—D. Stephani, Amplitude Modulation Tester, *Electronics World*, Jan. 1968, p 51.

DISPLACEMENT DETECTOR—Object being monitored is attached to movable top plate, which may be photographic film or etched metal having opertures only a few thousandths of an inch wide. Movement equal to aperture width changes light on photocell from maximum to zero. Resulting change in photocell current or impedance is then measured with conventional meter-driving circuit that can be calibrated to read displacement. "Solid State Photosensitive Devices," RCA, Harrison, N.J., p 25.

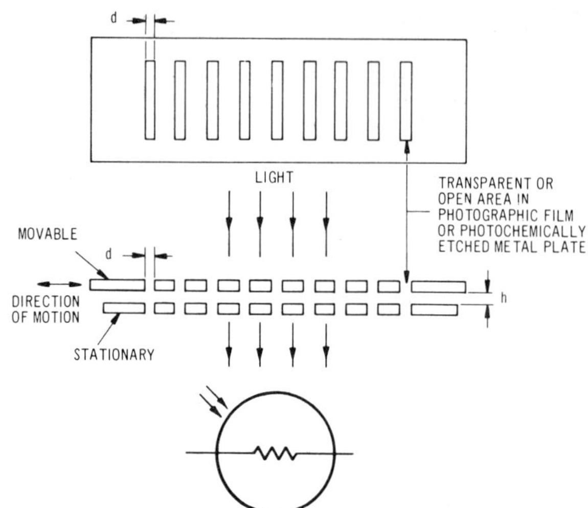

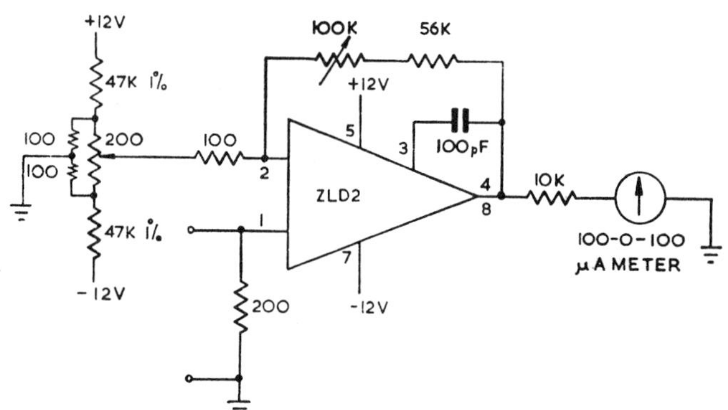

EXTENDING RANGE OF D-C MICROAMMETER—Uses Ferranti ZLD2 IC differential amplifier as d-c amplifier for converting 100-0-100 μA meter to rugged 10-μA meter. Offset of IC is eliminated by adjusting 200-ohm pot until output is zero for zero input. For calibration, apply known input current and adjust 100K pot until correct output reading is obtained. For 1% meter accuracy, temperature should be held within 3 C of calibration temperature.—Microlin Amplifiers ZLD2S and ZLD2T, Ferranti Ltd., Oldham, Lancs., England, No. 11, 1967, p 19.

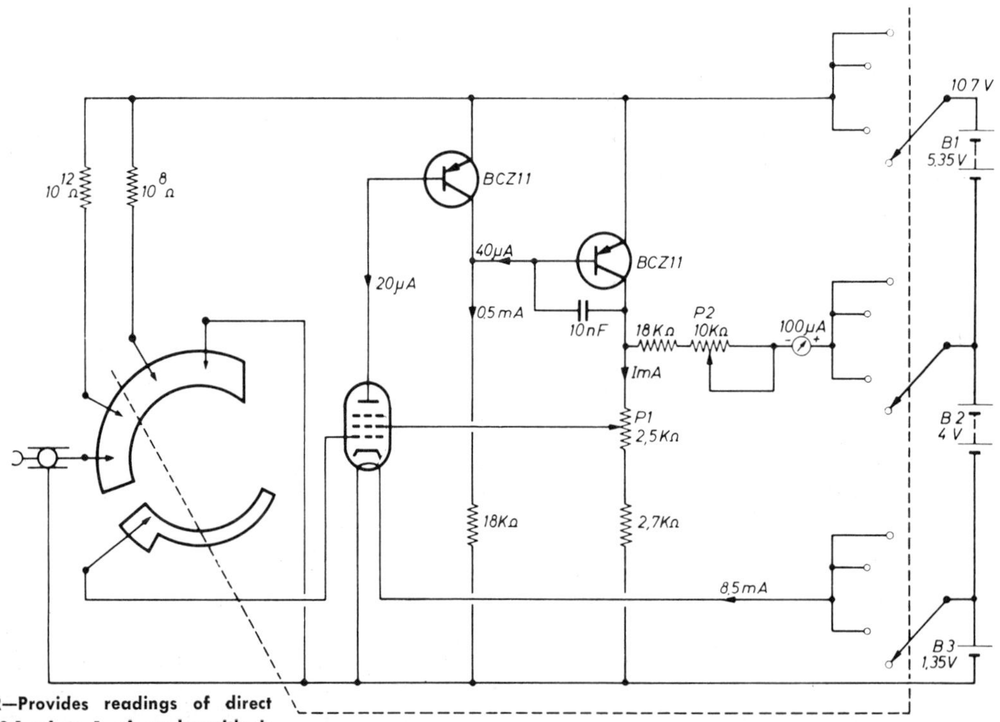

ELECTROMETER—Provides readings of direct currents from 0.1 pA to 1 μA on logarithmic scale, using Philips type 4068 electrometer tube. Report deals with measuring techniques and precautions for achieving maximum accuracy.—Electrometer Tubes, Philips, Pub. Dept., Elcoma Div., Eindhoven, The Netherlands, No. 11, 1965, p 6.

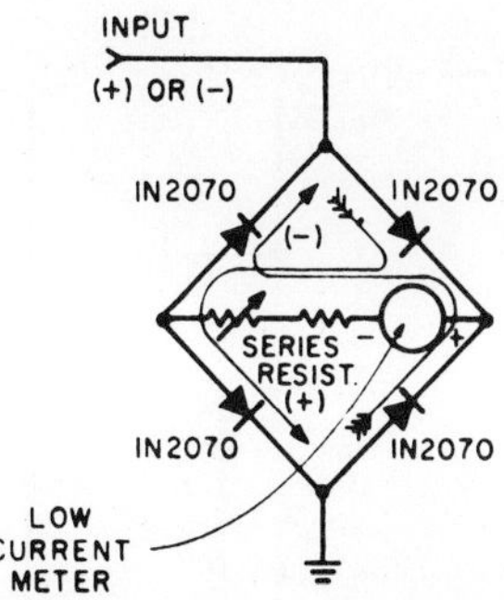

AUTOMATIC REVERSAL OF VOLTMETER—Low-loss diodes in bridge provide automatic reversal of polarity, without switching, when testing both npn and pnp transistors. Diodes are inexpensive and often cheaper than reversing switch, and do not introduce more than 10% error when measuring voltages above 5 V.—R. M. Mann, Low-Loss Diodes Reverse Meter Polarity, "400 Ideas for Design Selected from Electronic Design," Hayden Book Co., N.Y., 1964, p 152.

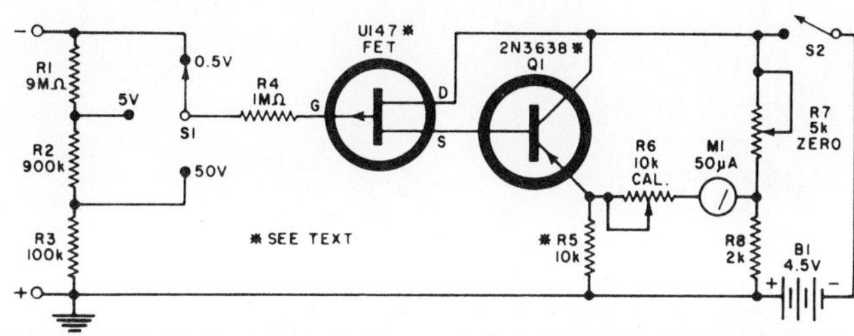

VTVM—Simple transistorized version of popular vacuum-tube voltmeter circuit uses inexpensive fet to give input impedance of 10 meg. Linear response permits using scale markings of meter. Battery drain is only 1 mA. Changing R7 to 2,500 ohms will give better resolution. (Changes are described in reader letter on p 12 of Nov. 1967 *Electronics World*.)—J. Randall, FET Voltmeter, *Electronics World*, Feb. 1967, p 63–64.

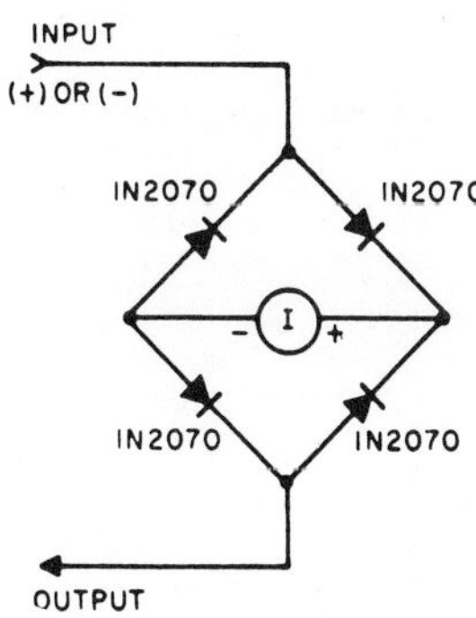

AUTOMATIC REVERSAL OF AMMETER—Low-loss diodes in bridge provide automatic reversal of polarity, without switching, when making current measurements in npn and pnp transistor test circuits. Error due to bridge is negligible except at extremely small currents, because leakage in diodes shunting meter is extremely low.—R. M. Mann, Low-Loss Diodes Reverse Meter Polarity, "400 Ideas for Design Selected from Electronic Design," Hayden Book Co., N.Y., 1964, p 152.

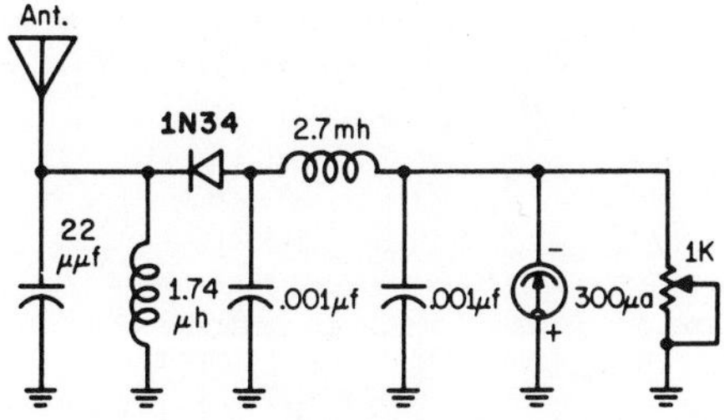

DIODE METER—Though low in sensitivity, will provide satisfactory indication of relative signal strength of transmitter in same room. Antenna is short length of insulated wire.—"Electronic Circuits Handbook," Vol. II, Cowan Pub. Corp., Port Washington, N.Y., 1966, p 89.

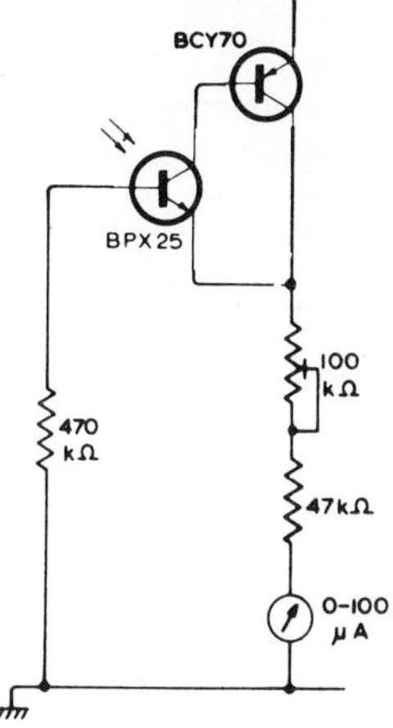

LINEAR LIGHT METER—Feedback across emitter resistor of BCY70 transistor stabilizes gain of BPX25 phototransistor. With values shown, 1,000 lux gives full-scale deflection of meter. May be calibrated either against standard light source or with another luxmeter.—Applications of Silicon Planar Phototransistor BPX25, Philips, Pub. Dept., Elcoma Div., Eindhoven, The Netherlands, No. 316, 1967.

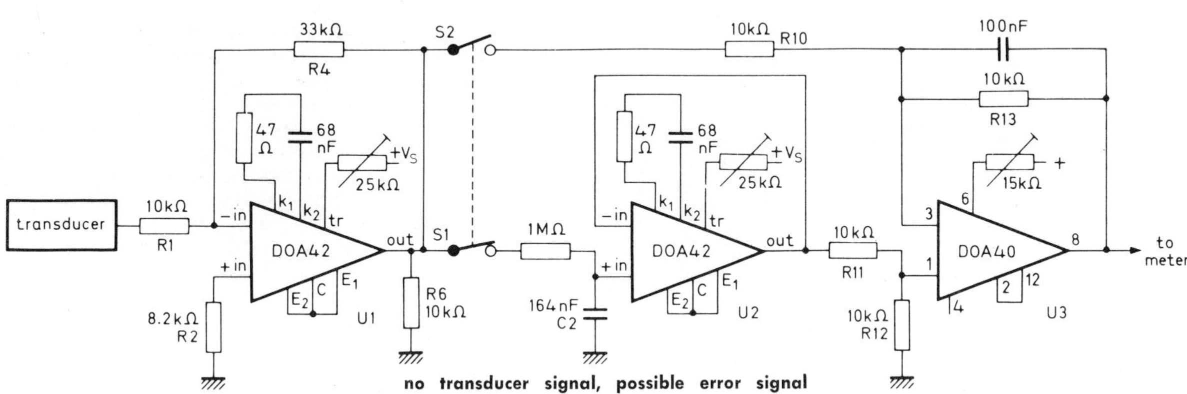

TRANSDUCER DRIFT COMPENSATION—Used to eliminate or greatly reduce zero error caused by drift in transducer and preamplifier of measuring circuit. Requires +15 V and −15 V supplies. With S1 closed (S2 open) and no transducer signal, possible error signal from transducer is amplified by opamp U1 and applied to opamp U2 connected as hold circuit feeding differential amplifier U3. After about 1 s, S2 is closed and transducer activated. Stored signal then cancels zero error, so measured value appears without error at output of U3.—P. Havas, Compensation of Transducer Zero Error, Philips, Pub. Dept., Elcoma Div., Eindhoven, The Netherlands, No. 78.

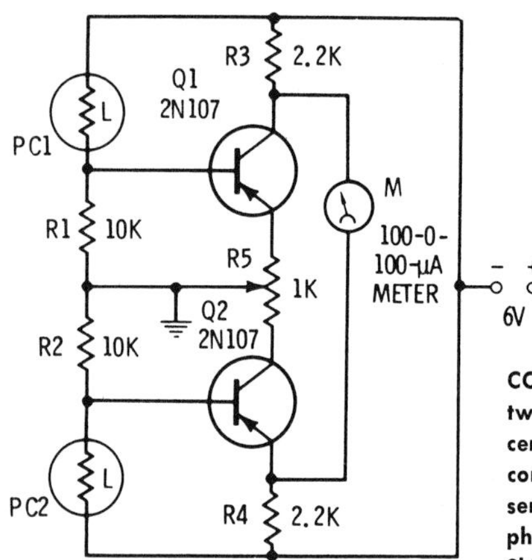

COMPARATOR—Circuit determines which of two photocells is illuminated and drives zero-center meter accordingly. May be used for comparing brilliance of two light sources, sensing position of vane moving between photocells, and comparing colors.—J. P. Shields, "Novel Electronic Circuits," H. W. Sams & Co., Indianapolis, Ind., 1968, p 80.

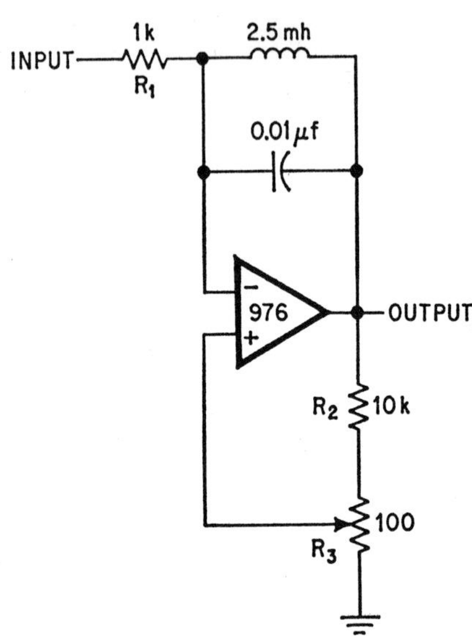

Q MULTIPLIER—Simple opamp circuit provides means for varying Q of tuned circuit with single pot. Developed for low-level measurements in communication receivers and active filters. Will operate up to 3 MHz. Values shown are for resonant frequency of 33 kHz. —R. C. Gerdes, Q-Multiplier Circuit Uses Op Amp With LC Feedback, *Electronics*, May 26, 1969, p 92.

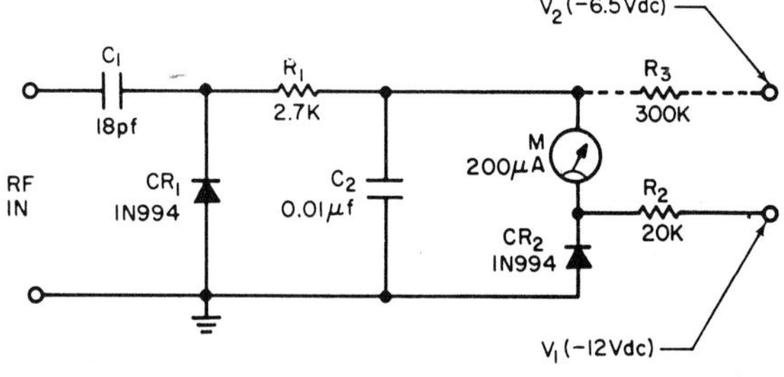

PEAK-READING VOLTMETER WITH DIODE—Addition of diode CR2 in series with meter of conventional peak-reading voltmeter improves its sensitivity, temperature characteristic, and low-level sensitivity and linearity. Extra diode also protects meter from current overload by opening above upper meter current limit as determined by R2 and V1. Performance is good up to 250 MHz, for input voltages below 0.4 V.—H. T. McAleer, Diode Improves Voltmeter's Linearity and Stability, *Electronic Design*, Nov. 22, 1965, p 65–67.

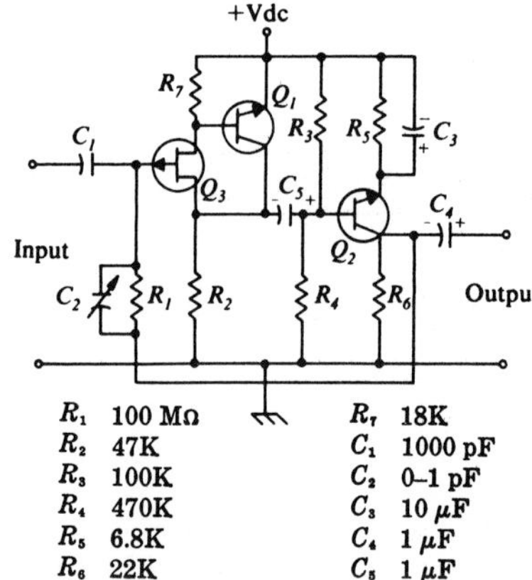

R_1	100 MΩ	R_7	18K
R_2	47K	C_1	1000 pF
R_3	100K	C_2	0–1 pF
R_4	470K	C_3	10 µF
R_5	6.8K	C_4	1 µF
R_6	22K	C_5	1 µF

ELECTROMETER AMPLIFIER—Uses fet to measure currents as small as 0.1 pA at room temperature with 1 Hz bandwidth and approaching theoretical noise limit. Should be used with external filter that limits bandwidth, for optimum noise performance. Q1 is 2N697, Q2 is 2N2484, Q3 is 2N2606, and supply is 12 V.—"Selected Electronic Circuitry," NASA SP-5046, 1966, Government Printing Office, Washington, D.C., p 3.

NOTE: To locate additional circuits in the category of this chapter, use the index at the back of this book. Check also the author's "Sourcebook of Electronic Circuits," published by McGraw-Hill in 1968.

CHAPTER 50
Medical Circuits

PACEMAKER—Tv-type blocking oscillator Q1 generates fixed pacing pulse at rate determined before implantation and connection to heart. Oscillator generates very low-power pulse for triggering Q2, which then makes C2 deliver 1-ms pulse to heart.—J. T. Prentice, Electronic Implants, *Electronics World*, June 1968, p 46–48.

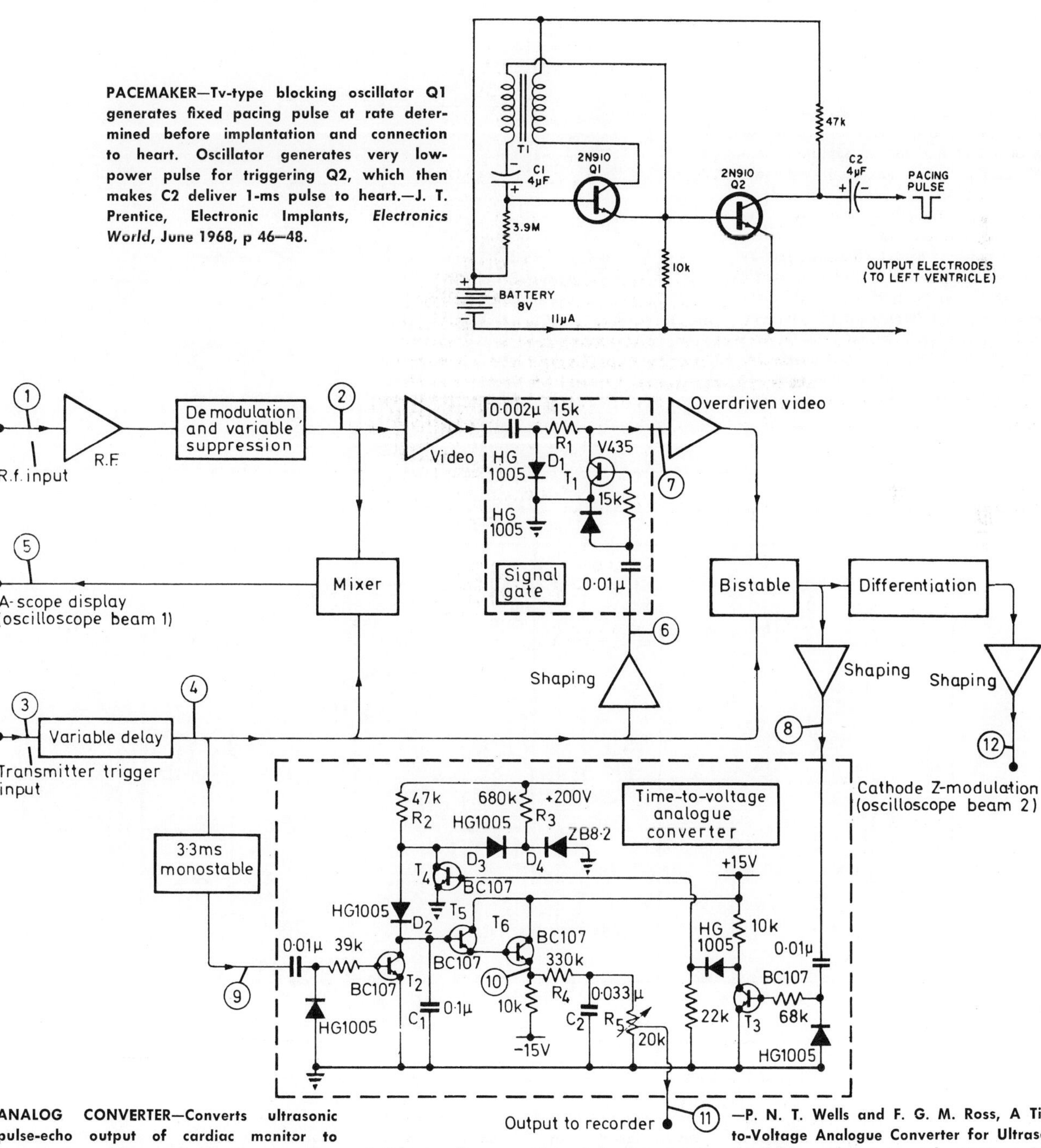

ANALOG CONVERTER—Converts ultrasonic pulse-echo output of cardiac monitor to square-wave pulses suitable for recording with high-speed ink-jet strip-chart recorders. Article describes operation of circuit in detail and gives examples of recordings obtained. —P. N. T. Wells and F. G. M. Ross, A Time-to-Voltage Analogue Converter for Ultrasonic Cardiology, *Ultrasonics*, July 1969, p 171–176.

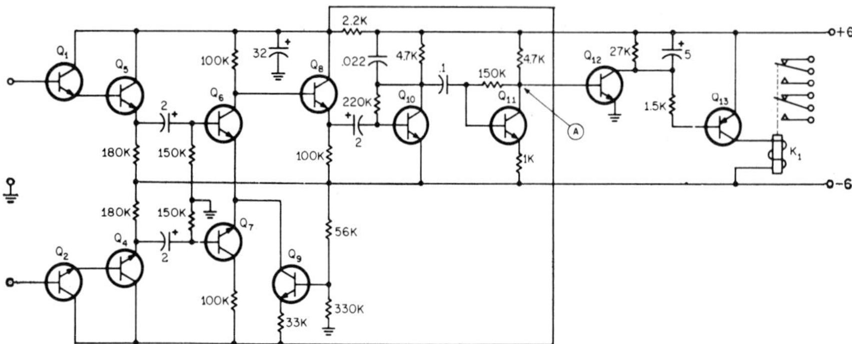

EMG KEYER—Electromyograph pulses picked up by silver electrodes held against stump muscle of amputee are fed to low-noise differential amplifier through impedance transformer. Output goes through conventional two-stage high-gain amplifier, detector, and d-c amplifier operating output relay used for keying amateur radio transmitter. Operator merely thinks of moving missing or paralyzed arm, to make relay operate. Bandwidth of amplifier is 50–500 Hz, corresponding to range of emg signals being picked up. Q13 is 2N-398 and other transistors are 2N708. Relay is Sigma SIL2500 or equivalent.—G. W. Horn, The Third Hand—An Aid for the Handicapped Operator, CQ, Feb. 1966, p 54–57.

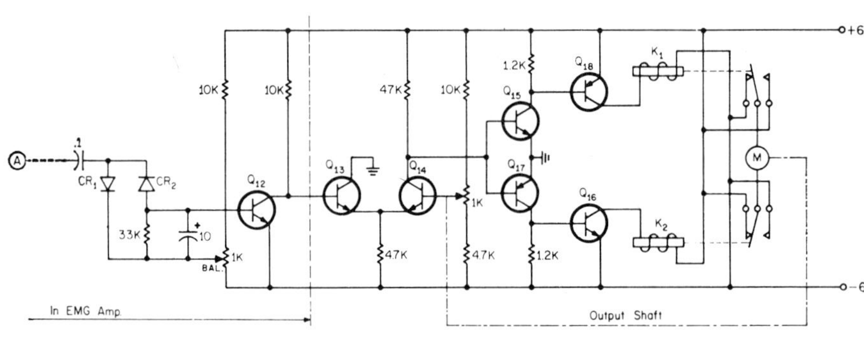

EMG SERVO—Used with electromyograph amplifier to convert amplified muscle potential (taken ahead of detector) to appropriate input for position servo providing continuous control of angular position of tuning knob for amateur radio transmitter or receiver. Position of output motor shaft is proportional at any instant to mental effort exerted by amputee on stump muscle. Relaxing muscle makes shaft return to zero position, because decreasing signal voltage pulls in other output relay and reverses motor. Q16 is BFY-56, Q17 2N398, Q18 BFY64, and others 2N-708.—G. W. Horn, The Third Hand—An Aid for the Handicapped Operator, CQ, Feb. 1966, p 54–57.

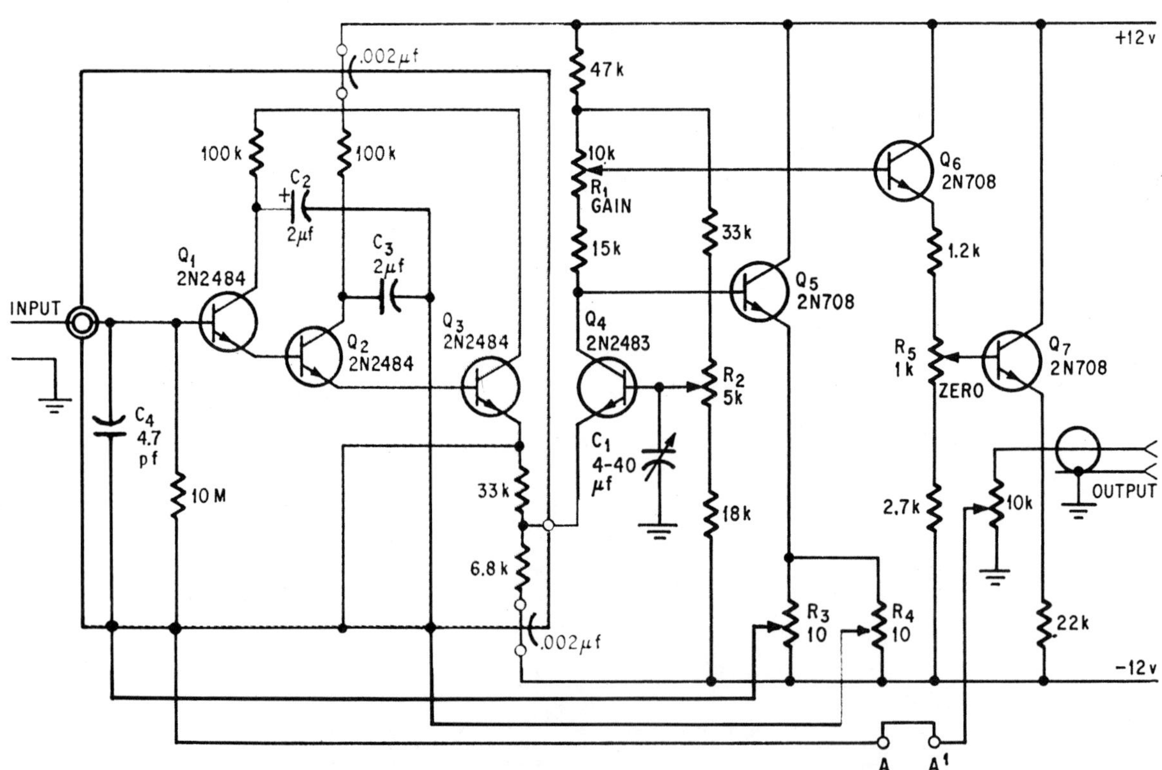

BIOELECTRIC PROBE AMPLIFIER—Used to amplify millivolt pulses produced in protoplasmic membrane, for feeding into recorder. First three transistors in Darlington configuration form negative-capacitance impedance converter, followed by d-c amplifier Q4 and emitter-followers Q6 and Q7 operating in cascade. Circuit presents 20,000-meg input resistance to probe, with input capacitance below 0.02 pF.—G. W. Horn, Feedback Reduces Bio Probe's Input Capacitance, *Electronics*, March 18, 1968, p 97–98.

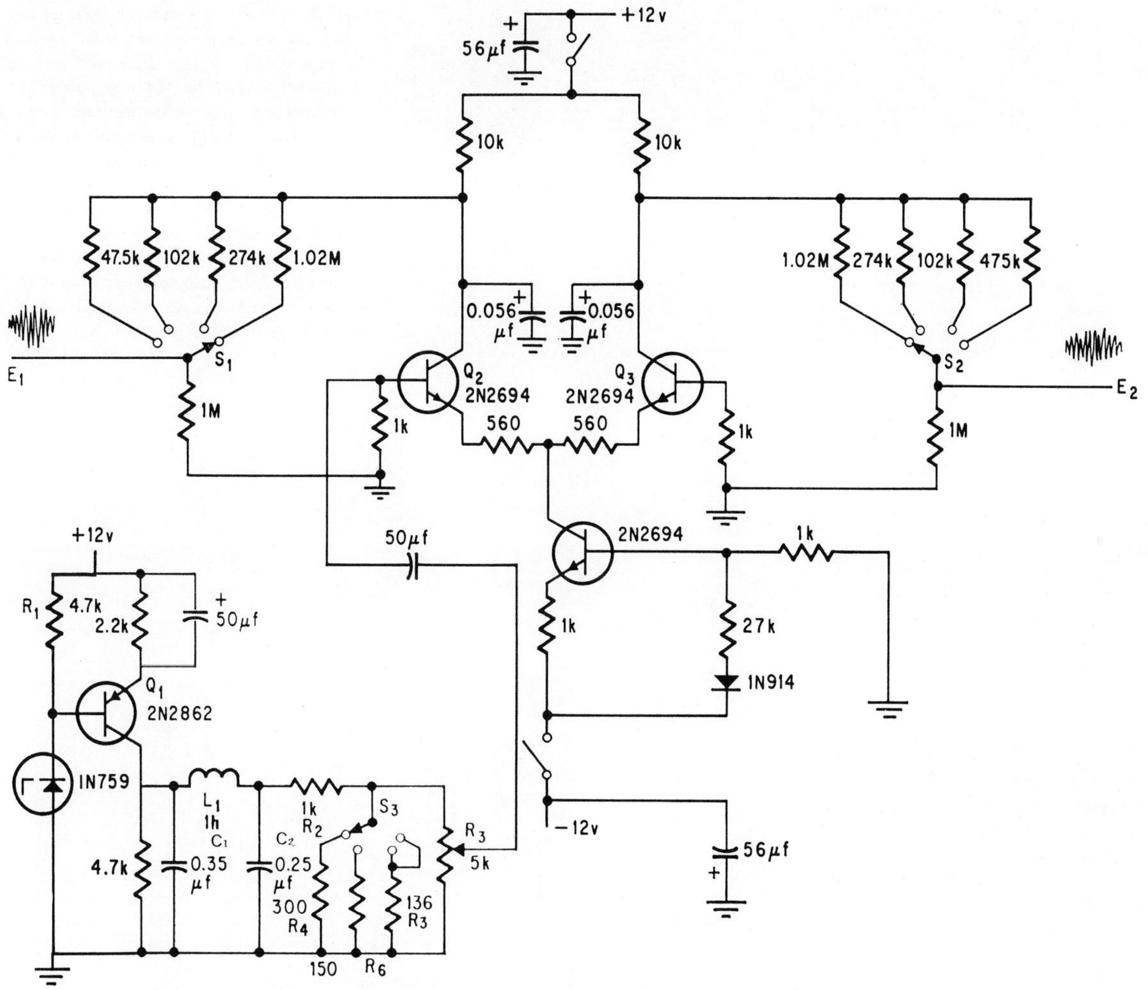

MUSCLE SIGNAL SIMULATOR—Simulates white noise generated in flexed muscle, for use in developing amplifiers and servomechanisms for controlling artificial limbs. Output of zener, serving as broad-spectrum noise generator, is amplified and filtered to give required 1-kHz bandwidth of noise.—W. Paisner, D. Antonelli, and W. Waring, Zener Simulates Muscle Signals, *Electronics*, June 10, 1968, p 111–112.

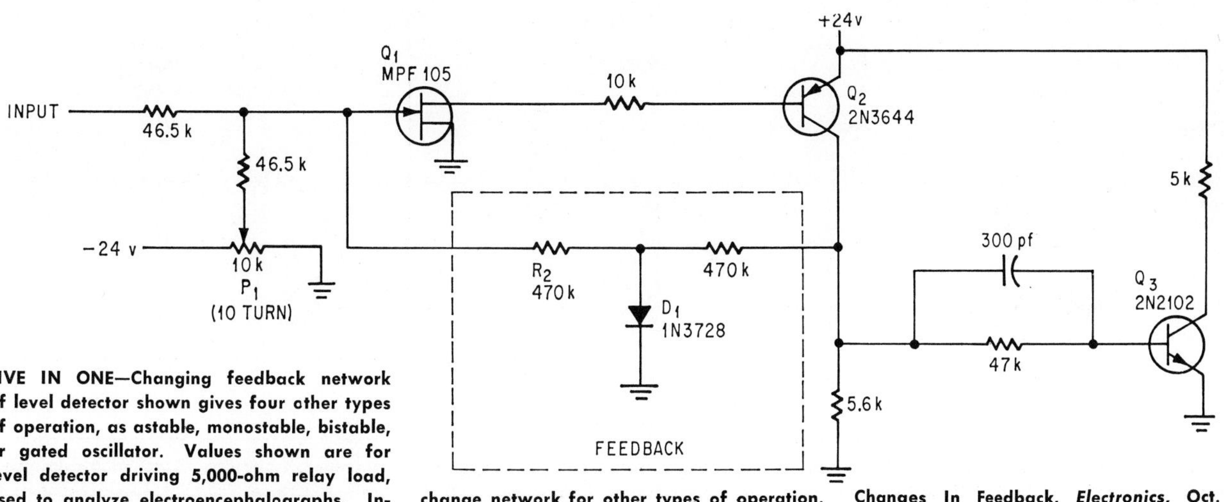

FIVE IN ONE—Changing feedback network of level detector shown gives four other types of operation, as astable, monostable, bistable, or gated oscillator. Values shown are for level detector driving 5,000-ohm relay load, used to analyze electroencephalographs. Input can be 0 to 20 V. Article tells how to change network for other types of operation. —G. Silverman, Five Valuable Circuits From Changes In Feedback, *Electronics*, Oct. 2, 1967, p 95–96.

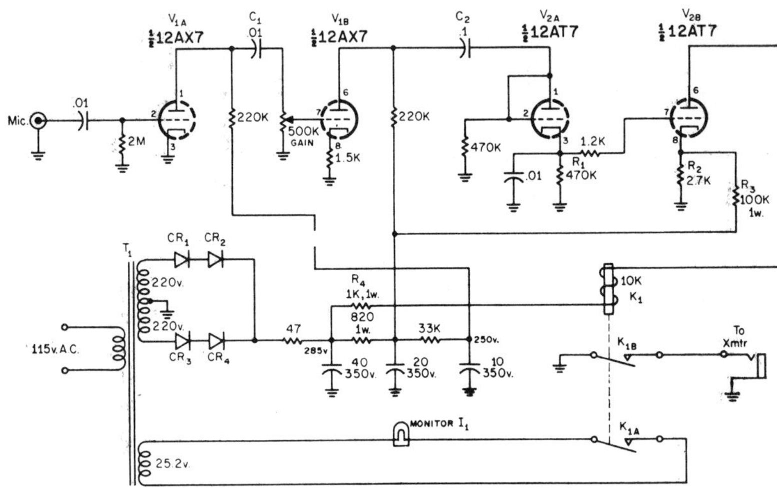

VOICE-OPERATED KEY—Developed for c-w amateur radio operators lacking full use of hands. Duration of sound at mike determines whether keying relay K1 produces dot or dash. Clearly spoken dah-dit-dah-dit dah-dah-dit-dah will give acceptable CQ in code after very little practice. Whistling also works. Other applications include keying of transmitter from magnetic tape recorder for on-the-air code classes.—A. Horst, The Vox Key, CQ, Jan. 1965, p 29–30.

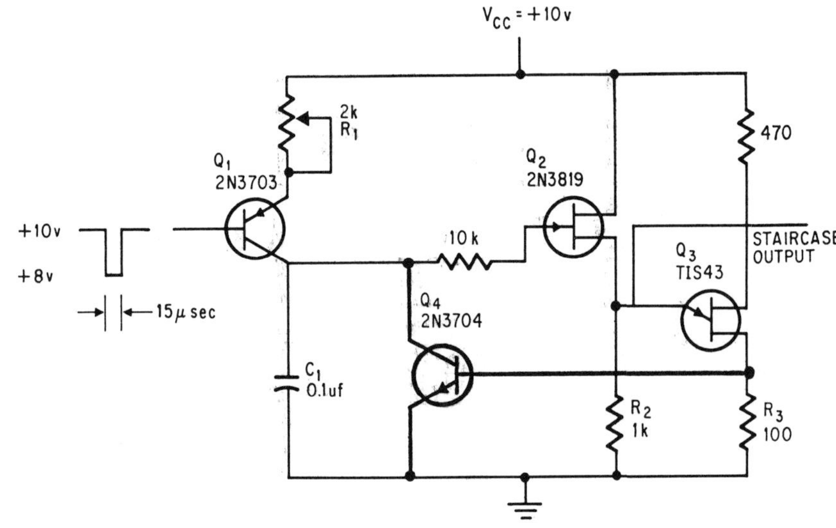

FET FLATTENS STEPS—Fet Q2 isolates waveforming capacitor from ujt of staircase generator, to prevent exponential decay or droop of staircase step voltage. Used as pulse counter, for accurately monitoring uterine contractions, heart beat, and respiration rate. —K. J. Bray, FET Keeps Long Staircase Steps Flat, *Electronics*, March 18, 1968, p 94.

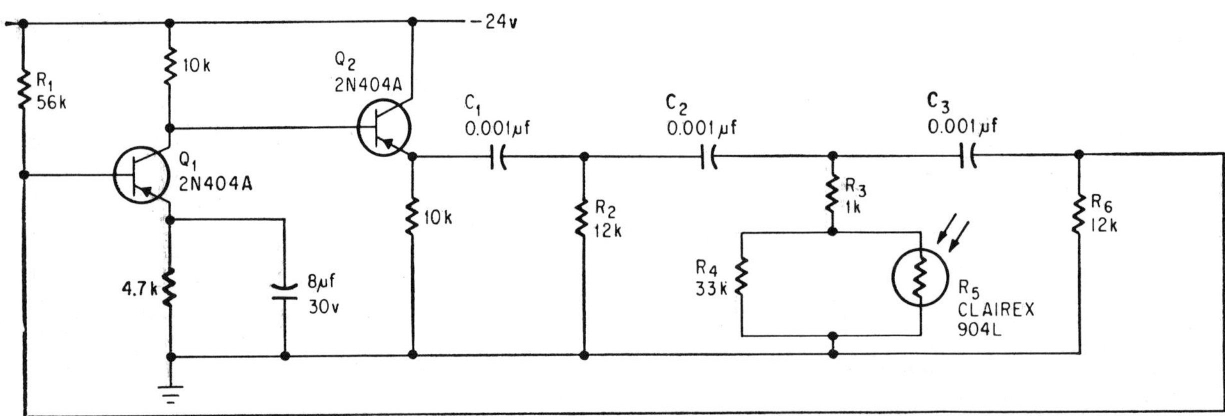

LIGHT-CONTROLLED OSCILLATOR—Addition of emitter-follower Q2 to phase-shift oscillator Q1 boosts output frequency 1.4 times, and gives greater frequency sensitivity to changes in light-sensitive resistor R5. One application is as psychological testing device that measures ability of subject to follow moving light source. For other applications, potentiometer in place of R5 will control frequency. —G. Silverman, Emitter Follower Enhances Oscillator's Frequency Variation, *Electronics*, Dec. 26, 1966, p 73–74.

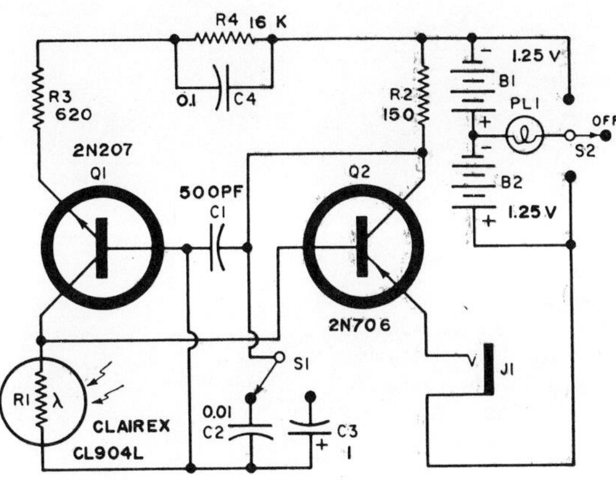

MOVEMENT SENSOR FOR BLIND—Used with interchangeable lenses to detect movements at various distances up to infinity, in science labs for blind students. Photoresistor R1 (Clairex CL904L or equivalent) produces frequency change in two-transistor RC feedback audio oscillator having small magnetic earphone in its output. PL1 is 1.25-V grain-of-wheat lamp used for cell illumination, as required for reading thermometer and sensing position of meter pointer.—Light Probe for the Blind, *Electronics World*, Nov. 1967, p 77.

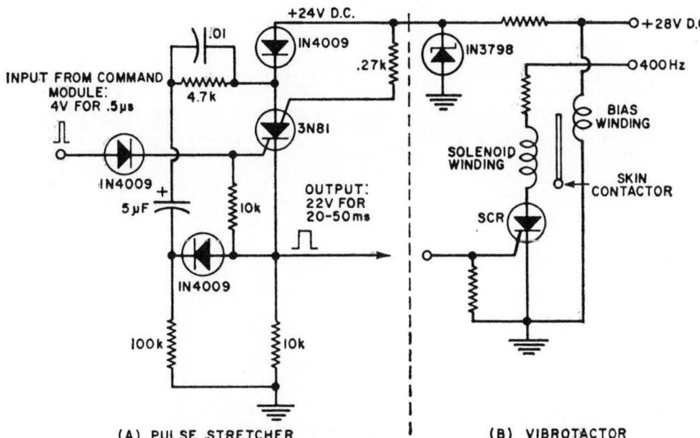

VIBROTACTOR—Developed for transmitting emergency signals to astronauts without using voice communication. Tiny vibrator, with solenoid winding, is attached to skin and actuated by pulses from communication link. Since taps on skin shorter than 0.5 μs cannot be felt by man, four-transistor pulse stretcher is used ahead of vibrator stage.—L. G. Lawrence, Communications Via Touch, *Electronics World*, May 1968, p 32–34 and 80.

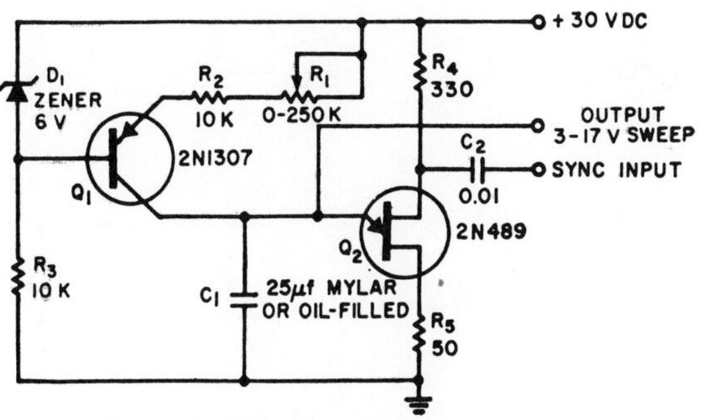

SLOW SWEEP FOR CARDIAC MONITOR—Slow linear sweep, adjustable by R1 from 1 to 30 s can be used for monitoring cardiac waveforms. Voltage ramp produced has less than 1% displacement error from linearity.—J. L. Aker, Unijunction Oscillator Gives 30-Sec Sweep, "400 Ideas for Design Selected from Electronic Design," Hayden Book Co., N.Y., 1964, p 189.

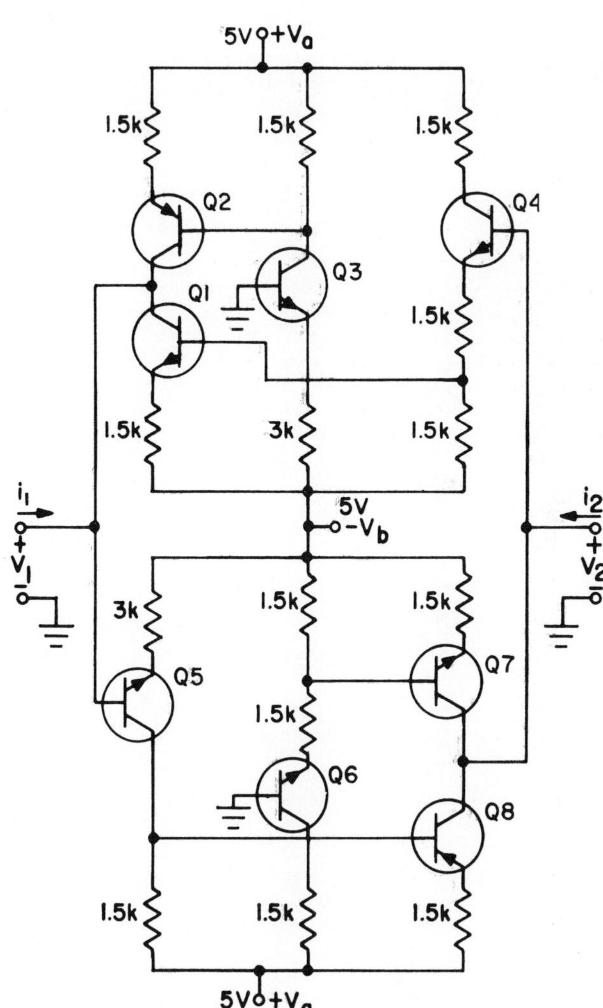

GYRATOR—Consists of two voltage-to-current negative-impedance converters, connected to produce output current proportional to input voltage. In addition, reverse transconductance makes input current proportional to output voltage. Serves as active filter for very low frequencies used in oceanography, seismology, and medical electronics. Article gives application circuits for specific frequencies.—J. L. Hogin, Active Filters, *Electronics World*, April 1969, p 58–60.

NERVE AMPLIFIER—Low-noise hybrid IC amplifier substitutes for electrometer tube in amplifying nerve and muscle-fiber impulses picked up by electrodes attached to body. Circuit has high input resistance and good linearity.—J. Y. Lettvin, Low-Noise Electrometer Amplifier, *EDN*, Sept. 1, 1969, p 69–70.

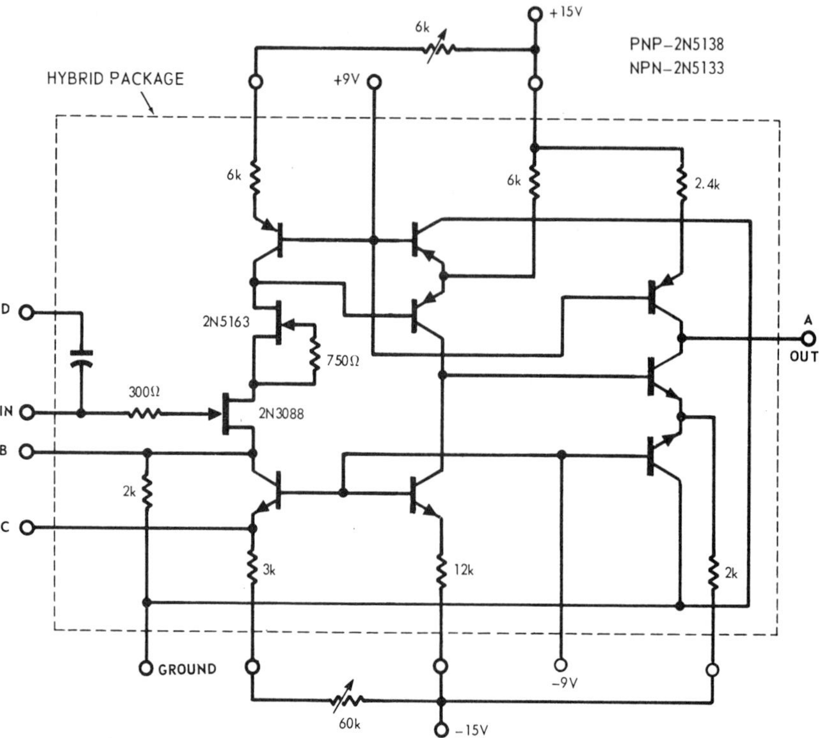

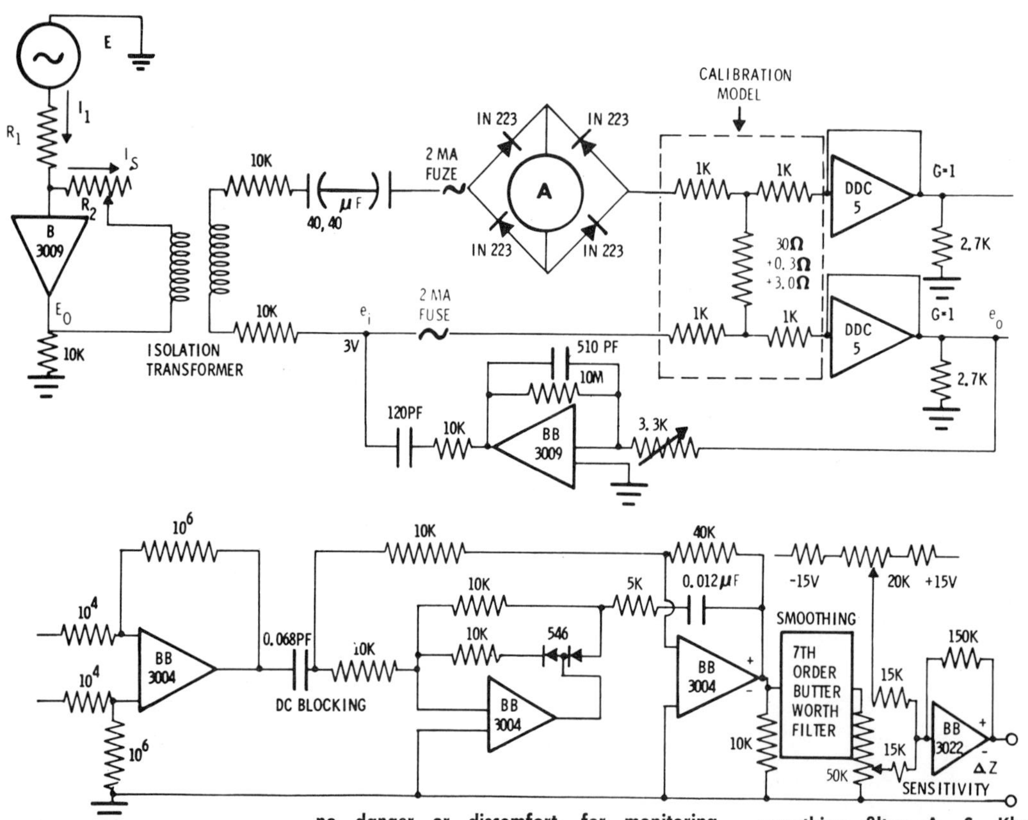

PLETHYSMOGRAPH—Low-frequency impedance plethysmograph provides current of 1 mA at frequencies as low as 10 Hz to subjects with no danger or discomfort, for monitoring impedance changes in 37 normal subjects under various conditions of lung ventilation. Output of BB3022 voltage comparator drives strip chart recorder through smoothing filter.—A. S. Khalafalla, S. P. Stackhouse, and O. H. Schmitt, Thoracic Impedance Gradient with Respect to Breathing, *IEEE Transactions on Bio-Medical Engineering*, July 1970, p 191–197.

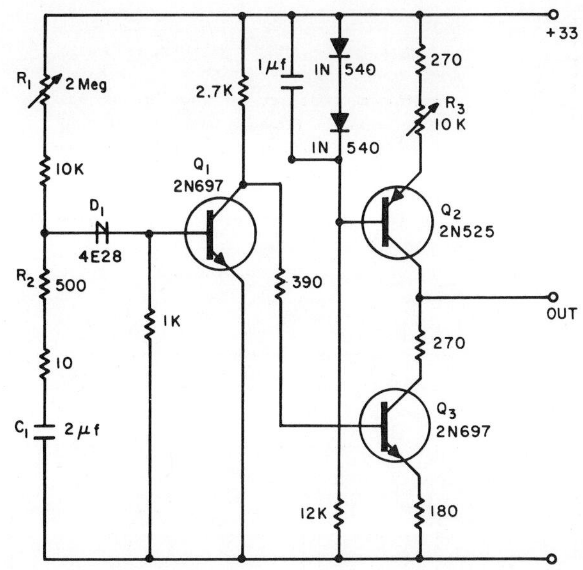

CONSTANT-CURRENT PULSES—Provides constant current within 3%, adjustable from 200 μA to 10 mA for pulses that are variable in frequency and duty cycle, with rise and fall times under 1 μs. Circuit is ideal for neurophysiological testing, pulse beta testing, and as driver for some types of sensors. Capacitor loading of output gives sawtooth with fast fall time and good linearity.—R. Dobkin, Pulse Generator Delivers a Constant Current, *Electronic Design*, March 15, 1965, p 63–64.

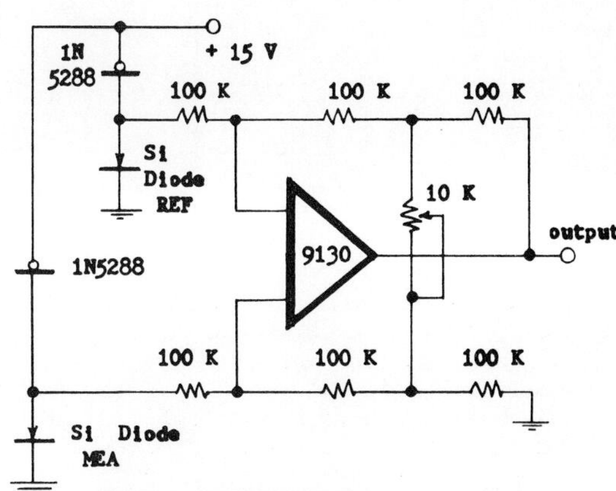

MEDICAL THERMOMETER—Uses one diode to establish reference temperature, and silicon diode to sense temperature being compared. If sensed temperature is lower than reference, output will go positive, and vice-versa. Output drives panel meter.—Two Electronic Thermometers for Medical/Industrial Use, Optical Electronics, Tucson, Ariz., No. 10075.

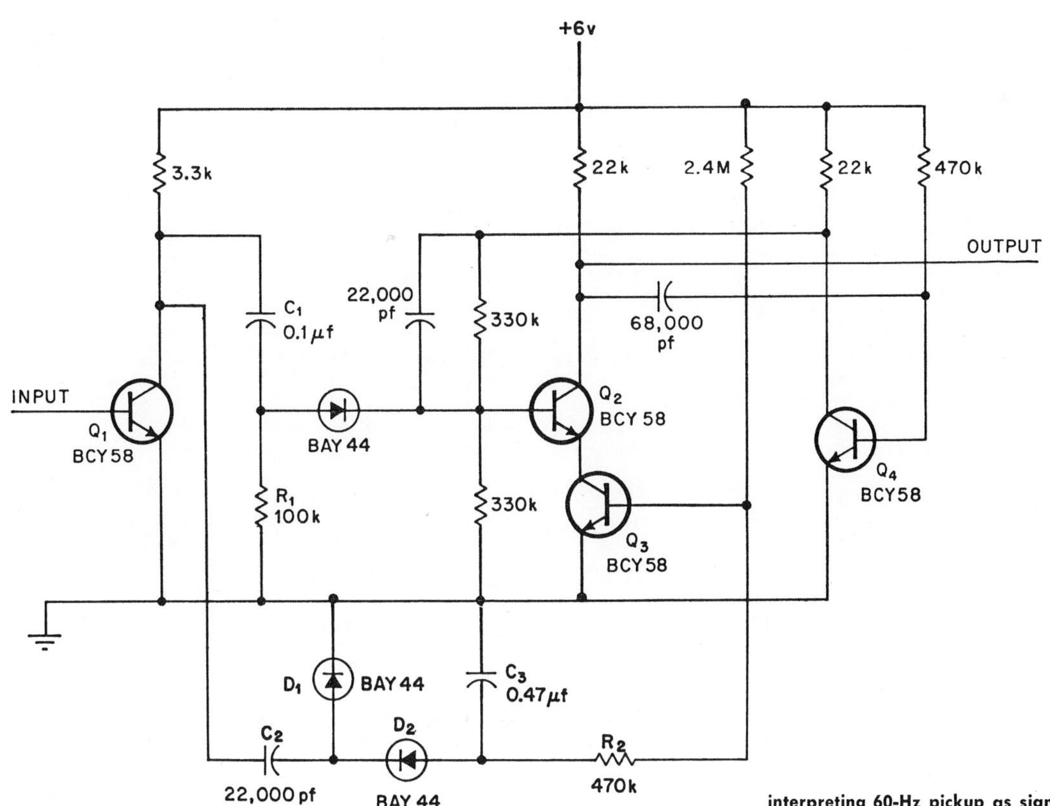

PACEMAKER CONTROL—Prevents false triggering by 60-Hz pickup from faulty system grounding leads, by suppressing input pulses above normal heart limit of 150 beats per minute or 2.5 Hz. Mono Q2-Q4 inhibits cardiac pacemaker when heart is operating on its own. Q3 and associated diode frequency-voltage converter prevent mono from interpreting 60-Hz pickup as sign of heart action and turning off pacemaker when it is actually needed.—V. Bicik, Monostable Protected Against 60-Hertz Pickup, *Electronics*, May 11, 1970, p 101.

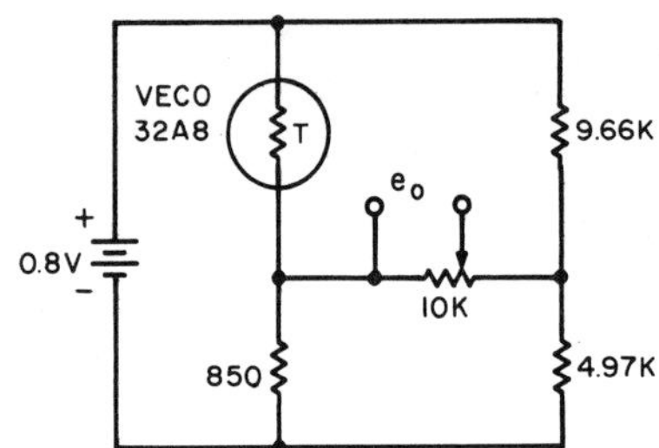

RECTAL TEMPERATURE MONITOR—Catheter-type thermistor probe in Wheatstone bridge circuit covers range of 30–50 C for studying temperature responses of dogs to various physical stimuli. Provides signal for driving standard d-c millivolt recorder. Source is 0.8 V.—M. Sapoff and R. M. Oppenheim, A Blanket Approach to a Linear Thermistor Network, *Electronic Design*, April 12, 1965, p 36 and 38–40.

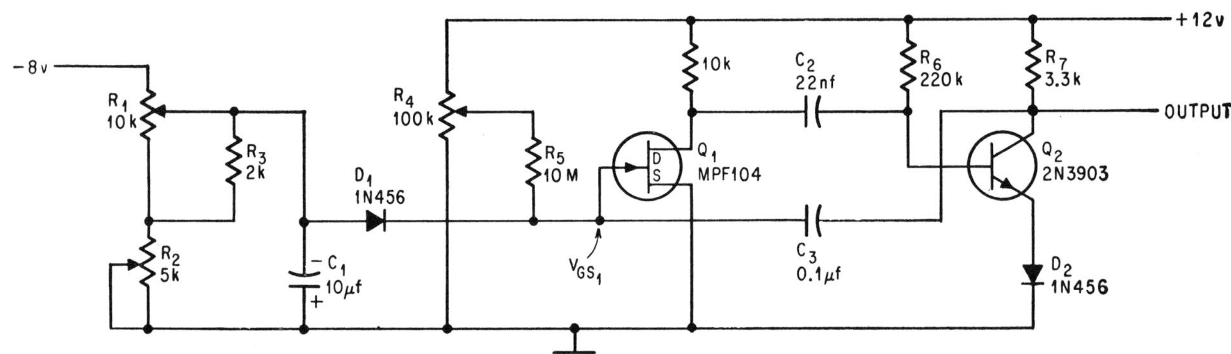

ON-OFF RATIOS FROM 20 TO 300—Developed for biomedical application requiring 3-ms pulses at repetition rates adjustable from 1 to 15 pps. Use of fet Q1 eliminates need for large electrolytics otherwise required for such widely spaced pulses. R1 adjusts prr, R4 establishes lowest frequency, and R2 establishes highest frequency.—E. A. Pfeiffer, Multivibrator Provides Short Pulses, Wide Spacing, *Electronics*, April 3, 1967, p 98–99.

NOTE: To locate additional circuits in the category of this chapter, use the index at the back of this book. Check also the author's "Sourcebook of Electronic Circuits," published by McGraw-Hill in 1968.

CHAPTER 51
Metal Detector Circuits

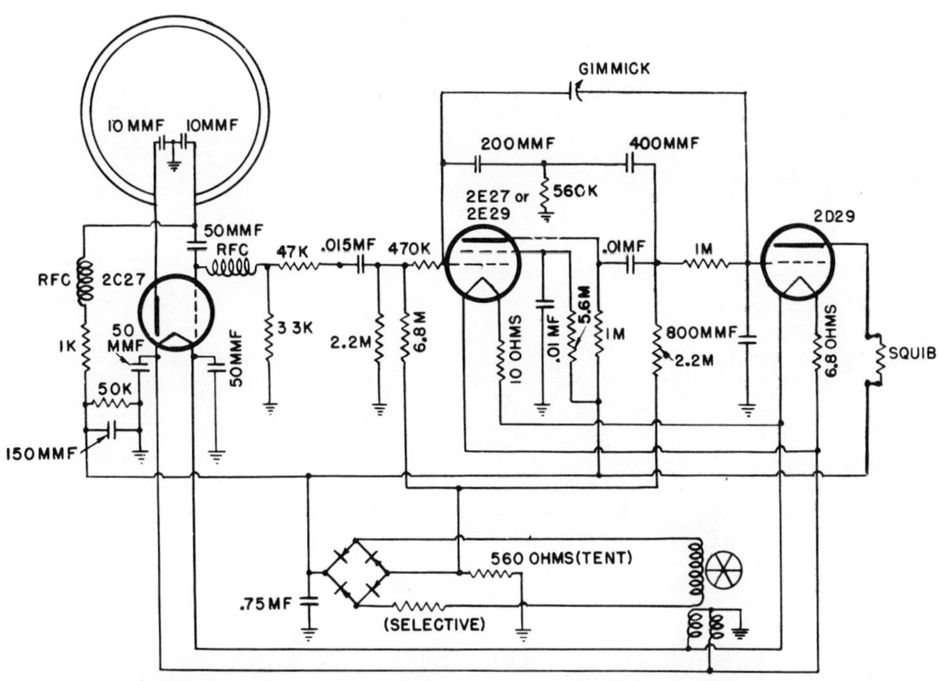

T-172 MORTAR SHELL FUZE—Major innovation in this proximity fuze circuit is loop antenna. Burst height over water was 23 ft. Uses reaction-grid-detector circuit.—A. V. Astin, Editor, "Radio Proximity Fuzes for Fin-Stabilized Missiles," Div. 4, NDRC, Vol. I, 1946 (available from Clearinghouse, Springfield, Va.), p 244.

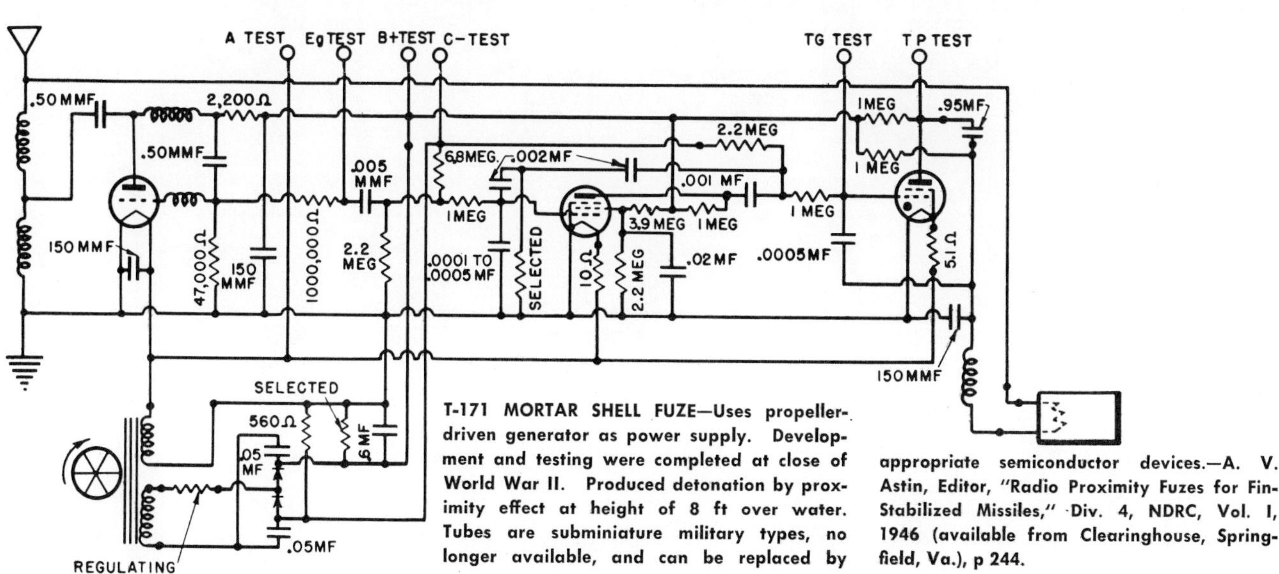

T-171 MORTAR SHELL FUZE—Uses propeller-driven generator as power supply. Development and testing were completed at close of World War II. Produced detonation by proximity effect at height of 8 ft over water. Tubes are subminiature military types, no longer available, and can be replaced by appropriate semiconductor devices.—A. V. Astin, Editor, "Radio Proximity Fuzes for Fin-Stabilized Missiles," Div. 4, NDRC, Vol. I, 1946 (available from Clearinghouse, Springfield, Va.), p 244.

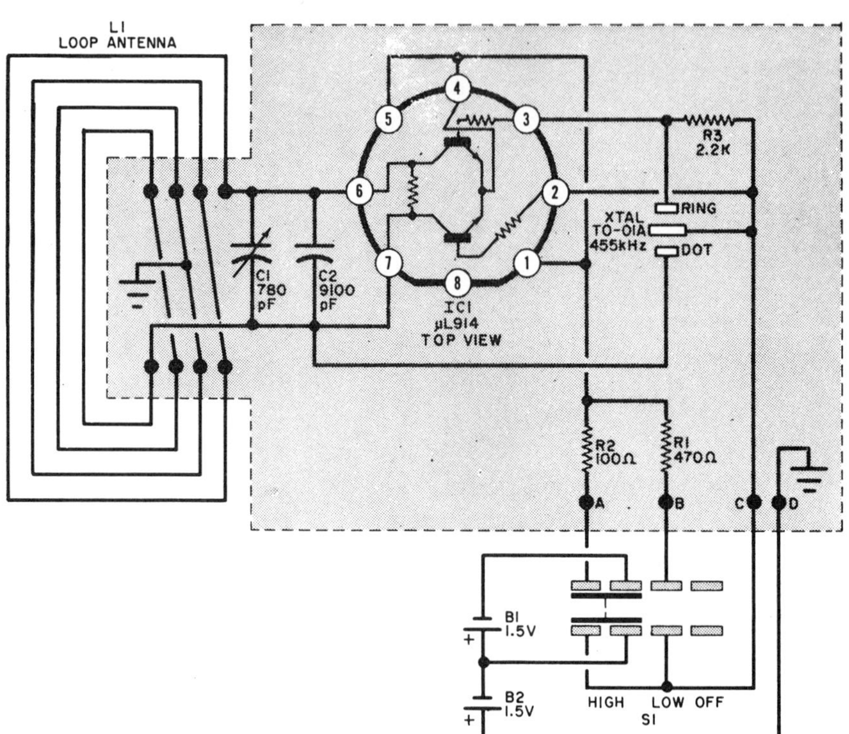

TRANSMITTER FOR IC METAL LOCATOR—Will locate pipes and valves buried as deep as 7 ft, and smaller objects at lesser depths if larger than coffee cans. Not intended for locating coins. Transmitter is 455-kHz IC oscillator controlled by ceramic Transfilter (XTAL), with single turn of four-conductor flat cable forming 9 x 11-inch loop, mounted at one end of 50-inch wood carrying rod. Receiver at other end of rod has similar loop feeding high-gain three-IC trf circuit tuned to 455 kHz, with loop oriented for null. Article gives construction details and sources for required parts.—D. Lancaster, Build IC-67 Metal Locator, *Popular Electronics*, Jan. 1967, p 41–48, 94, 96, 98, and 99.

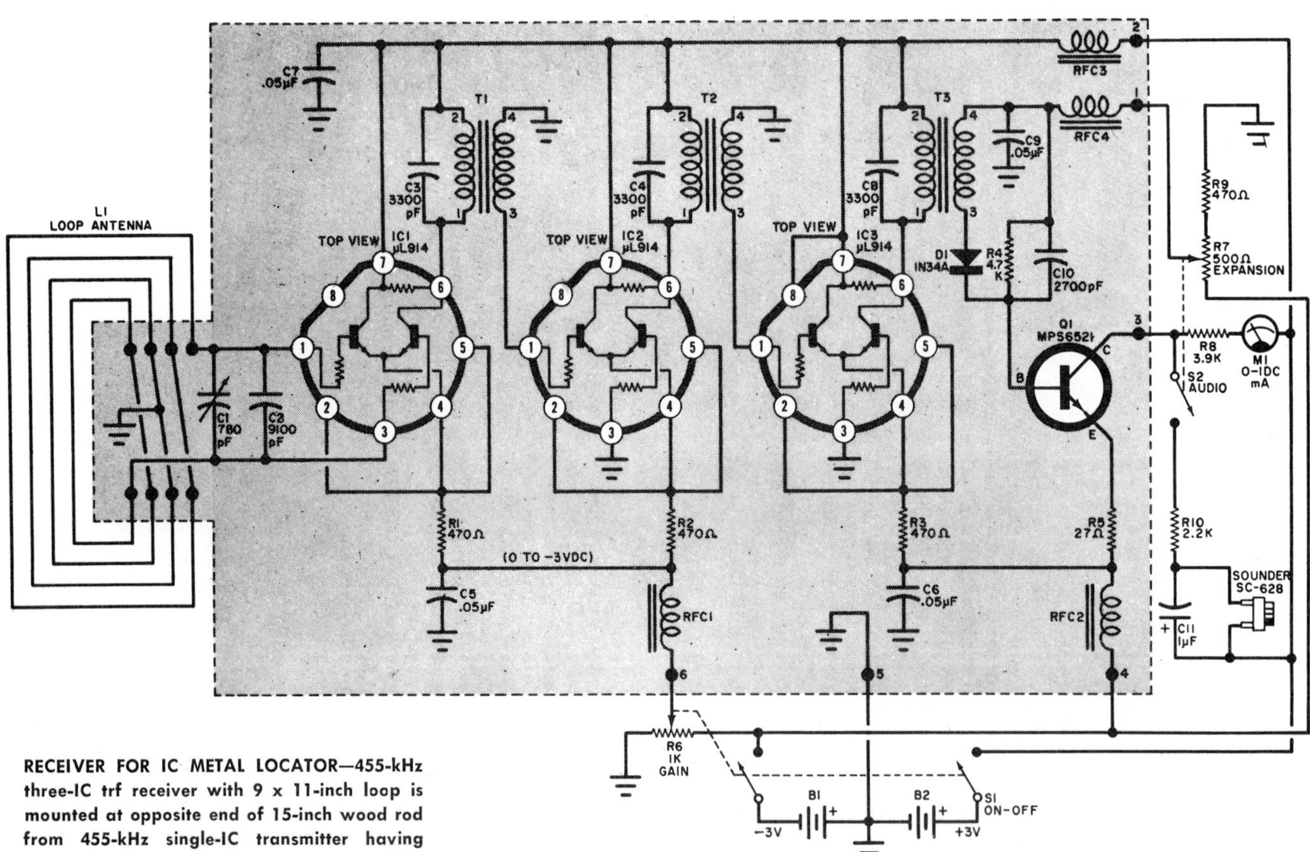

RECEIVER FOR IC METAL LOCATOR—455-kHz three-IC trf receiver with 9 x 11-inch loop is mounted at opposite end of 15-inch wood rod from 455-kHz single-IC transmitter having similar loop oriented for null. Provides both meter and audible indication for large buried metal objects. Article gives construction details and sources for required parts.—D. Lancaster, Build IC-67 Metal Locator, *Popular Electronics*, Jan. 1967, p 41–48, 94, 96, 98, and 99.

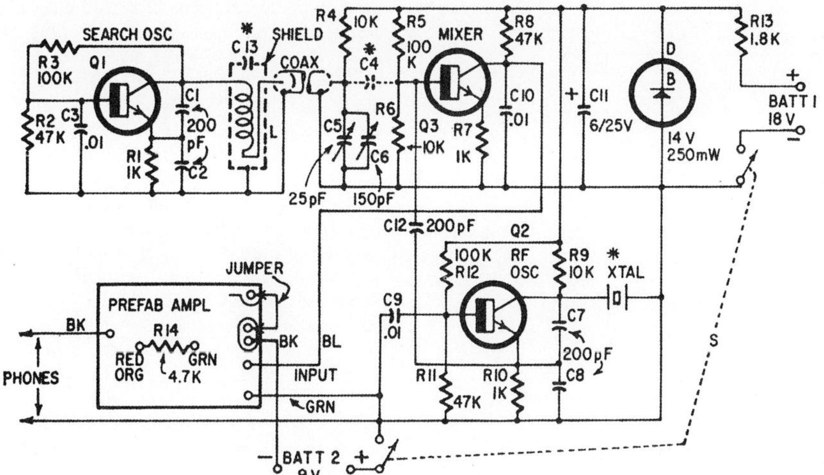

COIN-FINDER—Will detect dimes 4 inches from loop and gold or silver rings up to 5 inches away in dry or slightly damp ground. Uses 2,100-kHz surplus military crystal, but 160-meter amateur crystal will work if coil turns are adjusted. Search coil L is 8 turns of No. 24 plastic-covered hookup wire threaded through 3/8th-inch copper tubing bent into split ring 10½ inches in diameter. Article gives construction details. Transistors are npn with minimum beta of 30 and alpha cutoff above 3 MHz, such as 2N334, 2N1090, or 2N2926. IC audio amplifier is Lafayette 99R9039 or equivalent. Audio beat note in phone changes in frequency when search coil is near metal.—G. H. Gill, Summer Fun With a Sensitive Metal-Finder, *Radio-Electronics*, July 1966, p 55–57.

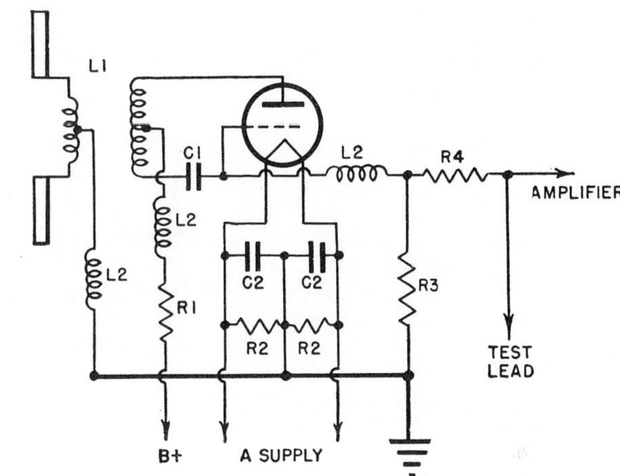

VT BOMB FUZE DETECTOR—Reaction-grid-detector circuit shown was used in M-166 bar-type bomb fuzes to initiate detonation at 50 to 100 feet above ground when dropped from aircraft. Antenna is nose of fuze. Coil values are adjusted to obtain required frequency and sensitivity. Values are: R1 1K; R2 3; R3 33K; R4 47K; C1 25 pF; C2 50 pF; Triode NR3A. Oscillator and antenna coils for L1 are wound on same core. L2 is r-f choke.—A. V. Astin, Editor, "Radio Proximity Fuzes for Fin-Stabilized Missiles," Div. 4, NDRC, Vol. I, 1946 (available from Clearinghouse, Springfield, Va.), p 225–226.

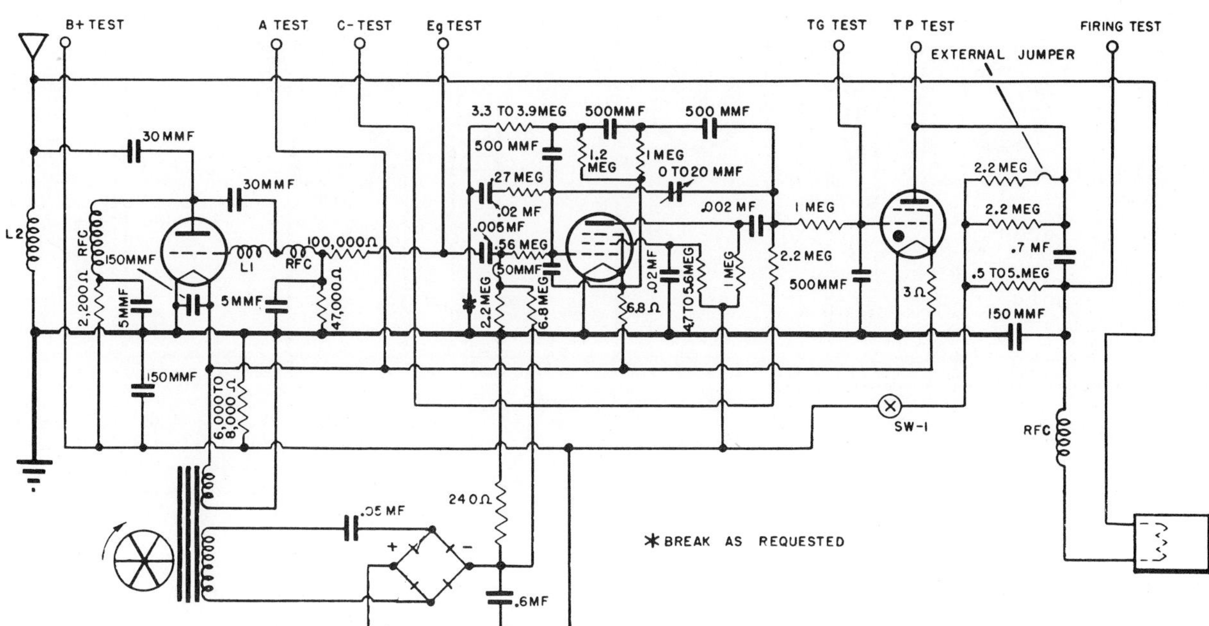

VT ROCKET FUZE—Developed just before end of World War II, as T-2005 rocket fuze. Intended for shipboard defense against attacking enemy aircraft. Fuze initiated detonation automatically when missile was within kill distance of aircraft. Tubes are subminiature military types, no longer available; modern versions undoubtedly use semiconductor devices.—A. V. Astin, Editor, "Radio Proximity Fuzes for Fin-Stabilized Missiles," Div. 4, NDRC, Vol. I, 1946 (available from Clearinghouse, Springfield, Va.), p 241–242.

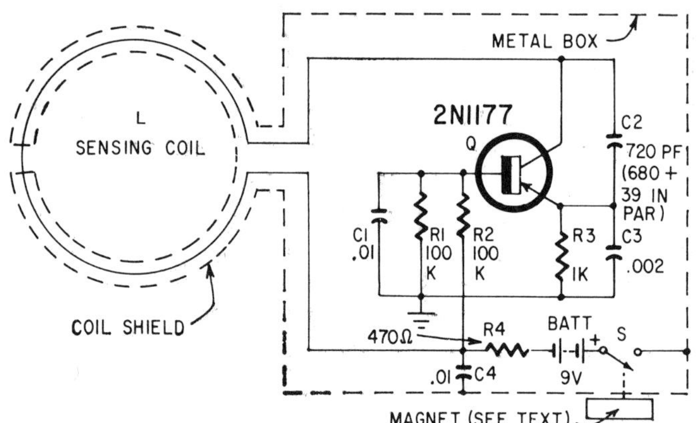

WATERPROOF ANCHOR-FINDER—Solder-sealed single-transistor transmitter suspended from boat is used with ordinary transistor radio in boat for locating lost outboard motors, anchors, or other relatively large metal objects under water. Beat-frequency oscillator should be added to radio, or coupling should be introduced between two i-f stages to make oscillating i-f serving same purpose. Transmitter operates at about 600 kHz. In depths greater than 30 ft, connect insulated antenna wire to receiver and run it parallel with transmitter suspension rope. Article gives construction details for search coil which is 4 turns of insulated wire threaded through 23-inch-diameter split ring of ½-inch copper tubing. Permanent magnet outside housing holds improvised magnetic-blade switch open; remove magnet to turn on transmitter.—O. Klippberg, Underwater Metal Hunting for Fun or Profit, *Radio-Electronics*, June 1966, p 38–39.

AUDIO-MODULATED 180-KHZ TRANSMITTER—Ujt relaxation oscillator Q2 produces low-frequency audio tone for modulating transistor r-f oscillator Q1 which radiates search signal from L1 (34 turns No. 22 enamel wound around 6.8 x 5.3-inch plastic case of transmitter). Receiver is mounted at other end of 30-inch support rod, with its loop at right angles to that of transmitter. Operating frequency is around 180 kHz. Intended for locating buried objects larger than pie pans, such as metal pails filled with gold coins. Article gives construction details.—C. D. Rakes, Treasure Witcher, *Science & Electronics*, April/May 1970, p 39–44 and 80.

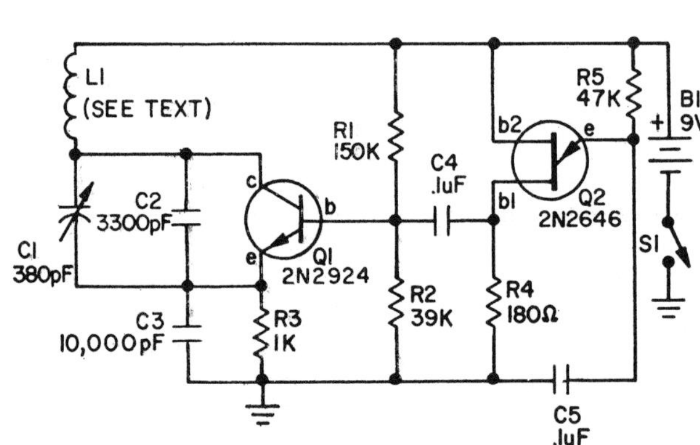

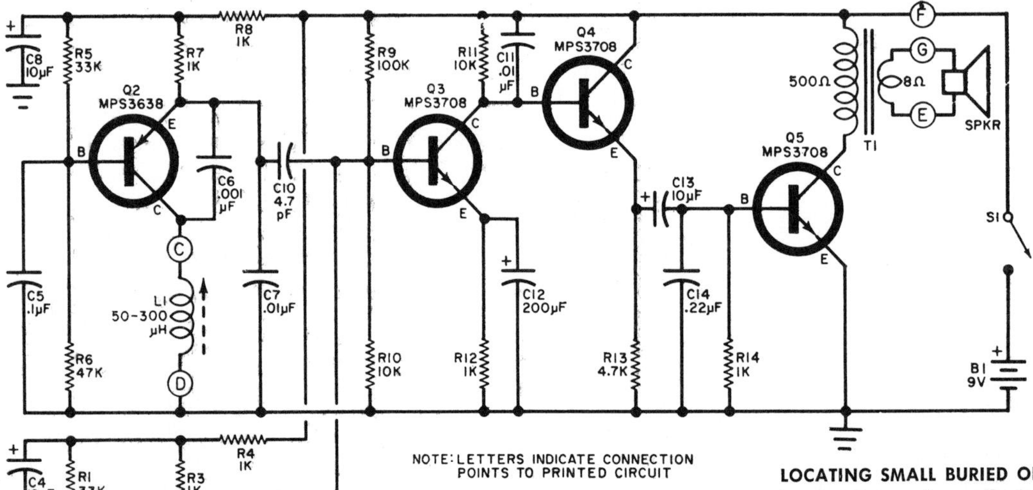

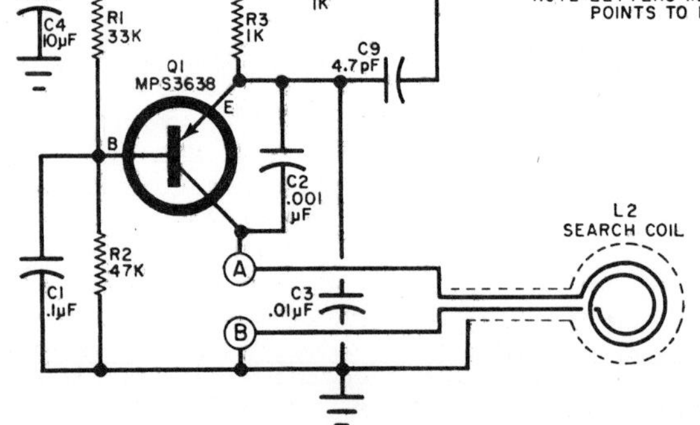

NOTE: LETTERS INDICATE CONNECTION POINTS TO PRINTED CIRCUIT

LOCATING SMALL BURIED OBJECTS—Designed for locating such small objects as coins or rings on beaches and bullets on old battlefields if not more than a few inches deep. Maximum detection depth for larger objects is about 2 ft. Uses single-loop circuit with two r-f oscillators, operating in range of 400 to 500 kHz, with detector and audio amplifier. Audio beat note from speaker changes in tone when search coil is near metal. Article gives construction and adjustment details.—D. Meyer, Build the "Beachcomber," *Popular Electronics*, July 1967, p 27–32 and 84.

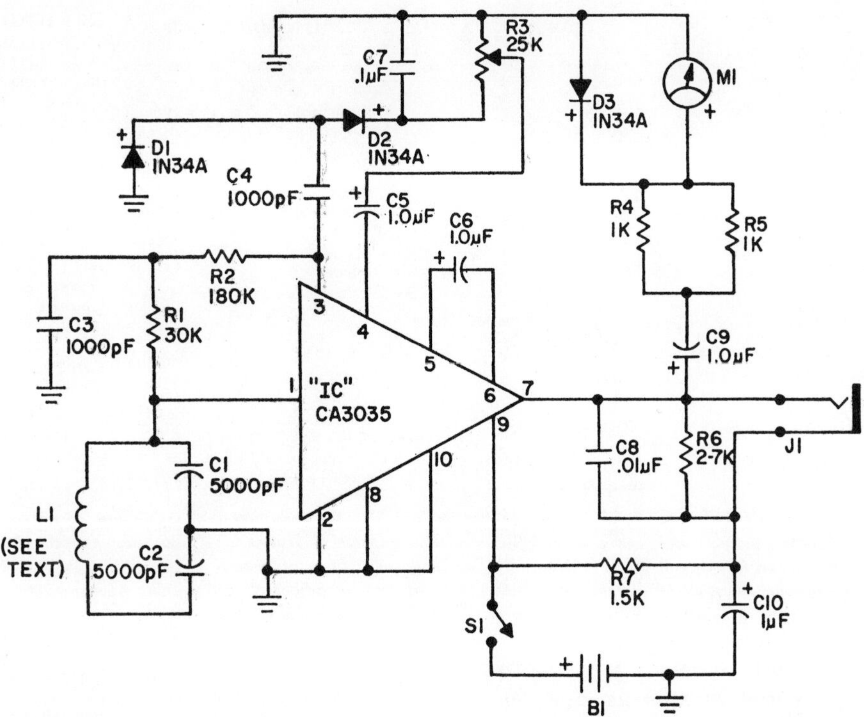

180-KHZ RECEIVER—Single IC is equivalent of three transistors in providing gain of 129 dB for amplifying tone-modulated signal picked up from transmitter at other end of 30-inch support rod when in presence of metal. Diode D2 demodulates signal after first IC stage, and other two IC stages amplify resulting audio tone sufficiently to drive 2,000-ohm headphones and indicating meter. Pickup loop L1 has 34 turns of No. 22 enamel wound around plastic case of receiver. Use 9-V battery such as Eveready 216BP. Meter is 500-μA d-c. Article gives construction details.—C. D. Rakes, Treasure Witcher, *Science & Electronics*, April/May 1970, p 39–44 and 80.

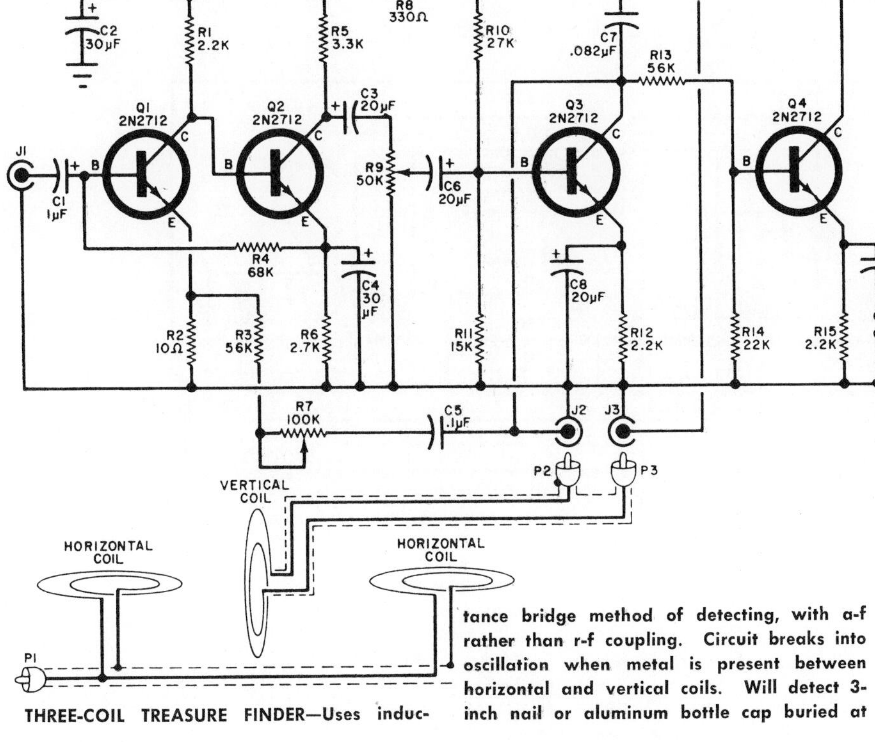

THREE-COIL TREASURE FINDER—Uses inductance bridge method of detecting, with a-f rather than r-f coupling. Circuit breaks into oscillation when metal is present between horizontal and vertical coils. Will detect 3-inch nail or aluminum bottle cap buried at depth of 2 inches, or garbage-can lid at 2½ ft. Has maximum sensitivity for iron objects. Each horizontal coil has 470 turns of No. 32 wire on 1½ x 3 inch form, and vertical coil has 870 turns on 1½ x 2¾ inch form. Article gives construction details. Tone in headphones has maximum volume when hidden metal is midway between vertical coil and either horizontal coil. Oscillators Q1 and Q3 are about 2 kHz.—L. Huggard, Build a "Different" Metal Locator, *Popular Electronics*, Feb. 1969, p 53–58.

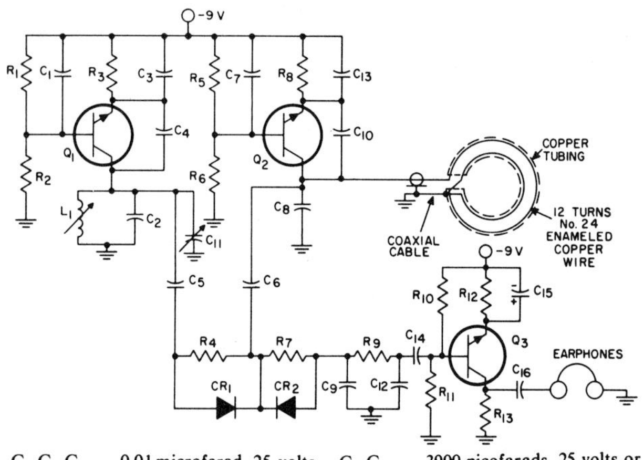

C_1 C_7 C_{14} = 0.01 microfarad, 25 volts or greater

C_2 = 1800 picofarads, 25 volts or greater

C_3 C_{13} = 3900 picofarads, 25 volts or greater

C_4 C_9 C_{10} = 0.001 microfarad, 25 volts or greater

C_5 C_6 = 0.004 microfarad, 25 volts or greater

C_8 = 680 microfarads, 25 volts or greater

C_{11} = 20 picofarads, variable type, Hammarlund No. MAC-20 or equivalent

C_{12} = 0.02 microfarad, 25 volts or greater

C_{15} = 50 microfarads, 6 volts, electrolytic

C_{16} = 0.1 microfarad, 25 volts or greater

CR_1 CR_2 = silicon rectifier, type 1N34A

R_1R_5 = 22,000 ohms, 1/2 watt, 10%

R_2R_6 = 47000 ohms, 1/2 watt, 10%

R_3R_8 = 2200 ohms, 1/2 watt, 10%

R_4 R_7 = 1 megohm, 1/2 watt, 10%

$_9$ = 68,000 ohms, 1/2 watt, 10%

R_{10} = 10,000 ohms, 1/2 watt, 10%

R_{11} = 91,000 ohms, 1/2 watt, 10%

R_{12} = 680 ohms, 1/2 watt, 10%

R_{13} = 6800 ohms, 1/2 watt, 10%

$Q_1Q_2Q_3$ = transistor, RCA SK3020

L_1 = 50 to 140 microhonries, adjustable

Copper tubing: 1/4-inch diameter, 3.14 feet (enough for loop of 1-foot diameter)

No. 24 enameled copper wire: about 40 feet (enough for 12 turns of 1-foot diameter and connections)

Coaxial cable: about 3 feet (exact amount depends on length of handle)

Earphones = 200 ohms

METAL DETECTOR—Can be used to locate buried treasure, underground pipes, and other buried metal objects. When search coil is near object, tone in earphone changes or cuts off completely. Uses two oscillators; Q1 is approximately 300 kHz as determined by L1 and C2, and Q2 operates at frequency determined by C11 and inductance of search coil and objects near it. L1 is adjusted for tone in phones, and C11 then adjusted for maximum sensitivity as indicated by motorboating sound. Book gives complete construction details.—"Hobby Circuits Manual," RCA, Harrison, N.J., HM-90, p 138.

FINDING HIDDEN BRASS NAILS—Oscillating detector frequency changes about 1 kHz when nonmagnetic screw or nail is in magnetic field near gap in cut toroid. Used to detect concealed fasteners that could wreck saw blades or tear sandpaper during refitting of wood deck or bulkhead of ship. Coil is in tank circuit of Colpitts oscillator, clamped to laminated copper plate acting as electrostatic shield. Change in oscillator frequency changes beat frequency output of receiver mixer, producing change in audio output.—D. B. Hoisington, Oscillator as Detector, *Electronics*, March 18, 1968, p 95.

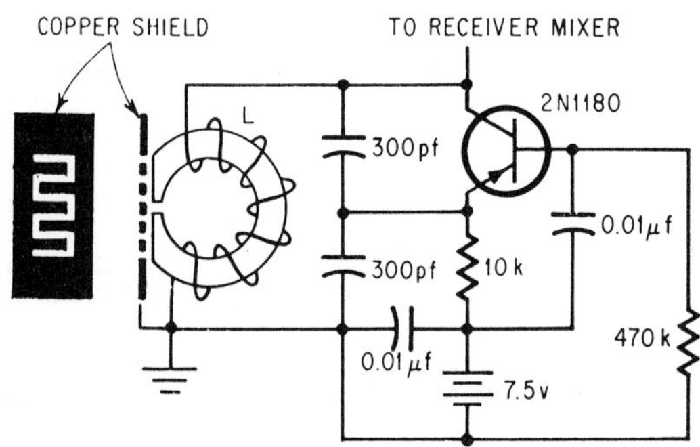

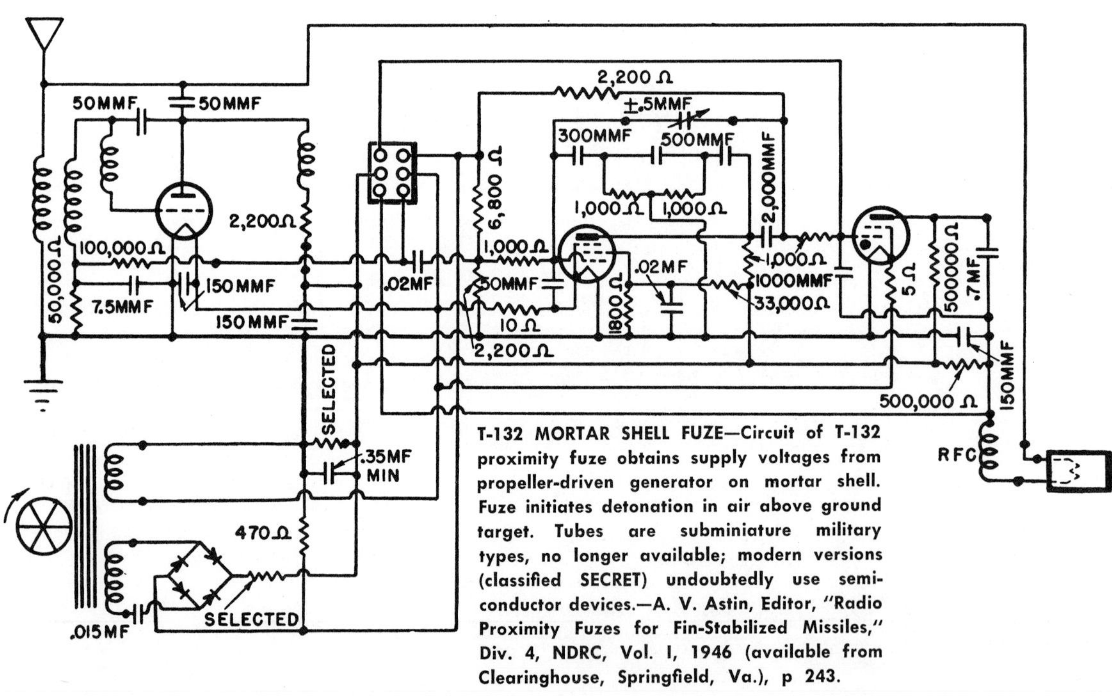

T-132 MORTAR SHELL FUZE—Circuit of T-132 proximity fuze obtains supply voltages from propeller-driven generator on mortar shell. Fuze initiates detonation in air above ground target. Tubes are subminiature military types, no longer available; modern versions (classified SECRET) undoubtedly use semiconductor devices.—A. V. Astin, Editor, "Radio Proximity Fuzes for Fin-Stabilized Missiles," Div. 4, NDRC, Vol. I, 1946 (available from Clearinghouse, Springfield, Va.), p 243.

IC BURIED-METAL DETECTOR—Consists of single-transistor transmitter using 2N2646 ujt as oscillator driving scr, to feed highly directional 4 by 6-inch loop L1 wound around transmitter housing. Receiving loop of same size is similarly wound around receiver using Westinghouse WC183T IC and GE-5 transistor Q2. Transmitter and receiver are mounted at opposite ends of 3-foot wood rod held horizontally several feet above ground while walking over area being searched. When loops are properly oriented at right angles to each other, with no metal in vicinity, nothing is heard in phones. Metal object within range gives 175-Hz tone in phones and unusual deflection of 1-mA d-c meter. Book gives construction and adjustment data. Values are: R1 15K; R2 220; R3 22; R4 470; R5, R6 270; R7 5K; R8 47K; R9 330K; R10 1.8K; C1 0.3 μF; C2 1 μF; C3, C5, C6 0.001 μF; C4 2,000 pF; C7, C10 0.003 μF; C8, C9, C11 10 μF; B1, B2 9 V, B3 4.5 V; D1, D2, D3 1N38B; D4 2N3228 scr; L1 74 turns #27 tapped two turns from end; L2 68 turns.—R. M. Brown, "Electronic Hobbyist's IC Projects Handbook," TAB Books, Blue Ridge Summit, Pa., 1968, p 116.

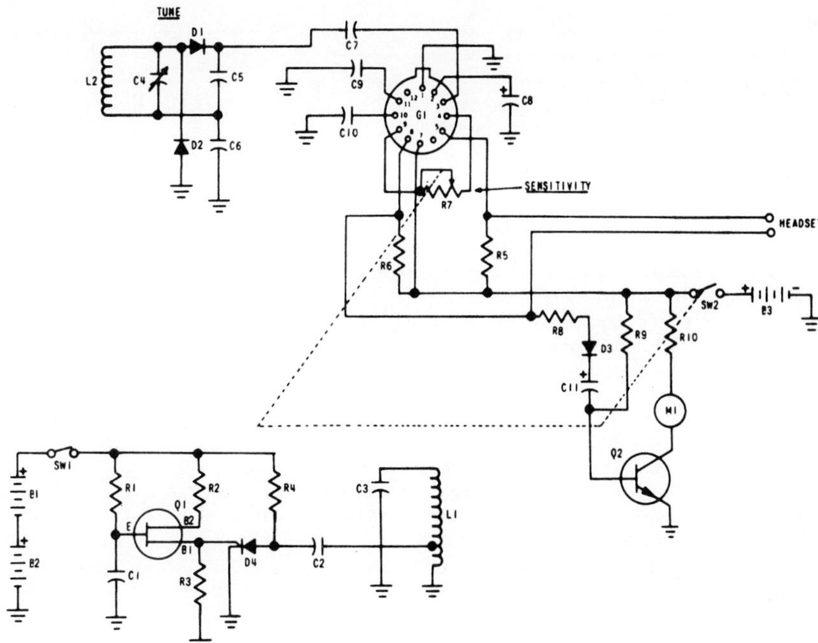

REACTION-GRID DETECTOR IN FUZE—Used in M-168 and T-92-E1 bomb fuzes to initiate detonation about 50 feet above ground or water. Antenna is nose of fuze. Values are: R1 100K; R2 47K; R3 2.2K; C1 5 pF; C2, C3 30 pF; C4 5 pF; C6, C22 150 pF; triode NR3A.—A. V. Astin, Editor, "Radio Proximity Fuzes for Fin-Stabilized Missiles," Div. 4, NDRC, Vol. I, 1946 (available from Clearinghouse, Springfield, Va.), p 225.

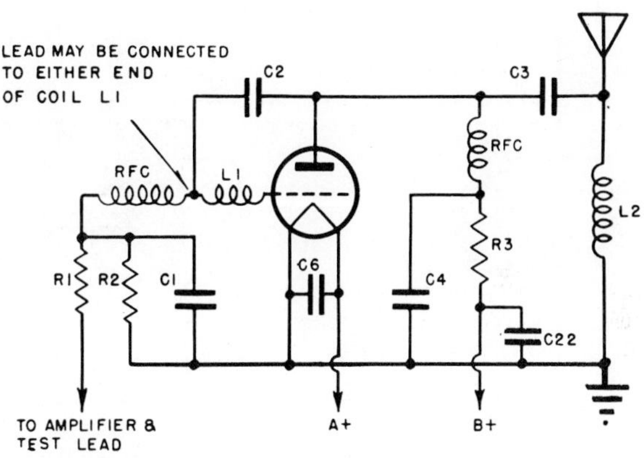

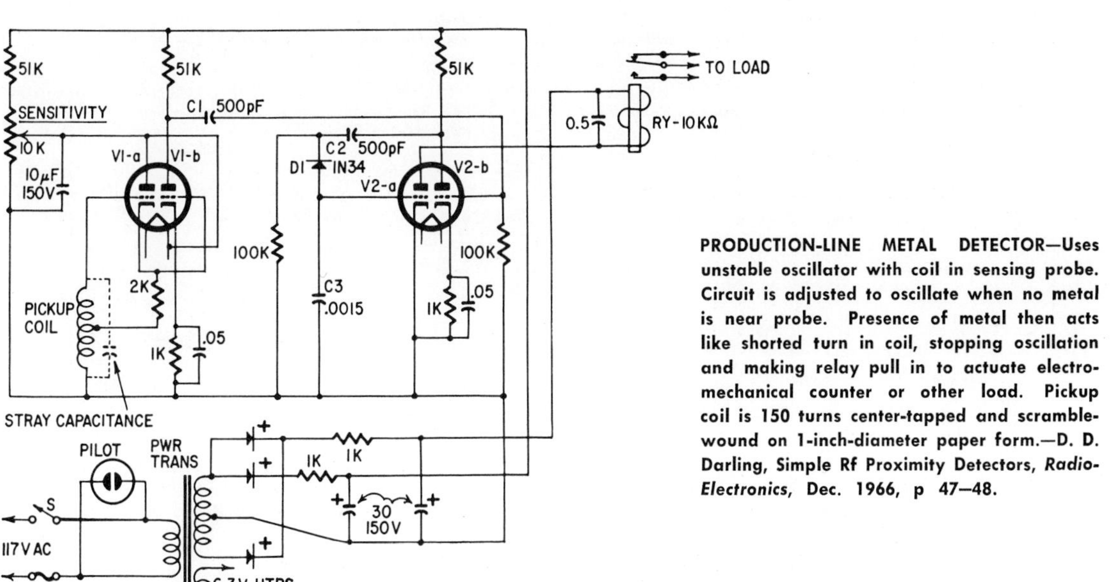

PRODUCTION-LINE METAL DETECTOR—Uses unstable oscillator with coil in sensing probe. Circuit is adjusted to oscillate when no metal is near probe. Presence of metal then acts like shorted turn in coil, stopping oscillation and making relay pull in to actuate electromechanical counter or other load. Pickup coil is 150 turns center-tapped and scramble-wound on 1-inch-diameter paper form.—D. D. Darling, Simple Rf Proximity Detectors, *Radio-Electronics*, Dec. 1966, p 47–48.

METAL DETECTOR—Will detect any metal. Nonmagnetic materials increase circuit losses of sensing inductor, thus reducing its inductance, whereas ferromagnetic materials reduce reluctance of magnetic circuits and thereby increase inductance. Can be used for locating metal, such as nails and shell particles, embedded in wood to be worked with machine tools, locating iron rods in reinforced concrete, locating pipes and wiring in walls, locating metal objects in cows before surgery, locating bullets at scene of murder, and tracing buried pipes. L1 and L2 are 550 turns of 0.2-mm enameled copper wound on ferroxcube type 4B rods 10 mm in diameter and 10 cm long. Transformer T has 180-turn primary and 200-turn c-t secondary of same wire wound on type 22/12-4C4 pot core without air gap. Frequency of oscillator TR1 is about 3 kHz. Article gives construction, alignment, and operating instructions.—J. F. van Oort, Brief Items of Interest, *Electronic Applications*, Philips, Pub. Dept., Elcoma Div., Eindhoven, The Netherlands, Vol. 25, No. 3, 1964–1965, p 123–128.

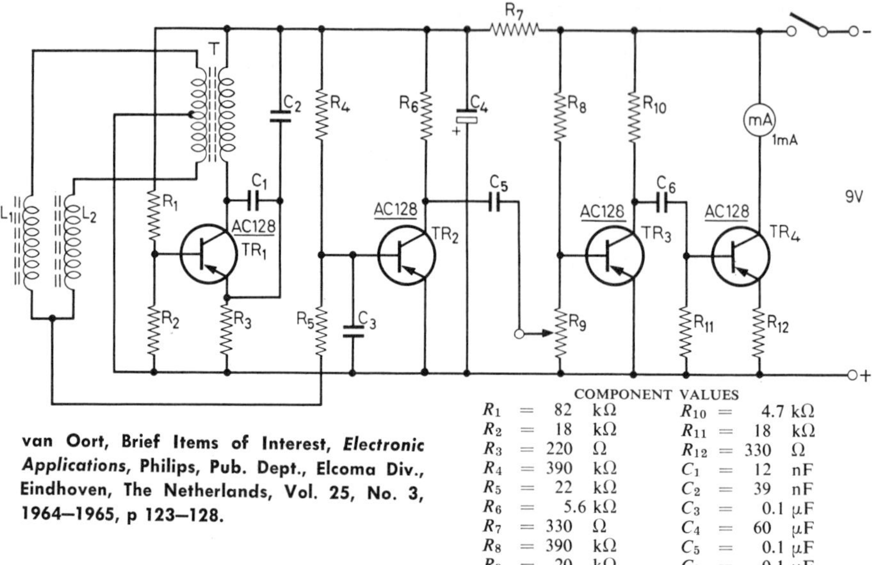

COMPONENT VALUES

R_1 = 82 kΩ		R_{10} = 4.7 kΩ	
R_2 = 18 kΩ		R_{11} = 18 kΩ	
R_3 = 220 Ω		R_{12} = 330 Ω	
R_4 = 390 kΩ		C_1 = 12 nF	
R_5 = 22 kΩ		C_2 = 39 nF	
R_6 = 5.6 kΩ		C_3 = 0.1 μF	
R_7 = 330 Ω		C_4 = 60 μF	
R_8 = 390 kΩ		C_5 = 0.1 μF	
R_9 = 20 kΩ		C_6 = 0.1 μF	

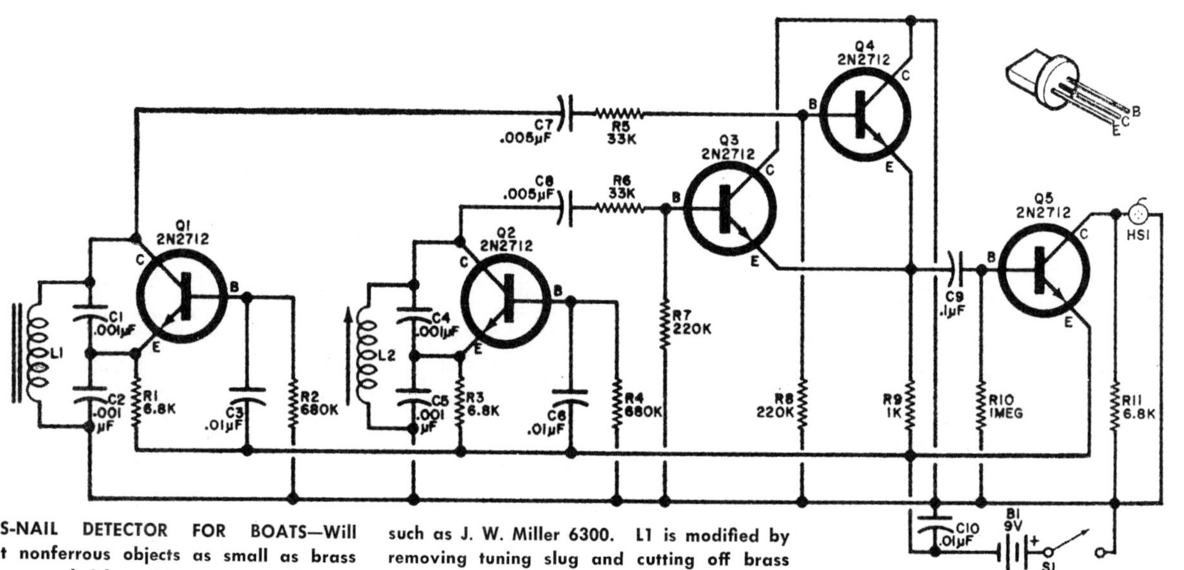

BRASS-NAIL DETECTOR FOR BOATS—Will detect nonferrous objects as small as brass brads concealed by paint, to prevent damage to sanders or power saws when working on boats. Will also detect magnetic objects, although maximum range is about 2 inches. L1 and L2 are high-Q ferrite antenna coils, such as J. W. Miller 6300. L1 is modified by removing tuning slug and cutting off brass tuning screw flush with core. Article gives other modifications required, along with construction details and sources for parts. Q1 and Q2 are audio oscillators that beat to produce audio tone in high-impedance earphone HSI which changes when L1 is near metal.—J. S. Simonton, Jr., Carpenter's Mate—Tiny Metal Locator for Tiny Metal, *Popular Electronics*, Sept. 1969, p 69–72.

NOTE: To locate additional circuits in the category of this chapter, use the index at the back of this book. Check also the author's "Sourcebook of Electronic Circuits," published by McGraw-Hill in 1968.

CHAPTER 52
Modulator Circuits

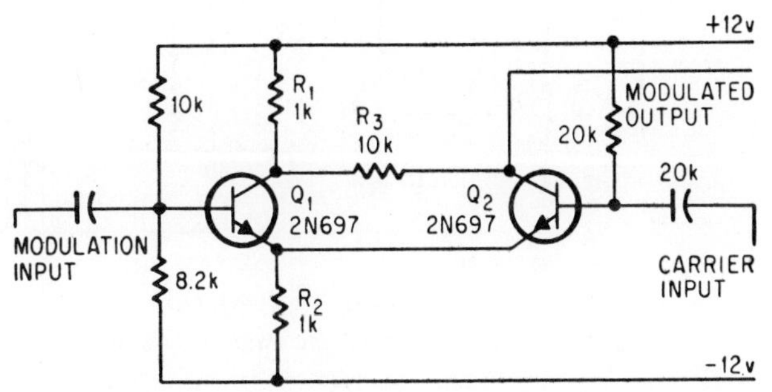

SUBAUDIO ON 2-KHZ SUBCARRIER—Requires only two transistors in simple differential amplifier circuit. Article also gives modification for amplitude modulation at radio frequencies.—A. Pichard, 100% Amplitude Modulation With Two Transistors, *Electronics*, June 12, 1967, p 104–105.

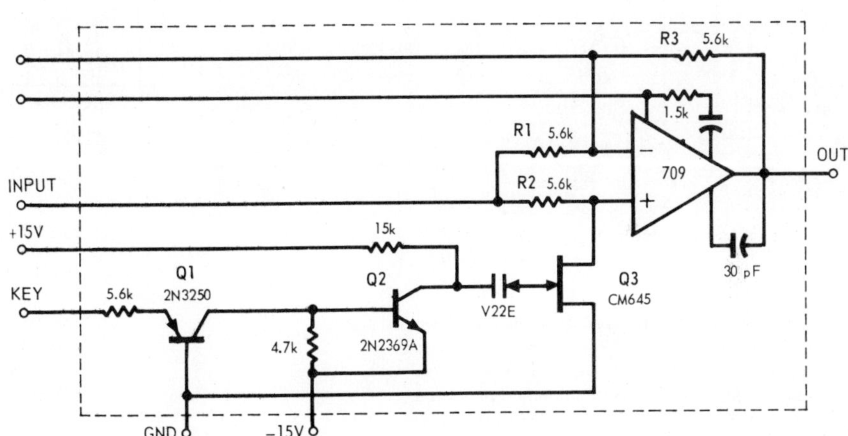

FULL-WAVE PHASE-SENSITIVE—Analog switch Q1-Q3 is controlled by key or reference signal, usually 0 to +3 V logic. With analog switch closed (key at 0 V), amplifier gain is −1. With switch open, gain is 0. May also be used as square-wave modulator. Frequency range is d-c to 500 kHz. Output voltage range is −9 V to +9 V.—F. L. Schmid, Full-Wave Phase-Sensitive Demodulator, *EDN*, Sept. 1, 1969, p 73.

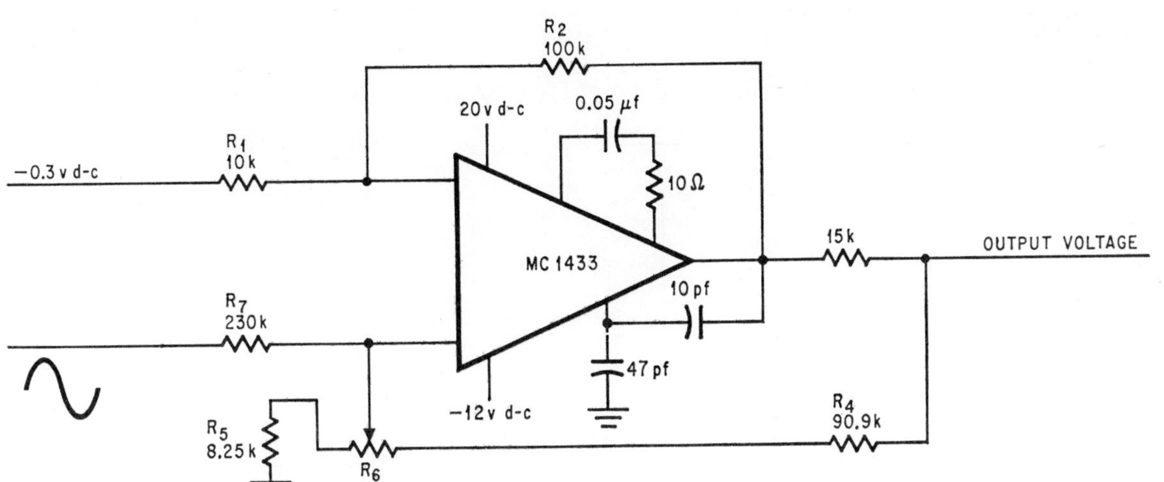

A-M WITHOUT CARRIER SUPPRESSION—IC opamp delivers modulating output that varies around d-c level, for amplitude modulation without carrier suppression in double balanced mixer. D-c input at upper left changes level along with a-c signal fed to noninverting input of IC.—K. Hanneman, Modulating Current Supplied by Op Amp, *Electronics*, Aug. 5, 1968, p 107.

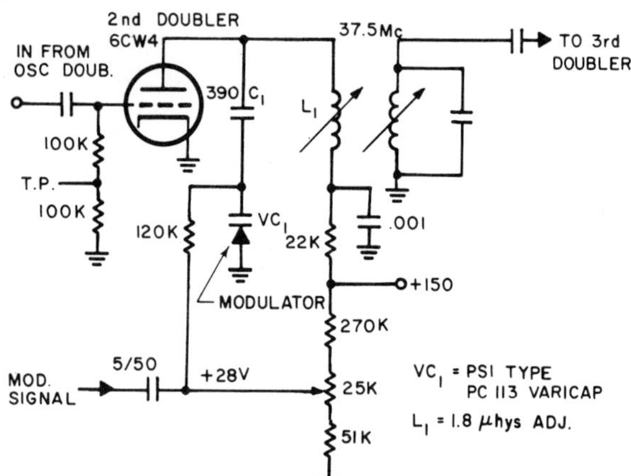

VARACTOR PHASE MODULATOR—Input of 7 V p-p produces 1 radian of phase modulation at 150 MHz from oscillator-doubler of crystal-controlled vhf signal generator.—G. Costa, VHF Signal Uses Varactor for Phase Modulation, *Electronic Design*, Oct. 26, 1964, p 58–59.

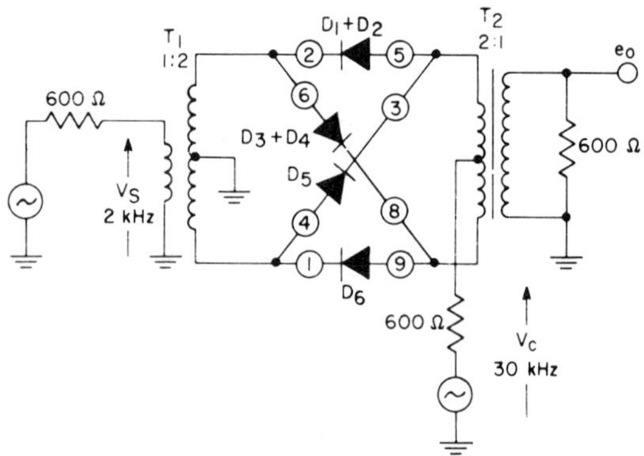

RING MODULATOR—Uses four diodes from CA3019 diode array for suppressing both carrier frequency and signal frequency, so output theoretically contains only upper and lower sidebands. For single-sideband transmission, one sideband can be eliminated by selective filtering.—"Linear Integrated Circuits," RCA, Harrison, N.J., IC-41, p 306.

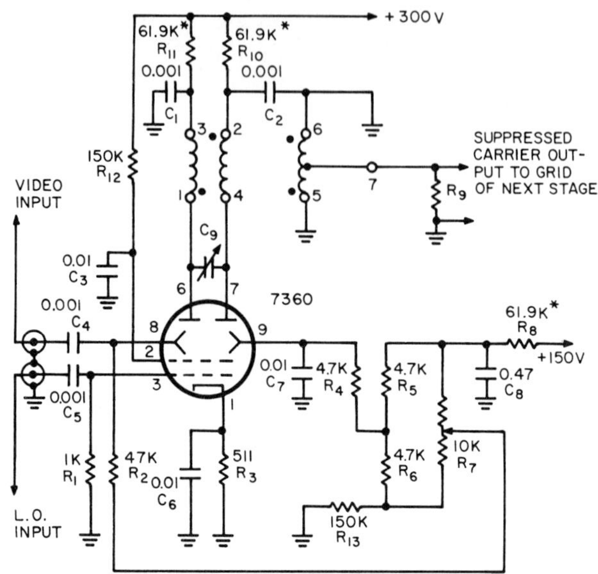

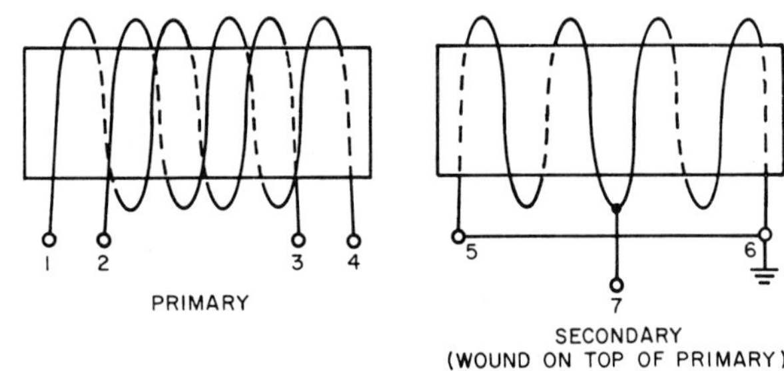

54-DB CARRIER SUPPRESSION—Special transformer simplifies nulling of carrier in balanced modulator using 7360 beam deflection tube. Transformer consists of bifilar primary, wound first and lacquered in position, and split secondary wound on top of primary.—J. L. Christensen and D. Johnson, Balanced Modulator Transformer Increases Carrier Suppression, *Electronic Design*, Jan. 18, 1969, p 46–47.

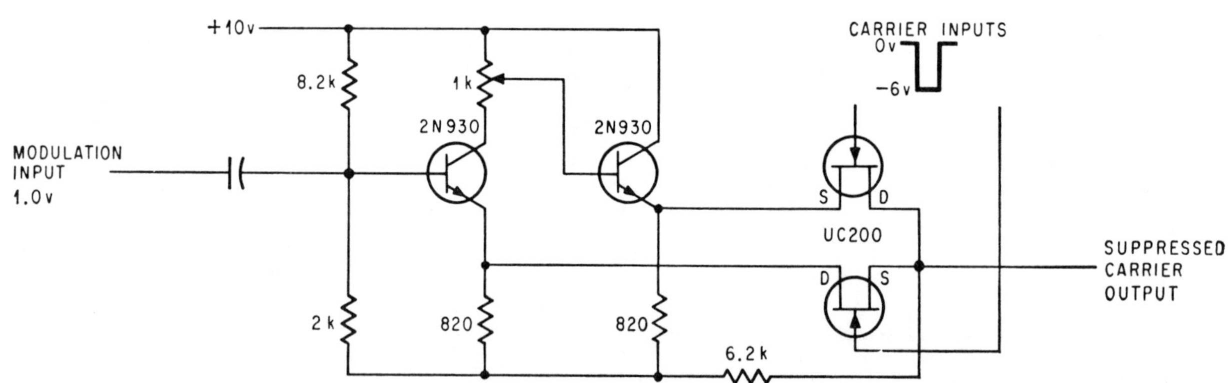

SWITCHED-FET SUPPRESSED-CARRIER—At 100 kHz modulated with 5 kHz, carrier signal rejection is 50 dB and modulation signal rejection 60 dB. Requires no transformers or complex balancing techniques. Modulating signal must be maintained below 1 V peak-to-peak. —C. H. McDermott, Suppressed Carrier Modulator With Noncritical Components, *Electronics*, Oct. 31, 1966, p 70.

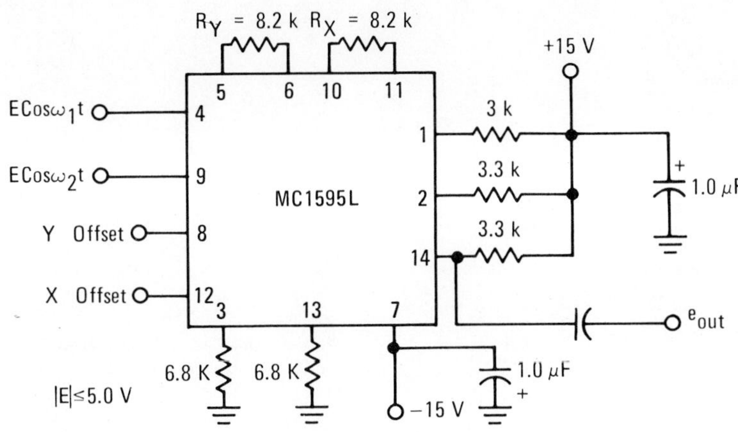

BALANCED MODULATOR—Uses IC linear multiplier as suppressed-carrier modulator, with 1.6-kHz audio tone on 40-kHz carrier as one application.—E. Renschler, The Monolithic Multiplier Breakthrough, "State-of-the-Art—Linears in Action," Motorola, Phoenix, Ariz., 1969, p 27–36.

40-KHZ BALANCED MODULATOR—Motorola monolithic multiplier serves as balanced modulator for 1.6-kHz input signal. Article tells how to design external circuits to handle maximum input voltage swing without introducing nonlinearity.—E. Renschler and D. Weiss, Try the Monolithic Multiplier as a Versatile A-C Design Tool, *Electronics*, June 8, 1970, p 100–105.

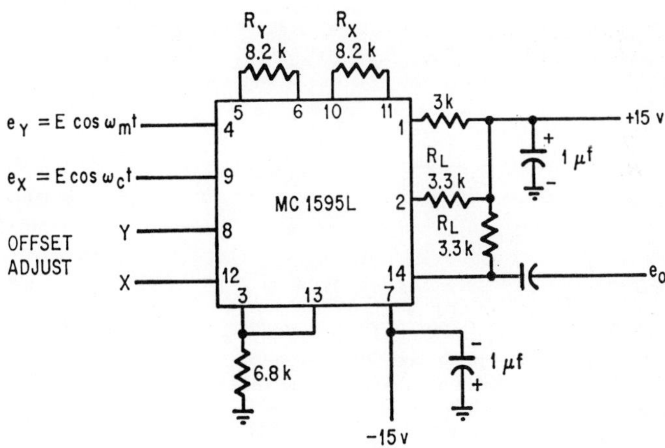

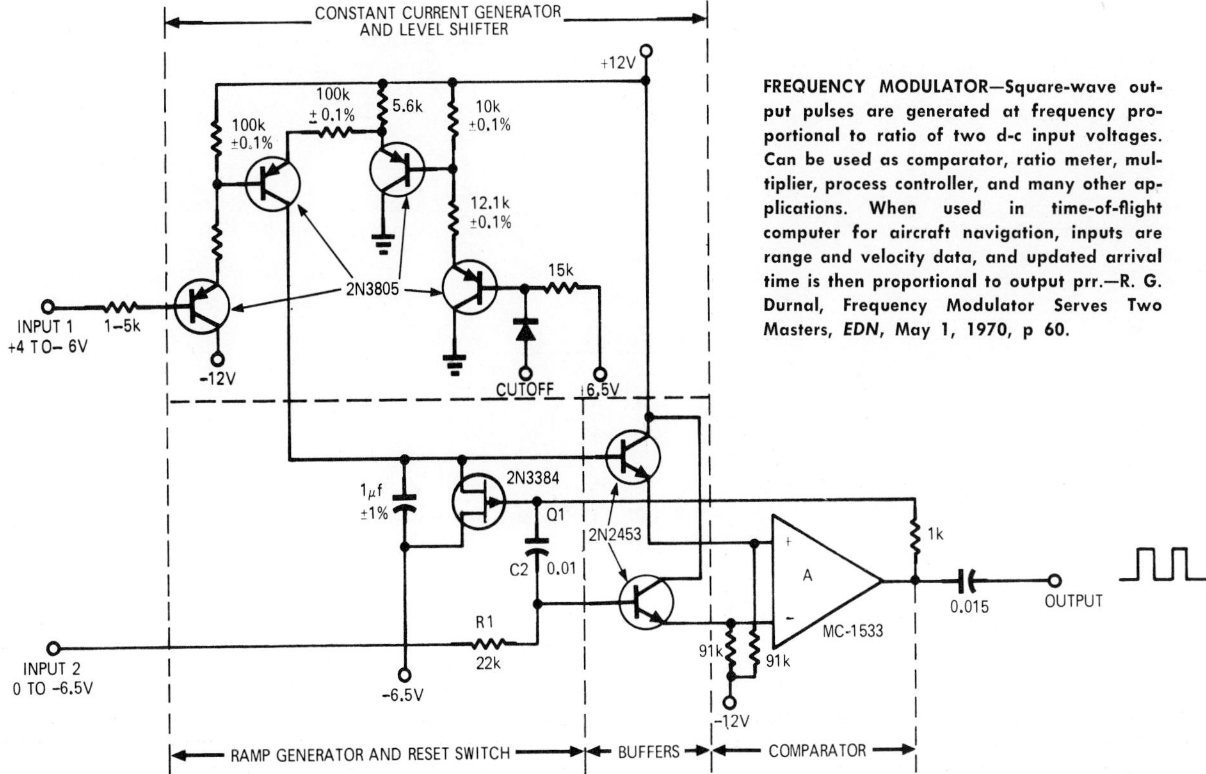

FREQUENCY MODULATOR—Square-wave output pulses are generated at frequency proportional to ratio of two d-c input voltages. Can be used as comparator, ratio meter, multiplier, process controller, and many other applications. When used in time-of-flight computer for aircraft navigation, inputs are range and velocity data, and updated arrival time is then proportional to output prr.—R. G. Durnal, Frequency Modulator Serves Two Masters, *EDN*, May 1, 1970, p 60.

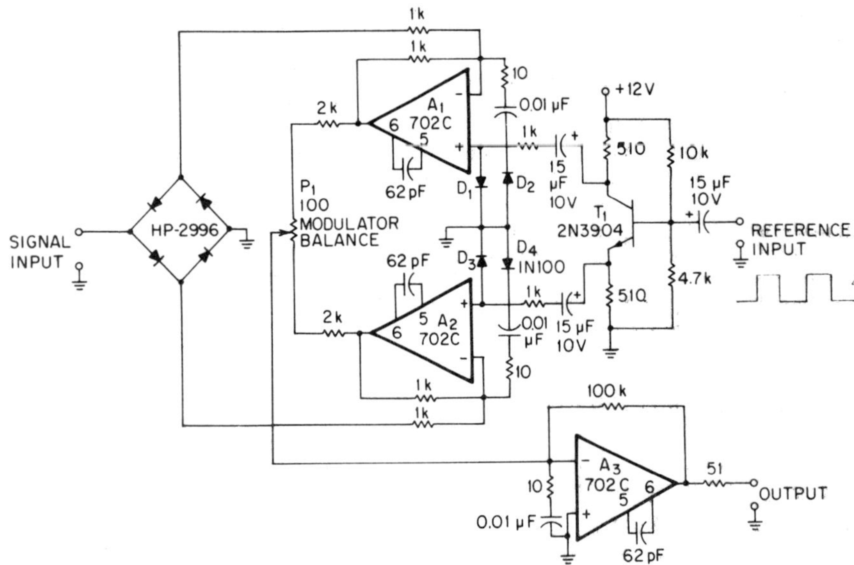

10 HZ—1 MHZ RING MODULATOR—Opamps replace transformers, to provide reliable operation over wide frequency range without component changes. A1 and A2 gate hot-carrier diodes and condition signal. Incoming signal is passed into each unity-gain amplifier during half of reference cycle and disconnected during other half. A3 sums outputs of A1 and A2.—J. R. Nielsen, Transformerless Ring Modulator, *EEE*, Feb. 1970, p 116.

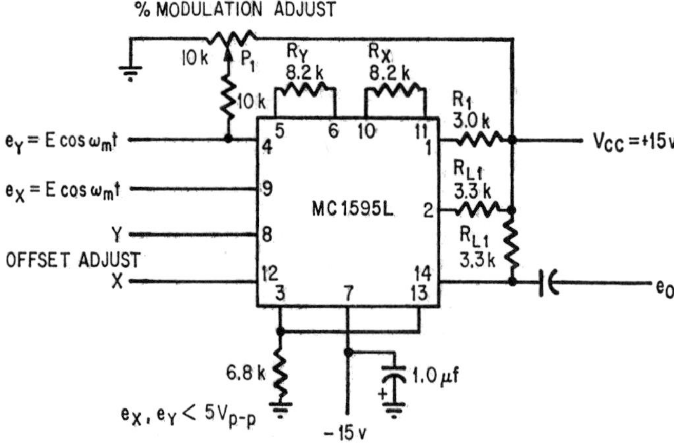

IC FOR A-M—Motorola monolithic multiplier performs amplitude modulation by adding d-c term to modulating signal with pot P1.—E. Renschler and D. Weiss, Try the Monolithic Multiplier as a Versatile A-C Design Tool, *Electronics*, June 8, 1970, p 100–105.

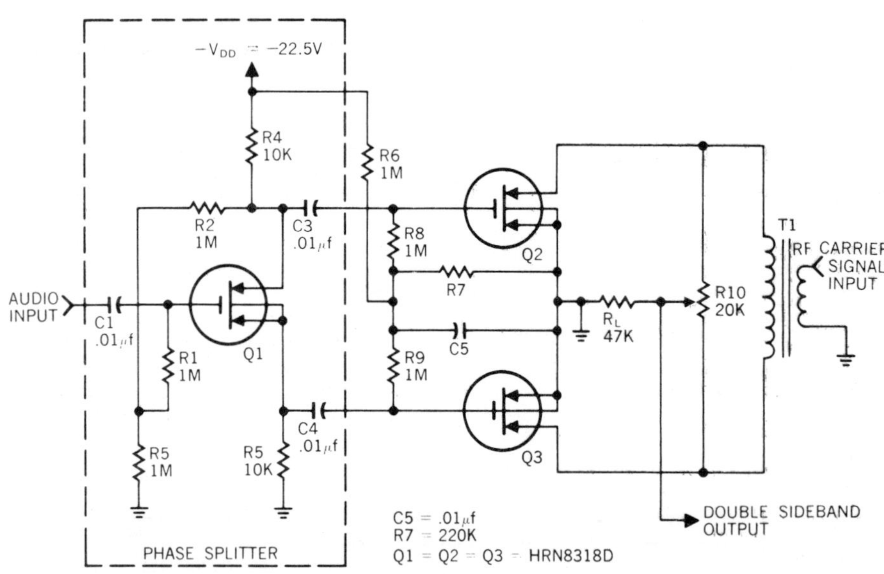

MOSFET BALANCED MODULATOR—Provides audio modulation of r-f carrier signal for double-sideband generation. Mosfet Q1 acts as phase splitter having extremely high input impedance, for driving other two mosfets out of phase to produce double sideband. R10 serves for balancing output signals accurately, for use in modulating linear r-f power amplifiers.—C. R. Perkins, "Application of MOSFET Devices to Electronic Circuits," Hughes, Newport Beach, Cal., 1968, p 42.

A-M WITH IC MULTIPLIER—Similar to balanced modulator, but with d-c term added by means of potentiometer 3. IC is Motorola linear four-quadrant multiplier. With careful alignment, 100% modulation is possible.—E. Renschler, The Monolithic Multiplier Breakthrough, "State-of-the-Art—Linears in Action," Motorola, Phoenix, Ariz., 1969, p 27–36.

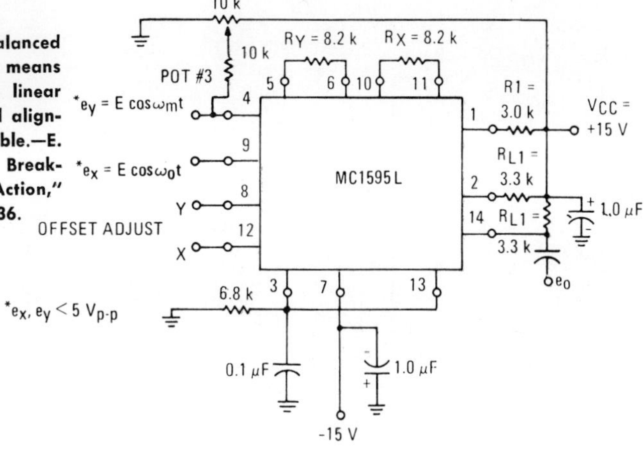

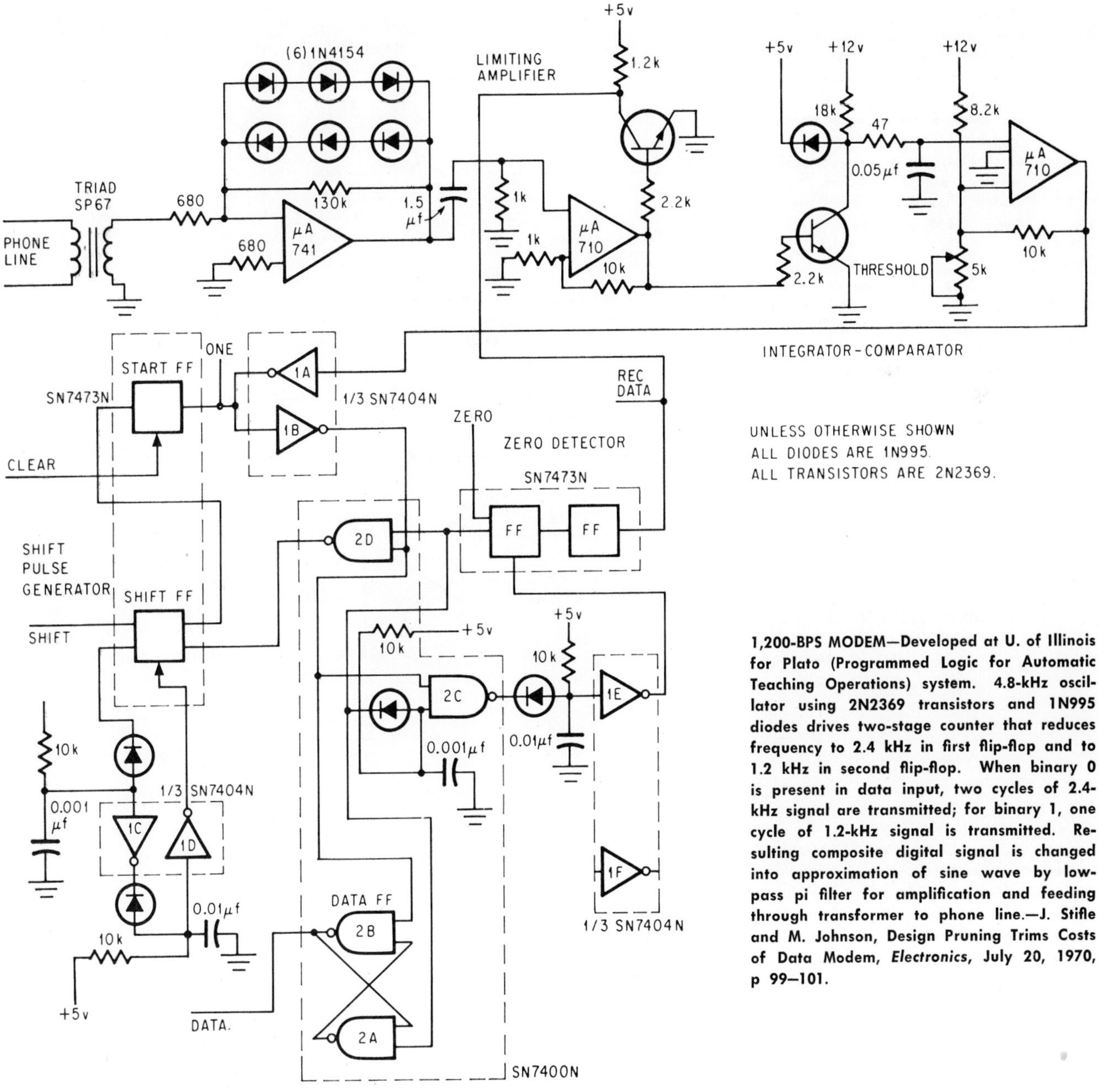

UNLESS OTHERWISE SHOWN
ALL DIODES ARE 1N995.
ALL TRANSISTORS ARE 2N2369.

1,200-BPS MODEM—Developed at U. of Illinois for Plato (Programmed Logic for Automatic Teaching Operations) system. 4.8-kHz oscillator using 2N2369 transistors and 1N995 diodes drives two-stage counter that reduces frequency to 2.4 kHz in first flip-flop and to 1.2 kHz in second flip-flop. When binary 0 is present in data input, two cycles of 2.4-kHz signal are transmitted; for binary 1, one cycle of 1.2-kHz signal is transmitted. Resulting composite digital signal is changed into approximation of sine wave by low-pass pi filter for amplification and feeding through transformer to phone line.—J. Stifle and M. Johnson, Design Pruning Trims Costs of Data Modem, *Electronics*, July 20, 1970, p 99–101.

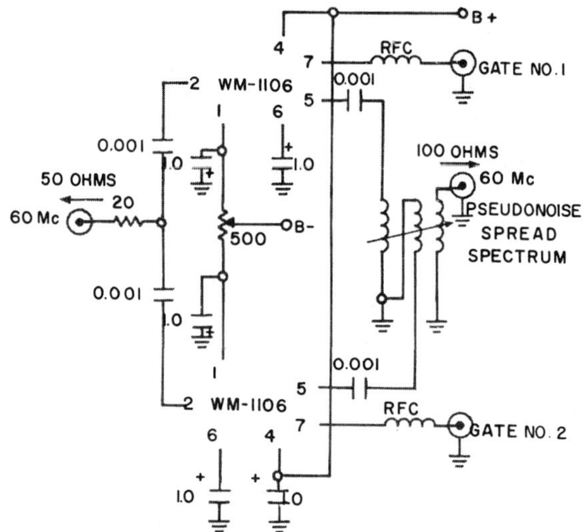

PHASE MODULATOR FOR 60-MHZ I-F—Provides 180-deg shift in phase of output signal each time switching signal is applied to modulator, to give coded noise-like output. Operates with pseudo-random code having maximum code rate of 5 megabits per second. Switching time is faster than 30 ns. Uses two gated IC video amplifiers fed in parallel, with outputs fed to push-pull transformer.—S. G. Shepherd and A. E. Seman, Design With Integrated Circuits at 60 Mc, *Electronic Design*, Aug. 2, 1965, p 30–33.

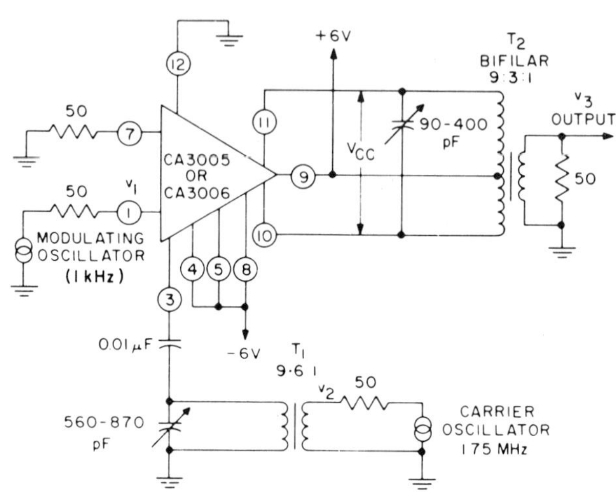

SUPPRESSED-CARRIER MODULATOR—Uses IC r-f amplifier as double-sideband modulator. Carrier suppression is function of bilateral symmetry and modulation-to-carrier drive ratio. Carrier output is 25 dB below double-sideband output when drive V1 is 10 mV and V2 is 31.5 mV.—"Linear Integrated Circuits," RCA, Harrison, N.J., IC-41, p 229.

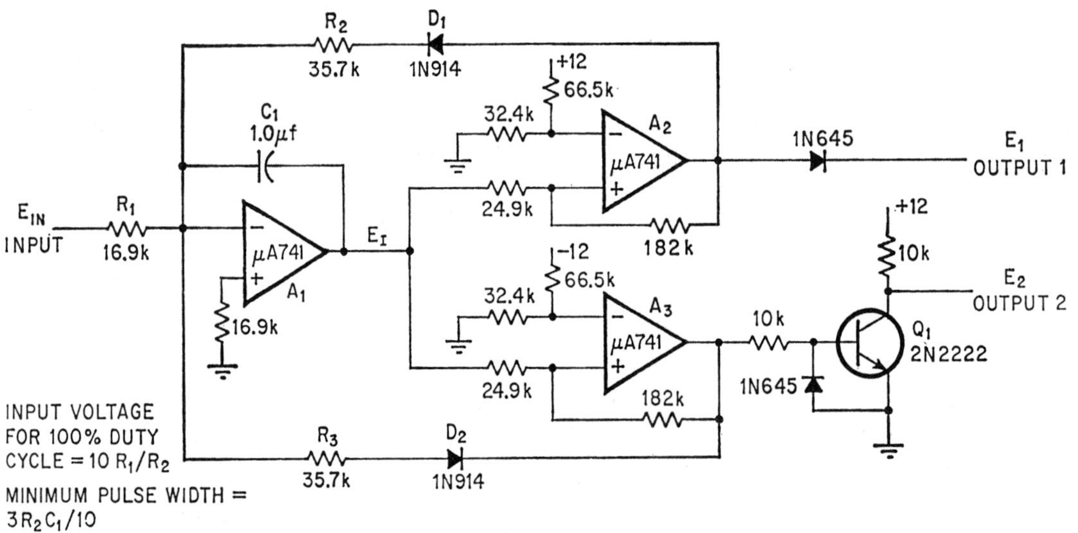

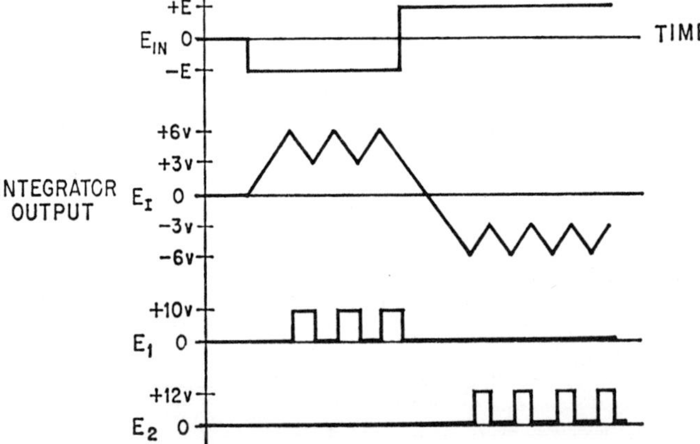

BANG-BANG SUBSTITUTE—Provides variations in pulse width and frequency for solenoid-type pneumatic valves in missile and space vehicles, to give both coarse and fine control having many advantages over conventional bang-bang systems. Circuit gives large savings in gas and energy consumption. For small control signals, valves are modulated with minimum pulse width for just barely opening valve. For large control signals, system changes to bang-bang mode.—W. A. Cooke, Pulse Modulator Regulates Pneumatic Valve Closure, *Electronics*, Sept. 1, 1969, p 80–81.

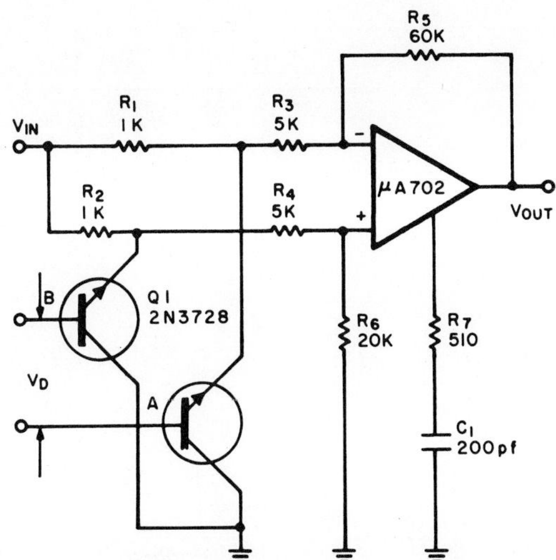

TRANSFORMERLESS MODEM—Uses Fairchild IC opamp as full-wave modulator-demodulator operating over wide range of frequencies. Input switch Q1 alternately switches IC from inverting (transistor A ON) to noninverting (transistor B ON) amplifier. Push-pull drive signal can be obtained from IC flip-flop. Values shown give gain of 10 and bandwidth of 10 MHz.—C. J. Amato, The Integrated Operational Amplifier: A Versatile and Economical Circuit, "Microelectronic Design," Hayden Book Co., N.Y., 1966, p 189–194.

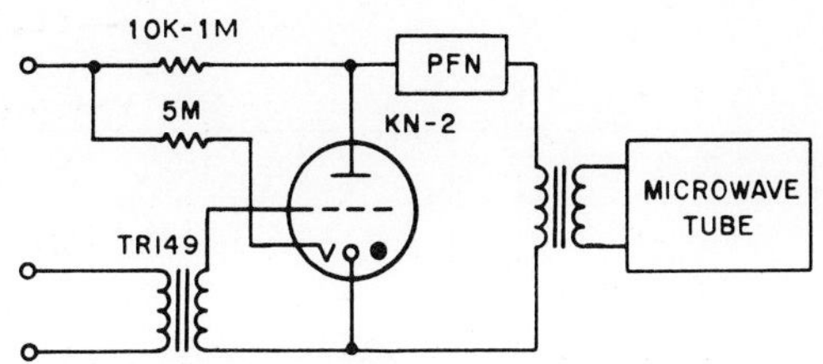

BEACON MODULATOR—Input pulse trips Krytron gas-filled switch tube, producing high peak current through pulse-forming network and output transformer, for pulse modulation of high-power microwave radar tube.—Krytrons—Cold Cathode Switch Tubes, EG&G, Boston, Mass., KR-100, 1968.

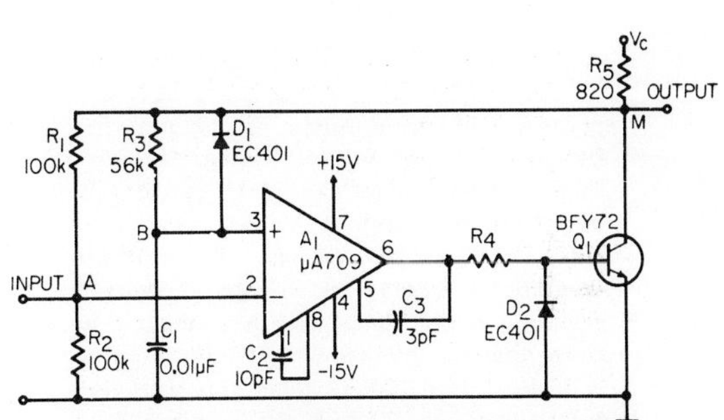

ANALOG MULTIPLIER—Single opamp connected as one-shot accepts input frequencies from 1 to 1,000 Hz and control voltages from 0.1 to 15 V, and delivers constant-width output pulses with amplitudes proportional to product of input frequency and d-c control voltage. Multiplication accuracy is 0.1%. Q1 may be any suitable switching transistor with low VCE.—B. Stojanovic, Pulse-Height Modulator Multiplies Voltage by Frequency, *EEE*, July 1968, p 99–100.

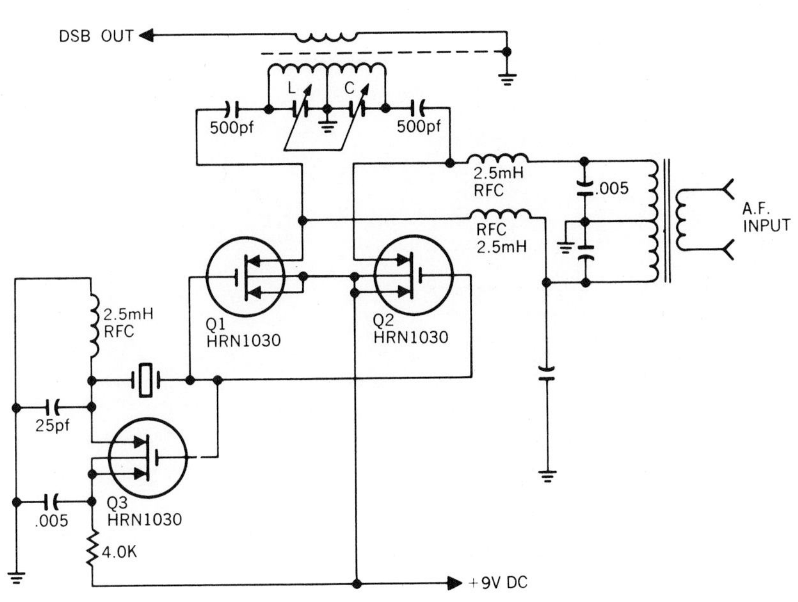

DOUBLE-SIDEBAND GENERATOR—Simple crystal oscillator drives two mosfet r-f switches that are modulated out of phase with audio input signal to generate double-sideband r-f carrier signal.—C. R. Perkins, "Application of MOSFET Devices to Electronic Circuits," Hughes, Newport Beach, Cal., 1968, p 43.

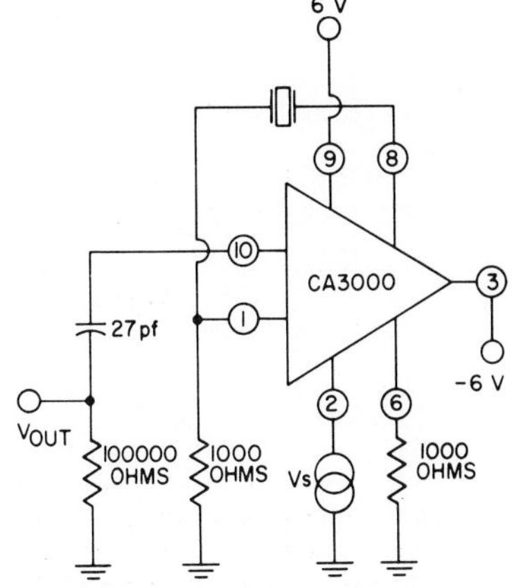

MODULATED CRYSTAL IC—Introduction of audio signal at terminal 2 of IC d-c amplifier operating as crystal oscillator gives a-m modulation. High-pass filter must be used at output. Carrier frequency may be up to 1 MHz, depending on crystal used.—"Linear Integrated Circuits," RCA, Harrison, N.J., IC-41, p 125.

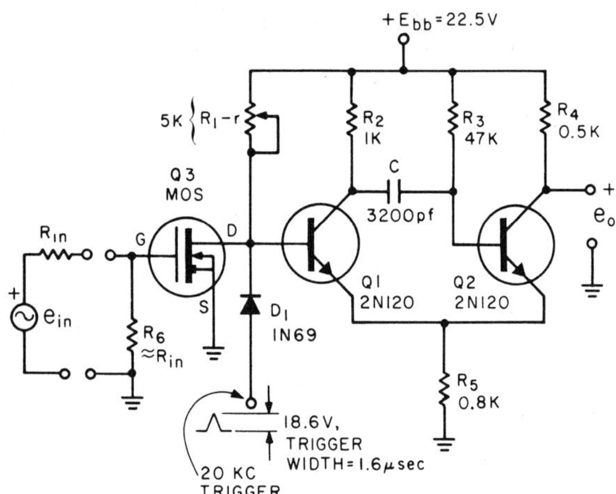

IC PDM—Audio input voltage varies resistance of mosfet Q3, which in turn varies base voltage of Q1 and duration of output pulse. Designed for construction as integrated-circuit chip. For peak input under 1 V, output pulse amplitude is above 2 V and modulation index is 0.25 to 0.75. Trigger rate of 20 kHz was chosen because it is high enough for sampling audio signal and low enough for easy filtering. Unmodulated pulse duration is 25 μs. Uses RCA insulated-gate depletion-type mosfet.—A. J. Wall, Converting a Pulse Modulator Into An Integrated Chip, *Electronic Design*, Feb. 17, 1964, p 60–65.

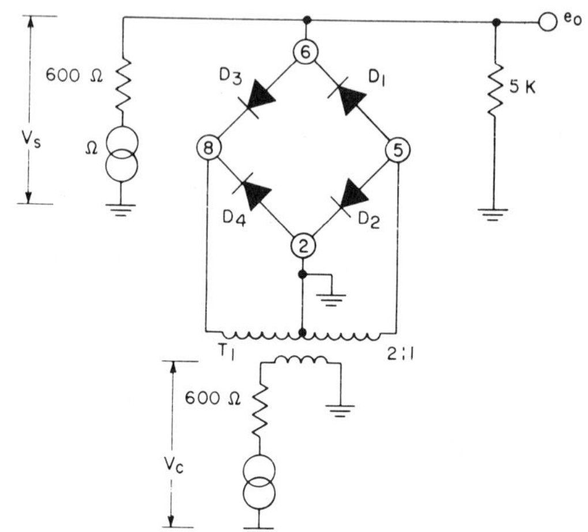

T_1—TECHNITROL No. 851166 OR EQUIV.

IC BALANCED MODULATOR—Uses CA3019 four-diode IC array in symmetrical bridge network that minimizes carrier frequency at output. Carrier of one polarity makes all diodes conduct and effectively short-circuits signal source. Carrier of opposite polarity cuts off all diodes and allows signal current to flow to load. If all diodes are identical, bridge is perfectly balanced and no carrier current reaches load.—"Linear Integrated Circuits," RCA, Harrison, N.J., IC-41, p 300.

NOTE: To locate additional circuits in the category of this chapter, use the index at the back of this book. Check also the author's "Sourcebook of Electronic Circuits," published by McGraw-Hill in 1968.

CHAPTER 53

Motor Control Circuits

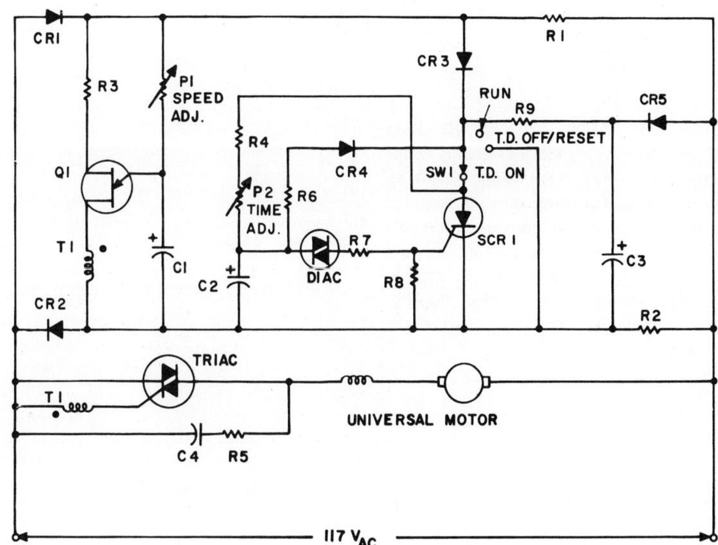

DIAC-TRIAC FULL-WAVE WITH DELAY—Built-in time delay for automatic turn-off permits setting P2 to turn off motor of mixer or other appliance automatically after desired period of operation. Circuit can be reset for next cake by switching SW1 to OFF/RESET position. RUN position bypasses delay. —A. A. Adem, Speed Controls for Universal Motors, General Electric, Syracuse, N.Y., No. 200.57, 1966, p 11.

CRI THROUGH CR5 GE AI4B
TI : I:I PULSE TRANFORMER (SPRAGUE IIZI2)

QI : GE	2N2646	CI : .IμF	50V	C4 .IμF	200V	R5-R6	100Ω	I/2W
DIAC : GE	ST2	C2 : 100μF	50V	RI-R2	33K I/2W	R7-R8	IK	I/2W
SCRI : GE	CI06B	C3 : .5μF	200V	R3	390Ω I/2W	PI	500K	I/2W
TRIAC : GE	SC40BX43			R4	IOK I/2W	P2	IM	I/2W
				R9	IOK 2W			

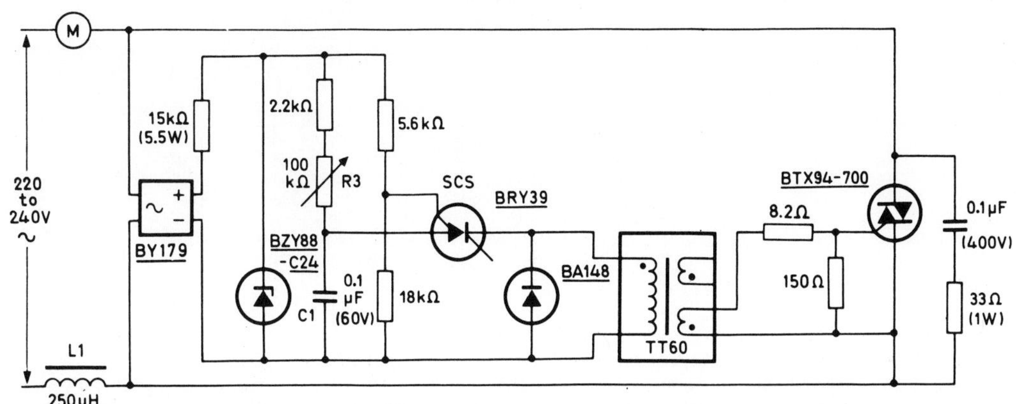

4.5-KW SQUIRREL-CAGE FAN MOTOR—Circuit has no hysteresis effect (no lag between change of speed setting and resultant change in motor speed). Circuit is designed for 220-250 V a-c line operation. Choke L1 limits steepness of current transients and helps suppress rfi.—G. J. Derksen and G. J. Tobisch, Philips, Pub. Dept., Elcoma Div., Eindhoven, The Netherlands, No. 80, 1970.

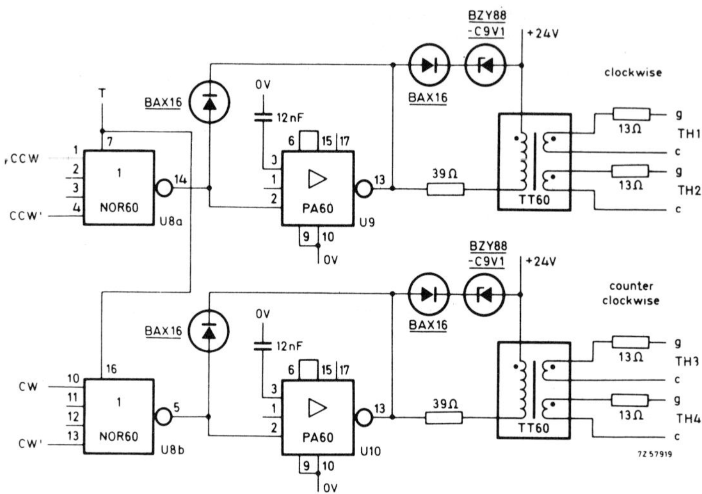

D-C MOTOR THYRISTOR TRIGGERING—Uses Philips IC unit to convert clockwise and counterclockwise commands from logic circuit to triggering required for operating d-c motor at either of two predetermined speed levels in either direction or stopping motor. Report describes operation in detail.—W. B. Rosink, Reversible Two-Speed D. C. Motor Supply, Philips, Pub. Dept., Elcoma Div., Eindhoven, The Netherlands, No. 79.

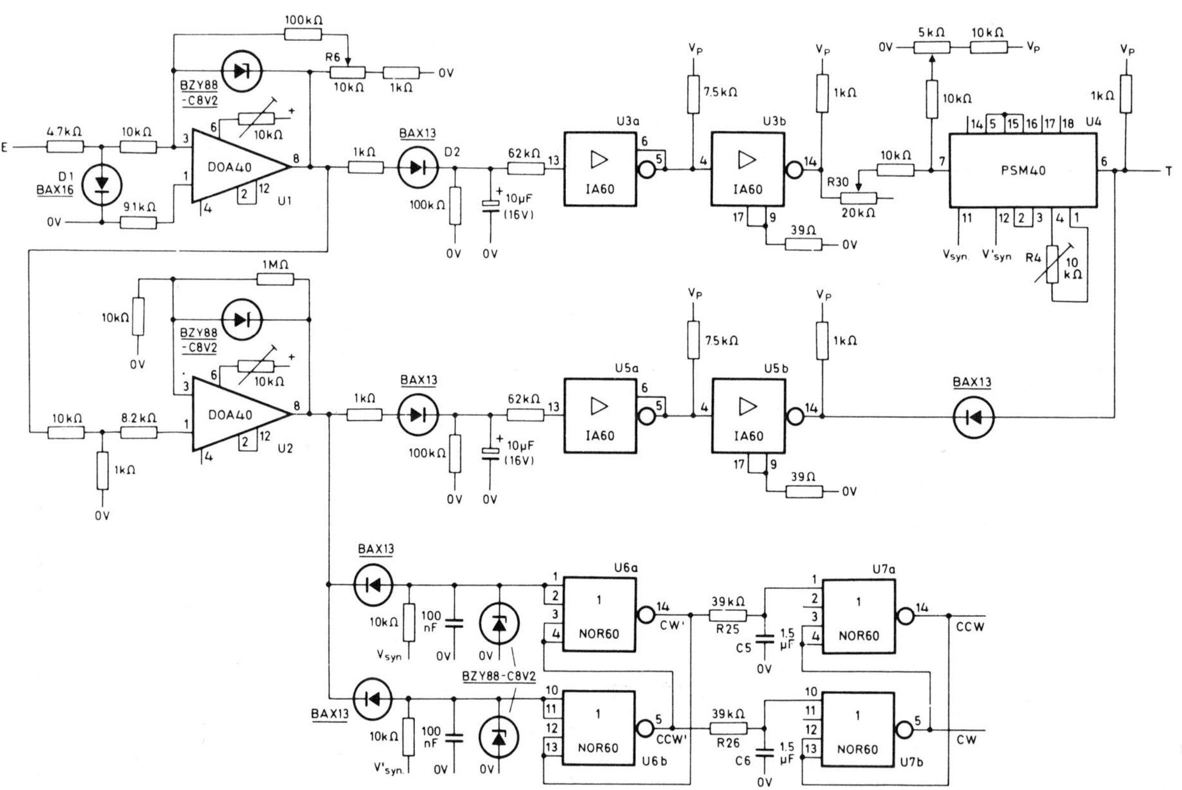

D-C MOTOR CONTROL LOGIC—Requires a-c control signal that can be varied in amplitude and phase, applied to terminal E. Gives control in both directions at two predetermined speeds. When control signal drops below certain value, motor changes from high to low speed. At still lower signal level, motor stops. If signal phase is then reversed, motor starts in opposite direction, and runs at low or high speed level depending on amplitude of control signal. Operation of Philips IC units is described in report. Output leads CCW, CW, and T go to thyristor triggering circuit for motor.—W. B. Rosink, Reversible Two-Speed D. C. Motor Supply, Philips, Pub. Dept., Elcoma Div., Eindhoven, The Netherlands, No. 79.

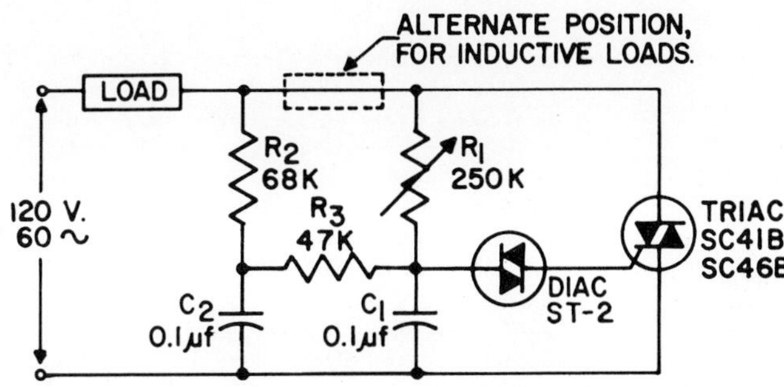

EXTENDED-RANGE FULL-WAVE—Use of extra capacitor C2 in basic 600-W diac-triac circuit extends range for reliable phase control, particularly at low output settings. Place load in alternate position for motors.—F. W. Gutzwiller and E. K. Howell, Economy Power Semiconductor Applications, General Electric, Syracuse, N.Y., No. 671.1, 1965, p 16.

BATTERY-VEHICLE CONTROLLER—Uses rapid-acting scr switch, known as Jones chopper, in series with d-c series motor to control speed of battery-powered vehicle such as golf cart. At low speeds, ON time is much less than OFF time so average voltage across motor is low. OFF time is changed by R2 in timer, for smooth control and high efficiency. Operates as variable-frequency constant-pulse-width system. Pulse repetition rate range is about 100 to 400 Hz. Values are for 36-V battery and maximum motor current of 110 A. Article gives design equations.—"SCR Manual," 4th Edition, General Electric, 1967, p 237–243.

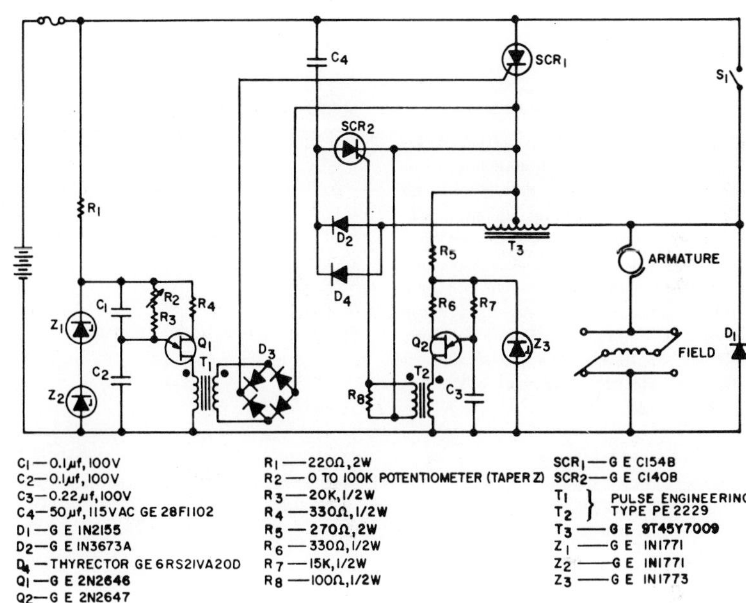

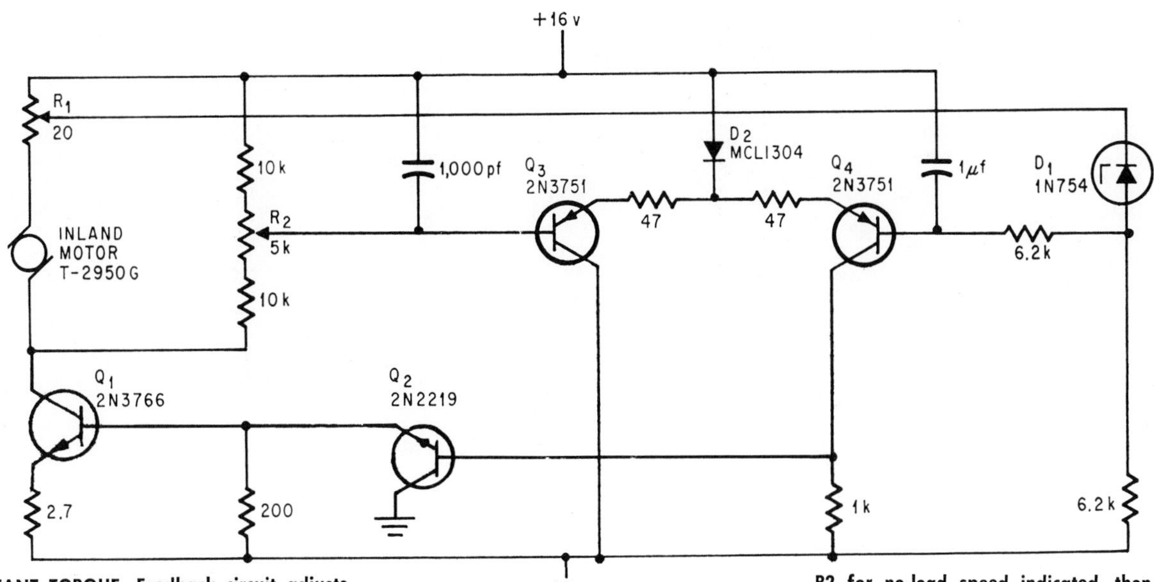

CONSTANT TORQUE—Feedback circuit adjusts voltage of d-c motor and inserts negative or positive adjustable resistance in series with motor, to offset typical variation of up to 20% in slope of torque-speed curve caused by variations in strength of permanent magnet. Used for constant-speed, constant-tension magnetic tape drive. To adjust for slope, set R2 for no-load speed indicated, then adjust R1 for proper torque with motor stalled.—E. S. Busby, Feedback Circuit Keeps Motor's Torque Constant, *Electronics*, Sept. 2, 1968, p 72.

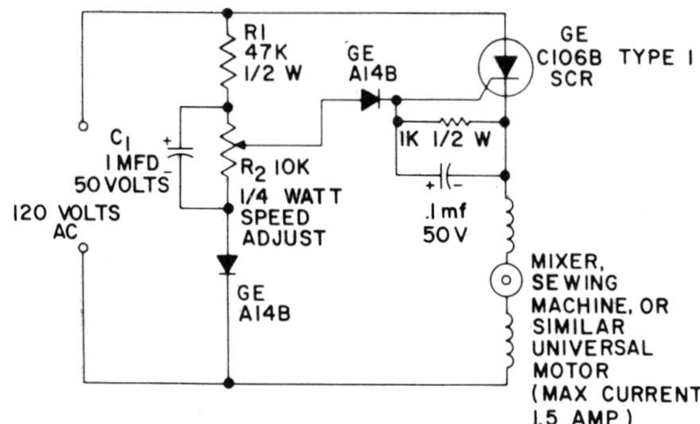

SEWING-MACHINE MOTOR CONTROL—Can be used in place of carbon-pile speed control for sewing machines, food mixers, and other household appliances using universal a-c/d-c motors. Speed-dependent feedback gives excellent torque even at slow speeds. C1 is optional, and may sometimes improve performance. A selenium 6RS5PX7 double diode assembly may be used in place of the two A14B silicon diodes shown.—Silicon Controlled Rectifier, General Electric, Syracuse, N.Y., No. 150.9, 1969.

UNIVERSAL-MOTOR CONTROL WITH SELF-TIMING—Shuts motor off automatically after predetermined time delay determined by setting of R3. R2 determines speed. Suitable for blenders and larger food mixers having motors rated at up to 2 A. Maximum obtainable delay with circuit shown is above 30 s. Pilot lamp remains on until main power switch is turned off, after timer stops motor.—D. R. Grafham, Using Low Current SCR's, General Electric, Syracuse, N.Y., No. 200.19, 1967, p 37.

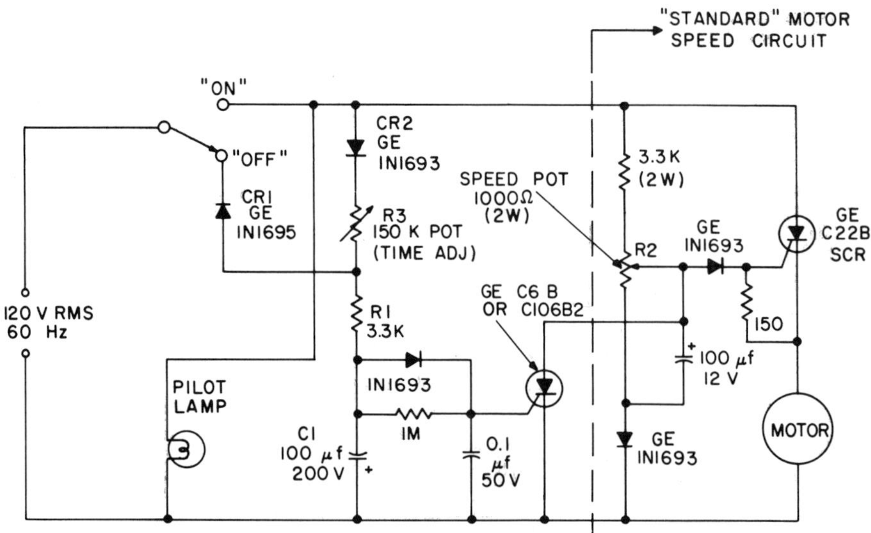

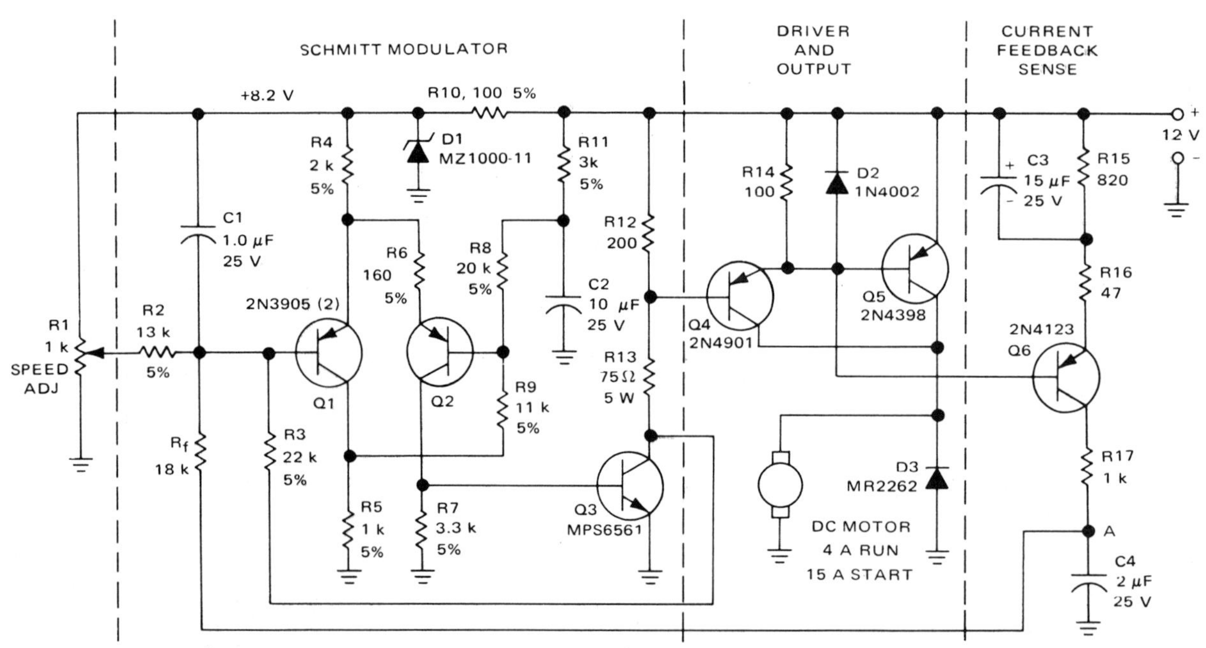

12-V PWM D-C CONTROL—Provides speed control of 12-V 4-A d-c motor, with good regulation at any given speed. Schmitt trigger Q1-Q2 and phase inverter Q3 produce variable-width variable-frequency pulse waveform whose duty cycle and frequency are a function of R1 and feedback current through Rf. Output of Schmitt modulator feeds Darlington-connected power amplifier Q4-Q5 that drives motor. Free-wheeling diode D3 suppresses inductive kickback of motor, while D2 protects Q5 from voltage transients of motor.—"Semiconductor Power Circuits Handbook," Motorola, Phoenix, Ariz., 1968, p 1—30.

HALF-WAVE CONTROL FOR SHUNT MOTOR—Provides speed control for d-c shunt motor designed for operation on half-wave rectified 120-V a-c supply. D1 provides field current, with D3 smoothing its waveform. Diac-scr combination supplies armature current, with D5 for smoothing. At end of each positive half-cycle, field voltage drops to zero and C1 discharges through D2. Voltage across C1 is thus zero at start of each positive half-cycle, regardless of setting of speed control R1. Voltage rating of scr is twice that required for resistive load, or 400 V, because of counter emf of armature at high speeds.—E. K. Howell, Speed Control for Shunt-Wound DC Motors, General Electric, Syracuse, N.Y., No. 200.44, 1965, p 5.

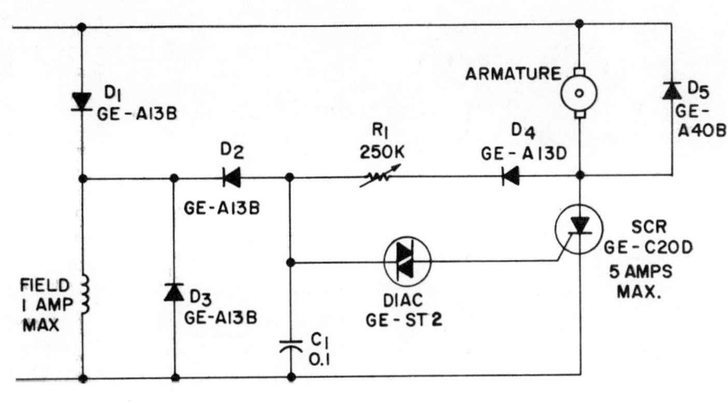

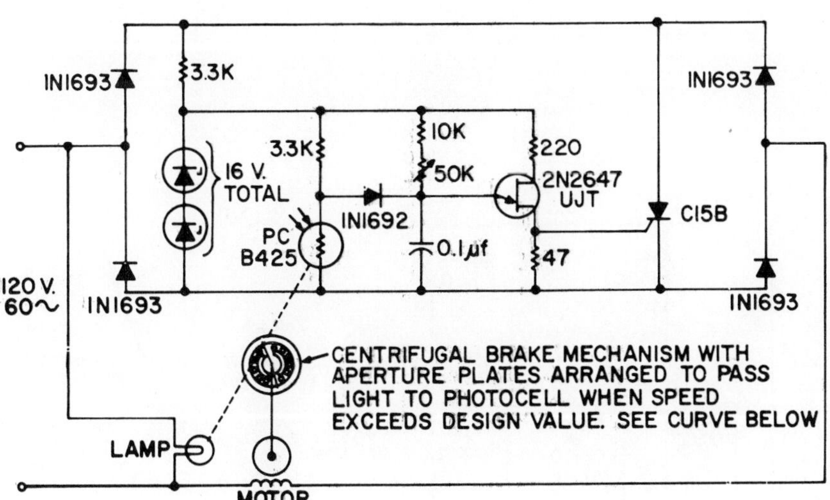

PHOTOELECTRIC-FEEDBACK A-C CONTROL—Centrifugal mechanism acts as variable shutter between lamp and photocell, to hold speed of induction motor constant within fairly tight limits.—F. W. Gutzwiller and E. K. Howell, Economy Power Semiconductor Applications, General Electric, Syracuse, N.Y., No. 671.1, 1965, p 21.

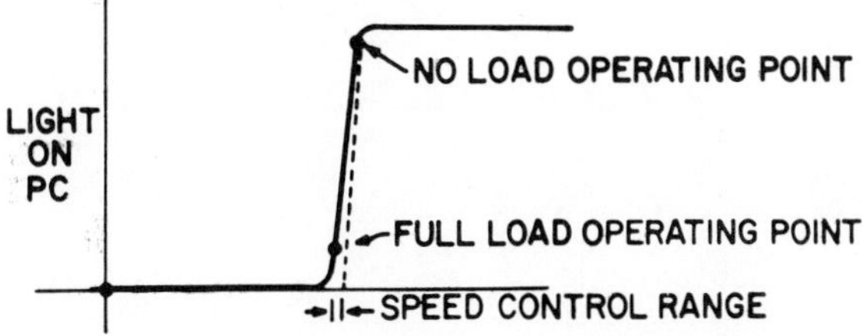

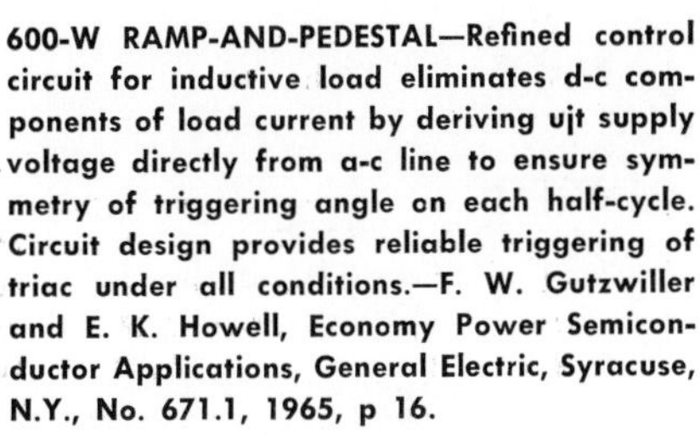
600-W RAMP-AND-PEDESTAL—Refined control circuit for inductive load eliminates d-c components of load current by deriving ujt supply voltage directly from a-c line to ensure symmetry of triggering angle on each half-cycle. Circuit design provides reliable triggering of triac under all conditions.—F. W. Gutzwiller and E. K. Howell, Economy Power Semiconductor Applications, General Electric, Syracuse, N.Y., No. 671.1, 1965, p 16.

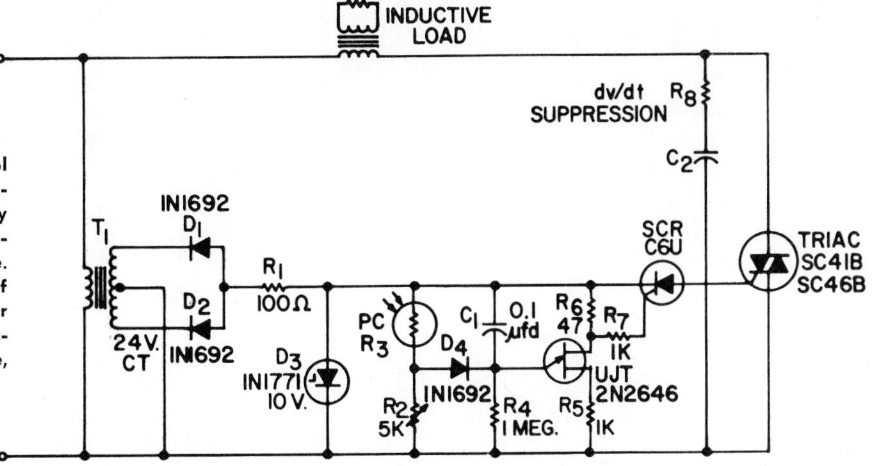

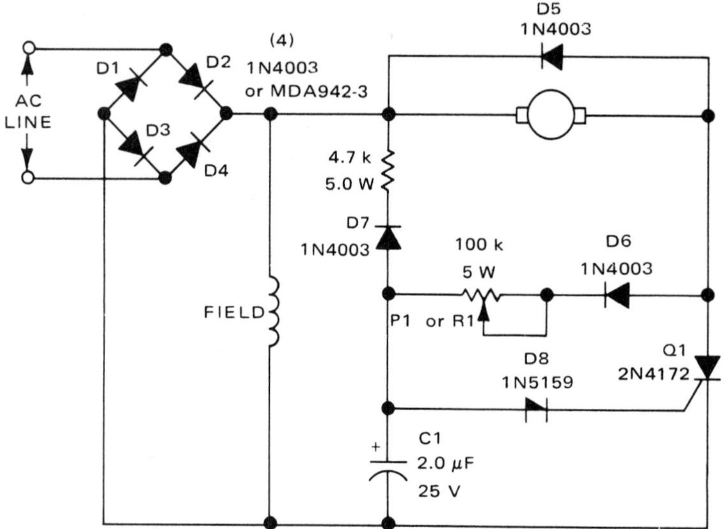

FULL-WAVE FOR SHUNT-WOUND—Power for $\frac{1}{15}$th-hp 5,000-rpm 115-V d-c motor is supplied from full-wave bridge. Free-wheeling diode D5 is necessary across armature for scr Q1 to turn off. Four-layer diode D8 provides stable firing point for Q1. Speed pulsations occurred only at very low speed settings. Provides much better speed regulation than with comparable half-wave control.—"Semiconductor Power Circuits Handbook," Motorola, Phoenix, Ariz., 1968, p 1–25.

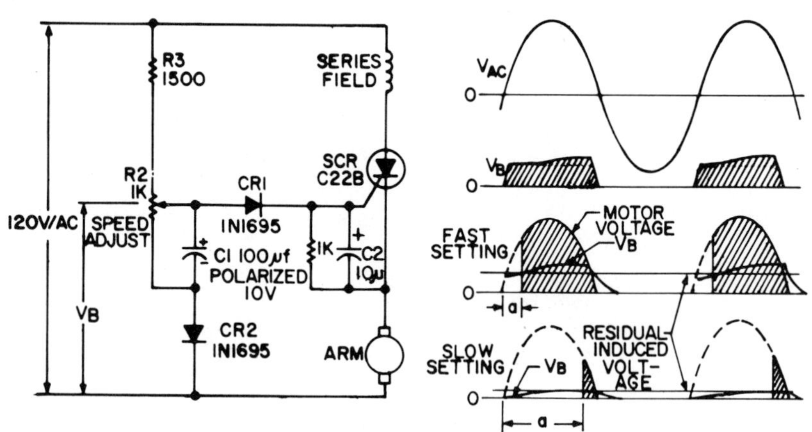

UNIVERSAL MOTOR CONTROL—Widely used for power tools and sewing machines. Compares voltage across capacitor with generated emf in armature to regulate motor speed. To avoid changing motor connections, series field may be left in armature circuit.—F. W. Gutzwiller and E. K. Howell, Economy Power Semiconductor Applications, General Electric, Syracuse, N.Y., No. 671.1, 1965, p 23.

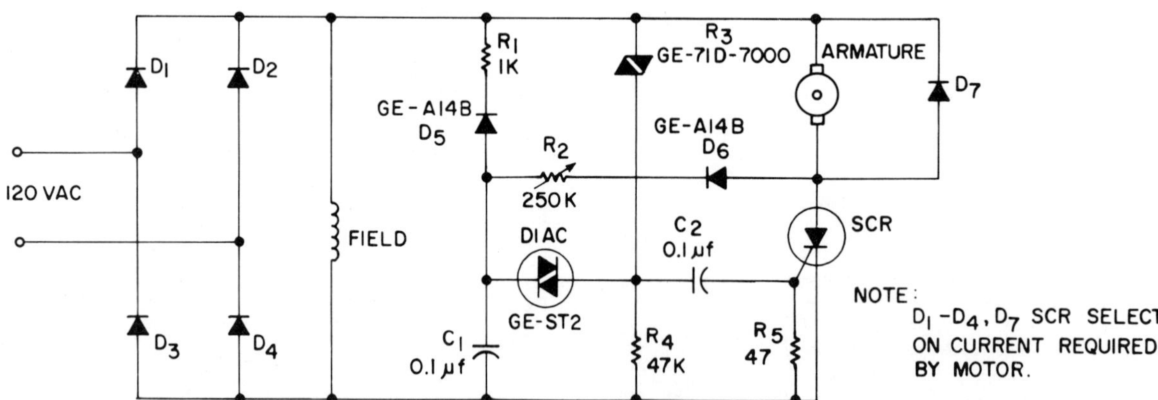

LINE-VOLTAGE COMPENSATION WITH SPEED CONTROL—Provides armature voltage control of 115-V d-c shunt motor operating from a-c line through bridge rectifier. Field is directly across rectifier. Compensation for changes in line voltage is provided only at reduced speeds, by shifting voltage required across C1 to produce triggering of scr.—E. K. Howell, Speed Control for Shunt-Wound DC Motors, General Electric, Syracuse, N.Y., No. 200.44, 1965, p 4.

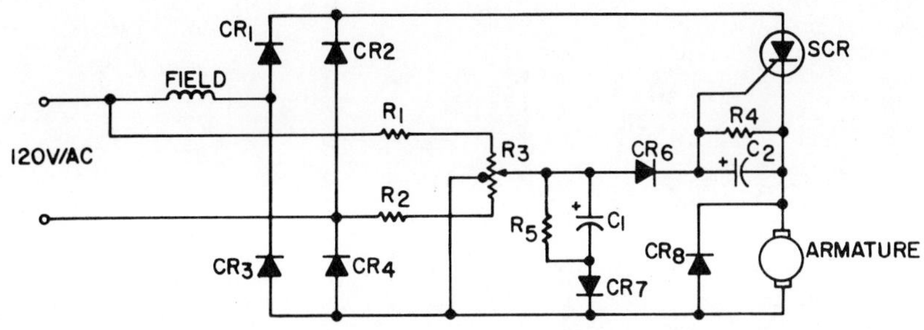

REVERSIBLE HALF-WAVE UNIVERSAL—Armature current is always in same direction because scr is fed by bridge rectifier. Direction of field current depends on which polarity of applied voltage is present at time scr conducts. Direction of rotation is changed by causing conduction in either positive or negative half-cycle of supply voltage. Feedback control of motor speed is achieved by comparing counter emf of armature with capacitor voltage.—F. W. Gutzwiller and E. K. Howell, Economy Power Semiconductor Applications, General Electric, Syracuse, N.Y., No. 671.1, 1965, p 23.

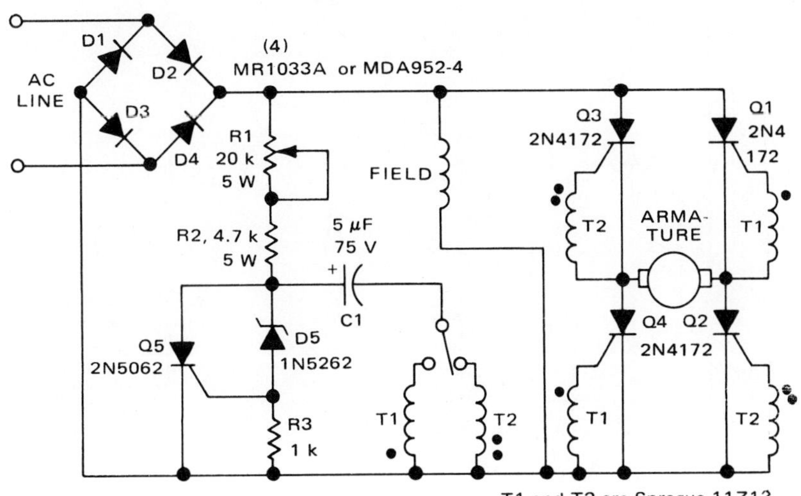

REVERSING SHUNT-WOUND—Controls both speed and direction of 1/15th-hp 5,000-rpm 115-V shunt-wound d-c motor. Field is connected across bridge rectifier and armature is in scr bridge. Switch reverses armature current and direction of rotation by triggering opposite diagonal pair of scr's. R1 controls speed.—"Semiconductor Power Circuits Handbook," Motorola, Phoenix, Ariz., 1968, p 1–27.

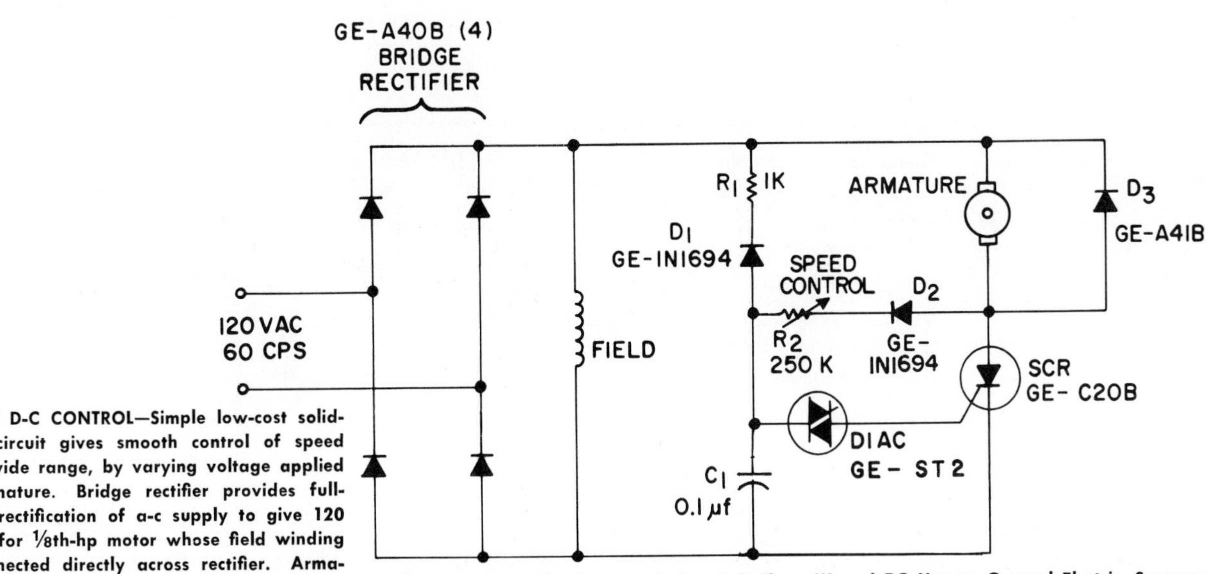

SHUNT D-C CONTROL—Simple low-cost solid-state circuit gives smooth control of speed over wide range, by varying voltage applied to armature. Bridge rectifier provides full-wave rectification of a-c supply to give 120 V d-c for 1/8th-hp motor whose field winding is connected directly across rectifier. Armature voltage is controlled by changing point in each half-cycle at which scr is turned on, with scr turning off only at end of each half-cycle.—E. K. Howell, Speed Control for Shunt-Wound DC Motors, General Electric, Syracuse, N.Y., No. 200.44, 1965, p 1.

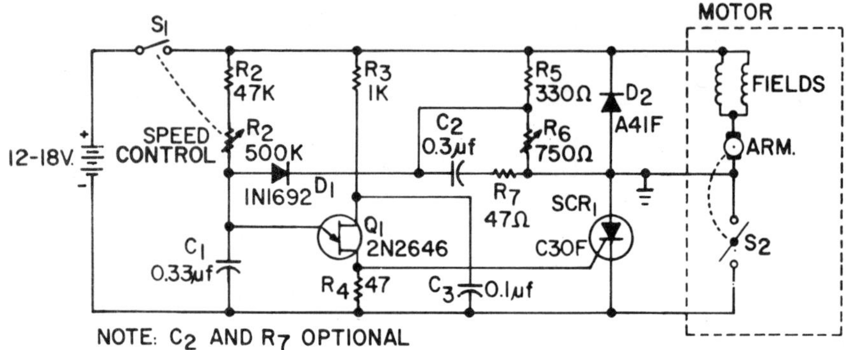

LOW-VOLTAGE D-C MOTOR CONTROL—Low-cost control operating from battery solves commutation problem with mechanical contact that bypasses scr twice per revolution of motor. Speed of motor is synchronous with that of ujt which turns on scr, giving very precise control of speed.—F. W. Gutzwiller and E. K. Howell, Economy Power Semiconductor Applications, General Electric, Syracuse, N.Y., No. 671.1, 1965, p 24.

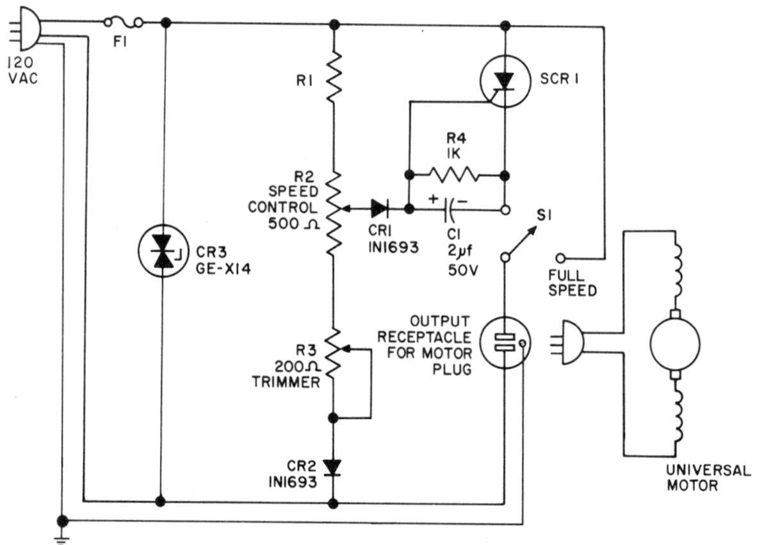

PLUG-IN SPEED CONTROL—Single black-box half-wave scr phase control can be used on variety of electric appliances and tools having series universal brush-type motors, such as with electric drills, power saws, sanders, lathes, fans, movie projectors, and food mixers or blenders. Requires no rewiring of motor. For motors rated 3 A max, use GE-X1 scr, 3-A fuse, and 2,500-ohm 4-W resistor for R1. For motors up to 5 A, use C30B scr, 5-A fuse, and 2,500-ohm 4-W resistor for R1. —"Hobby Manual," General Electric, Owensboro, Ky., 1965, p 131.

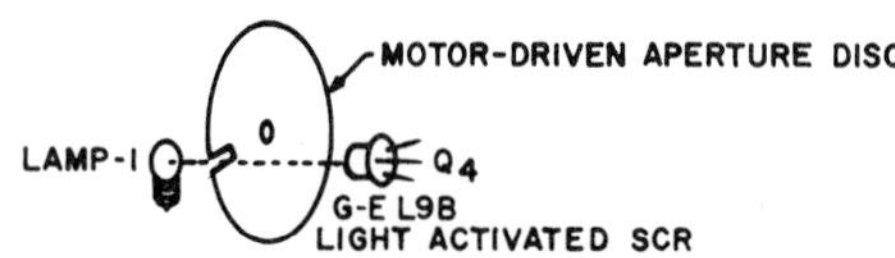

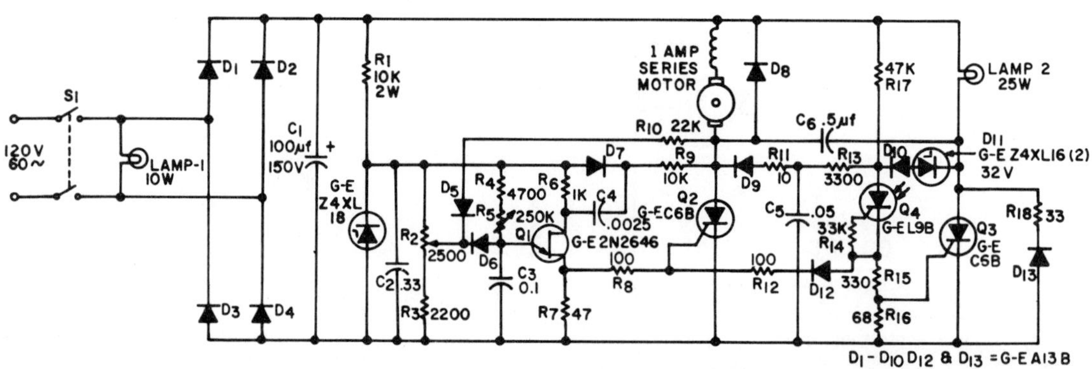

PRECISION SPEED CONTROL—Uses aperture disc on armature shaft to interrupt light from lamp to lascr and produce scr turnoff signal for ujt-synchronous drive through flip-flop and scr. Optional system eliminates wear of mechanical switch and does not load motor. Faster response time of lascr permits higher oscillator frequency and either higher motor speeds or multiple interruptions per revolution. Phase-detector principle employed produces linear output for full 360-deg range of phase error, with full output for any input frequency below reference frequency, and nearly zero output for inputs above reference.—E. K. Howell, Solid State Control for DC Motors Provides Variable Speed with Synchronous-Motor Performance, General Electric, Syracuse, N.Y., No. 200.43, 1965, p 7.

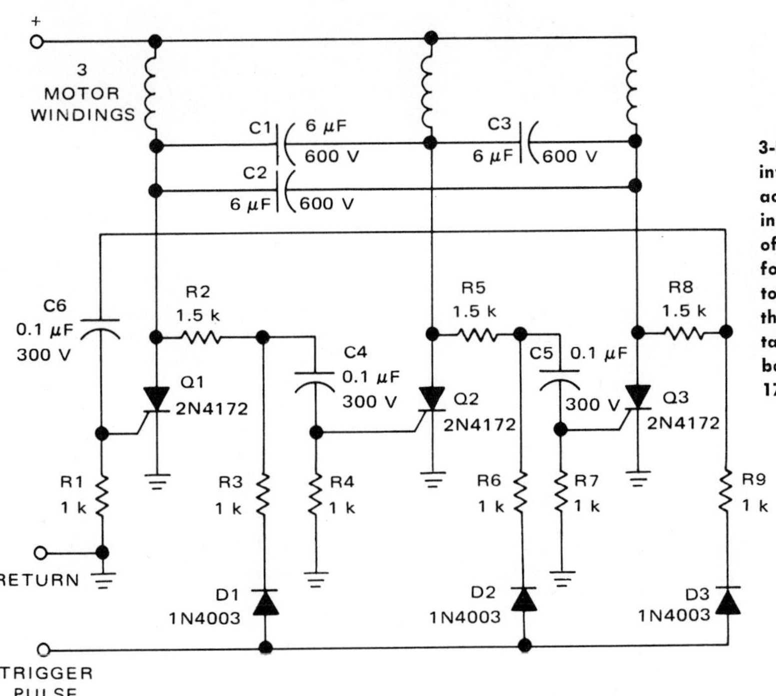

3-PHASE INDUCTION—Forced self-commutated inverter for three-phase induction motor is actually ring counter having one motor winding as load for each stage. Successive firings of scr's create moving flux field around stator for developing torque on rotor for speeds up to 7,200 rpm. Interchanging any two of the three windings with switches will reverse rotation.—"Semiconductor Power Circuits Handbook," Motorola, Phoenix, Ariz., 1968, p 1–17.

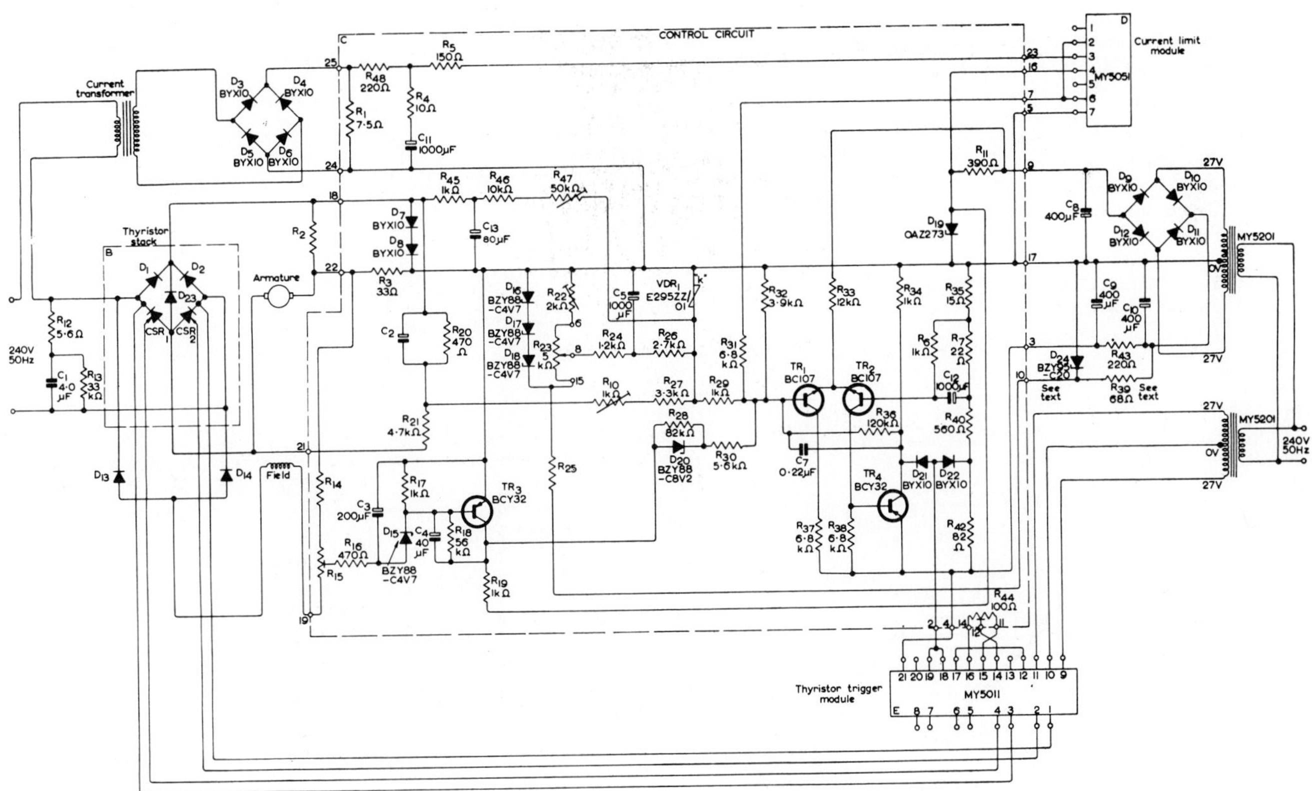

ARMATURE-VOLTAGE SPEED CONTROL—Uses bridge to measure back emf of motor, which is proportional to motor speed when field is constant. Short-term speed regulation against load change can be as good as 1% at full speed, and long-term regulation as bad as 10%. Chief causes of speed drift are changes in field flux caused by temperature rise in windings or changes in supply voltage. Designed for 5-hp d-c shunt motor. B is Mullard thyristor stack with current rating 1.5 times full-load motor current. D13 and D14 are Mullard BYX22-800 or others to suit field current. R2 is 1/10th of armature resistance, R14 is 1/64th of field resistance, and R15 is 1/32nd of field resistance. R25 is 330. D24 and R39 improve speed regulation.—J. Merrett, Thyristor Speed Control Circuit Design for D. C. Shunt Motors Supplied from A. C. Mains, Philips, Pub. Dept., Elcoma Div., Eindhoven, The Netherlands, No. 438, 1967.

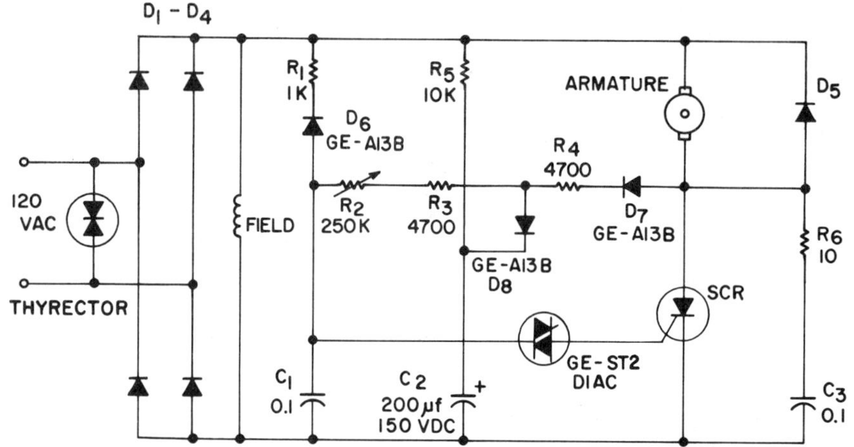

SOFT-START SHUNT D-C MOTOR CONTROL—Addition of R6 and C3 across scr improves commutation in basic armature voltage control circuit by limiting rate at which voltage is applied to scr after turnoff. If motor failed to commutate at low-speed setting, violent speed fluctuations would occur because it would be driven suddenly to high speed at which commutation occurs reliably. Thyrector across a-c line suppresses high-voltage transients that could damage semiconductors in circuit. R2 controls speed.—E. K. Howell, Speed Control for Shunt-Wound DC Motors, General Electric, Syracuse, N.Y., No. 200.44, 1965, p 3.

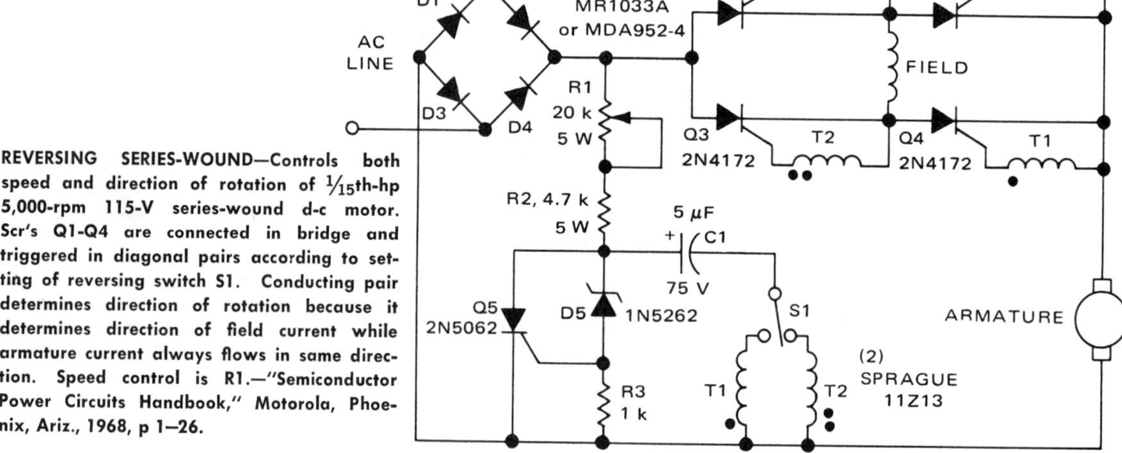

REVERSING SERIES-WOUND—Controls both speed and direction of rotation of 1/15th-hp 5,000-rpm 115-V series-wound d-c motor. Scr's Q1-Q4 are connected in bridge and triggered in diagonal pairs according to setting of reversing switch S1. Conducting pair determines direction of rotation because it determines direction of field current while armature current always flows in same direction. Speed control is R1.—"Semiconductor Power Circuits Handbook," Motorola, Phoenix, Ariz., 1968, p 1–26.

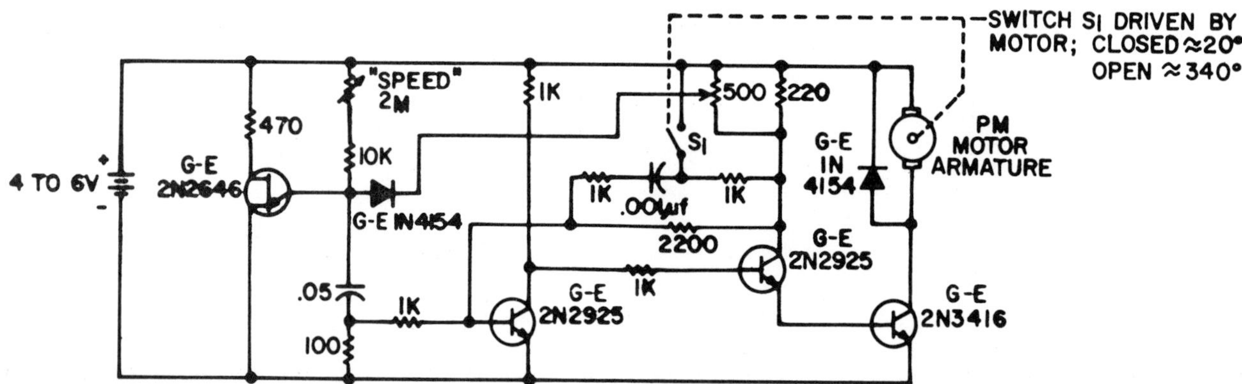

SMALL P-M MOTOR CONTROL—Four-transistor circuit provides adjustable speed control, synchronous with output of ujt relaxation oscillator, for small battery-operated permanent-magnet motors such as are used in phonographs, tape recorders, and recording instruments. Ujt oscillator drives flip-flop that energizes motor. Switch S1, driven by cam on armature shaft, reverses flip-flop and thereby interrupts motor current several times per revolution when closed momentarily by cams. With fixed oscillator frequency, motor speed can be changed in discrete octave steps by changing number of switch closures per revolution from 1 to 2 to 4 to 8, etc., mechanically or electrically.—E. K. Howell, Solid State Control for DC Motors Provides Variable Speed with Synchronous-Motor Performance, General Electric, Syracuse, N.Y., No. 200.43, 1965, p 7.

35-V P-M CONTROL—Uses step-down transformer and bridge rectifier to permit use of component values that give phase control of d-c motor over full half-cycle. Gives excellent speed control from stall up to 20,500 rpm. Small but not objectionable pulsation occurs at light loads and slow speeds, but effect vanishes when motor is fully loaded.—"Semiconductor Power Circuits Handbook," Motorola, Phoenix, Ariz., 1968, p 1–28.

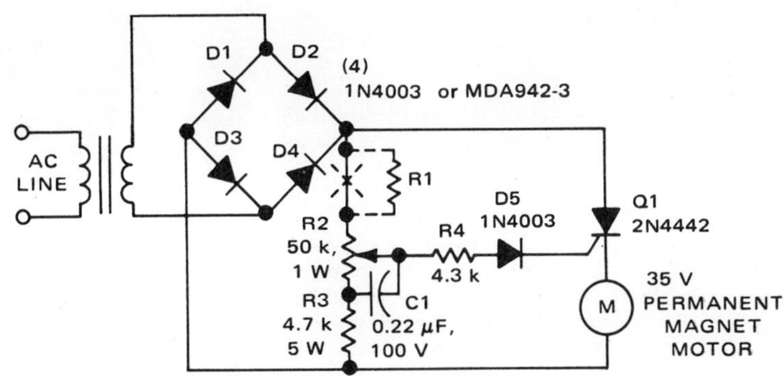

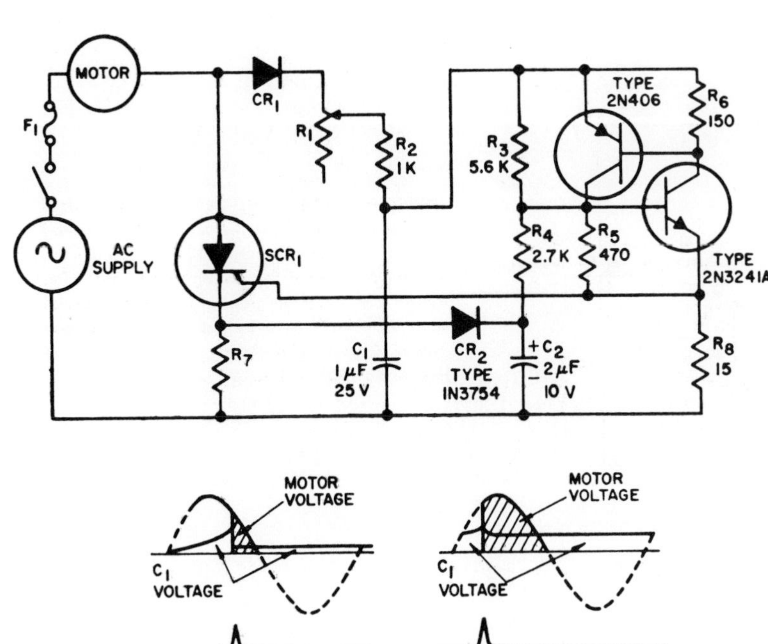

HALF-WAVE SCR WITH REGENERATIVE TRIGGERING—Uses two-transistor regenerative trigger approximating performance of avalanche diode. R7 must be matched with motor rating, in range from 0.1 ohm for larger universal motors to 1 ohm for smaller types. For scr ratings up to 25 A, CR1 is 1N3755 and R1 is 75K with 120-V a-c supply. —"Silicon Power Circuits Manual," RCA, N.J., SP-51, p 246.

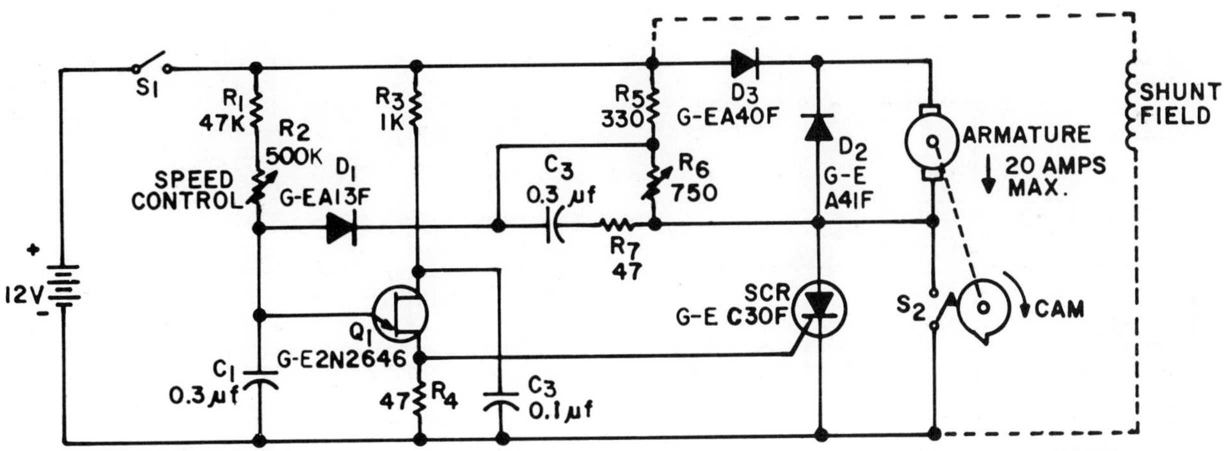

P-M MOTOR SYNCHRONOUS CONTROL—Maintains speed of shunt or permanent-magnet d-c motor at rate determined by output of variable-frequency ujt relaxation oscillator Q1. Each ujt output trigger makes scr pass motor current until cam switch on armature closes and bypasses scr. Motor is then without current until next trigger. Motor speed is held in synchronism with oscillator up to torque limit of motor, with that torque being maintained at all lower speeds down to locked rotor. However, with locked rotor, motor cannot be turned off because commutating switch S2 is not tripped; S1 must then be opened.—E. K. Howell, Solid State Control for DC Motors Provides Variable Speed with Synchronous-Motor Performance, General Electric, Syracuse, N.Y., No. 200.43, 1965, p 5.

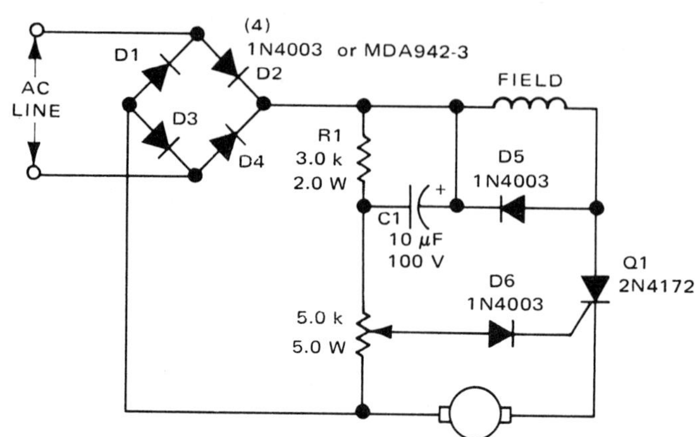

COMPENSATED FULL-WAVE DRIVE—Uses full-wave rectifier on a-c line to drive series-wound d-c motor, with scr providing speed control. Diode D5 provides current path for energy stored in inductive field of motor, to allow scr to turn off. Designed for 1/15th-hp 5,000-rpm 115-V d-c motor, but circuit is capable of controlling motors up to 1/4th-hp.—"Semiconductor Power Circuits Handbook," Motorola, Phoenix, Ariz., 1968, p 1–21.

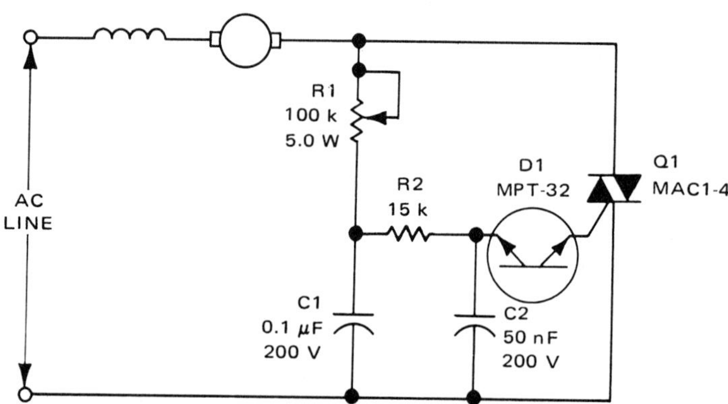

UNCOMPENSATED FULL-WAVE DRIVE—Uses three-layer diode D1 with triac for speed control of series-wound 115-hp 5,000-rpm 115-V d-c motor operating from a-c line. Motor can provide greater maximum torque than with half-wave control.—"Semiconductor Power Circuits Handbook," Motorola, Phoenix, Ariz., 1968, p 1–20.

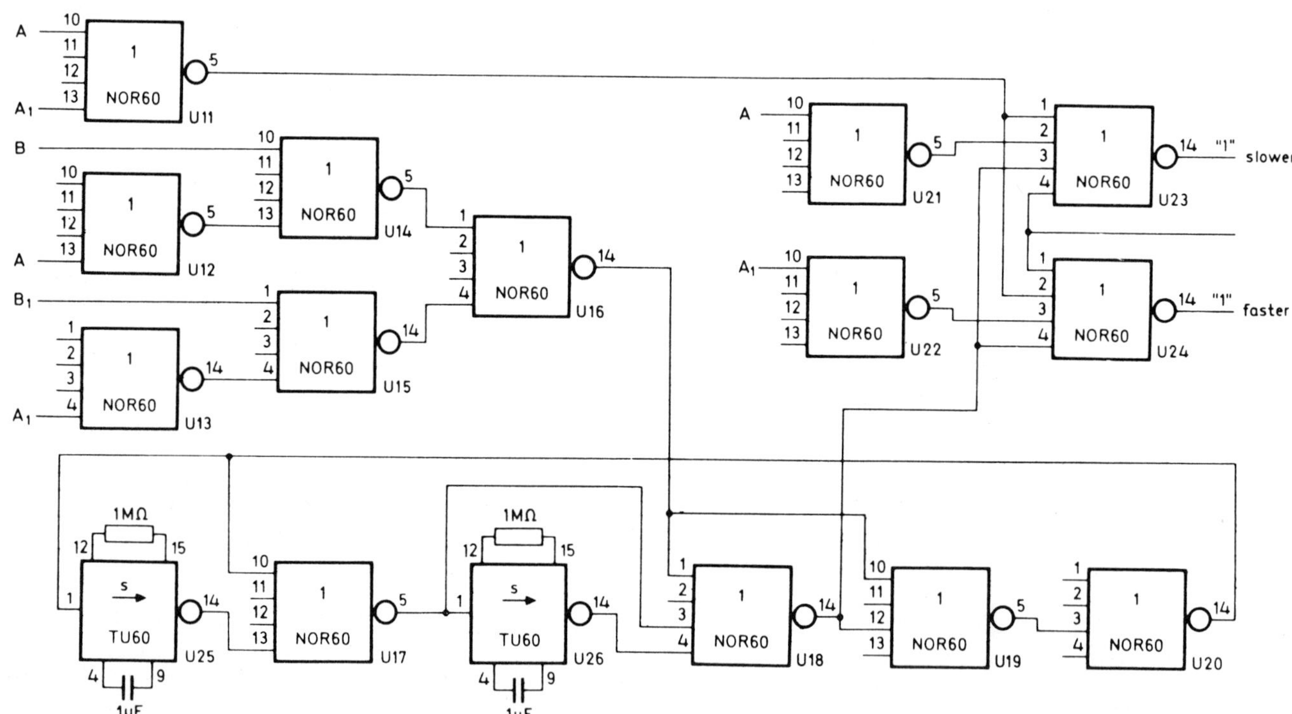

SPEED-SYNCHRONIZING LOGIC—Combination of Philips NOR60 and TU60 gates converts outputs of speed-synchronizing level detector to voltages required for speeding up or slowing down appropriate motor to give synchronization.—L. J. Lemmens, Control Circuit for Motor Speed Synchronization, Philips, Pub. Dept., Elcoma Div., Eindhoven, The Netherlands, No. 66.

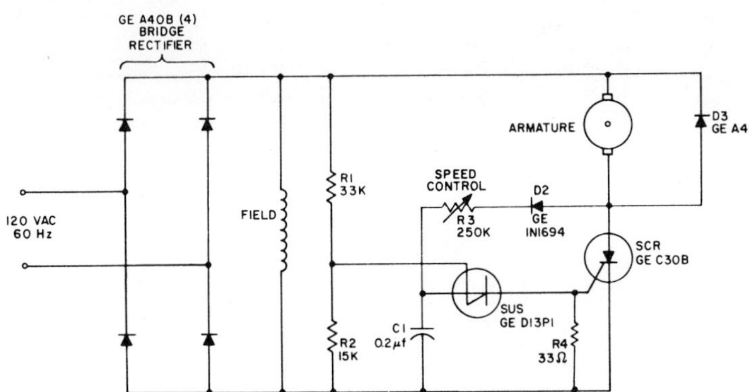

SHUNT-WOUND ½-HP D-C MOTOR CONTROL—Simple, low-cost solid-state speed control uses bridge rectifier for full-wave rectification of a-c supply. Field winding is permanently connected across d-c output of bridge. Provides smooth wide-range control of speed by controlling voltage applied to armature. Speed regulation is 10%.—"SCR Manual," 4th Edition, General Electric, 1967, p 213–215.

SPEED-SYNCHRONIZING LEVEL DETECTOR—Combination of Philips DOA40 opamps and DZD40 zero detectors delivers logic information on speeds to electric motors being synchronized, when d-c voltages proportional to speed are applied to inputs a and b by tachometers. If speed of motor M1 is higher than M2, output A is high and A1 is zero. If M2 is fast, A1 is high and A is zero. If difference in motor speeds is greater than limits covered by outputs A and A1, either B1 or B is zero depending on which motor is faster. Outputs are used to drive logic circuit that makes necessary speed corrections to give synchronization.—L. J. Lemmens, Control Circuit for Motor Speed Synchronization, Philips, Pub. Dept., Elcoma Div., Eindhoven, The Netherlands, No. 66.

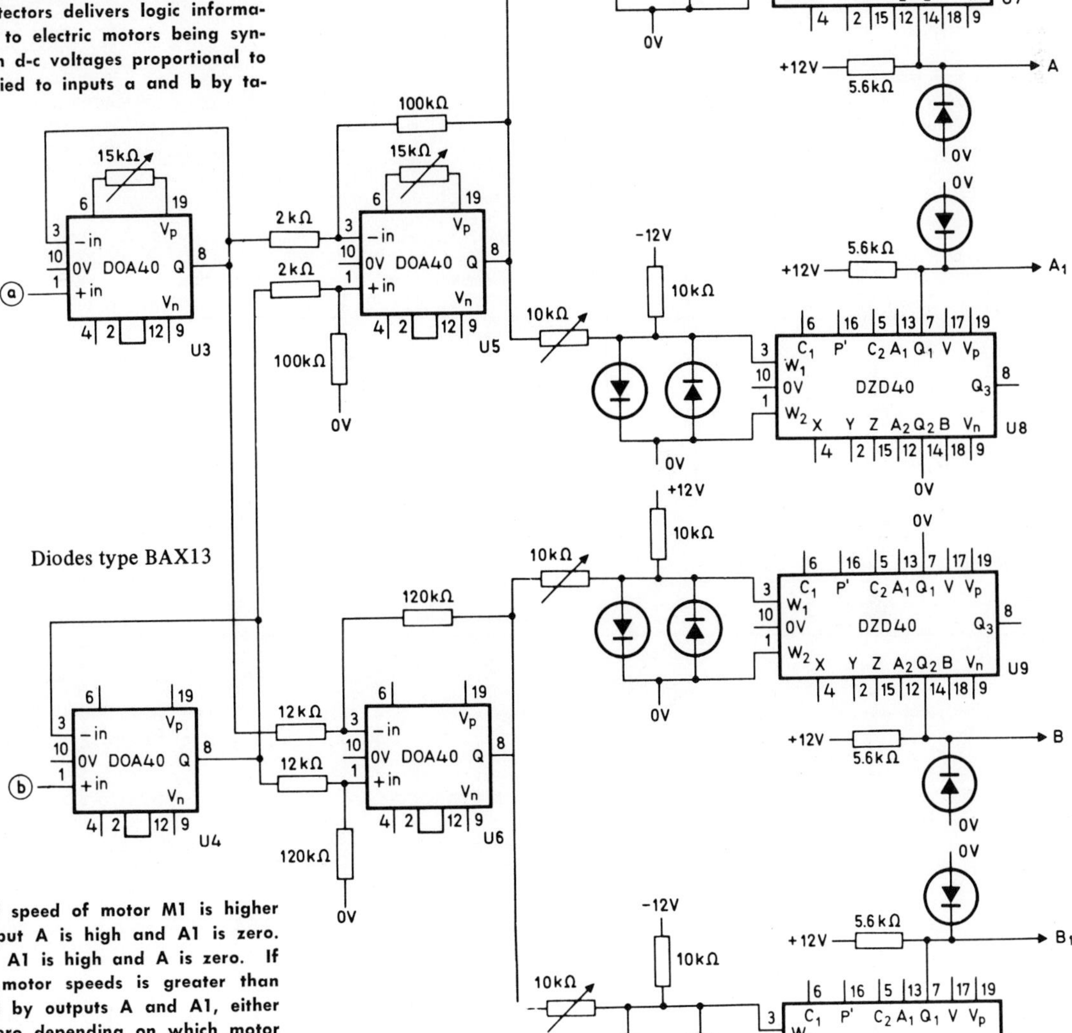

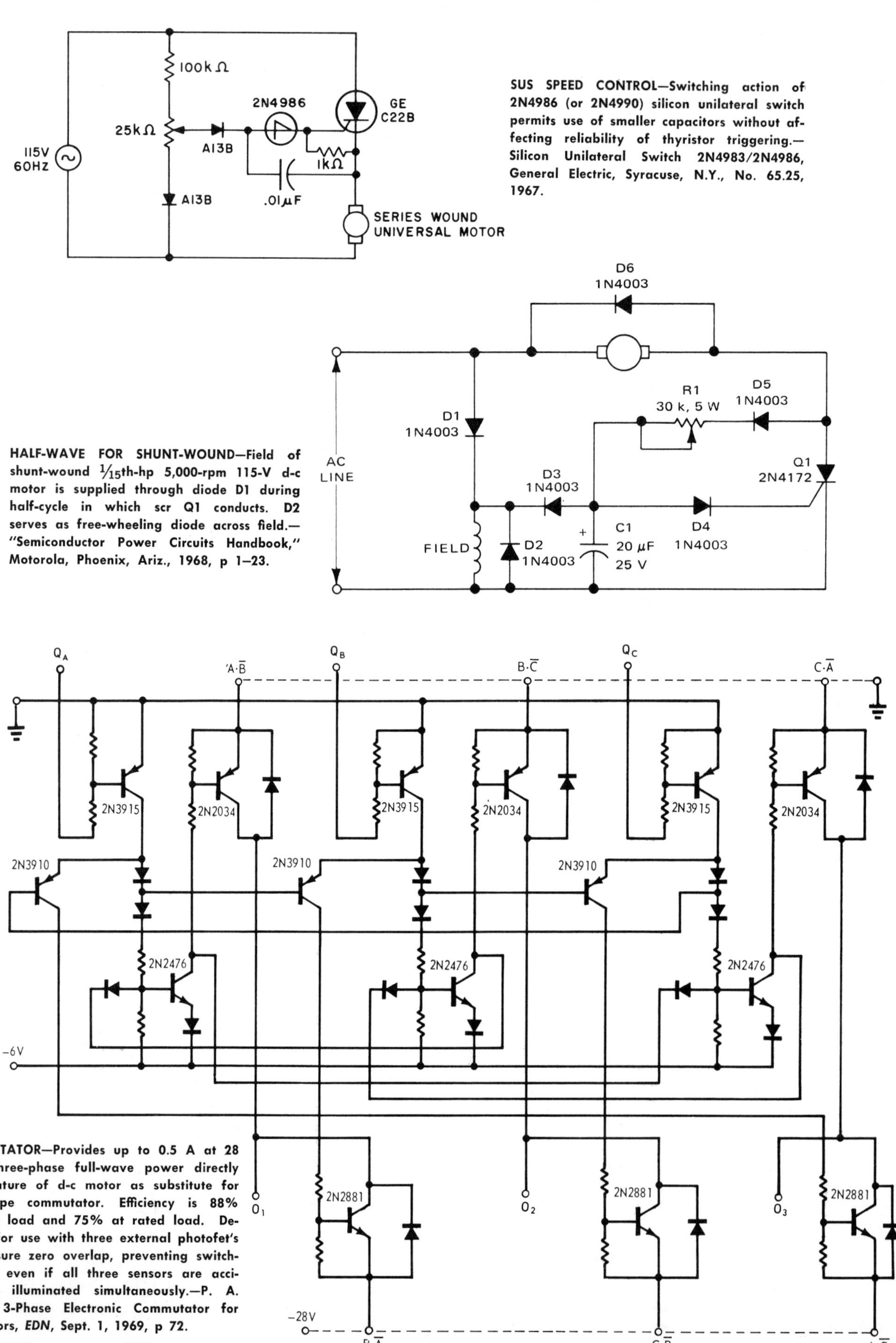

SUS SPEED CONTROL—Switching action of 2N4986 (or 2N4990) silicon unilateral switch permits use of smaller capacitors without affecting reliability of thyristor triggering.—Silicon Unilateral Switch 2N4983/2N4986, General Electric, Syracuse, N.Y., No. 65.25, 1967.

HALF-WAVE FOR SHUNT-WOUND—Field of shunt-wound 1/15th-hp 5,000-rpm 115-V d-c motor is supplied through diode D1 during half-cycle in which scr Q1 conducts. D2 serves as free-wheeling diode across field.—"Semiconductor Power Circuits Handbook," Motorola, Phoenix, Ariz., 1968, p 1–23.

COMMUTATOR—Provides up to 0.5 A at 28 V of three-phase full-wave power directly to armature of d-c motor as substitute for brush-type commutator. Efficiency is 88% at peak load and 75% at rated load. Designed for use with three external photofet's that assure zero overlap, preventing switch-through even if all three sensors are accidentally illuminated simultaneously.—P. A. Studer, 3-Phase Electronic Commutator for DC Motors, *EDN*, Sept. 1, 1969, p 72.

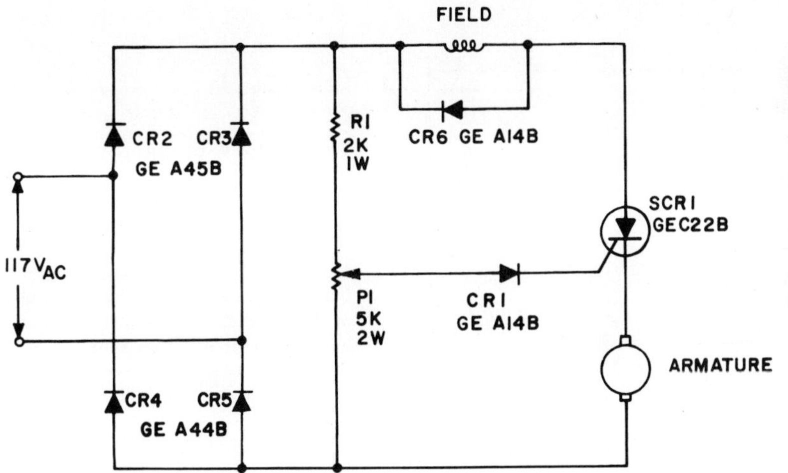

FULL-WAVE D-C MOTOR CONTROL WITH FEEDBACK—Requires separate connections for armature and field. Full-wave bridge supplies required d-c voltage for circuit and motor. Counter emf of armature provides feedback signal. One drawback is possibility of hunting at low speed settings, where there may not be sufficient time for scr to turn off. —A. A. Adem, Speed Controls for Universal Motors, General Electric, Syracuse, N.Y., No. 200.57, 1966, p 10.

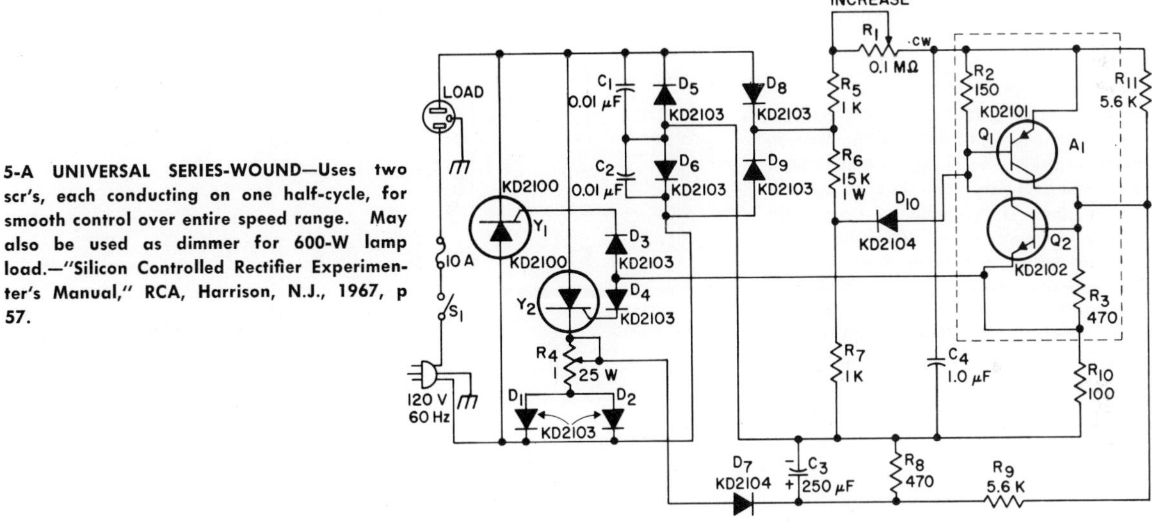

5-A UNIVERSAL SERIES-WOUND—Uses two scr's, each conducting on one half-cycle, for smooth control over entire speed range. May also be used as dimmer for 600-W lamp load.—"Silicon Controlled Rectifier Experimenter's Manual," RCA, Harrison, N.J., 1967, p 57.

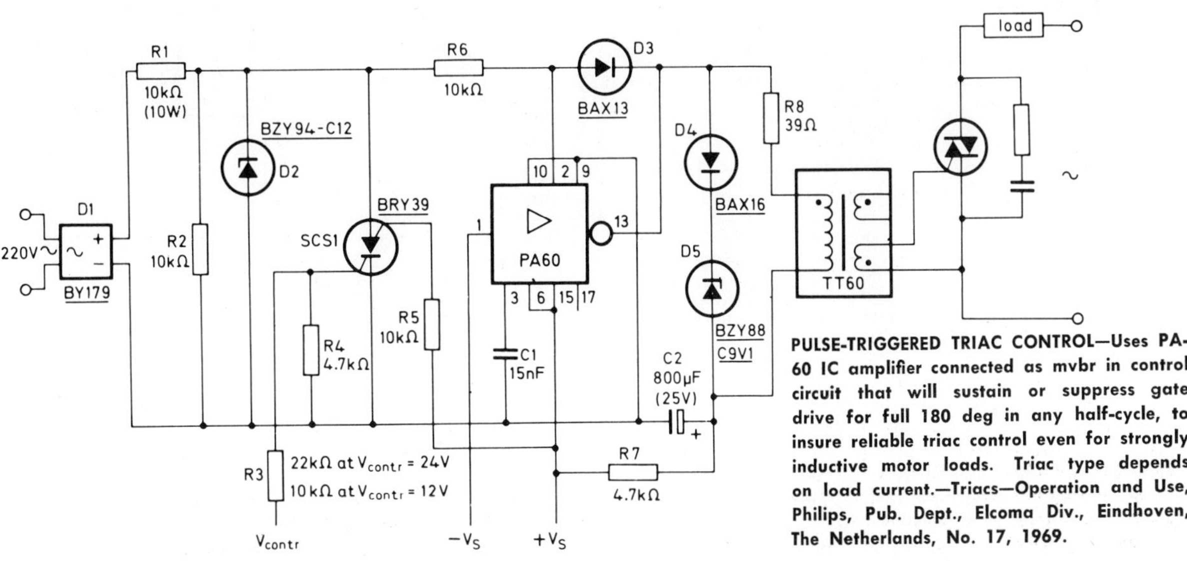

PULSE-TRIGGERED TRIAC CONTROL—Uses PA-60 IC amplifier connected as mvbr in control circuit that will sustain or suppress gate drive for full 180 deg in any half-cycle, to insure reliable triac control even for strongly inductive motor loads. Triac type depends on load current.—Triacs—Operation and Use, Philips, Pub. Dept., Elcoma Div., Eindhoven, The Netherlands, No. 17, 1969.

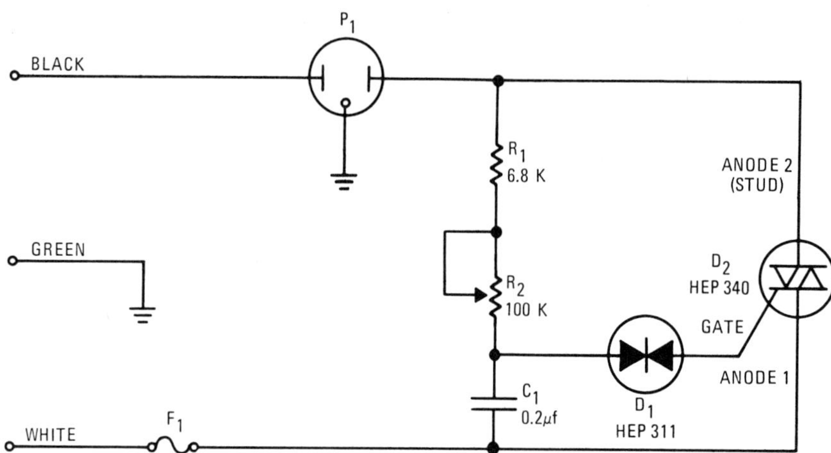

TRIAC POWER CONTROL—Simple and inexpensive control may be used for universal motors, incandescent lamps, or other devices to a maximum power of 600 W. Article gives construction details. P1 is polarized outlet. R2 varies speed or brightness from 0 to 98%, but for electric drills the torque will be low at low speeds. For continuous use at full load, mount triac D2 on heat sink to prevent overheating and loss of control.—"Solid State Projects Manual," Motorola, Phoenix, Ariz., 1968, p 55.

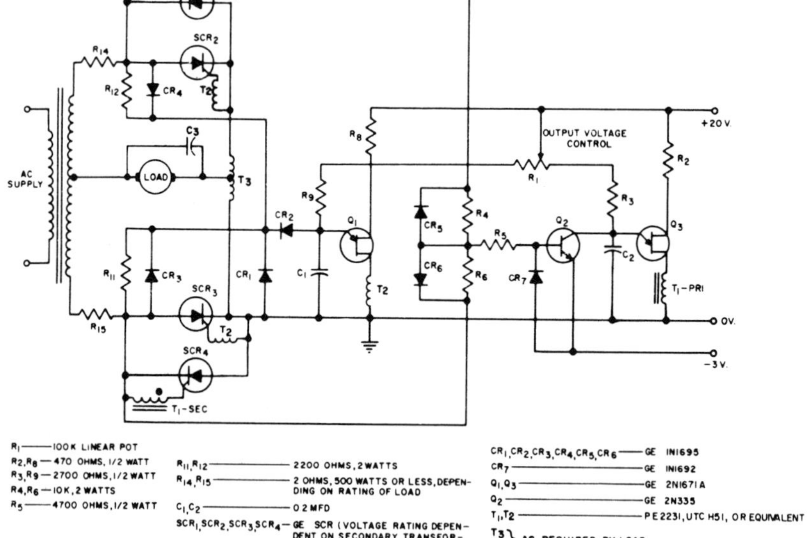

FULL-WAVE REVERSING D-C MOTOR DRIVE—Designed around SCR2-SCR3 with common cathodes controlled by ujt Q1 and SCR1-SCR4 with common anodes controlled by ujt Q3. Transistor clamp Q2 synchronizes firing of Q3 to anode voltages across SCR1 and SCR4. At extreme left-hand position of R1, full output voltage appears across load. When arm of R1 is moved to right of center, polarity of load is reversed. If R1 is moved rapidly through center position, plugging occurs (motor acts as generator).—"SCR Manual," 4th Edition, General Electric, 1967, p 216–217.

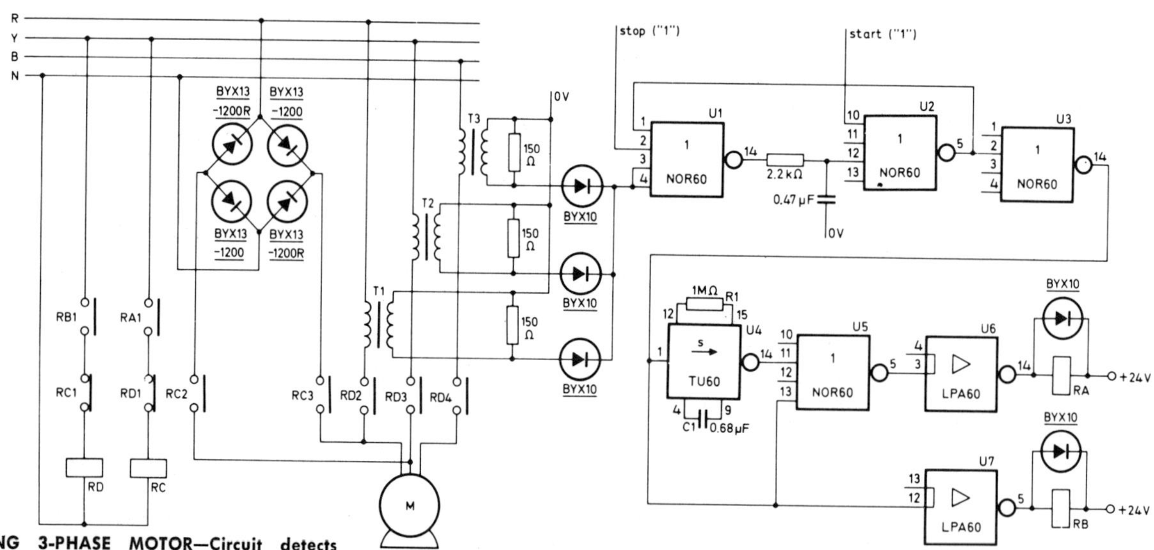

BRAKING 3-PHASE MOTOR—Circuit detects excessive drop in speed of motor and applies d-c braking current to windings to stop motor quickly and minimize disruption to sequence of operations on production line, then switches off braking current to avoid burning out motor winding. Uses Philips IC logic blocks.—Asynchronous Motor Braking Control, Philips, Pub. Dept., Elcoma Div., Eindhoven, The Netherlands, No. 92, 1970.

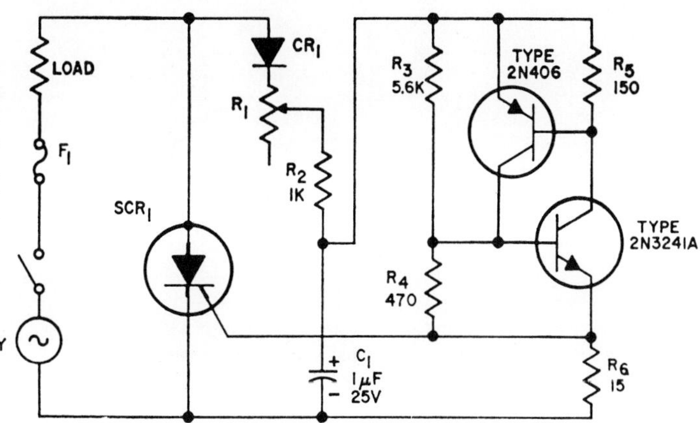

HALF-WAVE SCR WITHOUT REGULATION—Gives maximum conduction angle of about 170 deg and 8-V firing-voltage threshold. R1 is 75K speed control for 120-V scr's handling loads up to 25 A a-c, CR1 is 1N3755, and scr depends on load current rating.—"Silicon Power Circuits Manual," RCA, Harrison, N.J., SP-51, p 241.

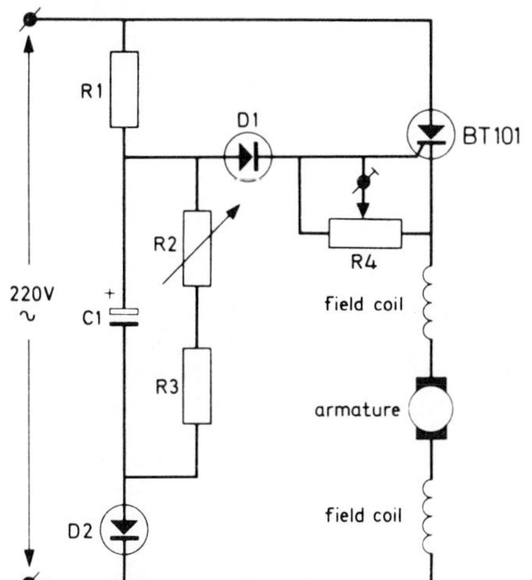

R1 = 4.7 kΩ, 7.0 W
R2 = 2.0 kΩ; 2.0 W
*R3 = 120 Ω; 0.5 W
R4 = 500 Ω; 0.5 W
*C1 = 47 μF; 63 V
D1, D2 = BYX10

* these values depend on the minimum speed requirement.

MIXER SPEED CONTROL—Single low-cost thyristor provides smooth continuous speed control of universal a-c motor for mixer or electric drill. R3 determines minimum speed setting. Typical speed ratio is 3:1. Requires only two connections to motor, as compared to circuits in which thyristor is between armature and one field coil.—Simple Speed Control for Small A. C. Series Motors, Philips, Pub. Dept., Elcoma Div., Eindhoven, The Netherlands, No. 17, 1968.

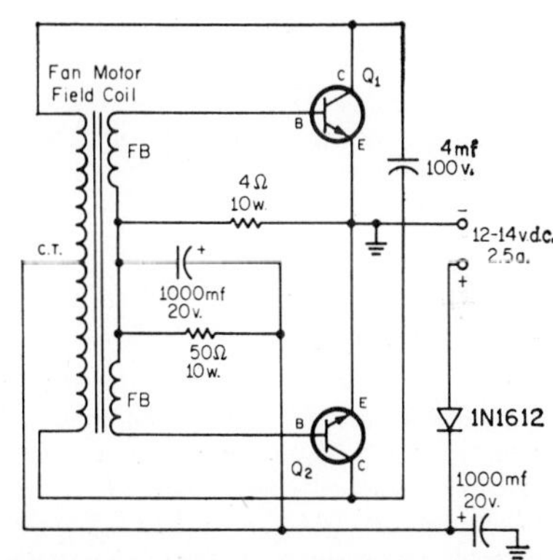

CONVERTER FOR FAN MOTOR—Operates from 12-V storage battery, drawing 2.5 A, and develops sufficient power to drive cooling fan motor at frequency of about 68 Hz without noise-producing d-c motor brushes. Motor can be ordinary rim-drive phonograph motor with field coil rewound as shown, or Gonset 115-011 motor available from Mamco, Racine, Wisc. Transistors are RCA 40251.—W. F. Frankart, Brushless D. C. Fan Motor, CQ, May 1966, p 49.

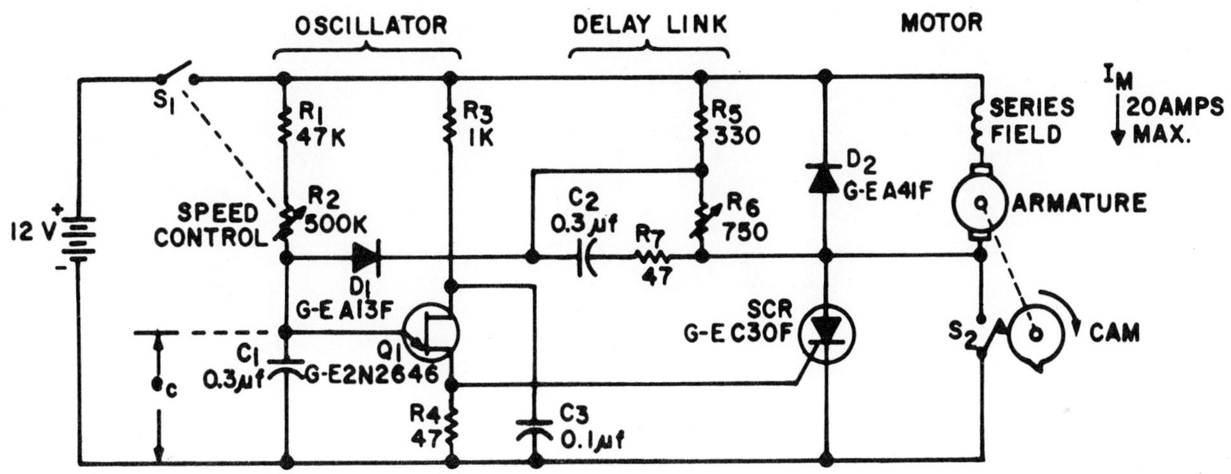

SYNCHRONOUS SERIES-MOTOR CONTROL—Relaxation oscillator Q1 generates trigger pulses for scr. With operation from d-c source, scr conducts current through motor until cam switch on armature closes and momentarily bypasses current around scr. Motor is then without current until arrival of next trigger. D2 eliminates most of arcing at S2. Article gives detailed description of circuit action during under-speed and over-speed conditions to maintain synchronism with ujt frequency.—E. K. Howell, Solid State Control for DC Motors Provides Variable Speed With Synchronous-Motor Performance, General Electric, Syracuse, N.Y., No. 200.43, 1965, p 4.

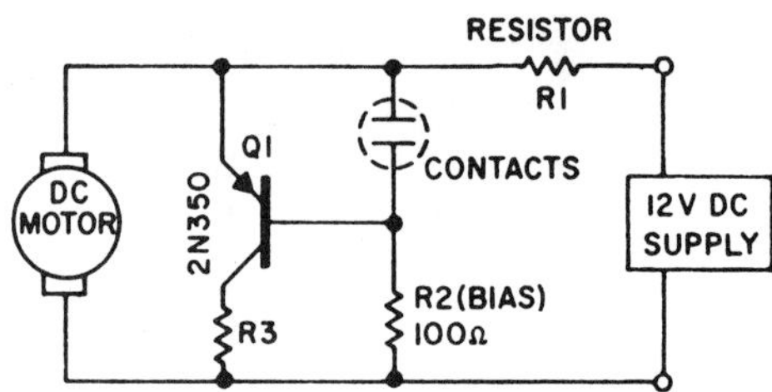

TRANSISTOR SUPPLEMENTS CENTRIFUGAL SWITCH—Q1 provides dynamic braking path for armature and improves speed regulation. When switch contacts open, Q1 is biased on through R2, to reduce arcing at contacts.—T. F. Bright, Bridge Circuit Temperature Stabilizes Relay Operation, "400 Ideas for Design Selected from Electronic Design," Hayden Book Co., N.Y., 1964, p 98.

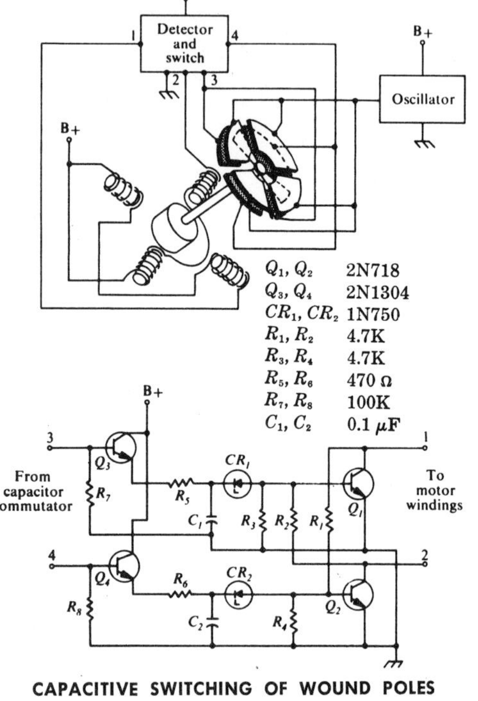

CAPACITIVE SWITCHING OF WOUND POLES—Can be used wherever d-c motors or a-c synchronous motors without brushes must operate with minimum maintenance. One set of four capacitor stator plates is provided for each wound pole of motor, and switching is accomplished by mounting capacitor rotor on motor shaft so it passes between stacked stator plates. Rotor plates should be insulated from shaft, and require no electrical connection because they merely serve to couple stator sections. Modulated output from stator is detected and used to switch appropriate wound poles of permanent-magnet motor. Amplitude of modulation is independent of speed, which means that capacitor system performs equally well for motor starting, running, and restarting from stall. D-c supply is 100 V and oscillator is 100-kHz sine-wave.—"Selected Electronic Circuitry," NASA SP-5046, 1966, Government Printing Office, Washington, D.C., p 70.

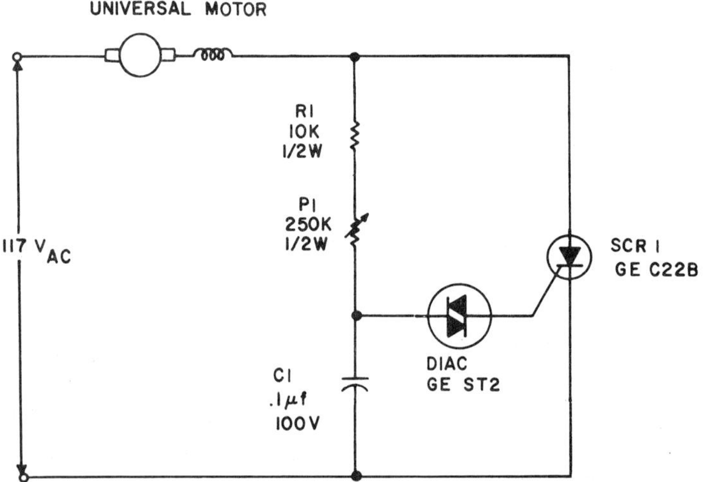

HALF-WAVE CONTROL WITHOUT FEEDBACK—Diac-triggered scr, for speed control of universal a-c/d-c motor, has wide control range, although absence of feedback signal makes motor slow down as load is increased. When load is removed, motor runs at no-load speed for setting of P1.—A. A. Adem, Speed Controls for Universal Motors, General Electric, Syracuse, N.Y., No. 200.47, 1966, p 3.

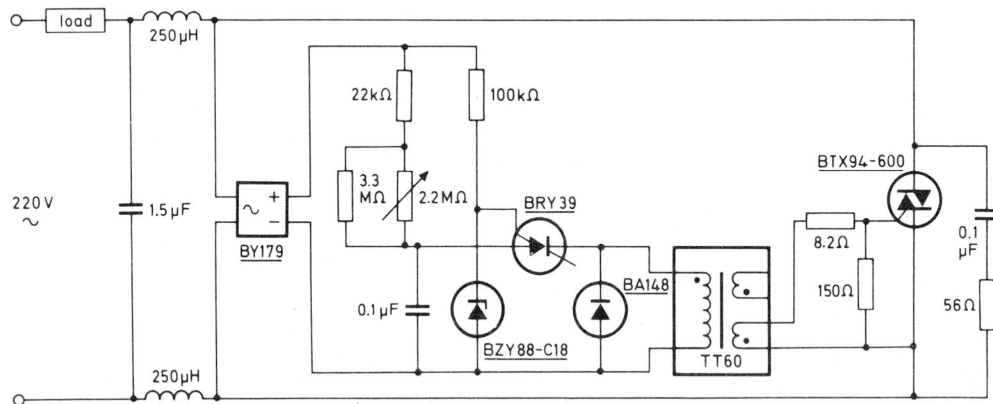

BASIC SCS CONTROL FOR TRIAC—Uses BRY39 silicon controlled switch with triac for controlling power to low-inductance loads such as lamps, heaters, and squirrel-cage fan motors. Control range is 20 to 170 deg. Large changes in line voltage affect trigger angle excessively for certain applications.—Triacs—Operation and Use, Philips, Pub. Dept., Elcoma Div., Eindhoven, The Netherlands, No. 17, 1969.

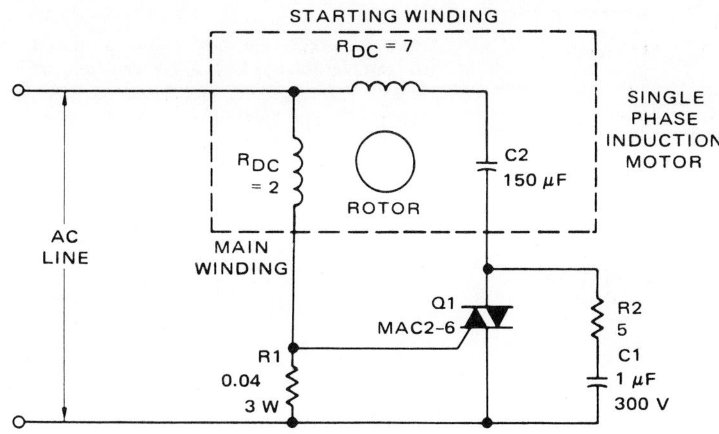

TRIAC MOTOR-STARTING SWITCH—Used to control starting winding of ½-V single-phase 115-V induction motor. Eliminates need for centrifugal switch that would cut out winding when rotor reaches about 75% of full-load speed. Operation is based on starting current in main winding being several times running current. Triac Q1 is triggered by drop across R1 whenever main-winding current exceeds threshold level. Values shown are for motor having peak starting current of 40 A and peak running current of 8 A, with triac triggering on only for currents above 12 A. Current drops below 12 A after about 12 cycles.—"Semiconductor Power Circuits Handbook," Motorola, Phoenix, Ariz., 1968, p 4–5.

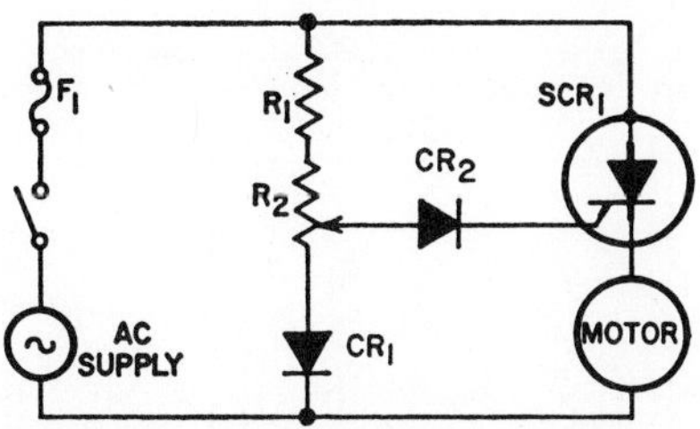

HALF-WAVE SCR WITH REGULATION—Highly effective for speed control of universal motors. Counter emf, which is function of speed, determines point in each positive half-cycle at which scr fires. Skip-cycling may occur at low speed settings of R2, making motor speed erratic. Uses 1N3755 for both diodes for motors drawing up to 25 A from 120-V a-c line. Book gives values of R1 and R2 for eight different scr types.—"Silicon Power Circuits Manual," RCA, Harrison, N.J., SP-51, p 244.

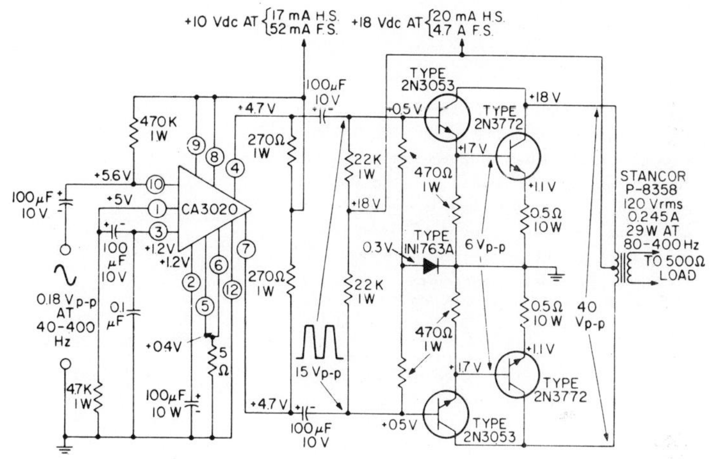

40–400 HZ CONTROL—Uses wideband IC amplifier to drive 500-ohm load through transformer and four-transistor power amplifier. May also be used as servo amplifier. Delivers 29 W.—"Linear Integrated Circuits," RCA, Harrison, N.J., IC-41, p 274.

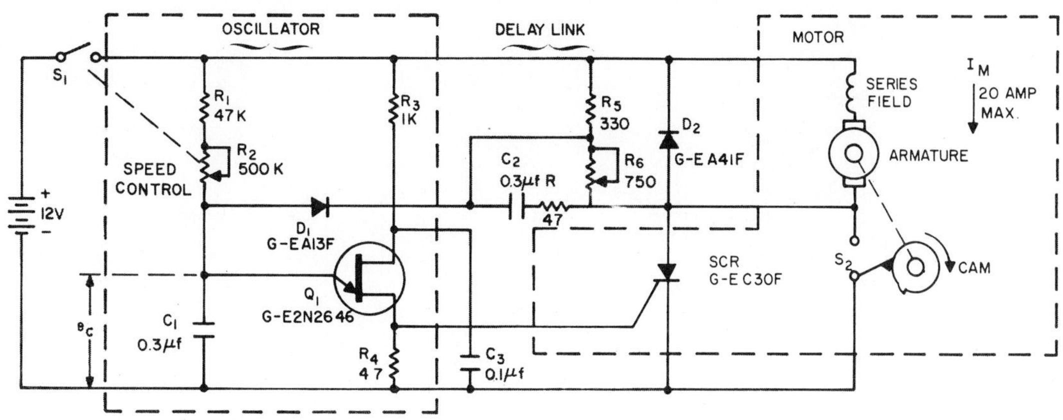

UJT-SCR CONTROL FOR SERIES MOTOR—Relaxation oscillator Q1 generates periodic pulses that trigger scr carrying motor current. At one or more points in rotation of motor shaft, cam bypasses current around scr to make it turn off (commutate). Time between turn-on by ujt and turn-off by scr depends on motor load. Arrangement provides high starting torque at any speed below desired synchronous speed that would otherwise require a-c synchronous motor. Use of cam switch gives simplicity and low cost.—E. K. Howell, Precise Speed Control, High Torque Can Now be Combined in DC Motors, *Electronic Design*, Dec. 6, 1965, p 20–25.

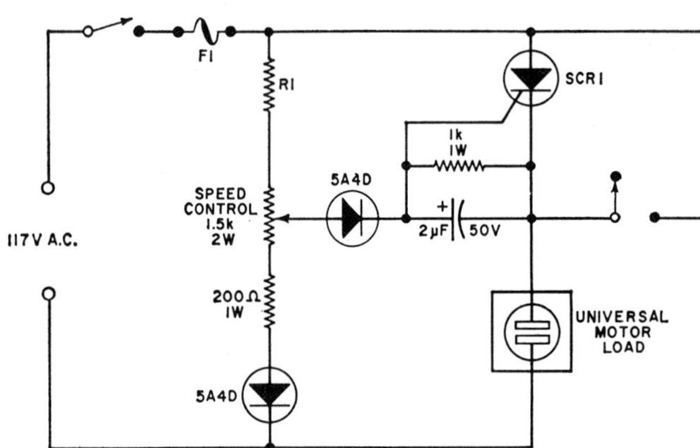

SPEED CONTROL—For 2-A universal motors use 2N1774 for SCR1, 3 A for F1, and 10K for R1. For 5-A motor use 2N685 for SCR1, 10 A for F1, and 5K for R1.—D. Cooper, SCR's and Triacs—the Revolution Continues, *Electronics World*, Aug. 1968, p 25–28.

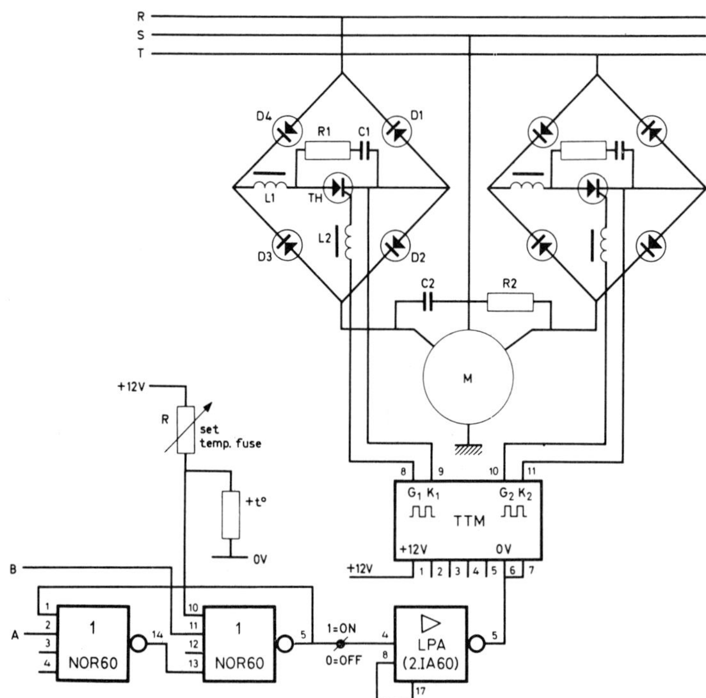

SWITCHING 3-PHASE MOTOR—Philips IC NOR circuits, power amplifier, and TTM thyristor trigger module, when connected to bridge circuits as shown, will switch on 3-hp 3-phase motor M when 1-level pulse is applied to input A, and will switch motor off when 1-level is applied to B. Temperature-sensitive PTC resistor provides overload protection. Values are: R1 22; R2 10; C1-C2 1 μF at 1,000 V; all diodes are BYX25/800R; thyristor TH is BTX12/600R. Thyristor bridges are identical.—C. Rosielle, "Control System Design Manual for 60-Series Norbits," Philips, Pub. Dept., Elcoma Div., Eindhoven, The Netherlands, 1968, p 147.

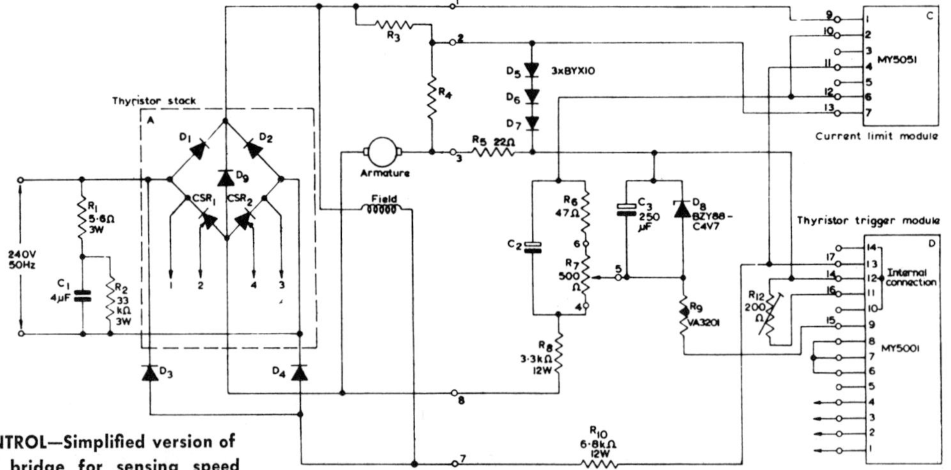

SIMPLE SPEED CONTROL—Simplified version of armature voltage bridge for sensing speed provides economical control for d-c shunt motor. R7 sets speed. Uses Mullard thyristor stack rated at twice motor full-load current, plus two other Mullard modules. Diodes D3 and D4 are Mullard BYX22-80, C2 is 20 μF, and R3 and R4 depend on armature resistance. Report gives complete design information.—J. Merrett, Thyristor Speed Control Circuit Design for D. C. Shunt Motors Supplied from A. C. Mains, Philips, Pub. Dept., Elcoma Div., Eindhoven, The Netherlands, No. 438, 1967.

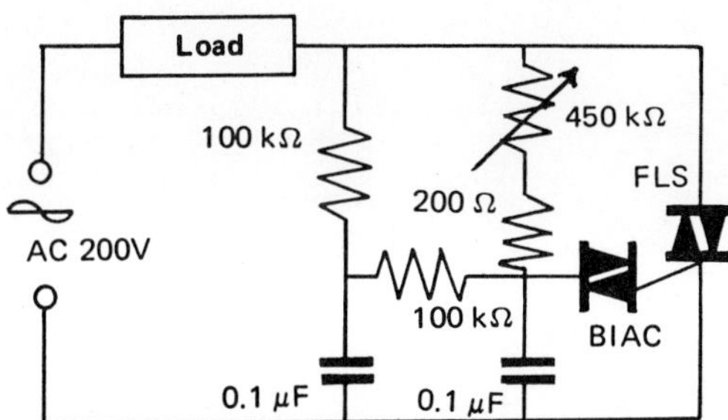

20-A MOTOR SPEED CONTROL—New five-layer FQO½ switching thyristor triggered by biac provides smooth wide-angle control of speed for a-c motors rated at up to 20 A. Will also handle lamp or heater loads. Speed control is 450K pot.—FLS Five-Layer Switch (Hitachi ad), *Journal of Asia Electronics Union*, No. 1, 1970, p 32.

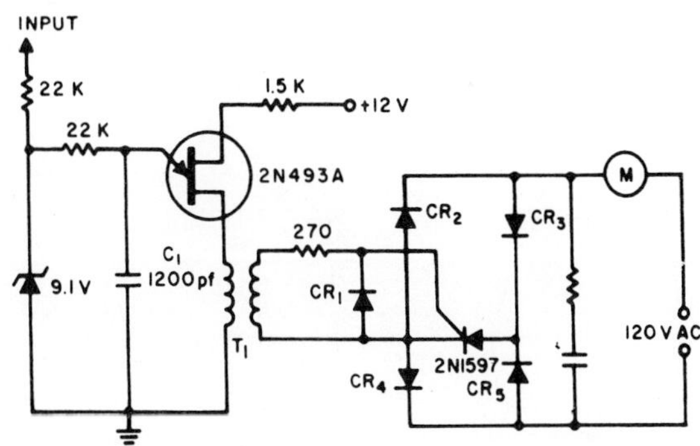

ELIMINATING SNEAK-PATHS—Provides electrical isolation between d-c control circuit and a-c line, without resorting to bulky isolation transformer. With bias as shown, ujt relaxation oscillator starts when C1 charges to 7 V. When input control voltage is increased above 7 V d-c to increase speed of motor, pulse repetition rate increases up to prr corresponding to zener limit of 9.1 V. T1 couples pulses to scr, to provide full-wave control of a-c motor through five-diode bridge. Series resistor and capacitor across bridge suppress motor-produced transients.—S. Steckler, Motor Control System Isolates AC Lines from DC Circuits, "400 Ideas for Design Selected from Electronic Design," Hayden Book Co., N.Y., 1964, p 217.

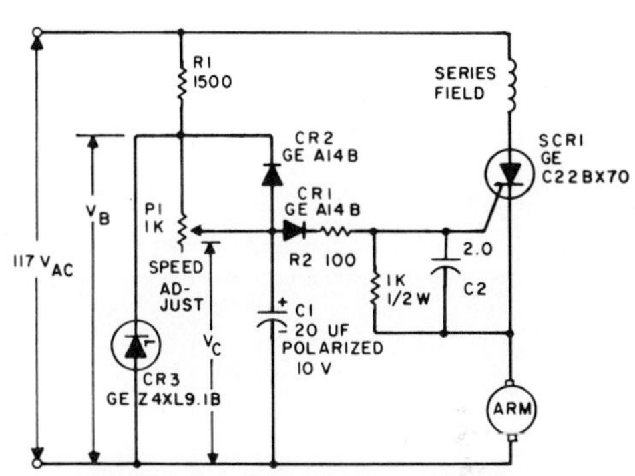

SLOW-SPEED HALF-WAVE WITH FEEDBACK—Gives stable operation at all speeds. Motor residual field provides speed feedback signal. Circuit permits very short scr conduction time, for stable operation at low speeds. Need for separate armature and field connections to motor is possible drawback.—A. A. Adem, Speed Controls for Universal Motors, General Electric, Syracuse, N.Y., No. 200.47, 1966, p 5.

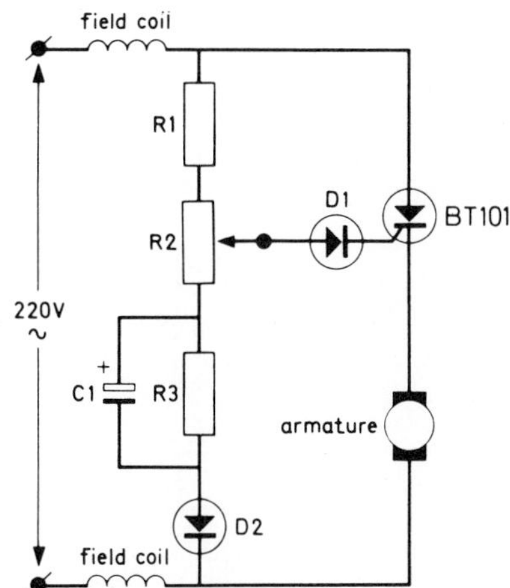

ELECTRIC DRILL SPEED CONTROL—Uses low-cost thyristor and minimum of other components to provide smooth continuous speed control above minimum speed setting determined by values of R3 and C1, which are typically 270 ohms and 16 μF. R1 is 5.6K, R2 is 1K, and diodes are BYX10. Developed for use with a-c series universal motors in hand drills, food mixers, and similar appliances.—Simple Speed Control for Small A. C. Series Motors, Philips, Pub. Dept., Elcoma Div., Eindhoven, The Netherlands, No. 17, 1968.

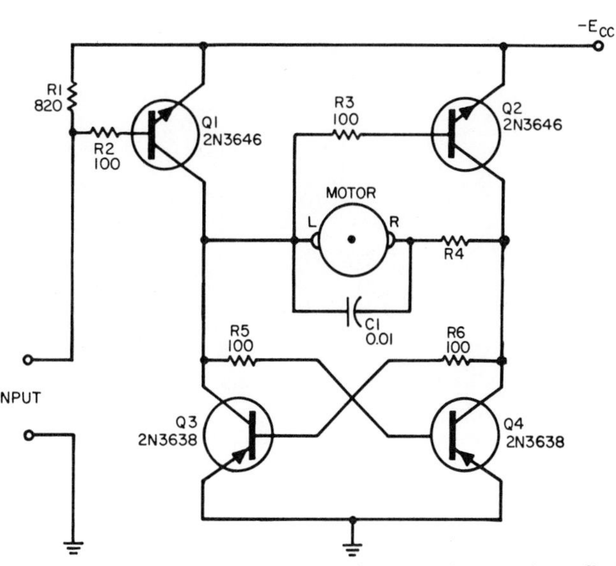

REVERSING SWITCH—With input open, permanent-magnet d-c motor runs in one direction. When input is shorted by ordinary switch, switching transistor, or other means, motor reverses. Closing switch makes Q1 and Q4 conduct, turning off Q2 and Q3. Applications include reversal of battery-powered tape recorders.—C. B. Smith, SPST Switch Reverses PM DC Motor Rotation, *Electronic Design*, April 26, 1967, p 245.

2-A UNIVERSAL FOR POWER TOOLS—Provides full-wave control over entire speed range, with essentially constant speed for any given setting of R1 under changing load conditions. Operates smoothly at low speeds, but motor may overheat because built-in fan cannot provide sufficient cooling air at low speeds. Intended only for universal series-wound motor, but can be used for dimming lamps up to 240-W.—"Silicon Controlled Rectifier Experimenter's Manual," RCA, Harrison, N.J., 1967, p 53.

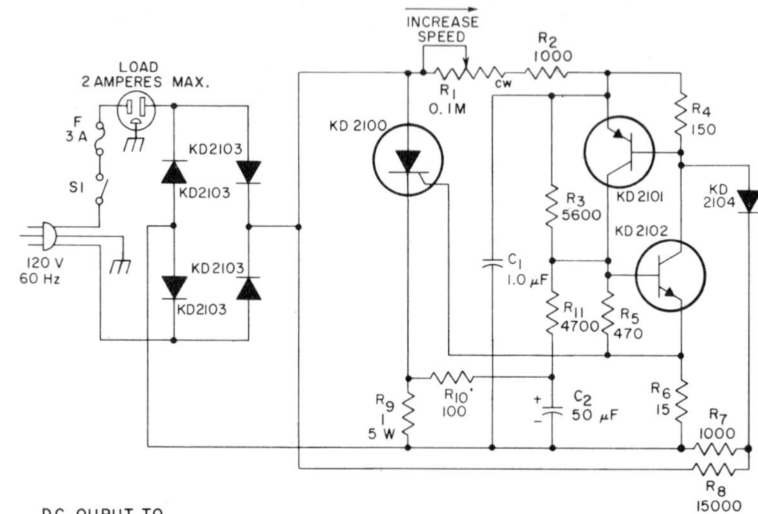

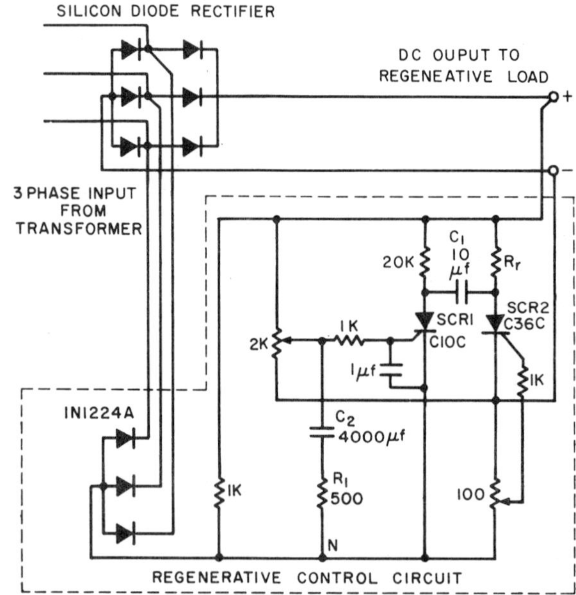

REGENERATIVE-LOAD POWER ABSORBER—Uses scr's in regenerative control circuit to absorb energy from regenerative loads such as elevator and crane motors. Is quiet, has adjustable time delay, and has long life. A-c line variations do not affect set point. Circuit values are for 1.5-kW regenerative control unit having 220 V at no-load. Regenerative load is picked up at 230 V and dropped out at 220 V.—S. P. Lee, Regenerative Load Energy Absorbed by SCR Circuit, *Electronic Design*, May 11, 1964, p 87–89.

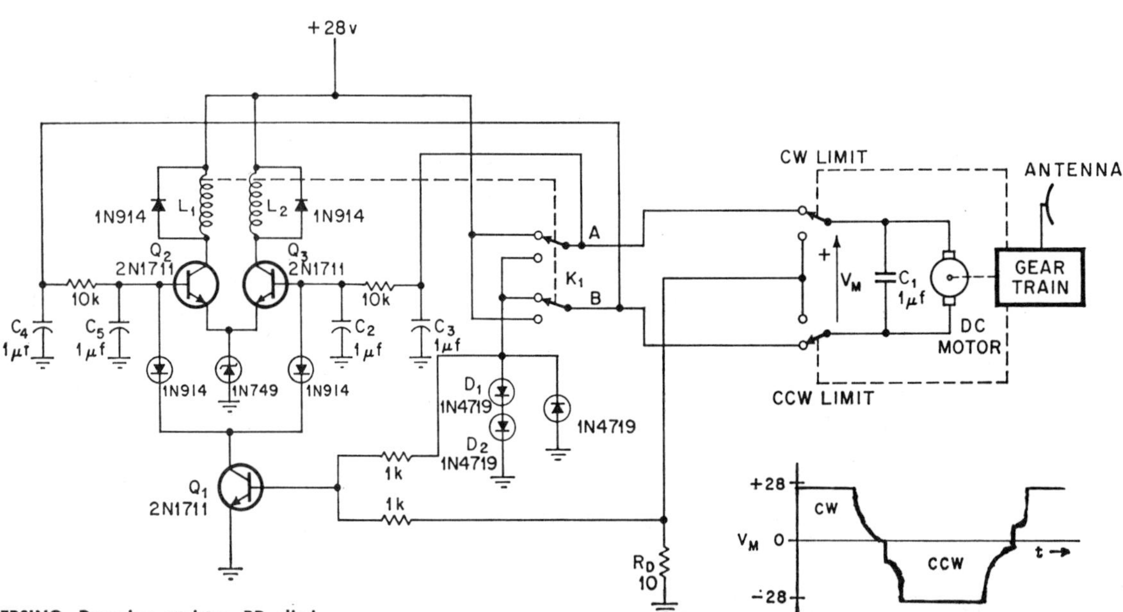

SELF-REVERSING—Damping resistor RD dissipates initial energy of motor when power is removed, and develops signal that turns on Q1 as motor is slowing down. When motor stops, Q3 turns on and pulses latching relay L to reverse motor connections. Can be used to reverse scan direction of motor-driven antenna when limit switch operates.—J. E. Bjornholt, Dynamic Braking EMF Signals Motor To Reverse, *Electronics*, June 22, 1970, p 84.

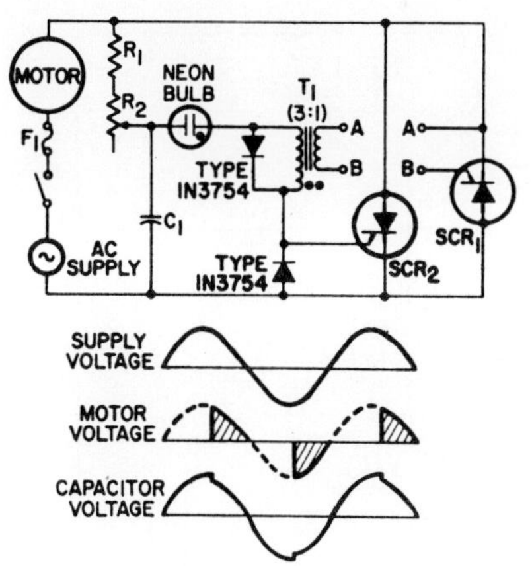

FULL-WAVE SCR WITHOUT REGULATION—Simple full-wave proportional control uses a-c phase shifting to provide gate phase-angle control. Small pulse transformer provides isolation. Conduction angle range is 30 to 150 deg. Book gives values of all components for eight different types of scr used with both 120-V and 240-V a-c lines.—"Silicon Power Circuits Manual," RCA, Harrison, N.J., SP-51, p 248.

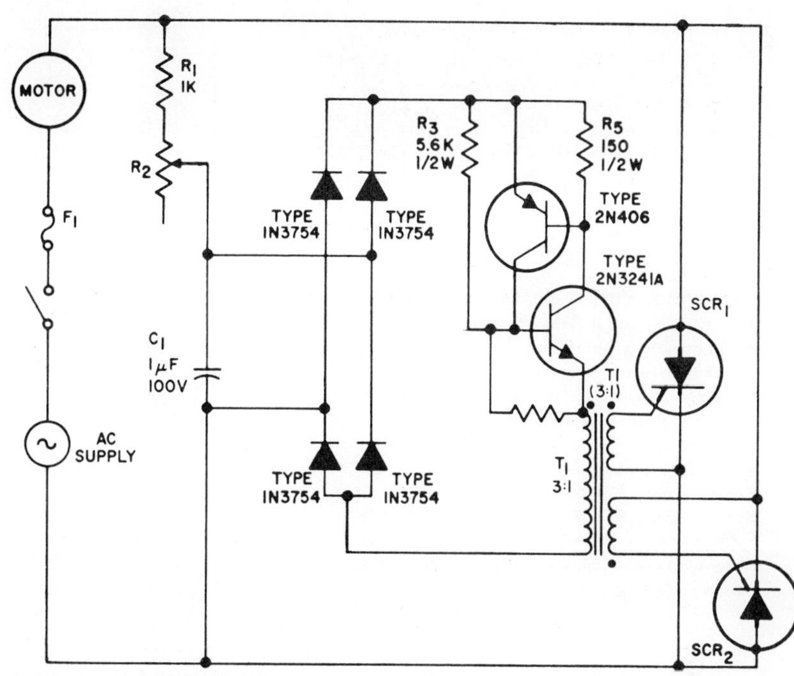

FULL-WAVE SCR UNREGULATED WITH 5—170 DEG CONDUCTION RANGE—Large conduction angle range is more desirable when higher power is to be controlled. For 120-V a-c supply, R2 is 75K and scr's depend on motor current rating. For 240-V a-c, R2 is 150K.—"Silicon Power Circuits Manual," RCA, Harrison, N.J., SP-51, p 249.

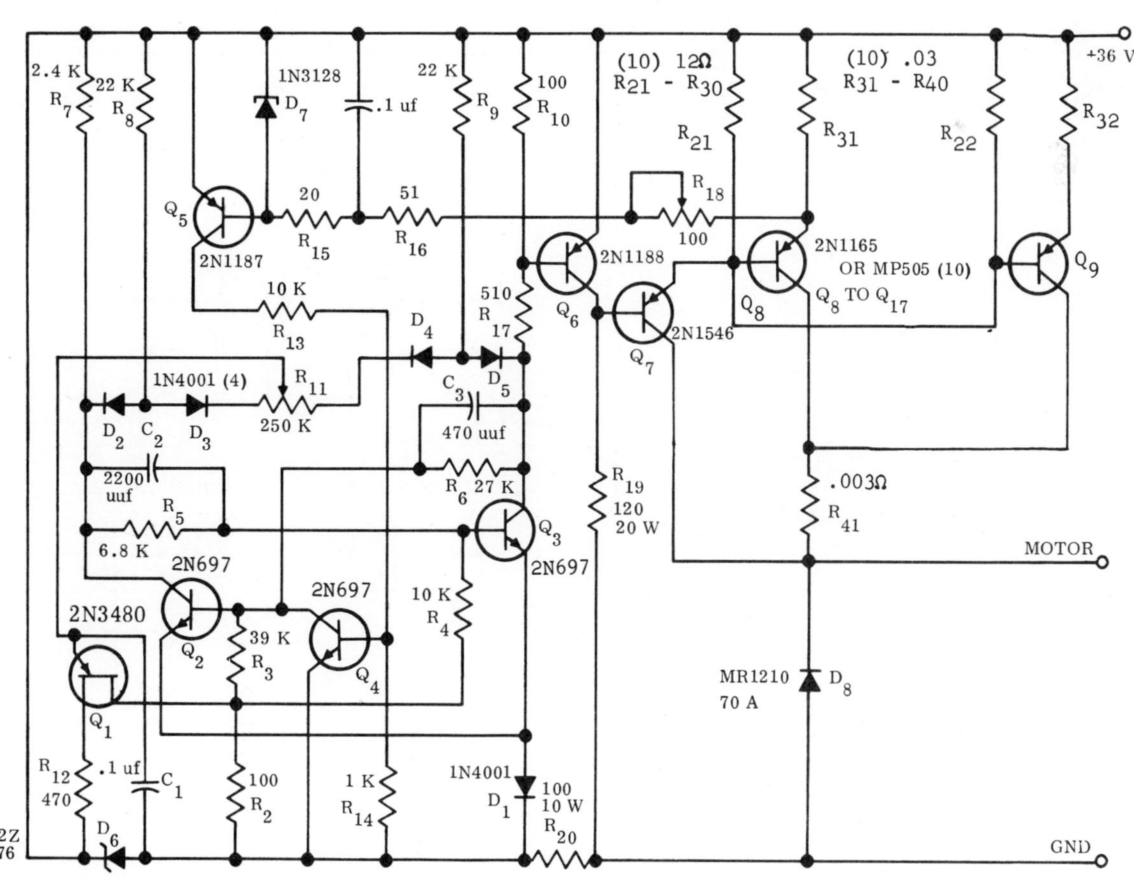

PWM CONTROL FOR 36-V GOLF CART—Handles up to 200 A under stall or starting conditions by using ten transistors in parallel for control of series d-c motor. Book tells how pulse width modulation is used to control speed.—"Circuits Manual," Motorola, Phoenix, Ariz., 1965, p 6-4-8.

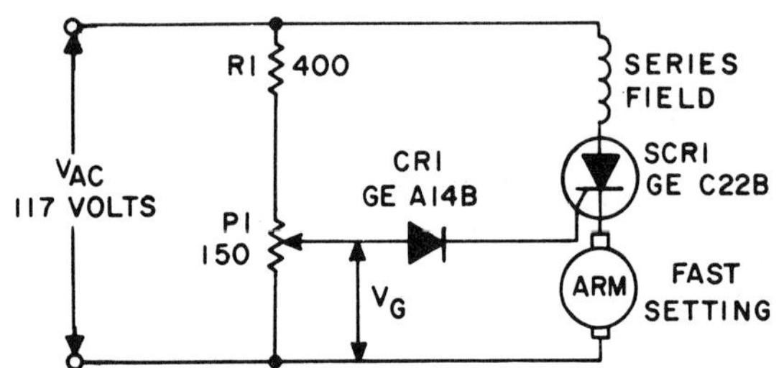

HALF-WAVE WITH FEEDBACK—Uses feedback by motor residual field to induce back emf in armature proportional to speed. Scr is located between armature and series field winding. When load on motor is increased, feedback action automatically advances firing angle of scr, thereby increasing motor torque while maintaining essentially constant speed. Chief drawback is 25-W power dissipation in R1-P1. Operation is unstable at low speeds. —A. A. Adem, Speed Controls for Universal Motors, General Electric, Syracuse, N.Y., No. 200.47, 1966, p 4.

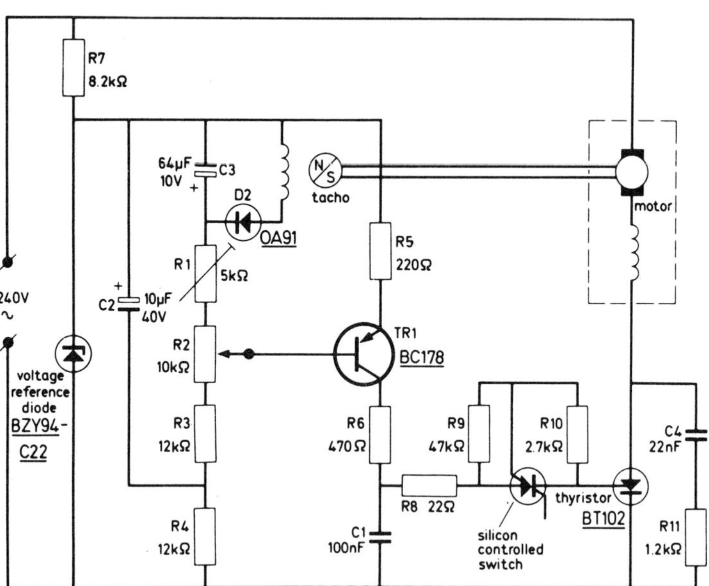

LOW-COST THYRISTOR CONTROL OF SMALL FHP MOTOR—Philips BT102 thyristor makes smooth, continuous speed control economical for sewing machines, food mixers, electric drills, and other appliances using small fractional-horsepower motors. Tachometer on motor shaft provides feedback to stabilize speed against variations in motor loading, while zener provides stabilization against line voltage changes. Thyristor is triggered by scs at point in each half-cycle corresponding to setting of speed control R2, to give 7:1 speed range. Tachometer is disk of ceramic magnetic material mounted on motor shaft, inducing pulses in coil wound on suitably shaped stator.—Series Motor Speed Control Systems with Tachometer, Philips, Pub. Dept., Elcoma Div., Eindhoven, The Netherlands, No. 6, 1968.

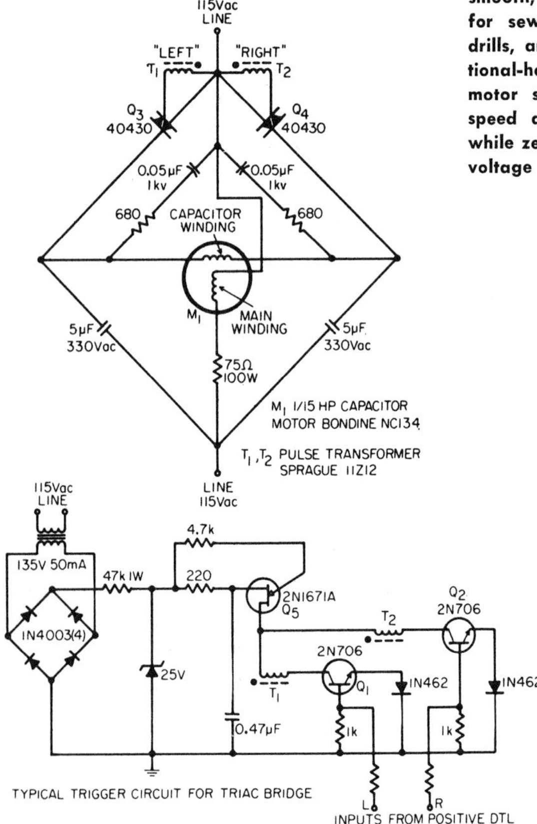

TRIACS REVERSE CAPACITOR MOTOR—Simple triac bridge controls direction of rotation for fractional-horsepower capacitor-start motor. Power is obtained from a-c motor line. Left and right rotation command signals are obtained from trigger circuit (shown also) through transformers T1 and T2, with trigger in turn controlled by low-level logic from flip-flop or other source.—High-Voltage Triacs Reverse Capacitor Motor, "Electronic Circuit Design Handbook," Tab Books, Blue Ridge Summit, Pa., p 33–34.

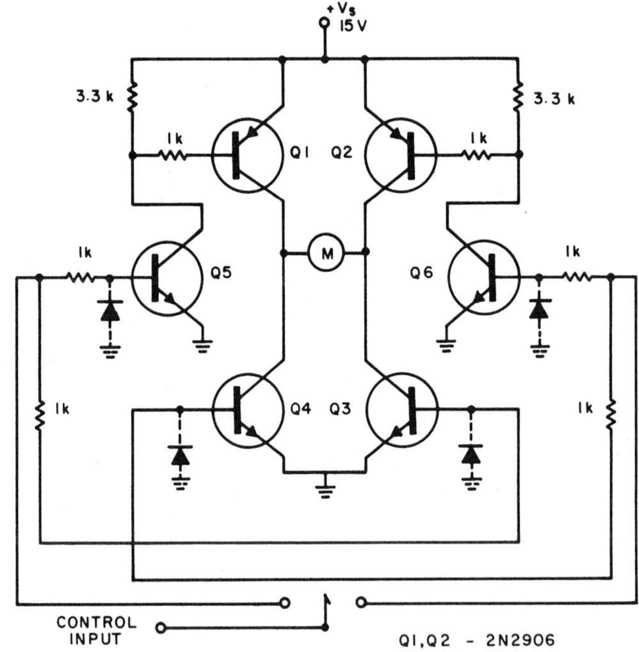

PROPORTIONAL D-C CONTROL—Drives 15-V d-c permanent-magnet motor rated at 100 mA. Bridge-type proportional control amplifier Q1-Q4 is driven by common-emitter stages Q5-Q6. Motor voltage varies from 9.5 to 14.7 V when control input voltage is increased from 0.8 to 2.5 V, with proportional change in speed. Control switch determines direction of rotation.—J. Ayer, Proportional DC Motor Control Requires Low-Level Inputs, *Electronic Design*, Aug. 15, 1968, p 236.

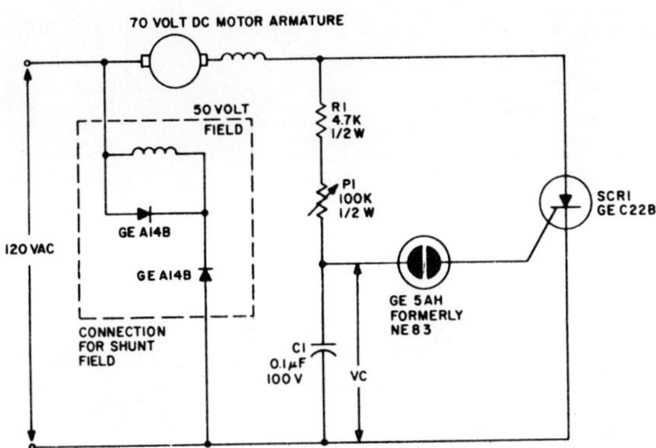

HALF-WAVE NEON-TRIGGERED—Simplest and lowest-cost speed control for universal, shunt, or p-m motors. Uses one scr and minimum number of components. Series network R1-P1-C1 supplies phase-shift signal to neon that triggers scr on at varying times in positive a-c half-cycles.—"SCR Manual," 4th Edition, General Electric, 1967, p 215.

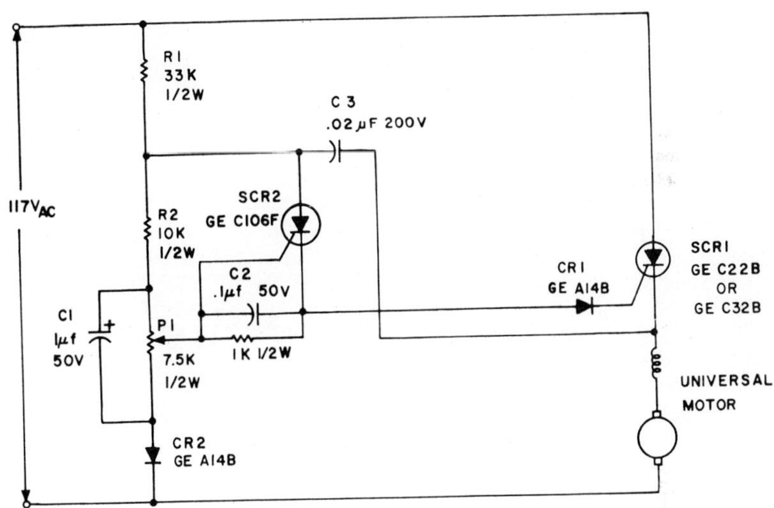

HALF-WAVE WITH IMPROVED SPEED REGULATION—Reliable and economical circuit with excellent performance at low speed is achieved by using ramp charge on C1 to provide stable triggering point for SCR2, which in turn delivers pulse rather than continuous current for triggering gate of SCR1.—A. A. Adem, Speed Controls for Universal Motors, General Electric, Syracuse, N.Y., No. 200.47, 1966, p 8.

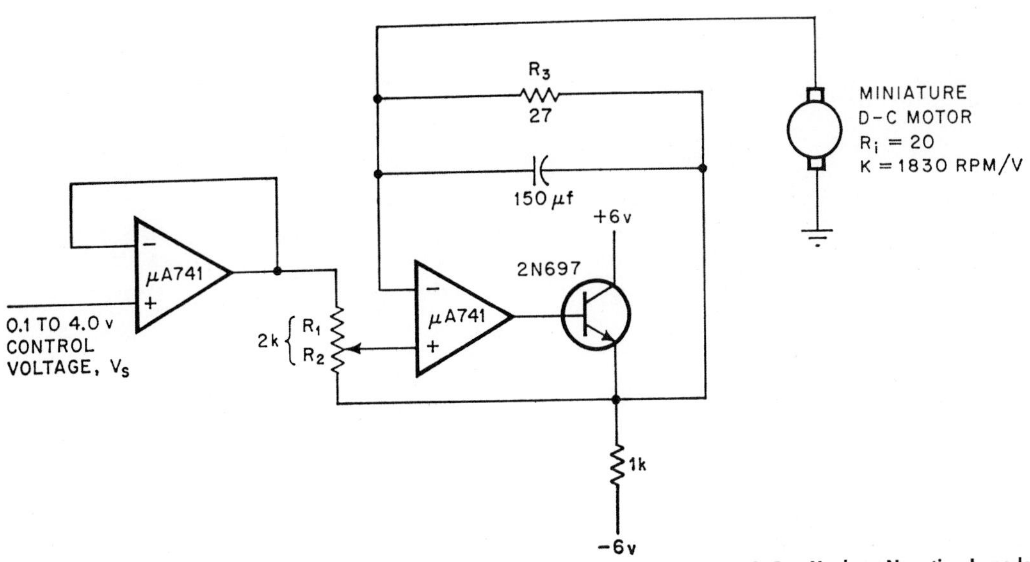

CONSTANT SPEED WITHIN 2%—Negative impedance in series with motor makes speed essentially independent of load. Opamp connected with both positive and negative feedback serves as negative impedance converter. Capacitor prevents circuit from oscillating.—S. Ben-Yaakov, Negative Impedance Stabilizes Motor's Speed, *Electronics*, Mar. 30, 1969, p 94.

FOUR-SPEED CONTROL—Provides four different speeds with permanent-magnet d-c motor energized from a-c line by means of thyristor whose conduction angle depends on difference between reference voltage of zeners and back emf of armature, to give two different washing speeds and two different spin-dry speeds for washing machine. Spin-dry cycle can be started before drum is completely drained, without risk of overheating motor. Heating element R1 for spin-drying is 14 ohms; R2 is 4.3K, R3 10K, R4 100-ohm pot, D1 and D2 BZY88/C7V5, D3 and D4 BYX10, D5 BYX38, and D6 BT101/500R.—W. Ebbinge and D. C. de Ruiter, Improved Speed Control for a Permanent Magnet Motor, Philips, Pub. Dept., Elcoma Div., Eindhoven, The Netherlands, No. 446, 1969.

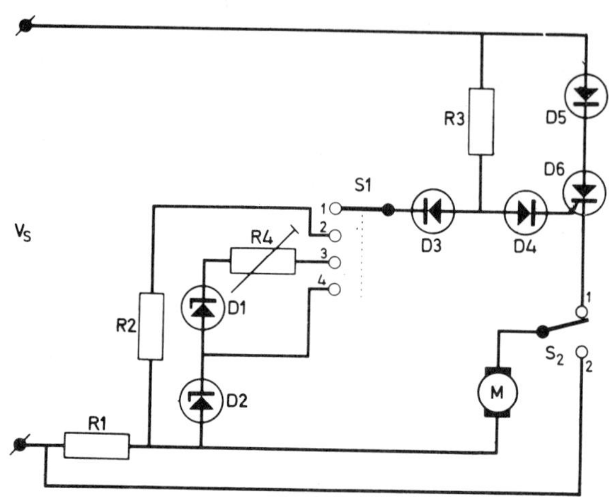

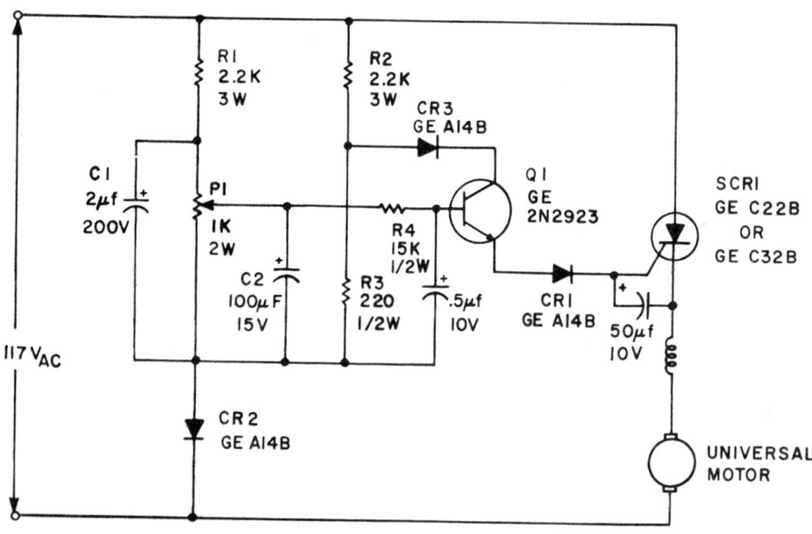

HIGH-PERFORMANCE UNIVERSAL-MOTOR CONTROL—Gives greatly improved speed-control performance at low speed settings. Choice of scr depends on motor rating.—A. A. Adem, Speed Controls for Universal Motors, General Electric, Syracuse, N.Y., No. 200.47, 1966, p 7.

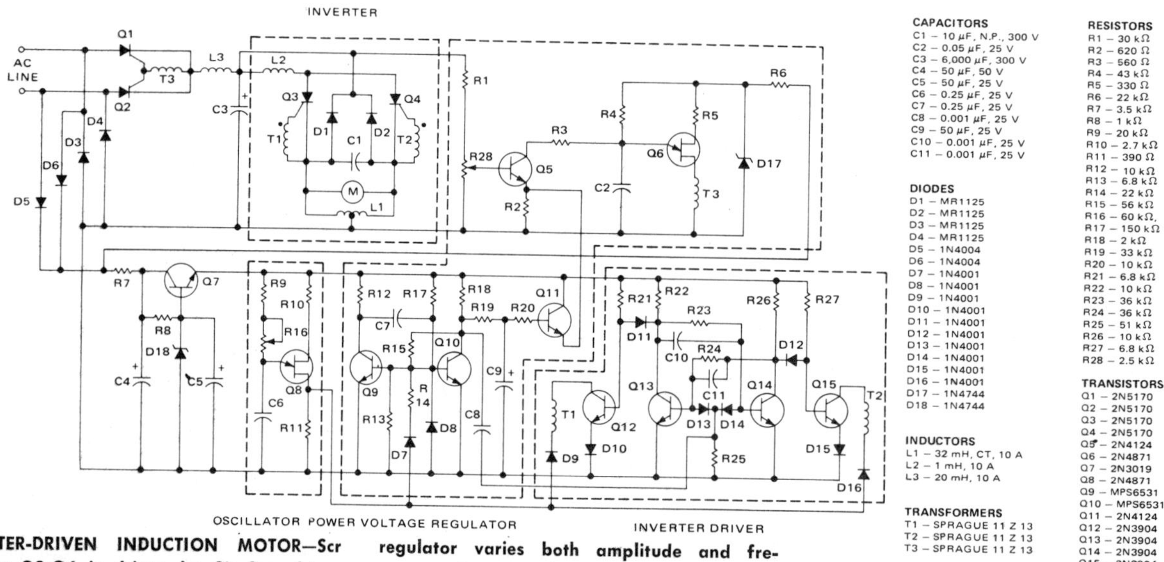

CAPACITORS
C1 – 10 μF, N.P., 300 V
C2 – 0.05 μF, 25 V
C3 – 6,000 μF, 300 V
C4 – 50 μF, 50 V
C5 – 50 μF, 25 V
C6 – 0.25 μF, 25 V
C7 – 0.25 μF, 25 V
C8 – 0.001 μF, 25 V
C9 – 50 μF, 25 V
C10 – 0.001 μF, 25 V
C11 – 0.001 μF, 25 V

DIODES
D1 – MR1125
D2 – MR1125
D3 – MR1125
D4 – MR1125
D5 – 1N4004
D6 – 1N4004
D7 – 1N4001
D8 – 1N4001
D9 – 1N4001
D10 – 1N4001
D11 – 1N4001
D12 – 1N4001
D13 – 1N4001
D14 – 1N4001
D15 – 1N4001
D16 – 1N4001
D17 – 1N4744
D18 – 1N4744

INDUCTORS
L1 – 32 mH, CT, 10 A
L2 – 1 mH, 10 A
L3 – 20 mH, 10 A

TRANSFORMERS
T1 – SPRAGUE 11 Z 13
T2 – SPRAGUE 11 Z 13
T3 – SPRAGUE 11 Z 13

RESISTORS
R1 – 30 kΩ
R2 – 620 Ω
R3 – 560 Ω
R4 – 43 kΩ
R5 – 330 Ω
R6 – 22 kΩ
R7 – 3.5 kΩ
R8 – 1 kΩ
R9 – 20 kΩ
R10 – 2.7 kΩ
R11 – 390 Ω
R12 – 10 kΩ
R13 – 6.8 kΩ
R14 – 22 kΩ
R15 – 56 kΩ
R16 – 60 kΩ,
R17 – 150 kΩ
R18 – 2 kΩ
R19 – 33 kΩ
R20 – 10 kΩ
R21 – 6.8 kΩ
R22 – 10 kΩ
R23 – 36 kΩ
R24 – 36 kΩ
R25 – 51 kΩ
R26 – 10 kΩ
R27 – 6.8 kΩ
R28 – 2.5 kΩ

TRANSISTORS
Q1 – 2N5170
Q2 – 2N5170
Q3 – 2N5170
Q4 – 2N5170
Q5 – 2N4124
Q6 – 2N4871
Q7 – 2N3019
Q8 – 2N4871
Q9 – MPS6531
Q10 – MPS6531
Q11 – 2N4124
Q12 – 2N3904
Q13 – 2N3904
Q14 – 2N3904
Q15 – 2N3904

INVERTER-DRIVEN INDUCTION MOTOR—Scr inverter Q3-Q4 is driven by flip-flop driver and ujt oscillator, with ujt frequency being twice that applied to motor because of divider action of flip-flops. Power voltage regulator varies both amplitude and frequency of motor voltage to get smooth speed control. Used with 1/6th-hp single-phase induction motor. Motor does not overheat even though circuit provides square-wave voltage. Book describes operation in detail. —"Semiconductor Power Circuits Handbook," Motorola, Phoenix, Ariz., 1968, p 1–14.

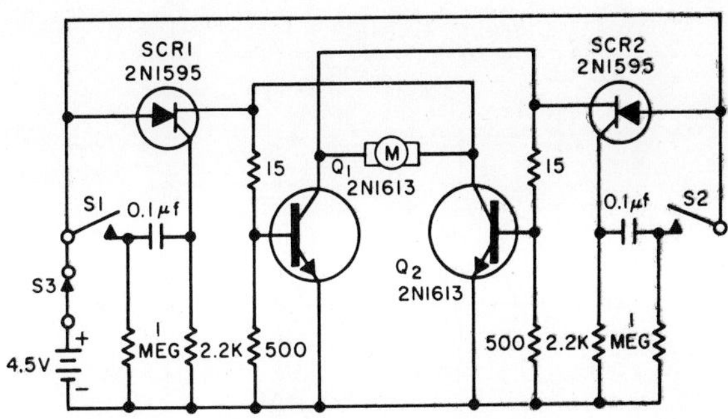

REVERSING D-C MOTOR—Closing S1 triggers SCR1 on to apply power to right-hand terminal of motor, and simultaneously saturates Q1 to ground other terminal of motor. Similarly, S2 sends current through motor in opposite direction to provide reversal. Used with 3-V 500-mA motor.—C. S. Pepper, SCR-Transistor Switch Allows DC Motor Reversal, *Electronic Design*, Feb. 17, 1964, p 93–94.

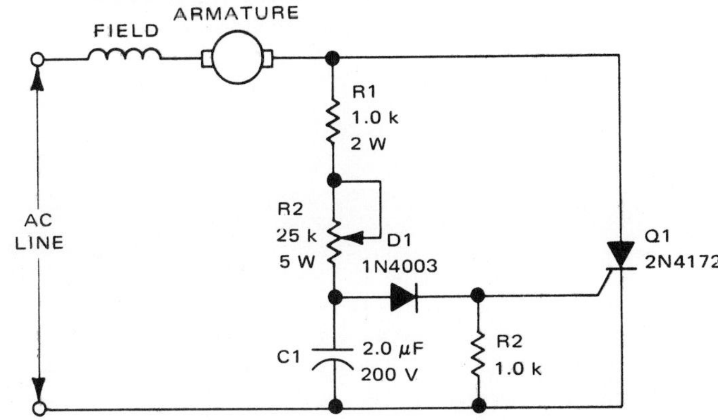

UNCOMPENSATED HALF-WAVE DRIVE—Controls speed of series-connected d-c motor by varying average voltage applied to motor. Operation is stable at low speeds for given load. Speed control R2 sets firing point of scr Q1. Used with $\frac{1}{15}$th-hp 5,000-rpm 115-V d-c motor on 120-V a-c line.—"Semiconductor Power Circuits Handbook," Motorola, Phoenix, Ariz., 1968, p 1–18.

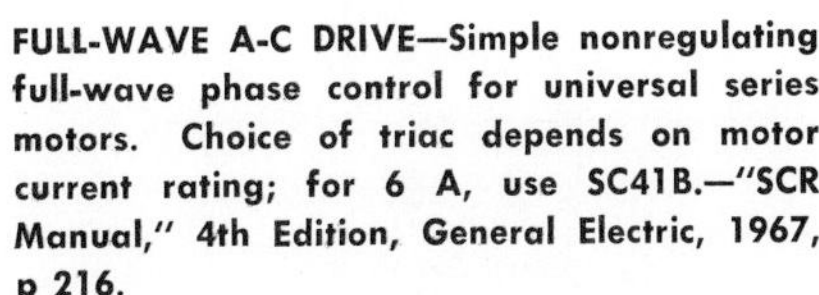

FULL-WAVE A-C DRIVE—Simple nonregulating full-wave phase control for universal series motors. Choice of triac depends on motor current rating; for 6 A, use SC41B.—"SCR Manual," 4th Edition, General Electric, 1967, p 216.

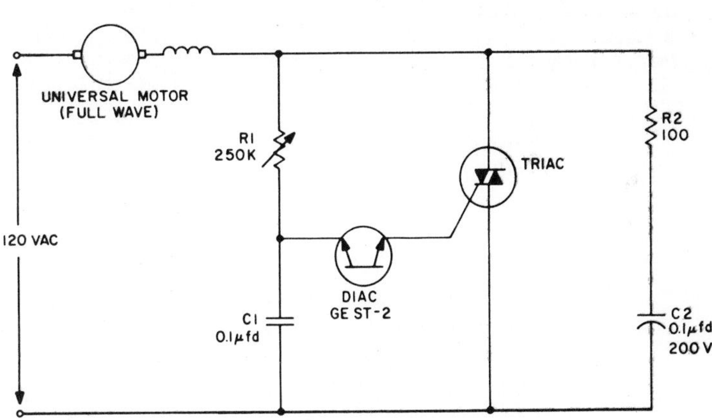

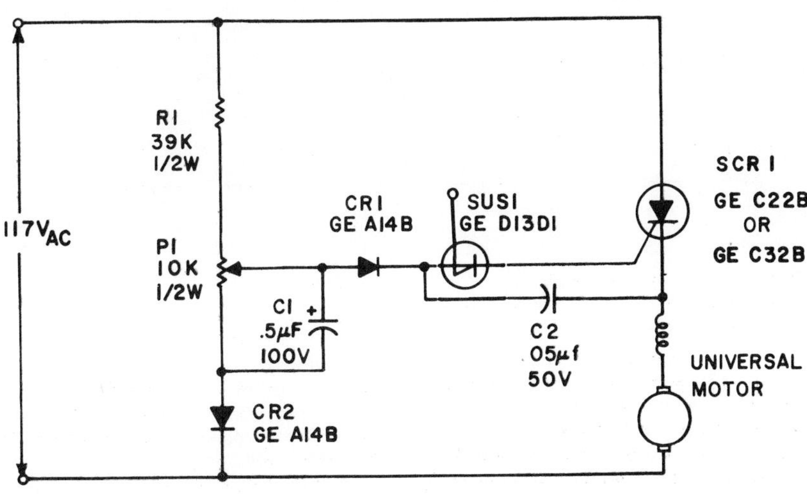

SUS-TRIGGERED UNIVERSAL CONTROL WITH FEEDBACK—Economical and reliable circuit provides good control at low speeds by using silicon unilateral switch to provide pulse rather than continuous current for triggering gate of scr. Motor residual field provides back emf for speed feedback signal. Component values for R1 and P1 are independent of scr used. Article gives changes needed for operation on 240 V.—A. A. Adem, Speed Controls for Universal Motors, General Electric, Syracuse, N.Y., No. 200.57, 1966, p 8.

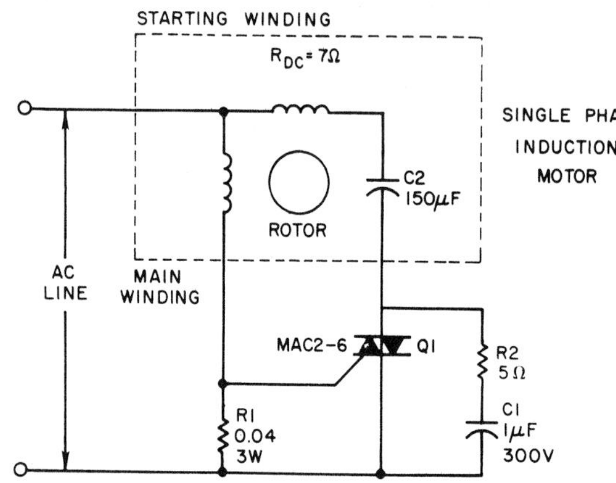

TRIAC STARTER FOR ½-HP INDUCTION—Replaces mechanical centrifugal switch in disconnecting start winding when motor reaches about 75% of full-load speed. Voltage across R1, proportional to current in main winding, gates triac; use slide-wire resistor initially to select correct trigger level.—G. V. Fay, Reliable Semiconductor Replaces Centrifugal Motor Starting Switch, *Electronic Design*, Aug. 16, 1969, p 248.

HALF-WAVE UNIVERSAL SERIES MOTOR CONTROL—Used in blenders, hand tools, vacuum cleaners, mixers, and light industrial applications. Gives equivalent of infinitely variable tap on motor. For full-speed operation with half-wave circuit, 80-V motor must be used. Article gives theory of operation in detail. Table gives values of components required for three different sizes of motors. —"SCR Manual," 4th Edition, General Electric, 1967, p 210–211.

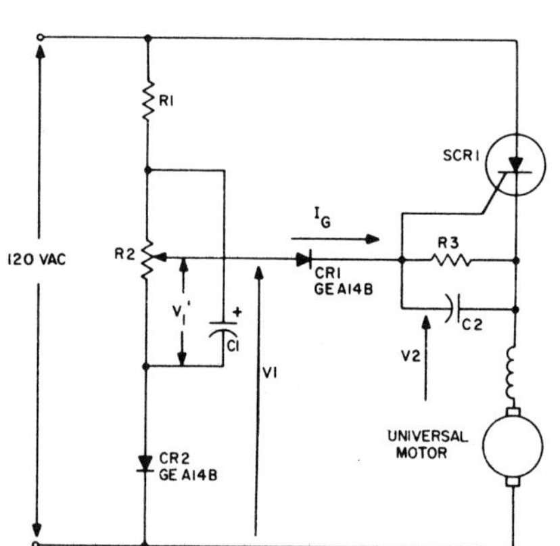

	LOW UP TO 1 AMP NAMEPLATE	MEDIUM UP TO 3 AMP NAMEPLATE	HIGH UP TO 15 AMP NAMEPLATE
R2	10K 1W	1K 2W	1K 2W
R1	47K 1/2 W	3.3K 2W	3.3K 2W
R3	1K 1/2W	150K 1/2 W OPTIONAL	150K 1/2 W OPTIONAL
C1	0.5μf 50V	10μf 50V	10μf 50V
C2	0.1 μf 10V	0.1μf 10V OPTIONAL	0.1μf 10V OPTIONAL
SCR1	GE C106B	GE C22BX70	GE C33B

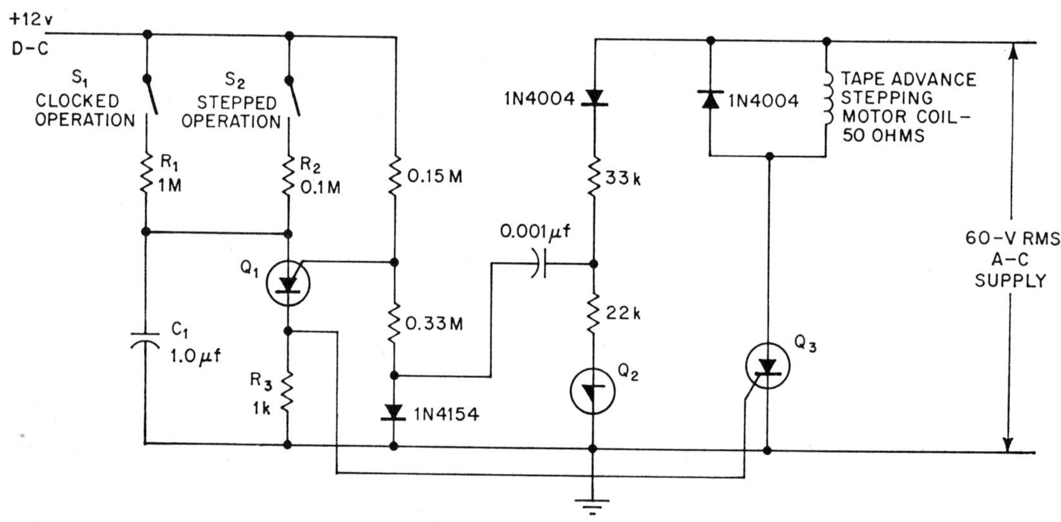

Q_1 – PROGRAMABLE UNIJUNCTION TRANSISTOR (GE TYPE D13T1)
Q_2 – SILICON UNILATERAL SWITCH (GE TYPE 2N4987)
Q_3 – SILICON-CONTROLLED RECTIFIER (GE TYPE C106B1)

PROGRAM-TAPE STEPPER—Inadvertent advance of d-c stepping motor by supply noise is minimized if motor is activated by a-c signal. Tape advance signal closes either S1 or S2, depending on mode of operation chosen. Closing S2 charges C1 to breakover point of programmable ujt Q1. When Q1 fires, scr Q3 is turned on during positive half-cycles of a-c supply voltage, energizing stepping motor that indexes tape. Sus Q2 ensures that scr is gated on at beginning of each positive half-cycle. In clocked mode, S1 opens and closes at prescribed time intervals of about 1 s, depending on time constant R1-C1.—J. H. Silverman, A-C Source Drives Tape-Stepping Motor, *Electronics*, Nov. 24, 1969, p 109.

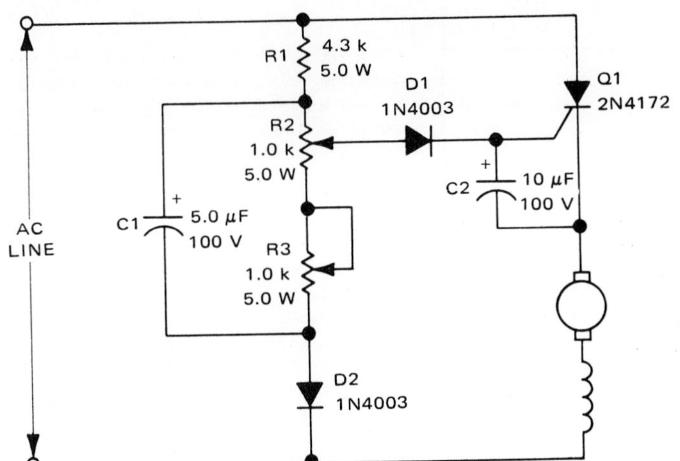

COMPENSATED HALF-WAVE DRIVE—Speed regulation is much better than for uncompensated drive. Back emf of motor provides feedback when scr is off, to compensate for changes in load. Used with 1/15th-hp 5,000-rpm 115-V d-c motor on 120-V a-c line.—"Semiconductor Power Circuits Handbook," Motorola, Phoenix, Ariz., 1968, p 1–19.

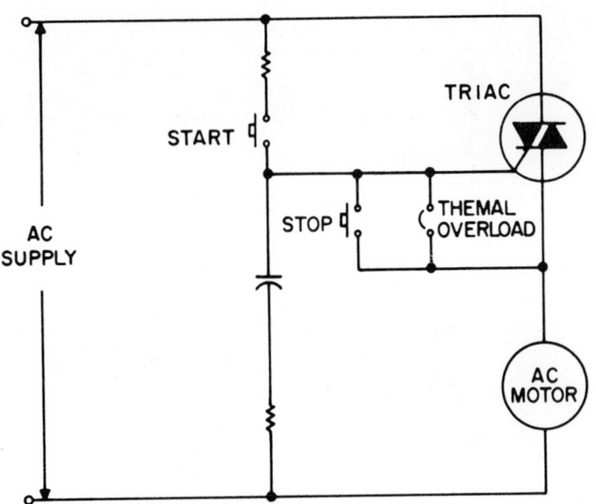

A-C MOTOR STARTER—Momentary closing of start button latches triac on and starts motor. Momentary closing of stop button, closing of thermal overload contact, or loss of line voltage stops motor. Resistor and capacitor values are given in specifications for triac chosen to match motor rating.—F. W. Gutzwiller and E. K. Howell, Economy Power Semiconductor Applications, General Electric, Syracuse, N.Y., No. 671.1., 1965, p 8.

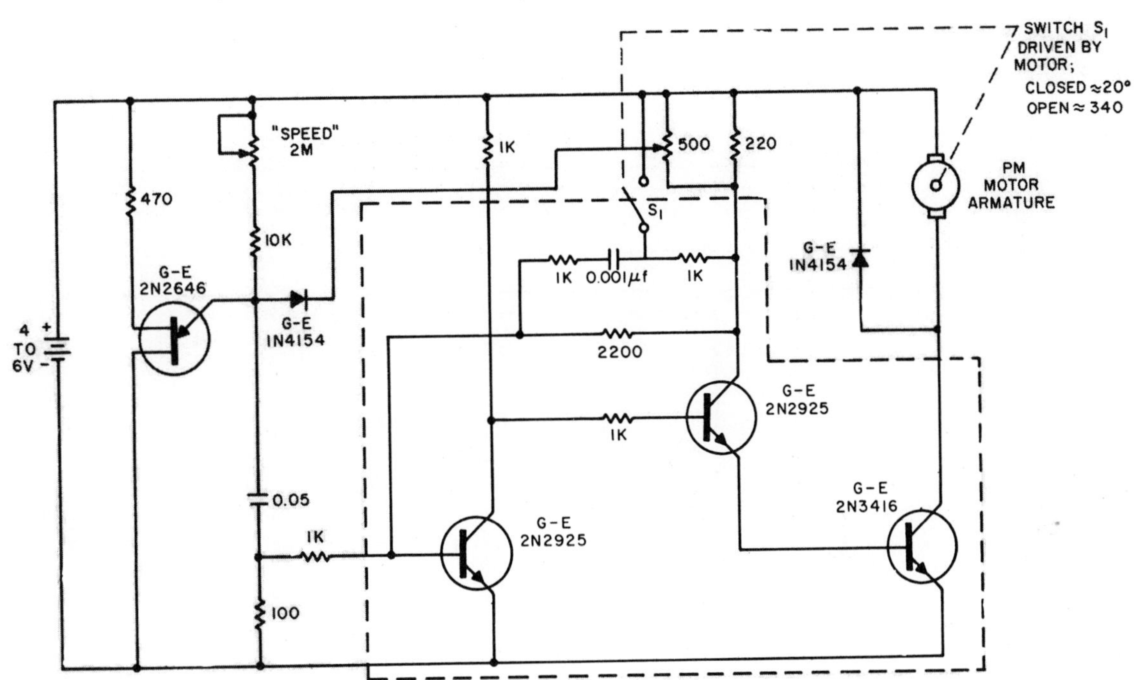

UJT CONTROL FOR P-M MOTOR—Ujt relaxation oscillator drives flip-flop to energize small battery-operated permanent-magnet motor. Rotation of motor shaft closes S1, reversing flip-flop and turning motor off. At low speeds, cam on motor shaft should close S1 several times per revolution. Motor speed can be changed in discrete octave steps by changing switch closures per revolution from 1 to 2 to 4 to 8, etc., either mechanically or electrically. Speed is synchronously related to oscillator frequency.—E. K. Howell, Precise Speed Control, High Torque Can Now be Combined in DC Motors, *Electronic Design*, Dec. 6, 1965, p 20–25.

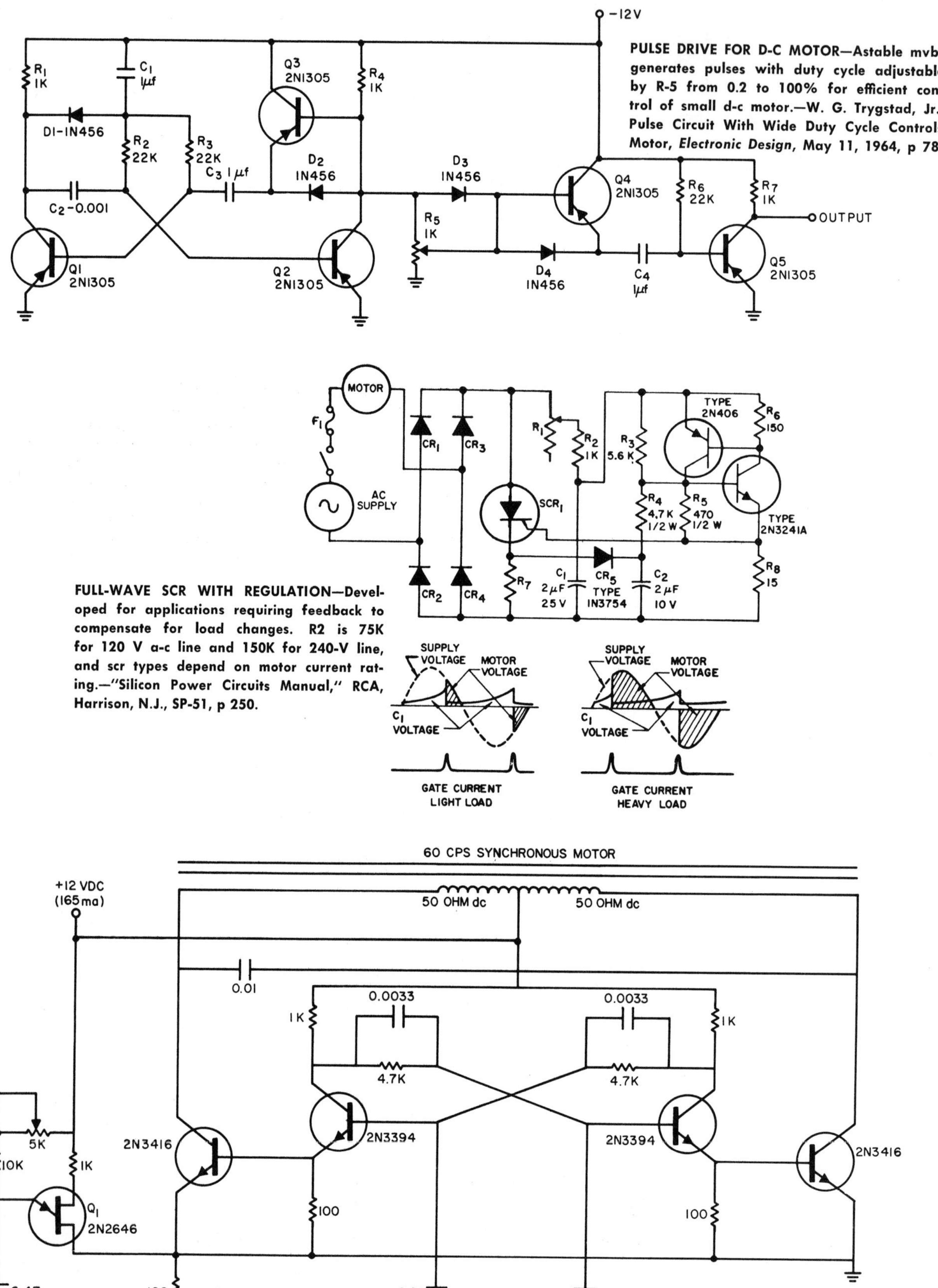

PULSE DRIVE FOR D-C MOTOR—Astable mvbr generates pulses with duty cycle adjustable by R-5 from 0.2 to 100% for efficient control of small d-c motor.—W. G. Trygstad, Jr., Pulse Circuit With Wide Duty Cycle Controls Motor, *Electronic Design*, May 11, 1964, p 78.

FULL-WAVE SCR WITH REGULATION—Developed for applications requiring feedback to compensate for load changes. R2 is 75K for 120 V a-c line and 150K for 240-V line, and scr types depend on motor current rating.—"Silicon Power Circuits Manual," RCA, Harrison, N.J., SP-51, p 250.

D-C DRIVE FOR SYNCHRONOUS MOTOR—Ujt-mvbr combination permits operation of synchronous clock motor, induction motor, or hysteresis synchronous motor from 12 V d-c supply. 2N3394's in mvbr are synchronized by ujt relaxation oscillator Q1 to give constant frequency. Mvbr drives 2N3416's operating with motor winding as d-c/a-c inverter. Motor must have center-tapped winding.—D. V. Jones, UJT and Multivibrator Form Brushless DC Motor, *Electronic Design*, Oct. 11, 1965, p 67–68.

CHAPTER 54
Multivibrator Circuits

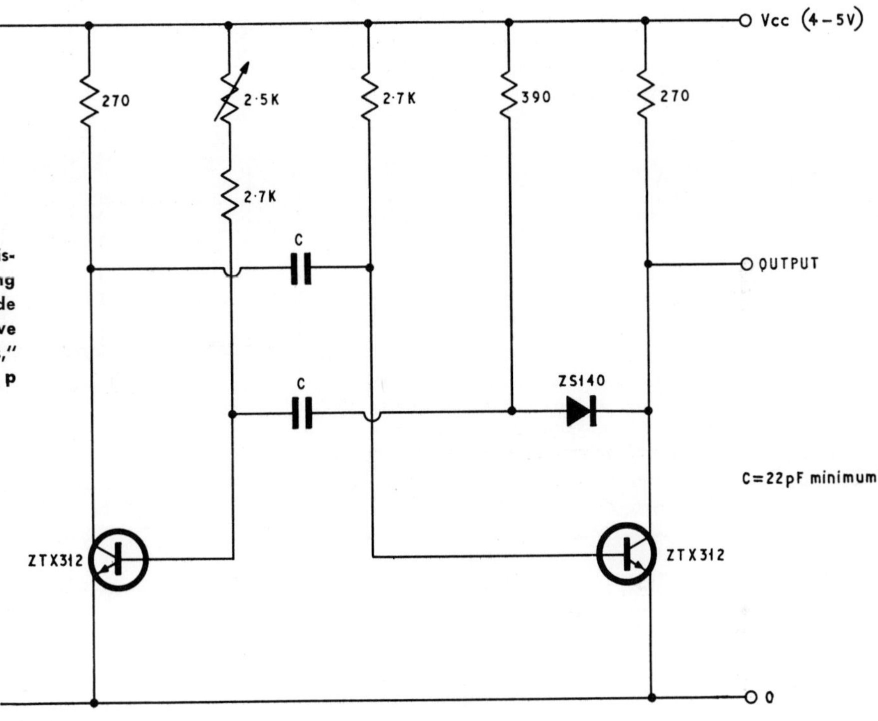

FAST RISE AND FALL TIMES—Ferranti transistors give 10-ns rise and fall times, permitting high repetition rates in simple saturated-mode circuit. Maximum working frequency is above 10 MHz.—"E-Line Transistor Applications," Ferranti Ltd., Oldham, Lancs., England, 1969, p 7.

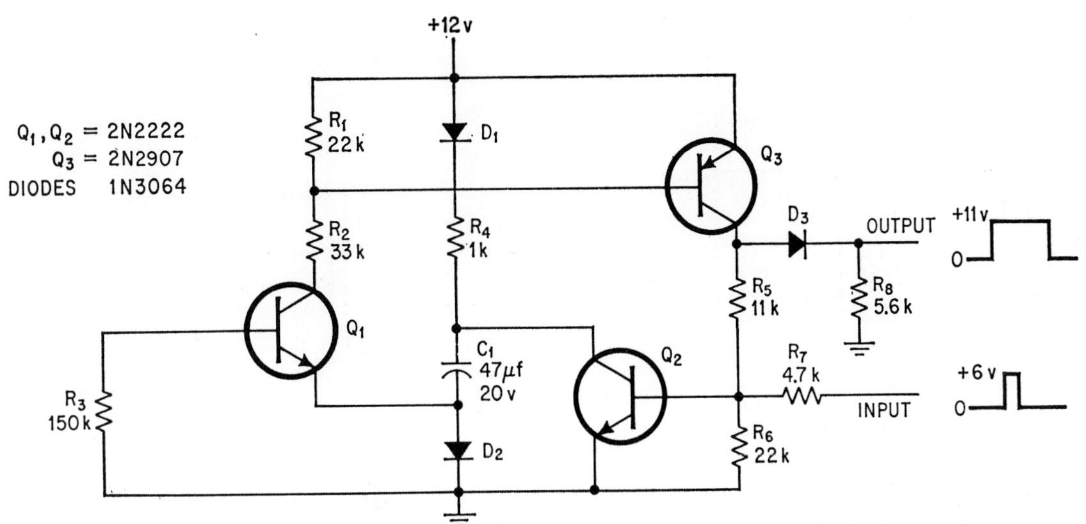

30-NA STANDBY CURRENT—Negligible standby power consumption makes circuit ideal for aerospace and medical projects. Has high noise immunity. Output pulse width is directly proportional to C1, and is 1 s for values shown. Reducing C1 gives pulse widths down to 5 μs.—E. J. Hoffman, One-Shot Multivibrator Requires No Standby Power, *Electronics*, May 26, 1969, p 91.

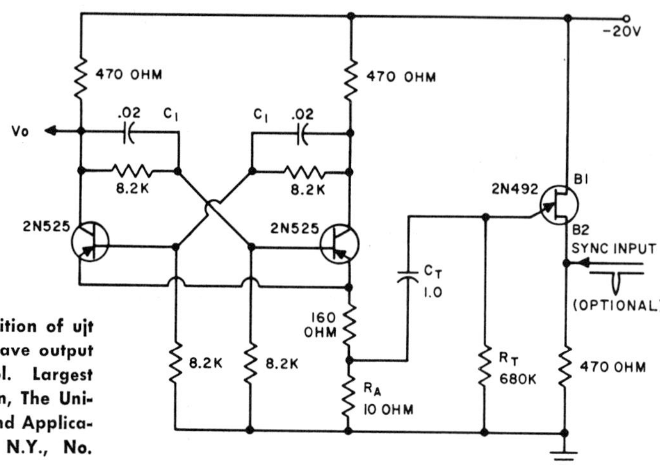

HYBRID SYMMETRICAL MVBR—Addition of ujt gives perfect symmetrical square-wave output without need for balance control. Largest capacitor is only 1 μF.—T. P. Sylvan, The Unijunction Transistor Characteristics and Applications, General Electric, Syracuse, N.Y., No. 90.10, 1965, p 52.

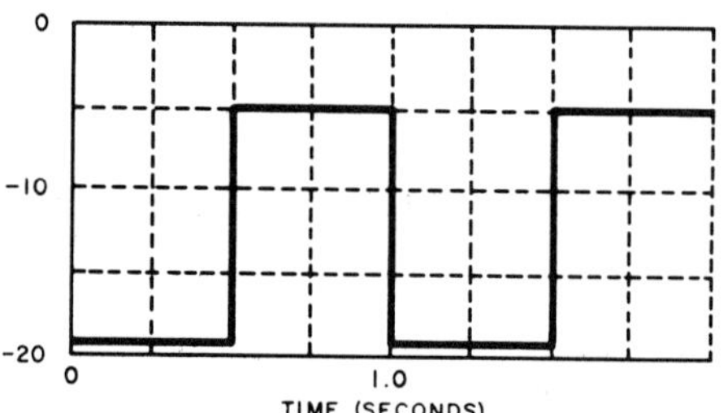

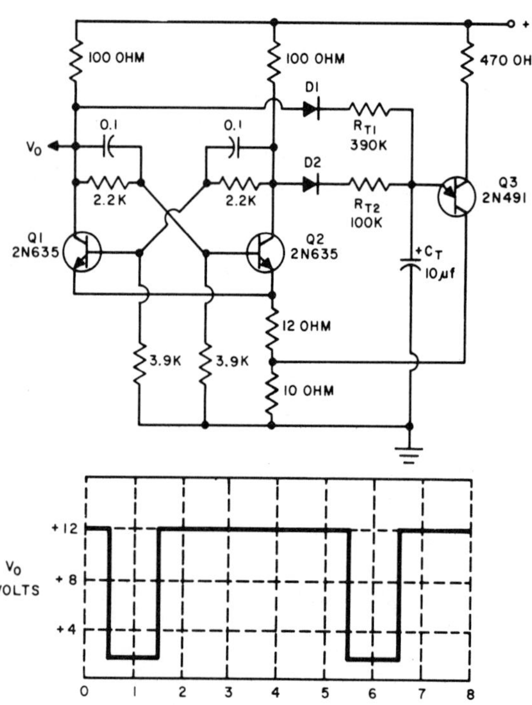

HYBRID UNSYMMETRICAL MVBR—Uses npn transistor flip-flop with ujt. Waveform shown is for values specified for RT; with potentiometers here, lengths of two parts of timing period can be adjusted over range of up to 1,000 to 1. Protective 3K resistors should then be in series with each pot.—T. P. Sylvan, The Unijunction Transistor Characteristics and Applications, General Electric, Syracuse, N.Y., No. 90.10, 1965, p 53.

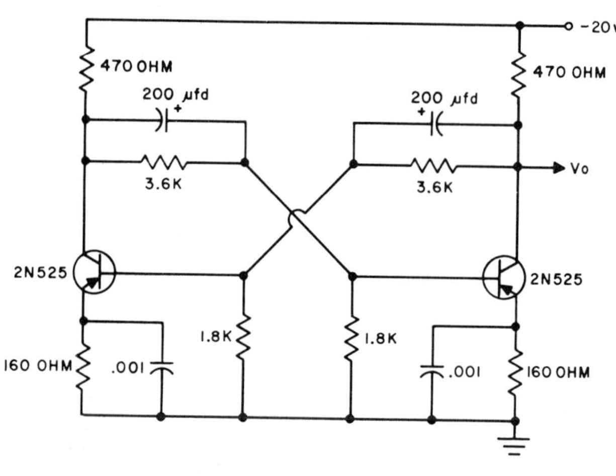

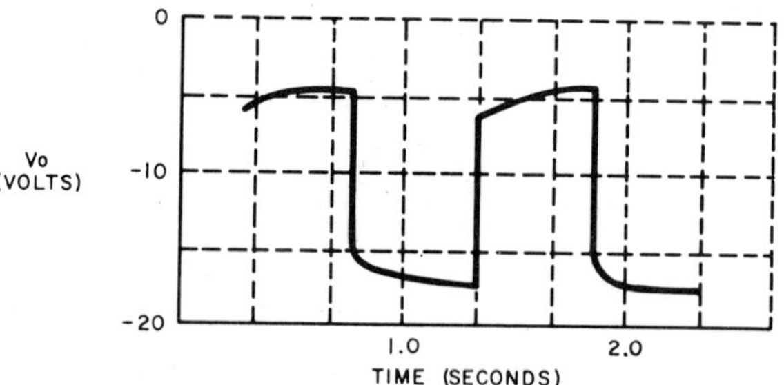

BASIC TWO-TRANSISTOR CIRCUIT—Included for comparison, because output waveform deviates considerably from ideal square wave. —T. P. Sylvan, The Unijunction Transistor Characteristics and Applications, General Electric, Syracuse, N.Y., No. 90.10, 1965, p 51.

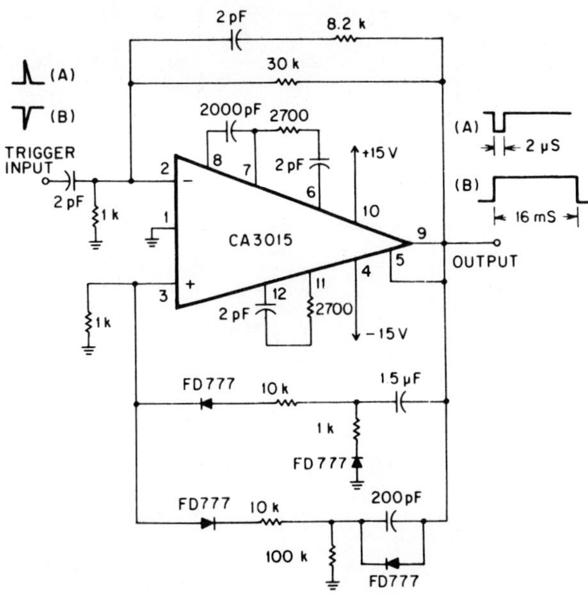

CONTROLLED BIPOLAR—Positive trigger input gives negative output pulse, while negative trigger gives positive pulse. Durations of both pulses are independently adjustable.—G. T. Flynn, Sequential Bipolar Multivibrator, *EEE*, April 1969, p 122–123.

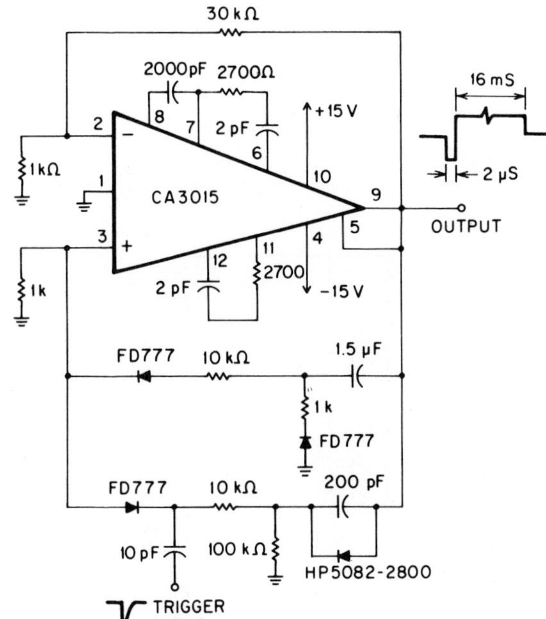

SEQUENTIAL BIPOLAR—Generates 2-μs negative pulse followed by 16-ms positive pulse, each time circuit is triggered. Will trigger as often as once every 20 ms. Output amplitudes are −7 and +7 V. Duration of each pulse is independently adjustable over wide range by changing circuit values.—G. T. Flynn, Sequential Bipolar Multivibrator, *EEE*, April 1969, p 122–123.

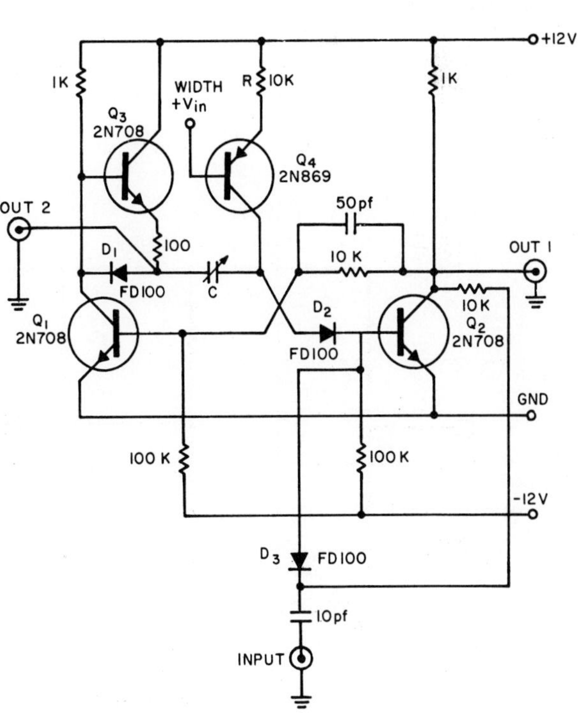

FAST-RECOVERY ONE SHOT—Pulse width of four-transistor mvbr is determined by d-c voltage applied to base of Q4.—G. Marosi, Four-Transistor Monostable Multi Shortens Recovery Time, *Electronic Design*, Aug. 17, 1964, p 201–202.

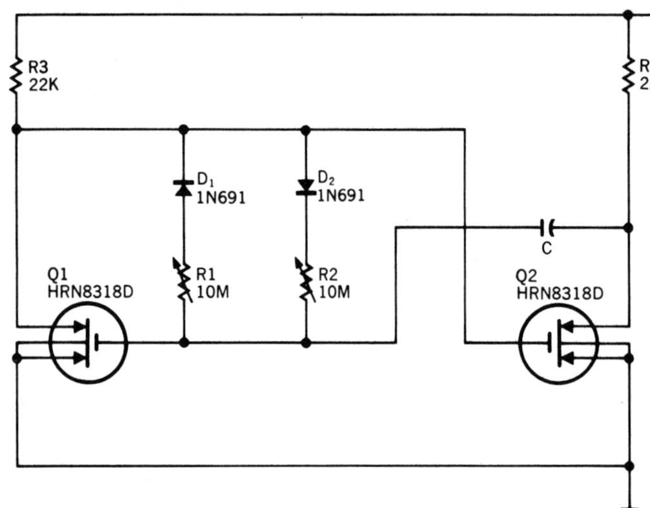

VARIABLE WIDTH AND DUTY CYCLE—Isolating and dividing timing resistor of astable mosfet mvbr into two controls gives independent control over pulse width and duty cycle, to form basis for highly flexible pulse generator. —C. R. Perkins, "Application of MOSFET Devices to Electronic Circuits," Hughes, Newport Beach, Cal., 1968, p 24.

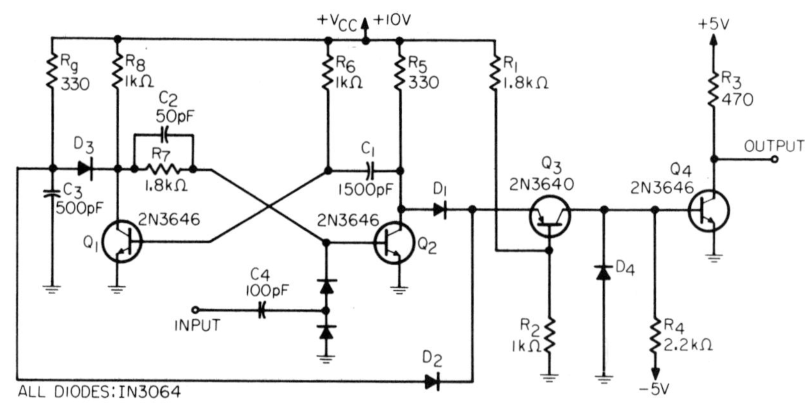

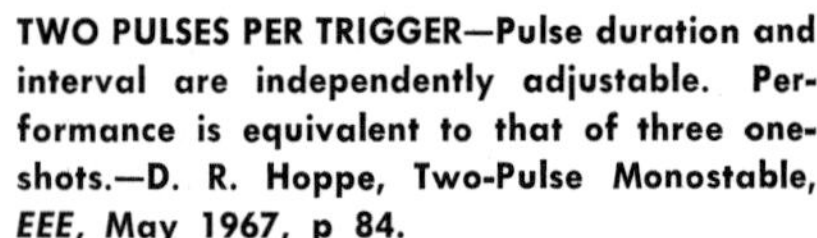
TWO PULSES PER TRIGGER—Pulse duration and interval are independently adjustable. Performance is equivalent to that of three one-shots.—D. R. Hoppe, Two-Pulse Monostable, *EEE*, May 1967, p 84.

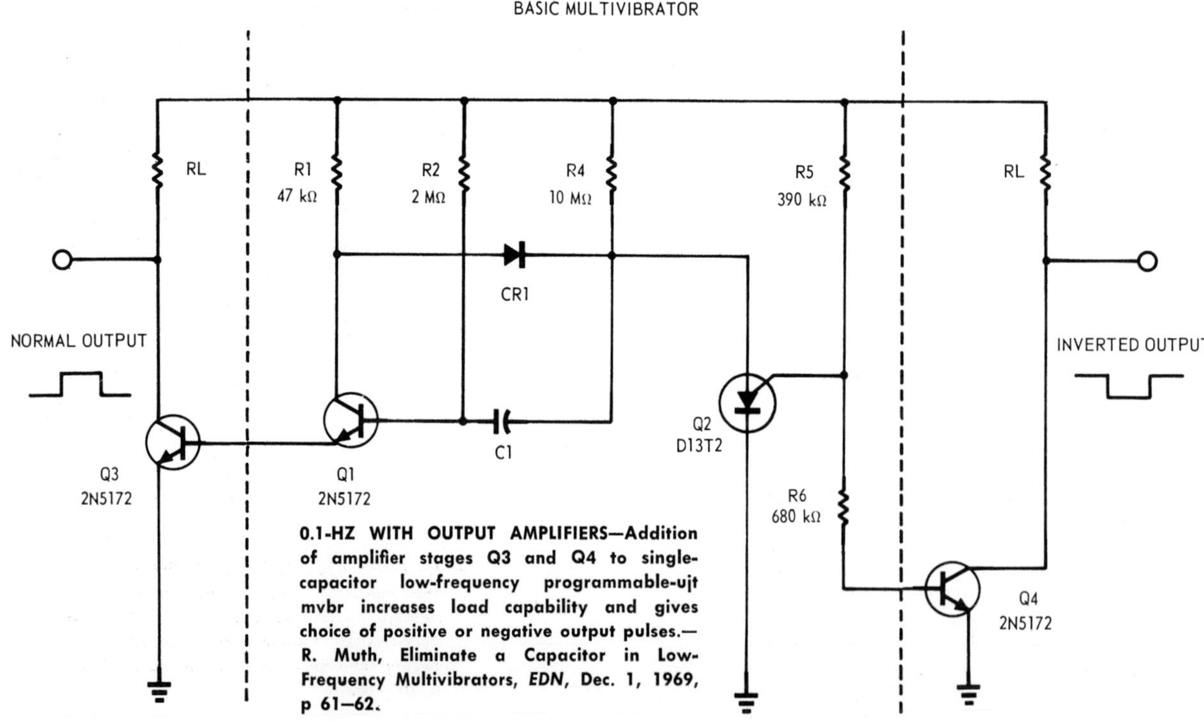

0.1-HZ WITH OUTPUT AMPLIFIERS—Addition of amplifier stages Q3 and Q4 to single-capacitor low-frequency programmable-ujt mvbr increases load capability and gives choice of positive or negative output pulses.—R. Muth, Eliminate a Capacitor in Low-Frequency Multivibrators, *EDN*, Dec. 1, 1969, p 61–62.

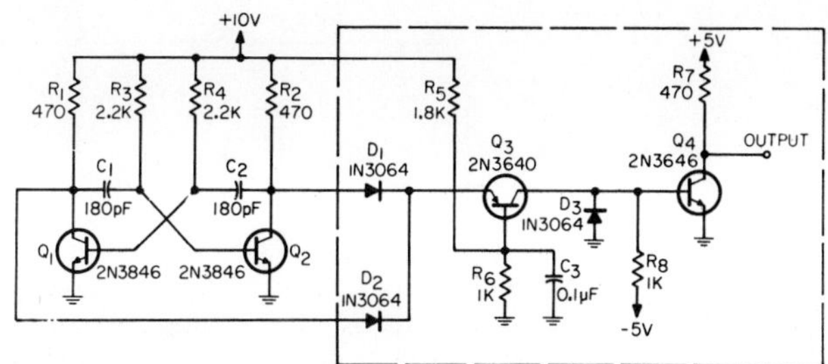

DOUBLER FOR MVBR—Circuit in dashed rectangle doubles output frequency of astable mvbr Q1–Q2 to extend operating range. May also be used with most other relaxation oscillators. Wiht values shown, output frequency is 5.5 MHz, pulse width 86 ns, rise time 15 ns, and fall time 5 ns.—D. R. Hoppe, Frequency Doubler for Relaxation Oscillators, *EEE*, Feb. 1967, p 147–148.

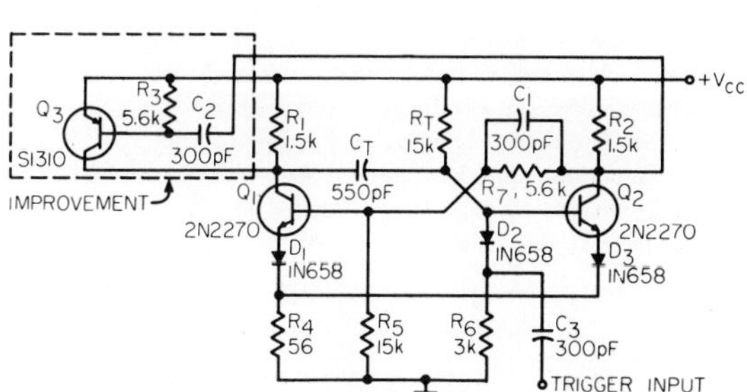

FAST-RECOVERY ONE-SHOT—Simple modification (dashed rectangle) cuts recovery time to 50 ns, as compared to about 6 μs for basic one-shot. Modification also improves output waveform and reduces dynamic output impedance.—M. Felcheck and W. Kirschner, Improved One-Shot with Fast Recovery, *EEE*, Oct. 1967, p 142–143.

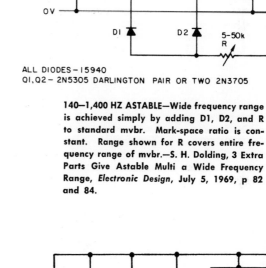

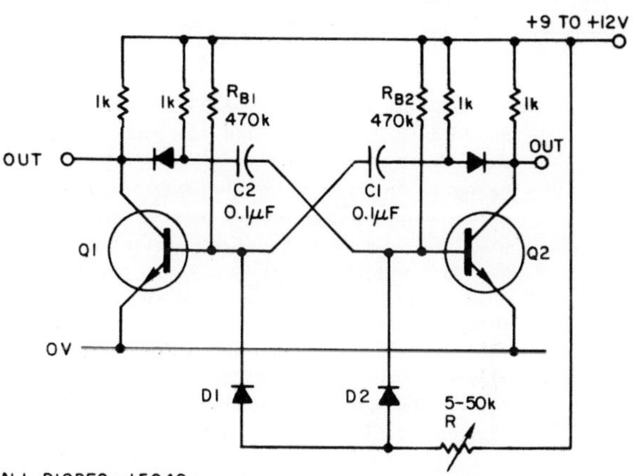

140–1,400 HZ ASTABLE—Wide frequency range is achieved simply by adding D1, D2, and R to standard mvbr. Mark-space ratio is constant. Range shown for R covers entire frequency range of mvbr.—S. H. Dolding, 3 Extra Parts Give Astable Multi a Wide Frequency Range, *Electronic Design*, July 5, 1969, p 82 and 84.

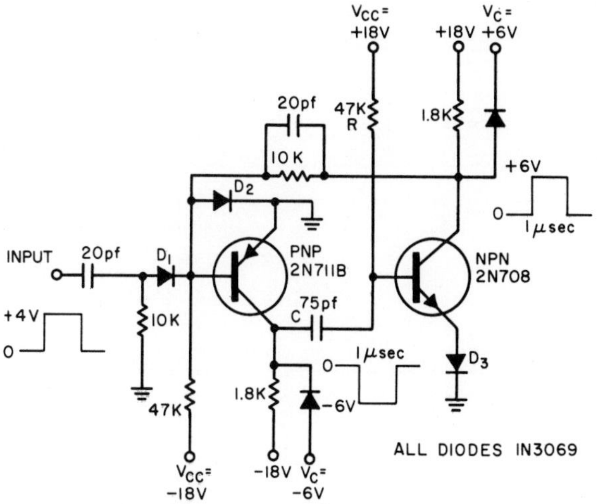

REGENERATIVE SHARPENING OF RISE TIME—Complementary transistors, connected as shown, speed transition time of monostable mvbr enough to make it indistinguishable from 40-ns rise and fall times of transistors themselves. Pulse repetition frequency is 960 kHz with values shown.—G. Klein, Monostable Multivibrator Has a Sharp Rise Time, *Electronic Design*, Feb. 17, 1964, p 88–89.

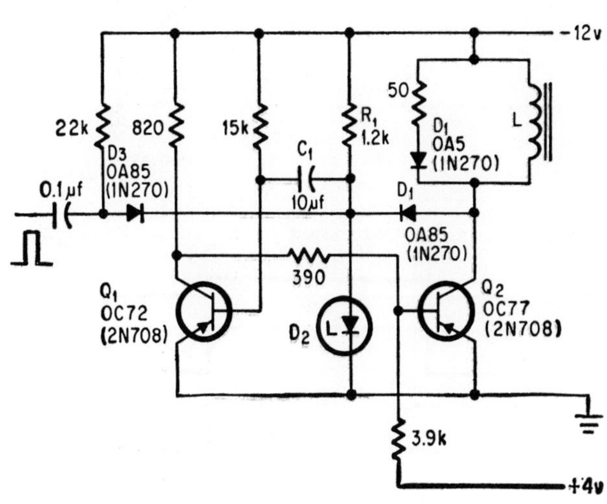

ZENER BLOCKS STRAY PULSES—Zener D2 acts with three conventional diodes in mvbr to block pulses from power supply and inductive load, and thereby prevent premature triggering.—R. Ilic, Diodes Provide Noise Immunity for Monostable Multivibrators, *Electronics*, Jan. 9, 1967, p 106–107.

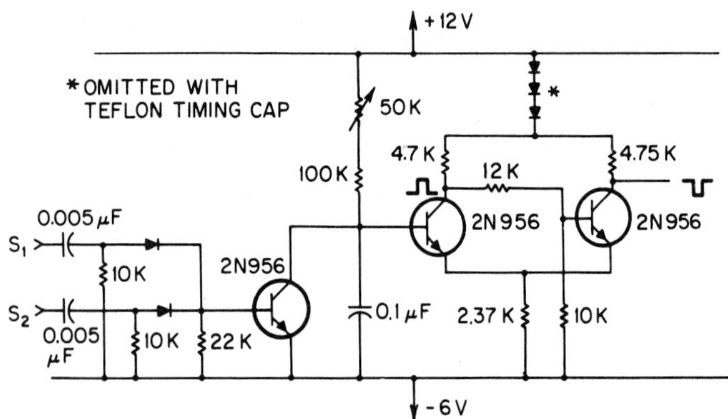

TRIGGERABLE-ANYTIME MONO—Consists of modified Schmitt trigger and one additional stage that performs function of mono without having its drawback of ignoring input triggers during output pulse. Circuit may be retriggered at any time from any number of sources. Triggers occurring during output pulse simply resaturate first transistor, discharging 0.1-μF capacitor to negative supply voltage and initiating normal pulse period. Values shown give 5-ms pulse width.—B. Pearl, A Retriggerable Pseudo-Mono, *EEE*, Dec. 1966, p 78–79.

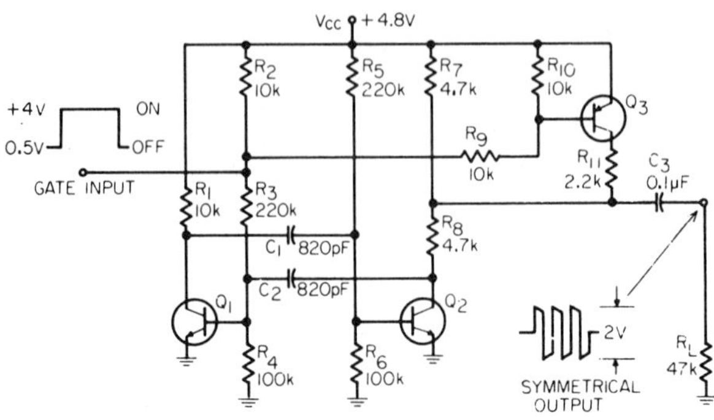

SYMMETRICAL A-C OUTPUT—Addition of Q3 to keyed mvbr eliminates d-c level shift of output that would cause severe distortion in a-c coupled load. Another advantage is that circuit starts instantly with full-width first pulse. Astable mvbr Q1-Q2 is keyed by switching charging voltage of C2. Mvbr oscillates at about 3 kHz for +4 V gate input, and is turned off when gate is below 1 V.—M. Converse, Keyed Multivibrator Produces Symmetrical A-C Output, *EEE*, Nov. 1968, p 141.

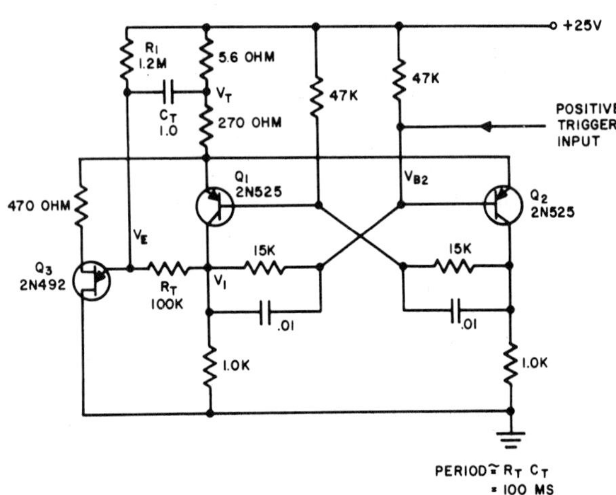

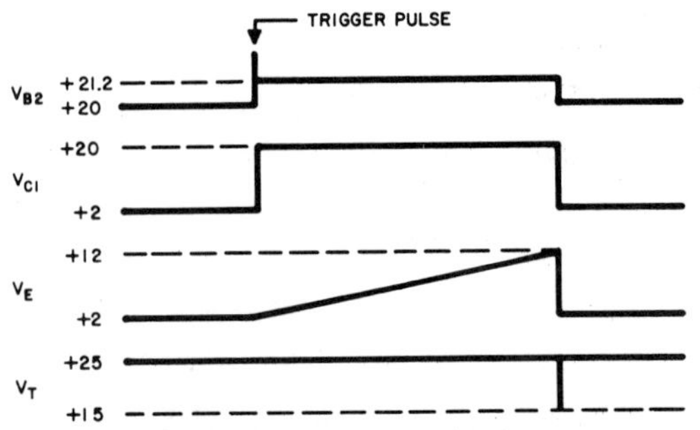

HYBRID ONE-SHOT—With basic circuit shown, all voltages return to initial values at end of timing cycle, so timing period is independent of trigger rate and duty cycle.—T. P. Sylvan, The Unijunction Transistor Characteristics and Applications, General Electric, Syracuse, N.Y., No. 90.10, 1965, p 55.

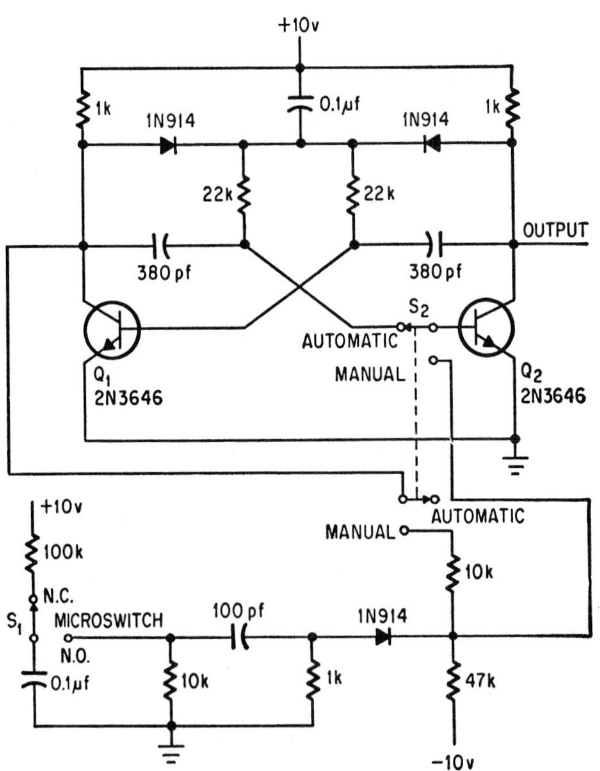

ASTABLE-MONO SWITCH—With S2 in automatic position, circuit runs as unsymmetrical astable mvbr generating 1.5-μs pulses at 150-kHz repetition rate, for testing counter and logic circuits at high switching speeds. Manual position gives one-shot action.—D. Haggen, Switch Converts Multivibrator from Astable to One-Shot, *Electronics*, Nov. 28, 1966, p 80.

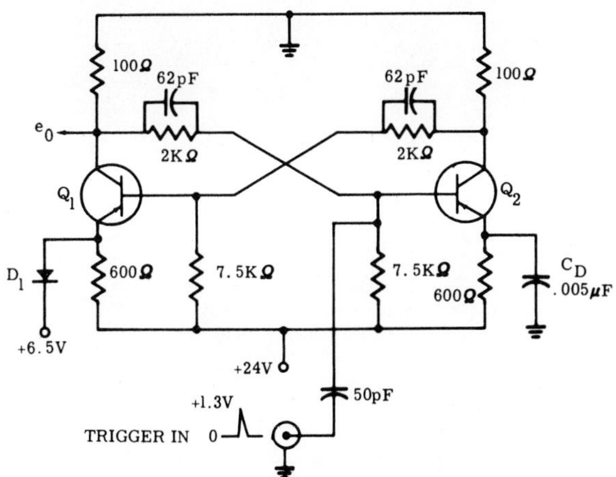

CURRENT-MODE MONO—Maximum repetition rate is 1MHz. Timing interval or delay in returning from quasi-stable to steady state is almost comparable to recovery time of capacitor.—"High Speed Switching Transistor Handbook," Motorola, Phoenix, Ariz., 1969, p 280.

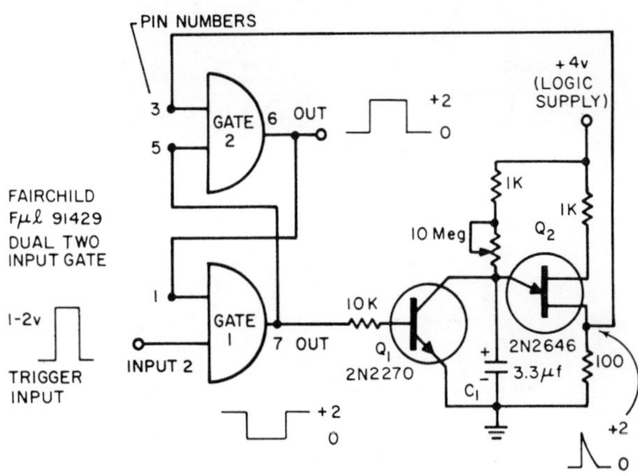

WIDE-RANGE ONE-SHOT—Combining two cross-coupled NAND gates with ujt gives stable, wide-range one-shot mvbr having complementary outputs, with delays of 100 ms to 20 s, in minimum space.—A. C. Ward, NAND Gates and UJT Form Stable Hybrid Monostable Multi, *Electronic Design*, April 26, 1965, p 45–46.

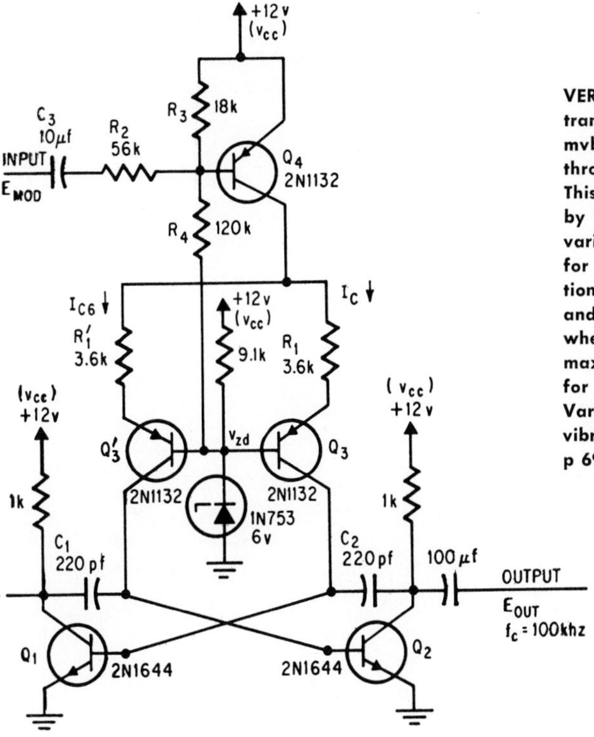

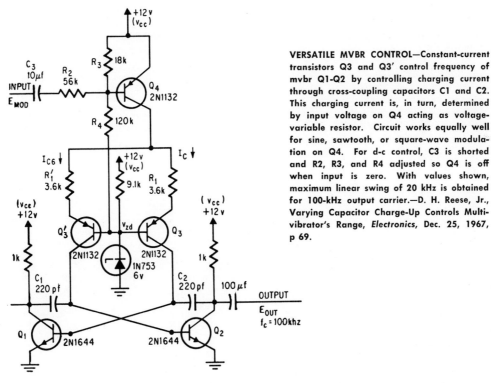

VERSATILE MVBR CONTROL—Constant-current transistors Q3 and Q3′ control frequency of mvbr Q1-Q2 by controlling charging current through cross-coupling capacitors C1 and C2. This charging current is, in turn, determined by input voltage on Q4 acting as voltage-variable resistor. Circuit works equally well for sine, sawtooth, or square-wave modulation on Q4. For d-c control, C3 is shorted and R2, R3, and R4 adjusted so Q4 is off when input is zero. With values shown, maximum linear swing of 20 kHz is obtained for 100-kHz output carrier.—D. H. Reese, Jr., Varying Capacitor Charge-Up Controls Multivibrator's Range, *Electronics*, Dec. 25, 1967, p 69.

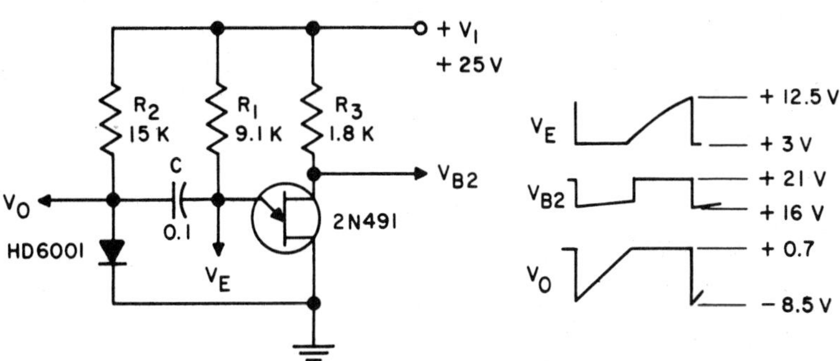

SINGLE-UJT MVBR—Frequency is about 1 kHz. Article gives equations for calculating times for the two periods shown in waveforms.—T. P. Sylvan, The Unijunction Transistor Characteristics and Applications, General Electric, Syracuse, N.Y., No. 90.10, 1965, p 74.

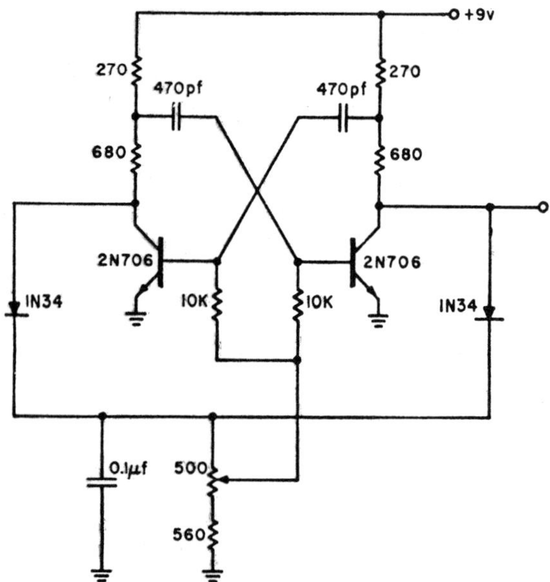

200—300 KHZ TUNABLE—Frequency is changed with 500-ohm pot. Base bias is obtained through diode network to ensure reliable starting.—M. W. Egerton, Tunable Multivibrator Starts Reliably, "400 Ideas for Design Selected from Electronic Design," Hayden Book Co., N.Y., 1964, p 184.

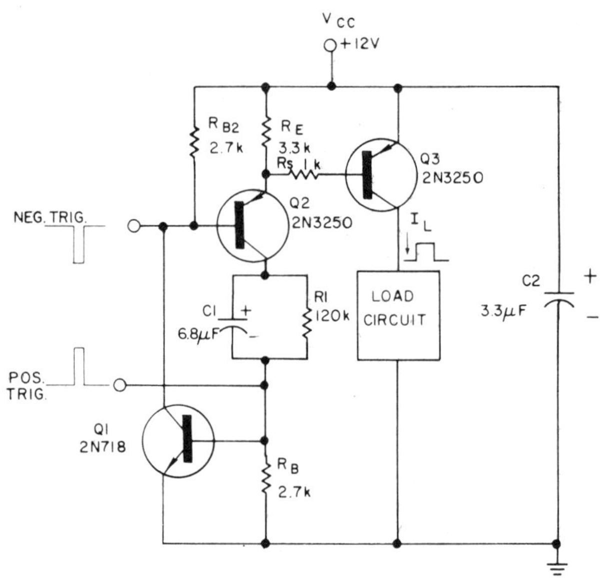

ONE-SHOT SWITCH—Three-transistor equivalent of scr applies power to d-c load when triggered by either positive or negative pulse. Circuit draws negligible standby current. Article gives equation for determining time load current is cut off.—D. Bron, Three-Transistor Circuit Functions as a One-Shot SCR, *Electronic Design*, March 1, 1970, p 81—83.

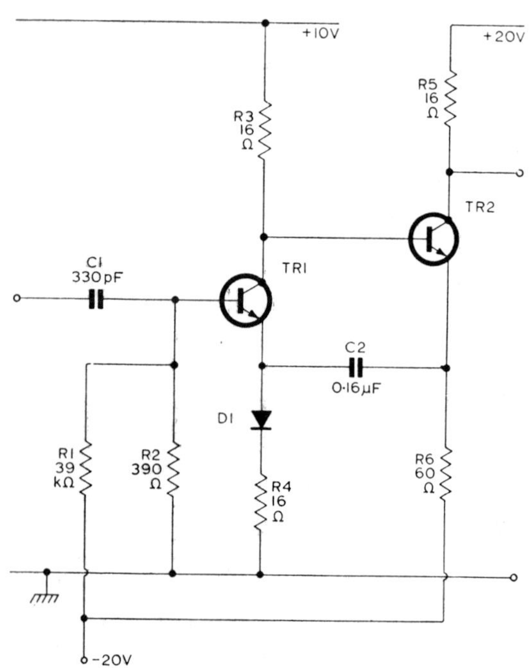

EMITTER-COUPLED MONO—Delivers 500-mA output pulse having duration of 1.25 μs. Transistors are BFY50, and diode is AAZ12.—Applications of the BFY50, BFY51 and BFY52, Philips, Pub. Dept., Elcoma Div., Eindhoven, The Netherlands, No. 428, 1965.

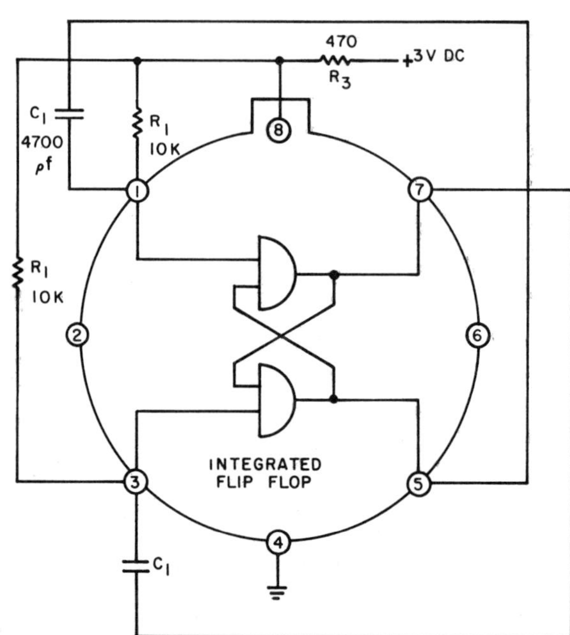

FREE-RUNNING IC FLIP-FLOP—Only five external components are needed to convert standard Fairchild or Amelco IC flip-flop to astable or free-running mvbr. R3 makes circuit self-starting. Article gives frequency equation.—G. Demjanenko, External Connection Converts Integrated Flip-Flop To Monostable, *Electronic Design*, Aug. 17, 1964, p 198—200.

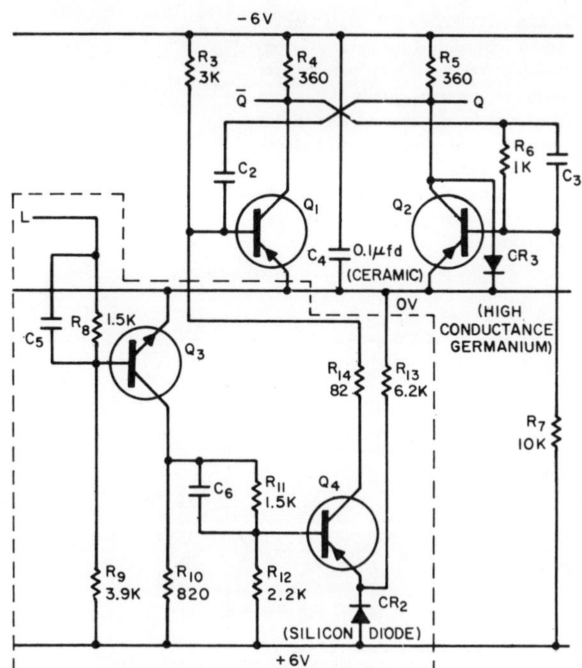

BACKWARD MONO—Changing capacitively coupled input of conventional monostable mvbr to direct coupling permits selecting one pulse from series of pulses, providing signal whenever pulse is missing from pulse train, and indicating null in servo system. Article describes each application in detail, with waveforms. Cost of parts is only a few dollars, even for 0.1-μs rise and fall times.—R. A. Karlin, The Backward Monostable: A Time-Delay Switch, *Electronic Design*, Jan. 4, 1965, p 58–61.

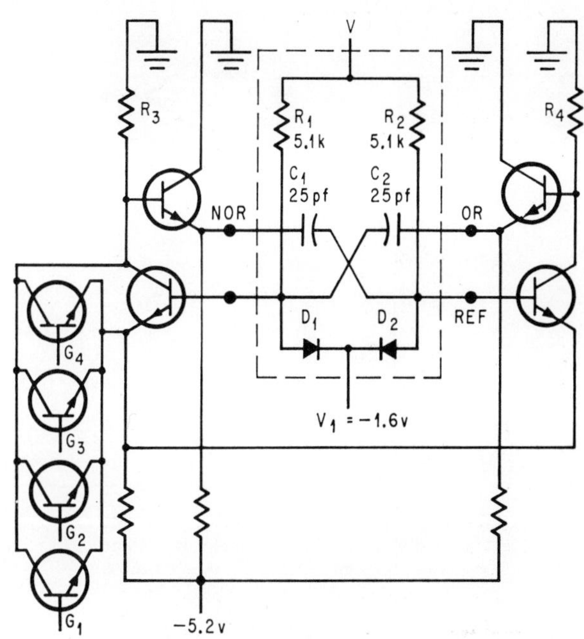

MULTI-INPUT ASTABLE IC—Components outside dashed box are on Motorola MC301 IC having emitter-coupled logic. Connection shown gives gated astable mvbr in which frequency is determined by values of components and supply voltage V. Oscillations stop when any one of the four input levels is high. Features include fast operation, externally controlled repetition rate, and multi-input start-stop control of operation.—A. Tojo, High Speed Multivibrator Controlled By Single ECL, *Electronics*, Sept. 18, 1967, p 109–110.

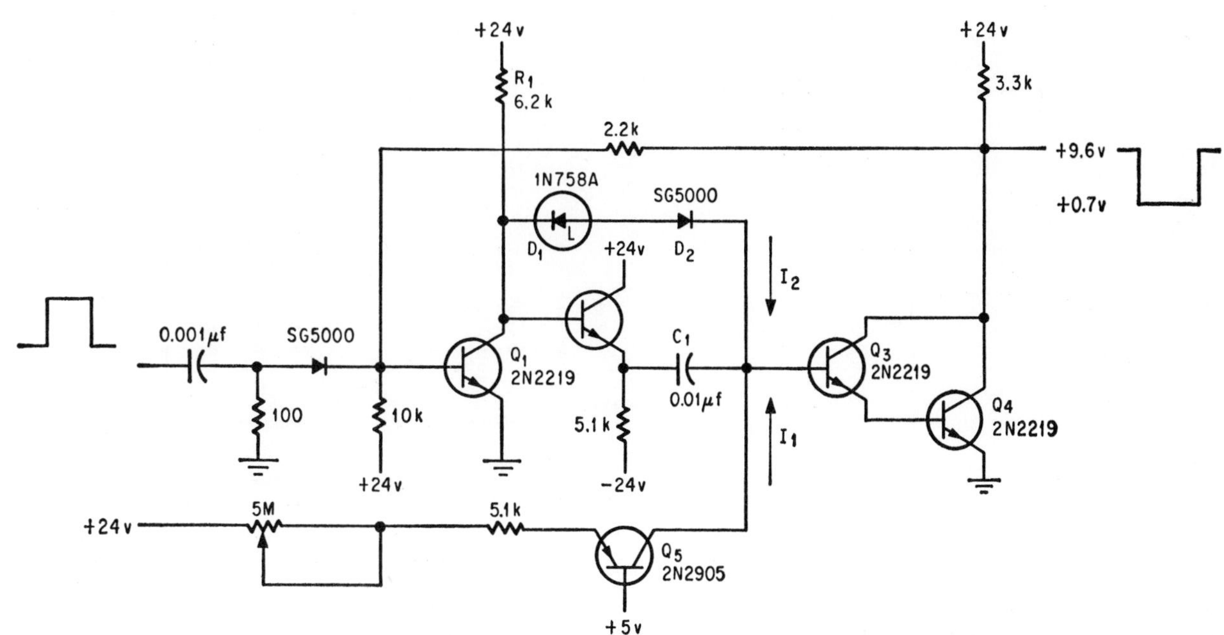

WIDER PULSES FASTER—Two extra diodes in mvbr using Darlington Q3-Q4 give high noise immunity and fast recovery time without limiting width of output pulse. In stable state, Q1 is off and Q3 and Q4 conduct heavily. With triggering, voltage across D1 and D2 falls below zener voltage and high resistance of D1 has effect of opening this diode path. Pulse width is then determined only by values of C1 and current I1.—A. J. Metz, Two Diodes Remove Pulse-Width Limitation, *Electronics*, June 12, 1967, p 105.

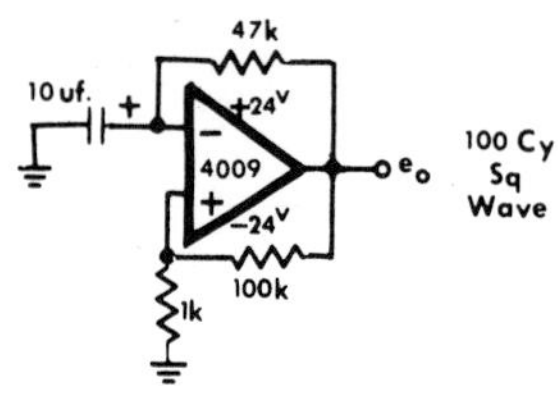

100-HZ SQUARE-WAVE OPAMP—Uses Model 4009 d-c opamp with only four external components. Positive feedback loop sets trigger threshold level of opamp, while R-C time constant in negative feedback loop sets charging time constant. Varying negative feedback resistor gives wide range of frequencies. —B. J. Losmandy, Operational Amplifier Applications for Audio Systems, Opamp Labs, Los Angeles, Cal., 1968.

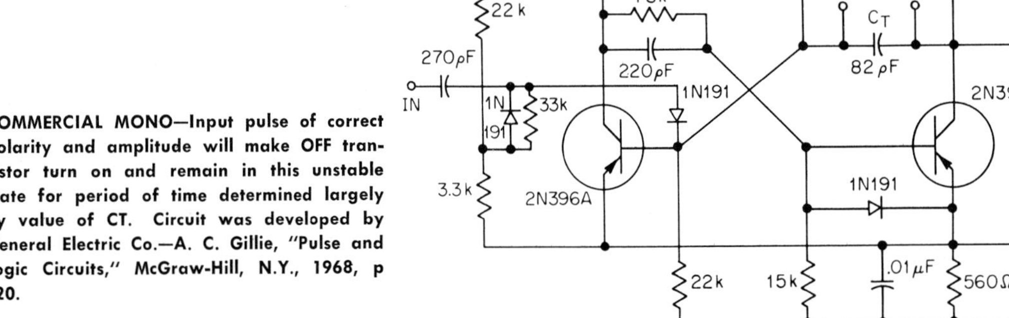

COMMERCIAL MONO—Input pulse of correct polarity and amplitude will make OFF transistor turn on and remain in this unstable state for period of time determined largely by value of CT. Circuit was developed by General Electric Co.—A. C. Gillie, "Pulse and Logic Circuits," McGraw-Hill, N.Y., 1968, p 220.

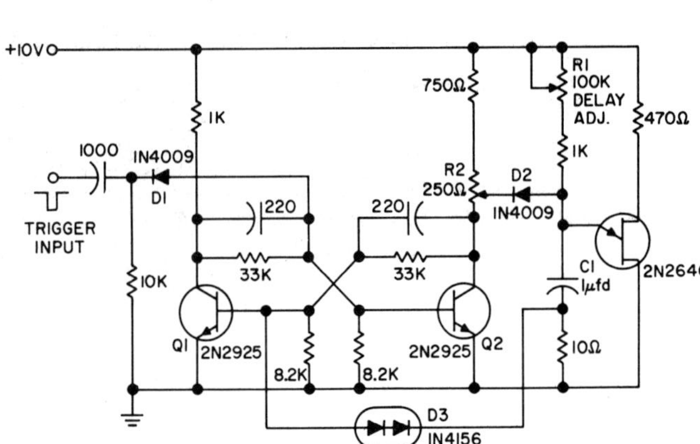

FAST-RECOVERY ONE-SHOT—Provides extremely wide range of duty cycles, good timing stability, and clean waveforms while using only low-cost components. Circuit can be retriggered immediately after completing timing cycle, without loss of timing accuracy.—"Unijunction Circuit Hints," General Electric, Syracuse, N.Y., Fig. 5.

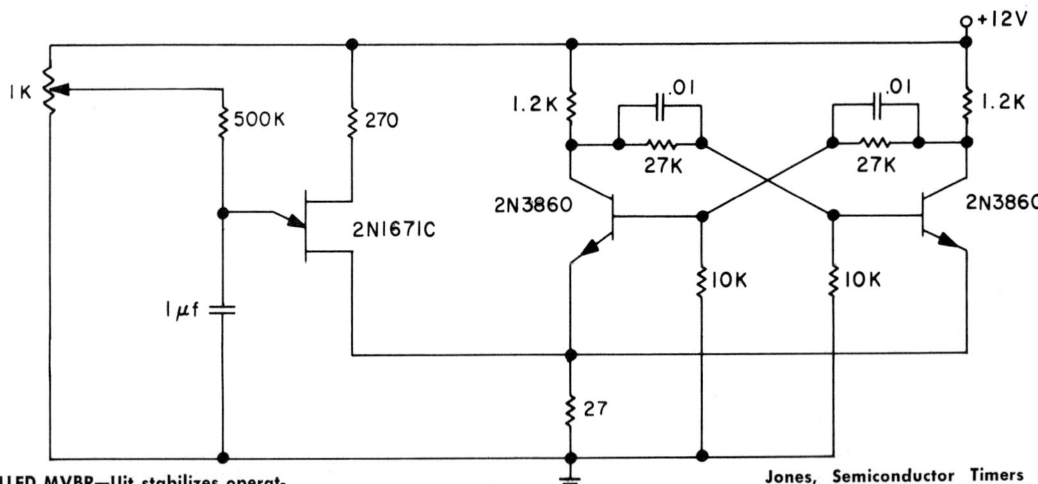

UJT-CONTROLLED MVBR—Ujt stabilizes operating frequency, making mvbr produce good 1-Hz square waves despite changes in supply voltage and ambient temperature.—D. V. Jones, Semiconductor Timers and Low Frequency Oscillators, General Electric, Syracuse, N.Y., No. 671.3, 1966, p 16.

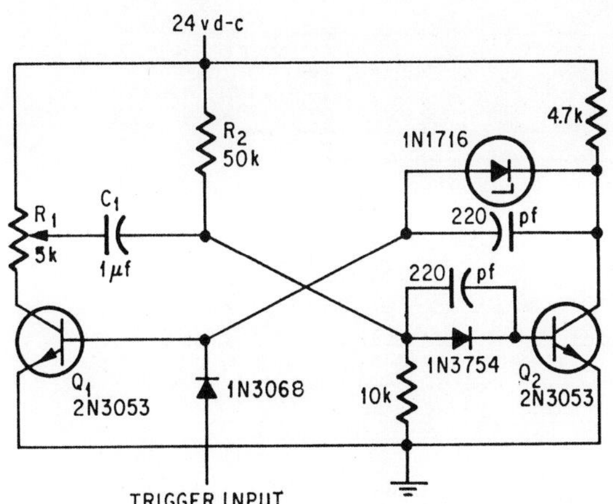

WIDER PULSES—By adjusting capacitor charging voltage as well as RC time constant in monostable mvbr, range of variation in output pulse width can be greater than 1,000:1. R1 adjusts charging voltage and R2 adjusts time constant.—P. Schiff, Voltage Adjustment Extends Multivibrator's Pulse Width, *Electronics*, Sept. 30, 1968, p 82–83.

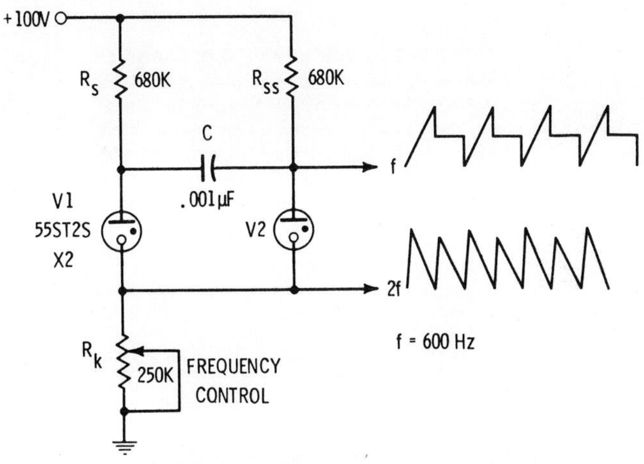

CATHODE-COUPLED ASTABLE NEON—600-Hz fundamental frequency is available, as well as alternate waveform at 1,200 Hz. Amplitudes of high-frequency signal are equal only on alternate cycles.—W. G. Miller, "Using and Understanding Miniature Neon Lamps," H. W. Sams & Co., Indianapolis, Ind., 1969, p 46.

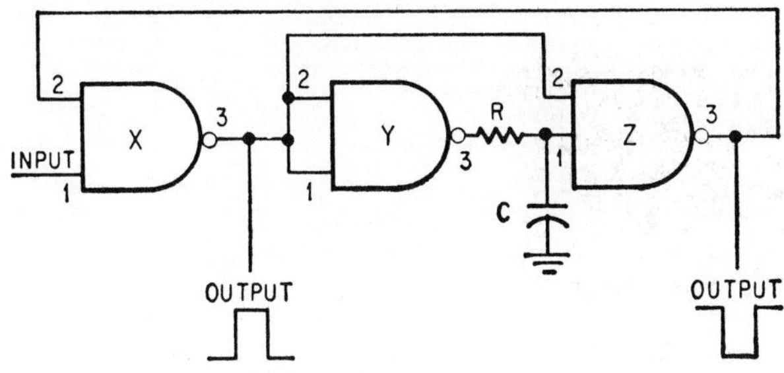

X, Y and Z are 3 of the 4 gates of a Sylvania SG223

CONSTANT PULSE WIDTH—Combining three NAND gates as shown gives fast monostable mvbr in which width of output pulse is independent of supply voltage and input pulse width. With 4 V for 1 level and less than 0.45 V for 0 level, period of monostable is 1.4 RC. To avoid gate overload, R should be below 220 ohms.—P. Sandland, Integrated Gates Form Fast Monostable Multivibrator, *Electronics*, June 26, 1967, p 108–109.

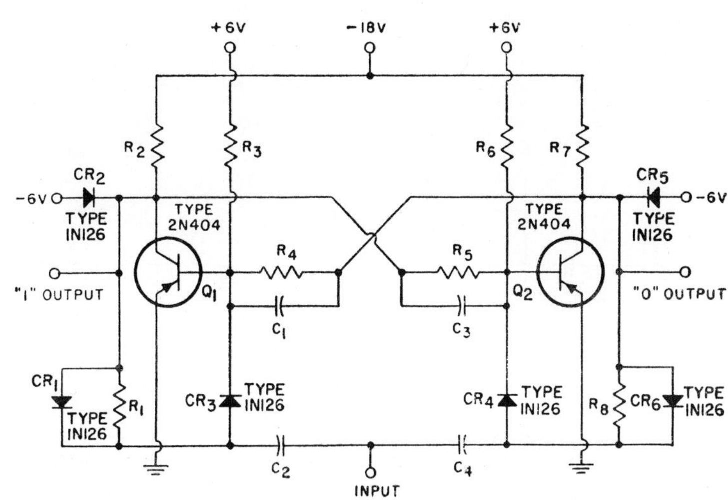

1-MHZ BISTABLE—Can be used for generating binary outputs for computer applications, or as electronic switch. Circuit is in stable state when either transistor is conducting and other transistor is cut off. States are switched each time positive trigger pulse is applied to input terminal at bottom center. Output, which may be taken from either stage, or both, is unit step voltage for single trigger and square wave for continuous periodic triggering of input. Frequency division of 2:1 is thereby obtained. Values: R1, R8 5.1K; R2, R7 1.2K; R3, R6 11K; R4, R5 2.7K; C1, C3 180 pF; C2, C4 430 pF.—"Transistor Manual," RCA, Harrison, N.J., SC-13, p 534.

SWITCHING BY SUPPLY VOLTAGE CHANGE—Insertion of zener in one coupling arm of bistable mvbr gives switching simply by changing d-c supply voltage. Can be used in overvoltage alarms, trigger circuits, and protective circuits.—A. R. Hayes, Multivibrator Switches With Supply Voltage Change, *Electronic Design*, April 13, 1964, p 74–75.

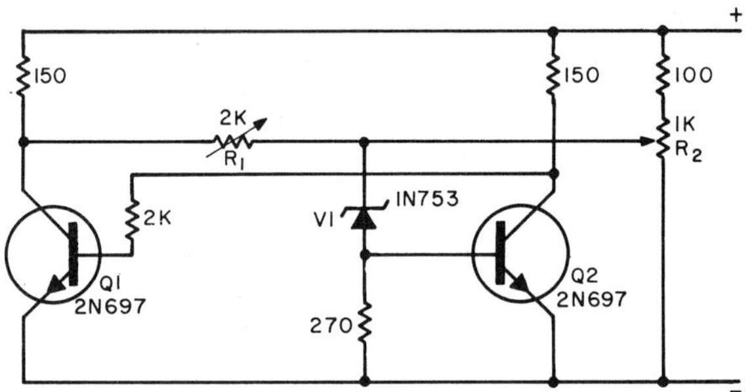

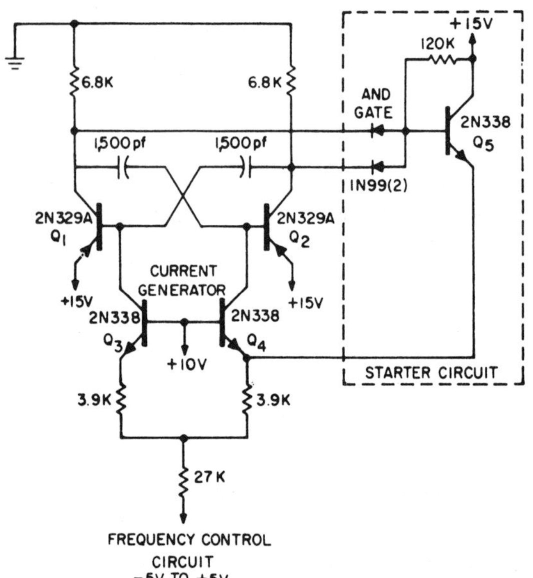

GATE PREVENTS TURN-ON STALL—Use of AND-gate starter (dashed rectangle) with symmetrical free-running mvbr provides protection from stalling at turn-on, without interfering with normal balanced operation.—M. T. Pett, Starter Circuit Prevents Stall of Free-Running Multi, "400 Ideas for Design Selected from Electronic Design," Hayden Book Co., N.Y., 1964, p 63.

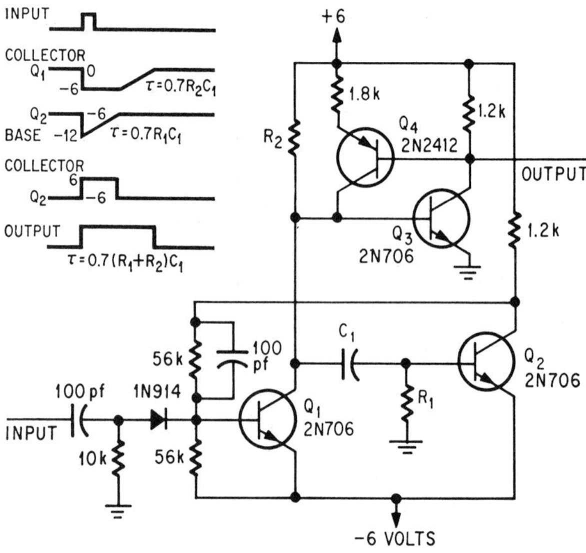

IMMEDIATE RETRIGGERING—Modification of single-shot mvbr gives timing capacitor C1 extra job of setting up circuit to receive next trigger pulse instantly, by reducing recovery time of circuit to zero. Duty cycle thus becomes essentially 100%. Values of R1, R2, and C1 are selected to give desired output pulse width.—J. L. Shagena and A. Mall, Single-Shot Multivibrator Has Zero Recovery Time, *Electronics*, Nov. 27, 1967, p 83.

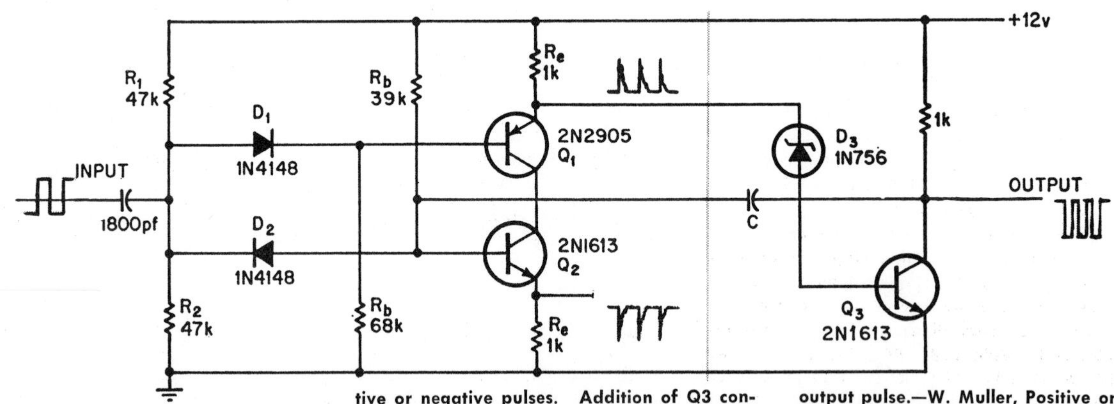

BIPOLAR ONE-SHOT—Use of complementary transistors permits triggering by either positive or negative pulses. Addition of Q3 converts circuit to monostable mvbr, for which single rectangular input pulse gives double output pulse.—W. Muller, Positive or Negative Pulses Trigger One-Shot Multivibrator, *Electronics*, Aug. 18, 1969, p 94.

OPTIMUM ASTABLE DESIGN WITH GRAPHS—Article contains design equations, graphs, and step-by-step procedure for optimizing ten design criteria for generating square-wave or unsymmetrical pulses with fastest possible rise time. Circuit shown is worked out as example, for 100-kHz pulses with width of 1 μs.—C. W. Davis, Plotting Produces Total Astable Design, *Electronic Design*, Sept. 13, 1965, p 60–63.

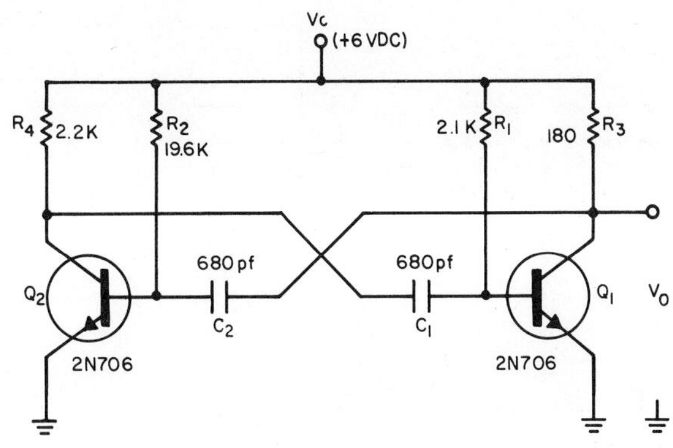

75-S ONE-SHOT FOR $3.50—Long-duration one-shot uses low-cost components, including dual-gate IC. Operates on supply as low as 2.6 V d-c. Input and output levels are compatible with standard micrologic.—R. W. Walton, Long-Duration One-Shot Uses Integrated Circuit, *EEE*, Oct. 1966, p 140.

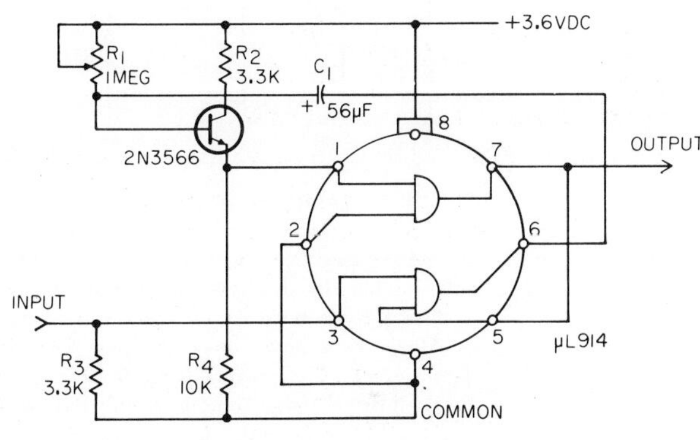

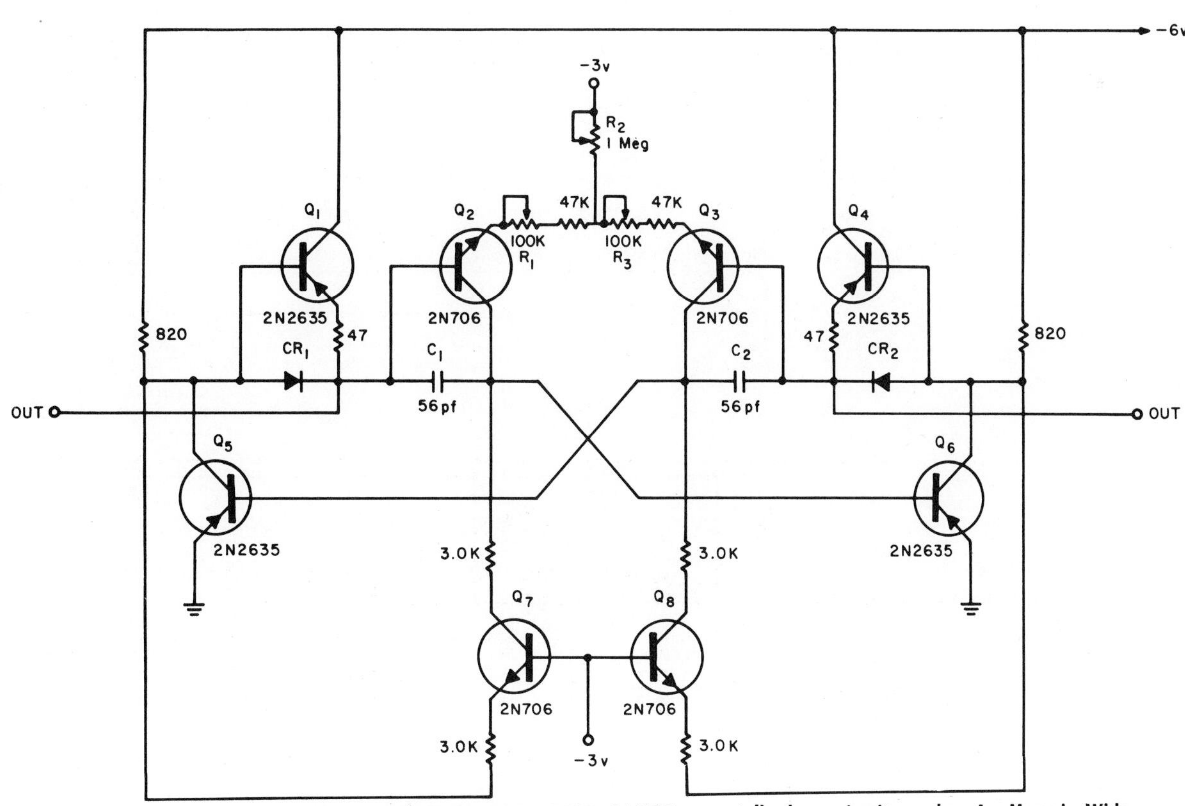

NOTE:
DIODES ARE 1N662

EIGHT TRANSISTORS GIVE WIDE RANGE—Additional transistors prevent locking of conventional mvbr into stable state, to give frequency range from 8 kHz to 3 MHz. Article tells how circuit works.—A. Marosi, Wide-Range Multivibrator Varies Frequency from 8 Kc to 3 Mc, *Electronic Design*, April 12, 1965, p 50.

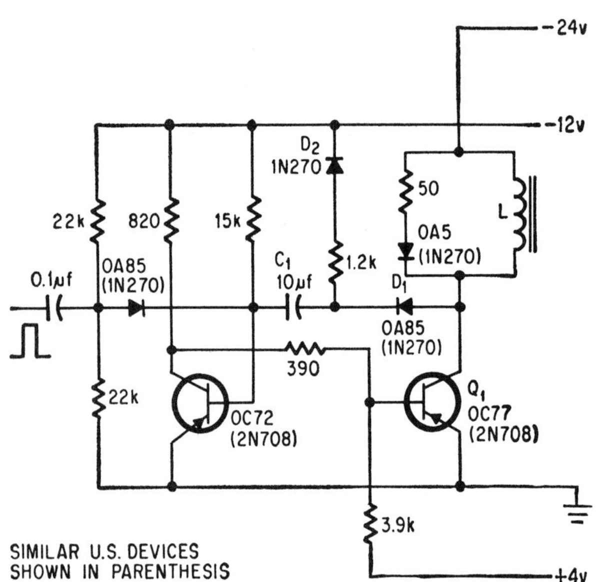

DIODES BLOCK STRAY PULSES—Arrangement prevents relay or other inductive load from affecting stability of mbvr, and at same time provides immunity to pulses coming from common power supply.—R. Ilic, Diodes Provide Noise Immunity for Monostable Multivibrators, *Electronics*, Jan. 9, 1967, p 106–107.

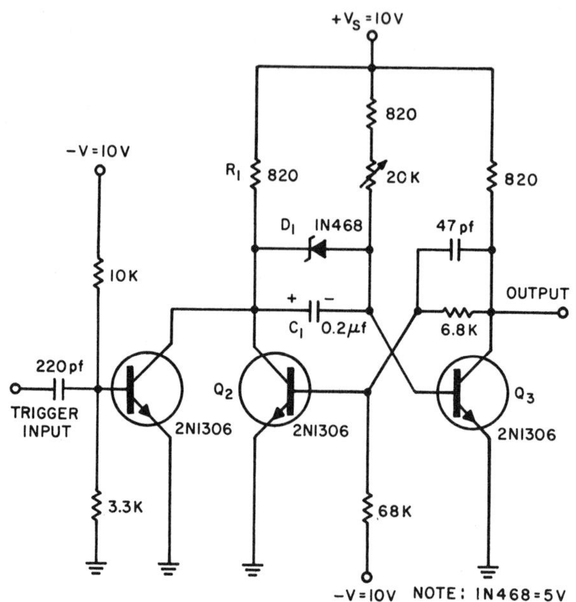

ZENER STABILIZES DELAY—Use of zener D1 across timing capacitor makes time delay independent of whether mono mvbr is triggered by random pulse pattern or by first pulse in burst of uniformly spaced pulses. Article tells how zener changes time delay equation.—G. Carsner, Zener Diode Stabilizes Monostable Delay Time, *Electronic Design*, Dec. 21, 1964, p 59–60.

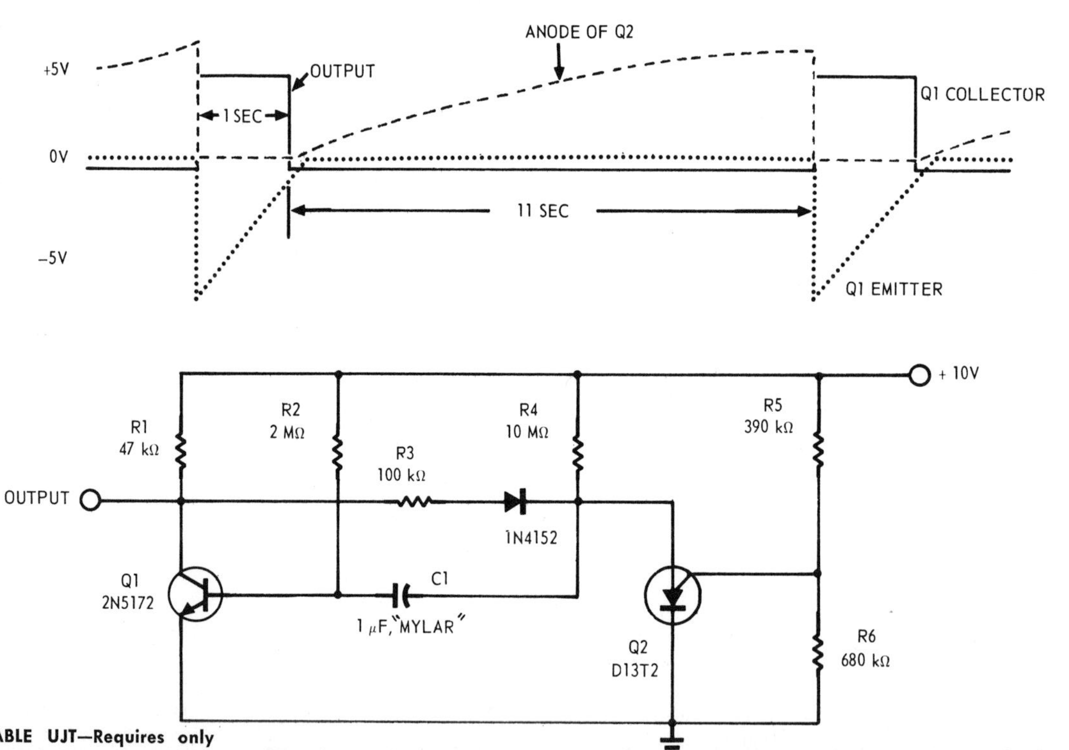

0.1-HZ PROGRAMMABLE UJT—Requires only one large and expensive film capacitor for operation well below 1 Hz. Changing value of C1 changes duration of OFF period. Load must be at least 50K.—R. Muth, Eliminate a Capacitor in Low-Frequency Multivibrators, *EDN*, Dec. 1, 1969, p 61–62.

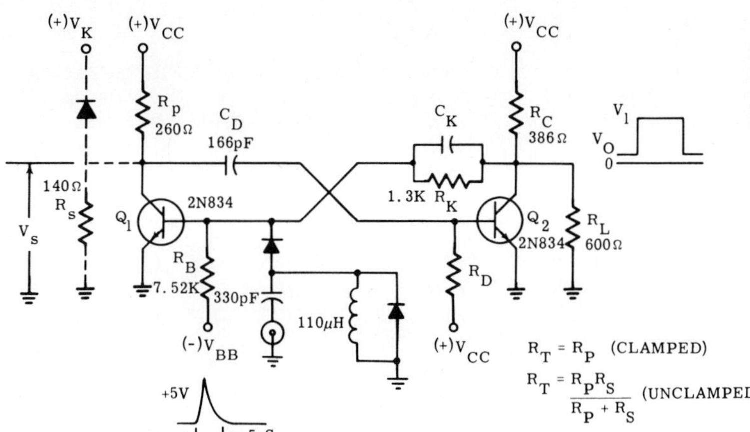

BASIC MONO—Also called one-shot or delay flop. Has one stable state, and one quasi-stable state into which it must be triggered, returning to stable state after given relaxation or delay time. Book gives procedure for calculating values of components.—"High-Speed Switching Transistor Handbook," Motorola, Phoenix, Ariz., 1969, p 235.

VOLTAGE-DIVIDER ASTABLE—Uses voltage divider in bias network. Frequency of operation is approximately equal to 1,000,000 divided by (0.025C + 2.5), where C is value of cross-coupling capacitor in pF, or about 375 kHz for values shown.—A. C. Gillie, "Pulse and Logic Circuits," McGraw-Hill, N.Y., 1968, p 213.

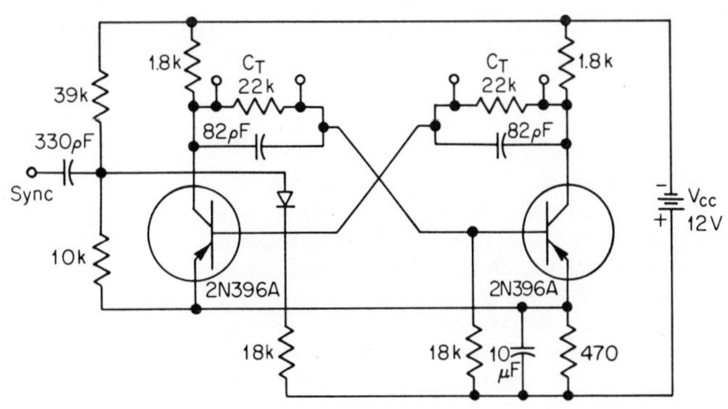

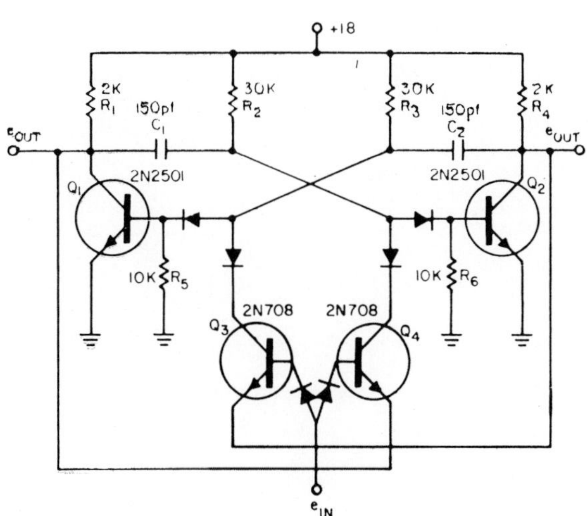

360-KHZ ASTABLE-BISTABLE—Addition of gating transistors Q3-Q4 to feedback paths of basic astable mvbr gives bistable operation. Circuit is free-running up to 360 kHz for fixed input, or changes state in binary fashion when input is pulsed.—T. Saunders, Modified Astable Multivibrator Also Operates in Bistable Mode, *Electronic Design*, Dec. 20, 1965, p 48–49.

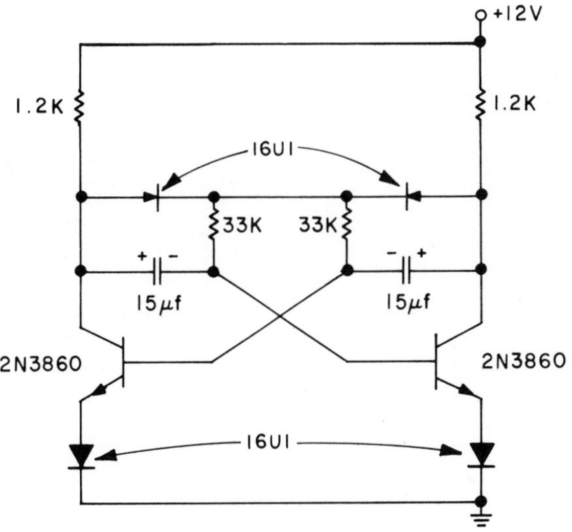

LOW-COST ASTABLE—Provides periods of 0.5 to 1 s. Upper 16U1 dual-diode assures startup by preventing lockup due to saturation of both transistors. Lower dual-diode protects transistors.—D. V. Jones, Semiconductor Timers and Low Frequency Oscillators, General Electric, Syracuse, N.Y., No. 671.3, 1966, p 16.

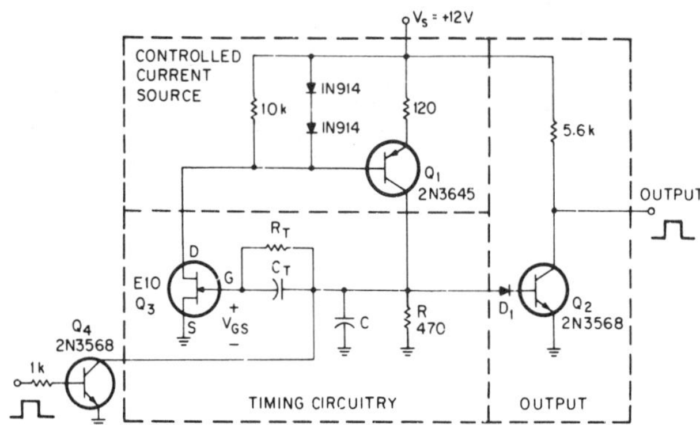

FALSE TRIGGERING—Current source isolates line noise from timing circuitry of one-shot mvbr, to prevent false triggering by line noise when using long time constants. Q1 and capacitor C provide required isolation. RT should be much larger than R, with 10K as minimum; this means that minimum pulse duration is about 50 μs. With 10 meg for RT and 330 μF for CT, time duration is 1 hr.—G. L. Schaffer, Current Source Improves Immunity of One-Shot, *EEE*, March 1969, p 126 and 128.

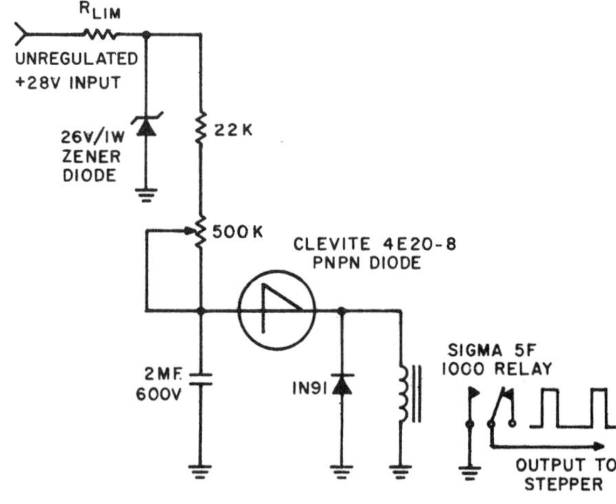

0.5–10 HZ WITH NOISE IMMUNITY—Shockley pnpn diode connected as free-running mvbr is unaffected by radiated noise of relays and other devices. Used to drive stepper relays at rate determined by setting of pot. Zener regulator prevents supply voltage changes from affecting frequency.—M. E. T. Swinnen, Multivibrator Immune to Radiated Noise, *Electronic Design*, Dec. 7, 1964, p 71–73.

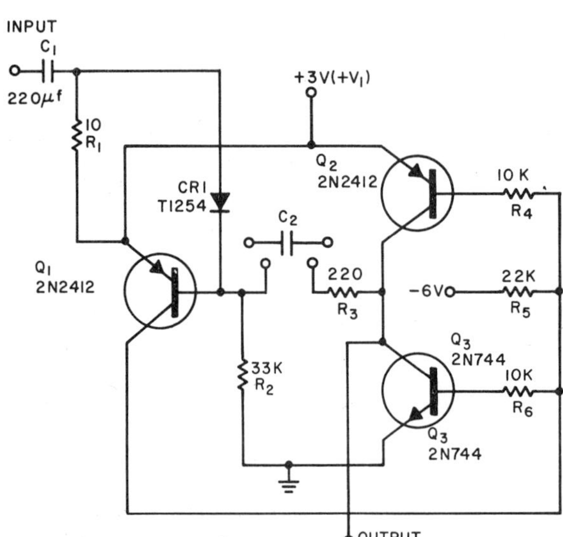

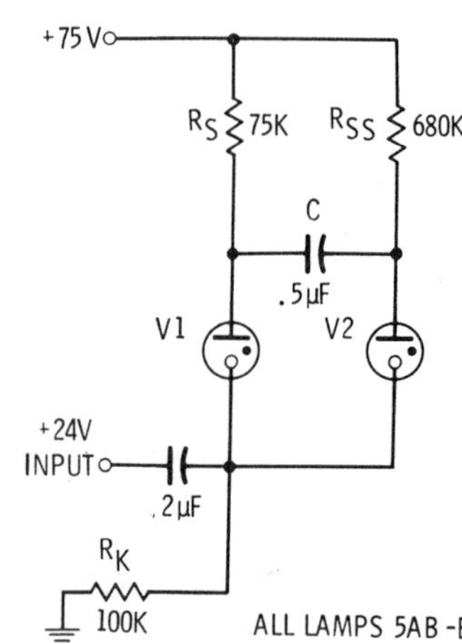

FAST-RECOVERY ONE-SHOT—At rest, Q1 and Q2 are ON, Q2 is OFF, and output is at ground. Positive input pulse changes all transistors, driving output to about 3 V positive. Value of coupling capacitor C2, acting with R2, determines holding time before circuit returns to original state. For 0.01 μF, output pulse is about 280 μs. Pulse width remains constant for duty cycles well above 90%.—D. Colin, Monostable Configuration Provides Unusually Fast Recovery Time, *Electronic Design*, Aug. 3, 1964, p 43.

MONOSTABLE NEON—V1 is normally on but is extinguished by 24-V input pulse which permits V2 to ignite. However, voltage across 100K resistor is not sufficient to keep V1 from firing, so circuit returns to stable state. Time V2 is on depends on time constant of 0.5-μF capacitor and two anode resistors.—W. G. Miller, "Using and Understanding Miniature Neon Lamps," H. W. Sams & Co., Indianapolis, Ind., 1969, p 50.

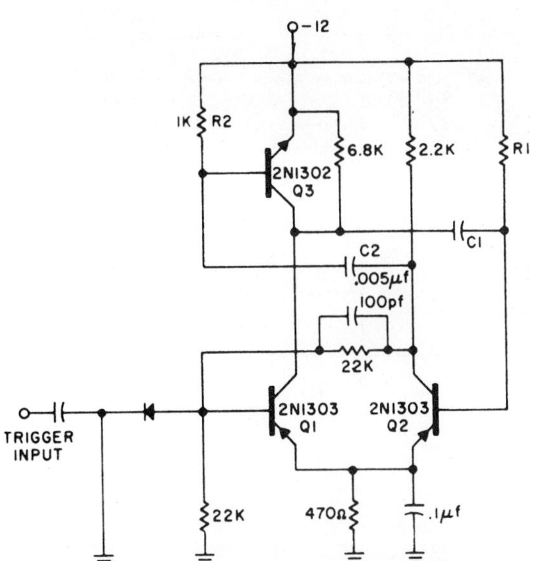

TRANSISTOR SPEEDS CAPACITOR DISCHARGE—Addition of Q3 to monostable mvbr provides regenerative discharging of timing capacitor at end of pulse period. Circuit has given fall times as short as 0.1 μs on pulse widths of 1 μs to 15 ms.—R. W. Allington, Extra Transistor Reduces Turn-Off Time in One-Shot Multi, "400 Ideas for Design Selected from Electronic Design," Hayden Book Co., N. Y., 1964, p 69.

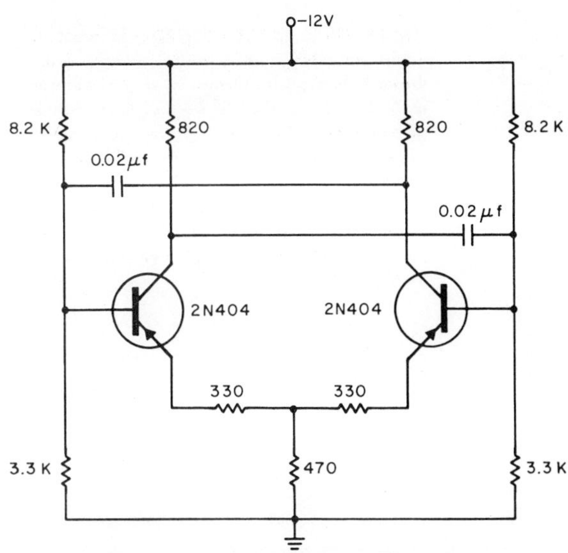

POSITIVE STARTING—Simple modification of standard mvbr, to prevent transistors from saturating, insures oscillation by precluding existence of stable state in which both transistors are on. Values shown give 100-kHz operation over wide temperature range.—N. O. Sokal, Free-Running Multi Has Sure-Fire Starting, *Electronic Design*, Jan. 6, 1964, p 80.

ZERO QUIESCENT POWER—When monostable mvbr is switched to its OFF condition, both transistors are nonconducting and no power whatsoever is drawn from supply. Circuit produces pulse widths ranging from several microseconds to several milliseconds. Both input and output are compatible with DTL or TTL devices.—M. Steele, Monostable Conserves Power, *EDN*, Dec. 15, 1969, p 61.

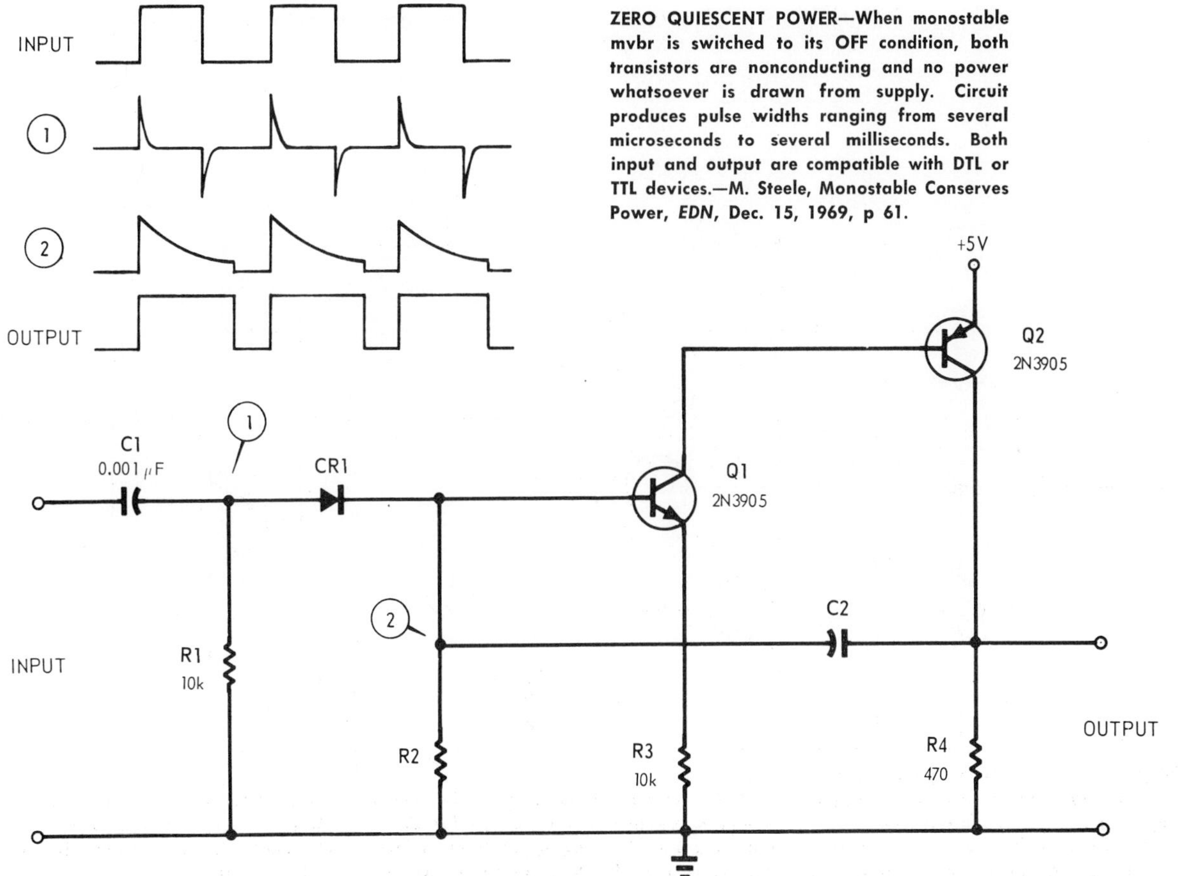

LINEAR PULSE WIDTH CONTROL—Monostable mvbr provides output pulse whose width varies linearily with respect to control voltage of 0-25 V d-c applied to base of Q4. Article gives equation for period of one-shot. Operation depends on use of emitter-follower constant-current generator. Pulse width range is about 3 to 80 μs.—R. S. Hughes, Pulse Width vs. Control Voltage Made Linear by Generator, *Electronic Design*, Dec. 21, 1964, p 56–58.

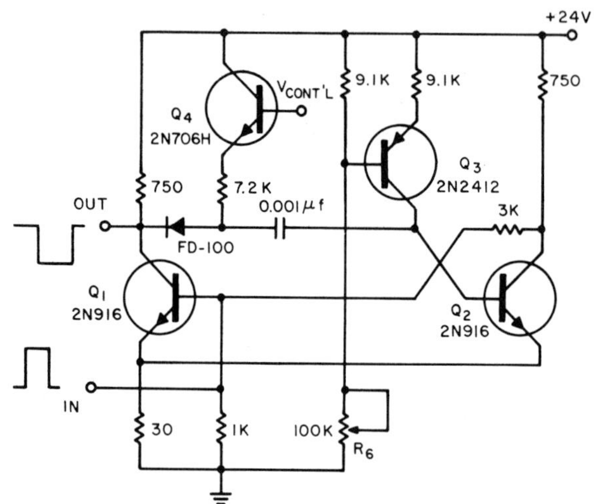

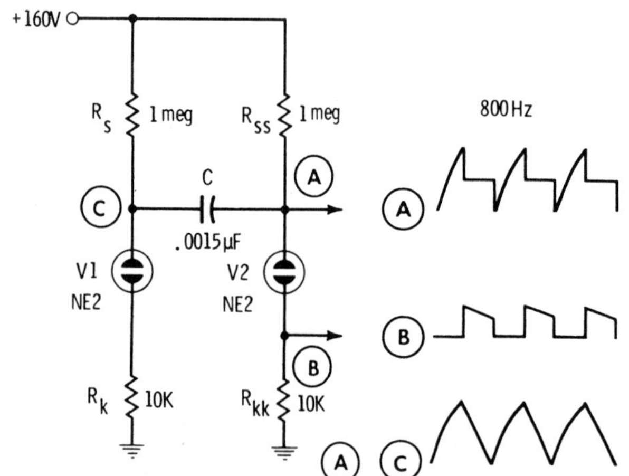

800-HZ ASTABLE NEON—Offers three symmetrical waveshapes by tapping circuit at different points. Square wave at B has 10-μs rise time, and top may be made flat by using diode clipper.—W. G. Miller, "Using and Understanding Miniature Neon Lamps," H. W. Sams & Co., Indianapolis, Ind., 1969, p 45.

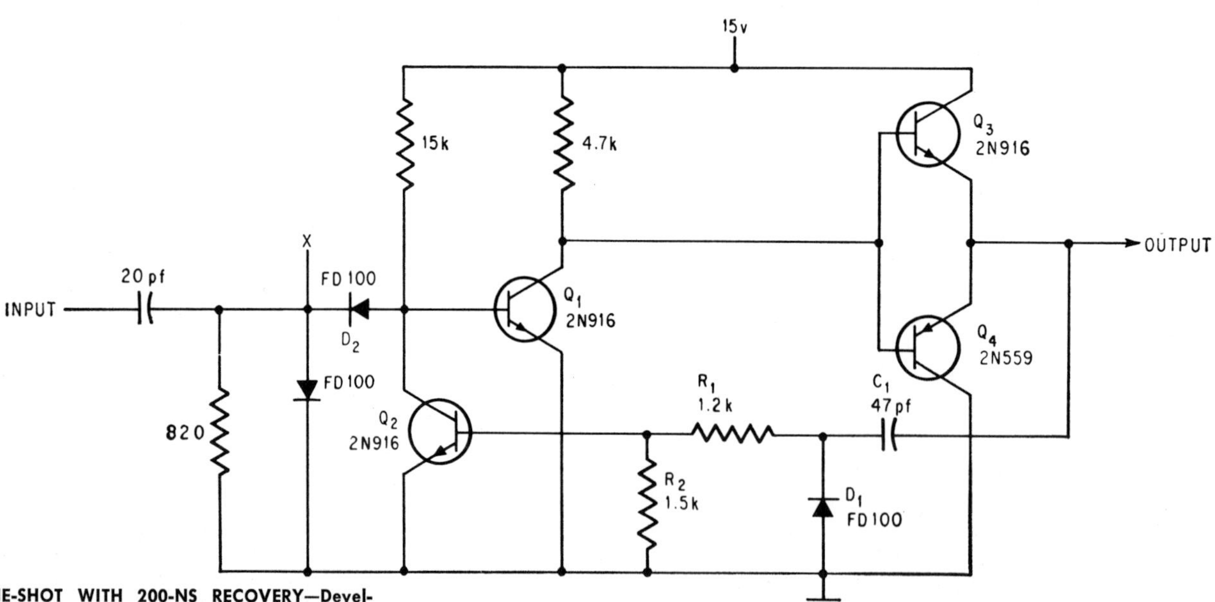

ONE-SHOT WITH 200-NS RECOVERY—Developed for computer and communications applications having very high pulse repetition rate. Has been used as pulse-averaging discriminator in f-m system having 200-kHz deviation of 1-MHz carrier. Input at point X clamps output to positive supply voltage for duration of pulse. Discharging C1 through low-impedance path D1-Q4 gives short recovery time. Pulse width generated is 600 ns.—J. J. Moran and R. M. Gloriosco, Narrow-Pulse One-Shot Recovers Quickly, *Electronics*, Jan. 9, 1967, p 107.

IMPROVED TRIGGERING OF MONO—Shaping of input trigger pulses by differentiating circuit C1-Rd makes performance of emitter-coupled mono more reliable. Will trigger reliably with pulses above 3.9 V for all values of d-c control voltage between 1.1 and 1.8 V, with this controlled range making output pulse duration vary between 1.1 and 8.35 ms. Recovery time is about 1.7 ms.—A. J. Duelm, Wiring Modification Improves Voltage Variable Delay Circuit, *Electronic Design*, Feb. 15, 1970, p 82 and 84.

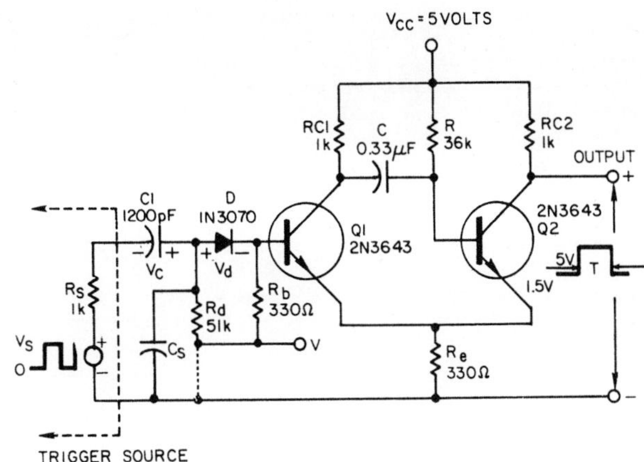

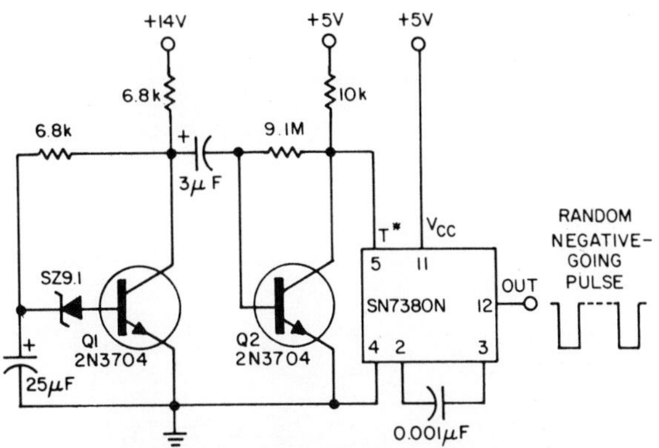

NOISE-TRIGGERED RANDOM PULSES—Provides random pulse spacings ranging from tens of microseconds to milliseconds, for TTL logic-level pulse generator. Uses Schauer SZ9.1 zener with Q1 as broad-spectrum noise generator. Q2 is biased so only higher-level noise spikes drive it to saturation and trigger IC mono mvbr. Varying noise generator supply voltage changes output rate.—R. J. Krusberg, Noise Spikes Trigger Random-Pulse Generator, *Electronic Design*, June 7, 1970, p 102.

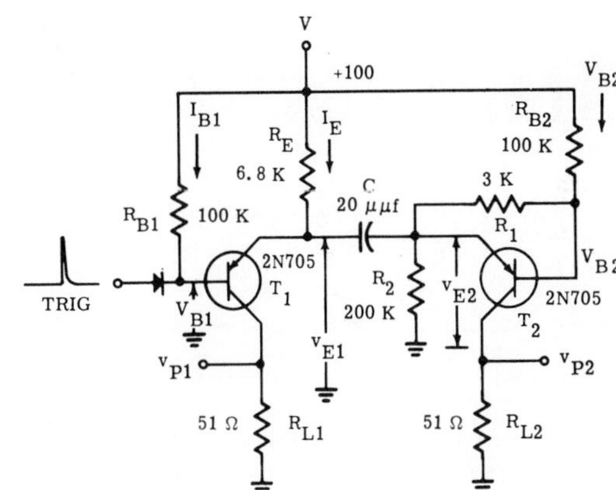

FAST-RISE MONO—Gives essentially square-wave output pulses with rise time of 1 ns, fall time of 2 ns, and duration from 12 ns to several μs. Will produce 12-ns pulses reliably at repetition rate of 20 MHZ.—"High Speed Switching Transistor Handbook," Motorola, Phoenix, Ariz., 1969, p 302.

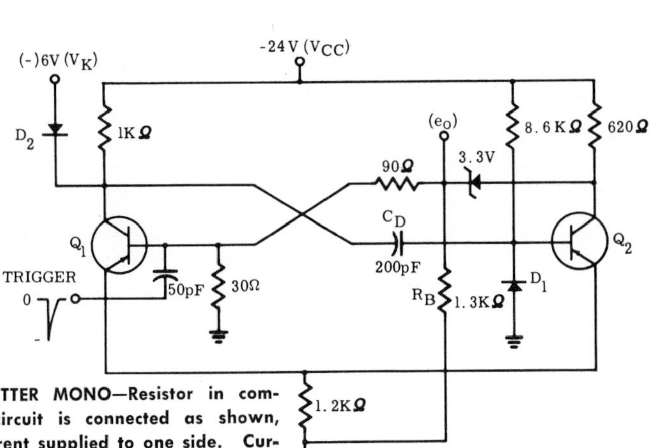

COMMON-EMITTER MONO—Resistor in common-emitter circuit is connected as shown, with base current supplied to one side. Current through RB holds D1 conducting and keeps Q2 on until Q1 is triggered. Recovery of circuit is rapid, permitting duty cycle as high as 80%. Circuit is sensitive to small trigger signals but insensitive to their level, so noise is not a problem.—"High Speed Switching Transistor Handbook," Motorola, Phoenix, Ariz., 1969, p 281.

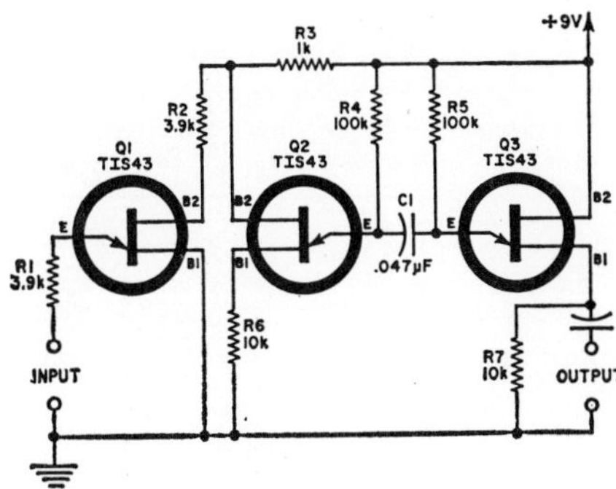

ON AND OFF—Both ujt's of mvbr are normally off. Input ujt Q1 provides rectangular pulse when positive input signal of sufficiently high level arrives, causing Q2 and Q3 to fire in sequence, after which circuit returns to rest. Will handle repetition rates up to 120 pps. Input must be at least 4.5-V positive-going pulse or 3-V rms sine-wave signal.—Ujt Monocycle Multivibrator, *Electronics World*, April 1969, p 61.

6-MIN PERIOD—Two 2N3436 fet's are connected as source followers, with two npn transistors serving as switches. Action is similar to that of ordinary mvbr and is self-starting. When C1 and C2 are 4 μF, rheostats can vary period over range from 8 ms to 6 min. With 100 pF, frequency range becomes 100 Hz to 3 MHz. Stability is good with long time constants because large electrolytics are not used.—G. Hanus and Y. Martinez, Stable Low Frequencies with FET-Bipolar Pairs, *Electronics*, Jan. 9, 1967, p 105.

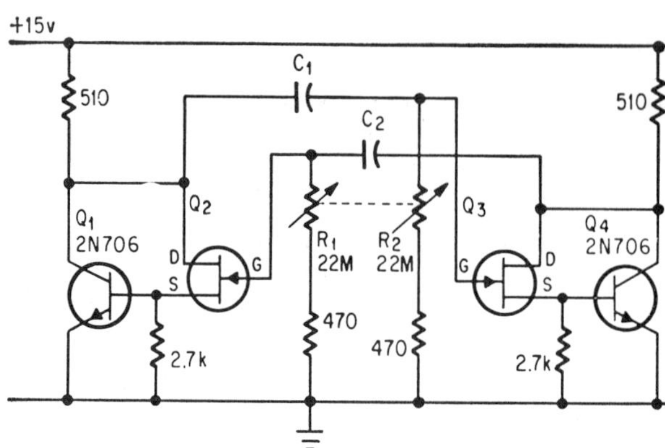

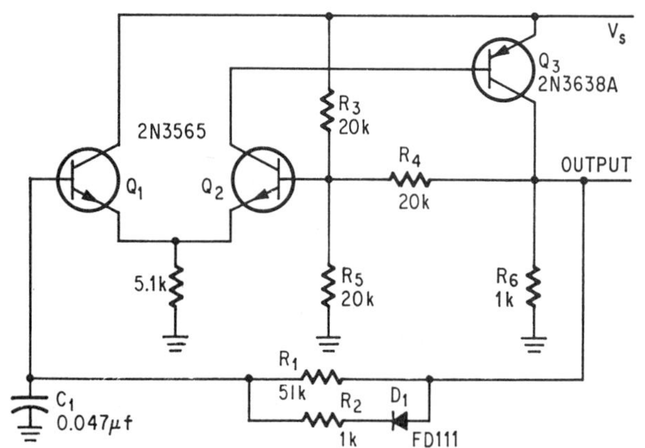

VARIABLE DUTY CYCLE—Switching of diode between two timing networks gives ratio of up to 500 to 1 between on and off times of unsymmetrical free-running mvbr. With values shown, frequency is 600 Hz, rise time 0.3 μs and fall time 4 μs. Article gives design equations. Supply voltage can drop 50% without affecting frequency.—L. Blaser, Waveform Generation Eased By Two Timing Networks, *Electronics*, Sept. 18, 1967, p 110–111.

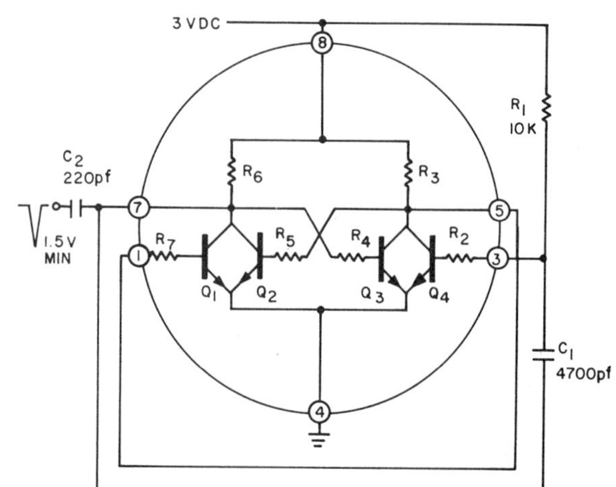

MAKING IC FLIP-FLOP GO MONO—Only two external components are needed to convert standard Fairchild or Amelco IC flip-flop for operation as monostable (one-shot) mvbr. Width of one-shot pulse in seconds is equal to 0.37 R1C1, where R1 is in ohms and C1 in farads. For values shown, width is 18 ms.—G. Demjanenko, External Connection Converts Integrated Flip-Flop To Monostable, *Electronic Design*, Aug. 17, 1964, p 198–200.

STABILIZING WITH DIODES—Compensating diodes D are added to astable mvbr to nullify transistor changes that cause frequency shifts in square-wave output. Article gives design equations. If used with highly stable power supply, temperature change from −10 to 90 C shifts output of 1-MHz mvbr only 10 Hz.—J. Teixeira, Diodes In a Multivibrator Lessen Frequency Variations, *Electronics*, July 8, 1968, p 93–94.

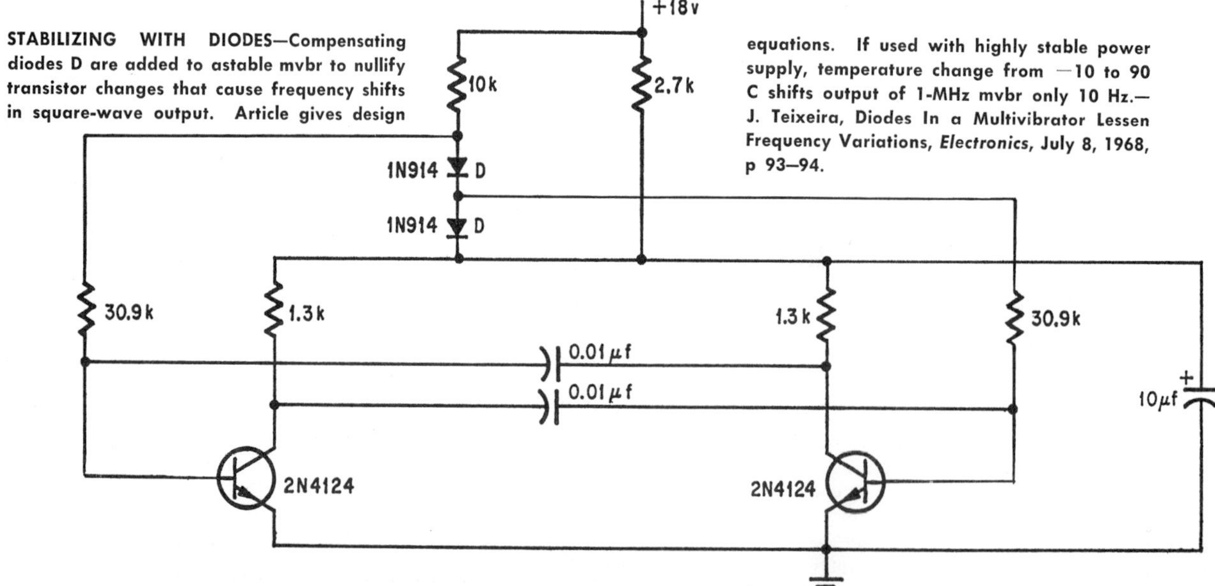

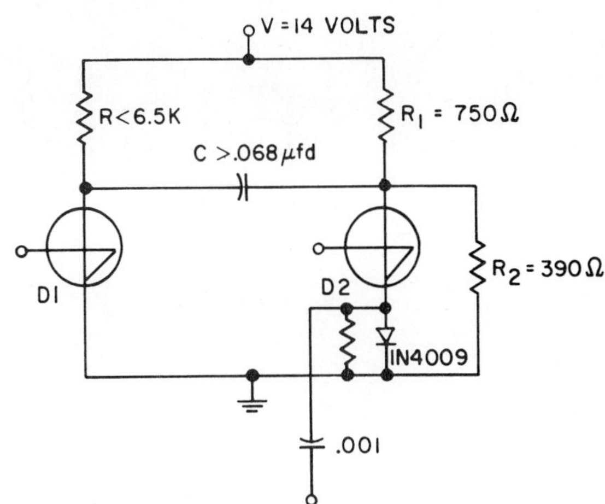

TWO-SUS ONE-SHOT—With silicon unilateral switches, circuit is capable of handling duty cycles above 85%. Requires positive-going switching voltage of 8 V applied to one sus to turn it on. Succeeding positive pulses then have no effect, but first negative-going pulse will turn on other sus and turn off the one that was conducting. After supply voltage is applied, sus having lowest switching voltage will be first to turn on. D1 and D2 are D13P1 sus switches.—W. R. Spofford, Jr., Applications of the New Silicon Bilateral Switch and the Silicon Unilateral Switch, General Electric, Syracuse, N.Y., No. 671.3, 1966, p 4.

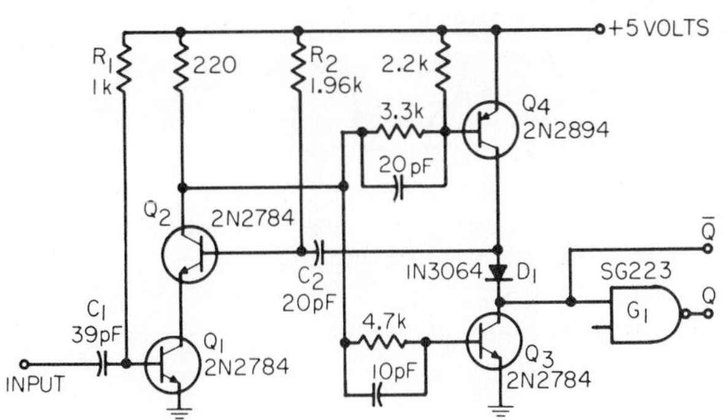

30-NS PULSE WIDTH FROM ONE-SHOT—Improved input trigger circuit permits generation of extremely fast pulses with width independent of trigger duration and amplitude. Requires negative trigger.—D. R. Hoppe, High Speed Saturated-Mode One-Shot, *EEE*, May 1968, p 122–123.

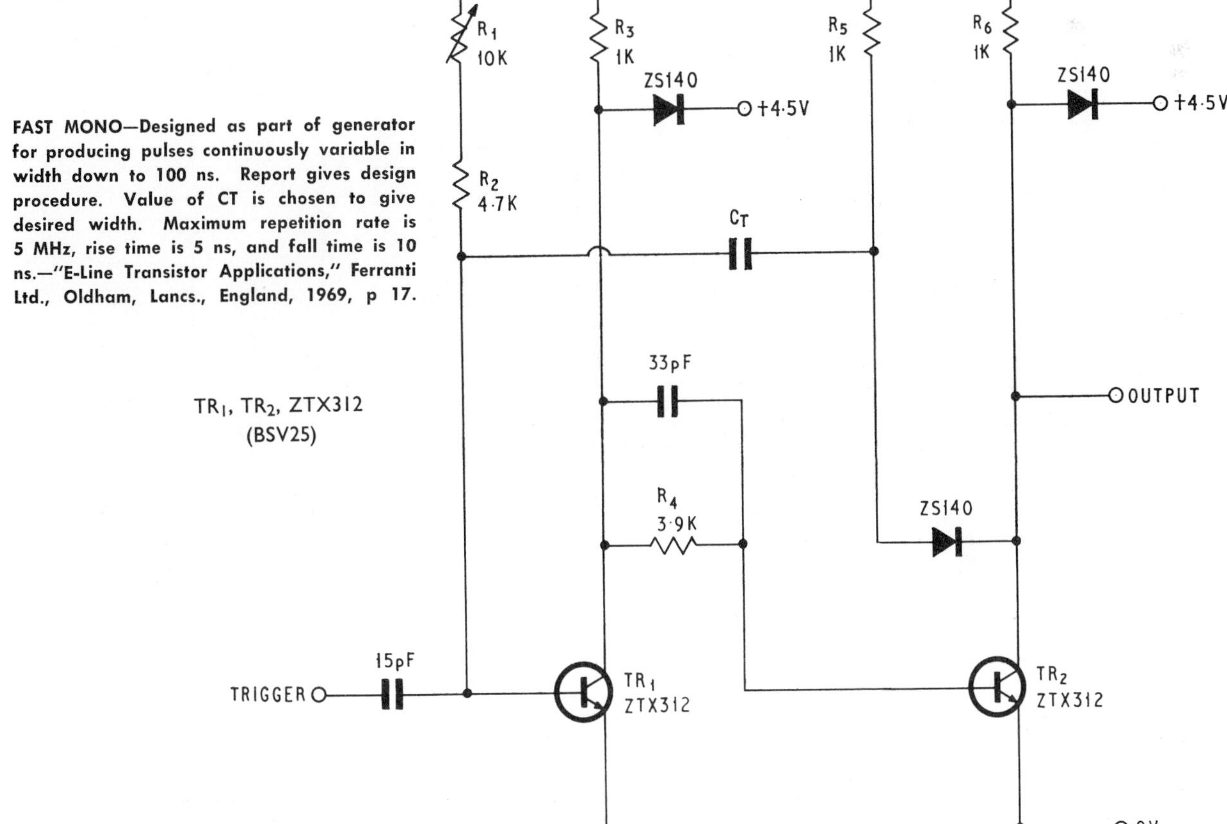

FAST MONO—Designed as part of generator for producing pulses continuously variable in width down to 100 ns. Report gives design procedure. Value of CT is chosen to give desired width. Maximum repetition rate is 5 MHz, rise time is 5 ns, and fall time is 10 ns.—"E-Line Transistor Applications," Ferranti Ltd., Oldham, Lancs., England, 1969, p 17.

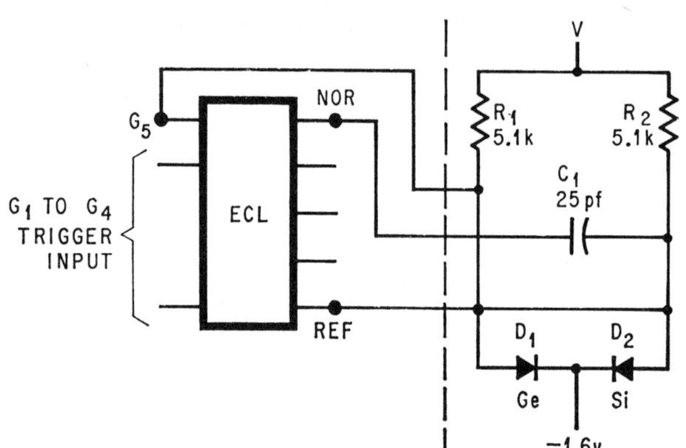

MULTI-INPUT MONO IC—Only five components, at right of dashed line, are needed with Motorola MC301 emitter-coupled logic IC to give monostable mvbr in which trigger signal at any one of the four inputs initiates oscillation. Frequency can be varied remotely by changing V.—T. Tojo, High Speed Multivibrator Controlled By Single ECL, *Electronics*, Sept. 18, 1967, p 109–110.

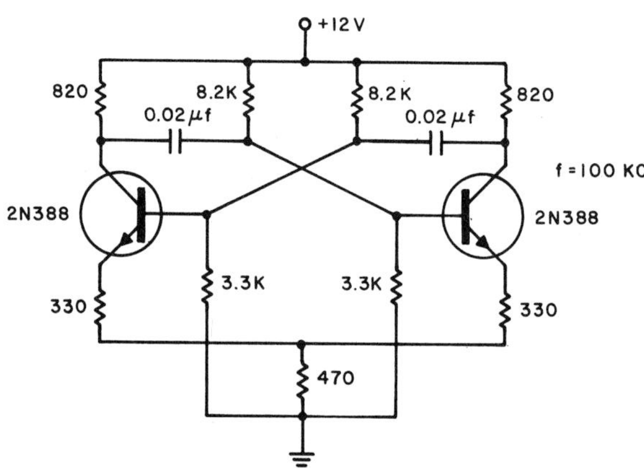

AVOIDING BOTH-ON CONDITION—Free-running mvbr is designed to preclude situation where both transistors are on and saturated, as might occur if both halves of circuit are well matched and power supply voltage comes on slowly. With transistors both in active region when on and with loop gain greater than one, circuit cannot exist stably with both transistors on.—N. O. Sokal, Trouble Spots in Circuits, *Electronic Design*, Nov. 9, 1964, p 32–37.

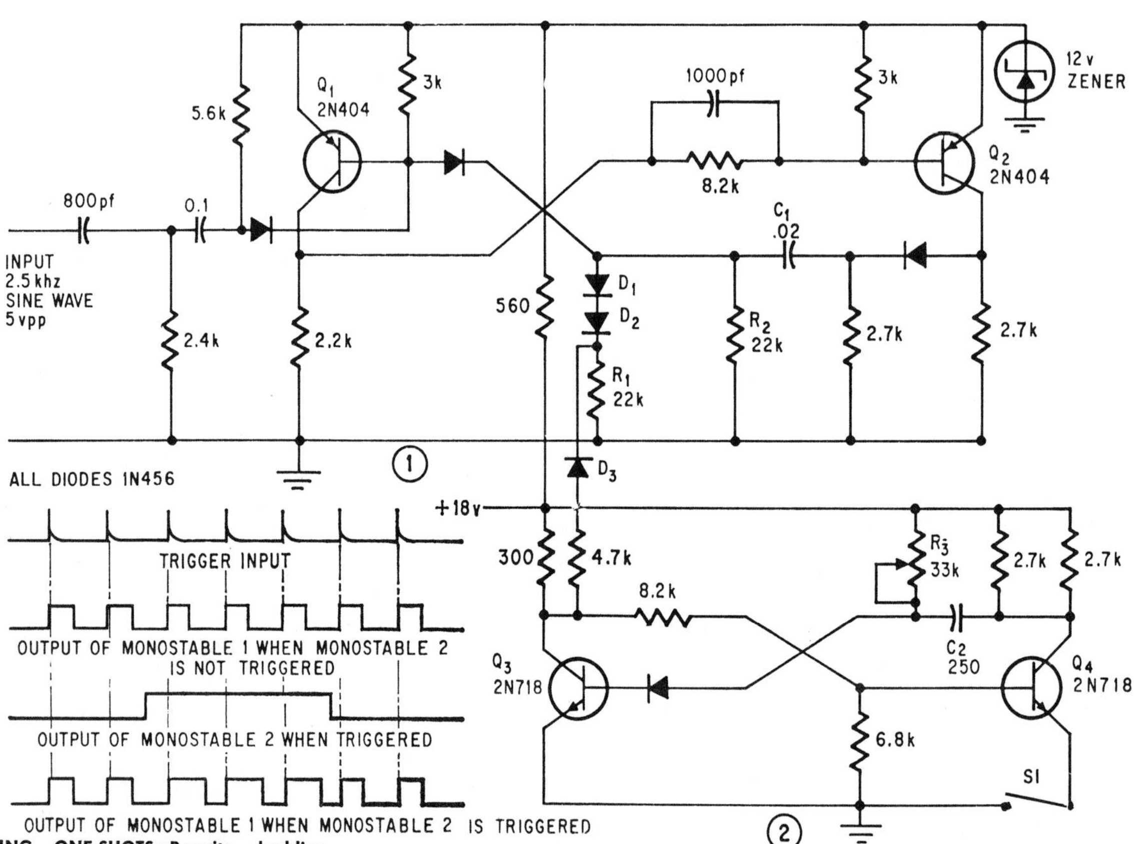

CASCADING ONE-SHOTS—Permits doubling pulse width for desired time interval. Initially, Q1 and Q3 are on, and Q2 and Q4 are off. Switch one is open, so 2.5-kHz sine-wave input triggers first mono. To increase pulse width, S1 is momentarily closed to trigger second mono. Duration of this mono, 0.7 x R3 x C2, determines how long wider pulses will be gated out. Output of mono 1 is at collector of Q2, and output of mono 2 is at collector of Q3.—K. Vijaya Raghavan, Two One-Shots Control Waveform's Pulse Width, *Electronics*, Jan. 6, 1969, p 93.

ZERO STANDBY POWER—One-shot draws no power from supply when in normal standby or OFF mode. When either d-c level or pulse turns on scr, values of R1 and C1 determine how long regenerative action is sustained before scr is turned off. With 10K and 10 μF, ON time is 270 ms, while with 1K and 1 μF, ON time is 5.5 ms. Article gives values for other times, along with design equations. —A. L. Lew, Zero (Quiescent) Power One-Shot, *EEE*, Dec. 1969, p 91.

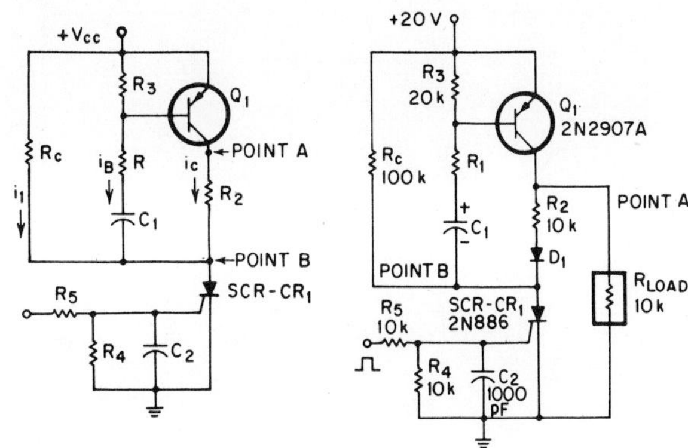

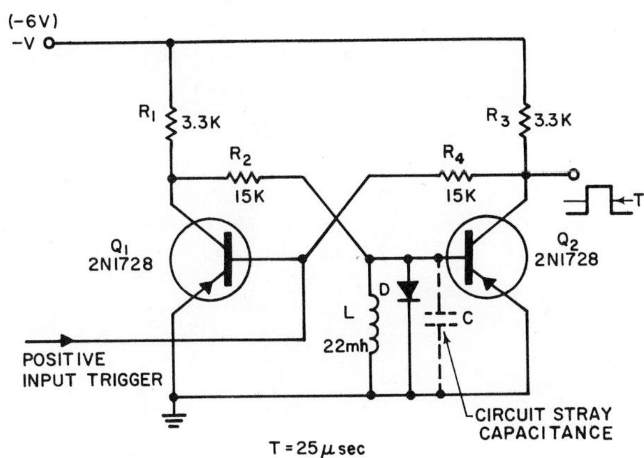

INDUCTOR-CONTROLLED—Use of inductor in place of conventional capacitor for controlling timing gives rise and fall times limited only by transistor switching speed. Capacitor charging curve is eliminated from output waveform. Circuit is stall-proof if small amount of resistance is used in series with inductor to bias transistors into their linear region; for circuit shown, d-c resistance of inductor was enough for this purpose.—R. J. Bouchard, Inductor Timing Improves Multivibrator Action, *Electronic Design*, July 20, 1964, p 78–80.

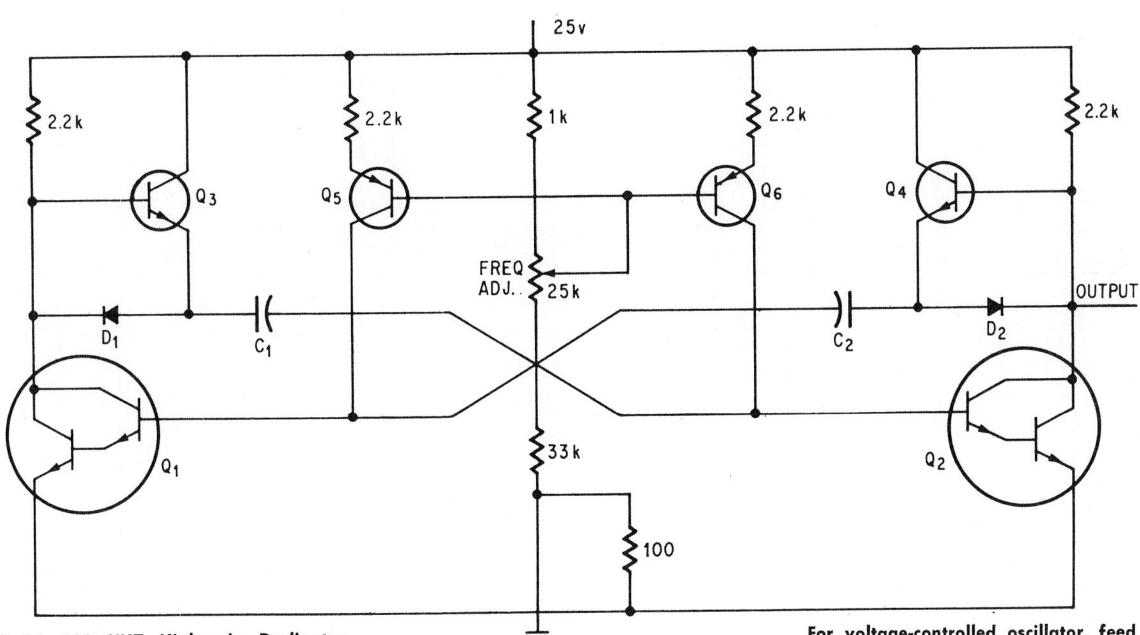

50 HZ TO 100 KHZ—High-gain Darlington transistors and quick-acting emitter-follower transistors broaden frequency range of free-running mvbr. Q3 and Q4 boost upper frequency limit by discharging C1 and C2 faster. Q5 and Q6 act as current sources, making linear tuning possible over range of 1,000 to 1 with 25K pot. When C1 and C2 are 250 pF, frequency range is 50 Hz to 100 kHz. For voltage-controlled oscillator, feed control voltage directly to bases of Q5 and Q6. Transistor types are not critical.—F. B. Golden, Darlington Transistors Widen Multivibrator's Range, *Electronics*, Nov. 25, 1968, p 82.

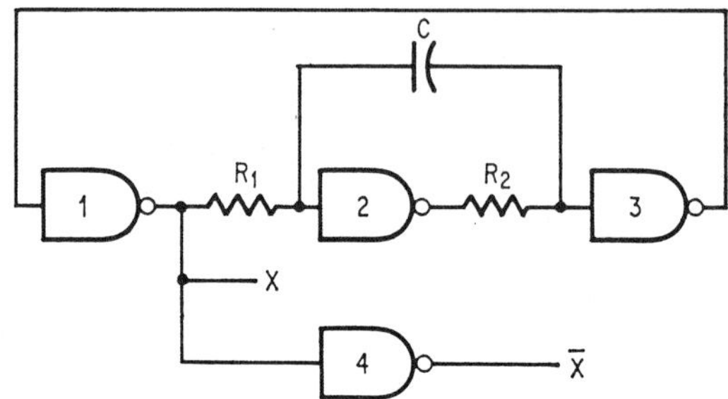

QUAD NAND GATE RUNS FREE—Low-cost mvbr is self-starting, with rise and fall times below 50 ns, complementary outputs, and wide frequency range. C and R2 control frequency, while R1 changes symmetry of output. With R1 and R2 both 510 ohms, output varies from 200 Hz to several MHz when C is varied from 10 μF to 100 pF.—O. Q. Flint, Jr., Free-Running Multivibrator Is Made with a NAND Gate, *Electronics*, Jan. 6, 1969, p 95–96.

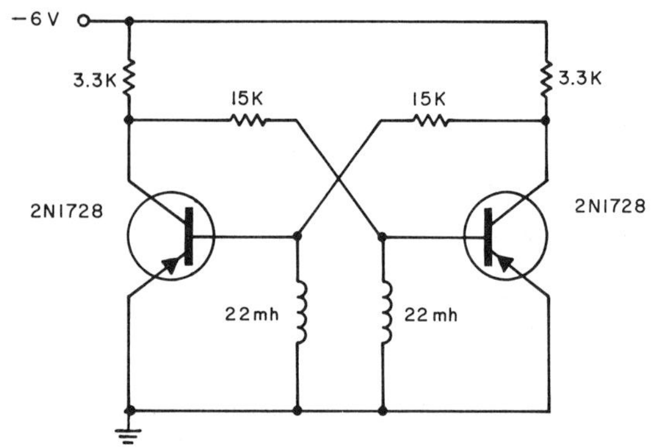

20-KHZ INDUCTOR-CONTROLLED—Use of inductors in place of capacitors gives rise and fall times limited only by transistor switching speeds. Circuit is stall-proof.—R. J. Bouchard, Inductor Timing Improves Multivibrator Action, *Electronic Design*, July 20, 1964, p 78–80.

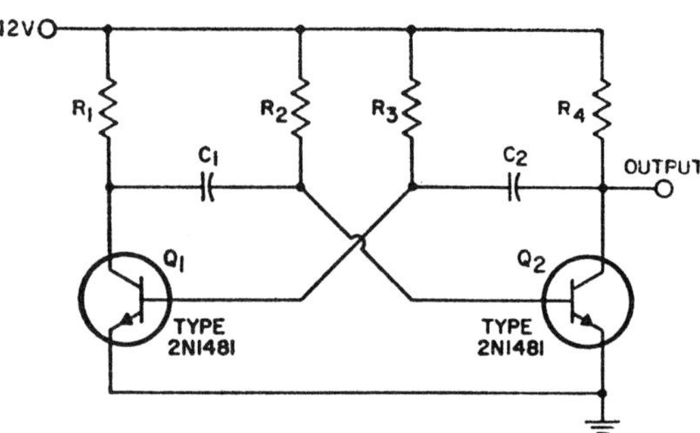

7-KHZ ASTABLE—Provides square-wave output with peak value equal to d-c supply voltage. Capacitors are 0.1 μF, R1 and R4 are 60 ohms, and R2 and R3 are IK.—"Transistor Manual," RCA, Harrison, N.J., SC-13, p 533.

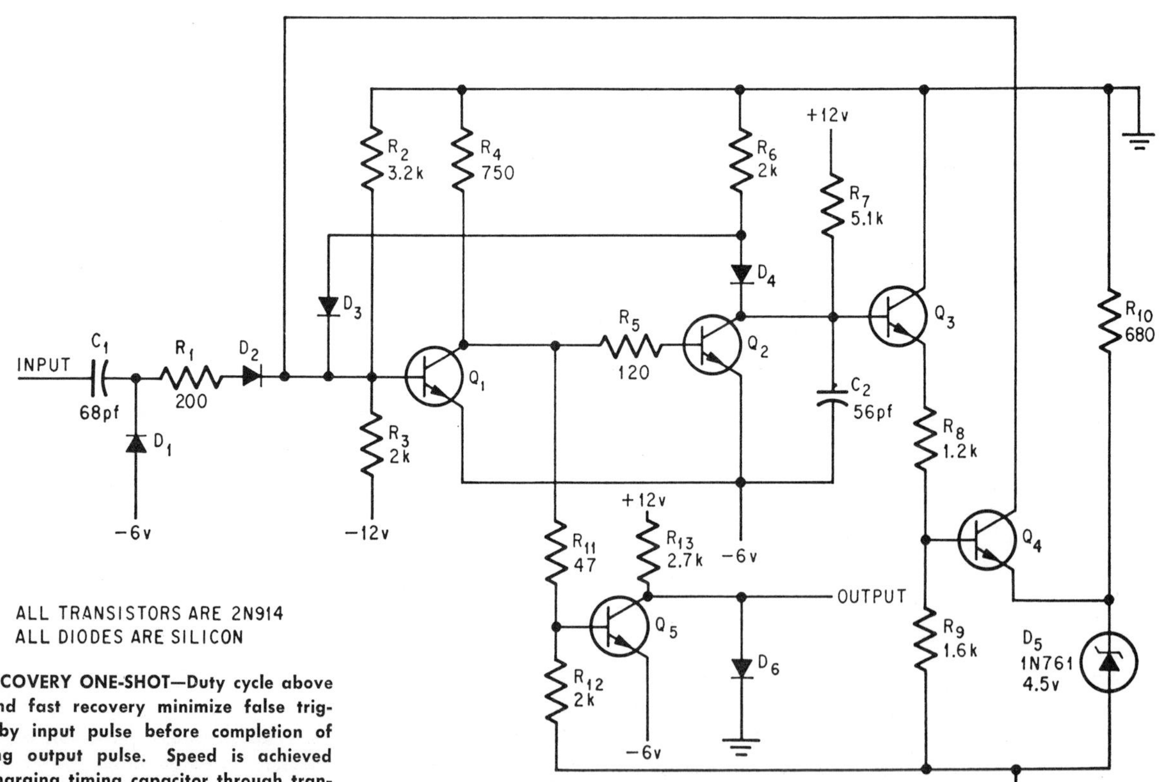

FAST-RECOVERY ONE-SHOT—Duty cycle above 95% and fast recovery minimize false triggering by input pulse before completion of preceding output pulse. Speed is achieved by discharging timing capacitor through transistor Q2 directly instead of through customary transistor. Output pulse width is 100 ns. Once timed interval has started, circuit is insensitive to input variations except for about 10 ns.—J. H. Williams, Full Duty Single Shot Recovers Fast, *Electronics*, March 31, 1969, p 89.

D-C COUPLING WITH DIODES—Multi-pellet diodes provide d-c level-shifting to give desired output voltage swing in astable mvbr. Operation is stable from several Hz to about 10 MHz. Only one capacitor is needed. Rise time is about 5 ns.—Silicon Multi-Pellet Diodes MPD200/MPD300/MPD400, General Electric, Syracuse, N.Y., No. 75.42, 1966.

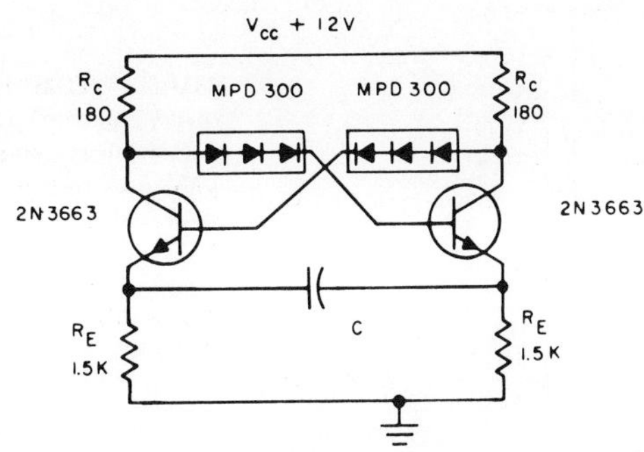

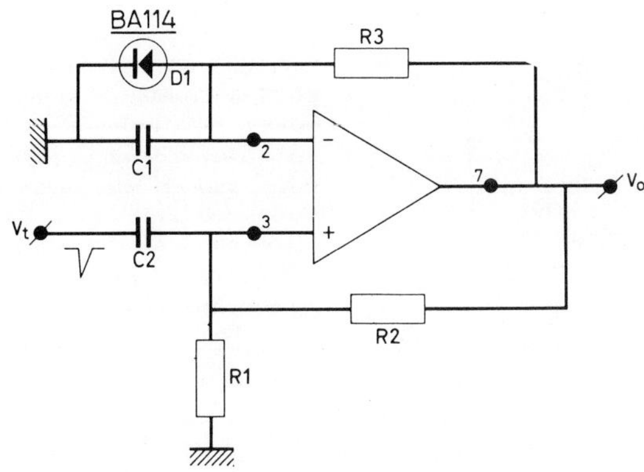

IC MONO—Uses Philips TAA241 difference amplifier as monostable mvbr that is saturated in its quiescent state and then has output of +10 V. Negative-going trigger makes output switch to new value of about −5 V. R1 is 8.2K, R2 and R3 are 100K, C1 is 10 nF, and C2 is 4.7 nF. With these values, pulse time is 175 μs, rise time 0.35 μs, fall time 0.7 μs, and delay time 0.3 μs.—J. Cohen and J. Oosterling, Applications of a Practical D. C. Difference Amplifier, Philips, Pub. Dept., Elcoma Div., Eindhoven, The Netherlands, No. 321, 1968.

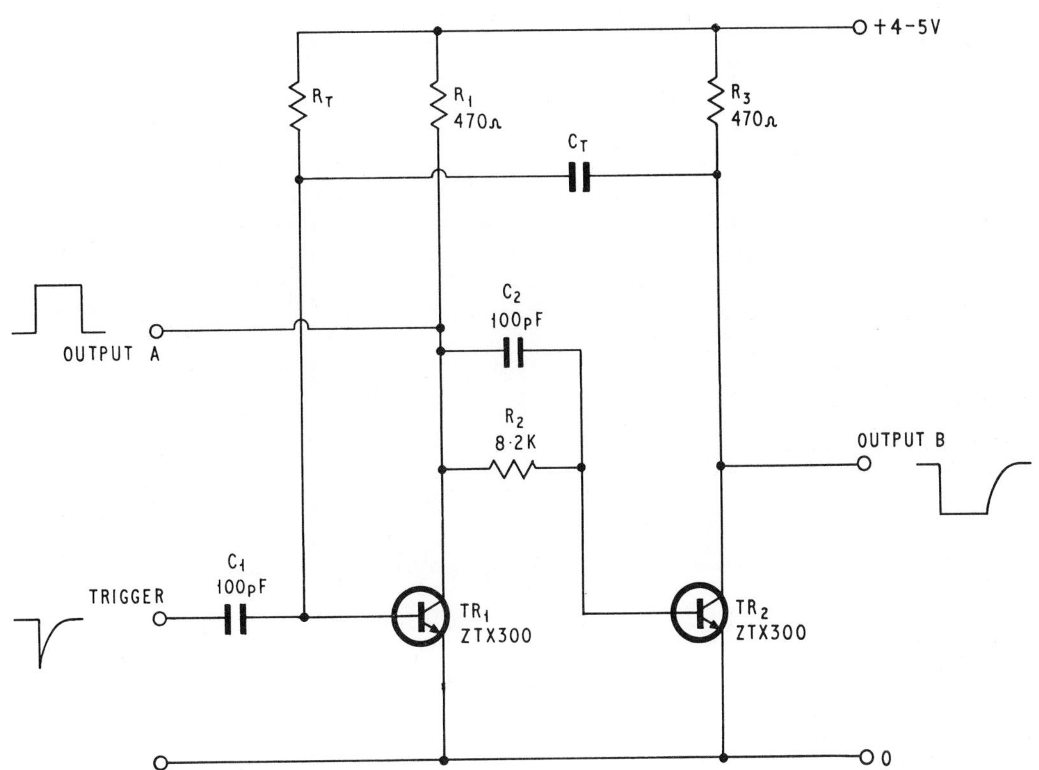

BASIC MONO—Minimum output pulse width is 1 μs. Report gives design procedure. One drawback is slow positive edge of output pulse from TR2, occurring because CT must recharge through R3. Report shows how to overcome this with diode from CT to output. —"E-Line Transistor Applications," Ferranti Ltd., Oldham, Lancs., England, 1969, p 14.

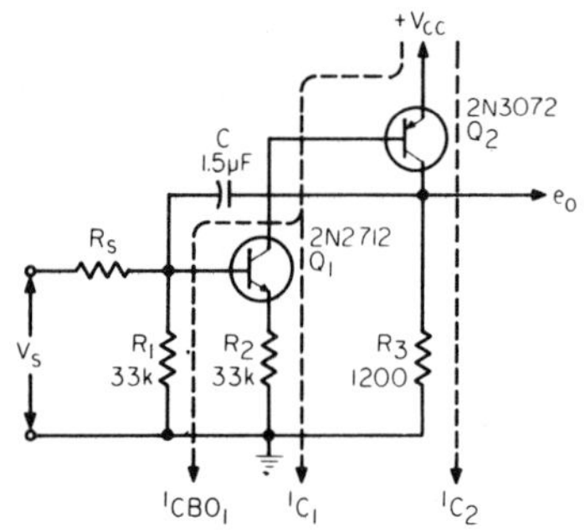

SIMPLIFIED ONE-SHOT—Complementary transistors give simplified design, with negligibly small quiescent currents (shown by dashed lines). Will also operate as free-running mvbr or as trigger by making minor changes in values of components.—A. C. Caggiano, Simplified One-Shot Multivibrator, *EEE*, Oct. 1967, p 140 and 142.

ASTABLE FROM IC AMPLIFIER—Uses Philips TAA293 general-purpose amplifier. Value of C determines period; 10 nF gives about 16 μs with high-to-low ratio of 0.6. Period for other values of C is in direct proportion to C down to 2 μs.—The TAA293 as a Schmitt Trigger and Multivibrator, Philips, Pub. Dept., Elcoma Div., Eindhoven, The Netherlands, No. 25, 1968.

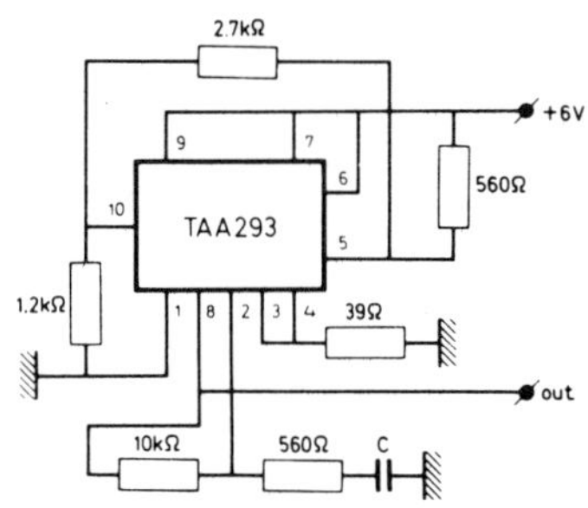

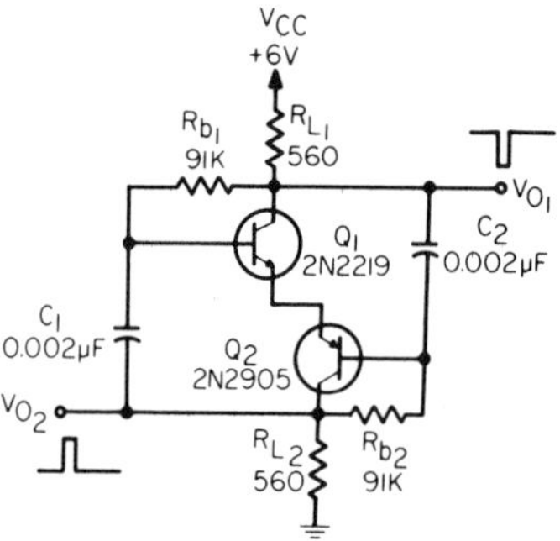

LOCK-UP IMMUNITY—With complementary transistors connected as shown, circuit is inherently self-starting, immune to lock-up, and useful over wide range of frequencies. Coincident positive and negative output pulses have equal amplitudes. With values shown, pulse width is about 2 μs and amplitude about half of supply voltage.—C. R. Bond, Complementary Series Multivibrator, *EEE*, Sept. 1967, p 135–136.

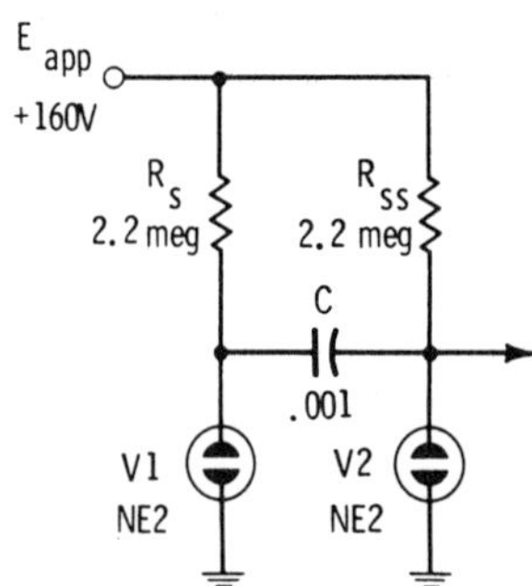

700-HZ ASTABLE NEON—Basic circuit may be modified by changing resistor values to obtain frequency up to 8 kHz.—W. G. Miller, "Using and Understanding Miniature Neon Lamps," H. W. Sams & Co., Indianapolis, Ind., 1969, p 43.

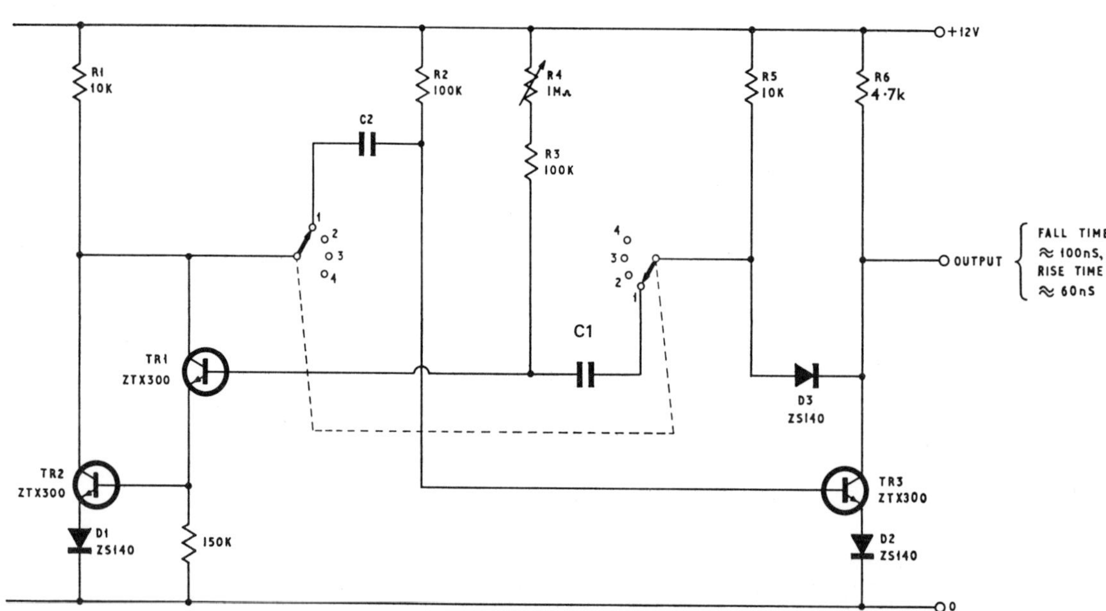

WIDE-RANGE MVBR—Gives pulse durations ranging from 26.5 μs to 66 s in nine ranges, by switching capacitors C1 and C2 which have identical values from 180 pF to 75 μF. TR1 and TR2 form Darlington pair giving required large value of base resistance for long pulse durations.—"E-Line Transistor Applications," Ferranti Ltd., Oldham, Lancs., England, 1969, p 8.

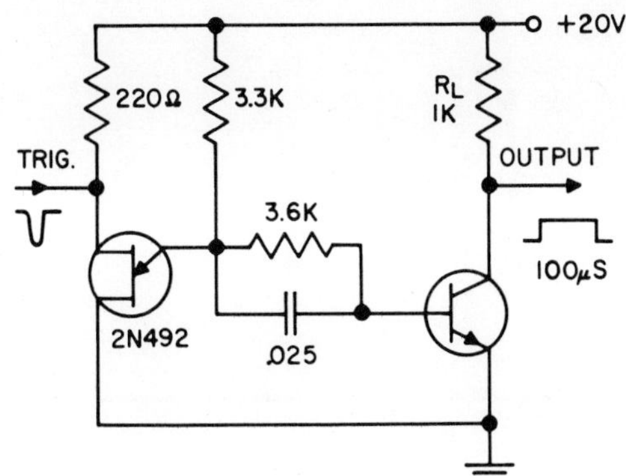

SINGLE-UJT ONE-SHOT—Addition of resistor between emitter and ground converts basic single-ujt mvbr to one-shot. Method of adding transistor output stage is also shown.—T. P. Sylvan, The Unijunction Transistor Characteristics and Applications, General Electric, Syracuse, N.Y., No. 90.10, 1965, p 76.

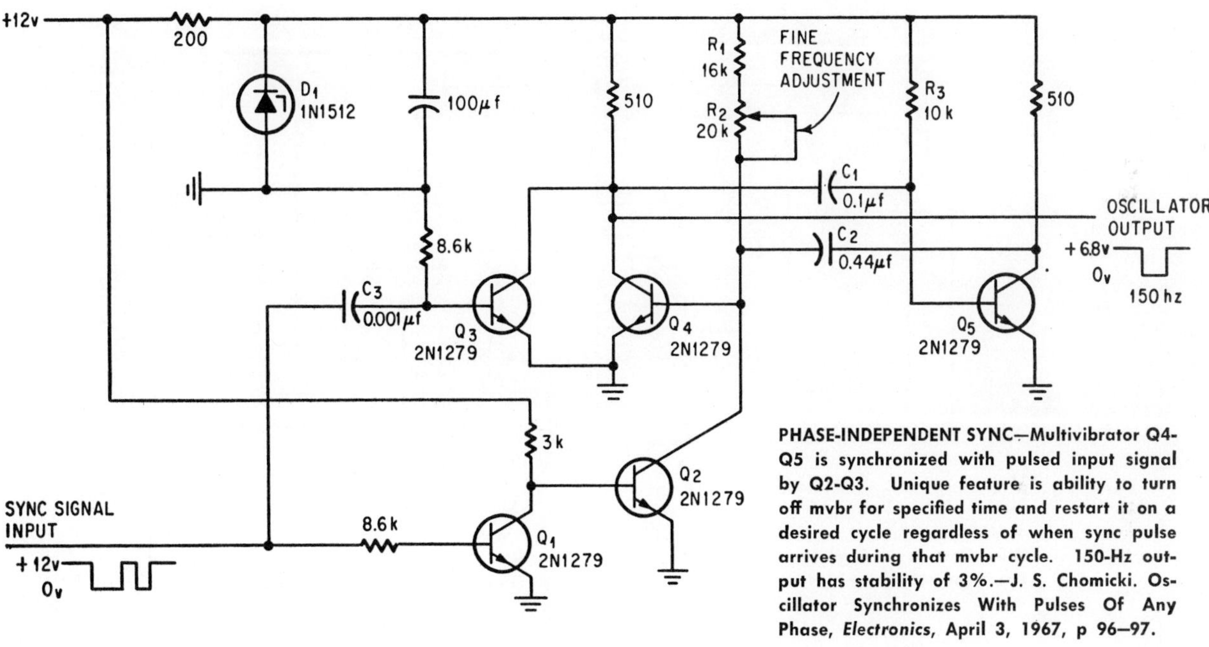

PHASE-INDEPENDENT SYNC—Multivibrator Q4-Q5 is synchronized with pulsed input signal by Q2-Q3. Unique feature is ability to turn off mvbr for specified time and restart it on a desired cycle regardless of when sync pulse arrives during that mvbr cycle. 150-Hz output has stability of 3%.—J. S. Chomicki. Oscillator Synchronizes With Pulses Of Any Phase, *Electronics*, April 3, 1967, p 96–97.

NOTE: To locate additional circuits in the category of this chapter, use the index at the back of this book. Check also the author's "Sourcebook of Electronic Circuits," published by McGraw-Hill in 1968.

CHAPTER 55
Noise Circuits

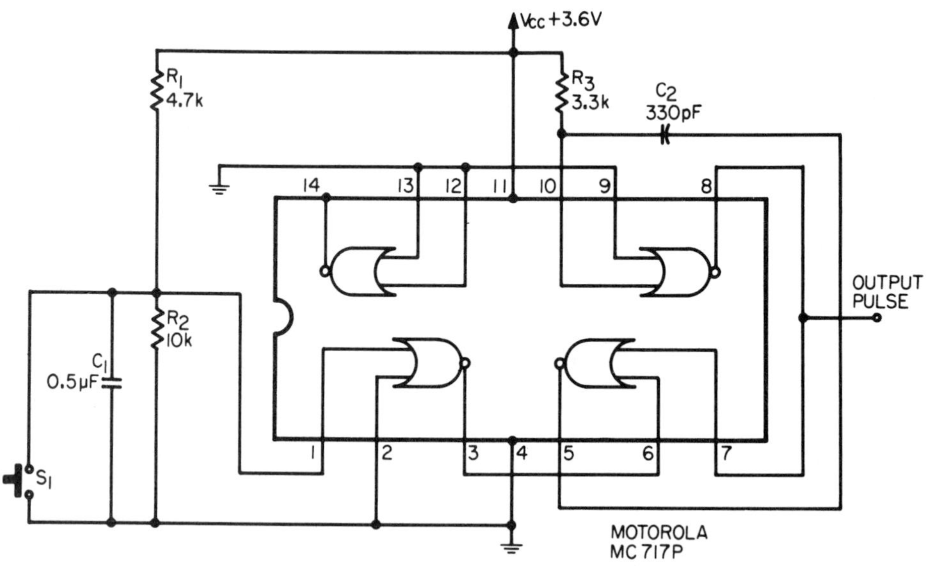

SWITCH NOISE ELIMINATOR—Closing S1 gives output pulses from 1 μs to 80 ms, with width depending on value of C2. Built around RTL four-gate NOR IC, functioning as one-shot driven by inverter. Switch noise is below noise threshold of IC, so one-shot sees clean fast trigger signal. I. Isrealy, IC One Shot Generates Short-Duration Pulses and Eliminates Switch Noise, *EEE*, March 1968, p 129–130.

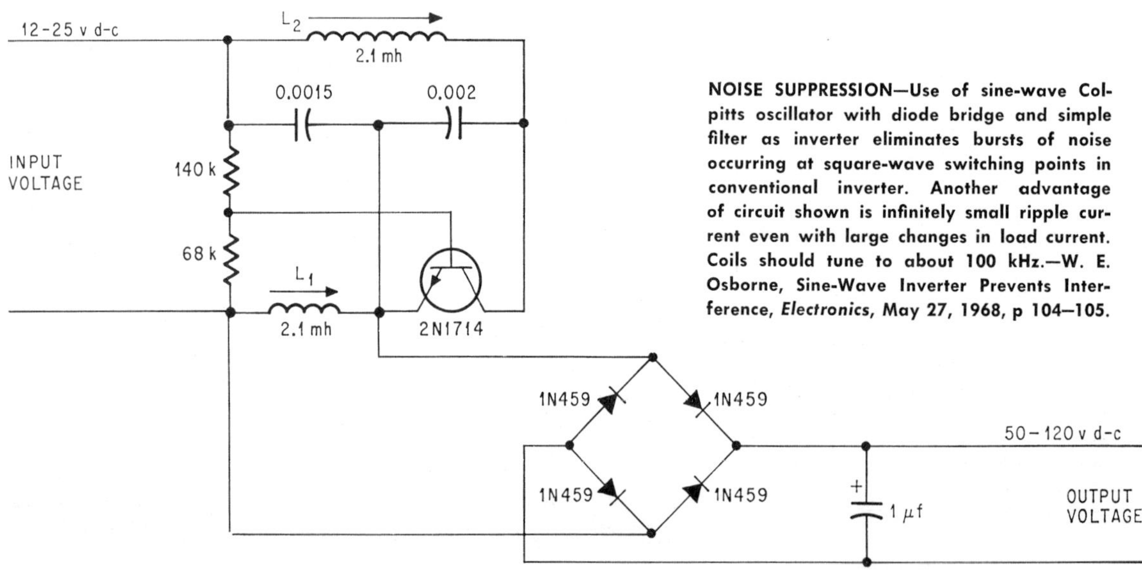

NOISE SUPPRESSION—Use of sine-wave Colpitts oscillator with diode bridge and simple filter as inverter eliminates bursts of noise occurring at square-wave switching points in conventional inverter. Another advantage of circuit shown is infinitely small ripple current even with large changes in load current. Coils should tune to about 100 kHz.—W. E. Osborne, Sine-Wave Inverter Prevents Interference, *Electronics*, May 27, 1968, p 104–105.

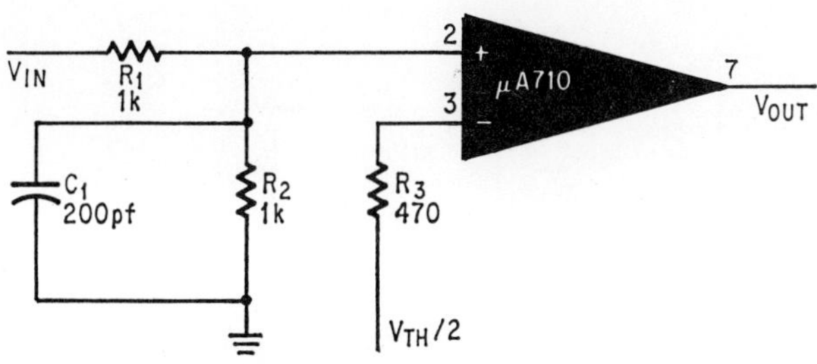

LONG-LINE NOISE SUPPRESSOR—IC opamp serves as preconditioner to improve signal-to-noise ratio in digital line. Divider R1-R2 permits handling large input signals (14 V). C1 shunts out fast noise spikes from high-gain Fairchild μA710 opamp. Output is generated when input exceeds half the threshold level established by reference voltage applied to terminal 3. Article contains thirteen other IC opamp application circuits.—J. F. Gifford and M. Markkula, Linear IC's: Part 5, Ins and Outs of Op Amps, *Electronics*, Nov. 27, 1967, p 84–93.

GRASS SIMULATOR—Random-noise generator covering 100 kHz to 8 MHZ, with content and level both adjustable, simulates radar return signal for use in test setup. Output is adjustable from 0 to 3 V p-p.—D. D. Lacey, Noise Generator Simulates Radar Return-Signal 'Grass,' *Electronic Design*, May 24, 1970, p 114.

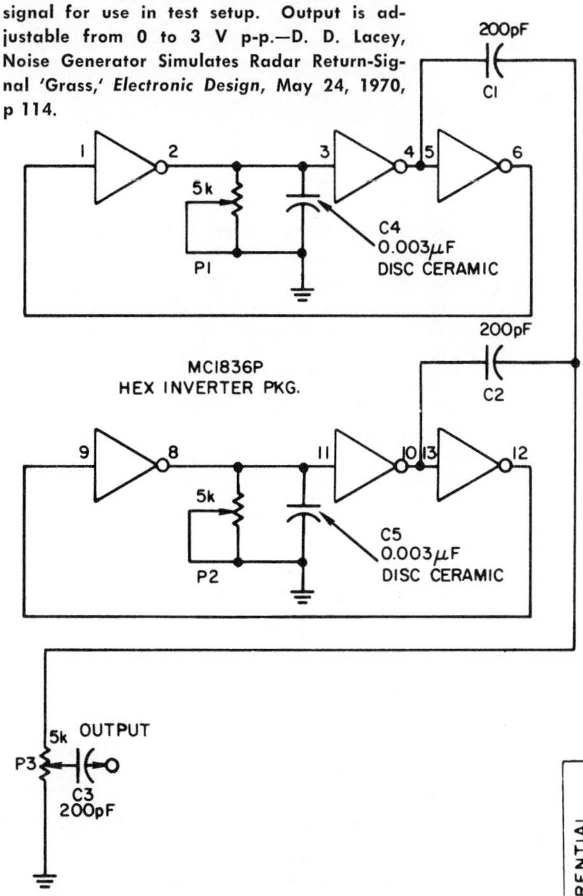

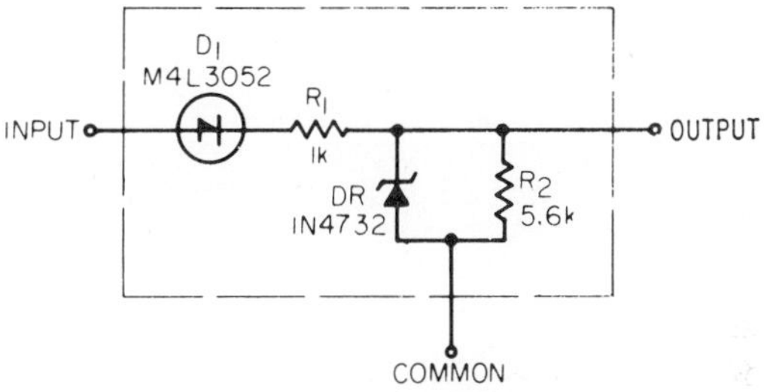

ACTIVE NOISE FILTER—Developed for timing and logic circuits of industrial electronic controls having lines long enough to pick up severe 60-Hz radiation. Works like Schmitt trigger though requiring no external d-c supply. Article includes table showing d-c switching levels and ripple at various noise frequencies.—P. A. Lajoie, Simple Solid-State Noise Filter for Industrial Logic Systems, *EEE*, Oct. 1968, p 124 and 126.

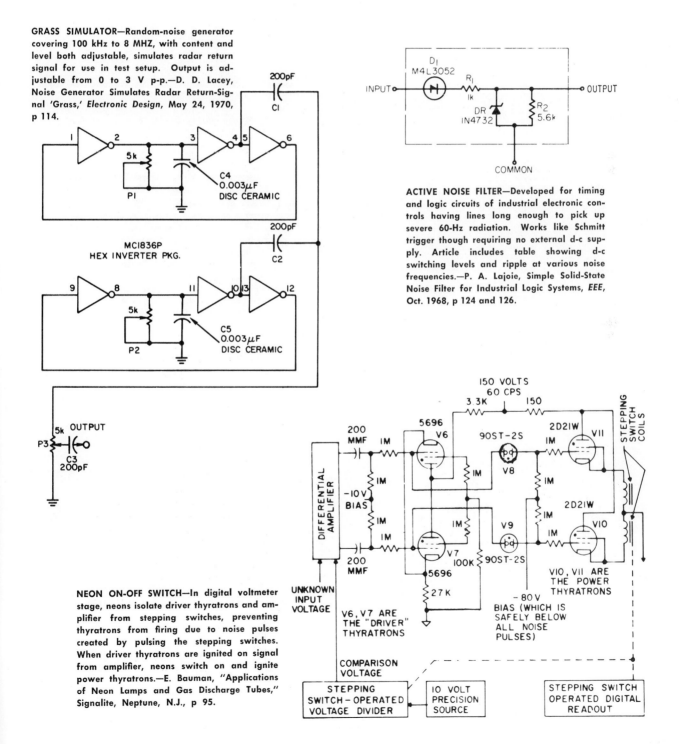

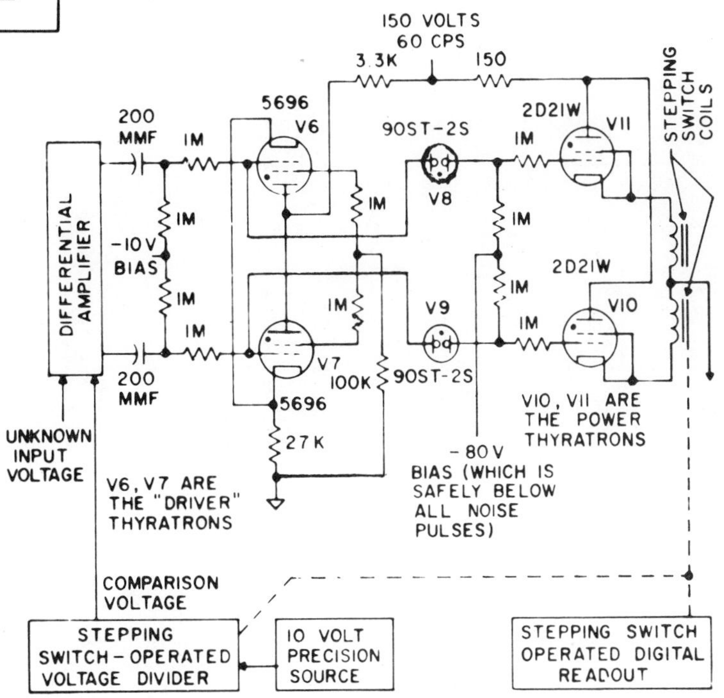

NEON ON-OFF SWITCH—In digital voltmeter stage, neons isolate driver thyratrons and amplifier from stepping switches, preventing thyratrons from firing due to noise pulses created by pulsing the stepping switches. When driver thyratrons are ignited on signal from amplifier, neons switch on and ignite power thyratrons.—E. Bauman, "Applications of Neon Lamps and Gas Discharge Tubes," Signalite, Neptune, N.J., p 95.

NOISE TO 500 KHZ—Avalanche diode noise source gives 1 to 2 mV into 50 ohms over frequency range of 2 kHz to over 500 MHz, for testing broadband video and r-f amplifier systems.—H. Penfield, Why Not The Avalanche Diode As An RF Noise Source? *Electronic Design*, April 12, 1965, p 32–35.

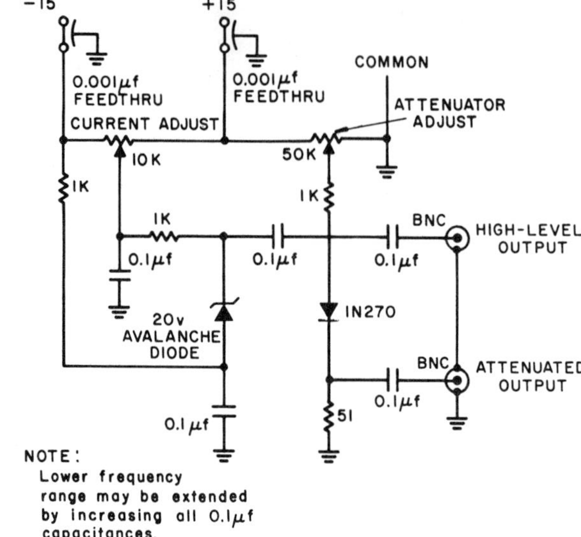

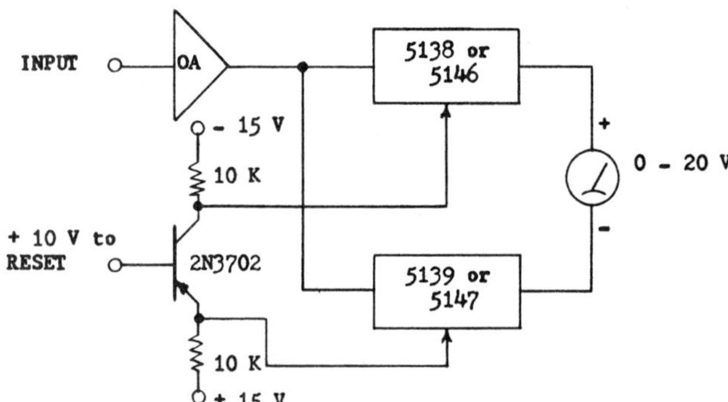

PEAK-READING NOISE METER—One module senses positive peaks of noise, while other senses negative peaks. Both outputs drive meter that reads p-p value of noise. Reset circuit provides both polarities, to reset both modules. Use OEI 5138 and 5139 modules for d-c to 10 kKz, and others for 10 MHz. When measuring very low-level signals, opamp preamp noise must be canceled by replacing meter circuit with opamp having offset voltage added to signal.—A Peak Reading Noise Meter, Optical Electronics, Tucson, Ariz., No. 10092.

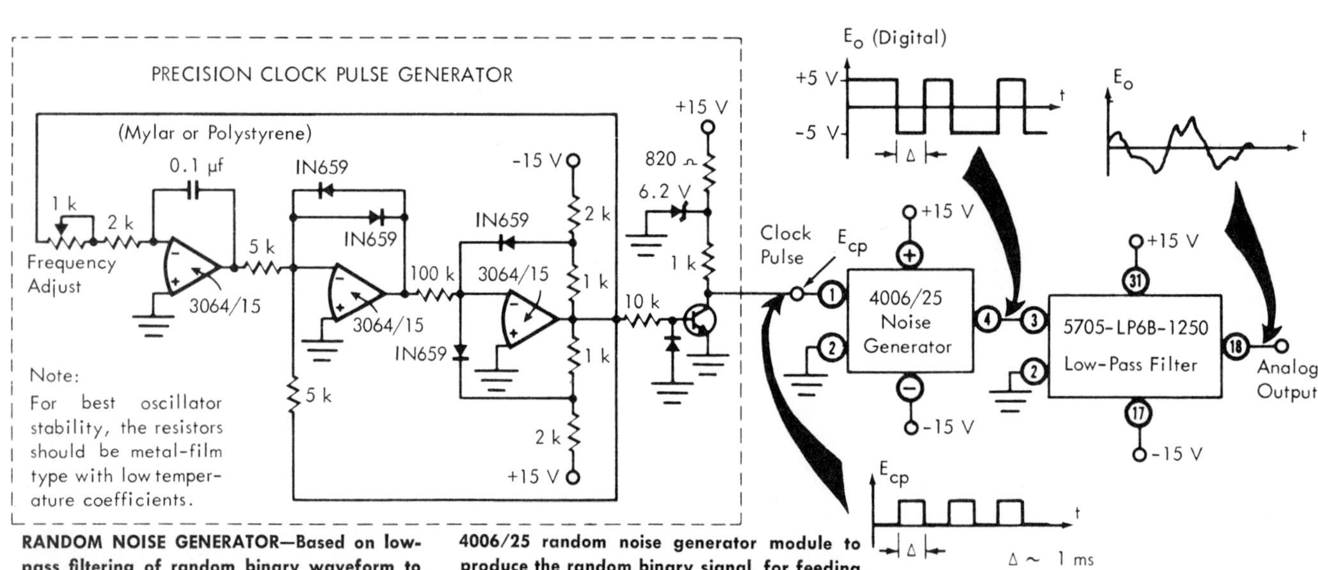

RANDOM NOISE GENERATOR—Based on low-pass filtering of random binary waveform to obtain analog noise source having known power spectral density and rms value. Clock signal is applied to Burr-Brown 4006/25 random noise generator module to produce the random binary signal, for feeding to low-pass filter module. Resulting noise signal has flat power spectrum from d-c to 1 kHz. Article gives design equations.—Burr-Brown Computer Designed Active Filters, Burr-Brown Research, Tucson, Ariz., No. PDS-203A, 1968.

CONTAMINATED-SIGNAL REJECTOR—Simple circuit compares signal with noise in pulse system and delivers squelch output for rejecting noise-contaminated signals. Can be used in pulse command and control applications, as well as for code communication. When desired series of pwm pulses reaches input, integrated value at A is insufficient to break down CR1. When noise is present with signal, however, CR1 breaks down and resulting signal at B turns Q2 off, making Q3 turn on and provide ground point for squelch.—"Selected Electronic Circuitry," NASA SP-5046, 1966, Government Printing Office, Washington, D.C., p 71.

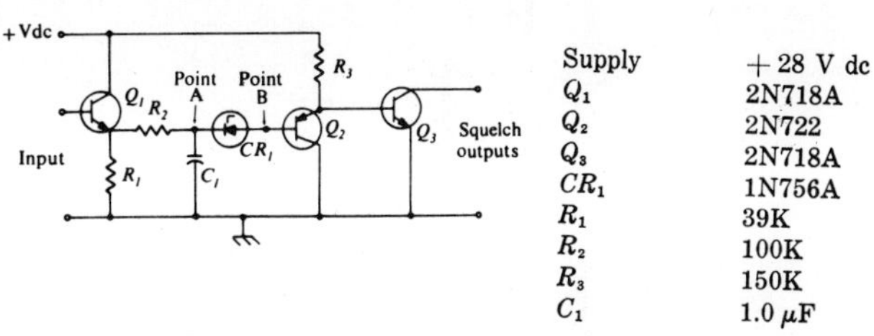

Supply	+28 V dc
Q_1	2N718A
Q_2	2N722
Q_3	2N718A
CR_1	1N756A
R_1	39K
R_2	100K
R_3	150K
C_1	1.0 μF

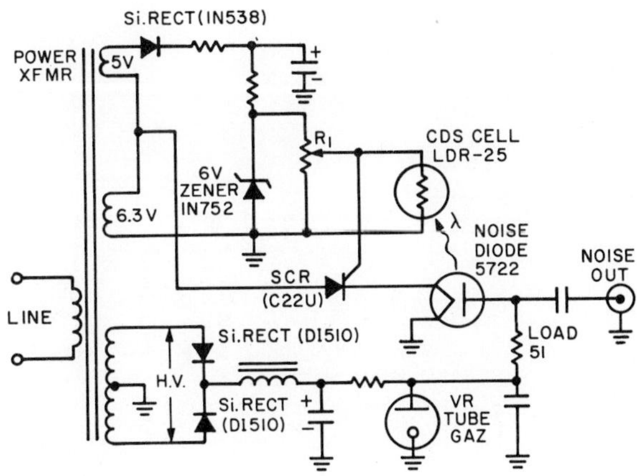

NOISE DIODE FILAMENT REGULATOR—Noise output current of temperature-limited noise diode is held constant at value determined by setting of R1, in range of 0.5 to 10 mA, by dual regulator and cadmium sulfide cell controlling conduction angle of scr. Cell monitors light output of noise diode, which increases with line voltage, to compensate for line voltage variations. Can be easily adapted for control of other noise sources.—H. D. Olson, Semiconductors Regulate Noise-Diode Plate Current, *Electronic Design*, March 16, 1964, p 108–109.

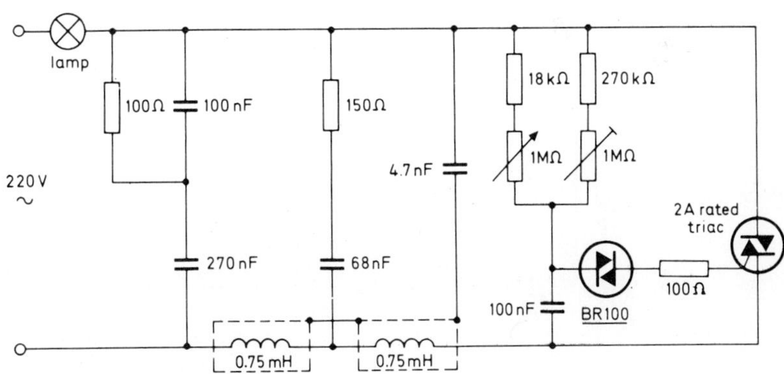

TRIAC RFI SUPPRESSION—Used when it is possible to insert chokes in series with line. Series resistors must then be added as shown to prevent oscillation, because load no longer acts as damping element between filter and control circuit.—Triacs—Operation and Use, Philips, Pub. Dept., Elcoma Div., Eindhoven, The Netherlands, No. 17, 1969.

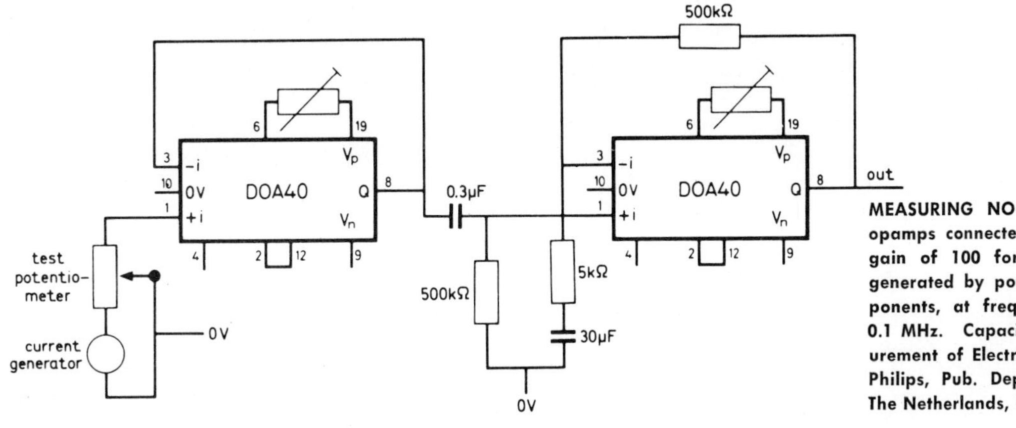

MEASURING NOISE—Two Philips DOA40 IC opamps connected as shown provide overall gain of 100 for measuring electrical noise generated by potentiometers and other components, at frequencies between 1 Hz and 0.1 MHz. Capacitor blocks d-c signal.—Measurement of Electrical Noise Using the DOA40, Philips, Pub. Dept., Elcoma Div., Eindhoven, The Netherlands, No. 28.

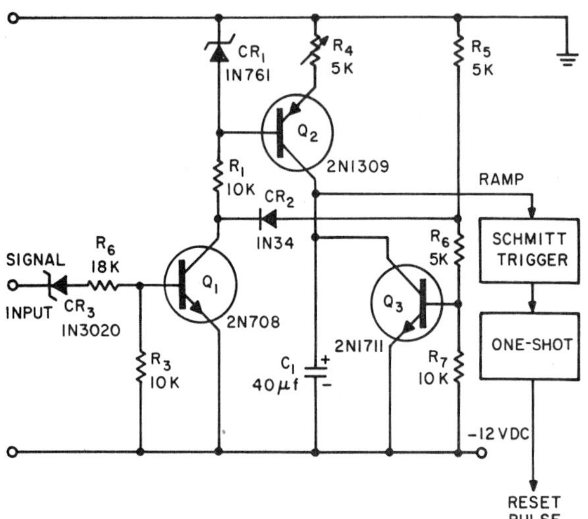

NOISE PULSE SUPPRESSOR—Pulse-width discriminator fires to provide output pulse for each input pulse exceeding level of zener CR3 and having width determined by setting of Schmitt trigger.—A. A. Dargis, Pulse Width Discriminator Rejects Narrow Noise Pulses, *Electronic Design*, Dec. 21, 1964, p 50.

KILLING TURN-ON AND TURN-OFF TRANSIENTS—Scr in solid-line portion of circuit (switch S closed) eliminates kilovolt spikes when inductive a-c load is turned off. Dotted portion of circuit eliminates turn-on transients (switch S is then left open). Both radiated and conducted r-f interference are eliminated. Can be used in paper-tape punches, tape transport motor drives, electric typewriters, and other a-c motor or solenoid devices.—J. L. Haynes, Reducing Transients in Switched Inductive Loads, *Electronics*, Oct. 17, 1966, p 88–89.

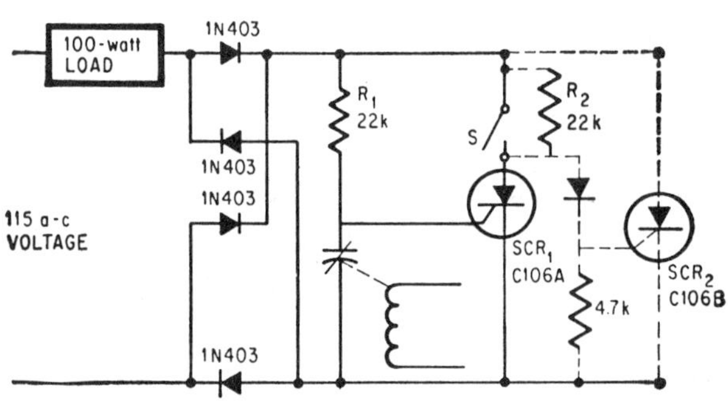

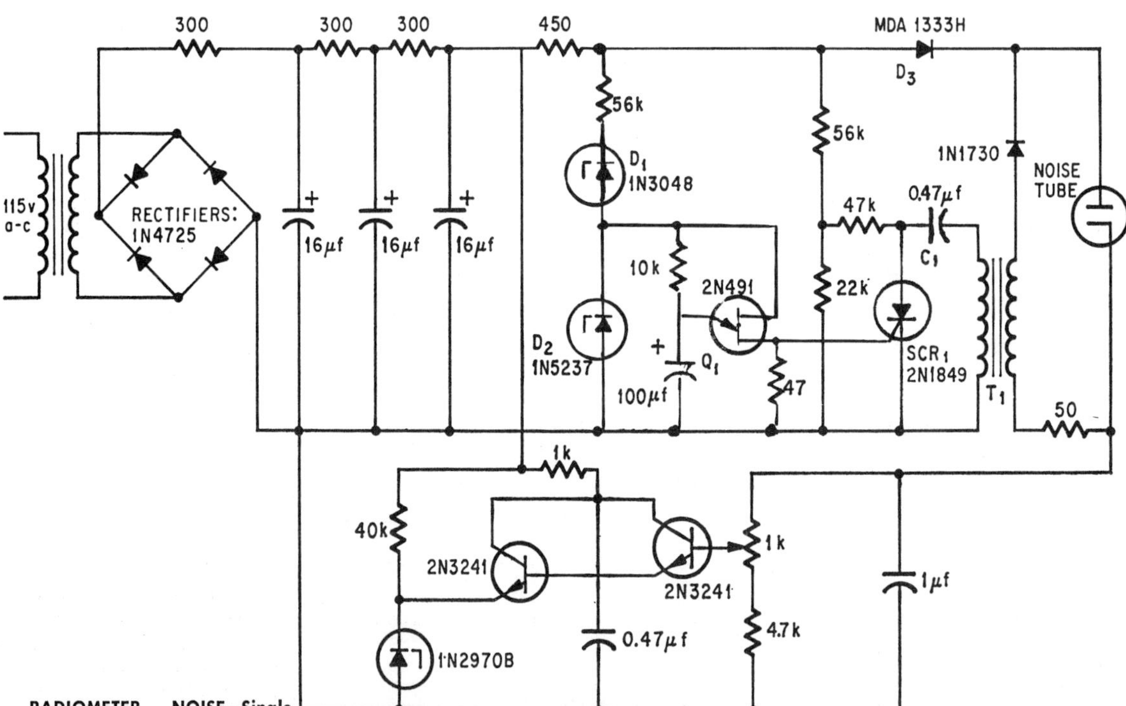

MEASURING RADIOMETER NOISE—Single power supply provides 7-kV pulse for ionizing gas-discharge noise tube and 300 V to keep it ionized. Ujt Q1 triggers SCR1 to generate pulse, then automatically switches to low-voltage operation. Shunt regulator, using two 2N3241 transistors with zener, keeps current constant to prevent variations in noise output. D3 can be seven 1N4725 diodes in series, costing much less than 1-kV prepotted stack shown.—J. M. Payne, Zeners and SCR Fire Gas Discharge Tube, *Electronics*, July 22, 1968, p 71.

2N3819
2N3820
2N708
2N708
IN—1
IN—2
OUT
+12

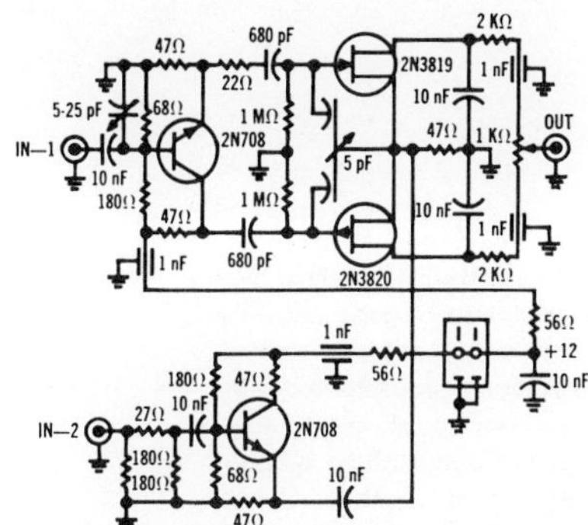

CORRELATOR—Provides 35 dB rejection of uncorrelated components for random signals in 10% band centered at 300 MHz, for radio astronomy applications. Complementary silicon fet's are used as direct multipliers while balancing out spurious responses.—Wideband Correlator Uses Complementary FETs for Signal Multiplication (Texas Instruments ad), *Electronics*, Oct. 31, 1966, p 107.

+30V
R1
68k
R2
680k
C2
220pF
T1
2N3483
OUTPUT
Ve
C1
0.01μF
D1

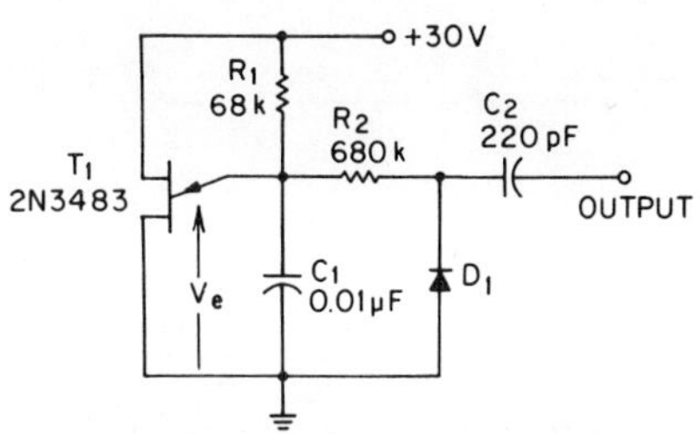

0.5–500 MHZ A-M NOISE GENERATOR—Requires only diode, ujt, and four other components. Amplitude of output is sufficient for checking operation of a-m receiver on any h-f and vhf band without switching or tuning, by feeding noise output to input of receiver.—R. A. Reitmeyer, Jr. and R. A. Gilson, Simple Wideband A-M Noise Generator, *EEE*, Feb. 1970, p 116–117.

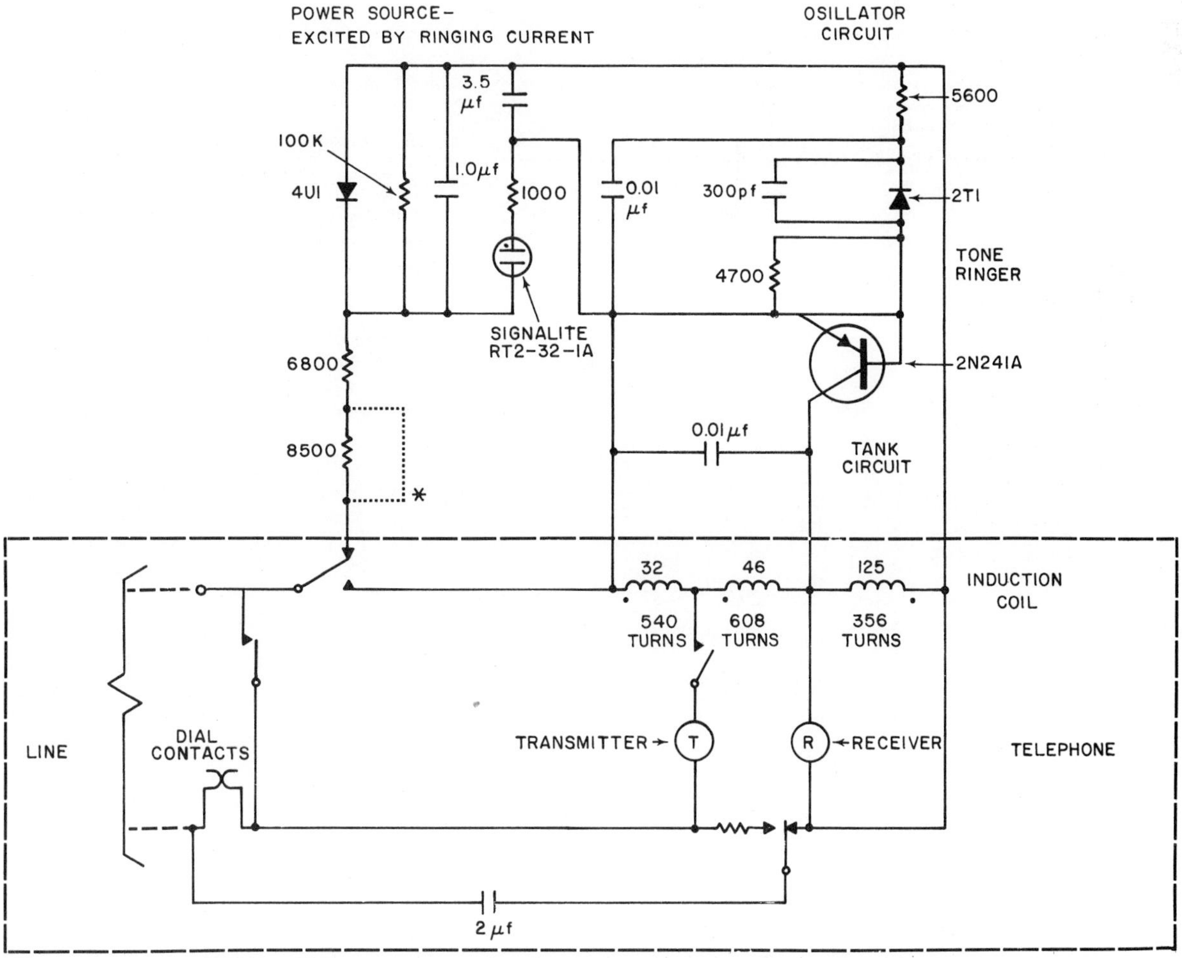

POWER SOURCE-
EXCITED BY RINGING CURRENT
OSILLATOR
CIRCUIT
3.5
μf
5600
100K
4UI
1.0μf
1000
0.01
μf
300pf
2TI
TONE
RINGER
4700
SIGNALITE
RT2-32-IA
6800
2N241A
0.01μf
8500
TANK
CIRCUIT
*
32
46
125
INDUCTION
COIL
540
TURNS
608
TURNS
356
TURNS
LINE
DIAL
CONTACTS
TRANSMITTER
T
R
RECEIVER
TELEPHONE
2μf

* INSERT JUMPER TO DECREASE LEVEL

DIALING SIGNAL SUPPRESSOR—Neon glow lamp in Ericofon handset suppresses undesirable dial-tapping sound that could sometimes activate another extension or telephone. Application requires that breakdown voltage of neon remain constant within 8% over life of telephone. Lamp has radioactive material that stabilizes its breakdown voltage. Circuit also shows tone oscillator that replaces conventional bell ringer and is activated by same 20-Hz ringing voltage.—E. Bauman, Glow Lamp Prevents Telephone Dial Tapping, *Electronic Design*, Dec. 21, 1964, p 46–48.

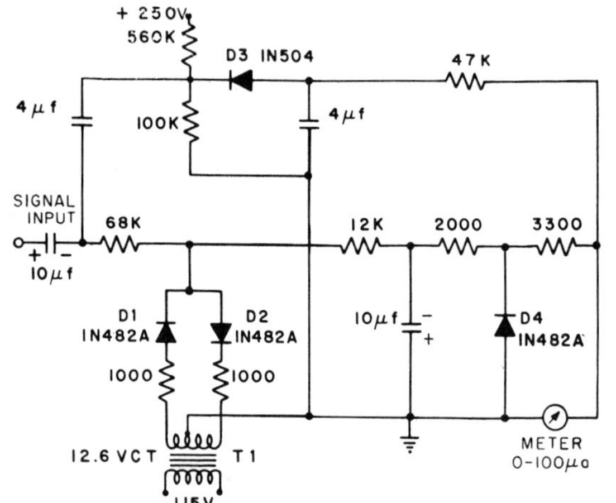

TUNING 60-HZ SIGNAL BURIED IN NOISE—Uses synchronous modulation to get peak output level of desired signal at power-line frequency even though buried in noise exceeding it by one or two orders of magnitude. Output actuates meter through RC filter having time constant of about 0.04 s.—H. L. Kahn, Peak Voltage Indicator Solves Tuning Problem, *Electronic Design*, Jan. 20, 1964, p 84–85.

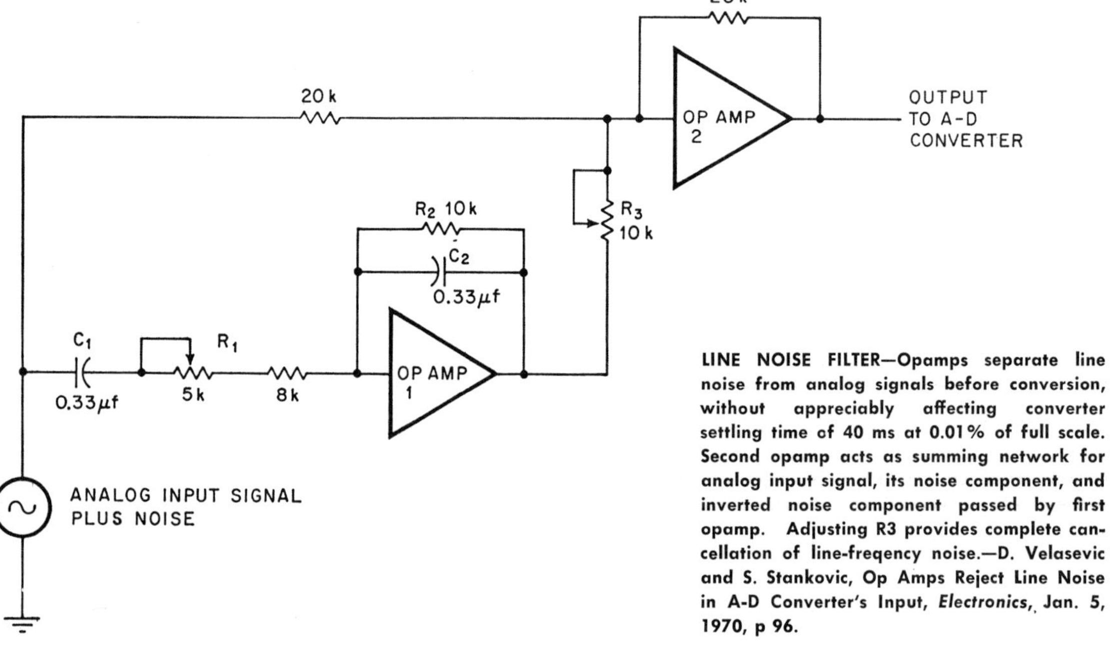

LINE NOISE FILTER—Opamps separate line noise from analog signals before conversion, without appreciably affecting converter settling time of 40 ms at 0.01% of full scale. Second opamp acts as summing network for analog input signal, its noise component, and inverted noise component passed by first opamp. Adjusting R3 provides complete cancellation of line-freqency noise.—D. Velasevic and S. Stankovic, Op Amps Reject Line Noise in A-D Converter's Input, *Electronics*, Jan. 5, 1970, p 96.

NOTE: To locate additional circuits in the category of this chapter, use the index at the back of this book. Check also the author's "Sourcebook of Electronic Circuits," published by McGraw-Hill in 1968.

CHAPTER 56
Operational Amplifier Circuits

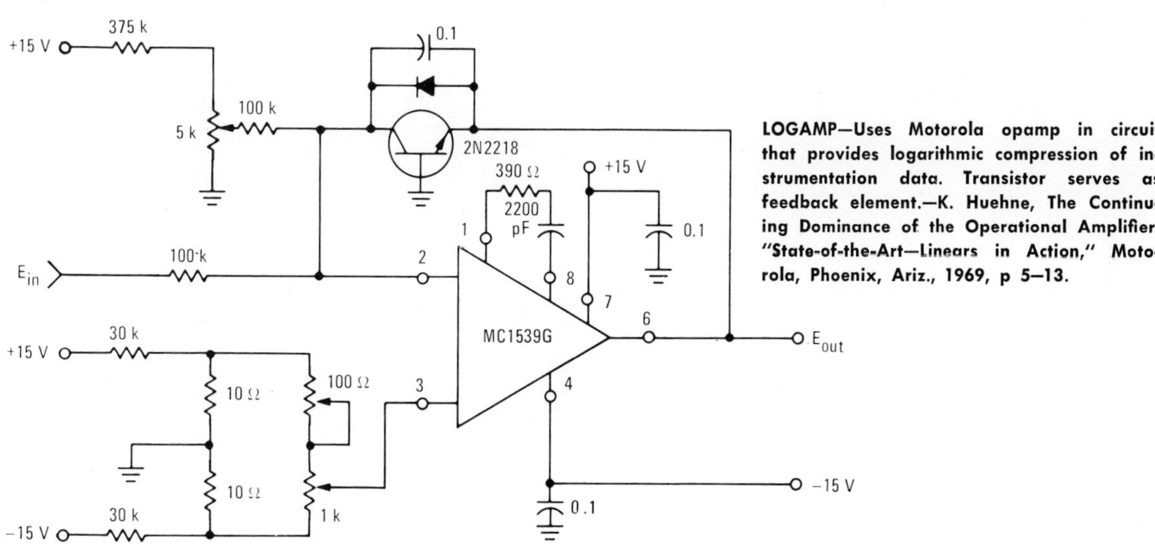

LOGAMP—Uses Motorola opamp in circuit that provides logarithmic compression of instrumentation data. Transistor serves as feedback element.—K. Huehne, The Continuing Dominance of the Operational Amplifier, "State-of-the-Art—Linears in Action," Motorola, Phoenix, Ariz., 1969, p 5–13.

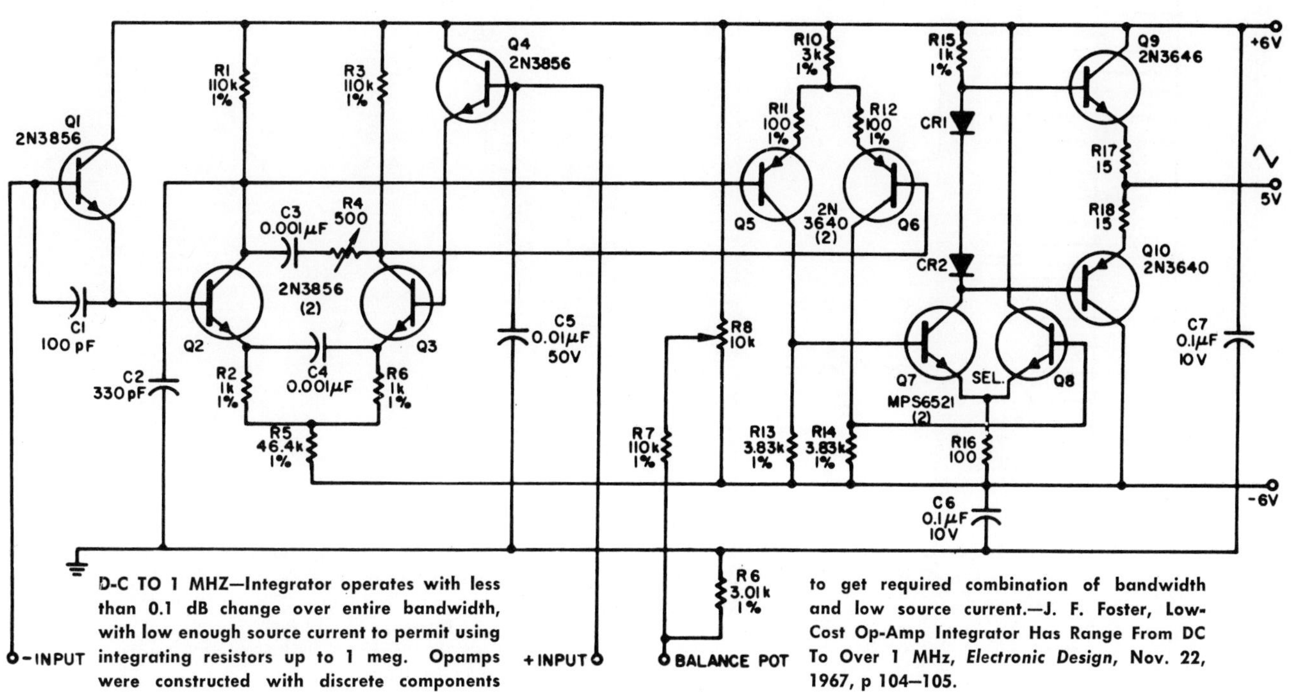

D-C TO 1 MHZ—Integrator operates with less than 0.1 dB change over entire bandwidth, with low enough source current to permit using integrating resistors up to 1 meg. Opamps were constructed with discrete components to get required combination of bandwidth and low source current.—J. F. Foster, Low-Cost Op-Amp Integrator Has Range From DC To Over 1 MHz, *Electronic Design*, Nov. 22, 1967, p 104–105.

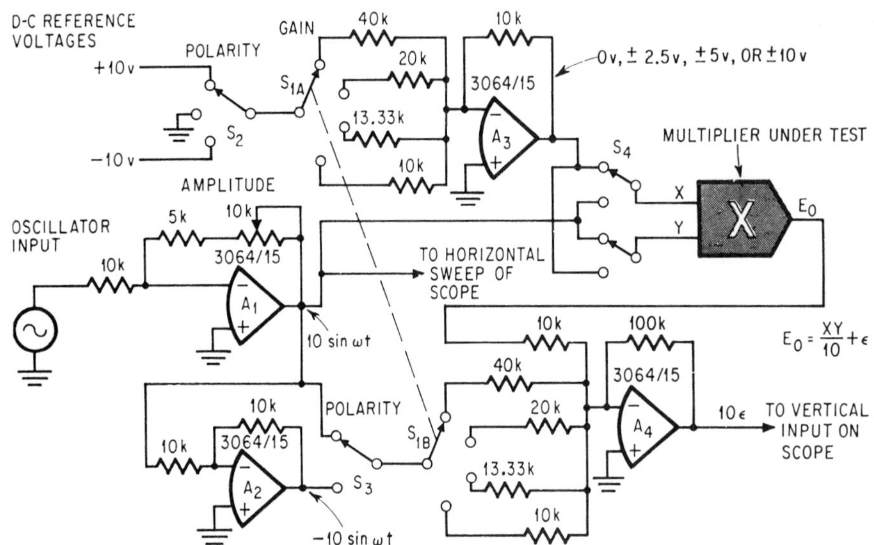

ANALOG MULTIPLIER TESTER—Combination of four opamps and scope serves for measuring gain and offset errors of analog multipliers quickly, efficiently, and accurately. S1 gives choice of four d-c input voltages—0, 2.5, 5, and 10 V—with either polarity, and also sets gain for multiplier. Amplitude of sine-wave input is not critical. Same test setup will measure frequency response of multiplier.—T. Cate, Top Performance from Analog Multipliers? Much Depends on Errors Gauged in Your Circuit, *Electronics*, April 13, 1970, p 114–117.

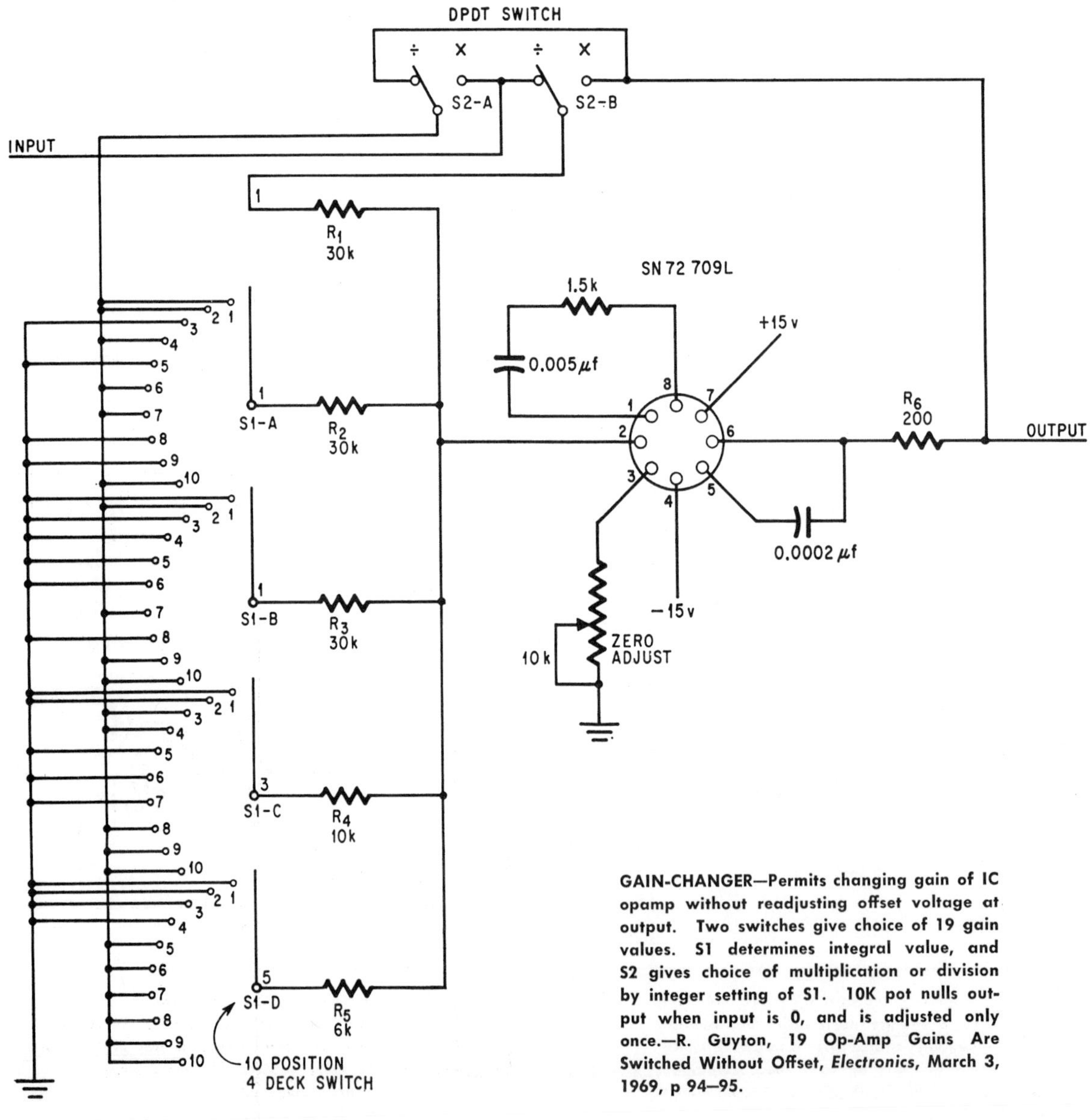

GAIN-CHANGER—Permits changing gain of IC opamp without readjusting offset voltage at output. Two switches give choice of 19 gain values. S1 determines integral value, and S2 gives choice of multiplication or division by integer setting of S1. 10K pot nulls output when input is 0, and is adjusted only once.—R. Guyton, 19 Op-Amp Gains Are Switched Without Offset, *Electronics*, March 3, 1969, p 94–95.

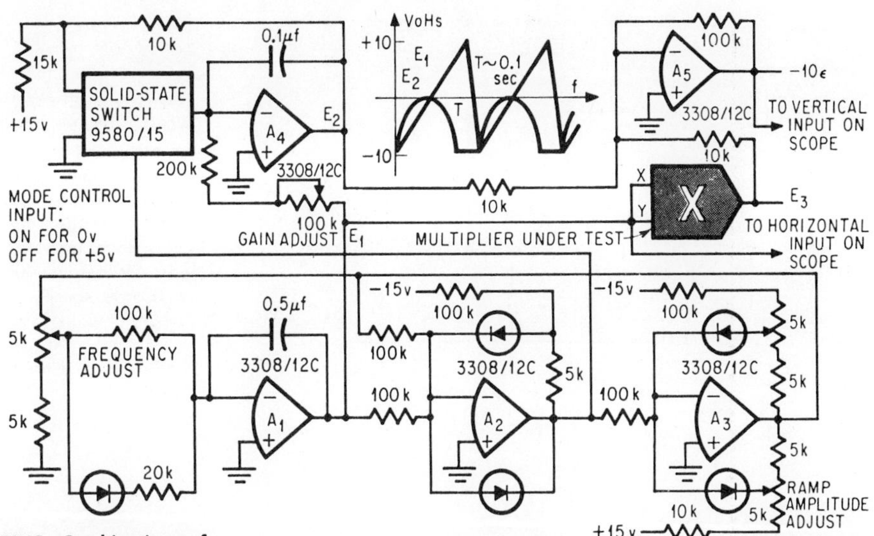

SQUARING-MODE TESTING—Combination of five low-cost fet-input opamps, IC solid-state switch, and scope serves for testing squaring accuracy of quarter-square or variable-transconductance-type analog multipliers. Two equal inputs are integrated to give ramp functions, which in turn are integrated and resulting curves subtracted from ramps to determine multiplier error. Article gives relevant equations and graphs.—T. Cate, Top Performance from Analog Multipliers? Much Depends on Errors Gauged in Your Circuit, *Electronics*, April 13, 1970, p 114–117.

INCREASING INPUT VOLTAGE RANGE—Bootstrapping bias supply (in dashed box at top) for unity-gain IC opamp permits use with three to four times normal input voltage limit of 7 V. Output current is 700 mA. Stability is excellent. High open-loop gain (about 2,000 at 400 Hz) eliminates crossover distortion.—D. R. Younge, Bootstrapping Bias Supply Increases IC Voltage Capacity, *Electronics*, Oct. 28, 1968, p 90–91.

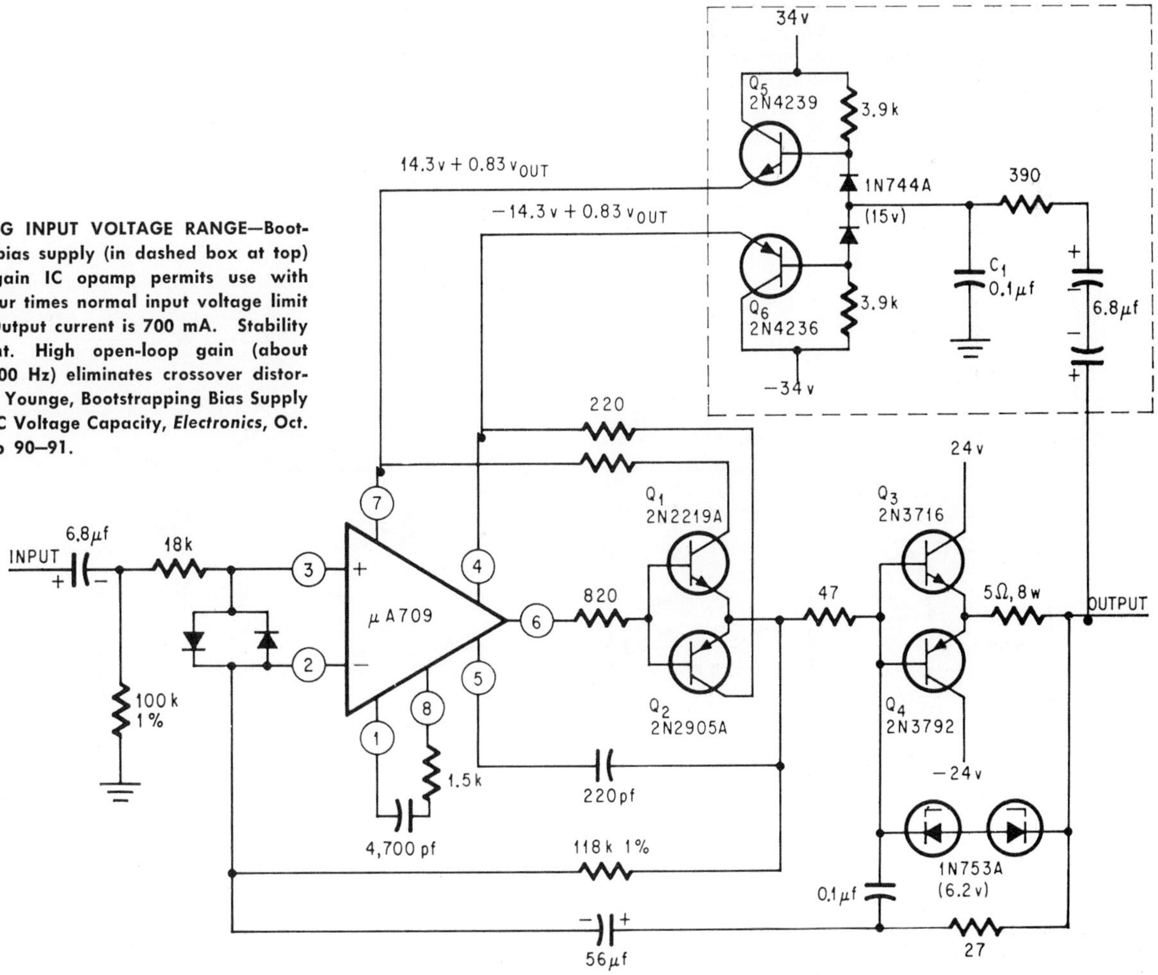

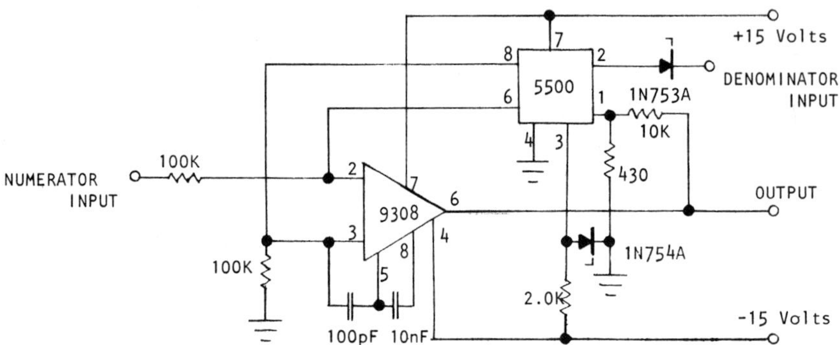

TWO-QUADRANT ANALOG DIVIDER—Input and output signal levels are 10 V full scale. Numerator and output are bipolar but denominator is positive only. Division is obtained by connecting analog multiplier 5500 in feedback loop of opamp.—Applying the Model 5500 Monolithic Analog Multiplier, Optical Electronics, Tucson, Ariz., No. 10138.

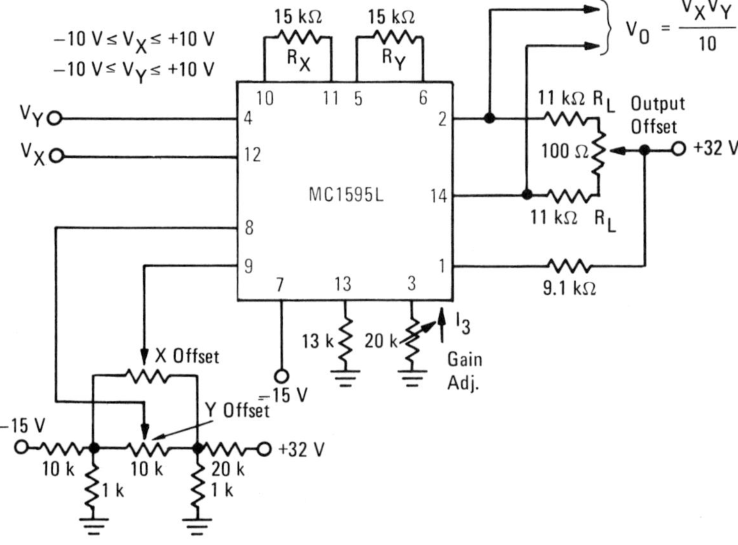

IC MULTIPLIER—Accommodates input voltages over range of −10 V to +10 V. Output dynamic swing will ride 22-V common-mode level. Frequency response is down 3 dB at 4.5 MHz.—E. Renschler, The Monolithic Multiplier Breakthrough, "State-of-the-Art—Linears in Action," Motorola, Phoenix, Ariz., 1969, p 27–36.

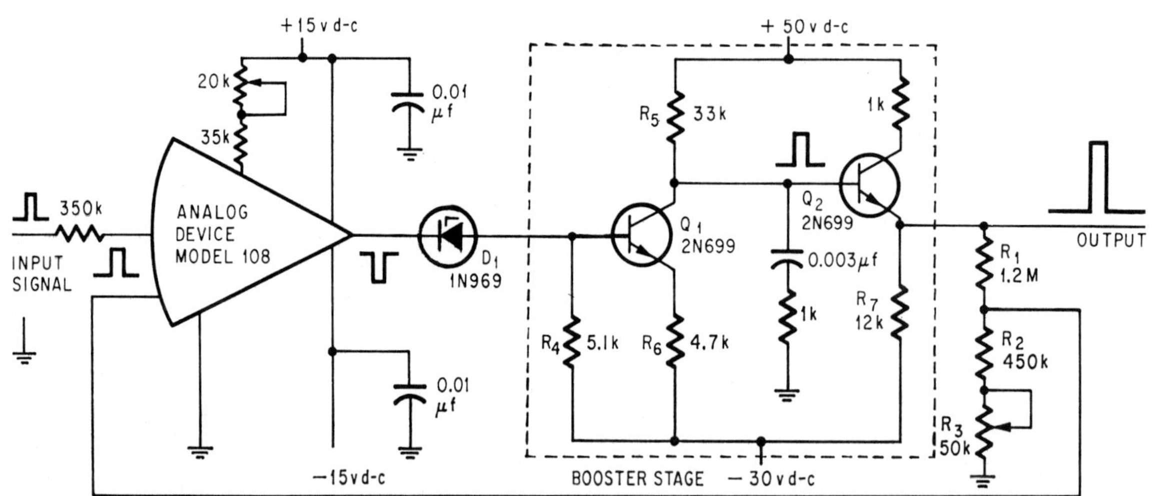

VOLTAGE BOOSTER—Two transistors and zener diode give high output voltage from low-voltage opamp having good gain and stability. Can be used to measure phase angle changes as small as 0.01%.—A. Freilich, Boosting Op-Amp Output With Two Transistors, *Electronics*, June 10, 1968, p 110–111.

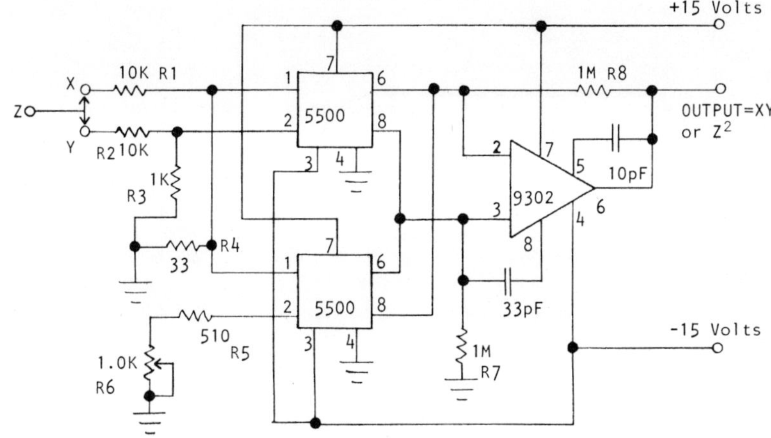

BIPOLAR SQUARING—Consists of four-quadrant multiplier having 10 V input and output signal levels of both polarities. Bandwidth is d-c to 10 kHz, but may be increased by changing R7 and R8 to 100K. When inputs are connected together as shown, circuit becomes squaring amplifier. R6 adjusts offset at Y input or adjusts symmetry of output parabola when squaring.—Applying the Model 5500 Monolithic Analog Multiplier, Optical Electronics, Tucson, Ariz., No. 10138.

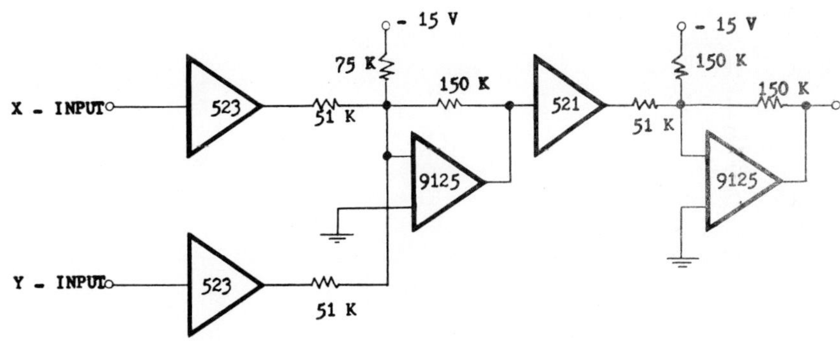

SQUARE ROOT OF SUM OF SQUARES—Uses five OEI IC's to square X and Y inputs. First 9125 opamp sums the squares, 521 performs square root, and 9125 at output cancels offset so output is absolute value of input function. Inputs and outputs are all positive.—Generating Square Root of Sum of Squares Function, Optical Electronics, Tucson, Ariz., No. 10085.

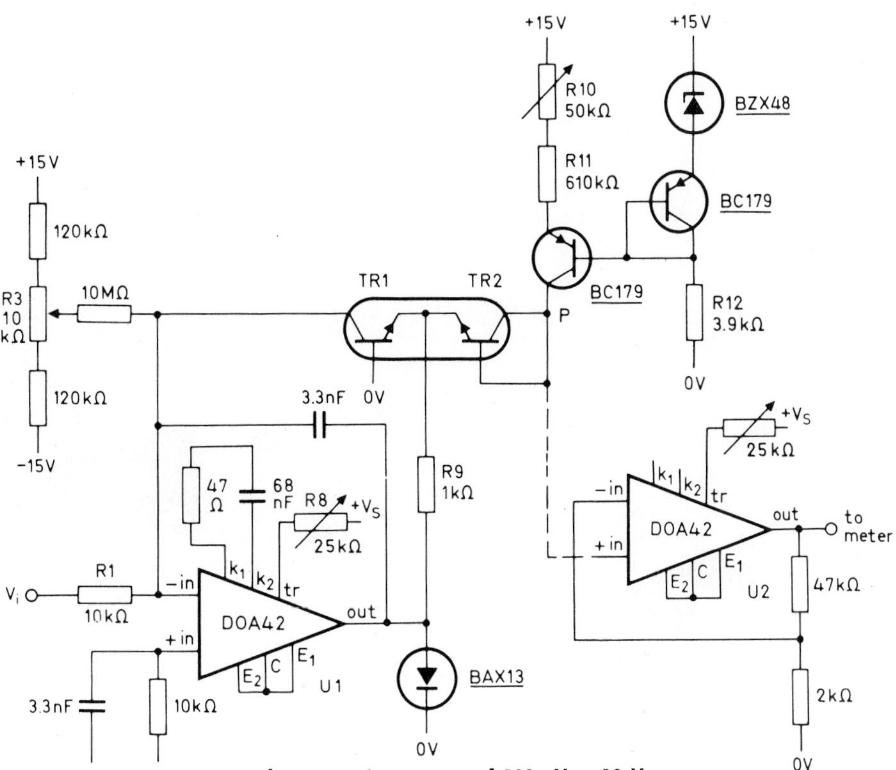

LOGAMP—Uses logarithmic voltage-current relationship in semiconductor junction to provide, by means of feedback in Philips DOA42 IC opamp, output which is logarithm of input voltage over input range of 100 μV to 10 V. Opamp at lower right may be added as buffer and amplifier for logarithmic signal. Transistors TR1 and TR2 can be selected examples of BCY87 having high hFE at low IC values. Circuit is suitable for positive input voltages only.—A. Schechtman, A Logarithmic Amplifier, Philips, Pub. Dept., Elcoma Div., Eindhoven, The Netherlands, No. 86.

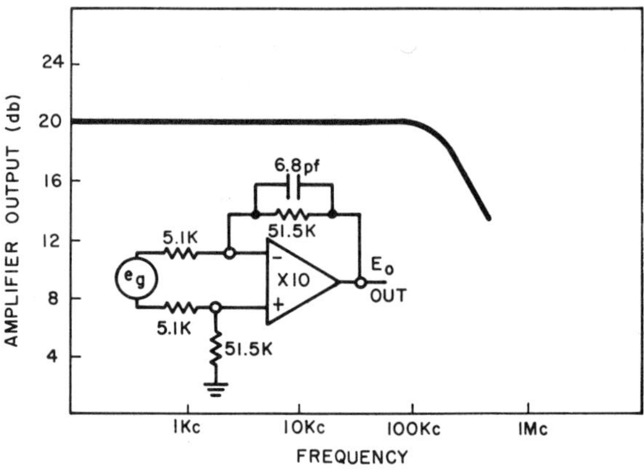

IC DIFFERENCE AMPLIFIER—Provides gain of 20, with frequency response shown by curve. IC can be SN521, or SN522 having added emitter-follower for greater drive capability. —L. Housey and G. McFarland, Using Integrateds as Feedback Amplifiers, *Electronic Design*, March 2, 1964, p 49–52.

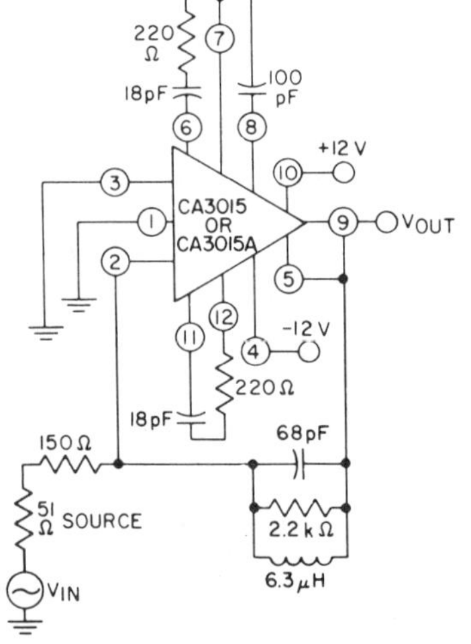

10-MHZ R-L-C BANDPASS—Gain is about 20 dB at resonance, and 3-dB bandwidth is about 1 MHz. Inputs are effectively grounded.—"Linear Integrated Circuits," RCA, Harrison, N.J., IC-41, p 262.

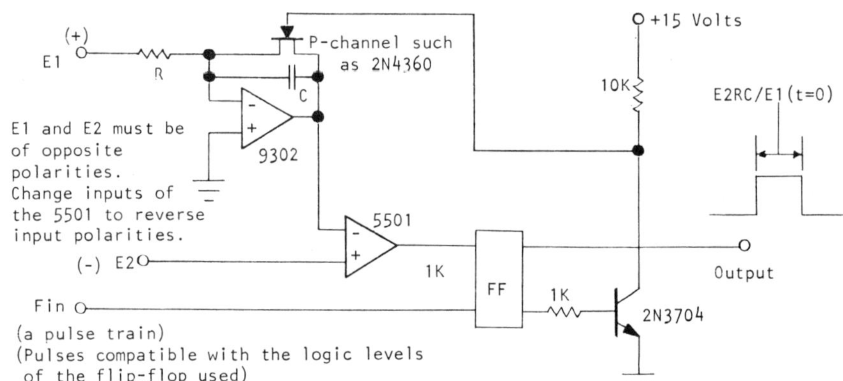

ANALOG DIVIDER—Analog input E1 drives integrator, while analog input E2 is reference level of analog comparator. When integrator output is greater than reference, comparator sets flip-flop FF, which changes state at next clock pulse, making fet reset integrator and start process over again. End of clock pulse resets flip-flop. Output is rectangular pulse train. Flip-flop may be any RS type having sufficient speed for clock rate used.—An Average Value Analog Divider, Optical Electronics, Tucson, Ariz., No. 10145.

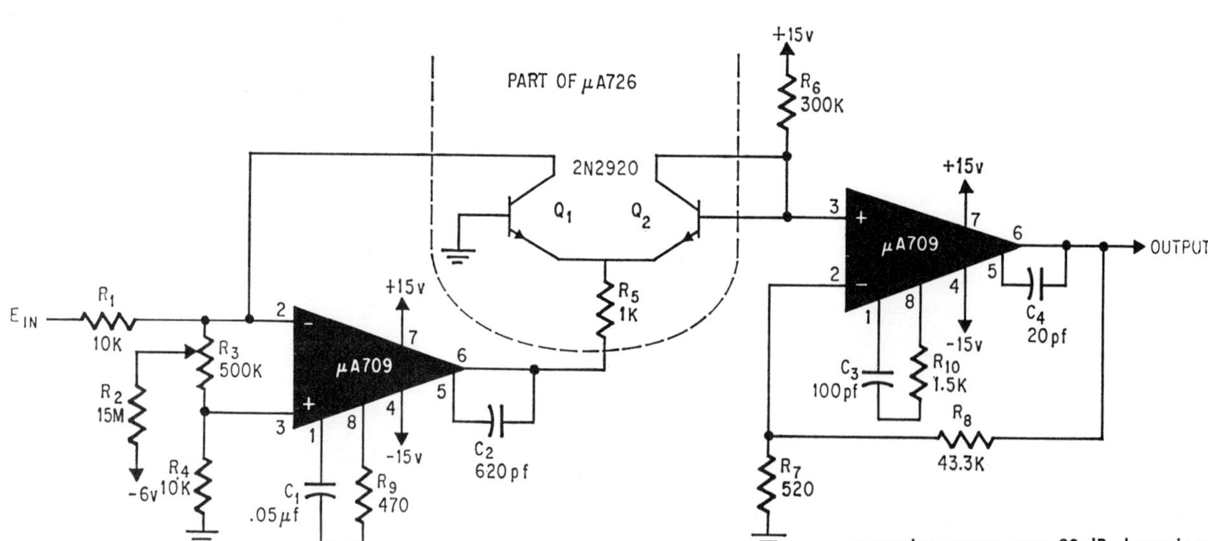

LOG AMPLIFIER—Two Fairchild μA709 IC opamps and transistor pair from temperature-compensated IC differential amplifier together serve to multiply and divide signals in true logarithmic fashion. The transistors, connected as feedback stage between IC's, add the two signal levels after they have been converted to logarithmic form. Logarithmic conversion occurs over 80-dB dynamic range and wide temperature range.—J. F. Gifford and M. Markkula, Linear IC's: Part 5, Ins and Outs of Op Amps, *Electronics*, Nov. 27, 1967, p 84–93.

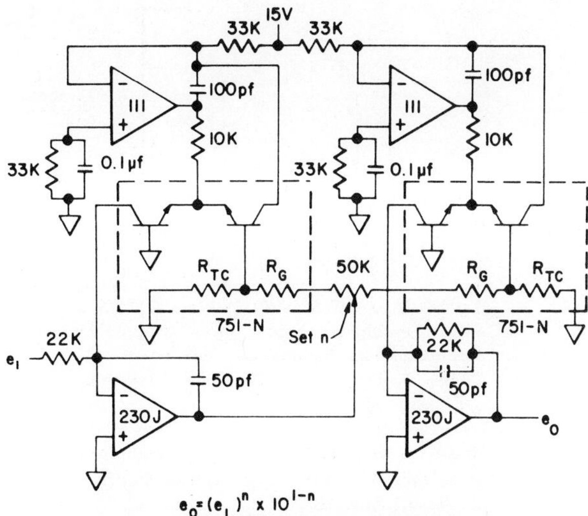

EXPONENTIAL FUNCTION OF VOLTAGE—Exponent generated is adjustable between 0.25 and 4 by means of single potentiometer. Dashed rectangles are Analog Devices 751N log modules; 111 is reference opamp and 230J is chopper-stabilized opamp.—W. Borlase and E. David, Design of Temperature Compensated Log Circuits Employing Transistors and Operational Amplifiers, Analog Devices, Cambridge, Mass., E020-10-3/69, p 12.

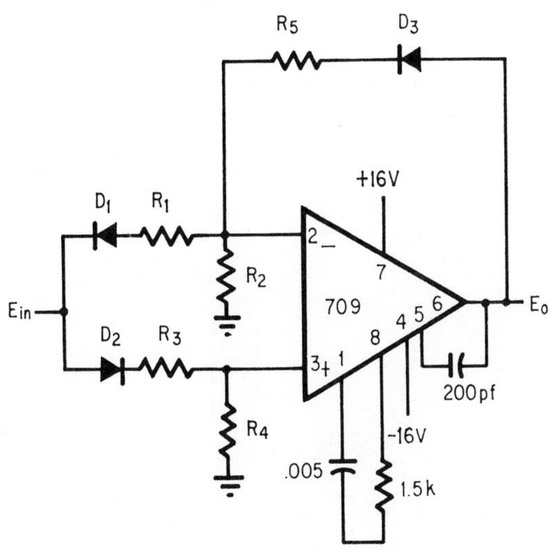

ABSOLUTE VALUES—Requires only single IC opamp for converting d-c input voltages of either polarity to their absolute value. Accuracy is 0.1% from 0 to 50 C for bipolar inputs of 0.5 to 15 V. Article tells how input polarity changes transfer function. R1 through R5 have equal values, and forward resistances of all three diodes are identical. —W. Spani, Absolute Value Circuit Needs Only One Op Amp, *Electronics*, Jan. 20, 1969, p 89.

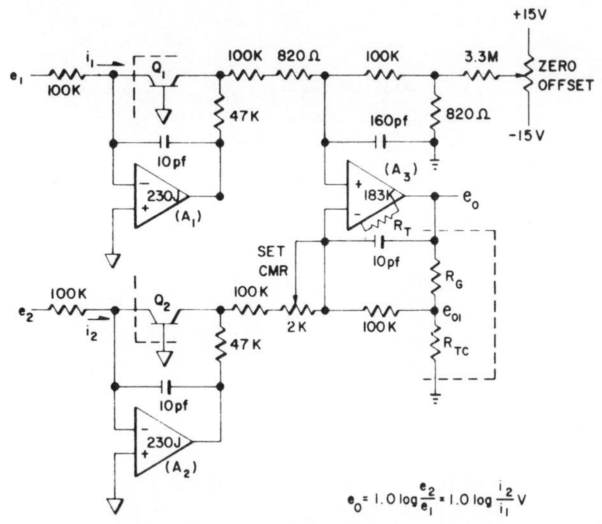

PRECISION LOG OF VOLTAGE OR CURRENT RATIO—Provides accurate logarithmic conversion on both inputs. Uses Analog Devices 230J chopper-stabilized amplifiers with 751N log element for positive inputs (dashed rectangle) or 751P for negative inputs. Differential amplifier 183K is high-impedance type. Circuit includes common mode response zeroing control and zero offset control.—W. Borlase and E. David, Design of Temperature Compensated Log Circuits Employing Transistors and Operational Amplifiers, Analog Devices, Cambridge, Mass., E020-10-3/69, p 12.

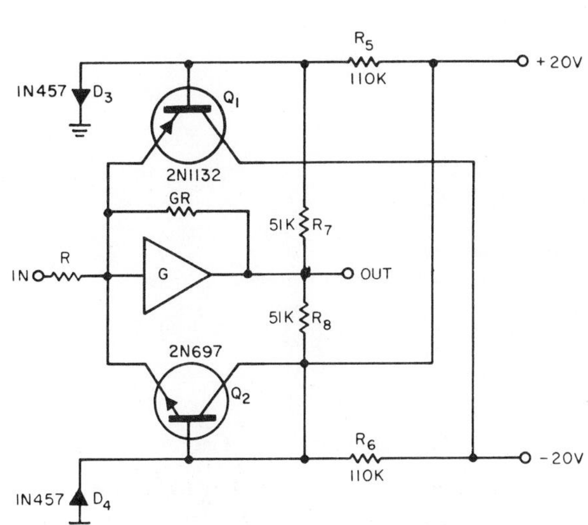

OPAMP LIMITER—Modification of differential amplifier circuit Q1-Q2 serves to limit output of opamp G to plus or minus 10 V. Coupling and biasing resistors are not in feedback loop, so arrangement gives good hard limiting.—P. A. Ralatos, Reset Circuit Independent of Amplitude and Polarity, *Electronic Design*, Oct. 25, 1965, p 70 and 72.

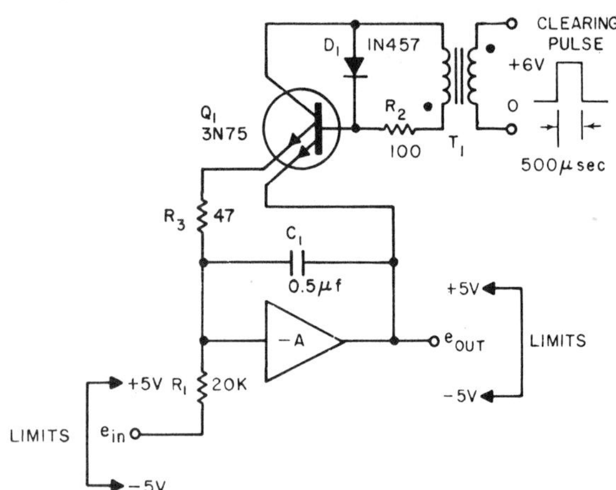

T_1 = 400 OHMS, 1:1 RATIO MINIATURE AUDIO TRANSFORMER

CLEARING—Combination of dual-emitter transistor Q1, transformer, and diode D1 clears integrator by discharging its capacitor when clearing pulse is applied, without producing d-c leakage path between either end of C1 and control signal. Circuit will reset integrator to within 10 mV of zero.—J. A. Wisnia, Dual-Emitter Transistor Clears Integrator Circuit, *Electronic Design*, June 7, 1965, p 41–42.

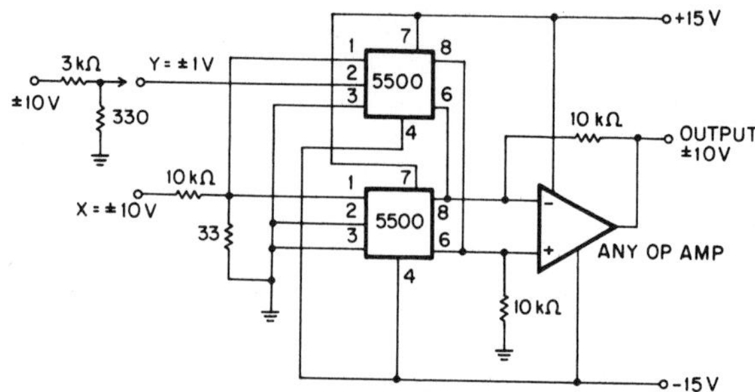

FOUR-QUADRANT MULTIPLIER—Two OEI 5500 analog multipliers feed opamp to provide product of two inputs over four quadrants. Opamp is not critical. Output is 10 V full-scale with either polarity when R is 100K. Frequency response depends on opamp up to 10 MHz.—Two and Four Quadrant Multipliers using the OEI Model 5500, Optical Electronics, Tucson, Ariz., No. 10140.

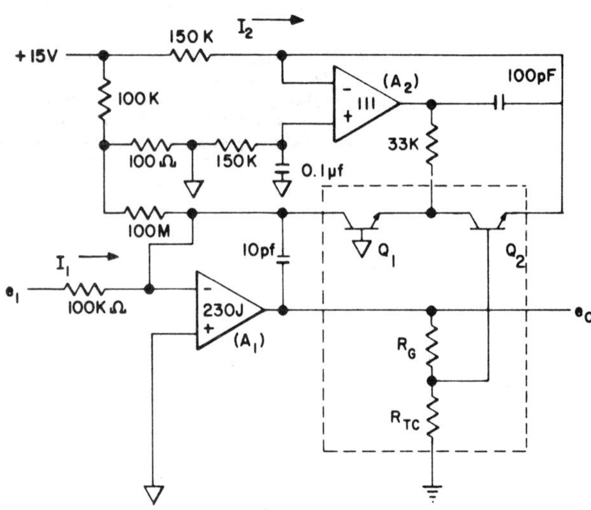

INPUT RANGE:

$1mV < e_1 < 10V$ or $10nA < I_1 < 100\mu A$

$$-e_o = 1.0 \log \frac{e_1 R_R}{e_R R_1} = \log \frac{e_1 \times 150K}{15 \times 100K} = \log \frac{e_1}{10} (V)$$

$$\tau = \left(\frac{1}{40I} R_E\right) C_f, \; I_{min} = \frac{15mV}{100M\Omega} = 150 \text{ pA}$$

$$\tau_{min} = \left(\frac{1}{40 \times 1.5 \times 10^{-10}} + 33K\right) 10^{-11} \approx 1.6 \text{ ms}$$

LOG OF VOLTAGE OR CURRENT—Provides logarithmic compression of inputs to 230J chopper-stabilized amplifier over wide dynamic range (10 pA to 100 μA). Dashed rectangle is Analog Devices 751N log element for positive inputs (use 751P for negative inputs).—W. Borlase and E. David, Design of Temperature Compensated Log Circuits Employing Transistors and Operational Amplifiers, Analog Devices, Cambridge, Mass., E020-10-3/69, p 11.

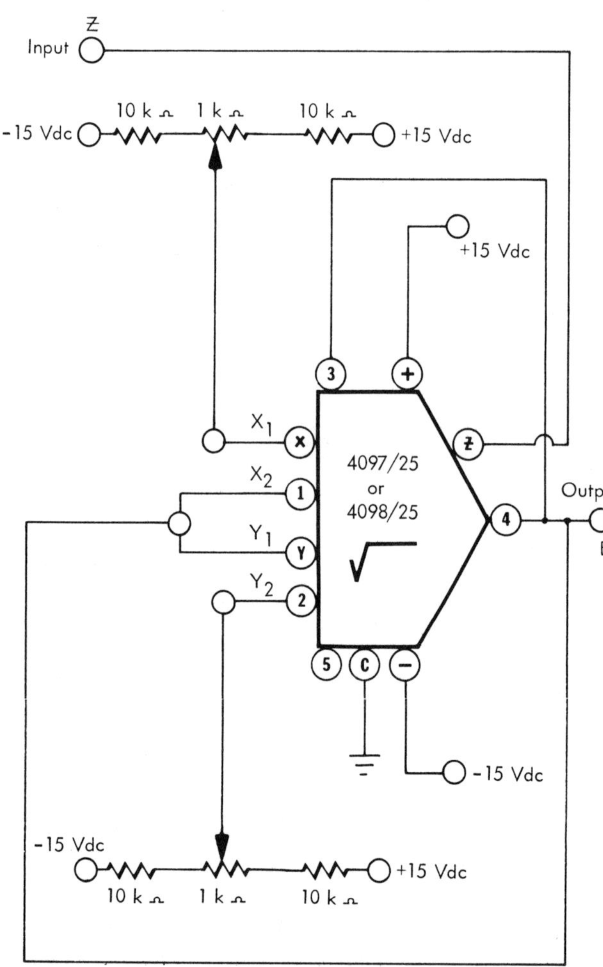

$E_o = \sqrt{10|Z|}$, where $-10 \leq Z \leq 0$.

SQUARE-ROOTING—Connection shown for Burr-Brown differential-input multiplier-divider package provides noninverting square-root mode of operation with offset nulling. Multiplier is used to square output signal. Report discusses causes of square-rooting errors.—Differential Input Multiplier/Dividers, Burr-Brown Research, Tucson, Ariz., PDS-201A-2, 1969.

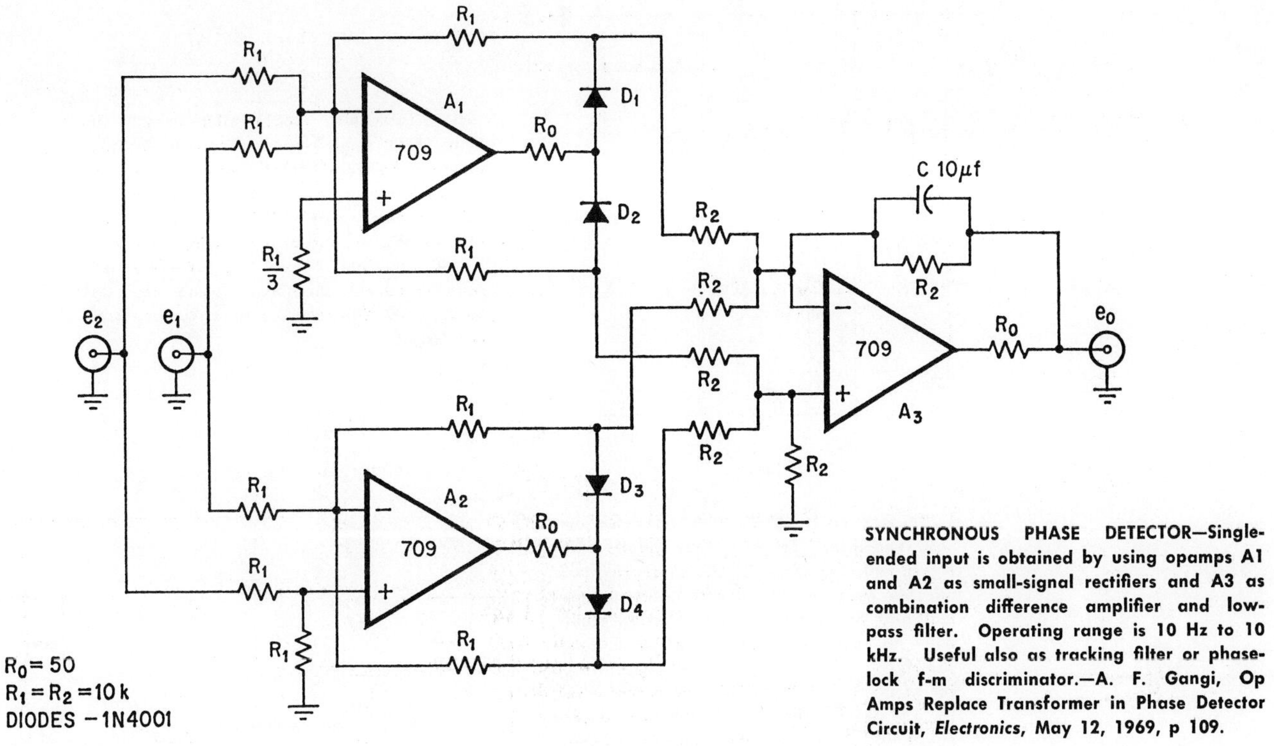

SYNCHRONOUS PHASE DETECTOR—Single-ended input is obtained by using opamps A1 and A2 as small-signal rectifiers and A3 as combination difference amplifier and low-pass filter. Operating range is 10 Hz to 10 kHz. Useful also as tracking filter or phase-lock f-m discriminator.—A. F. Gangi, Op Amps Replace Transformer in Phase Detector Circuit, *Electronics*, May 12, 1969, p 109.

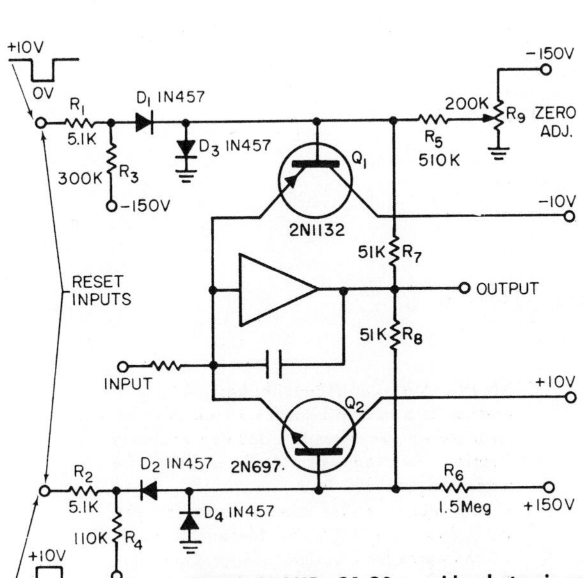

RESETS OPAMP—Q1-Q2 provide electronic reset for integrating opamp regardless of output amplitude or polarity. Differential IC current amplifier is gated ON for reset period and provides full-signal negative feedback, to convert integrator to zero-gain amplifier. Article describes function of integrating capacitor across opamp, whose value is chosen to give desired discharge rate.—P. A. Ralatos, Reset Circuit Independent of Amplitude and Polarity, *Electronic Design*, Oct. 25, 1965, p 70 and 72.

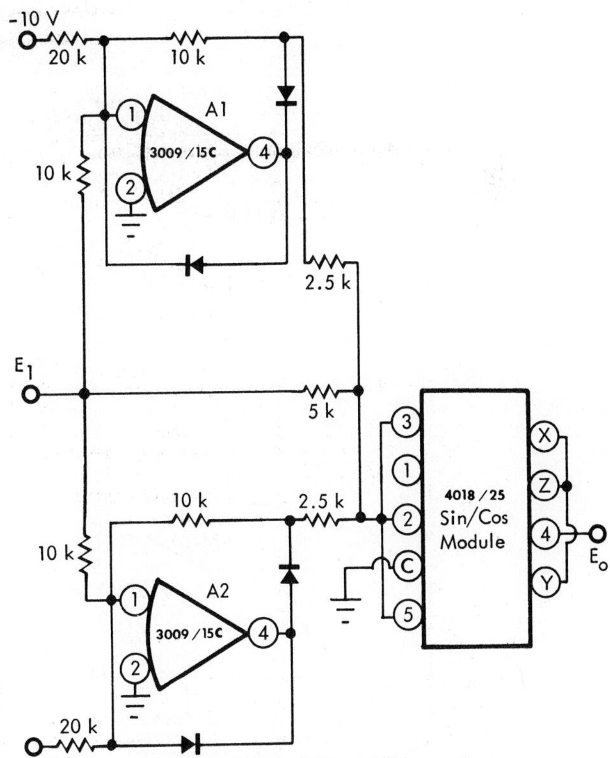

FOUR-QUADRANT SINE—Addition of two opamps to Burr-Brown 4018/25 two-quadrant sine-cosine generator module gives four-quadrant response. Equations are given. For 0.1% overall accuracy, all resistors should be trimmed to 0.01% of indicated values.—Sine/Cosine Function Generator, Burr-Brown Research, Tucson, Ariz., PDS-210, 1968, p 5.

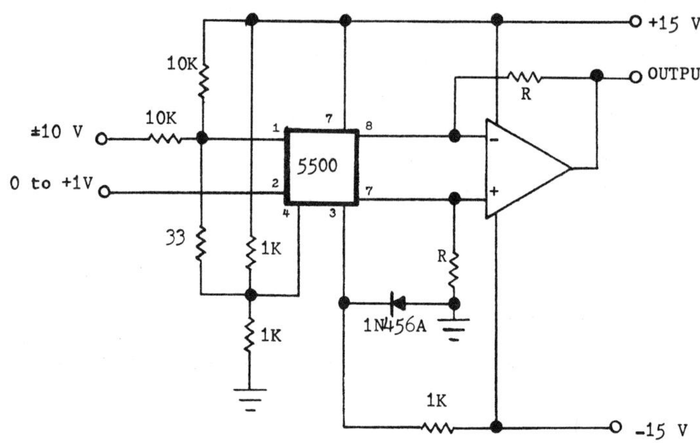

TWO-QUADRANT MULTIPLIER—Uses OEI Model 5500 single-chip analog multiplier providing differential output equal to product of two inputs. Opamp at output is not critical, and may be OEI 9302, 9125, etc. Value of R determines output amplitude; 100K gives 10 V full-scale bipolar output.—Two and Four Quadrant Multipliers using the OEI Model 5500, Optical Electronics, Tucson, Ariz., No. 10140.

CUBIC FUNCTION GENERATOR—Uses two low-cost unmatched fet squaring circuits with forced-matching scaling factor to approximate matched fet pairs. Used with quarter-square multiplier and summing and inverting amplifiers to generate cubic function. Circuit shown squares over 60-dB output signal range for inputs from 100 to 10,000 Hz when driven by sine wave. Article covers theory, design equations, and other applications for squarer. —T. F. Bogart, Jr., Matched Transistors Pass for FET Squarers, *Electronic Design*, Nov. 8, 1965, p 36–41.

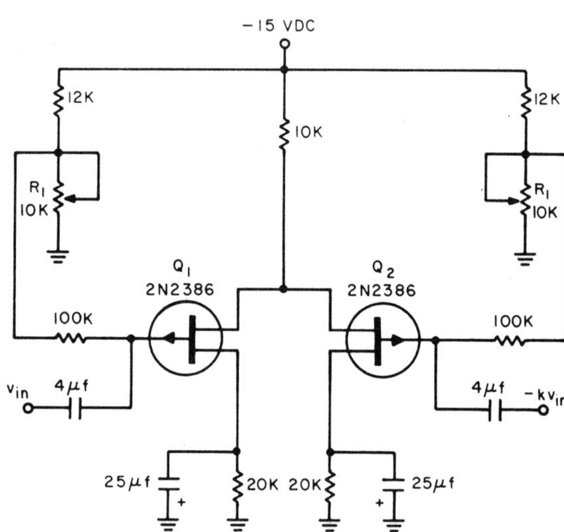

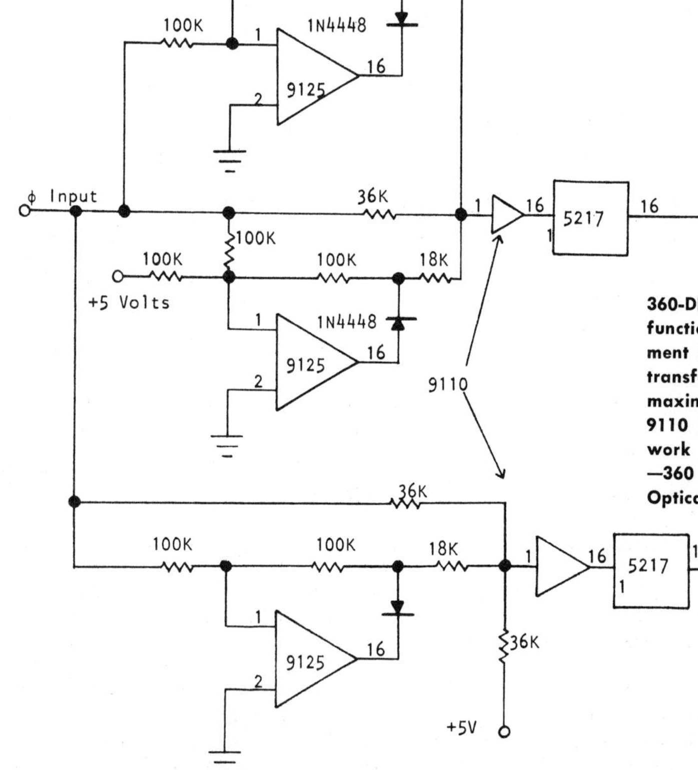

360-DEG SINE-COSINE—With basic OEI sine-function and opamp modules, circuit arrangement shown generates full 360-deg nonlinear transfer function. Useful bandwidth for maximum accuracy is d-c to 1 kHz. Model 9110 modules buffer summing resistor network and drive 5217 sine function modules. —360 Degree Sine/Cosine Function Generator, Optical Electronics, Tucson, Ariz., No. 10154.

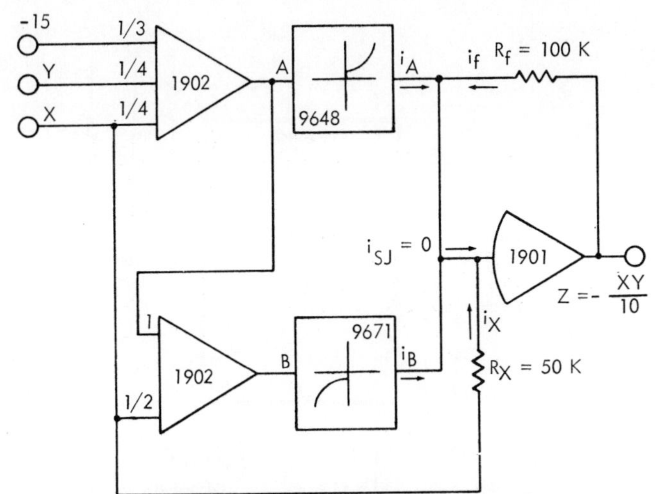

FOUR-QUADRANT MULTIPLIER—Combines Burr-Brown 9648 and 9671 squaring modules with three high-gain d-c opamps to give four-quadrant multiplication of input signals at X and Y. Output opamp is connected as summing amplifier.—Negative Input General Purpose Squaring Module, Burr-Brown Research, Tucson, Ariz., PDS-180A, 1968.

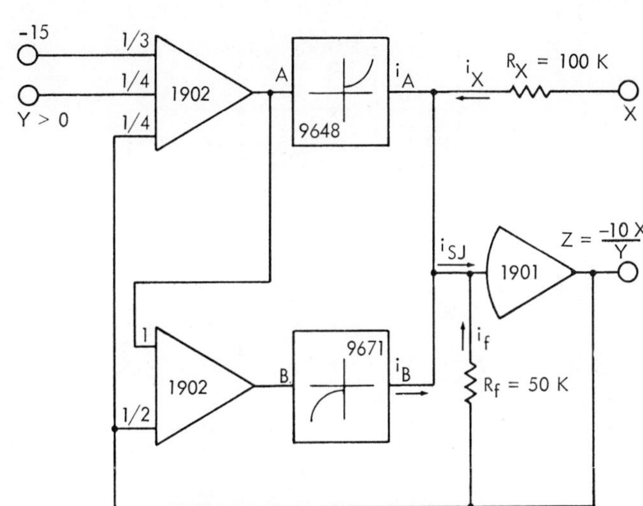

TWO-QUADRANT DIVIDER—Combines Burr-Brown 9648 and 9671 squaring modules with three high-gain d-c opamps to give two-quadrant division of signal at X by signal at Y.—Negative Input General Purpose Squaring Module, Burr-Brown Research, Tucson, Ariz., PDS-180A, 1968.

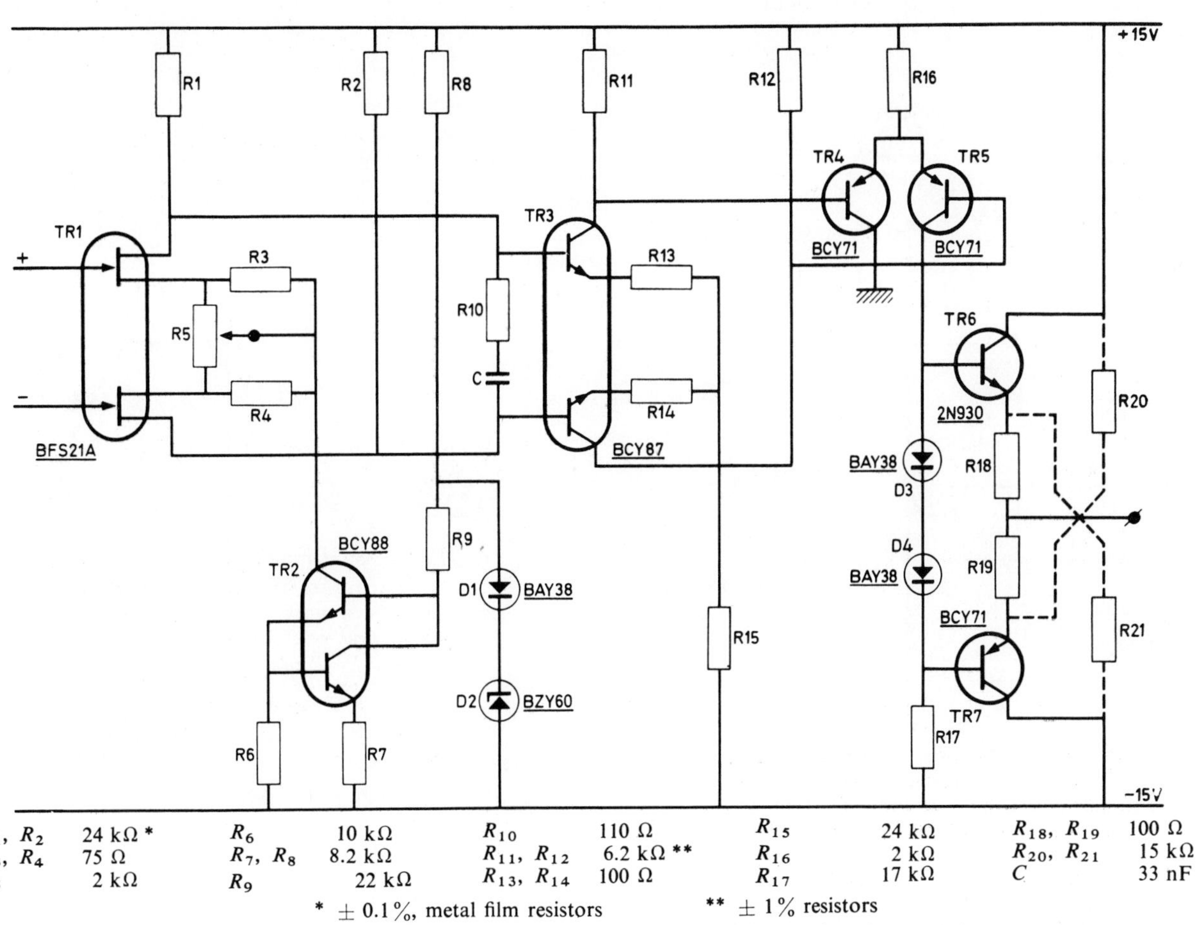

R_1, R_2	24 kΩ *	R_6	10 kΩ	R_{10}	110 Ω	R_{15}	24 kΩ	R_{18}, R_{19}	100 Ω
R_3, R_4	75 Ω	R_7, R_8	8.2 kΩ	R_{11}, R_{12}	6.2 kΩ **	R_{16}	2 kΩ	R_{20}, R_{21}	15 kΩ
R_5	2 kΩ	R_9	22 kΩ	R_{13}, R_{14}	100 Ω	R_{17}	17 kΩ	C	33 nF

* ± 0.1%, metal film resistors ** ± 1% resistors

DIFFERENTIAL FET INPUT—Fet pair in first stage reduces bias and offset currents by factor of 1,000 as compared to bipolar transistors. Unity-gain bandwidth is 10 MHz, open-loop voltage gain 99 dB, and slewing rate with compensation network is 10 V per μs. Report gives design equations.—B. J. M. Overgoor, An Operational Amplifier with Differential FET Input, Philips, Pub. Dept., Elcoma Div., Eindhoven, The Netherlands, No. 332, 1969.

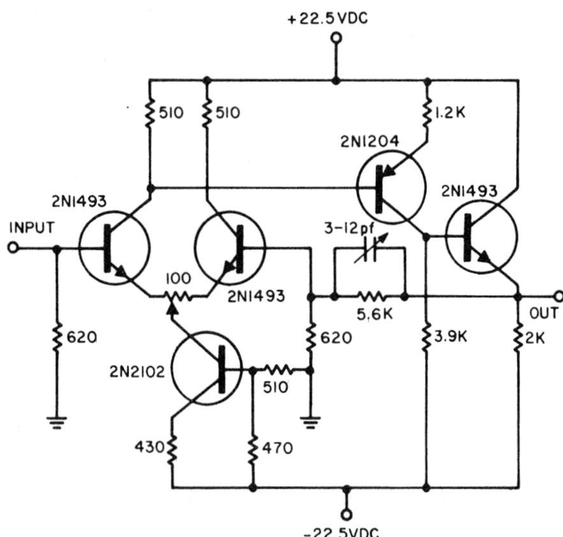

2 W FROM D-C TO 12 MHZ—Instability is avoided by limiting gain of each stage and using feedback for handling large voltage swings. Output stage can handle 20-V swing into 200 ohms, or 2 W for square wave. Bandwidth is flat within 3 dB and rise time is 25 ns.—R. H. McMorrow, Modified Operational Amplifier Has Flat Bandwidth to 12 Mc, *Electronic Design*, Aug. 30, 1965, p 47–48.

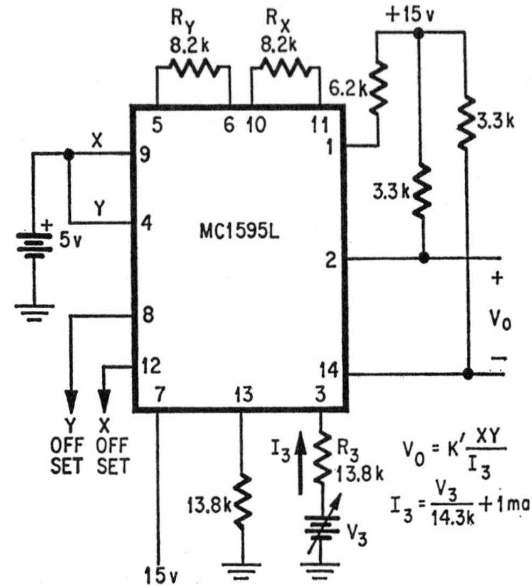

IC MULTIPLIER-DIVIDER—Motorola monolithic multiplier provides simultaneous multiplication and division when used with component values shown.—E. Renschler and D. Weiss, Try the Monolithic Multiplier as a Versatile A-C Design Tool, *Electronics*, June 8, 1970, p 100–105.

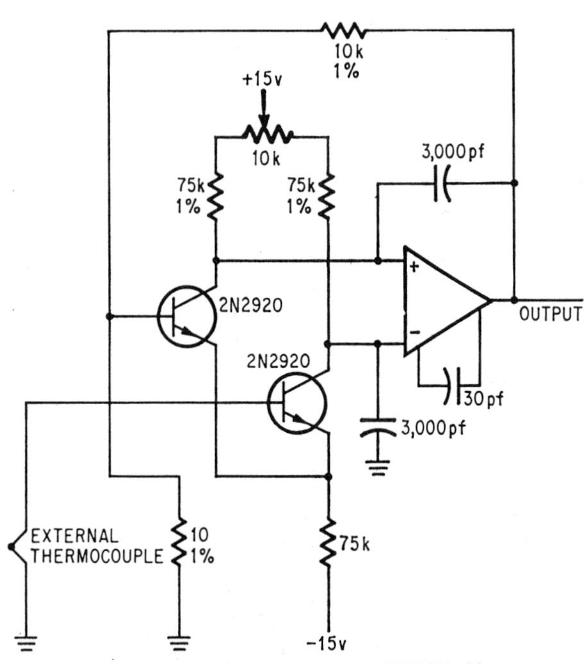

OFFSET VOLTAGE DRIFT SUPPRESSION—Bias current drift compensation techniques for IC amplifier, described in article, are here applied to complete amplifier having monolithic transistor pair as preamp. Null potentiometer unbalances collector load resistors so zero output is obtained for zero input. Change of 1 V in either supply makes offset voltage change only about 10 μV. Temperature drift is low, comparing favorably with that of expensive chopper-stabilized amplifiers.—R. J. Widlar, Linear IC's: Compensating For Drift, *Electronics*, Feb. 5, 1968, p 90–93.

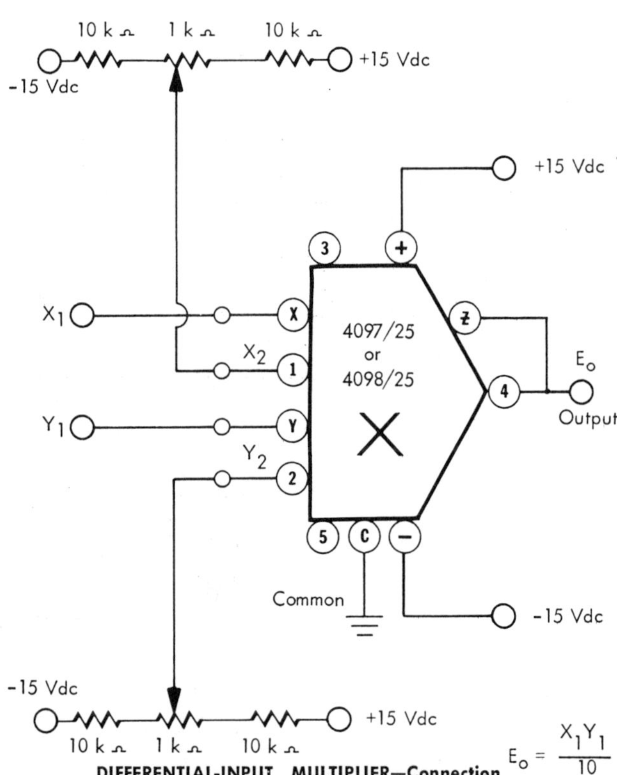

DIFFERENTIAL-INPUT MULTIPLIER—Connection shown for Burr-Brown multiplier-divider package multiplies inputs at X1 and Y1 with improved accuracy by using offset nulling principle. Accuracy is 2% of full-scale for 4097 and 1% for 4098. Report discusses offset errors.—Differential Input Multiplier/Dividers, Burr-Brown Research, Tucson, Ariz., PDS-201A-2, 1969.

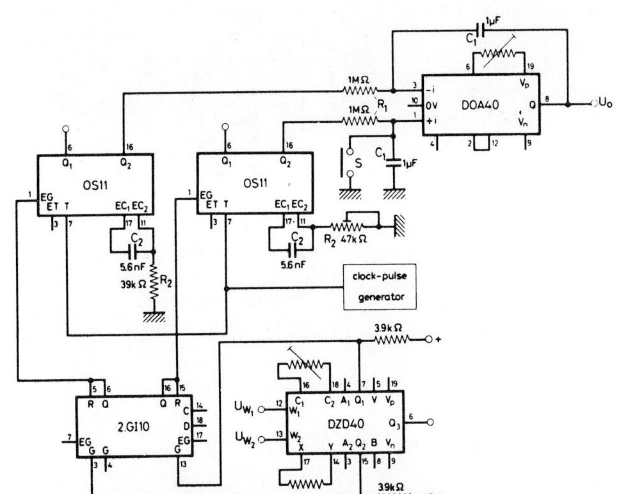

ANALOG CONTROL OF VOLTAGE—Output voltage Uo of Philips DOA40 IC opamp is proportional to difference between input signal voltages applied to OS11 IC monostable mvbr's. Multivibrators are connected to DZD40 zero detector and to common clock pulse generator. Output voltage is returned to zero by operating reset switch S to short out C1.—Electronic Potentiometer With 40- and 10-Series Circuit Blocks, Philips, Pub. Dept., Elcoma Div., Eindhoven, The Netherlands.

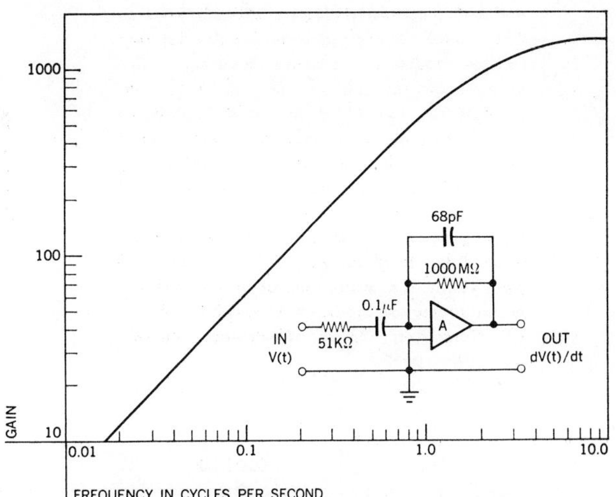

DIFFERENTIATOR—Uses high-gain Philbrick USA-3 opamp with capacitive input and resistive feedback. Developed for observing transverse dHS effect in bismuth at liquid helium temperatures. Output drives X-Y recorder.—R. D. Brown III, New Methods for De Haas-Shubnikov Measurements, *IBM Journal*, Nov. 1966, p 462–471.

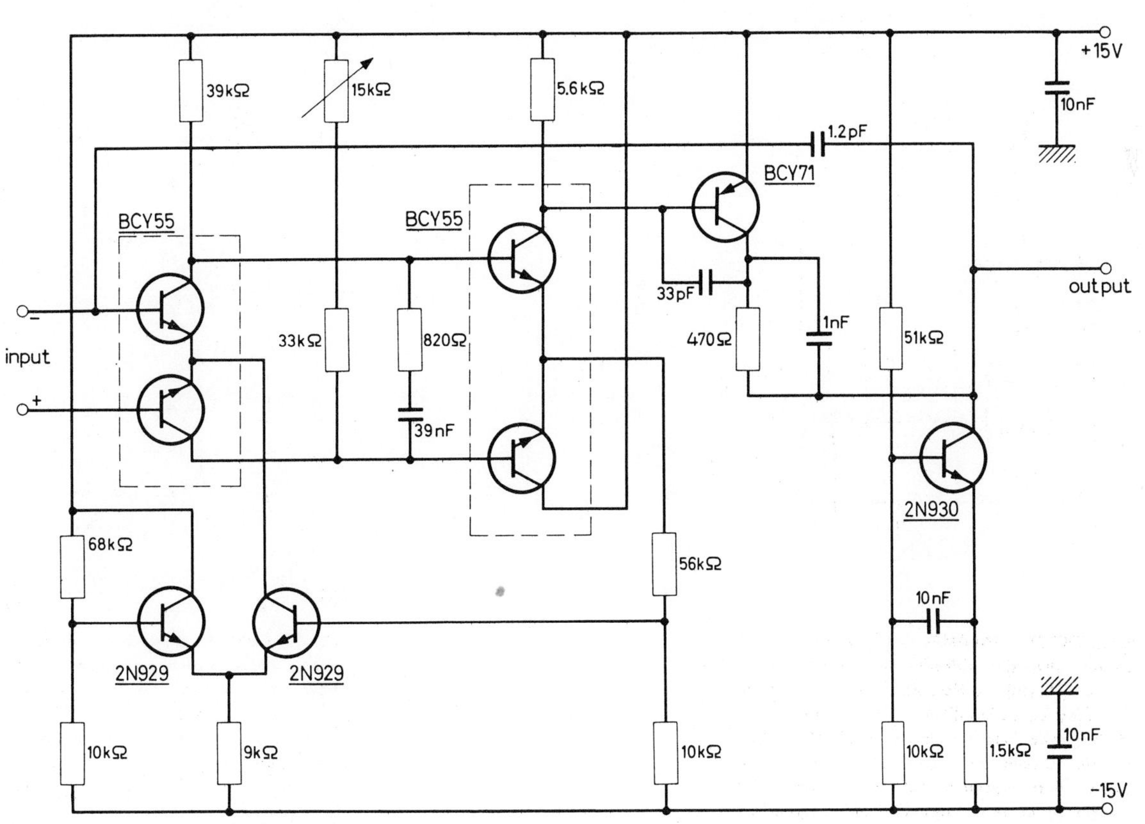

HIGH-GAIN D-C DIFFERENTIAL AMPLIFIER—Provides open-loop d-c gain of 200,000, differential input impedance of 100,000 ohms, common-mode input impedance of 20 meg, output impedance of 10K, unity-gain bandwidth of 9 MHz, and common-mode rejection ratio of 94 dB. Suitable for operational use in amplifying signal by known and accurately determined factor. Article includes mathematical discussion of amplification errors.—J. Oosterling and S. Sijtstra, Operational Amplifiers, *Electronic Applications*, Philips, Pub. Dept., Elcoma Div., Eindhoven, The Netherlands, Vol. 26, No. 4, p 116–188.

A-C/D-C LOGARITHMIC CONVERTER—Uses OEI Model 269 four-decade bipolar logamp having frequency response covering entire audio spectrum down to d-c. Output is instantaneous log of input. With sine-wave input, output is rounded-top steep-sided waveform, with amplitude still equal to log of input peak amplitude. Compression of amplifier means that entire four decades of input produce output from 250-mV full-scale peak down to about 25 mV for minimum input. With d-c input, output is d-c voltage equal to log of input.—A Logarithmic AC to DC Converter, Optical Electronics, Tucson, Ariz., No. 10082.

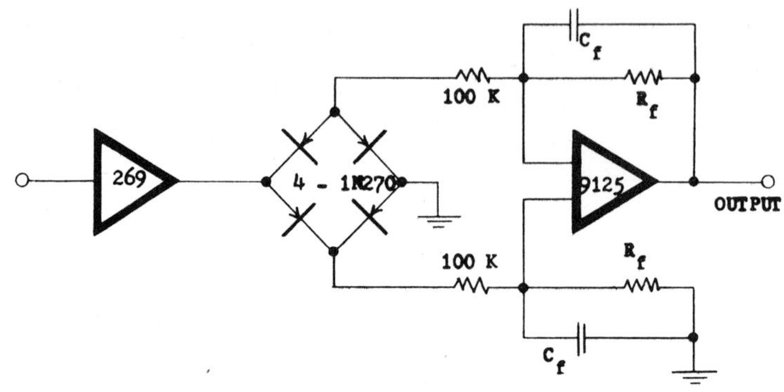

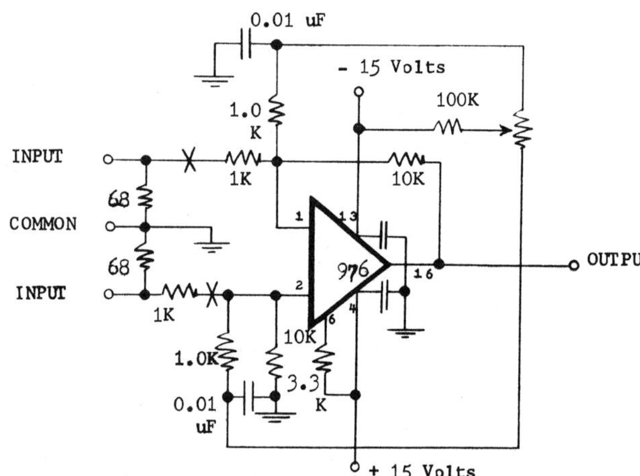

BALANCED TERMINATION—Required for transducers and other signal sources having long lines. If common-mode voltage exists between both inputs and signal ground, opamp can reject voltage as common-mode signal. Arrangement shown provides for nulling of d-c unbalance with pot. Capacitors may be inserted in d-c lines at points marked X. Use 16 μF. High-frequency response for −3 dB is about 3 MHz.—An AC Coupled Balanced Input Pre-Amplifier, Optical Electronics, Tucson, Ariz., No. 10115.

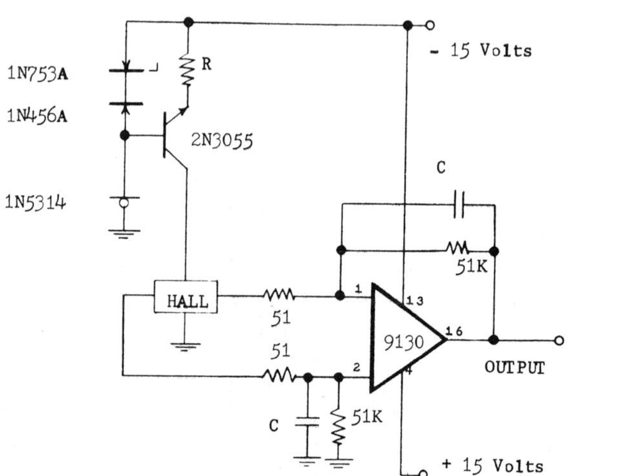

HALL-EFFECT PREAMP—OEI Model 9130 opamp provides differential input required for amplifying differential output voltage that may be as small as a few mV per gauss of magnetic field passing through Hall-effect device. Circuit has gain of 1,000, which means that placement of Hall device with respect to earth's magnetic field may affect output. Frequency response extends from d-c to about 1,000 Hz. Linearity is good if bias current is set properly.—A Hall Effect Device Pre-Amplifier, Optical Electronics, Tucson, Ariz., No. 10118.

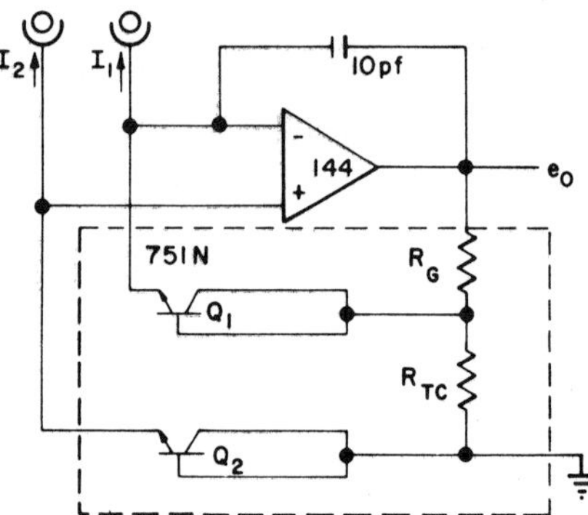

$$e_0 = 1.0 \log \frac{I_2}{I_r}(V), \quad 10^{-9}A < I_1 < 10^{-7}A, \quad 10^{-9}A < I_2 < 10^{-4}A$$

$$\tau \approx \frac{1}{40 I_1}\left(\frac{R_G + R_{TC}}{R_{TC}}\right) \times 10^{-11} \approx \frac{4 \times 10^{-12}}{I_1} \text{ sec}, \quad \frac{1}{40 I_1} >> R_G$$

LOG OF CURRENT RATIO—Combines Analog Devices 751N matched transistor pair and calibrated voltage divider module with Model 144 fet amplifier to provide logarithm of ratio of two input currents greater than a nanoampere each. Diode-connected transistors are reversible. Used in colorimetry, where overall accuracy of 0.1 dB can be maintained.—W. Borlase and E. David, Design of Temperature Compensated Log Circuits Employing Transistors and Operational Amplifiers, Analog Devices, Cambridge, Mass., E020-10-3/69, p 10.

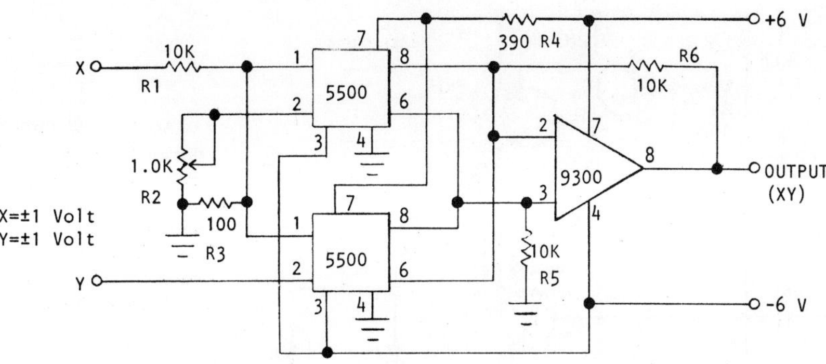

FOUR-QUADRANT FOR D-C TO 10 MRZ—Uses OEI 5500 analog multipliers. Bandwidth is limited only by slew rate or frequency response of 9300 opamp. Output is 1 V full scale.—Applying the Model 5500 Monolithic Analog Multiplier, Optical Electronics, Tucson, Ariz., No. 10138.

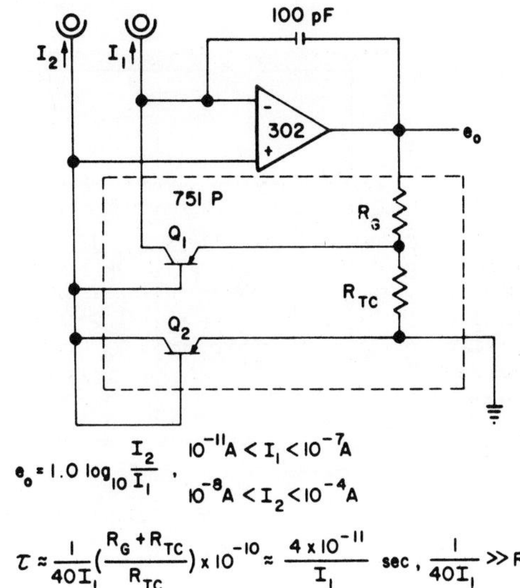

$$e_o = 1.0 \log_{10}\frac{I_2}{I_1}, \quad 10^{-11}A < I_1 < 10^{-7}A, \quad 10^{-8}A < I_2 < 10^{-4}A$$

$$\tau \approx \frac{1}{40I_1}\left(\frac{R_G + R_{TC}}{R_{TC}}\right) \times 10^{-10} \approx \frac{4 \times 10^{-11}}{I_1} \text{ sec}, \quad \frac{1}{40I_1} \gg R_G$$

LOG OF CURRENT RATIO WITHOUT REVERSIBILITY—Analog Devices 751P log element is transdiode-connected, for handling currents from few picoamperes to hundreds of nanoamperes with good accuracy. Model 302 amplifier error currents are much smaller than lowest signal currents which can be converted. Transdiode connection means loss of reversibility, so use 751P for negative input currents or 751N for positive input currents.—W. Borlase and E. David, Design of Temperature Compensated Log Circuits Employing Transistors and Operational Amplifiers, Analog Devices, Cambridge, Mass., E020-10-3/69, p 11.

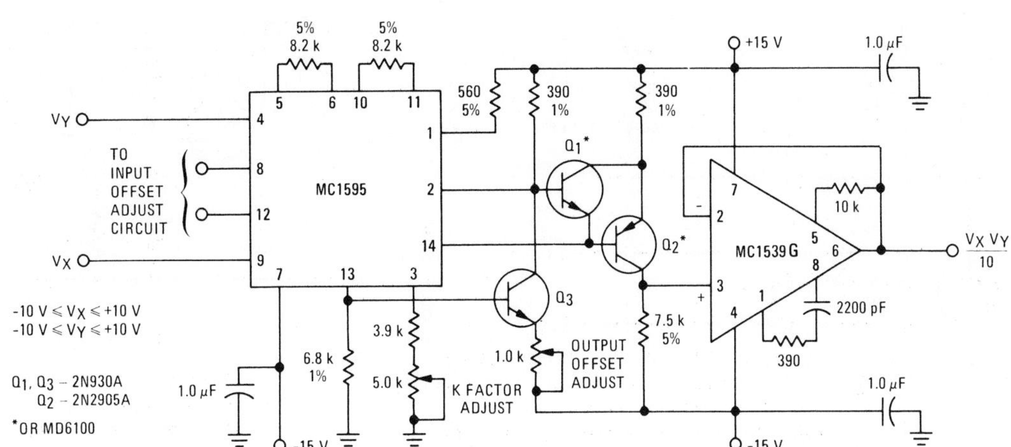

MULTIPLY WITH DISCRETE LEVEL SHIFT—Circuit takes differential output current and translates directly to ground reference, using inexpensive discrete components. Upper frequency limit depends only on 7.5K resistor and straight capacitance at output. High output impedance, with resulting limitation on drive capability, is overcome by using opamp voltage follower at output. Input IC is Motorola MC1595 linear four-quadrant multiplier.—E. Renschler, The Monolithic Multiplier Breakthrough, "State-of-the Art—Linears in Action," Motorola, Phoenix, Ariz., 1969, p 27–36.

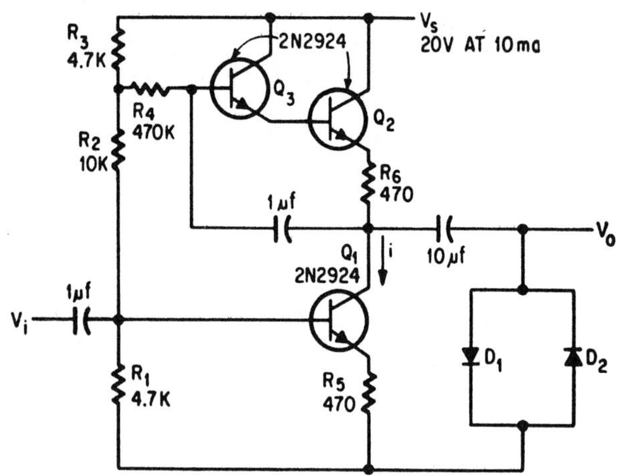

ANALOG MULTIPLICATION—Two diodes driven by three-transistor Darlington current generator form low-cost logarithmic amplifier providing multiplication at 1 kHz over 3-decade signal range. Diodes are 1N914 silicon planar units.—J. F. Delpech, Logarithmic Amplifier Has 66-dB Range, *Electronics*, Oct. 17, 1966, p 89–90.

IC NONINVERTING OPAMP—Provides gain of 20 dB, 100-kHz bandwidth for 5,000-ohm source impedance, and frequency response shown by curve. IC can be SN521, or SN522 having added emitter-follower for greater drive capability.—L. Housey and G. McFarland, Using Integrateds as Feedback Amplifiers, *Electronic Design*, March 2, 1964, p 49–52.

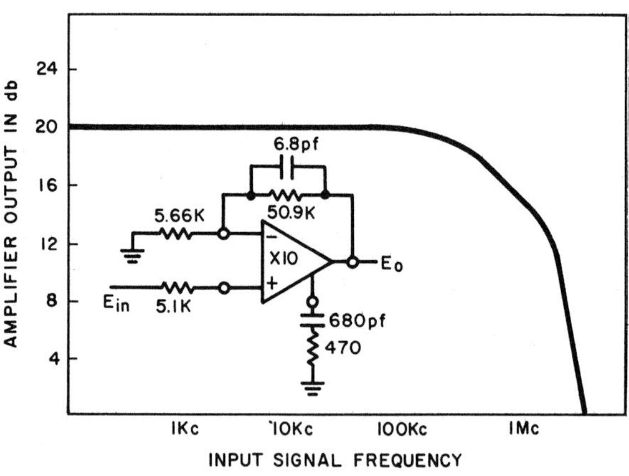

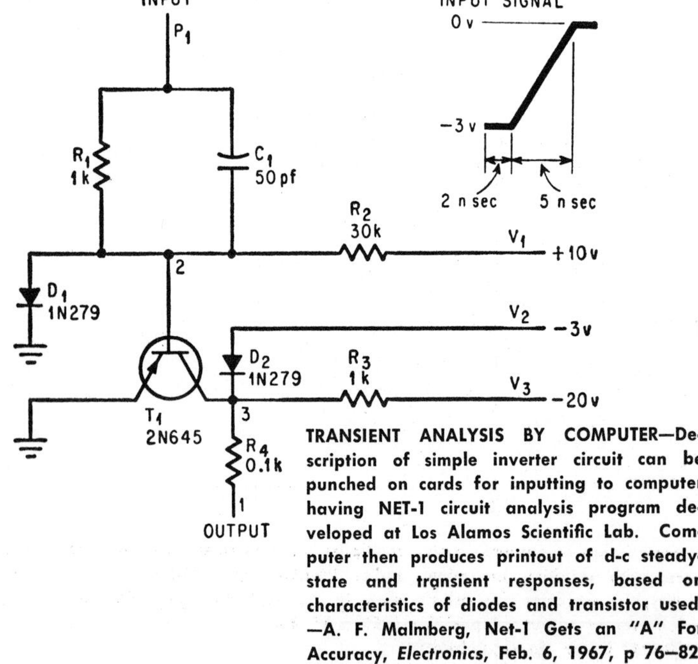

TRANSIENT ANALYSIS BY COMPUTER—Description of simple inverter circuit can be punched on cards for inputting to computer having NET-1 circuit analysis program developed at Los Alamos Scientific Lab. Computer then produces printout of d-c steady-state and transient responses, based on characteristics of diodes and transistor used. —A. F. Malmberg, Net-1 Gets an "A" For Accuracy, *Electronics*, Feb. 6, 1967, p 76–82.

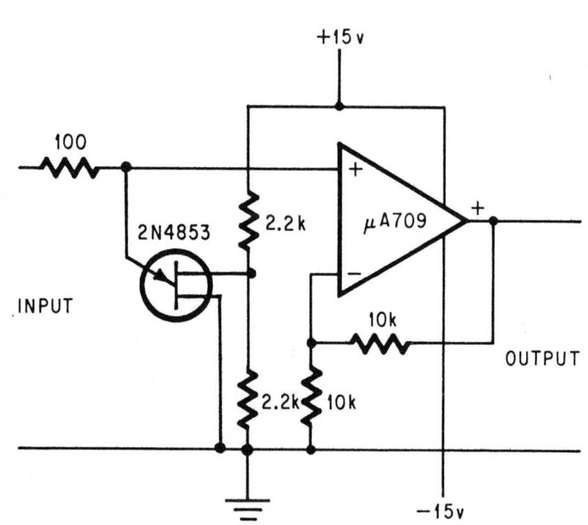

TRANSIENT PROTECTION—Large positive-going voltage transients at input of IC opamp are suppressed by using ujt at input to serve as variable threshold limiter and maintain resistance of about 3 gigohms. To limit negative transients, use complementary ujt instead of or with this circuit.—R. Chapman, UJT Protects Op Amp From Voltage Transients, *Electronics*, Nov. 25, 1968, p 83.

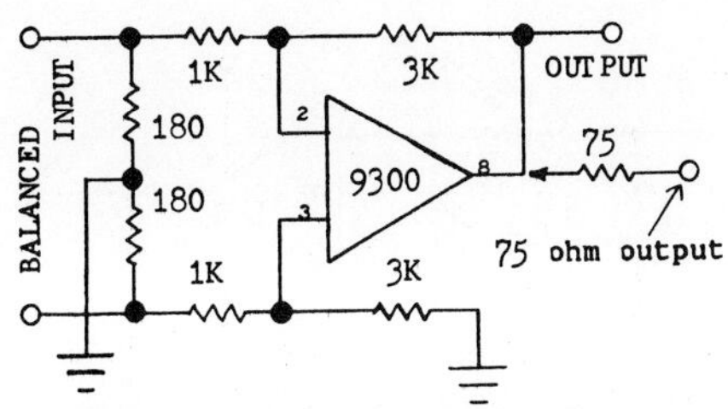

DIFFERENTIAL WITH GAIN OF 3—When driven from balanced line, bandwidth is well above 10 MHz. Input impedance is 300 ohms. Uses OEI 9300 opamp.—Applying the Model 9300 Monolithic Operational Amplifier, Optical Electronics, Tucson, Ariz., No. 10134.

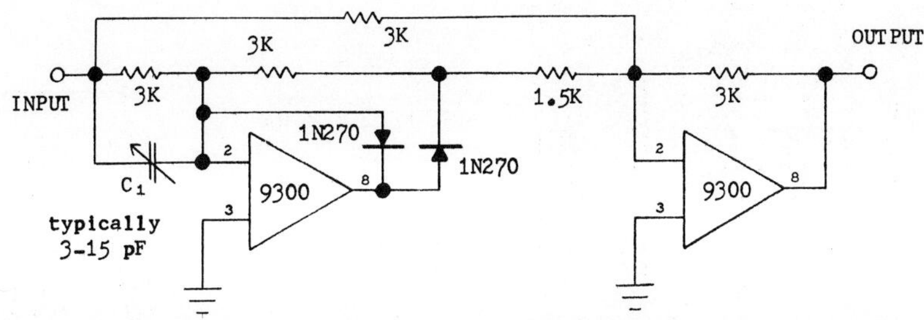

WIDE-BAND ABSOLUTE-VALUE—Provides accurate full-wave rectification of input, from d-c to 5 MHz for 1 V peak output, using two OEI 9300 opamps.—Applying the Model 9300 Monolithic Operational Amplifier, Optical Electronics, Tucson, Ariz., No. 10134.

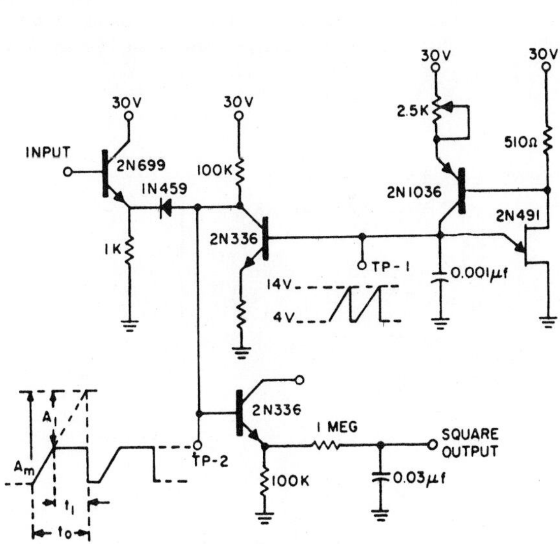

SQUARER—Output voltage of circuit is directly proportional to square of d-c input voltage.—R. L. Colcord, Circuit Squares DC Input Voltage, "400 Ideas for Design Selected from Electronic Design," Hayden Book Co., N.Y., 1964, p 83.

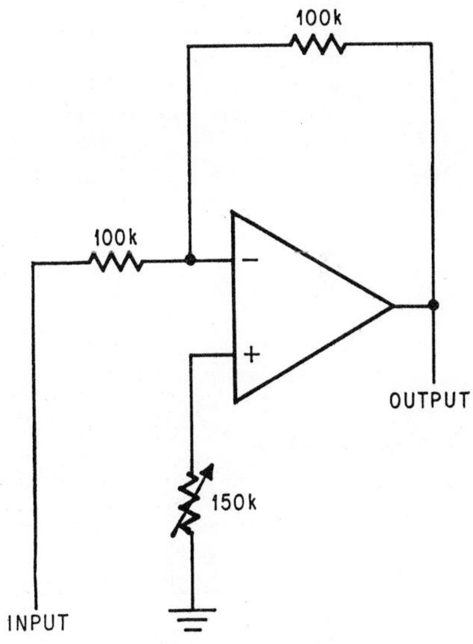

SUMMING AMPLIFIER—Variable resistor provides bias current compensation for linear IC used with fixed source impedance. Temperature characteristics are excellent, but arrangement works only for fixed values of feedback resistors.—R. J. Widlar, Linear IC's: Compensating For Drift, *Electronics*, Feb. 5, 1968, p 90–93.

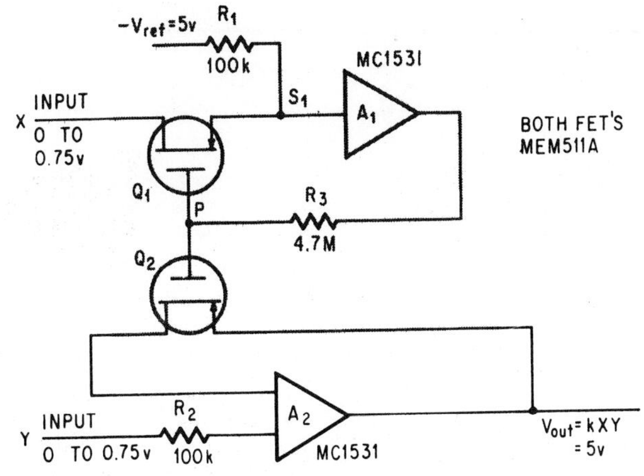

IC MULTIPLIER—Input signals X and Y are combined by fet's operated as voltage-variable resistors by keeping signal voltages below 0.75-V pinchoff of these fet's. Opamps A1 and A2 then make output proportional to product of X and Y. Useful in desktop computers.—B. Shore, Pocket-Size Analog Computer Divides and Multiplies, *Electronics*, Dec. 25, 1967, p 66–67.

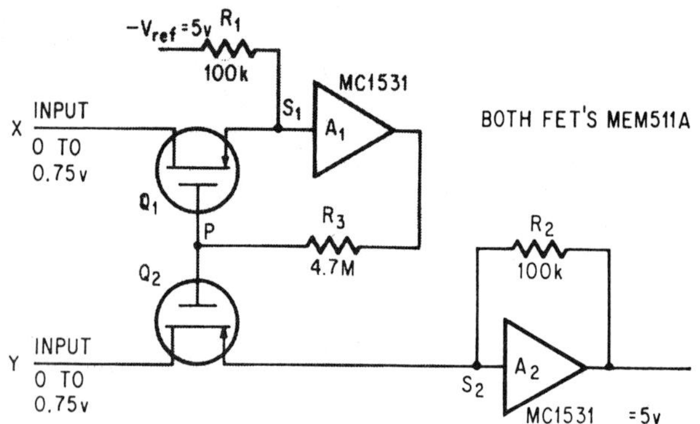

IC DIVIDER—Input signals X and Y are combined by fet's operated as voltage-variable resistors by keeping signal voltages below 0.75-V pinchoff. Opamps then make output proportional to quotient Y/X. Used in desktop analog computers.—B. Shore, Pocket-Size Analog Computer Divides and Multiplies, *Electronics*, Dec. 25, 1967, p 66–67.

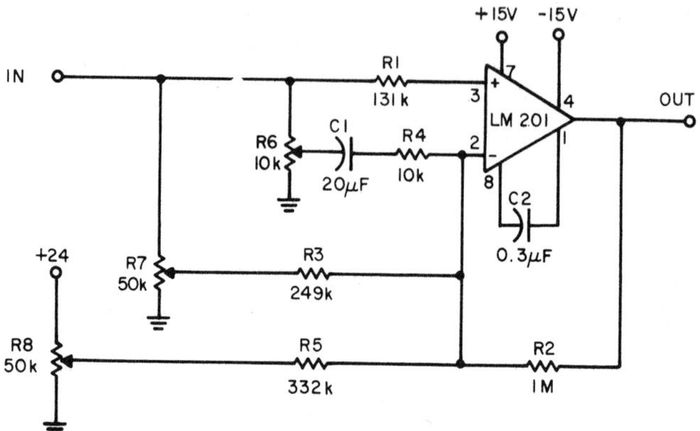

TRACKING WITHOUT CAPACITIVE INPUT—Has independent adjustments for gain, offset, and differentiating time constant. Output drifts only 10 mV per day and 0.25 mV per deg C.—J. Harris, A Tracking Differentiator Has Noncapacitive Input, *Electronic Design*, Aug. 15, 1968, p 238.

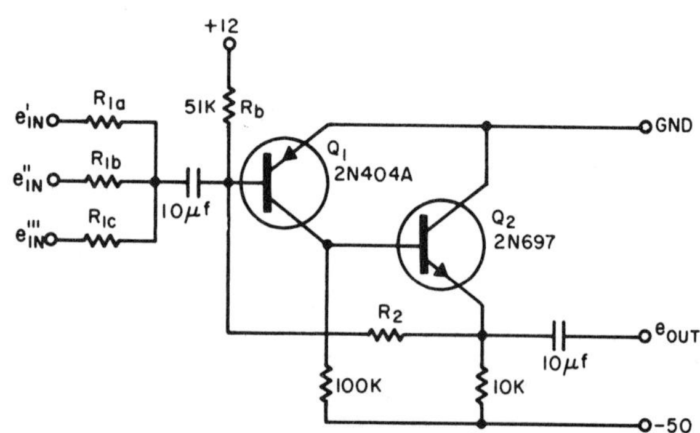

ALGEBRAIC SUMMING—Minor modifications in input of two-stage operational inverter convert it into excellent summing amplifier having gains up to 10, depending on values used for input resistors and R2.—W. Rosenbluth, Two-Stage Transistor Replaces Precision Operational Inverter, *Electronic Design*, April 12, 1965, p 54–56.

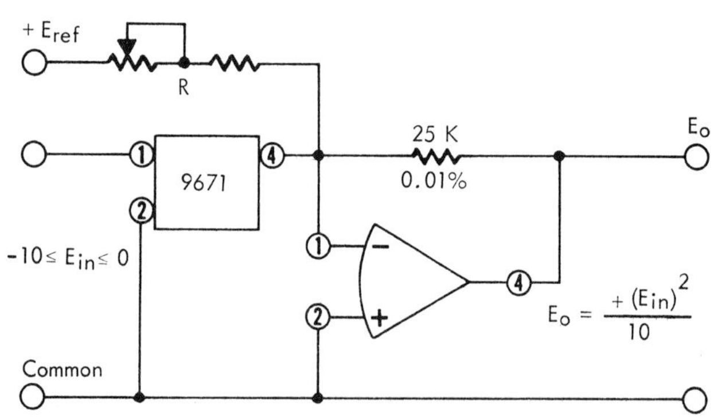

SQUARING CIRCUIT—Burr-Brown general-purpose negative-input 9671 squaring module may be used with variety of standard opamps to provide current into opamp summing junction that is proportional to square of applied negative input voltage. Module requires +15 V and −15 V from external regulated power supply.—Negative Input General Purpose Squaring Module, Burr-Brown Research, Tucson, Ariz., PDS-180A, 1968.

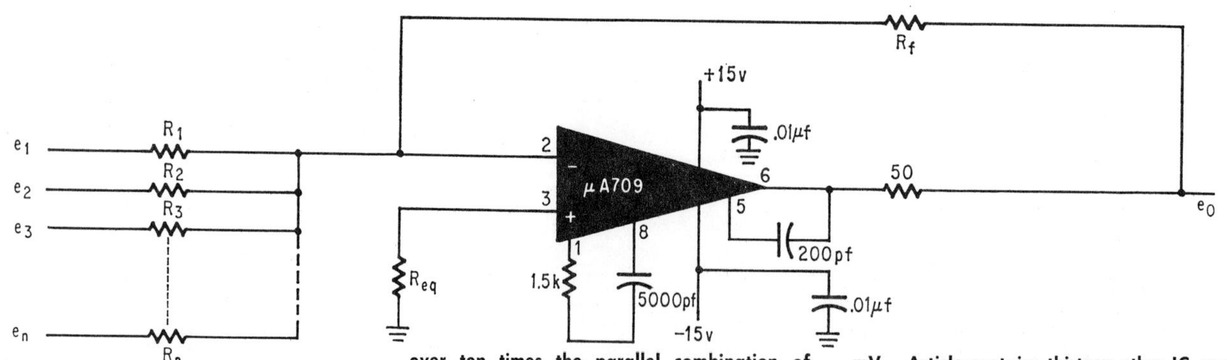

SUMMING—Circuit using Fairchild μA709 IC opamp can sum many input signals with high accuracy, provided input resistance of IC is over ten times the parallel combination of feedback resistor Rf and the source resistors. With three inputs and with input resistors and Rf all 20,000 ohms, maximum error is only 30 mV. Article contains thirteen other IC opamp application circuits.—J. F. Gifford and M. Markkula, Linear IC's: Part 5, Ins and Outs of Op Amps, *Electronics*, Nov. 27, 1967, p 84–93.

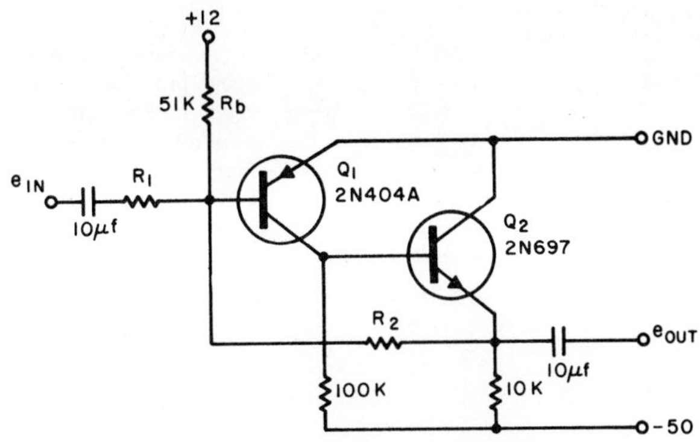

OPTIMUM TWO-STAGE INVERTER—Provides constant input impedance and unity gain of opamp, along with broadband 180-deg phase shift at much lower cost and less complexity. Output impedance is low, and gain is independent of transistor parameters. Can be used in analog computer to invert 400-Hz sine and square-wave signals. Gain depends on R2; if R1 is 50K, gain will be unity if R2 is 50.85K.—W. Rosenbluth, Two-Stage Transistor Replaces Precision Operational Inverter, *Electronic Design*, April 12, 1965, p 54–56.

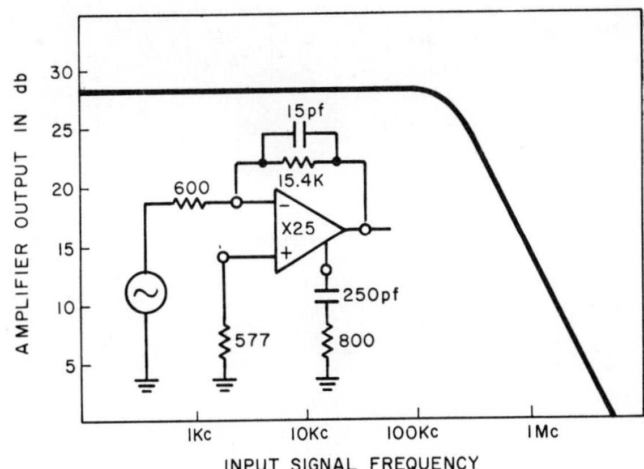

IC INVERTING OPAMP—Provides gain of 28 dB, bandwidth of 100 kHz, and choice of inverting or noninverting input. Frequency response is shown by curve. IC can be SN521, or SN522 having added emitter-follower for greater drive capability.—L. Housey and G. McFarland, Using Integrateds as Feedback Amplifiers, *Electronic Design*, March 2, 1964, p 49–52.

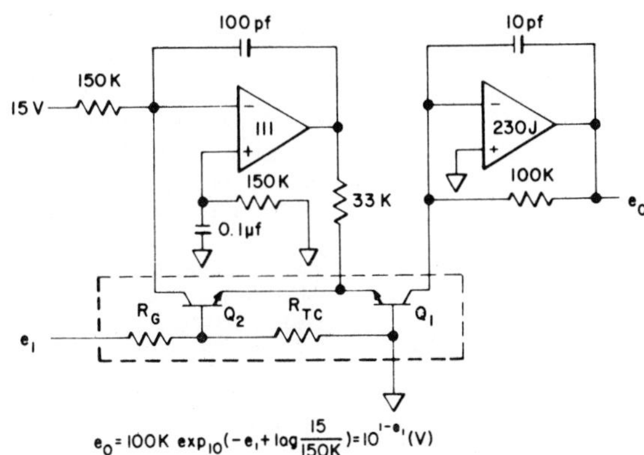

ANTILOG OF VOLTAGE—Uses Analog Devices 751N log module (dashed rectangle) for positive inputs or 751N for negative inputs, with model 111 reference opamp and 230J chopper-stabilized opamp. With input varying from 0 to 5 V, output will vary from 10 V to 100 μV, representing one decade of output voltage change per volt of input voltage change.—W. Borlase and E. David, Design of Temperature Compensated Log Circuits Employing Transistors and Operational Amplifiers, Analog Devices, Cambridge, Mass., E020-10-3/69, p 12.

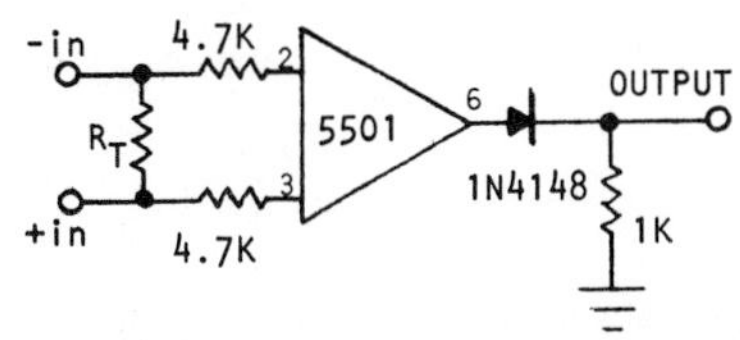

DIGITAL LINE RECEIVER—Uses analog comparator IC to detect differential digital signal that may be riding on some common-mode signal. Positive supply voltage is set for logic-compatible output voltage level. Line termination shown eliminates reflection problems of long line lengths, if RT is chosen for best match.—Applying the Model 5501 Monolithic Analog Comparator, Optical Electronics, Tucson, Ariz., No. 10147.

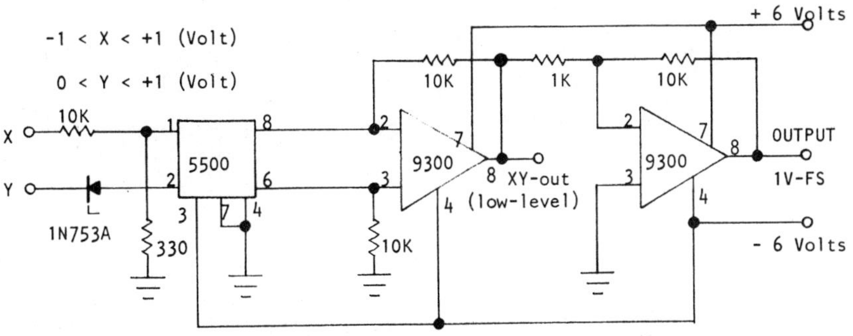

TWO-QUADRANT FOR D-C TO 10 MHZ—OEI Model 5500 analog multiplier and two opamps give wideband multiplier function at 1 V output.—Applying the Model 5500 Monolithic Analog Multiplier, Optical Electronics, Tucson, Ariz., No. 10138.

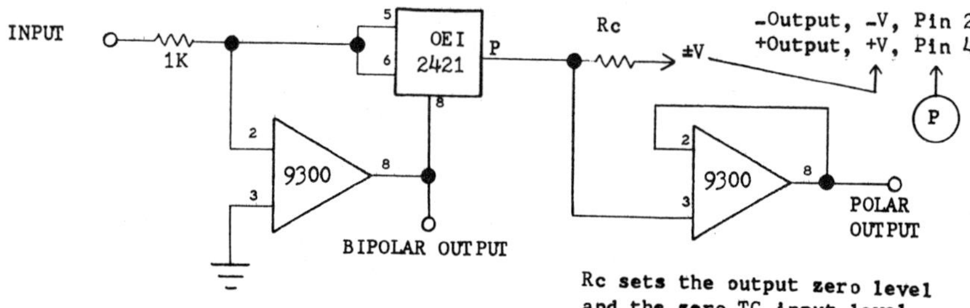

POLAR LOGAMP—Two opamps and Model 2421 diode cluster having log characteristics give 250-mV peak output, inverted in polarity from input, as temperature-compensated polar logamp or as wideband bipolar logamp.—Applying the Model 9300 Monolithic Operational Amplifier, Optical Electronics, Tucson, Ariz., No. 10134.

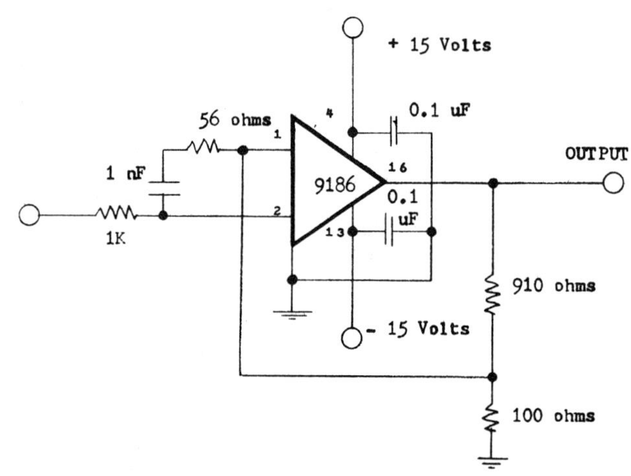

VOLTAGE FOLLOWER—Uses OEI Model 9186 uhf opamp with compensation for stabilizing as voltage follower with gain of 10, bandwidth of 30 MHz, and normal slewing rate of 600 V per μs.—A Wide Band Voltage Follower, Optical Electronics, Tucson, Ariz., No. 10108.

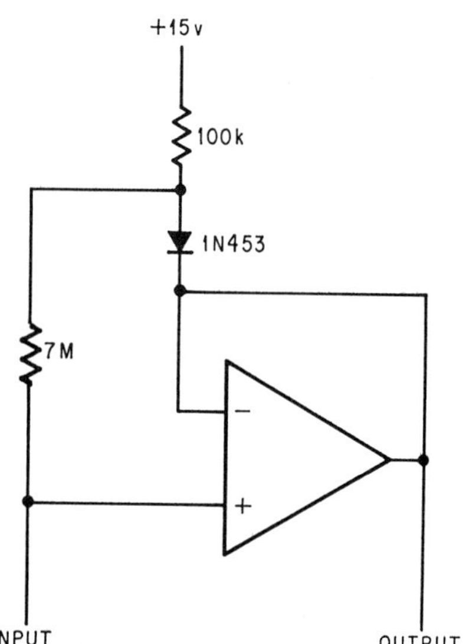

BOOTSTRAPPING STOPS DRIFTS—Germanium diode and selected 7-meg resistor provide bias current compensation for voltage-follower configuration of IC amplifier. Diode bootstrapping to amplifier output provides high input impedance.—R. J. Widlar, Linear IC's: Compensating For Drift, *Electronics*, Feb. 5, 1968, p 90–93.

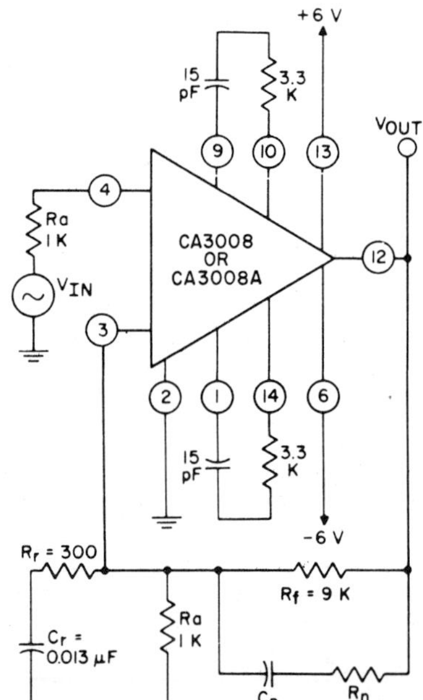

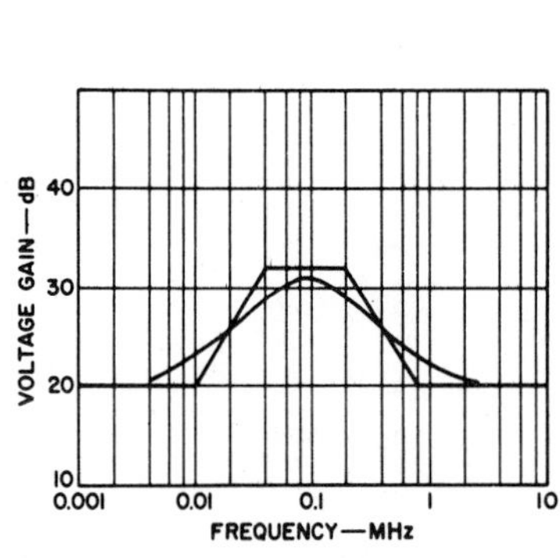

SYNTHESIZING PEAKED RESPONSE—Noninverting IC opamp duplicates transfer function expressed by equation given in book, to give peaked response shown.—"Linear Integrated Circuits," RCA, Harrison, N.J., IC-41, p 250.

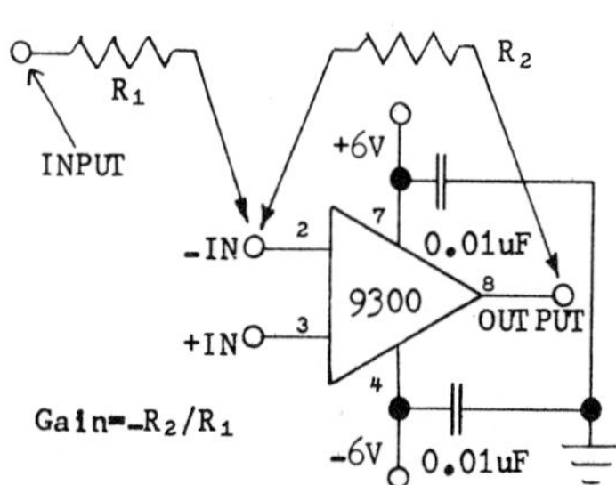

ADJUSTABLE-GAIN AMPLIFIER—Gain depends on ratio of values used for R2 and R1. Circuit requires common ground point. Power supply bypass capacitors should be disc ceramic or equivalent high-frequency types. Use metal-film resistors for maximum bandwidth. OEI 9300 opamp has 6 dB/octave rolloff over entire operating frequency range to 100 MHz.—Applying the Model 9300 Monolithic Operational Amplifier, Optical Electronics, Tucson, Ariz., No. 10134.

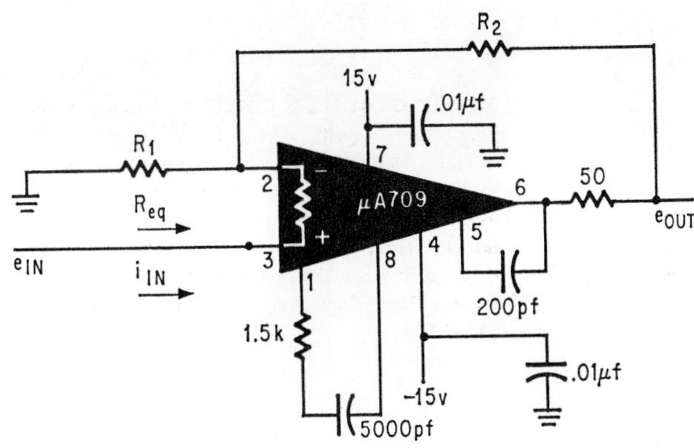

IC BUFFER—Uses Fairchild μA709 opamp to provide any gain from unity to 25,000 without loading source. Closed-loop gain is determined by values used for R1 and R2. Equivalent input resistance can easily be made greater than 10 meg. Article contains 13 other IC opamp application circuits.—J. F. Gifford and M. Markkula, Linear IC's: Part 5, Ins and Outs of Op Amps, *Electronics*, Nov. 27, 1967, p 84–93.

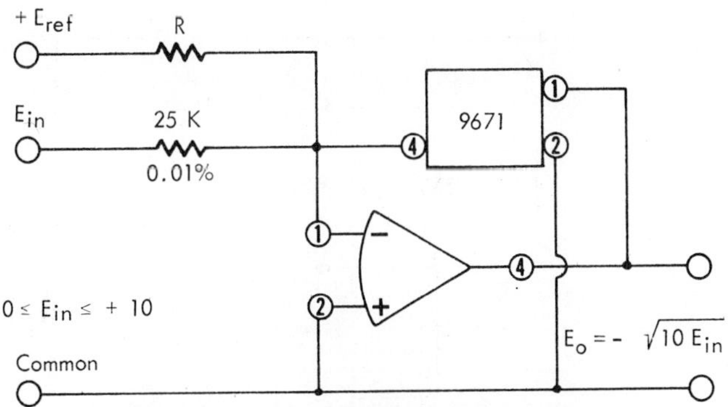

SQUARE-ROOT CIRCUIT—Burr-Brown 9671 squaring module is placed in feedback path of standard opamp, to produce at output the square root of an input signal between zero and 10 V. Accuracy is poor for small input amplitudes.—Negative Input General Purpose Squaring Module, Burr-Brown Research, Tucson, Ariz., PDS-180A, 1968.

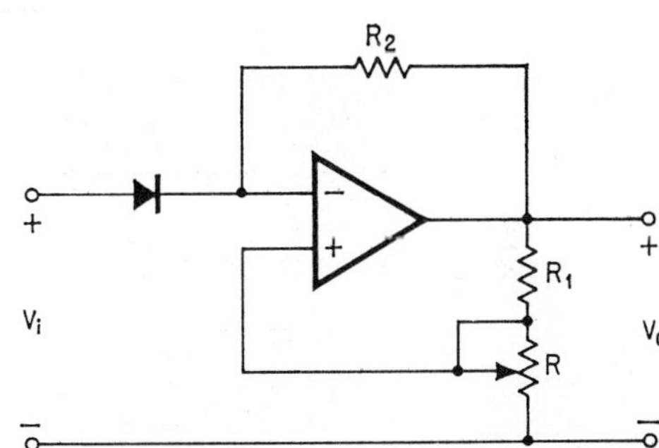

ANTILOG OPAMP—Extends logarithmic relation between forward current and voltage of silicon diode by canceling bulk resistance effect of diode at higher currents. Opamp is Fairchild μA702; R is 20, R1 is 500, and R2 is 1K. Common mode rejection of opamp makes grounding of reference terminals unnecessary.—S. Franco, Op Amp Log Circuit Eliminates Diode Bulk-Resistance Effects, *Electronics*, June 9, 1969, p 101.

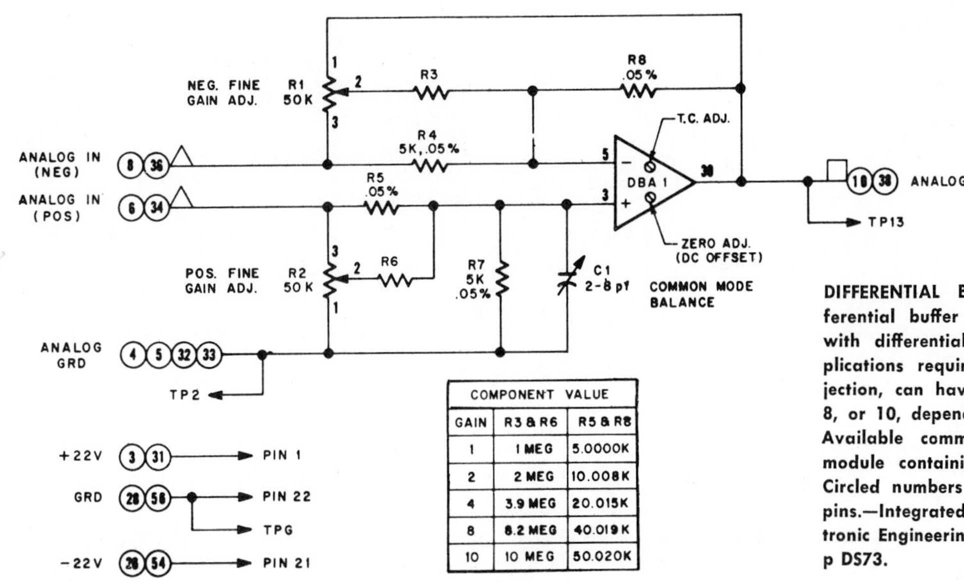

COMPONENT VALUE		
GAIN	R3 & R6	R5 & R8
1	1 MEG	5.0000K
2	2 MEG	10.008K
4	3.9 MEG	20.015K
8	8.2 MEG	40.019K
10	10 MEG	50.020K

DIFFERENTIAL BUFFER—General-purpose differential buffer amplifier, designed for use with differential multiplexer and other applications requiring high common-mode rejection, can have differential gains of 1, 4, 8, or 10, depending on resistor values used. Available commercially as D-4083 plug-in module containing IC and all components. Circled numbers are etched board connector pins.—Integrated Circuit Logic Cards, Electronic Engineering Co., Santa Ana, Cal., 1969, p DS73.

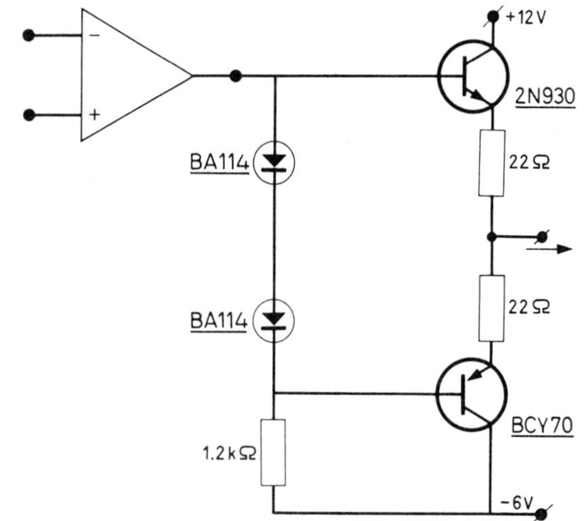

BOOSTING OUTPUT CURRENT—Adding complementary pair of emitter-followers to Philips TAA241 difference amplifier gives higher output current. Emitter resistors are used to prevent thermal runaway.—J. Cohen and J. Oosterling, Applications of a Practical D. C. Difference Amplifier, Philips, Pub. Dept., Elcoma Div., Eindhoven, The Netherlands, No. 321, 1968.

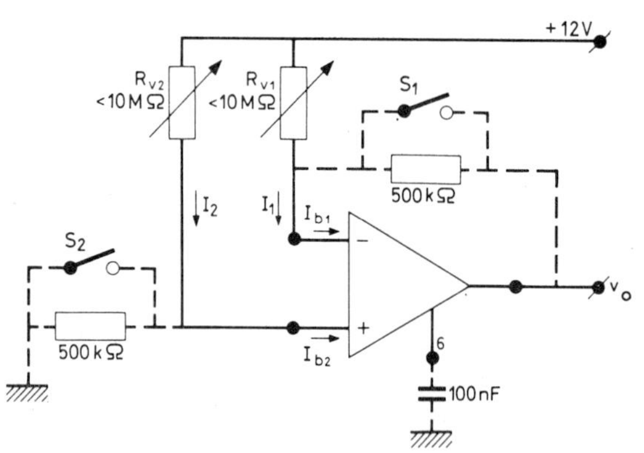

ERROR COMPENSATION—Uses Philips TAA241 difference amplifier with provision for compensating errors introduced by bias or offset current. Potentiometer adjustment procedure is given in report.—J. Cohen and J. Oosterling, Applications of a Practical D. C. Difference Amplifier, Philips, Pub. Dept., Elcoma Div., Eindhoven, The Netherlands, No. 321, 1968.

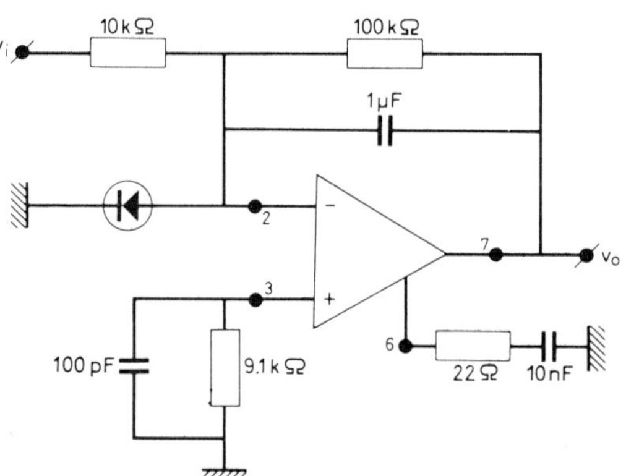

DIFFERENCE AMPLIFIER AS INTEGRATOR—Uses Philips TAA241 difference amplifier in connection that prevents feedback capacitor from being continuously charged by offset voltage. Circuit will operate satisfactorily only above its break frequency, which for values shown is 1.6 Hz.—J. Cohen and J. Oosterling, Applications of a Practical D. C. Difference Amplifier, Philips, Pub. Dept., Elcoma Div., Eindhoven, The Netherlands, No. 321, 1968.

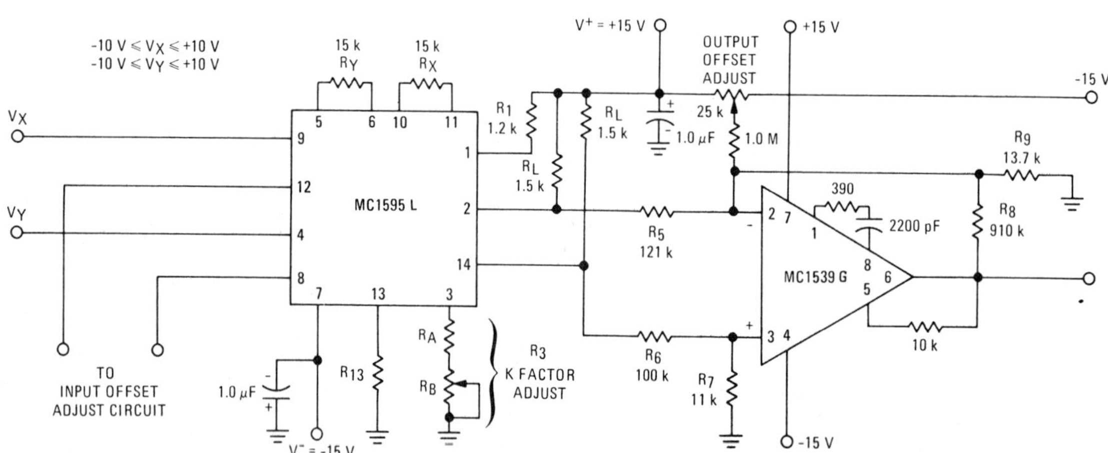

MULTIPLY WITH OPAMP LEVEL SHIFT—Accommodates input voltages from −10 V to +10 V without using 32-V supply. IC multiplier is set up to provide product of input voltages divided by 75, and opamp supplies fixed closed-loop gain of 7.5.—E. Renschler, The Monolithic Multiplier Breakthrough, "State-of-the-Art—Linears in Action," Motorola, Phoenix, Ariz., 1969, p 27–36.

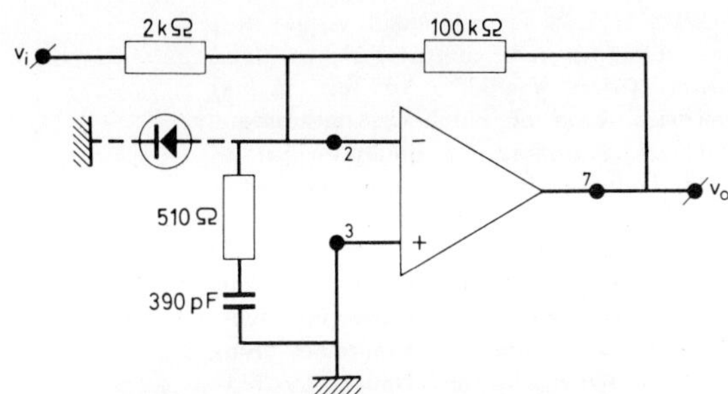

INVERTING AMPLIFIER WITH GAIN OF 50—Full-power frequency is 500 kHz and wideband noise voltage 2 mV rms. Uses Philips TAA241 difference amplifier.—J. Cohen and J. Oosterling, Applications of a Practical D. C. Difference Amplifier, Philips, Pub. Dept., Elcoma Div., Eindhoven, The Netherlands, No. 321, 1968.

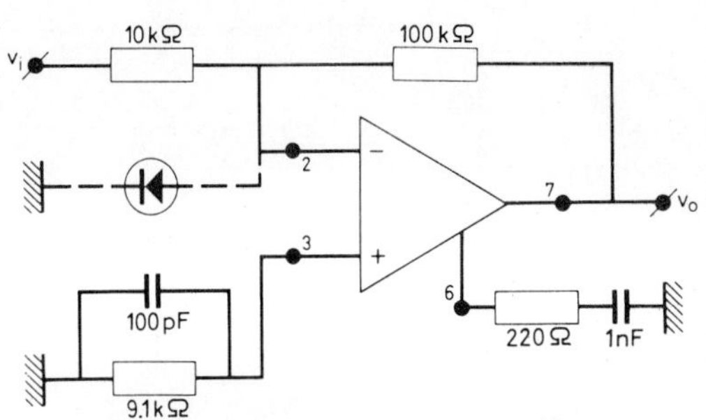

INVERTING AMPLIFIER WITH GAIN OF 10—Full-power frequency is 30 kHz and wideband noise voltage is only 0.5 mV rms. Uses Philips TAA241 difference amplifier.—J. Cohen and J. Oosterling, Applications of a Practical D. C. Difference Amplifier, Philips, Pub. Dept., Elcoma Div., Eindhoven, The Netherlands, No. 321, 1968.

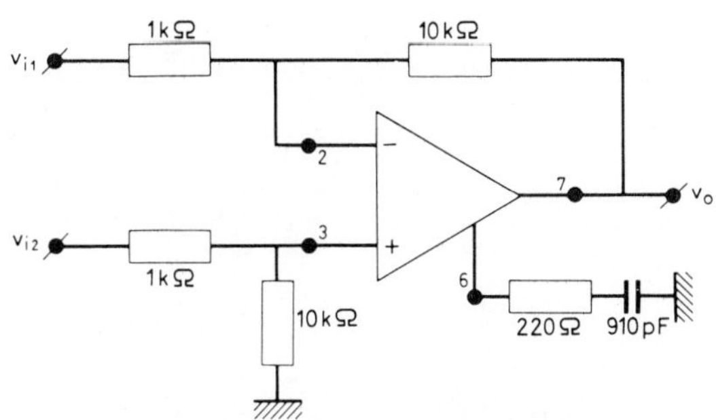

SUBTRACTING AMPLIFIER—Uses Philips TAA-241 difference amplifier in circuit giving gain of 10 that is flat within 1 dB up to 8 MHz.—J. Cohen and J. Oosterling, Applications of a Practical D. C. Difference Amplifier, Philips, Pub. Dept., Elcoma Div., Eindhoven, The Netherlands, No. 321, 1968.

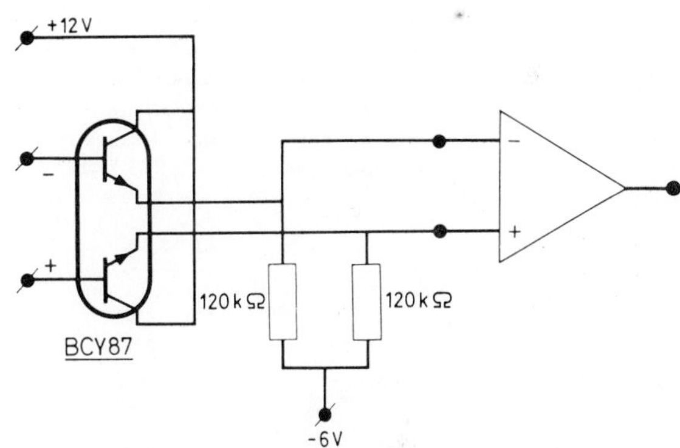

BOOSTING INPUT IMPEDANCE—Pair of emitter-followers ahead of Philips TAA241 difference amplifier increases input impedance and/or permits operation with smaller input current.—J. Cohen and J. Oosterling, Applications of a Practical D. C. Difference Amplifier, Philips, Pub. Dept., Elcoma Div., Eindhoven, The Netherlands, No. 321, 1968.

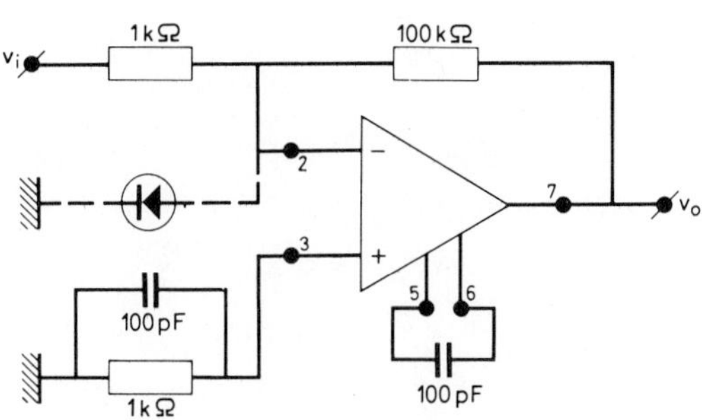

INVERTING AMPLIFIER WITH GAIN OF 100—Will supply 10 V output at full-power frequency limit of 350 kHz. Wideband noise voltage at output is 1.2 mV rms from 2 Hz to 1 MHz. Uses Philips TAA241 difference amplifier.—J. Cohen and J. Oosterling, Applications of a Practical D. C. Difference Amplifier, Philips, Pub. Dept., Elcoma Div., Eindhoven, The Netherlands, No. 321, 1968.

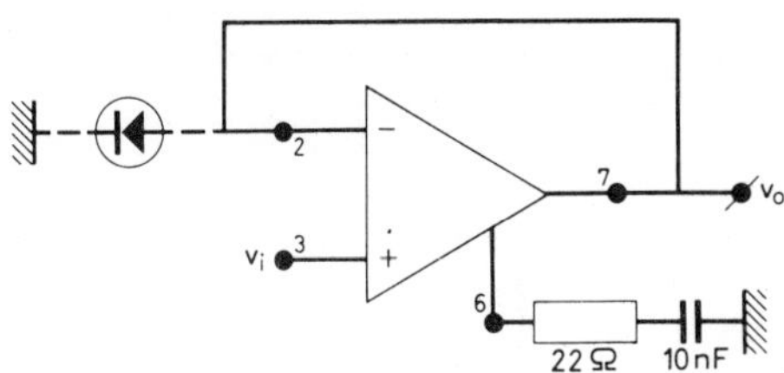

FOLLOWER—Connection shown, for use with Philips TAA241 difference amplifier, gives unity gain. Input impedance is 7 meg and output impedance very low. Can handle signals from +0.5 V to −0.4 V. Response is flat to 2 MHz.—J. Cohen and J. Oosterling, Applications of a Practical D. C. Difference Amplifier, Philips, Pub. Dept., Elcoma Div., Eindhoven, The Netherlands, No. 321, 1968.

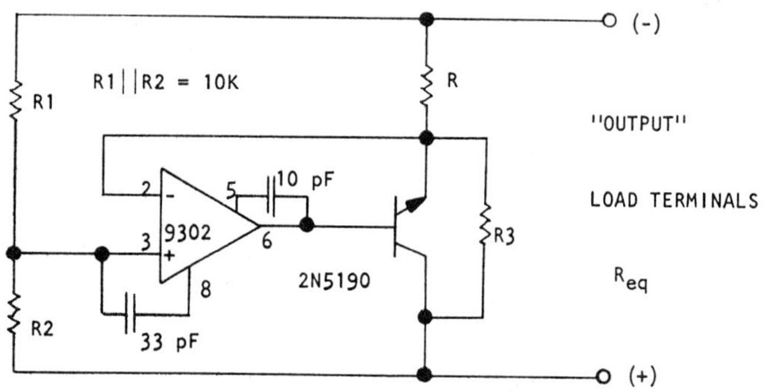

ACTIVE RESISTOR—Two-terminal output has same voltage-current characteristic as fixed resistor. Offers possibility of cost saving, small size, ease of obtaining nonstandard values of resistance, and ability to act as load or ballast at low resistance values. Behaves like shunt regulator. Noninverting input of opamp senses fraction of load voltage and attempts to maintain this voltage (across R) the same as at noninverting input. Bandwidth is 1 MHz. R3 suppresses transients.—An Active Resistor, Optical Electronics, Tucson, Ariz., No. 10148.

ROOT-MEAN-SQUARE CIRCUIT—Operations of square and square-rooting are combined to give rms averaging circuit accepting bipolar inputs. Uses two Burr-Brown 9671 squaring modules combined with four standard opamps. Averaging time of circuit is determined by choice of values for low-pass filter elements R2-C1. Filter bandwidth should be small compared to bandwidth of signal being measured.—Negative Input General Purpose Squaring Module, Burr-Brown Research, Tucson, Ariz., PDS-180A, 1968.

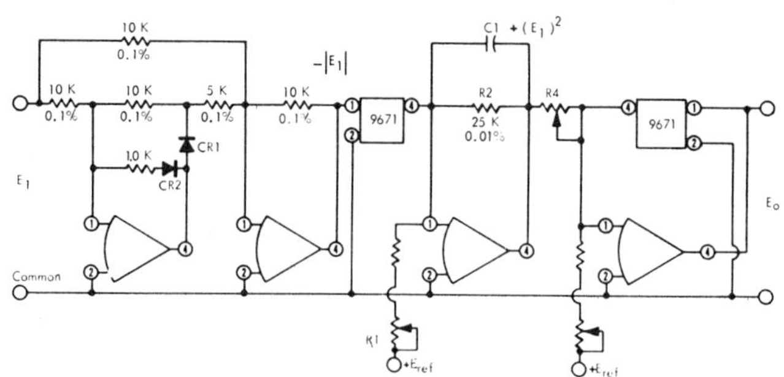

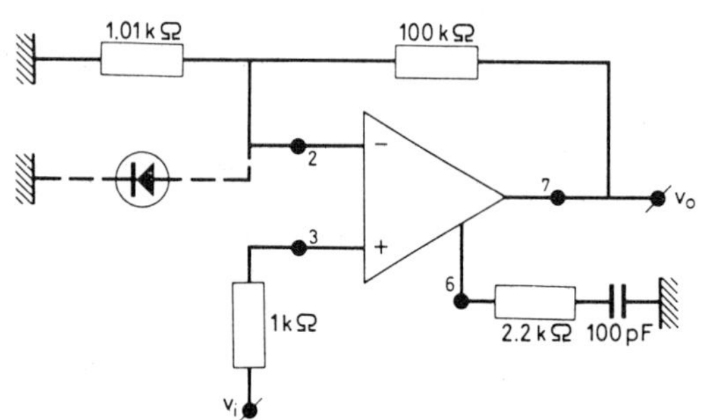

NONINVERTING WITH 100 GAIN—Uses Philips TAA241 difference amplifier. Wideband noise voltage is 1.1 mV rms. Frequency response is flat to 1 MHz.—J. Cohen and J. Oosterling, Applications of a Practical D. C. Difference Amplifier, Philips, Pub. Dept., Elcoma Div., Eindhoven, The Netherlands, No. 321, 1968.

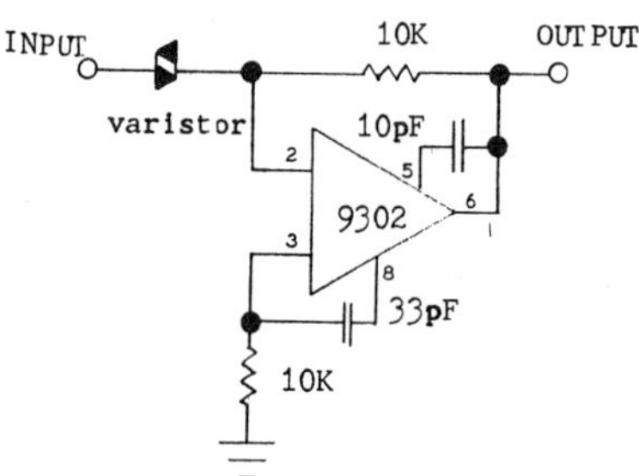

EXPANSION FUNCTION—Thyrite varistor and OEI opamp together give expansion function having exponent greater than unity. By selecting varistor, squaring, cubic, and quadratic functions may be created.—Applying the Model 9302 Monolithic Operational Amplifier, Optical Electronics, Tucson, Ariz., No. 10135.

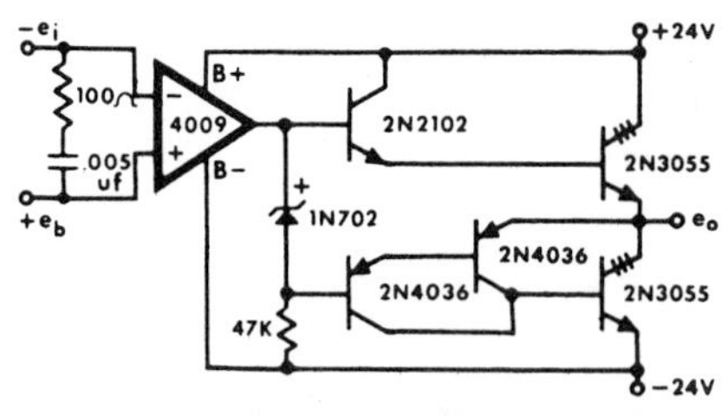

50-W OPERATIONAL POWER AMPLIFIER—Uses pair of silicon transistors in output stage, upper of which is driven by emitter-follower fed by opamp, in Darlington configuration. 320-kHz rolloff network between inputs of opamp ensures stability down to unity gain. Circuit provides closed-loop gain from 2 to about 20.—B. J. Losmandy, Operational Amplifier Application for Audio Systems, Opamp Labs, Los Angeles, Cal., 1968.

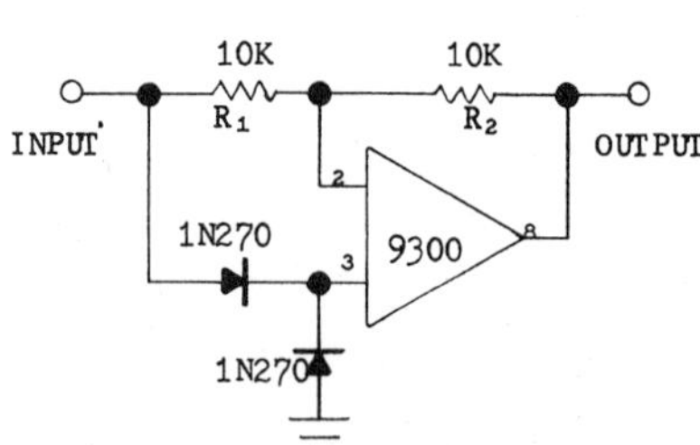

ABSOLUTE-VALUE CIRCUIT—Use of germanium gold-bonded diodes with OEI opamp improves high-frequency operation and low-level signal operation beyond that obtained with silicon diodes. Circuit has positive output, made negative by reversing both diodes. Useful bandwidth is d-c to 100 kHz.—Applying the Model 9300 Monolithic Operational Amplifier, Optical Electronics, Tucson, Ariz., No. 10134.

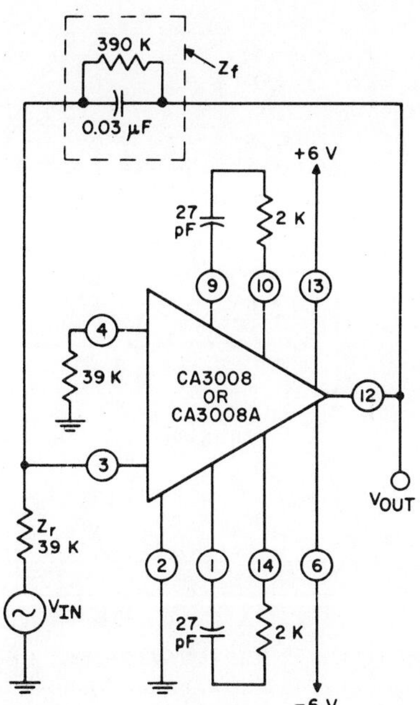

IC OPAMP AS INTEGRATOR—External circuit provides d-c feedback, so offset voltage cannot continuously charge feedback capacitor until amplifier limits. D-c gain is 20 dB. Weighting factor of integration is about 1 ms. —"Linear Integrated Circuits," RCA, Harrison, N.J., IC-41, p 252.

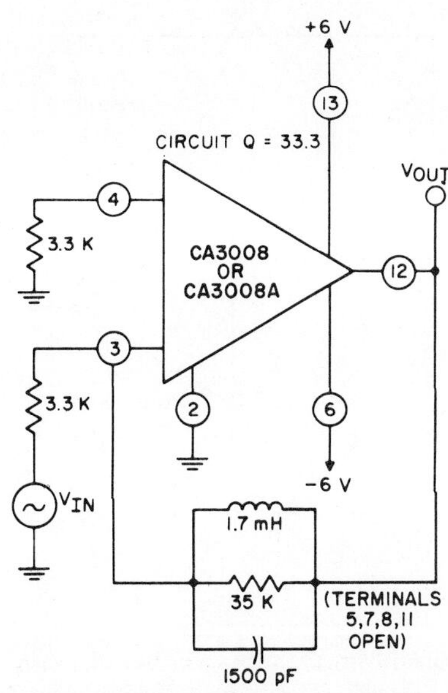

100-KHZ NARROW-BAND—Inverting-type IC opamp is connected as tuned amplifier having peak response shown.—"Linear Integrated Circuits," RCA, Harrison, N.J., IC-41, p 251.

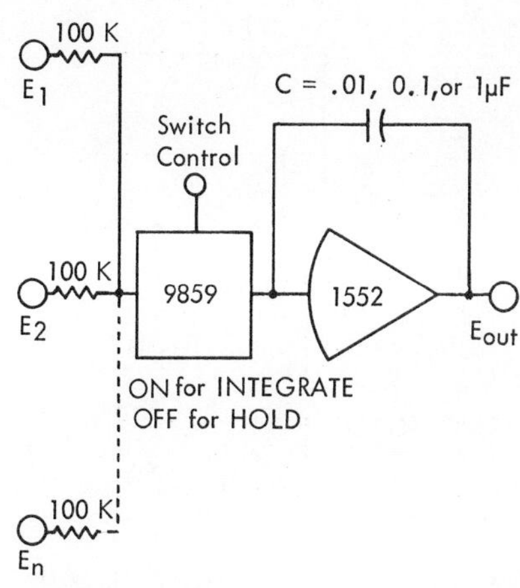

ANALOG INTEGRATOR—Burr-Brown 9859/15 electronic switch feeds opamp to give choice of either integrate or hold modes of operation. With integrate mode (produced by +5 V at switch control), circuit behaves like low fixed resistance and can accommodate input currents up to 1 mA. In hold mode, switch resistance is almost infinite, isolating summing inputs from amplifier. Chief error is due to switching time, which is under 10 μs.—Integrate/Hold Electronic Switch, Burr-Brown Research, Tucson, Ariz., PDS 189, 1967.

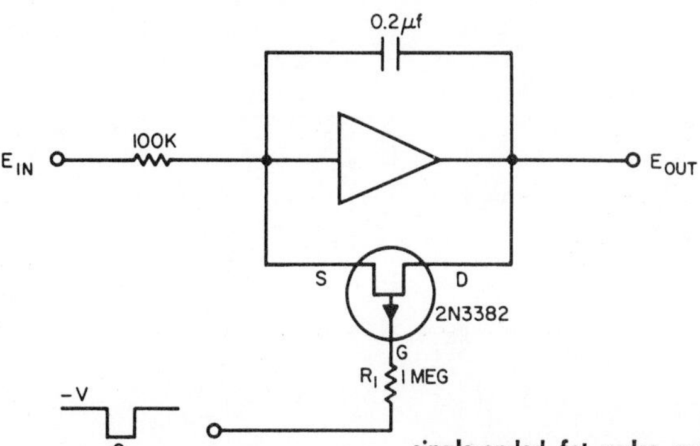

LIMITER AND RESETTER—Electronically variable limiter for opamp has very high input impedance for controlling pulse, while acting as single-ended fet pulse gate for resetting of opamp integrator.—P. A. Ralatos, FET Limits and Resets Operational Amplifiers, *Electronic Design*, Nov. 8, 1965, p 54–56.

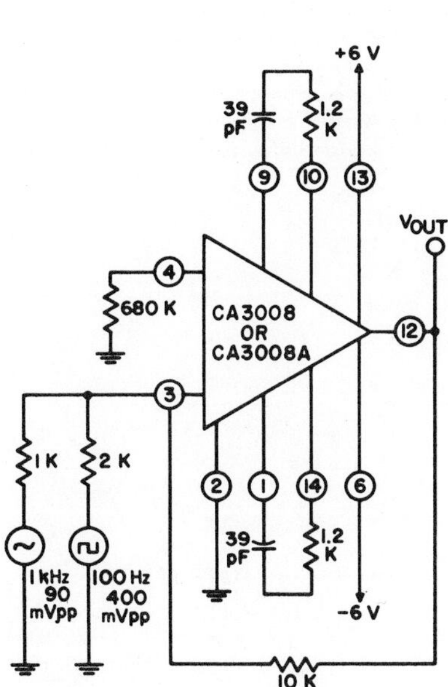

SCALING ADDER—Uses IC opamp with inverting feedback for summing and weighting two different input signals. Weighting is possible because virtual ground existing at junction of feedback resistor and inverting input terminal 3 isolates each signal channel from others.—"Linear Integrated Circuits," RCA, Harrison, N.J., IC-41, p 254.

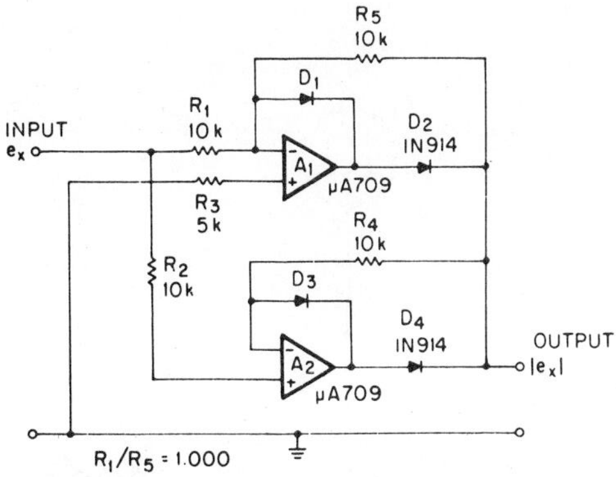

ABSOLUTE VALUE—Provides high accuracy yet requires only one pair of accurately matched resistors (R1 and R5). Opamp A1 serves as inverter and A2 as voltage follower. Input can be up to 1 kHz, which is adequate for analog-digital converter system.—M. A. Smither, Improved Absolute-Value Circuit, *EEE*, March 1969, p 124.

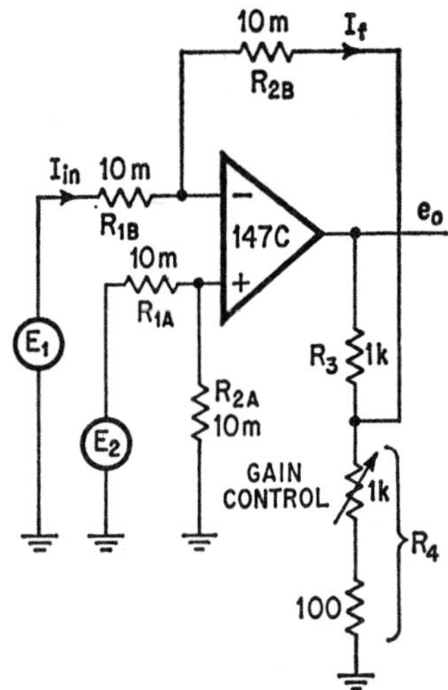

VARIABLE-GAIN IC—Provides continuously adjustable gain with single pot, for matching circuit sensitivity to input signal levels. Input attenuation network R3-R4 minimizes common-mode errors. Circuit gain can be varied from less than unity to very high upper limit. —W. D. Miller, Minimizing Common-Mode Errors in a Variable-Gain Amplifier, *Electronics*, June 23, 1969, p 104.

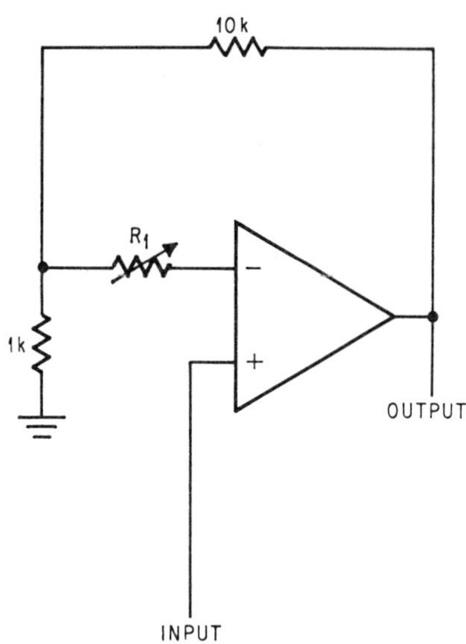

NONINVERTING AMPLIFIER—Variable resistor R1 provides bias current compensation for linear IC that has fixed source impedance. R1 should be three times source impedance. Will handle wide temperature range, and is unaffected by power supply or common mode variations.—R J. Widlar, Linear IC's: Compensating For Drift, *Electronics*, Feb. 5, 1968, p 90–93.

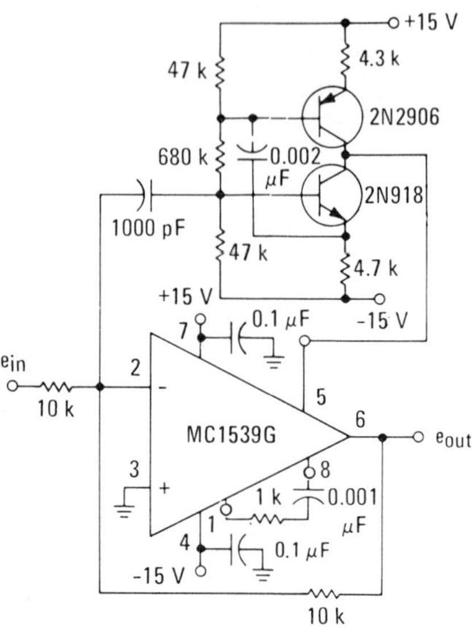

UNITY-GAIN FEED-FORWARD—First two stages of Motorola opamp are bypassed for high frequency and signal is inserted at input to third stage. Gives output of 10 V p-p at 1 MHz. Operating information is given in Motorola Application Note AN-439. —K. Huehne, The Continuing Dominance of the Operational Amplifier, "State-of-the-Art—Linears in Action," Motorola, Phoenix, Ariz., 1969, p 5–13.

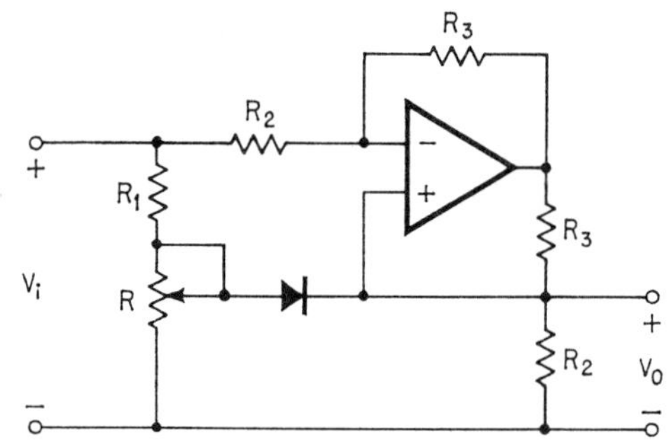

LOG OPAMP—Opamp cancels bulk resistance effect of silicon diode, to permit working with larger forward currents in logarithmic amplifier. Opamp is Fairchild µA702; R1 is 500, R2 and R3 are 1K, and R is 20.. Common mode rejection of opamp makes grounding of reference terminals unnecessary. —S. Franco, Op Amp Log Circuit Eliminates Diode Bulk-Resistance Effects, *Electronics*, June 9, 1969, p 101.

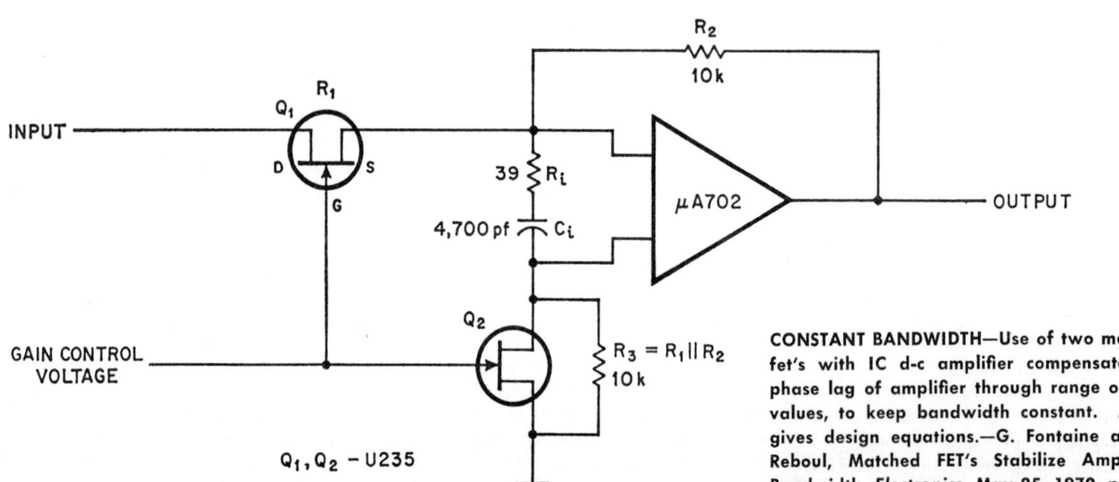

CONSTANT BANDWIDTH—Use of two matched fet's with IC d-c amplifier compensates for phase lag of amplifier through range of gain values, to keep bandwidth constant. Article gives design equations.—G. Fontaine and G. Reboul, Matched FET's Stabilize Amplifier's Bandwidth, *Electronics*, May 25, 1970, p 93.

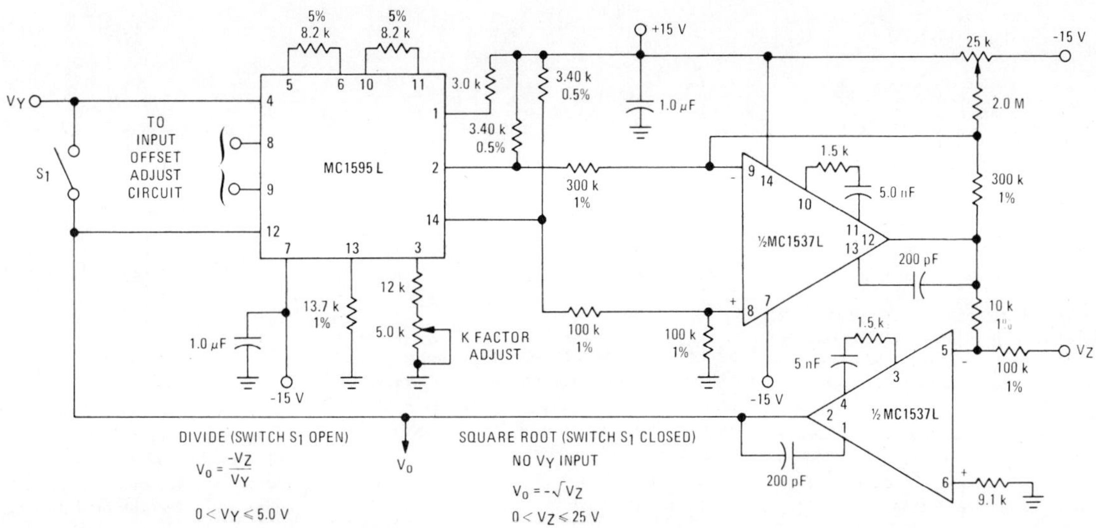

SQUARE ROOT WITH MULTIPLIER AND DUAL OPAMP—Also performs division of two input voltages, when multiplier is used in opamp feedback loop.—E. Renschler, The Monolithic Multiplier Breakthrough, "State-of-the-Art—Linears in Action," Motorola, Phoenix, Ariz., 1969, p 27–36.

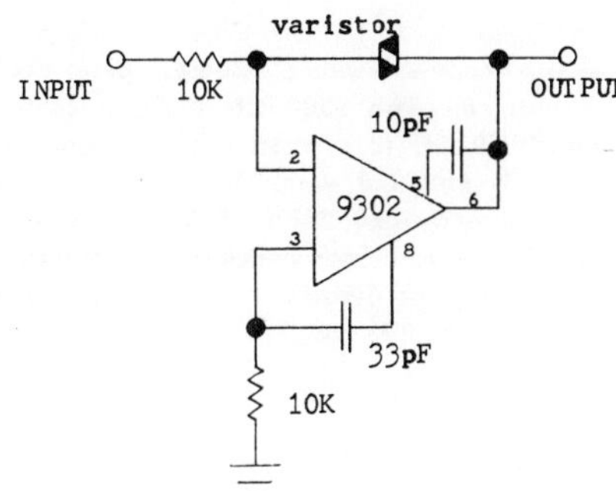

ROOTING FUNCTION—OEI opamp circuit combined with thyrite varistor gives function having exponent less than unity. Opamp permits full 10-V swing with either polarity to 100 kHz but varistor may reduce this bandwidth. Single varistors provide exponents of 0.25 to 0.5, and combination of varistors with or without resistors and diodes gives wide variety of other nonlinear functions.—Applying the Model 9302 Monolithic Operational Amplifier, Optical Electronics, Tucson, Ariz., No. 10135.

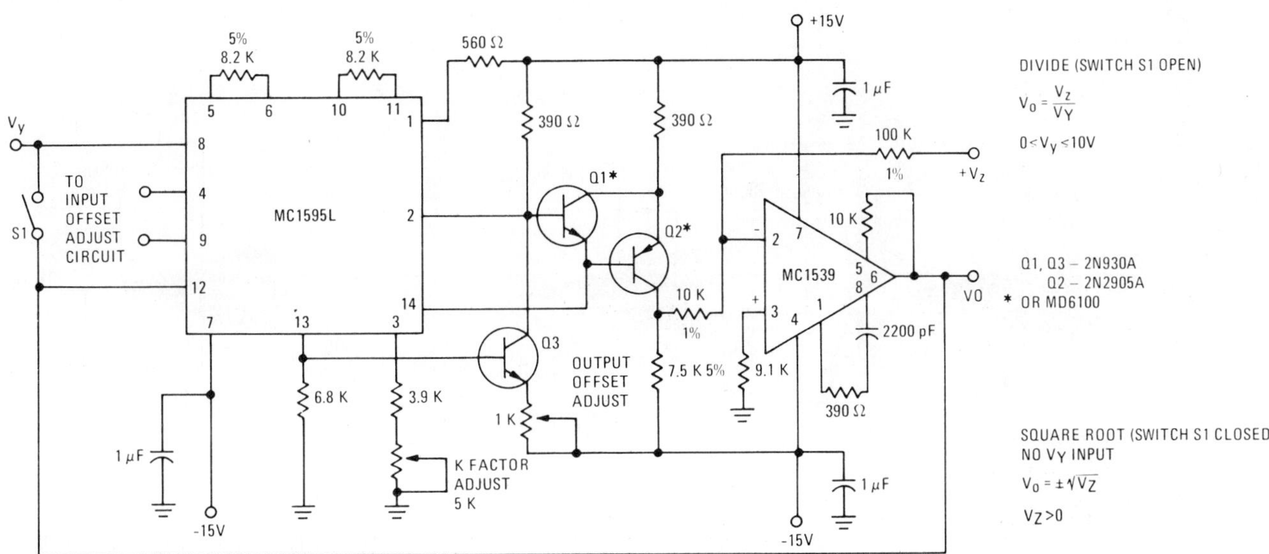

DIVIDE AND SQUARE ROOT—Combination of Motorola opamp and linear four-quadrant multiplier used as feedback element provides functions of division or square root, along with discrete level shift. Operating information is given in Motorola Application Note AN-490.—K. Huehne, The Continuing Dominance of the Operational Amplifier, "State-of-the-Art—Linears in Action," Motorola, Phoenix, Ariz., 1969, p 5–13.

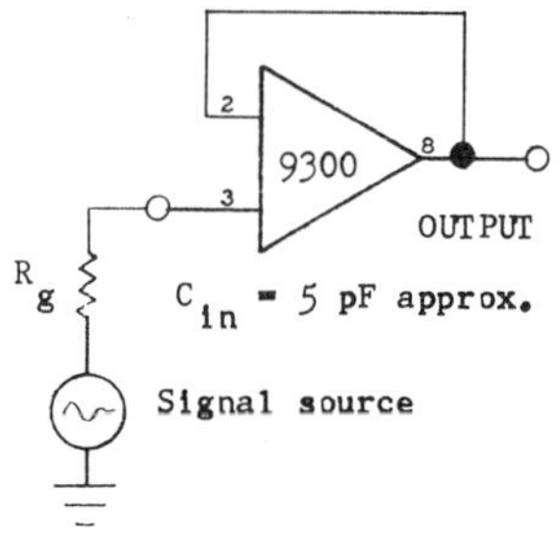

POSITIVE VOLTAGE FOLLOWER—Uses OEI 9300 opamp as unity-gain amplifier serving as buffer for signal source when driving lower-impedance circuit or transmission line. Requires 6-V bipolar supply. With 1,000-ohm generator impedance, bandwidth is above 10 MHz.—Applying the Model 9300 Monolithic Operational Amplifier, Optical Electronics, Tucson, Ariz., No. 10134.

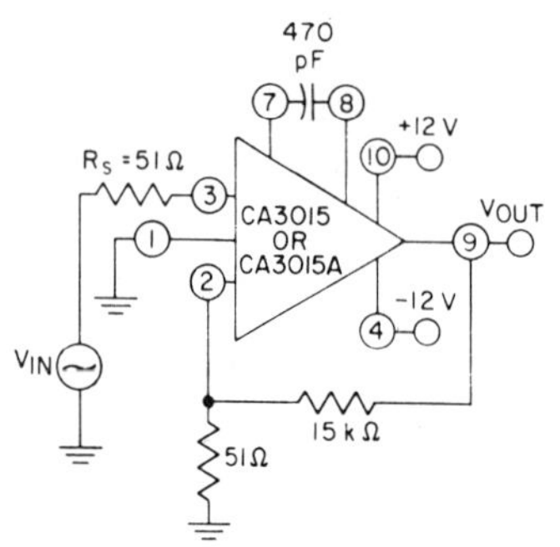

50-DB NONINVERTING—IC opamp with phase-lead compensation has 3-dB bandwidth of 3.5 MHz and unity-gain crossover at 150 MHz.—"Linear Integrated Circuits," RCA, Harrison, N.J., IC-41, p 260.

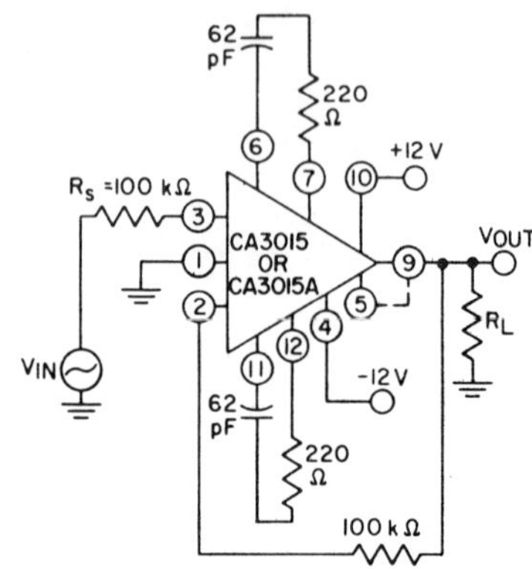

VOLTAGE FOLLOWER—Connection shown for IC opamp, with terminals 5 and 9 shorted, will transform 3.4 V p-p from 100,000-ohm source to 470-ohm load. Higher voltage swing may be obtained by increasing positive supply voltage.—"Linear Integrated Circuits," RCA, Harrison, N.J., IC-41, p 263.

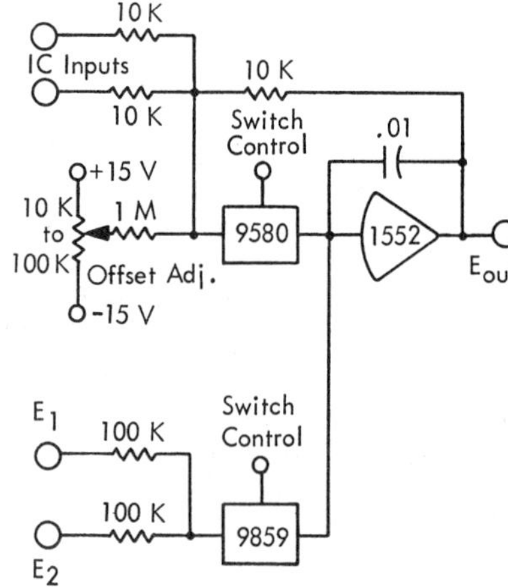

THREE-MODE CONTROL—Uses two electronic switch modules feeding opamp. Reset mode is obtained with 9580 ON (0 V at control) and 9859 OFF (0 V at its control). Compute mode is obtained with 9580 OFF (+5 V at control) and 9859 ON (+5 V). Hold mode is obtained with both switches off.—Integrate/Hold Electronic Switch, Burr-Brown Research, Tucson, Ariz., PDS 189, 1967.

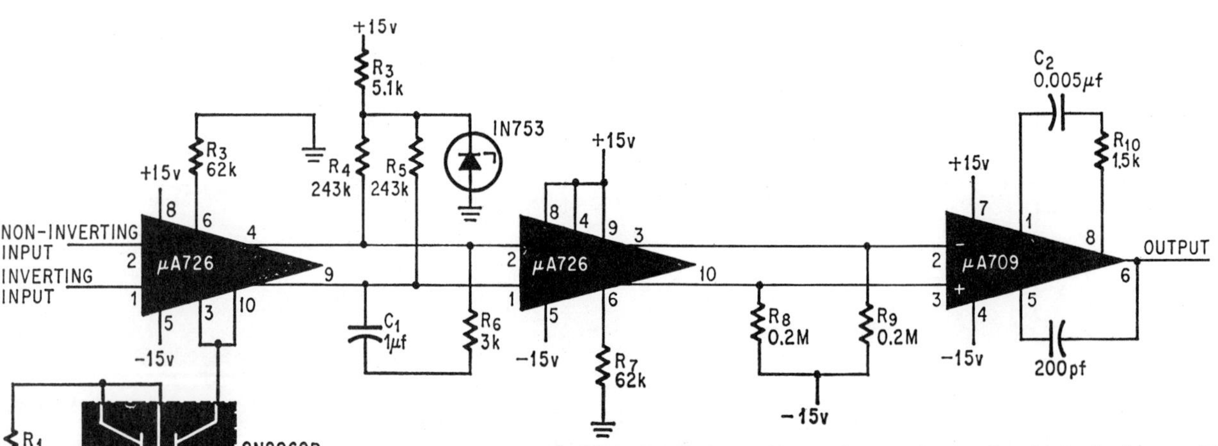

LOW-LEVEL TRANSDUCER SIGNALS—Provides gain of 3,000,000 for transducer signals as low as a few millivolts, with high input impedance and high stability. First two IC opamps are Fairchild μA726, used for temperature stabilization and to prevent loading of high-impedance transducers. Fairchild μA709 opamp at right provides most of gain. Same gain can be obtained without middle IC if stability requirement is less stringent, by changing values of some components to those given in article. 2N2060B is transistor-pair IC.—J. F. Gifford and M. Markkula, Linear IC's: Part 5, Ins and Outs of Op Amps, *Electronics*, Nov. 27, 1967, p 84–93.

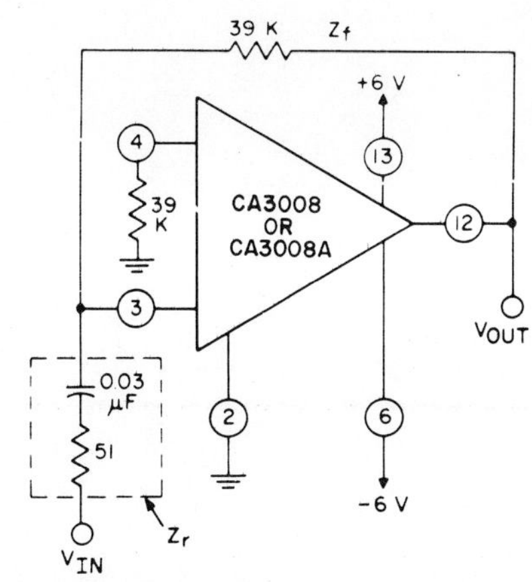

DIFFERENTIATOR—IC opamp with connections shown will serve as differentiating circuit, giving output peak for each side of square-wave input.—"Linear Integrated Circuits," RCA, Harrison, N.J., IC-41, p 253.

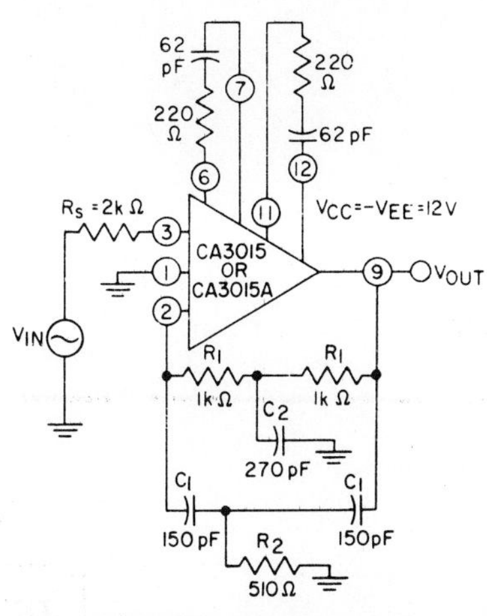

TWIN-T BANDPASS—With values shown, gain is peak of 33 dB at 1 MHz and 3-dB bandwidth is about 0.1 MHz with twin-T network in feedback loop.—"Linear Integrated Circuits," RCA, Harrison, N.J., IC-41, p 261.

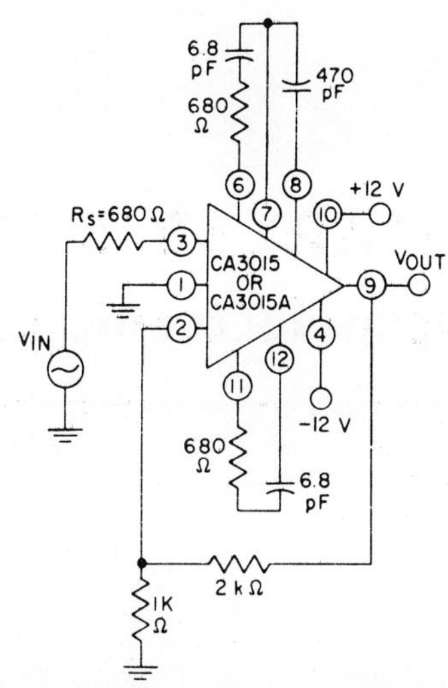

10-DB GAIN AT 42 MHZ—Uses noninverting IC opamp with phase-lead and phase-lag compensation. Response peaks about 2 dB at 20 MHz.—"Linear Integrated Circuits," RCA, Harrison, N.J., IC-41, p 261.

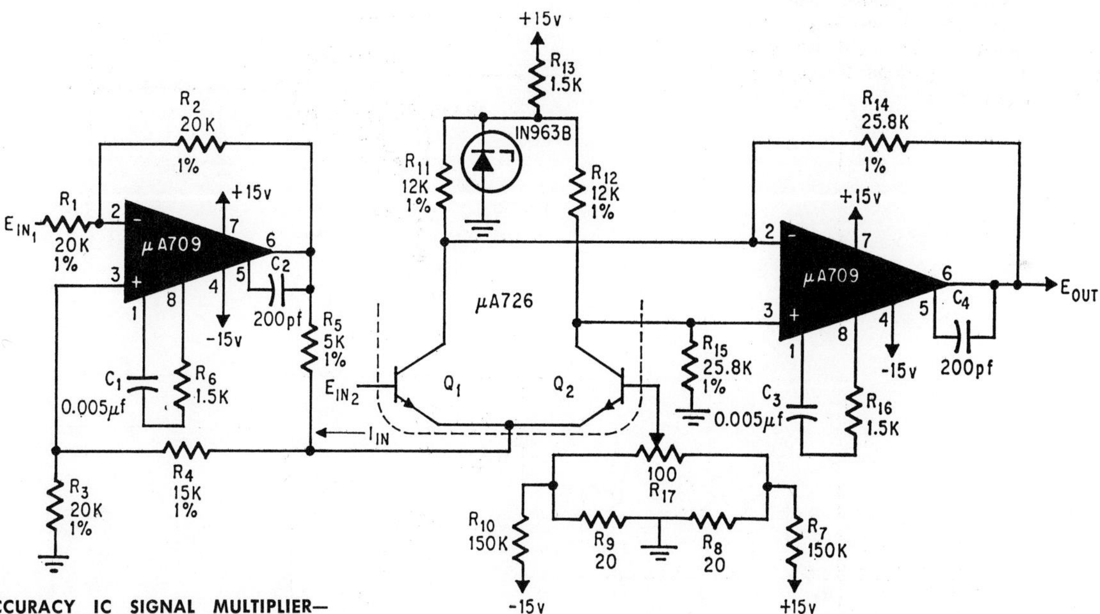

HIGH-ACCURACY IC SIGNAL MULTIPLIER—First Fairchild µA709 IC opamp supplies current proportional to one positive input voltage. Other input is fed directly to base of Q1 in differential pair of µA726 IC that multiplies. Second µA709 converts resulting output current to voltage having desired scale factor, with low output impedance.—J. F. Gifford and M. Markkula, Linear IC's: Part 5, Ins and Outs of Op Amps, *Electronics*, Nov. 27, 1967, p 84–93.

NOTE: To locate additional circuits in the category of this chapter, use the index at the back of this book. Check also the author's "Sourcebook of Electronic Circuits," published by McGraw-Hill in 1968.

CHAPTER 57
Optoelectronic Circuits

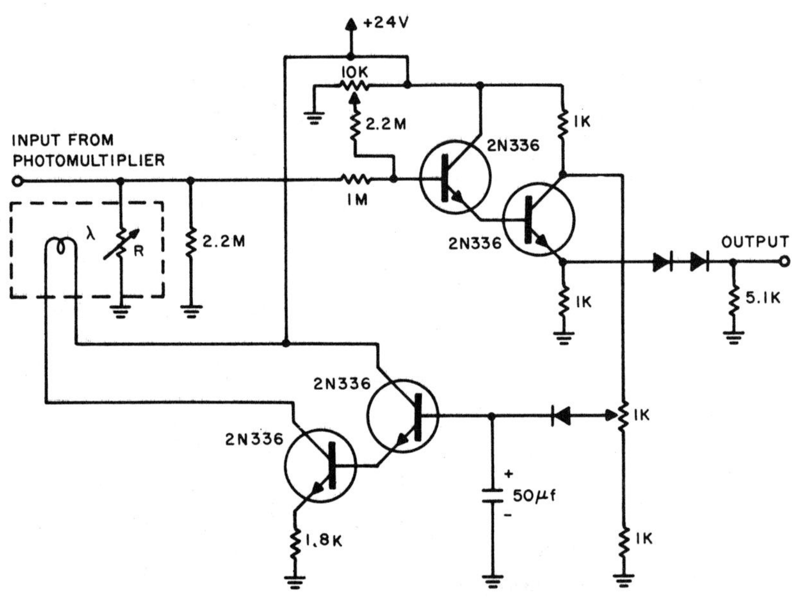

FAX PHOTOMULTIPLIER AMPLIFIER—Raytheon Raysistor lamp-photoconductor, similar to CK1116 but with extremely small filaments for fast response (dashed box), improves response speed of baseband photomultiplier amplifier for AN/GXC-5 portable facsimile system that transmits graphic material. Diodes can be 1N2069.—H. Weisbecker, Designing a Feedback System? Control It With a Photo Emitter-Sensor, *Electronic Design*, Aug. 30, 1965, p 32 and 34–35.

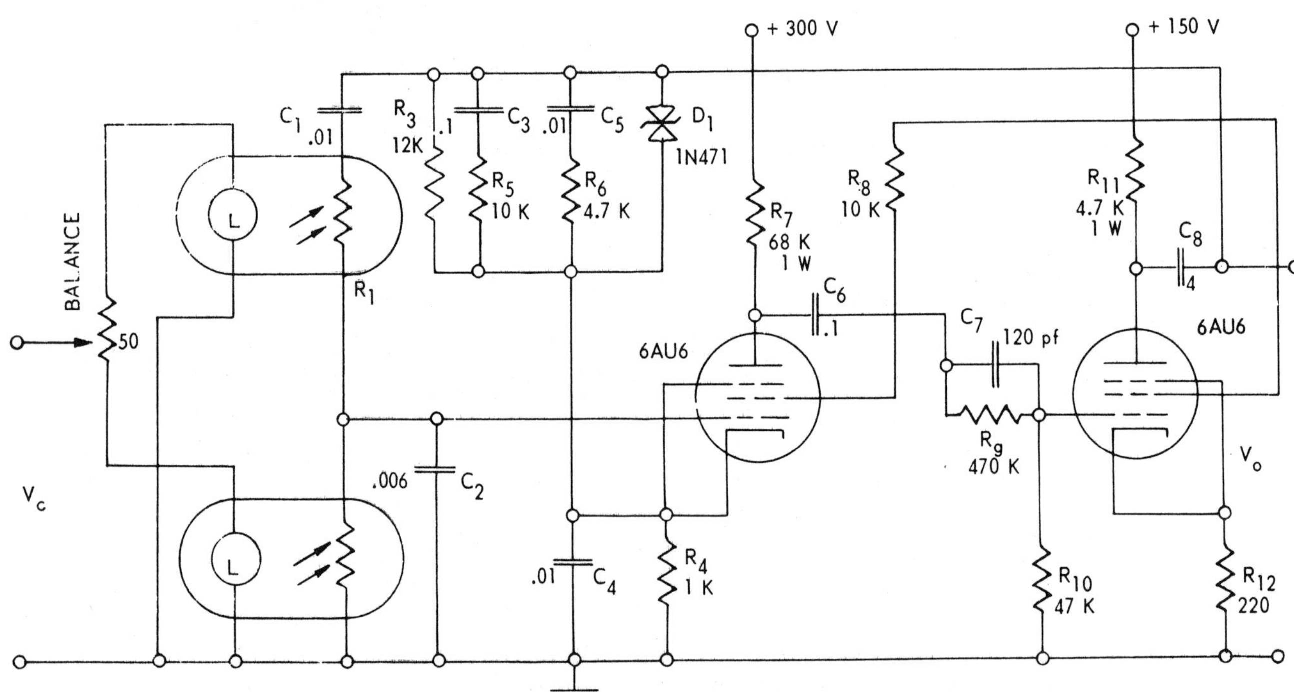

WIEN-BRIDGE VCO—Changing d-c control voltage applied to lamps of CK1102 or CK-1112 Raysistor pair changes values of photocell resistances in arms of bridge, to vary output frequency over range of 10 Hz to 50 kHz. Output has constant amplitude within 1 dB and is reasonably sinusoidal.—Raysistor Optoelectronic Devices, Raytheon, Quincy, Mass., 1967, p 20.

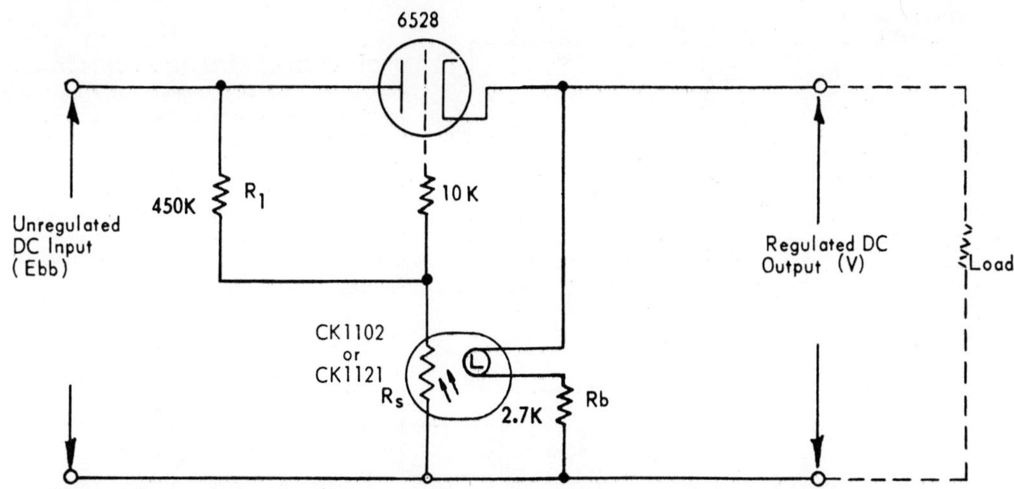

RAYSISTOR CONTROL—Uses combination lamp and photocell in single package to sense output voltage and apply appropriate controlled voltage to grid of series regulator triode. Report gives design calculations. Good regulation is obtained for 100 V d-c output when input varies from 200–400 V.—Raysistor Optoelectronic Devices, Raytheon, Quincy, Mass., 1967, p 13.

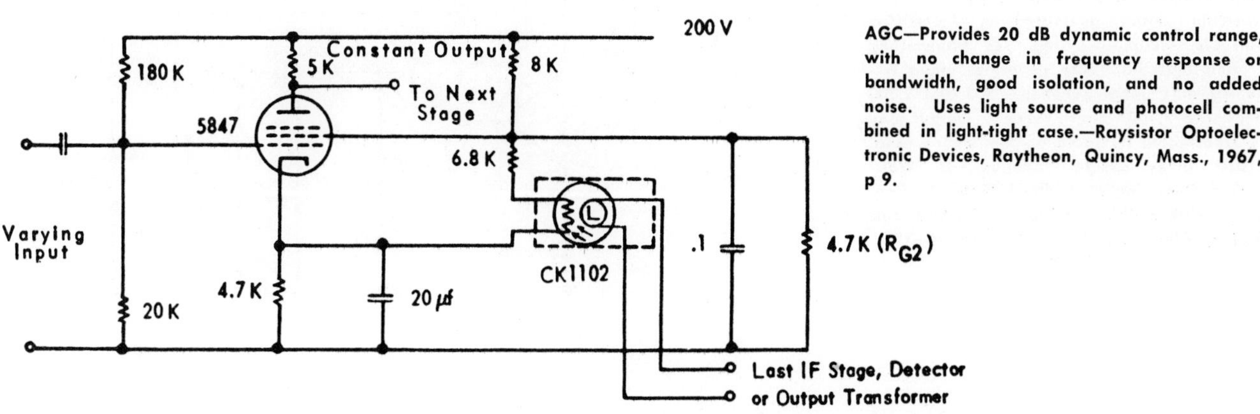

AGC—Provides 20 dB dynamic control range, with no change in frequency response or bandwidth, good isolation, and no added noise. Uses light source and photocell combined in light-tight case.—Raysistor Optoelectronic Devices, Raytheon, Quincy, Mass., 1967, p 9.

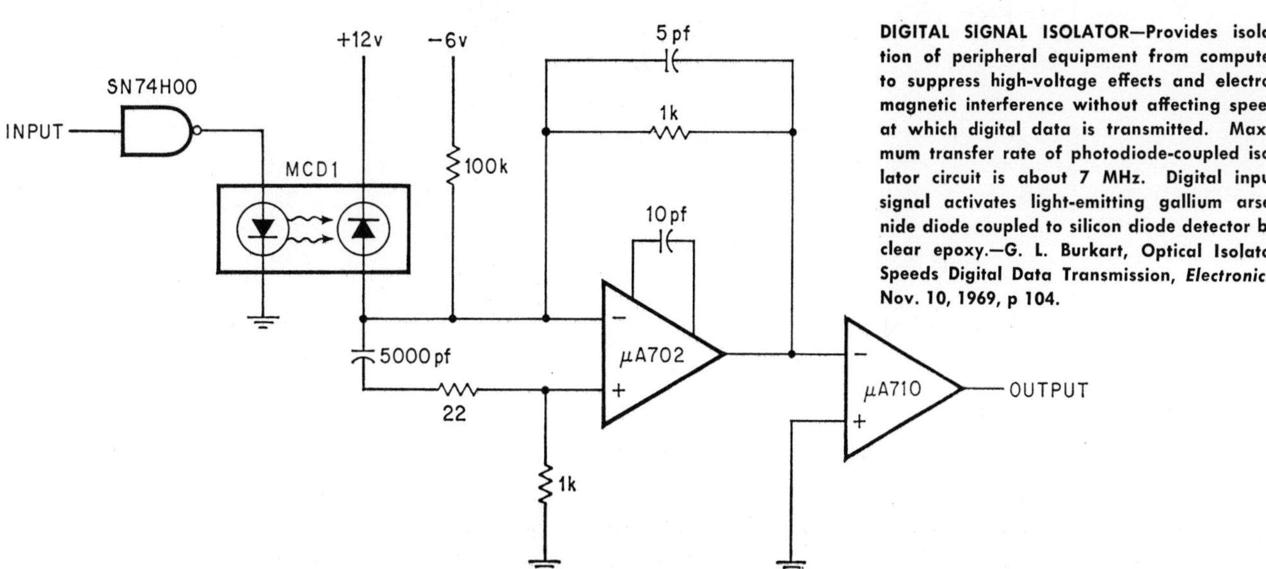

DIGITAL SIGNAL ISOLATOR—Provides isolation of peripheral equipment from computer to suppress high-voltage effects and electromagnetic interference without affecting speed at which digital data is transmitted. Maximum transfer rate of photodiode-coupled isolator circuit is about 7 MHz. Digital input signal activates light-emitting gallium arsenide diode coupled to silicon diode detector by clear epoxy.—G. L. Burkart, Optical Isolator Speeds Digital Data Transmission, *Electronics*, Nov. 10, 1969, p 104.

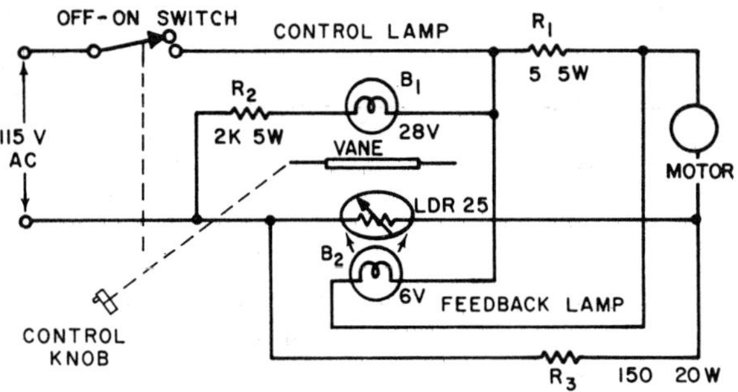

PHOTOELECTRIC APPLIANCE CONTROL—Low-cost speed control for small universal motor in kitchen appliances or for lamp loads up to 60 W requires only cadmium sulfide cell, lamp, and knob-controlled vane. Additional 6-V lamp provides optoelectronic feedback for speed regulation. Performance equals that of two scr's back-to-back.—Bargain Components, *Electronic Design*, Oct. 12, 1964, p 44–45.

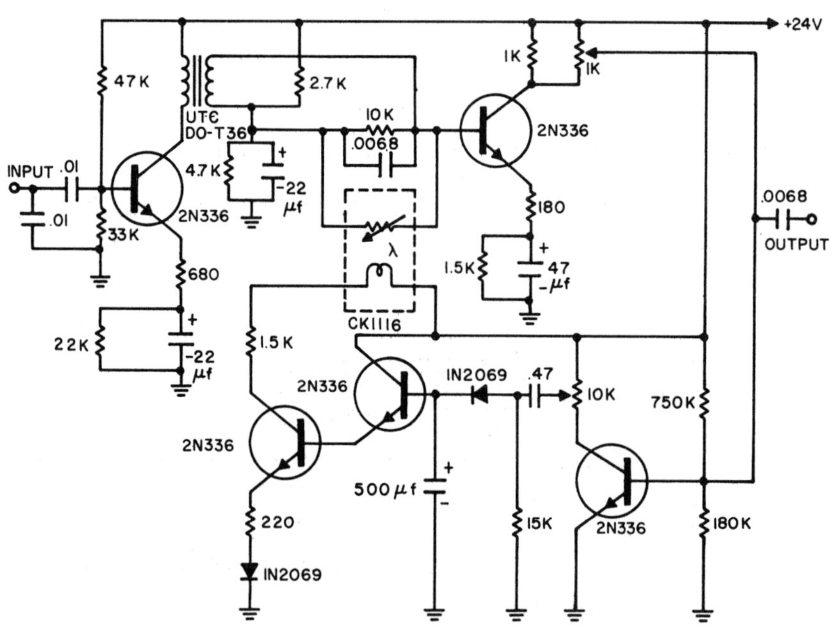

BACKGROUND CONTROL FOR A-M FAX—Raytheon CK1116 lamp-photoconductor (dashed box) and Darlington in feedback loop provide background control for a-m facsimile signal generated in AN/GXC-5 portable facsimile system for transmitting graphic material. Also generates audio frequency-shift signal between 1,500 and 2,300 Hz, below 2,400-Hz a-m carrier. Output may be transmitted by radio or over phone lines. Article gives design equations.—H. Weisbecker, Designing a Feedback System? Control It With a Photo Emitter-Sensor, *Electronic Design*, Aug. 30, 1965, p 32 and 34–35.

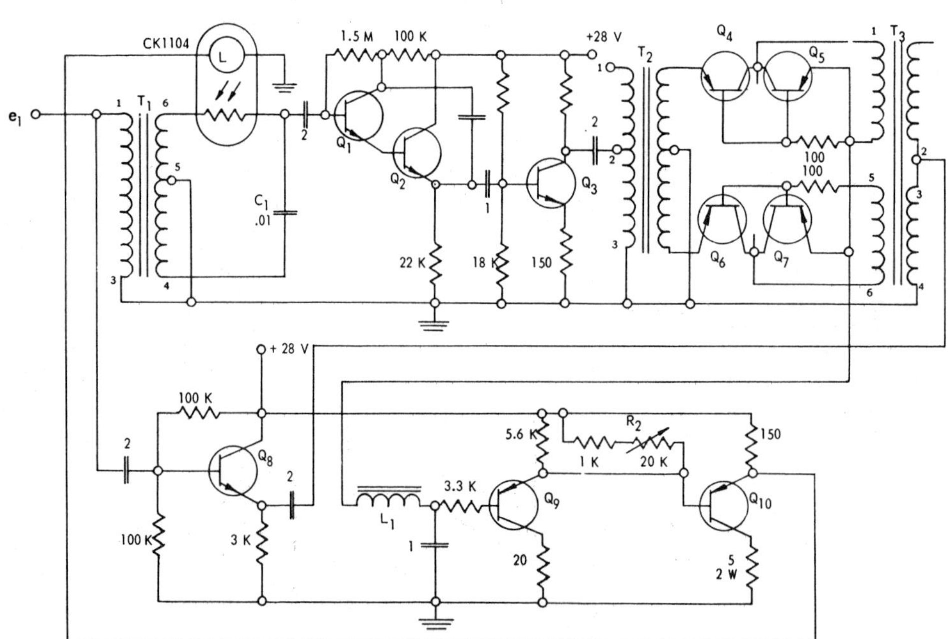

AUDIO PHASE SHIFTER—Raysistor serves as variable resistance in servo loop, to provide constant phase shift of 90 deg within 2 deg from 200 to 2,000 Hz. Initial control voltage applied to Raysistor lamp, value of C1, and operating frequency range are mutually interdependent, and affected by choice of transistors.—Raysistor Optoelectronic Devices, Raytheon, Quincy, Mass., 1967, p 23.

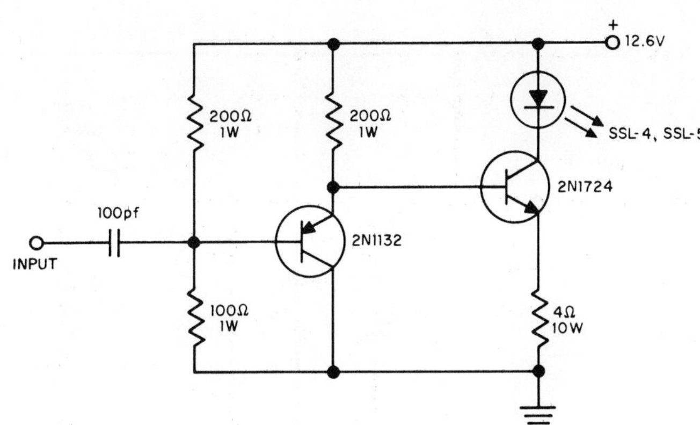

LIGHT-BEAM MODULATOR—Two-transistor modulator is linear up to 80% modulation of light beam generated by gallium arsenide solid-state lamp. Bandwidth is 30 Hz to 250 kHz.—L. M. Hertz, Solid State Lamps—Part II, General Electric, Cleveland, Ohio, No. 3-0121, 1970, p 8.

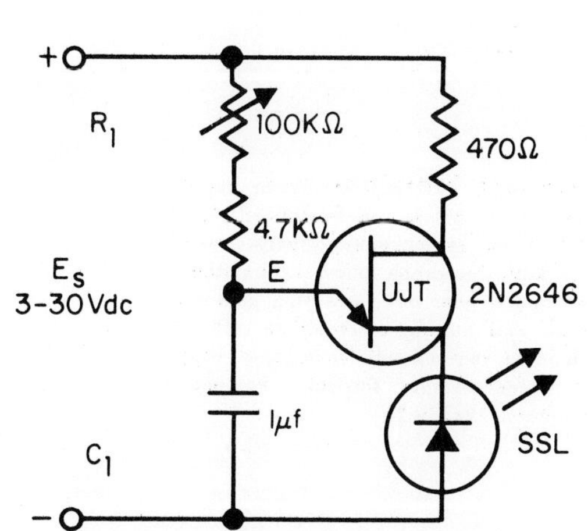

LAMP DRIVE—Simple ujt pulse generator gives 20-ms fast-rise pulses for driving solid-state lamps. R1 changes frequency, and C1 changes frequency range and pulse width. With 15-V supply, frequency range is 10 to 200 pps.—L. M. Hertz, Solid State Lamps—Part II, General Electric, Cleveland, Ohio, No. 3-0121, 1970, p 23.

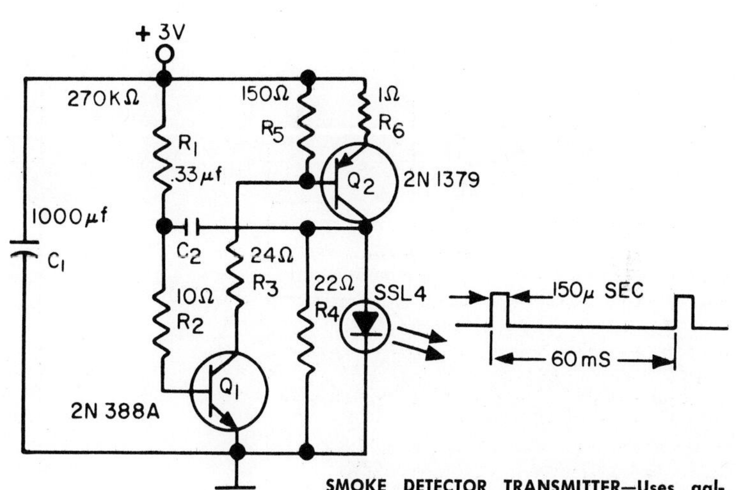

SMOKE DETECTOR TRANSMITTER—Uses gallium arsenide lamp pulsed at 10 pps by relaxation oscillator Q1-Q2. Draws only 0.7 mA from pair of D flashlight cells. Used with four mirrors to provide 8-inch optical path to sensor in receiver.—L. M. Hertz, Solid State Lamps—Part II, General Electric, Cleveland, Ohio, No. 3-0121, 1970, p 31.

BLOCKING-OSCILLATOR DRIVE FOR SSL—Flashes from solid-state lamp are controlled by applying trigger voltage to blocking oscillator.—L. M. Hertz, Solid State Lamps—Part II, General Electric, Cleveland, Ohio, No. 3-0121, 1970, p 8.

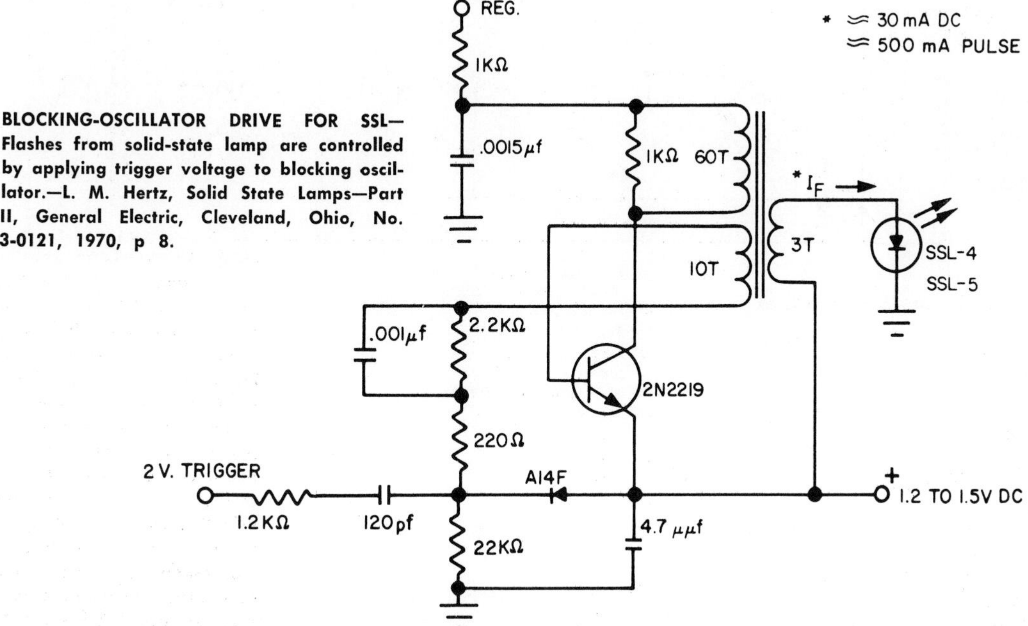

LIGHT-BEAM MODULATOR—Gallium arsenide solid-state lamp can be modulated at frequencies up to 100 MHz, depending on SSL used, with conventional r-f transistor power amplifier. Transistor types depend on frequency and on power requirements of SSL used.—L. M. Hertz, Solid State Lamps—Part II, General Electric, Cleveland, Ohio, No. 3-0121, 1970, p 6.

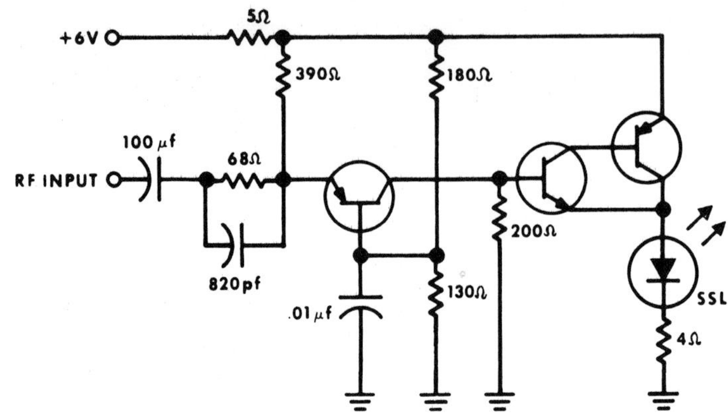

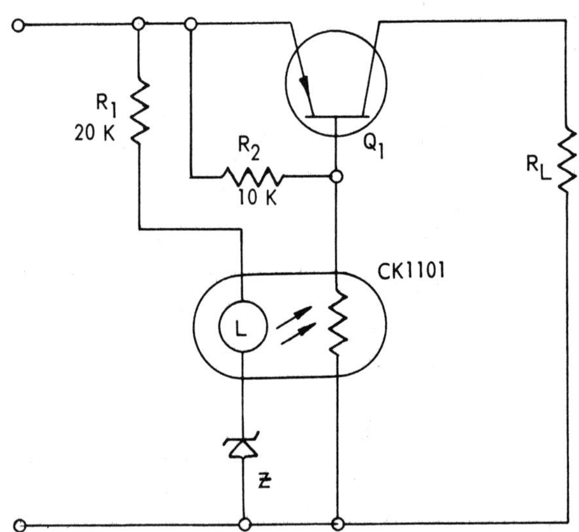

UNDERVOLTAGE PROTECTION—When supply voltage drops below predetermined level established by zener, voltage across neon lamp in Raysistor drops below extinguishing voltage and it goes out, increasing photocell resistance and turning off transistor Q1, to drop load current essentially to zero.—Raysistor Optoelectronic Devices, Raytheon, Quincy, Mass., 1967, p 26.

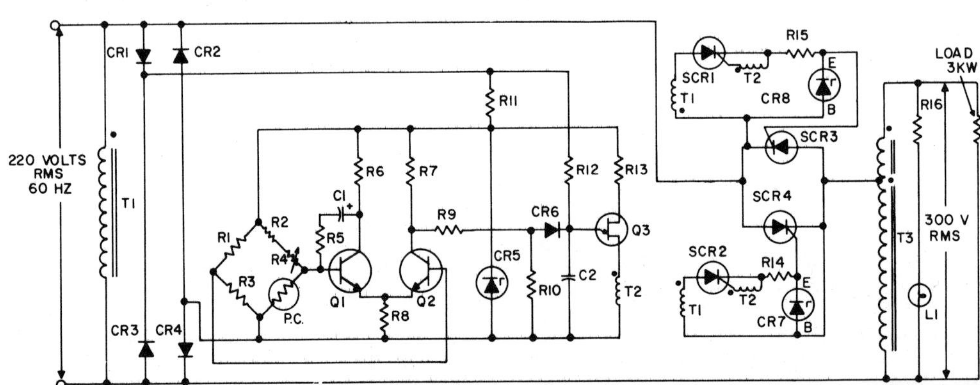

ALL RESISTORS ±10% AND 1/2 WATT EXCEPT WHERE MARKED

CR1 THRU CR4 - G.E. A13D OR A14D
CR5 - G.E. Z4XL22
CR6 - G.E. A13F OR A14F
CR7 - CR8 - G.E. 16L1423
C1 - 10MF, 25 VDC G.E. 62F204 MINIATURE TUBULAR WET SLUG CAP.
C2 - 0.22 UF, 50 VDC ±10% G.E. 75F3R5-244A
Q1 - Q2 - G.E. 2N2925
Q3 - G.E. 2N2646
SCR1 - SCR2 - G.E. C6U or C106Y
SCR3 - SCR4 - G.E. C135E OR C35E
T1 - 220 V RMS PRIMARY 12 V RMS SECONDARY 100 MA RMS RATED SECONDARY CURRENT

T2 - PULSE TRANSFORMER 1:1:1 ALADDIN PART NO. 90-2398
T3 - TURNS RATIO 1:1.82 4KVA
R1 - 22K
R2 - 2.2K
R3 - 18K
R4 - 10K MULTI-TURN TRIM POT
R5 - 10K
R6 - 2.2K
R7 - 2.2K
R8 - 2.2K
R9 - 5.6K
R10 - 47K
R11 - 8.2K, 10 WATT
R12 - 1.5MEG
R13 - 1K
R14 - R15 - 220 OHM
R16 - 9K ±5%, 14 WATTS

3-KW A-C VOLTAGE REGULATOR—Holds a-c load voltage constant at 300 V for a-c line drop from 220 V to 190 V, and allows output to drop only 1.5 V for input jump to 250 V. Lamp L1 across load, sealed into photocell PC as GE PL5B1, gives sensing of phase-controlled true rms load voltage, which is initially adjusted to desired 300 V by trimpot R4 in bridge. Article describes circuit operation in detail, tells how to adapt for soft-start during initial transient condition when circuit is turned on, and shows how to use as current regulator.—J. L. Brookmire, AC Voltage or Current Regulator Featuring Closed-Loop Feedback Control, General Electric, Syracuse, N.Y., No. 200.46, 1966.

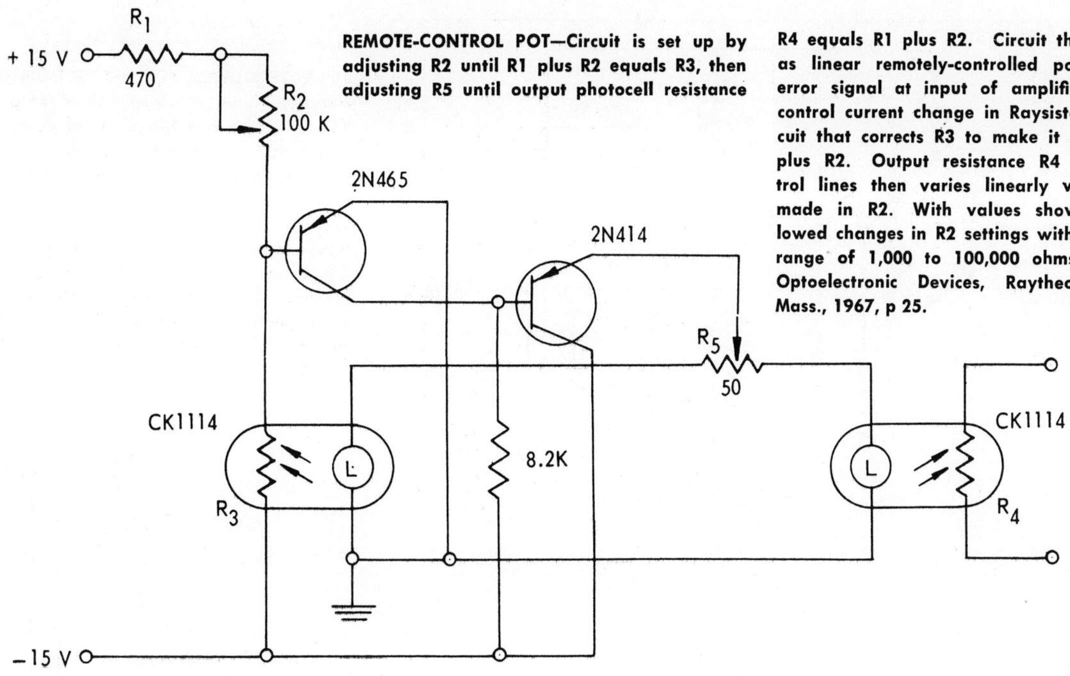

REMOTE-CONTROL POT—Circuit is set up by adjusting R2 until R1 plus R2 equals R3, then adjusting R5 until output photocell resistance R4 equals R1 plus R2. Circuit then operates as linear remotely-controlled pot in which error signal at input of amplifier produces control current change in Raysistor lamp circuit that corrects R3 to make it equal to R1 plus R2. Output resistance R4 across control lines then varies linearly with change made in R2. With values shown, R4 followed changes in R2 settings within 5% over range of 1,000 to 100,000 ohms.—Raysistor Optoelectronic Devices, Raytheon, Quincy, Mass., 1967, p 25.

ISOLATED-INPUT TRIGGER FOR TRIAC—6-V lamp, which may be energized remotely from battery, is sealed in box with cadmium sulfide photocell. When lamp is on, photocell triggers triac just after start of each half-cycle, to give full-wave switching of loads up to 6 A. Use RCA 40429 triac for 120 V and 40430 for 240 V.—R. M. Marston, 20 Triac Circuits, *Radio-Electronics*, June 1970, p 51–53 and 97.

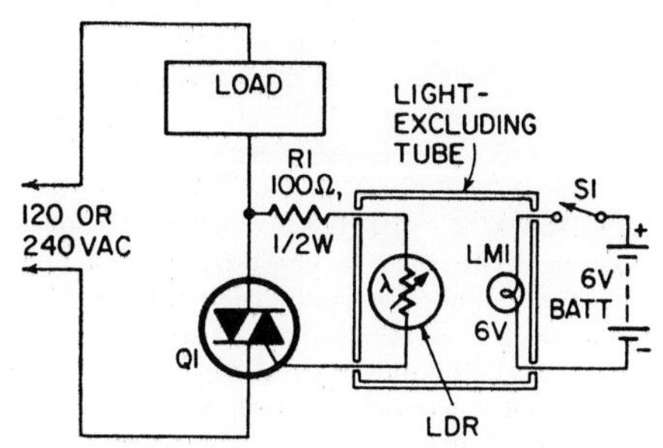

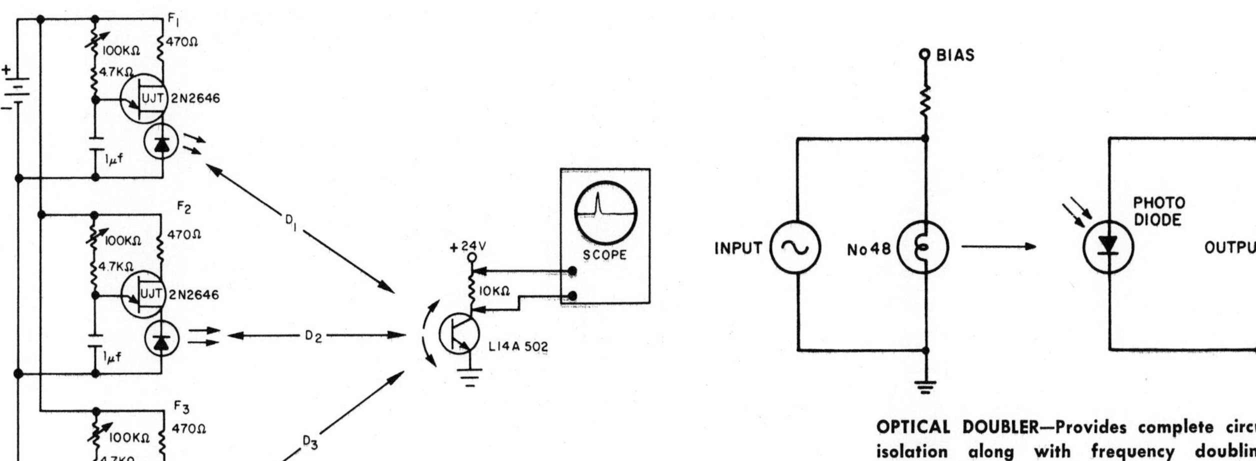

POSITION DETECTOR—Three ujt oscillator circuits each drive solid-state lamp SSL-5C at different pulsing rate. As L14A502 planar silicon phototransistor is rotated about its light-detecting center, each radiated light pulse in turn can be seen on scope, for determination of position of phototransistor.—L. M. Hertz, Solid State Lamps—Part II, General Electric, Cleveland, Ohio, No. 3-0121, 1970, p 22.

OPTICAL DOUBLER—Provides complete circuit isolation along with frequency doubling. Range is from d-c to 500 Hz for lamp shown, to 2 kHz for No. 2128 lamp, and to 10 kHz for pinlite. With switched d-c bias that extinguishes lamp on negative half-cycle, programmed output of f or 2f can be obtained. Distortion is low.—R. Dobkin, Simple Low-Frequency Doubler Provides Isolation, *Electronic Design*, Dec. 21, 1964, p 54–55.

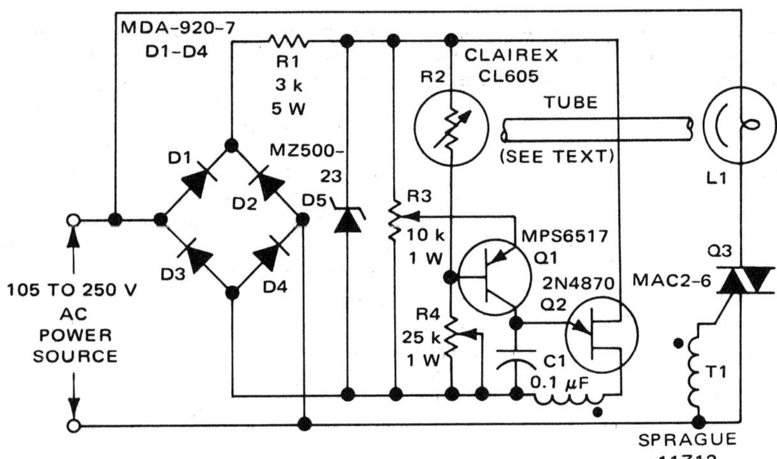

100-V REGULATOR FOR PROJECTION LAMP—Holds rms voltage across 150-W lamp within 2% of 100 V rms for all input voltages between 105 and 250 V a-c. Uses photoelectric feedback to firing circuit Q1-Q2 which controls conduction angle of triac Q3. Photocell senses red glow of back of reflector inside lamp, as heated by filament, to get integration of light output by mass of reflector and thereby eliminate 60-Hz modulation of filament.—"Semiconductor Power Circuits Handbook," Motorola, Phoenix, Ariz., 1968, p 3–27.

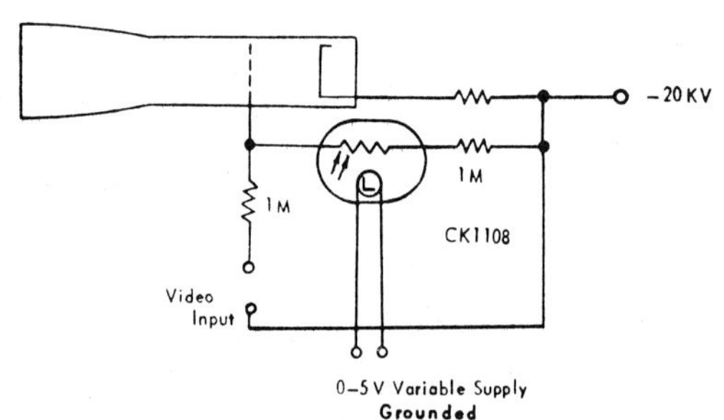

AUTOMATIC CONTRAST CONTROL—When lamp of Raysistor is energized by amplified video signal, automatic contrast control is obtained over range of 60 dB along with up to 25 kV isolation. Lamp filament provides automatic averaging effect because of its thermal inertia.—Raysistor Optoelectronic Devices, Raytheon, Quincy, Mass., 1967, p 15.

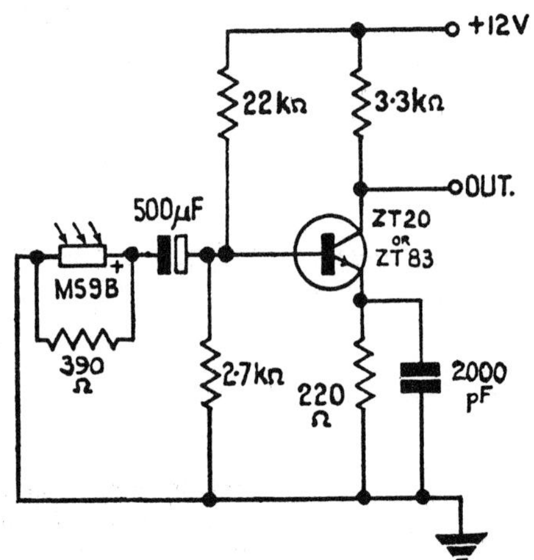

TAPE READER FOR PULSED LIGHT CIRCUITS—Designed for use with gallium arsenide and gallium phosphide lamps that can be pulsed at high repetition rates, to give low-drift performance of chopper amplifier without using chopper transistor. With low duty cycle, higher peak light intensities can be obtained than are available from fixed light sources. Can also be used for reading punched cards. —Silicon Photocell Applications, Ferranti Ltd., Oldham, Lancs., England, No. 9, 5/67, p 10.

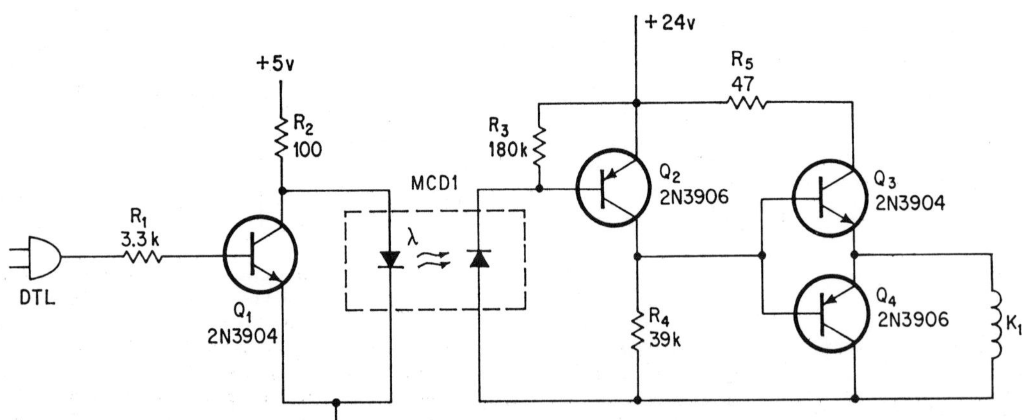

RELAY ISOLATOR—Gallium arsenide light-emitting diode, optically coupled to silicon p-i-n photodiode, combine to produce complete electrical isolation between IC driver and 400-ohm relay, thus eliminating relay noise and spikes. With no light reaching photodiode detector through light pipe, photodiode is at maximum impedance of 5 gigohms, Q2 and Q3 do not conduct and relay is not energized.—W. Otsuka, Photodiode Coupled Pair Isolates DTL from a Relay, *Electronics*, July 21, 1969, p 82.

CHAPTER 58
Oscillator Circuits—A-F

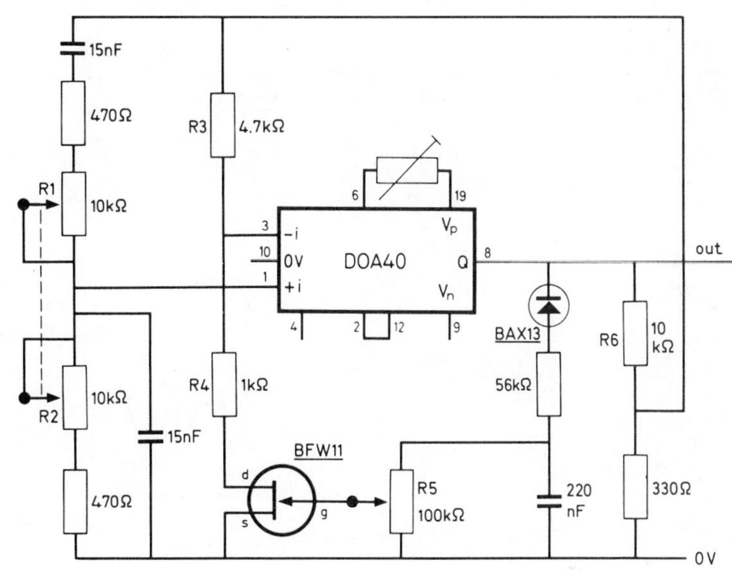

1–15 KHZ WIEN BRIDGE—Uses Philips DOA40 IC opamp. With 12-V supply, output is 18 V p-p sine wave (about 6 V rms). Ganged pots in two branches of bridge control frequency. When set at 2,000 Hz, output did not drift more than 2 Hz during 8 hours of operation.—Wien Bridge Oscillator Using the DOA40, Philips, Pub. Dept., Elcoma Div., Eindhoven, The Netherlands, No. 27.

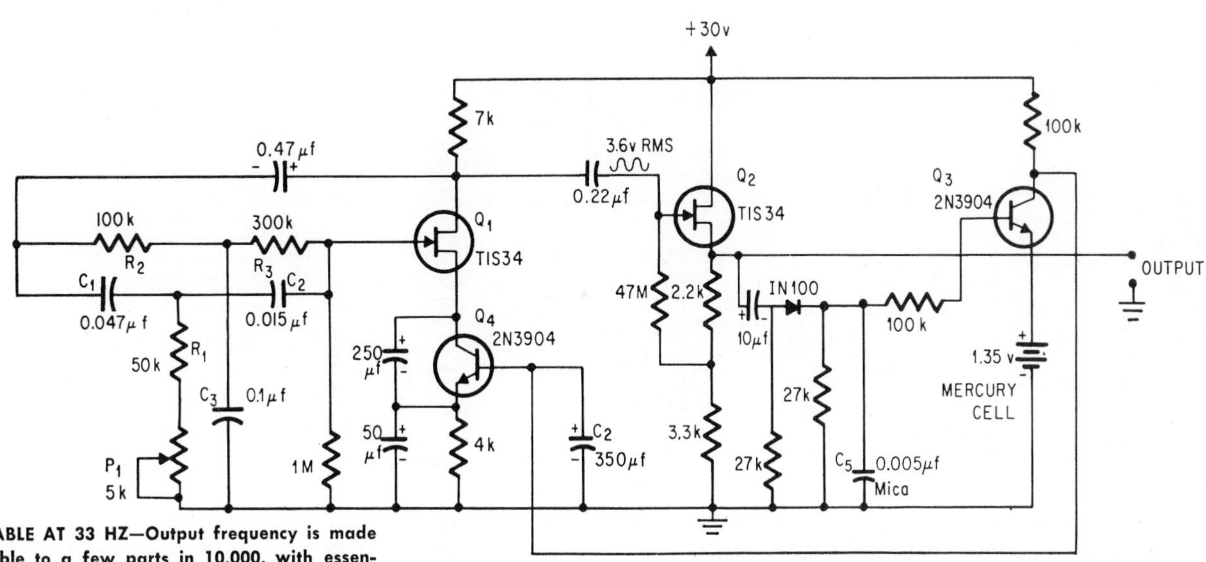

STABLE AT 33 HZ—Output frequency is made stable to a few parts in 10,000, with essentially constant output voltage, by adding negative feedback to fet oscillator Q1 having unbalanced parallel-T network. Output of Q1 at 33 Hz is fed through buffer Q2 and rectified to charge integrating capacitor C5. Voltage across C5 is compared to stable d-c reference (1.35-V mercury cell) in difference amplifier Q3 and error signal is applied to base of Q4 to vary bias of Q1 and compensate for output amplitude variations.—L. Mourlam, Jr., Feedback Loop Stabilizes FET Oscillator, *Electronics*, Sept. 4, 1967, p 97.

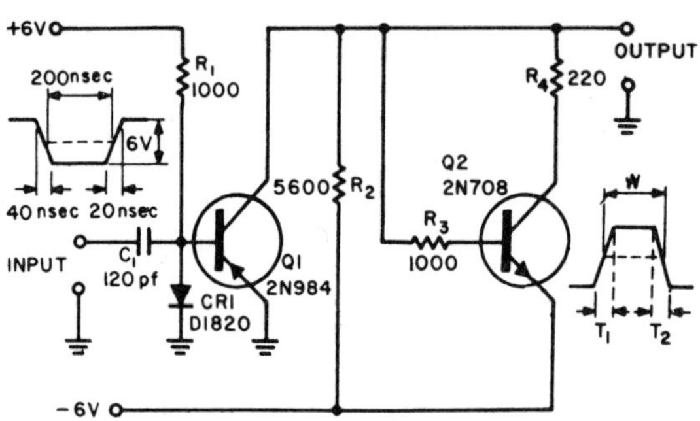

0–10 MHZ TRANSFORMERLESS BLOCKING—Furnishes narrow fast-rise pulse from low-impedance output, with value of C1 determining width of pulse. Requires −6 V trigger with fall time below 40 ns. Operates from d-c to above 10 MHz.—C. A. Karrfalt, Blocking Oscillator Operates Without Transformer,

	NO LOAD	220pf LOAD
W	56 nsec	70 nsec
T_1	12 nsec	25 nsec
T_2	15 nsec	99 nsec

"400 Ideas for Design Selected from Electronic Design," Hayden Book Co., N.Y., 1964, p 190–191.

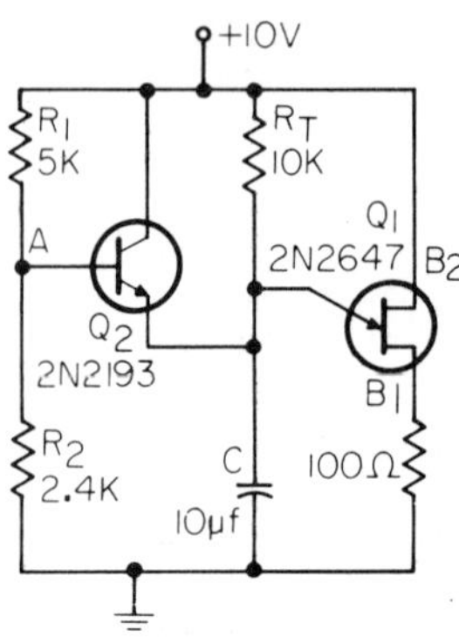

ELIMINATING UJT START-UP ERROR—Addition of transistor to basic ujt oscillator compensates for timing error due to time taken to charge capacitor during first cycle after power is applied. Q2 saturates when power is applied, charging C rapidly. Q2 is then cut off, and current then flows into C conventionally through timing resistor Rt.—J. V. Crowling, Modified UJT Oscillator Has No Timing Error, *EEE*, Dec. 1966, p 120–121.

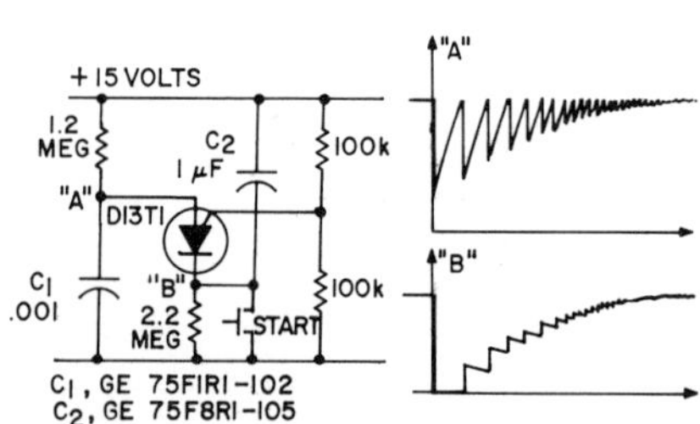

CHIRP OSCILLATOR—Uses D13T1 programmable ujt. Oscillation starts when switch is open, with decreasing amplitude as shown, and stops in about 1 s or until switch is closed.—W. R. Spofford, Jr., The D13T—A Programmable Unijunction Transistor, General Electric, Syracuse, N.Y., No. 90.70, 1967, p 9.

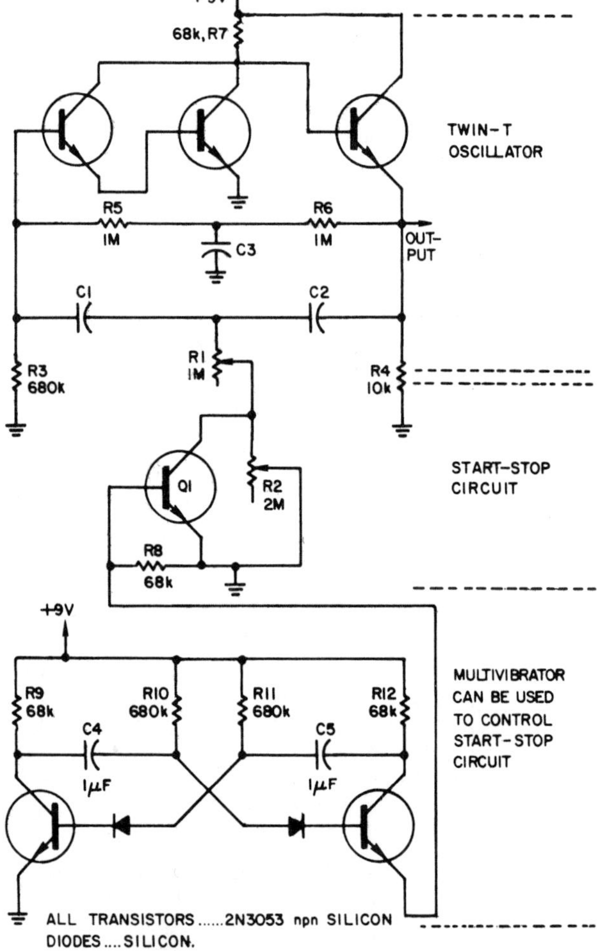

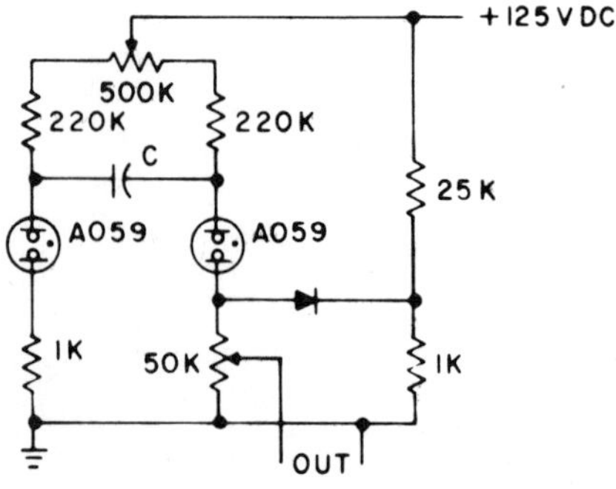

1–10 HZ NEON—Simple subaudio dual relaxation oscillator uses close-tolerance neon lamps. Clamping diode type is not critical.—E. Bauman, "Applications of Neon Lamps and Gas Discharge Tubes," Signalite, Neptune, N.J., p 35.

KEYED TWIN-T—Produces 1 pps of 160-Hz signal when C1 and C2 are 1,000 pF and C3 is 2,000 pF. Amount of regeneration in oscillator is determined by R1 and R2 in series; these are adjusted so circuit will not oscillate unless R2 is short-circuited by Q1. Rate at which oscillation builds up will then depend on setting of R1, and rate of decay by setting of R2. Mvbr turns Q1 on and off.—D. E. Johnson, Circuit Keys Twin-T Oscillator Without Generating Transients, *Electronic Design*, Aug. 16, 1969, p 246 and 248.

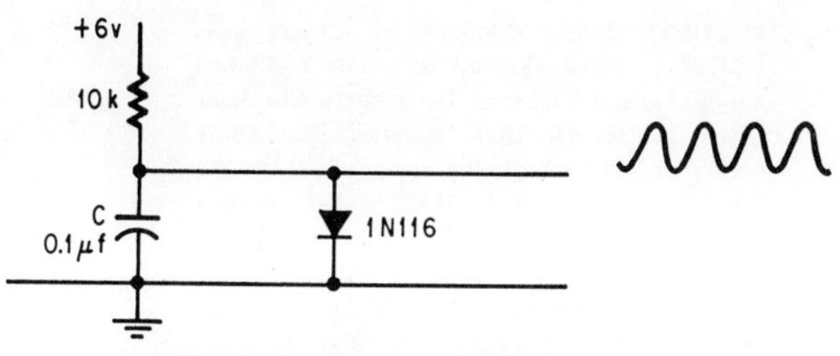

CRYOGENIC-DIODE OSCILLATOR—Low-cost cryogenic diode cooled by liquid nitrogen exhibits negative resistance required for relaxation oscillator operating in range of 30 Hz to 30 kHz, depending on value of C. Output amplitude ranges from 0.4 to 1.5 V, depending on diode used. Stability is excellent.—E. Elad, Low Temperature Triggers Diode Relaxation Oscillator, *Electronics*, Aug. 21, 1967, p 90.

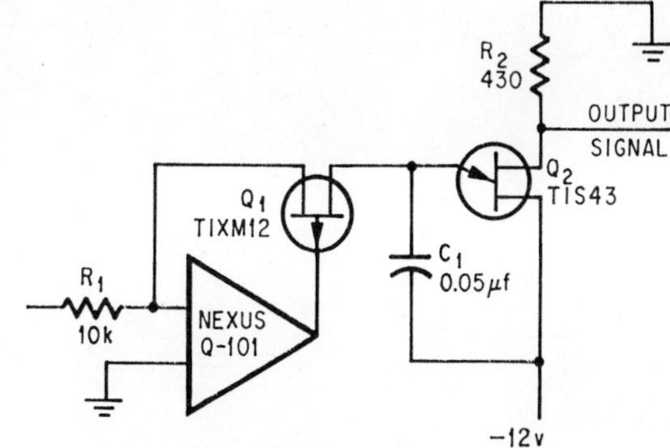

CONSTANT-CURRENT CHARGING—IC opamp with fet supplies charging current for ujt relaxation oscillator Q2, to give differential linearity better than 0.1% for output frequency varying from 0 to 1,400 Hz.—J. M. Kootsey, FET and IC Keep Oscillator Linear, *Electronics*, Aug. 19, 1968, p 84.

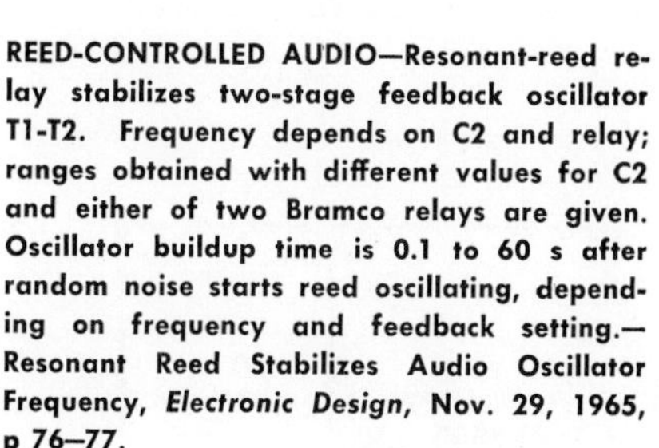

REED-CONTROLLED AUDIO—Resonant-reed relay stabilizes two-stage feedback oscillator T1-T2. Frequency depends on C2 and relay; ranges obtained with different values for C2 and either of two Bramco relays are given. Oscillator buildup time is 0.1 to 60 s after random noise starts reed oscillating, depending on frequency and feedback setting.—Resonant Reed Stabilizes Audio Oscillator Frequency, *Electronic Design*, Nov. 29, 1965, p 76–77.

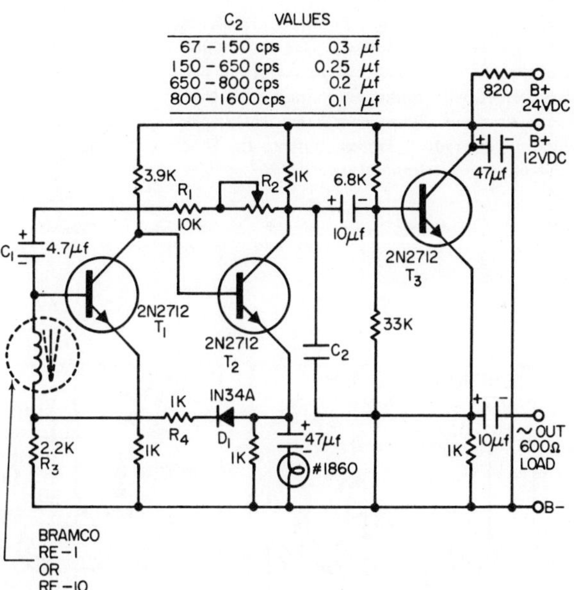

C_2	VALUES
67 – 150 cps	0.3 μf
150 – 650 cps	0.25 μf
650 – 800 cps	0.2 μf
800 – 1600 cps	0.1 μf

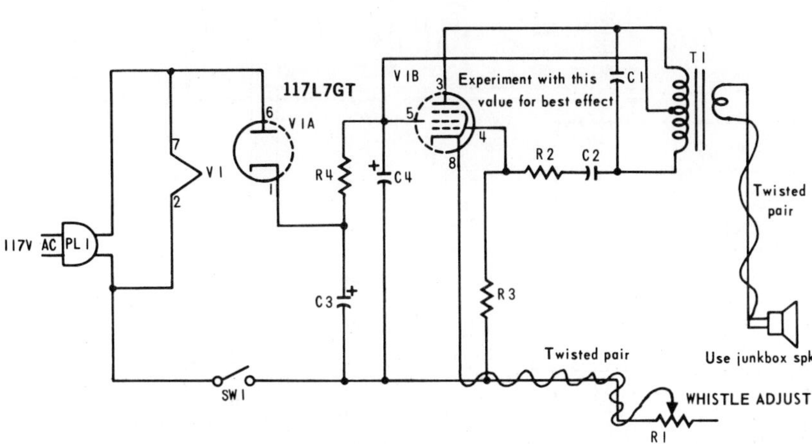

TRAIN WHISTLE—R1, which may be remotely located, determines tone of whistle. Place it near train controls, with speaker at other end of track layout. T1 is audio output transformer with 5K primary and 4 or 8 ohm secondary. Other values are: C1 0.047 μF, but try other values for best tone; C2 0.015 μF; C3-C4 20 μF; R1 2K pot; R2 2.7K; R3 39K; R4 270.—R. M. Brown, "104 Simple One-Tube Projects," Tab Books, Blue Ridge Summit, Pa., 1969, p 107.

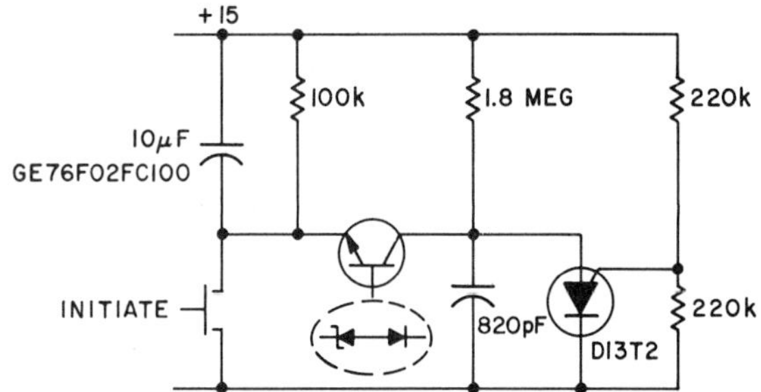

PRE-TIMED 1-KHZ OSCILLATOR—Circuit uses D13T2 programmable ujt as 1-kHz oscillator. Timing section is formed by 2N2926 transistor (used as zener), 100K resistor, and 10-μF capacitor. When power is applied, D13T2 latches up. Pushing INITIATE switch charges capacitor to full 15 V. Circuit then oscillates until capacitor discharges to point where D13T2 latches up again.—W. R. Spofford, Jr., The D13T—A Programmable Unijunction Transistor, General Electric, Syracuse, N.Y., No. 90.70, 1967, p 9.

A-F TONES WITH H RESONATOR—Twintron H-shaped piezoelectric resonator with Q of 4,000 is used with single transistor to generate audio tone that can be tuned from 20 kHz down to fraction of hertz. Over 1,000 stations can be connected to tone communication system, each having its distinct tone frequency for actuating Twintron receiving resonator at central station. One application is automatic reading of electric meters in private homes with tones transmitted over telephone lines.—H. Baker and J. R. Cressey, H-Shaped Resonators Signal Upturn In Tone Telemetering, *Electronics*, Oct. 2, 1967, p 99–106.

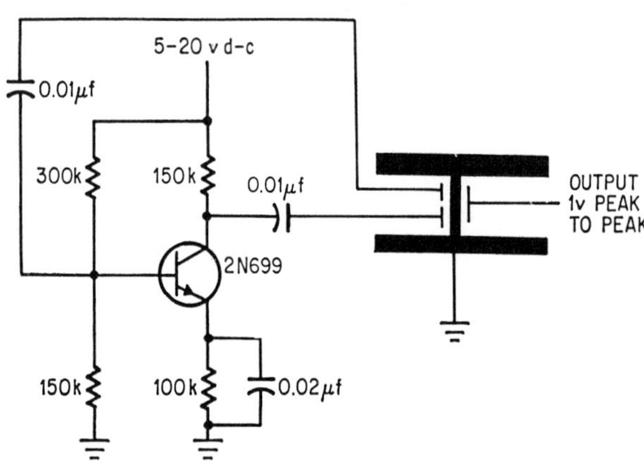

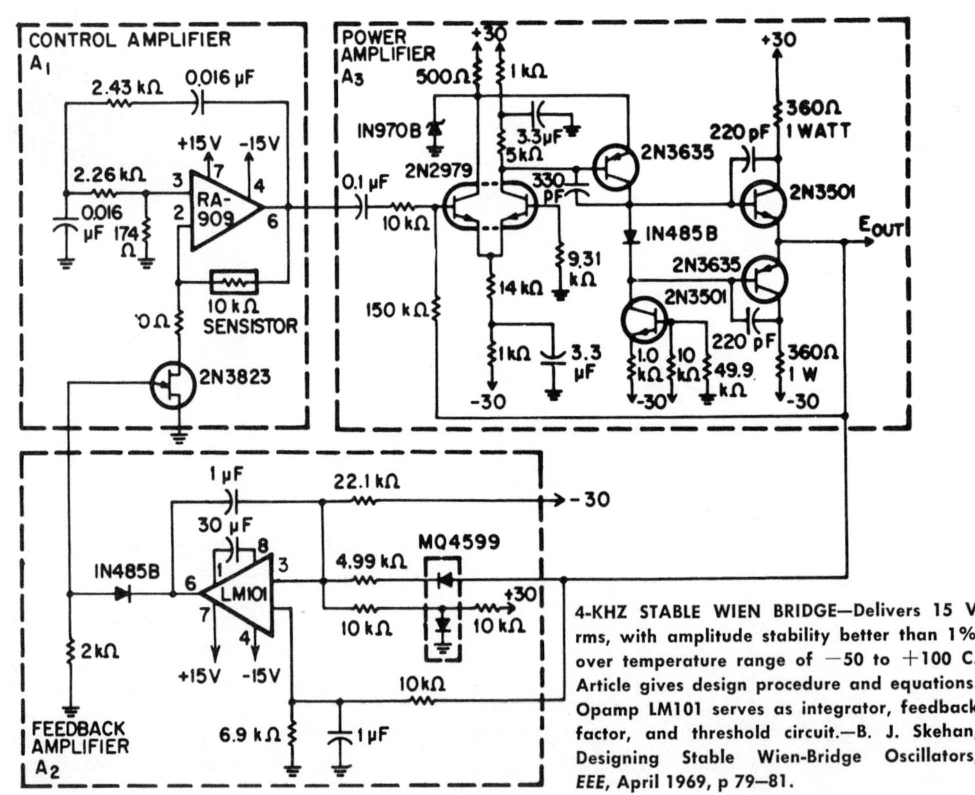

4-KHZ STABLE WIEN BRIDGE—Delivers 15 V rms, with amplitude stability better than 1% over temperature range of −50 to +100 C. Article gives design procedure and equations. Opamp LM101 serves as integrator, feedback factor, and threshold circuit.—B. J. Skehan, Designing Stable Wien-Bridge Oscillators, *EEE*, April 1969, p 79–81.

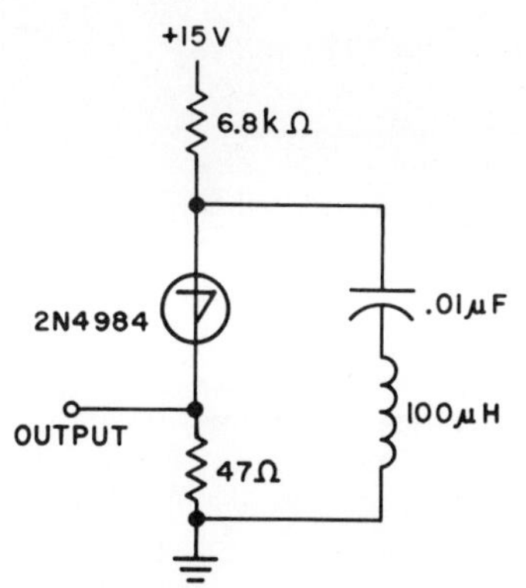

10 KHZ WITH SUS—Capacitor charges until 8-V switching voltage of silicon unilateral switch is reached. Sus then switches on, and resulting discharge through inductor causes current to ring. When ringing current drops below holding current, sus opens and charging cycle repeats. May also be used with 2N4989 sus.—Silicon Unilateral Switch 2N-4984/2N4985, General Electric, Syracuse, N.Y., No. 65.27, 1967.

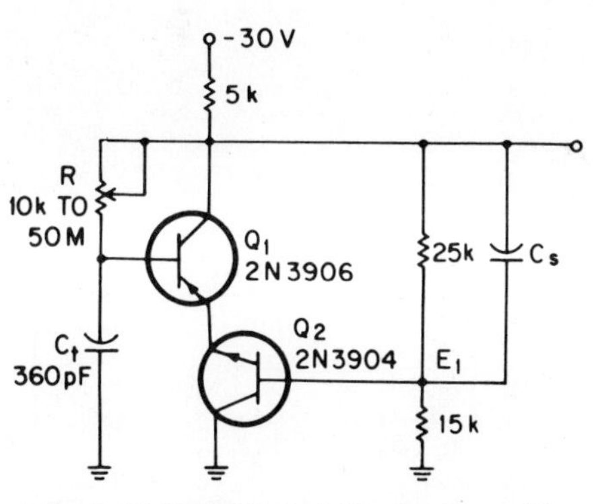

5,000:1 FREQUENCY RANGE—Simple modification of basic relaxation oscillator greatly increases range over which frequency is controlled by R. Q1 draws base current only from timing capacitor Ct, speeding transition from blocking to conduction.—G. R. Latham IV, A 5000:1 Frequency-Range Oscillator, *EEE*, April 1970, p 101–102.

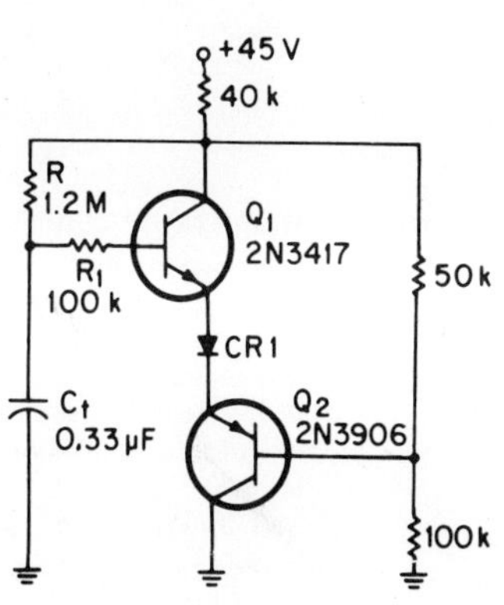

2-HZ RELAXATION—Discharge time of Ct is increased by placing R1 in series with base of Q1 in modification of relaxation oscillator, to permit generating frequencies down to 2 Hz without increasing size of R to point where it is affected by high humidity. Temperature stability may be as poor as 10%, but this is adequate for many low-frequency applications.—G. R. Latham IV, A 5000:1 Frequency-Range Oscillator, *EEE*, April 1970, p 101–102.

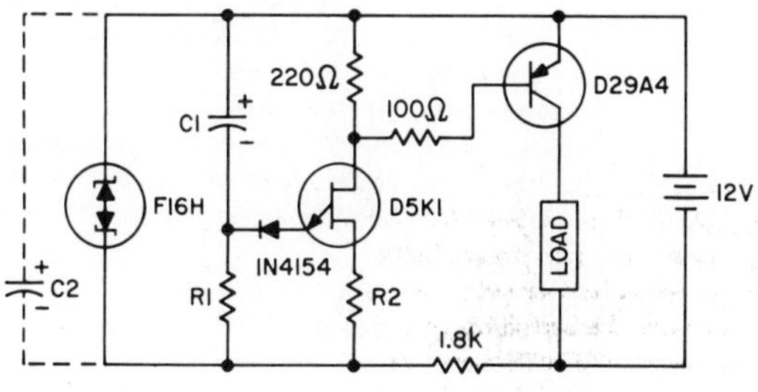

0.1-HZ RELAXATION—Delivers 20-ms-wide pulse every 10 s. R1 is 100K; R2 is 220 ohms, adjusted for optimum temperature compensation. C1 and C2 are 100-μF 20-V solid tantalum.—Silicon Complementary Unijunction Transistor D5K1, General Electric, Syracuse, N.Y., No. 60.15, 1967.

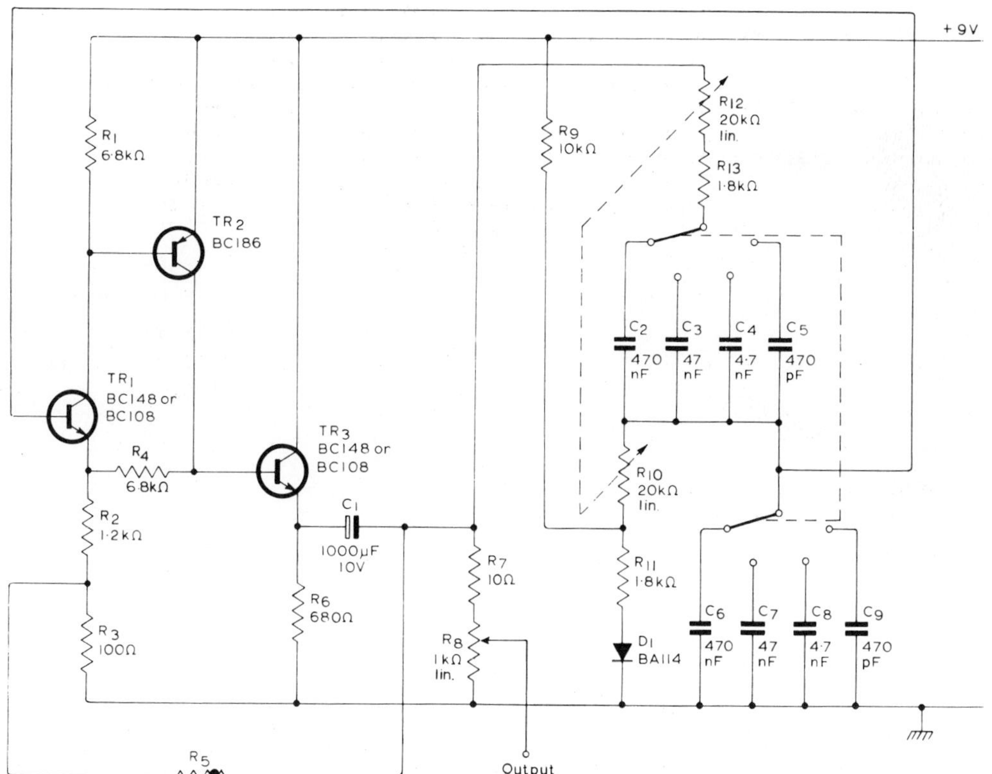

15–200,000 HZ AUDIO SIGNAL GENERATOR—Wien-bridge oscillator supplies 1-V rms output over entire frequency range, which is covered in four bands: 15–200 Hz; 150–2,000 Hz; 1,500–20,000 Hz; 15,000–200,000 Hz. Will operate with any supply voltage from 6 to 10 V. R5 is STC type R53 thermistor.—"Transistor Audio and Radio Circuits," Mullard Ltd., London, 1969, p 178.

STABILIZING AUDIO OSCILLATOR—Arrangement acts as pulse-excited tuned circuit, with no need to make adjustment for loop gain of unity as normally required with IC opamp sine-wave oscillator. When output voltage is low, negative feedback loop is open and amplifier gain is high. Output then tends to increase rapidly because positive feedback path is closed. As soon as one diode conducts, gain drops to value determined by negative feedback loop. Pot regulates output amplitude. Frequency is determined by values of R and C in Wien bridge.—L. Molyneux, Op Amp Sine Wave Oscillator Uses Diodes for Stability, *Electronics*, March 17, 1969, p 97.

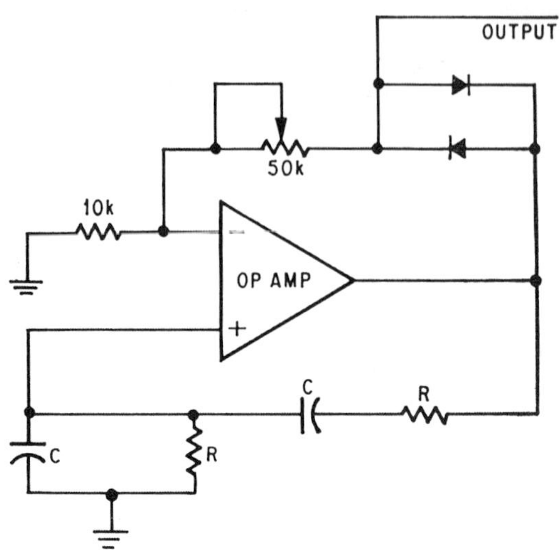

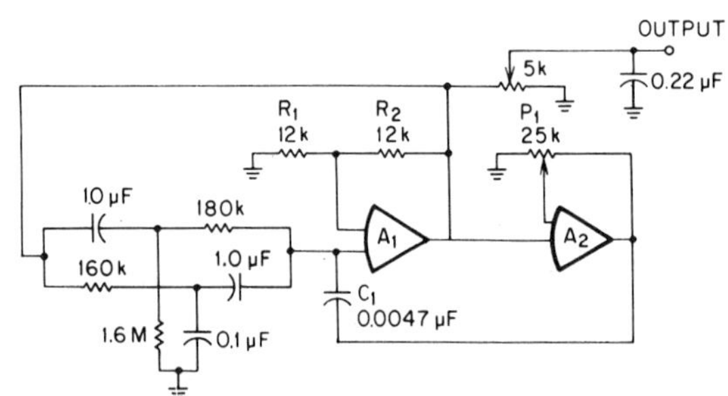

1-HZ SINE-WAVE—Twin-T network with two opamps generates very low frequencies with low distortion and stable amplitude. Oscillator runs free for most of each cycle, but is pushed for short time as output approaches zero from either direction.—J. Potzick, Low-Frequency Sine-Wave Oscillator, *EEE*, March 1970, p 130.

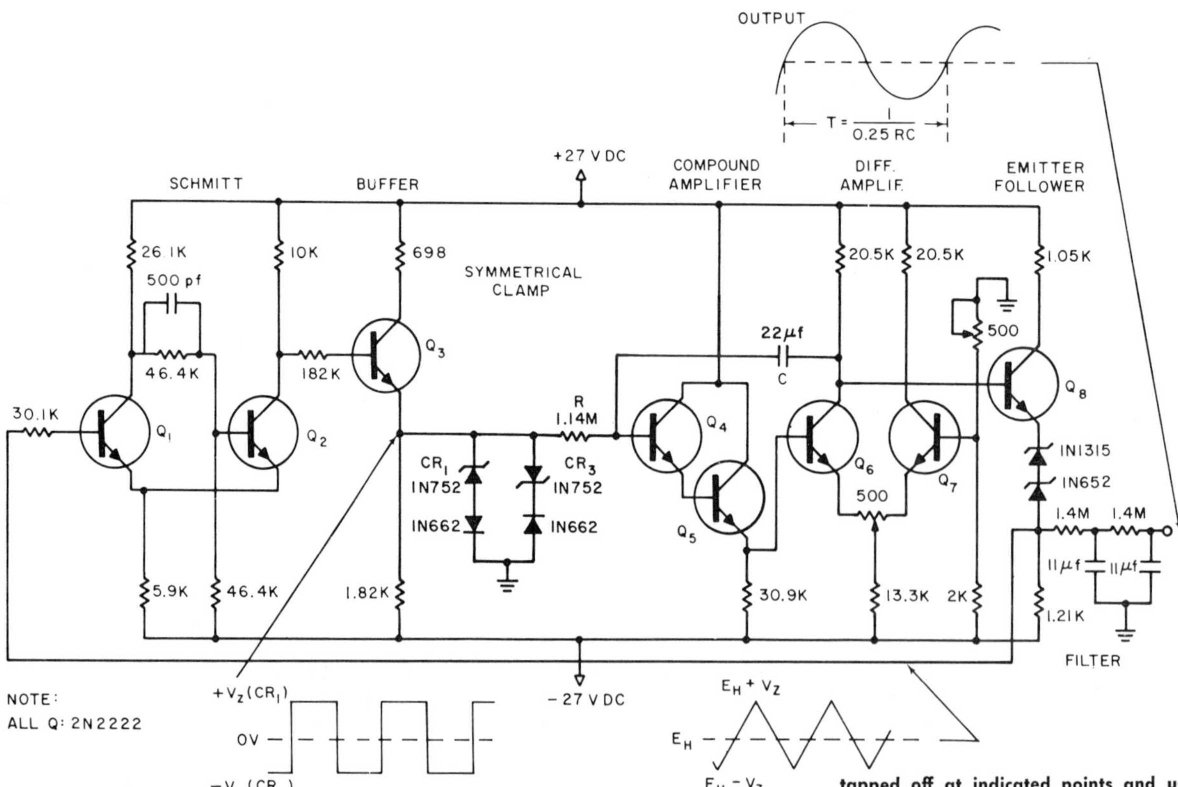

SINUSOIDAL SUBAUDIO—Frequency of five-stage oscillator network is determined by values of R and C in diode integrator circuit that couples differential amplifier to high-input-impedance compound amplifier. Square-waves and triangular waves may be tapped off at indicated points and used for long time delays or very slow cro traces.—J. N. Bequette, Sub-Audio Sinusoids Generated by Integrator Feedback Loop, *Electronic Design*, June 7, 1965, p 38.

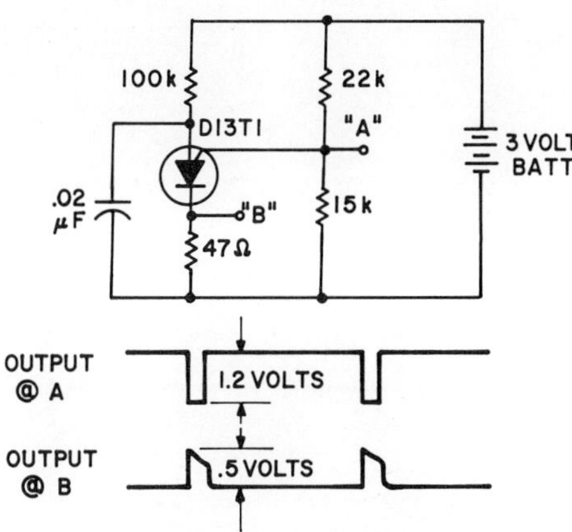

3-V RELAXATION OSCILLATOR—Operates from two flashlight cells, generating 1 kHz with choice of two different waveforms shown. Uses D13T1 programmable ujt, which is low-power triode thyristor. Battery drain is low.—W. R. Spofford, Jr., The D13T—A Programmable Unijunction Transistor, General Electric, Syracuse, N.Y., No. 90.70, 1967, p 8.

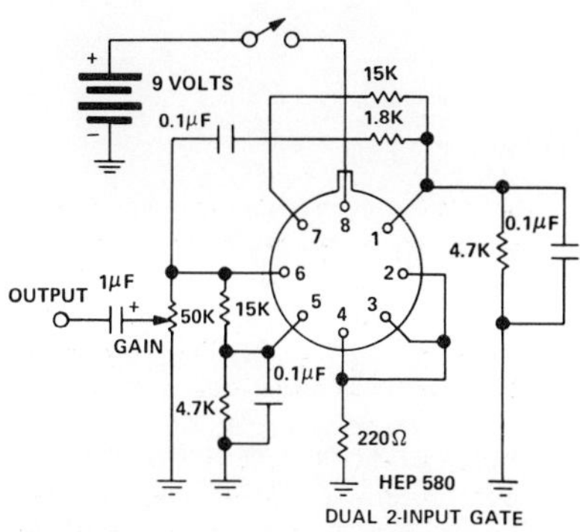

1,000-HZ IC—Features adjustable sine-wave output from 0 to 2 V p-p, fixed at about 1,000 Hz, for general audio testing.—"Tips on Using IC's," Motorola, Phoenix, Ariz., HMA-32, 1968.

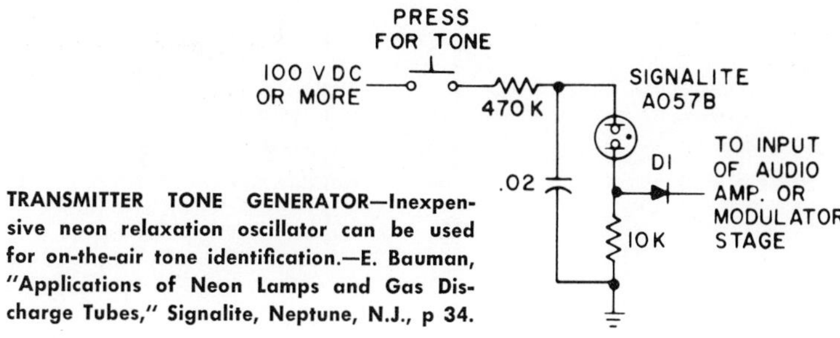

TRANSMITTER TONE GENERATOR—Inexpensive neon relaxation oscillator can be used for on-the-air tone identification.—E. Bauman, "Applications of Neon Lamps and Gas Discharge Tubes," Signalite, Neptune, N.J., p 34.

NOTE: To locate additional circuits in the category of this chapter, use the index at the back of this book. Check also the author's "Sourcebook of Electronic Circuits," published by McGraw-Hill in 1968.

CHAPTER 59
Oscillator Circuits—R-F

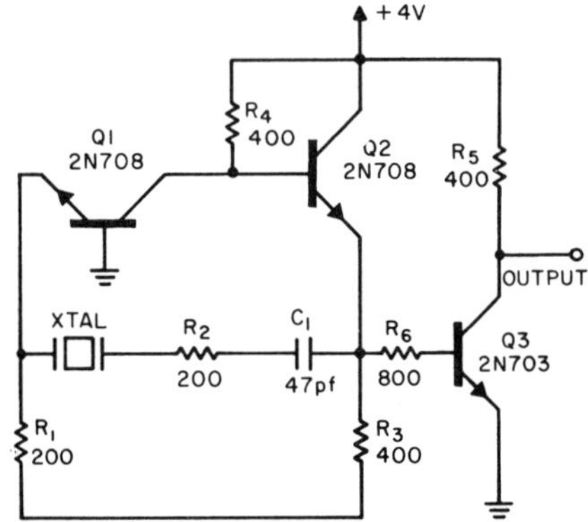

8-MHZ THIN-FILM CRYSTAL—Article gives step-by-step procedure for adapting crystal oscillator to version shown, suitable for thin-film hybrid construction using attached active devices (crystal and transistors), then gives instructions for constructing circuit by deposition through masks in vacuum chamber.—L. W. Sumney and C. E. Holland, Fabricate Your Own Thin-Film Oscillator, *Electronic Design*, March 30. 1964, p 52–56.

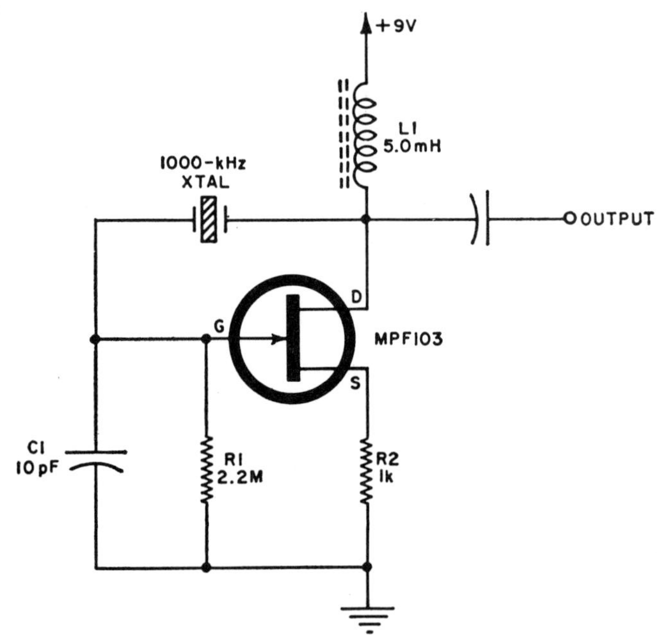

1-MHZ PIERCE—With high-activity crystal, clean sine-wave output is obtained. Without loading, drain current should be about 30 μA; higher current, above 500 μA, is due to parasitic oscillations—the chief drawback of this simple circuit.—F. H. Tooker, FET Sine-Wave Crystal Oscillators, *Electronics World*, June 1969, p 33 and 83.

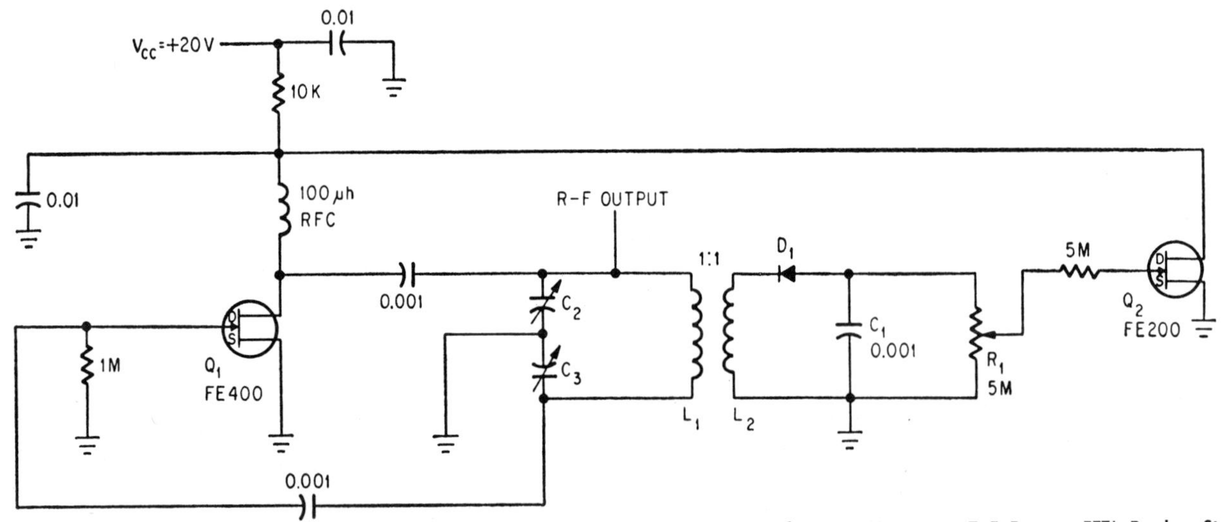

SUBAUDIO TO GHZ WITH FET—Features of manually tuned circuit shown are low cost, load leveling for constant-voltage output, low noise, stability, tunability and sweepability over wide frequency range, and unloaded output up to 15 V peak-to-peak in 300 to 400 MHz range.—T. F. Prosser, FET's Produce Stable Oscillators, *Electronics*, Oct. 3, 1966, p 102–103.

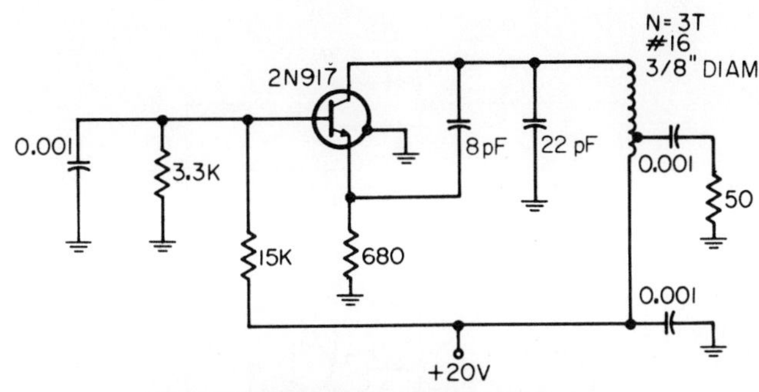

BIPOLAR-TRANSISTOR 100-MHZ—Chief drawback of conventional silicon transistor oscillator is relatively large change in frequency with temperature, as compared to fet oscillator at same frequency. Total drift is about 70 kHz from nominal 100 MHz for 70 C temperature change.—C. L. Farell, Designing FET Oscillators, *EEE*, Jan. 1967, p 86–90.

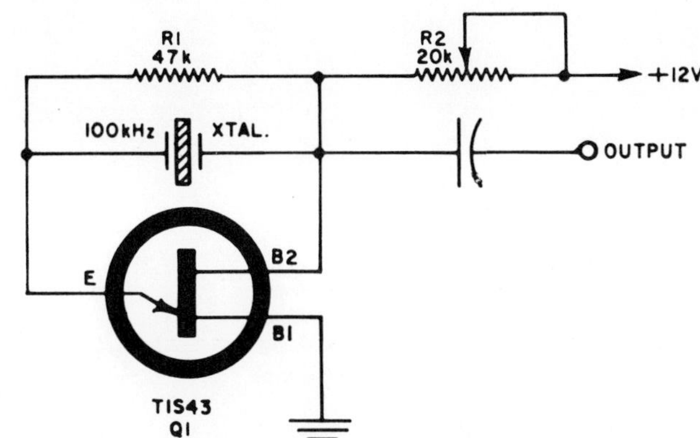

UJT CRYSTAL—Useful for generating 100 kHz when efficiency and waveform purity are relatively unimportant. Both are affected by supply voltage, adjusted here by R2.—F. H. Tooker, Ujt Sine-Wave Generators, *Electronics World*, Feb. 1969, 82.

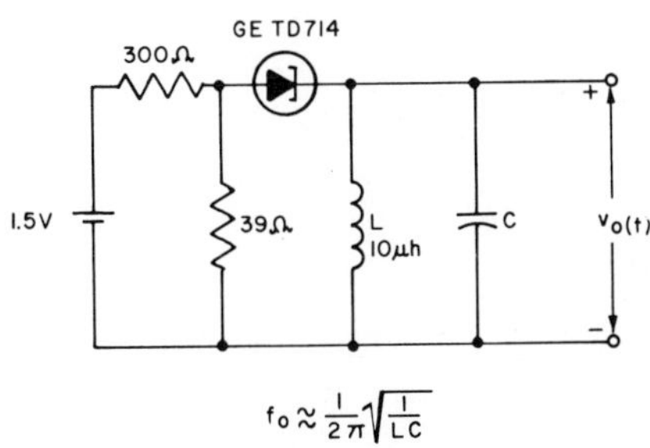

TUNNEL-DIODE OSCILLATOR—Simple parallel LC oscillator gives good sine-wave output, though limited to relatively low power.—W. R. Spofford, Jr., Applications For The New Low Cost TD 700 Series Tunnel Diodes, General Electric, Syracuse, N.Y., No. 90.66, 1967, p 6.

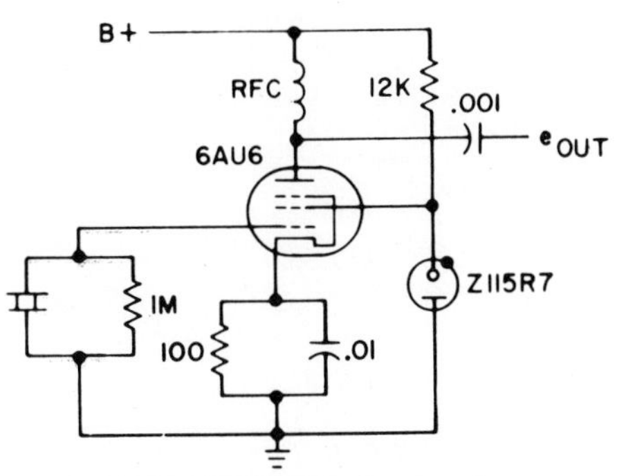

OSCILLATOR REGULATOR—Prevents frequency drift and output level changes in crystal oscillator due to power supply voltage variations. Neon lamp regulates to within 1 V of 115 V. Plate supply should be about 150 V to insure breakdown of regulator.—E. Bauman, "Applications of Neon Lamps and Gas Discharge Tubes," Signalite, Neptune, N.J., p 80.

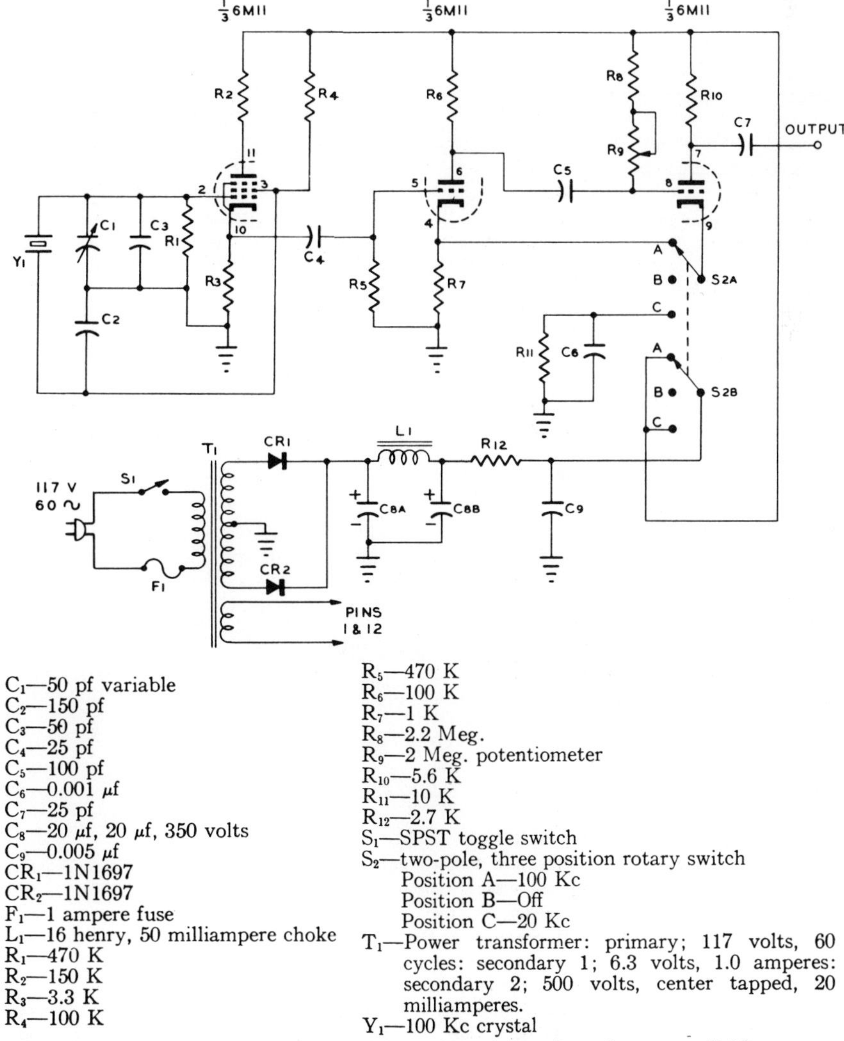

C_1—50 pf variable
C_2—150 pf
C_3—50 pf
C_4—25 pf
C_5—100 pf
C_6—0.001 μf
C_7—25 pf
C_8—20 μf, 20 μf, 350 volts
C_9—0.005 μf
CR_1—1N1697
CR_2—1N1697
F_1—1 ampere fuse
L_1—16 henry, 50 milliampere choke
R_1—470 K
R_2—150 K
R_3—3.3 K
R_4—100 K
R_5—470 K
R_6—100 K
R_7—1 K
R_8—2.2 Meg.
R_9—2 Meg. potentiometer
R_{10}—5.6 K
R_{11}—10 K
R_{12}—2.7 K
S_1—SPST toggle switch
S_2—two-pole, three position rotary switch
Position A—100 Kc
Position B—Off
Position C—20 Kc
T_1—Power transformer: primary; 117 volts, 60 cycles: secondary 1; 6.3 volts, 1.0 amperes: secondary 2; 500 volts, center tapped, 20 milliamperes.
Y_1—100 Kc crystal

100 AND 20 KHZ FREQUENCY STANDARD—Uses single compactron and single 100-kHz crystal with switch that provides optional 20-kHz output from frequency divider connection.—"Essential Characteristics," General Electric, Owensboro, Ky., 1969, p 352.

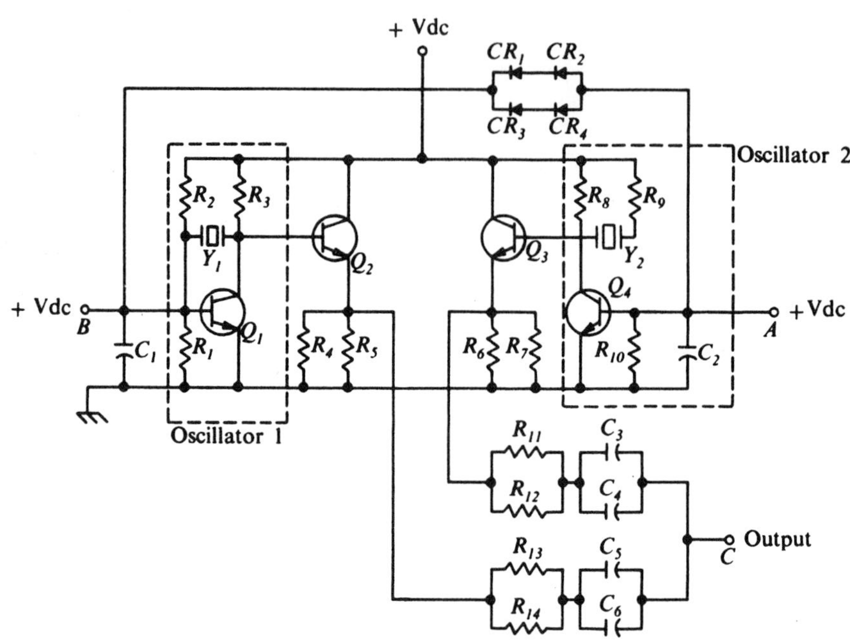

DUAL REDUNDANT OSCILLATOR—Maintains critical oscillator operation by automatic switching between two identical crystal oscillators, either of which will supply correct frequency and output amplitude to next stage or module. Oscillator 1 is prime and under normal conditions feeds its signal through amplifier Q2 to point C. If the amplitude of oscillator 1 drops below selected value, bias is removed from oscillator 2 so it can take over. All transistors are 4210AA and all diodes 1N658. Other values are: R1 and R10 120K; R2 2 meg; R3 and R8 10K; R4-R7 2K; R9 1.8 meg; R11-R14 3.9K; C1 220 pF; C2 120 pF; C3-C6 0.01 μF.—"Selected Electronic Circuitry," NASA SP-5046, 1966, Government Printing Office, Washington, D.C., p 14.

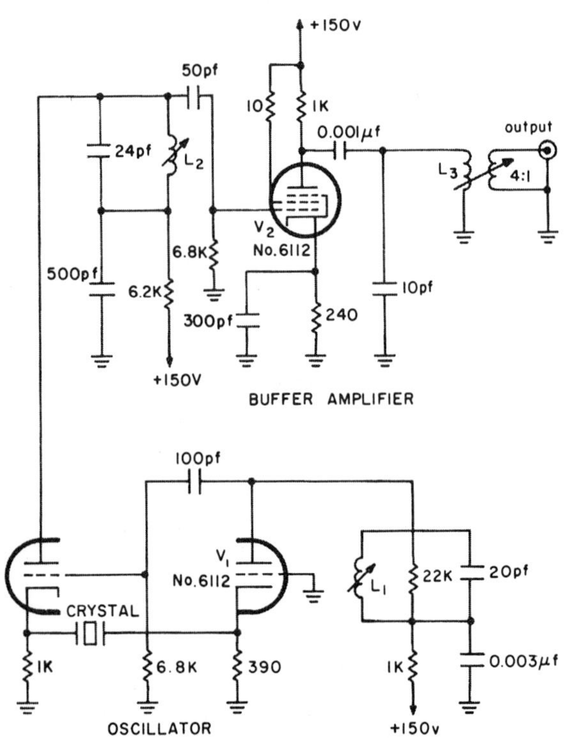

PHASED-RADAR VHF OSCILLATOR—Cathode-coupled crystal oscillator and buffer amplifier were developed for use in binary combination of oscillators and mixers for generating large number of discrete frequencies required in electronic scanning radar. Gives excellent reliability and stability in range of 10 to 70 MHz, with undesired second harmonic over 30 dB below fundamental.—G. F. Ross, Binary Generation of Frequencies Saves on Hardware, *Electronic Design*, Nov. 23, 1964, p 38–42 and 44–47.

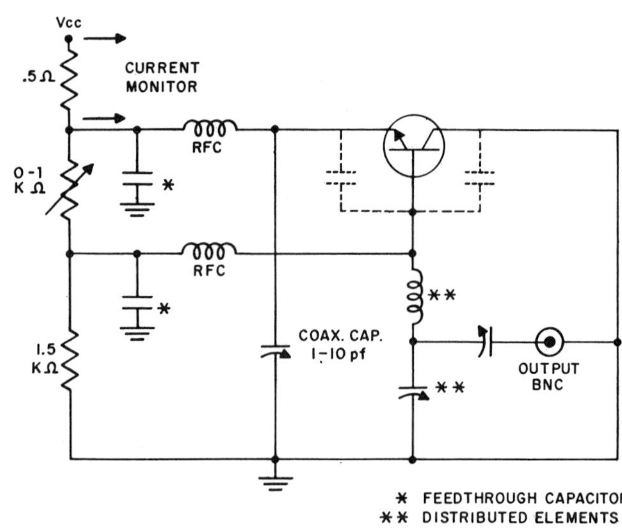

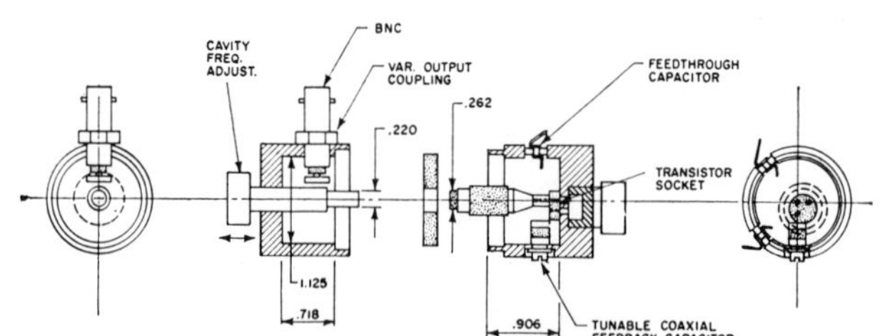

600–1,100 MHZ POWER OSCILLATOR—Uses coaxial cavity for which equivalent circuit is shown below. Suitable for pulse or c-w operation. Either 2N3533 or 2N3866 overlay type of uhf transistor may be used. Article covers design and includes performance graphs.—O. L. Meyer and D. C. Auth, Overlay UHF Transistors as CW and Pulsed Power Oscillators, *Microwave Journal*, Aug. 1969, p 59–66.

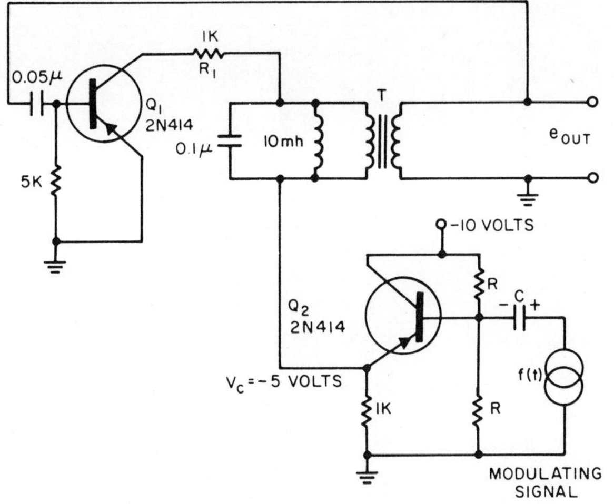

MULTI-PURPOSE A-M OSCILLATOR—Amplitude-modulated oscillator operates as collector-modulated class B amplifier for studying properties of a-m systems. Carrier frequency is 5 kHz. Values of biasing resistors R depend on impedance of modulating signal generator, and C depends on modulating frequency.—R. Brander and L. S. Bobrow, Low Cost 2-Stage Circuit Forms Versatile AM Oscillator, *Electronic Design*, May 10, 1965, p 42 and 44.

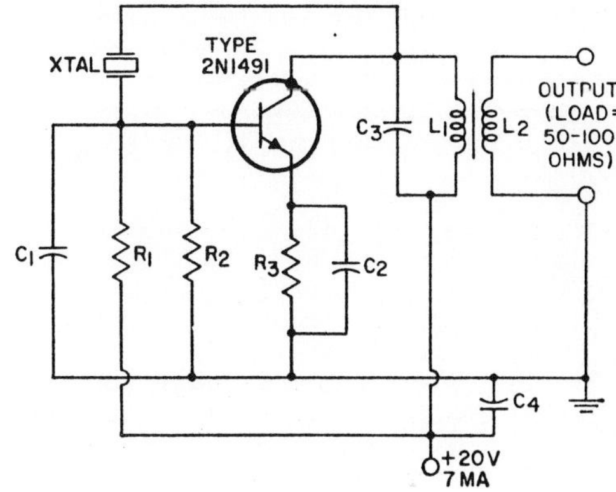

27-MHZ CRYSTAL—Provides stable 4-mW output from common-emitter circuit, using positive feedback from collector to base through crystal. Values: R1 9.1K; R2 680; R3 200; C1 20 pF; C2, C4 0.01 μF; C3 22 pF; L1 15 turns No. 22 enamel on CTC LS5 form with powdered iron slug; L2 2 turns No. 18 enamel on cold end of L1; XTAL 27 MHz.—"Transistor Manual," RCA, Harrison, N.J., SC-13, p 507.

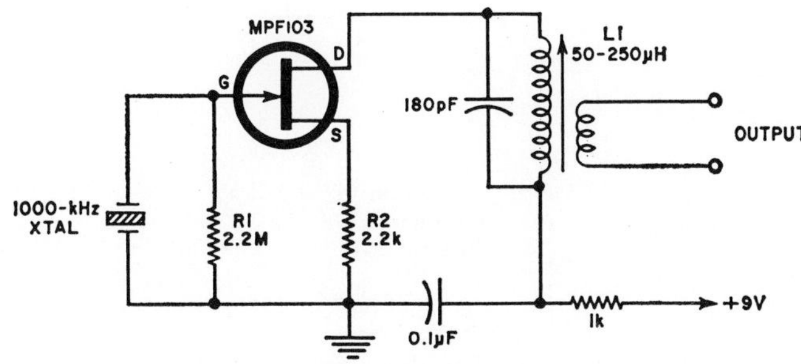

1-MHZ TUNED-DRAIN FET—Uses link output. Puts out clean sine wave when core of L1 is adjusted to tune drain tank slightly higher than crystal frequency, so drain current is minimum of about 150 μA unloaded.—F. H. Tooker, FET Sine-Wave Crystal Oscillators, *Electronics World*, June 1969, p 33 and 83.

100-KHZ CRYSTAL FET—Offers excellent frequency stability at low current drain, with harmonics out to 100 MHz. Q1 and Q2 are Motorola HEP-801 and HEP-50 respectively. Choke L1 is Miller 6304 or equivalent. Article gives construction and calibration details.—"Field Effect Transistor Projects," Motorola, Phoenix, Ariz., 1966, p 48–56.

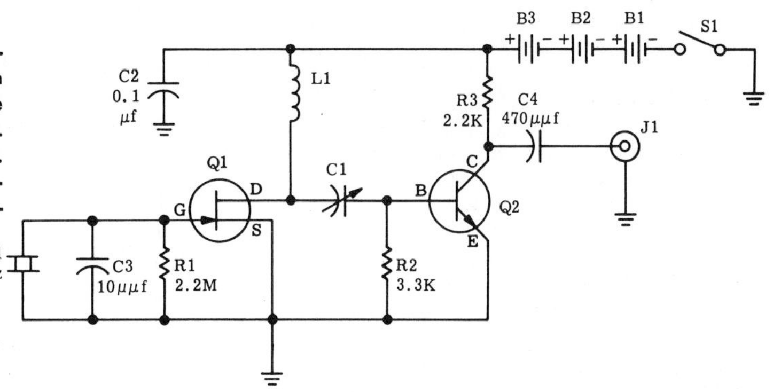

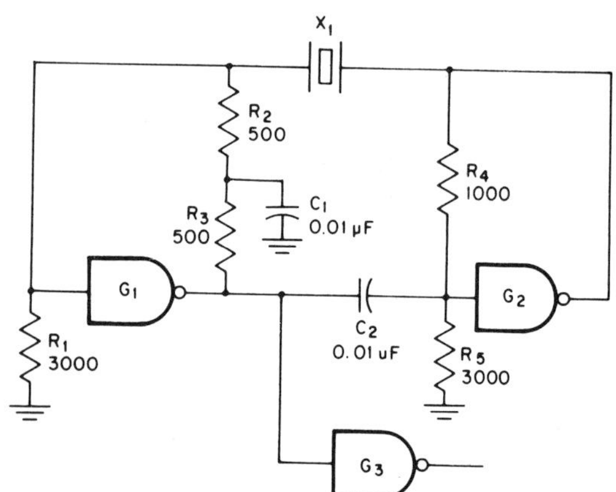

1–3 MHZ THREE-GATE CRYSTAL—Any gates in DTL/TTL families can be used if they are buffer type with low output impedance in high or low state. 932 buffer was used in circuit. Frequency stability is essentially that of crystal, which operates in series mode on fundamental frequency. May be powered by 5 V of logic gates or any other value between 3.8 and 7 V d-c. Output is square wave with about 40% duty cycle.—S. D. Culp, Crystal Oscillator, *EEE*, July 1970, p 87.

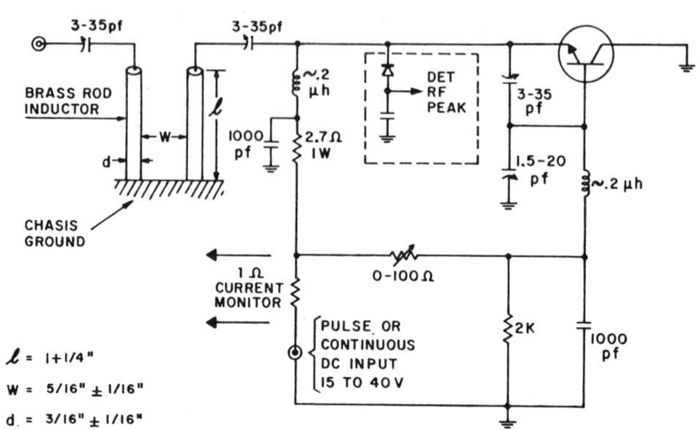

350–750 MHZ POWER OSCILLATOR—Tunable lumped-circuit oscillator for pulsed or c-w operation can use either 2N3553 or 2N3866 overlay type of uhf transistor. Article covers design and includes performance graphs. —O. L. Meyer and D. C. Auth, Overlay UHF Transistors as CW and Pulsed Power Oscillators, *Microwave Journal*, Aug. 1969, p 59–66.

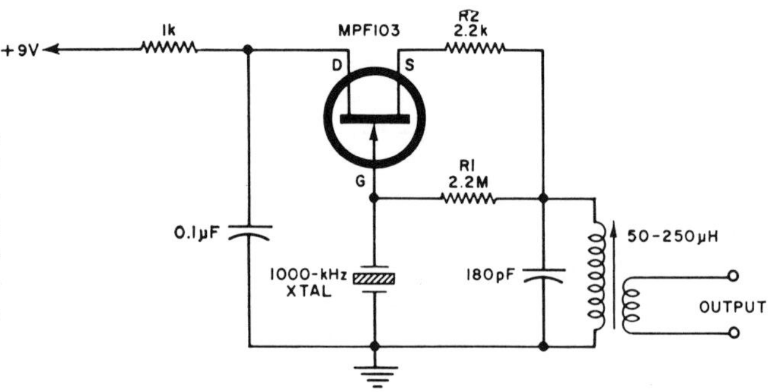

1-MHZ GROUNDED-DRAIN COLPITTS FET—Adjusting core of output transformer for minimum drain current gives cleanest sinewave output. Grounded-drain configuration makes circuit less susceptible to stray fields and capacitances.—F. H. Tooker, FET Sine-Wave Crystal Oscillators, *Electronics World*, June 1969, p 33 and 83.

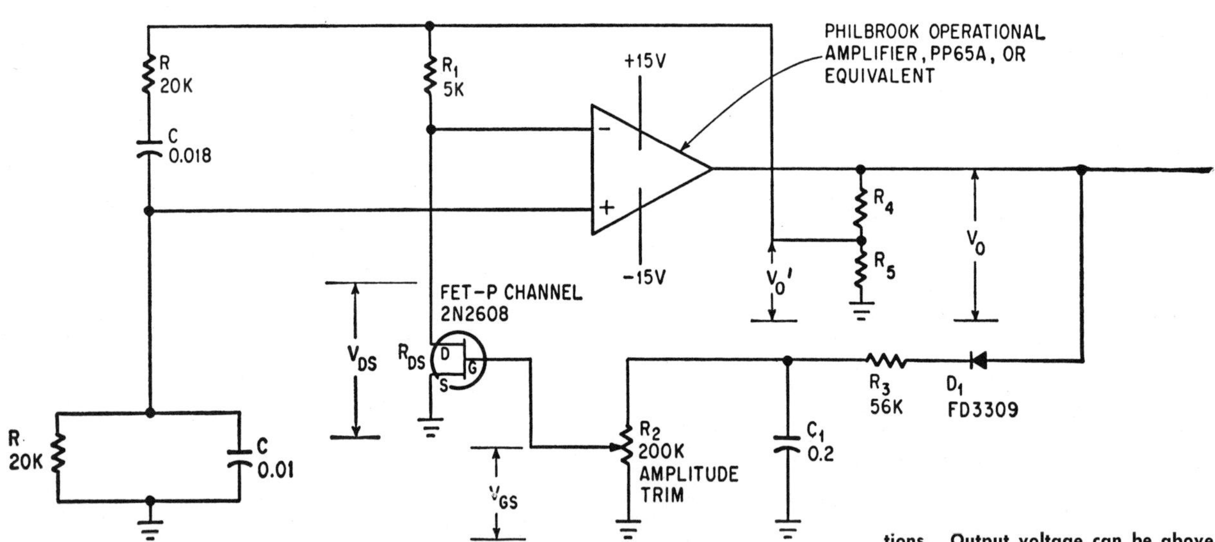

FET STABILIZES OPAMP BRIDGE OSCILLATOR—Arrangement provides distortionless output over full range from d-c to 100 kHz. Depends on fact that an fet acts like linear variable resistance when its drain-source voltage approaches zero. Article gives design equations. Output voltage can be above 10 V.—J. J. Panico, FET Stabilizes Amplitude Of Wien Bridge Oscillator, *Electronics*, Oct. 3, 1966, p 107.

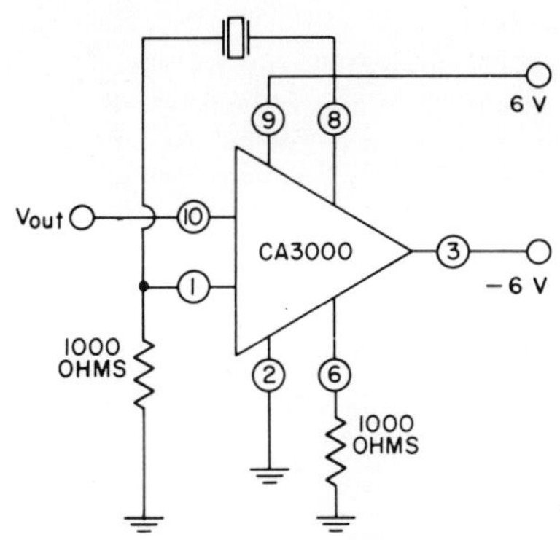

CRYSTAL IC—Use of two external resistors and quartz crystal with IC d-c amplifier gives crystal oscillator operating up to 1 MHz depending on crystal used. Output is taken from collector that is not connected to crystal (terminal 10), and has waveform about halfway between sine and square wave.—"Linear Integrated Circuits," RCA, Harrison, N.J., IC-41, p 125.

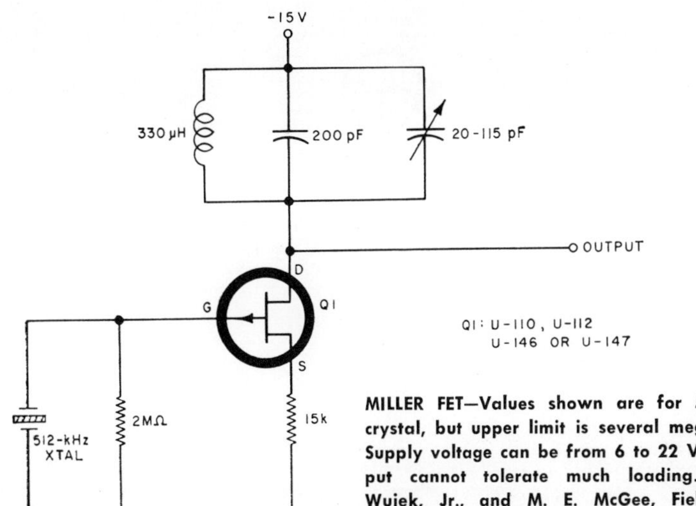

MILLER FET—Values shown are for 512-kHz crystal, but upper limit is several megahertz. Supply voltage can be from 6 to 22 V. Output cannot tolerate much loading.—J. H. Wujek, Jr., and M. E. McGee, Field-Effect Transistor Circuits, *Electronics World*, May 1967, p 32–33 and 75.

TWO-FREQUENCY CRYSTAL OSCILLATOR—With negative voltage applied to supply terminal, transistor operates in inverted mode and 500-kHz crystal X1 determines output frequency. With positive supply, 600-kHz crystal determines output frequency. Adding capacitors as shown by dashed lines gives single output terminal. Frequencies may be remotely selected.—J. M. Tewksbury, Bilateral Crystal Oscillator Has Two-Frequency Output, "400 Ideas for Design Selected from Electronic Design," Hayden Book Co., N.Y., 1964, p 179.

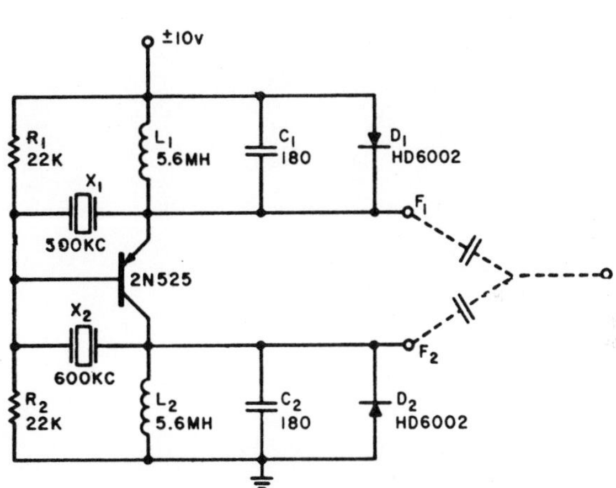

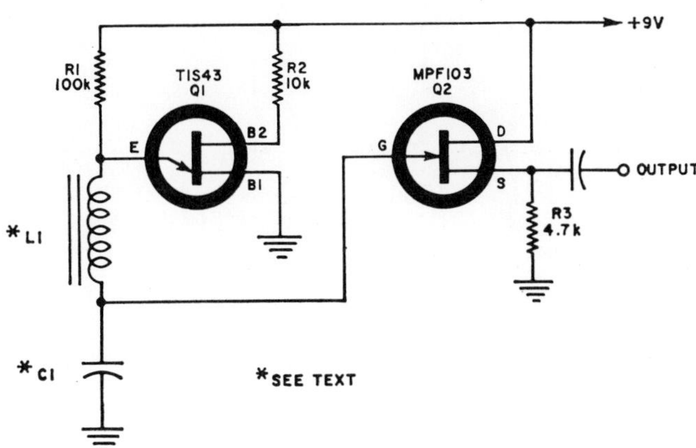

400-HZ UJT SINE-WAVE—Output frequency ranges from 100 Hz to 100 kHz, depending on L1 and C1. For 400-Hz sine-wave output with acceptable waveform purity, C1 is 0.047 μF and L1 is 3-H a-f choke.—F. H. Tooker, Improving Sawtooth Linearity, *Electronics World*, Feb. 1969, p 84.

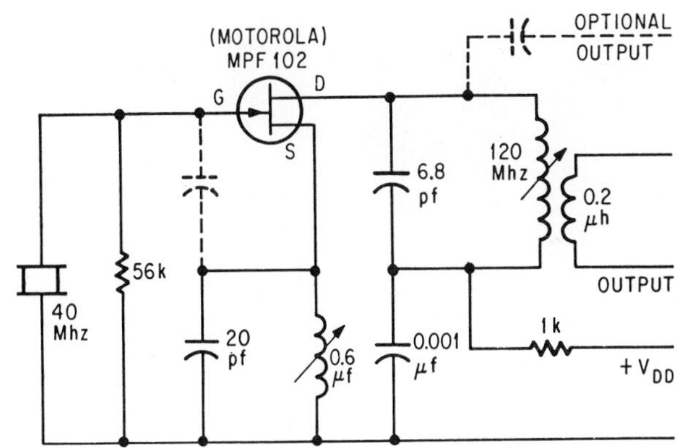

FET IN CRYSTAL TRIPLER—High gate-to-source impedance of fet minimizes crystal loading in vhf-uhf oscillator-multiplier. Tank circuit in source lead is tuned to about 0.7 times 40-MHz fundamental of crystal.—F. B. Cupp, FEB Cuts Down Crystal Loading, *Electronics*, Sept. 18, 1967, p 111.

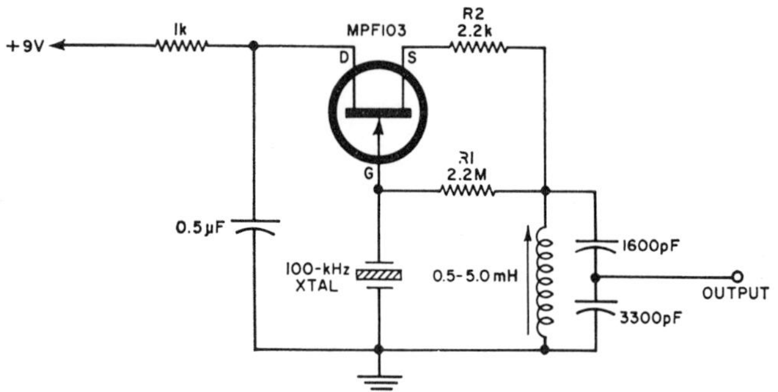

100-KHZ GROUNDED-DRAIN COLPITTS FET—Sine-wave output is cleanest when tank coil is adjusted for minimum drain current. Useful as signal source for time-base generators in digital counter.—F. H. Tooker, FET Sine-Wave Crystal Oscillators, *Electronics World*, June 1969, p 33 and 83.

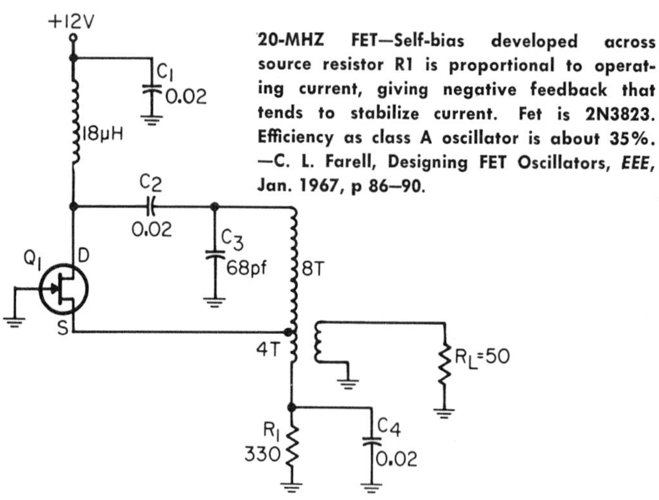

20-MHZ FET—Self-bias developed across source resistor R1 is proportional to operating current, giving negative feedback that tends to stabilize current. Fet is 2N3823. Efficiency as class A oscillator is about 35%. —C. L. Farell, Designing FET Oscillators, *EEE*, Jan. 1967, p 86–90.

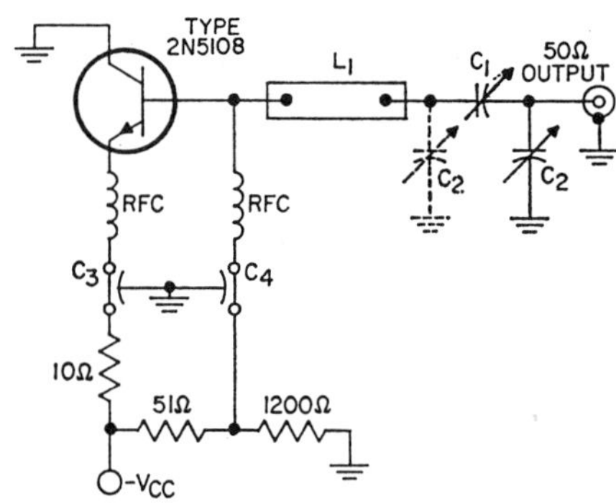

1.68-GHZ L-BAND OSCILLATOR—Collector of transistor connects directly to ground plane of stripline circuit board. Power output is over 0.3 W at 20% efficiency when operating from 25-V d-c supply. L1 is 0.75-inch section of 50-ohm microstripline; can be operated at any frequency from 1 to 2 GHz by changing length of L1 slightly. With 0.8-inch line, frequency is 1.5 GHz. Values: C1, C2 0.35–3.5 pF piston; C3, C4 470 pF; RFC 5 turns No. 28 on 0.125" form.—"Silicon Power Circuits Manual," RCA, Harrison, N.J., SP-51, p 364.

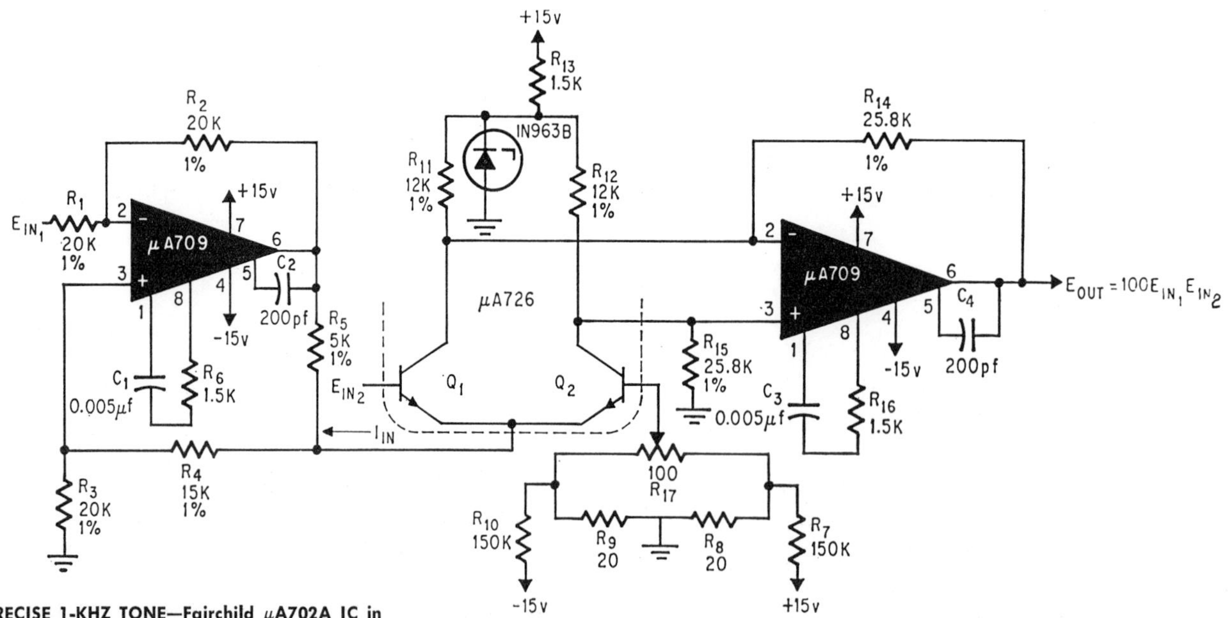

PRECISE 1-KHZ TONE—Fairchild µA702A IC in fet circuit provides agc to minimize instabilities and prevent limiting. Can be used as precision tone generator, timing signal generator, or for computation. Negative feedback through R3 stabilizes gain and makes it independent of IC characteristics. Positive feedback to noninverting input is made equal to negative feedback by agc, to give undistorted 8-V sine-wave output.—J. F. Gifford and M. Markkula, Linear IC's: Part 5, Ins and Outs of Op Amps, *Electronics*, Nov. 27, 1967, p 84–93.

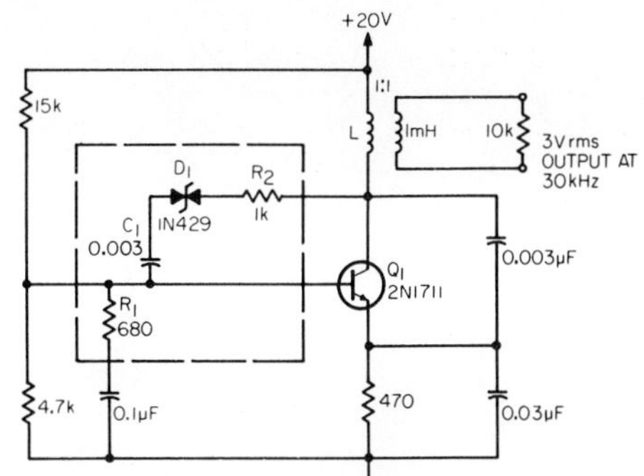

30-KHZ CONSTANT-AMPLITUDE—Zener D1 stabilizes operating conditions and output amplitude of emitter-feedback oscillator. Distortion in sine-wave output is less than 1%, and amplitude stability for combined variations of 0–65 C temperature change, 18-22 V d-c supply voltage change, and load change from 10K to infinity is less than 5%. —M. Feller, Amplitude-Stabilized Oscillator, *EEE*, April 1967, p 139–140.

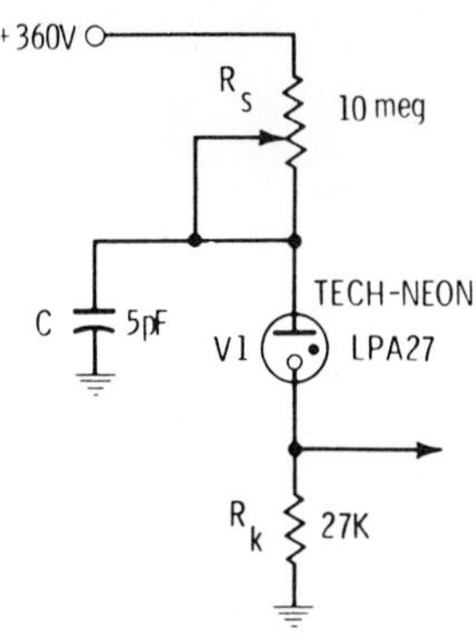

30–40 KHZ NEON—Neon chosen has very fast deionization time to maintain high-frequency stability. Sine-wave amplitude varies from 1 to 14 V into 1-meg load.—W. G. Miller, "Using and Understanding Miniature Neon Lamps," H. W. Sams & Co., Indianapolis, Ind., 1969, p 41.

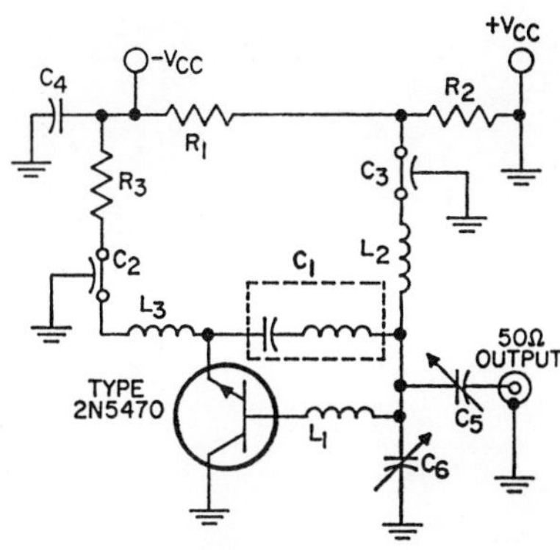

1.8–2.3 GHZ TUNABLE—With 24-V supply, delivers 0.3 W at 16% efficiency with Hartley oscillator circuit. Values: R1 51; R2 1.2K; R3 10; C1 0.82 pF; C2, C3 100 pF; C4 0.01 pF; C5, C6 0.35–3.5 pF; L1 0.05" length No. 22 wire.—"Silicon Power Circuits Manual," RCA, Harrison, N.J., SP-51, p 365.

SPLIT-DRAIN FET—Tuned-drain tuned-gate crystal oscillator puts out clean sine wave when L1 is set for minimum drain current of about 150 μA unloaded.—F. H. Tooker, FET Sine-Wave Crystal Oscillators, *Electronics World*, June 1969, p 33 and 83.

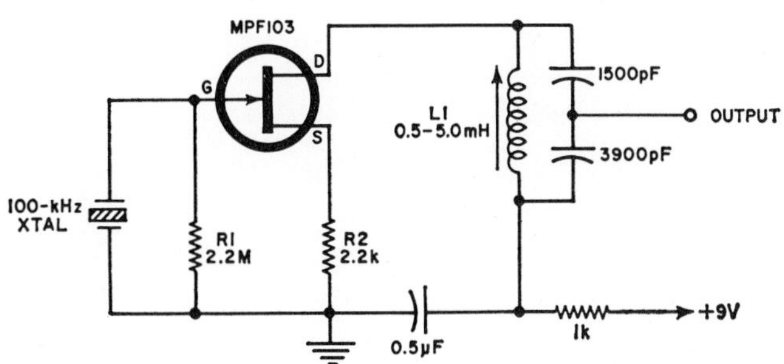

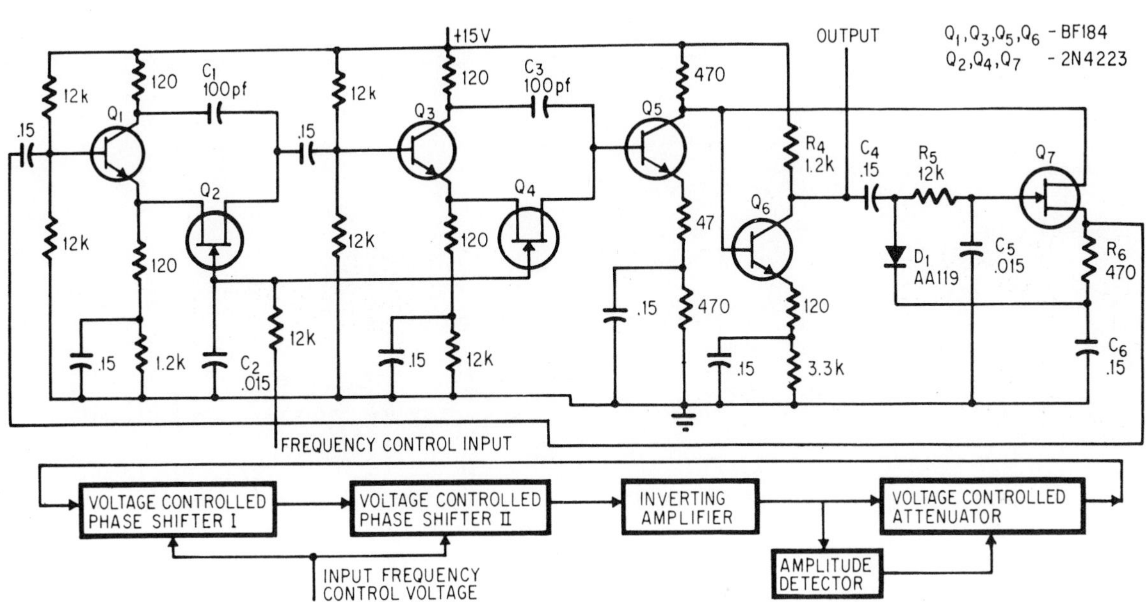

0.5–5 MHZ FET-TUNED R-C—Field-effect transistors acting as variable resistors tune R-C oscillator over decade range with control voltage of 4.8 to 7.2 V. Oscillator output amplitude is constant within 1 dB. Other frequency ranges can be obtained by changing capacitor values. Two phase shifters, phase inverter, amplifier, and attenuator are connected in loop. Circuit oscillates at frequency in which total phase shift is 360 deg. Voltage-controlled attenuator Q7 is driven by amplitude detector Q6 to provide constant output voltage.—K. van der Geer, FET's Tune RC Oscillator Over Decade Range, *Electronics*, Feb. 17, 1969, p 96.

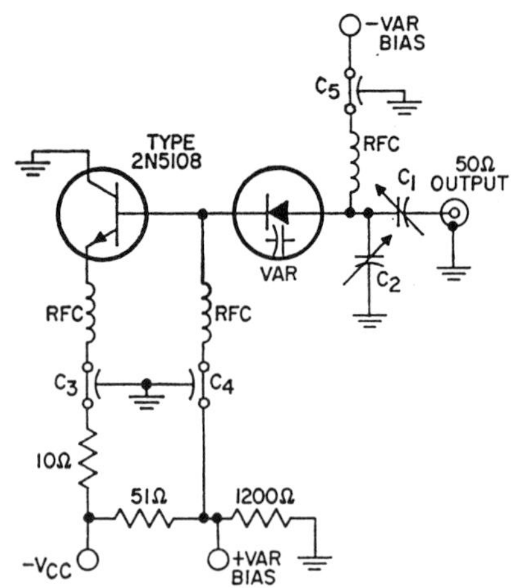

1–1.5 GHZ VARACTOR-TUNED—Delivers 600 mW over entire range when tuned with high-Q varactor diode having control range of 0 to 22 V and transistor collector supply of 28 V. Values: C1, C2 1–7 pF piston; C3-C5 470 pF; RFC 0.1 μH.—"Silicon Power Circuits Manual," RCA, Harrison, N.J., SP-51, p 365.

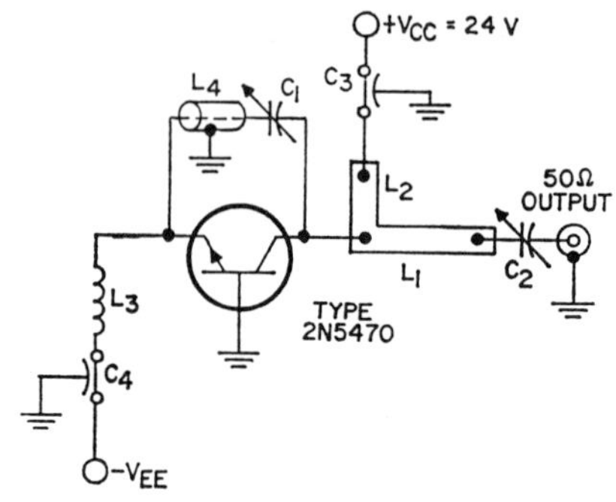

1.8–2.2 GHZ COLPITTS—Phase-resonant loop L4-C1 provides necessary feedback. With 24-V supply, power output is about 0.3 W. Values: C1, C2 0.35–3.5 pF; C3, C4 100 pF; L1, L2 microstripline (dimensions given in book); L3 5 turns; L4 50-ohm coax 1.5" long. —"Silicon Power Circuits Manual," RCA, Harrison, N.J., SP-51, p 366.

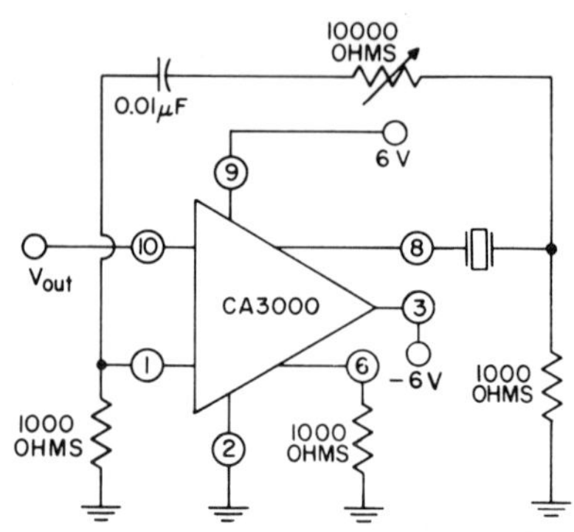

VARIABLE-FEEDBACK CRYSTAL IC—Adjustable feedback path for IC d-c amplifier permits adjusting crystal oscillator to give pure sine wave. Frequency depends on crystal used, and can be up to 1 MHz. Collector tuning (terminal 10) will extend frequency range above 10 MHz.—"Linear Integrated Circuits," RCA, Harrison, N.J., IC-41, p 125.

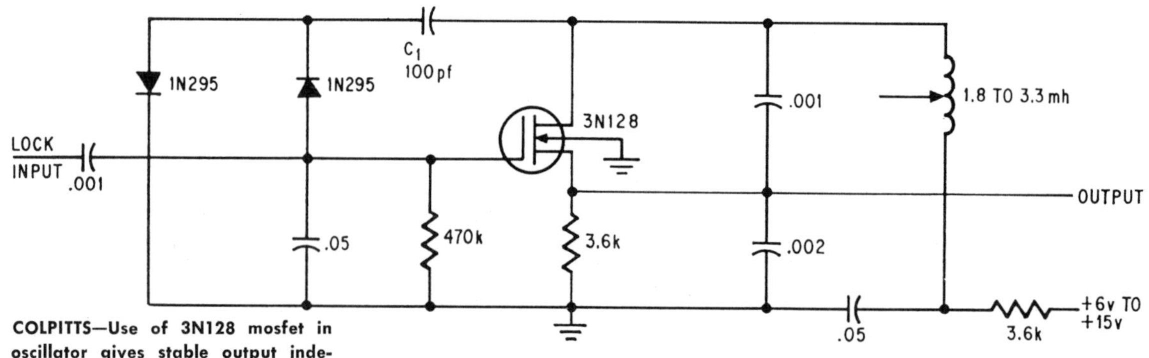

MOSFET COLPITTS—Use of 3N128 mosfet in Colpitts oscillator gives stable output independently of load and supply voltage changes, and improves waveform symmetry. Circuit can be frequency-locked to external oscillator through input coupling capacitor.—N. H. Brown, MOS FET Stabilizes Oscillator's Output, *Electronics*, Feb. 3, 1969, p 80.

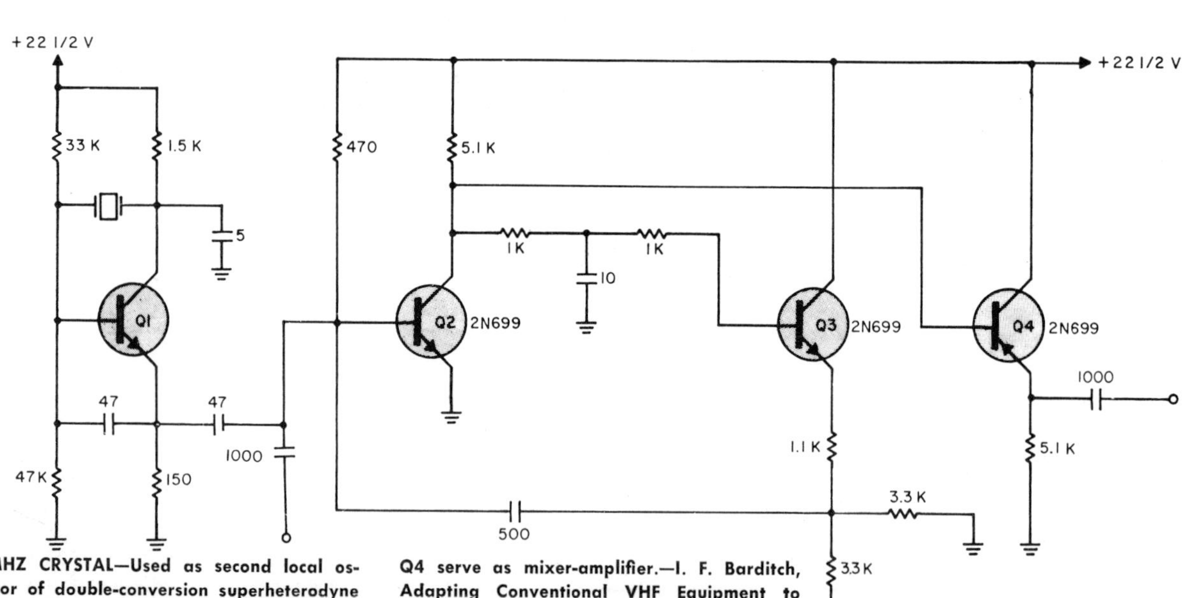

30-MHZ CRYSTAL—Used as second local oscillator of double-conversion superheterodyne f-m receiver developed for printed-circuit card construction. Q1 can be 2N699. Q2-Q4 serve as mixer-amplifier.—I. F. Barditch, Adapting Conventional VHF Equipment to Molecular Electronics, *Electronic Design*, Feb. 17, 1964, p 44–51.

CHAPTER 60
Phase Control Circuits

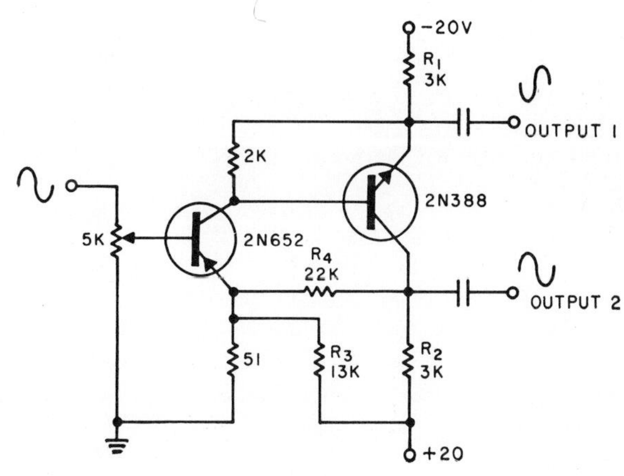

PHASE SPLITTER WITH GAIN OF 150—Direct-coupled complementary pair with feedback provides voltage gain and equal outputs 180 deg out of phase. Values of R1 and R2 must be changed according to output impedance and R3 then adjusted to give circuit bias for desired operating level of output transistor.—R. E. Risely, DC Phase Splitter Adds Voltage Gain, *Electronic Design*, Feb. 3, 1964, p 46 and 48.

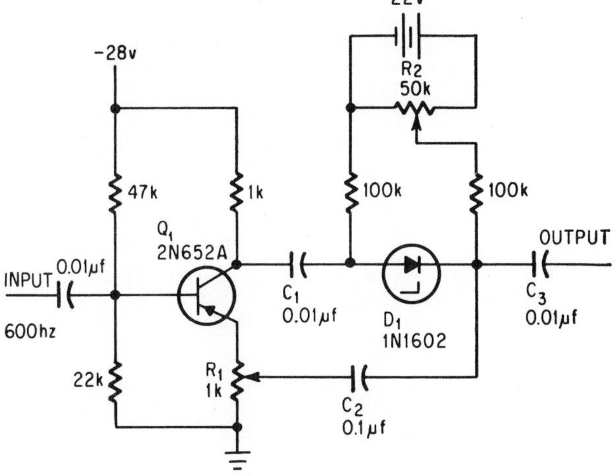

VOLTAGE-VARIABLE SHIFTER—Can be used as a-c motor speed control for mixers, blenders, and drills, where firing point of scr is changed. Can also serve as correction circuit in feedback loop of automatic phase control system. Phase angle of low-frequency input signal can be shifted up to 70 deg without distorting waveform. As adjustable phase reference, one circuit can control many servomechanisms. Reduction of 5:1 in output amplitude over phase-shifting range can be cut to 1.2:1 by adjusting R1.—T. T. Kalal, Zener Diode Controls Variable Phase Shifter, *Electronics*, Dec. 26, 1966, p 72–73.

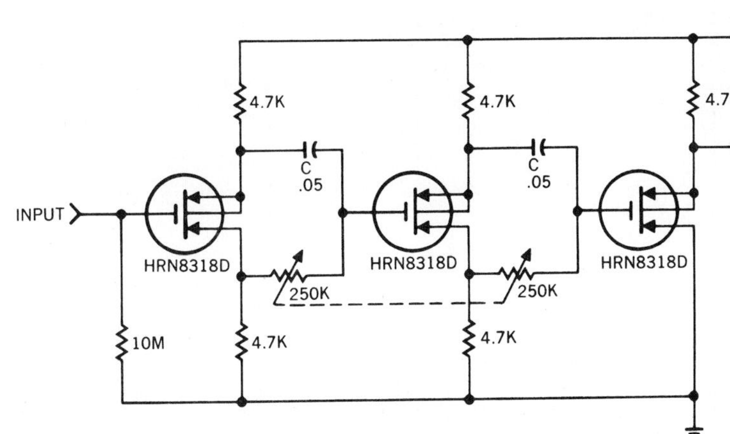

MOSFET TWO-STAGE PHASE SHIFTER—Ganged control permits shifting phase of 400-Hz signal over full range of 0 to 180 deg. Can be used to generate pulse or signal having known phase difference from that of reference signal.—C. R. Perkins, "Application of MOSFET Devices to Electronic Circuits," Hughes, Newport Beach, Cal., 1968, p 26.

CONSTANT-AMPLITUDE PHASE SHIFTER—Shifts sinusoidal signal over 180-deg range, and reversal of input leads provides additional 180-deg shift. Maintains constant output amplitude and low output impedance. Used for phase-locking amplifiers.—J. J. Shin, Signals Shifted 180 Deg as Amplitude Remains Constant, *Electronics*, May 12, 1969, p 110.

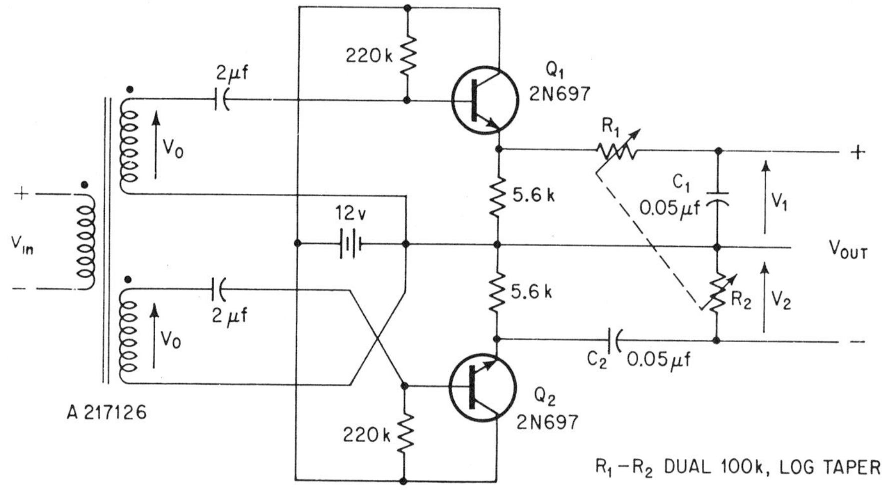

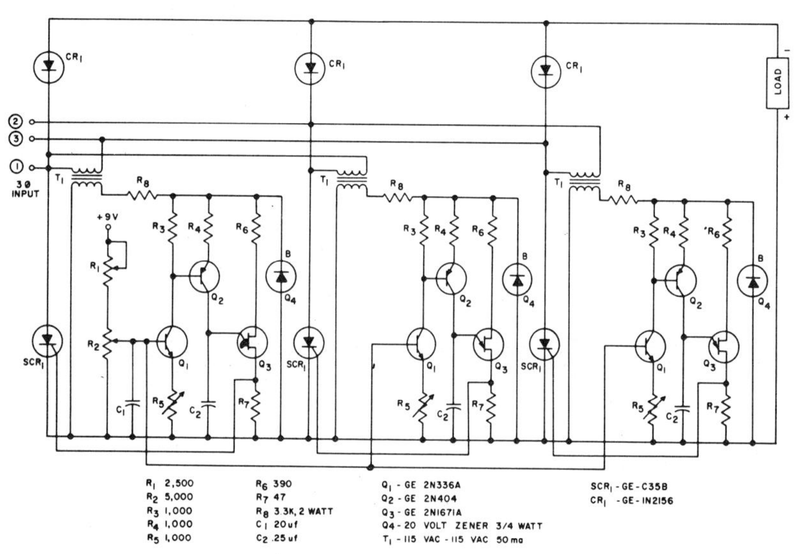

THREE-PHASE WITH STEPLESS 0–100% CONTROL—Uses separate triggering of each phase for varying d-c output voltage smoothly down to zero, for applications such as ring counters, flip-flops, and magnetic firing controls. Will not fall out of synchronism. Power output depends on scr's used. Tracking accuracy, controlled by pots R5, is accurate within 1 deg at 60 Hz.—J. D. Atherly, F. W. Gutzwiller, and F. Pastore, Three Phase SCR Firing Circuits for DC Power Supplies, General Electric, Syracuse, N.Y., No. 200.21, 1962.

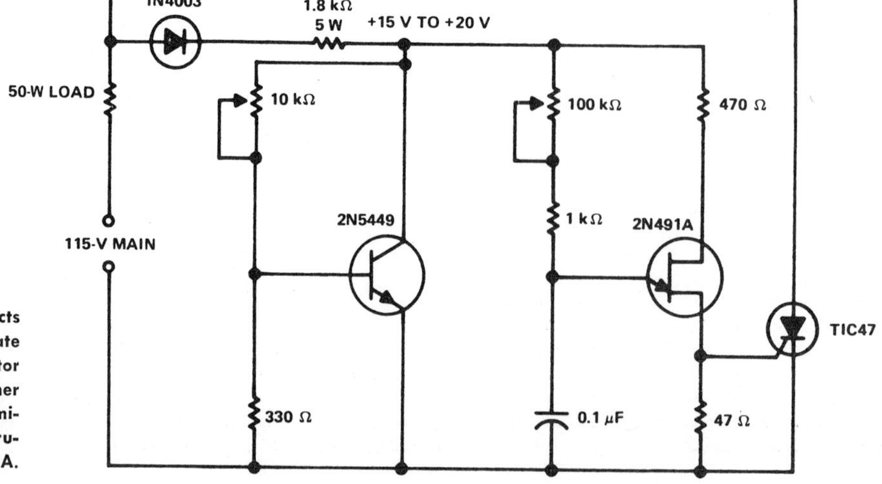

50-W HALF-WAVE A-C CONTROL—Conducts over range of 10 to 170 deg on alternate half-cycles. May be used for heater or motor control, as relay driver, or as lamp dimmer if flicker is not objectionable.—Preferred Semiconductors and Components, Texas Instruments, Dallas, Texas, CC101, 1968, p 7108A.

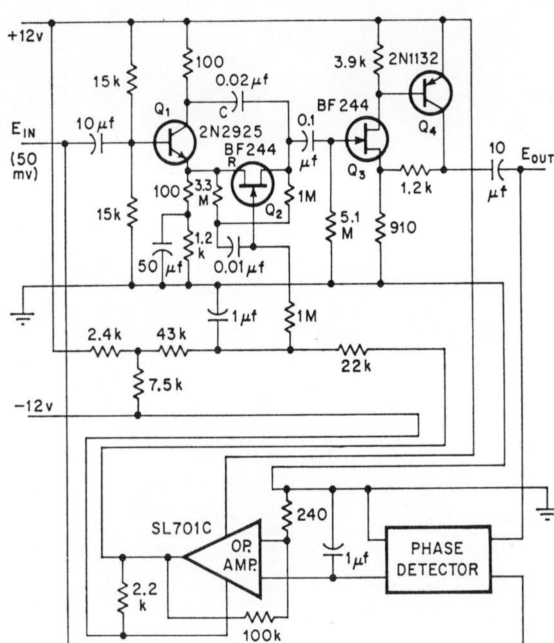

FREQUENCY-INDEPENDENT 90-DEG SHIFTER—Will produce 90-deg shift independently of frequency in audio range, for producing circular sweeps on crt. Can also be used for phase measurements where calibrated 0–90 deg phase shifter is formed by adding signal to quadrature component. Fet is used as variable resistance in R-C phase shifter, with resistance controlled by feedback from phase detector and opamp.—J. Kalinski, Variable FET Resistance Gives 90 Deg Phase Shifts, *Electronics*, July 20, 1970, p 88.

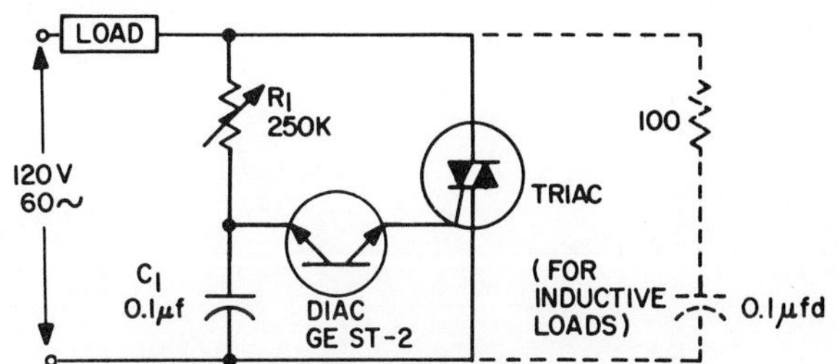

FULL-WAVE DIAC-TRIAC—Simplicity makes circuit ideal for many lamp, heater, and fan speed controls, despite limited control range and large hysteresis effect at low outputs. Choice of triac depends on load to be handled.—"SCR Manual," 4th Edition, General Electric, 1967, p 139–140.

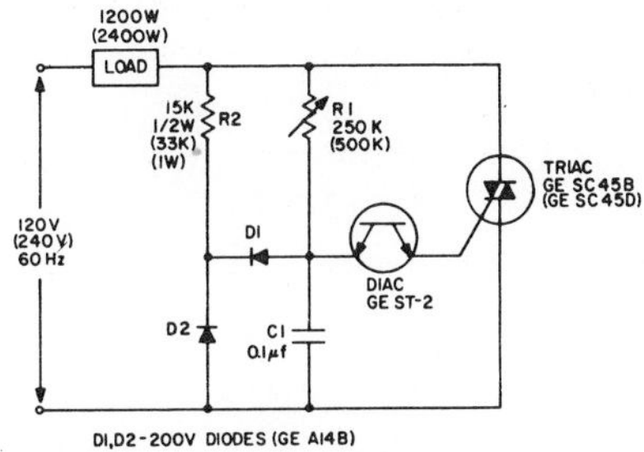

FULL-WAVE WITH ALTERNATE RESET—Uses diode to reset capacitor at end of each positive half-cycle. Does not reset at end of negative half-cycle, but snap-on effect is negligible.—"SCR Manual," 4th Edition, General Electric, 1967, p 188.

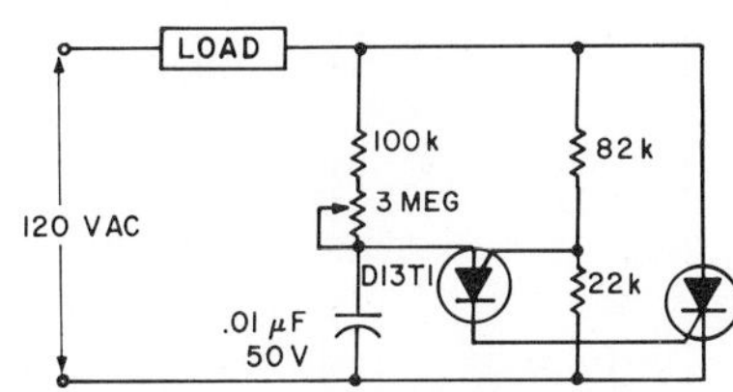

LINE-OPERATED SCR TRIGGER—Uses D13T1 triode thyristor as programmable ujt in phase control circuit that derives required interbase voltage directly from a-c line. Potentiometer in resistor divider controls point in each cycle at which scr (at right) is triggered.—W. R. Spofford, Jr., The D13T—A Programmable Unijunction Transistor, General Electric, Syracuse, N.Y., No. 90.70, 1967, p 7.

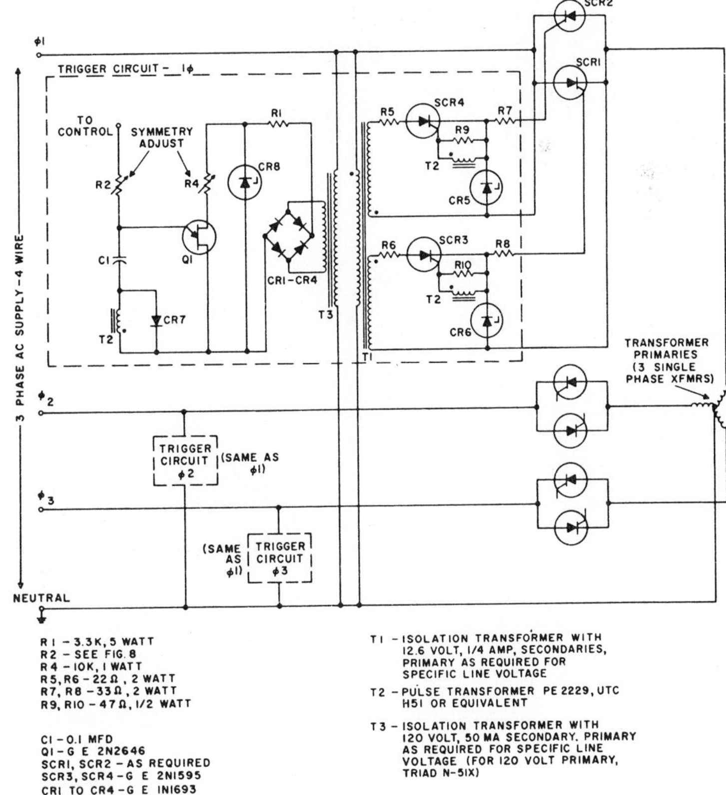

FULL-RANGE THREE-PHASE CONTROL—Used in four-wire a-c system feeding three wye-connected transformers. One pair of scr's is in series with each line, and transformer neutral is connected to system neutral. Trigger circuits are between line and neutral of each phase. Ujt triggers pilot scr's. Article has five circuit variations for controlling the three ujt's from single master signal.—"SCR Manual," 4th Edition, General Electric, 1967, p 205–207.

MANUAL SCR CONTROL—Basic manually controlled scr with ujt covers full range from minimum to maximum power. Zener clamps voltage of control circuit to fixed level.—"SCR Manual," 4th Edition, General Electric, 1967, p 189–190.

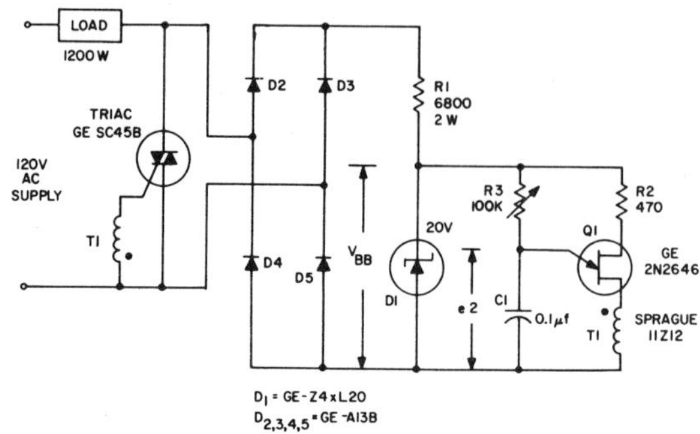

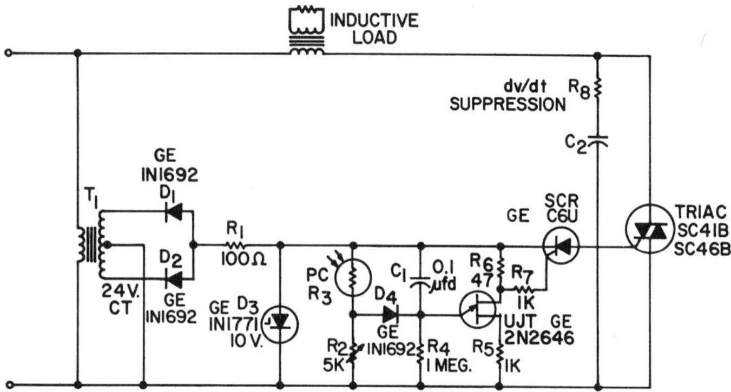

RAMP AND PEDESTAL CONTROL—Designed for inductive loads. Rectified supply voltage is used with small pilot scr to give continuous drive to triac gate after triggering, to hold triac on until load current is high enough for triac to latch.—J. H. Galloway, Using the Triac for Control of AC Power, General Electric, Syracuse, N.Y., No. 200.35, 1966, p 12.

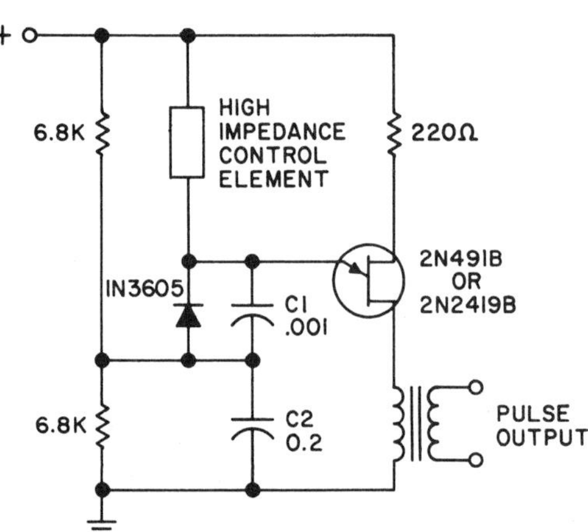

HIGH-GAIN UJT—Simple modification of conventional ujt-scr phase-control circuit increases effective gain up to 10,000 times, giving equivalent of several stages of transistor amplification. Article covers choice of capacitor values to give desired output pulse amplitude.—"Unijunction Circuit Hints," General Electric, Syracuse, N.Y., Fig. 2.

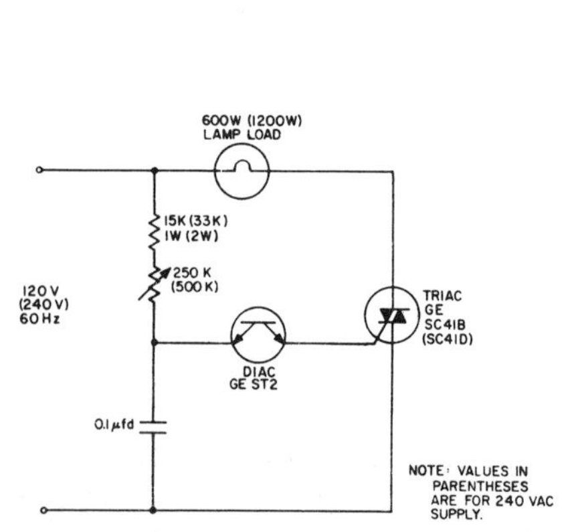

FULL-WAVE WITH REDUCED SNAP-ON—Control circuit is connected to supply to reduce snap-on effect wherein load current jumps suddenly to value from which it is smoothly controlled. This allows capacitor to recharge slightly between triggering point and end of half-cycle.—"SCR Manual," 4th Edition, General Electric, 1967, p 188.

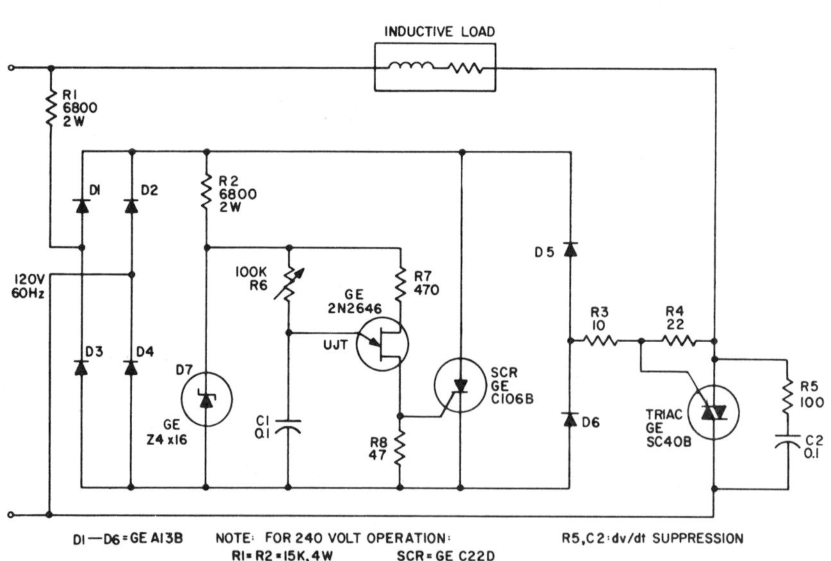

TRANSFORMERLESS TRIGGER—In smaller and lower-cost version of phase control for inductive a-c loads, bridge rectifier supplies power to ujt trigger and holding current to scr. If triggering occurs before turn-off of triac, scr will be turned on and held by current through R1.—"SCR Manual," 4th Edition, General Electric, 1967, p 197–198.

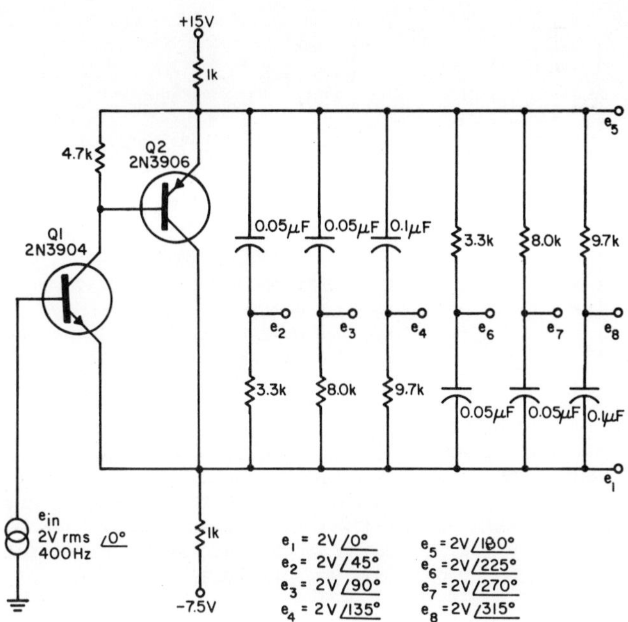

EIGHT-OUTPUT SHIFTER—Provides outputs 45 deg apart from 0 to 360 deg with constant amplitude and with phase nearly independent of load impedance. Output impedance is 2 ohms.—A. G. Lloyd, Multioutput Phase Shifter Uses One Transistor, *Electronic Design*, Oct. 25, 1967, p 130 and 132.

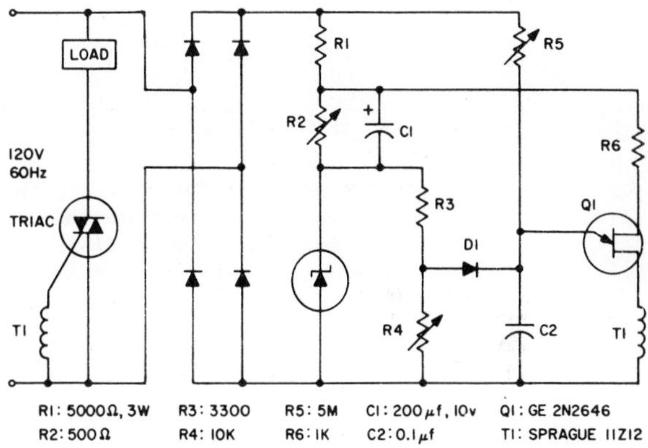

LINE-VOLTAGE COMPENSATION—R2 and C1 add to zener voltage a d-c voltage proportional to a-c supply voltage, to serve as ujt interbase voltage. Reducing supply voltage reduces interbase and peak-point voltages of ujt, to make triggering occur earlier on ramp and compensate for line voltage drop. Holds rms output voltage constant within 5% for 50% change in supply voltage.—"SCR Manual," 4th Edition, General Electric, 1967, p 195–196.

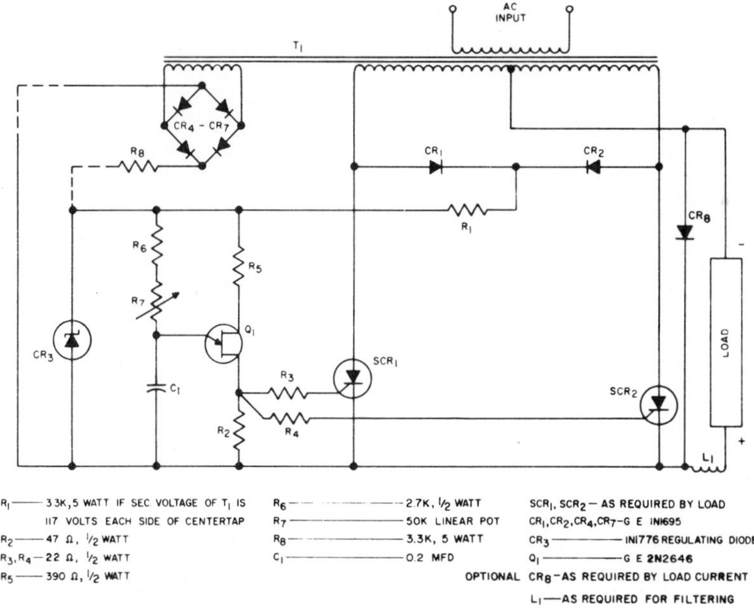

PHASE-CONTROLLED D-C SUPPLY—D-c voltage across load can be steplessly adjusted by R7 from maximum to zero, with scr's in single-phase center-tapped phase-controlled rectifier. Single ujt Q1 develops gate signal to fire both scr's on alternate half-cycles. At 60 Hz, R7 varies firing angle from 10 deg for maximum load power to 180 deg for fully off. —"SCR Manual," 4th Edition, General Electric, 1967, p 199–200.

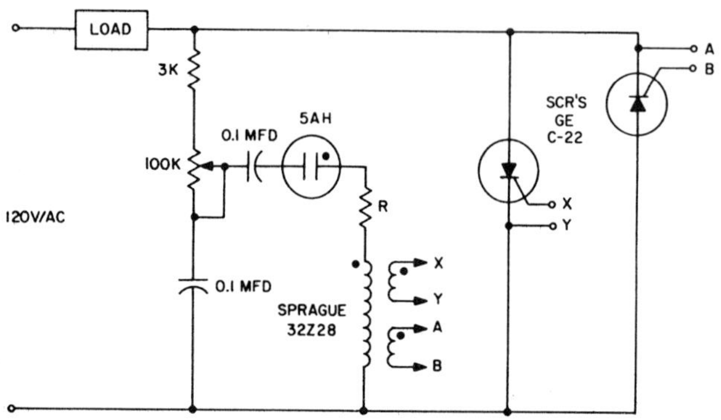

FULL-WAVE NEON-SCR TRIGGER—Transformer-coupled full-wave a-c phase-controlled circuit uses 5AH neon as trigger for two-terminal system. Pulse transformer allows scr's to alternate in firing. Loss of load voltage is only about 5% of what it would be without control circuit.—"SCR Manual," 4th Edition, General Electric, 1967, p 199.

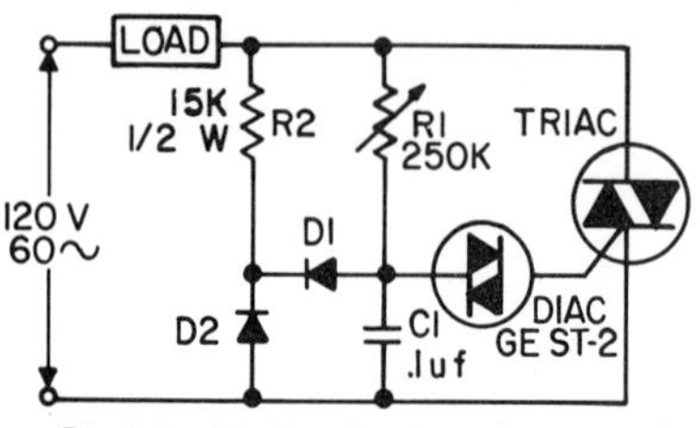

D1, D2 - 200V DIODES (GE A14B)

HYSTERESIS-FREE TRIAC CONTROL—Timing capacitor is reset to same level after each positive half-cycle, to provide uniform initial condition for phase-control operation. Arrangement is useful only for resistive loads such as lamps and heaters, because firing angle is not symmetrical throughout range from minimum to maximum load power. Choice of triac depends on load. For 220 V, change R1 to 500K, R2 to 22K, and D1-2 to A14D.—J. H. Galloway, Using the Triac for Control of AC Power, General Electric, Syracuse, N.Y., No. 200.35, 1966, p 8.

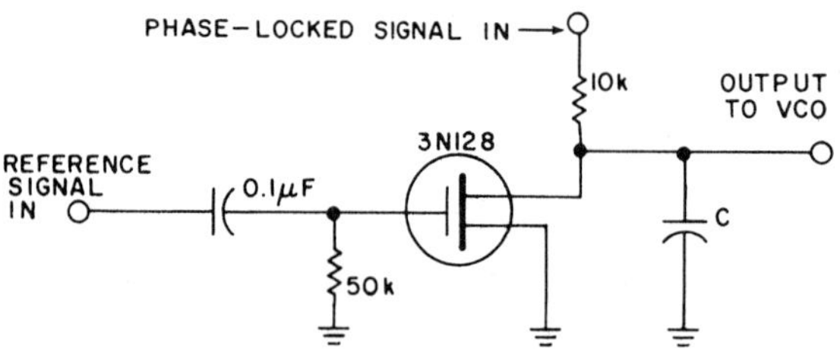

PHASE-LOCK DETECTOR—Mosfet operating in variable-resistance region provides d-c output voltage proportional to phase difference between input signal and reference signal. Used to drive vco of function generator. Value of C is chosen so its reactance is very much less than 10,000 ohms at oscillator frequency.—G. Worstell, Phase-Lock Detector Requires No External Power Supply, *Electronic Design*, Oct. 25, 1969, p 107.

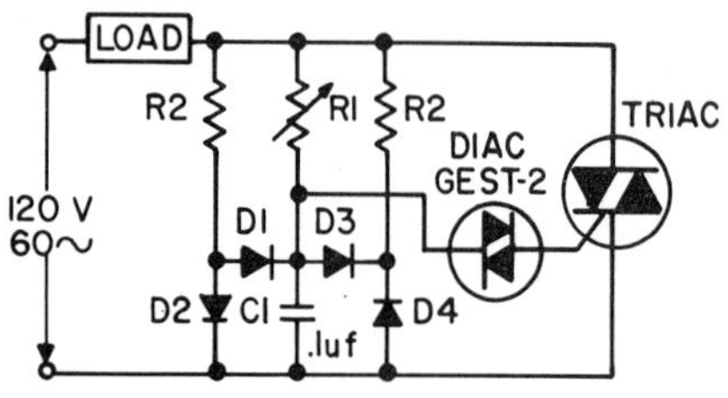

R1 - 250K POT.
R2, R3 - 15K 1/2 W
D1, D2, D3, D4 - 200V DIODES (GE A14B)

TRIAC CONTROL OF INDUCTIVE LOADS—Provides symmetrical firing for hysteresis-free operation of inductive loads. Choice of triac depends on load. For 220 V, change R1 to 500K, R2 and R3 to 22K, D1-D4 to A14D, and use 400-V triac.—J. H. Galloway, Using the Triac for Control of AC Power, General Electric, Syracuse, N.Y., No. 200.35, 1966, p 8.

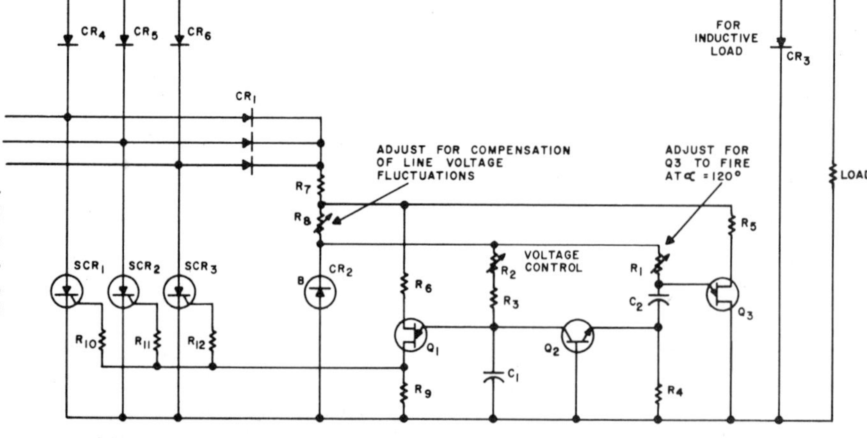

CR_1 -(3) GE IN1695
CR_2 - 20 VOLT, 1 WATT ZENER DIODE, IN1527
CR_3, CR_4, CR_5, CR_6, - AS REQUIRED FOR LOAD (GE IN2156)
SCR_1, SCR_2, SCR_3 - AS REQUIRED FOR LOAD (GE C35B)
Q_1, Q_3, - GE 2N1671A Q_2 - GE 2N635
R_1 - 10K POT
R_2 - 20K POT
R_3 - 470 OHMS
R_4 - 100 OHMS
R_5, R_6 - 390 OHMS
R_7, - 3.3K, 2W
R_8 - 500 OHM POT, 2W
R_9 - 100 OHMS
R_{10}, R_{11}, R_{12} - 25 OHMS
C_1 - 0.5 MFD
C_2 - 1.0 MFD

THREE-PHASE WITH COMMON TRIGGER—Operates from three-phase 117-V a-c line and provides control of d-c output voltage from zero to practically 100% of maximum theoretical value. Effect of transients is minimized. Firing circuit cannot fall out of synchronism with a-c power system. When d-c voltage is raised from zero, it jumps abruptly to 25% and then rises steplessly above that value; this is not objectionable for such applications as lamp and heater control. Similarly, when control voltage is reduced below 25%, output jumps abruptly to zero.—J. D. Atherly, F. W. Gutzwiller, and F. Pastore, Three Phase SCR Firing Circuits for DC Power Supplies, General Electric, Syracuse, N.Y., No. 200.21, 1962.

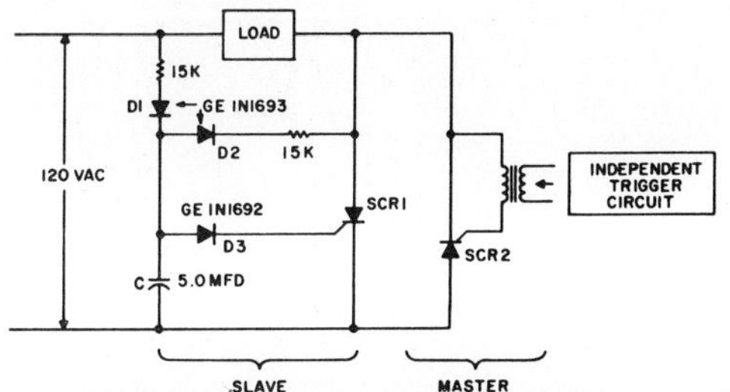

FULL-WAVE SLAVE CONTROL—Half-wave SCR2 circuit is triggered externally on one half-cycle at predetermined phase angle. On next half-cycle, slave circuit triggers SCR1 at same phase angle, to give full-wave phase control of load current. Both scr's are C11/C20.—"SCR Manual," 4th Edition, General Electric, 1967, p 69.

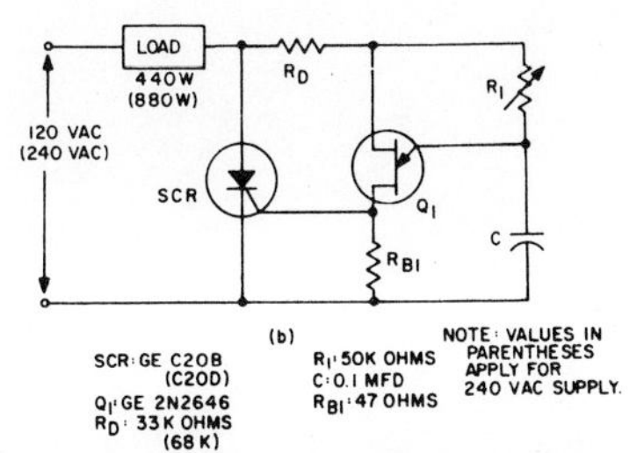

HALF-WAVE WITH UJT CAPACITOR RESET—Uses basic ujt relaxation oscillator to trigger scr during positive half-cycles of a-c line. Capacitor is reset at end of each positive half-cycle, by discharging through ujt, to prevent cycle-skipping caused by residual charge on half-cycles when scr is not triggered.—"SCR Manual," 4th Edition, General Electric, 1967, p 185–186.

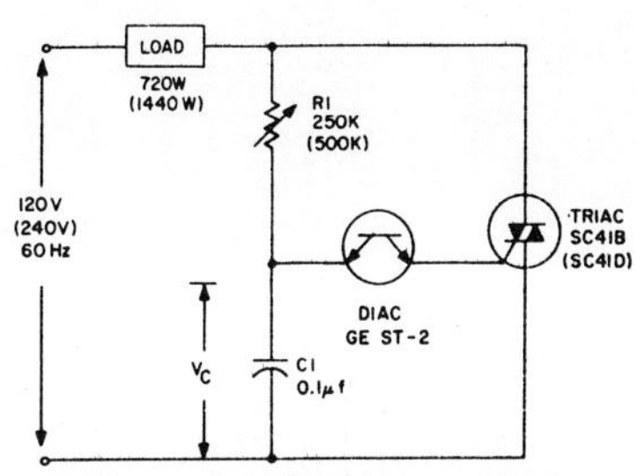

DIAC-TRIAC FULL-WAVE—Circuit is simplest full-wave phase control. R1 determines load current. Chief drawback is snap-on effect, wherein load current jumps suddenly to value from which it is smoothly controlled.—"SCR Manual," 4th Edition, General Electric, 1967, p 187–188.

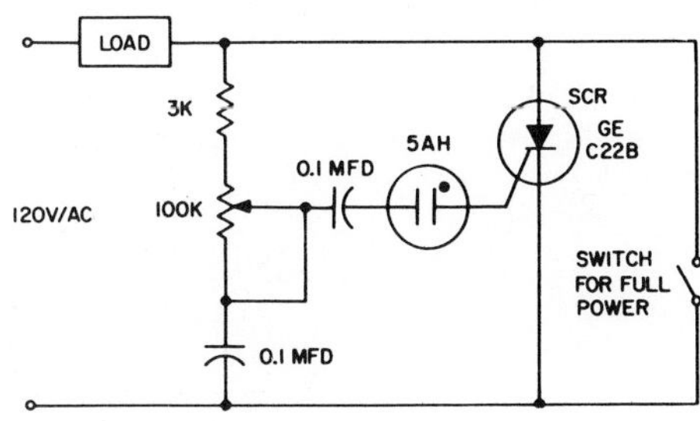

HALF-WAVE NEON-SCR TRIGGER—Combines low cost of R-C diode phase control circuit with improved performance of 5AH neon that triggers when voltage across capacitors reaches breakdown level of neon. Control range is from full off to 95% of half-wave rms output voltage.—"SCR Manual," 4th Edition, General Electric, 1967, p 198–199.

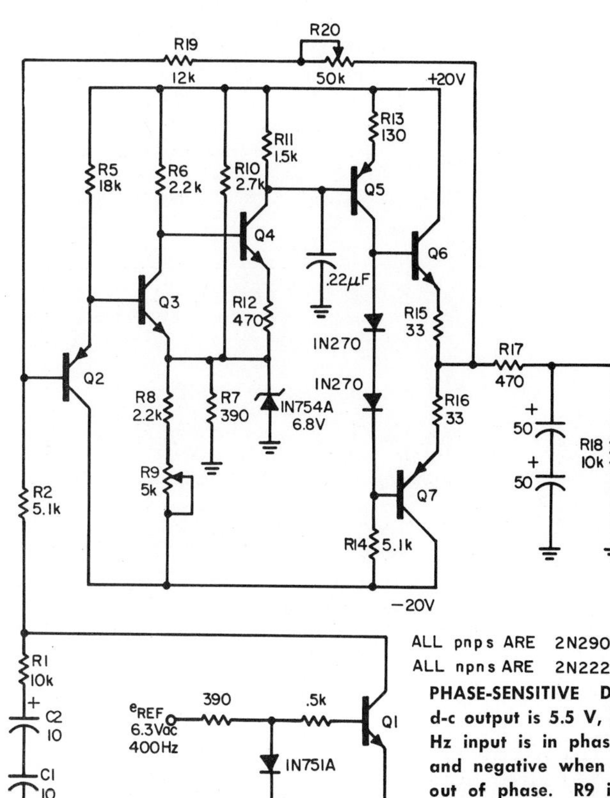

ALL pnps ARE 2N2907
ALL npns ARE 2N2222A

PHASE-SENSITIVE DEMODULATOR—Maximum d-c output is 5.5 V, being positive when 400-Hz input is in phase with 400-Hz reference, and negative when input and reference are out of phase. R9 is zero adjust.—N. Nekomoto, Linear Demodulator Combines High Output and Phase Sensitivity, *Electronic Design*, Oct. 11, 1967, p 100 and 102.

+10V
47K
2.2K
A
C_1
1μf
1μf
IN
1μf
Q_1
OUT
B
2.5K
R_1
22K
2.2K

170-DEG PHASE SHIFTER—Used in servos and other phase-sensitive systems to buck out residual phase shift. Transistor acts only as phase splitter, to provide complementary outputs from which desired value can be obtained by adjusting R1. Operates from 600 to 4,000 Hz, using 2N1306 transistor.—Transistorized Phase Shifter, "Electronic Circuit Design Handbook," Tab Books, Blue Ridge Summit, Pa., p 20.

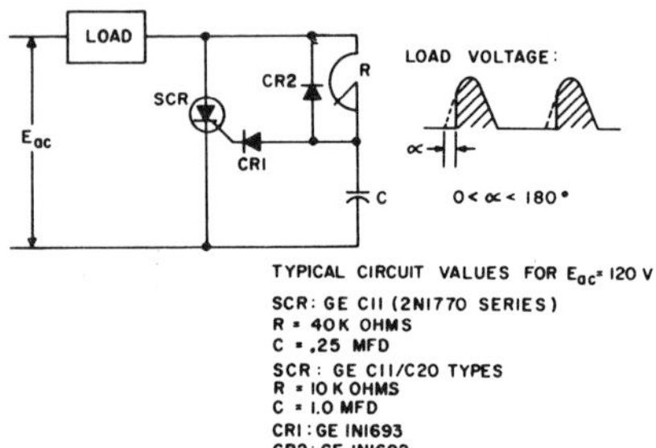

HALF-WAVE SCR—Gives full 180-degree phase control of half-wave load current.—"SCR Manual," 4th Edition, General Electric, 1967, p 69.

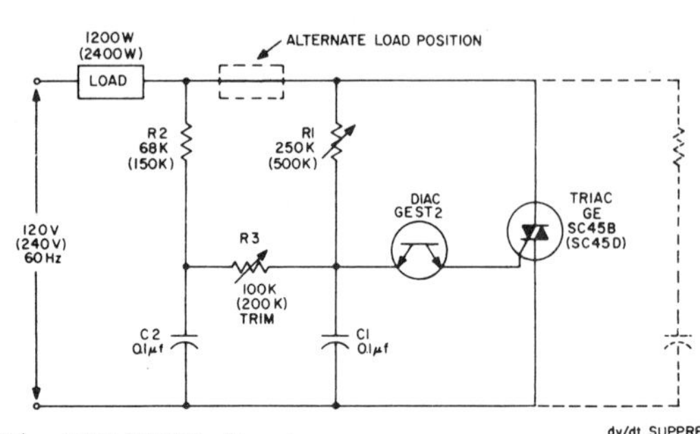

EXTENDED-RANGE FULL-WAVE—Has very little snap-on effect. C2 recharges C1 after triggering. R3 is adjusted to compensate for use of wide-tolerance components. Values in parentheses are for 240-V a-c line.—"SCR Manual," 4th Edition, General Electric, 1967, p 189.

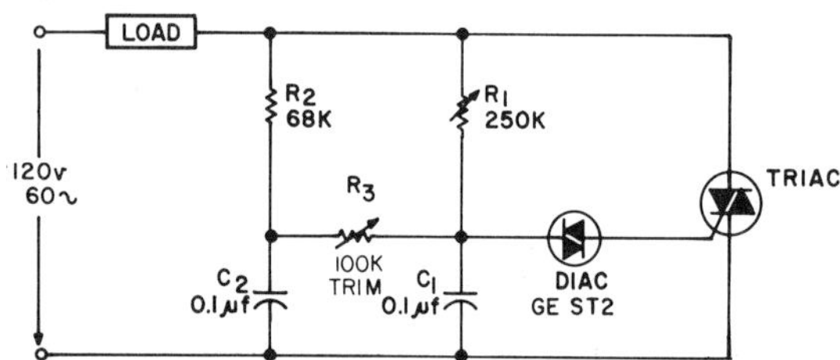

FULL-WAVE TRIAC CONTROL—Provides smooth phase-shift control with R1 over range of from 5 to 95% of full load power, although subject somewhat to line voltage variations. R3 is adjusted so triac just drops out of conduction when R1 is brought to maximum resistance (minimum load power). Circuit has some hysteresis. Choice of triac depends on load. For 220 V, change R1 to 500K, R2 to 120K, and R3 to 200K.—J. H. Galloway, Using the Triac for Control of AC Power, General Electric, Syracuse, N.Y., No. 200.35, 1966, p 8.

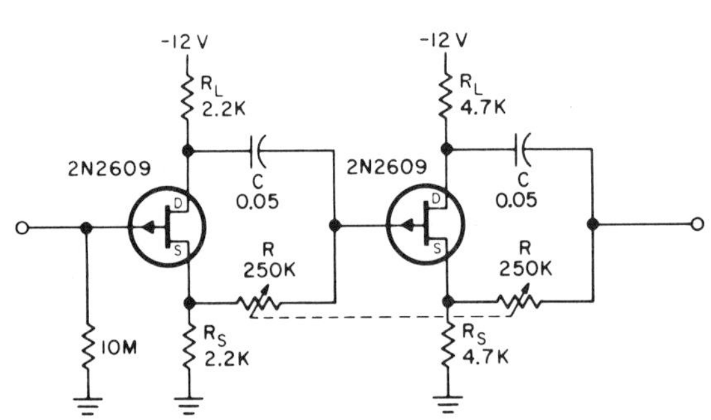

360-DEG FET SHIFTER—Each stage provides adjustable shift of 0 to 180 deg, depending on setting of ganged controls R.—"FET Circuit Ideas," Siliconix, Sunnyvale, Cal., 1966.

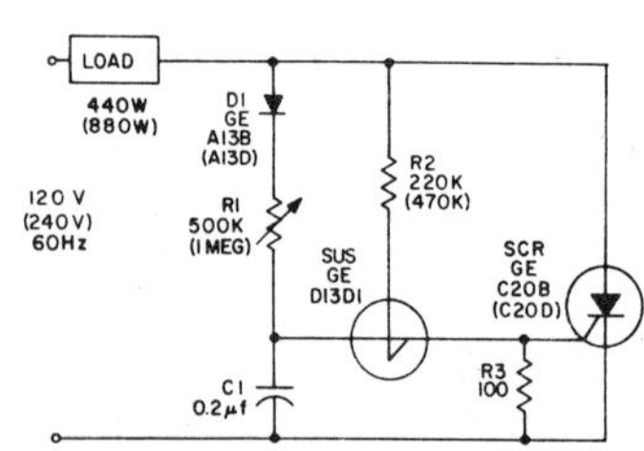

HALF-WAVE WITH SUS CAPACITOR RESET—Uses basic silicon unilateral switch (sus) relaxation oscillator to trigger scr at controlled triggering angle during positive half-cycles of a-c line. If switching voltage is not reached during one positive half-cycle, sus trigger does not switch and high residual voltage is left on C1, causing cycle-skipping. This is avoided by forcing sus to switch at end of each positive half-cycle with R2 current when line voltage goes negative. Values in parentheses are for 240 V a-c.—"SCR Manual," 4th Edition, General Electric, 1967, p 185–186.

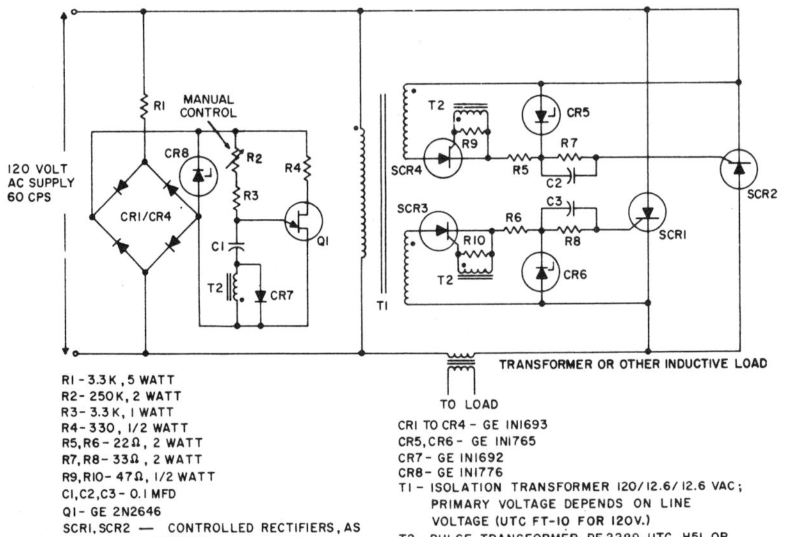

TRIGGER FOR INDUCTIVE LOADS—Designed for phase-controlled scr's feeding inductive a-c load. Obtains synchronization from a-c supply voltage rather than from scr voltage. Trigger signal is continuous for most of desired conduction period. Ujt Q1 is connected across a-c line by bridge rectifier, for triggering on both halves of a-c cycle.—"SCR Manual," 4th Edition, General Electric, 1967, p 196–197.

CHAPTER 61
Phonograph Circuits

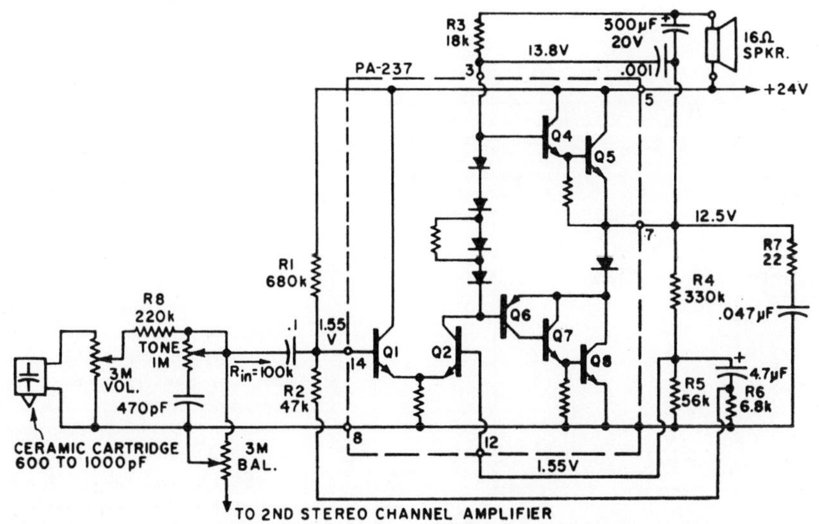

4-W IC PHONO AMPLIFIER—Bootstrapping of R2 to increase input impedance is possible because input and output of G-E integrated circuit are in phase. Article analyzes circuit performance at different volume control settings.—D. V. Jones, Audio-Frequency Integrated Circuits, *Electronics World*, July 1968, p 54–56.

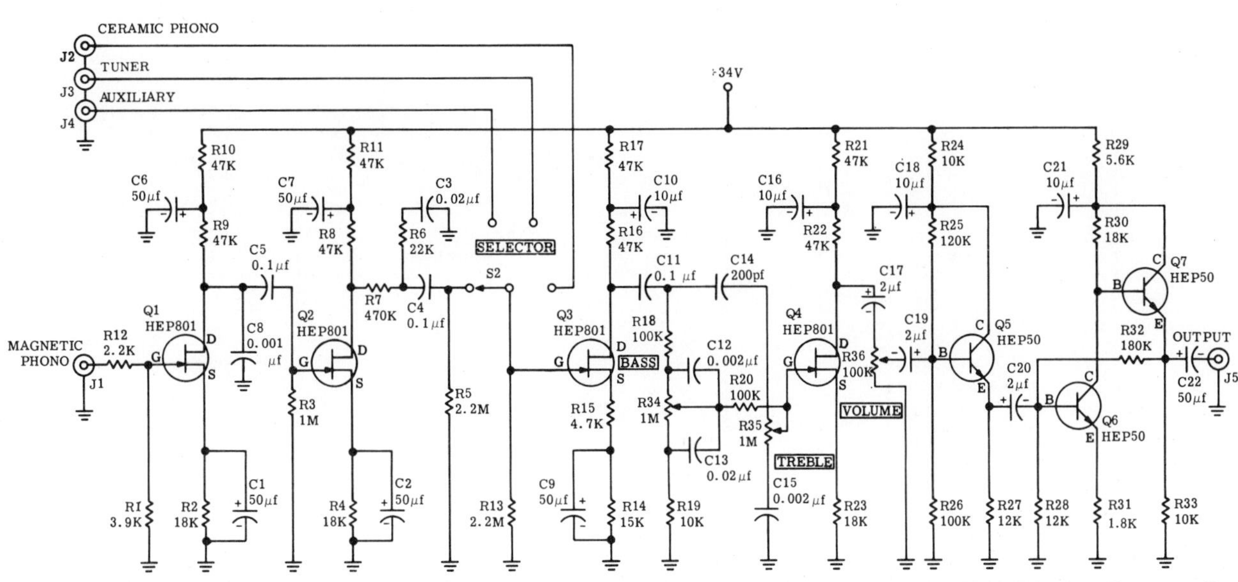

FET MONO AUDIO—Serves as complete control center for high- and low-impedance audio sources, including tone controls and necessary equalization for each source. Article gives construction details, including circuit of 34-V power supply using 117/25 V Stancor P6469 transformer, HEP177 full-wave bridge rectifier, and single 2,000-μF filter capacitor.—"Field Effect Transistor Projects," Motorola, Phoenix, Ariz., 1966, p 57–74.

1.5-W LINE-OPERATED AMPLIFIER—Output stage is powered directly from rectified a-c line, while driver transistor gets its voltage from extra winding on phonograph motor after rectification.—D. E. Lancaster, Plastic Power Transistors—Advantages and Applications, *Electronics World*, Feb. 1968, p 50–52.

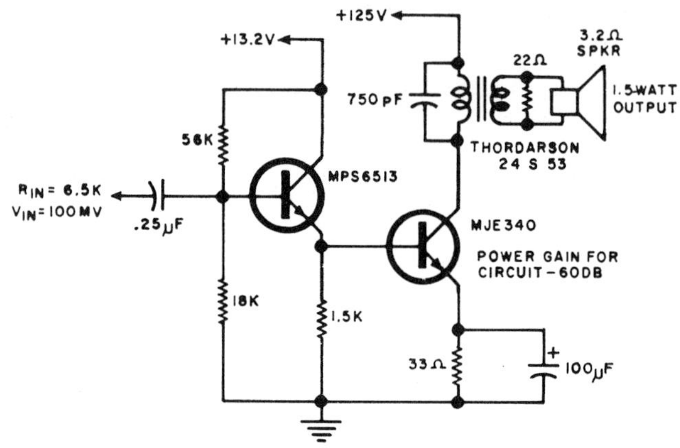

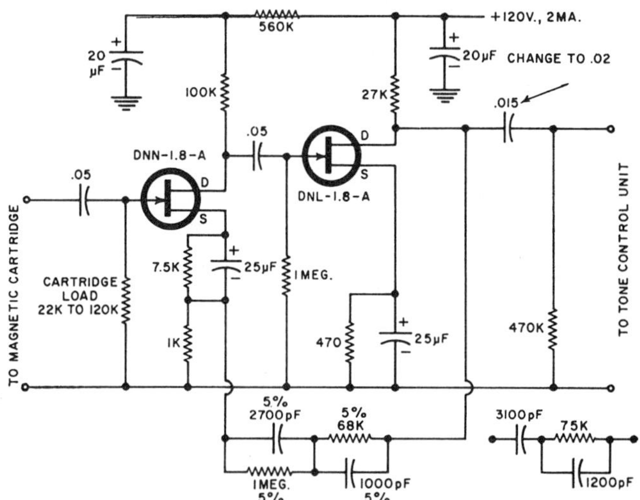

FET PHONO EQUALIZER-PREAMP—High-quality performance is obtained with this voltage amplifier design, which provides proper biasing for field-effect transistors. Feedback network at bottom center gives exact RIAA equalization. Alternative network at lower right (with 0.015 capacitor changed to 0.02) is preferable for organ music having pronounced low frequencies. Gain is 40 dB, and overload-to-noise ratio is 104 dB. Noise level is 7 dB lower than best tube circuit, overload level is 5 dB higher, and dynamic range is much greater than with conventional transistors.—W. A. Rheinfelder, Phono Equalizer Uses FET's, *Electronics World*, April 1966, p 32–33 and 93.

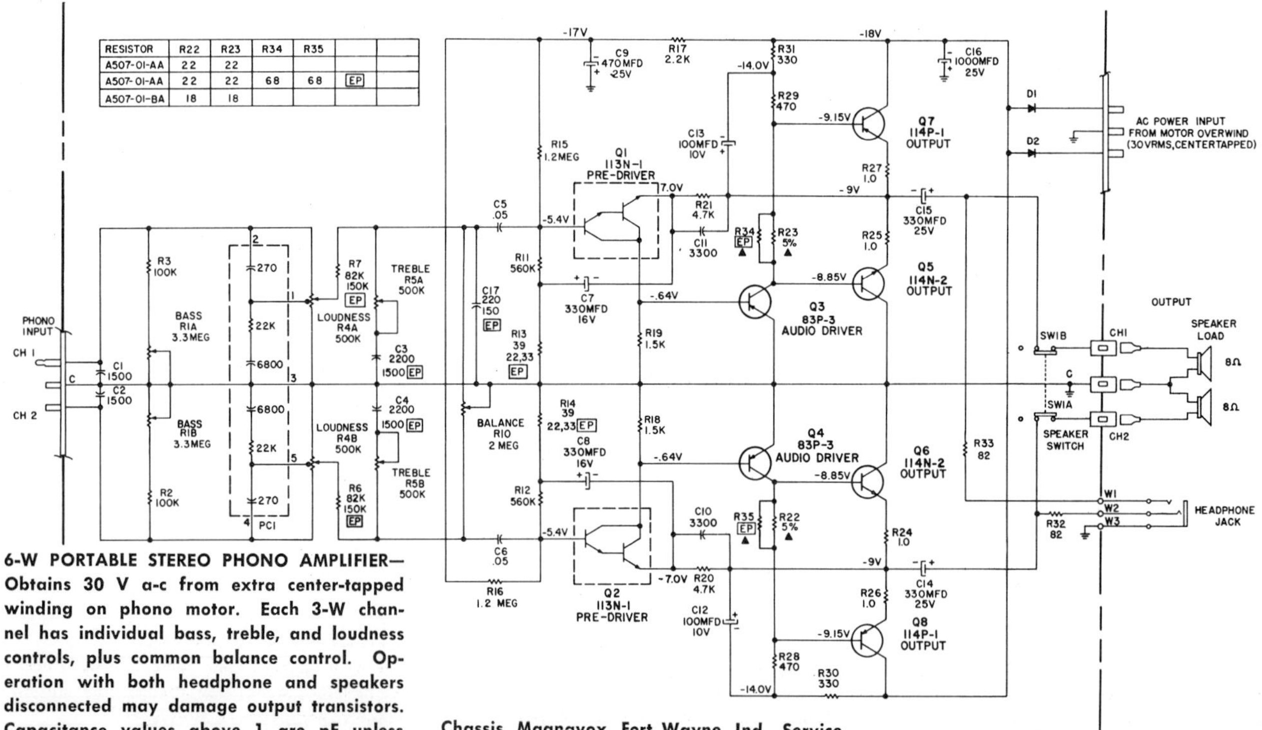

RESISTOR	R22	R23	R34	R35		
A507-01-AA	22	22				
A507-01-AA	22	22	68	68	EP	
A507-01-BA	18	18				

6-W PORTABLE STEREO PHONO AMPLIFIER—Obtains 30 V a-c from extra center-tapped winding on phono motor. Each 3-W channel has individual bass, treble, and loudness controls, plus common balance control. Operation with both headphone and speakers disconnected may damage output transistors. Capacitance values above 1 are pF unless otherwise indicated.—A507 Series Amplifier Chassis, Magnavox, Fort Wayne, Ind., Service Manual 4340, 1969.

1-W IC FOR CERAMIC CARTRIDGE—Use of PA234 IC minimizes number of external components needed for phono amplifier. A-c feedback network is independent of d-c feedback network. Speaker coupling capacitor serves also as a-c bypass capacitor across d-c bias resistors.—Dwight V. Jones, 1 Watt IC Amplifier for Ceramic Phono Cartridge, General Electric, Syracuse, N.Y., No. 90.77, 1969.

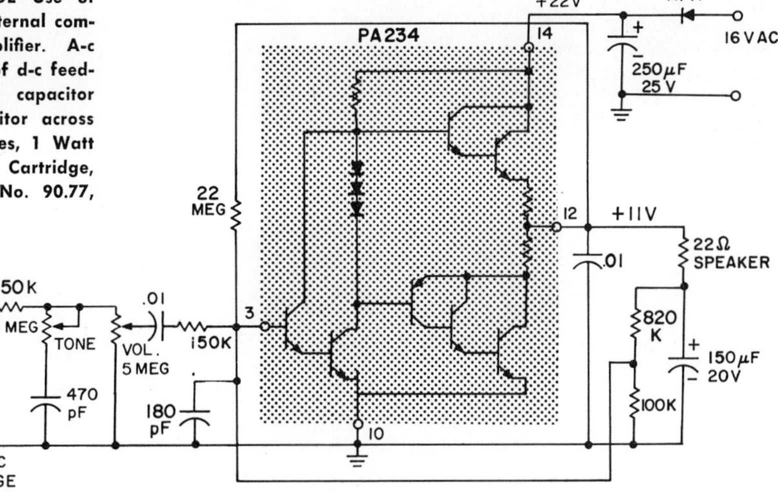

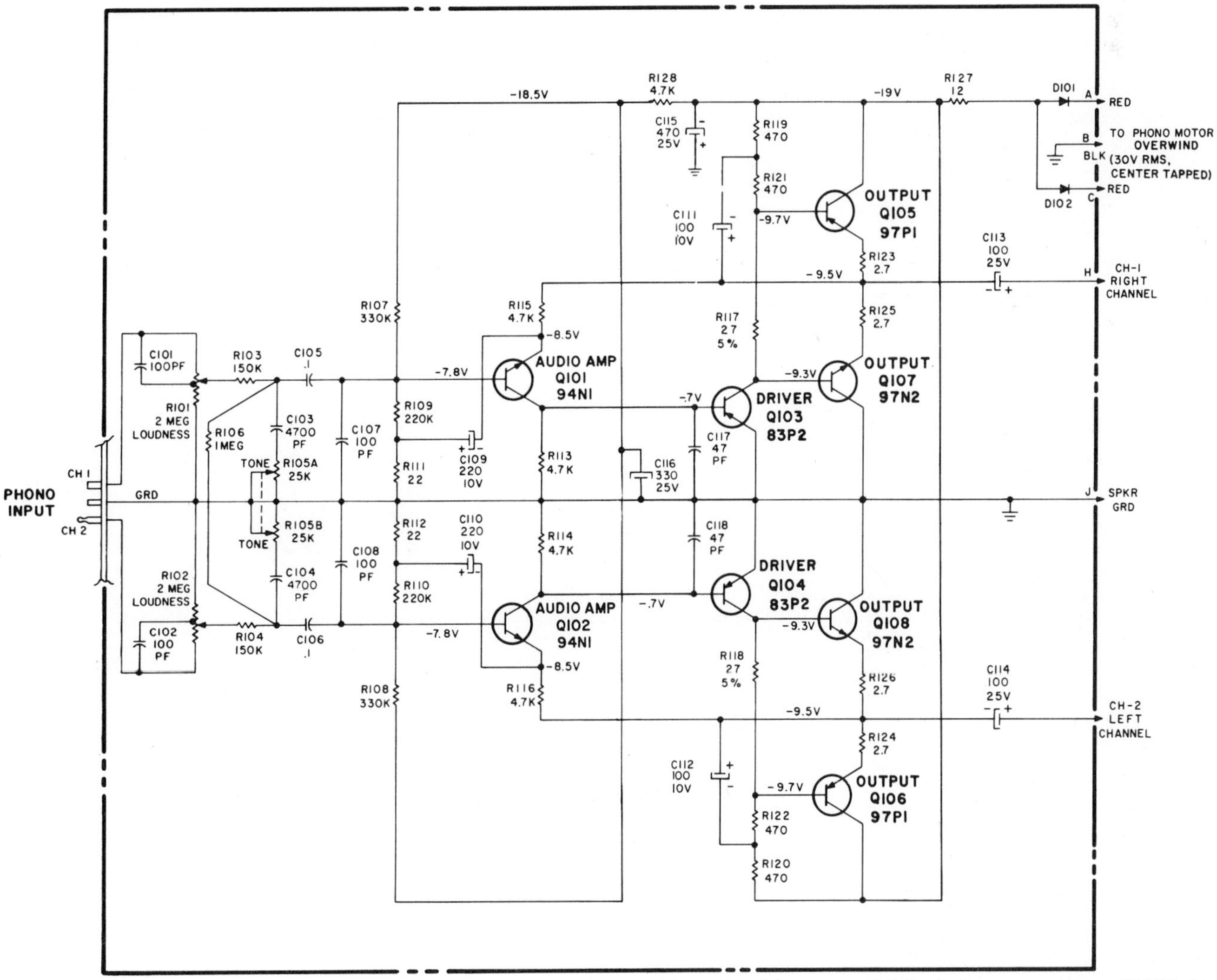

3 W WITH EIGHT TRANSISTORS—Provides 1.5 W per channel of music power output, for use in portable stereo phonograph having extra winding on motor for supplying 30 V a-c to rectifiers for amplifier. Complementary-symmetry output stage drives speaker directly for each channel. Transistors have special Magnavox type numbers.—A509 Series Amplifier Chassis, Magnavox, Fort Wayne, Ind., Service Manual 4341, 1970.

3-W RECORD-PLAYER AMPLIFIER—Designed for use with cartridges having 300-mV output, such as crystal units. R10 acts with C4 as simple treble control. Speaker provides low-voltage supply (with C6) for collector of TR1.—"Transistor Audio and Radio Circuits," Mullard Ltd., London, 1969, p 44.

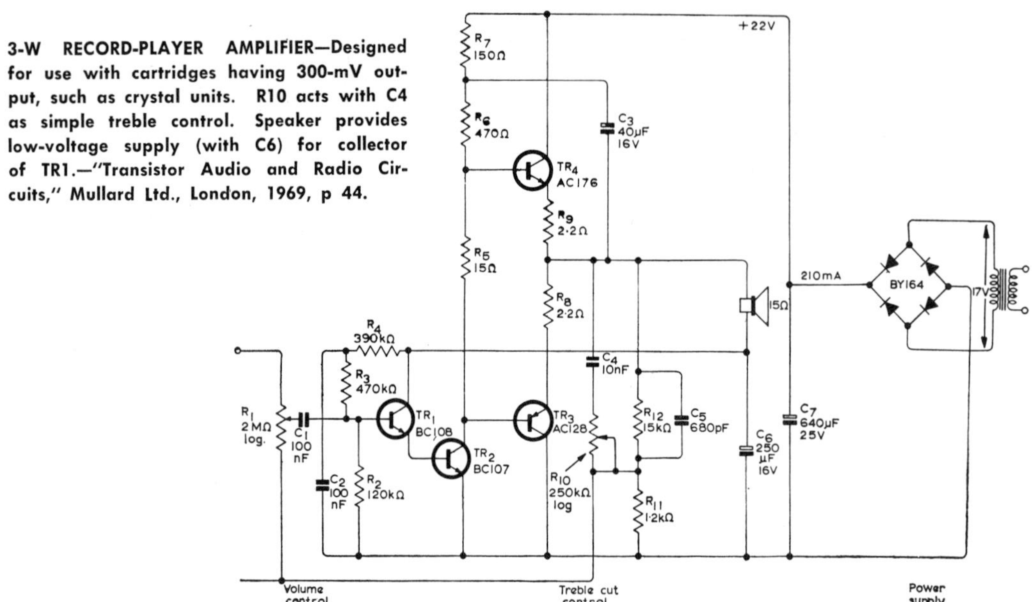

MICRO-ELECTRONICS NO.	R1
RS8310	47K
RS8312	68K
RS8314	100K
RS8316	150K
RS8318	220K
SUBSTITUTION CHART FOR R1	

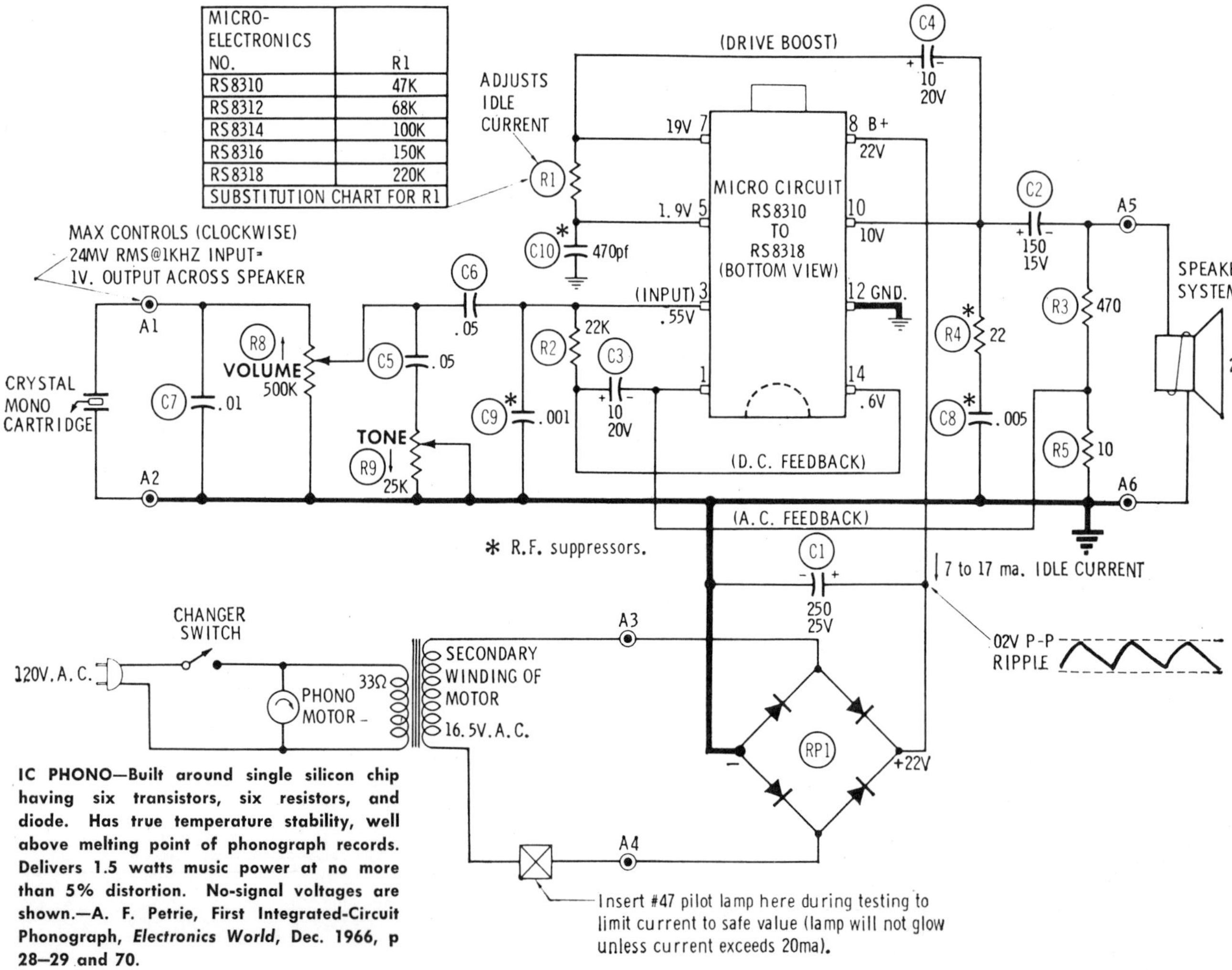

IC PHONO—Built around single silicon chip having six transistors, six resistors, and diode. Has true temperature stability, well above melting point of phonograph records. Delivers 1.5 watts music power at no more than 5% distortion. No-signal voltages are shown.—A. F. Petrie, First Integrated-Circuit Phonograph, *Electronics World*, Dec. 1966, p 28–29 and 70.

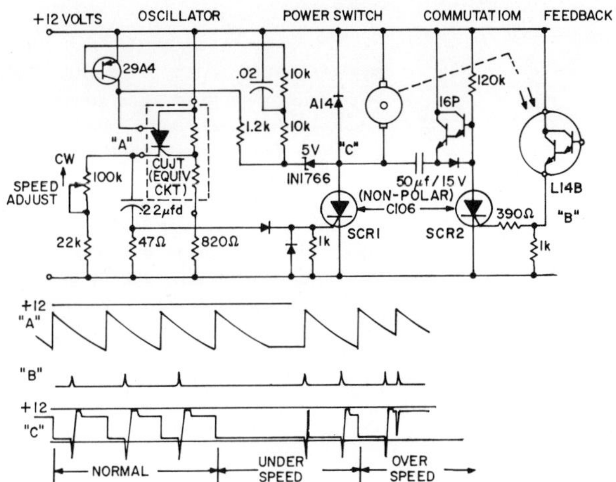

PHONO MOTOR SPEED CONTROL—Complementary ujt 3N81 (dashed box) is used in free-running relaxation oscillator to stabilize speed of d-c motor drive for portable phonographs and tape recorders. Light reflected off disc on motor is sensed by phototransistor L14B, turning SCR2 on and turning off SCR1. When 0.22-μF capacitor charges to peak point and fires, SCR1 comes on again and process repeats itself to make motor synchronous with oscillator. Article describes operation in detail.—W. R. Spofford, Jr., Complementary Unijunction Transistor, General Electric, Syracuse, N.Y., No. 90.72, 1968, p 15.

STEREO PHONO PREAMP—Has 50,000-ohm input impedance for magnetic cartridges and delivers up to 10 mV for audio power amplifier. Both channels are identical, each with its own RIAA feedback network. Article gives design procedure. If gain control is used between preamp and amplifier, it should be 25,000 to 100,000 ohms, without blocking capacitor.—J. G. Holbrook, The Engineer's Stereo Preamp, *Electronics World*, May 1968, p 44–45.

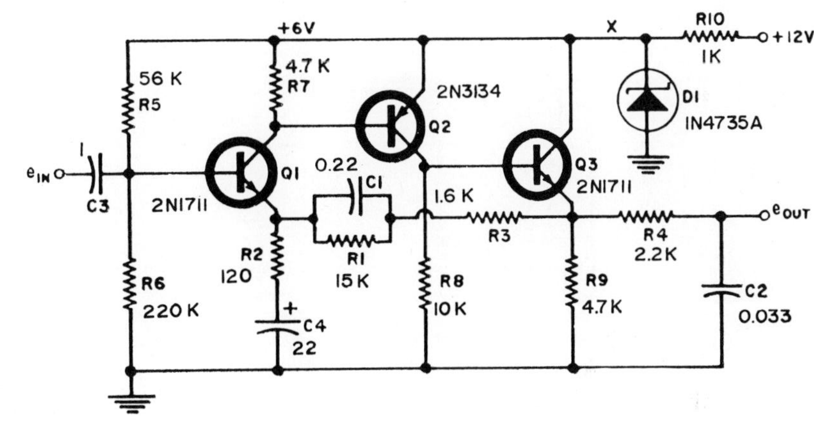

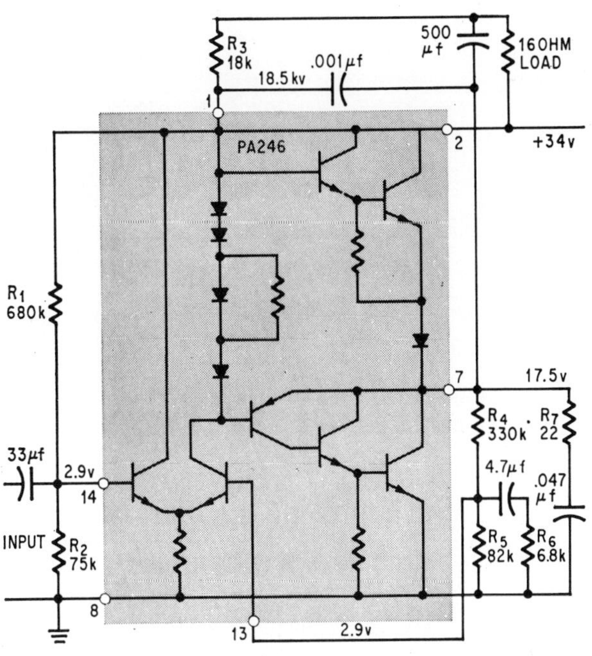

5-W AUDIO IC—Complete phonograph amplifier is obtained simply by adding resistors and capacitors to General Electric PA246 IC audio amplifier. Frequency response is 30 Hz to 100 kHz. Designed for 0.5-V signal from phono pickup and 16-ohm speaker load. Can also be used in radios and tape recorders. Requires 34-V supply.—IC Audio Amplifier Puts Out 5 Watts, *Electronics*, Nov. 25, 1968, p 111–112.

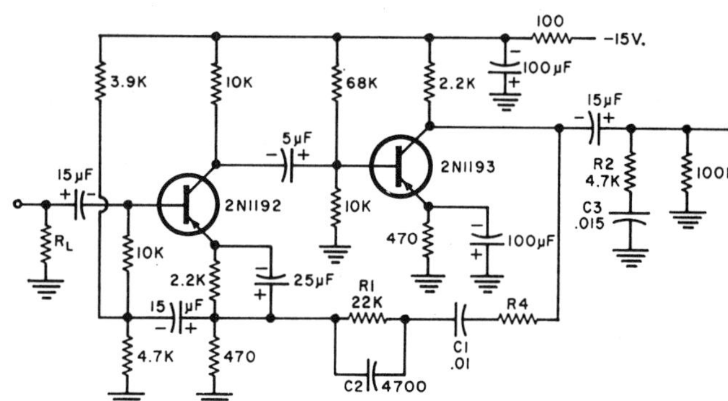

GERMANIUM-TRANSISTOR PHONO PREAMP—Feedback gives RIAA equalization and offsets inherent base-emitter nonlinearity, to give high fidelity along with required high input impedance and low output impedance. Gain is 40 dB. Current drain is 5 mA, and overload-to-noise ratio is 85 dB.—W. A. Rheinfelder, Phono Equalizer Uses FET's, *Electronics World*, April 1966, p 32–33 and 93.

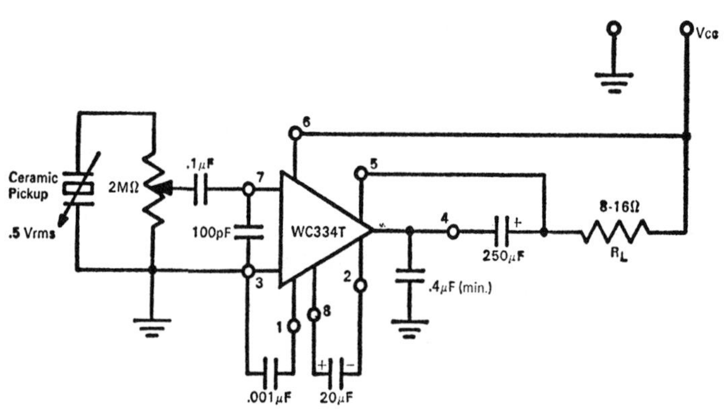

SINGLE-IC PHONO AMPLIFIER—Provides 25 dB gain for 0.5 V rms output of ceramic pickup and delivers 1 W to 8-ohm speaker at 5% harmonic distortion.—Westinghouse To Unveil IC Device, *Electronic News*, Aug. 21, 1967, p 84.

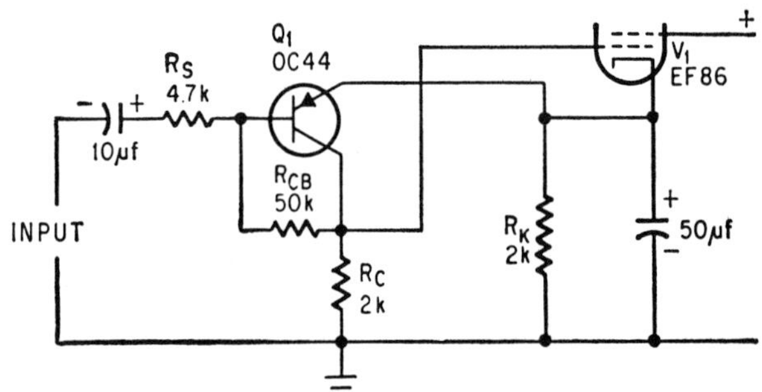

GAIN BOOSTER FOR MAGNETIC CARTRIDGE—Single transistor boosts gain of tube preamp for crystal cartridge by 10, to permit use of magnetic cartridge without adding step-up transformer or extra separately powered tube stage. Cathode bias of tube is supply voltage for transistor.—Y. L. Li, Cathode Voltage Boosts Amplifier Gain Tenfold, *Electronics*, May 15, 1967, p 95.

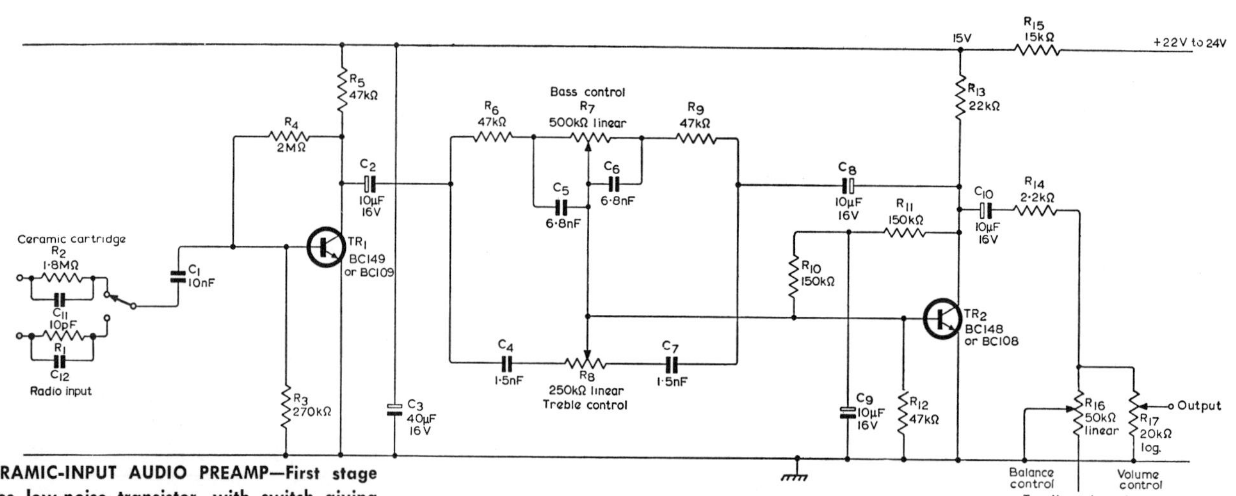

CERAMIC-INPUT AUDIO PREAMP—First stage uses low-noise transistor, with switch giving choice of ceramic cartridge or radio input. Choose R1 experimentally to give required sensitivity with radio used, then choose C12 to give with R1 an 18-µs time constant. Balance control is provided for stereo use.—"Transistor Audio and Radio Circuits," Mullard Ltd., London, 1969, p 42.

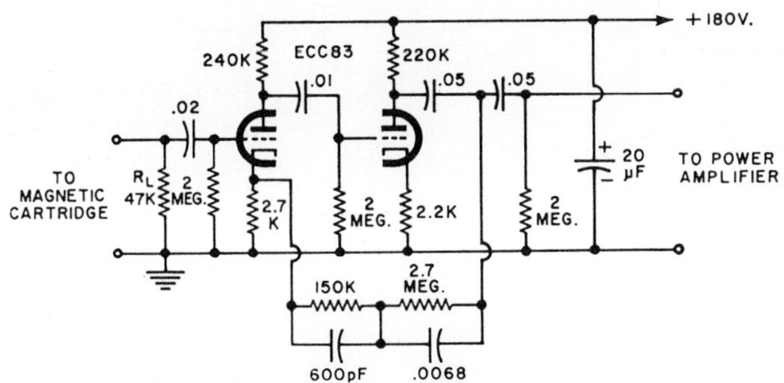

LOW-NOISE PHONO PREAMP—Feedback from last anode into first cathode uses network trimmed to give exact RIAA equalization. Gain is 40 dB.—W. A. Rheinfelder, Phono Equalizer Uses FET's, *Electronics World*, April 1966, p 32–33 and 93.

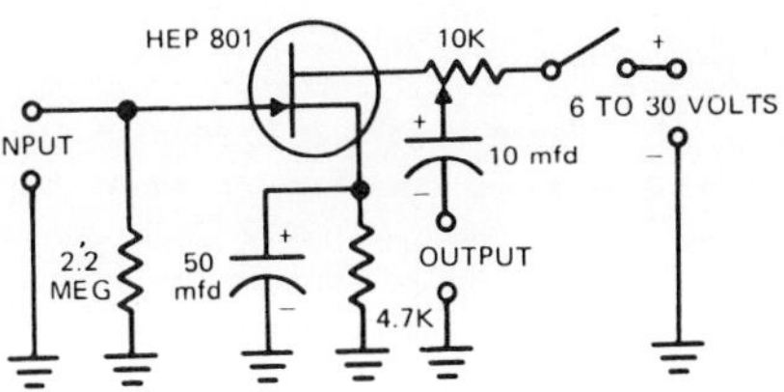

FET MICROPHONE OR PHONO—Gives excellent frequency response over wide range of supply voltages for ceramic or crystal microphone or phono cartridge.—"Tips on Using FET's," Motorola, Phoenix, Ariz., HMA-33, 1969.

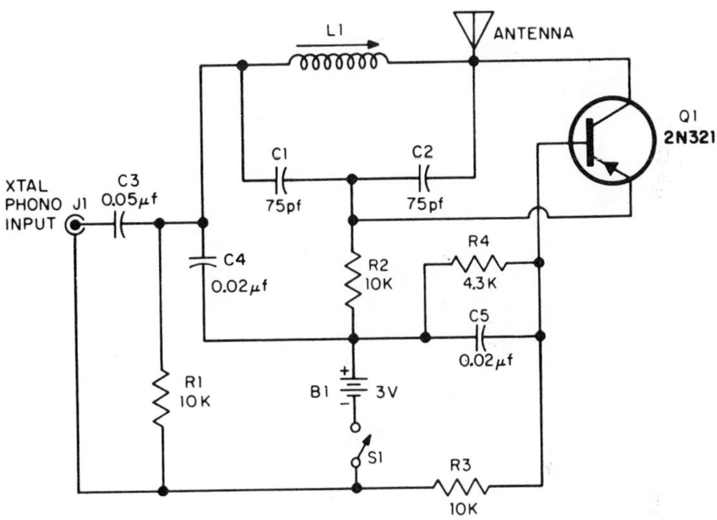

WIRELESS PHONO OSCILLATOR—Developed to broadcast phono pickup signal of inexpensive phonograph to high-quality a-m receiver nearby, for better audio reproduction. Antenna is limited to 10 feet by law. L1 is ferrite vari-loopstick, used for tuning to dead-spot at low end of broadcast band on receiver.—"A Modern Transistor Workbook," Radio Shack, Boston, Mass., 1965, p 15.

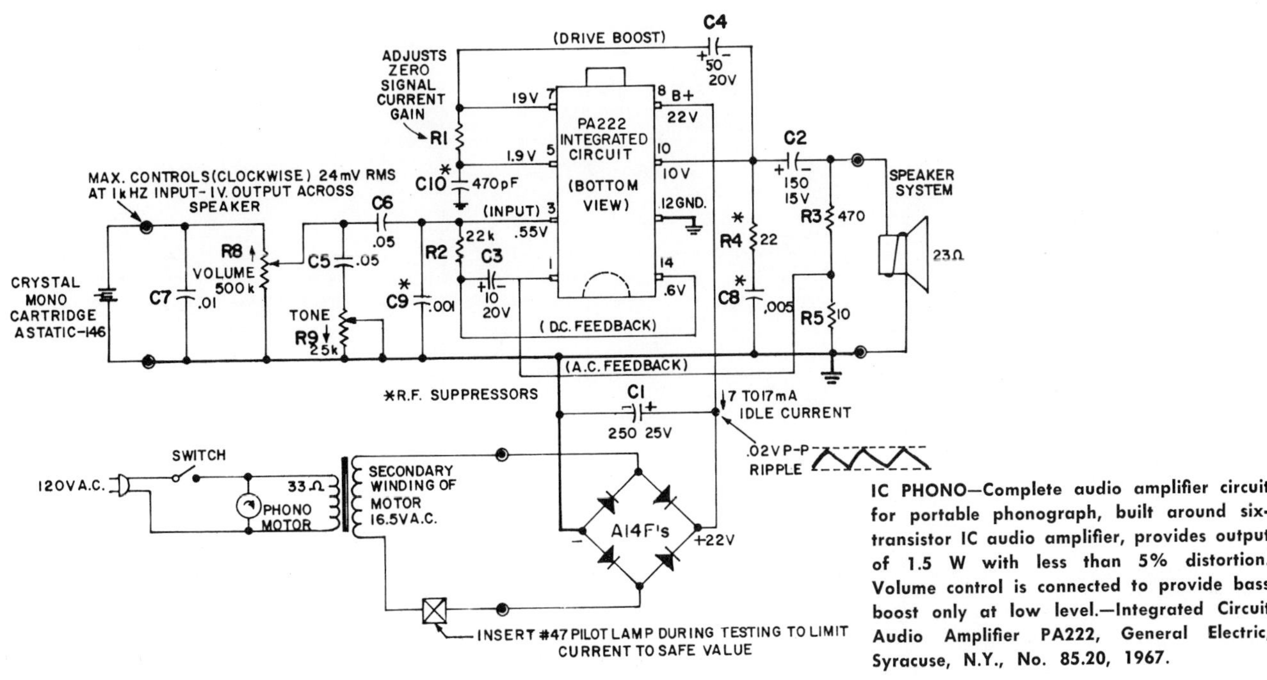

IC PHONO—Complete audio amplifier circuit for portable phonograph, built around six-transistor IC audio amplifier, provides output of 1.5 W with less than 5% distortion. Volume control is connected to provide bass boost only at low level.—Integrated Circuit Audio Amplifier PA222, General Electric, Syracuse, N.Y., No. 85.20, 1967.

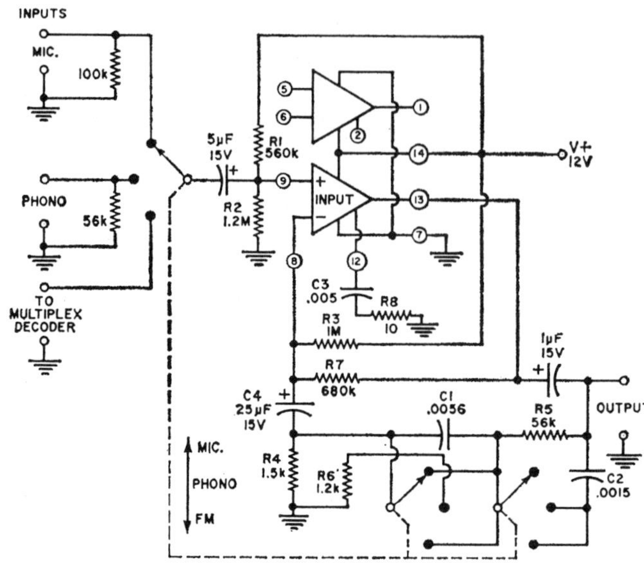

DUAL-CHANNEL IC PREAMP—Uses two operational amplifiers on single chip, similar to Motorola MC1302P IC. External connections are shown for only one channel; other channel is wired identically to terminals 1, 2, 5, and 6. Used in H. H. Scott Series 2500 a-m/f-m compact stereo radio-phonos. Maximum output is 3 V.—D. R. von Recklinghausen, IC Op-Amp Hi-Fi Preamplifier, *Electronics World*, June 1968, p 44–45.

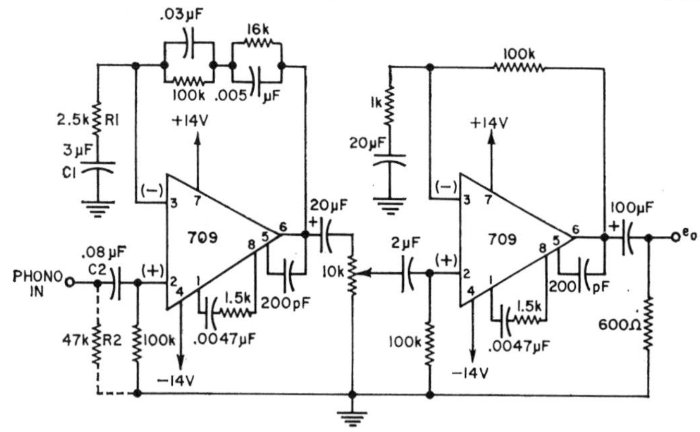

RIAA PHONO PREAMP—Designed for magnetic phono cartridge. Uses either Fairchild μA709 or National LM709 IC opamp with compensating R-C networks in feedback loop of first amplifier. Requires 6-mV input at 1 kHz to give 4-dBm reference output level. Circuit rejects signals below 20 Hz to minimize transients.—S. L. Silver, IC Op Amps Boost Audio Circuit Performance, *Electronics World*, Sept. 1968, p 30–32.

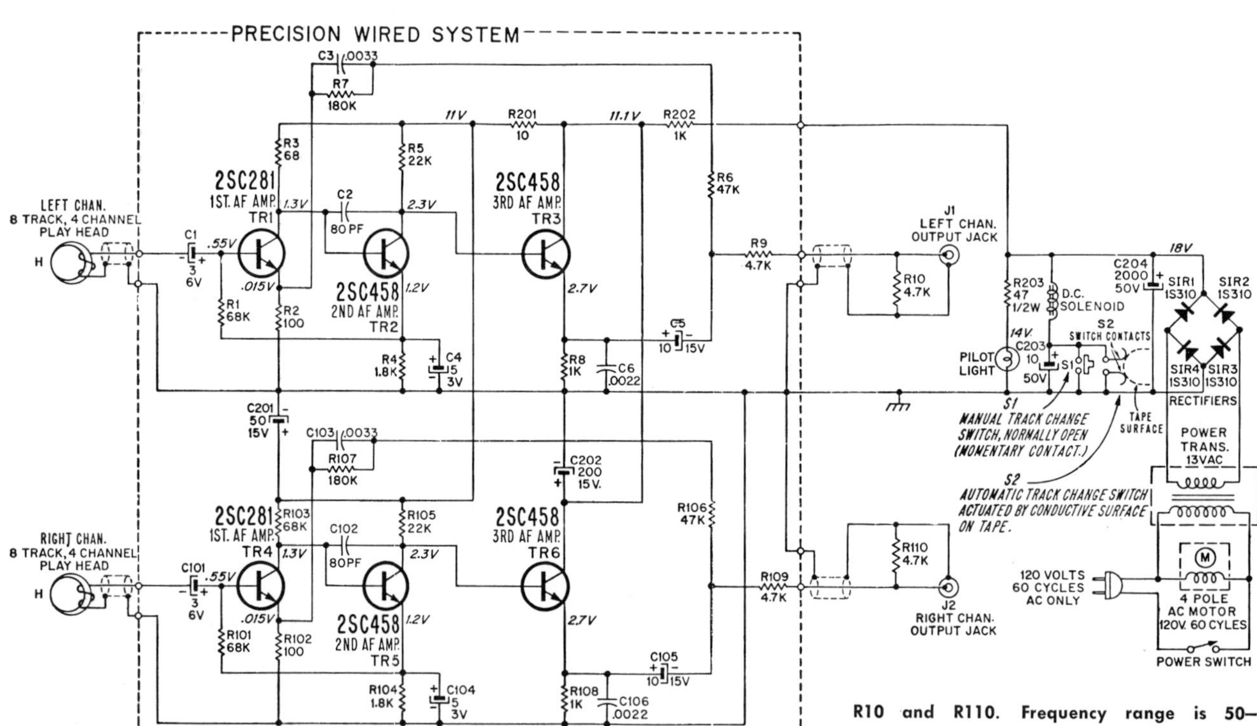

STEREO CARTRIDGE PLAYER—Delivers 0.1 V per channel into 200K impedance, for driving transistor amplifiers. To obtain 0.2-V output for tube amplifiers, clip 4.7K resistors R10 and R110. Frequency range is 50–10,000 Hz.—Cartridge Tape Player STP631, Admiral, Bloomington, Ill., Service Manual S1213, 1969.

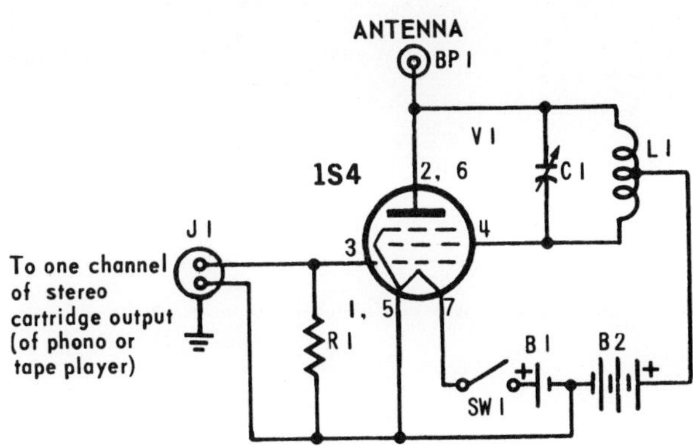

STEREO PHONO OSCILLATOR—Can be used with a-m radio to convert monaural phonograph for stereo records. Change to stereo cartridge, feed one channel to regular phono amplifier, and connect other to J1 for broadcasting to radio used for second channel. For good stereo effect, place radio about 7 ft from phonograph. Tune radio to dead spot, and adjust C1 until music is heard while playing stereo record. Antenna can be few feet of wire (legal limit is 10 ft). Values are: B1 1.5 V; B2 30 V; C1 365 pF; R1 510K; L1 182 turns No. 30 enamel center-tapped on 5/8" form.—R. M. Brown, "104 Simple One-Tube Projects," Tab Books, Blue Ridge Summit, Pa., 1969, p 166.

2-W IC PHONOGRAPH—Uses GE PA-237 integrated circuit for driving 16-ohm speaker, with ceramic cartridge at input. Minimum cartridge output of 0.5 V gives 2 W power output with about 2% total harmonic distortion at 1 kHz.—Dwight V. Jones, Monolithic 2 Watt Integrated Amplifier—Characteristics and Applications, General Electric, Syracuse, N.Y., No. 90.73, 1968, p 12.

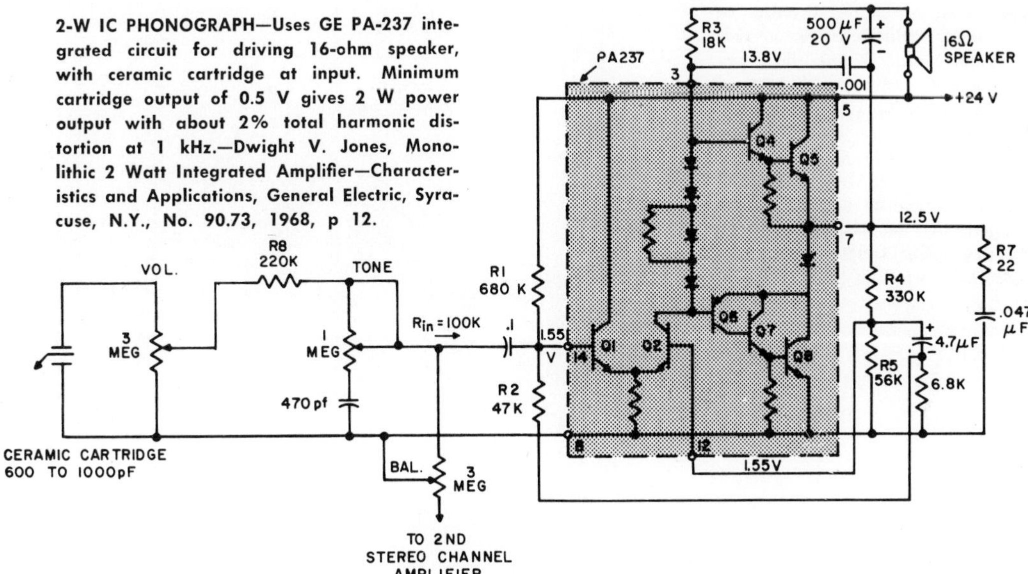

NOTE: To locate additional circuits in the category of this chapter, use the index at the back of this book. Check also the author's "Sourcebook of Electronic Circuits," published by McGraw-Hill in 1968.

CHAPTER 62
Photoelectric Circuits

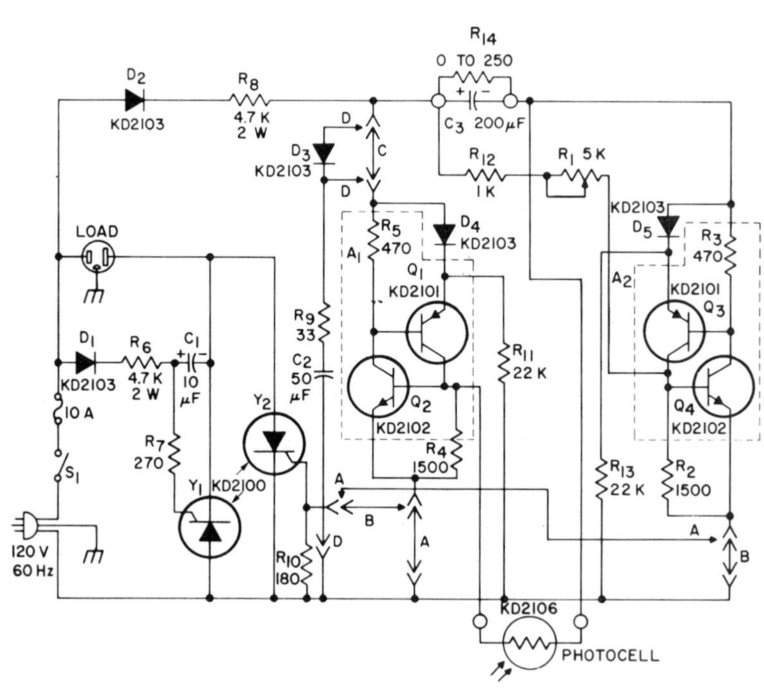

LIGHT-OPERATED ON-OFF SWITCH—Different combinations of wiring give choice of operating methods. With wiring A, increase in light turns off load. With wiring B, increase in light turns on load. With wiring combination of A and C, increase in light turns off load but it is turned back on again when light level increases to level determined by setting of R1, as required for automatic night lamp in vacant homes or for street lamp control. Connection D, for R9 and C2, is optional latching circuit. Maximum load is 600 W.—"Silicon Controlled Rectifier Experimenter's Manual," RCA, Harrison, N.J., p 106.

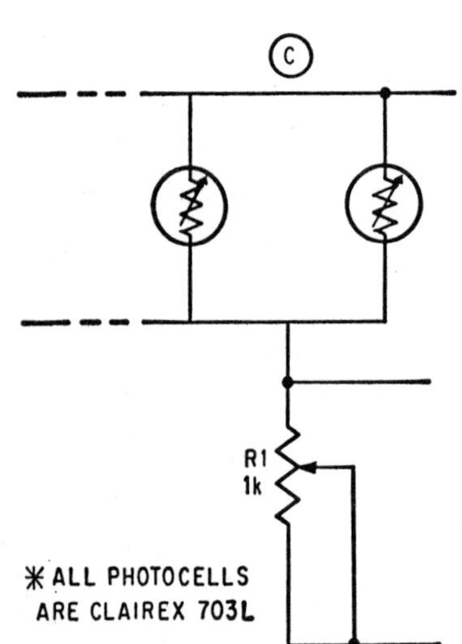

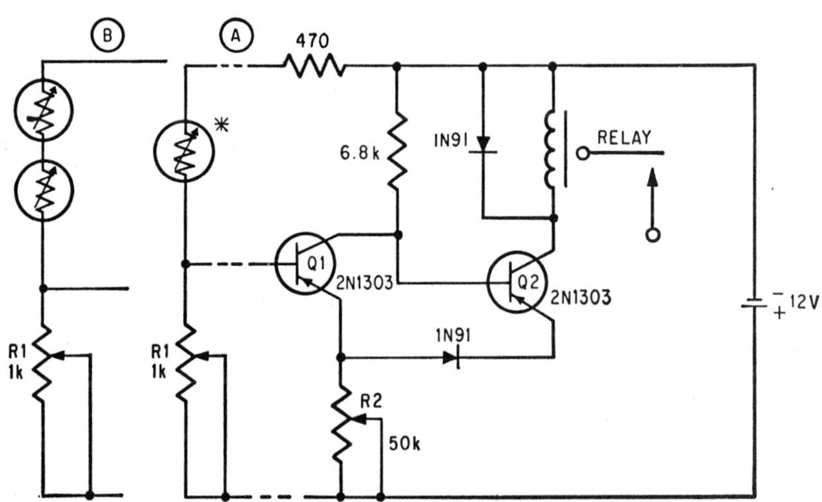

SCHMITT TRIGGER DRIVES RELAY FASTER—Ordinary photoelectric control relay is tripped directly at high speed in response to small changes in light intensity on photoconductive cell connected into basic Schmitt trigger. With circuit configuration A, relay pulls in when light drops. With B, both cells must be illuminated for relay dropout, thus giving AND logic function. With C, illumination on either cell makes relay drop out, to give OR logic function. Reversing locations of R1 and cells gives relay pull-in with increasing light; R1 should then be increased to 50K.—R. A. Farrall, Light-activated Schmitt Triggers Control Relay, *Electronics*, May 15, 1967, p 98.

2-A PHOTOSWITCH—Provides on-off action. When light on photocell exceeds predetermined level set by R4, relay releases and turns off lamp or other load. When light drops below same level, relay pulls in and turns on lamp load again. Values: R1 150; R2 5.6; R3 470; R4 250; C1 5 μF; F1 3 A; CR1 SK3031; CR2 SK3030; Q1 SK3005; Q2 SK3020; photocell KD2016; relay 1.35K 12 V.—"Hobby Circuits Manual," RCA, Harrison, N.J., HM-90, p 87.

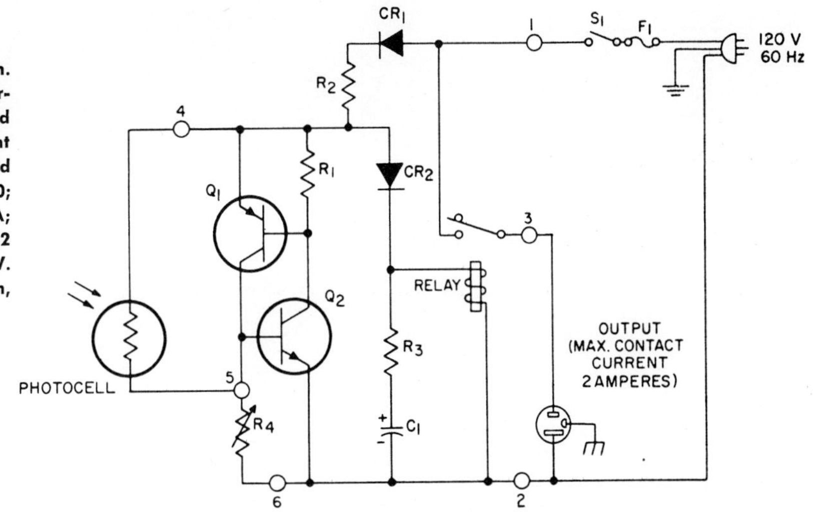

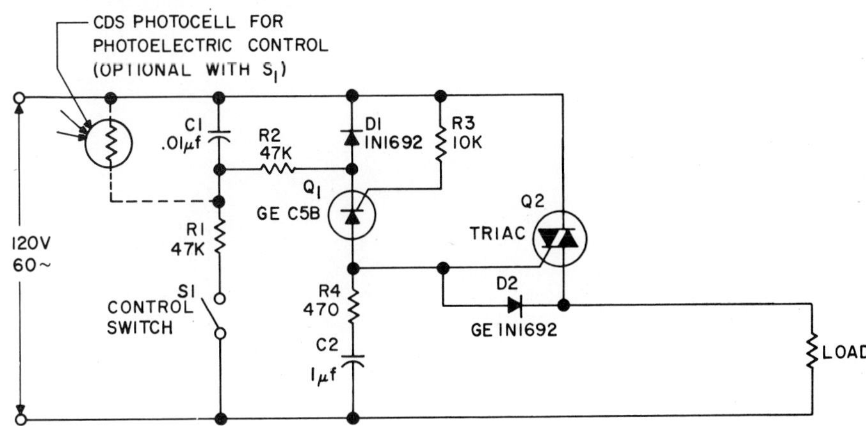

SYNCHRONOUS SWITCHING—When photocell resistance increases or control switch is closed, scr-triac combination turns on load current only at next instant when a-c supply voltage passes through zero. Similarly, light on photocell or opening of switch does not turn off load until current next passes through zero. This gives minimum disturbance to power supply when switching, with conduction only for integral number of whole cycles. Eliminates rfi and audio filtering problems. With transformers or other inductive loads, eliminates fuse-blowing nuisance caused by surge of magnetizing current.—J. H. Galloway, Using the Triac for Control of AC Power, General Electric, Syracuse, N.Y., No. 200.35, 1966, p 15.

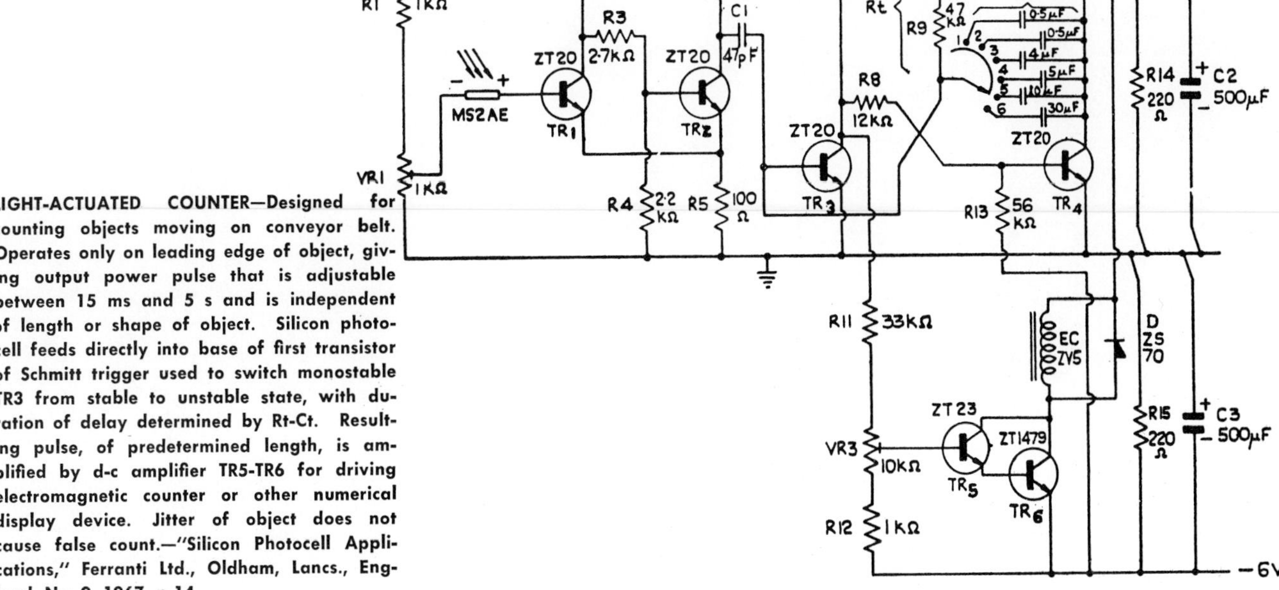

LIGHT-ACTUATED COUNTER—Designed for counting objects moving on conveyor belt. Operates only on leading edge of object, giving output power pulse that is adjustable between 15 ms and 5 s and is independent of length or shape of object. Silicon photocell feeds directly into base of first transistor of Schmitt trigger used to switch monostable TR3 from stable to unstable state, with duration of delay determined by Rt-Ct. Resulting pulse, of predetermined length, is amplified by d-c amplifier TR5-TR6 for driving electromagnetic counter or other numerical display device. Jitter of object does not cause false count.—"Silicon Photocell Applications," Ferranti Ltd., Oldham, Lancs., England, No. 9, 1967, p 14.

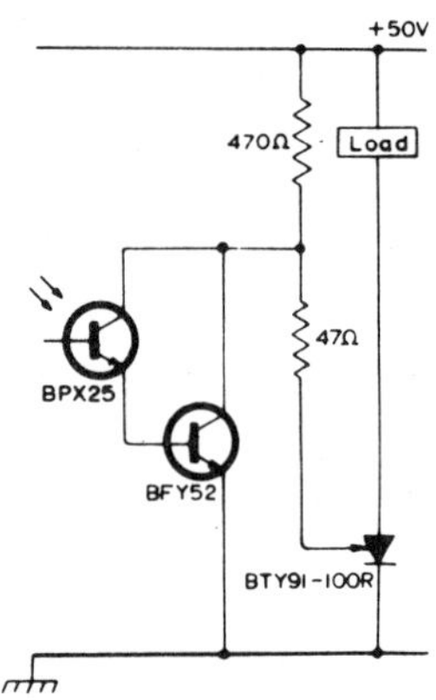

DARKNESS-ON D-C SWITCH—When light on phototransistor drops below 1,000 lux, transistor generates trigger that turns on thyristor handling up to 16 A load current.—Applications of Silicon Planar Phototransistor, BPX25, Philips, Pub. Dept., Elcoma Div., Eindhoven, The Netherlands, No. 316, 1967.

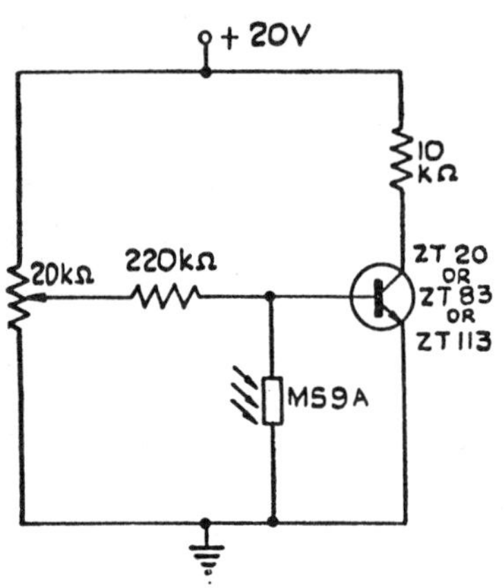

SILICON PHOTOCELL TURNS OFF TRANSISTOR—Illumination on cell generates signal that turns off transistor. Can be used in punched tape readers.—"Silicon Photocell Applications," Ferranti, Oldham, Lancs., England, No. 9, 1967, p 6.

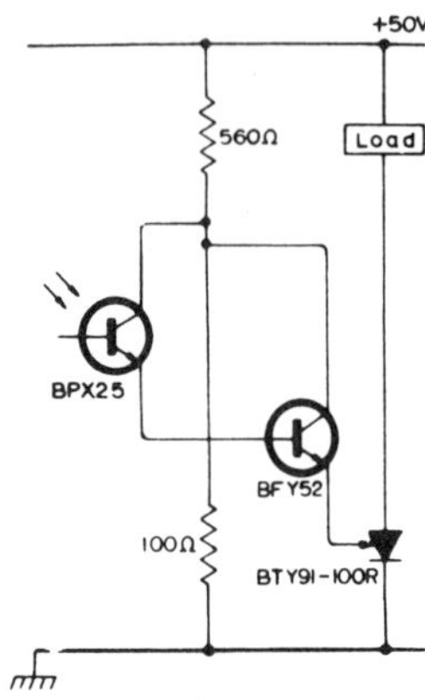

DARKNESS-OFF D-C SWITCH—With phototransistor dark, transistor has no base current and no collector current, so thyristor is held off. Light produces trigger that turns on thyristor to apply power to load. Requires 1,000 lux to turn on 16-A load.—Applications of Silicon Planar Phototransistor BPX25, Philips, Pub. Dept., Elcoma Div., Eindhoven, The Netherlands, No. 316, 1967.

LIGHT-CURTAIN GUARD FOR MACHINES—Fail-safe a-c system uses light source that is modulated by operating small-filament lamp in series with rectifier from a-c line, to give high 50-Hz (or 60-Hz) flicker content. With modulated light, system will fail safe either if normally conducting transistor becomes short-circuited or normally nonconductive transistor becomes open circuit. Curtain of light is projected across throat of punch press, power shears, or other dangerous machines, so operator cannot insert hand through curtain without interrupting at least one beam of light and pulling in machine-stopping relay.—"Silicon Photocell Applications," Ferranti Ltd., Oldham, Lancs., England, No. 9, 1967, p 18.

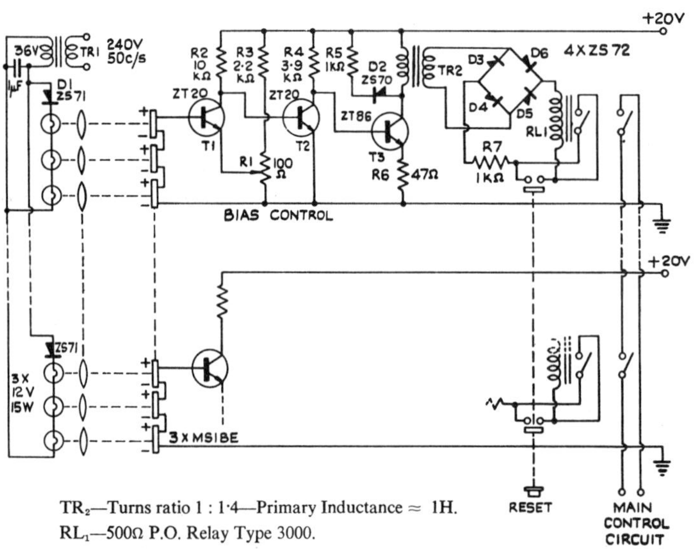

TR₂—Turns ratio 1 : 1·4—Primary Inductance ≈ 1H.
RL₁—500Ω P.O. Relay Type 3000.

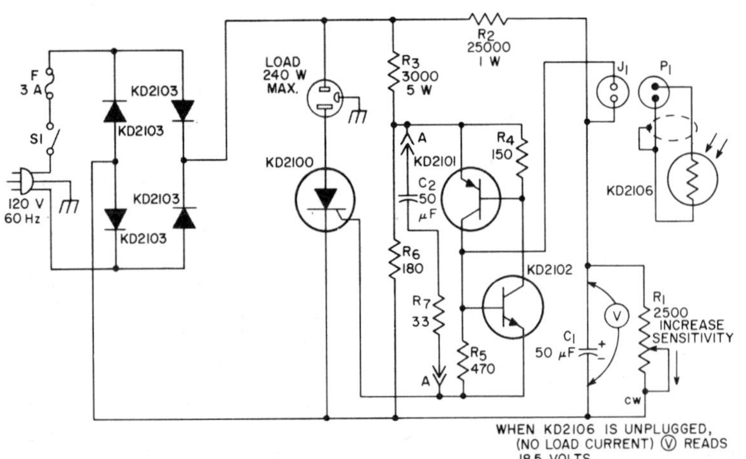

LIGHT-OPERATED TURN-ON SWITCH—Will switch on lamp, heater, or universal motor up to 240 W at predetermined light level determined by setting of R1. C2 and R7 form optional latching circuit that keeps load on until line switch S1 is opened. Applications include turning on advertising signs when illuminated by auto headlights, turning on dock lights with spotlight or flashlight when boat is returning after dark, and turning on lights at darkness.—"Silicon Controlled Rectifier Experimenter's Manual," RCA, Harrison, N.J., 1967, p 100.

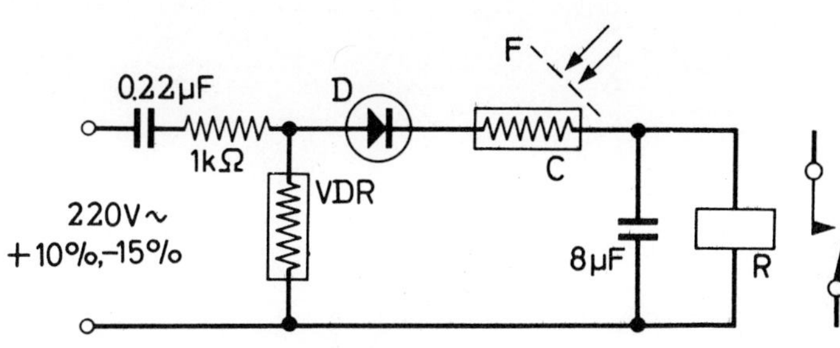

220-V A-C TWILIGHT SWITCH—Relay releases at darkness, turning on lamp load. Cell is cadmium sulfide RPY20; diode is BYX10; VDR is voltage-dependent resistor E 299 DG/P248; R is 1K; C1 0.22 μF; C2 8 μF; relay is 20K with make at 45 V and break at about 20 V. Capacitor across relay prevents pull-in by flashes of light.—M. Donkers and E. B. G. Nijhof, The Application of Cadmium-Sulphide Photo-Conductive Cell RPY20 In Automatic Twilight Switches, Philips, Pub. Dept., Elcoma Div., Eindhoven, The Netherlands, No. 424, 1964.

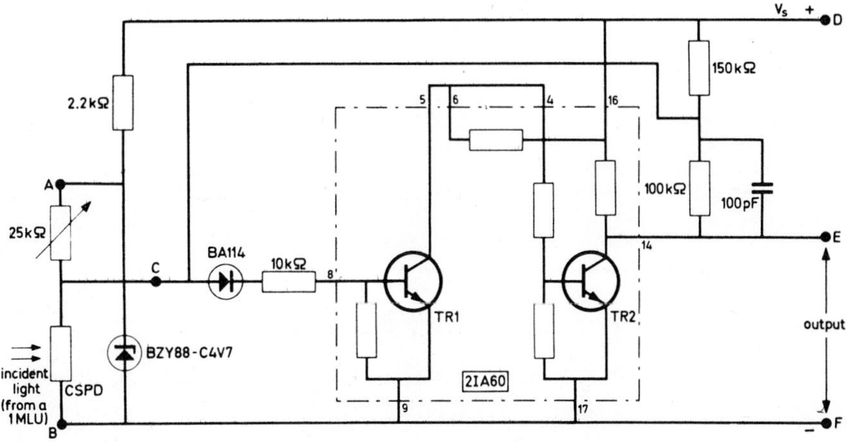

LOW-COST IC PHOTORELAY—Uses Philips 21-A60 two-transistor IC as amplifier for photocell. Intended for use in industrial control installations where distance between light source and photocell is under 8 ft. Pulse-shaping action of IC improves usefulness of output signal for driving up to 20 counting or logic units. Interruption of light on cell makes voltage across unloaded output terminals approach supply voltage.—Photoelectric Detecting System Using Light Sensor CSPD and Lamp Unit 1MLU, Philips, Pub. Dept., Elcoma Div., Eindhoven, The Netherlands, No. 12, 1968.

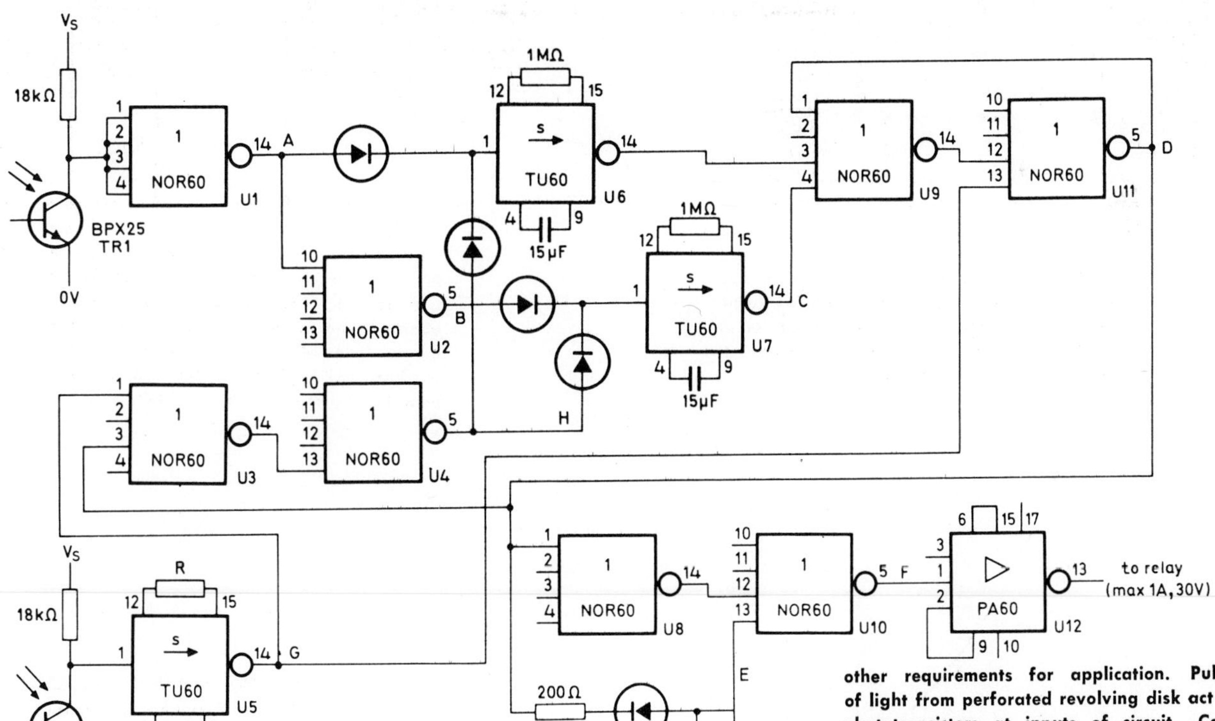

Diodes type BAX13

FURNACE-EMPTYING DETECTOR—Basic circuit detects long absences of action in industrial process where action can be converted into pulses of light. Originally developed to control slow emptying of furnace into hopper suspended on scales, so weight and time are registered and hopper emptied automatically if nothing dribbles out for 15 s. Uses combination of Philips IC gates connected as shown to provide required time delay and other requirements for application. Pulses of light from perforated revolving disk act on phototransistors at inputs of circuit. Complete cycle consists of rotation of disk in given direction from initial position, pause detection to determine whether disk is stationary for longer than 15 s, and return of disk to initial position. Cycle-terminating relay cannot operate again until disk is back home for start of new cycle.—H. Magro, Detection of Long-Duration Pauses in Machine Operations, Philips, Pub. Dept., Elcoma Div., Eindhoven, The Netherlands, No. 67.

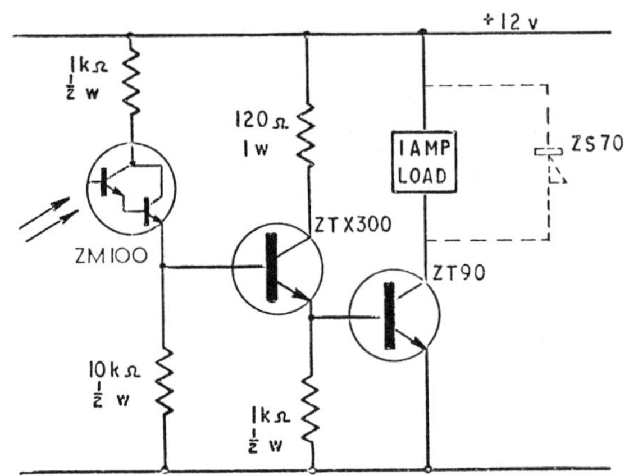

HIGH-SENSITIVITY PHOTO-DARLINGTON RELAY—Addition of two transistor amplifier stages to Ferranti ZM100 photo-Darlington permits turning on 1-A load with light level of only 2 lumens per sq ft.—A Photo Darlington Pair, Ferranti, Oldham, Lancs., England, No. 36, 1968.

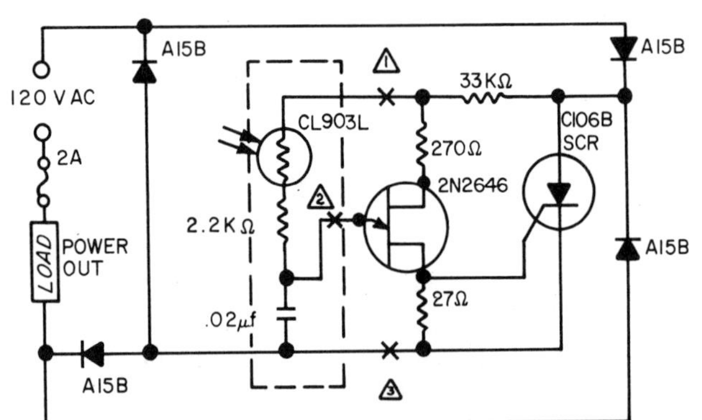

2-A PHOTORELAY—Load current varies with intensity of light reaching photoconductive cell. Ujt relaxation oscillator frequency varies with resistance of photocell, to change firing angle of scr and thereby change average current to load.—L. M. Hertz, "Solid State Lamps—Part II," General Electric, Cleveland, Ohio, No. 3-0121, 1970, p 21.

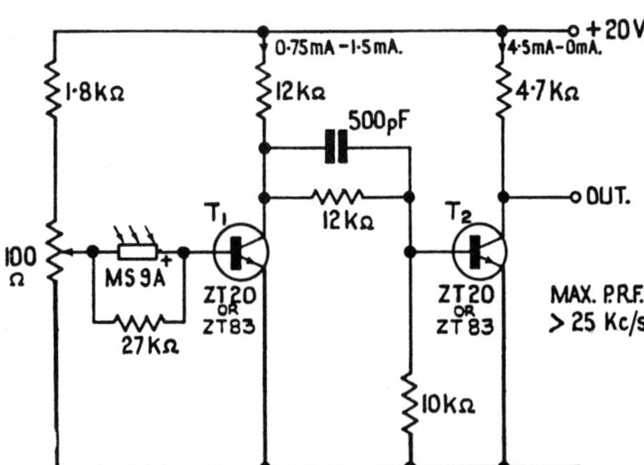

PUNCHED CARD READER—Tiny silicon photocell with two-stage d-c amplifier is suitable for light intensities of 1,000 to 3,000 lumens per square foot, as commonly used in punched card or tape readers in which reading is done while card is stationary.—"Silicon Photocell Applications," Ferranti Ltd., Oldham, Lancs., England, No. 9, 1967, p 7.

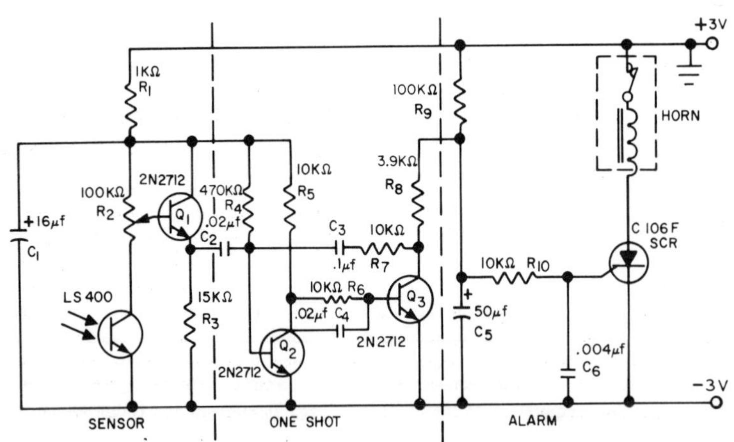

SMOKE DETECTOR RECEIVER—Responds to 10-pps pulsed light beam from transmitter. Optical path through area being monitored is 8 inches long, with four mirrors each ¼ inch square. One-shot triggers scr to turn on 1.5-V bicycle-horn alarm if smoke interrupts pulsed beam. Draws only 3 mA from pair of D flashlight cells when horn is off.—L. M. Hertz, "Solid State Lamps—Part II," General Electric, Cleveland, Ohio, No. 3-0121, 1970, p 31.

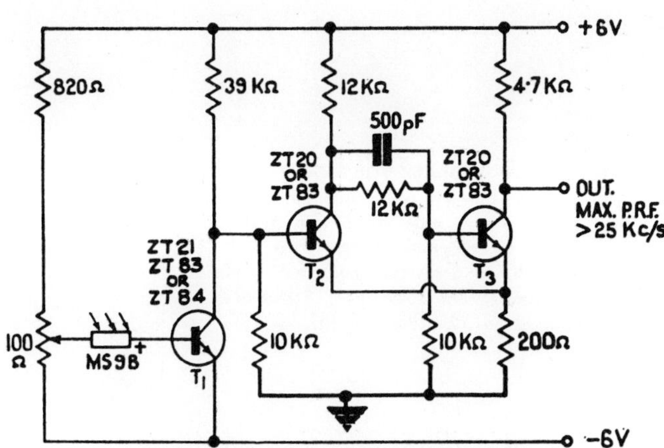

HOT-STRIP DETECTOR—Use of single-transistor d-c coupled amplifier stage between silicon photocell and input to Schmitt trigger T2-T3 gives operation down to light levels of 10 foot-candles, as required for detection of hot strip in rolling mills.—"Silicon Photocell Applications," Ferranti Ltd., Oldham, Lancs., England, No. 9, 1967, p 11.

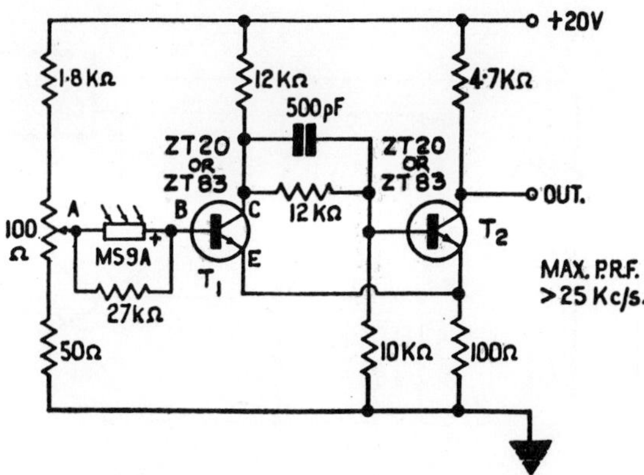

MOVING TAPE READER—Silicon-photocell circuit uses Schmitt trigger instead of straight d-c amplifier, for applications involving reading of holes in slow-moving punched cards or tape. Since circuit switches rapidly from one state to the other, operation is independent of card or tape speed.—"Silicon Photocell Applications," Ferranti Ltd., Oldham, Lancs., England, No. 9, 1967, p 7.

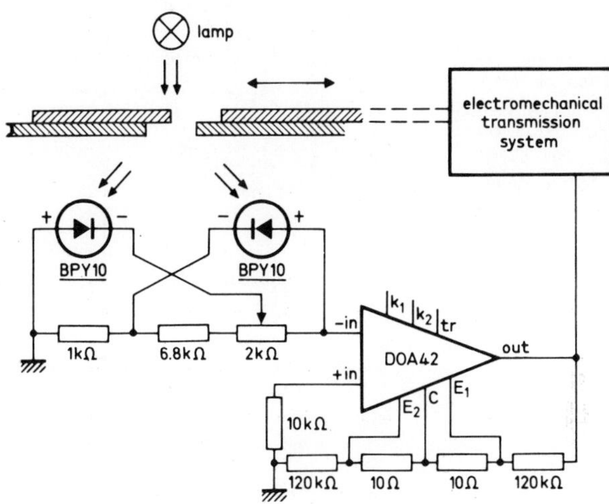

DISPLACEMENT DETECTION—Circuit minimizes effect of spread in parameters and changes in parameters with time and temperature. Purpose of circuit is to maintain two plates in predetermined position with respect to each other, with both photocells then receiving equal illumination. Uses Philips DOA42 opamp having voltage gain of 12,000 to drive electromechanical positioning system in correct direction for rebalancing photocells.—J. van Stam, Accurate Positioning With Photocells, Philips, Pub. Dept., Elcoma Div., Eindhoven, The Netherlands, No. 81.

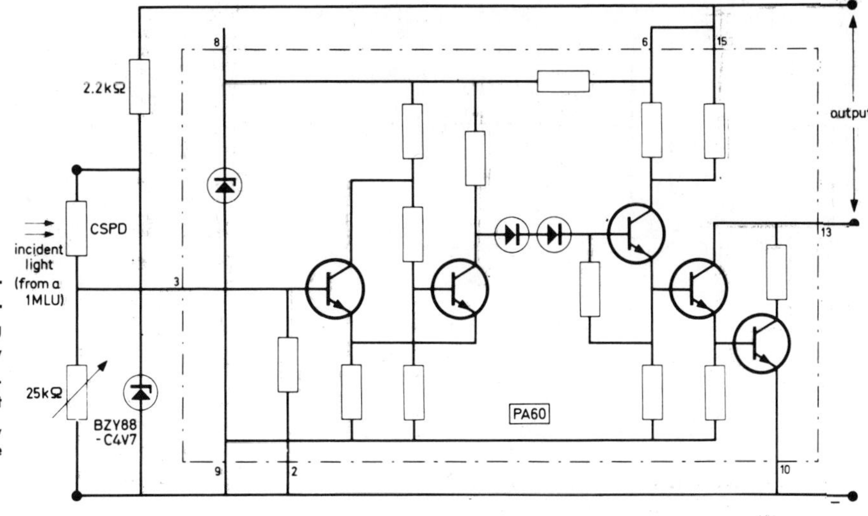

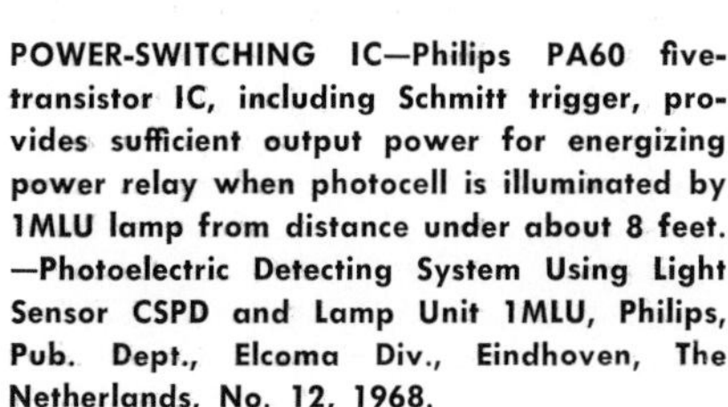
POWER-SWITCHING IC—Philips PA60 five-transistor IC, including Schmitt trigger, provides sufficient output power for energizing power relay when photocell is illuminated by 1MLU lamp from distance under about 8 feet. —Photoelectric Detecting System Using Light Sensor CSPD and Lamp Unit 1MLU, Philips, Pub. Dept., Elcoma Div., Eindhoven, The Netherlands, No. 12, 1968.

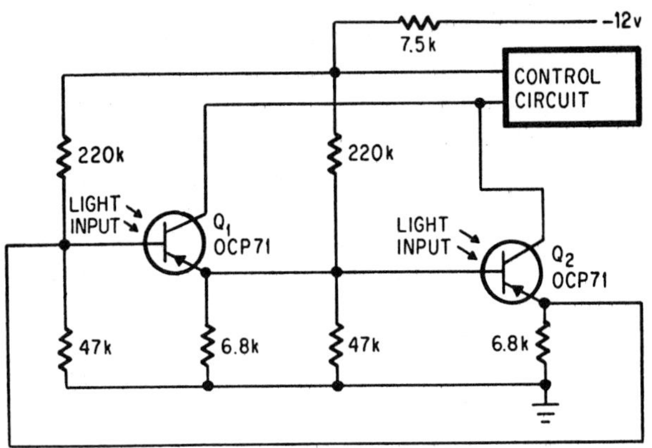

REGENERATIVE FEEDBACK FOR TWO PHOTOTRANSISTORS—Cascade connection with feedback gives current gain of 20 for typical illumination, as compared to gain of 4 without feedback.—R. Sivaswamy, Current Feedback Enhances Phototransistor Sensitivity, *Electronics*, June 12, 1967, p 103.

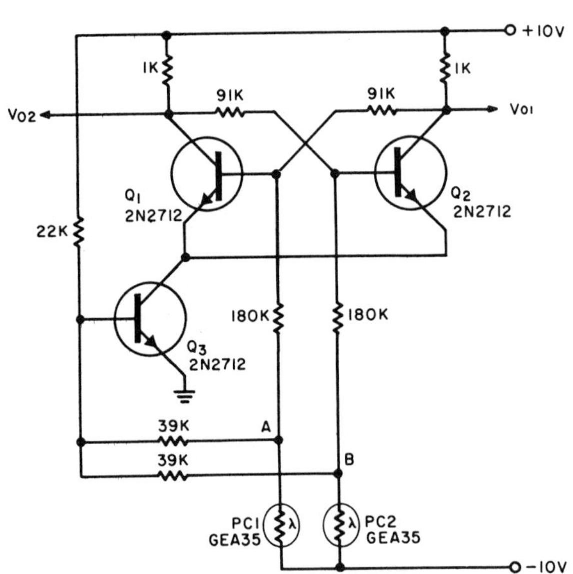

DIRECTION INDICATOR—Low-cost circuit actuates flip-flop to indicate direction of interruption of light beam by moving object. Output is negative-going at VO1 if object blocks light to PC1 before PC2. For object moving in opposite direction, output is negative-going at VO2.—H. J. Hildebrandt, Photocell Control Indicates Direction of Motion, *Electronic Design*, Oct. 12, 1964, p 80–81.

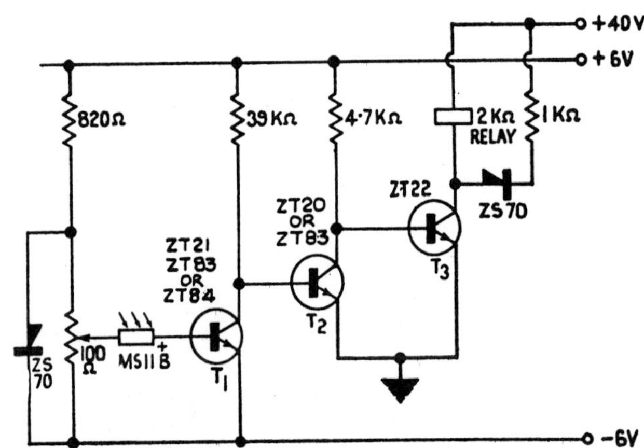

HIGH-GAIN PHOTORELAY—Three-stage direct-coupled amplifier with current gain of 10,000 gives reliable operation of telephone relay with light intensities as low as 1 lumen per sq ft on silicon photocell.—"Silicon Photocell Applications," Ferranti Ltd., Oldham, Lancs., England, No. 9, 1967, p 11.

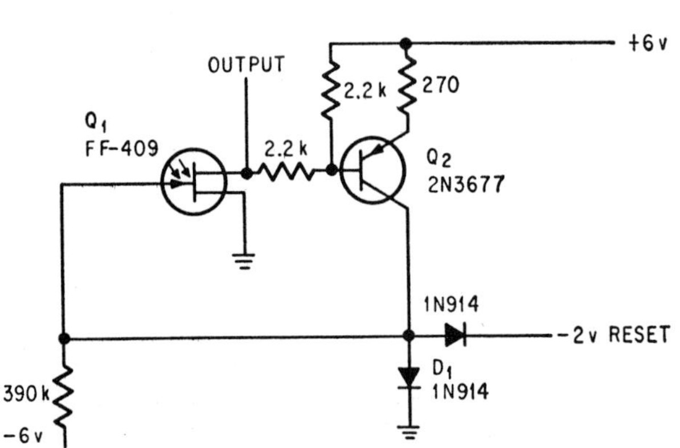

LOW-DRAIN FET LIGHT CONTROL—No power is dissipated by circuit in darkness, thus conserving battery life. Chief drawback is poor noise immunity, even though light-sensitive fet arrangement gives high voltage gain and high sensitivity.—B. R. Smith, Light-Sensitive FET, *Electronics*, Nov. 14, 1966, p 124–125.

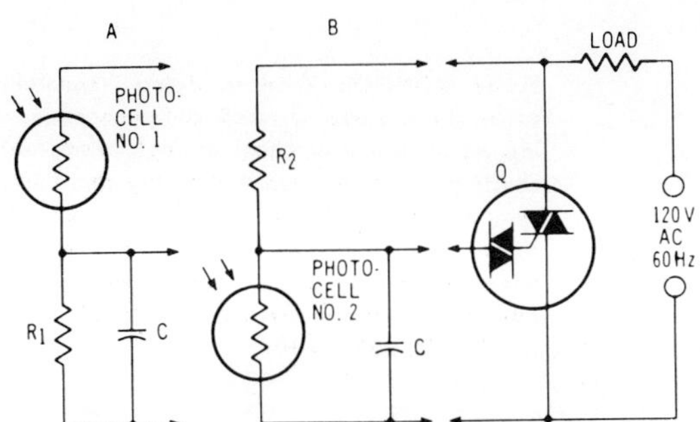

INTERNAL-TRIGGER TRIAC—Will control 720 W at up to 6 A. With connection A, load is energized when photocell is illuminated. With B, drop in light energizes load. Photocells are RCA 4453, triac is RCA-40431 silicon with internal trigger, R1 is 6.8K, and R2 is 13K.—"Solid State Photosensitive Devices," RCA, Harrison, N.J., p 22.

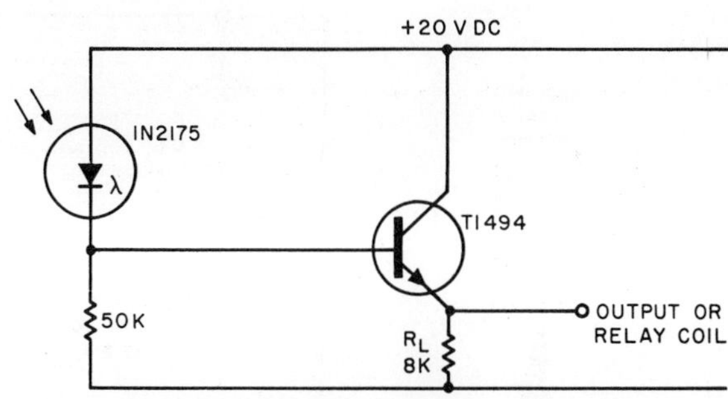

SENSOR, TRANSISTOR, AND RELAY—Emitter-follower is used between 1N2175 and 8,000-ohm relay for impedance transformation. Emitter voltage can also be used to drive amplifier, flip-flop, trigger, counter, or scr. Relay pull-in current is 1.2 mA.—D. Abel, Light Sensors—Bright Future for an Expanding Technology, *Electronic Design*, Feb. 17, 1964, p 76–79.

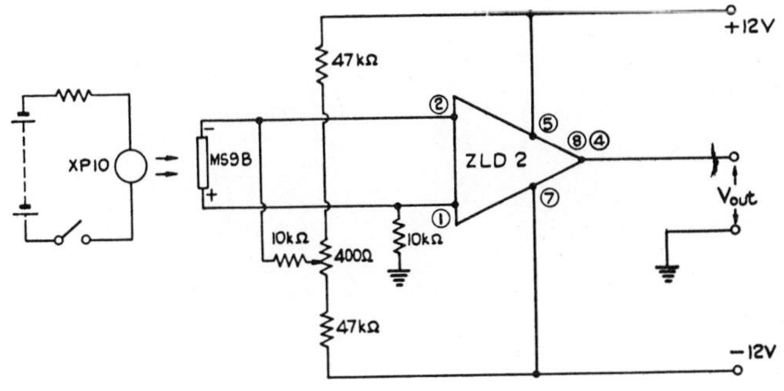

PUSH-PULL IC PHOTORELAY—Uses Ferranti ZLD2 differential d-c amplifier with silicon photocell at input, illuminated by Ferranti XP10 gallium phosphide light-emitting diode 0.05 inch from active face of photocell. Full output swing of 10 V is obtained with 100% interruption of light beam by punched paper tape or shutter.—"Silicon Photocell Applications," Ferranti Ltd., Oldham, Lancs., England, No. 9, 1967, p 13.

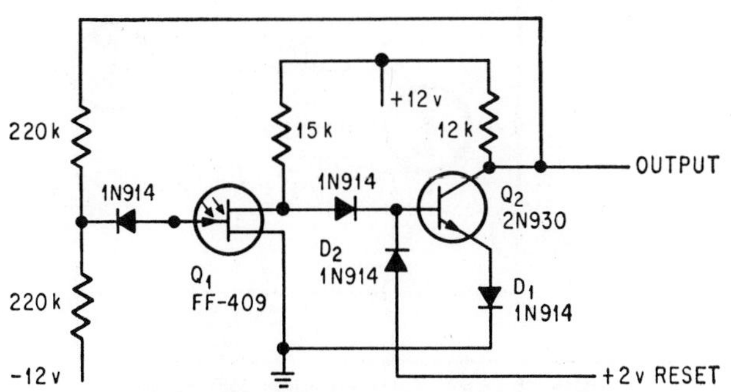

FET DOOR-OPENER—Light saturates fet Q1 and turns off npn transistor Q2 to provide positive output voltage, as required for garage-door openers, smoke detectors, and paper-break detectors. High voltage gain (above 100,000) and sensitivity of 0.1 foot-candle make circuit useful also in star trackers. Has good noise immunity.—B. R. Smith, Light-Sensitive FET, *Electronics*, Nov. 14, 1966, p 124–125.

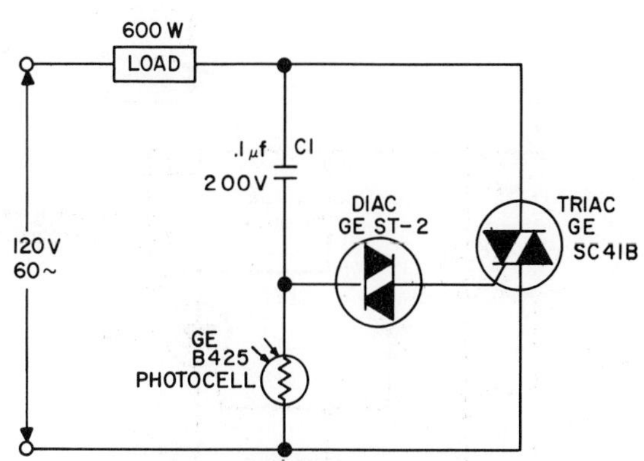

DIAC-TRIAC CONTROL—When photocell is dark, voltage across diac rises rapidly with a-c line voltage during each half-cycle, triggering diac early in cycle. When illumination makes photocell resistance drop below 2K, diac is not triggered and load power is shut off. For 240 V, change C1 to 0.1 μF.—J. H. Galloway, Using the Triac for Control of AC Power, General Electric, Syracuse, N.Y., No. 200.35, 1966, p 15.

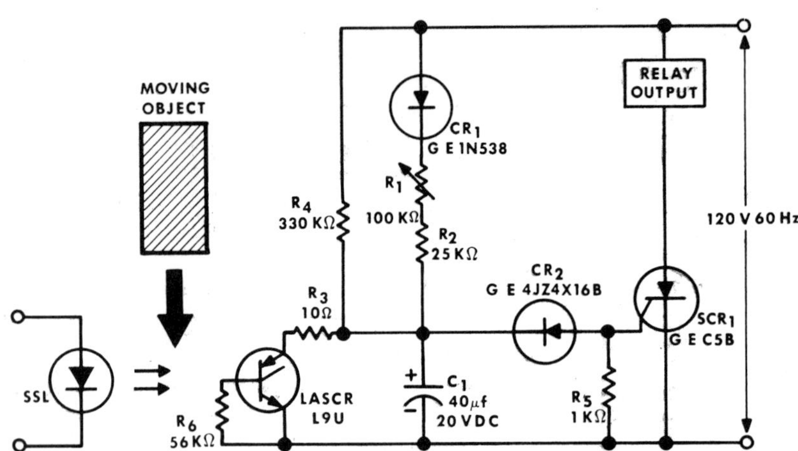

FLOW MONITOR—Used to detect impending catastrophic jams of small components moving down conveyor chute at high speed and shutting down line, while ignoring small self-clearing pile-ups. R1 controls amount of beam interruption permitted before relay is energized.—L. M. Hertz, "Solid State Lamps—Part II," General Electric, Cleveland, Ohio, No. 3-0121, 1970, p 18.

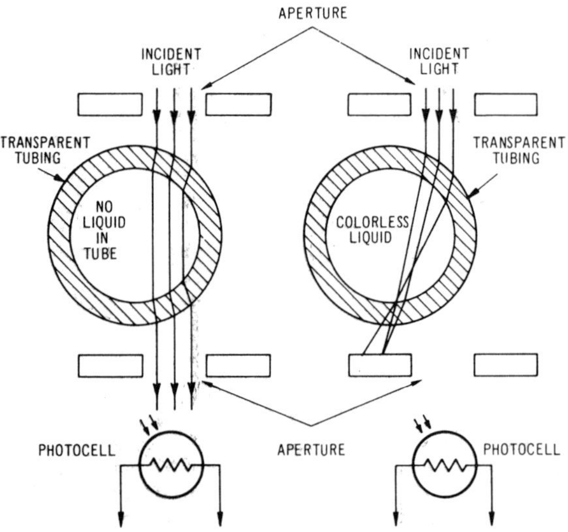

COLORLESS-LIQUID DETECTOR—Photocell is initially positioned so light passes through empty glass tube to photocell. Apertures should be positioned so light goes through near inner edge of tubing, as shown. When liquid is present, it refracts light away from photocell. Any simple photoelectric relay circuit can be used to convert change in photocell impedence to relay or indicator operation.—"Solid State Photosensitive Devices," RCA, Harrison, N.J., p 27.

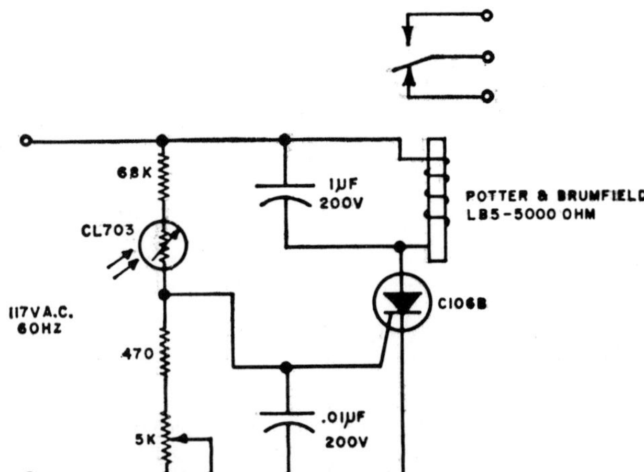

SCR CONTROL—Simple line-operated modern control uses scr to pull in relay when illumination on photocell increases to predetermined level set by potentiometer.—J. G. Rabinowitz, Photocells—Types, Characteristics, and Applications, *Electronics World*, Sept. 1968, p 23–26.

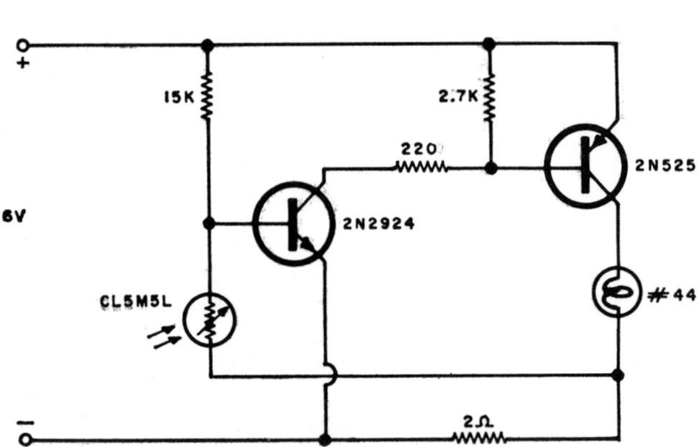

SUNSET LAMP—Turns on night light or masthead lamp on boat when twilight falls. Uses modified complementary Schmitt trigger in which transistors conduct heavily when dark resistance of photocell goes above 1,500 ohms. In daylight, photocell drops below 500 ohms, transistors turn off, and battery drain drops to 400 μA.—J. G. Rabinowitz, Photocells—Types, Characteristics, and Applications, *Electronics World*, Sept. 1968, p 23–26.

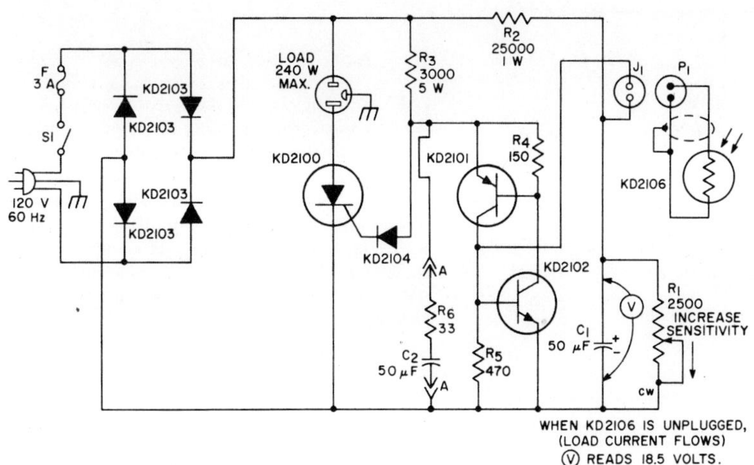

LIGHT-OPERATED TURN-OFF SWITCH—R1 determines level at which circuit interrupts power to lamp, heater, or universal motor up to 240 W. R6 and C2 provide optional latching to hold load off until line switch S1 is opened.—"Silicon Controlled Rectifier Experimenter's Manual," RCA, Harrison, N.J., 1967, p 103.

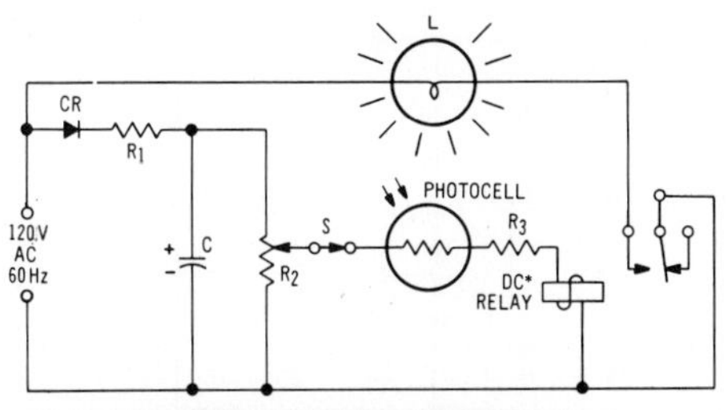

LIGHT-RESPONSIVE ALARM—Illumination on photocell, by burglar turning on room lights or flashlight, energizes relay to turn on outdoor lights, alarm, or hi-fi stereo recording of vicious barking dog. Values: R1 5.6; R2 25K; R3 2K; C 8 μF; CR 1N1763A; photocell 7163; relay 10K at 2 mA.—"Solid State Photosensitive Devices," RCA, Harrison, N.J., p 24.

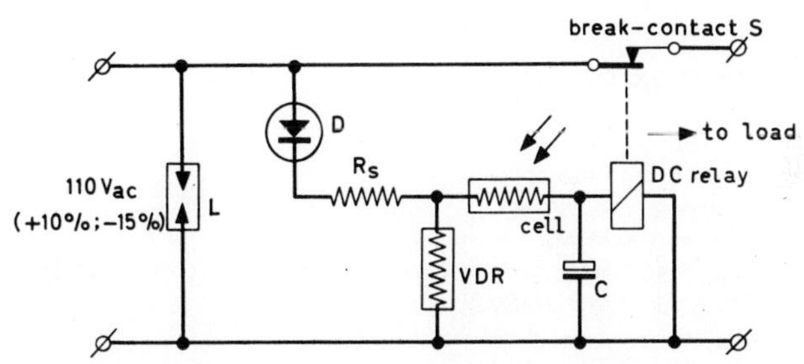

TWILIGHT SWITCH—Electrolytic capacitor across relay makes circuit insensitive to short light flashes and prevents relay from chattering as twilight falls and decreasing illumination on photocell increases impedance of cell to make relay release and apply power to lamp load. Lightning arrester (Sigma Instruments A112) protects photocell from transients above 2 kV produced by lightning in power line. Diode is BYX10; Rs 3.3K; C 8 μF; photocell RPY20; VDR voltage-dependent resistor E 298 GD/A262; relay is 21.8K, with make at 45 V d-c and break at 18 V d-c.—M. Donkers and E. B. G. Nijhof, The Application of Cadmium-Sulphide Photo-Conductive Cell RPY20 In Automatic Twilight Switches, Philips, Pub. Dept., Elcoma Div., Eindhoven, The Netherlands, No. 424, 1964.

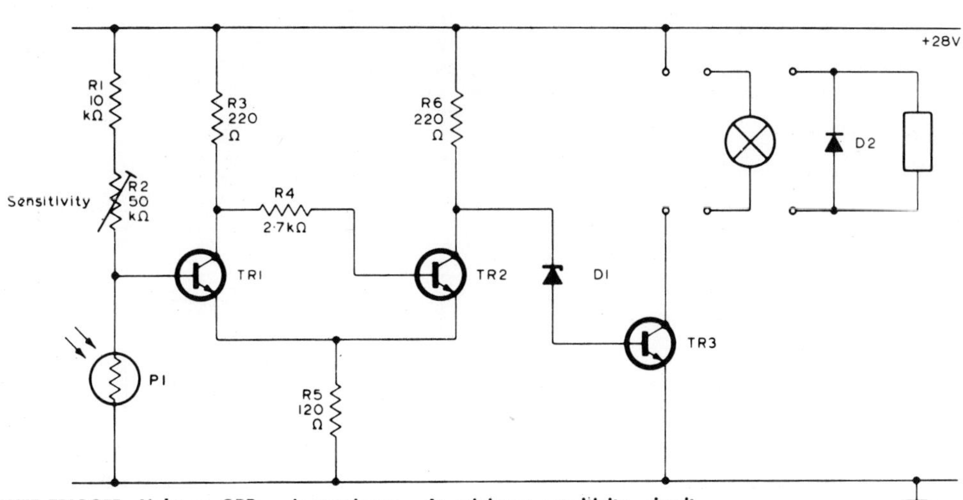

DRIVE FOR SCHMITT TRIGGER—Light on ORP-12 photocell triggers circuit and energizes lamp or relay load at level determined by R2. If set to trigger at 0.1 lux, circuit will be triggered again and lamp turned off when illumination rises to 0.11 lux and sensitivity is maximum. At minimum sensitivity, circuit triggers at 3.2 lux and retriggers to turn off lamp at 6.5 lux. Chief advantage of using Schmitt trigger is that output is switched very rapidly and does not remain in condition of high dissipation for long. Lamp load can be up to 6 W. TR1 and TR2 are BFY52, TR3 is BFY51, and D1 is OAZ215.—Applications of the BFY50, BFY51 and BFY52, Philips, Pub. Dept., Elcoma Div., Eindhoven, The Netherlands, No. 428, 1965.

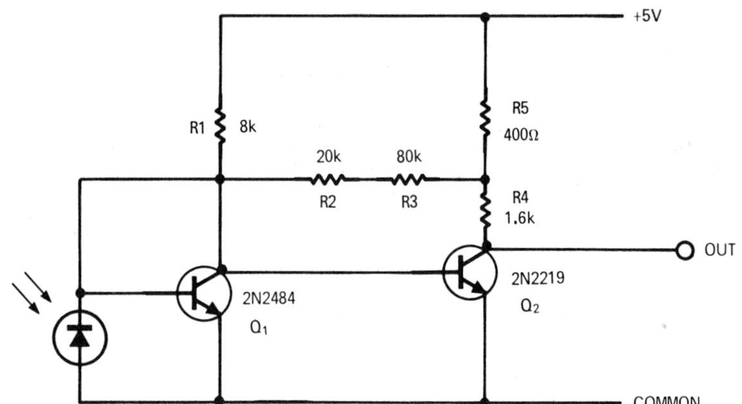

CARD READER—Schmitt trigger controlled by photovoltaic cell operating in diode mode provides consistent output from punched card or punched paper tape reader head assembly for light levels ranging from 100 to 1,000 foot-candles. Output is compatible with TTL or DTL logic and independent of erratic movement of cards or tape.—T. B. Stephenson, One Hole, One Pulse From Flutterless Card Reader, *EDN*, Feb. 15, 1970, p 59.

LIGHT-INTERRUPTION CONTROL—When beam between solid-state lamp and light-activated scs is interrupted, anode of silicon unilateral switch goes positive on next positive cycle of a-c line, triggering sus and scr to energize load for as long as light beam is interrupted. —L. M. Hertz, "Solid State Lamps—Part II," General Electric, Cleveland, Ohio, No. 3-0121, 1970, p 16.

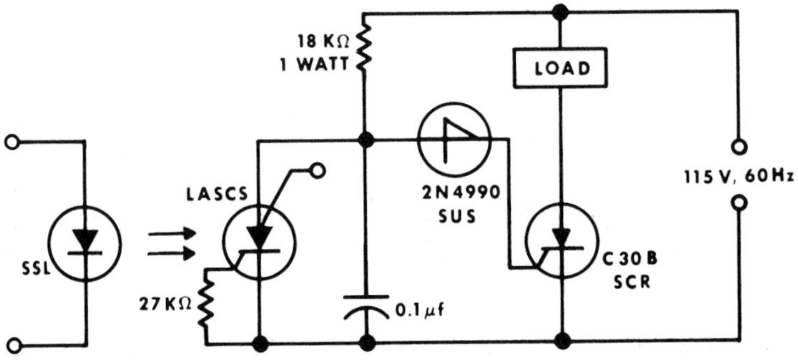

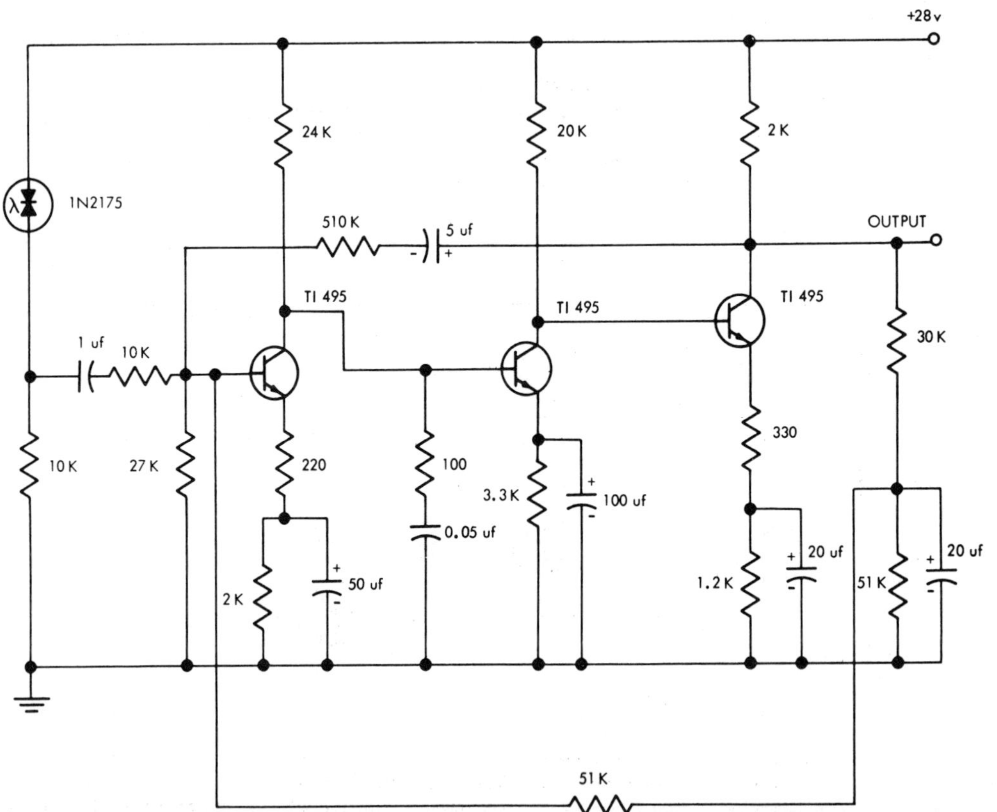

PHOTODUODIODE PREAMP—Provides voltage amplification of 30 dB, flat within 1 dB from 10 Hz to 20,000 Hz, for signal output of 1N-2175 npn, diffused silicon photoduodiode. Applications include high-speed reading of punched cards and punched tape, light measurement, conveyor-line counting, and military light-detection systems. Output obtained across 1K load resistor is 4 V p-p.—"Preferred Semiconductors and Components," Texas Instruments, Dallas, Texas, CC101, 1968, p 27804.

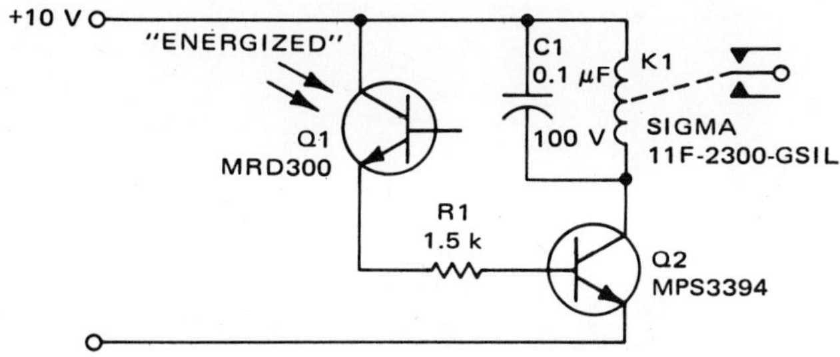

SIMPLE LIGHT-OPERATED RELAY—200 foot-candles on phototransistor Q1 saturates Q2 and pulls in d-c relay. C1 protects Q2 from inductive voltage spike of relay coil.—"Semiconductor Power Circuits Handbook," Motorola, Phoenix, Ariz., 1968, p 6–38.

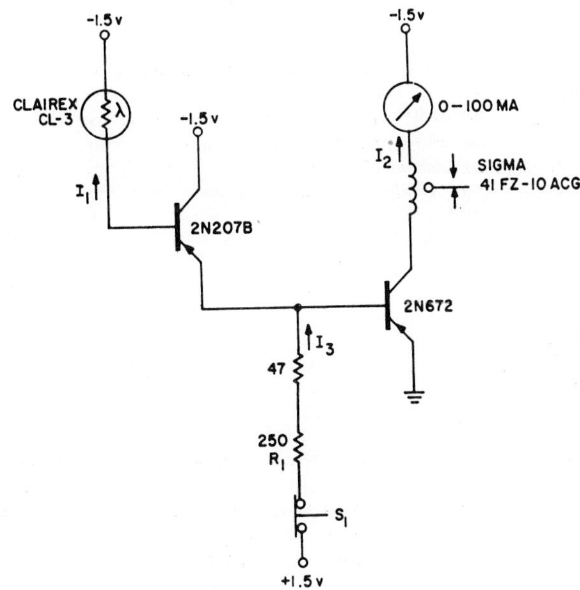

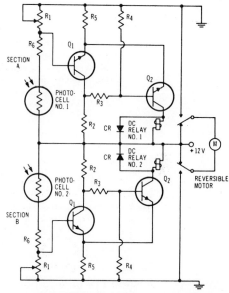

HIGH-SENSITIVITY DETECTOR—Differential amplifier circuit gives relay operation for very small percentage change in light on photocell. Can be used in light-beam burglar alarm systems and machine-tool safety systems. R1 is decreased until current I2 is just sufficient to hold relay in when photocell illumination is normal. Decrease of fraction of foot-candle in light then makes I2 drop about 20 mA, releasing relay and tripping alarm. S1 must then be open momentarily to energize relay and reset system.—E. S. Gordon, Photoelectric Circuit Operates With High Light Resolution, "400 Ideas for Design Selected from Electronic Design," Hayden Book Co., N.Y., 1964, p 107.

LIGHT-CONTROLLED SERVO—Two 12-V photocell-Schmitt triggers connected back-to-back apply no voltage to motor when both photocells are illuminated. When either photocell is dark, its relay pulls in and energizes motor for rotation in corresponding direction. Values: R1 5K; R2 820; R3 270; R4 820; R5 10; R6 1K; CR RCA-40266; Q1 40234; Q2 40084; photocells SQ2508; relays 96 ohms 12 V (shown de-energized).—"Solid State Photosensitive Devices," RCA, Harrison, N.J., p 27.

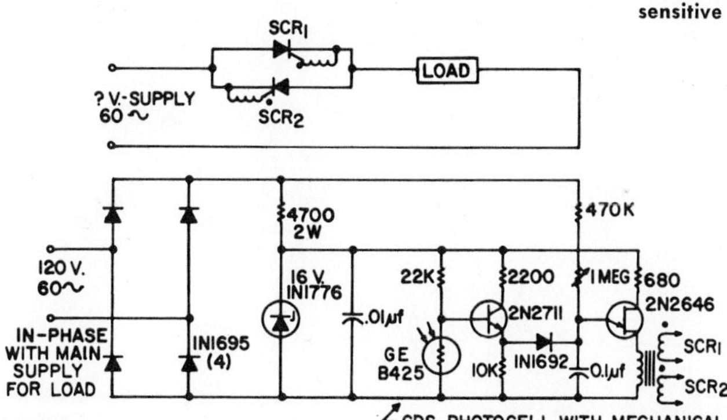

RAMP-AND-PEDESTAL CONTROL—Photocell determines pedestal voltage to which capacitor is charged through transistor at beginning of each half-cycle. Capacitor then continues to charge along adjustable ramp until ujt triggers and fires load scr's through transformer. With lamp load for illumination control, rms voltage across load can be regulated by exposing photocell to small pilot lamp connected across load. For regulation of load current, low-voltage high-current lamp is connected in series with load and placed near photocell. For proportional control of load in response to mechanical position, sensing element should drive shutter between lamp and photocell.—F. W. Gutzwiller and E. K. Howell, Economy Power Semiconductor Applications, General Electric, Syracuse, N.Y., No. 671.1, 1965, p 12.

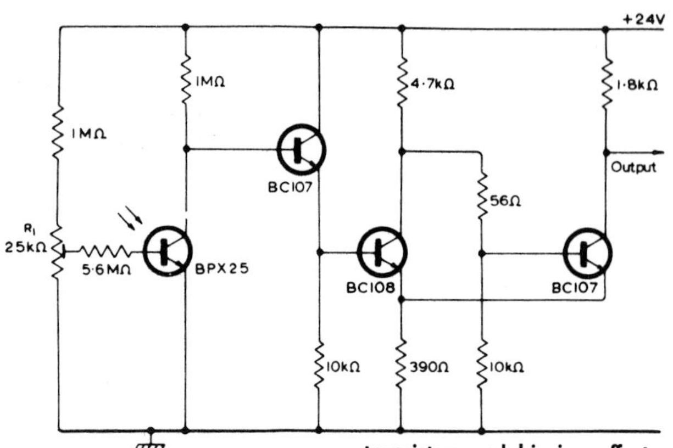

REDUCING DARK CURRENT—Illumination of only 10 lux produces output voltage change of about 20 V in high-sensitivity circuit having backlash of only about 0.5 lux. Dark current is reduced by connecting high resistance between base and emitter of phototransistor, and biasing effect resulting therefrom is overcome with connection shown. Adjust R1 until phototransistor in dark is just cut off.—Applications of Silicon Planar Phototransistor BPX25, Philips, Pub. Dept., Elcoma Div., Eindhoven, The Netherlands, No. 316, 1967.

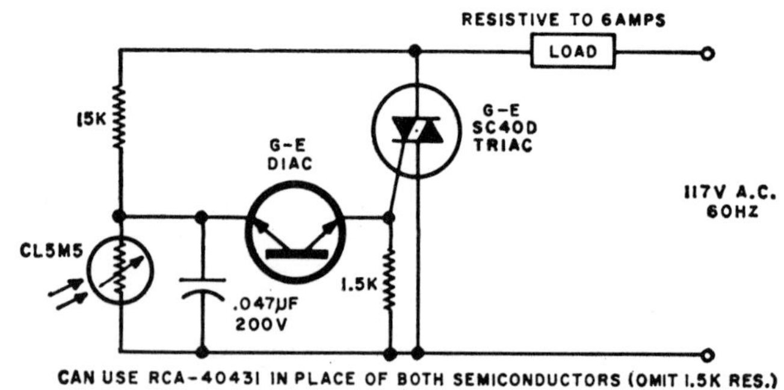

6-A TRIAC CONTROL—With illumination on photocell, triac turns off power to load.—J. G. Rabinowitz, Photocells—Types, Characteristics, and Applications, *Electronics World*, Sept. 1968, p 23–26.

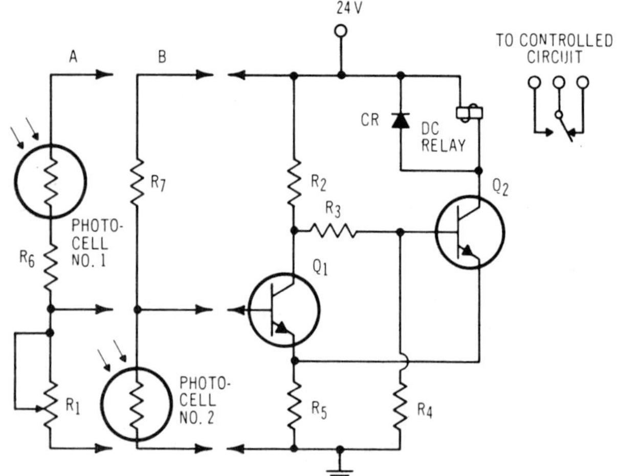

24-V SCHMITT TRIGGER—With connection A, relay is energized when light drops below value determined by setting of R1. With connection B, relay is energized when light rises above predetermined level. Values: R1 1K; R2, R3 2.2K; R4 300; R5 12; R6 10K; R7 75K; CR 40266; Q1, Q2 40084; photocell No. 1 SQ2508; photocell No. 2 SQ2519; relay 360 ohms 24 V.—"Solid State Photosensitive Devices," RCA, Harrison, N.J., p 21.

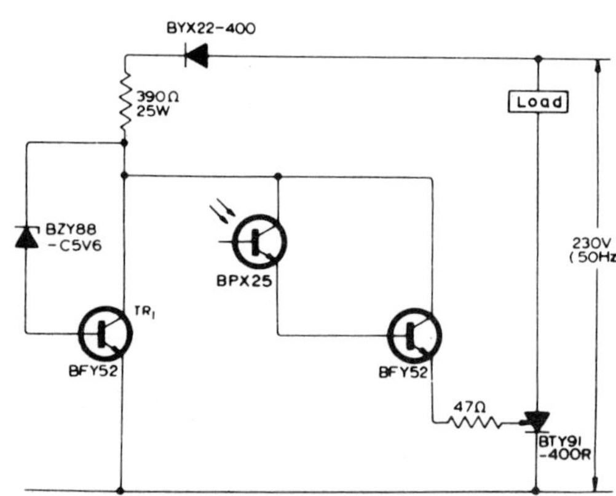

A-C POWER CONTROL—When light on phototransistor rises above about 700 lux, thyristor is triggered and turns on load current up to 16 A from a-c line. Circuit does not latch on because thyristor disconnects supply from load at end of each positive half-cycle. Circuit retriggers about 6 deg past zero voltage if phototransistor still has sufficient illumination.—Applications of Silicon Planar Phototransistor BPX25, Philips, Pub. Dept., Elcoma Div., Eindhoven, The Netherlands, No. 316, 1967.

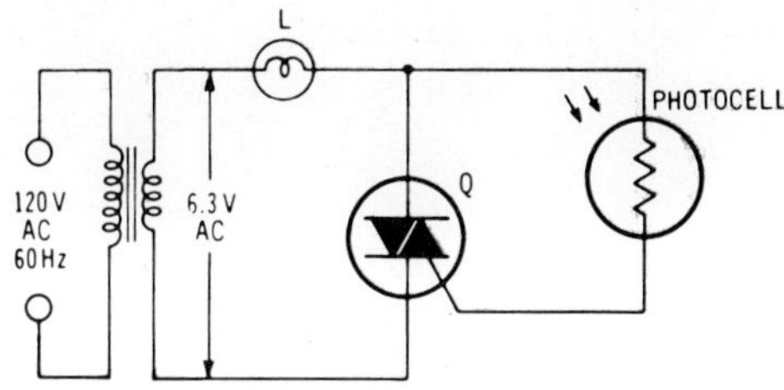

6.3-V A-C TRIAC CONTROL—Light makes photocell impedance drop, and resulting increase in cell current triggers triac on. Will handle lamp or other load currents up to 2.5 A, with 15 W maximum. Triac Q is RCA-40528 and photocell is SQ2519.—"Solid State Photosensitive Devices," RCA, Harrison, N.J., p 21.

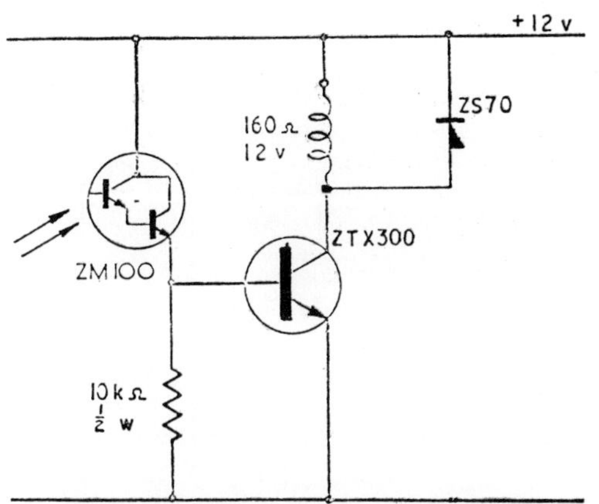

PHOTO-DARLINGTON WITH AMPLIFIER—Transistor provides sufficient additional gain for operating relay when light level on Ferranti ZM100 photo-Darlington is below 50 lumens per sq ft.—A Photo Darlington Pair, Ferranti, Oldham, Lancs., England, No. 36, 1968.

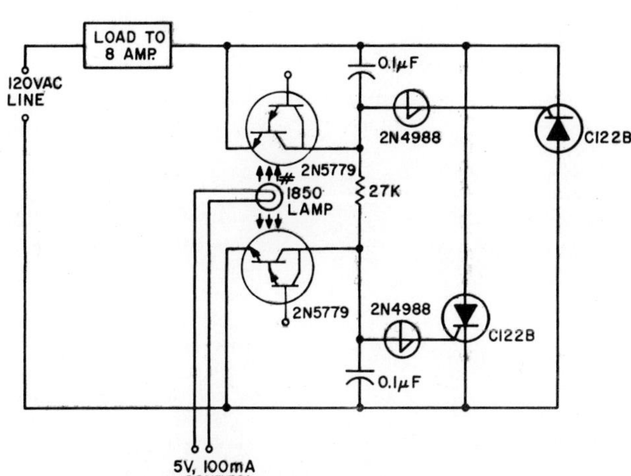

PHOTO-DARLINGTON AMPLIFIER—Two 2N-5779 npn planar silicon glass-housing transistors in Darlington connection are illuminated by lamp whose intensity varies with control current, for control of loads up to 1,000 W. By increasing 27K resistor to 56K and using C122D scr's, load can be 2,000 W at 240 V.—Light Sensor 2N5777-2N5780, General Electric, Syracuse, N.Y., No. 55.46, 1969.

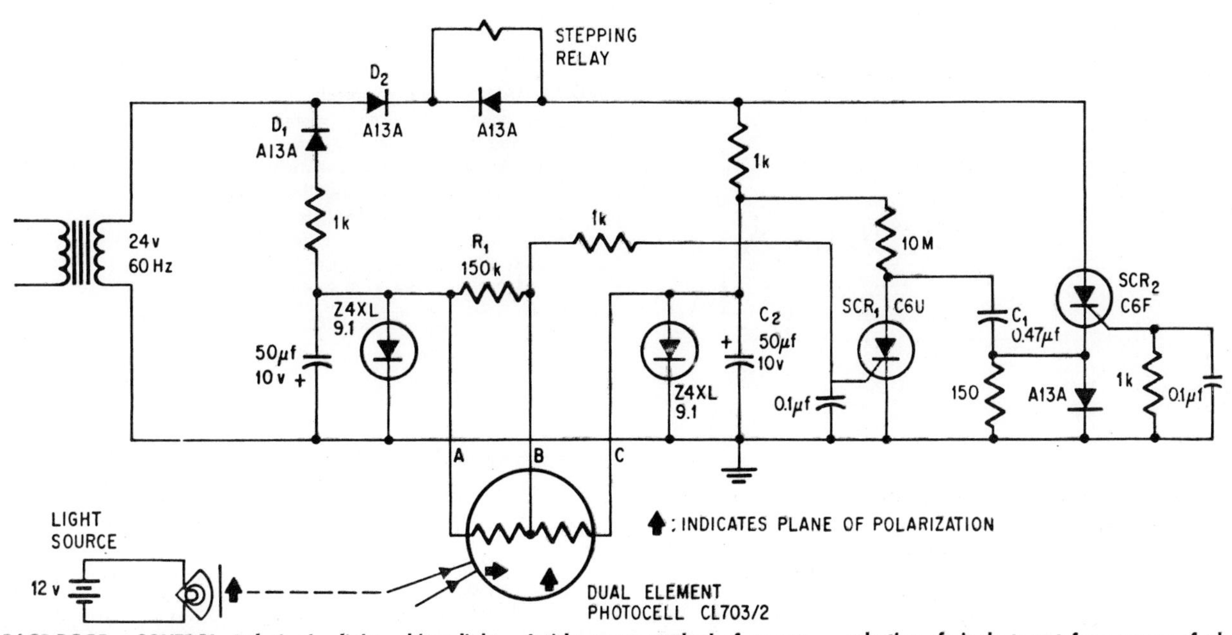

GARAGE-DOOR CONTROL—Polarized light source on moving vehicle can trigger photocell of control up to 50 feet away, without risk of accidental triggering by stray or ambient light. Article covers method of mounting horizontal and vertical polarizing filters in system. Can be adapted for variety of other remote control applications, including selection of single target from group of photocells.—E. K. Howell, Polarized Light Triggers Remote Control System, *Electronics*, Jan. 23, 1967, p 88–90.

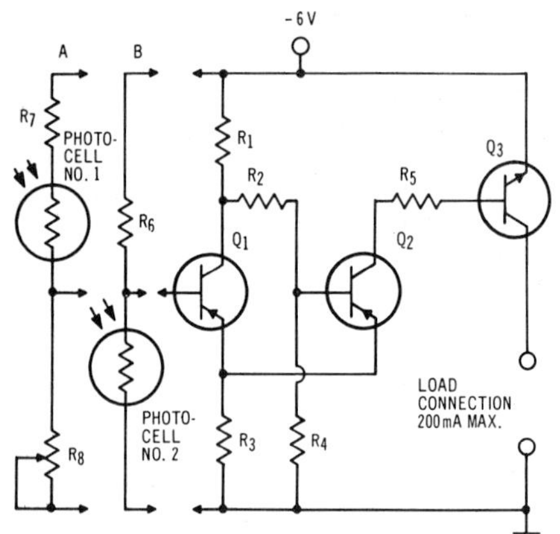

RCA PHOTOCELLS:
No. 1, TYPE SQ2508
No. 2, TYPE SQ2520

Q_1, Q_2: RCA-2N404
Q_3: RCA-2N388
R_1, R_2: 1200
R_3: 22
R_4: 1200
R_5: 390
R_6: 3900
R_7: 1000
R_8: 1000

6-V SCHMITT TRIGGER—With photocell connection A, load is energized when light drops below predetermined level set by R8. With connection B, load is energized when illumination rises above predetermined level.—"Solid-State Photosensitive Devices," RCA, Harrison, N.J., p 20.

SINGLE-APERTURE POSITION INDICATOR—If photocells are uniformly spaced on circumference of circle, with lamp and aperture mounted on radius arm, meter will indicate angular position of aperture by reading maximum voltage when only photocell No. 1 is illuminated and minimum voltage when lowest cell (No. 5) is illuminated. All resistors are equal, and can be any value that gives reasonable power dissipation for d-c voltage source used, while giving desired full-scale voltage at meter for light on first photocell. For conditions shown, with light on No. 3 cell, meter voltage is equal to source voltage multiplied by ratio of sum of R3, R4, and R5 to sum of all five resistances.—"Solid State Photosensitive Devices," RCA, Harrison, N.J., p 26.

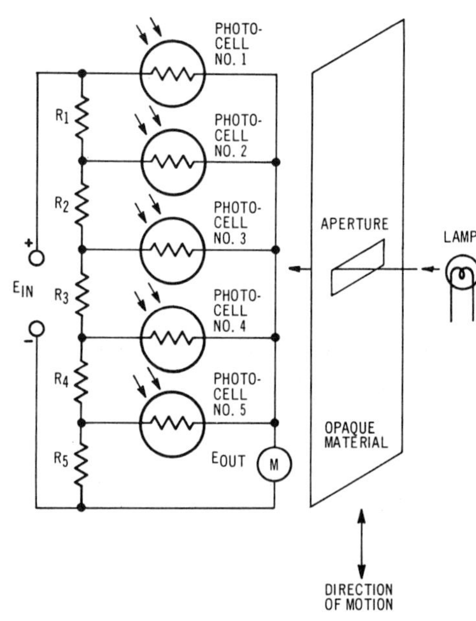

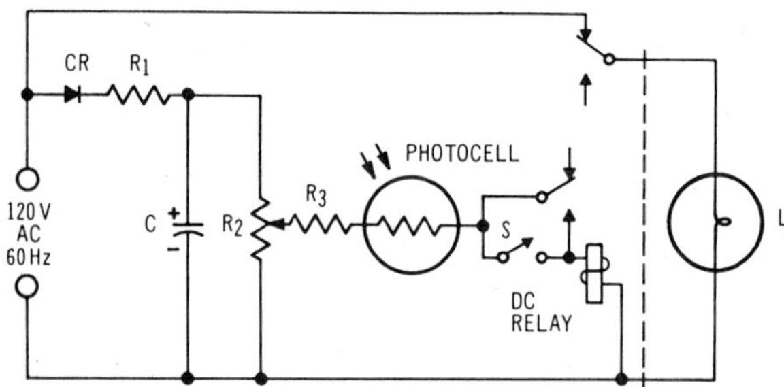

BURGLAR LAMP—When photocell is illuminated and switch S closed, current flows through photocell and relay, so lamp is not energized. At twilight, relay opens and lamp is connected directly across a-c line. Used to discourage burglars when home is unoccupied. Open S to reset. Values: R1 5.6; R2 25K; R3 2K; C 8 μF; CR 1N1763A; photocell 7163; relay 10K at 3.5 mA.—"Solid State Photosensitive Devices," RCA, Harrison, N.J., p 23.

SENSITIVE LIGHT-OPERATED LINE SWITCH—Cadmium sulfide photocell turns triac on through Schmitt trigger Q2-Q3 when light level falls below preset value determined by R4. Circuit has very little backlash, so only small change in light level is needed to make triac turn on or off. Load can be up to 6 A, using RCA 40429 triac for 120 V and 40430 for 240 V.—R. M. Marston, 20 Triac Circuits, *Radio-Electronics*, June 1970, p 51–53 and 97.

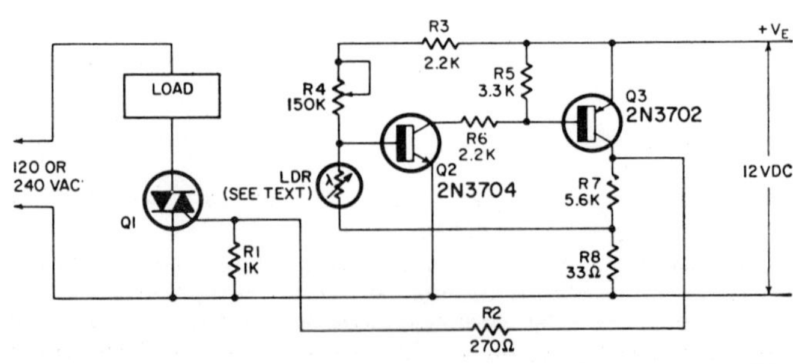

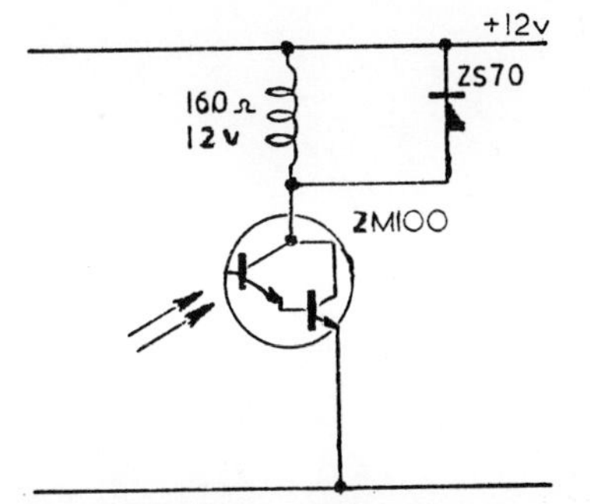

PHOTO-DARLINGTON RELAY—Uses Ferranti ZM100 photo-Darlington having high sensitivity at low light levels. Maximum dissipation rating of 300 mW at room temperature can be increased 50% by mounting on heat sink. 60-W lamp 8 inches away will produce the required 50 lumens per sq ft to switch relay.—A Photo Darlington Pair, Ferranti, Oldham, Lancs., England, No. 36, 1968.

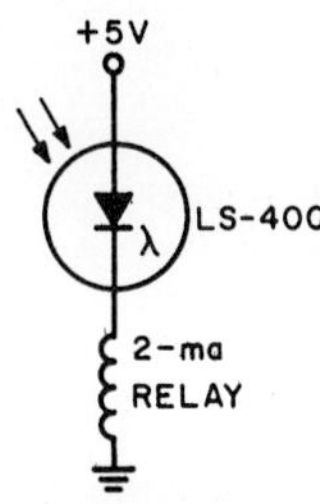

SENSOR AND RELAY—High sensitivity of Texas Instruments LS-400 npn silicon planar light sensor permits direct drive of 2-mA relay from 5-V source, eliminating need for transistor amplifier stage. Relay will pull in on minimum light intensity of 600 footcandles.—D. Abel, Light Sensors—Bright Future for an Expanding Technology, *Electronic Design*, Feb. 17, 1964, p 76–79.

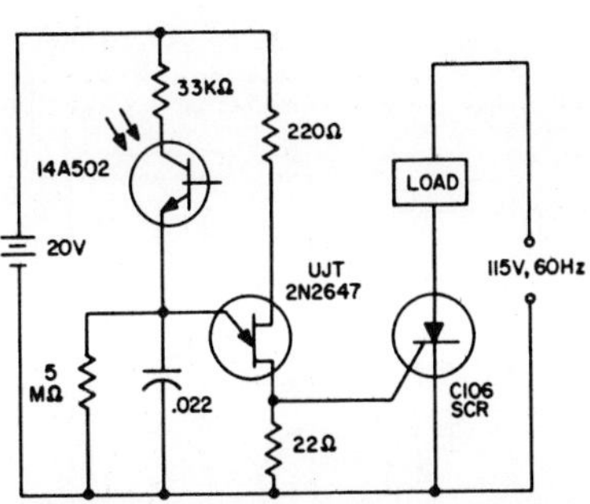

HIGH-SENSITIVITY LIGHT-PRESENCE DETECTOR—Phototransistor and ujt allow much lower levels of light to actuate scr. When light reaches phototransistor, ujt becomes relaxation oscillator, at frequency considerably above 60 Hz. Scr is then turned on early in positive half of each cycle.—"SCR Manual," 4th Edition, General Electric, 1967, p 299.

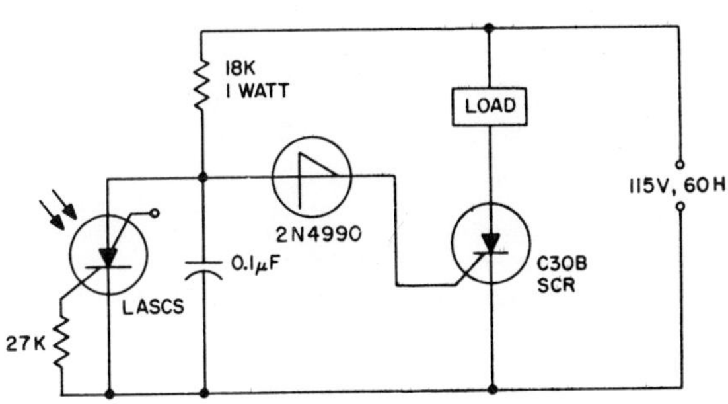

LIGHT-INTERRUPTION DETECTOR—When light on light-activated silicon controlled switch (lascs) is interrupted, anode voltage of 2N-4990 unilateral switch goes positive on next positive half-cycle, triggering switch and scr. Load is then energized for as long as there is no light on lascs.—"SCR Manual," 4th Edition, General Electric, 1967, p 298.

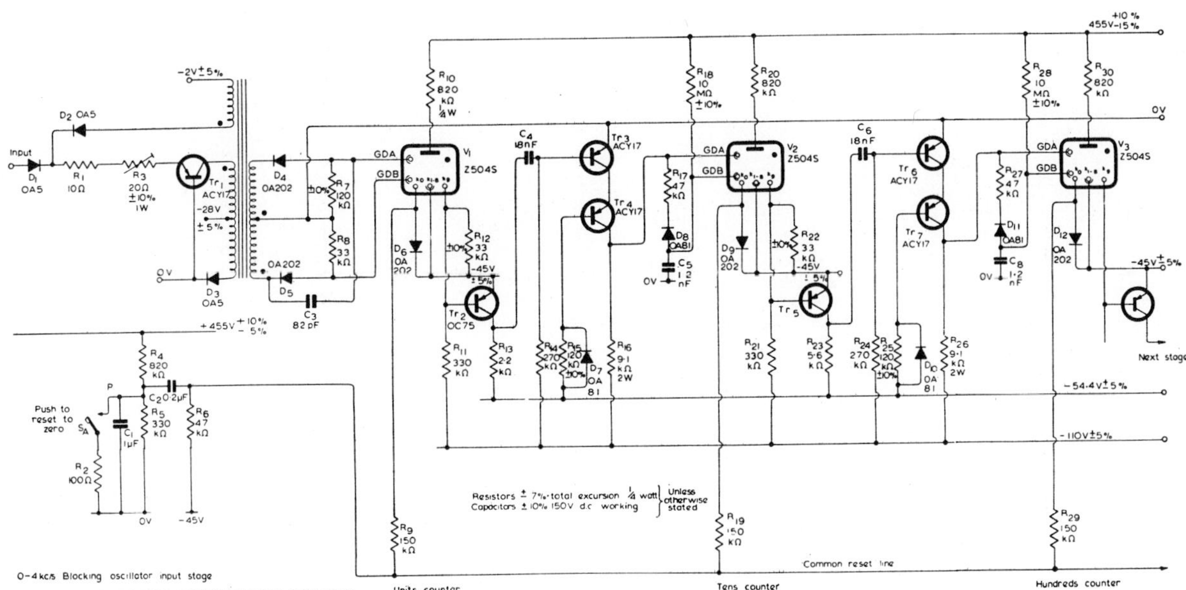

PHOTOELECTRIC-INPUT SIX-DECADE SCALER—Will count up to 25 objects per second moving through light beam if ORP60 cadmium sulfide cell is used with 2,000-lux level, and up to 13 objects per second with 1,000-lux RPY15 cell. Four additional decades may be added, each having gas-filled Z504S decade counter and three-transistor pulse-shaper coupler.—G. C. Chappell and G. F. Jeynes, Transistor Coupling Circuits for the Z504S Stepping Tube, Philips, Pub. Dept., Elcoma Div., Eindhoven, The Netherlands, No. 15, 1965, p 26–38.

AT AMPLIFIER LOCATION
VOLUME-CONTROL AT REMOTE LOCATION
ELECTROSTATIC SHIELD (FINE MESH SCREEN)
SHIELDED LEAD
L
R
1
2
e_{IN}
e_{OUT}
LIGHT-TIGHT BOX
LIGHT-TIGHT PARTITION

REMOTE POT—Permits adjusting volume of hi-fi or p-a system from practically any desired distance, using only battery and pot R at remote location. When arm of A is at 1, upper lamp is out and lower lamp is lit, so lower photocell has minimum resistance and provides maximum attenuation of audio signal.—"Solid State Photosensitive Devices," RCA, Harrison, N.J., p 27.

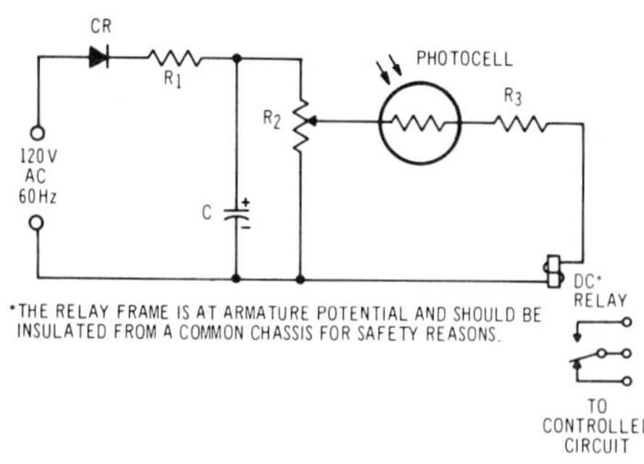

120-V A-C PHOTORELAY—Will operate at light levels as low as 1 foot-candle. R2 adjusts sensitivity of circuit. Suitable for either on-off control or gradual changes in illumination. Values: R1 5.6; R2 25K; R3 2K; C 8 μF; CR 1N1763A; photocell 7163; relay 10K at 2.5 mA.—"Solid State Photosensitive Devices," RCA, Harrison, N.J., p 21.

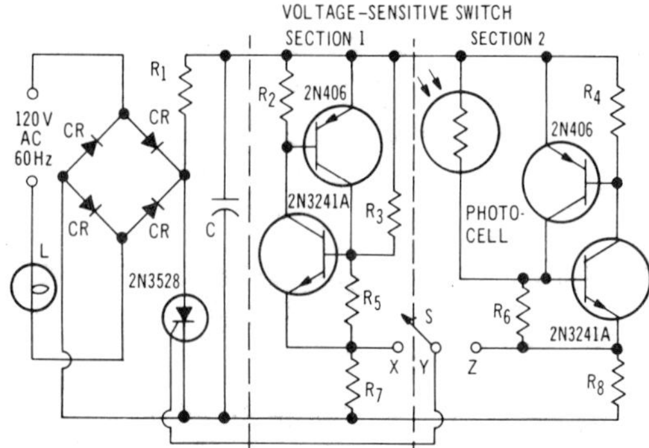

120-V A-C SCR CONTROL FOR 150 W—Switch S reverses operation of circuit; when set at X, scr is on when photocell is dark, and increase in light makes it turn off load. When set at Z, load is energized by increase in light level. Values: R1 4.7K; R2, R4 150; R3 56K; R5, R6 4.7K; R7, R8 15; C 0.22 μF; CR 1N2861A; photocell 7163; load L 150 W.—"Solid State Photosensitive Devices," RCA, Harrison, N.J., p 22.

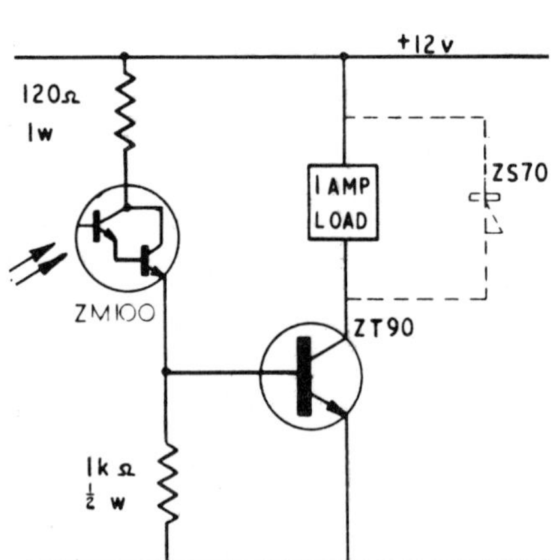

PHOTO-DARLINGTON FOR 1-A LOAD—When illumination on Ferranti ZM100 photo-Darlington is above 50 lumens per sq ft, only one transistor amplifier stage is required to turn on 1-A load. Inductive loads require diode in parallel to reduce voltage transients.—A Photo Darlington Pair, Ferranti, Oldham, Lancs., England, No. 36, 1968.

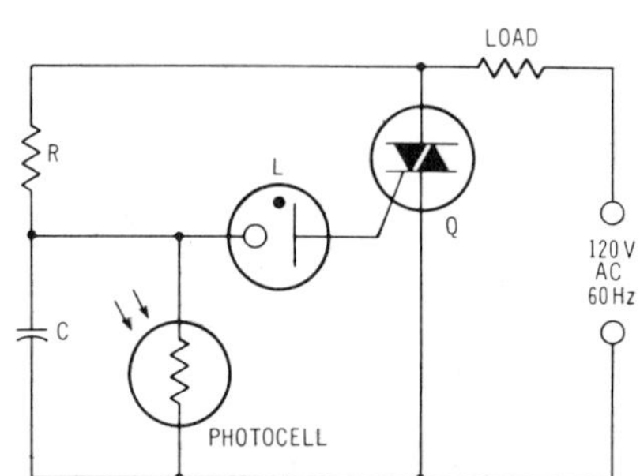

120-V A-C TRIAC CONTROL—When photocell is dark, its impedance is high and C charges to firing voltage of neon L, triggering triac on and delivering power to load. Increase in light reduces photocell impedance, so C cannot charge enough to fire neon and trigger triac; load is then off. Q can be RCA 40429, 40485, or 40575 silicon triac. Photocell is RCA 7163, L is 5AH neon, C is 0.1 μF, and R is 15K.—"Solid State Photosensitive Devices," RCA, Harrison, N.J., p 22.

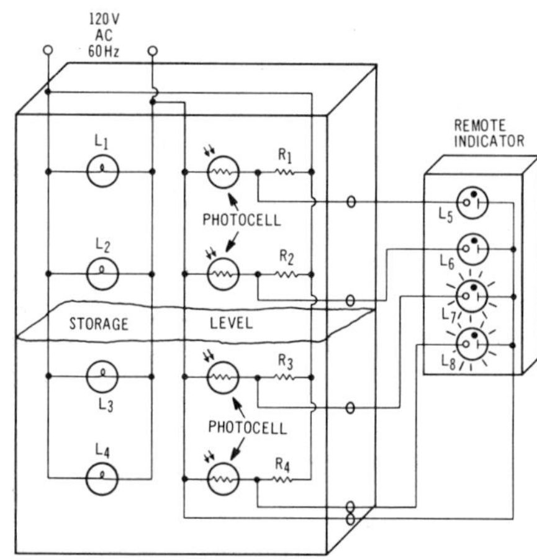

BIN LEVEL INDICATOR—Can be used with any number of levels. When grain or other dry material in bin blocks light from lamp to photocell, associated neon 3AG lamp comes on. Highest lamp glowing on indicator panel corresponds to level in bin. Photocells are RCA SQ 2503 and resistors are 330K.—"Solid State Photosensitive Devices," RCA, Harrison, N.J., p 26.

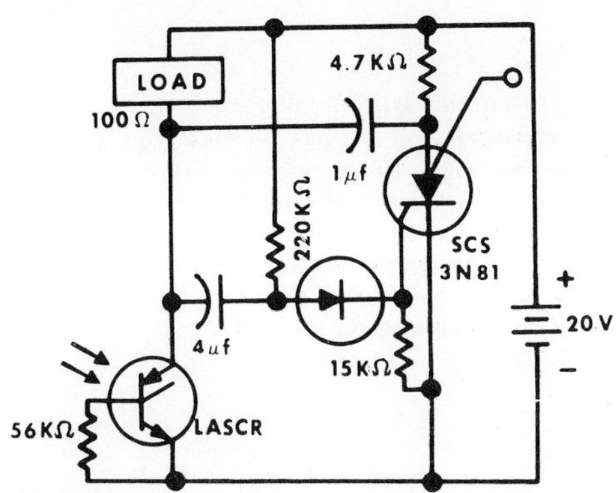

LIGHT-TRIGGERED ONE-SHOT—With no light on lascr, scs conducts but load is off. Short pulse of light on lascr turns it on and turns off scs. Load, which may be indicator lamp, is then energized. After delay of about 0.6 s while 4-μF capacitor charges through 220K, scs is turned on and lascr is commutated off. Useful for detecting presence of pulses of light lasting longer than some minimum time. For longer pulses, lascr remains conducting and indicator stays on.—L. M. Hertz, "Solid State Lamps—Part II," General Electric, Cleveland, Ohio, No. 3-0121, 1970, p 16.

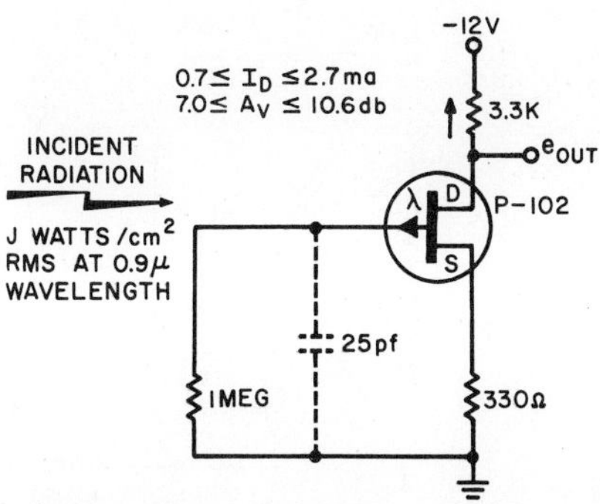

CHOPPED-LIGHT DETECTOR—Photo-fet in simple circuit provides 8 dB gain for chopped incident light, in much less space than photodiode-transistor combination. Upper frequency limit is about 7 kHz.—M. Shipley, Using Photo Field-Effect Transistors, *Electronic Design*, Aug. 31, 1964, p 76.

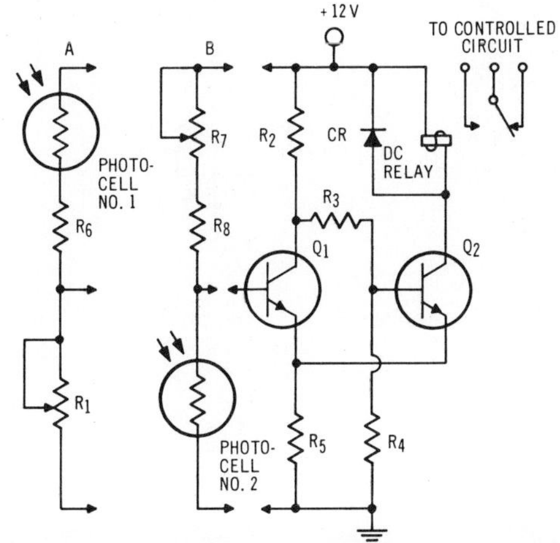

12-V SCHMITT TRIGGER—With connection A, relay is energized when light drops below value determined by setting of R1. With connection B, relay is energized when light rises above level set by R7. Values: R1 5K; R2 820; R3 270; R4 820; R5 10; R6 1K; R7 10K; R8 1.2K; CR 40266; Q1 40234; Q2 40084; photocell No. 1 SQ2508; photocell No. 2 SQ-2536; relay 96 ohms 12 V.—"Solid-State Photosensitive Devices," RCA, Harrison, N.J., p 20.

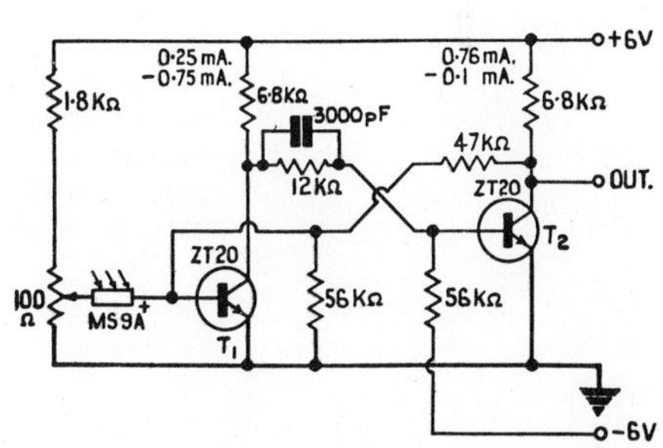

TAPE READER WITH ECCLES-JORDAN TRIGGER—Gives reliable reading of holes in moving punched cards or tape, for light intensities of 1,000 to 3,000 lumens per sq ft. Ambient temperature can be up to 100 C.—"Silicon Photocell Applications," Ferranti Ltd., Oldham, Lancs., England, No. 9, 1967, p 8.

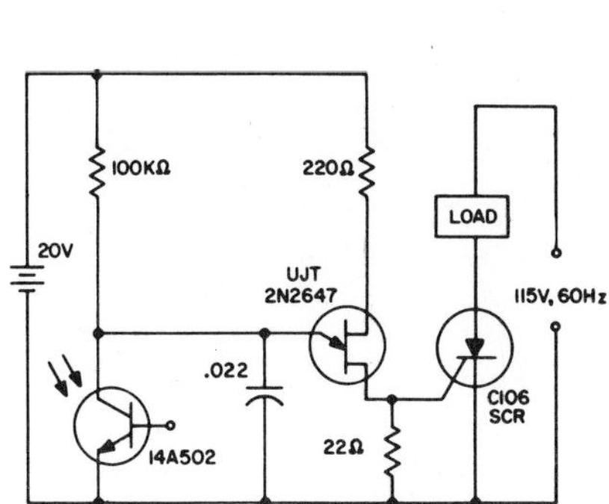

HIGH-SENSITIVITY LIGHT-ABSENCE DETECTOR—When phototransistor is dark, ujt operates as relaxation oscillator and energizes scr and load on positive half-cycles.—"SCR Manual," 4th Edition, General Electric, 1967, p 299.

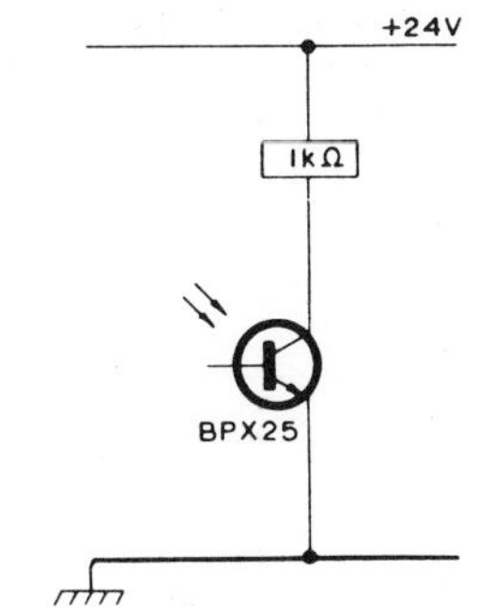

DIRECT CONTROL OF RELAY—With 24-V 1,000-ohm relay, illumination of about 10,000 lux will energize relay. Lower illumination can be used with higher-resistance relay.—Applications of Silicon Planar Phototransistor BPX25, Philips, Pub. Dept., Elcoma Div., Eindhoven, The Netherlands, No. 316, 1967.

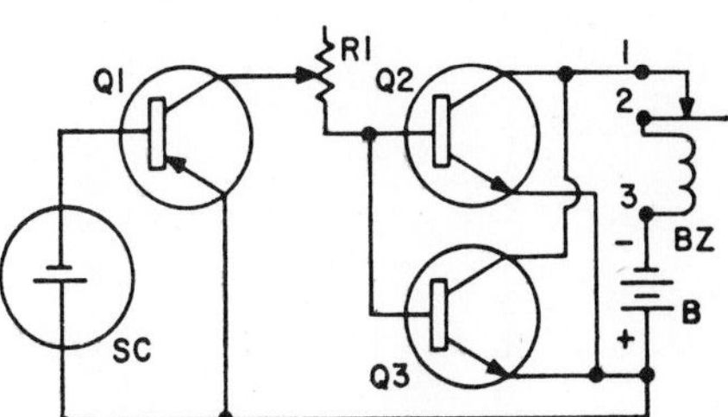

SOLAR-CELL BUZZER—Flashlight beam on solar cell makes pnp transistor Q1 turn on paralleled npn transistors Q2 and Q3 to close 3-V flashlight-cell circuit to small buzzer. R1 is 50K pot. Transistor types are not critical, and may be low-cost units. Solar cell and other parts are available from Radio Shack, 730 Commonwealth Ave., Boston, Mass.—Light Operated Buzzer, *Elementary Electronics*, Jan.–Feb. 1968, p 14.

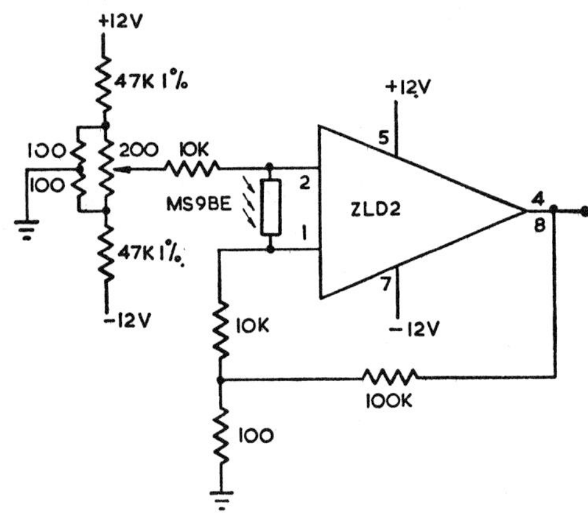

IC TRIGGER—Ferranti ZLD2 IC differential amplifier is operated with positive feedback to give triggering when silicon photocell generates voltage in excess of 5-mV input hysteresis value. Potentiometer serves to compensate for offset voltage of amplifier.—Microlin Amplifiers ZLD2S and ZLD2T, Ferranti Ltd., Oldham, Lancs., England, No. 11, 1967, p 19.

POSITION-SENSING SERVO—Two silicon MS-9B photocells mounted side by side are illuminated by single narrow beam of light. Relative movement between beam and photocells causes one photocell to generate more output than the other, for amplification by Ferranti ZLD2 IC differential amplifier. Polarity of output depends on which photocell has more illumination. Output is zero for equal illumination. Gain is 100 with parallel voltage feedback as shown.—Microlin Amplifiers ZLD2S and ZLD2T, Ferranti Ltd., Oldham, Lancs., England, No. 11, 1967, p 20.

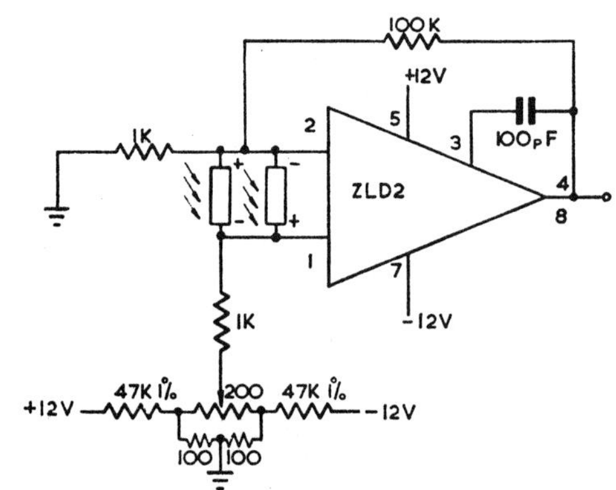

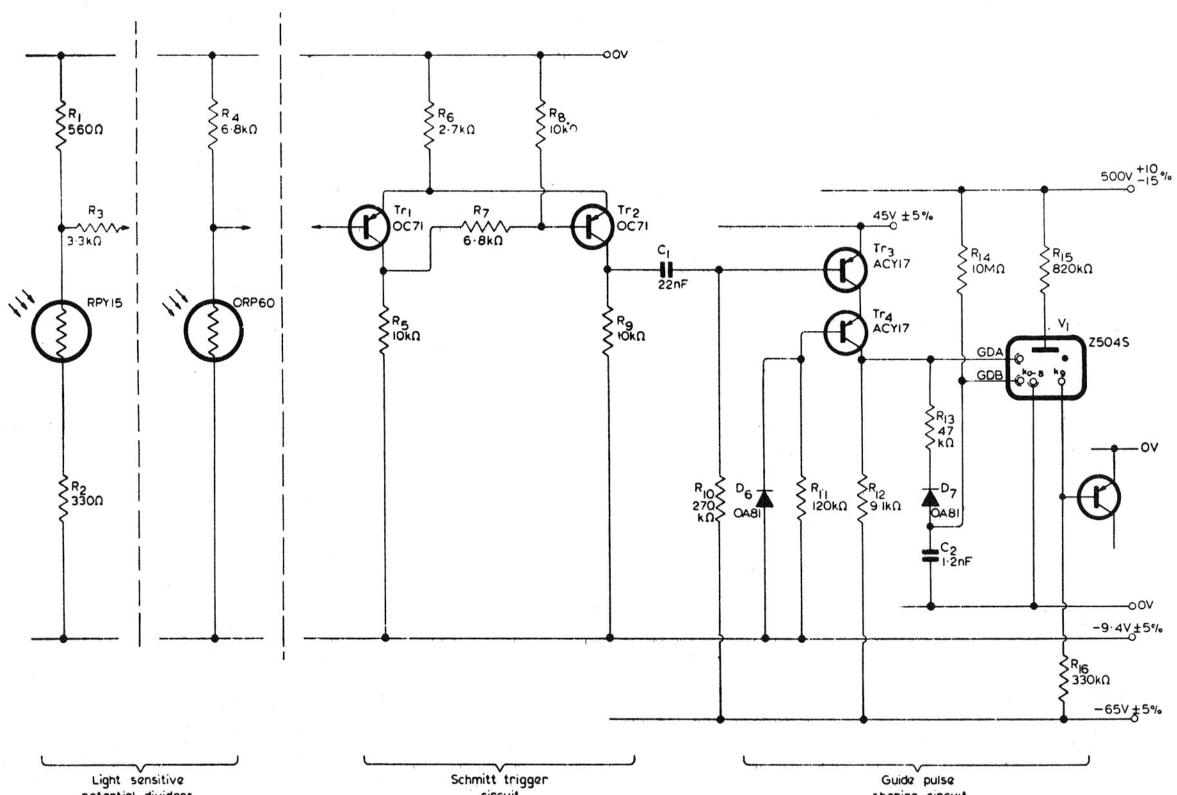

25-HZ PHOTOELECTRIC COUNTER—Will count objects moving through light beams at speeds up to 25 objects per second if ORP60 cadmium sulfide input network is used; this requires illumination level of at least 2,000 lux, falling to background level below 10 lux when object interrupts light beam. Alternative RPY15 cell requires only 1,000 lux but counting speed is limited to 13 objects per second. Photocell drives Schmitt trigger that generates pulse with required rise time to operate ACY17 cascode circuit feeding Z504S cold-cathode decade stepping tube.—G. C. Chappell and G. F. Jeynes, Transistor Coupling Circuits for the Z504S Stepping Tube, Philips, Pub. Dept., Elcoma Div., Eindhoven, The Netherlands, No. 15, 1965, p 26–38.

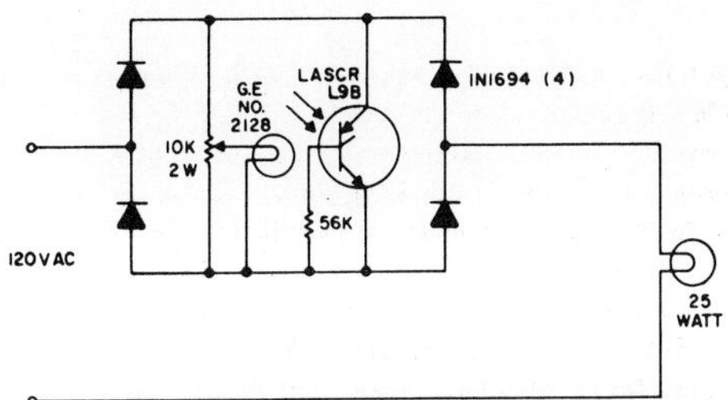

TINY 25-W PHASE CONTROL—Consists only of miniature lamp, lascr, four small diodes, and two resistors, almost fitting in walnut shell. Can be used for continuous phase control of small heating element such as soldering iron and for dimming lamps up to 25 W. At low applied voltages, miniature lamp will still reach lascr firing level in about 3 Hz because of its small low-mass filament. Lamp voltage drops to zero when lascr fires, protecting lamp and resetting it for next half-cycle. Lamp should touch lascr.—E. K. Howell, The Light Activated SCR, General Electric, Syracuse, N.Y., No. 200.34, 1965.

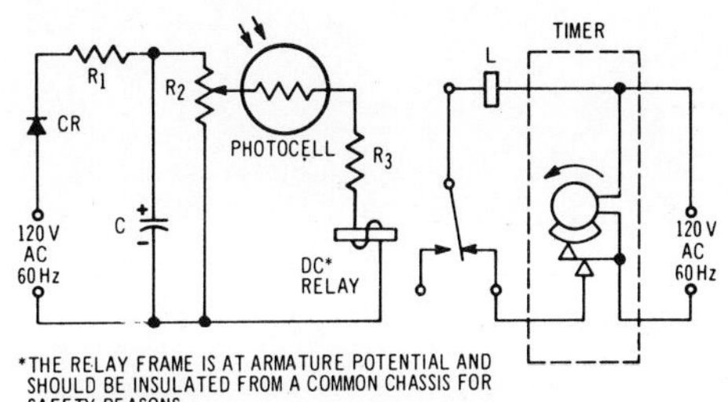

*THE RELAY FRAME IS AT ARMATURE POTENTIAL AND SHOULD BE INSULATED FROM A COMMON CHASSIS FOR SAFETY REASONS.

TWILIGHT TURN-ON AND CLOCK TURN-OFF—For window display lights in stores. 24-hour timer is set so its contacts close in mid-afternoon and open at desired turn-off time for display in late evening. Lights cannot come on in daylight, however, because relay is energized when photocell is illuminated. At twilight, photocell impedance goes up, relay drops out, current flows through lamp load, and timer takes over. Values: R1 5.6; R2 25K; R3 2K; C 8 μF; CR 1N1763A; photocell 7163; timer Intermatic T101.—"Solid State Photosensitive Devices," RCA, Harrison, N.J., p 23.

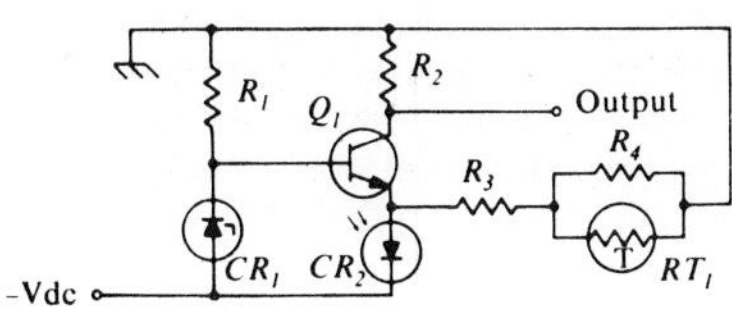

Supply	−4 V dc
CR_1	1N758
CR_2	1N2175
R_1	1.2K
R_2	510K
R_3	82K
R_4	1.8 Ω

DIRECT-COUPLED PHOTODIODE SWITCH—Uses low-cost components to provide temperature compensation, for accurate sensing of light in control applications. Responds to very slow changes in illumination.—"Selected Electronic Circuitry," NASA SP-5046, 1966, Government Printing Office, Washington, D.C., p 88.

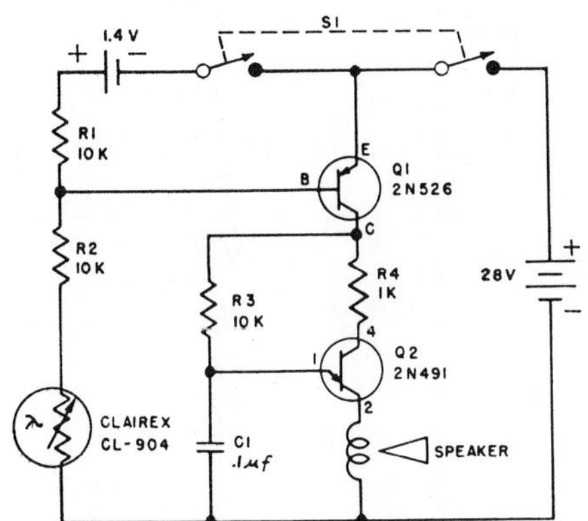

VIEWING PANEL LAMP REMOTELY—Photocell in housing is taped or otherwise fastened over panel lamp, to actuate 1,000-Hz oscillator that drives speaker. When lamp comes on, tone can be heard by technician working at rear of equipment or elsewhere. Eliminates need for setting up mirrors or walking around equipment to observe effect of each change on front-panel indicator lamp.—E. S. Kennedy, Monitor for Hidden Indicators, *Electronics World*, Aug. 1968, p 76.

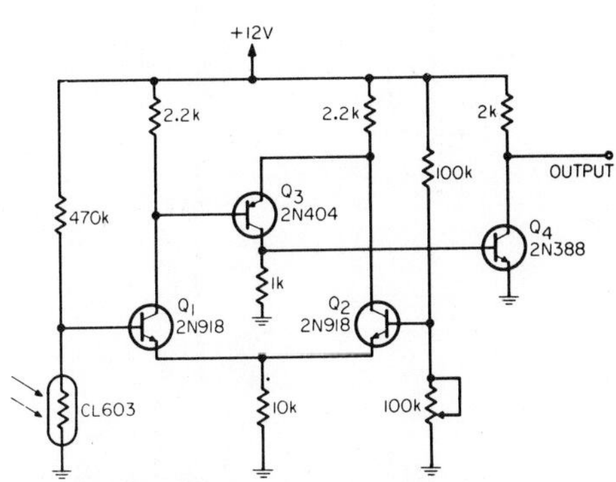

VARIABLE-THRESHOLD AMPLIFIER—When incident light on photocell reaches predetermined threshold level set by 100K pot, circuit switches rapidly from 12 V output to 0 output, for driving standard logic. Low current drain permits battery operation. Developed to detect change from daylight to darkness and automatically select best operating frequency for radio transmitter. Will function equally well for other applications with thermistor or humidity sensor in place of photocell.—C. Becklein, Photocell Threshold Circuit, *EEE*, April 1967, p 139.

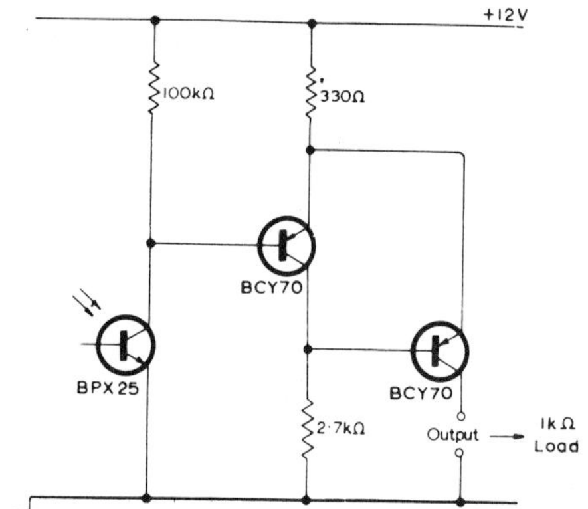

BISTABLE AMPLIFIER—Operates with illumination levels as low as 50 lux. Will drive electronic counter at speeds up to 6,000 counts per second. When phototransistor is illuminated above 50 lux, circuit has no output. Without illumination, output is 8 mA at 8 V into 1K load. Suitable for elevator door-safety control, level indicator, card reader, batch counter, or burglar alarm applications.—Applications of Silicon Planar Phototransistor BPX25, Philips, Pub. Dept., Elcoma Div., Eindhoven, The Netherlands, No. 316, 1967.

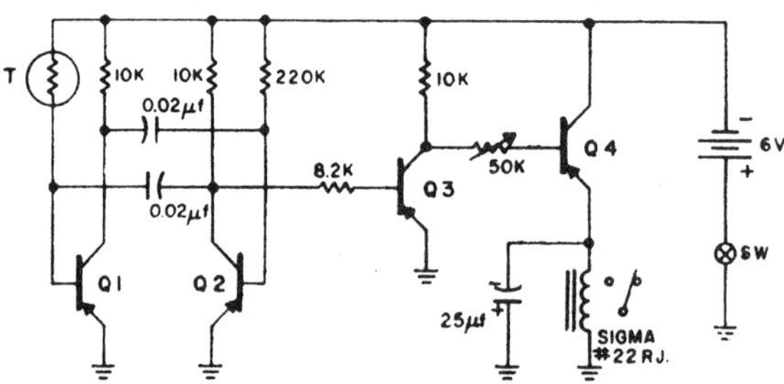

BURGLAR ALARM—Hupp class-2 cadmium sulfide photocell T varies frequency of free-running mvbr Q1-Q2 in accordance with variations of incident light. With full illumination, duty cycle of oscillator pulse train is about 15%. When beam of light is interrupted, as by intruder, duty cycle increases to about 65%. Amplifier Q3 drives emitter-follower Q4 to keep relay normally energized. Relay opens when beam is broken or power fails, to trip alarm connected to contacts. With small focusing lens on photocell, interruption of beam from ordinary two-cell flashlight over 200 ft away will trip alarm, even in presence of high ambient light. Transistor types are not critical.—J. Porter, A Cadmium Sulfide Photocell Indicator, "400 Ideas for Design Selected from Electronic Design," Hayden Book Co., N.Y., 1964, p 103.

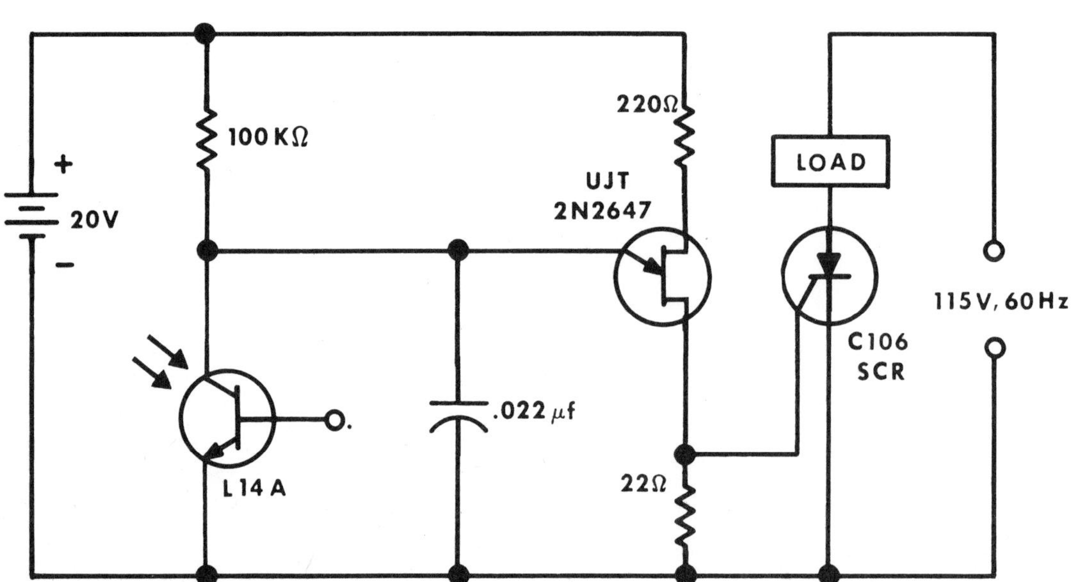

HIGH-SENSITIVITY LIGHT DETECTOR—Energizes load on positive half-cycles when light is removed from phototransistor, with ujt then operating as relaxation oscillator.—L. M. Hertz, "Solid State Lamps—Part II," General Electric, Cleveland, Ohio, No. 3-0121, 1970, p 11.

NOTE: To locate additional circuits in the category of this chapter, use the index at the back of this book. Check also the author's "Sourcebook of Electronic Circuits," published by McGraw-Hill in 1968.

CHAPTER 63
Photography Circuits

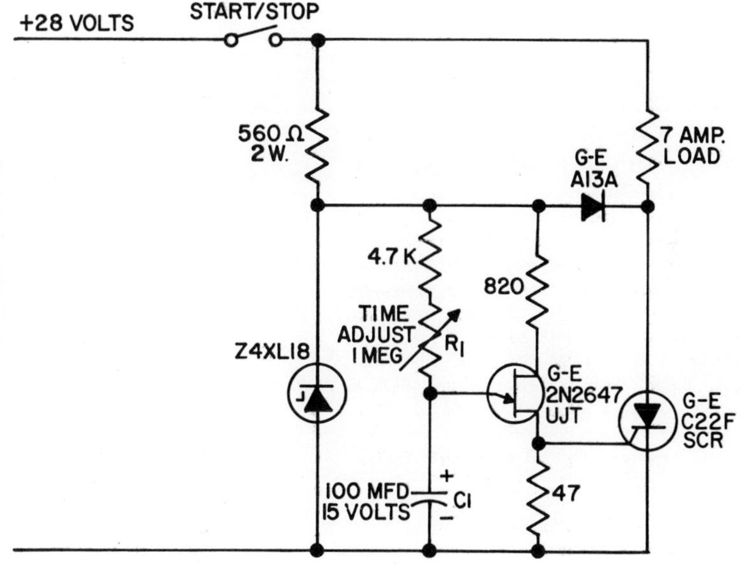

D-C DELAY RELAY—Turns off 7-A load at precise predetermined time after switch is closed, from 1 to 60 s, as determined by setting of R1. For shorter delays, use smaller values for R1 and C1. Applications include enlarger control in photography, process control, alarms, etc.—F. W. Gutzwiller and E. K. Howell, Economy Power Semiconductor Applications, General Electric, Syracuse, N.Y., No. 671.1, 1965, p 3.

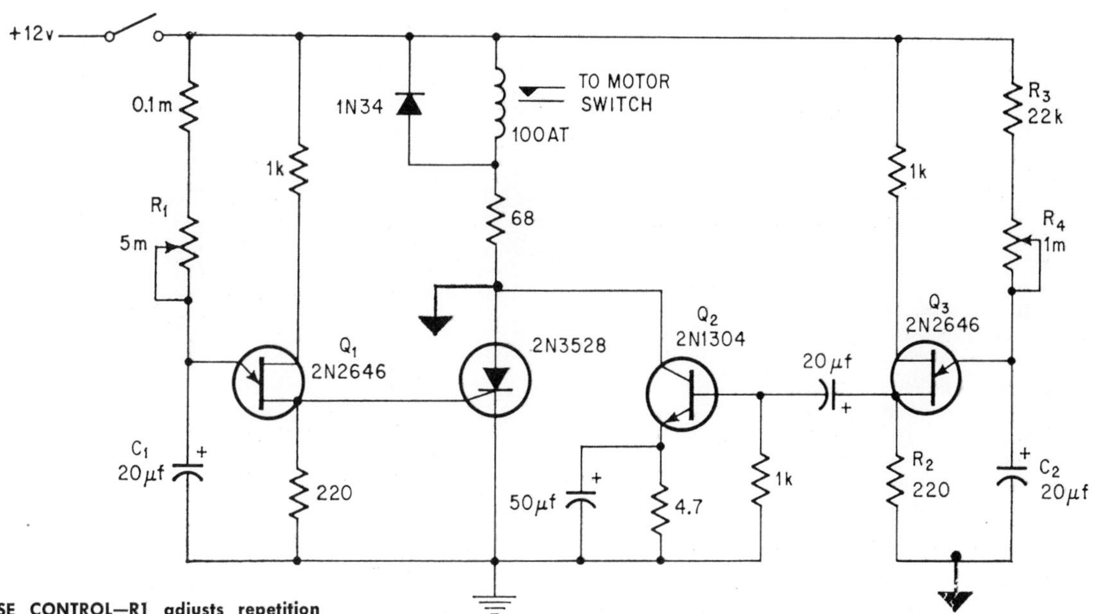

TIME-LAPSE CONTROL—R1 adjusts repetition rate of output pulse over range of 2–60 s between pulses, and R4 adjusts pulse duration from 0.5 to 25 s. Applications include shutter control in time-lapse photography, control of strip-chart recorders, starting and stopping of motors connected to relay contacts, and handling of other small loads either directly or through relay. When C1 is charged to firing voltage of ujt Q1, scr is turned on and relay is energized. Since scr has negligible voltage drop when conducting, its anode is at virtual ground. This places junction of R2 and C2 also at virtual ground, and C2 charges until it fires Q3 and thereby turns on Q2 to open scr and relay. Cycle then repeats.—T. T. Kalal, Pulse Width Varied by a "Switched Ground," *Electronics*, April 28, 1969, p 77.

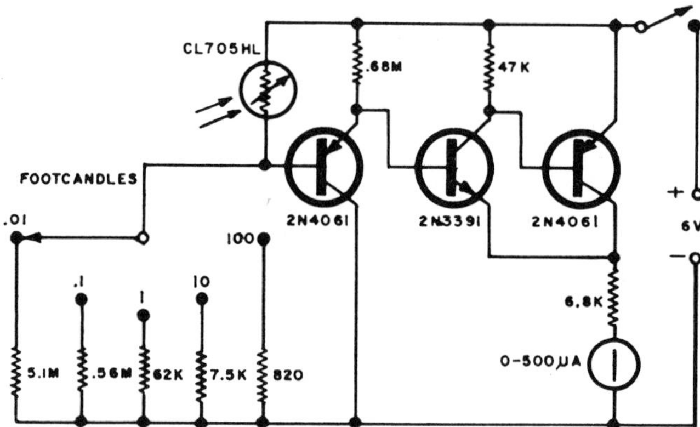

FIVE-RANGE PHOTOMETER—Ranges from 0.01 to 100 foot-candles are in decade steps. Load resistors for photocell are chosen so each range gives full-scale meter reading.—J. G. Rabinowitz, Photocells—Types, Characteristics, and Applications, *Electronics World*, Sept. 1968, p 23–26.

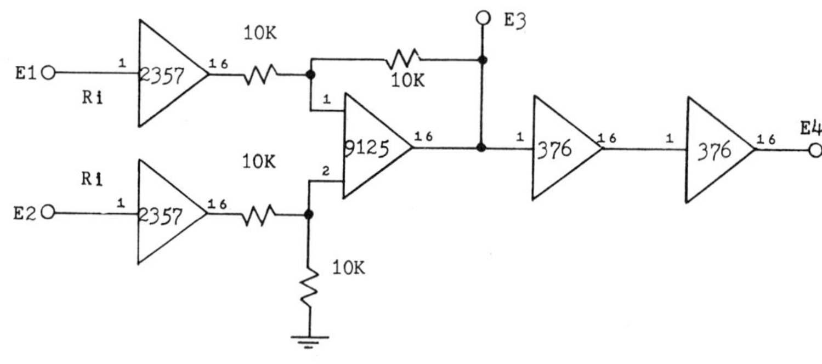

SPECTROPHOTOMETER OUTPUT CONVERTER—First three modules convert measured transmission value at particular wavelength to density value by obtaining difference of two logarithms. Next two modules (complement of 2357) are required only when obtaining exposure from density. Dynamic range is 90 dB for d-c to 1 kHz, or 40 dB for d-c to 100 kHz. Ri is 1,000 ohms for 10-V full-scale input. Light-sensitive current devices may be used in place of E1 and E2.—Conversion of Transmission to Density and Density to Exposure, Optical Electronics, Tucson, Ariz., No. 10133.

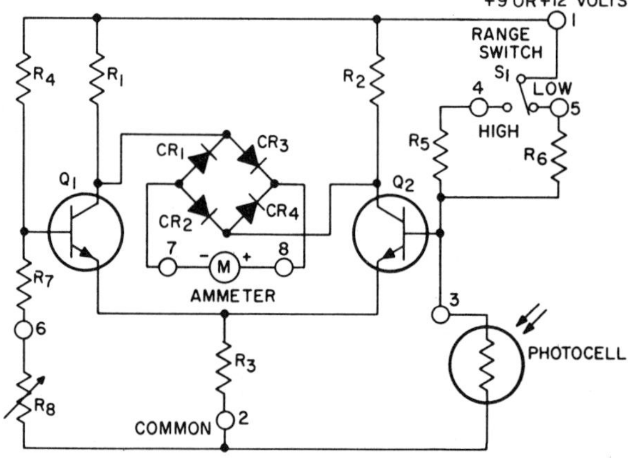

ENLARGER EXPOSURE METER—After correct exposure time is determined experimentally with test negative, photocell of meter is placed on easel at center of interest, and R8 is adjusted for zero meter deflection with test negative. Negative to be printed is then inserted in enlarger, photocell is moved to center of interest for that negative, and iris of enlarger is adjusted for zero deflection. Photocell is removed, printing paper inserted, and exposure made for same time as test negative. Low range of meter covers 0.2–6 foot-candles, and high range 6–400 foot-candles.—"Hobby Circuits Manual," RCA, Harrison, N.J., HM-90, p 78.

$CR_1CR_2CR_3CR_4$ = silicon rectifier, type 1N270
M = meter, 0 to 1 milliampere, 12 volt, or 0 to 500 microamperes, 9 volt
Photocell = RCA KD2106
Q_1Q_2 = transistor, RCA SK3020
$R_1R_2R_7$ = 4700 ohms, 1/2 watt, 10%
R_3 = 2200 ohms (12 volts), 3300 ohms (9 volts), 1/2 watt, 10%
R_4 = 47,000 ohms, 1/2 watt, 10%
R_5 = 100,000 ohms, 1/2 watt, 10%
R_6 = 10,000 ohms, 1/2 watt, 10%
R_8 = potentiometer, 50,000 ohms, linear taper
S_1 = range switch, single-pole, double-throw

TIMER FOR ENLARGER—Print-exposure timer gives adjustable delays from fraction of second to 1 min for automatic turn-off of printer or enlarger after exposure is started. Timing accuracy is 2%. Will handle relay or other loads up to 5 A. T1 is 12.6-V filament transformer such as Triad F25X. MR1 is 24-V a-c relay such as Potter & Brumfield MR5A.—"Hobby Manual," General Electric, Owensboro, Ky., 1965, p 164.

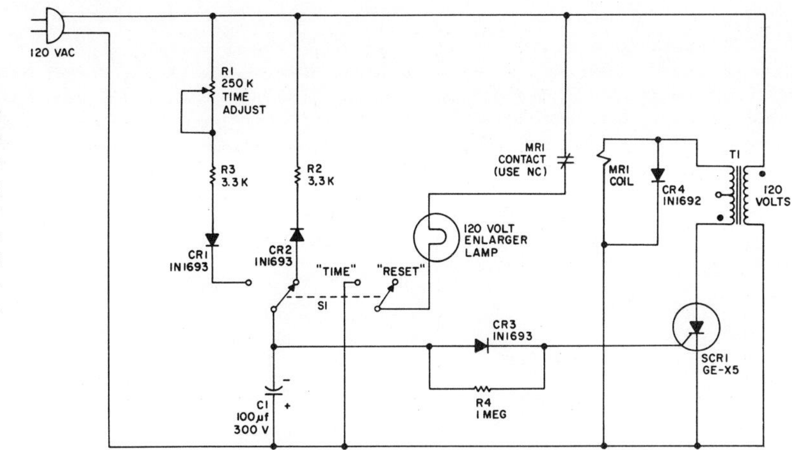

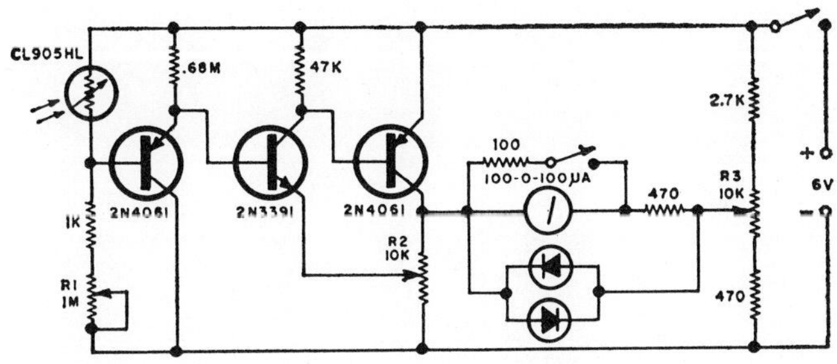

DARKROOM EASEL PHOTOMETER—Sensitive circuit can be used for measurements or comparisons over wide range of light levels. R1 may be calibrated in exposure time, R2 in paper contrast or filter number, and R3 in relative paper speed.—J. G. Rabinowitz, Photocells—Types, Characteristics, and Applications, *Electronics World*, Sept. 1968, p 23–26.

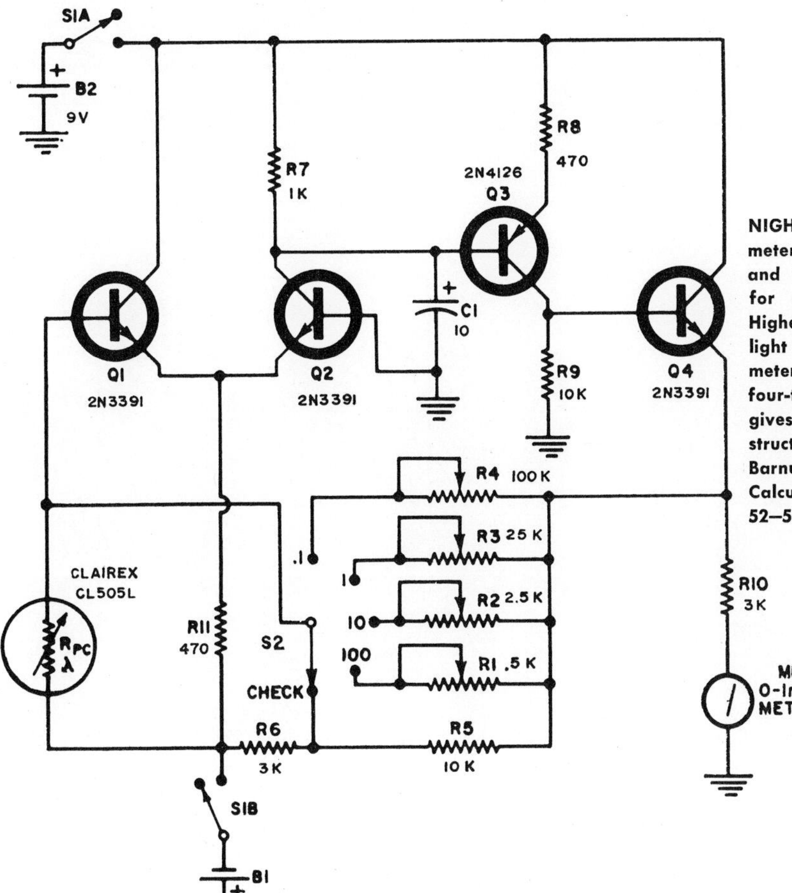

NIGHT EXPOSURE METER—Incident-reading meter with ranges of 0.01–0.1, 0.1–1, 1–10, and 10–100 footcandles is sensitive enough for low-light-level night photography. Higher ranges can serve also for reflected-light measurements and as enlarger exposure meter. Uses cadmium sulfide photocell with four-transistor differential amplifier. Article gives theory of operation, along with construction and calibration procedures.—J. L. Barnum, Design of a Light Meter & Exposure Calculator, *Electronics World*, May 1969, p 52–54 and 78–79.

LAB PHOTOMETER—Gives high sensitivity, wide range, and high accuracy for measurement of film transmission density, reflection coefficient, and very low values of light intensity. Logarithmic relation of anode voltage to light flux, necessary for linear density scale, is obtained by stabilizing anode current of XP1110 photomultiplier with EL81. High-voltage supply is stabilized at about 2,000 V with series connection of 25 ZZ1000 gas tubes. When indicating voltmeter M is calibrated in densities (density = log 1/transmission), the four ranges are for densities of 0–1, 1–2, 2–3, and 3–4. Report covers design and calibration.—A 4-Decade Linear Density Scale Photometer Equipped with the XP1110 Photomultiplier Tube, Philips, Pub. Dept., Elcoma Div., Eindhoven, The Netherlands, No. 318, 1967.

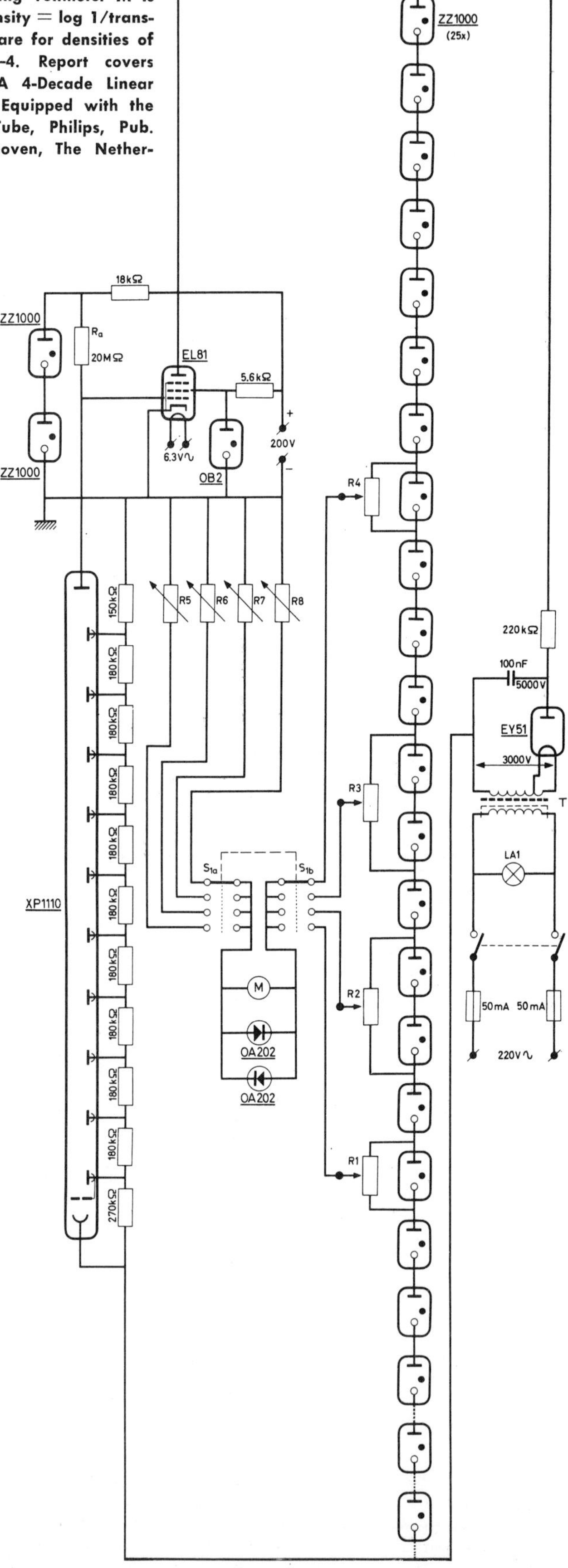

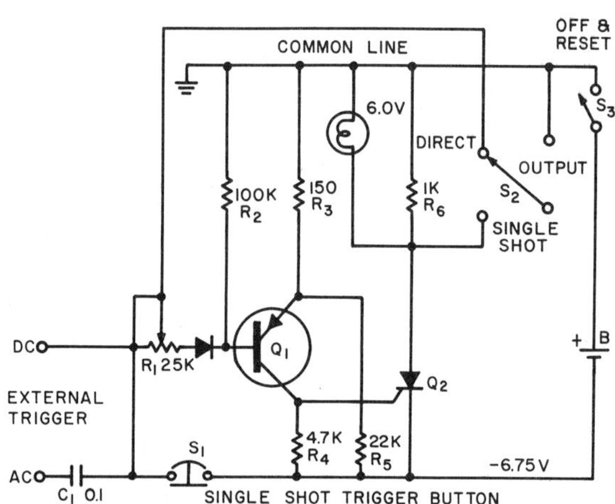

ONE-SHOT TRIGGER FOR SINGLE-SWEEP PHOTO—Camera lens is opened, sweep is triggered by applying external trigger or pushing button, and lens is closed. Eliminates smearing that occurs when recurrent trace is not completely synchronized with sweep speed. Input signal of about 0.6 V will fire trigger and give 6-V output for external-trigger input of scope. Q2 is operated at low voltage and current, so can be any inexpensive scr. Q1 can be almost any pnp transistor.—A. M. Schotz, One Shot Triggers Scope For Single Sweep, *Electronic Design*, Jan. 6, 1964, p 82 and 84.

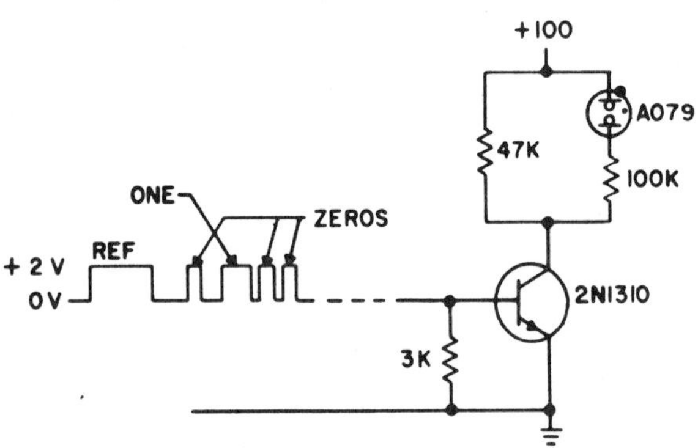

FILM TIME-CODE MARKER—Light from transistor-driven neon lamp marks time information in binary code on 35-mm instrumentation film.—E. Bauman, "Applications of Neon Lamps and Gas Discharge Tubes," Signalite, Neptune, N.J., p 153.

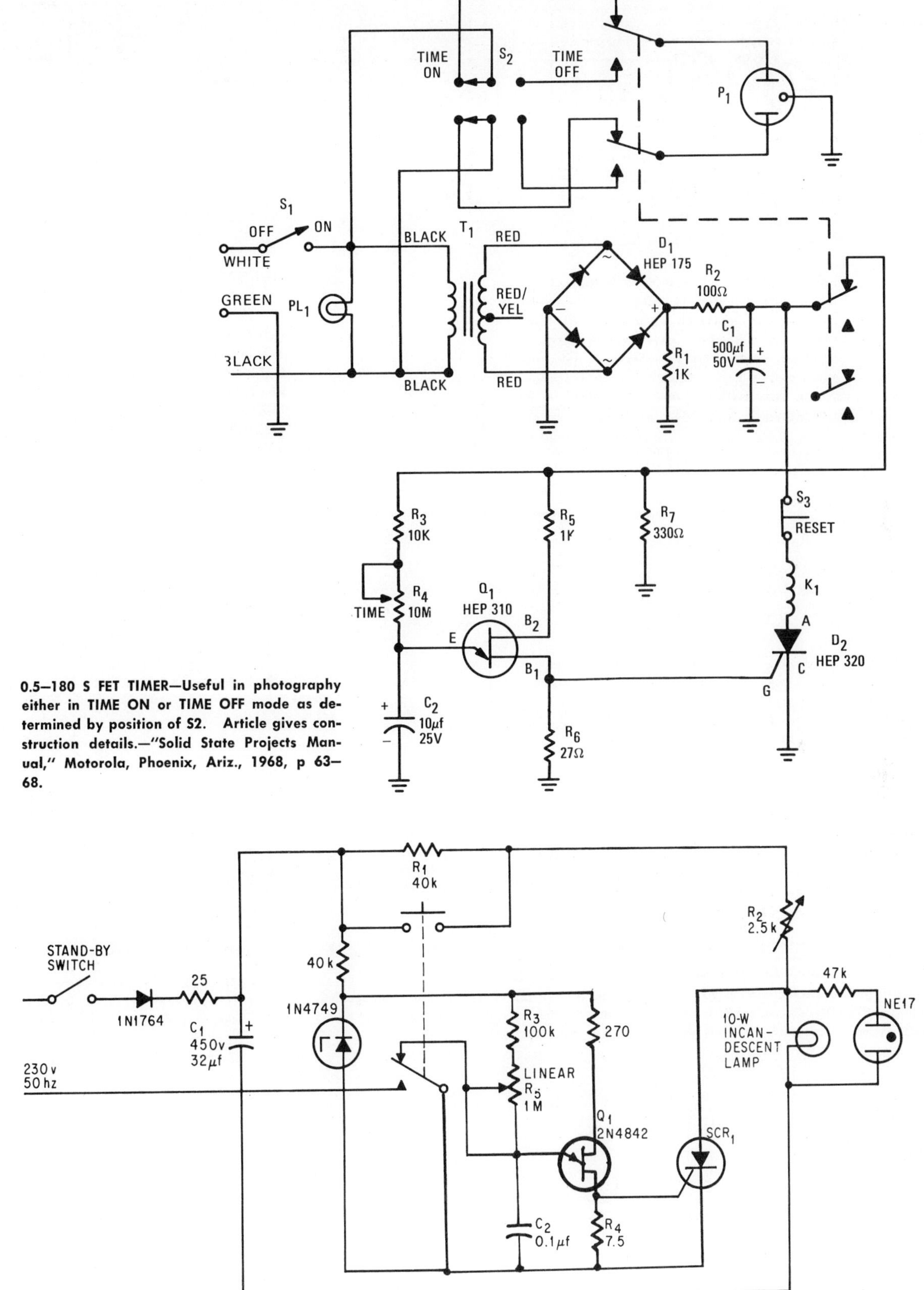

0.5–180 S FET TIMER—Useful in photography either in TIME ON or TIME OFF mode as determined by position of S2. Article gives construction details.—"Solid State Projects Manual," Motorola, Phoenix, Ariz., 1968, p 63–68.

PRINTER CONTROL—When standby switch is closed, rectified 320 V d-c across C1 supplies 6.2 mA to 10-W incandescent lamp for photographic printer, to keep filament temperature close to visible illumination point. Pressing switch of ujt-scr timer shorts R1 to send 43 mA through lamp to give maximum illumination for printing and initiate timing. C2 then charges through R3 and R5 until Q1 fires and gates scr on, to shunt lamp and terminate exposure. Releasing timer switch then restores standby condition. R5 controls time.—D. Lior, Photographic Printer Controlled by UJT-SCR Timer, *Electronics*, March 18, 1968, p 96–97.

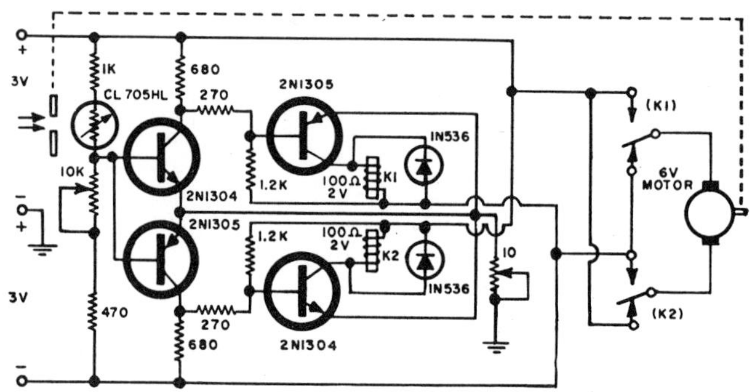

PHOTOELECTRIC APERTURE CONTROL—Servo motor moves shutter to adjust aperture until resistance of photocell equals that of load circuit potentiometer. Uses two complementary Schmitt triggers to actuate motor control relays.—J. G. Rabinowitz, Photocells—Types, Characteristics, and Applications, *Electronics World*, Sept. 1968, p 23–26.

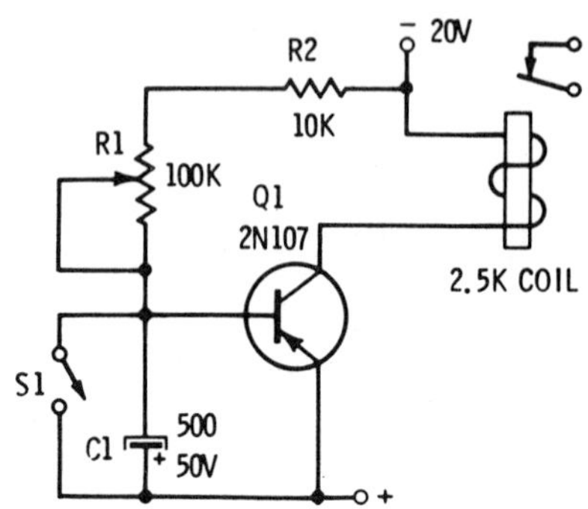

PHOTOGRAPHIC TIMER—Timing cycle begins when S1 is opened, removing short across C1. When C1 charges sufficiently, base current flows through Q1 and relay is energized, opening relay contacts and cutting off power to lamp or other load. Increasing value of R1 lengthens timing cycle.—J. P. Shields, "Novel Electronic Circuits," H. W. Sams & Co., Indianapolis, Ind., 1968, p 91.

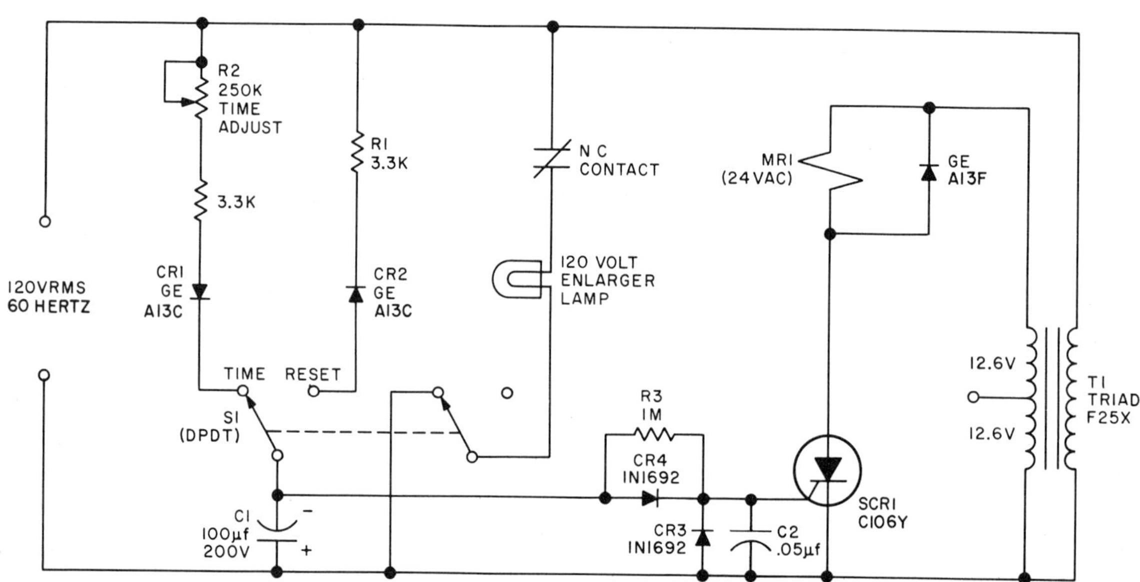

ENLARGER PHOTOTIMER—When S1 is at RESET, C1 is charged to peak negative value of supply voltage (165 V) and enlarger lamp is off. When S1 is set at TIME, enlarger lamp comes on and C1 discharges at rate determined by setting of R2 until its voltage has become sufficiently positive (about 2 V) to trigger scr and energize relay to turn off enlarger lamp. R2 gives range of 0.01 to 60 s for exposures.—D. R. Grafham, Using Low Current SCR's, General Electric, Syracuse, N.Y., No. 200.19, 1967, p 29.

NOTE: To locate additional circuits in the category of this chapter, use the index at the back of this book. Check also the author's "Sourcebook of Electronic Circuits," published by McGraw-Hill in 1968.

CHAPTER 64

Power Supply Protection Circuits

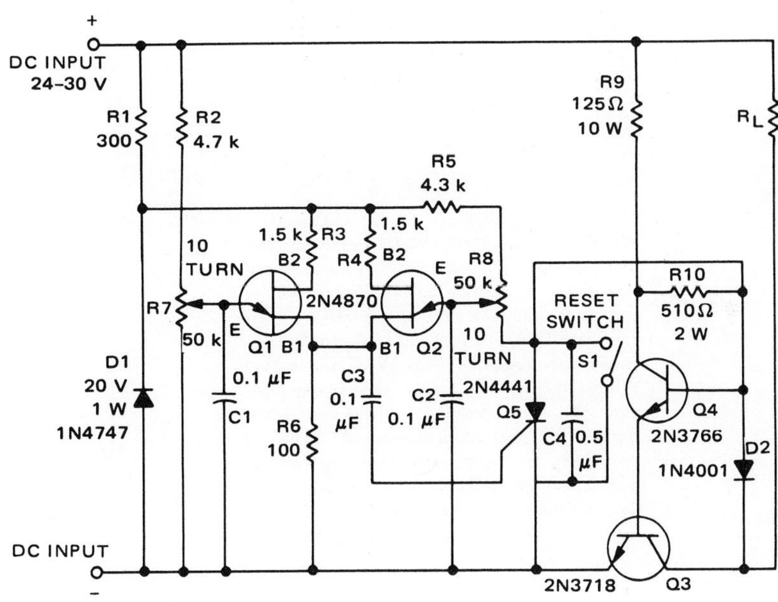

D-C CIRCUIT BREAKER—Protects load against transient voltage or current overload. Acts in 4 to 10 μs, as compared to 8 ms for mechanical circuit breakers. Requires momentary closing of S1 for resetting. R8 sets overcurrent trip point and R7 sets overvoltage point; both are precision 10-turn pots.—"Semiconductor Power Circuits Handbook," Motorola, Phoenix, Ariz., 1968, p 4–18.

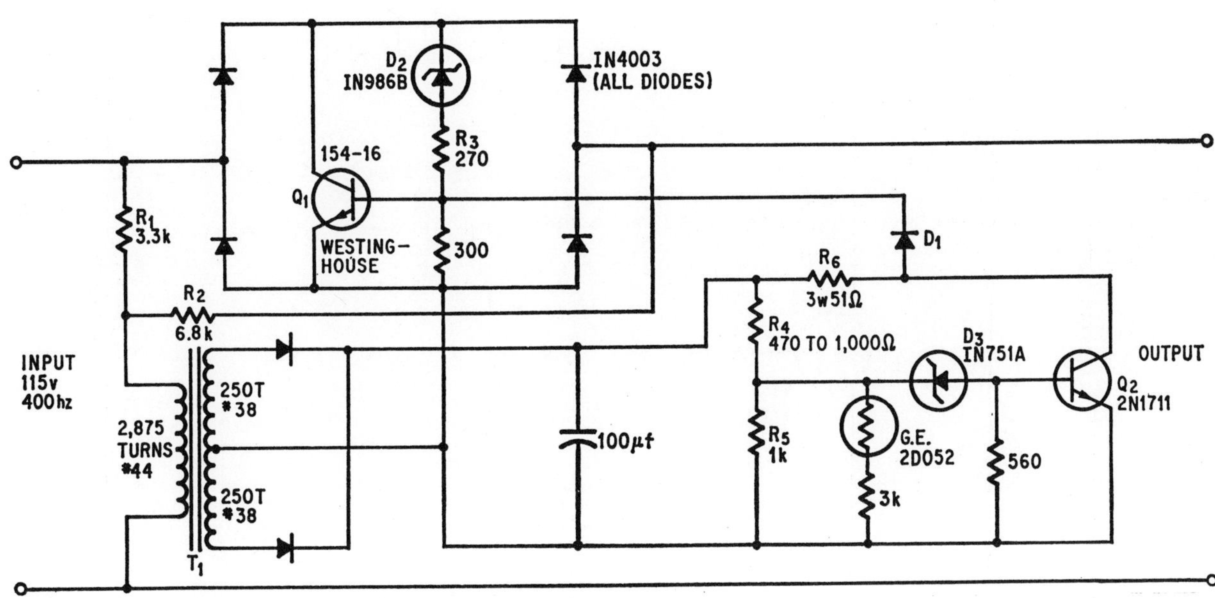

SURGE LIMITER—Circuit shown was designed for use in series-type regulator for airborne military power supplies requiring protection from long-term voltage transients on both a-c and d-c supply lines. Circuit shown is for system normally drawing 1 A and having turn-on surge of 3 A. For normal output, series transistor is saturated. When output exceeds preset level, error voltage is developed and amplified to bring series transistor out of saturation and thereby maintain output at desired level.—M. Kanner, Nonstop Limiter Absorbs Transients, *Electronics*, May 26, 1969, p 106–107.

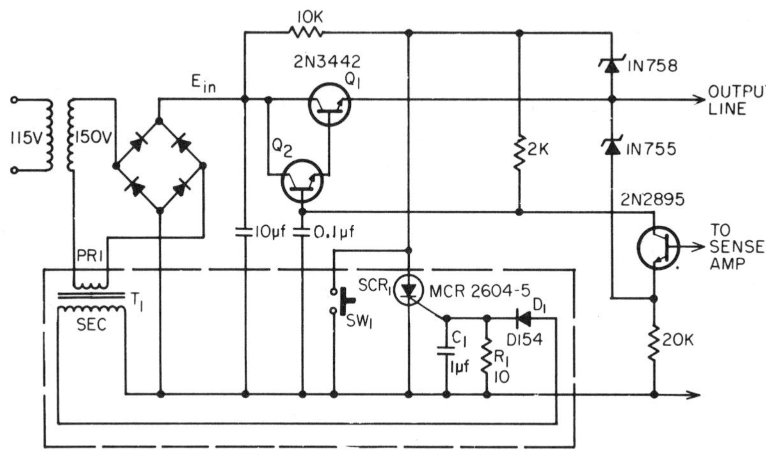

OVERLOAD-SAMPLING CURRENT TRANSFORMER—T1 samples current supplied to series voltage regulator. Rectified sample of current triggers scr when predetermined value of overload current is reached. This removes base current from Q1 and Q2, turning off both transistors. Circuit can be reset manually with SW1 or by interrupting input voltage. T1 has 8-turn primary and 120-turn secondary on EI-187 core.—S. J. Arnold, Current Transformer Gives Fast Overload Protection, *EEE*, Sept. 1966, p 146.

TRANSISTOR CURRENT LIMITERS—Protects current-limiting series transistor Q2 from excessive power dissipation by breaking circuit for overloads, short-circuits, or excessive supply voltage. Load current is adjustable and stable over range of 1 to 10 A, and output voltage is only 3 V below 35-V supply voltage. C1 slows down rate of current interruption, to prevent breaking of circuit by transients; for faster current interruption, C1 may be omitted.—R. K. Manherz, Solid-State Current-Limiter Functions as Circuit Breaker, *Electronic Design*, March 15, 1965, p 59–60.

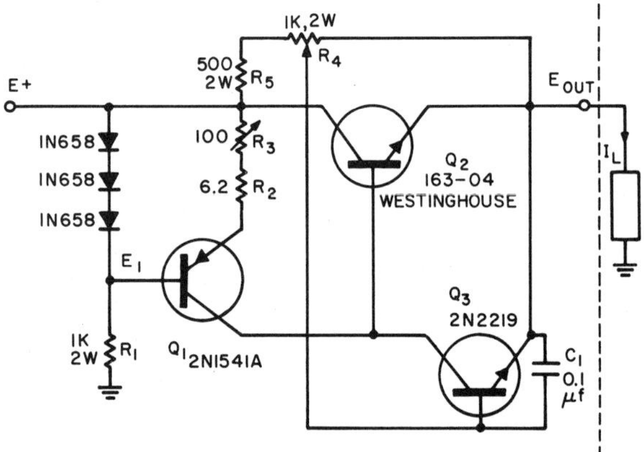

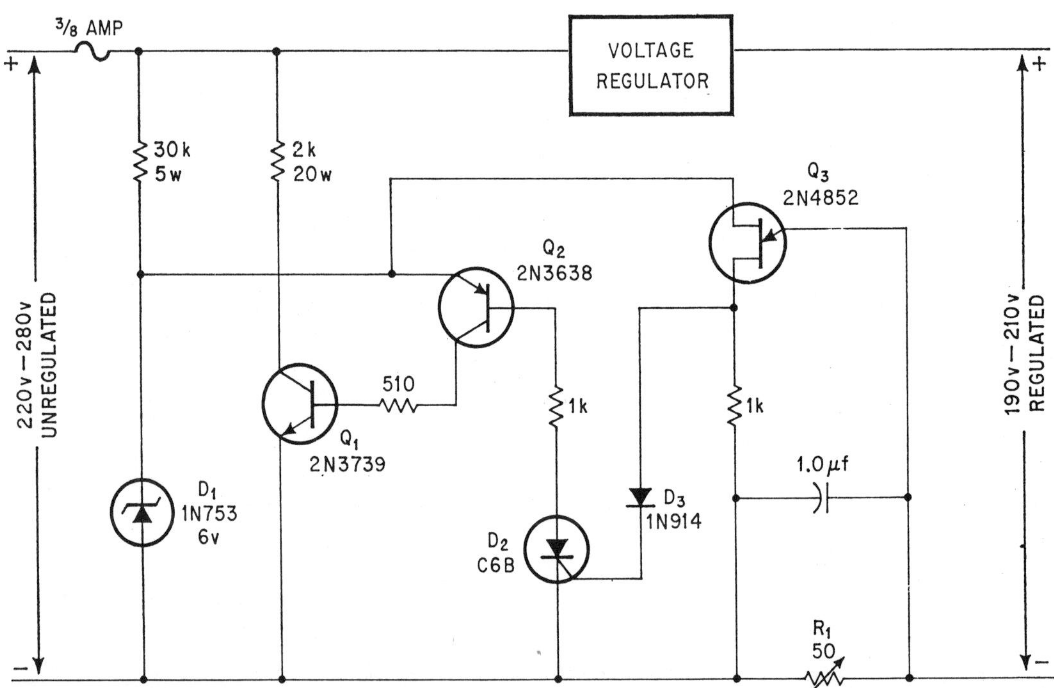

OVERCURRENT—Ujt circuit is activated only when current capability of associated regulated power supply is exceeded. Current-sensing resistor R1 is initially adjusted to keep ujt Q3 off until current rating of supply is exceeded. Overcurrent then turns on Q3, scr D2, Q2, and Q1 in turn, and current drawn by Q1 blows fuse to protect transistors of voltage regulator.—J. Durnin and M. DeCicco, Unijunction Circuit Prevents Damage to Transistors, *Electronics*, June 9, 1969, p 100–101.

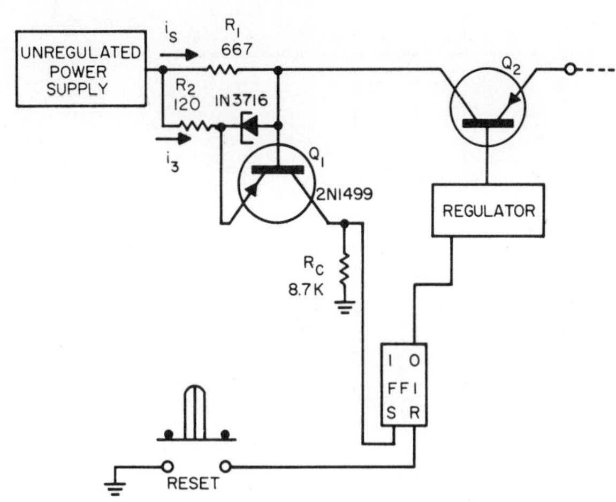

CURRENT OVERLOAD—Tunnel diode and transistor provide better protection than fuse against current overload of power supply. Fast switching speed of diode provides shutdown before overload current can damage series-regulating transistor Q2. Values shown give cutoff at 1 A; article gives design equations for other cutoff values.—R. B. Jones, Tunnel Diode Provides Fast Current-Overload Detection, *Electronic Design*, Nov. 22, 1965, p 62.

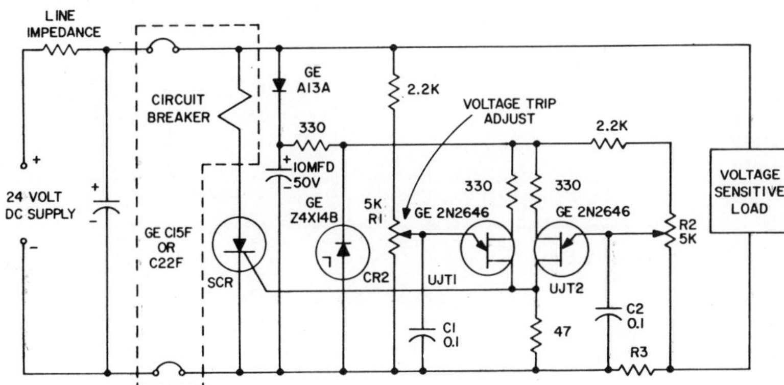

HIGH-SPEED CROWBAR—Useful for protecting d-c circuits against input line voltage transients and load shorts. If d-c supply voltage exceeds value determined by setting of R1, UJT1 fires and triggers SCR. Full supply voltage is then applied to trip coil of circuit breaker to open supply line. Circuit also loads d-c bus instantly to prevent load voltage from rising until breaker has time to operate.—"SCR Manual," 4th Edition, General Electric, 1967, p 158–159.

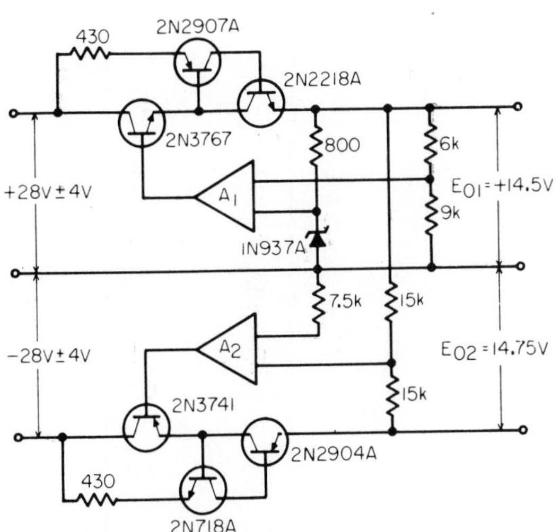

BUILT-IN PROTECTION—Addition of upper two transistors and 430-ohm resistor to conventional series regulator having IC opamp provides overvoltage protection for IC if series regulator fails or becomes shorted. Similar protection circuit is used in lower regulator providing regulated −14.75 V from −28 V.—A. P. Bjork, Overvoltage-Protection Circuit for EC Power Supplies, *EEE*, Dec. 1968, p 101–102.

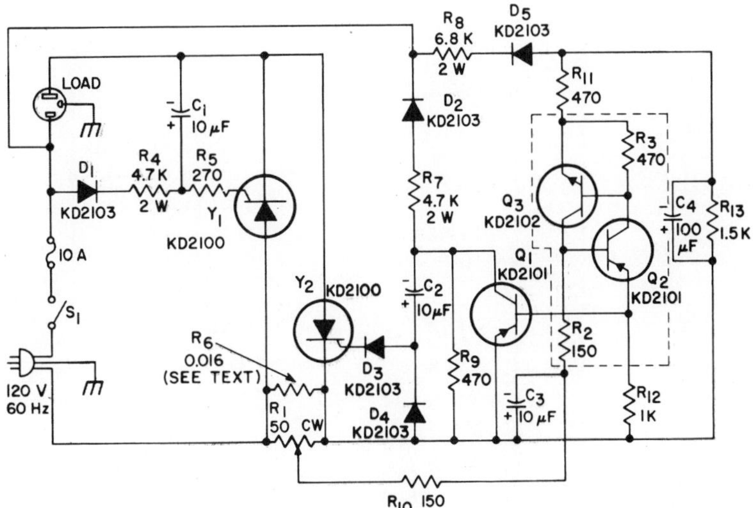

600-KW OVERLOAD SWITCH—Uses regenerative switch (dashed rectangle) that conducts when overload condition as preset by R1 occurs. This turns off scr's Y1 and Y2, interrupting power to load. Line switch must be opened momentarily to reset after overload clears up.—"Silicon Controlled Rectifier Experimenter's Manual," RCA, Harrison, N.J., 1967, p 123.

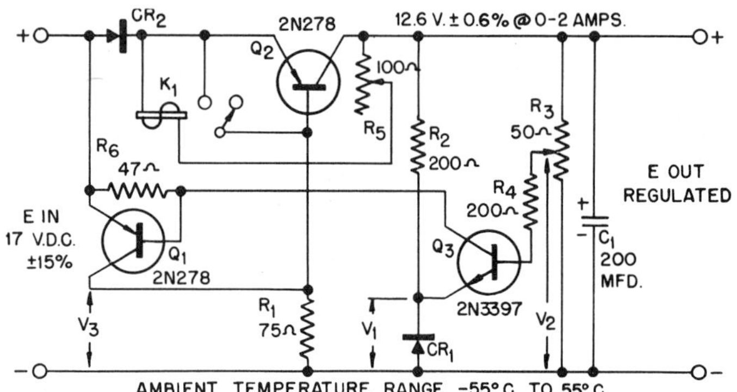

RELAY-PROTECTED VOLTAGE REGULATOR—Consists of proportional voltage regulator that delivers constant 12.6 V d-c output within 0.6% while 17-V d-c input is varying 15%. When voltage across series regulator transistor Q2 rises above preset value determined by setting of R5, voltage-sensitive relay K1 operates and shorts emitter of Q2 to its base, thereby turning off collector current of Q2. Excess voltage could be caused by large increase in input voltage, overload, or shorted output. Fuse or circuit breaker would not react in time to protect circuit from damage under these conditions. CR1 is 1N1770 and CR2 is 1N3491.—Voltage Regulator, Delco Radio, Kokomo, Indiana, No. 3-B, 1965.

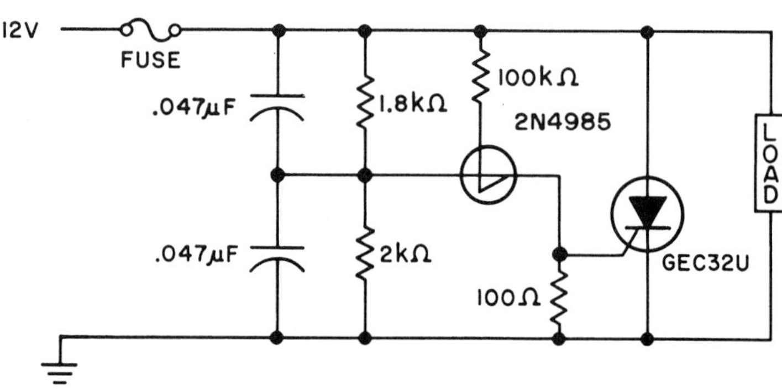

OVERVOLTAGE PROTECTION—Combination of 2N4985 silicon unilateral switch and scr blows line fuse for overvoltage. Circuit triggers between 13.2 and 14 V for rapidly rising voltages, and between 14 and 17 V for slowly increasing voltages. May also be used with 2N4989 sus.—Silicon Unilateral Switch 2N-4984/2N4985, General Electric, Syracuse, N.Y., No. 65.27, 3/67.

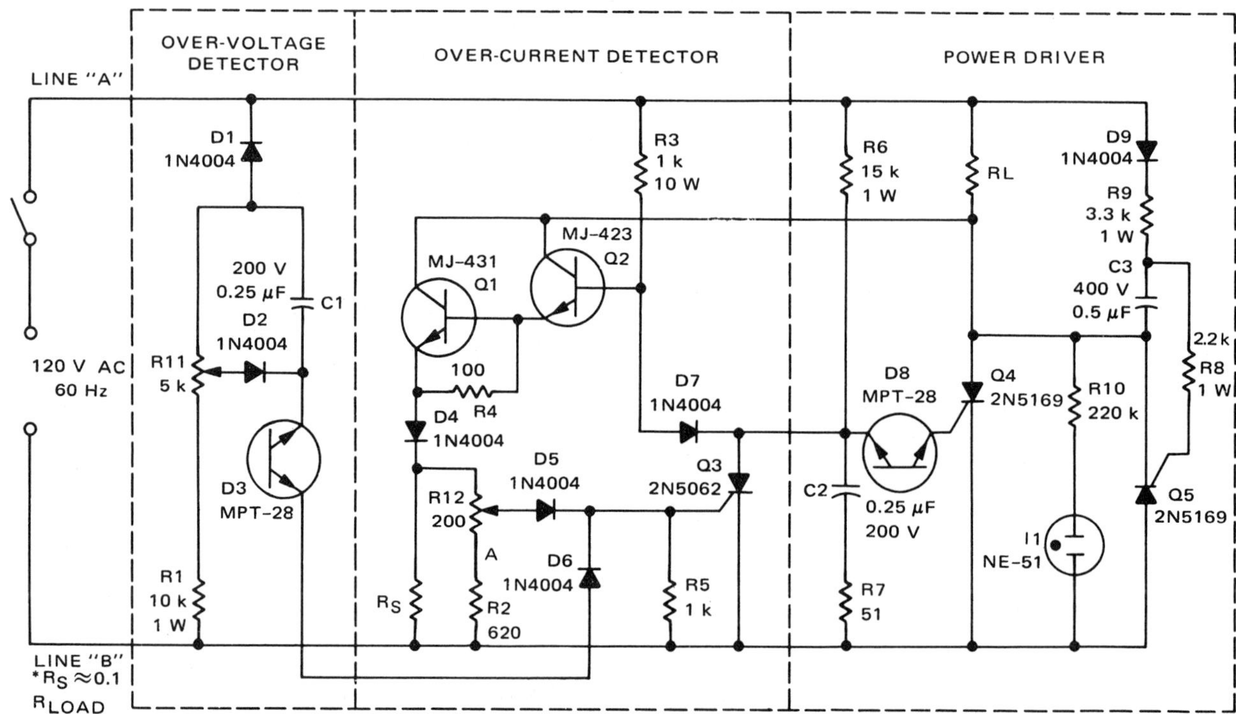

A-C OVERVOLTAGE AND OVERCURRENT PROTECTION—Protects resistive load RL in power driver from excessive voltage as well as excessive current. Scr Q5 is slave-fired by Q4 which carries load current. Overcurrent detector prevents D8 from firing Q4 and thus prevents load from being connected across line in event of short-circuit. Overvoltage detector senses negative half-cycles of line voltage and similarly prevents Q4 from turning on as long as overvoltage exists. Setting of R11 determines overvoltage level at which load is disconnected. Circuit resets automatically.—"Semiconductor Power Circuits Handbook," Motorola, Phoenix, Ariz., 1968, p 4–14.

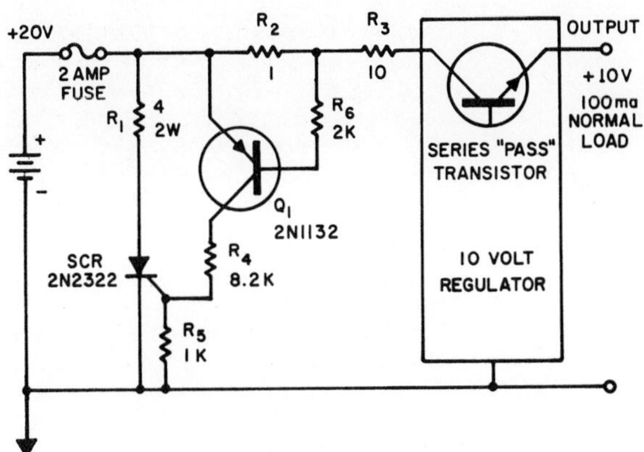

FUSE BLOWER—Protects series-pass transistor from burnout even for direct short across regulator output, by acting faster than series transistor. R2 provides voltage drop proportional to short-circuit current, which turns Q1 on when drop is about 0.7 V. Scr then turns on quickly and blows fuse. R3 prevents turn-on surge current from blowing fuse.—P. Galluzzi, SCR Arrangement Improves Short-Circuit Protection, *Electronic Design*, Sept. 28, 1964, p 55–56.

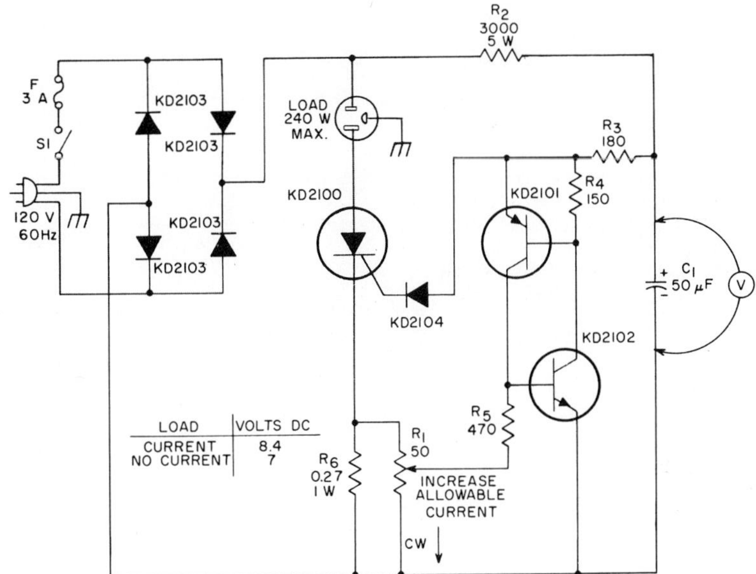

OVERLOAD SWITCH—Serves as electronic circuit breaker that interrupts power to load at predetermined overload point determined by setting of R1. Can be used for heater and universal motor loads up to 240 W. Incandescent lamp load can be protected only if R1 is turned to maximum-current setting before S1 is closed, to allow for high starting current through low cold resistance of lamp, then turned back to desired trip setting. Photoflood lamps cannot be used.—"Silicon Controlled Rectifier Experimenter's Manual," RCA, Harrison, N.J., 1967, p 120.

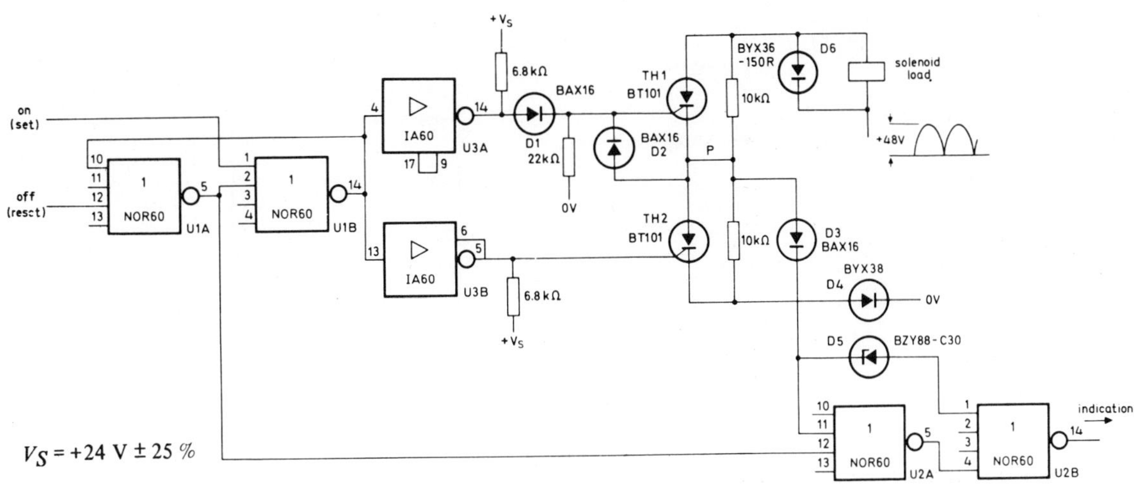

THYRISTOR SHORT-CIRCUIT ALARM—Combination of Philips IC gates and opamps trips alarm when either of series thyristors conducts when trigger is off. Solenoid then pulls in and removes power from thyristors. Used to prevent unwanted and possibly dangerous operation of machine when thyristors control electromagnetic clutch.—D. Hofman, Fault Detection and Display Circuit For a Thyristor Operated Load, Philips, Pub. Dept., Elcoma Div., Eindhoven, The Netherlands, No. 73.

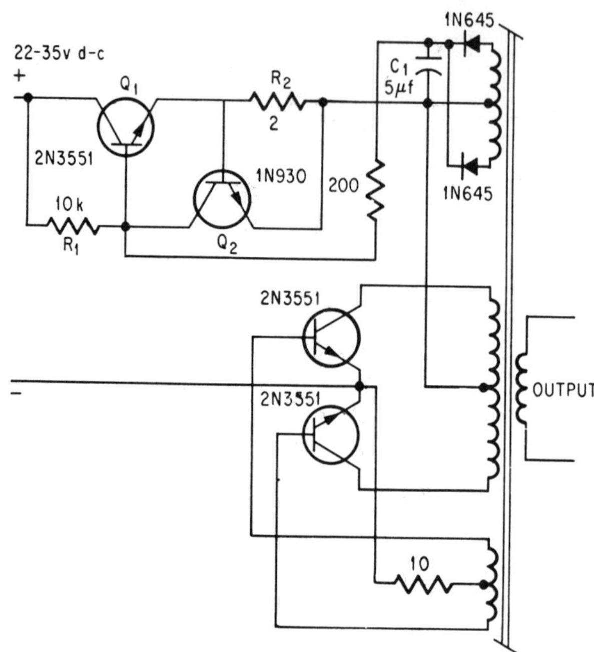

PROTECTING SATELLITE SUPPLY—Current-limiting feedback loop between inverter and d-c supply of spacecraft prevents inverter or output shorts from draining battery pack. When high-surge current boosts drop across R2 and biases Q2 into conduction, Q1 is forced into cutoff. Current-limiting resistor R1 and Q2 are then in series with line in place of R2, to limit battery current drain.—R. Burkett, Feedback Protects Spacecraft's Power Supply, *Electronics*, Jan. 8, 1968, p 91.

DARLINGTONS AS OVERLOAD FUSE—Arrangement shown for series regulator gives overload protection of power supply without adding scr and transistors. As load increases, conduction in Darlington pair increases. Voltage regulation continues until Q3 reaches its maximum current as determined by zener and value chosen for R3. Output voltage drops as load increases, until Q3 turns off. Darlingtons then turn off, deactivating power supply. After overload is eliminated, resetting can be manual or automatic command.—F. J. Messina, Power Supply Regulator Uses Fewer Parts, *Electronics*, Jan. 6, 1969, p 94.

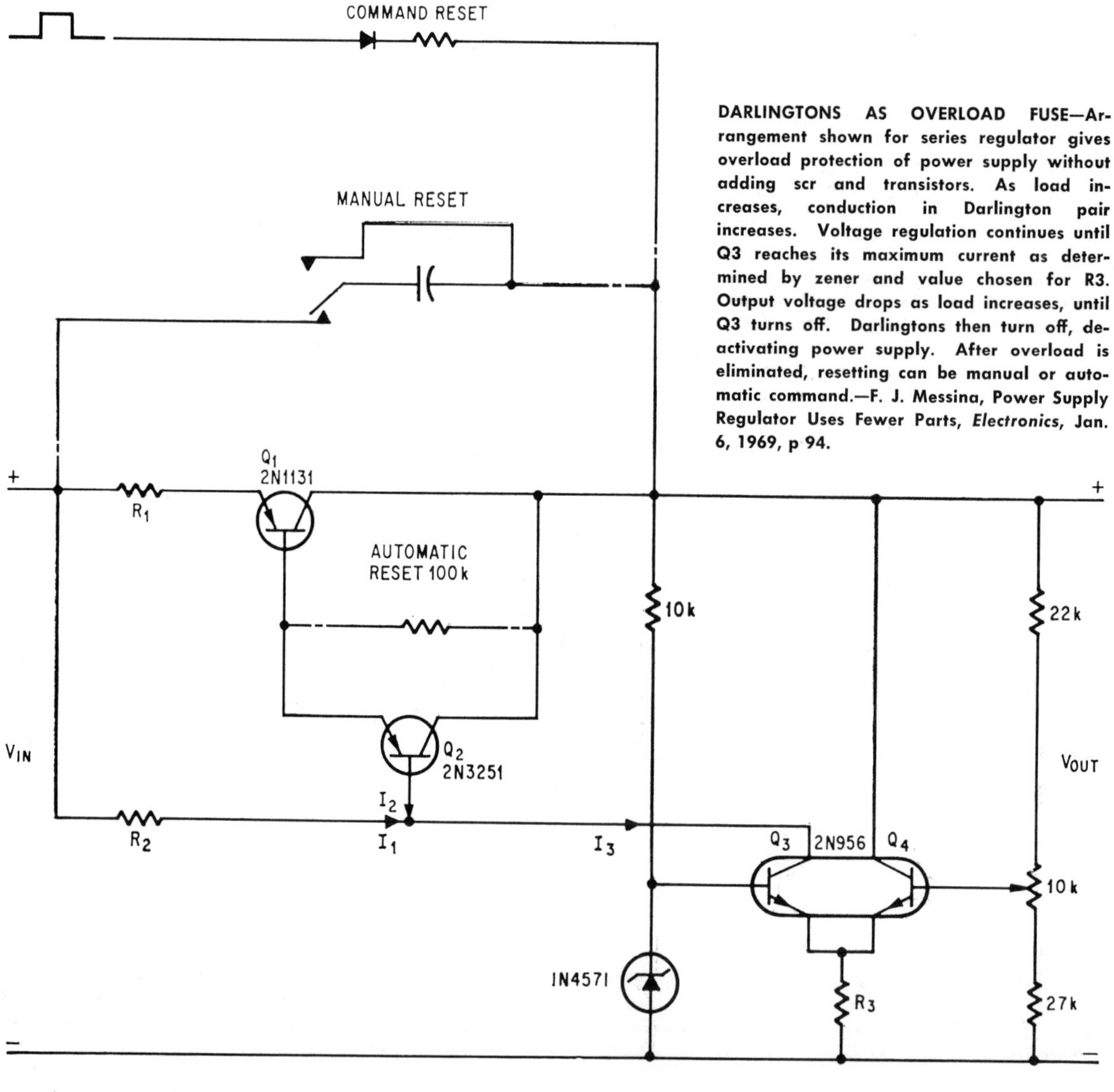

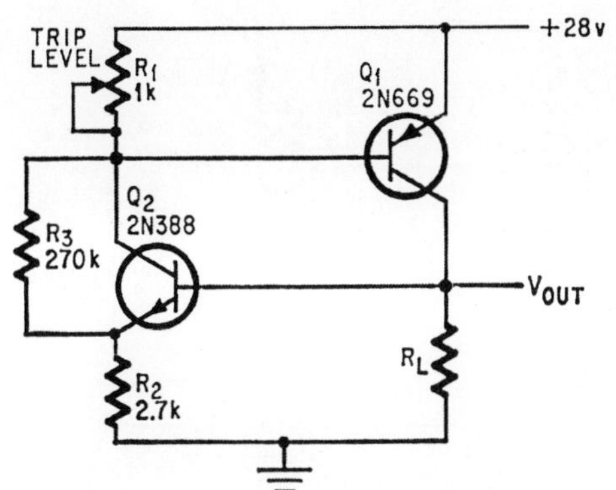

AUTOMATIC-RESET BREAKER—Solid-state breaker trips within 100 μs after load is shorted, and reduces fault current to zero within 500 μs, for protection of printed-circuit wiring and interconnections. Ideal for universal lab power supplies. Automatic reset reapplies power after interval depending on leakage in Q1.—C. J. Ulrick, Power Supply Breaker Acts in 100 Microseconds, *Electronics*, Feb. 3, 1969, p 79.

FAULTS AND OVERLOADS—Provides on-off power control, eliminating need for self-destructing fuses and for circuit breakers that are too slow to protect semiconductors. Time constant of R2-C1 prevents tripping by transient overloads such as start-up of incandescent lamps. Allowable current gain for load is 0 to 5 A, and circuit will limit overload to 7 A for shorted output.—A. J. Marek, Solid-State Relay/Circuit Breaker, *EEE*, June 1969, p 141–142.

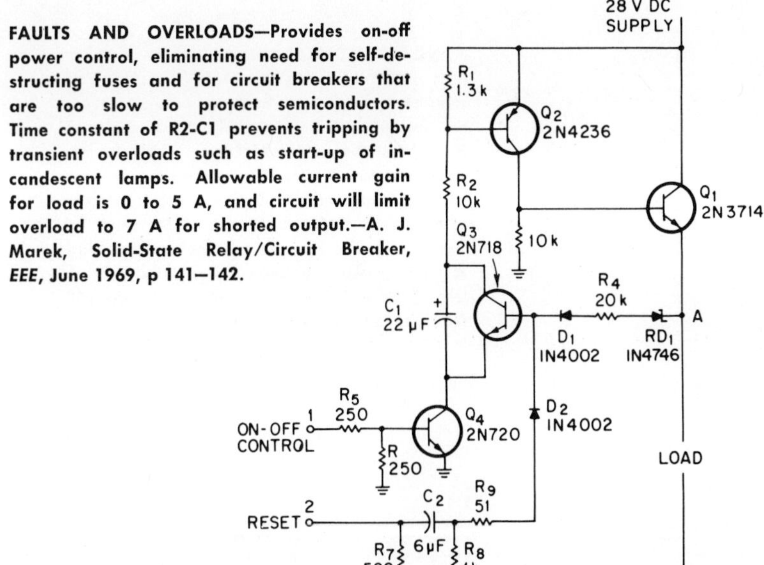

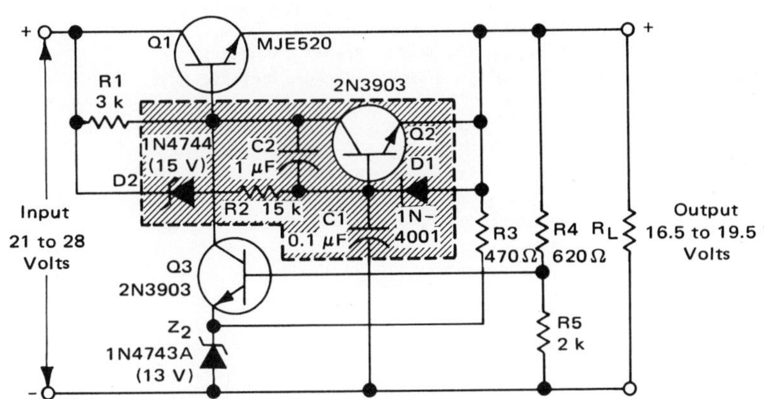

PROTECTING SERIES-PASS REGULATOR—Addition of inexpensive components shown in shaded area protects series-pass regulator against shorted output and restores normal operation automatically when short is removed. Under normal operating conditions, protective circuit is biased off and does not affect regulator action. Speed of protective action is limited only by storage and fall time of series-pass transistor Q1, which is about 1 ms.—"Semiconductor Power Circuits Handbook," Motorola, Phoenix, Ariz., 1968, p 3–30.

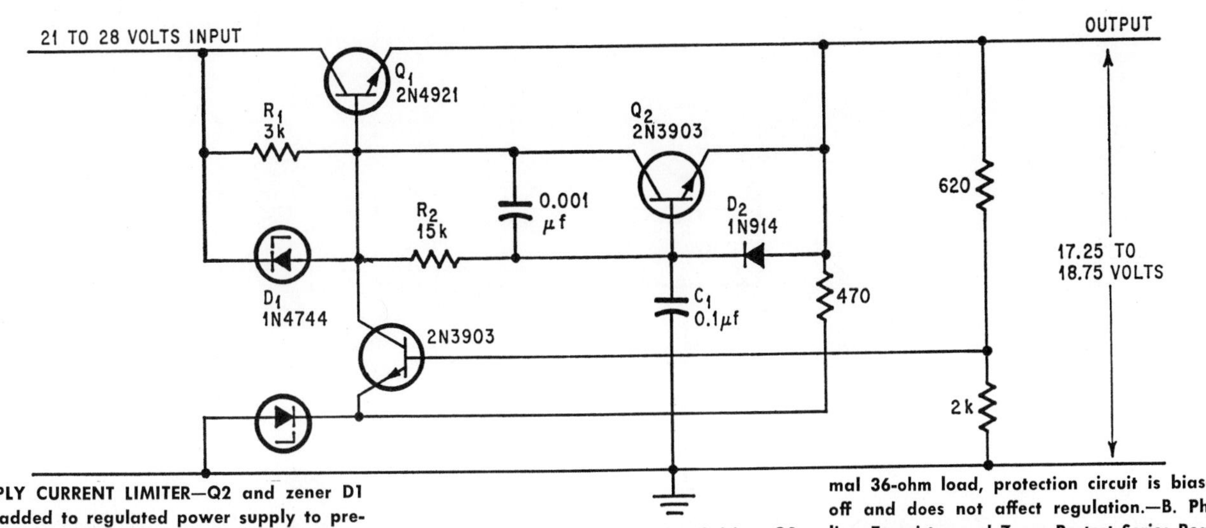

SUPPLY CURRENT LIMITER—Q2 and zener D1 are added to regulated power supply to prevent series transistor Q1 from damage by load short before fuse blows. With short, zener D1 draws reverse current and drives Q2 into saturation, cutting off Q1. With normal 36-ohm load, protection circuit is biased off and does not affect regulation.—B. Phillips, Transistor and Zener Protect Series Regulator, *Electronics*, July 8, 1968, p 92.

MANUAL-RESET BREAKER—Solid-state breaker trips within 100 μs after load is shorted, and reduces fault current to zero within 500 μs, for protection of printed-circuit wiring and interconnections. Ideal for universal lab power supplies. Pushbutton must be momentarily pressed manually to reset breaker after short. Leakage current of Q1 must be low enough so it cannot turn itself on and reapply power to load after fault.—C. J. Ulrick, Power Supply Breaker Acts in 100 Microseconds, *Electronics*, Feb. 3, 1969, p 79.

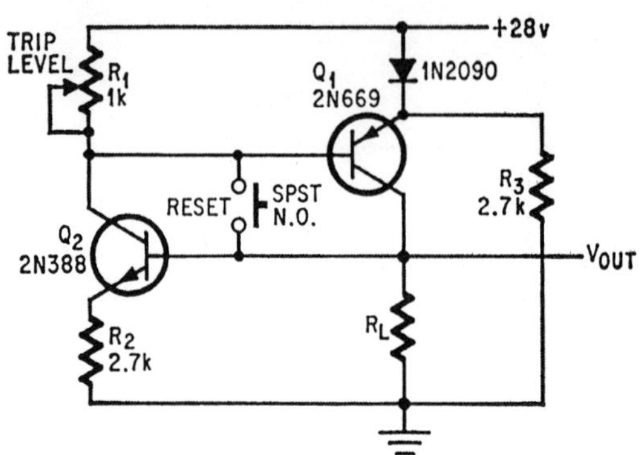

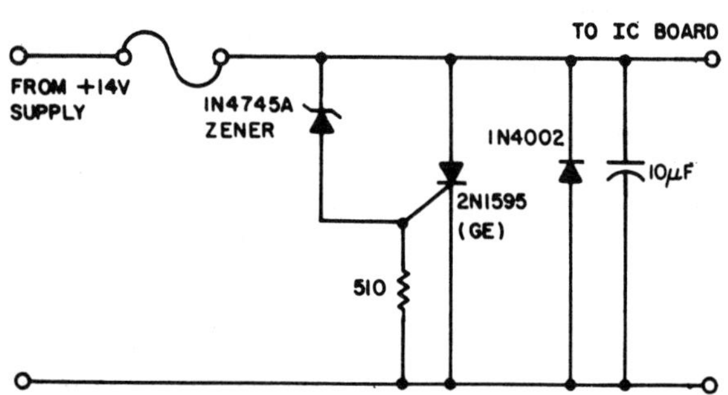

$6 INSURANCE FOR IC—Inserted between 14-V supply and IC load to protect against over-voltages caused by supply failures or noise spikes, and against wrong polarities caused by human errors. Uses 1N4002 silicon diode to blow fuse before reverse voltage damages IC's. Capacitor protects against spikes and prevents them from producing unnecessary crowbar action by scr and diode.—A. Geiersbach, Low-Cost Circuit Can Protect a Boardful of High-Cost ICs, *Electronic Design*, May 10, 1969, p 138.

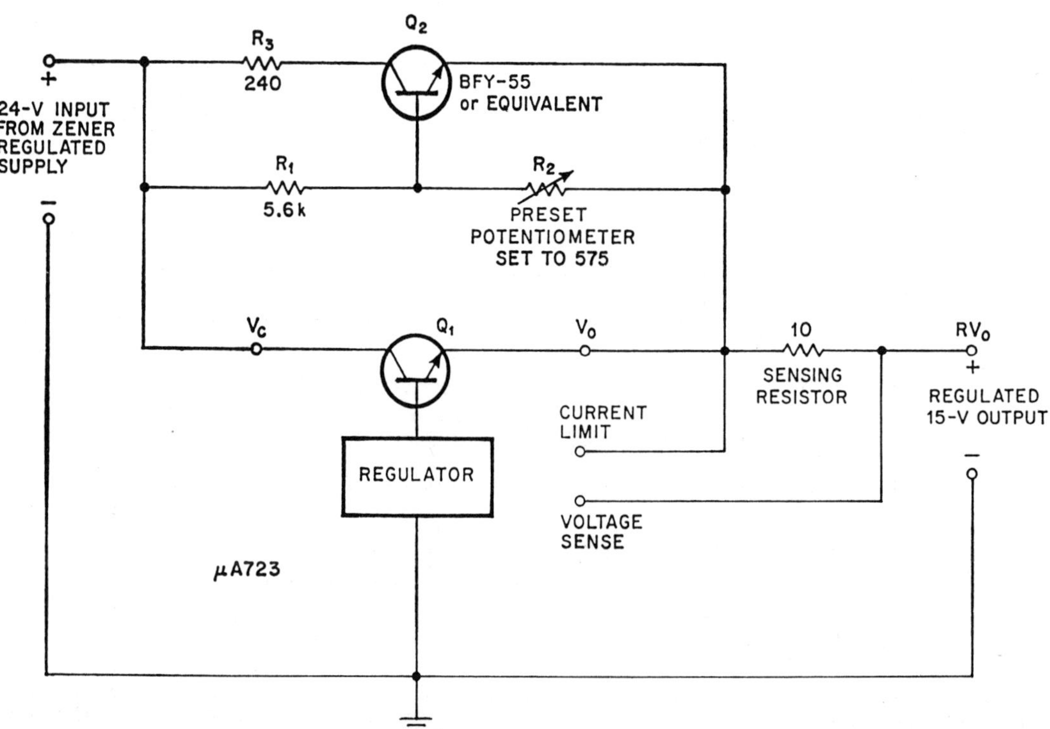

SERIES REGULATOR PROTECTION—Addition of Q2 network across series-pass transistor terminals of μA723 IC voltage regulator provides short-circuit protection. Article tells how to compute resistor values for use with other voltages and currents in series-type voltage regulators.—W. Granter, Short-Circuit Protection for Voltage Regulators, *Electronics*, April 27, 1970, p 91.

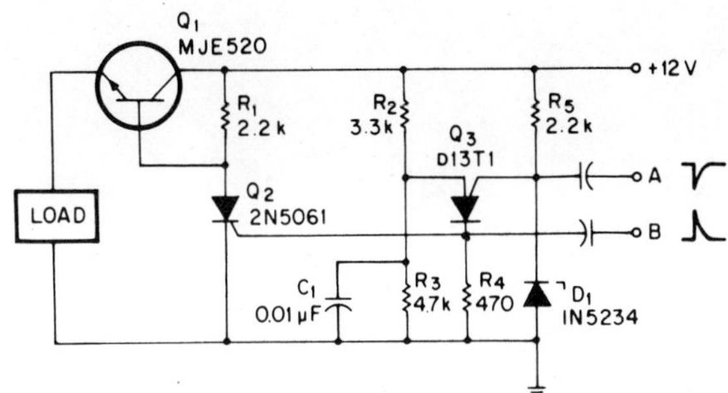

OVERVOLTAGE TRIP CIRCUIT—When supply voltage rises above value set by ratio R2-R3, programmable ujt Q3 fires and generates complementary pulses A and B that may be used to trigger alarm circuits or serve other functions. In addition, firing of Q3 turns on Q2, to cut off Q1 and load. Circuit stays off after circuit trips, until supply voltage is shut off so Q2 can commutate and reset circuit.—V. R. Laul, Adjustable-Overvoltage Circuit Breaker, *EEE*, April 1970, p 101.

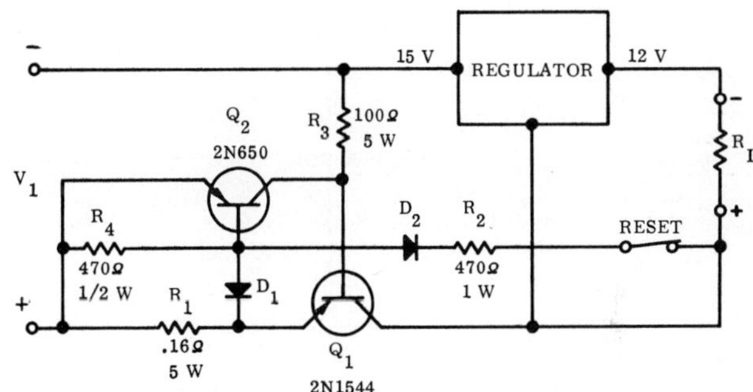

5.5-A ELECTRONIC FUSE—Switching action occurs in 90 µs, for protection of transistors in 12-V 5-A regulated power supply. When fuse acts, Q2 is on and Q1 off, so power is bypassed around transistors in regulator. Circuit is reset, after removing overload, by momentarily opening reset switch to remove power.—"Circuits Manual," Motorola, Phoenix, Ariz., 1965, p 8–2–3.

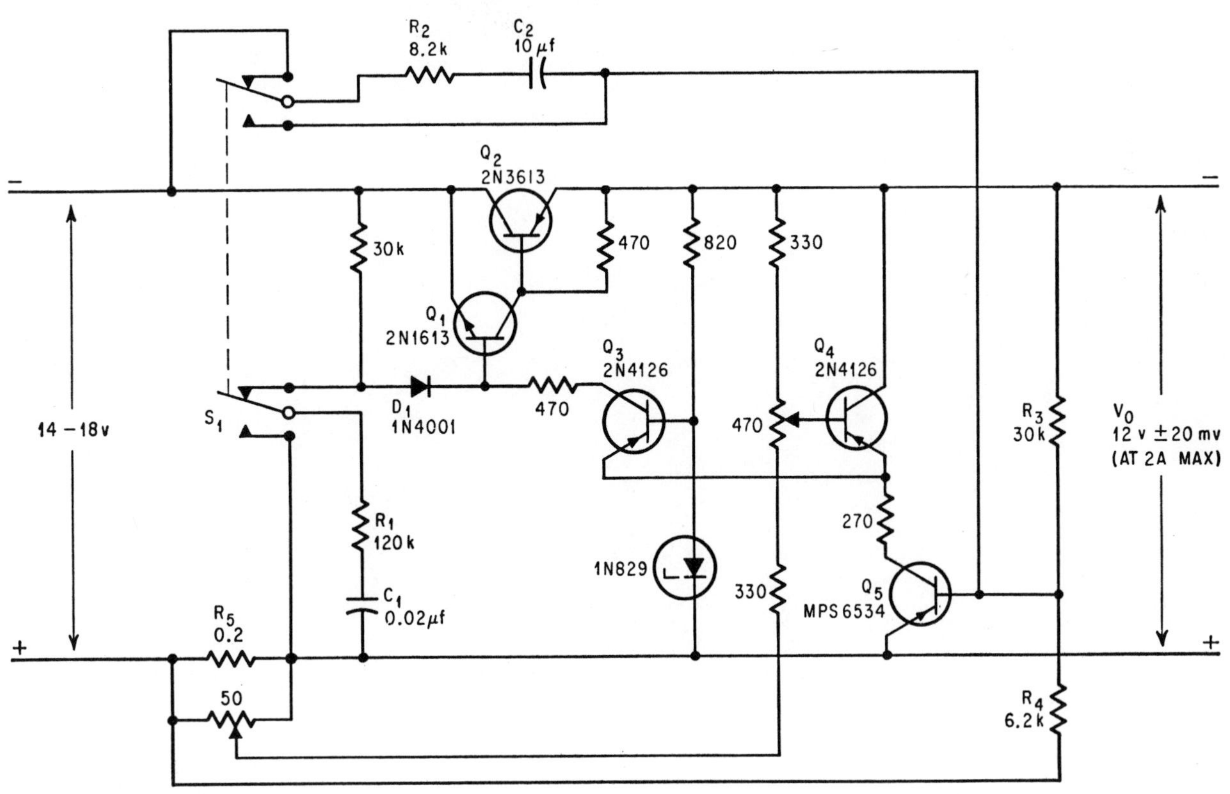

SERIES REGULATOR OVERLOAD—Single transistor Q5 is cut off by drop across R5 when output current of regulated 12-V supply increases beyond permissible maximum value, turning off regulator. Circuit has good temperature stability. Protection is achieved at much lower cost than with conventional flip-flop or scr and separate d-c supply.—S. Walko, Single Transistor Protects Power Supply from Overload, *Electronics*, June 12, 1967, p 102–103.

PROTECTIVE PREREGULATOR FOR SERIES TRANSISTOR—Circuit shown in dashed area decreases heat dissipation of series-pass transistor, making large heat sink unnecessary. Scr is normally conducting. When power supply voltage exceeds zener breakdown, scr cuts off. Average power dissipation of pass transistor is product of current drawn and zener voltage.—P. Pohl, Zener in Preregulator Limits Series Transistor Dissipation, *Electronics*, Oct. 27, 1969, p 98.

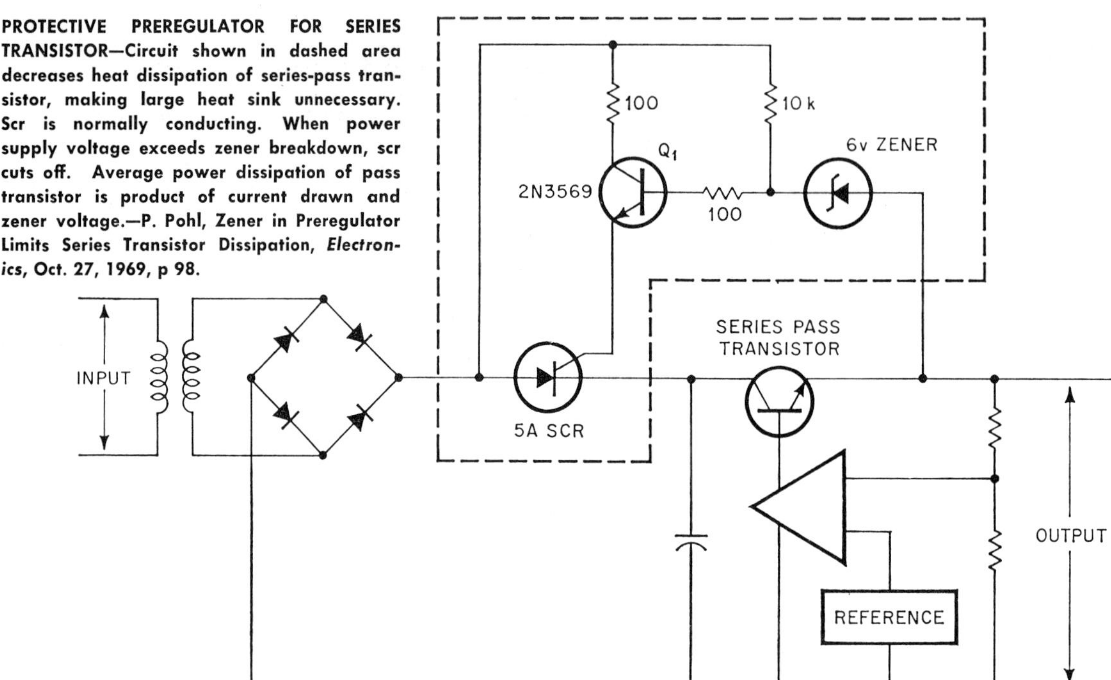

NOTE: To locate additional circuits in the category of this chapter, use the index at the back of this book. Check also the author's "Sourcebook of Electronic Circuits," published by McGraw-Hill in 1968.

CHAPTER 65
Protection Circuits

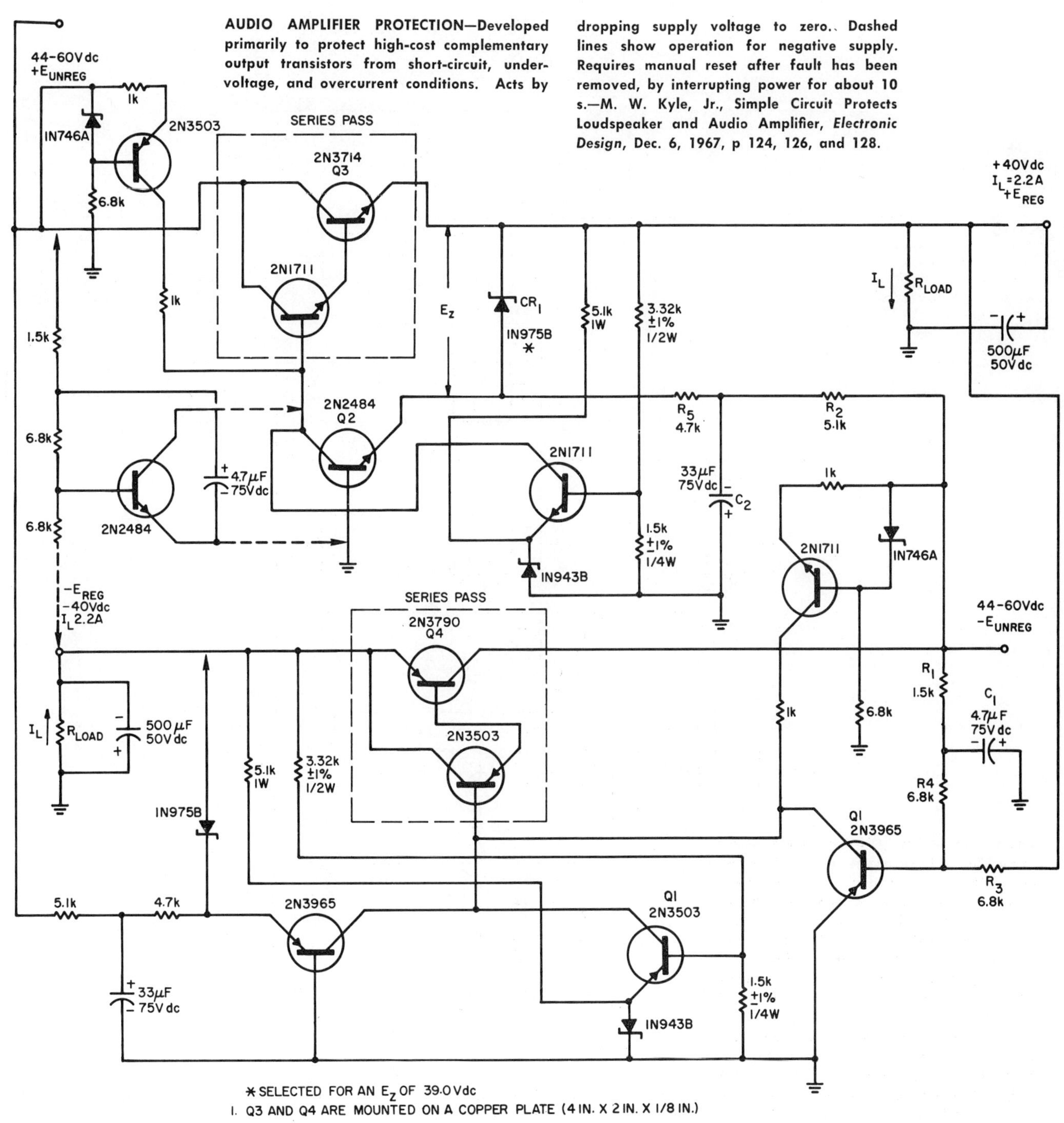

AUDIO AMPLIFIER PROTECTION—Developed primarily to protect high-cost complementary output transistors from short-circuit, undervoltage, and overcurrent conditions. Acts by dropping supply voltage to zero.. Dashed lines show operation for negative supply. Requires manual reset after fault has been removed, by interrupting power for about 10 s.—M. W. Kyle, Jr., Simple Circuit Protects Loudspeaker and Audio Amplifier, *Electronic Design*, Dec. 6, 1967, p 124, 126, and 128.

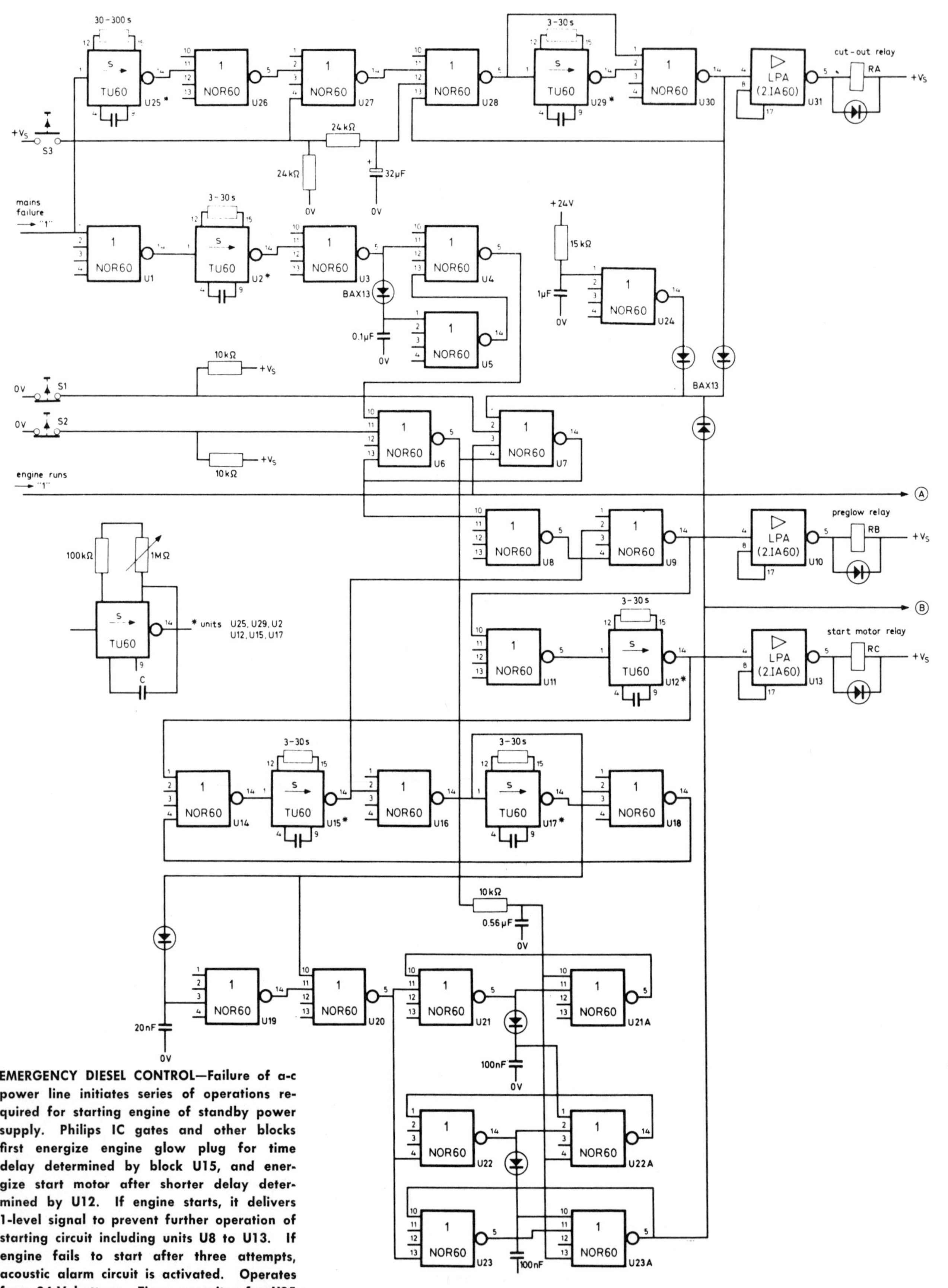

EMERGENCY DIESEL CONTROL—Failure of a-c power line initiates series of operations required for starting engine of standby power supply. Philips IC gates and other blocks first energize engine glow plug for time delay determined by block U15, and energize start motor after shorter delay determined by U12. If engine starts, it delivers 1-level signal to prevent further operation of starting circuit including units U8 to U13. If engine fails to start after three attempts, acoustic alarm circuit is activated. Operates from 24-V battery. Timer capacitor for U25 is 320 μF and all other timer capacitors are 32 μF. Leads at right go to warning and alarm circuit.—W. Klein, Control Circuit for Emergency Diesel Generator, Philips, Pub. Dept., Elcoma Div., Eindhoven, The Netherlands, No. 74.

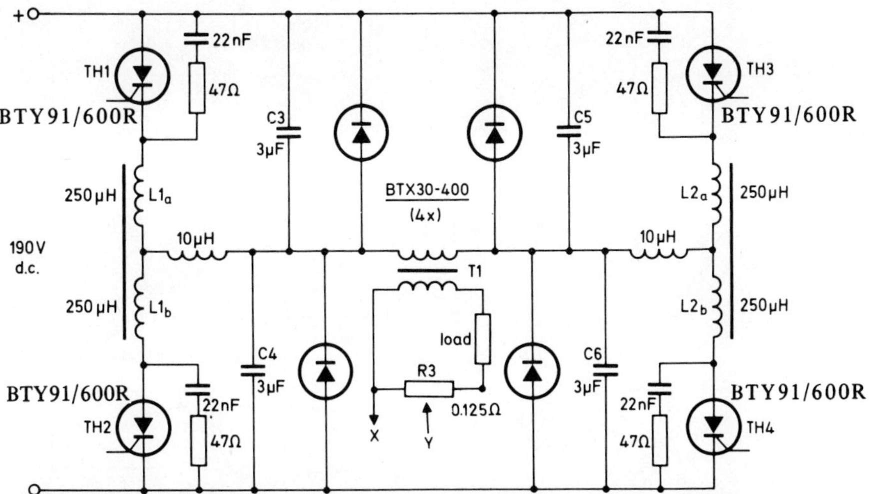

1.5-KW THYRISTOR BRIDGE INVERTER—Converts 190-V d-c to 220-V 400-Hz power. Includes trigger connected to thyristor gates and overload sensor connected to points X and Y, for protecting thyristors from overload. T1 has 190-turn primary and 220-turn secondary. —N. Bergstra and R. v. d. Linden, Overload Current Protection for a Bridge Inverter, Philips, Pub. Dept., Elcoma Div., Eindhoven, The Netherlands, No. 95, 1970.

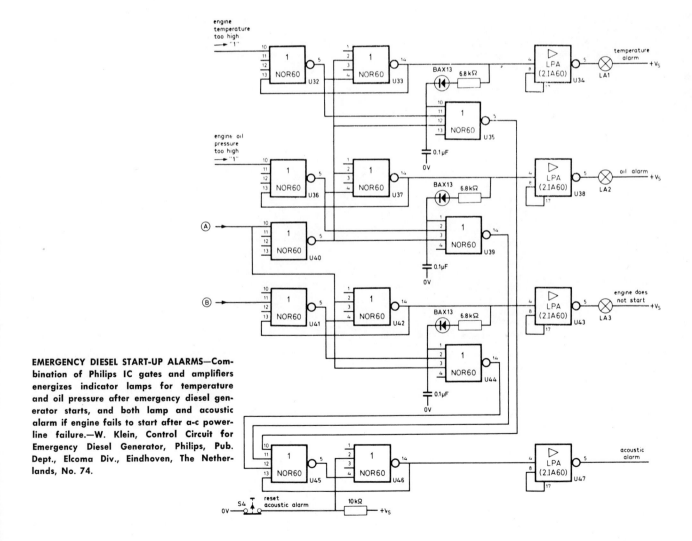

EMERGENCY DIESEL START-UP ALARMS—Combination of Philips IC gates and amplifiers energizes indicator lamps for temperature and oil pressure after emergency diesel generator starts, and both lamp and acoustic alarm if engine fails to start after a-c power-line failure.—W. Klein, Control Circuit for Emergency Diesel Generator, Philips, Pub. Dept., Elcoma Div., Eindhoven, The Netherlands, No. 74.

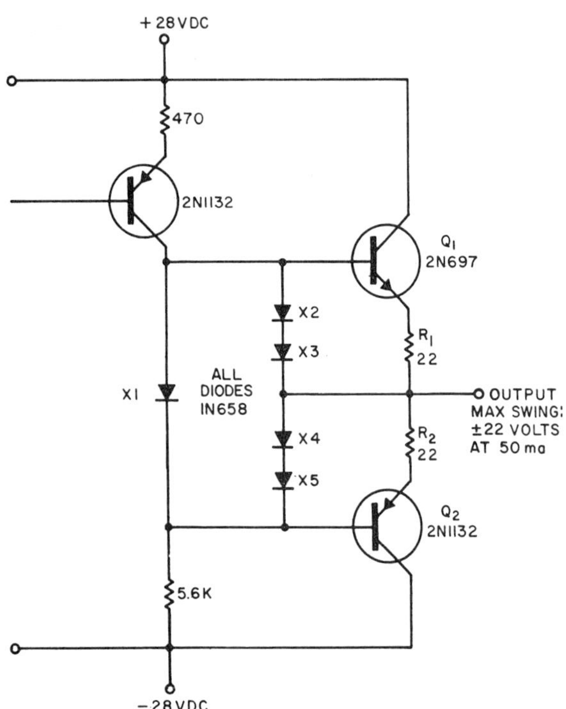

OUTPUT TRANSISTOR PROTECTION—Maximum current through either output transistor of complementary pair Q1-Q2 is limited to 50 mA. Diode X1 provides forward bias that is self-compensating for temperature and minimizes crossover distortion.—R. S. Young, Complementary Output Stage Provides Short Circuit Protection, *Electronic Design*, June 22, 1964, p 71–73.

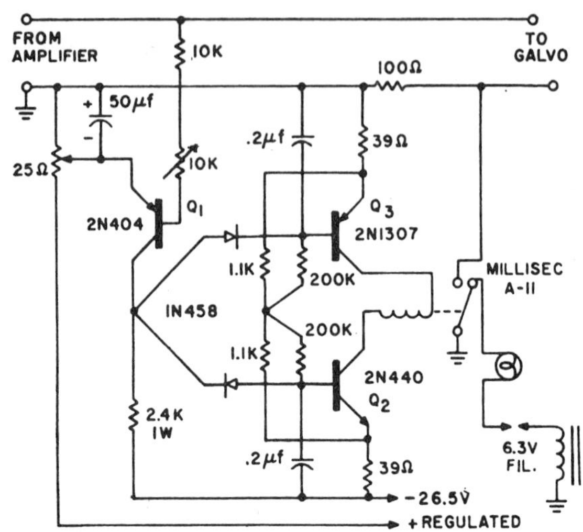

GALVANOMETER GUARD—Overload safety circuit prevents damage to high-frequency galvanometer driven by very low impedance amplifier. Protection is achieved by using relay to switch 100-ohm resistor into ground line to bypass galvanometer current on either positive or negative overvoltage. 10K pot in base circuit of Q1 adjusts sensitivity.—T. B. Whiteley, Transistor, Relay Switch Safeguard Sensitive Galvanometer, "400 Ideas for Design Selected from Electronic Design," Hayden Book Co., N.Y., 1964, p 145.

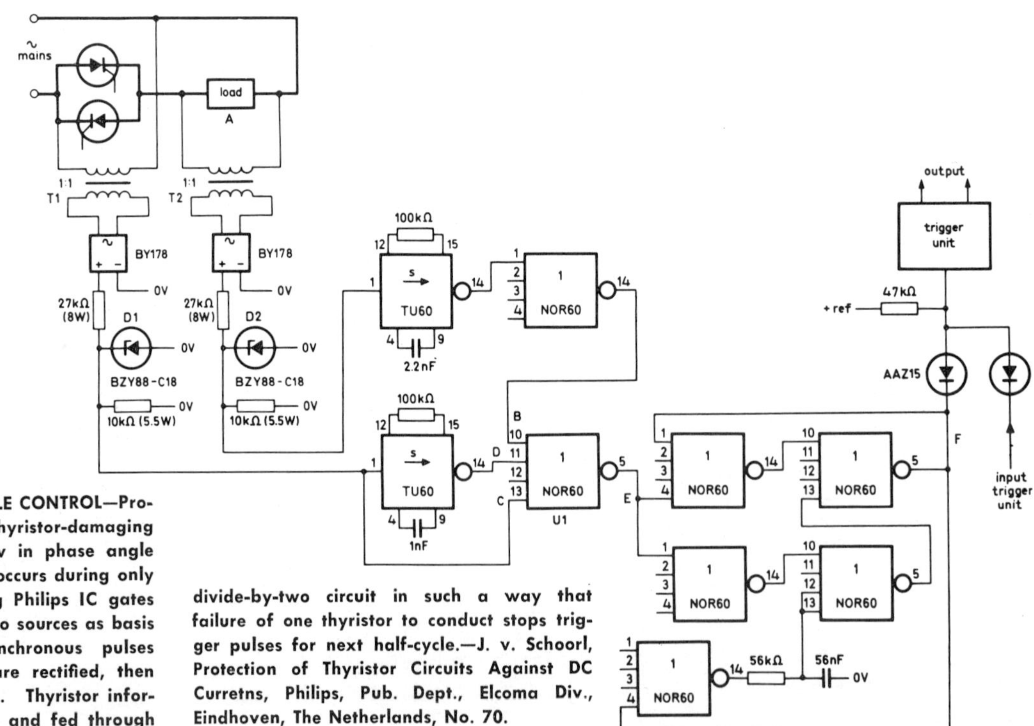

THYRISTORS IN PHASE ANGLE CONTROL—Provides protection against thyristor-damaging direct current that can flow in phase angle control circuit if conduction occurs during only half of cycle. Circuit using Philips IC gates obtains information from two sources as basis for protective action. Synchronous pulses from line transformer T1 are rectified, then limited to 18 V by zener D1. Thyristor information is obtained from T2 and fed through divide-by-two circuit in such a way that failure of one thyristor to conduct stops trigger pulses for next half-cycle.—J. v. Schoorl, Protection of Thyristor Circuits Against DC Curretns, Philips, Pub. Dept., Elcoma Div., Eindhoven, The Netherlands, No. 70.

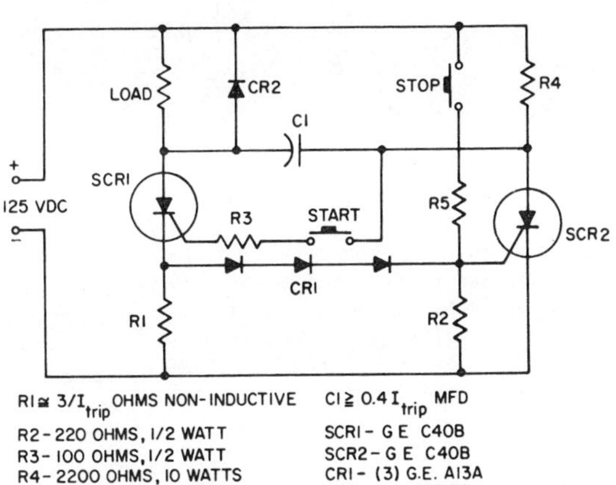

16-A D-C SCR FLIP-FLOP CIRCUIT BREAKER—Circuit is basically parallel capacitor-commutated flip-flop. Pressing start button momentarily makes SCR1 conduct and deliver power to load. Pressing stop button momentarily will interrupt load. If load current exceeds forward voltage drop across diode string CR1 and gate firing requirement of SCR2, load is interrupted automatically in less than half a cycle. Value of R1 and number of diodes determine level at which circuit will trip out. For values shown, maximum trip current should not exceed 100 A. Even with fault current rise of 10 million amperes per second, breaker will interrupt fault in 20 μs and keep peak fault current below 50 A.—"SCR Manual," 4th Edition, General Electric, 1967, p 156–158.

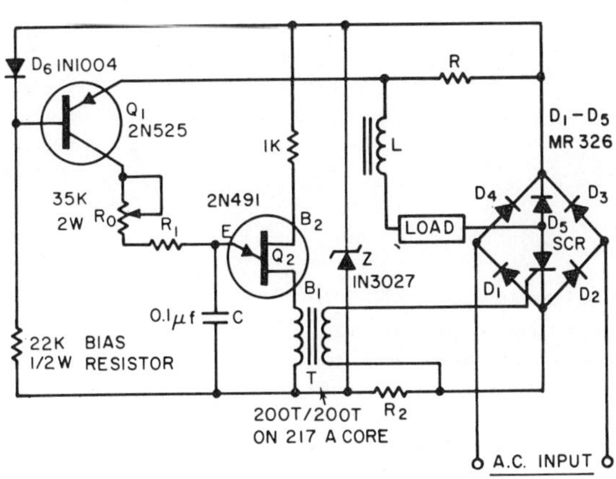

STARTING-CURRENT SURGE LIMITER—Protects components from damage by initial current surge through loads having low initial impedance, such as capacitors and incandescent lamps. Circuit converts voltage source seen by load into current source for duration of start-up. R-L time constant should be chosen to match duration of transient.—B. Berman, Q-R-L Network Limits Surge to Low-Starting Loaded SCR, *Electronic Design*, April 12, 1965, p 52–53.

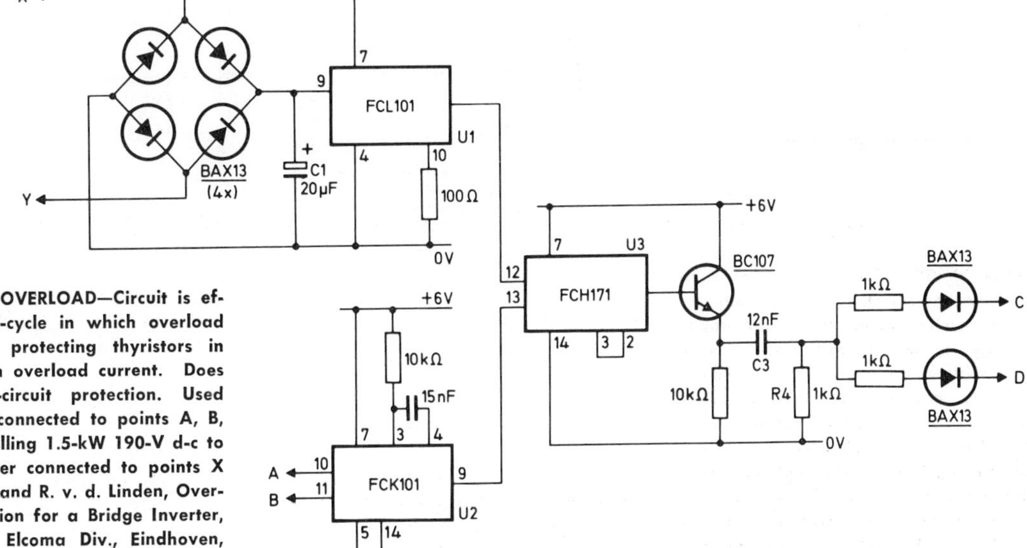

THYRISTOR BRIDGE OVERLOAD—Circuit is effective on first half-cycle in which overload current occurs, for protecting thyristors in bridge inverter from overload current. Does not provide short-circuit protection. Used with trigger circuit connected to points A, B, C, and D, for controlling 1.5-kW 190-V d-c to 220-V 400-Hz inverter connected to points X and Y.—N. Bergstra and R. v. d. Linden, Overload Current Protection for a Bridge Inverter, Philips, Pub. Dept., Elcoma Div., Eindhoven, The Netherlands, No. 95, 1970.

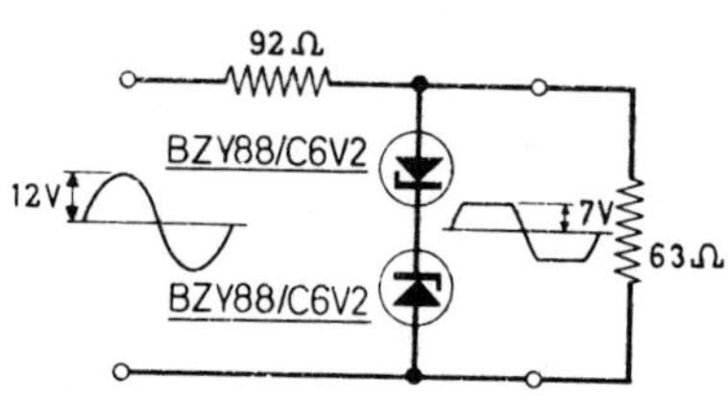

ZENER SPIKE CLIPPER—Two zeners in antiphase serve as full-wave stabilized amplitude limiter than can be used to protect other circuit elements against voltage surges or spikes. Clipping occurs at zener voltage level regardless of input voltage, but higher input makes output waveform more square so load takes more power.—Zener Diodes and Their Applications, Philips, Pub. Dept., Elcoma Div., Eindhoven, The Netherlands, No. 17, 1966.

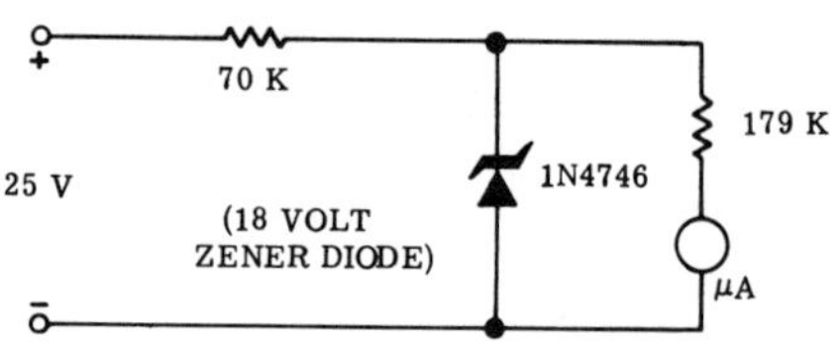

ZENER PROTECTS MICROAMMETER—18-V zener prevents overloading of 100-μA meter movement without affecting meter linearity. Chief advantage over thermal protection is instantaneous action of zener, provided repeatedly and indefinitely with no reset time. —"Zener Diode Handbook," Motorola, Phoenix, Ariz., 1967, p 7–13.

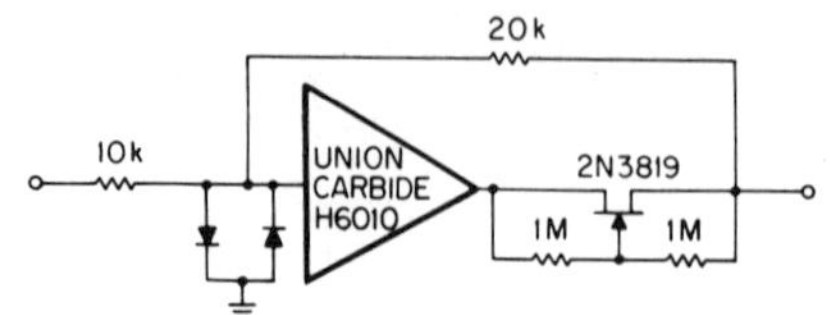

OPAMP PROTECTION—Inexpensive fet at output of opamp provides protection against voltage source up to 40 V applied even momentarily to output by limiting maximum output current to 10 mA. Effect on performance of opamp is almost negligible. Diodes similarly protect against excessive input voltages.—J. D. Spaihts, FET Protection for Opamps, *EEE*, Feb. 1970, p 115.

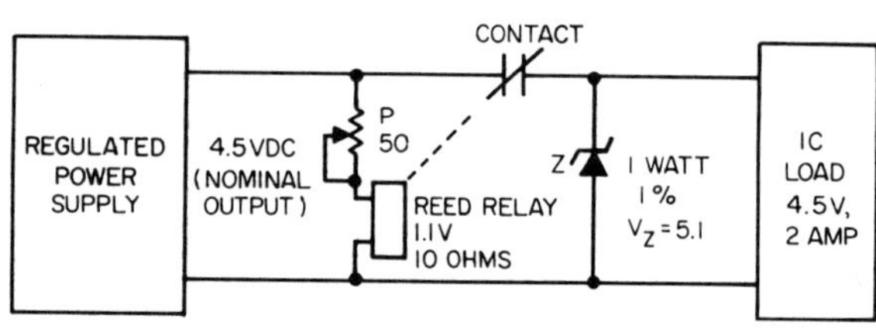

IC OVERVOLTAGE PROTECTION—Reed relay and zener diode protect low-voltage IC module from regulated power supply defect by clamping supply voltage at safe 5.1 V if, for example, failure of series-pass transistor in supply shoots voltage up to 9 V. Reed relay is then energized to open IC supply circuit before zener gets too hot.—J. J. McManus, Integrated Circuit Protected by Reed Relay-Diode Combination, *Electronic Design*, Nov. 29, 1965, p 78.

SCR LOAD PROTECTION—Prevents shorted scr from dumping excessive current into load. Bucking diode across load draws high current during normally missing half-cycle when scr fails, forcing fuse to blow. Load-shunting diode may be damaged before fuse blows unless application permits inserting sufficiently high limiting resistance in series with load. —J. T. Lamb, Shunt Diode Protects Load in SCR Circuit, *Electronic Design*, Oct. 25, 1969, p 109.

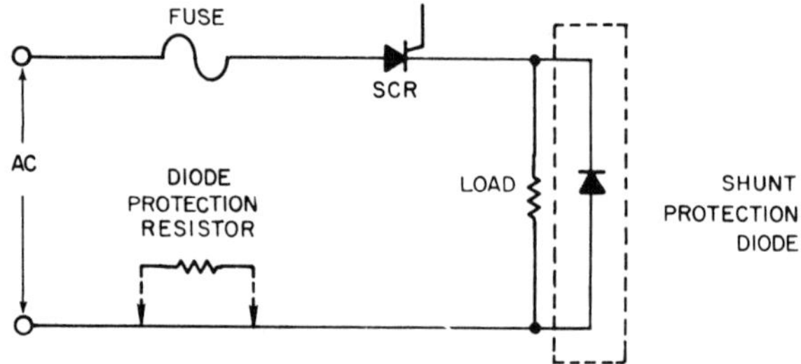

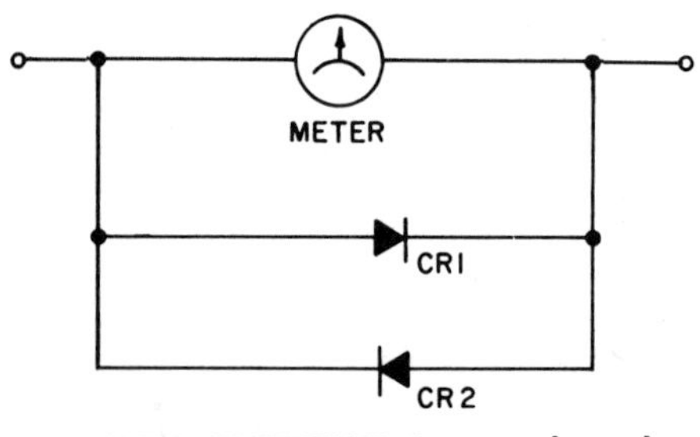

D-C METER PROTECTION—Low-cost low-voltage low-current silicon rectifiers such as 1N1692, connected across meter with opposite polarity as shown, will protect 50-μA meter of typical multimeter against heavy fault currents without introducing more than 1% error. With 1-A overload current, meter current is less than 1 mA because rectifiers begin conducting heavily when voltage across them exceeds about 0.5 V. For higher fault current, use higher-current rectifiers such as GE-X4.—"Hobby Manual," General Electric, Owensboro, Ky., 1965, p 156.

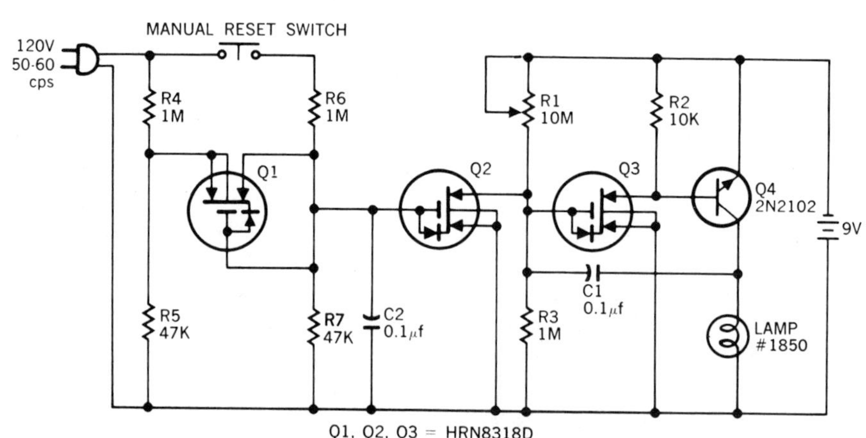

POWER FAILURE INDICATOR—Flasher is turned on by a-c line power failure, and keeps flashing until manual reset switch is operated, as indication that a-c line power has been interrupted. One application is for a-c power system serving unattended refrigerators or freezers, where power failure could cause food spoilage.—C. R. Perkins, "Application of MOSFET Devices to Electronic Circuits," Hughes, Newport Beach, Cal., 1968, p 46.

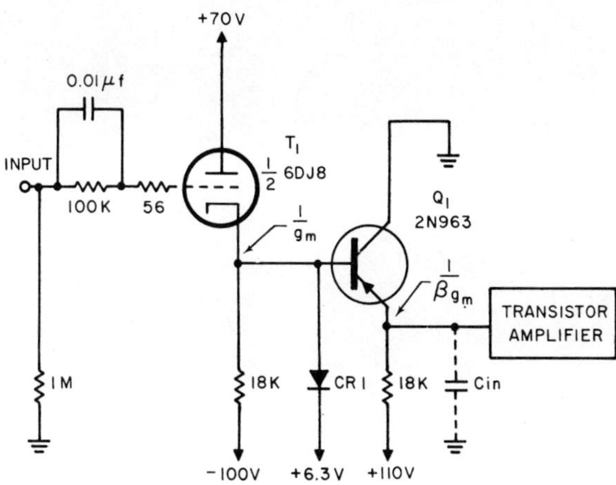

OVERLOAD PROTECTION—Triode cathode follower in cascade with emitter follower provides very low output impedance (below 10 ohms) and protects against large d-c overloads. Article describes operation.—L. A. Egherman, Emitter-Follower Circuit Protects Against Overloads, *Electronic Design*, March 15, 1965, p 61–62.

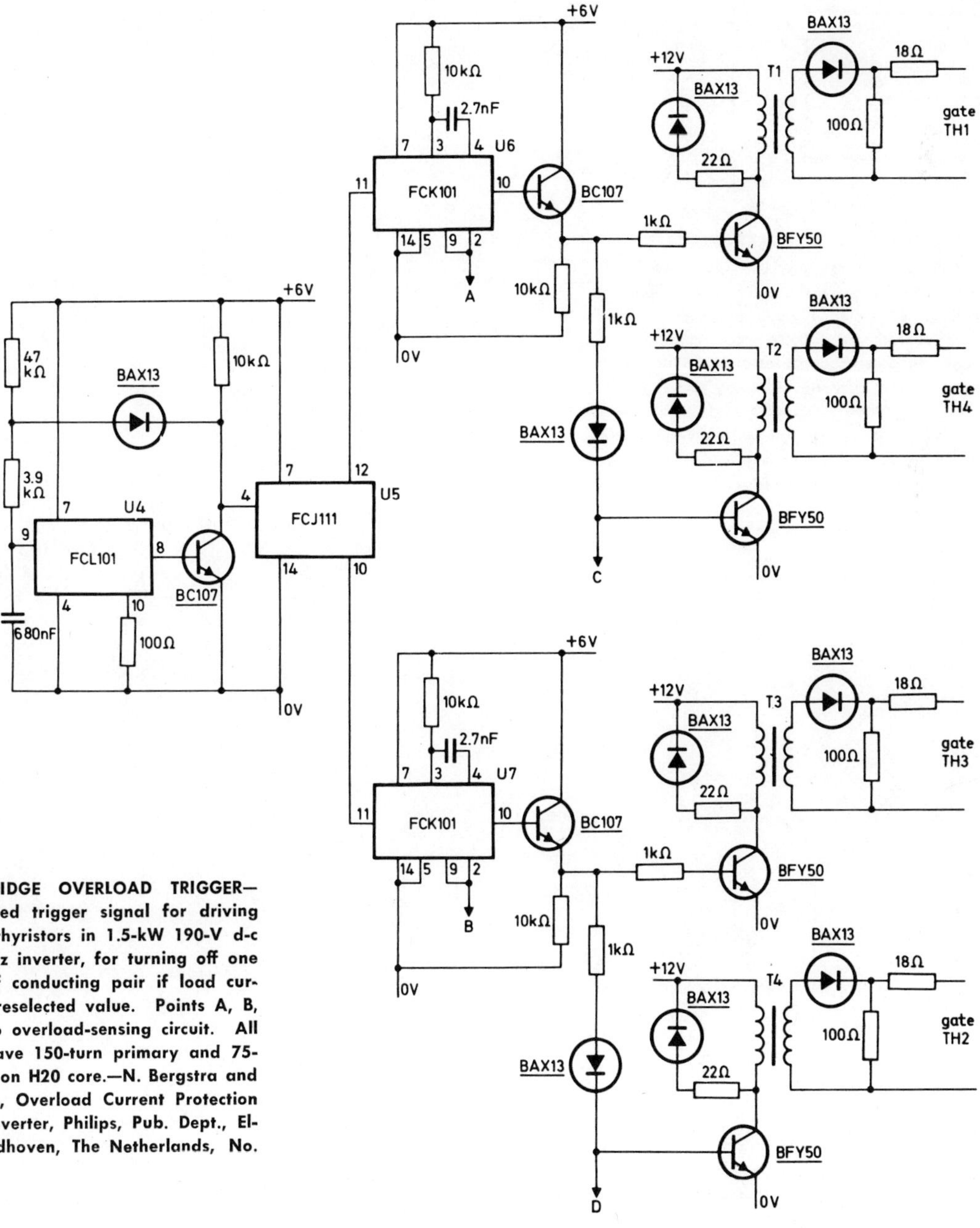

THYRISTOR BRIDGE OVERLOAD TRIGGER—Provides required trigger signal for driving gates of four thyristors in 1.5-kW 190-V d-c to 220-V 400-Hz inverter, for turning off one of thyristors of conducting pair if load current exceeds preselected value. Points A, B, C, and D go to overload-sensing circuit. All transformers have 150-turn primary and 75-turn secondary on H20 core.—N. Bergstra and R. v. d. Linden, Overload Current Protection for a Bridge Inverter, Philips, Pub. Dept., Elcoma Div., Eindhoven, The Netherlands, No. 95, 1970.

MULTIPLE-LAMP FAILURE—NE2 neons, shunting 28-V incandescent lamps connected as loads for Darlington Q1-Q2, glow only for lamp failure. Circuit values are not critical and depend mainly on current ratings of lamps. Q1 can be 2N718A, Q2 2N1613, diodes 1N-4245, R1 47K, and other resistors 100K.—D. A. Vaughan, Combination Lamp Driver and Failure Indicator, *EEE*, May 1969, p 117–118.

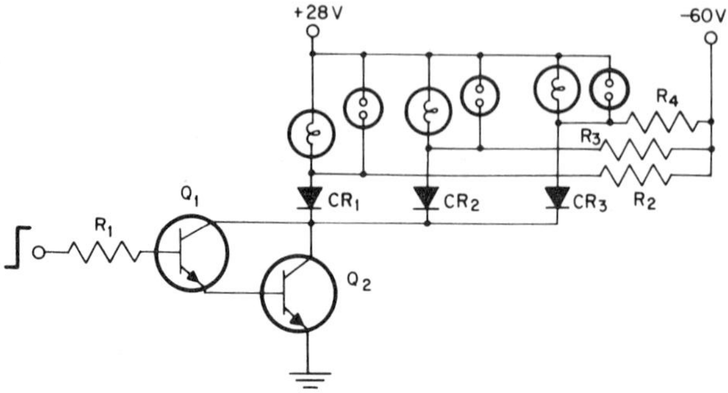

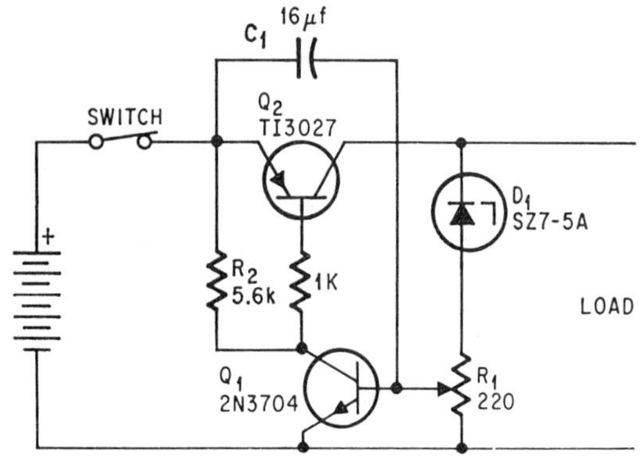

NICKEL-CADMIUM BATTERY—Prevents complete discharge by sensing when battery voltage falls below zener point of D1 and then turning off Q2 to open circuit. Prevents buildup of gas pressure and rupturing of cell, and increases battery life. Switch must be opened after each protective action, so C1 can discharge and permit turn-on.—D. L. Haskard, Voltage Sensor Limits Discharge in Batteries, *Electronics*, April 1, 1968, p 62.

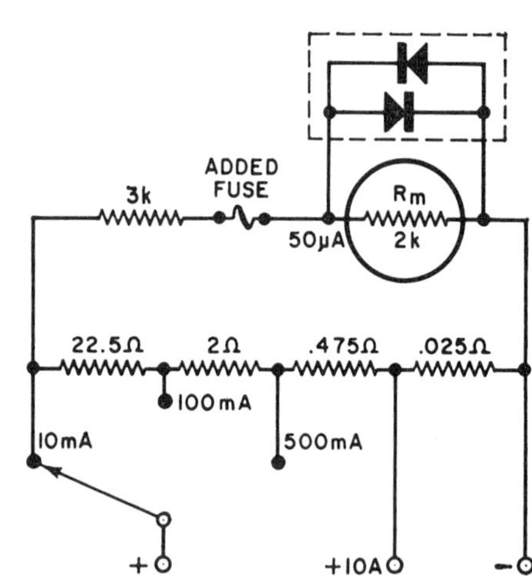

PROTECTOR DIODES FOR SIMPSON 260—Two Ohmite silicon diodes can be added to protect meter from current-range overloads. Bussmann AGX fast-blow 0.125-A instrument fuse can be added for extra protection, although 3,000-ohm resistor already in circuit will act as current limiter.—A. A. Mangieri, Diode Meter Protectors, *Electronics World*, Nov. 1966, p 56–57 and 76.

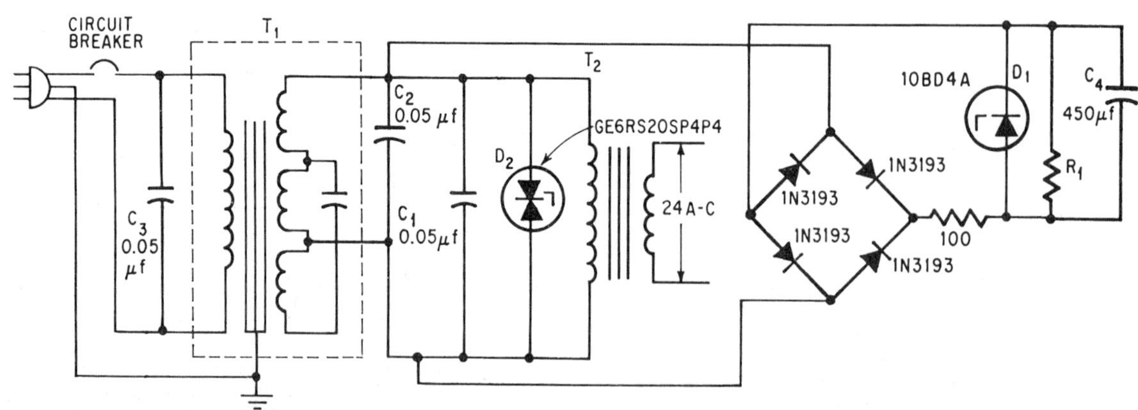

MIDNIGHT LINE SURGE CLIPPER—Protects refrigerators, freezers, and control equipment from damage by high line voltage surges that occur in late evening hours. Bridge rectifier and its load R1-C4, connected to a-c line filter, clips peaks of transients to keep voltage in filter at 117 V a-c.—L. E. Greenlee, Bridge Rectifier Clips Dangerous Voltages, *Electronics*, March 4, 1968, p 89–90.

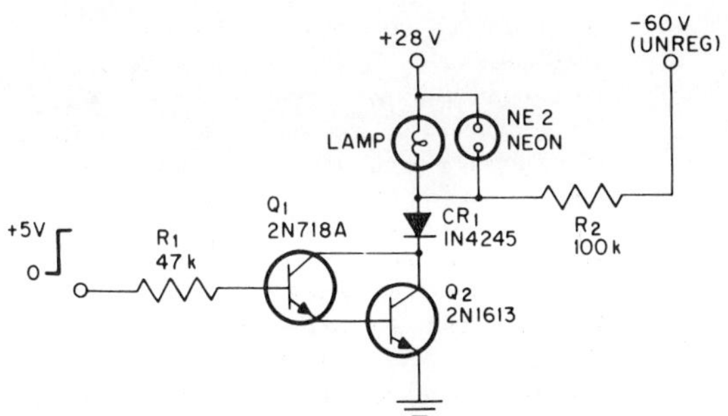

LAMP FAILURE—Provides reliable indication of failure of incandescent indicator lamp for critical information on instrument panel. Lamp being monitored is load for two-stage Darlington amplifier. Neon lamp connected across indicator glows only when incandescent lamp burns out.—D. A. Vaughan, Combination Lamp Driver and Failure Indicator, *EEE*, May 1969, p 117–118.

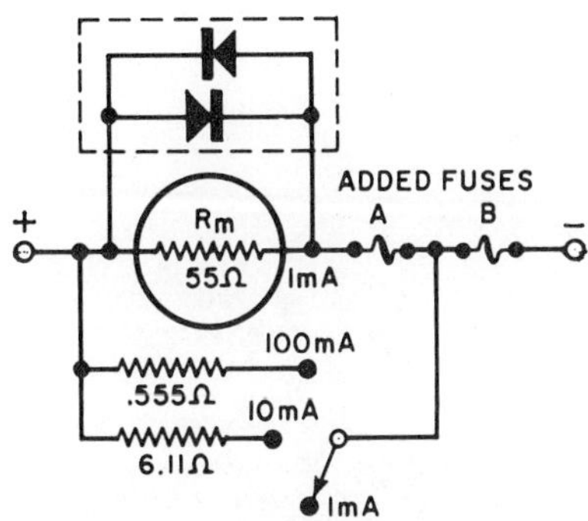

PROTECTING CURRENT RANGES OF VOM—Two Ohmite OMC7111 silicon diodes in parallel back-to-back provide protection against overloads of either polarity. Since diodes are connected directly between test leads, fuses must be added to protect against accidental overvoltage. Use ⅛-A fuses, which will break circuit in 1 s at 220 mA.—A. A. Mangieri, Diode Meter Protectors, *Electronics World*, Nov. 1966, p 56–57 and 76.

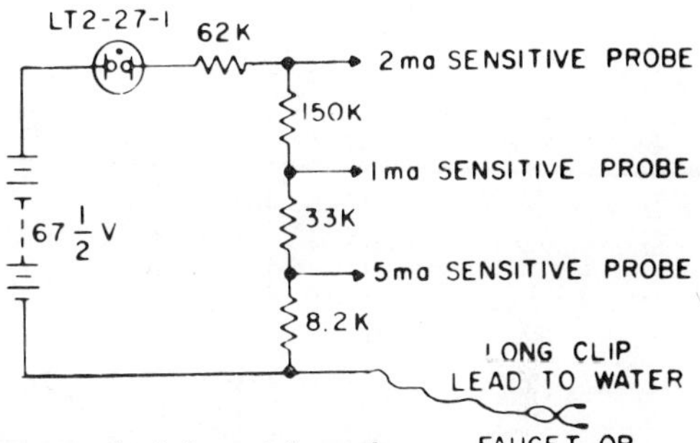

LEAKAGE CURRENT—Shock hazard from electrical appliances due to insulation leakage is determined by neon lamp indication. Anything above 5 mA is considered dangerous and makes neon glow.—E. Bauman, "Applications of Neon Lamps and Gas Discharge Tubes," Signalite, Neptune, N.J., p 146.

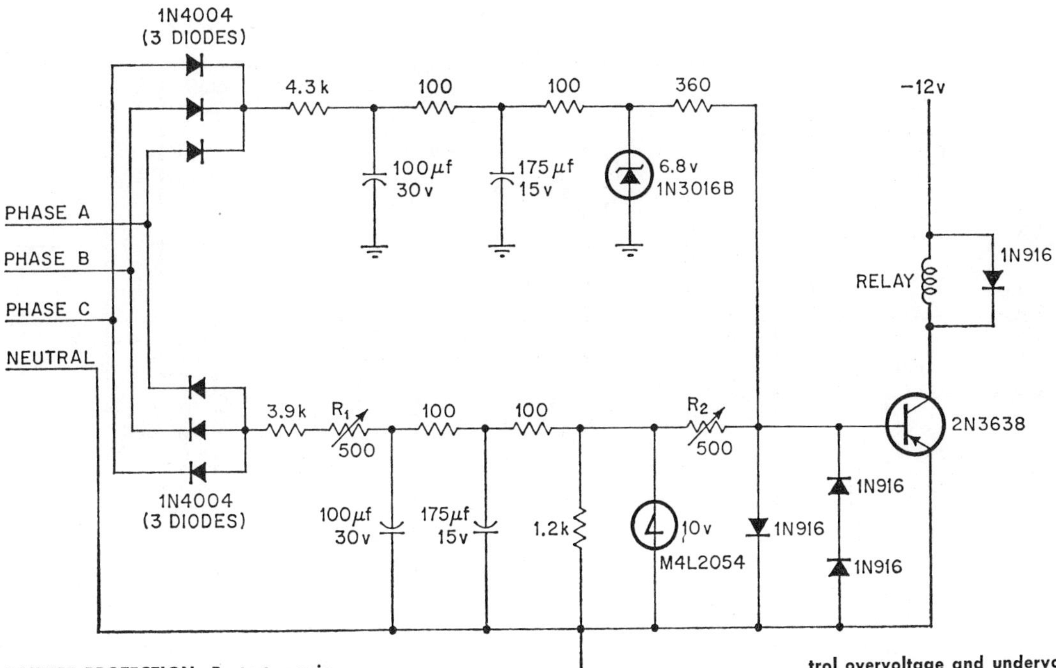

POWER FAILURE PROTECTION—Protects equipment from loss of one phase or from high or low line voltage. Compares sum of three-phase line voltages with regulated supply voltage and removes power from equipment when necessary. Settings of R1 and R2 control overvoltage and undervoltage trip points; controls are interlocking.—D. K. Smith, Monitor Guards Three Ways Against Power Failures, *Electronics*, Oct. 27, 1969, p 97–98.

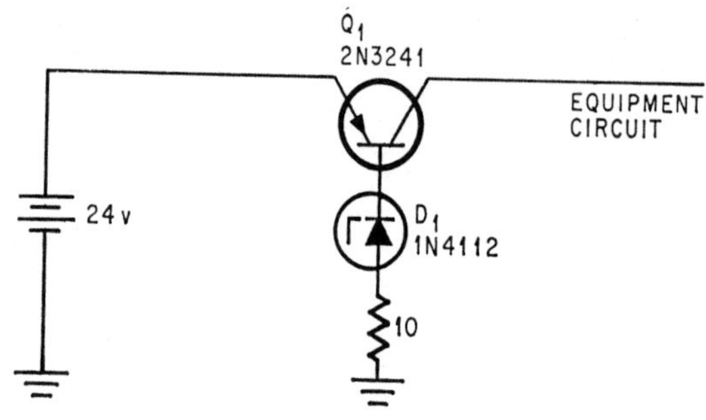

DEAD-BATTERY CUTOFF—Simple transistor arrangement with zener opens line between load and 24-V battery when battery discharges down to 18 V and affects accuracy of calibrating equipment. Particularly desirable for nickel-cadmium batteries because they can be destroyed if discharged below 30% of full capacity. For external indicator that comes on when line opens, place 24-V lamp between emitter and collector of Q1.—E. R. DeLoach, Transistor and Zener Monitor Calibration, *Electronics*, June 24, 1968, p 102.

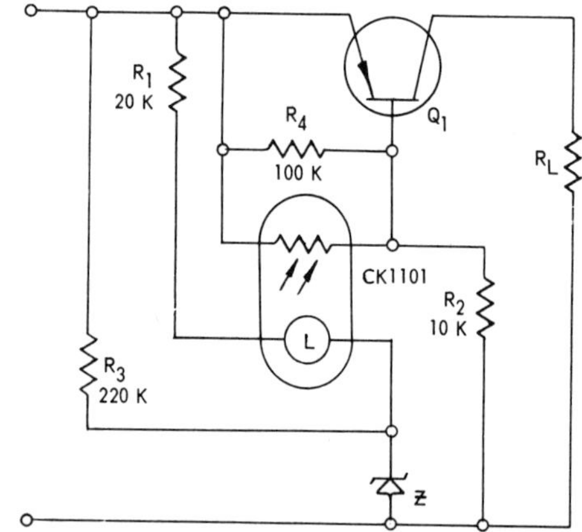

OVERVOLTAGE PROTECTION—At low voltage levels, transistor Q1 is saturated because photocell resistance of Raysistor acts as bias resistor. At overvoltage level determined by firing voltage of zener and neon in Raysistor, lamp fires and makes photocell resistance drop to low level, cutting off transistor and removing load voltage.—Raysistor Optoelectronic Devices, Raytheon, Quincy, Mass., 1967, p 27.

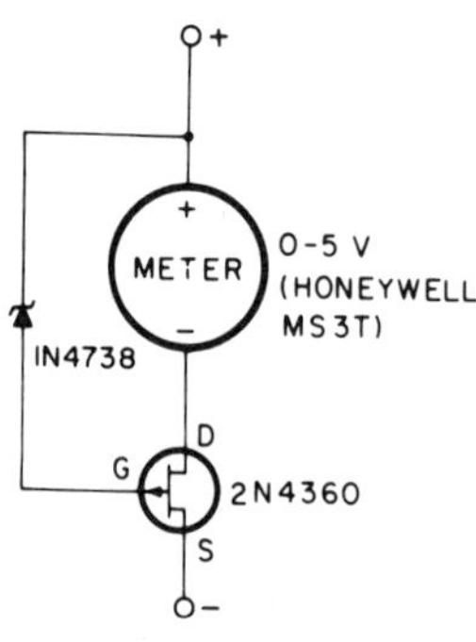

UJT-ZENER PROTECTION—Provides meter protection with only two components, without causing errors by loading external circuit. Developed for application where voltages measured were 2 to 3 V but with accidental overloads up to 14 V occasionally. Even with 16 V, voltage across meter is only 6.7 V. —R. L. Charnley, FET Provides Automatic Meter Protection, *EEE*, March 1969, p 128.

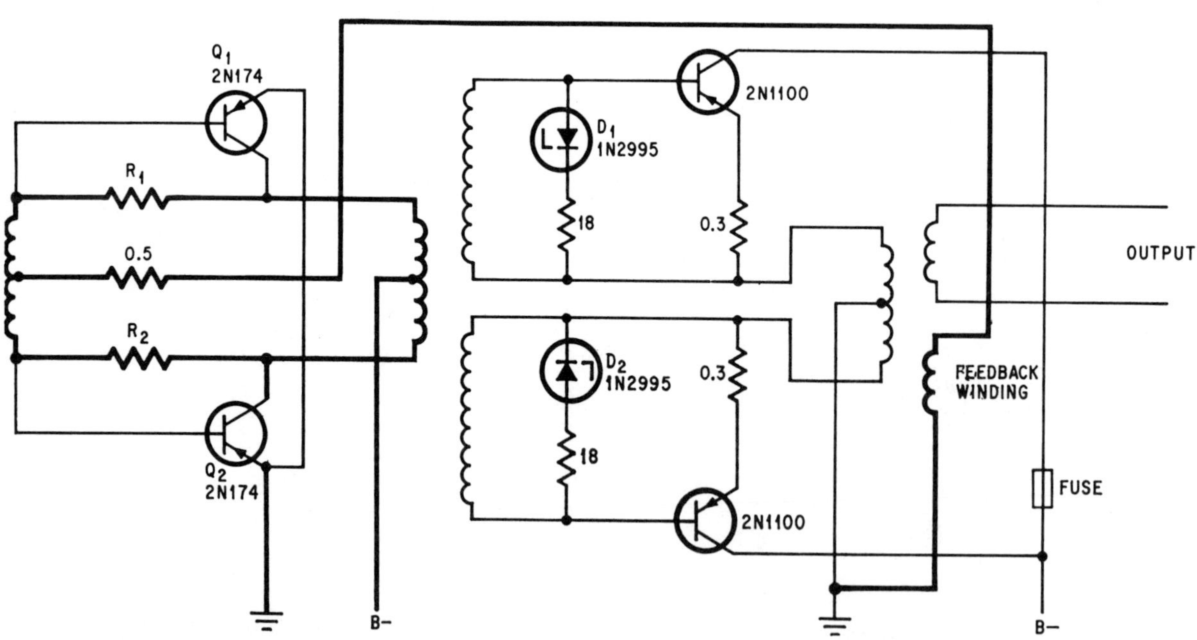

PROTECTING POWER TRANSISTORS—Inductive feedback circuit shown in heavy line acts on driver stage of audio amplifier when output shorts or opens, to interrupt drive current and thereby protect output power transistors from breakdown or thermal runaway.—G. S. Lehsten, Feedback Protects Amplifier During Load Failures, *Electronics*, Dec. 25, 1967, p 68–69.

IONIZATION GAGE—For aerospace sounding rocket, neon lamp with high breakdown voltage prevents d-c amplifier of cold-cathode ionization gage from being overloaded by abrupt rise in input current before external circuitry can switch in appropriate series resistor. Use of neon instead of zener diode maintains accuracy of gage readings.—E. Bauman, "Applications of Neon Lamps and Gas Discharge Tubes," Signalite, Neptune, N.J., p 91.

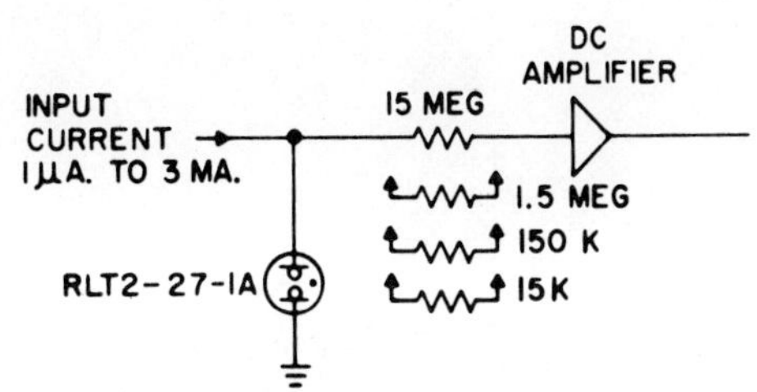

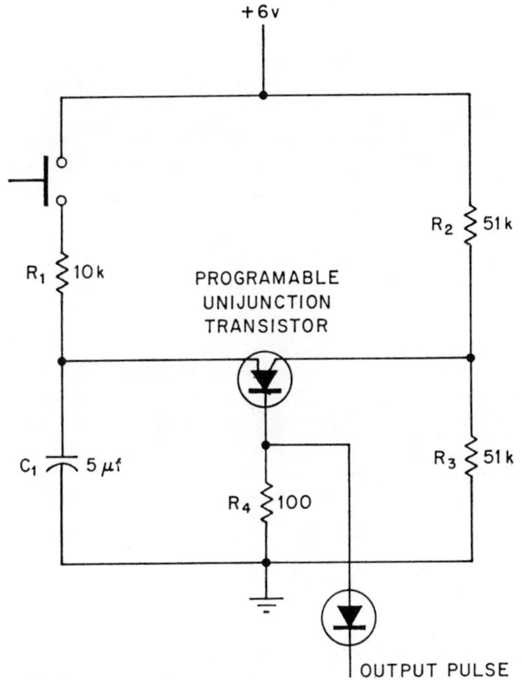

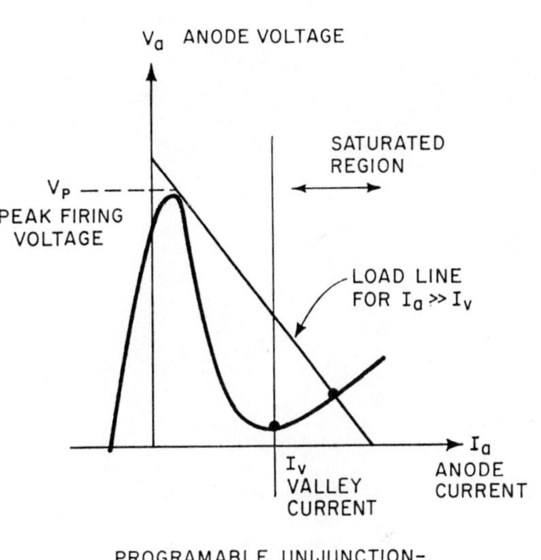

PROGRAMABLE UNIJUNCTION-TRANSISTOR CURVE

SWITCH BOUNCE ELIMINATOR—Programmable ujt generates clean pulses, free of switch contact bounce, over wide range of supply voltages. When switch is closed, C1 charges until it reaches peak firing voltage of ujt, then discharges through ujt to produce positive output voltage across R4. Circuit is immune to accidental triggering by transients or to contact bounce produced by switch.—C. Brogado, Unijunction Device Eliminates Contact Bounce, *Electronics*, April 13, 1970, p 106.

NOTE: To locate additional circuits in the category of this chapter, use the index at the back of this book. Check also the author's "Sourcebook of Electronic Circuits," published by McGraw-Hill in 1968.

CHAPTER 66
Pulse Generator Circuits

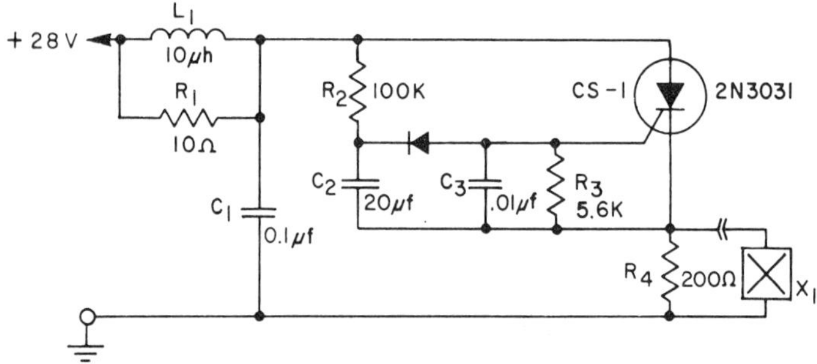

SQUIB FIRING—Energy for firing squib X1 is supplied through scr by 28-V d-c supply. To prevent scr from firing when anode voltage is applied rapidly, input network L1-R1-C1 limits rate of voltage rise. Time delay network R2-C2 and diode fire scr 1 s after circuit is armed by connecting to power supply.—High Reliability Squib Firing Circuits, Solid State Products, Salem, Mass., No. 3.

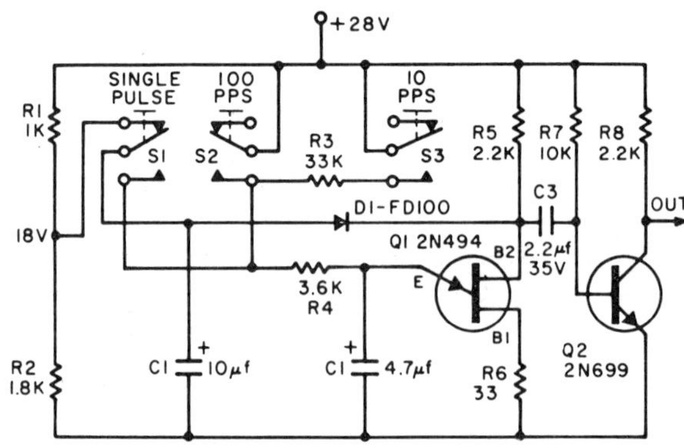

10 AND 100 PPS PLUS ONE-SHOT—Originally used as pulse source for stepping motors. Pulse width and repetition rate can be adjusted to any reasonable ratio, essentially independently; width is 850 μs for values shown.—G. E. Singleton, Pulse Generator Gives Low Frequency Otuput, *Electronic Design*, Jan. 20, 1964, p 79 and 81.

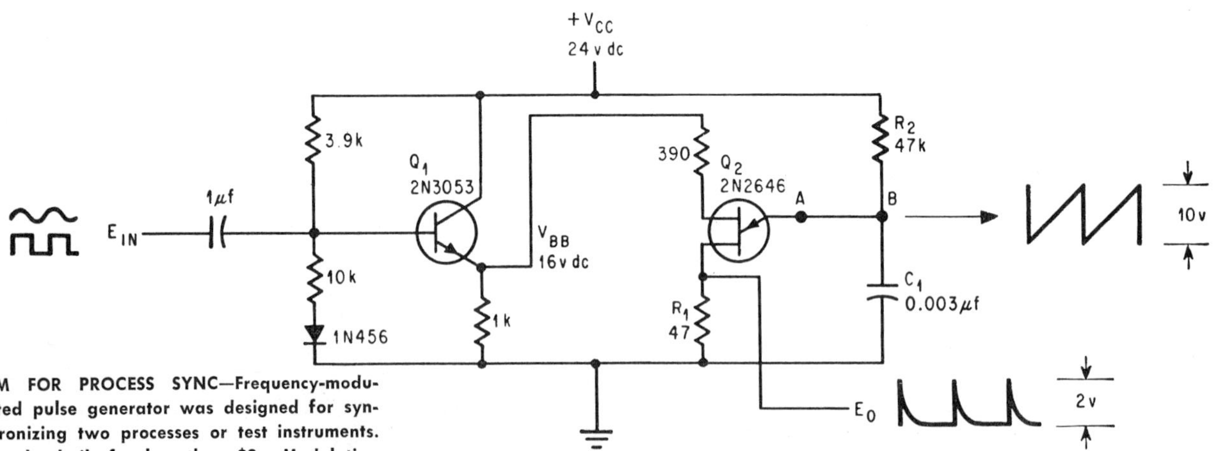

F-M FOR PROCESS SYNC—Frequency-modulated pulse generator was designed for synchronizing two processes or test instruments. Can be built for less than $3. Modulating input signal can be sinusoidal, square, or any other shape. Amplitude of input determines period of output, which is up to 0.0001 s for value shown, and frequency of input sets rate at which output changes. Increasing value of C1 increases period; above 10 μF, insert 1 ohm per μF between A and B to protect emitter of ujt Q2.—G. M. Nickus, Frequency-Modulated Output from Low-Cost Unijunction, *Electronics*, Nov. 14, 1966, p 122.

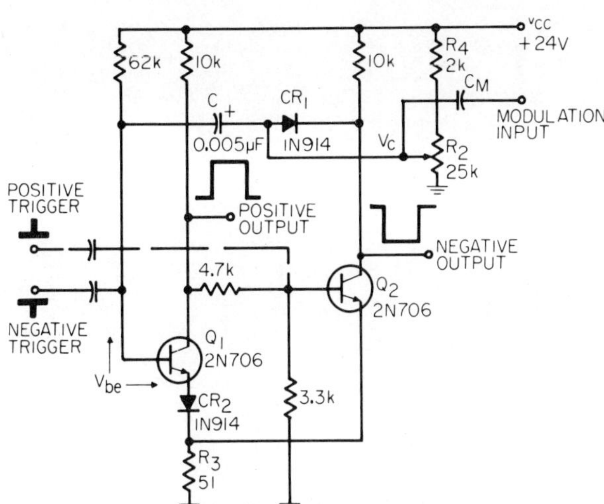

100:1 PWM—Modification of one-shot permits changing pulse width by means of R2, or externally with either d-c voltage or a-c modulation signal.—S. J. Erst, Improved Monostable Multivibrator Allows Wide Range of Pulse-Width Control, *EEE*, Jan. 1969, p 114–115.

SELF-POWERED GENERATOR—Produces sharp output pulse, with rise time of 100 ns during 50-μs fall time of 6-V rectangular input signal. Q1 and Q3 are 2N2894; Q2 is 2N2369; all diodes are 1N4153; R1 and R4 100K; R2 3K; R3 10K; C1 0.1 μF.—"Selected Electronic Circuitry," NASA SP–5046, 1966, Government Printing Office, Washington, D.C., p 57.

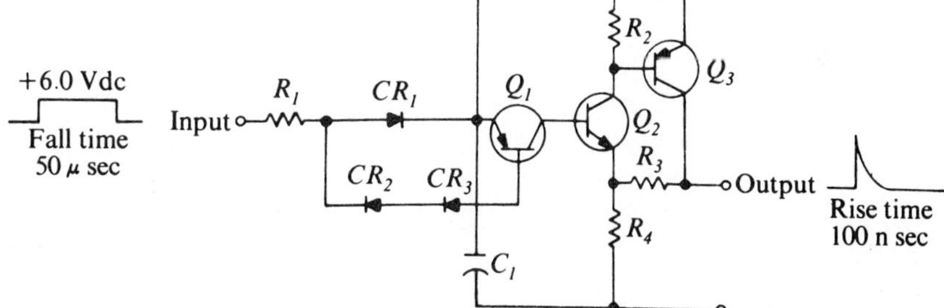

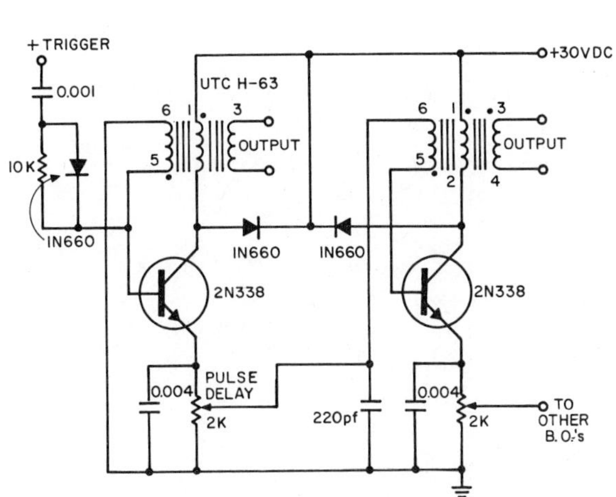

ADJUSTABLE PULSE TRAINS—Eight identical cascaded blocking oscillators generate pulse train in which spacing between pulses in adjacent oscillators is adjustable in range from 0.1 to 0.9 of previous pulse width. Pulse width is largely determined by values of R and C connected to emitter. Waveform at emitter is triangular, so potentiometer can adjust triggering time of next oscillator without affecting pulse width.—G. Mader, Blocking Oscillators Simplify Adjustable Interpulse Spacing, *Electronic Design*, July 6, 1964, p 52.

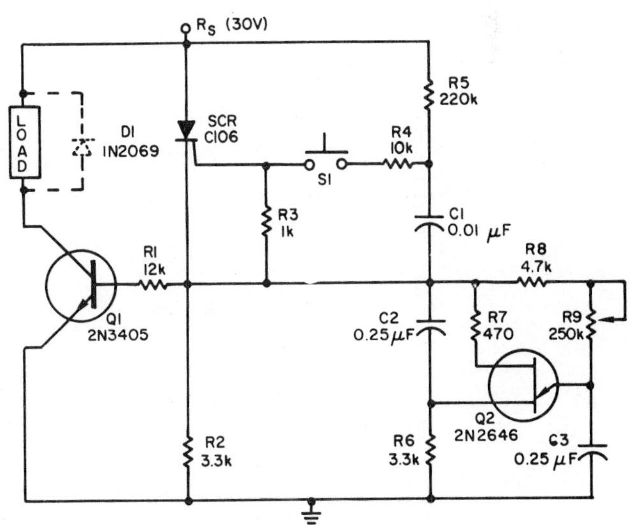

CONSTANT PULSE WIDTH—Random-duration closing of S1 produces fixed-duration output pulse with width adjustable by R9 from 2.5 to 100 ms. May be used as pulse stretcher, pulse shortener, and contact-bounce eliminator. Varying supply voltage from 15 V to 45 V produces less than 0.2-ms change in output pulse duration.—R. W. Murre, Any Switch Closure Produces a Fixed-Duration Output Pulse, *Electronic Design*, Feb. 1, 1969, p 72 and 74.

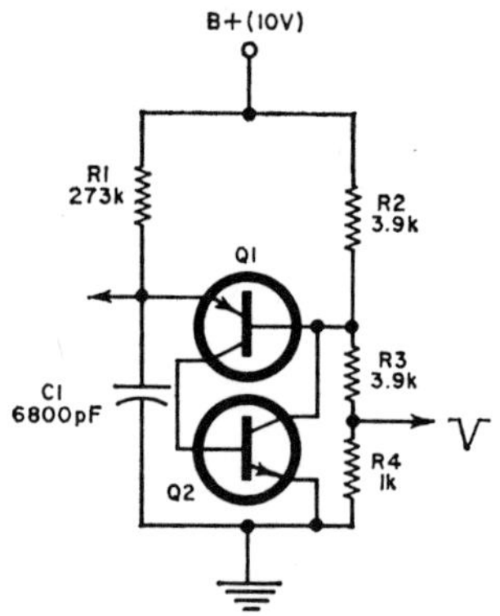

TRANSISTOR RELAXATION OSCILLATOR—Two ordinary transistors connected as shown will equal performance of ujt relaxation oscillator. Component values are for 1 kHz.—W. A. Vincent, Using Transistors as Negative-Resistance Devices, *Electronics World*, June 1969, p 38–40 and 62.

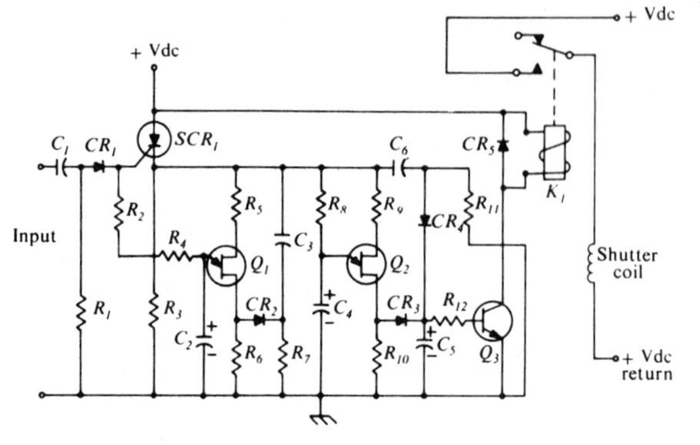

Supply	+ 20 Vdc
SCR_1	2N886
CR_1 through CR_5	1N645
K_1	BR5–1K
Q_1, Q_2	2N1671B
Q_3	2N930
C_1	0.01 μF
C_2, C_4	10 μF
C_3	0.1 μF
C_5	2.7 μF
C_6	1 μF
R_1	100K
R_2	2.2K
R_3	4.7K
R_4	68K
R_5, R_6, R_9, R_{10}	100 Ω
R_7	10K
R_8	33K
R_{11}	3.3K
R_{12}	27K

MULTIPULSE GENERATOR—Circuit was developed at Goddard Space Flight Center to generate pulses about 150 ms apart for operating shutter used to protect optical system from excessive light. Input trigger pulse turns on SCR1 to initiate capacitor-charging action for generating required pulses.—"Selected Electronic Circuitry," NASA SP-5046, 1966, Government Printing Office, Washington, D.C., p 24.

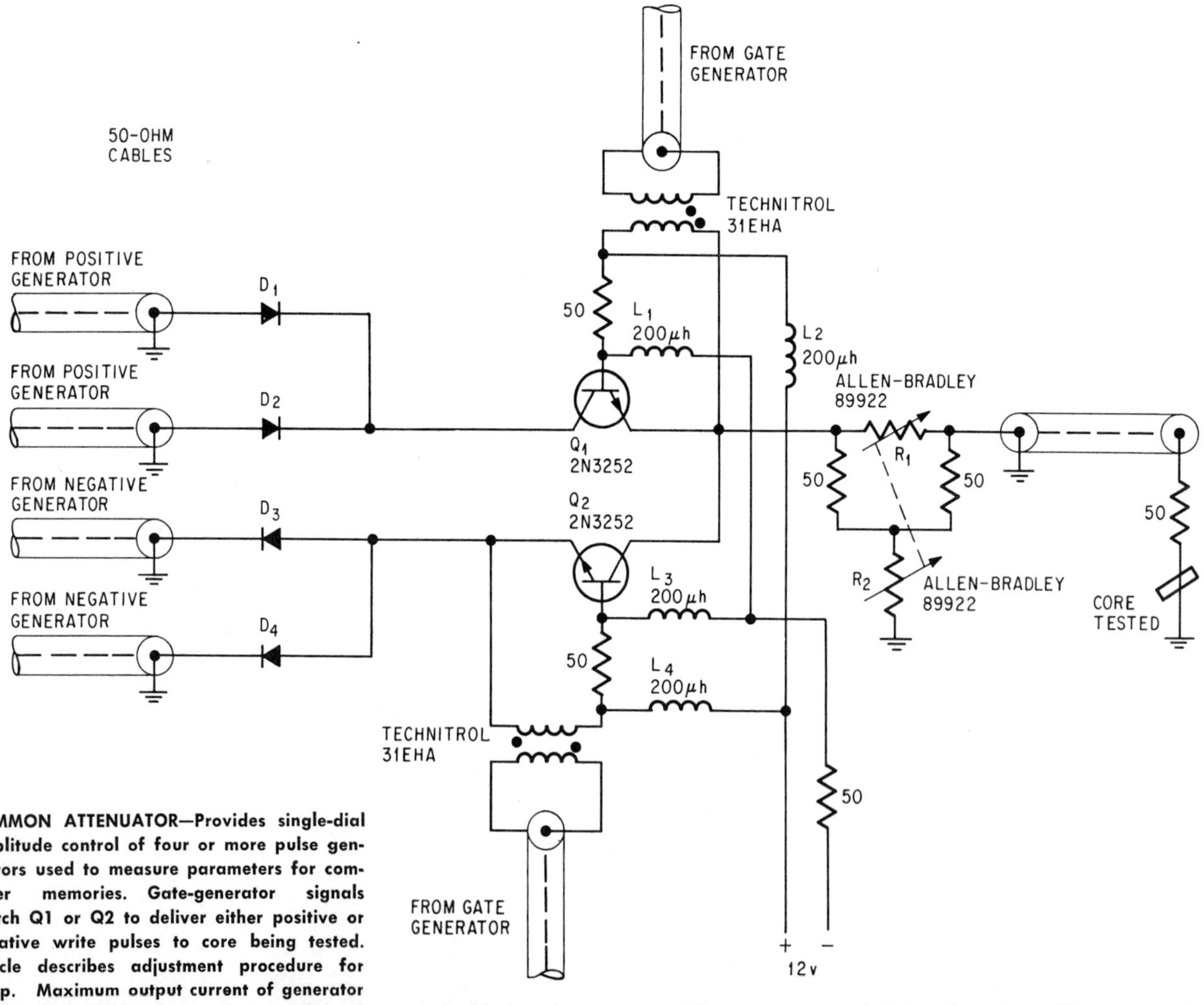

COMMON ATTENUATOR—Provides single-dial amplitude control of four or more pulse generators used to measure parameters for computer memories. Gate-generator signals switch Q1 or Q2 to deliver either positive or negative write pulses to core being tested. Article describes adjustment procedure for setup. Maximum output current of generator is 1 A into 50-ohm load. Repeatability of amplitude settings is limited only by attenuator backlash and generator stability.—W. M. Chu, Single Control Adjusts Outputs of Several Pulse Generators, *Electronics*, July 10, 1967, p 82–83.

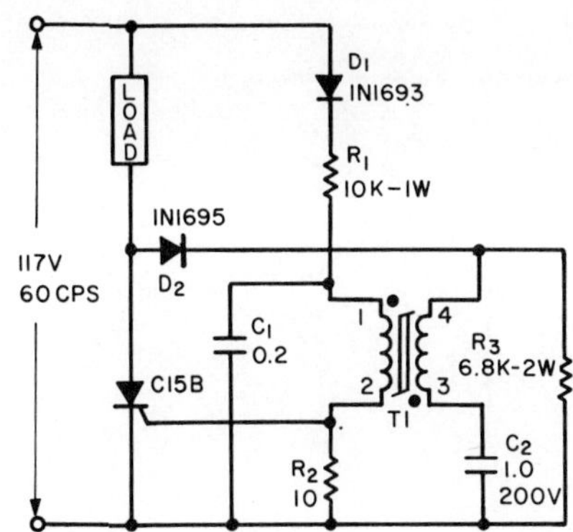

10-A PULSES AT 160 V—Scr with simple magnetic firing circuit switches half-cycles of line voltage to give high-power pulses for industrial control circuit application.—T. P. Sylvan, SCR Quarter-Wave Rectifier Forms High-Power Pulses, *Electronic Design*, April 27, 1964, p 95–97.

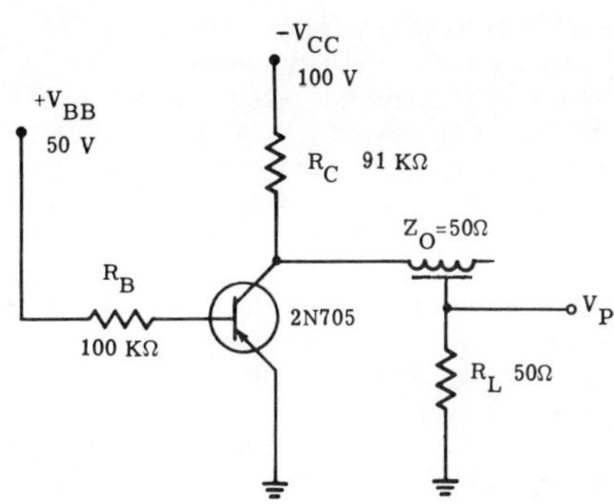

DELAY-LINE GENERATOR—Uses 50-ohm delay line Z with transistor operating in avalanche mode to generate positive or negative pulses with controllable amplitude and duration. To get negative pulses with circuit shown, load RL is placed in series with emitter-ground connection of transistor. VCC and RC affect repetition rate, but rate is primarily determined by value of line capacitance and therefore by pulse width. Pulse amplitude is changed by using different line impedance and transistor.—"High Speed Switching Transistor Handbook," Motorola, Phoenix, Ariz., 1969, p 295.

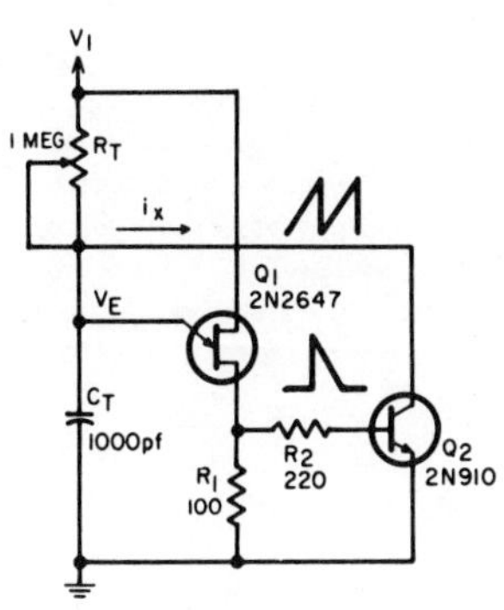

500-KHZ UJT RELAXATION—Single transistor and resistor extend frequency range of basic ujt.—M. Graminga, Modified Unijunction Oscillator Reaches 500 kHz, *EEE*, Sept. 1966, p 144.

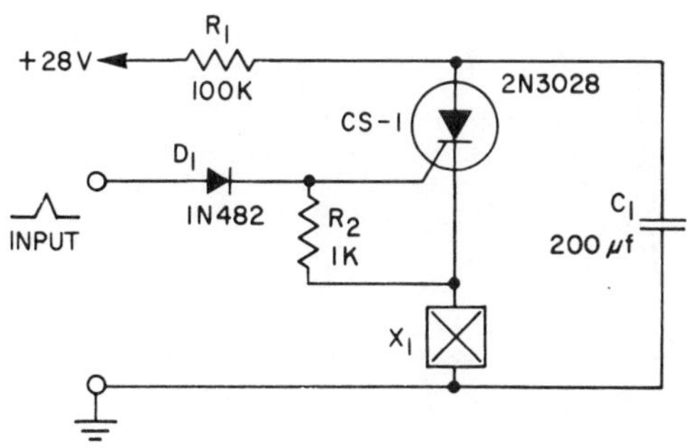

FIRING EXPLOSIVE BOLT—C1 stores energy for firing squib X1. Positive 1-mA pulse fires scr, making C1 discharge through squib. Circuit resets automatically after test firing, allowing C1 to recharge. Can be used for detonation and for rocket engine ignition.—High Reliability Squib Firing Circuits, Solid State Products, Salem, Mass., No. 3.

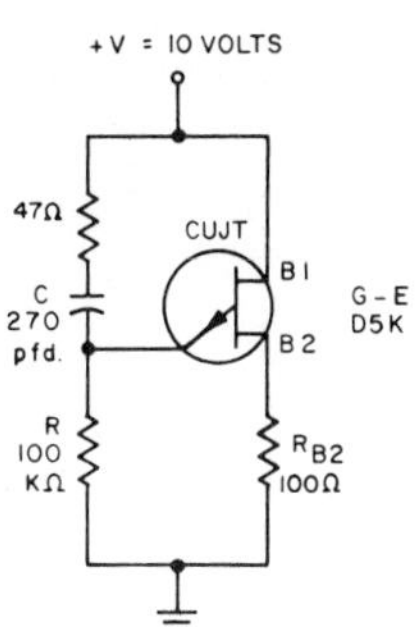

50-KHZ COMPLEMENTARY UJT—Operates as relaxation oscillator with good immunity to supply voltage changes.—W. R. Spofford, Jr., Complementary Unijunction Transistors, General Electric, Syracuse, N.Y., No. 90.72, 1968, p 10.

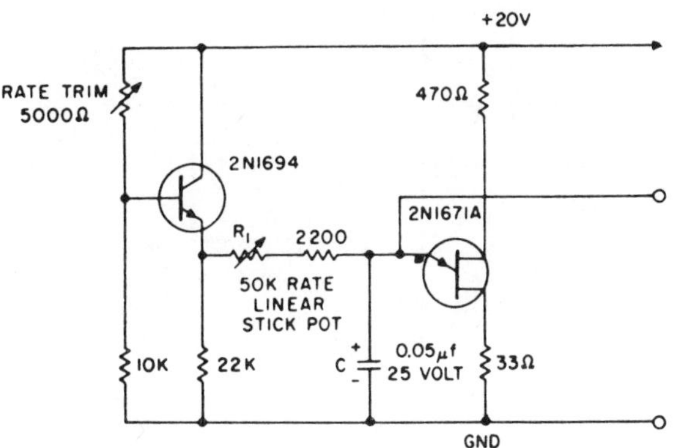

FREQUENCY-CALIBRATED POT IN UJT RELAXATION—High stability of ujt relaxation oscillator permits calibrating settings of potentiometers. Center frequency is approximately 1,000 Hz, with R1 providing at least one decade of variation and with trim control providing at least one octave of variation. Trim pot is independent of R1.—J. H. Phelps, Unijunction Oscillator Has Frequency Trim Control, "400 Ideas for Design Selected from Electronic Design," Hayden Book Co., N.Y., 1964, p 177.

ONE, TWO, THREE, OR BURST—Versatile pulse generator costing about $20 delivers combinations of 5-V pulses in frequency range of 400 to 15,000 Hz. With R3 at maximum, R2 is adjusted to give single pulse when power is applied. R3 is then adjusted to give double- or triple-pulse groups or to give continuous burst of pulses. Q1 may be any transistor serving as inverter and isolation stage.—G. Lawson, A Four-Layer Diode Forms Double-Pulse Generator, *Electronic Design*, April 26, 1967, p 243.

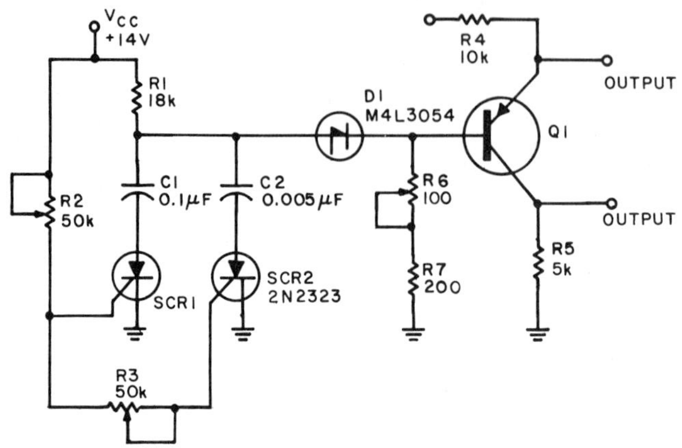

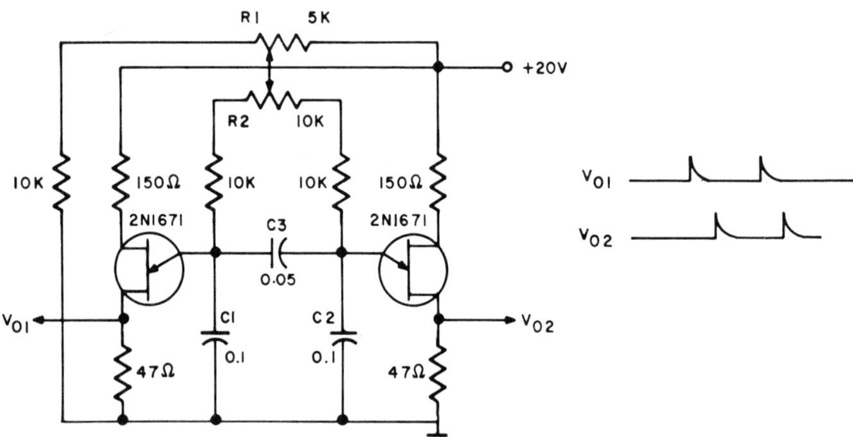

VARIABLE-PHASE DOUBLE-PULSE GENERATOR—Delivers high-power pulses alternately from two separate outputs, as required for such applications as firing an scr paralleled inverter having noninductive load. Circuit consists of two ujt relaxation oscillators, synchronized through C3, with R2 controlling the phase difference between outputs and R1 controlling frequency over range of 200 to 800 Hz. Output pulses are about 4 V peak and 10 μs wide.—T. P. Sylvan, The Unijunction Transistor Characteristics and Applications, General Electric, Syracuse, N.Y., No. 90.10, 1965, p 78.

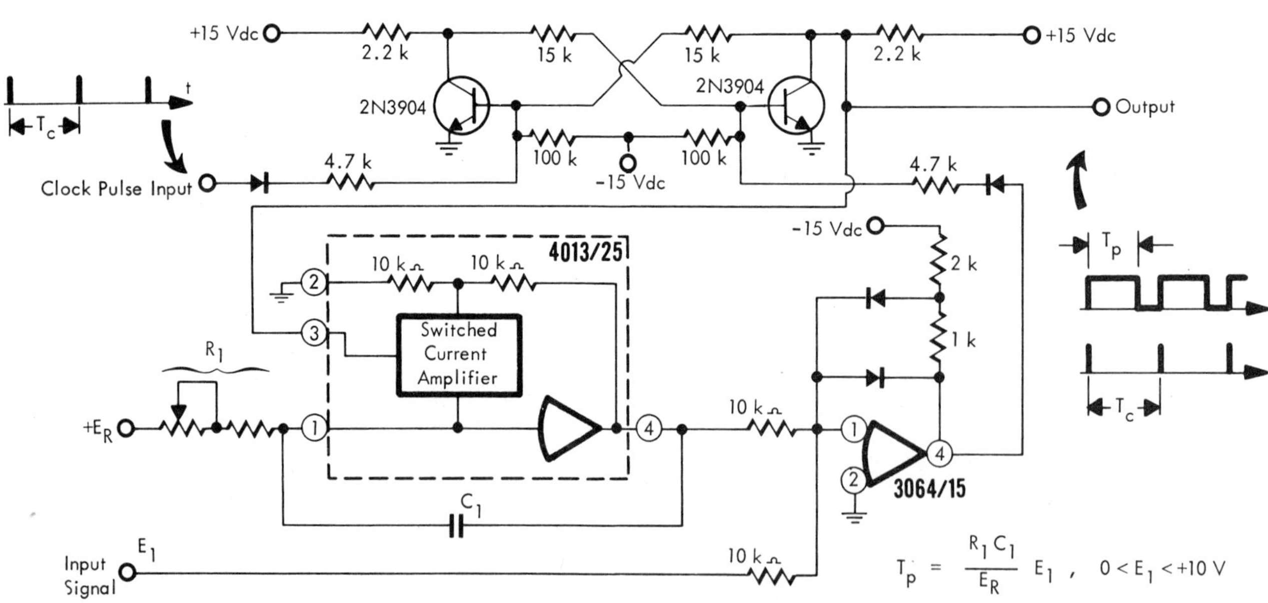

VOLTAGE TO PULSE WIDTH—With connections shown for Burr-Brown 4013/25 switched integrator, very linear and stable synchronized pulse-width modulator is obtained. Pulse train provides clocking signal to which output pulse train is synchronized. Pulse width of output is linear function of input signal voltage E1. Values of ER, C1, and R1 are chosen according to dynamic range and pulse repetition rate desired. If clock is 1 kHz and input voltage varies from 0.1 to 10 V, C1 can be 0.01 μF and R1 90K.—Sample/Hold Modules, Burr-Brown Research, Tucson, Ariz., PDS-211, 1969, p 10.

RELAXATION OSCILLATOR—Uses npn diffused silicon breakdown diode and minimum of other components to produce sharp output pulses. Breakdown voltage of T142A is in range of 28 to 36 V, so battery supply voltage must be enough for capacitor to charge through series resistor enough to exceed breakdown voltage and give desired repetition rate.—"Preferred Semiconductors and Components," Texas Instruments, Dallas, Texas, CC101, 1968, p 24108.

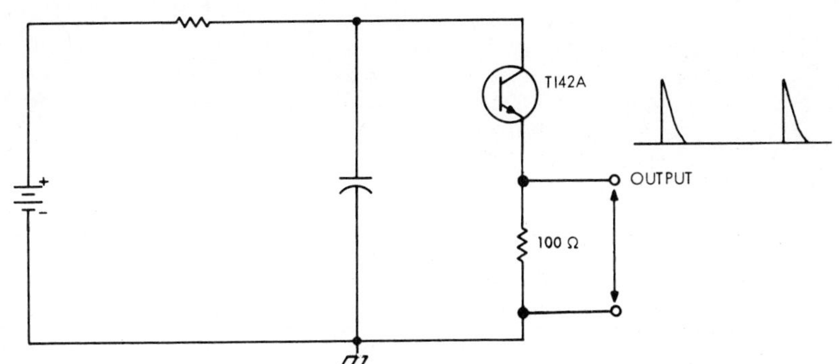

NOISE-IMMUNE NEON ONE-SHOT—Switching of neon tube converts a-c voltage or long d-c gate into short 20-V output pulse having less than 1-μs rise time. Circuit locks out other signals as long as trigger signal is present, and is immune also to signals and noise for predetermined time after removal of trigger. Product of R2 and C1 determines lockout time.—A. M. Patlach, Neon Tube Circuit Forms One-Shot Pulse Generator, *Electronic Design*, June 7, 1965, p 38–39.

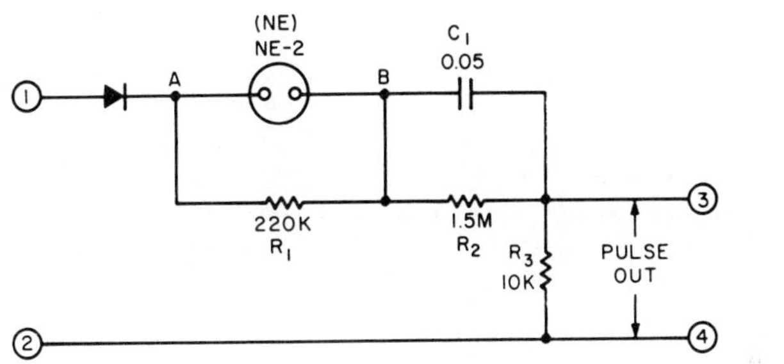

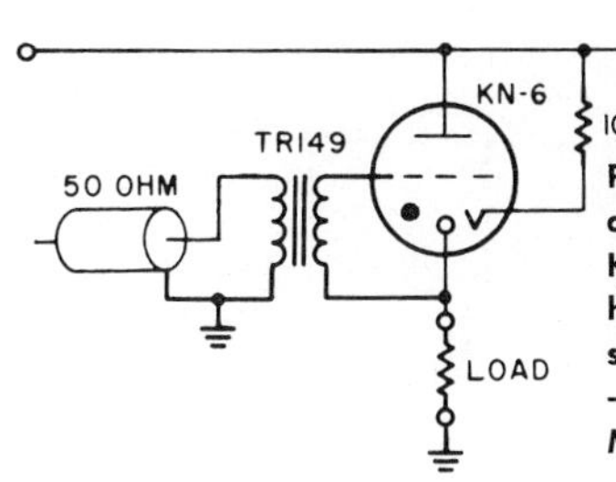

PULSE FORMER—Input pulse from 50-ohm coax is stepped up by transformer to trip Krytron gas-filled switch tube that produces high peak current for short duration, around several ns, through resistive load.—Krytrons—Cold Cathode Switch Tubes, EG&G, Boston, Mass., KR-100, 1968.

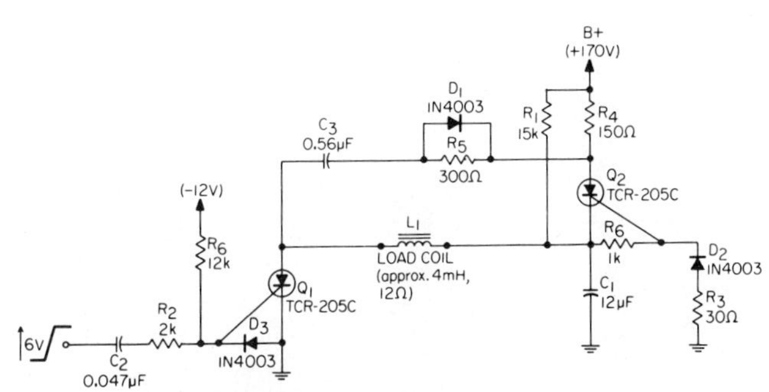

PRINT HAMMER DRIVE—Dual scr delay flop (monostable mvbr) delivers constant-energy pulses to solenoids of line printer hammers or paper tape punches, at repetition rates above 100 pps. Output is 170 V at 5 A. Circuit resets automatically.—S. W. Piccione, SCRs Simplify Monostable Coil-Driver, *EEE*, Nov. 1967, p 129–130.

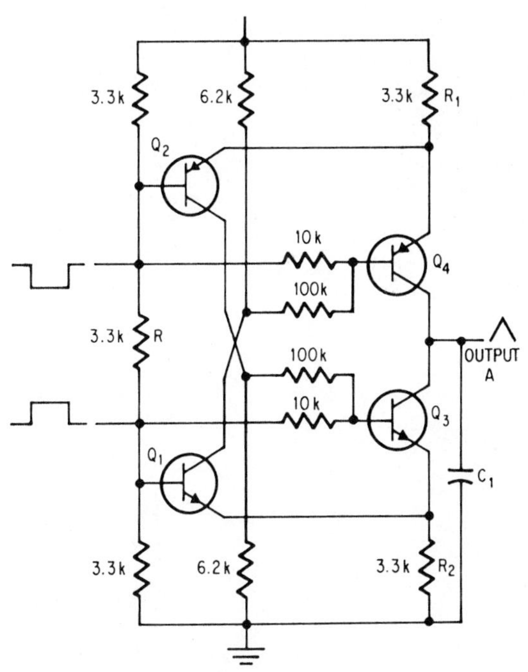

PWM—Arrangement shown requires only single capacitor on IC triangular-wave generator for pulse-width modulation in audio amplifiers. Also produces two square-wave outputs. Charging of C1 by collector current of Q4 forms leading edge of sawtooth.—O. Baade, One Capacitor Makes IC a Pulse-width Modulator, *Electronics*, Sept. 2, 1968, p 71.

NOTE: To locate additional circuits in the category of this chapter, use the index at the back of this book. Check also the author's "Sourcebook of Electronic Circuits," published by McGraw-Hill in 1968.

CHAPTER 67
Pulse Shaping Circuits

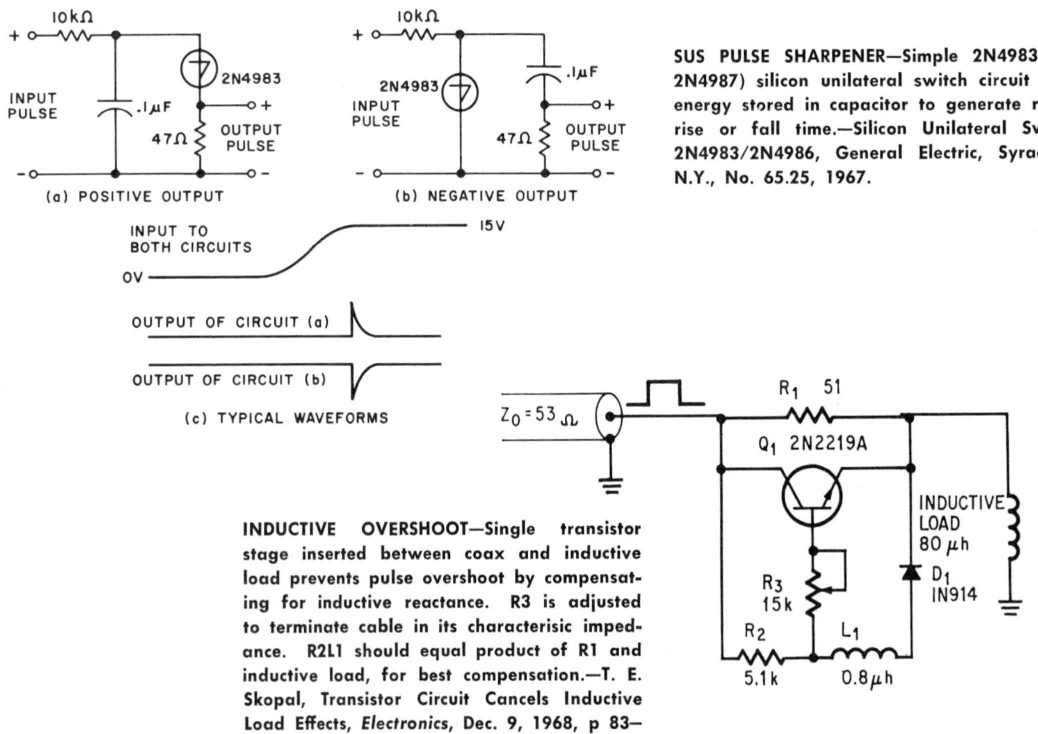

SUS PULSE SHARPENER—Simple 2N4983 (or 2N4987) silicon unilateral switch circuit uses energy stored in capacitor to generate rapid rise or fall time.—Silicon Unilateral Switch 2N4983/2N4986, General Electric, Syracuse, N.Y., No. 65.25, 1967.

INDUCTIVE OVERSHOOT—Single transistor stage inserted between coax and inductive load prevents pulse overshoot by compensating for inductive reactance. R3 is adjusted to terminate cable in its characterisic impedance. R2L1 should equal product of R1 and inductive load, for best compensation.—T. E. Skopal, Transistor Circuit Cancels Inductive Load Effects, *Electronics*, Dec. 9, 1968, p 83–84.

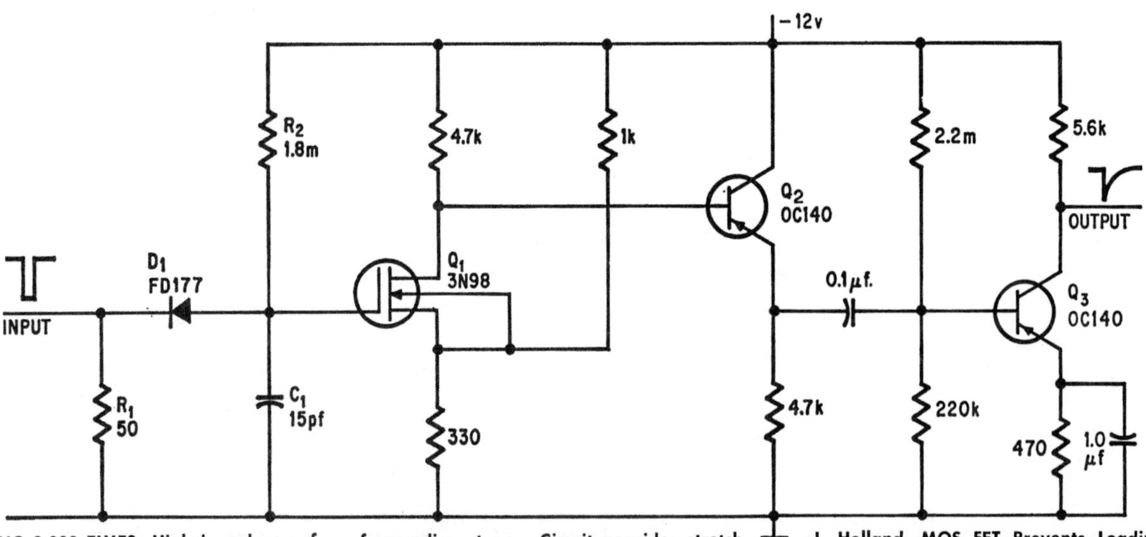

STRETCHING 2,000 TIMES—High impedance of mosfet transistor, in circuit for stretching narrow pulses by large factors, prevents loading of preceding stage. Circuit provides stretching factor of about 2,000 for 2.5-ns negative-going pulse having peak of at least 0.5 V. —J. Holland, MOS FET Prevents Loading By a Pulse Stretcher, *Electronics*, March 3, 1969, p 95.

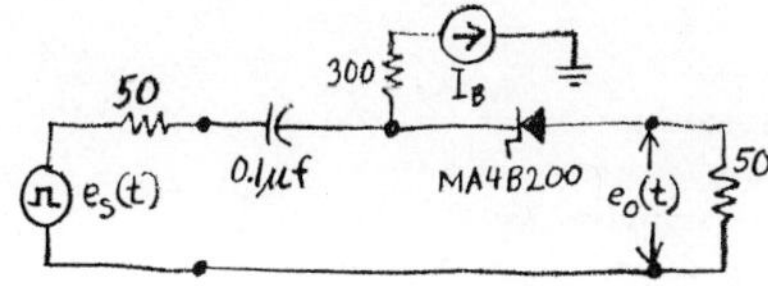

TRAILING-EDGE SHARPENER—Charge-controlled diode in series with load reduces output voltage until it switches into high-impedance state. For 5-ns fall time of input pulse, sharpening action reduces fall time of output pulse to less than 1 ns.—B. Siegal, Simpler Digital Circuits in a Snap, *Electronics*, June 9, 1969, p 105–108.

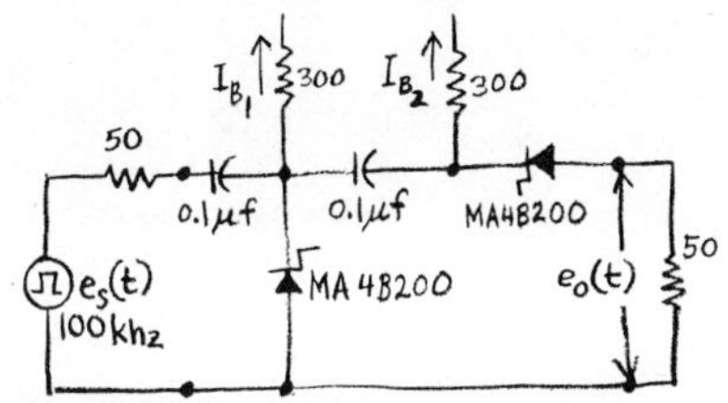

PULSE SQUARER—Combination of series and shunt charge-controlled diodes sharpens both leading and trailing edges of pulses in digital circuits. By varying bias currents, circuit will also serve for pulse position control and variable pulse width control.—B. Siegal, Simpler Digital Circuits in a Snap, *Electronics*, June 9, 1969, p 105–108.

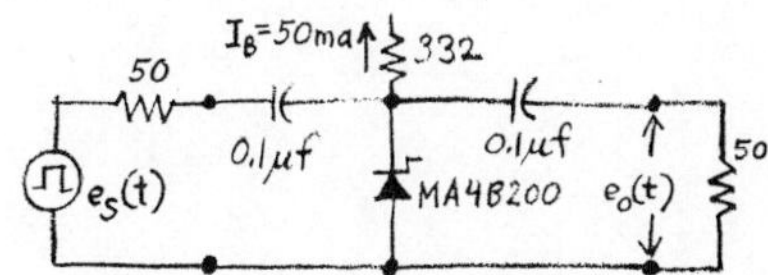

LEADING-EDGE SHARPENER—Charge-controlled diode is connected across load to present low impedance that holds output voltage low until all its stored charge is removed, then switches to high-impedance state. Output pulse is narrower than input pulse by amount of delay time. With values shown, input rise time is about 12 ns, and output rise time is narrowed to less than 1 ns.—B. Siegal, Simpler Digital Circuits in a Snap, *Electronics*, June 9, 1969, p 105–108.

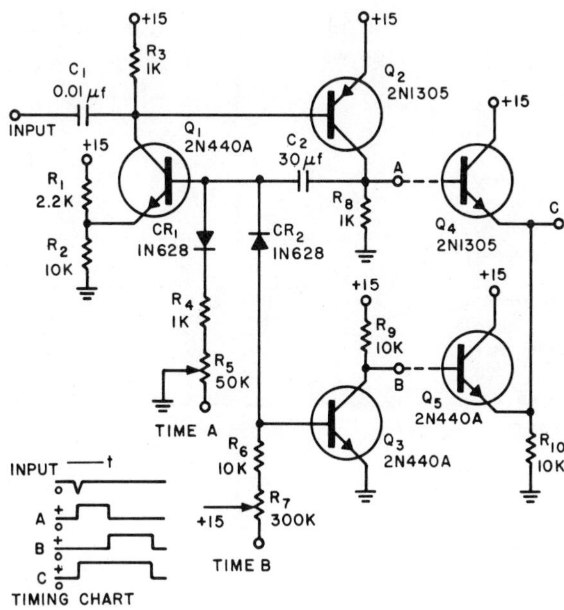

PULSE WIDENER—Modification of monostable mvbr gives equivalent of two standard mvbr circuits, for applications requiring elongated output pulse. For values shown, pulse width A can be adjusted from 0.05 to 1.8 s and B from 0.1 to 4.5 s. By adding OR gate Q4-Q5, width of output pulse at C becomes sum of times A and B. Circuit may also be used to provide timing function with zero recovery time and duty cycle approaching 100%.—R. W. Fergus, Modified Multivibrator Has Elongated Pulse Output, *Electronic Design*, March 15, 1965, p 59.

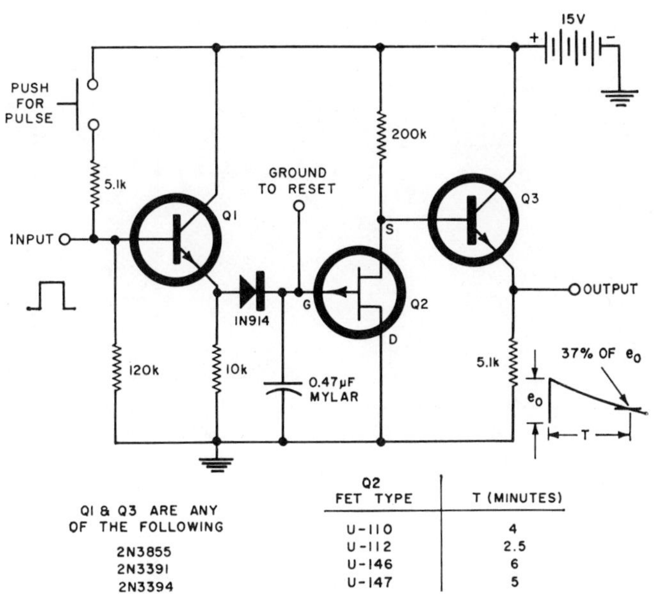

Q1 & Q3 ARE ANY OF THE FOLLOWING
2N3855
2N3391
2N3394

Q2 FET TYPE	T (MINUTES)
U-110	4
U-112	2.5
U-146	6
U-147	5

PULSE STRETCHER—Senses peak amplitude and holds this voltage level for much longer than width of pulse. External source can be used in place of pulse-initiating switch. Q1 and Q3 provide impedance transformation and isolate fet Q2 from source and load. Pulse can be stretched as long as 30 hours by using expensive fet with low gate leakage and selecting diode and capacitor with very low leakage.—J. H. Wujek, Jr., and M. E. McGee, Field-Effect Transistor Circuits, *Electronics World*, May 1967, p 32–33 and 75.

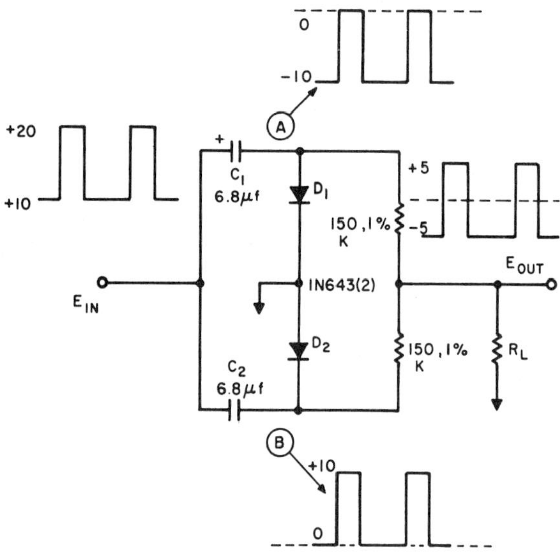

CENTERING WITH DIODES—Delivers output pulse having equal amplitudes above and below ground, when incoming pulse has variable amplitude and duty cycle. C1 and D1 provide positive clamping, so signal at A is reproduction of input shifted below d-c ground. Similarly, C2 and D2 provide negative clamp as at B. Resistor network acts as instantaneous adder to provide desired result. —T. B. Hooker, Circuit Provides Pulse Equally Centered About Ground, *Electronic Design*, Nov. 9, 1964, p 79.

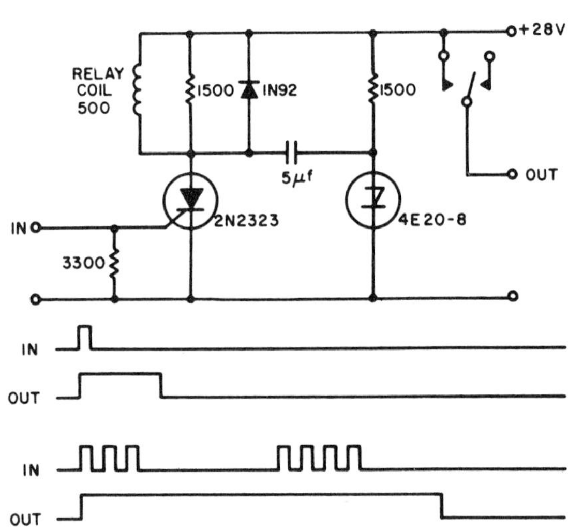

SCR PULSE STRETCHER—Will detect 3-V pulses as short as 20 μs, either singly or in trains, and stretch them as shown by waveforms. For values shown, relay is energized about 50 ms for single pulse. For repetition rates above 20 per second, relay remains energized during entire pulse train, but releases within 50 ms after last pulse in train.—A. Balint, SCR Pulse Stretcher Resets After Pulse Train, "400 Ideas for Design Selected from Electronic Design," Hayden Book Co., N.Y., 1964, p 40.

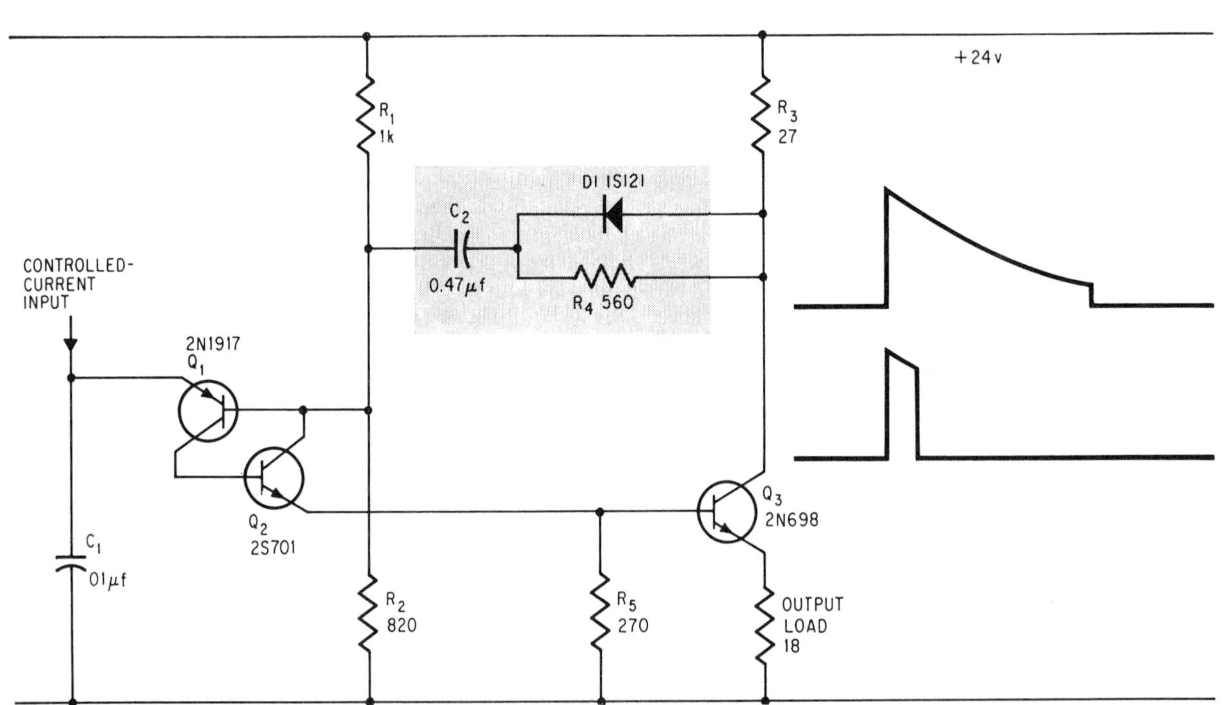

TRAILING-EDGE SHAPER—Feedback network is used between avalanche-switching input circuit and output stage of pulse generator to turn off Q1-Q2 sharply at desired interval after Q3 conducts, to shorten exponential decay time by factor of 10. The resulting sharper decay permits use of trailing edge of output pulse for triggering other circuits. With R5 as potentiometer, pulse width may be varied.—K. J. Foord, Simple Feedback Network Shapes Trailing Edges, *Electronics*, Oct. 2, 1967, p 96–97.

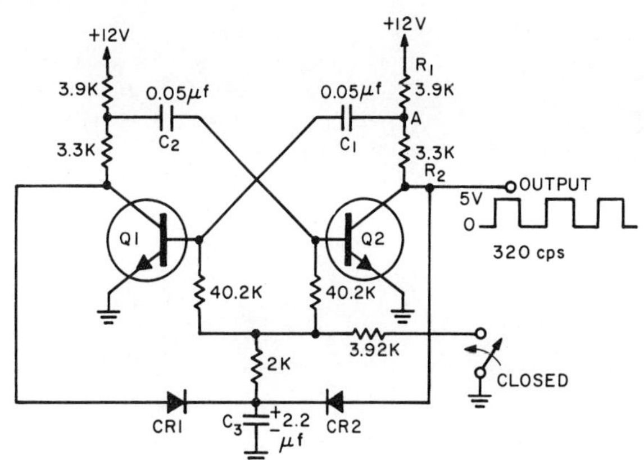

RISE-TIME BOOSTER—Rise time of conventional square-wave oscillator is greatly increased by connecting C1 and C2 to split collector loads of transistors. Circuit also provides clipping of output waveform.—P. D. Gargiulo, Fast Rise Times From Slow Circuits, *Electronic Design*, April 27, 1964, p 93–94.

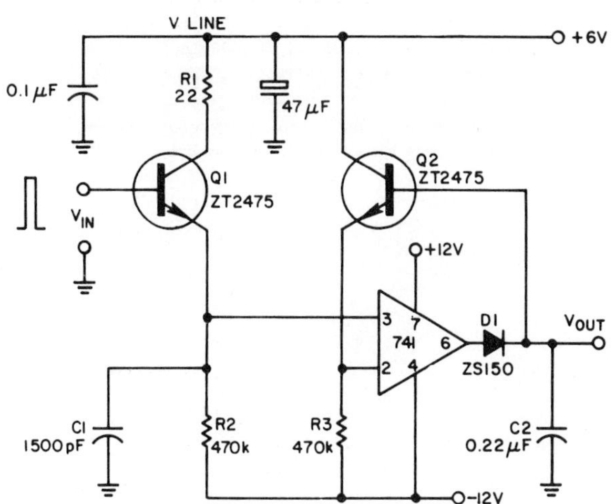

PEAK-HOLDING SPIKE STRETCHER—Will hold level of single pulse as narrow as 20 ns, with peak ranging from several hundred mV to 5 V, while increasing width of pulse up to 100,000,000 times.—I. D. Crawford, Pulse Stretcher Remembers Level of Narrow Spike, *Electronic Design*, June 7, 1970, p 96.

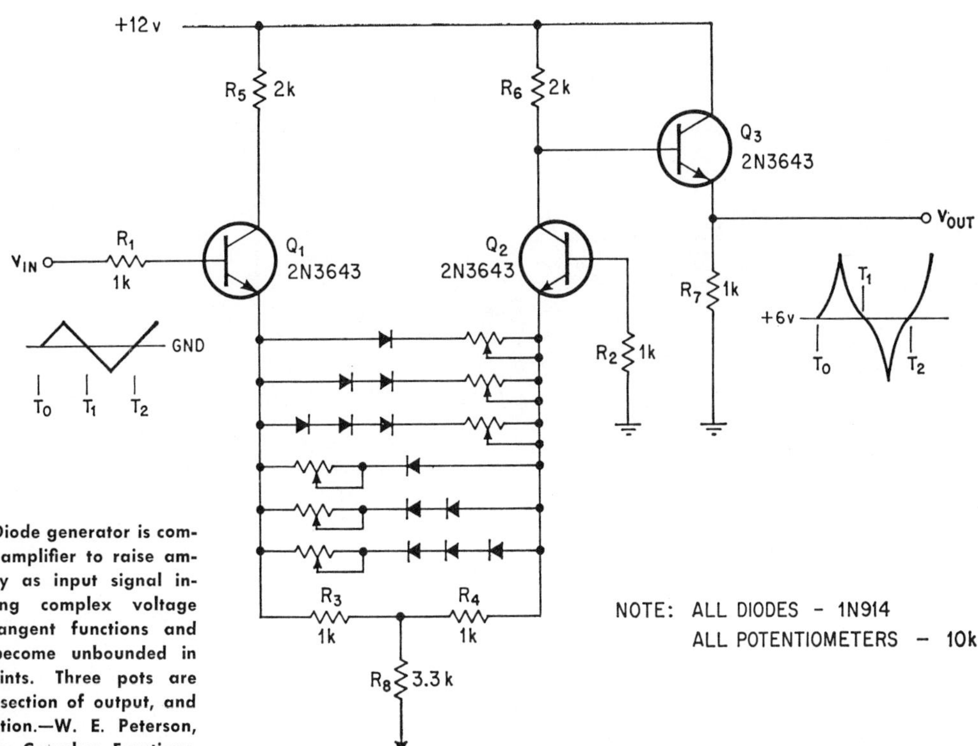

TANGENT FUNCTION—Diode generator is combined with differential amplifier to raise amplifier gain sequentially as input signal increases, for generating complex voltage waveforms such as tangent functions and other functions that become unbounded in magnitude at key points. Three pots are used to shape positive section of output, and three for negative section.—W. E. Peterson, Diode Generator Yields Complex Functions, *Electronics*, Oct. 13, 1969, p 95.

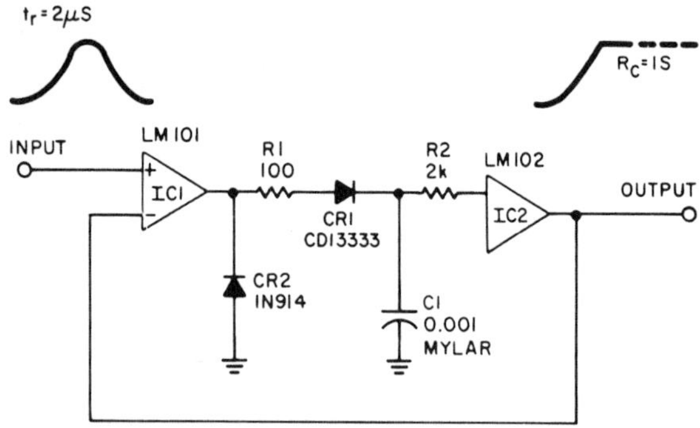

PULSE STRETCHER—Uses negative feedback for opamps to give unity gain. When positive pulse having rise time above 2 μs is fed to first opamp, positive output of opamp charges stretching capacitor C1 through R1 and CR1. When pulse dies away, CR1 becomes reverse-biased and C1 discharges with long time constant. Stretched output is thus obtained from second opamp serving as voltage follower. Typical pulse-stretching R-C time is 1 s for 3-V pulse. Dynamic range is over 200.—J. H. McQuaid, Linear Pulse Stretcher has Wide Dynamic Range, *Electronic Design*, July 5, 1969, p 80 and 82.

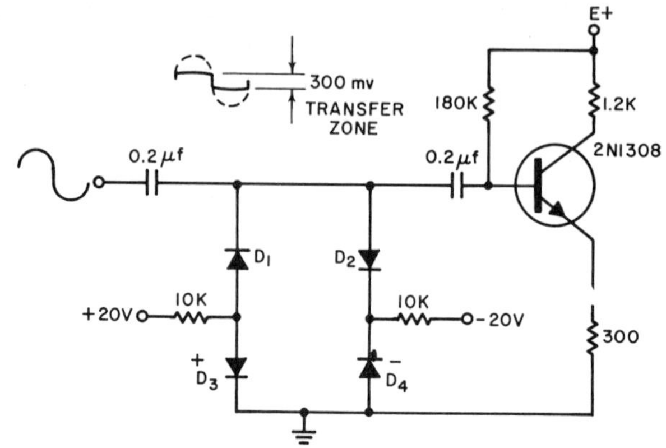

BIDIRECTIONAL CLIPPER—Symmetrically limits excursion of input signal about its average value. Transfer zone is only 300 mV. If all diodes are same type, allowed signal excursion will be nearly zero, because it is only as large as variations in diodes. For larger signals, use all silicon diodes, such as 1N459 for D1 and D2, and 1N456 for D3 and D4.—V. J. Kaneski, Simple Bidirectional Clipper Has Small Transfer Zone, *Electronic Design*, June 22, 1964, p 68–69.

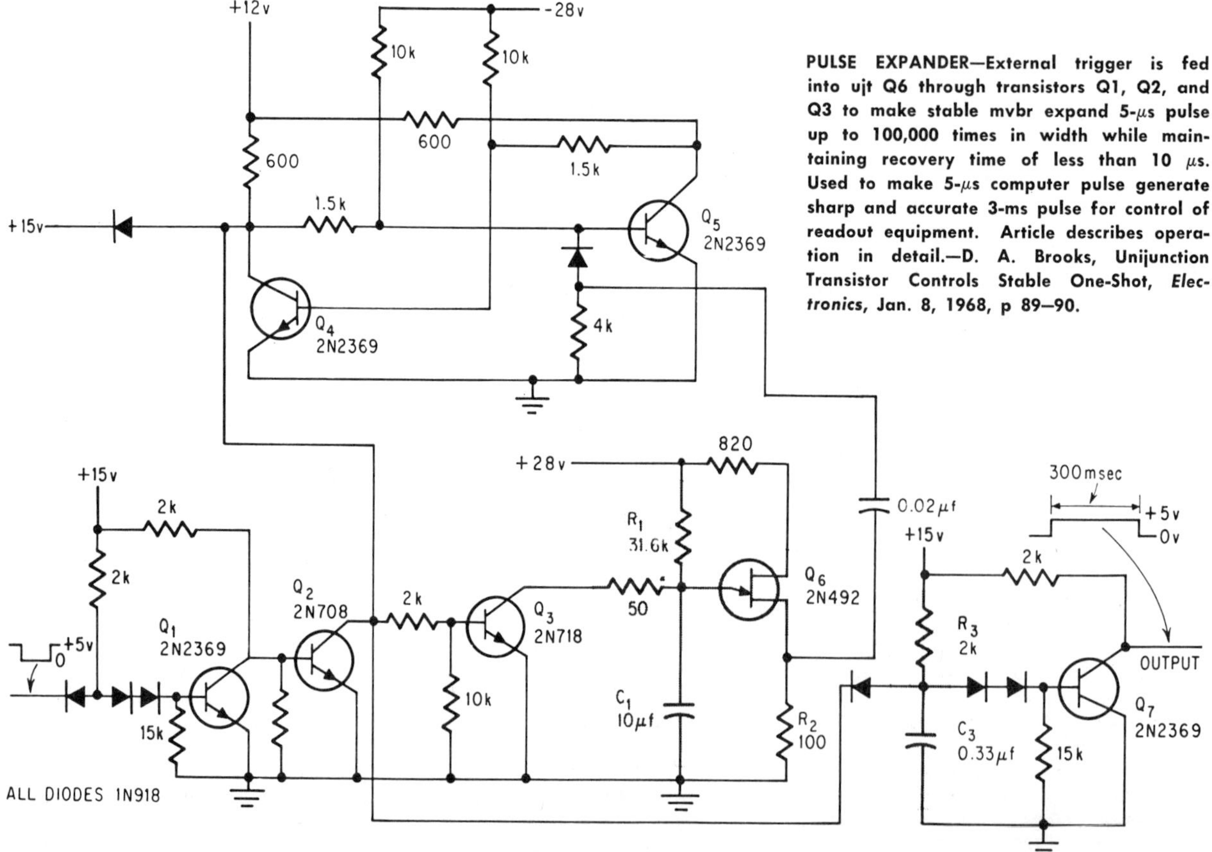

PULSE EXPANDER—External trigger is fed into ujt Q6 through transistors Q1, Q2, and Q3 to make stable mvbr expand 5-μs pulse up to 100,000 times in width while maintaining recovery time of less than 10 μs. Used to make 5-μs computer pulse generate sharp and accurate 3-ms pulse for control of readout equipment. Article describes operation in detail.—D. A. Brooks, Unijunction Transistor Controls Stable One-Shot, *Electronics*, Jan. 8, 1968, p 89–90.

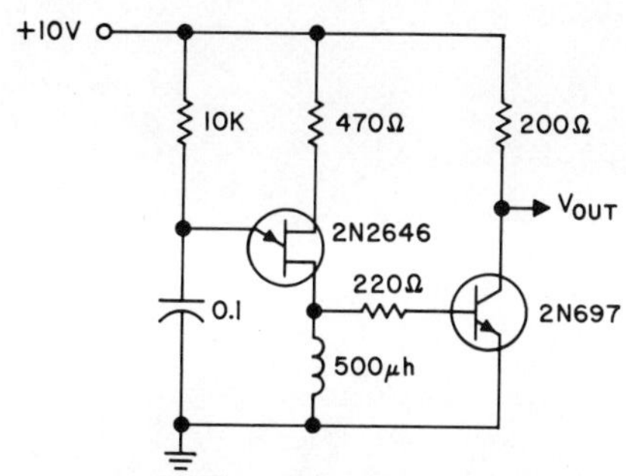

UJT SHAPER—Use of inductance in ujt relaxation oscillator cuts rise and fall times to 0.3 μs for 12-μs pulse width. With 47-ohm resistor in place of inductance, rise time is same, but fall time goes up to 3 μs.—"Unijunction Circuit Hints," General Electric, Syracuse, N.Y., Fig. 1.

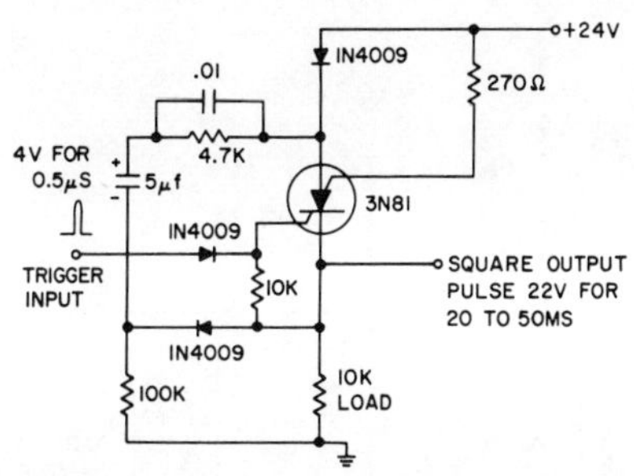

STRETCHER—Provides both amplification and widening of 4-V 0.5-μs trigger input pulse, with 5-μF capacitor and 4.7K resistor determining stretch interval and same capacitor with 100K resistor determining circuit recovery time. Gives square-wave output of 20 to 50 ms at 22 V.—Planar Silicon Controlled Switch 3N81/3N82, General Electric, Syracuse, N.Y., No. 65.16, 1964.

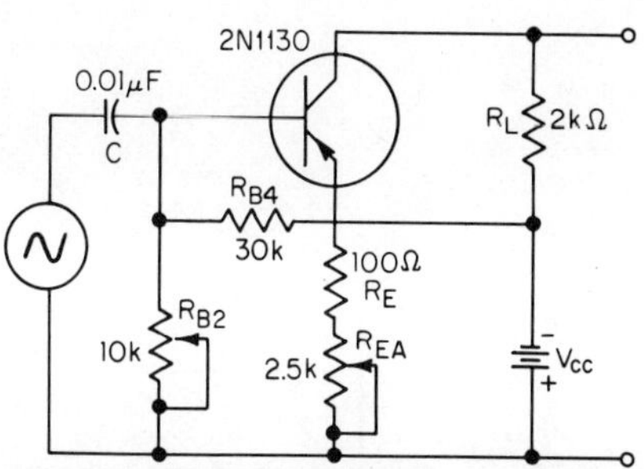

SINE-DRIVEN TRAPEZOIDAL—Gives trapezoidal output waveform for sine-wave input voltage large enough to drive transistor alternately into saturation and into cutoff. Typical value for battery is 10 V. Output is produced by clipping of input.—A. C. Gillie, "Pulse and Logic Circuits," McGraw-Hill, N.Y., 1968, p 278.

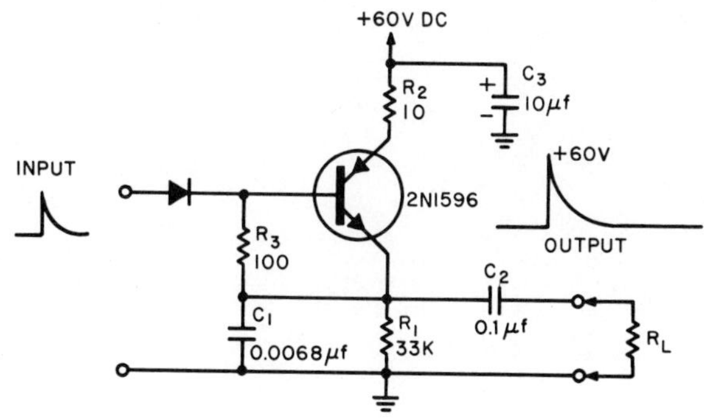

SCR AMPLIFIES ONLY LEADING EDGE—2N1596 scr acts as low-impedance pulse amplifier, eliminating need for shut-off for circuit requiring only leading edge of pulse. Pulse period of 8 ms is determined by C1, R1, C2, and load. Article gives operating details.—A. J. Fishman, Shut-Off is Not Required in SCR Pulse Amplifier, *Electronic Design*, March 16, 1964, p 107–108.

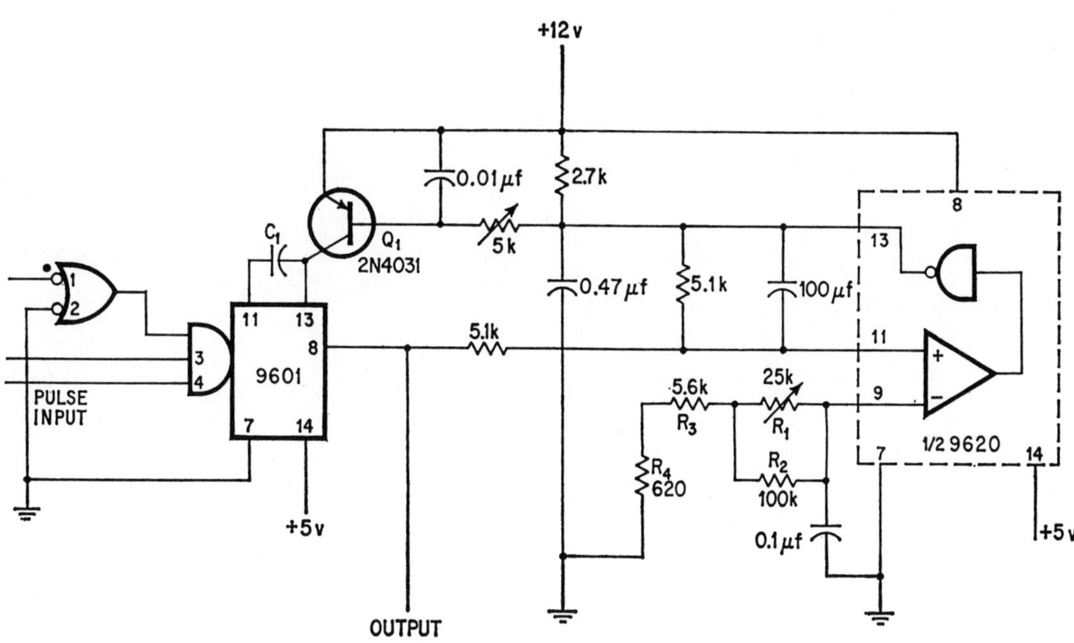

CONSTANT DUTY CYCLE—Single-shot mvbr coupled to integrator delivers output pulse train with constant duty cycle while matching output frequency to changing input frequency. Circuit permits varying frequency of pulse generator over wide range without simultaneously adjusting pulse width control. Duty cycle can be set anywhere from 7% to 93% over frequency range of 100 to 1,000 kHz if C1 is 500 pF.—W. Ross, Pulse Train Frequency Varied as Duty Cycle Stays Constant, *Electronics*, July 21, 1969, p 84.

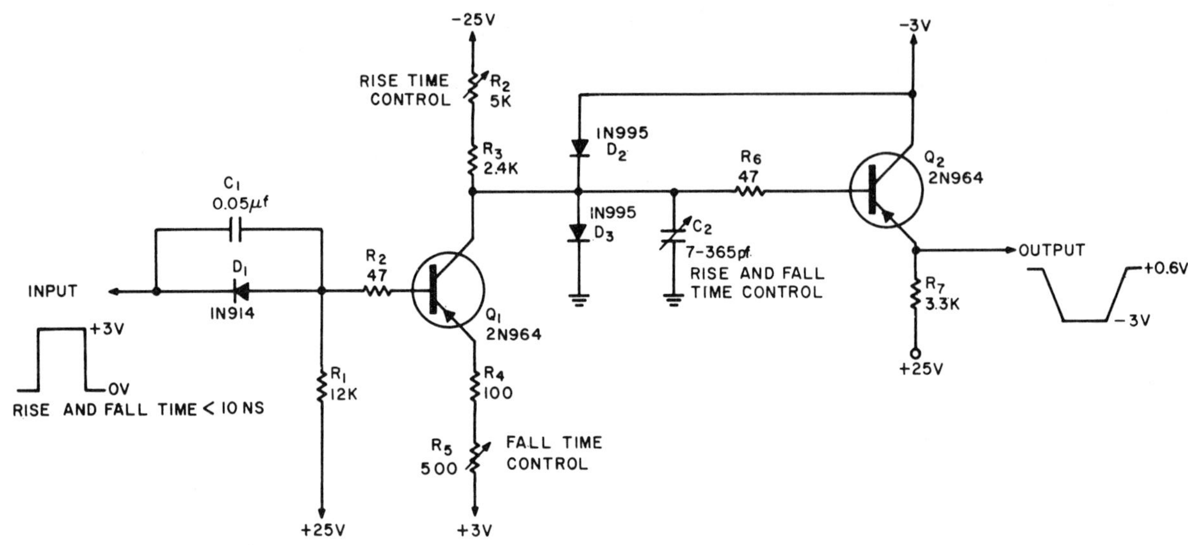

SQUARE TO TRAPEZOIDAL—Converts positive square waves into negative pulses having adjustable linear rise and fall times. With controls R2 and R5 set at minimum, C2 will vary output rise and fall times over range of 10 to 200 ns. Rise time only is affected by R2, while R5 changes both rise and fall times. With larger values for these adjustable components, rise and fall times can be increased to ms range.—D. N. Lee, Trapezoidal Generator Forms Variable Linear Ramps, *Electronic Design*, Dec. 7, 1964, p 66–67.

NOTE: To locate additional circuits in the category of this chapter, use the index at the back of this book. Check also the author's "Sourcebook of Electronic Circuits," published by McGraw-Hill in 1968.

CHAPTER 68
Radiation Circuits

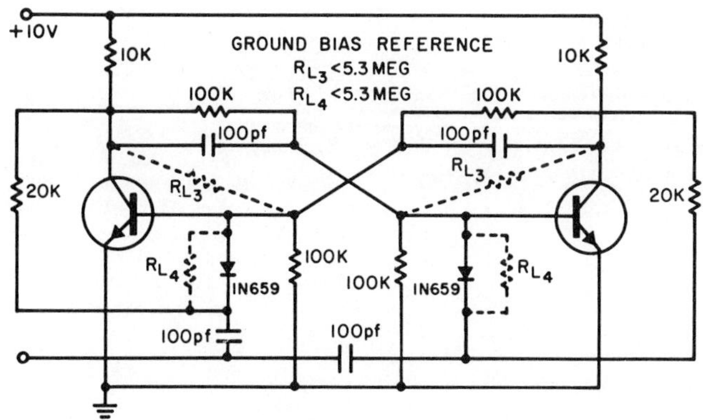

UNHARDENED—Even with special transistors, flip-flop shown is sensitive to radiation because its relatively low base-collector off-current makes it vulnerable to being turned off by transient pulse. Article discusses techniques for hardening such circuits for military equipment. Dashed lines show resistance paths that can carry radiation-induced leakage currents.—Designing Hardened Equipment: Several Methods Are Useful, *Electronic Design*, June 8, 1964, p 46 and 48–51.

HARDENED SCR SWITCHING TIME—Article gives equations into which measured parameters of components without radiation can be inserted for predicting response under radiation. Circuit shown is used to display on cro, in manner suitable for photographing, switching time of scr under test. Pulses are simultaneously applied to gate and anode. When anode pulse disappears, scr turns off until next gate and anode pulses arrive. Equation then gives performance under radiation.—J. T. Finnell, Jr. and F. W. Karpowich, Skipping the Hard Part of Radiation Hardening, *Electronics*, March 4, 1968, p 122–127.

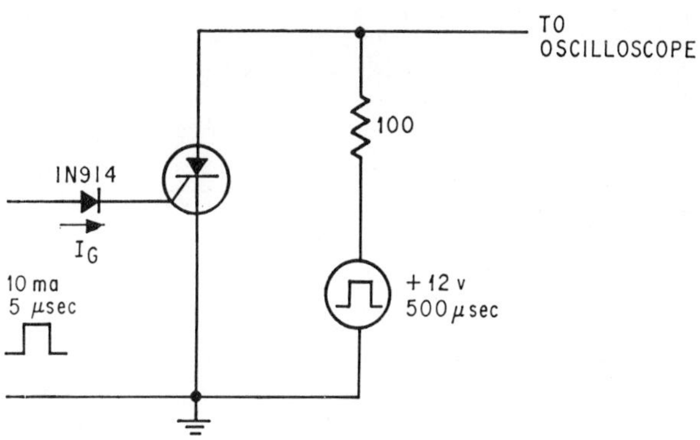

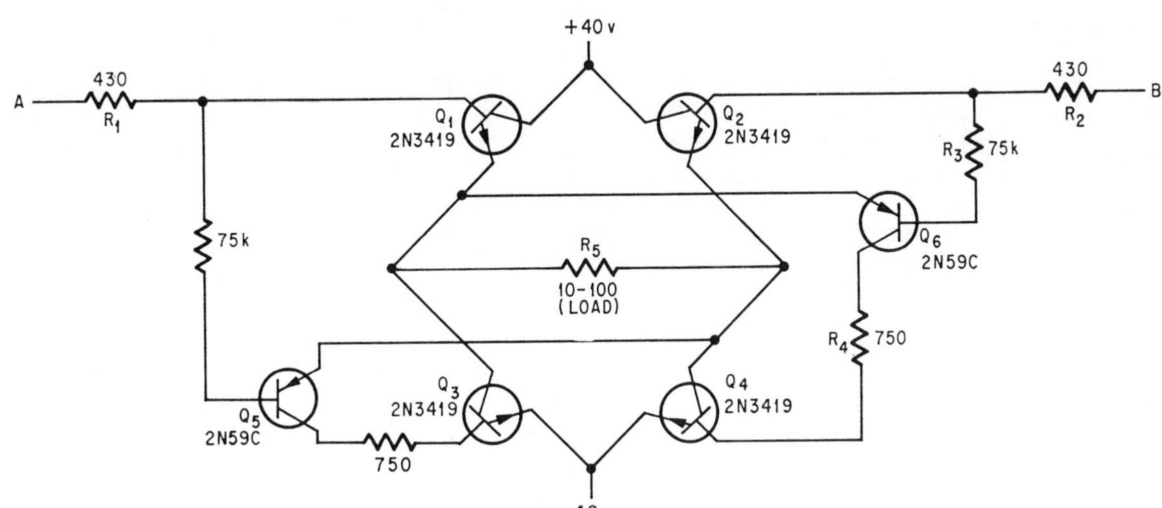

REACTOR ROD DRIVE—Bridge amplifier controls 100-W d-c motor for positioning control rods in nuclear reactor. Q5 and Q6 provide isolation between input and output and ensure class B operation. Load current is proportional to difference between voltages A and B.—M. A. Hassan and T. A. Greinevitch, Bridge Amplifier Provides Isolation, *Electronics*, Sept. 30, 1968, p 83.

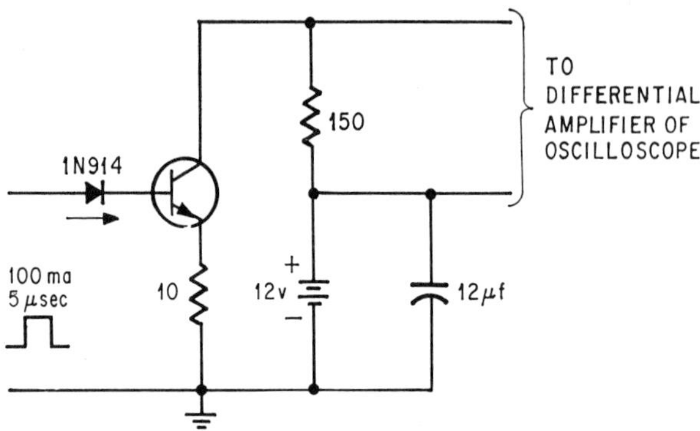

HARDENED TRANSISTOR STORAGE TIME—Article gives equations into which measured parameters of components without radiation can be inserted for predicting response under radiation. Circuit shown is used with cro to measure time required for transistor under test to recover after being driven into saturation by leading edge of pulse. Values are for 2N2222 transistor, which gave saturation or storage time of 3 μs. Equation gives storage time under gamma dose rate of 0.1 terarad/s as 4 μs, as compared to 3.8 μs measured under actual radiation.—J. T. Finnell, Jr. and F. W. Karpowich, Skipping the Hard Part of Radiation Hardening, *Electronics*, March 4, 1968, p 122–127.

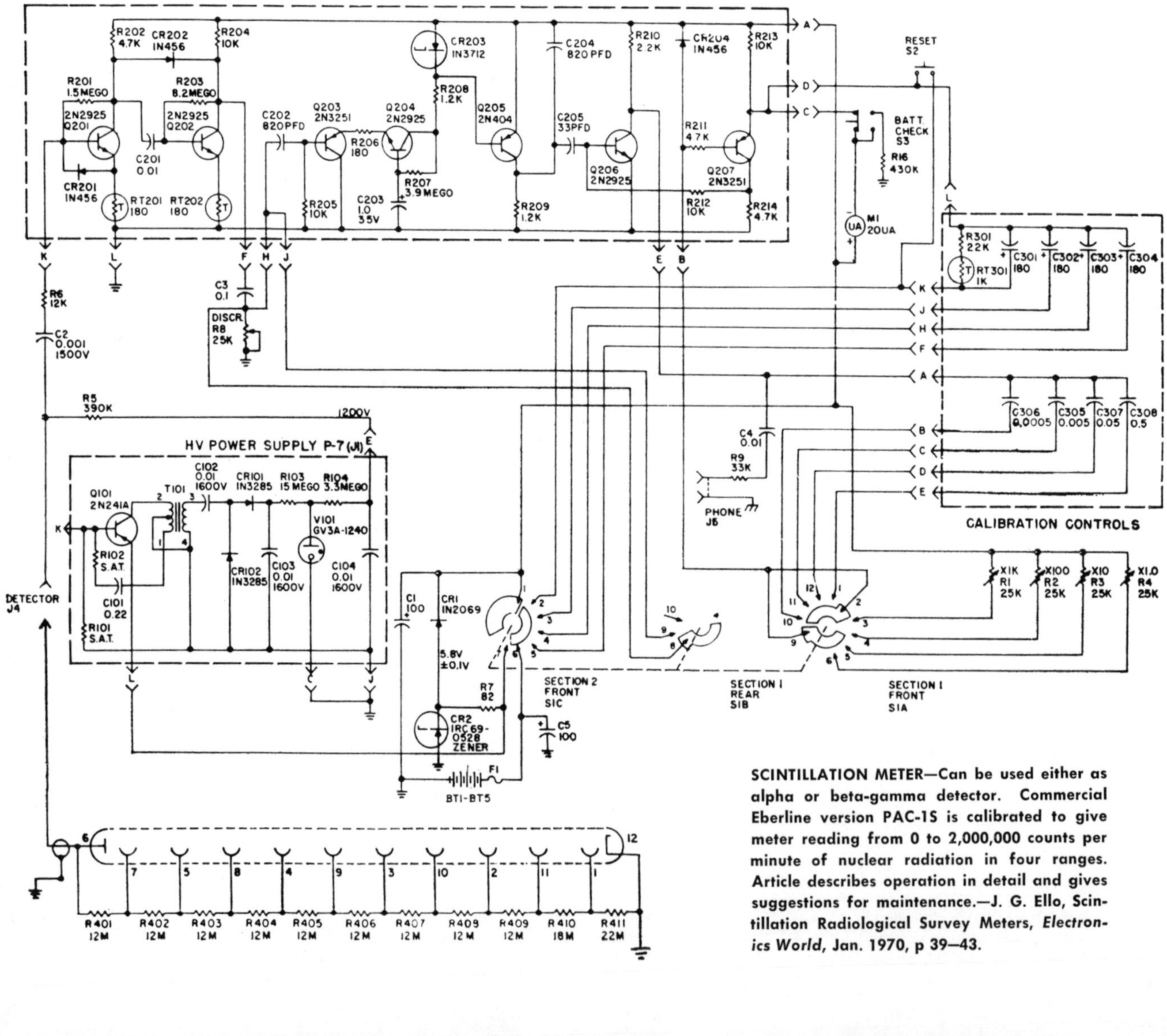

SCINTILLATION METER—Can be used either as alpha or beta-gamma detector. Commercial Eberline version PAC-1S is calibrated to give meter reading from 0 to 2,000,000 counts per minute of nuclear radiation in four ranges. Article describes operation in detail and gives suggestions for maintenance.—J. G. Ello, Scintillation Radiological Survey Meters, *Electronics World*, Jan. 1970, p 39–43.

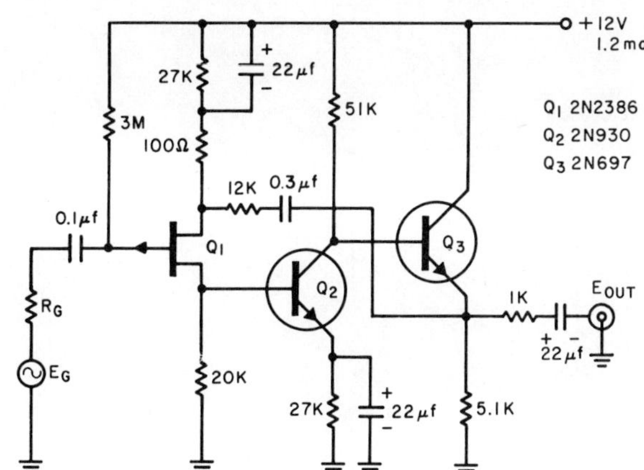

LOW NOISE FOR RADIATION DETECTOR—Silicon fet input stage has high input impedance and low noise level, to provide maximum signal transfer from high-impedance photovoltaic radiation detector. Amplifier stages Q2 and Q3 have direct coupling, with over-all a-c feedback loop to give desired frequency response. Over-all voltage gain is 115 at 1 kHz.—C. R. Seashore, Field-Effect Input Stage Gives Low-Noise Preamp, *Electronic Design*, May 25, 1964, p 70–71.

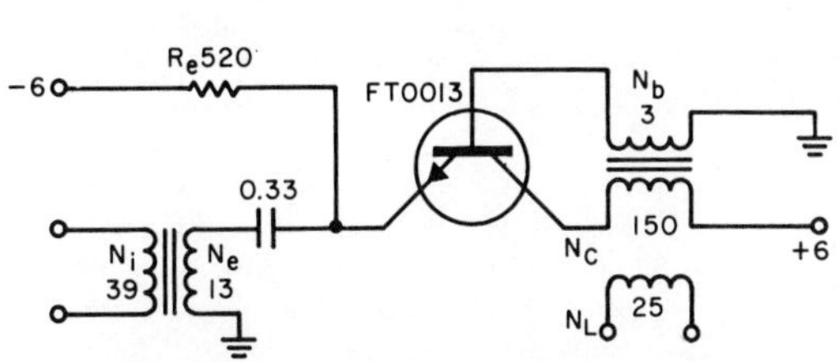

HARDENED—Common-base preamp, using special high-frequency small-signal transistor having short carrier transit time, loses only 3 dB of gain in high-radiation environment. Has stabilized voltage gain, with input impedance increased by negative feedback to base. Requires exact input and output power matching. Article gives circuit hardening techniques.—Designing Hardened Equipment: Several Methods Are Useful, *Electronic Design*, June 8, 1964, p 46 and 48–51.

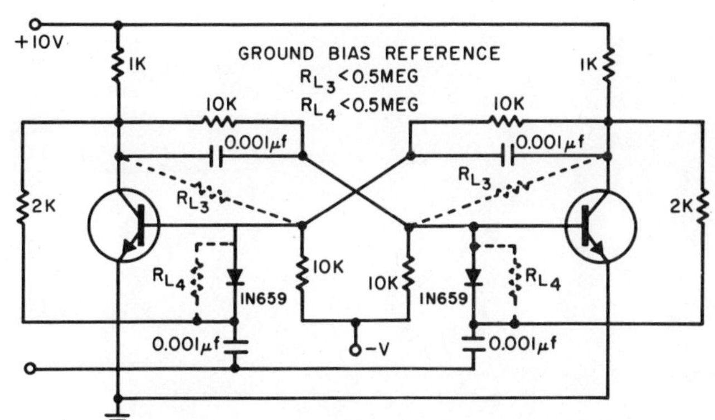

HARDENED FLIP-FLOP—Circuit is designed for reliable operation in high neutron fluxes, as required in military equipment. Base bias circuitry is designed to prevent turn-off by transient pulse. Dashed lines show resistance paths that can carry radiation-induced leakage currents. Special transistors are used. Article discusses circuit hardening techniques. —Designing Hardened Equipment: Several Methods Are Useful, *Electronic Design*, June 8, 1964, p 46 and 48–51.

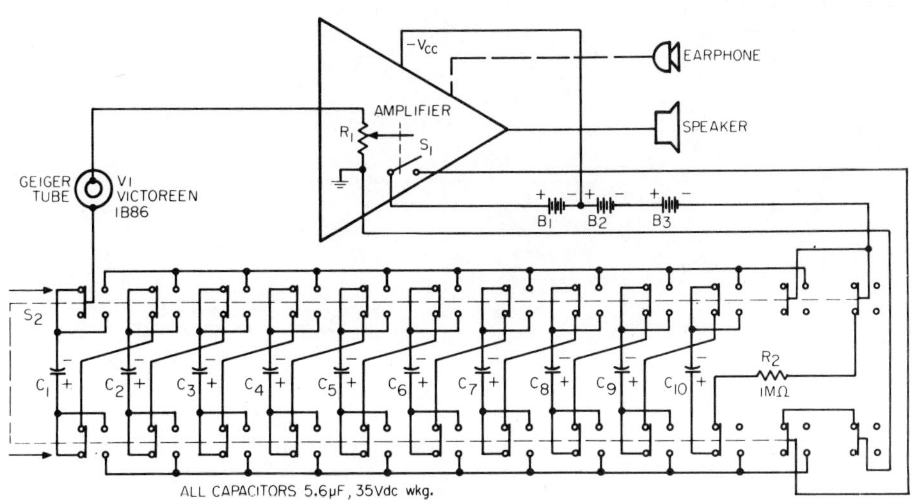

SWITCHED-CAPACITOR GEIGER—Printed-circuit switch charges capacitors in parallel to 27 V, then connects all capacitors in series with battery to give 300 V d-c required for Geiger tube. Counter will operate over 30 min on single charge of capacitors. Uses three small 9-V batteries in series.—D. J. Pistulka, Passive D-C Converter for Geiger Counter, *EEE*, June 1967, p 137.

BISTABLE NUCLEAR-REACTOR TRIP-ALARM DRIVER—Uses Fairchild IC opamp, with radiation-monitoring transducer fed through R1 to noninverting input. Since 0–10 V range of sensor is outside input limits of IC, level-set pot is returned to −12 V to shift input signal level to zero. Once adjusted, increase of a few mV above this threshold makes IC switch on and operate relay driver and alarm. Triggering repeatability is order of magnitude better than can be obtained with more expensive discrete-component circuits.—K. A. Zimmerman, The Integrated Operational Amplifier: A Versatile and Economical Circuit, "Microelectronic Design," Hayden Book Co., N.Y., 1966, p 189–194.

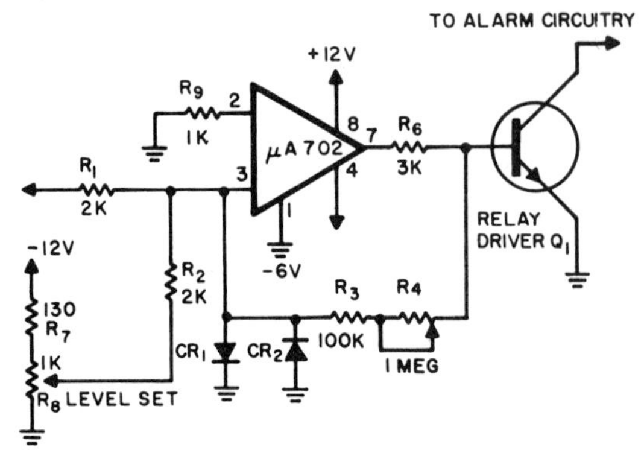

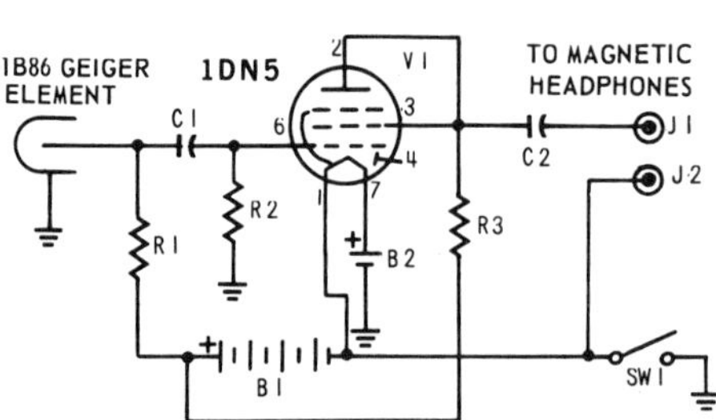

GEIGER COUNTER—Operates from 1.25-V cell B2 and 300-V battery B1, using Victoreen 1B86 Geiger element. Values are: C1-C2 0.025 μF; R1-R2 4.8 meg; R3 1.2 meg. Some clicking is always heard, due to normal background radiation on earth. Increase in clicking indicates strong source of radiation, such as lost shipment of uranium or radium. —R. M. Brown, "104 Simple One-Tube Projects," Tab Books, Blue Ridge Summit, Pa., 1969, p 122.

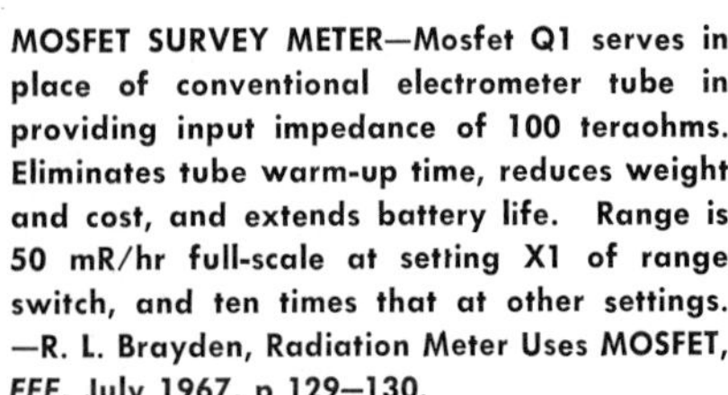

MOSFET SURVEY METER—Mosfet Q1 serves in place of conventional electrometer tube in providing input impedance of 100 teraohms. Eliminates tube warm-up time, reduces weight and cost, and extends battery life. Range is 50 mR/hr full-scale at setting X1 of range switch, and ten times that at other settings. —R. L. Brayden, Radiation Meter Uses MOSFET, *EEE*, July 1967, p 129–130.

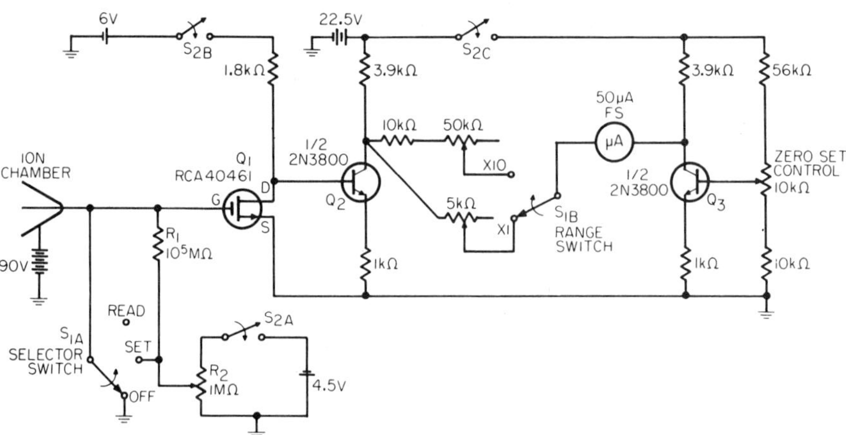

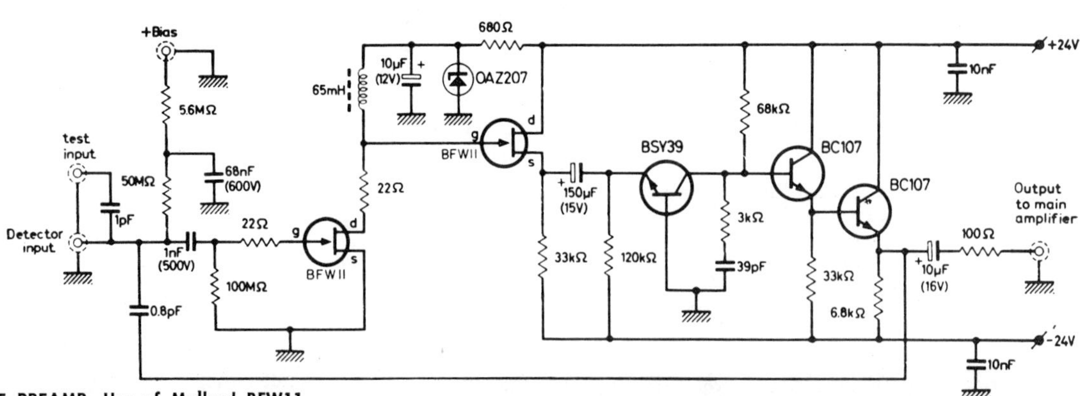

LOW-NOISE PREAMP—Use of Mullard BFW11 fet's significantly reduces noise as compared to that with conventional bipolar transistors when used with high-impedance radiation sensor.—Reduce Pre-Amplifier Noise in Solid State Radiation Detector, *Sasco Electronic News*, England, Sept. 1969, p 2.

CHAPTER 69
Receiver Circuits

IN-FLIGHT AIRCRAFT RECEIVER—Nonradiating pocket-size receiver using diode detector and two audio stages permits listening to 110–135 MHz pilot-ground transmission while flying, or control-tower transmissions while visiting airport. Range is about 500 ft from transmitter. Signals are picked up with three-turn loop antenna wound around base of plastic pillbox containing entire receiver. —"Hobby Manual," General Electric, Owensboro, Ky., 1965, p 74.

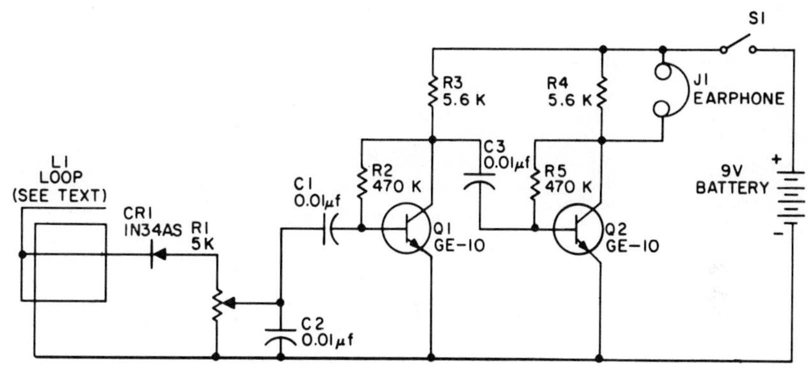

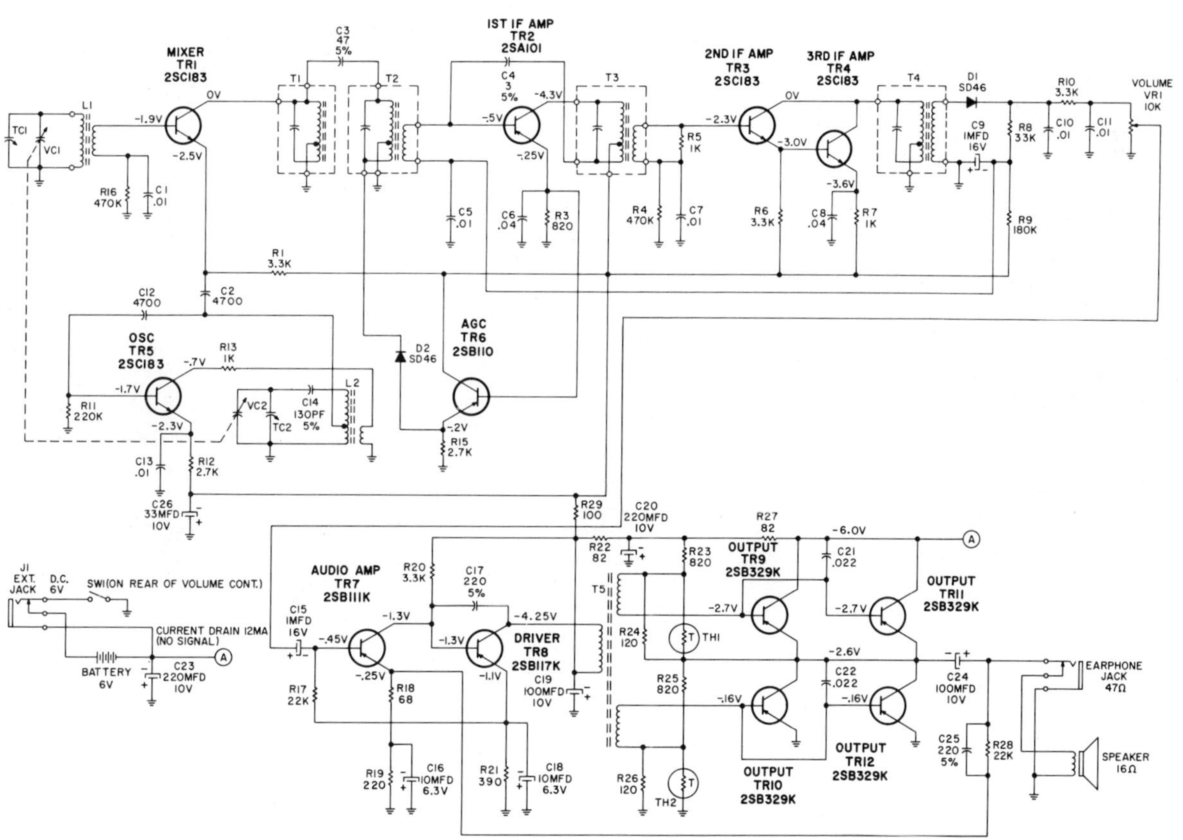

12-TRANSISTOR A-M PORTABLE—Operates from four 1.5-V Eveready 1015 AA cells or equivalent or from separate 6-V d-c adapter for a-c line. All capacitors with values less than 1 are in μF, and greater than 1 in pF. No-signal battery drain is 12 mA. Covers 535–1605 kHz.—1R1005 AM Portable Radio, Magnavox Service Manual 1439, 1969.

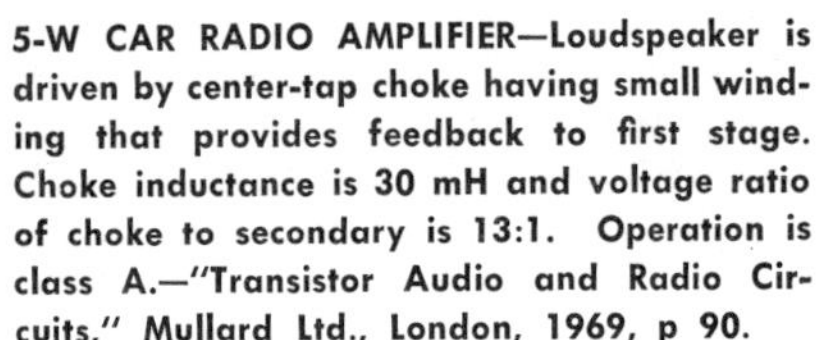

5-W CAR RADIO AMPLIFIER—Loudspeaker is driven by center-tap choke having small winding that provides feedback to first stage. Choke inductance is 30 mH and voltage ratio of choke to secondary is 13:1. Operation is class A.—"Transistor Audio and Radio Circuits," Mullard Ltd., London, 1969, p 90.

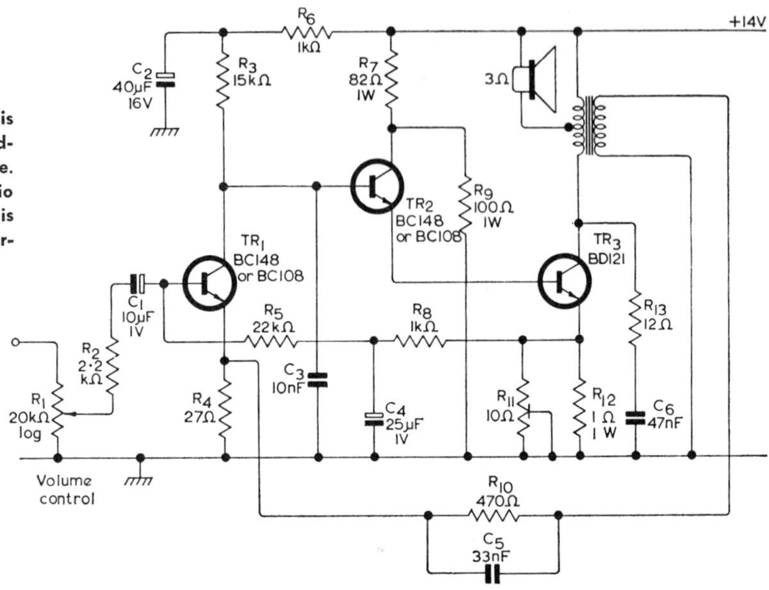

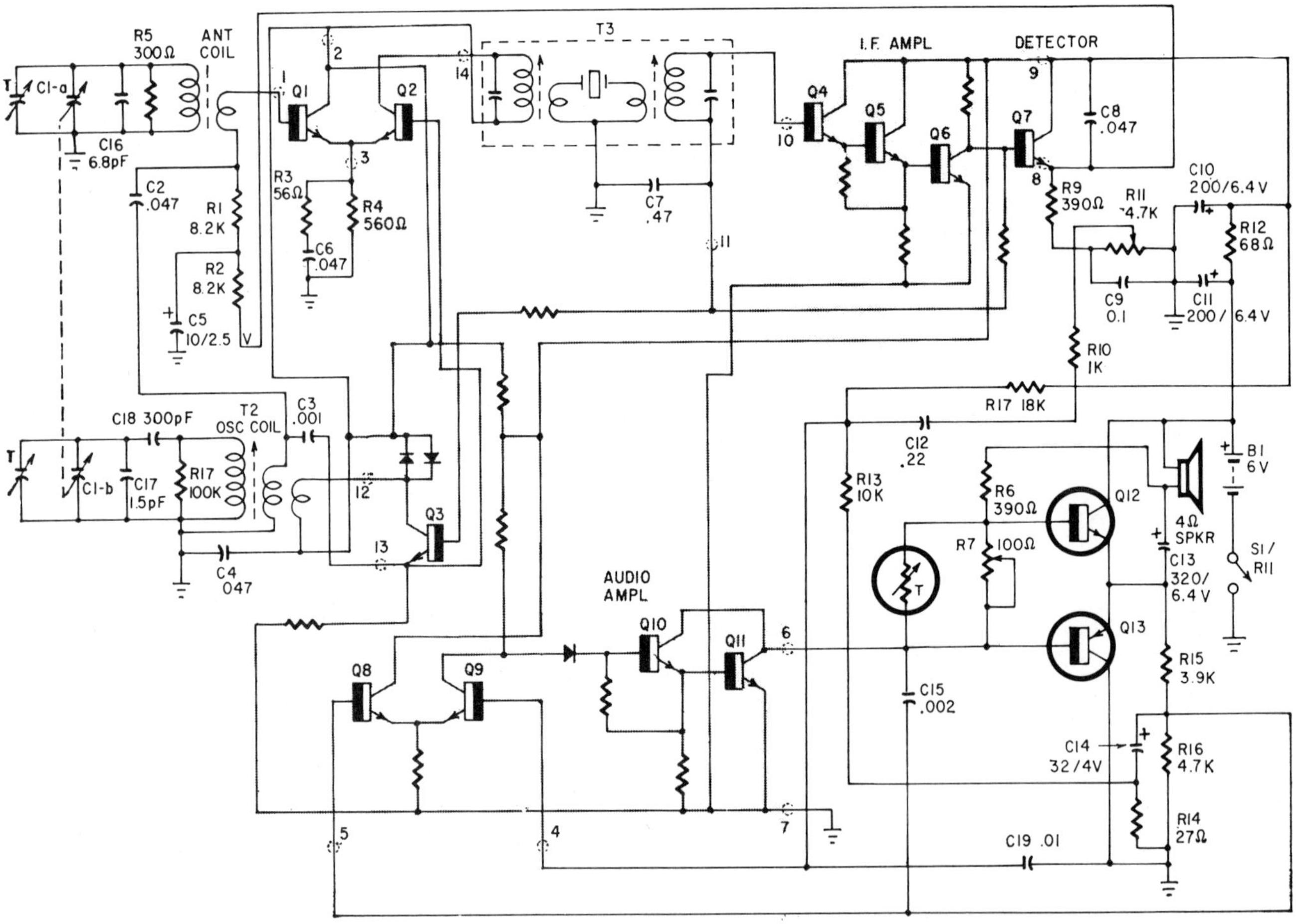

PORTABLE A-M RADIO—Single Amperex TAD-100 IC (shaded area) includes all active stages for driving earphone, and requires only two additional transistors for speaker (Q12 is 2N4105 and Q13 is 2N4106). Output power is then 1.5 W into 4-ohm speaker. T3 is Amperex 822-410-42010 ceramic i-f filter. C1 is 280-pF two-section tuning capacitor. Article gives construction details.—L. Auer and H. Thanos, Experiment With One-IC Radio, *Radio-Electronics*, Nov. 1969, p 49–51.

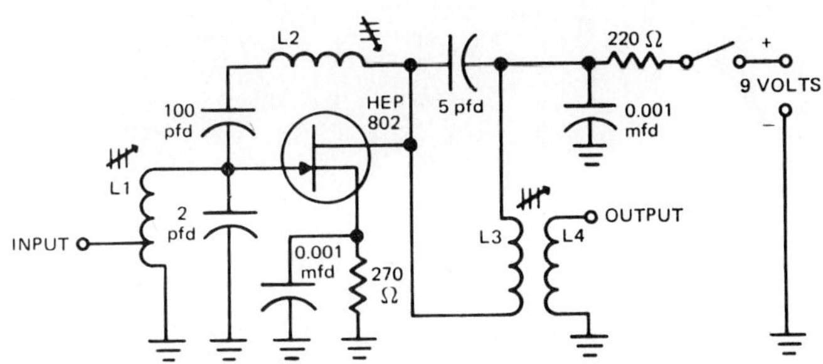

150-MHz FET—Battery-operated circuit gives 14-dB gain with low noise for 2-meter receiver. Coils L1, L2, L3, and L4 are respectively 5¼ turns tapped at 1¼ turns No. 26, 9½ turns No. 34, 5 turns No. 26, and 1¼ turns No. 26 at low end of L3, all wound on brass-slug ceramic forms.—"Tips on Using FET's," HMA-33, Motorola, Phoenix, Ariz., 1969.

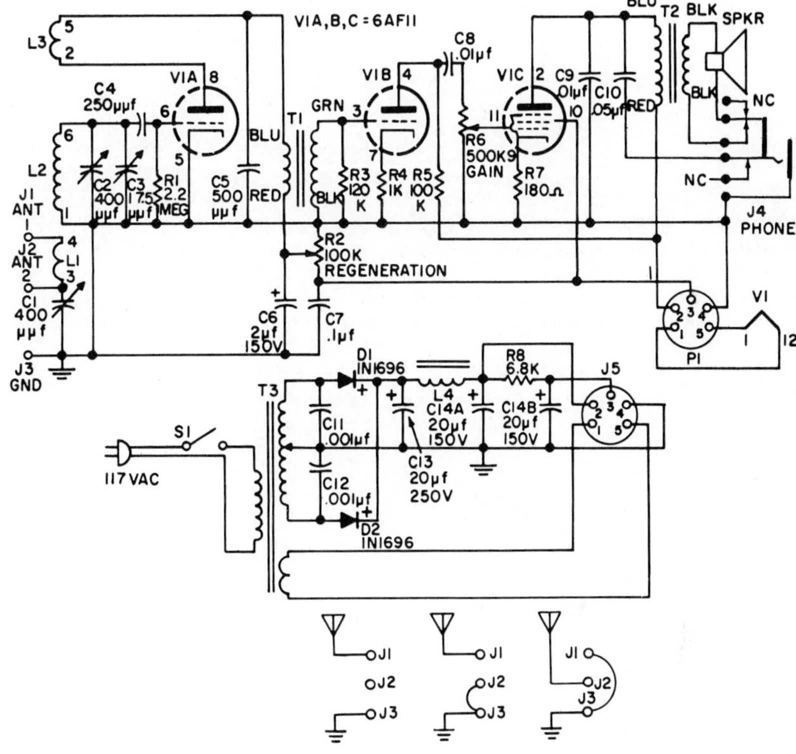

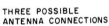

1-COMPACTRON S-W RECEIVER—Covers 250 kHz to 16 MHz with plug-in coils. Uses triode regenerative detector, triode audio voltage amplifier, and pentode power amplifier. Choice of antenna connections is provided to increase selectivity and tune out dead spots. Can serve as backup in case larger receiver breaks down. Article gives construction details and coil-winding data.—"Hobby Manual," General Electric, Owensboro, Ky., 1965, p 108.

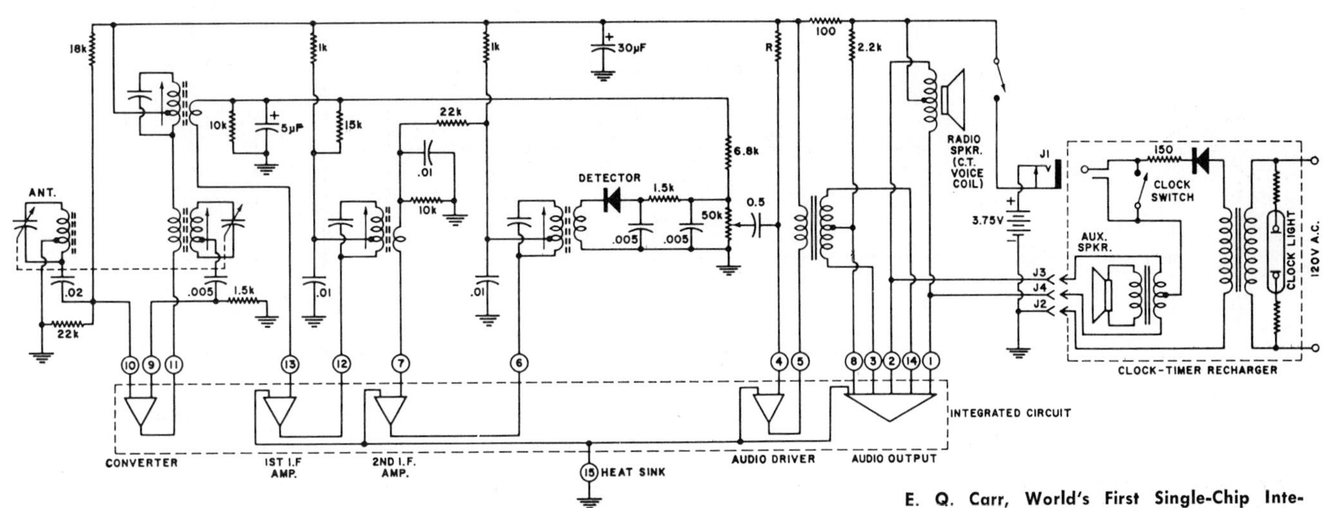

IC RADIO—G-E Model P1740 radio uses single 15-lead integrated circuit for all active components. External components include battery charger in clock-timer.—J. R. Cacciola and E. Q. Carr, World's First Single-Chip Integrated-Circuit Radio, *Electronics World*, Nov. 1966, p 44–46.

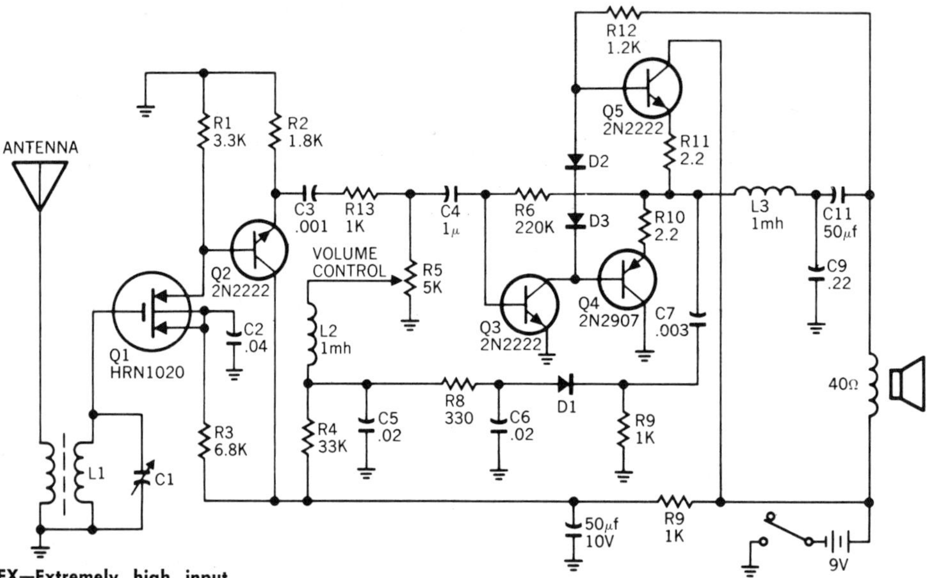

MOSFET A-M REFLEX—Extremely high input impedance of mosfet makes input tank circuit determine selectivity. Q2 buffers signal into low-impedance input of reflex amplifier Q3-Q4-Q5 that amplifies both r-f and audio signals. R-f output signal is filtered and fed to peak detector formed by R9, D1, C6, R8, C5, and L2. Resulting audio signal is fed through volume control R5 back into amplifier and filtered into speaker.—C. R. Perkins, "Application of MOSFET Devices to Electronic Circuits," Hughes, Newport Beach, Cal., 1968, p 39.

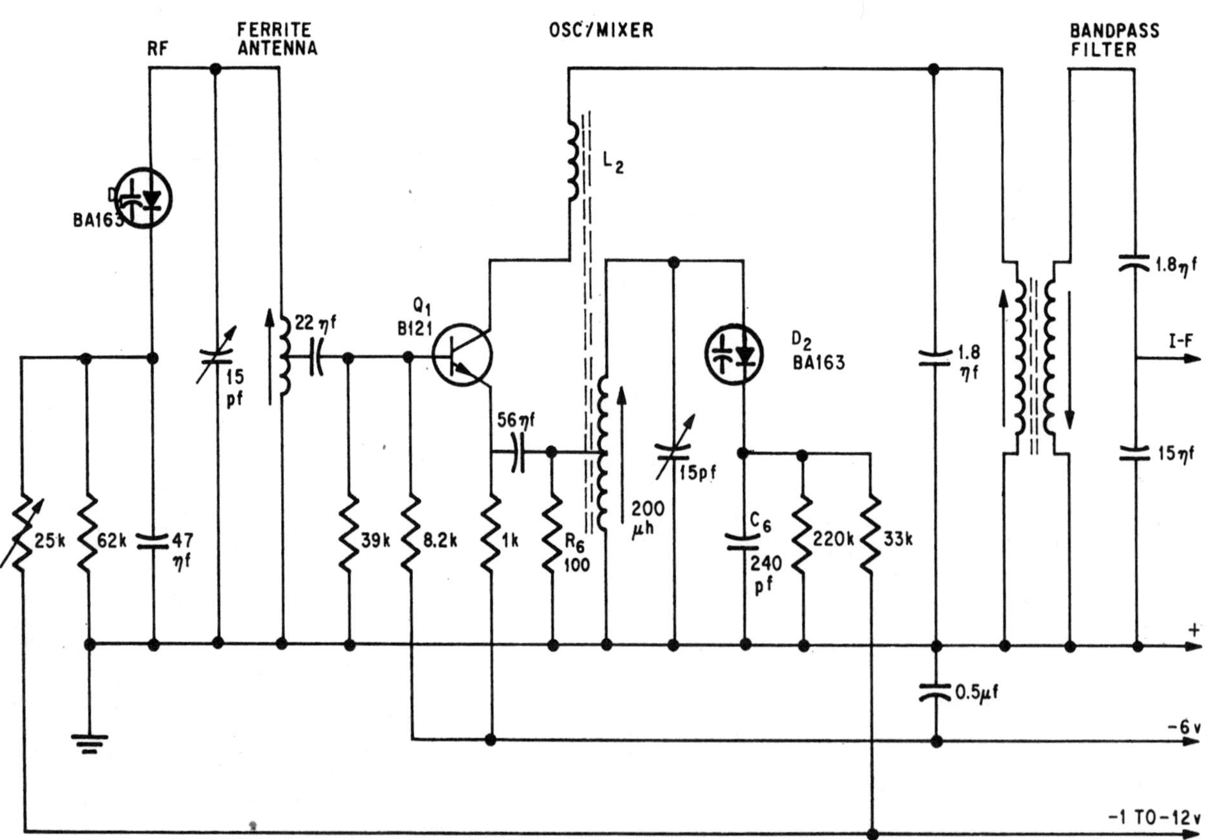

A-M VARACTOR-DIODE TUNER—Developed in Europe for covering 510–1,610 kHz broadcast band. Provides tuning accuracy and stability needed for pushbutton tuning. Self-oscillating mixer transistor Q1 operates in common-base mode. Maximum voltage required for tuning across band is 12 V. Varactor diodes should be matched.—H. Keller, Overcoming Design Problems in Varactor-Diode Tuners, *Electronics*, Jan. 6, 1969, p 88–92.

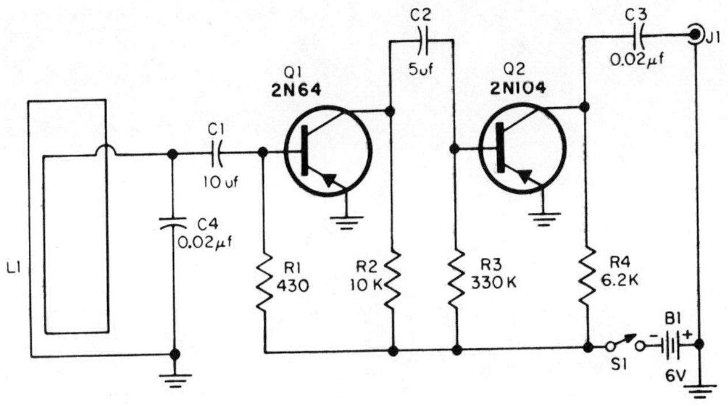

VLF WHISTLER RECEIVER—Covers vlf portion of r-f spectrum, from 4 to 16 kHz, for listening to whistlers (descending-frequency whistles caused by lightning), chirping and clicking sounds at sunrise known as dawn chorus, and sounds associated with launching of spacecraft and firing of nuclear explosions. Navy code broadcasts on 14.8 kHz may also be heard. Loop antenna is 200 turns of No. 25 enameled wire wound on frame consisting of two 4-ft pieces of wood formed into X by notching. Rotate loop to point where power-line hum is minimum. J1 should go to high-impedance input of hi-fi amplifier.—"A Modern Transistor Workbook," Radio Shack, Boston, Mass., 1965, p 43.

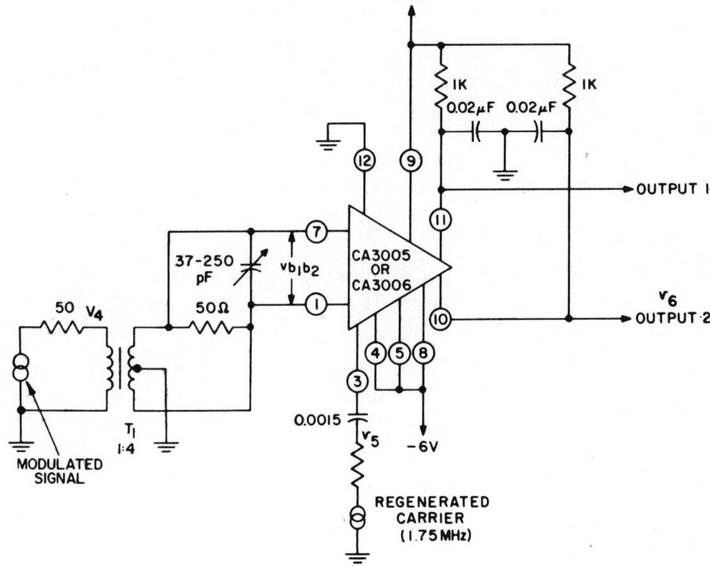

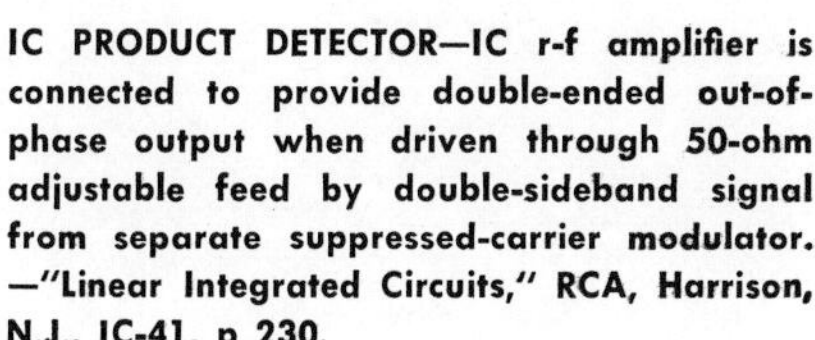

IC PRODUCT DETECTOR—IC r-f amplifier is connected to provide double-ended out-of-phase output when driven through 50-ohm adjustable feed by double-sideband signal from separate suppressed-carrier modulator. —"Linear Integrated Circuits," RCA, Harrison, N.J., IC-41, p 230.

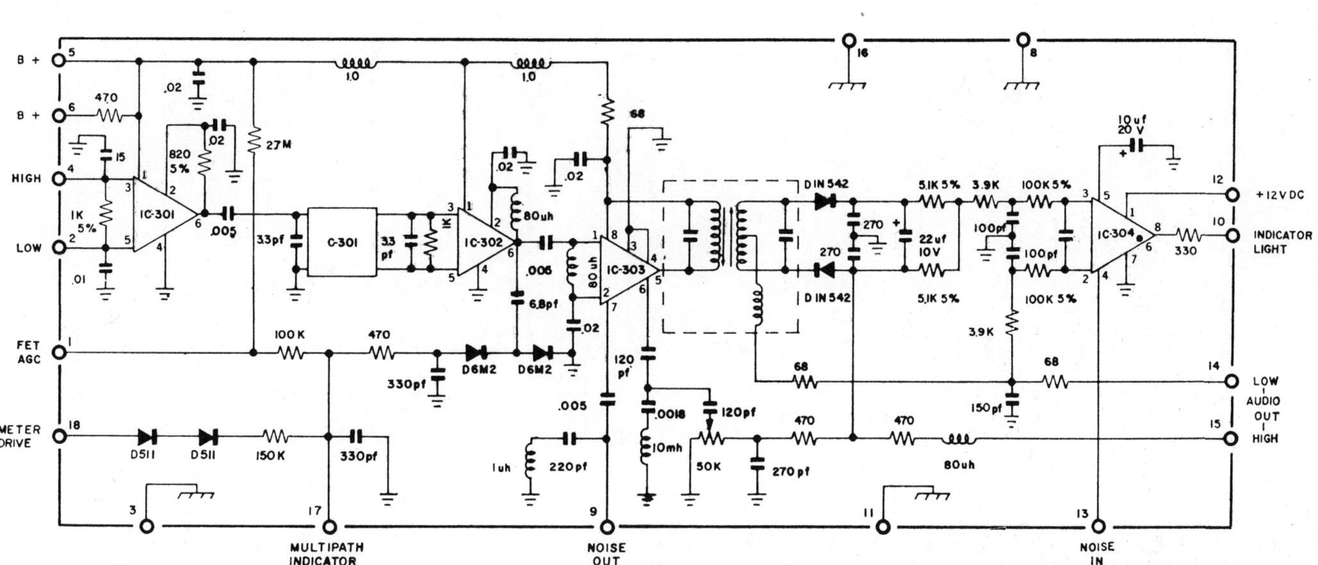

HI-FI I-F WITH IC—Uses integrated circuits designed for H. H. Scott f-m receivers by Motorola, with quartz crystal filter (C-301) between first two IC's to improve phase linearity over entire bandwidth. Output terminal 10 drives "Perfect Tune" lamp to show exact tuning of stereo signal.—L. W. Fish, Jr., and K. J. Peter, New Concepts in Hi-Fi Receiver Design, *Electronics World*, Feb. 1969, p 32–34 and 69–70.

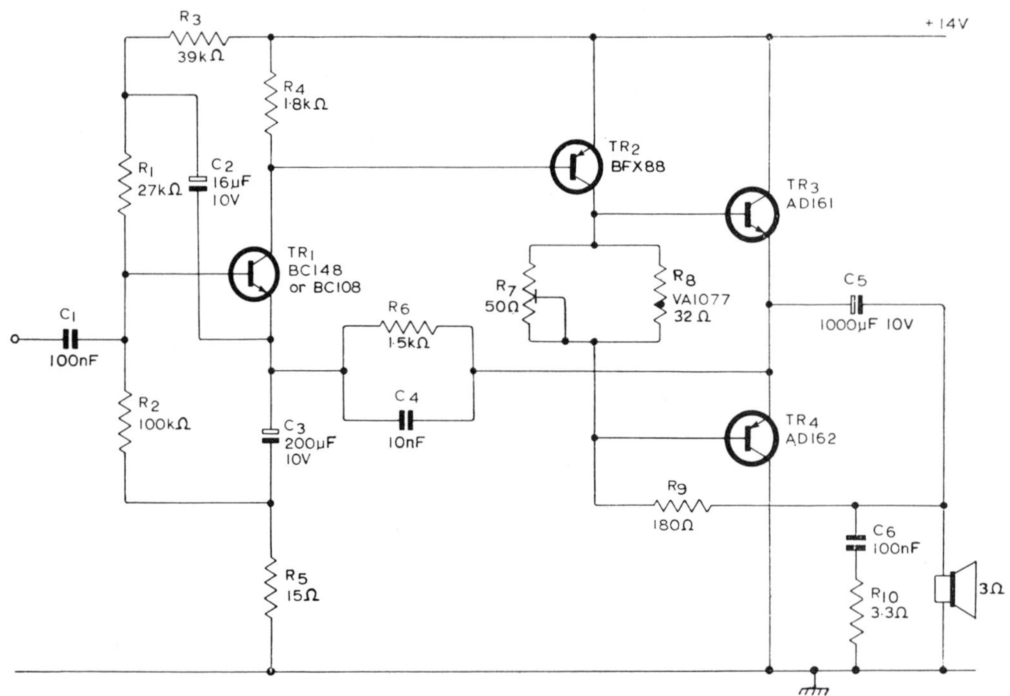

6-W CLASS B AMPLIFIER—Designed for use in car radio. Circuit is conventional except that decoupling capacitor C2 in input stage is returned to emitter of TR1 instead of to chassis; this reduces effect of ripple in supply and increases input resistance by bootstrapping base resistor.—"Transistor Audio and Radio Circuits," Mullard Ltd., London, 1969, p 92.

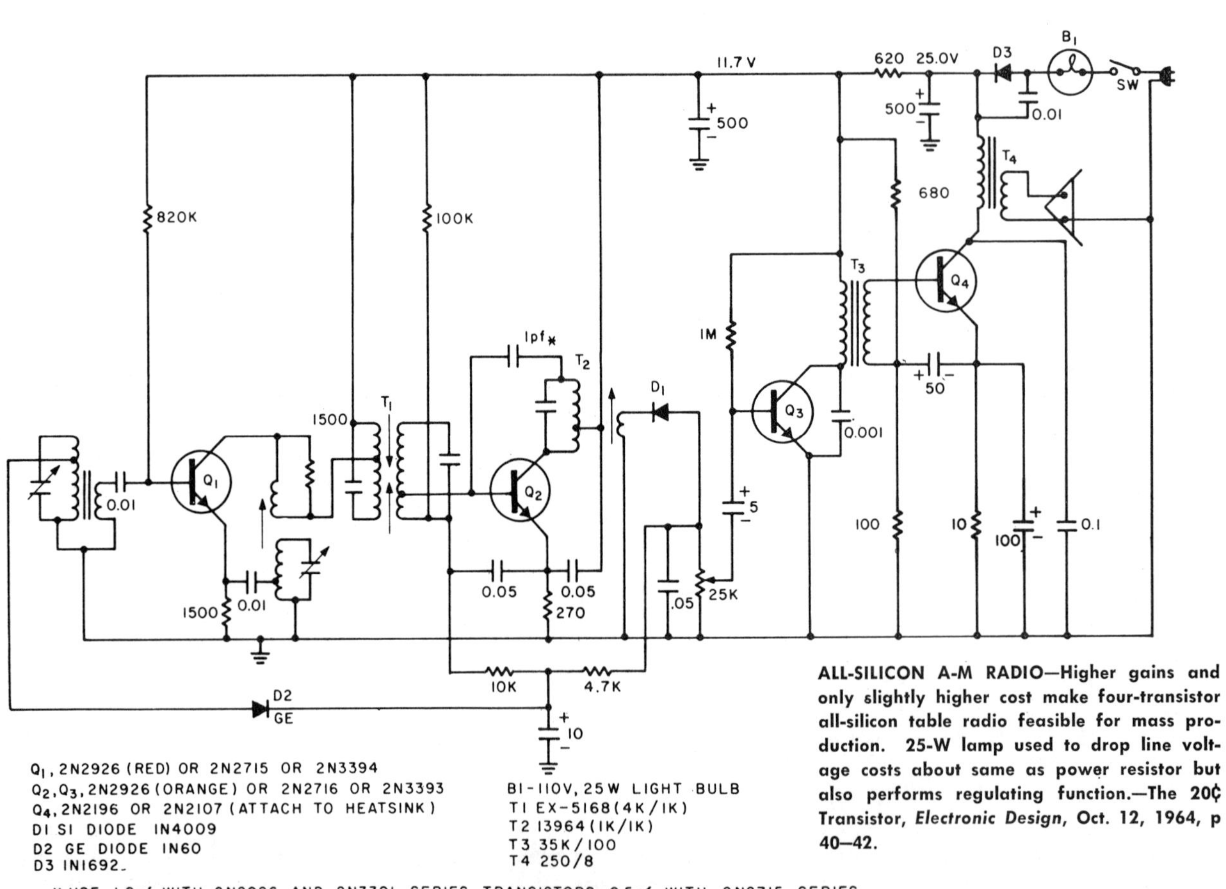

ALL-SILICON A-M RADIO—Higher gains and only slightly higher cost make four-transistor all-silicon table radio feasible for mass production. 25-W lamp used to drop line voltage costs about same as power resistor but also performs regulating function.—The 20¢ Transistor, *Electronic Design*, Oct. 12, 1964, p 40–42.

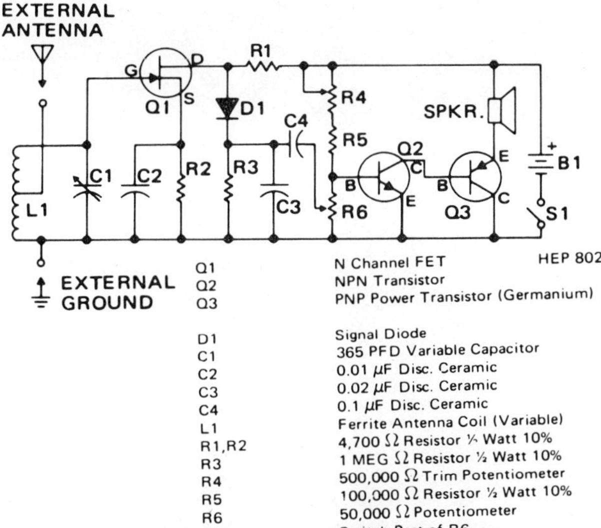

EXTERNAL ANTENNA
EXTERNAL GROUND
R1
R4
R5
R6
Q1
Q2
Q3
D1
C4
SPKR.
B1
S1
C1
C2
R2
R3
C3
L1
Q1 N Channel FET HEP 802
Q2 NPN Transistor
Q3 PNP Power Transistor (Germanium)
D1 Signal Diode
C1 365 PFD Variable Capacitor
C2 0.01 μF Disc. Ceramic
C3 0.02 μF Disc. Ceramic
C4 0.1 μF Disc. Ceramic
L1 Ferrite Antenna Coil (Variable)
R1,R2 4,700 Ω Resistor ¼ Watt 10%
R3 1 MEG Ω Resistor ½ Watt 10%
R4 500,000 Ω Trim Potentiometer
R5 100,000 Ω Resistor ½ Watt 10%
R6 50,000 Ω Potentiometer
S1 Switch Part of R6

3-TRANSISTOR A-M RADIO—Use of fet as r-f amplifier contributes to selectivity and gain of trf circuit feeding diode detector and two-transistor audio amplifier driving small speaker. Requires 12 V, obtained from eight 1.5-V cells in series. R6 is volume control, and R4 is bias adjustment.—Calectro Handbook, GC Electronics, Rockford, Ill., FR-69-C, p 41.

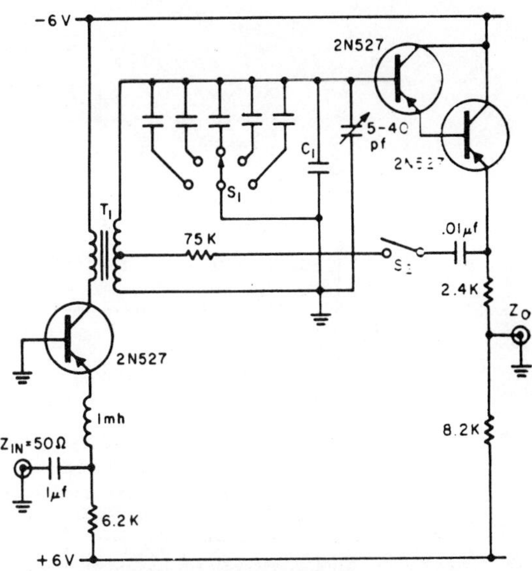

VLF RECEIVER—Uses Darlington circuit as Q-multiplier to give good selectivity over entire vlf band. T1 has 1:15 turns ratio. All transistors are 2N527. Output can be fed to ordinary R-C amplifiers to give desired output level.—R. W. Couch, Simple VLF Receiver Uses Single Tuned Stage, "400 Ideas for Design Selected from Electronic Design," Hayden Book Co., N.Y., 1964, p 33.

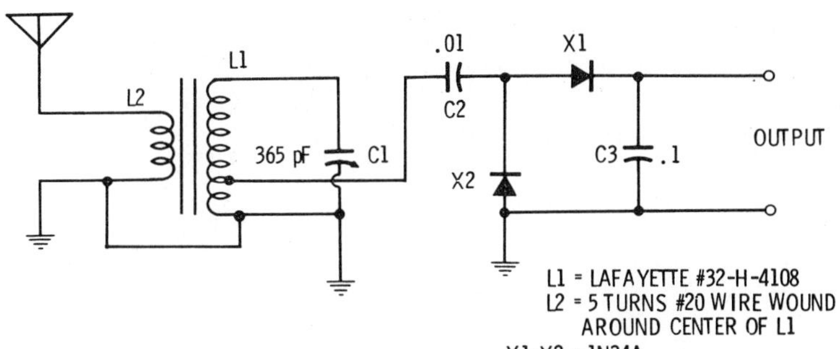

VOLTAGE-DOUBLER CRYSTAL SET—Gives best performance with crystal headphones or when connected to high-impedance input of audio amplifier. The longer the antenna, the louder the signal.—J. P. Shields, "Novel Electronic Circuits," H. W. Sams & Co., Indianapolis, Ind., 1968, p 64.

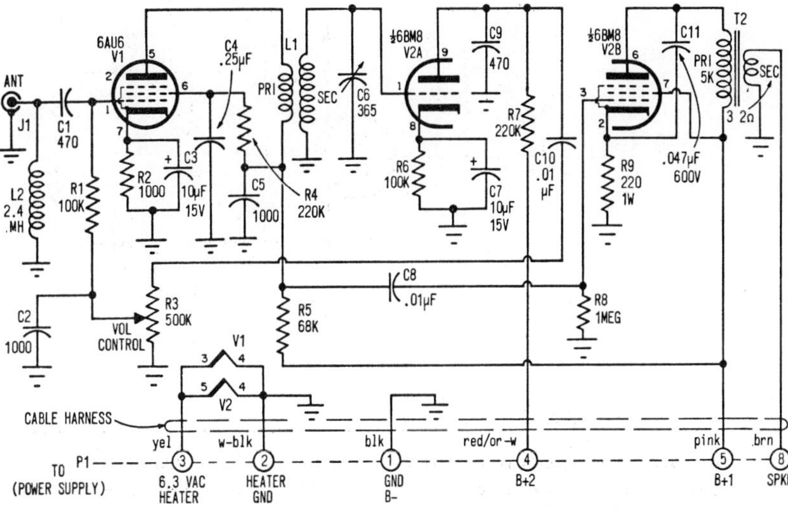

TWO-TUBE BROADCAST-BAND REFLEX—First tube, V1, serves as r-f amplifier and then as a-f amplifier, to minimize number of components required. Article gives construction details, including those for a-c power supply required.—C. Green, Build Twofer-Flex, *Radio-TV Experimenter*, June–July 1969, p 37–41.

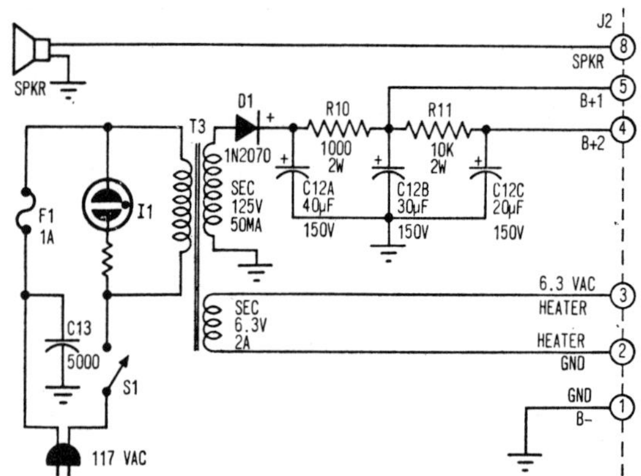

REFLEX-RECEIVER SUPPLY—Output terminals are numbered to correspond to those of two-tube broadcast-band reflex receiver shown in this chapter. Article gives construction details. I1 is NE-51H neon lamp.—C. Green, Build Twofer-Flex, *Radio-TV Experimenter*, June—July 1969, p 37—41.

DOUBLE-SIDEBAND
SUPPRESSED CARRIER
1.701 + 1.609 MHz

PRODUCT DETECTOR—Uses IC i-f amplifier with only three external components for handling suppressed-carrier signals. Output capacitor provides filtering for high-frequency components of oscillator signal at output. Gain is maximum for oscillator voltage range of 1 to 2 V.—"Linear Integrated Circuits," RCA, Harrison, N.J., IC-41, p 158.

IMPROVING SHORT-WAVE RECEIVER SELECTIVITY—Insertion of Miller 8902-B IC i-f strip, including detector, ahead of audio in budget-priced short-wave receiver boosts gain 100X (40 dB) and gives additional 18 dB of selectivity at 10 kHz. Receiver must have 455-kHz i-f. Will operate with either positive or negative grounds. Selectivity is greatly improved by using Miller 8901-B i-f transformer ahead of module. Article gives construction details and instructions for connecting to set. C2 is 0.01 μF.—H. Friedman, The 100Xer, *Elementary Electronics*, Mar.—Apr. 1970, p 43—48.

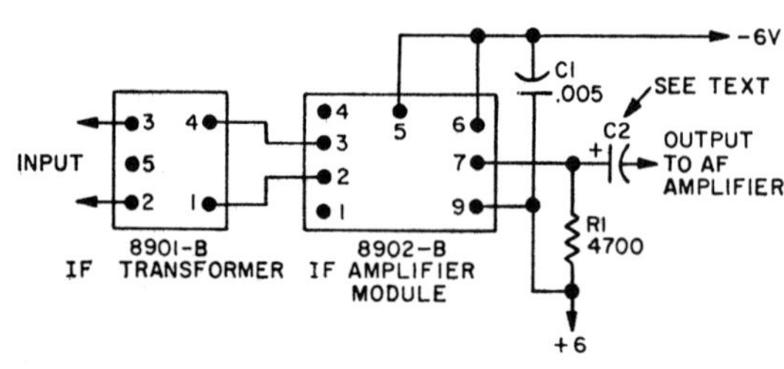

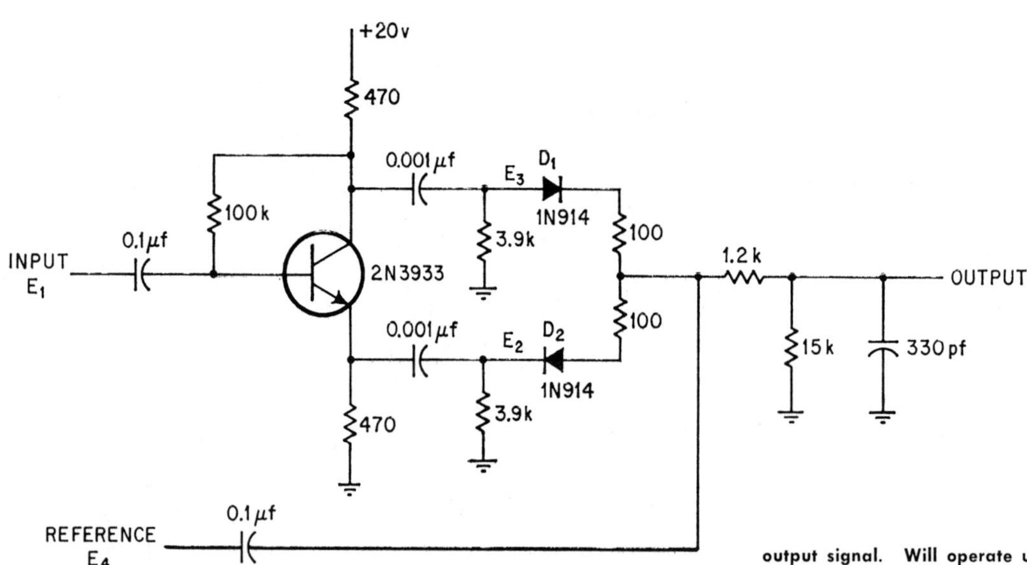

TRANSFORMERLESS PHASE-SENSITIVE DETECTOR—Extracts phase and amplitude modulation data from 20-MHz i-f signals. Incoming signals reach both diodes simultaneously but out of phase. Reference voltage combines with diode outputs by vector addition to give output signal. Will operate up to 30 MHz.—A. H. Hargrove, IC-Size Phase Detector Doesn't Need Any Inductors, *Electronics*, Aug. 4, 1969, p 91—92.

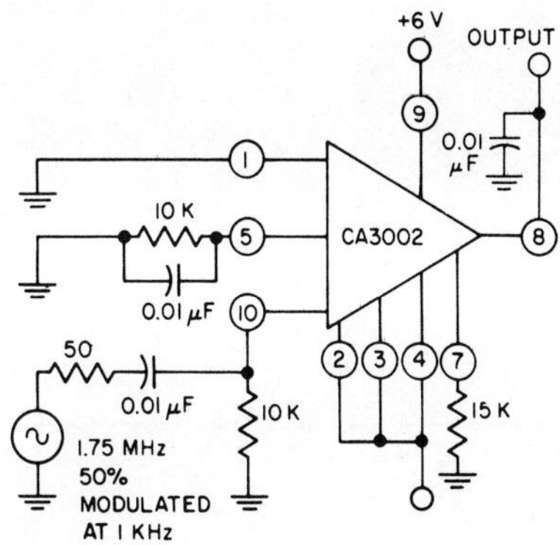

ENVELOPE DETECTOR—Uses IC i-f amplifier with fixed 15K resistor connected externally to reduce emitter current of output transistor, to give operating point providing required nonlinearity for detection of audio modulation signal. Distortion is below 3% for input signals from 12 to 60 mV.—"Linear Integrated Circuits," RCA, Harrison, N.J., IC-41, p 156.

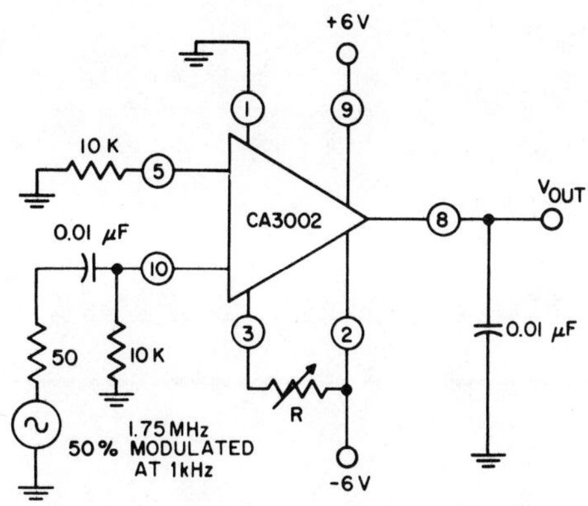

ENVELOPE DETECTOR—Operation of IC i-f amplifier with external connections shown gives envelope detector with distortion below 3% for input signals from 10 to 100 mV. Filter capacitor across output removes r-f signal from detected audio output.—"Linear Integrated Circuits," RCA, Harrison, N.J., IC-41, p 156.

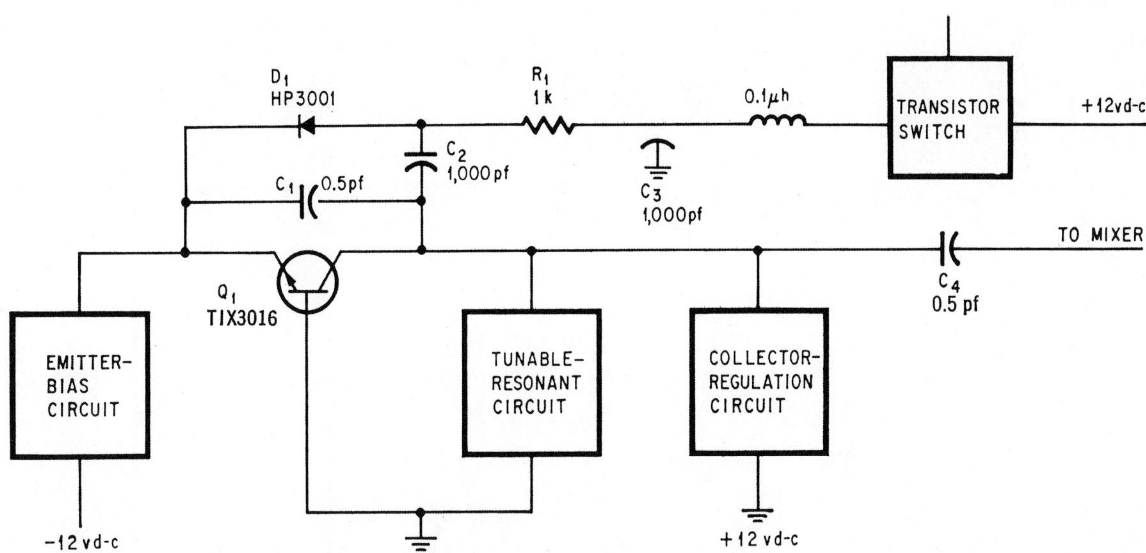

FAST-ON OSCILLATORS—Tunable oscillators in wide-spectrum communication equipment are kept in oscillation continuously to prevent transistor warmup delay, with p-i-n diode D1 shunting out signal until receiver is tuned to that band. When signal is desired, command signal is applied to transistor switch, restoring naturally high resistance of diode and providing oscillations within 50 ms.—A. Barone, P-I-N Diodes Turn On Microwave Bands Faster, *Electronics*, April 29, 1968, p 67.

NOTE: To locate additional circuits in the category of this chapter, use the index at the back of this book. Check also the author's "Sourcebook of Electronic Circuits," published by McGraw-Hill in 1968.

CHAPTER 70
Regulated Power Supply Circuits

12 V AT 100 MA WITH REFERENCE AMPLIFIER—Uses zener and npn silicon transistor packaged together, such as RA-1 to RA-3B, to perform functions of voltage reference and error voltage amplifier for precision power supply. Output voltage regulation is better than 0.3% for line voltage variations of 10%. Output is 12 V at 100 mA.—T. P. Sylvan, An Integrated Reference Amplifier For Precision Power Supplies, General Electric, Syracuse, N.Y., No. 90.15, 1963.

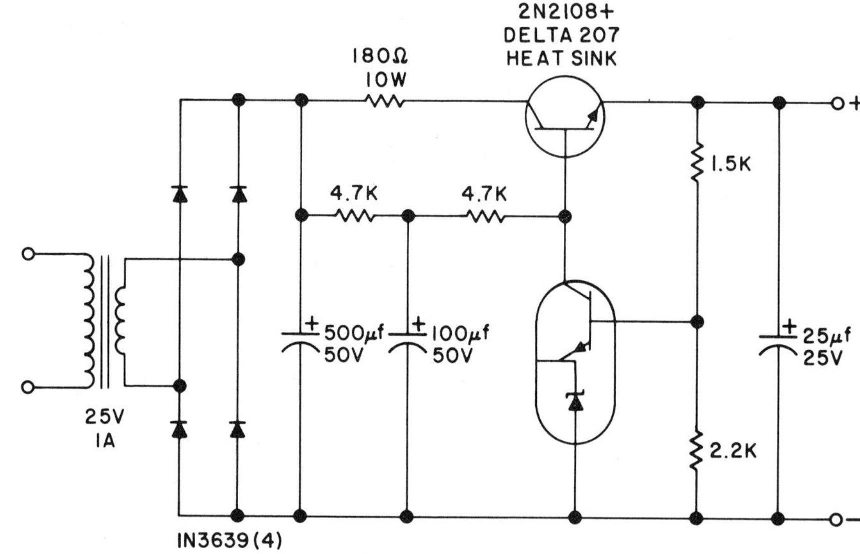

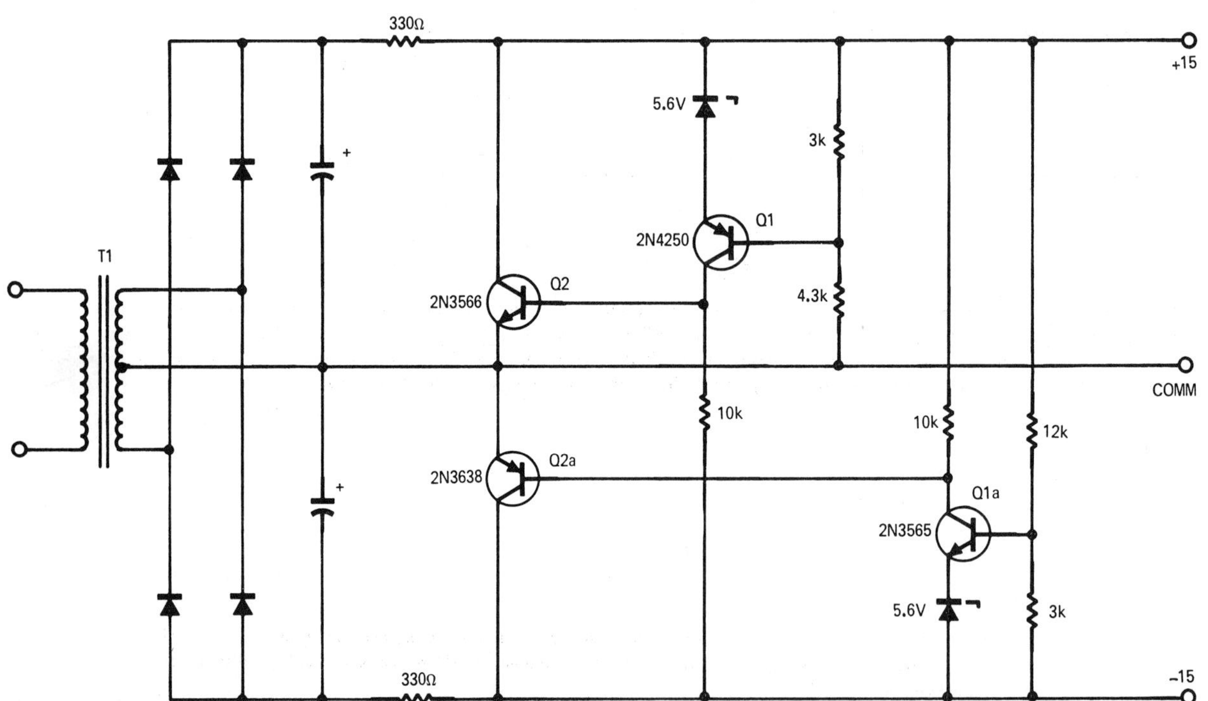

BIPOLAR 15 V—Provides sufficient power for up to four average-size IC's, delivering up to 25 mA with only 1-mV p-p ripple. Voltage regulation is within 0.2% for loads from 600 ohms to infinity and a-c line voltage changes from 105 to 125 V. Uses high-beta shunt regulator driven by current source Q1. —R. W. Forsberg, Shunt Regulator Has Optimized Gain, *EDN*, May 15, 1970, p 53.

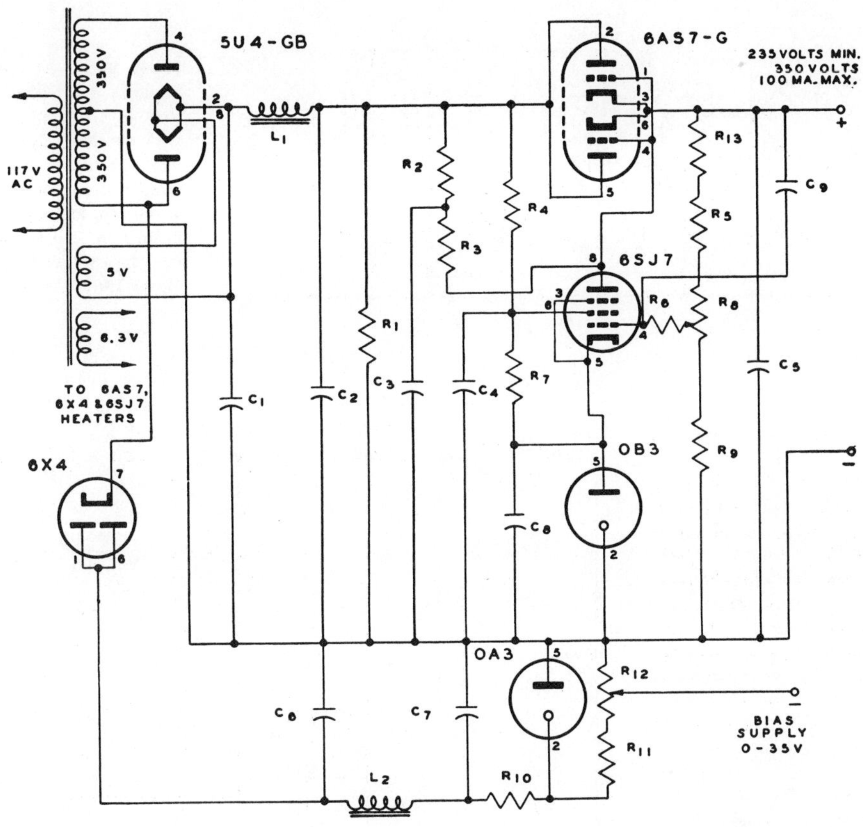

C_1 C_2—16 μf 600V
C_3 C_8—1 μf 600V
C_4—8 μf 450V
C_5—4 μf 600V
C_6 C_7—40 μf 450V
C_9—0.1 μf 600V

L_1—15 H 200 Ma
L_2—15 H 60 Ma
R_1—470 K
R_2 R_9 R_{13}—330 K
R_3—100 K
R_4—20 K 10 Watt

R_5 R_6—1 Meg
R_7—10 K 10 Watt
R_8—500 K Pot.
R_{10}—20 K 5 Watt
R_{11}—5 K 5 Watt
R_{12}—5 K Pot. 5 Watt

350 V AT 100 MA PLUS BIAS—All-tube version of series regulator uses separate diode for adjustable 0–35 V negative bias supply.—"Essential Characteristics," General Electric, Owensboro, Ky., 1969, p 348.

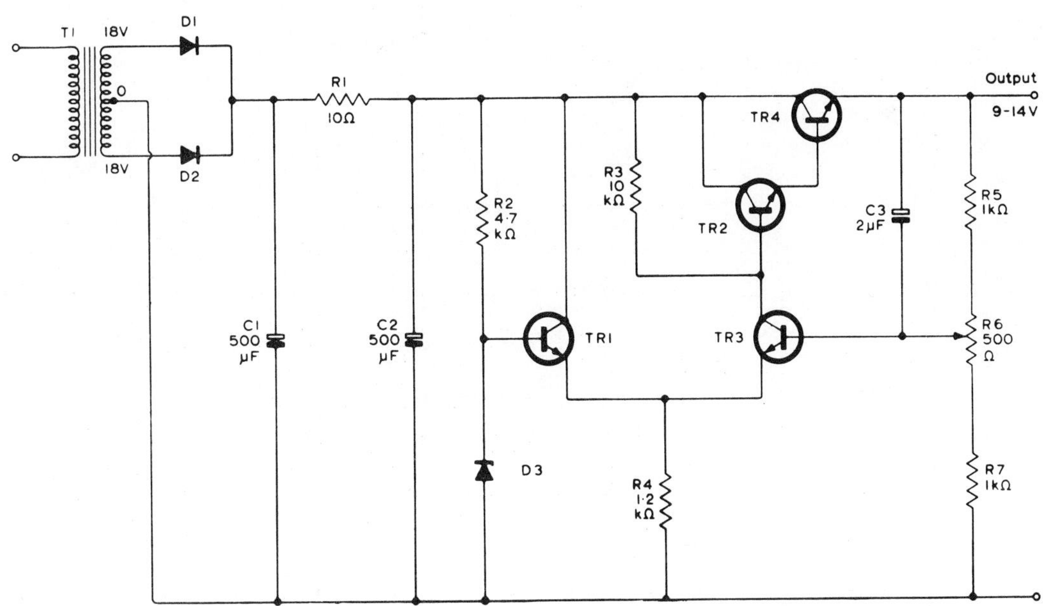

14 V WITH LONG-TAILED PAIR—Two of four BFY52 transistors are arranged as long-tailed-pair differential amplifier giving higher gain and better regulation than conventional three-transistor regulator. Changes in output current do not affect current or voltage of zener D3. Regulation is 1.5% over output voltage range of 9 to 14 V, with load currents up to 250 mA.—Applications of the BFY50, BFY51 and BFY52, Philips, Pub. Dept., Elcoma Div., Eindhoven, The Netherlands, No. 428, 1965.

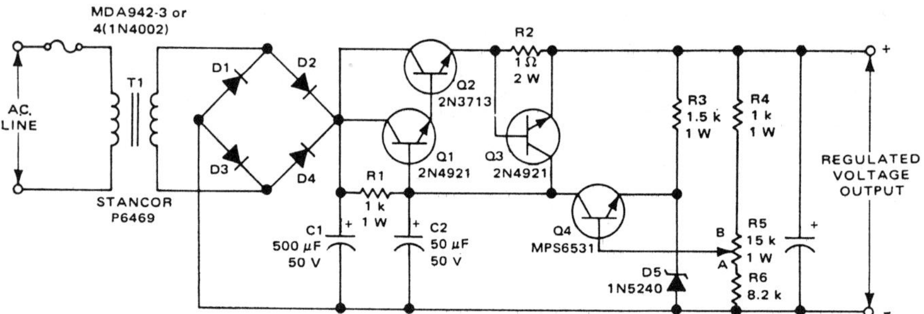

11—32 V D-C AT 700 MA—Use of series-pass regulators provides extremely good regulation, low ripple, and low output impedance, with excellent dynamic response. Can readily be adapted for remote voltage sensing, remote programming, and current-regulating or current-limiting applications. Overcurrent protection is provided by R2 and Q3.—G. V. Fay, Series-Pass Regulators, *Electronics World*, March 1969, p 48 and 78.

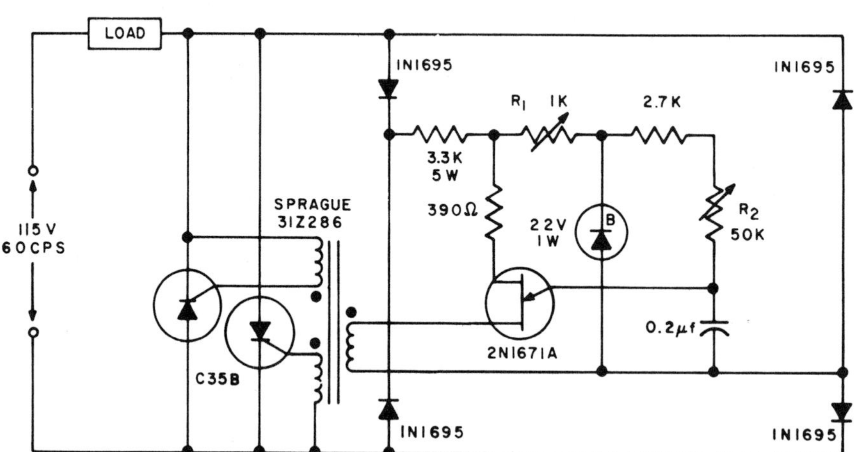

HIGH-POWER REGULATED A-C SUPPLY—Output current depends on ratings of scr's, and for those shown is 32 A (3.7 kW). Uses a-c phase control, with regulation for changes in line voltage. R1 makes peak voltage increase as line voltage increases, thereby retarding firing angle of scr's and reducing voltage applied to load. R1 can be adjusted to hold load voltage constant for given variation in line voltage. R2 determines output voltage. Size and cost are only one-tenth of comparable constant-voltage transformer and Variac.—T. P. Sylvan, The Unijunction Transistor Characteristics and Applications, General Electric, Syracuse, N.Y., No. 90.10, 1965, p 79.

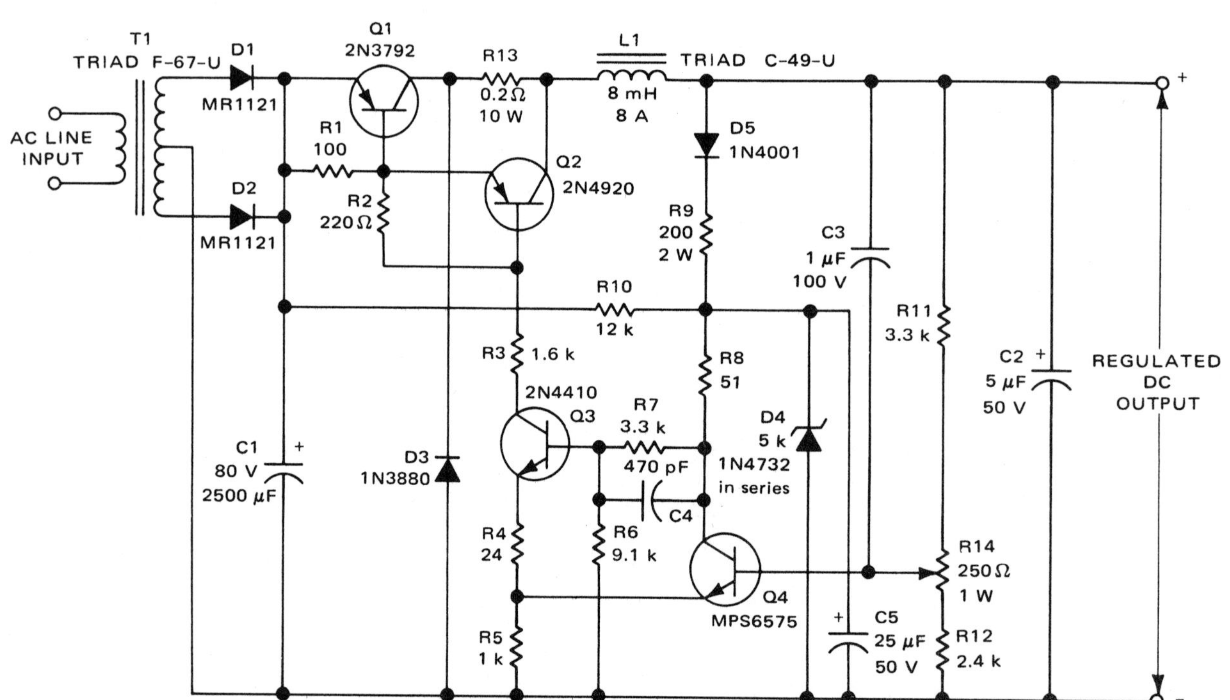

38-V D-C PWM SWITCHING PREREGULATOR—Uses voltage-sensing property of Schmitt trigger Q3-Q4 to provide drive for Darlington series switch Q1-Q2. With values shown, operating frequency is about 16.5 kHz and is essentially constant from no load to full load of 5 A. Output voltage drops only about 150 mV below 38 V at full load.—"Semiconductor Power Circuits Handbook," Motorola, Phoenix, Ariz., 1968, p 3–21.

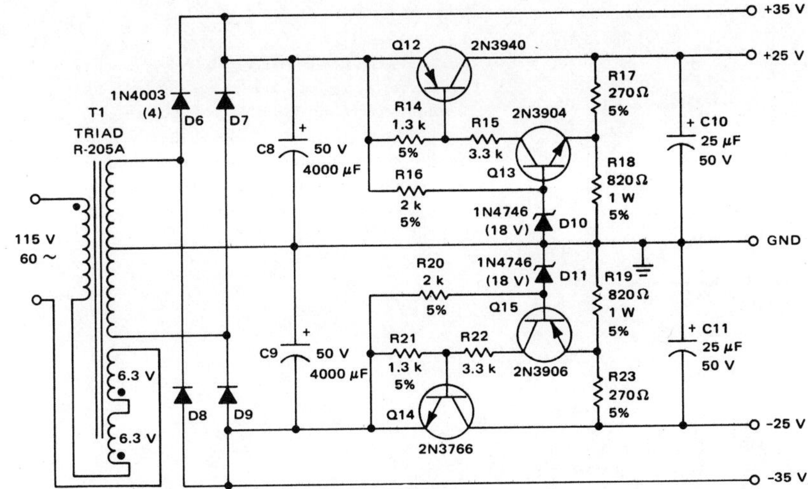

AUDIO AMPLIFIER TEST SUPPLY—Developed for testing 50-W audio amplifiers. Provides filtered but unregulated 35-V outputs of both polarities for output transistors and zener-regulated 25 V for input stages. Two 6.3-V windings are used as bucking voltages because secondary voltage of transformer was too high. Both positive and negative supplies should come on at same time, to prevent damage to transistors if power is applied to only one side.—"Semiconductor Power Circuits Handbook," Motorola, Phoenix, Ariz., 1968, p 5—50.

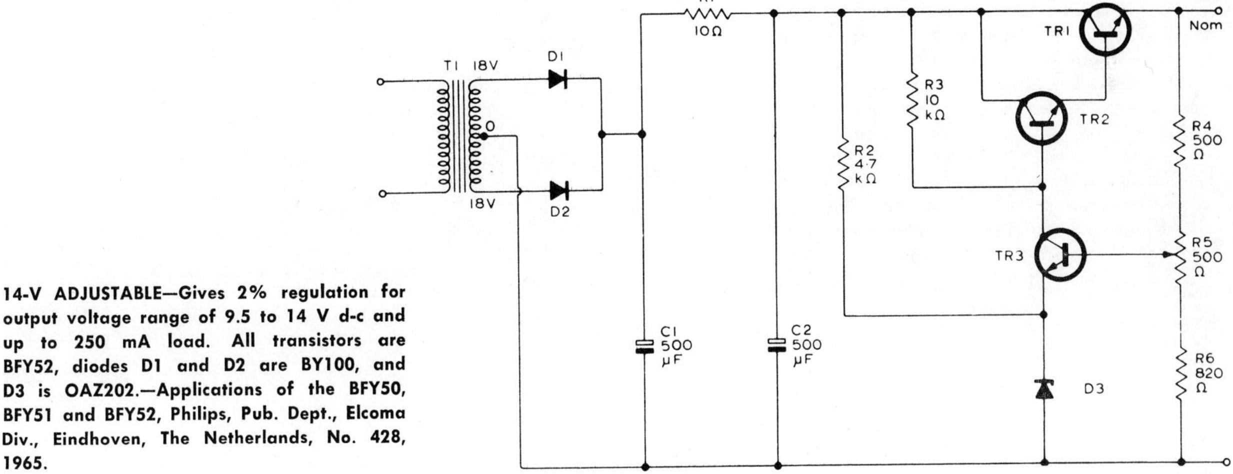

14-V ADJUSTABLE—Gives 2% regulation for output voltage range of 9.5 to 14 V d-c and up to 250 mA load. All transistors are BFY52, diodes D1 and D2 are BY100, and D3 is OAZ202.—Applications of the BFY50, BFY51 and BFY52, Philips, Pub. Dept., Elcoma Div., Eindhoven, The Netherlands, No. 428, 1965.

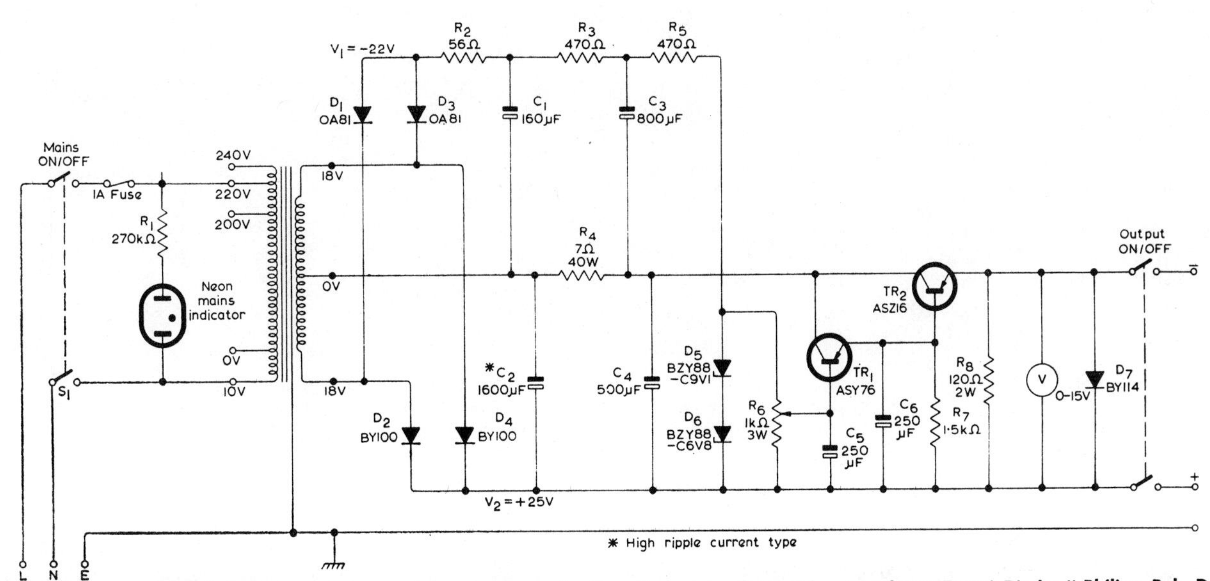

BENCH SUPPLY FOR TRANSISTORS—Output is adjustable from 0 to 15 V d-c at 0.5 A and partially stabilized, to meet requirements of most transistor circuits. Cannot be damaged by accidental short-circuits, as long as transformer secondary can supply 2.5 A.—"Voltage Regulator (Zener) Diodes," Philips, Pub. Dept., Elcoma Div., Eindhoven, The Netherlands, p 38.

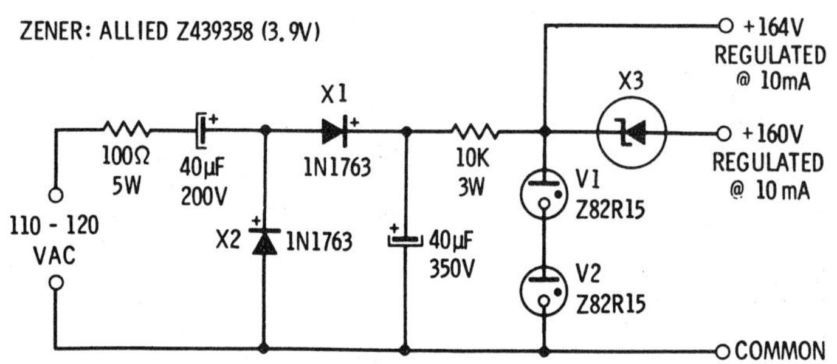

164-V NEON-REGULATED SUPPLY—Provides two stable voltages at low current, for applications such as counters, oscillators, and timers. Consists of half-wave voltage doubler, neon regulator, and zener diode.—W. G. Miller, "Using and Understanding Miniature Neon Lamps," H. W. Sams & Co., Indianapolis, Ind., 1969, p 80.

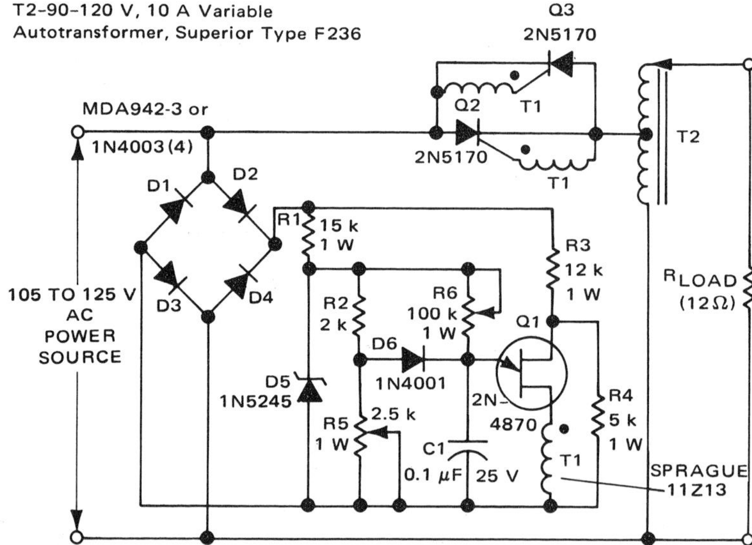

120-V A-C REGULATOR—Circuit holds voltage across 12-ohm load within 2% of 120 V by regulating 90-V input to stepup transformer T2. Load current is 10 A. Circuit has no feedback, but regulation is provided by T2. Q2 and Q3 are both pulsed at same time by ujt Q1 through T1, but only the one that is forward-biased by supply voltage at that instant turns on. R5 and R6 interact and may require several adjustments after load change or supply voltage change, to keep load voltage exactly at 120 V.—"Semiconductor Power Circuits Handbook," Motorola, Phoenix, Ariz., 1968, p 3–28.

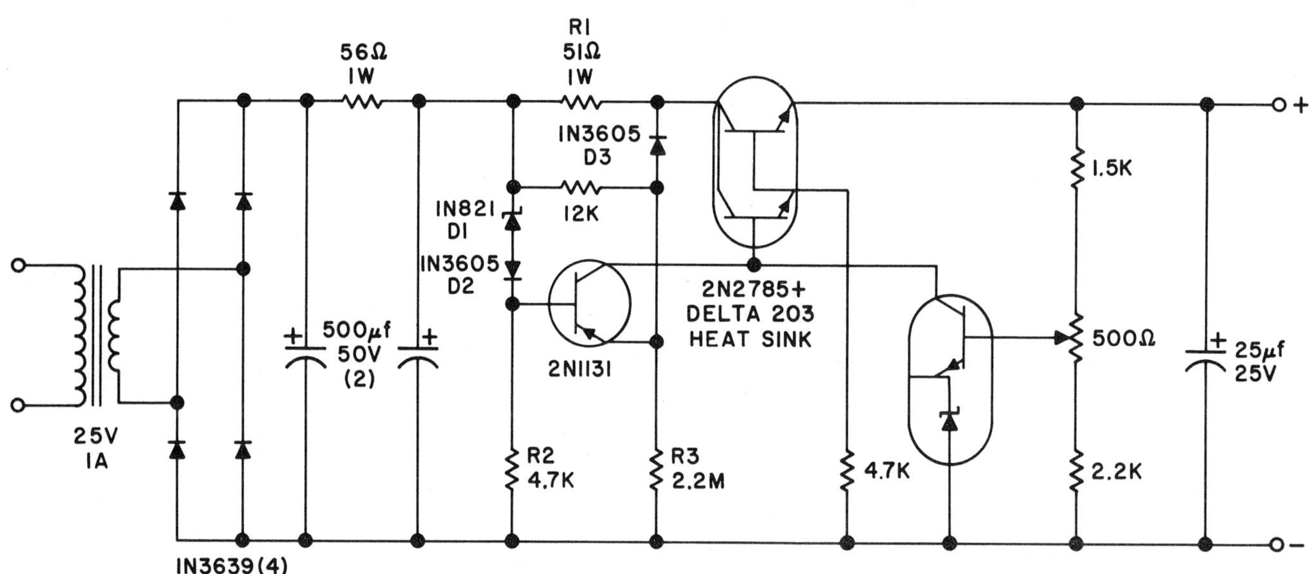

REFERENCE AMPLIFIER WITH DARLINGTON—Change in 12-V output voltage is less that 0.0001% for 10% change in a-c line voltage. Output current is 100 mA. 2N2785 Darlington is used as series regulator. R3 is adjusted to optimize regulation. Output impedance is 0.03 ohm, while ripple and noise at full load are below 10 µV.—T. P. Sylvan, An Integrated Reference Amplifier for Precision Power Supplies, General Electric, Syracuse, N.Y., No. 90.15, 1963.

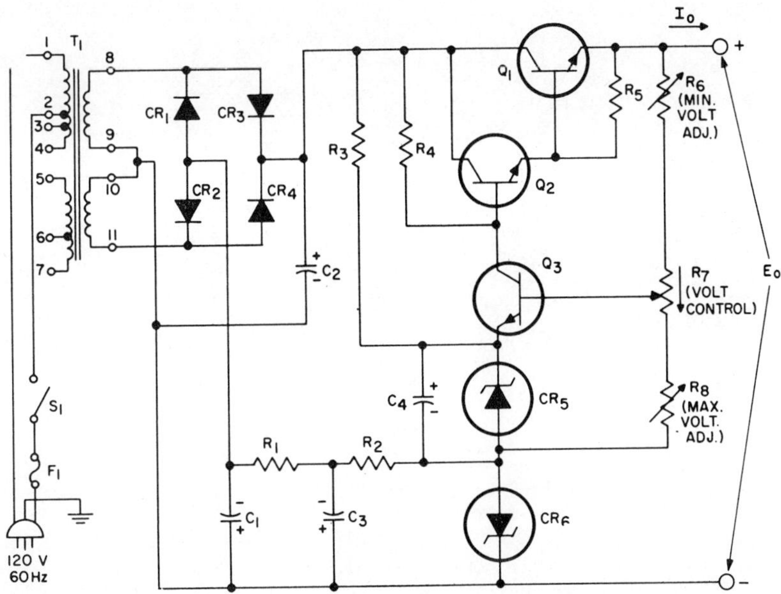

C_1C_3 = 500 microfarads, 25 volts, electrolytic
C_2 = 5000 microfarads, 25 volts, electrolytic
C_4 = 100 microtarads, 10 volts, electrolytic
$CR_1CR_2CR_3CR_4$ = silicon rectifier, RCA SK3030
CR_5 = zener diode, 6.8 volts, 1 watt
CR_6 = zener diode, 12 volts, 1 watt
F_1 = fuse, 1 ampere, 120 volts
Q_1 = transistor, RCA SK3027
Q_2Q_3 = transistor, RCA SK3020
R_1R_5 = 220 ohms, 1/2 watt, 10%
R_2 = 470 ohms, 1/2 watt, 10%
R_3 = 6800 ohms, 1/2 watt, 10%
R_4 = 10,000 ohms, 1/2 watt, 10%
R_6 R_8 = trimmer potentiometer, 5000 ohms, Mallory MTC-1 or equivalent
R_7 = potentiometer, 5000 ohms, linear taper
S_1 = switch, 120 volts, 1 ampere, single-pole, single-throw
T_1 = transformer, primary 115 volts, secondary 15 volts, 1 ampere, Stancor No. TP-4 or equivalent

12-V VARIABLE-VOLTAGE—Full-range supply provides maximum of 1 A at any voltage up to 12 V, operating from a-c line. Regulator section uses two zeners connected in opposition.—"Hobby Circuits Manual," RCA, Harrison, N.J., HM-90, p 54.

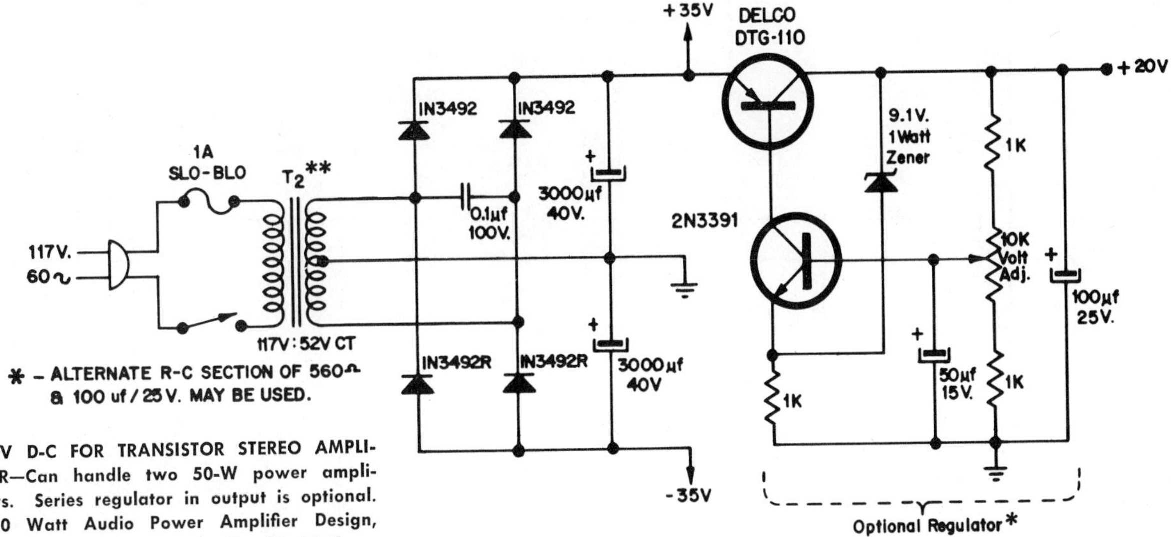

*** - ALTERNATE R-C SECTION OF 560Ω & 100 uf/25V. MAY BE USED.**

20-V D-C FOR TRANSISTOR STEREO AMPLIFIER—Can handle two 50-W power amplifiers. Series regulator in output is optional. —50 Watt Audio Power Amplifier Design, Delco Radio, Kokomo, Ind., No. 36, 1967.

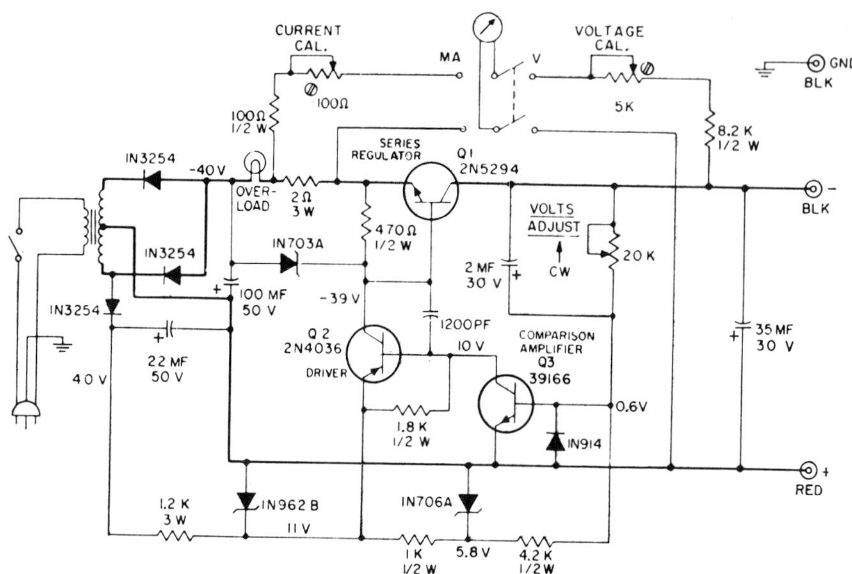

0–20 V AT 20 MA—Commercially available at $48 for single output or $87 for two identical units sharing common power transformer. Overload-indicator lamps glow brightly when output current appreciably exceeds full rated load of 200 mA. Output is continuously adjustable down to zero, with negative-feedback regulator circuit maintaining constant voltage with low ripple at any setting, regardless of variations in load or a-c line voltage.—RCA Models WP-700A, WP-702A Power Supplies, *Electronics World*, March 1969, p 68–69.

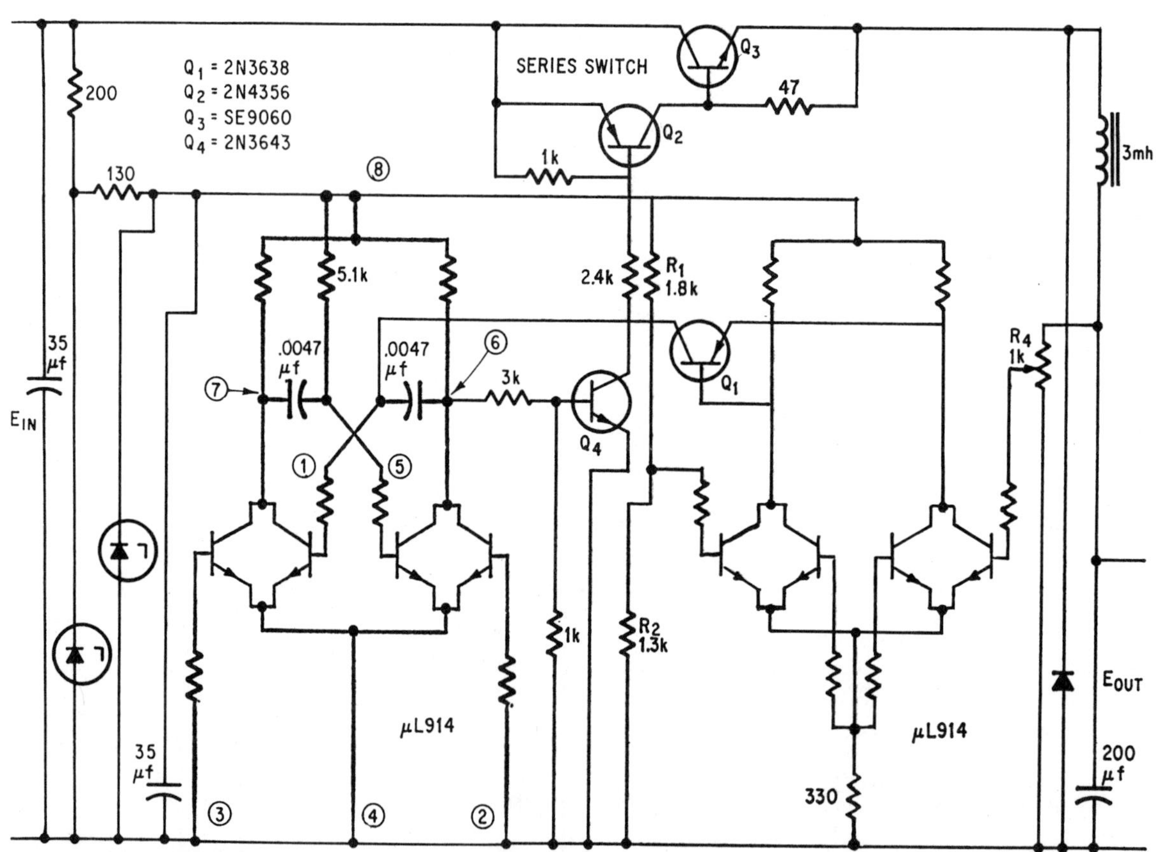

10-V IC SWITCHING REGULATOR—Two RTL AND gates, one used as differential amplifier and the other as astable mvbr, give load regulation of 0.2% from no load to 1 A for output of 10 V. Output ripple is less than 20 mV p-p. Differential amplifier (at right) operates as error detector by sensing difference between reference voltage set by R1-R2 and output voltage tapped by R4. Amplifier then produces error current from Q1 that changes duty cycle of IC mvbr at left and series switch Q3.—M. English, Voltage Regulator Built From Two AND Gates, *Electronics*, Dec. 23, 1968, p 57.

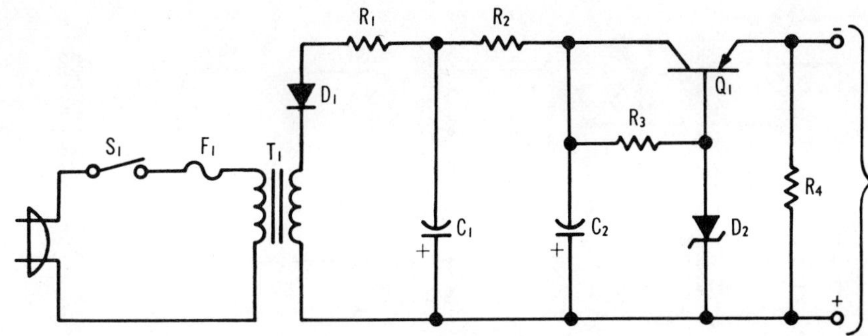

10 V at 250 MA—Furnishes well-filtered and stable voltage, for any transistor circuit requiring 9 to 10 V. Article gives construction details. Parts values are: R1 1; R2 2.4; R3 150; R4 200; C1-C2 500 μF; D1 HEP154; D2 HEP101; Q1 HEP230; F1 0.25 A; T1 117 V:12.6 V Triad F-25X.—"Solid State Projects Manual," Motorola, Phoenix, Ariz., 1968, p 41–43.

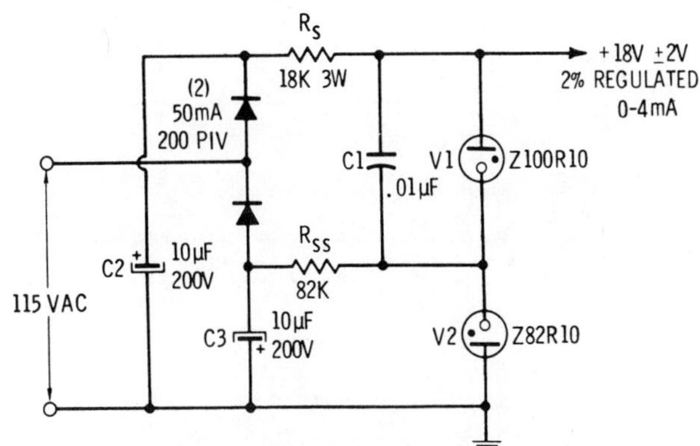

LOW-VOLTAGE NEON REGULATOR—18-V reference is achieved at output by algebraic addition of negative 100-V maintaining voltage of V1 to positive 82 V of V2. Regulator features common ground and is accurate over wide temperature range.—W. G. Miller, "Using and Understanding Miniature Neon Lamps," H. W. Sams & Co., Indianapolis, Ind., 1969, p 34.

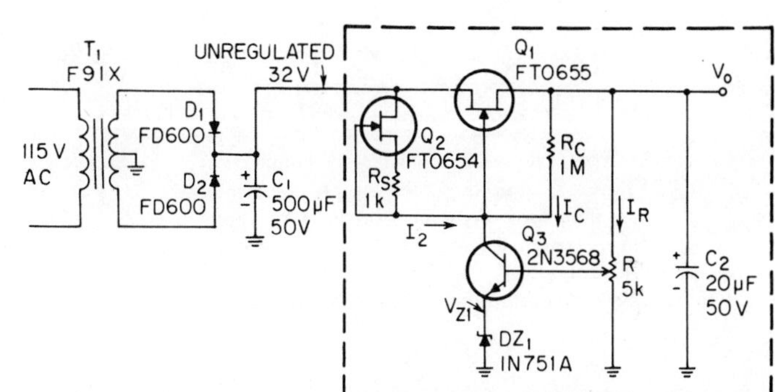

20 V AT 100 MA—Provides 0.5% regulation and short-circuit protection at parts cost under \$10. To convert to negative supply, change both n-channel fet's to p-channel and change Q3 to pnp transistor.—H. Wu, Designing Power Supplies with FETs, *EEE*, Dec. 1968, p 68–69.

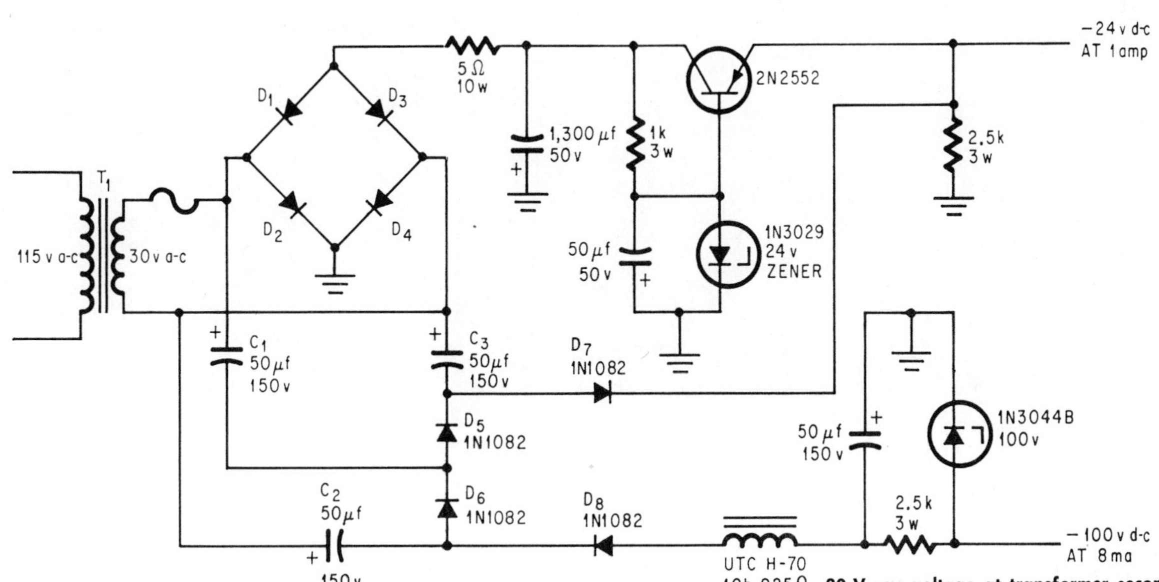

24 and 100 V WITH DIODE MULTIPLIERS—Can provide one output in range of 100 to 200 V and another below 50 V with single transformer secondary. Each capacitor-diode multiplier boosts no-load d-c output of previous stage an amount equal to 1.4 times 30-V rms voltage at transformer secondary.—M. E. Converse, Multiplier Stages Replace Power-Supply Transformer, *Electronics*, Dec. 9, 1968, p 84.

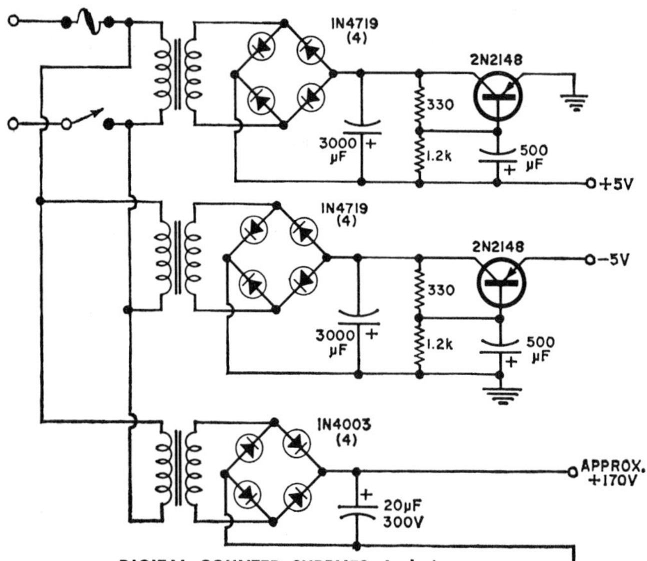

DIGITAL COUNTER SUPPLIES—Isolation transformer is used in 170-V supply, and 6.3-V 3-A filament transformers in the 5-V supplies for precision 50-MHz CB frequency monitor. —F. E. Cody, A 50-MHz Digital Counter, *Electronics World*, March 1969, p 40–42 and 61.

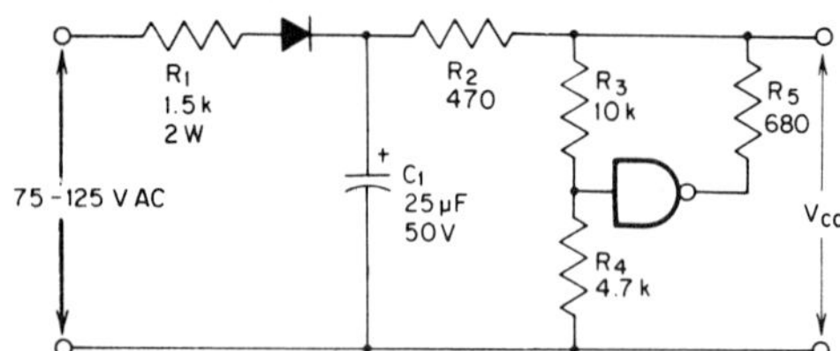

12 V D-C FROM A-C LINE—Unused gate in Amelco 303CJ multiple-gate IC may be connected as shown to provide regulated 12 V d-c for digital IC and reed relay. Other NAND or NOR gates could be used as well. Will provide up to 10 mA.—B. Horn, Spare IC Gate Serves as Regulator, *EEE*, Feb. 1970, p 115–116.

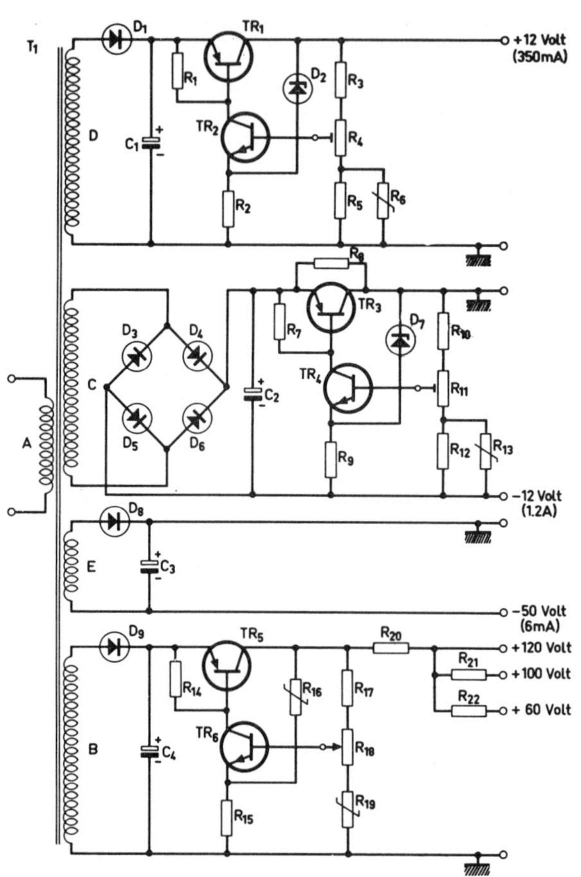

DESK CALCULATOR SUPPLY—Report gives design procedure for meeting power supply requirements for various types of small transistorized calculators, with one circuit as example. Intended for operation from 220-V 50-Hz line, but transformer winding data in report can readily be adjusted for 120-V operation. Provides 3% stabilization for 12-V outputs, and 8% stabilization for higher outputs. Series regulators are used with zeners and voltage-dependent resistors in low-voltage supplies.—A. P. Tanis, Design of Power Supply Units for Electronic Calculators, Philips, Pub. Dept., Elcoma Div., Eindhoven, The Netherlands, No. 833, 1967.

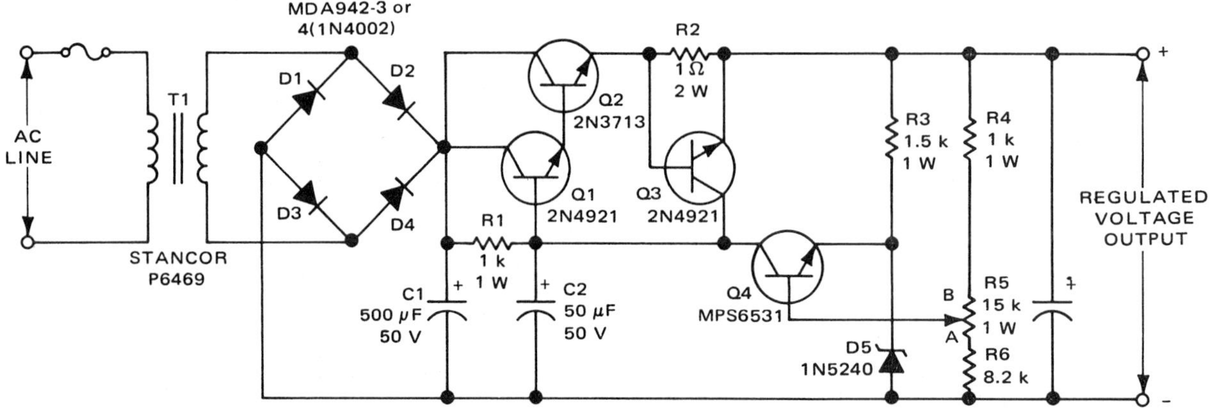

32-V D-C WITH OVERCURRENT PROTECTION—Output voltage is adjustable over range of 11 to 32 V by R5, with overcurrent protection provided by R2 and Q3. Circuit values were chosen to limit maximum current to about 700 mA, which means that voltage regulation is degraded for loads above 500 mA at higher output voltages and above 600 mA for outputs below 25 V.—"Semiconductor Power Circuits Handbook," Motorola, Phoenix, Ariz., 1968, p 3–12.

12-V 500-MA CONTINUOUSLY VARIABLE—Ripple is below 1%. CB is circuit breaker used in tv receivers. Almost any lower-level pnp transistor can be substituted for the 2N-414.—M. S. Rifkin, Variable Low-Voltage Power Supply, *Electronics World*, Oct. 1967, p 79.

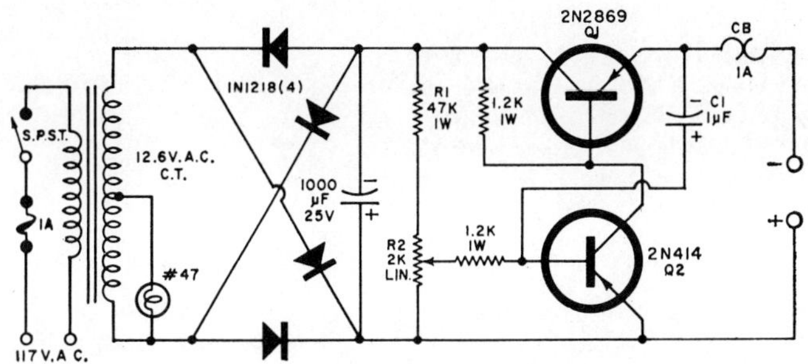

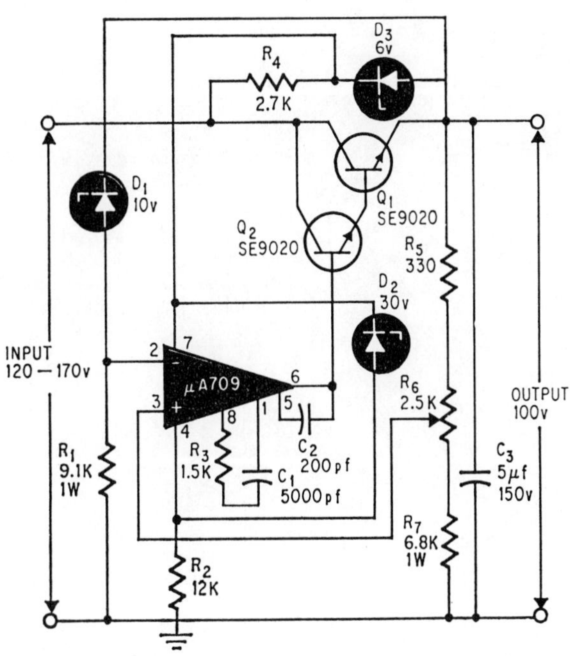

100 V D-C FROM A-C LINE—Modified bootstrap arrangement, with Fairchild μA709 opamp as control element, gives regulation better than 0.01% for output adjustment range of 60 V below maximum. Power transistors are used. Article contains 13 other IC opamp application circuits. D1, D2, and D3 are zeners.—J. F. Gifford and M. Markkula, Linear IC's: Part 5, Ins and Outs of Op Amps, *Electronics*, Nov. 27, 1967, p 84–93.

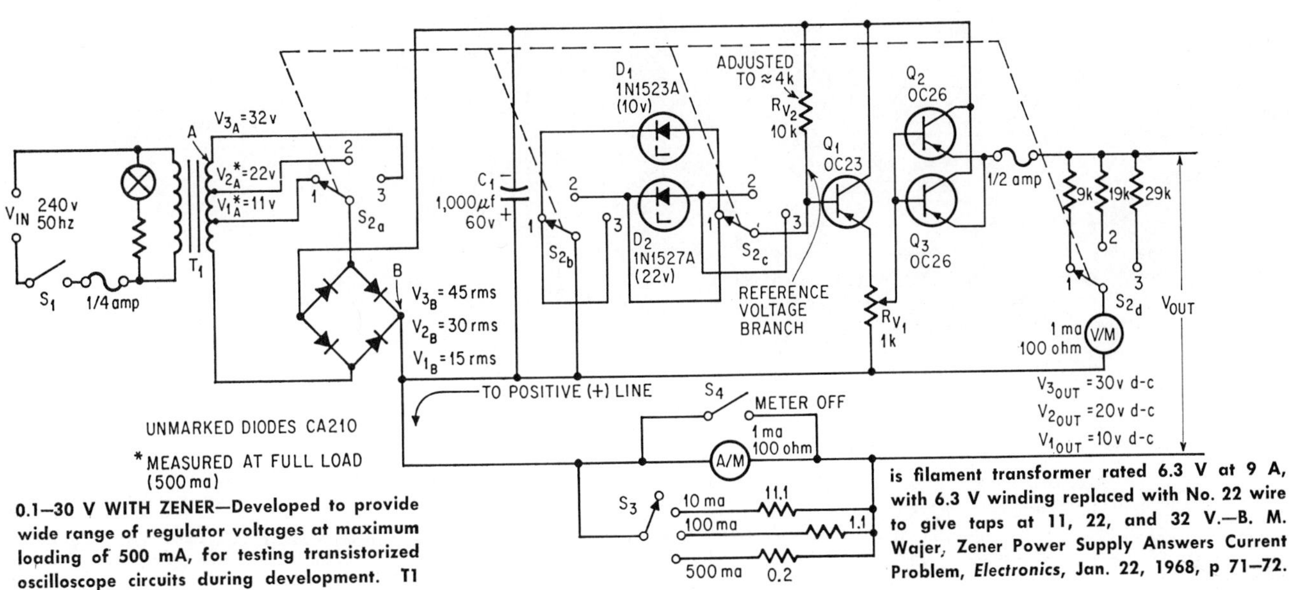

0.1–30 V WITH ZENER—Developed to provide wide range of regulator voltages at maximum loading of 500 mA, for testing transistorized oscilloscope circuits during development. T1 is filament transformer rated 6.3 V at 9 A, with 6.3 V winding replaced with No. 22 wire to give taps at 11, 22, and 32 V.—B. M. Wajer, Zener Power Supply Answers Current Problem, *Electronics*, Jan. 22, 1968, p 71–72.

DIFFERENTIAL LOW-VOLTAGE REFERENCE—Output voltage is difference between maintaining voltages of neon lamps at points A and B.—W. G. Miller, "Using and Understanding Miniature Neon Lamps," H. W. Sams & Co., Indianapolis, Ind., 1969, p 32.

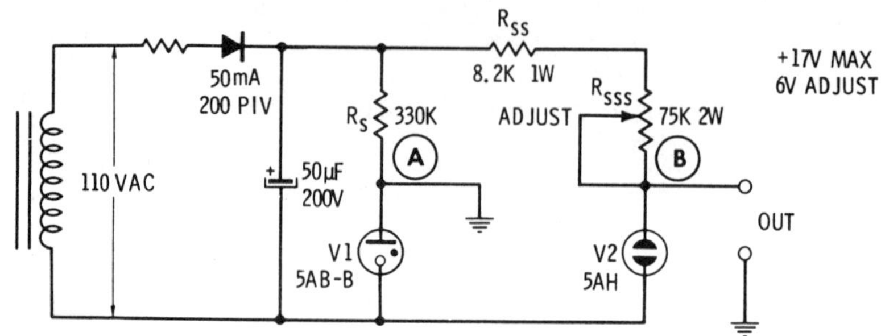

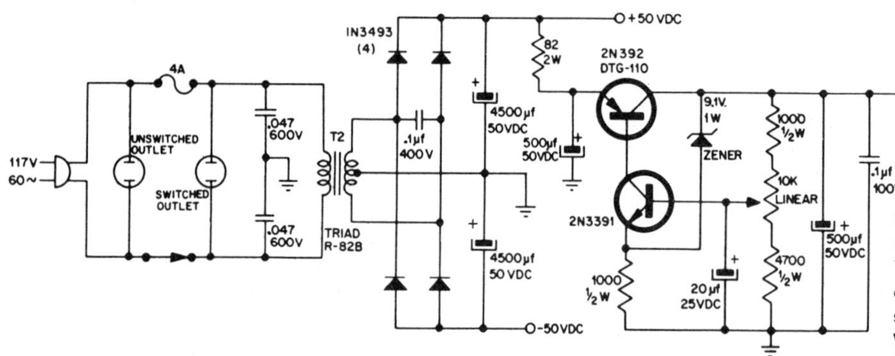

30 AND 50 V D-C FOR TRANSISTOR STEREO—Provides unregulated balanced 50-V, plus 30-V regulated, for handling both 80-W channels of all-transistor stereo system. Regulator is series-type using zener for reference.—160 Watt Stereo Audio Power Amplifier Design, Delco Radio, Kokomo, Ind., No. 35, 1968.

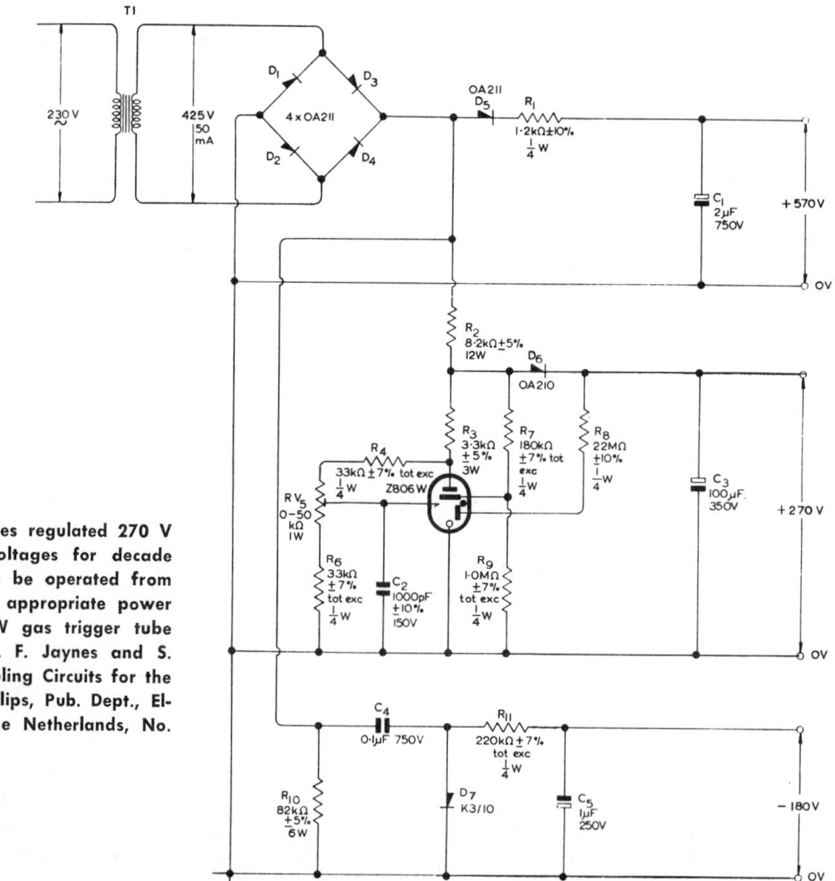

COUNTER SUPPLY—Provides regulated 270 V and two unregulated voltages for decade counter tube chain. Can be operated from 120 V a-c line by using appropriate power transformer. Uses Z806W gas trigger tube as voltage regulator.—G. F. Jaynes and S. Zilkha, Trigger Tube Coupling Circuits for the Z504S Stepping Tube, Philips, Pub. Dept., Elcoma Div., Eindhoven, The Netherlands, No. 15, 1965, p 16–25.

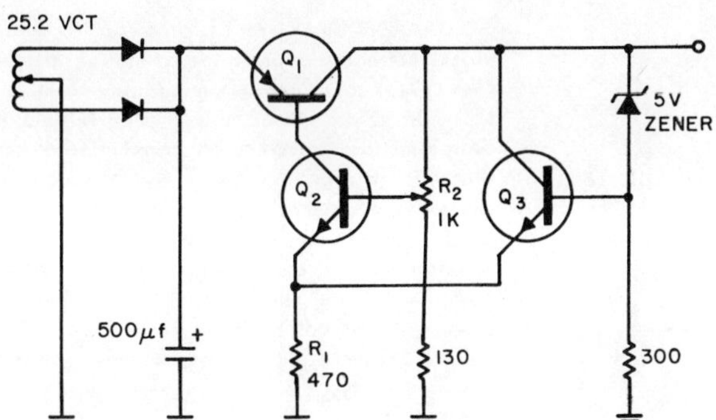

7–15 V WITH OVERLOAD PROTECTION—Uses one pnp and two npn transistors with other inexpensive components. Overload cutout current increases with output voltage setting of R2. Choose Q1 to withstand full d-c input voltage under short-circuit conditions.—W. F. McCarthy, Regulator Power Supply Improves Overload Protection, *Electronic Design*, Sept. 14, 1964, p 71.

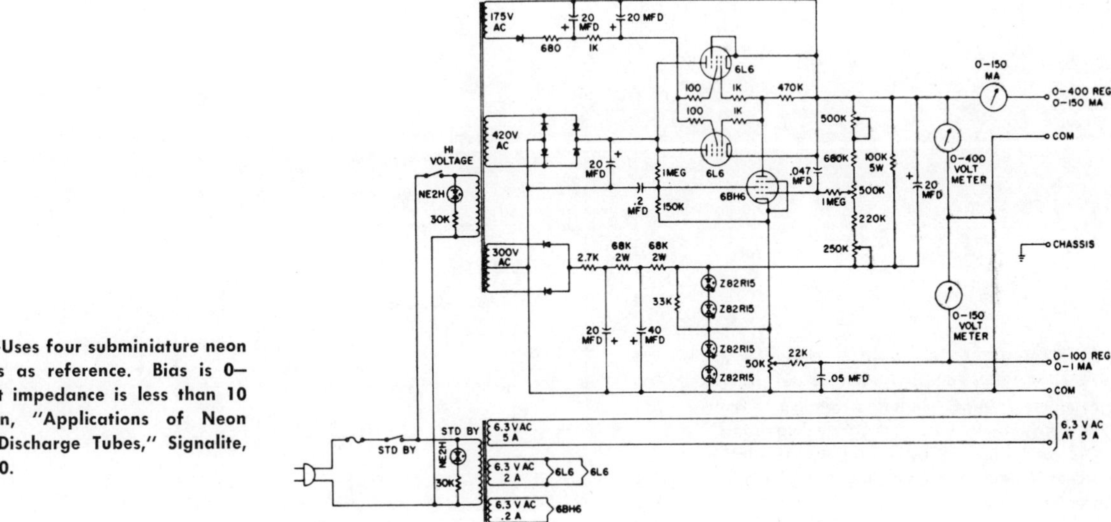

0–400 V SUPPLY—Uses four subminiature neon voltage regulators as reference. Bias is 0–100 V and output impedance is less than 10 ohms.—E. Bauman, "Applications of Neon Lamps and Gas Discharge Tubes," Signalite, Neptune, N.J., p 90.

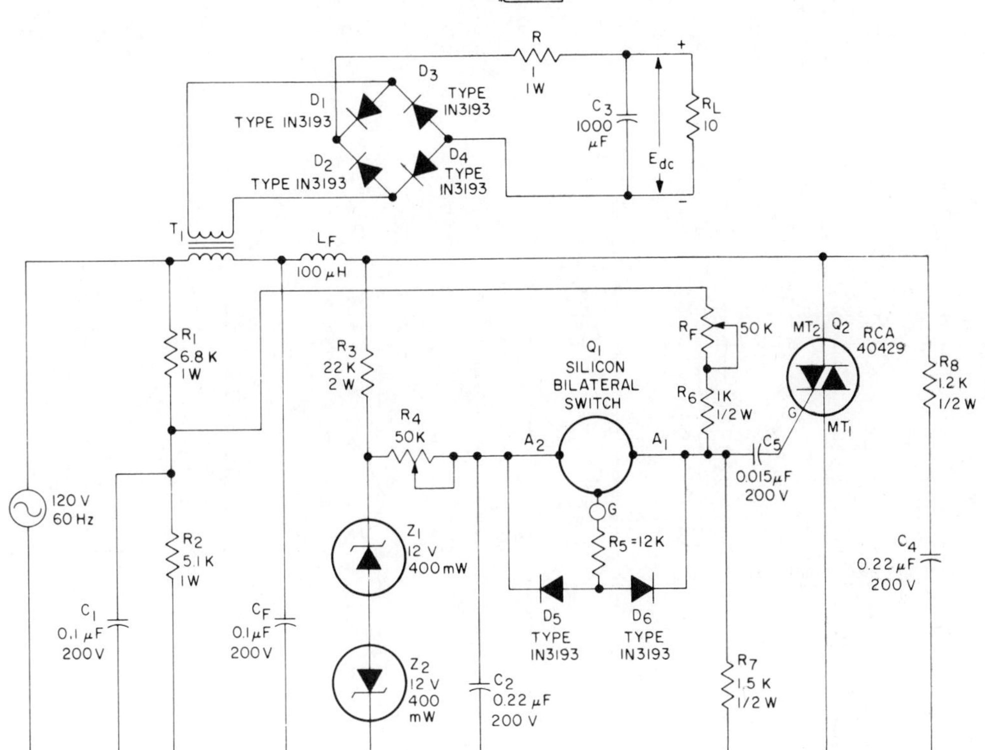

STABLE D-C SUPPLY—Power supply section uses full-wave bridge with R-C filter to provide d-c voltage of about 6 V. Regulator on primary side of line transformer T1 is phase-controlled triac with rfi suppression network. Voltage across 10-ohm load varies less than 2% for 20% change up or down in line voltage.—G. J. Granieri, AC Voltage Regulators Using Thyristors, RCA, Harrison, N.J., No. AN-3886, 1969.

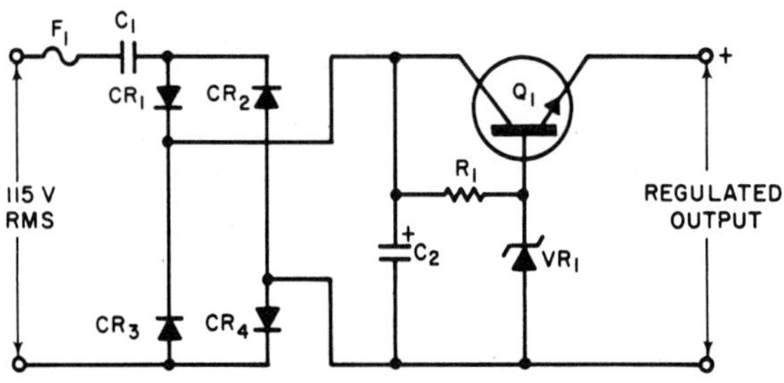

NO TRANSFORMER—Series capacitor C1 provides voltage-producing function of transformer to save space and reduce cost of low-voltage d-c power supply using full-wave bridge-rectifier circuit with conventional series voltage regulator Q1. Ideal for battery chargers. Value of C1 is chosen to give desired rectifier output voltage, and VR1 is selected for desired regulated output. Other components are conventional power supply sizes and are not critical.—A. T. Crane, Capacitor Replaces Transformer in Low Voltage Power Supply, *Electronic Design*, April 12, 1965, p 57.

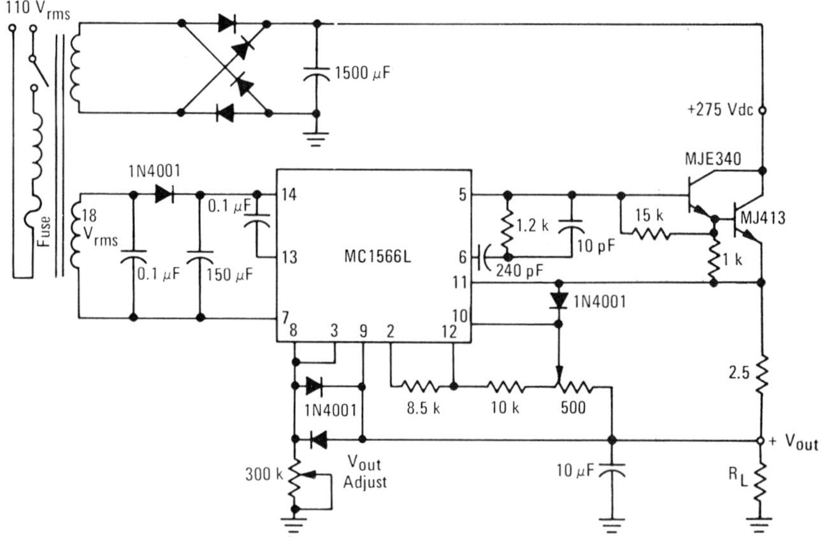

0–250 V D-C AT 0.1 A—Uses Motorola MC-1566 IC high-voltage regulator to provide complete voltage regulation right up to limiting current.—D. Kesner, Voltage Regulators—Old and New, "State-of-the-Art—Linears in Action," Motorola, Phoenix, Ariz., 1969, p 14–20.

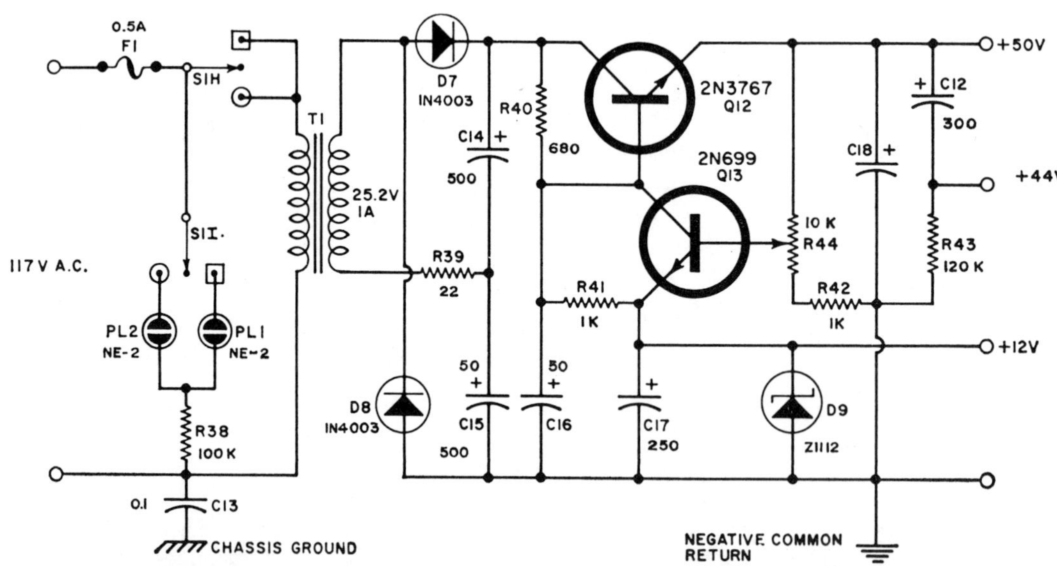

REGULATED 12, 44, and 50 V—Uses conventional voltage doubler with readily available power transformer. Zener D9 provides 12 V for reference, while Q12 and Q13 provide series-shunt regulation that minimizes ripple. Designed for use with transistor curve tracer. —M. Chan, Transistor Curve Tracer, *Electronics World*, Jan. 1968, p 55–58, 60, and 66.

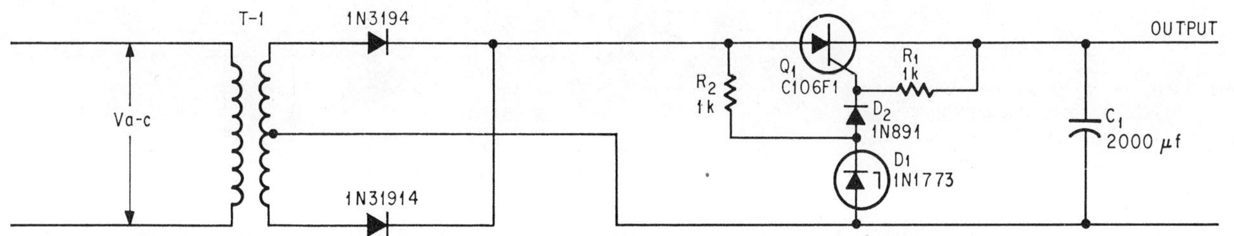

$3 SCR REGULATOR—Developed for use with consumer equipment in which cost of conventional regulated power supply would be prohibitive. Regulation is fair; for input range of 95 to 130 V, d-c output range is 11 to 12.5 V for outputs up to 0.3 A, after which transformer gradually saturates and impairs regulation.—P. Volkov, Inexpensive SCR Regulator For Consumer Equipment, *Electronics*, Feb. 5, 1968, p 88–89.

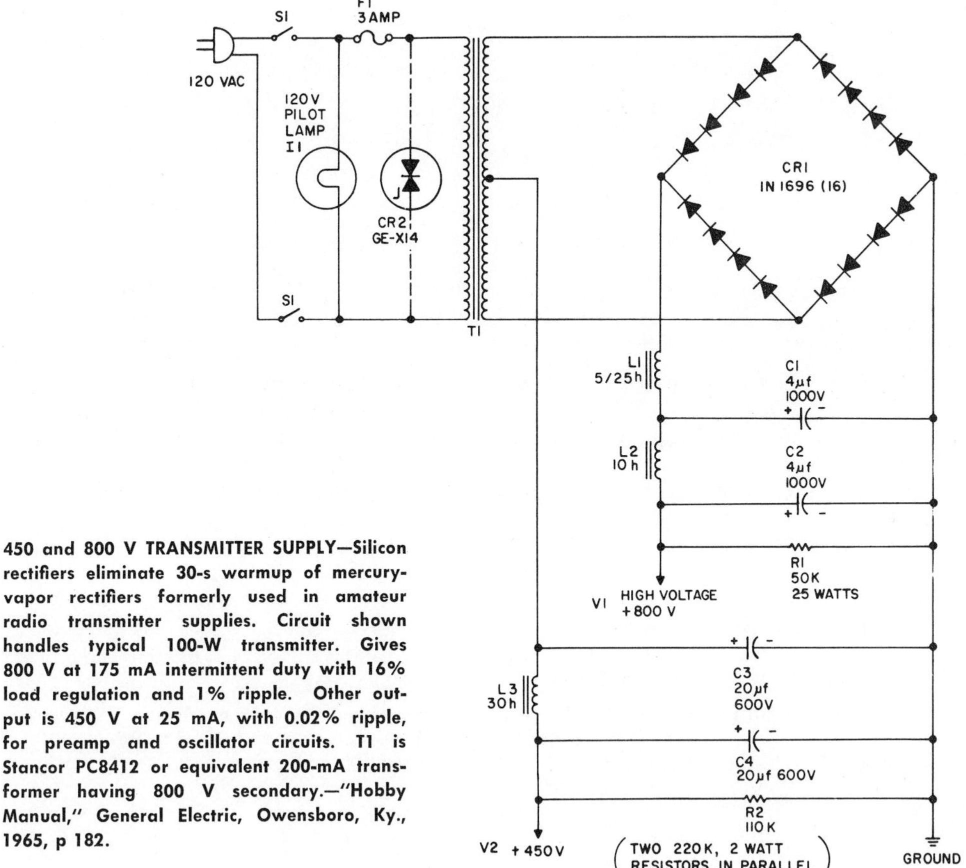

450 and 800 V TRANSMITTER SUPPLY—Silicon rectifiers eliminate 30-s warmup of mercury-vapor rectifiers formerly used in amateur radio transmitter supplies. Circuit shown handles typical 100-W transmitter. Gives 800 V at 175 mA intermittent duty with 16% load regulation and 1% ripple. Other output is 450 V at 25 mA, with 0.02% ripple, for preamp and oscillator circuits. T1 is Stancor PC8412 or equivalent 200-mA transformer having 800 V secondary.—"Hobby Manual," General Electric, Owensboro, Ky., 1965, p 182.

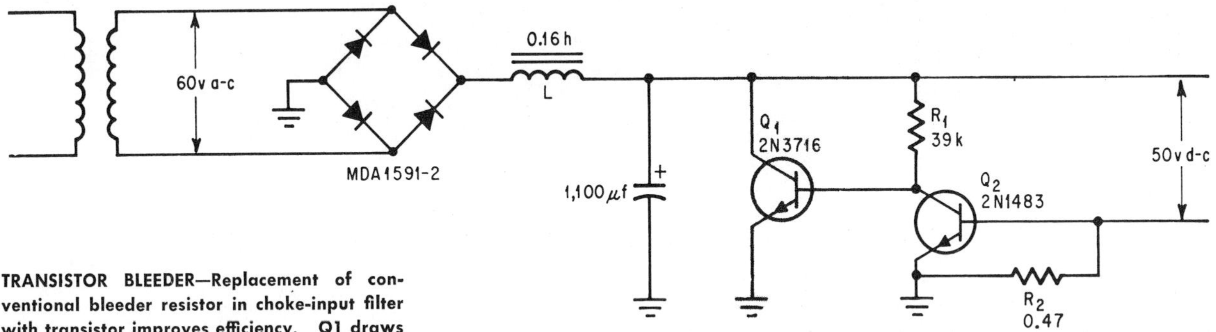

TRANSISTOR BLEEDER—Replacement of conventional bleeder resistor in choke-input filter with transistor improves efficiency. Q1 draws 520 mA at no load, just above critical value at which choke loses filtering capability. At full load of 3 A, bleeder transistor current is negligible.—C. K. Fitzsimmons, Transistor Replaces Bleeder and Regulates Power Supply, *Electronics*, Jan. 22, 1968, p 70–71.

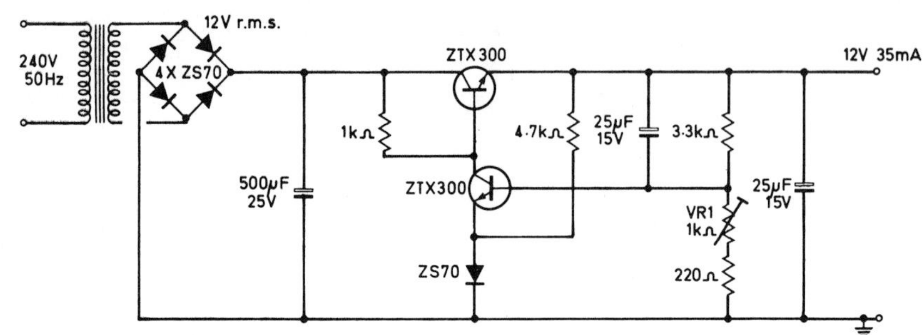

LOW-RIPPLE 12 V AT 35 MA—With values shown, ripple in 12-V output is only about 15 mV p-p.—E-Line Transistor Applications, Ferranti Ltd., Oldham, Lancs., England, 1969, p 47.

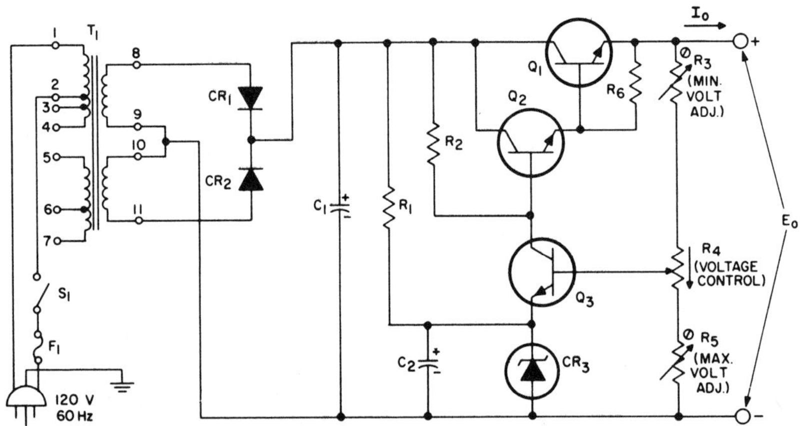

C_1 = 5000 microfarads, 25 volts, electrolytic
C_2 = 100 microfarads, 6 volts, electrolytic
CR_1CR_2 = silicon rectifier, RCA SK3030
CR_3 = zener diode, 3.9 volts, 1/2 watt
F_1 = fuse, 1 ampere, 120 volts
Q_1 = transistor, RCA SK3027
Q_2Q_3 = transistor, RCA SK3020
R_1 = 6800 ohms, 1/2 watt, 10%
R_2 = 10,000 ohms, 1 watt, 10%
R_3 R_5 = trimmer potentiometer, 5000 ohms, Mallory MTC-1 or equivalent
R_4 = potentiometer, 5000 ohms, linear tape:
S_1 = switch, 120 volts, 1 ampere, single-pole, single-throw
T_1 = transformer, primary 115 volts, secondary 15 volts, 1 ampere, Stancor No. TP-4 or equivalent

4.5 TO 12 V AT 1 A—Provides limited range of adjustment for output voltage. Regulation is provided by series transistor Q1, with zener serving as voltage reference for control transistors Q2 and Q3.—"Hobby Circuits Manual," RCA, Harrison, N.J., HM-90, p 53.

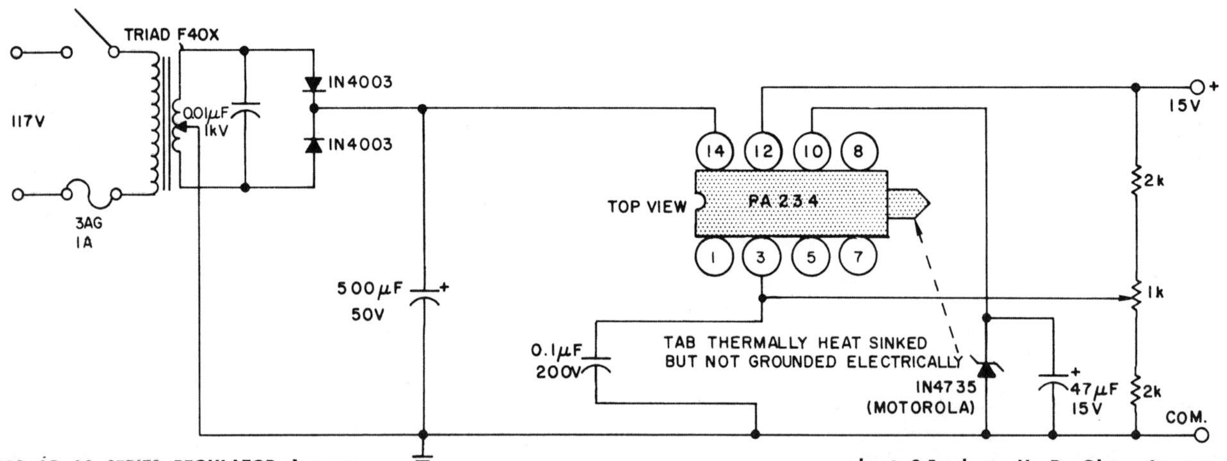

AUDIO IC AS SERIES REGULATOR—Inexpensive 1-W PA234 IC audio amplifier connected as shown provides regulated 15 V at up to several hundred mA, at lower cost than discrete components. Output impedance is about 2.5 ohms.—H. D. Olson, Inexpensive Audio IC Serves as Regulator, *Electronic Design*, Nov. 8, 1969, p 101.

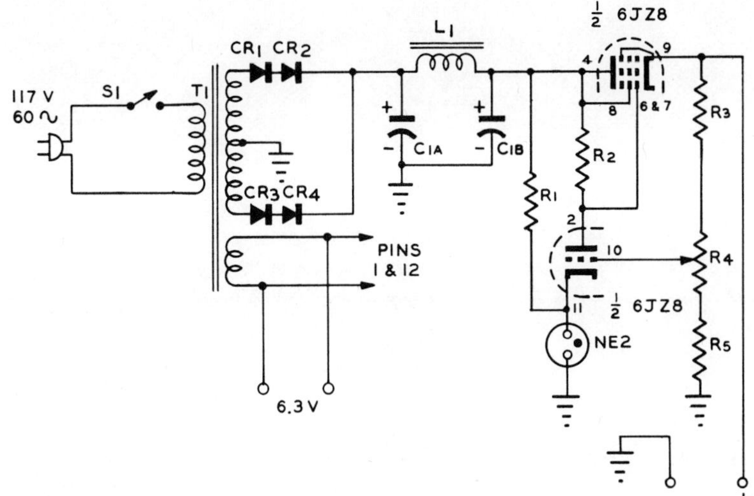

250 V WITH COMPACTRON—R4 permits adjusting regulated output from 150 V at 40 mA to 250 V at 60 mA. Pentode section of 6JZ8 compactron is in load circuit as series regulator, with triode section controlling grid bias of pentode. Intended for small receivers and converters. Diodes are 1N1696. Other values are: L1 8-H 75-mA Stancor C1355; T1 Stancor PC8419 with 6.3 V 3 A and 480 V CT 70 mA secondaries; R1 2.2 meg; R2-R4 1 meg; R5 470K.—"Hobby Manual," General Electric, Owensboro, Ky., 1965, p 187.

12 V AT 0.5 A—Two-transistor shunt regulator and 12-V reference battery provide 0.25% regulation. Battery current drain is negligible. Q1 must be able to dissipate same power as load.—R. Selleck, Transistor Shunt Regulator Improves Voltage Control, *Electronic Design*, June 8, 1964, p 73–74.

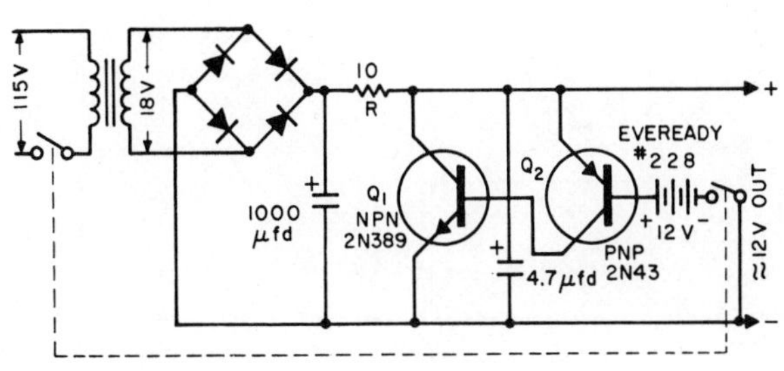

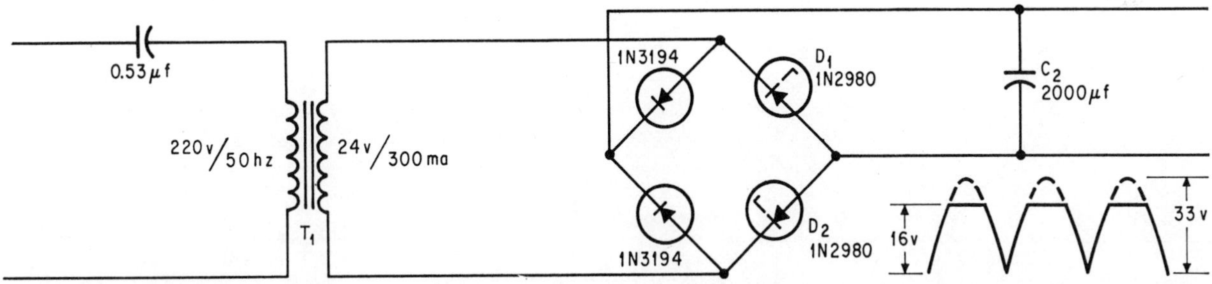

MAGNETIC-RESONANCE CURRENT-LIMITING—With zener diodes in bridge-rectifier power supply, regulating-current drain of diodes is limited by saturation of power supply. Transformer then acts as inductance between its primary and secondary, and this in turn forms low-Q series resonant circuit with capacitor in primary, to limit current flow. With circuit shown, load current remains above about 250 mA until output voltage reaches 16 V, after which current drops rapidly and reaches zero at about 17 V. Article gives design equation. Peak-clipping action makes output voltage easy to filter.—O. A. Horna, Magnetic Resonance Limits Zener Diode Current, *Electronics*, Dec. 11, 1967, p 97–98.

NOTE: To locate additional circuits in the category of this chapter, use the index at the back of this book. Check also the author's "Sourcebook of Electronic Circuits," published by McGraw-Hill in 1968.

CHAPTER 71
Regulator Circuits

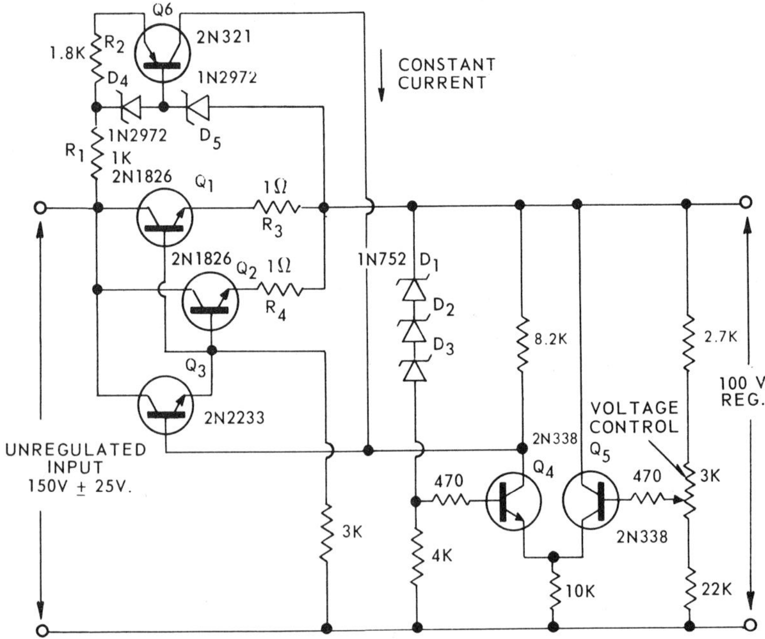

100 V AT 4 A—Holds d-c output constant within 0.2 V for maximum load variation and 25 V swing in unregulated 150-V input. Paralleled series-regulator transistors are used in design to stay well within safe-area ratings. Three 5-V zeners in series give better temperature coefficient than 15-V zener. Preregulator Q6 supplies constant current to differential amplifier and driver, to help eliminate ripple current.—"Silicon Power Transistor Handbook," Westinghouse, Youngwood, Pa., p 6–19.

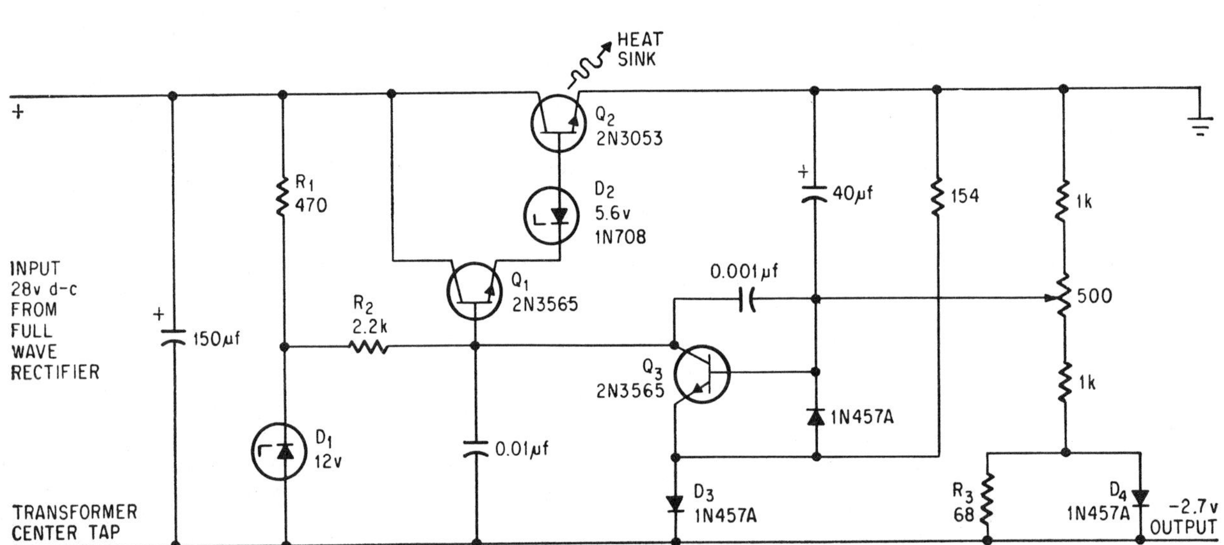

2.7-V REPLACEMENT FOR MERCURY CELL—Gives 0.01% regulation from 28-V d-c line and load regulation of 1%, at parts cost under $7. Zener diode D2 in regulator boosts operating voltage of amplifier that detects voltage differences. D1 merely acts with R1 to establish constant voltage source at junction with R2, making Q1 less susceptible to input line variations.—E. Luttrell, Low Voltage Supply Produces Good Regulation at Low Cost, *Electronics*, Jan. 23, 1967, p 91.

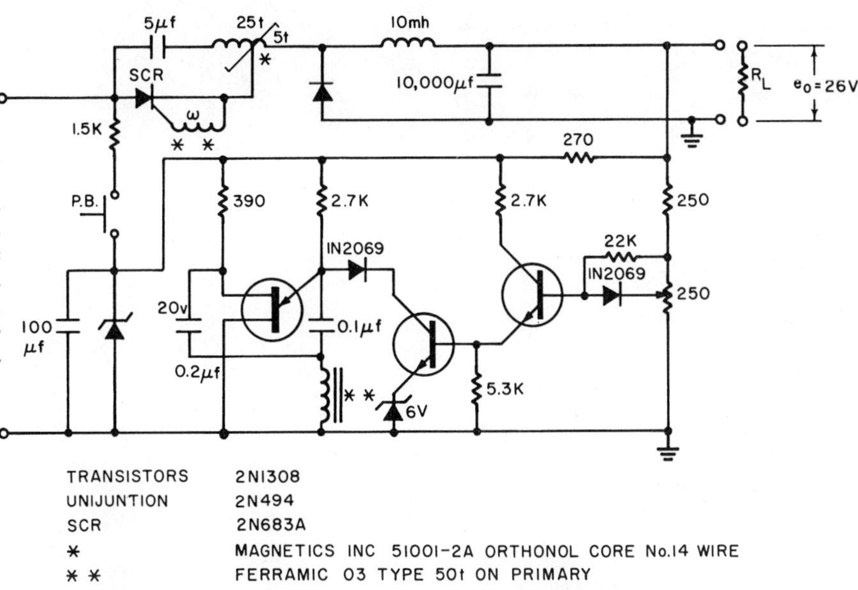

SWITCHING-MODE REGULATOR—Uses scr in commutating circuit. Output voltage is compared with voltage across reference diode and difference used to control current flow into frequency control section of ujt oscillator whose pulses trigger scr on. Frequency of ujt thus controls output voltage. Article describes operation in detail and gives design equations.—R. T. Windecker, Which Device for High-Power Switching?, *Electronic Design*, Sept. 14, 1964, p 64–69.

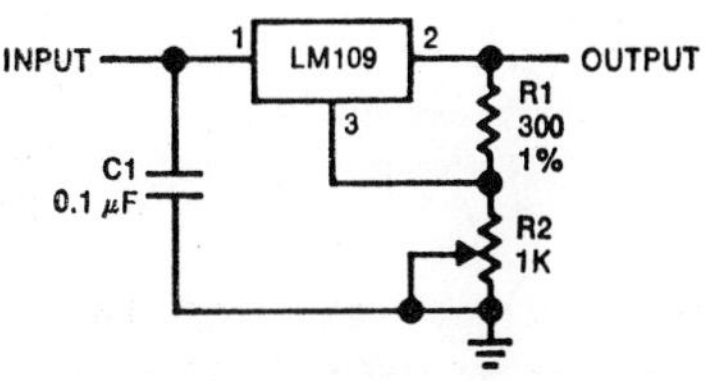

IC REGULATOR FOR LOGIC SUPPLY—Requires only three connections to provide regulation and thermal overload protection for standard 5-V digital logic power supply. Gives output currents over 1 A.—Adjustable-Output Regulator (National Semiconductor ad), *Electronic News*, June 8, 1970, p 11.

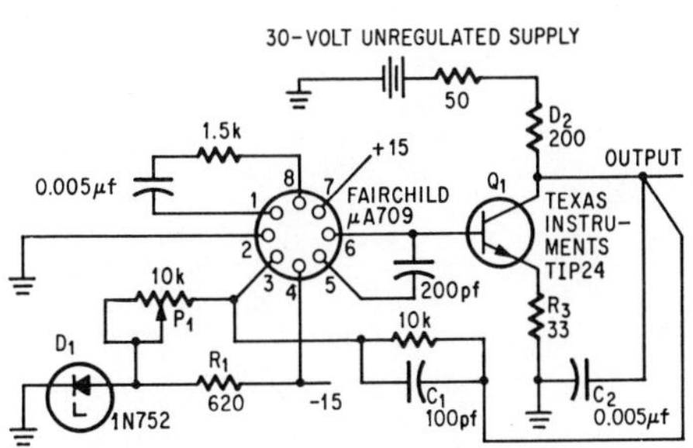

OPAMP REGULATES AND PROTECTS—Shunt regulator Q1 drives Fairchild IC operational amplifier, with zener D1 serving as voltage reference. P1 adjusts opamp gain, thereby changing output voltage over range of 6 to 25 V. At 15 V, load current can vary from 0 to 60 mA with little effect on voltage. Short-circuit current is limited to 120 mA. External low-power zeners provide 15-V supply voltages for IC.—R. D. Guyton, IC Operational Amplifier Makes Supply Short-Circuit Proof, *Electronics*, Sept. 18, 1967, p 106.

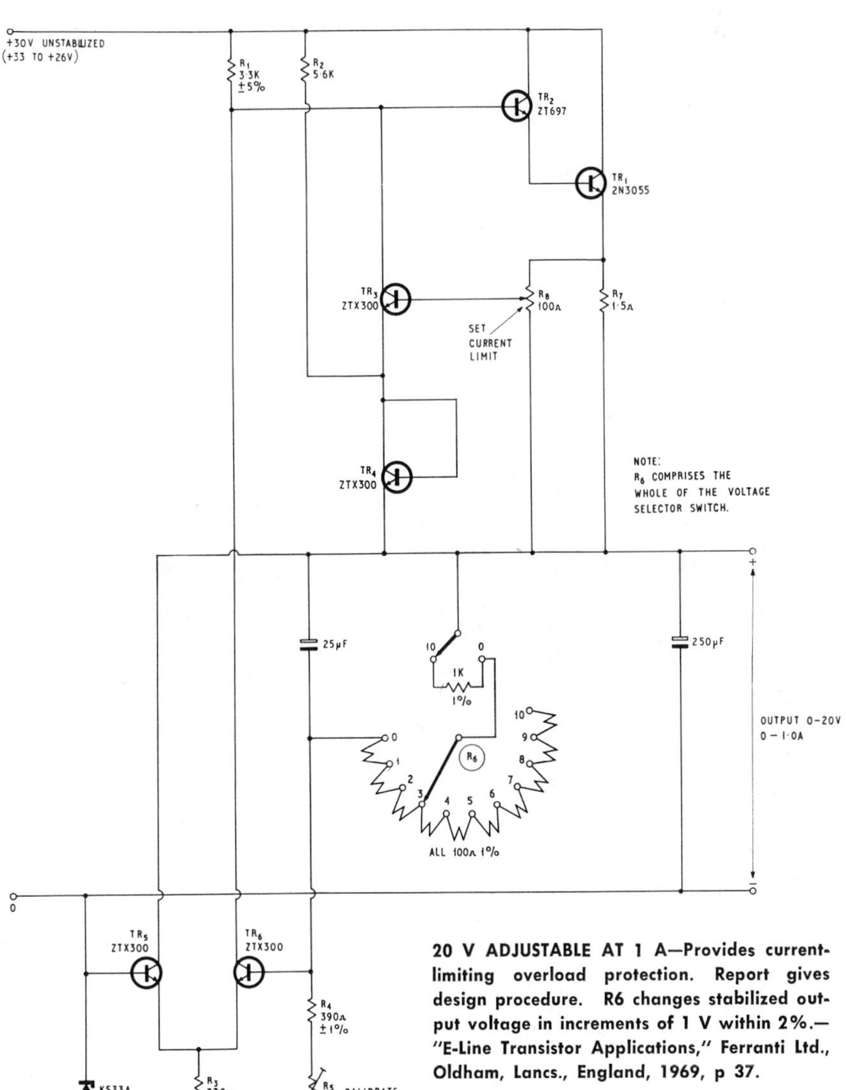

20 V ADJUSTABLE AT 1 A—Provides current-limiting overload protection. Report gives design procedure. R6 changes stabilized output voltage in increments of 1 V within 2%.—"E-Line Transistor Applications," Ferranti Ltd., Oldham, Lancs., England, 1969, p 37.

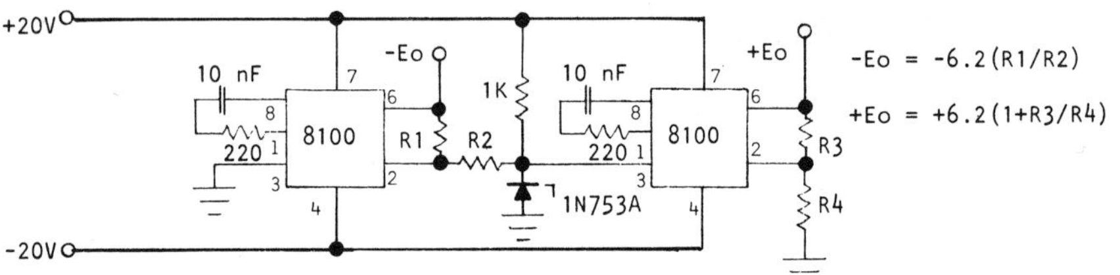

COMMON-REFERENCE DUAL REGULATOR—Provides two voltages having different values and opposite polarities, regulated by means of one zener diode. Voltage values are determined by resistor values.—Applying the Model 8100 Monolithic Voltage Regulator, Optical Electronics, Tucson, Ariz., No. 10141.

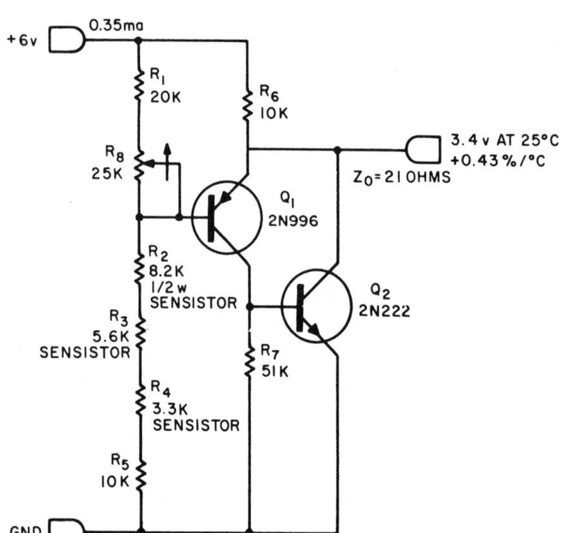

TEMPERATURE COMPENSATION—Uses sensistors to temperature-stabilize voltage at which ranges are changed in count-rate meter. Output of 3.4 V is adjustable. Temperature coefficient is +0.43%.—S. Thomas, N-Decade Count-Rate Meter, *Electronic Design*, March 15, 1965, p 34–39.

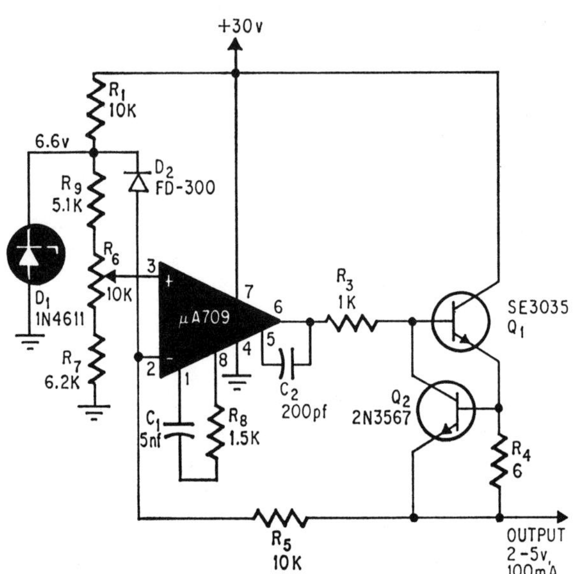

IC VOLTAGE-LOWERING REGULATOR—Uses Fairchild μA709 opamp operating at unity gain, with its input tapped across zener reference D1. Q2 provides surge protection. Article contains 13 other IC opamp application circuits.—J. F. Gifford and M. Markkula, Linear IC's: Part 5, Ins and Outs of Op Amps, *Electronics*, Nov. 27, 1967, p 84–93.

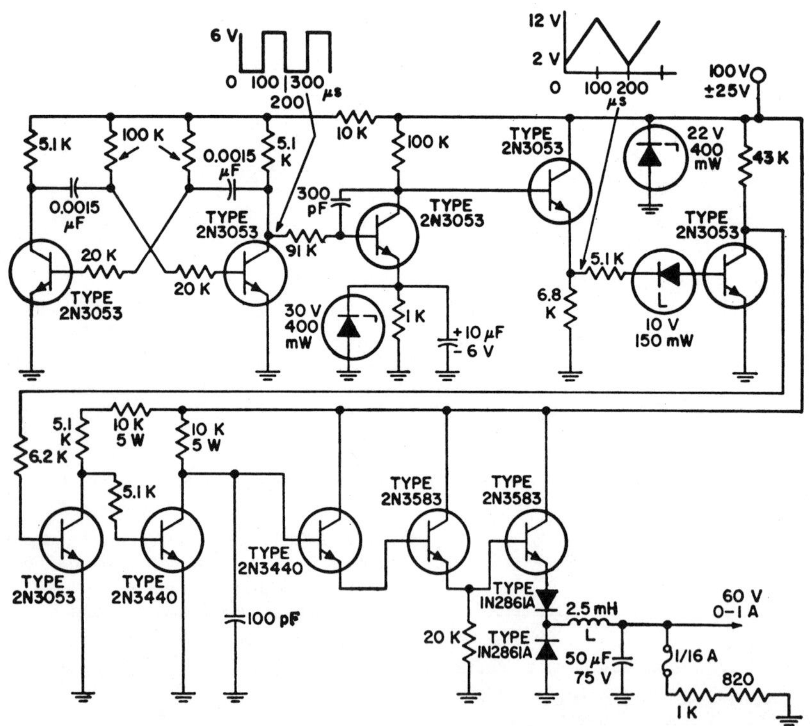

STEP-DOWN SWITCHING REGULATOR—Can be used as d-c step-down transformer for obtaining low d-c voltage from a-c line. Input to regulator is 100 V d-c obtained from line through rectifier, and output is 60 V d-c for loads up to 1 A.—"Silicon Power Circuits Manual," RCA, Harrison, N.J., SP-51, p 225.

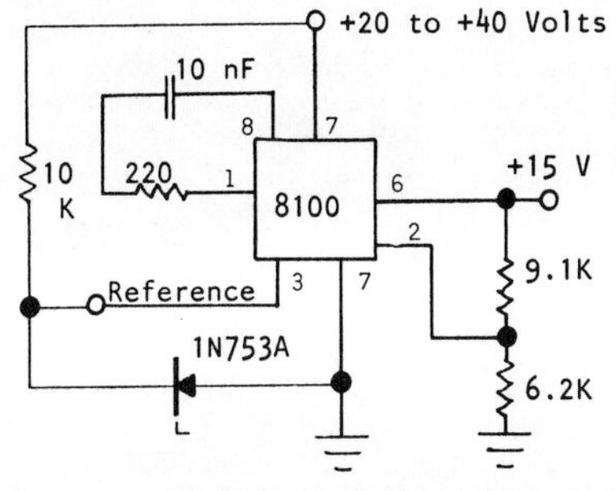

POSITIVE SWITCHING REGULATOR—Output voltage is equal to 99% of reference voltage. Small amount of positive feedback causes regulator to switch. Average voltage across output smoothing capacitor is sensed and used to govern output voltage level and switching activity of 8100.—Applying the Model 8100 Monolithic Voltage Regulator, Optical Electronics, Tucson, Ariz., No. 10141.

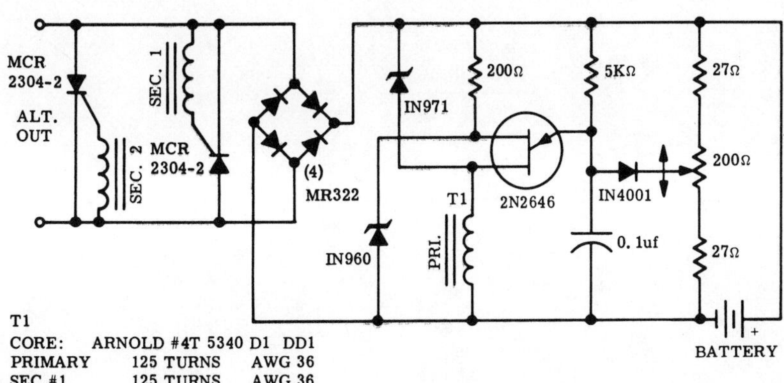

T1
CORE: ARNOLD #4T 5340 D1 DD1
PRIMARY 125 TURNS AWG 36
SEC #1 125 TURNS AWG 36
SEC #2 125 TURNS AWG 36
TRIFILAR WOUND

OUTBOARD-ENGINE ALTERNATOR REGULATOR—Controls 15-A d-c charging current to storage battery by shorting output of p-m alternator field when battery is charged, when scr's are triggered by voltage-sensitive ujt circuit. Shorting output does not appreciably increase maximum output current of alternator. Serves to protect bridge rectifiers against high-voltage stress otherwise occurring if alternator circuit were opened.—"Zener Diode Handbook," Motorola, Phoenix, Ariz., 1967, p 8-8.

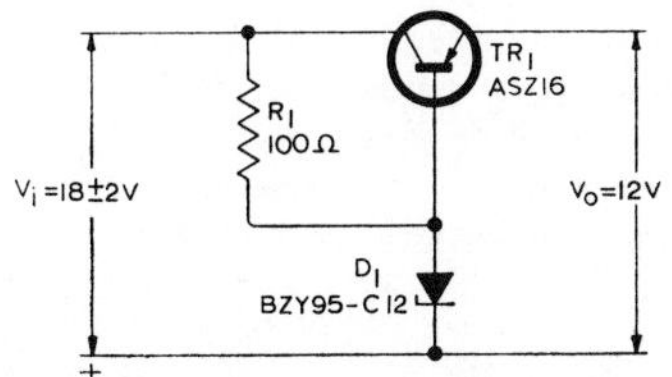

SERIES TRANSISTOR WITH ZENER—Provides essentially constant output of 12 V d-c at 250 mA for input of 16 to 20 V d-c. Book gives design equations.—"Voltage Regulator (Zener) Diodes," Philips, Pub. Dept., Elcoma Div., Eindhoven, The Netherlands, p 35.

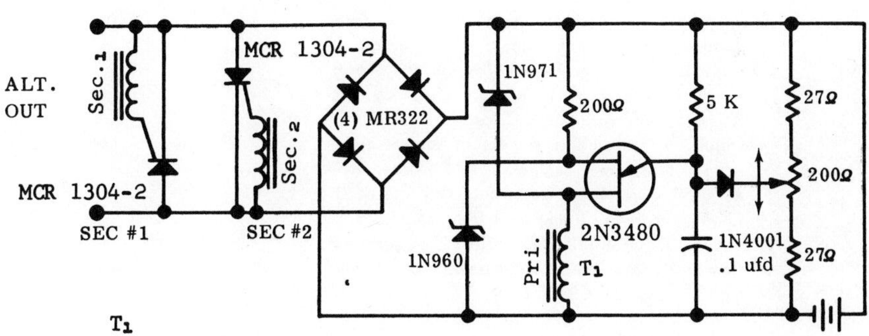

T_1

CORE: ARNOLD #4T 5340 D1 DD1
PRIMARY 125 TURNS AWG 36
SEC #1 125 TURNS AWG 36
SEC #2 125 TURNS AWG 36
TRIFILAR WOUND

BATTERY

OUTBOARD-ENGINE ALTERNATOR REGULATOR—Designed for alternators having permanent-magnet fields. Regulates 15-A charging current for battery by shorting output of alternator when triggered by ujt voltage-sensing circuit. With most alternators, shorting does not appreciably increase output current. Avoids damaging bridge rectifiers with inductive voltage spikes that would occur if output circuit were opened.—"Circuits Manual," Motorola, Phoenix, Ariz., 1965, p 8-4-3.

22–30 V SERIES REGULATOR—Uses three paralleled transistors in series with load to hold output voltage constant by varying load current. Reference is zener CR connected with reverse bias. Gives line regulation within 1% and load regulation within 0.5%. R9 varies output voltage. Values: R1 1.2K; R2, R4, R6 0.1; R3 2K; R5 570; R7 270; R8, R10 1K; R9 1K pot; C1 1 μF; C2 100 μF; CR 12-V zener.—"Transistor Manual," RCA, Harrison, N.J., SC-13, p 515.

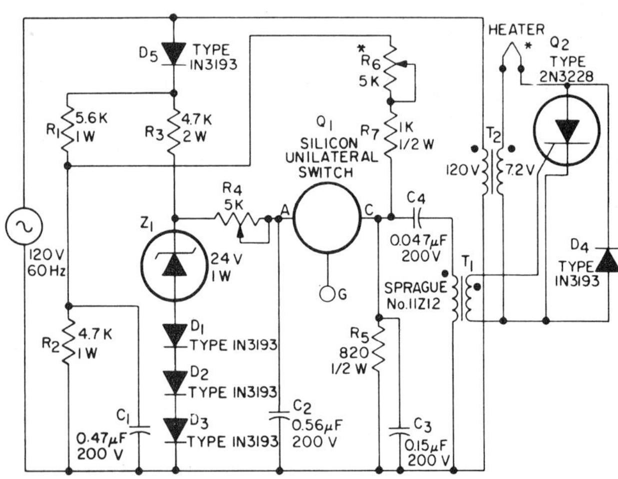

* IN THE CLOSED-LOOP REGULATOR R_6 IS REPLACED BY A PHOTOCELL RCA SQ2520 AND A POTENTIOMETER IN SERIES WITH A 6-VOLT INCANDESCENT LAMP IS CONNECTED IN PARALLEL WITH THE HEATER TERMINALS
NOTE: ALL RESISTOR VALUES ARE IN OHMS

CONSTANT LAMP VOLTAGE—Used to maintain constant voltage across heater of tube or filament of incandescent lamp. Full voltage is applied for one half-cycle through D4, while other half-cycle is phase-controlled by scr to provide regulation. Circuit is open-loop regulator with built-in protection against open or short-circuited component. Q1 has thyristor characteristics approximating those of ideal four-layer diode, switching at about 8 V.—G. J. Granieri, AC Voltage Regulators Using Thyristors, RCA, Harrison, N.J., Application Note AN-3886, 1969.

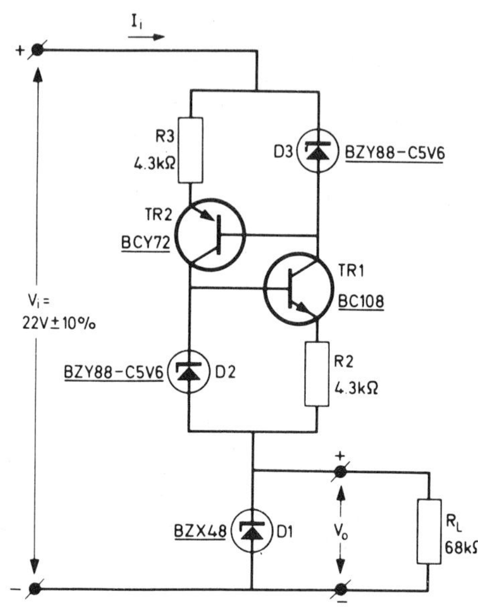

COMPLEMENTARY CONSTANT-CURRENT SOURCE—Highly stable constant-current source provides stabilized 6.5 V d-c output across load for input voltage as low as 18.5 V.—High-Stability Reference Diodes BZX47 Family, Philips, Pub. Dept., Elcoma Div., Eindhoven, The Netherlands, No. 331, 1968.

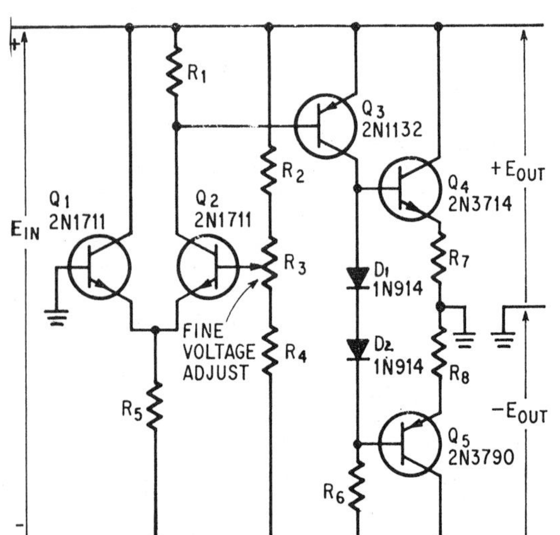

POSITIVE AND NEGATIVE VOLTAGES—Shunt regulator can provide any combination of positive and negative output voltages whose sum is equal to output of single regulated supply. Differential amplifier Q1-Q2 compares ground reference (formed by R2-R3-R4) to ground. Table gives values of components for two combinations of input and output voltages.—A. J. Mayle, Shunt Regulator Provides Dual Output Voltages, *Electronics*, Oct. 14, 1968, p 121–122.

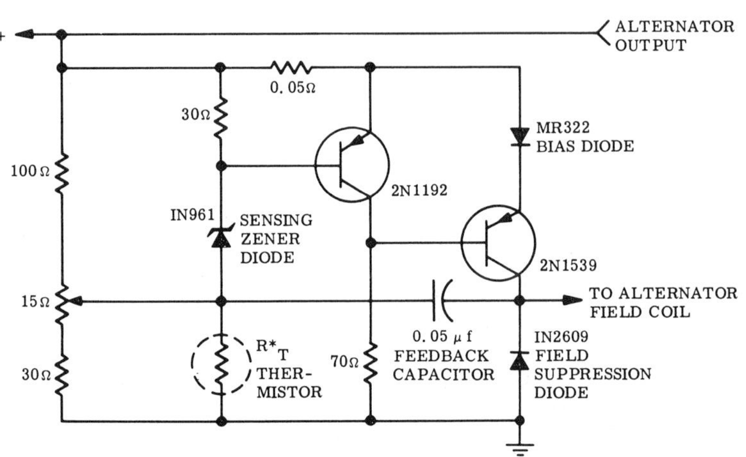

* THE VALUE OF R_T DEPENDS ON THE SLOPE OF THE VOLTAGE REGULATION VERSUS TEMPERATURE CURVE.

ALTERNATOR VOLTAGE REGULATOR—Monitors battery voltage level, allowing charging current to flow from alternator when battery voltage is low, and switching off charging current when battery is fully charged. Uses 1N2609 diode across alternator field to prevent buildup of high induced voltage when coil current is interrupted. Switching action occurs many times per second, to keep battery fully charged at all times.—"Zener Diode Handbook," Motorola, Phoenix, Ariz., 1967, p 8-4.

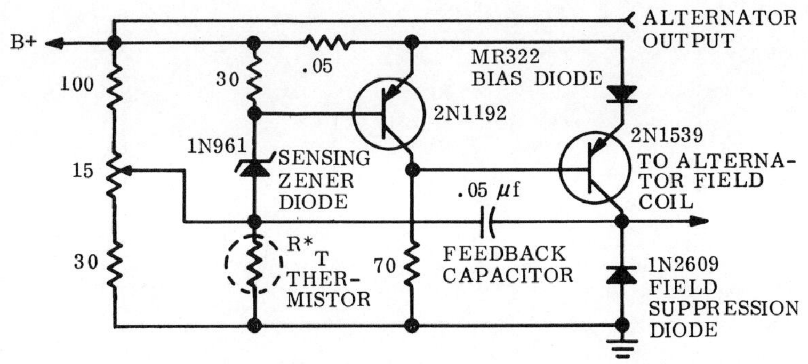

ALTERNATOR VOLTAGE REGULATOR—Used to control charging rate of auto storage battery. Switching action occurs many times per second, to keep battery charge essentially constant at maximum value for optimum operation. Choice of thermistor resistance depends on slope of curve for voltage regulation vs temperature.—"Circuits Manual," Motorola, Phoenix, Ariz., 1965, p 8-3-2.

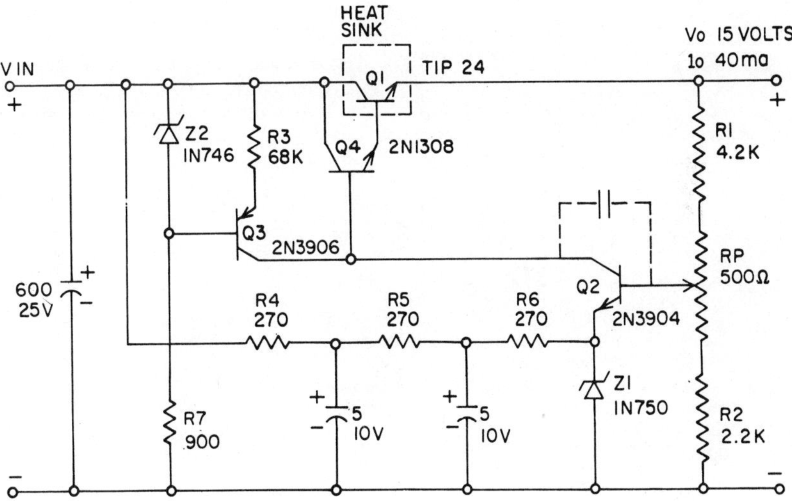

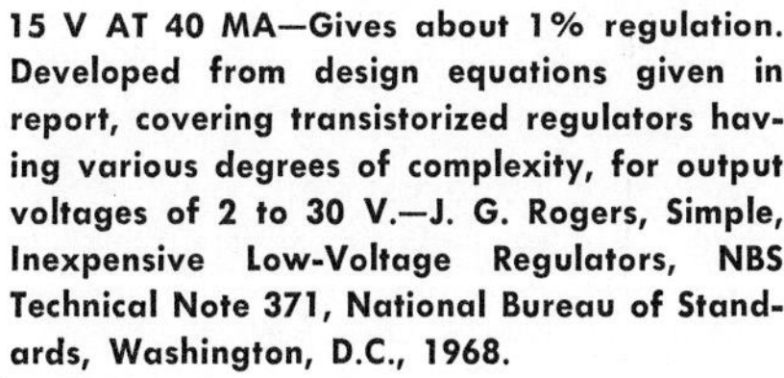
15 V AT 40 MA—Gives about 1% regulation. Developed from design equations given in report, covering transistorized regulators having various degrees of complexity, for output voltages of 2 to 30 V.—J. G. Rogers, Simple, Inexpensive Low-Voltage Regulators, NBS Technical Note 371, National Bureau of Standards, Washington, D.C., 1968.

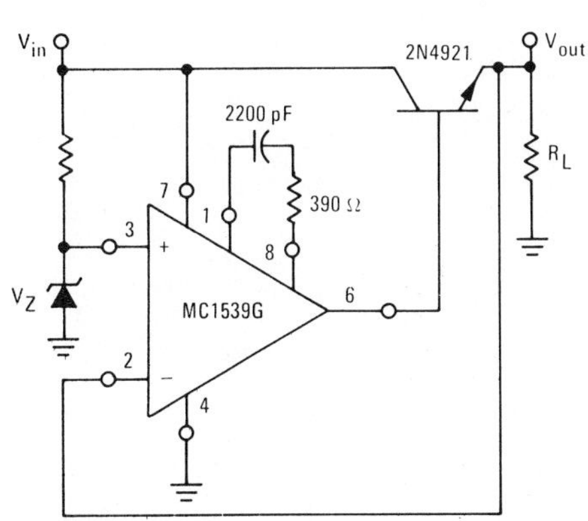

ERROR-SENSING OPAMP—Motorola opamp compares output voltage of power supply with zener reference voltage and adjusts current through series-pass transistor accordingly. Opamp derives its own operating power from input voltage. Load regulation is better than 0.1% for currents up to 300 mA.—K. Huehne, The Continuing Dominance of the Operational Amplifier, "State-of-the-Art—Linears in Action," Motorola, Phoenix, Ariz., 1969, p 5—13.

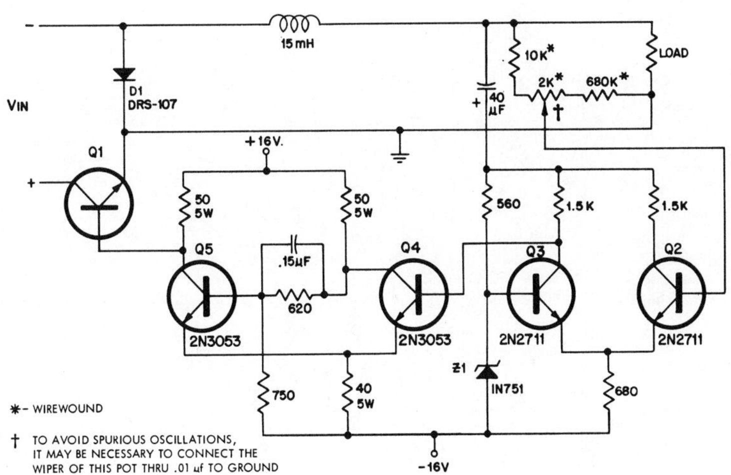

PWM SWITCHING REGULATOR—With d-c input varying 25 V above and below 250 V, output is constant at 200 V within fraction of volt for 2-A load current. Efficiency varies with power output, in range of 80% to 92%. Differential amplifier Q2-Q3 senses proportional amount of ripple present in output, compares it with reference zener, and delivers error signal to trigger Q4-Q5 for turning series transistor Q1 on or off in accordance with load requirements. Off and on times of Schmitt trigger change with load, as also does switching frequency, to give pulse width modulation.—Pulse Width Modulated Switching Regulator, Delco Radio, Kokomo, Ind., No. 39, 1967.

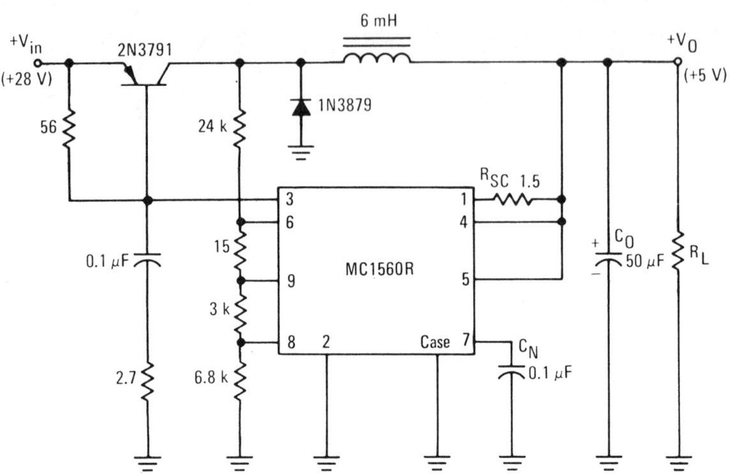

SWITCHING REGULATOR—Self-oscillating circuit using IC voltage regulator serves as efficient switching regulator.—D. Kesner, Voltage Regulators—Old and New, "State-of-the-Art—Linears in Action," Motorola, Phoenix, Ariz., 1969, p 14–20.

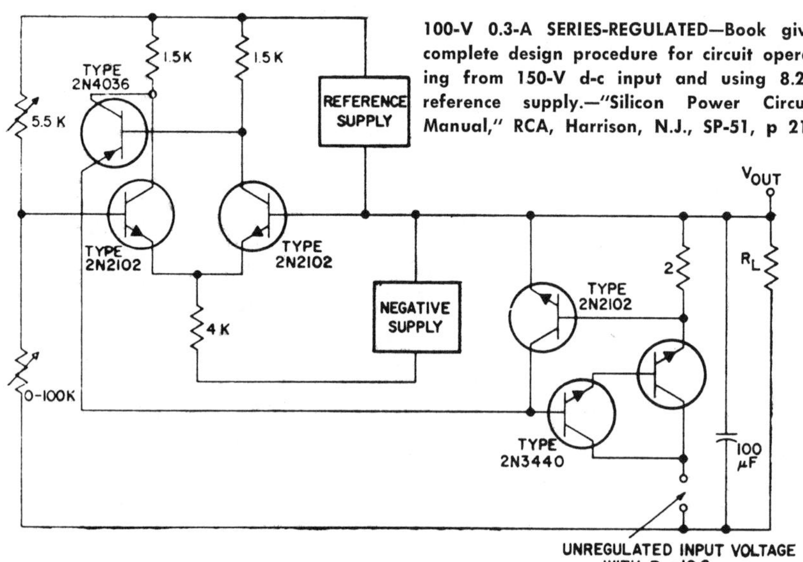

100-V 0.3-A SERIES-REGULATED—Book gives complete design procedure for circuit operating from 150-V d-c input and using 8.2-V reference supply.—"Silicon Power Circuits Manual," RCA, Harrison, N.J., SP-51, p 215.

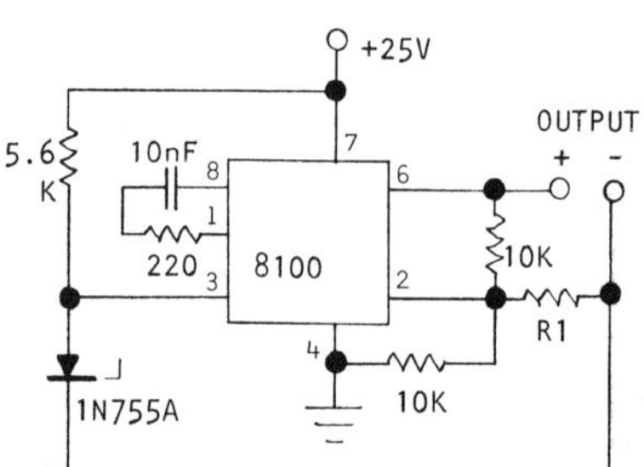

LONG-LINE COMPENSATION—Used to overcome poor regulation in system having remote sensing of many physically scattered loads. Insertion of small amount of positive feedback into IC regulator causes voltage to increase in proportion to increasing load current.—Applying the Model 8100 Monolithic Voltage Regulator, Optical Electronics, Tucson, Ariz., No. 10141.

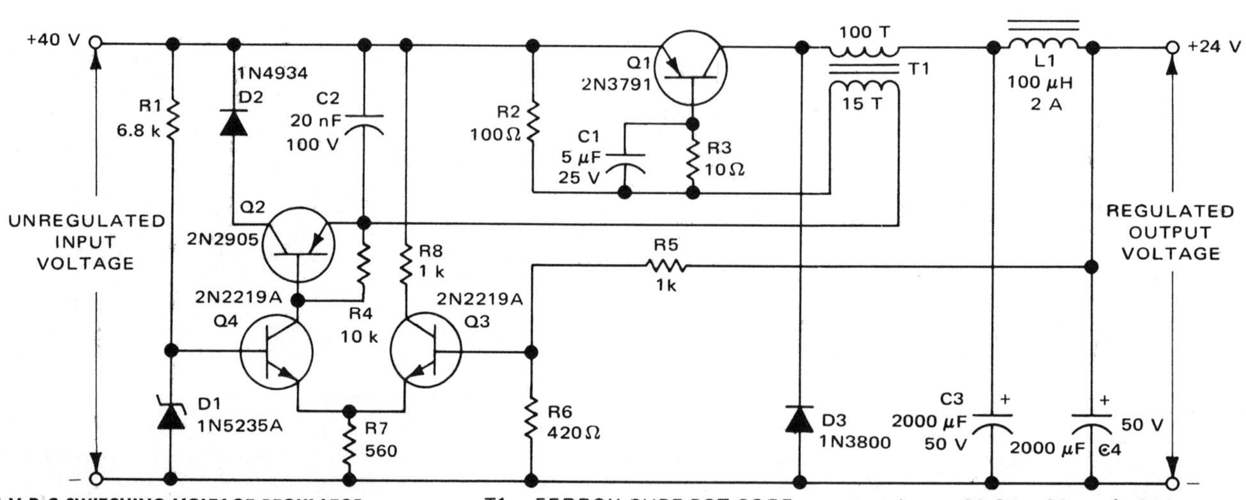

T1 – FERROX CUBE POT CORE 3622P-3E; 100 T PRIMARY 15 T SECONDARY

24-V D-C SWITCHING VOLTAGE REGULATOR—Output is held within 1% of 24 V for load currents of 100 mA to 2 mA and for supply voltage changes of 10% above and below 40 V d-c. Power switching transistor Q1 is controlled by feedback winding of T1 and transistors Q2-Q4. Q3 and Q4 serve as differential voltage comparator with zener D1. Maximum frequency of blocking oscillator action is 6 kHz at highest input voltages.—"Semiconductor Power Circuits Handbook," Motorola, Phoenix, Ariz., 1968, p 3–15.

PROPORTIONAL VOLTAGE REGULATOR—Provides 12 V at 2 A while d-c input varies as much as 15% in either direction from 17 V. Voltage proportional to output is compared to that of reference diode CR4, differential signal is amplified by Q3, and resulting output is used to control current through series transistor Q1 in such a way that voltage across load remains constant. Best suited for applications requiring very low internal impedance to a-c load currents.—Pulse Width Modulated Voltage Regulator, Delco Radio, Kokomo, Ind., No. 9B, 1965.

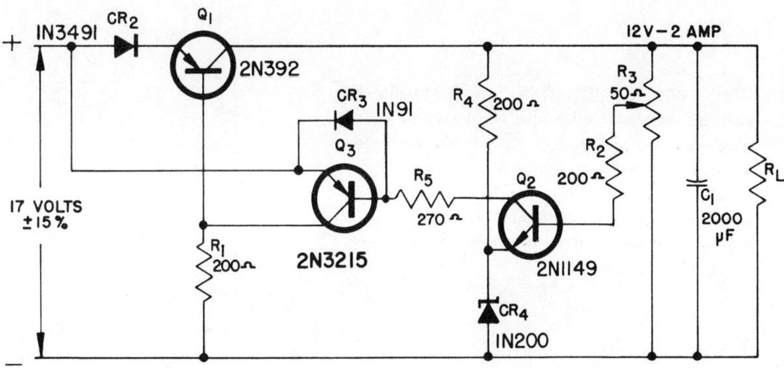

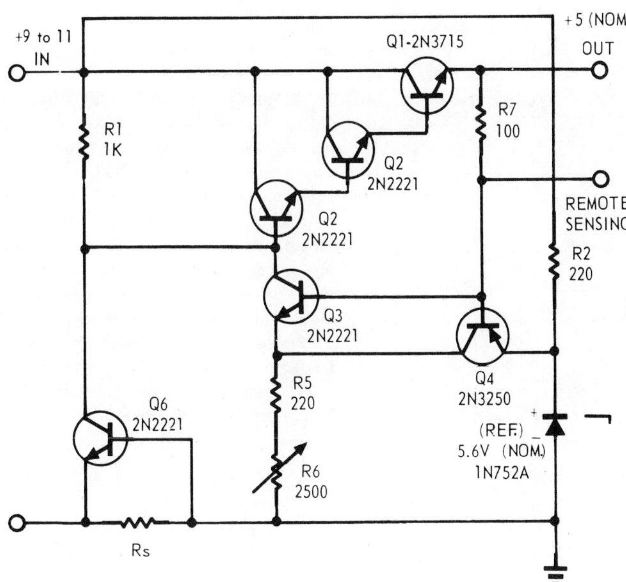

5 V FOR HIGH-CURRENT LOGIC—High-power pass transistor Q1 permits handling large currents up to limits of heat sink used. Includes short-circuit protection and connection for remote sensing of output voltage. Location of Rs ahead of control loop damps supply impedance and improves stability.—R. C. Sanford, 'Perfect' Regulator Satisfies Logic Circuits, *EDN*, Dec. 15, 1969, p 51–53.

500-W A-C LINE VOLTAGE REGULATOR—Holds a-c output voltage within 2% of 120 V for a-c input line voltage range of 90–140 V. Uses phase-controlled triac Q2 to adjust voltage applied to output transformer. Control circuit is basic ramp-and-pedestal type for scr. Article gives adjustment procedure and load options. Some types of a-c motors may not function properly on output because of its harmonic content.—S. Zimmer, 500 Watt AC Line Voltage and Power Regulator, General Electric, Syracuse, N.Y., No. 201.12, 1965.

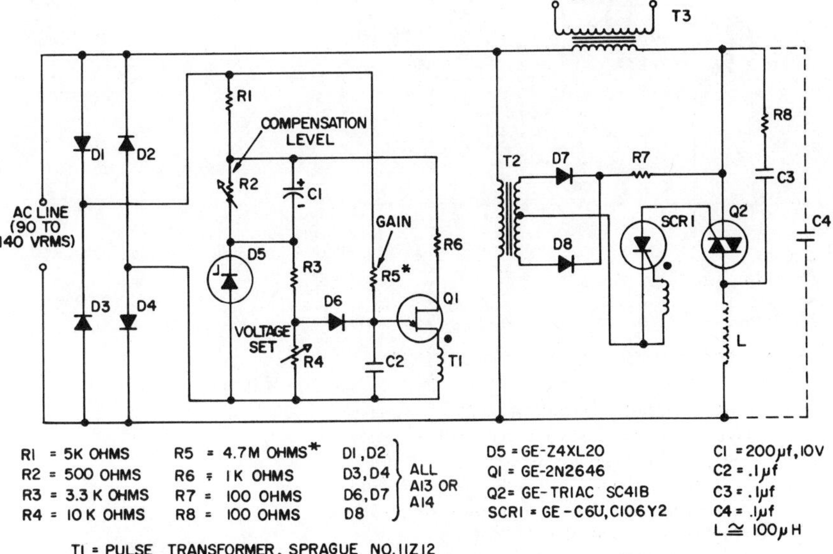

R1 = 5K OHMS
R2 = 500 OHMS
R3 = 3.3 K OHMS
R4 = 10 K OHMS
R5 = 4.7M OHMS*
R6 = 1 K OHMS
R7 = 100 OHMS
R8 = 100 OHMS
D1, D2; D3, D4; D6, D7; D8 — ALL A13 OR A14
D5 = GE-Z4XL20
Q1 = GE-2N2646
Q2 = GE-TRIAC SC41B
SCR1 = GE-C6U, C106Y2
C1 = 200μf, 10V
C2 = .1μf
C3 = .1μf
C4 = .1μf
L ≅ 100μH

T1 = PULSE TRANSFORMER, SPRAGUE NO. 11Z12
T2 = 24 VOLTS CT 300mA, KNIGHT #612476
T3 = SEE DESCRIPTION OF FIG. NO. 1 IN TEXT
*FOR ADJUSTABLE GAIN, USE VARIABLE RESISTOR HERE.

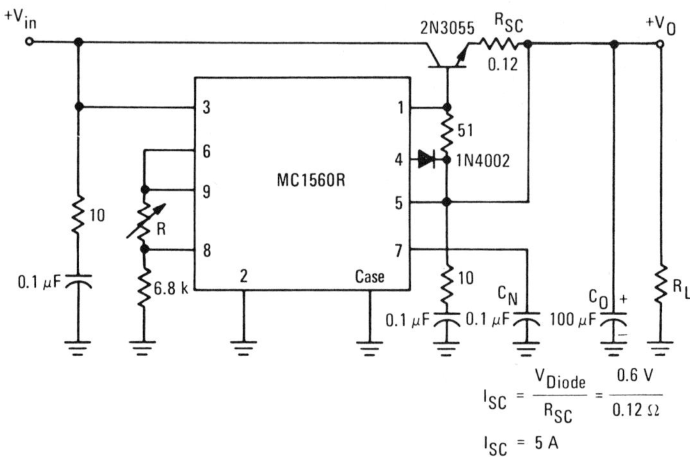

NPN CURRENT BOOSTER—Uses Motorola IC voltage regulator with npn transistor to boost maximum output current available at regulated output voltage above 500-mA rating for IC alone. Input voltage is 20 V.—D. Kesner, Voltage Regulators—Old and New, "State-of-the-Art—Linears in Action," Motorola, Phoenix, Ariz., 1969, p 14–20.

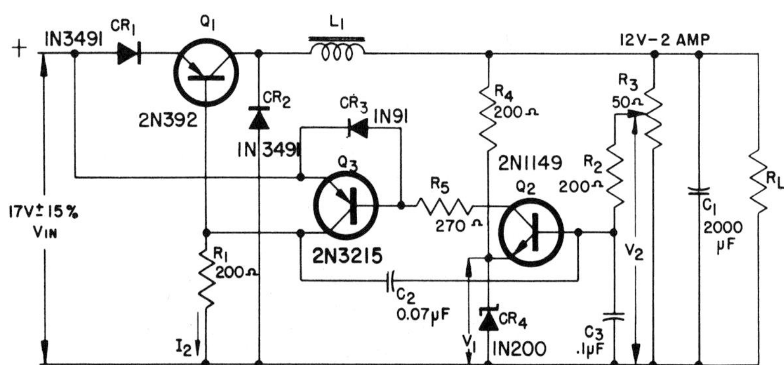

SWITCHING VOLTAGE REGULATOR—Gives efficiencies as high as 80%, even when d-c input voltage is several times larger than d-c output voltage. Q2-Q3 form free-running mvbr whose duty cycle is function of current flowing into base of Q2. Mvbr turns Q1 on and off in such a manner as to keep voltage across load constant. Report gives design criteria. Operates satisfactorily only when ripple in source and load voltages is at frequency substantially below switching frequency of regulator.—Pulse Width Modulated Voltage Regulator, Delco Radio, Kokomo, Ind., No. 9B, 1965.

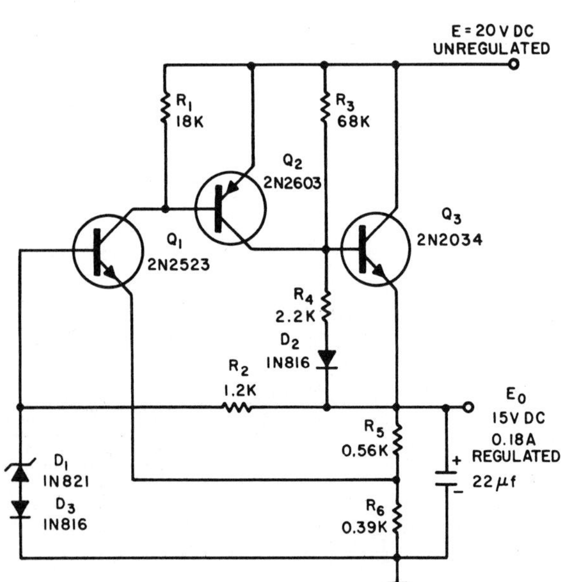

SHORT-CIRCUIT STABLE—Provides stability over wide temperature range, with no more components than for non-short-circuit-stable voltage regulator. Regulation from no load to 180 mA is 0.7%. Regulation for 15% change in unregulated 20-V supply is also 0.7%. Article gives design equations.—R. L. Moser, Self-starting Voltage Regulator is Short-circuit Stable, *Electronic Design*, Feb. 15, 1965, p 79–81.

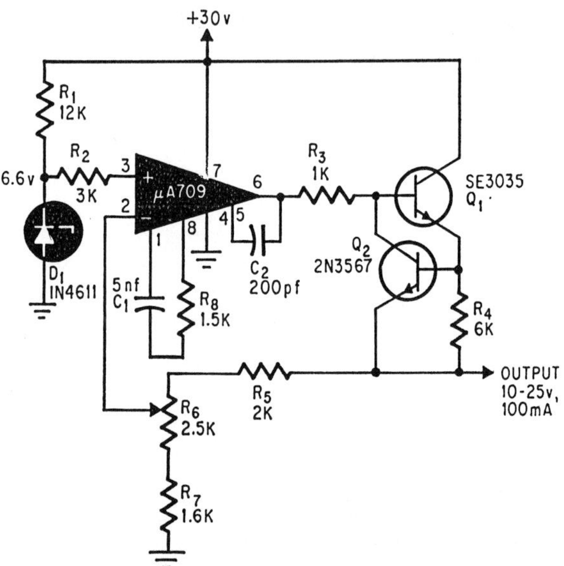

IC VOLTAGE-RAISING REGULATOR—Operates from single positive supply, using Fairchild μA709 opamp, and delivers precisely regulated output voltage above that of temperature-dependent zener reference D1. Q2 provides surge protection when output exceeds 100 mA. Article contains 13 other IC opamp application circuits.—J. F. Gifford and M. Markkula, Linear IC's: Part 5, Ins and Outs of Op Amps, *Electronics*, Nov. 27, 1967, p 84–93.

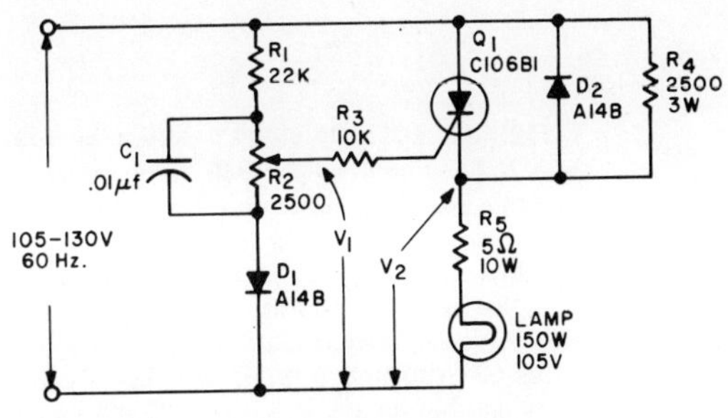

LAMP VOLTAGE REGULATOR—Simple regulator, designed for specific 150-W lamp, measures lamp power by measuring filament resistance. During negative half-cycle, lamp receives full current through D2. At beginning of positive half-cycle, R4 provides bias current to develop voltage V2 that depends on lamp resistance, for comparison with reference voltage V1. Phase-controlled triggering of scr occurs when V1 is more positive than V2. Drawbacks are 13-W power dissipation in R4 and R5 and flicker noticeable with peripheral vision.—E. K. Howell, Small Scale Integration in Low Cost Control Circuits, General Electric, Syracuse, N.Y., No. 671.9, 1968, p 20.

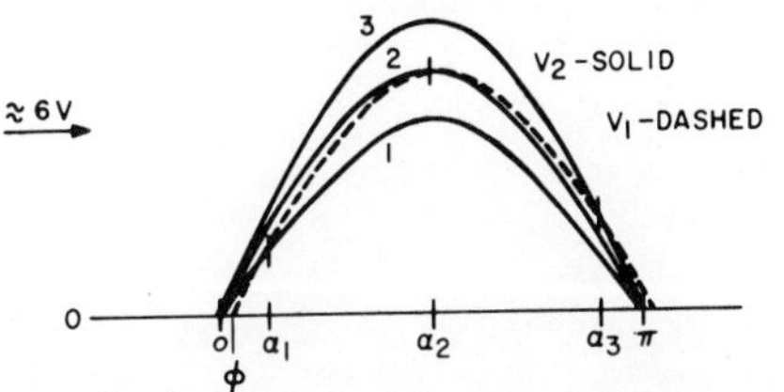

CASE 1 : LAMP R LOW, TRIGGERING ADVANCES TO α_1; LOW LINE VOLTAGE.
CASE 2 : LAMP R NORMAL, TRIGGERING AT α_2; MEDIAN LINE VOLTAGE.
CASE 3 : LAMP R HIGH, TRIGGERING AT α_3; HIGH LINE VOLTAGE.
NOTE: GAIN & STABILITY CONTROLLED BY C_1 (PHASE SHIFT ϕ)

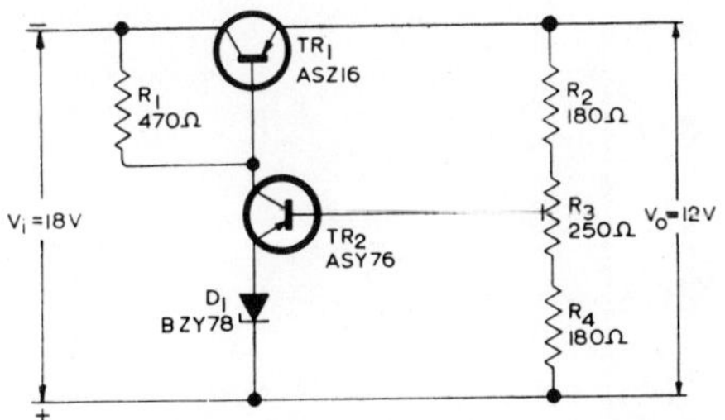

12 V AT 50 MA FROM 18 V D-C—Two-transistor series regulator uses zener as reference. Use of amplifier stage TR2 to control series transistor reduces output impedance of supply and thus greatly improves stabilization factor. —"Voltage Regulator (Zener) Diodes," Philips, Pub. Dept., Elcoma Div., Eindhoven, The Netherlands, p 43.

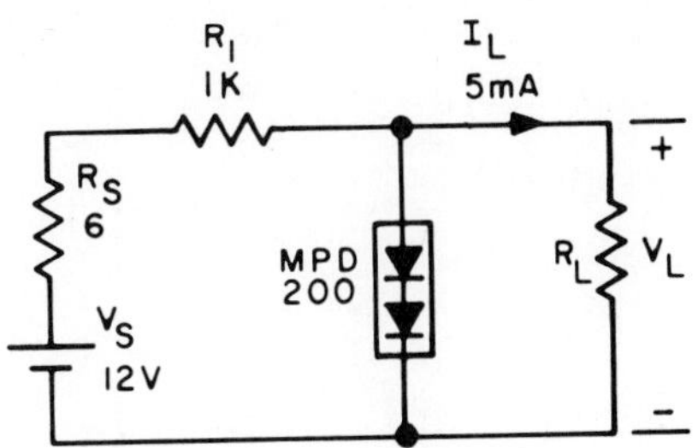

12-V DIODE REGULATOR—Multi-pellet diode provides good regulation (about 0.5%) against change in voltage source for transistors. Output impedance of regulator is about 5 ohms, and efficiency is high compared to that of resistive voltage-divider regulator for same impedance.—Silicon Multi-Pellet Diodes MPD200/MPD300/MPD400, General Electric, Syracuse, N.Y., No. 75.42, 1966.

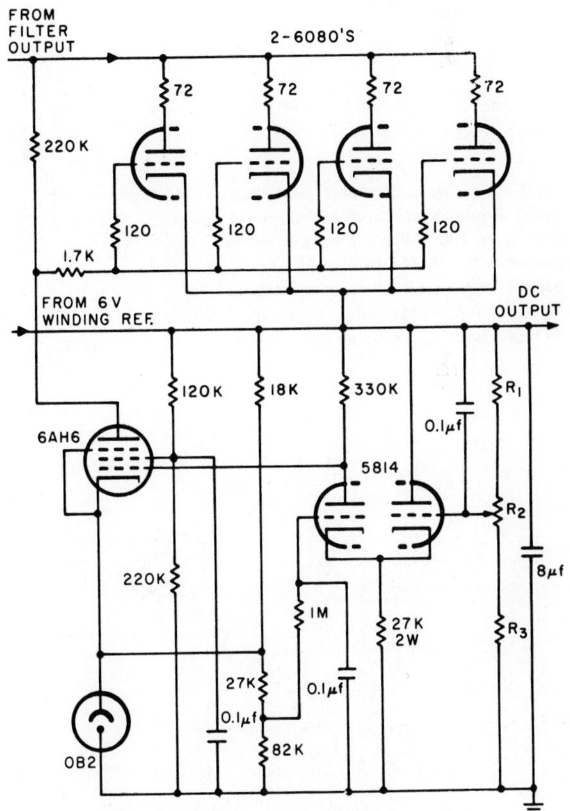

REDUCING OUTPUT IMPEDANCE—Modification of series-regulator power supply for servo provides 400 mA with dynamic impedance below 1 ohm at frequencies from 1 Hz to 100 kHz. Two-stage double-differentiated d-c amplifier is referenced to constant d-c voltage of 0B2. Corrected output signal of 6AH6 final amplifier is applied to grids of series regulators to keep output voltage constant within very narrow limits despite load changes.—E. G. Fonda, Servo-Modification Improved Dynamic Impedance, *Electronic Design*, Feb. 3, 1964, p 48 and 50.

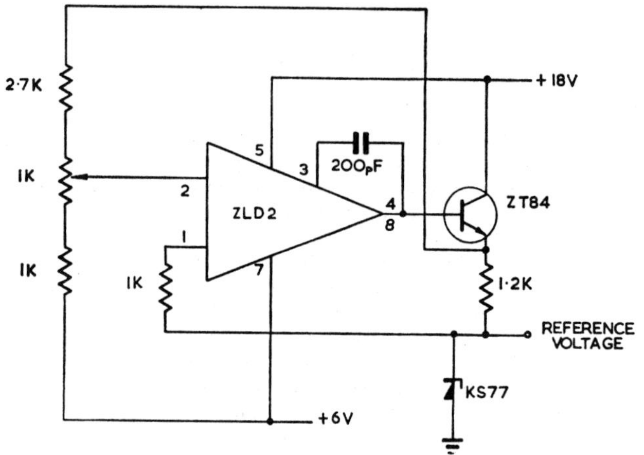

REFERENCE VOLTAGE SUPPLY—Reference voltage is generated by Ferranti KF77 reference voltage package, which has high stability if operating current is held within 5% of 5 mA. Combination of Ferranti ZLD2 IC differential amplifier and npn transistor provide this current with required stability over temperature range of —50 to 120 C and with large variations in d-c supply voltages. Potentiometer is adjusted to give 5 mA accurately through KS77.—Microlin Amplifiers ZLD2S and ZLD2T, Ferranti Ltd., Oldham, Lancs., England, No. 11, 1967, p 16.

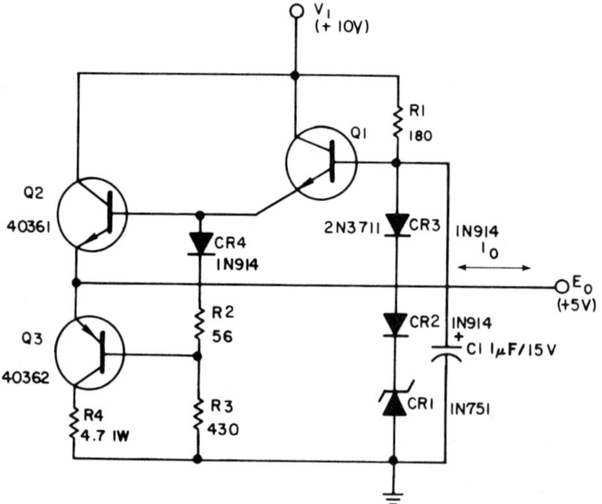

COMBINATION CURRENT SOURCE AND SINK—Provides constant 5-V output by sinking up to 100 mA when output voltage rises above 5 V. Zener CR1 establishes value of output voltage.—R. S. Conero, Voltage Regulator is a Current Source or Sink, *Electronic Design*, June 7, 1970, p 102.

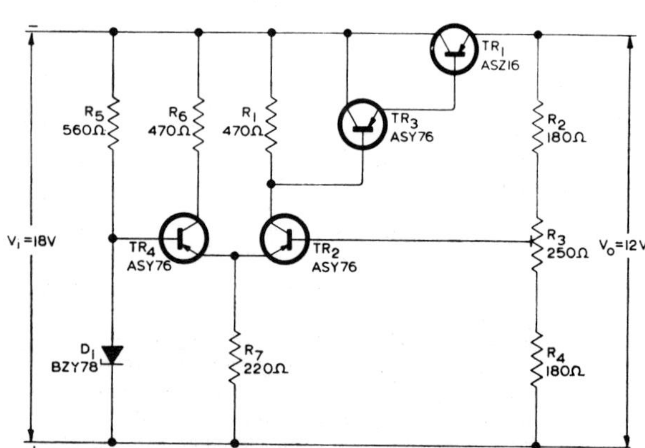

12 V WITH TEMPERATURE COMPENSATION—Effects of temperature changes on TR2 are reduced to about 0.045% per deg C by adding similar transistor TR4 to series regulator. Arrangement does not compensate for effect of temperature changes on zener, however.—"Voltage Regulator (Zener) Diodes," Philips, Pub. Dept., Elcoma Div., Eindhoven, The Netherlands, p. 44.

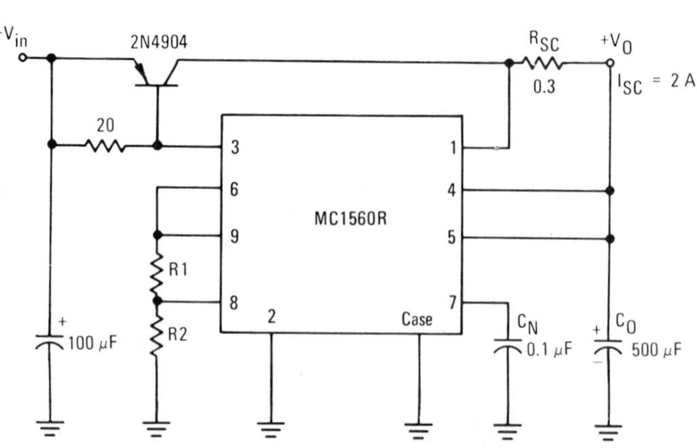

PNP CURRENT BOOSTER—Uses Motorola IC voltage regulator with pnp transistor to boost maximum output current above 500-mA rating for IC alone. Input voltage is 20 V.—D. Kesner, Voltage Regulators—Old and New, "State-of-the-Art—Linears in Action," Motorola, Phoenix, Ariz., 1969, p 14–20.

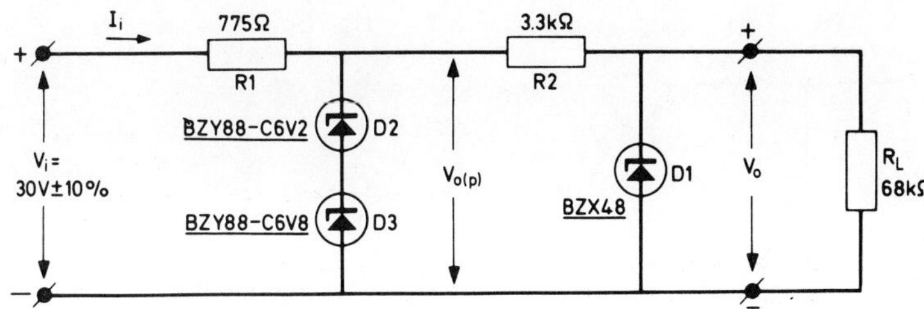

PRESTABILIZATION—Two zeners stabilize input voltage, to make output zener much more effective in holding output voltage at desired 6.5 V d-c.—High-Stability Reference Diodes BZX47 Family, Philips, Pub. Dept., Elcoma Div., Eindhoven, The Netherlands, No. 331, 1968.

DOUBLE SHUNT-DIODE 12-V REGULATOR—Use of two multi-pellet diodes instead of one gives much better regulation (about 0.07%) against voltage source changes.—Silicon Multi-Pellet Diodes MPD200/MPD300/MPD400, General Electric, Syracuse, N.Y., No. 75.42, 1966.

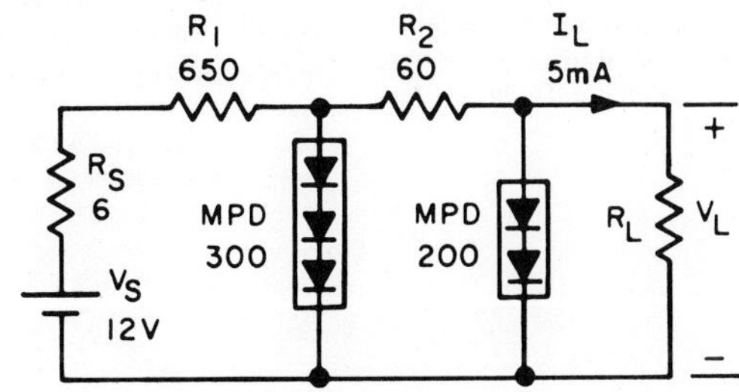

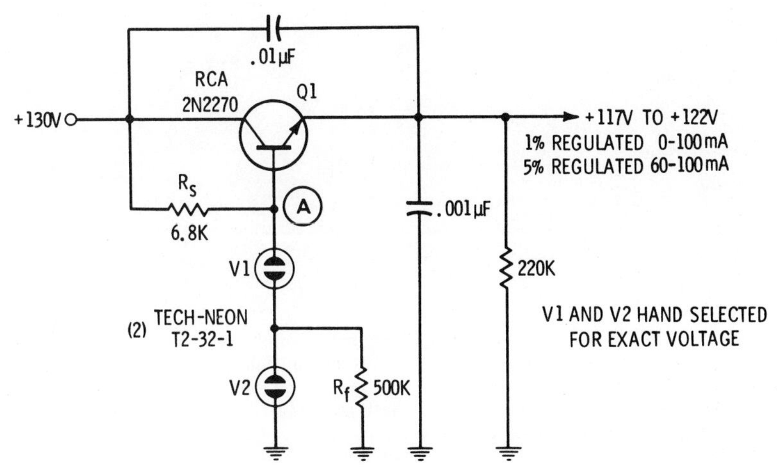

TWO-NEON VOLTAGE REGULATOR—Output voltage is sum of maintaining voltages of neons minus 0.6 V junction drop of transistor.—W. G. Miller, "Using and Understanding Miniature Neon Lamps," H. W. Sams & Co., Indianapolis, Ind., 1969, p 35.

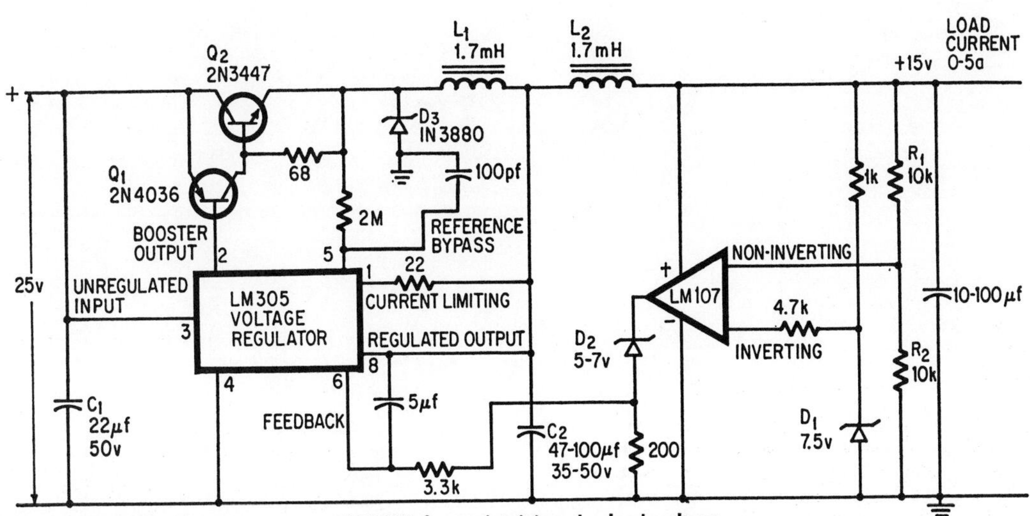

15-V SWITCHING REGULATOR—Operates at 20-kHz switching rate. Shunt opamp provides additional d-c loop voltage gain of up to 100,000 for maintaining d-c load voltage within few microvolts for load currents of 0 to 5 A.—W. L. Brown, IC's Save Power, Boost Efficiency of Regulated Power Supplies, *Electronics*, July 20, 1970, p 94–97.

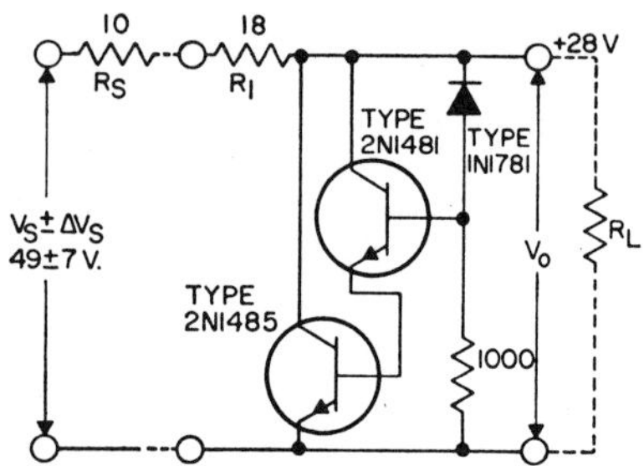

28-V SHUNT REGULATOR—Holds output voltage constant within 0.0125 V of 28 V for input changes of 7 V above and below 49 V d-c. Book gives detailed design procedure. —"Silicon Power Circuits Manual," RCA, Harrison, N.J., SP-51, p 218.

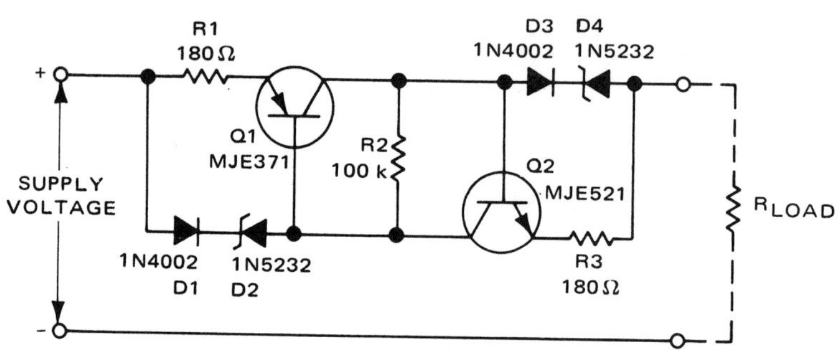

70-MA D-C TWO-TERMINAL CURRENT REGULATOR—Provides current regulation only if supply voltage is greater than sum of voltage drops across all four diodes, which is 12.5 V for components shown. Level of current regulation is diode drop divided by value of R1 (or R3). Circuit can be operated at regulated current levels up to 700 mA if supply voltage is above 13.5 V.—"Semiconductor Power Circuits Handbook," Motorola, Phoenix, Ariz., 1968, p 3–25.

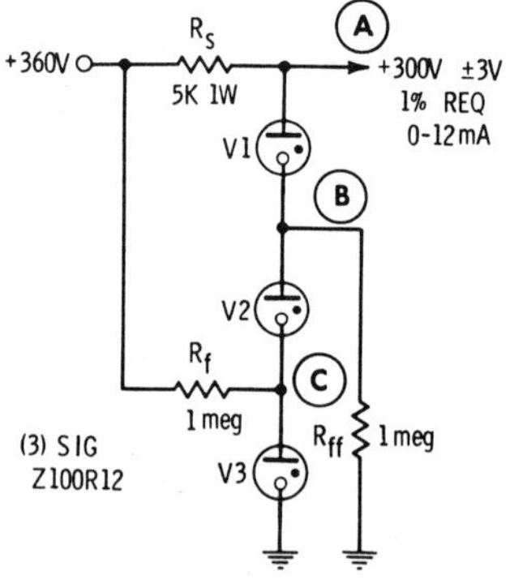

300-V THREE-LAMP REGULATOR—Neon lamps are initially ionized by current through 1-meg shunts which also permit use of supply voltage less than sum of breakdown voltages of lamps.—W. G. Miller, "Using and Understanding Miniature Neon Lamps," H. W. Sams & Co., Indianapolis, Ind., 1969, p 30.

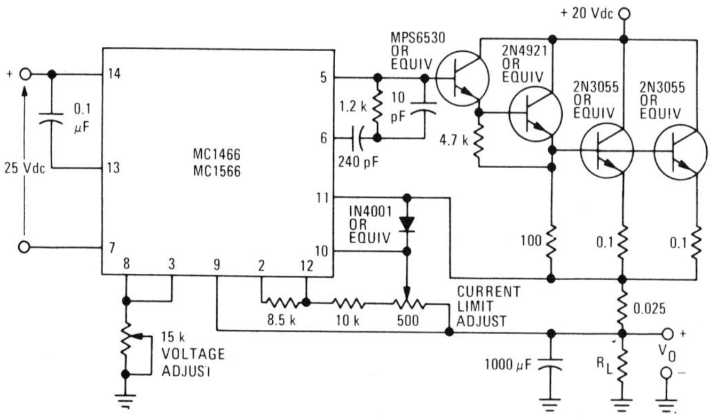

0–5 V D-C AT 10 A—Uses precision wide-range Motorola IC voltage and current regulator, with output voltage and current both adjustable. Both line and load voltage regulation are 0.01% plus 1 mV, and current regulation is 0.1% plus 1 mA.—Precision Wide-Range Voltage and Current Regulator MC1566L/MC1466L, Motorola, Phoenix, Ariz., DS9130, 1969.

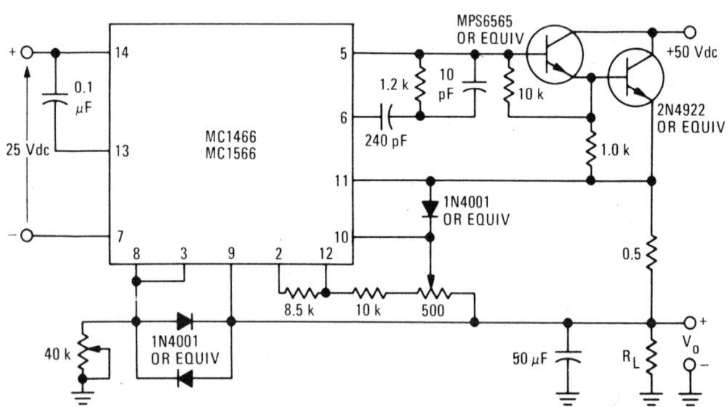

0–40 V D-C AT 0.5 A—Gives laboratory power supply performance, with line and load voltage regulation 0.01% plus 1 mV, using Motorola IC for stepping up 25-V d-c source voltage.—Precision Wide-Range Voltage and Current Regulator MC1566L/MC1466L, Motorola, Phoenix, Ariz., DS9130, 1969.

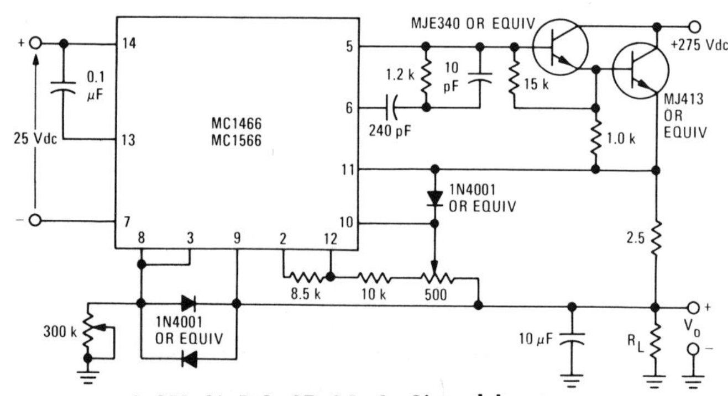

0–250 V D-C AT 0.1 A—Gives laboratory power supply performance, with line and load voltage regulation 0.01% plus mV, using Motorola IC for stepping up 25-V d-c source voltage.—Precision Wide-Range Voltage and Current Regulator MC1566L/MC1466L, Motorola, Phoenix, Ariz., DS9130, 1969.

IMPROVING EFFICIENCY—Permits lower unregulated input voltage to series-pass regulator for low-voltage (5–6 V) regulated output for IC circuits. With circuit shown, no device junctions are in series with output to subtract from available output voltage. Pnp differential pair Q1-Q2 drives pseudo-Darlington Q3-Q4. Handles loads up to 300 mA with 1% regulation.—W. G. Jung, High-Efficiency Series Regulator, *EEE*, April 1970, p 100–101.

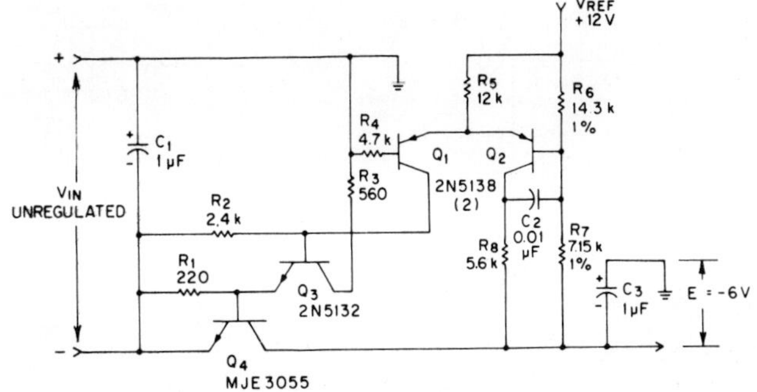

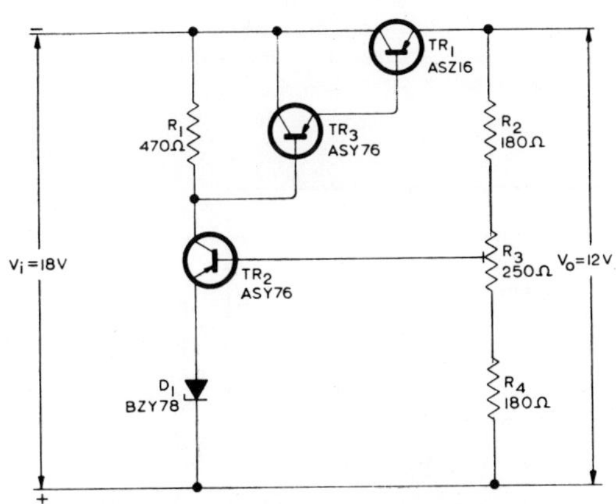

12 V AT 360 MA FROM 18 V D-C—Addition of third transistor amplifier stage to series regulator boosts maximum load current, although at expense of increased ripple in output.—"Voltage Regulator (Zener) Diodes," Philips, Pub. Dept., Elcoma Div., Eindhoven, The Netherlands, p 43.

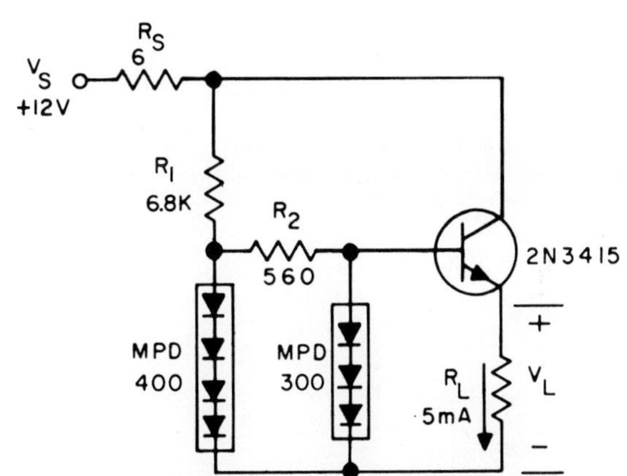

12-V DOUBLE-DIODE WITH EMITTER-FOLLOWER—Addition of transistor improves both efficiency and regulation in transistor supply applications.—Silicon Multi-Pellet Diodes MPD-200/MPD300/MPD400, General Electric, Syracuse, N.Y., No. 75.42, 1966.

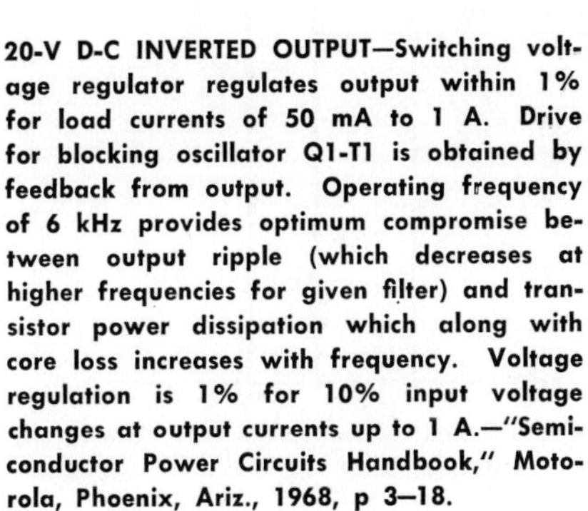
20-V D-C INVERTED OUTPUT—Switching voltage regulator regulates output within 1% for load currents of 50 mA to 1 A. Drive for blocking oscillator Q1-T1 is obtained by feedback from output. Operating frequency of 6 kHz provides optimum compromise between output ripple (which decreases at higher frequencies for given filter) and transistor power dissipation which along with core loss increases with frequency. Voltage regulation is 1% for 10% input voltage changes at output currents up to 1 A.—"Semiconductor Power Circuits Handbook," Motorola, Phoenix, Ariz., 1968, p 3–18.

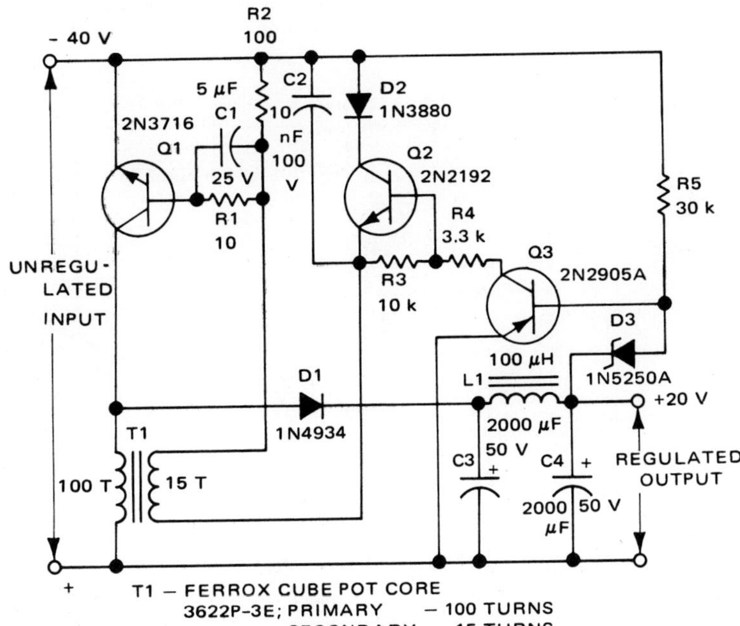

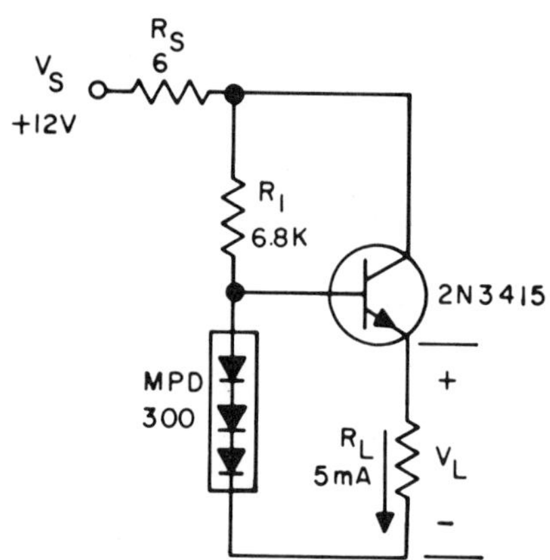

DIODE REGULATOR WITH EMITTER-FOLLOWER—Addition of cathode follower to diode voltage regulator gives higher efficiency and better regulation against voltage source changes. Output impedance is higher than with diode alone.—Silicon Multi-Pellet Diodes MPD200/MPD300/MPD400, General Electric, Syracuse, N.Y., No. 75.42, 1966.

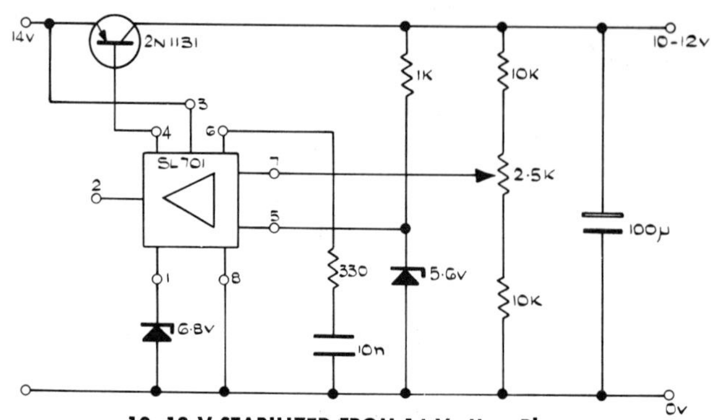

10–12 V STABILIZED FROM 14 V—Uses Plessey high-gain d-c amplifier with two zeners and series regulator transistor to give stabilization ratio of over 1,000 and output resistance less than 0.1 ohm.—R. C. Foss and B. J. Green, The SL700 Series and Applications, Plessey, Swindon, England, No. 7.

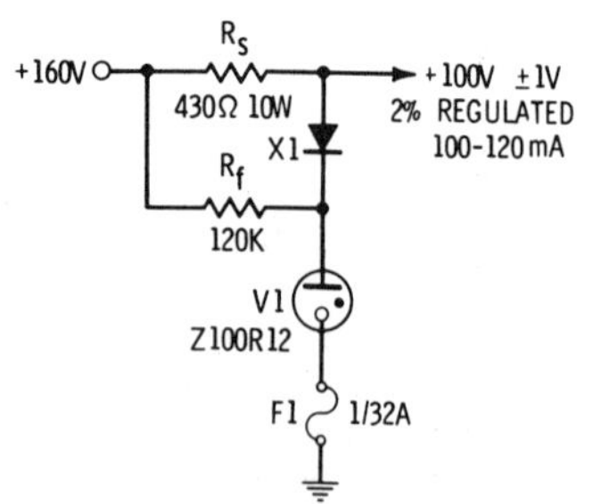

HIGH-CURRENT NEON REGULATOR—Permits load currents many times maximum rating of lamp. Fuse protects neon if load is removed or reduced. X1 may be any 400-piv 200-mA or better diode.—W. G. Miller, "Using and Understanding Miniature Neon Lamps," H. W. Sams & Co., Indianapolis, Ind., 1969, p 32.

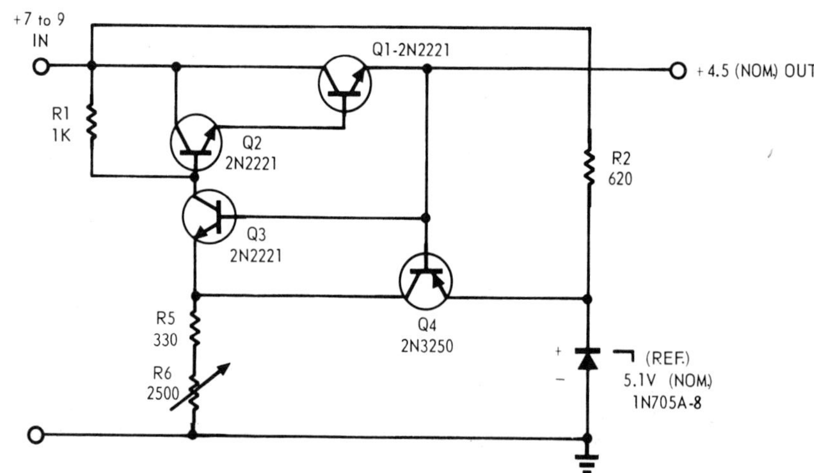

4.5 V AT 100 MA FOR LOGIC—Simple regulator acts like trigger having two stable states, corresponding to conditions before and after change in load current. Darlington pass transistor acts as emitter-follower. Developed for logic circuits in which line regulation is much less important than load regulation.—R. C. Sanford, 'Perfect' Regulator Satisfies Logic Circuits, *EDN*, Dec. 15, 1969, p 51–53.

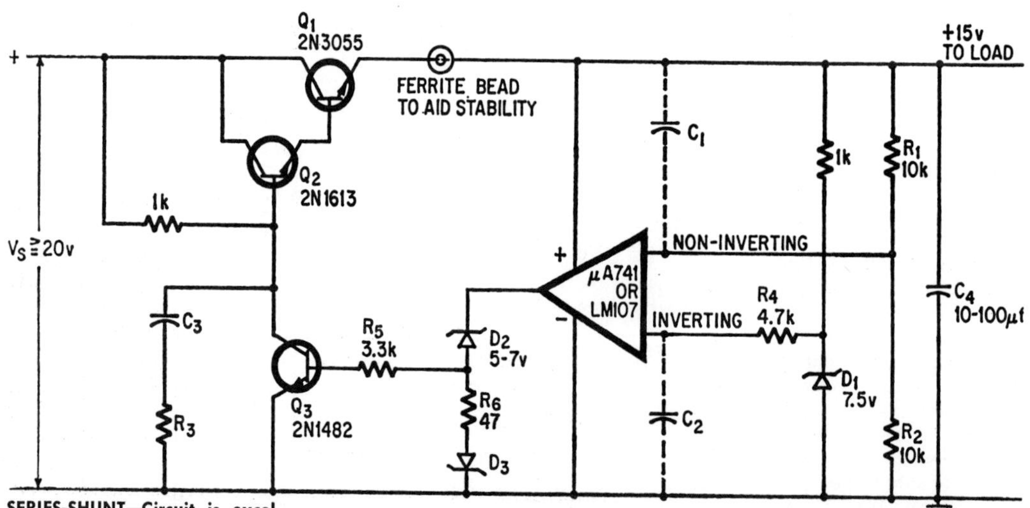

15-V LINEAR SERIES-SHUNT—Circuit is excellent for use when desired output is large fraction of source voltage. Dashed lines indicate optional components, with C2 for noise suppression and C1 for loop stabilization. Values of C1, C3, and R3 are chosen to minimize load voltage overshoot when driving fast-switching load.—W. L. Brown, IC's Save Power, Boost Efficiency of Regulated Power Supplies, *Electronics*, July 20, 1970, p 94–97.

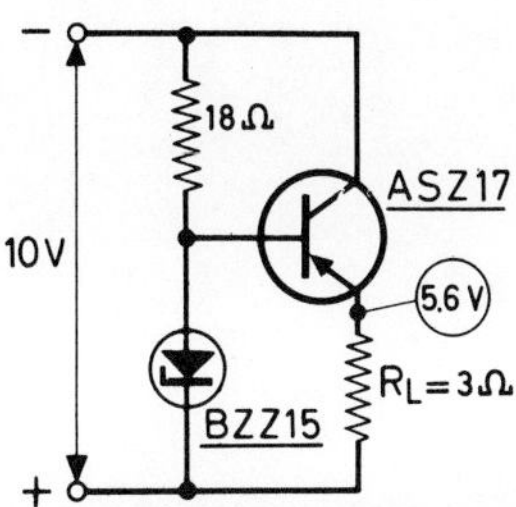

5.6 V D-C WITH ZENER AND TRANSISTOR—Power transistor, mounted on same heat sink with power zener, but electrically insulated, provides voltage stabilization at higher power level than zener alone.—Zener Diodes and Their Applications, Philips, Pub. Dept., Elcoma Div., Eindhoven, The Netherlands, No. 17, 1966.

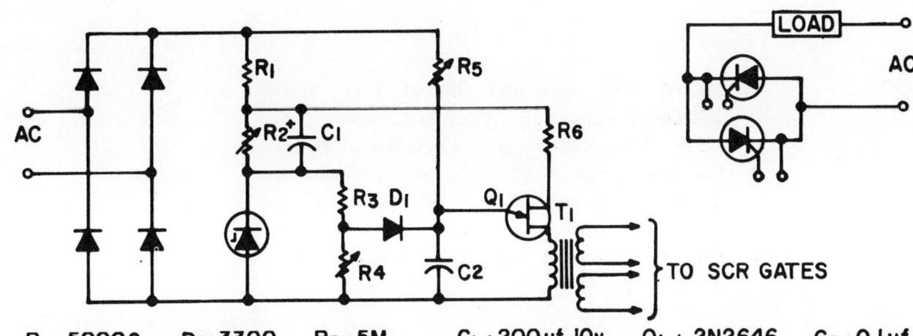

R_1 : 5000Ω R_3: 3300 R_5 : 5M C_1 : 200μf, 10v Q_1 : 2N2646 C_2 : 0.1μf
R_2: 500Ω R_4: 10K R_6 : 1K

A-C LINE VOLTAGE COMPENSATION—Ramp-and-pedestal control depends on relationship between pedestal height and peak point voltage of ujt. Cosine-shaped ramp provides good regulation over wide range of a-c input voltages.—F. W. Gutzwiller and E. K. Howell, Economy Power Semiconductor Applications, General Electric, Syracuse, N.Y., No. 671.1, 1965, p 13.

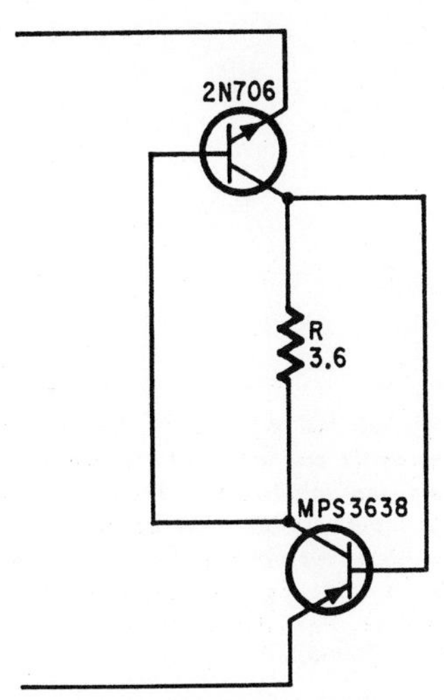

REGULATING BELOW ZENER MINIMUM—Two transistors and resistor provide zener action for regulating voltages below 2-V zener minimum. Arrangement has 1.5-V zener characteristic and zero dynamic impedance from 20 to 150 mA. When applied voltage is greater than 1.4 V, both transistors begin to conduct.—H. Stadler, Transistor "Zener" has Zero Dynamic Impedance, *Electronics*, March 31, 1969, p 86–87.

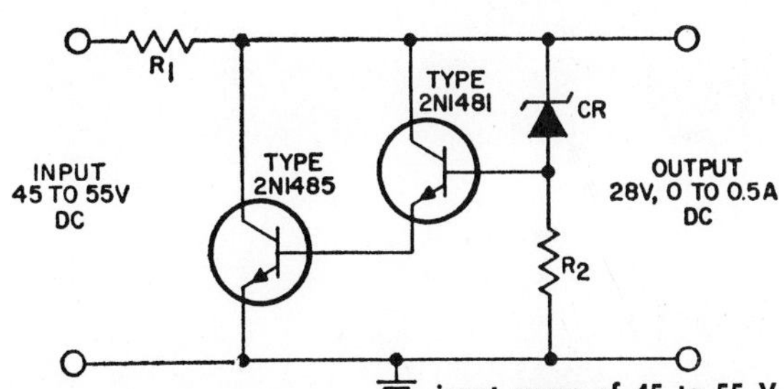

28-V SHUNT—Simple two-transistor shunt-type regulator holds output voltage constant within 0.5% for load currents up to 0.5 A, over d-c input range of 45 to 55 V. CR is 27-V reference diode, R1 is 28, and R2 is 1,000.—"Transistor Manual," RCA, Harrison, N.J., SC-13, p 516.

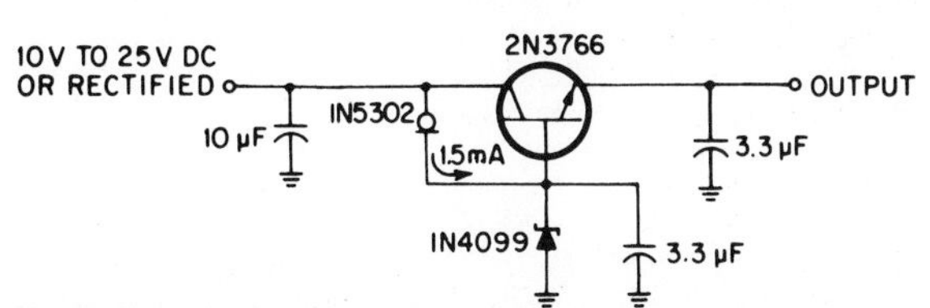

EXTENDING ZENER RANGE—Constant-current diode added to conventional zener of series regulator extends range of reference voltage, for handling wide range of input voltages. With values shown, regulator delivers 40 mA at nominal 6 V d-c.—P. Kestenbaum, Fixed Bias Extends Zener Range, *EEE*, May 1970, p 103–104.

R_1 –1K 5 Watt
R_2 –5.6K
R_3 –68K 1 Watt
*R_4 –6.34K ½ Watt
†R_5 –5K Pot.
*R_6 –191K 1 Watt
R_7 –5600Ω
R_8 –5600Ω
*R_9 –121K 1 Watt
R_{10}–150K

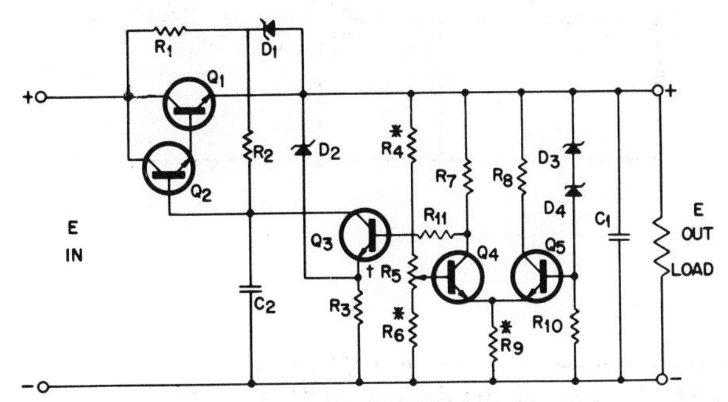

R_{11}–120K
D_1 –IN1767
D_2 –IN4735A
D_3 –IN4735A
D_4 –IN4734A
Q_1 –DTS413
Q_2 –2N3439
Q_3 –2N2711
Q_4 Q_5 –2N2712
C_1 –5mfd 450V
C_2 –0.01mfd 1 KV

* DENOTES HIGH-STABILITY FIXED FILM RESISTORS
† WIRE WOUND LOW TEMPERATURE COEFFICIENT

SERIES D-C VOLTAGE REGULATOR—Provides output of 290 V d-c for loads up to 600 mA, with regulation better than 0.5% for 15% change in 320-V d-c input voltage. Report describes sensing and correcting operation of circuit in detail. Circuit is not overload-proof.—DC Voltage Regulator With High Voltage Silicon Transistors, Delco Radio, Kokomo, Ind., No. 38, 1966.

70-MA D-C CURRENT REGULATOR WITH ZENER—Combination of 5.6-V zener and value of R2 gives current regulation at 70 mA for load range of 10 to 50 ohms. Value of R1 is not critical. Circuit has good regulation with temperature.—"Semiconductor Power Circuits Handbook," Motorola, Phoenix, Ariz., 1968, p 3–24.

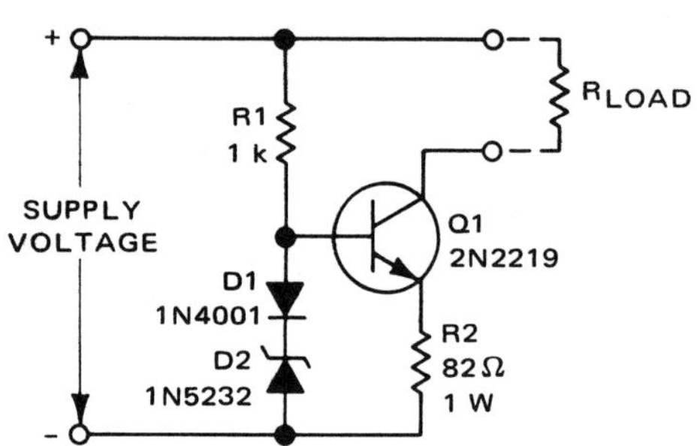

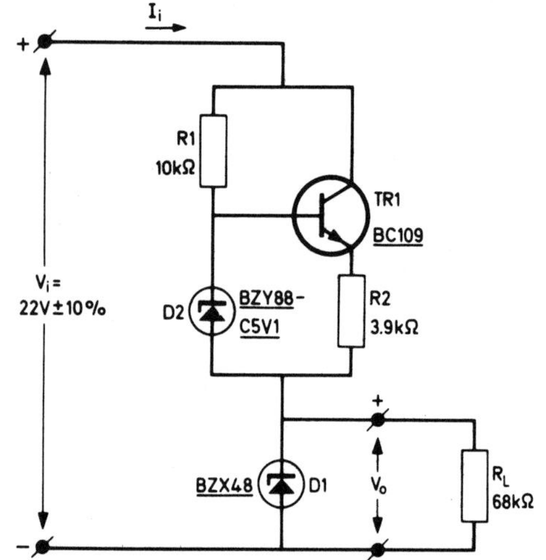

CONSTANT-CURRENT SOURCE—Use of two-terminal constant-current generator to stabilize input current permits use of lower input voltage than with voltage prestabilizer. With 2 mA supplied to reference diode D1, 100 μA is supplied to load at essentially constant 6.5 V d-c.—High-Stability Reference Diodes BZX47 Family, Philips, Pub. Dept., Elcoma Div., Eindhoven, The Netherlands, No. 331, 1968.

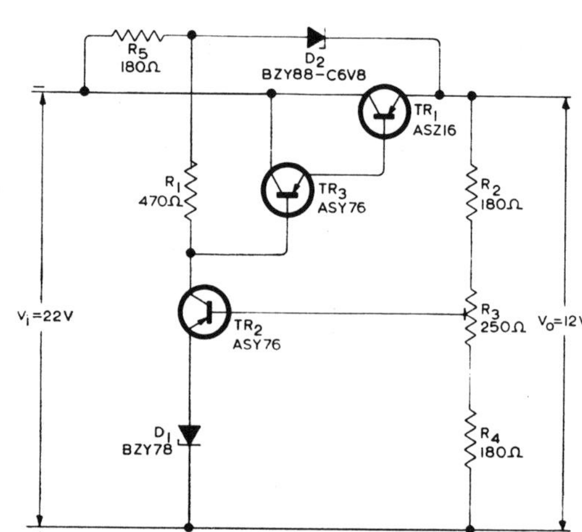

12 V AT 360 MA WITH LOW RIPPLE—Additional zener D2 acts with R5 to reduce amount of ripple fed into output through R1 and TR3, but input voltage must be increased to 22 V to allow for voltage drop across these components.—"Voltage Regulator (Zener) Diodes," Philips, Pub. Dept., Elcoma Div., Eindhoven, The Netherlands, p 44.

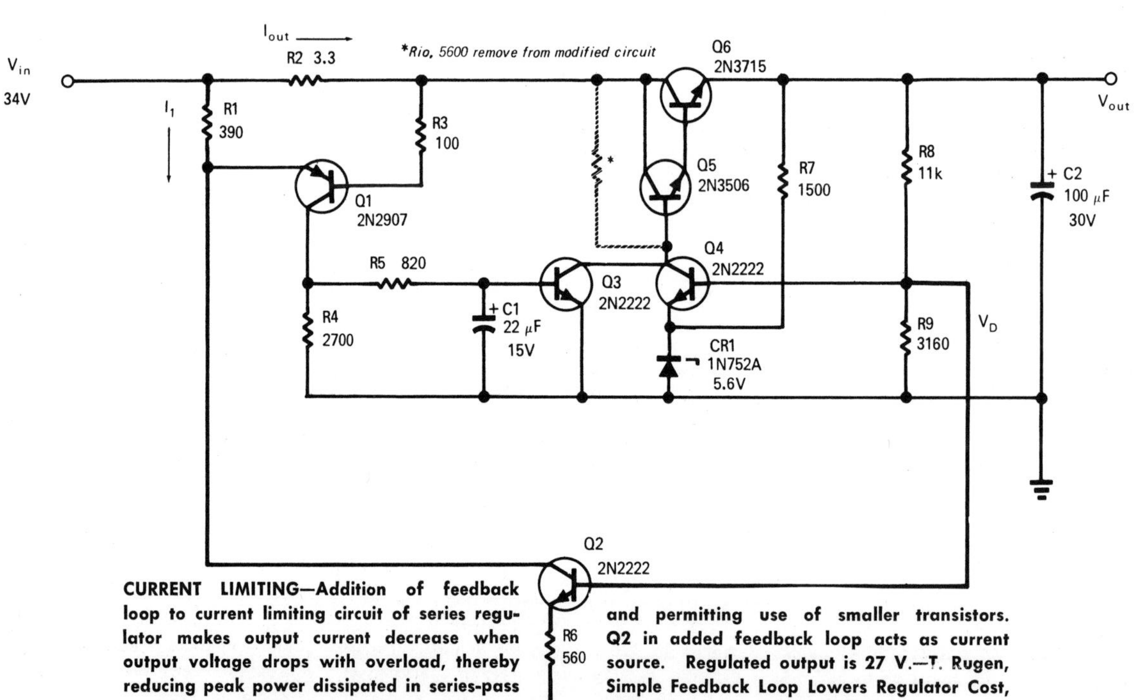

CURRENT LIMITING—Addition of feedback loop to current limiting circuit of series regulator makes output current decrease when output voltage drops with overload, thereby reducing peak power dissipated in series-pass transistor, reducing heat sink requirements, and permitting use of smaller transistors. Q2 in added feedback loop acts as current source. Regulated output is 27 V.—T. Rugen, Simple Feedback Loop Lowers Regulator Cost, *EDN*, June 1, 1970, p 55–56.

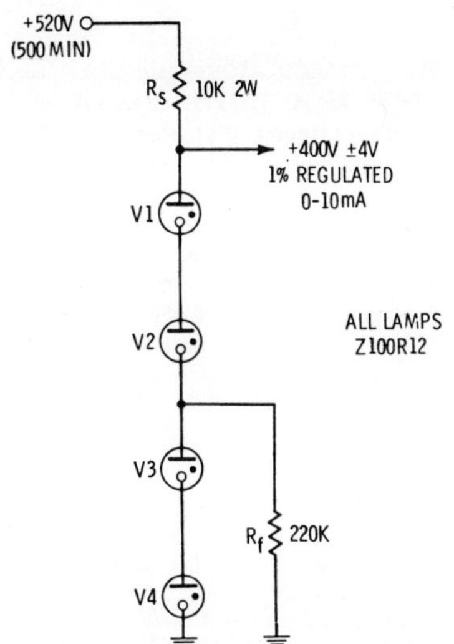

400-V NEON REGULATORS—Adding lamps in series permits higher reference voltages. Use of additional resistors lowers supply voltage requirements, as in circuit at right. All neons are Z100R12.—W. G. Miller, "Using and Understanding Miniature Neon Lamps," H. W. Sams & Co., Indianapolis, Ind., 1969, p 30.

DUAL 15-V REGULATOR—Uses pair of OEI regulator chips with circuit in which only one reference is needed. One adjustment sets output voltage for both positive and negative outputs. Developed for opamps requiring tracking in which any change in negative output voltage causes corresponding change in positive output. Range is 12 to 18 V.—Applying the Model 8100 Monolithic Voltage Regulator, Optical Electronics, Tucson, Ariz., No. 10141.

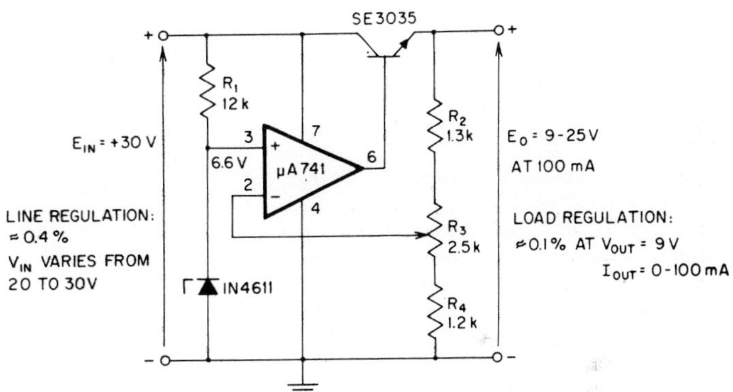

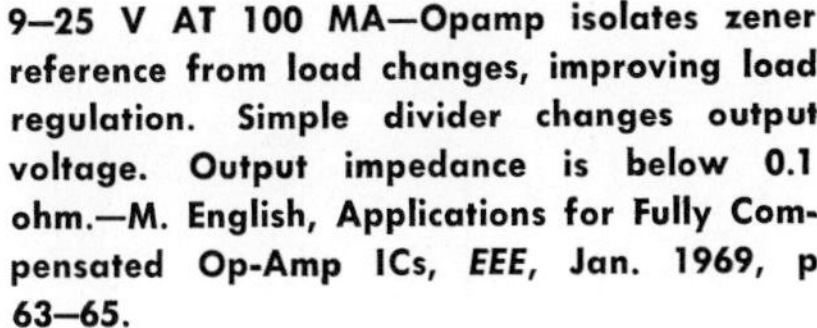
9–25 V AT 100 MA—Opamp isolates zener reference from load changes, improving load regulation. Simple divider changes output voltage. Output impedance is below 0.1 ohm.—M. English, Applications for Fully Compensated Op-Amp ICs, *EEE*, Jan. 1969, p 63–65.

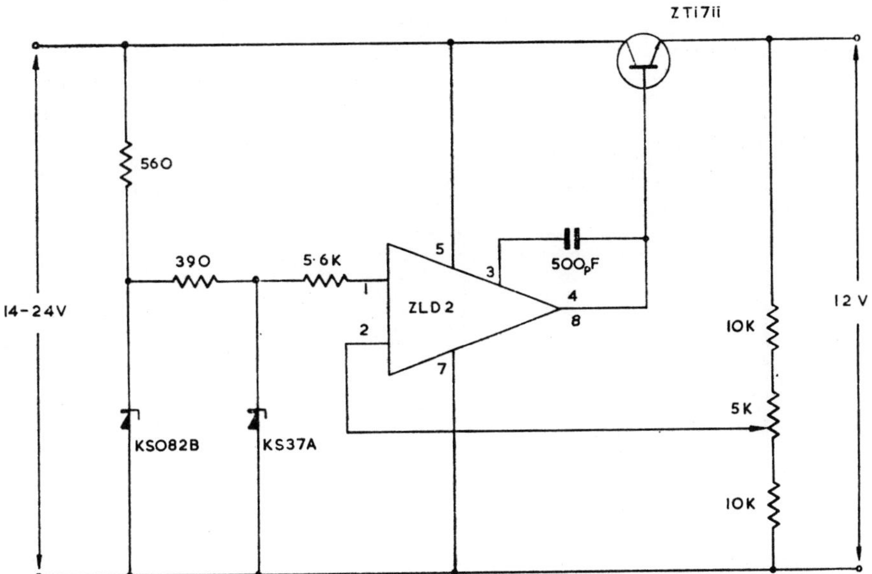

STABILIZED D-C SUPPLY—Uses Ferranti ZLD2 IC as d-c error signal amplifier, with noninverting input held at constant voltage derived from reference diodes. Inverting input receives error signal proportional to output voltage stabilized by series power transistor. Output voltage deviates from desired 12 V by only 5 mV per volt of change in input voltage.—Microlin Amplifiers ZLD2S and ZLD-2T, Ferranti Ltd., Oldham, Lancs., England, No. 11, 1967, p 15.

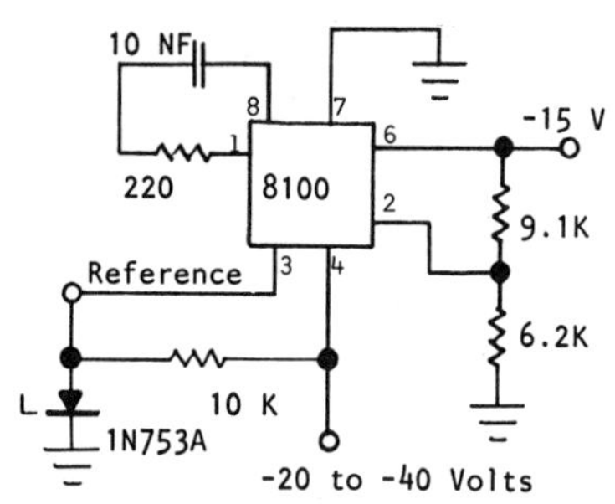

NEGATIVE SWITCHING REGULATOR—Negative regulated output voltage is essentially same as negative reference voltage.—Applying the Model 8100 Monolithic Voltage Regulator, Optical Electronics, Tucson, Ariz., No. 10141.

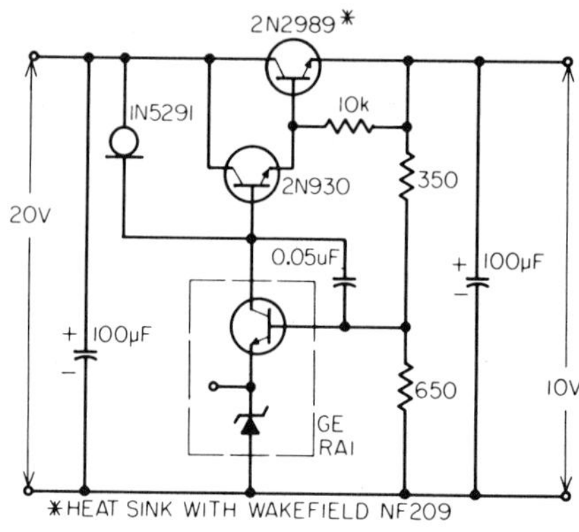

DIODE PREREGULATOR—Field-effect current-regulator diode 1N5291 functions as constant-current source that eliminates effect of input variations on bias voltage of 2N930 error amplifier in series voltage regulator. Designed for 200-mA load current. Load regulation is 0.1% from zero to full load, and line regulation is 0.02%.—A. Butvidas, CRD Simplifies Design of Voltage Regulators, *EEE*, May 1968, p 124 and 126.

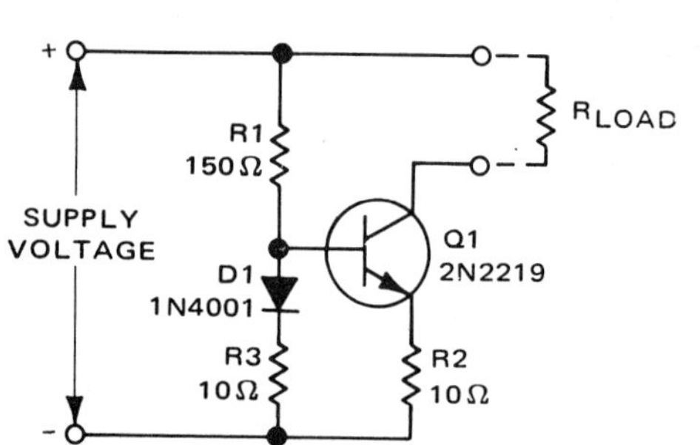

70-MA D-C CURRENT REGULATOR WITH SINGLE DIODE—Provides very good current regulation for loads from 10 to 100 ohms if supply voltage is held constant. Voltage drops across R2 and R3 are equal, and level of current regulation is equal to drop across R2 divided by resistance of R2.—"Semiconductor Power Circuits Handbook," Motorola, Phoenix, Ariz., 1968, p 3–24.

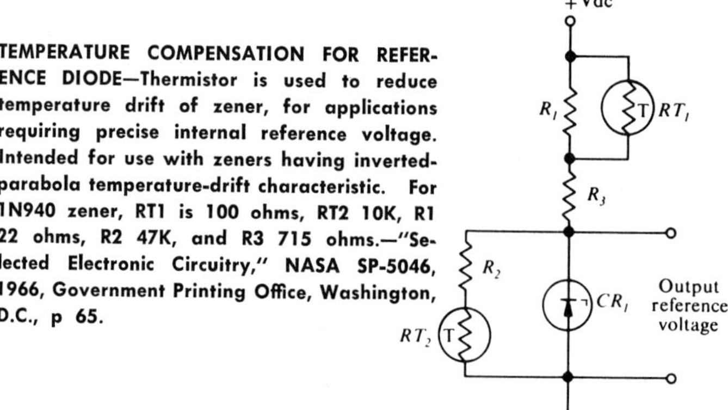

TEMPERATURE COMPENSATION FOR REFERENCE DIODE—Thermistor is used to reduce temperature drift of zener, for applications requiring precise internal reference voltage. Intended for use with zeners having inverted-parabola temperature-drift characteristic. For 1N940 zener, RT1 is 100 ohms, RT2 10K, R1 22 ohms, R2 47K, and R3 715 ohms.—"Selected Electronic Circuitry," NASA SP-5046, 1966, Government Printing Office, Washington, D.C., p 65.

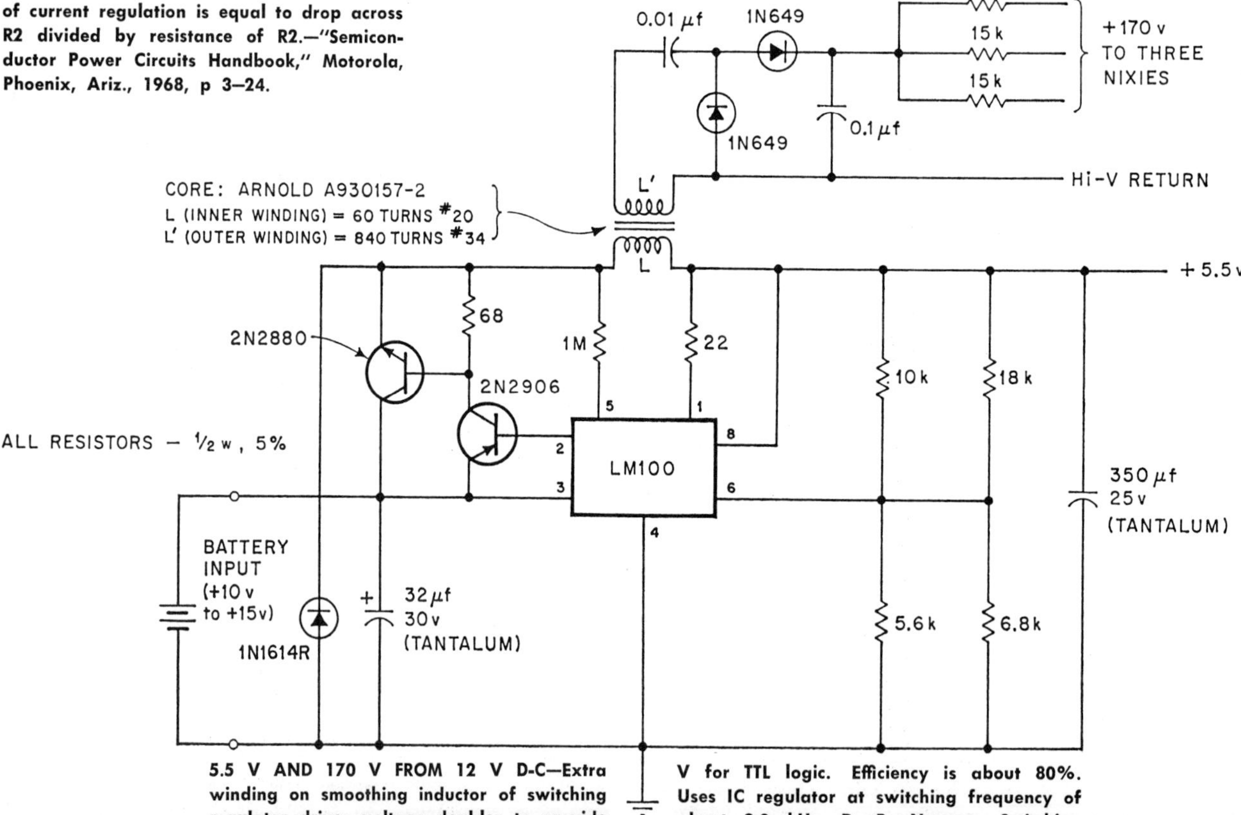

5.5 V AND 170 V FROM 12 V D-C—Extra winding on smoothing inductor of switching regulator drives voltage doubler to provide 150 to 210 V d-c needed for Nixie display tubes. Circuit also provides regulated 5.5 V for TTL logic. Efficiency is about 80%. Uses IC regulator at switching frequency of about 9.8 kHz.—D. B. Newton, Switching Regulator Drives IC's and Nixies Off Battery, *Electronics*, July 6, 1970, p 77.

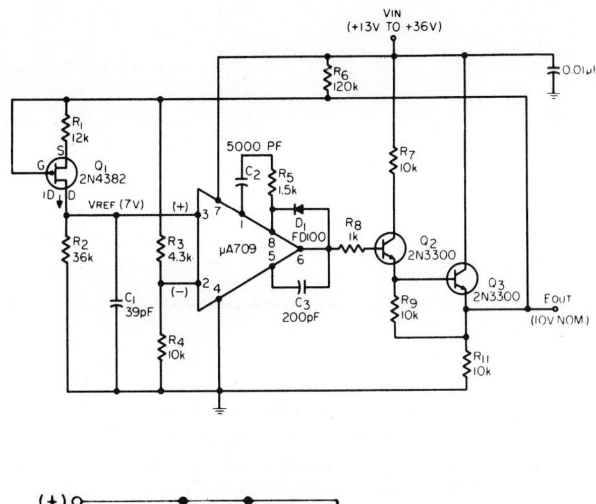

FET CONSTANT-CURRENT REFERENCE—Q1 supplies constant current to R2 to produce voltage drop as reference for d-c voltage regulator. Reference voltage can be much smaller than 6-V lower limit of most zeners. Temperature coefficient is adjustable and can either be set to low value or set to compensate for temperature effects in other circuits. Modified Darlington Q2-Q3 supplies output current up to 250 mA. Temperature coefficient depends on fet drain current.—C. N. Gold, Zenerless Regulator with Adjustable Tempco, *EEE*, Aug. 1967, p 128–129.

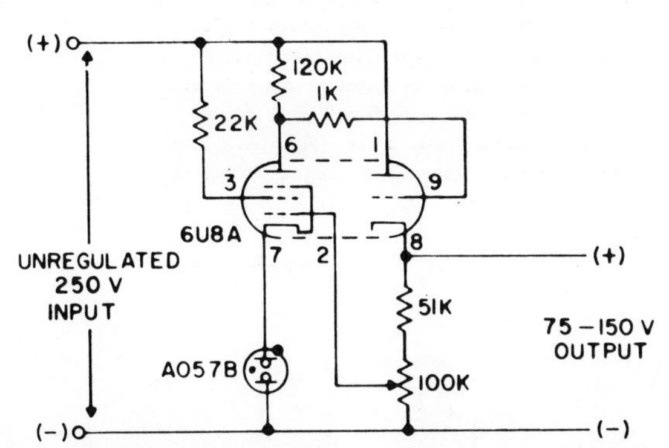

REGULATION AT LOW POWER—Neon sets reference level and its maintaining voltage establishes lower limit for voltage regulation. Potentiometer permits output voltage to be set at any value between 75 and 150 V.—E. Bauman, "Applications of Neon Lamps and Gas Discharge Tubes," Signalite, Neptune, N.J., p 88.

+
RLOAD
R1
470Ω
SUPPLY
VOLTAGE
Q1
2N2219
D1
MZ2360
D2
MZ2360
R2
10Ω
−

70-MA D-C CURRENT REGULATOR WITH BIASING DIODES—Current level at which regulation occurs is equal to 0.7-V drop across D2 divided by value of R2, because base-emitter voltage of Q1 matches drop across D1. Current remains essentially constant over load range of 10 to 100 ohms.—"Semiconductor Power Circuits Handbook," Motorola, Phoenix, Ariz., 1968, p 3–24.

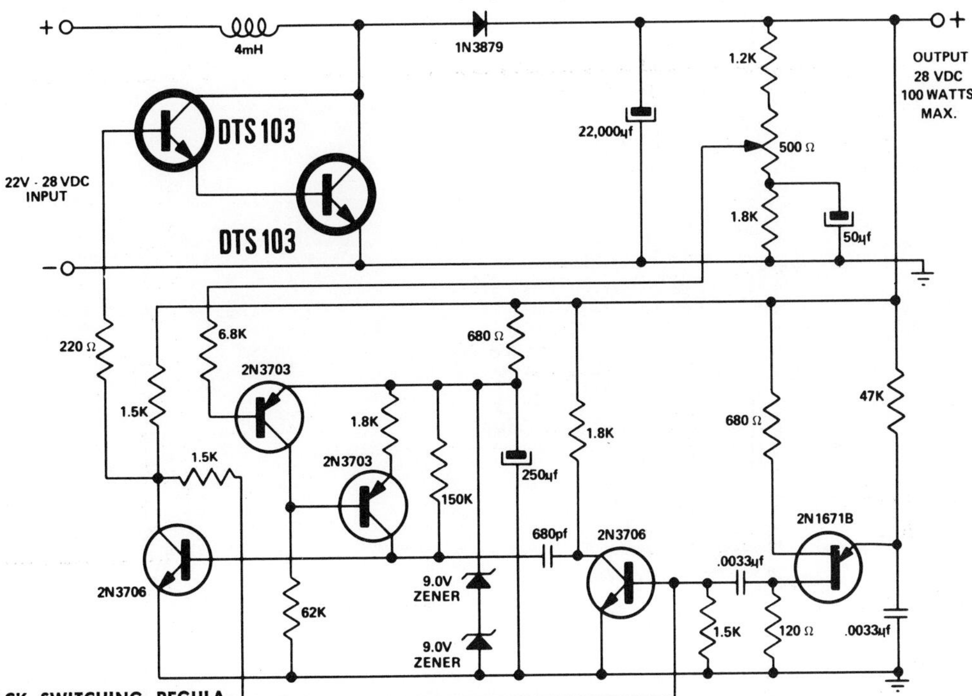

100-W 28-V FLYBACK SWITCHING REGULATOR—Provides efficient regulation by pulse width modulation at output voltages as high as 6 V above d-c input voltage. Switching rate of 9 kHz is provided by oscillator that triggers monostable mvbr, with mvbr also receiving voltage-sensing signals from output that determine pulse width. Efficiency is 87% at 80 W and better than 80% for other power outputs down to 15 W. Developed for use in aircraft.—28 Volts Flyback Regulator Switching, Delco Radio, Kokomo, Ind., No. 42, 1968.

CHAPTER 72
Relay Circuits

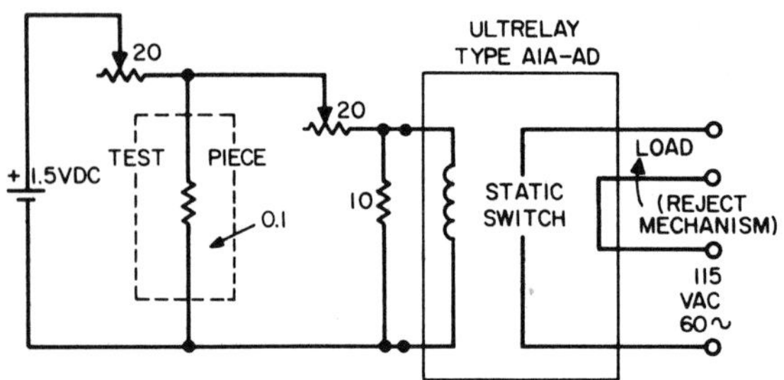

0.1-OHM RESISTANCE CHANGE DETECTOR—Uses Airborne Accessories ultrasensitive static relay in bridge circuit for production testing of components whose resistance value is critical. Static switch contains magamp-driven scr that can be used to activate solenoid reject mechanism that either labels or removes faulty test piece.—Sensitive Static Relay Detects Resistance Limits, *Electronic Design*, Nov. 29, 1965, p 75.

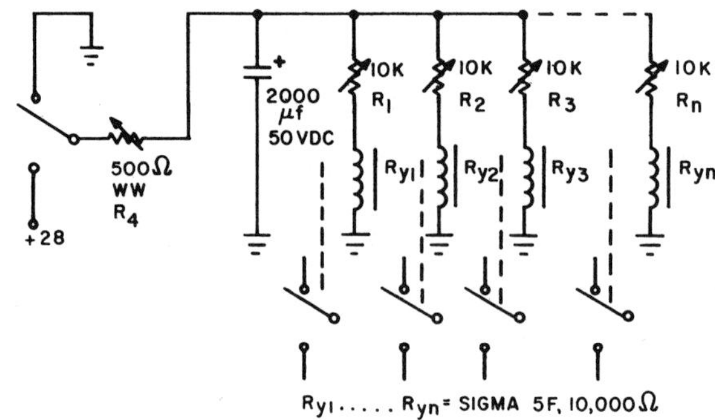

SEQUENCING OF RELAY PULL-INS—Series pot for each relay is set for pull-in voltage desired. When switch is set at 28 V, capacitor charges through R4, and each relay pulls in when capacitor voltage reaches preset value. When switch is released, relays drop out in reverse order of pull-in.—M. E. Swinnen, Relay Arrangement Simplifies Contact Sequencing, *Electronic Design*, Nov. 23, 1964, p 62.

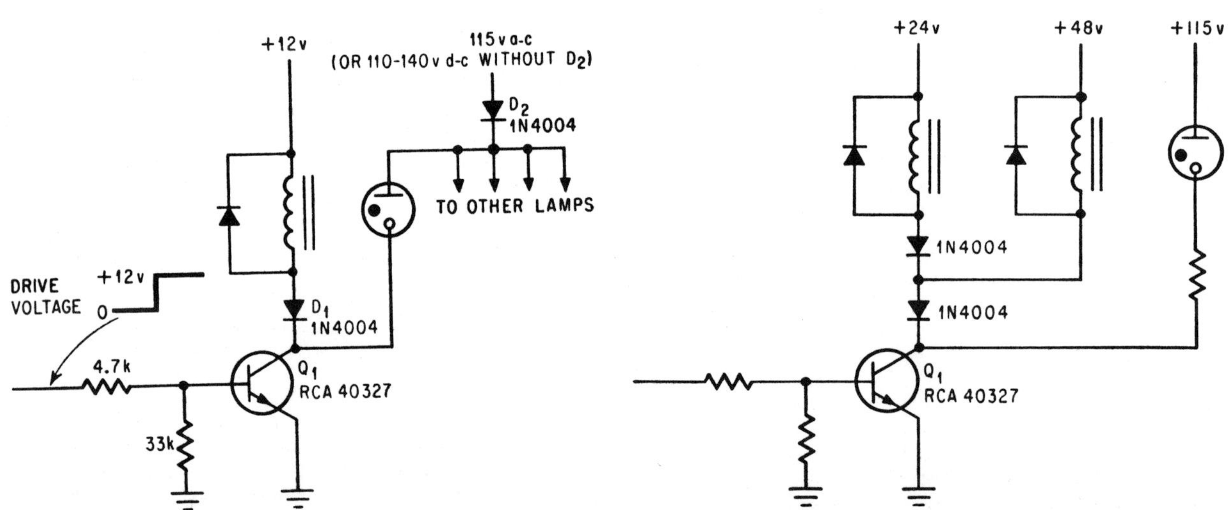

TRANSISTOR DRIVES RELAY AND NEONS—Addition of isolation diode to conventional relay driver permits turning on neon lamps and operating relay with single transistor. Circuit at right shows how to add isolation diodes for driving two or more relays having different supply voltages.—J. H. Silverman, Diode Isolator Combines Relay and Lamp Driver, *Electronics*, May 1, 1967, p 72.

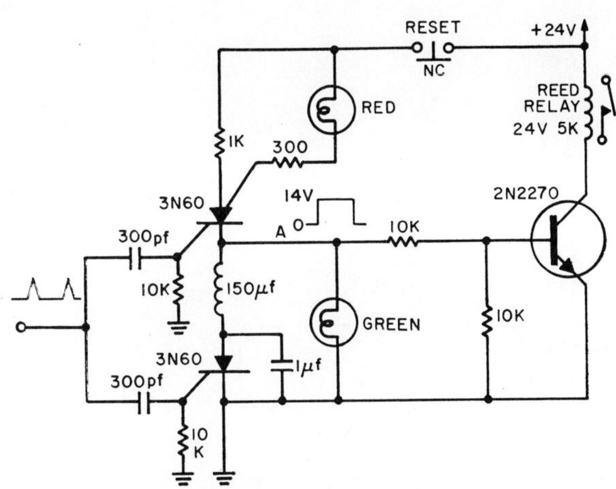

TWO-STEP LOCKOUT—First input pulse produces voltage step at output. Second input pulse makes output return to different level, followed by reed relay lockout. Developed for use in counters. Uses two 3N60 silicon controlled switches in series, lower of which cannot be fired until upper switch is fired. Input pulses must be below 5 V to prevent both switches from firing on first pulse. Lamps show circuit condition. When lower switch fires, on second pulse, transistor pulls in relay and holds it until reset switch is pushed.—B. Soroka, Lockout Circuit Operates With Single Line Input, *Electronic Design*, March 30, 1964, p 72–73.

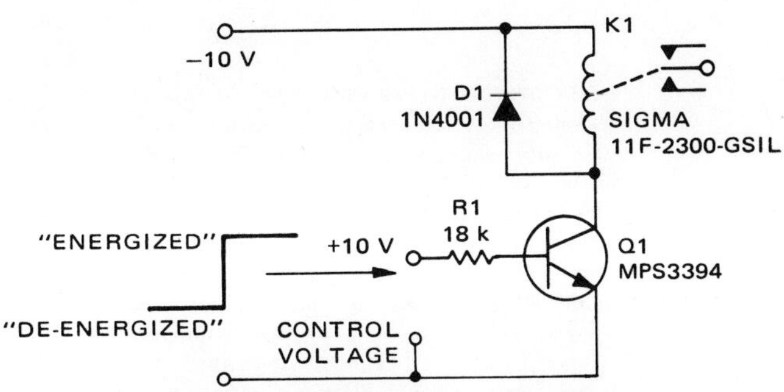

TRANSISTOR CONTROL—D-c relay is controlled by 0.5-mA signal current applied to transistor. Diode protects transistor from inductive voltage spike of relay coil.—"Semiconductor Power Circuits Handbook," Motorola, Phoenix, Ariz., 1968, p 6–37.

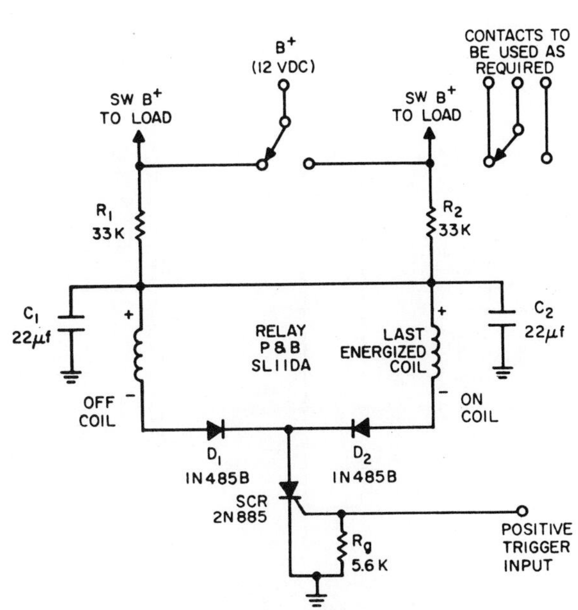

PULSES FLIP LATCHING RELAY—Positive trigger inputs applied to scr serve to alternate contacts of latching relay. Circuit draws very little power and provides current overload protection for coil. Time between successive trigger pulses should be greater than 2RC to give sufficient time for charging of coil capacitor.—J. S. Poole, SCR Pulse-Follower Circuit Alternates Latching Relay, *Electronic Design*, Dec. 20, 1965, p 51–52.

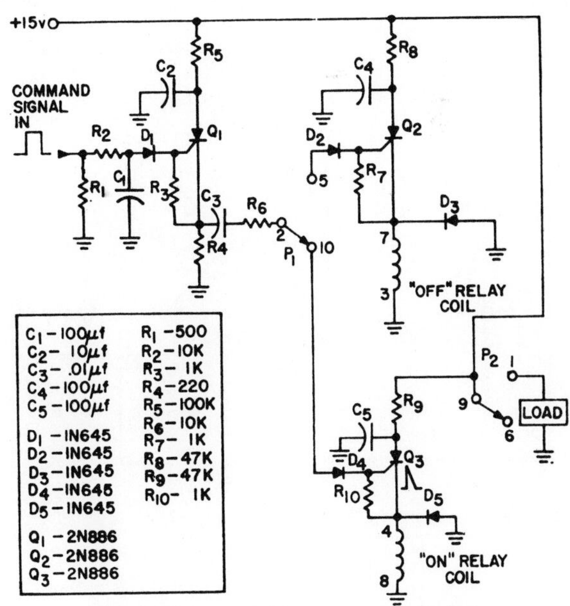

LATCHING WITH PULSES—Load is switched on and off by consecutive command signal pulses, with minimum signal power. Uses three scr's and dpdt magnetic latching relay. Circuit is shown with poles P1 and P2 in position corresponding to energizing of ON relay coil. Filter network R1-R2-C1 desensitizes circuit to random noise spikes.—J. N. Libby and J. C. Schaffert, SCR Relay Flips, Flops on Consecutive Commands, "400 Ideas for Design Selected from Electronic Design," Hayden Book Co., N.Y., 1964, p 110.

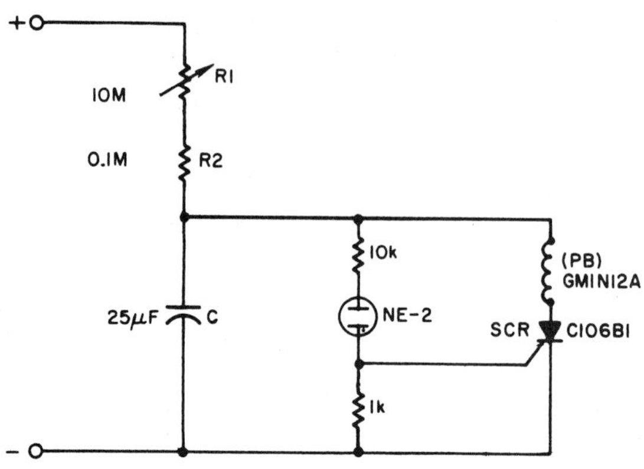

TIMER DRIVES STEPPER—With 90-V d-c supply, stepping relay is operated at 5-minute intervals with values shown, with interval determined by R1-C. R2 determines minimum time. With half-wave rectified a-c line power, interval is 10 minutes. Can also be used with ordinary relay or other inductive load. Neon conducts at about 65 V and triggers scr, to make C discharge through relay coil and scr.—L. Eaton, Low-Power Timer Drives Stepping Relay, *Electronic Design*, Aug. 16, 1969, p 238 and 240.

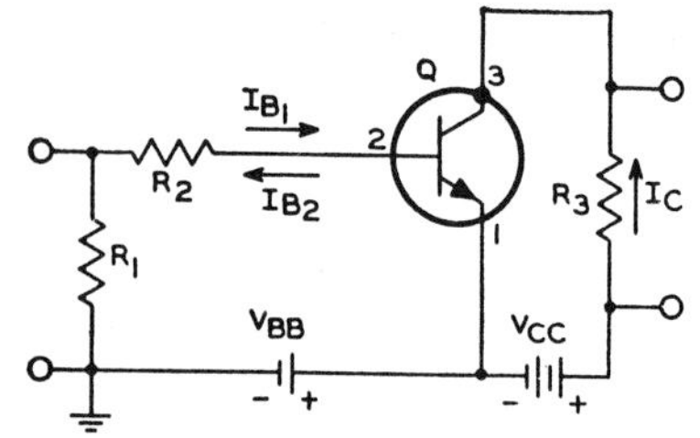

RELAY DRIVER—Uses 2N1483 npn silicon power transistor for energizing solenoid or relay. Delay time is only 0.2 μs and pulse rise and fall times about 1 μs. Values: R1 50; R2 700; R3 59; V-BB 8.5 V; V-CC 12 V. —"Transistor Manual," RCA, Harrison, N.J., SC-13, p 167.

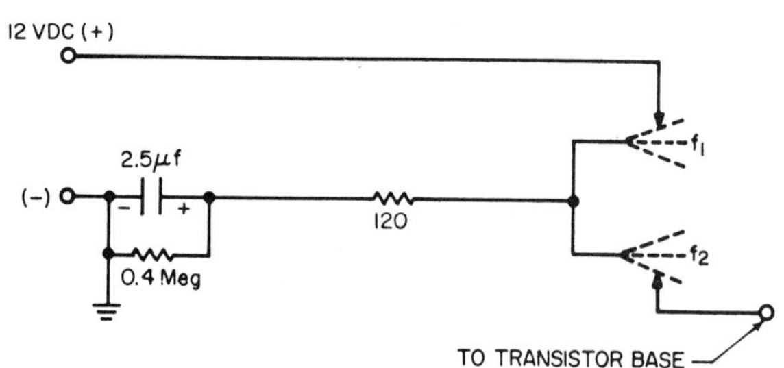

TWO-FREQUENCY AUDIO DECODER—Provides decoding for control function only when the two reeds of Bramco signal-coil relay are activated in sequence by their respective different frequencies. First frequency, f1, charges capacitor. Second frequency, f2, transfers capacitor charge to transistor base (or tube grid) for control action. Bleeder resistor across capacitor prevents switching action by undesired codes.—Multiple-Reed Relay Acts as 2-Frequency Decoder, *Electronic Design*, Nov. 29, 1965, p 71.

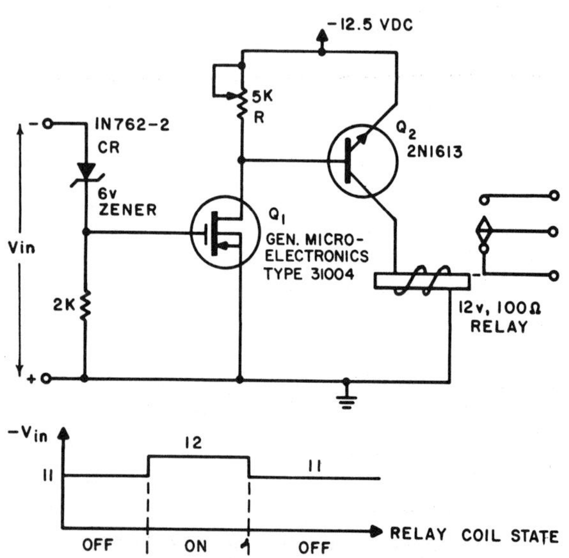

LOW-COST DIFFERENTIAL RELAY—Sharp-turn-on characteristic of mosfet Q1 gives reliable operation of inexpensive common relay on voltage differential less than 1 V. Pull-in and drop-out levels can be changed, to place 1-V differential level at any desired location in range of 1 to 12 V, by appropriate choice of zener and value of R.—L. G. Cowles, MOS Transistor Provides Sharp Differential Relay Switching, *Electronic Design*, March 29, 1965, p 32.

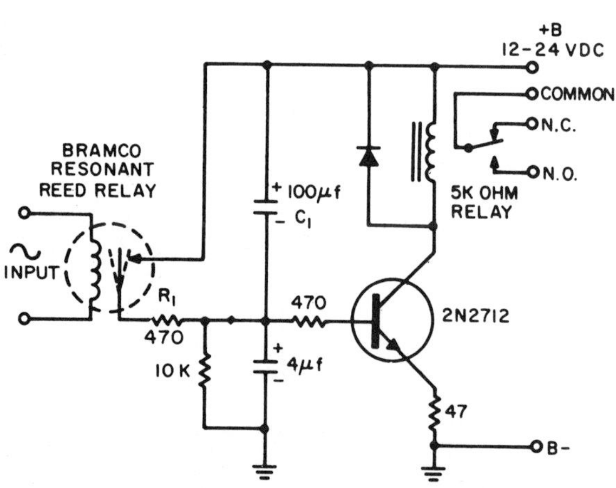

TIMED LOCKUP OF LATCHING CIRCUIT—Contacts of frequency-selective resonant-reed relay discharge C1 through R1 to make transistor conduct and pull in power relay at desired time interval after input signal is applied. When reed stops vibrating after input signal is removed, C1 charges up to transistor cutoff point, and power relay is then released. Lockup time is 5 to 10 s for value of C1 shown.—Resonant Reed Controls Timed Latching Relay, *Electronic Design*, Nov. 29, 1965, p 80.

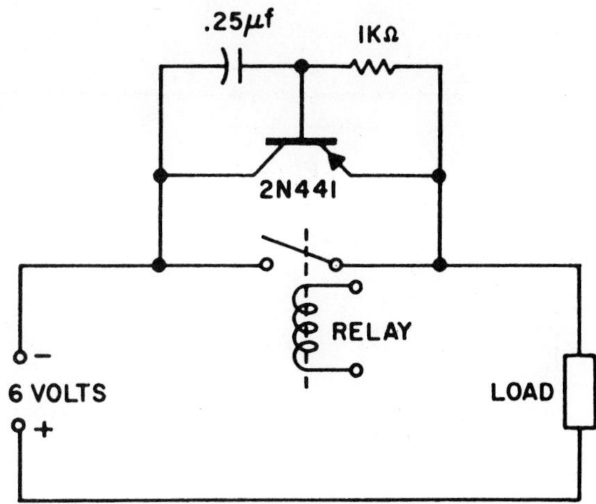

CONTACT ARC SUPPRESSION—Transistor supplements capacitor action in suppressing arc occurring when relay contacts open. With no suppression, peak voltage across opening contacts was 640 V. Capacitor alone reduced this to 340 V, and capacitor-transistor combination brought peak down to 12 V.—M. Dickey, Amplified Capacitor Suppresses Arc More Completely, "400 Ideas for Design Selected from Electronic Design," Hayden Book Co., N.Y., 1964, p 100–101.

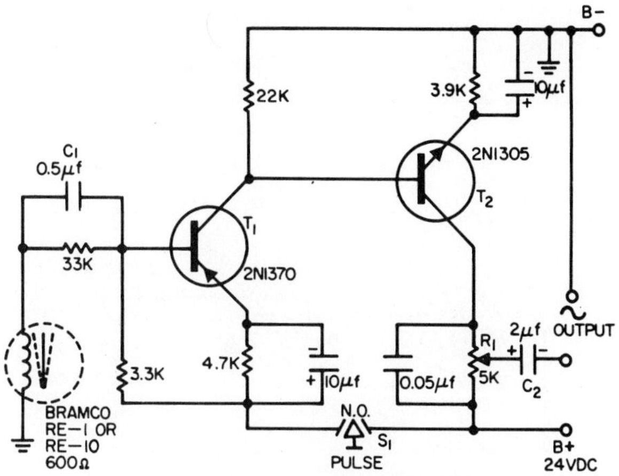

DAMPED TONE GENERATOR—Damped audio tone with extremely narrow bandwidth is generated each time reed relay is pulsed. Tone is amplified by T1 and clipped to desired level by T2.—Resonant Reed-Relay Produces Pulsed Tone, *Electronic Design*, Nov. 29, 1965, p 74.

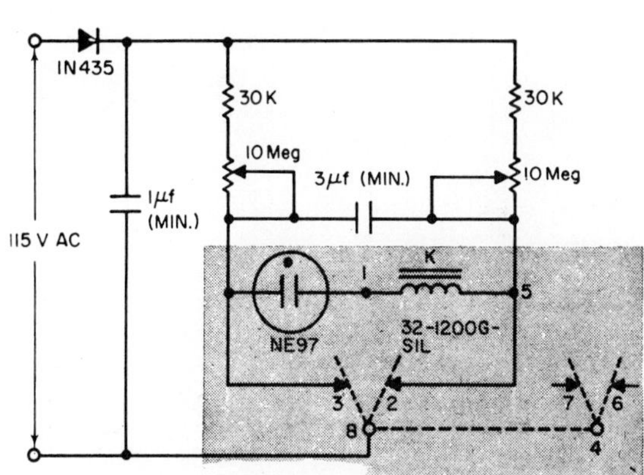

20-MINUTE FLIP-FLOP—Bistable magnetic-latching polarized relay and neon lamp serve as free-running mvbr having cycling times up to 20 min, depending on settings of pots and size of capacitor used between them.—Polarized Latching Relay Forms Free-Running Flip-Flop, *Electronic Design*, Nov. 29, 1965, p 74.

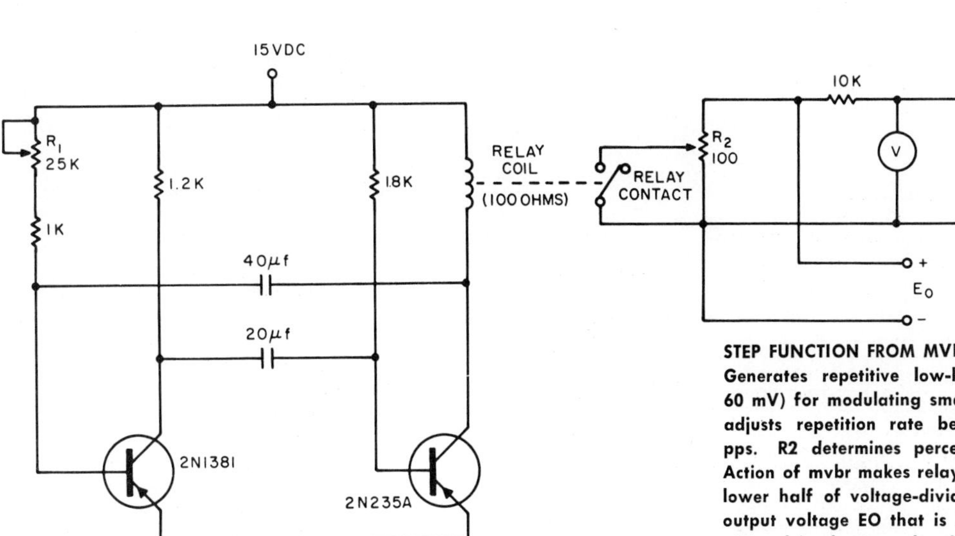

STEP FUNCTION FROM MVBR-PULSED RELAY—Generates repetitive low-level steps (up to 60 mV) for modulating small d-c signals. R1 adjusts repetition rate between 0.1 and 8 pps. R2 determines percentage modulation. Action of mvbr makes relay contacts short out lower half of voltage-divider R2 to generate output voltage EO that is between 0 and 60 mV and is about one-hundredth of monitored voltage V.—Pulsed Relay Generates Low-Level Step Functions, *Electronic Design*, Nov. 29, 1965, p 81.

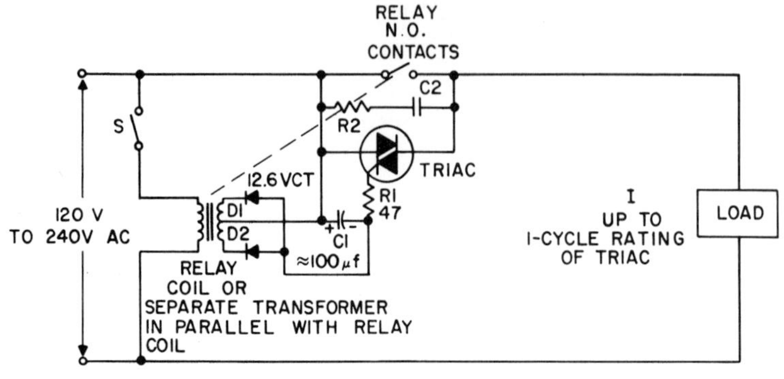

TRIAC CONTACT-PROTECTOR—When switch is closed, relay is energized and triac is fired, sending current through load. Since triac stays on as long as load current flows, there is no arcing of contacts while they bounce. Furthermore, load current flows through contacts when they are closed, rather than through triac, so heat dissipation in triac is negligible. When switch is opened, relay contacts open but triac remains fired long enough to eliminate contact arcing because it opens only at natural current-zero time. Circuit can thus be used for load currents higher than relay or triac could handle alone.—J. H. Galloway, Using the Triac for Control of AC Power, General Electric, Syracuse, N.Y., No. 200.35, 1966, p 13.

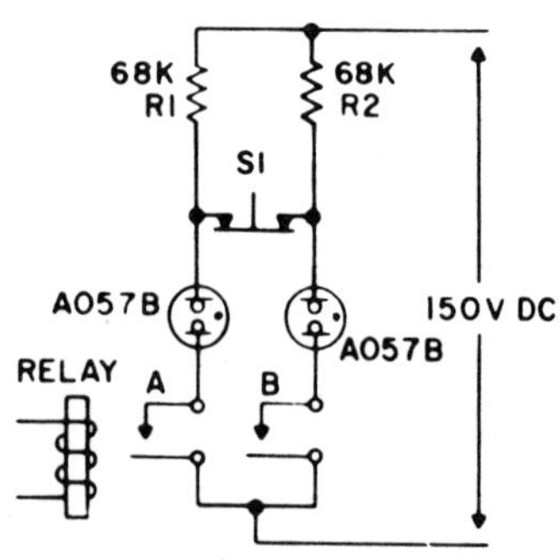

CONTACT-CLOSING SEQUENCE—Both neons should glow when S1 is closed. With S1 open, neon which glows shows which contact closed first. If neither lamp lights, both contacts closed simultaneously.—E. Bauman, "Applications of Neon Lamps and Gas Discharge Tubes," Signalite, Neptune, N.J., p 144.

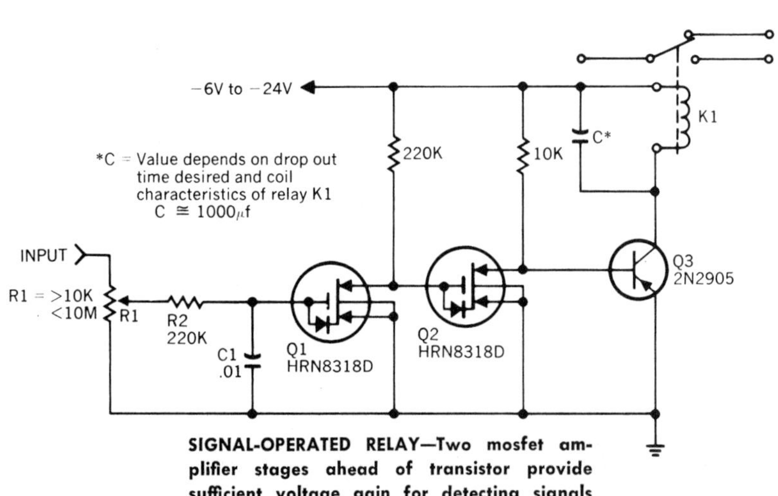

SIGNAL-OPERATED RELAY—Two mosfet amplifier stages ahead of transistor provide sufficient voltage gain for detecting signals as low as 2 V and energizing relay.—C. R. Perkins, "Application of MOSFET Devices to Electronic Circuits," Hughes, Newport Beach, Cal., 1968, p 35.

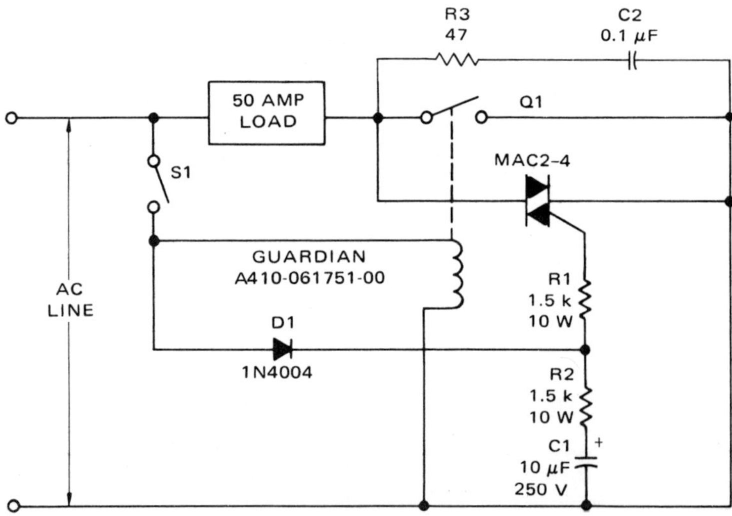

TRIAC SUPPRESSES CONTACT ARCING—Triac turns on during first positive half-cycle after S1 is closed, and carries load current before relay coil has had time to close its contacts. Similarly, triac conducts for several cycles after relay contacts open, because of energy stored in C2. Maximum voltage across contacts is only about 1 V when they open, permitting use of smaller relay and reducing noise of relay closing. Triac shown will handle loads up to 50 A.—"Semiconductor Power Circuits Handbook," Motorola, Phoenix, Ariz., 1968, p 4–7.

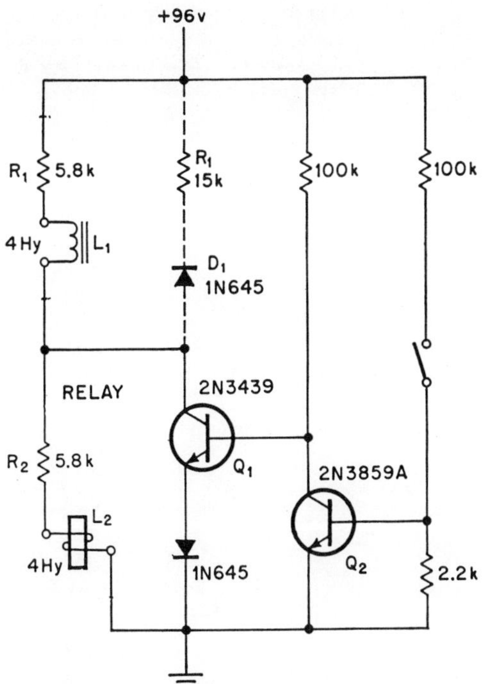

FASTER RELAY—Shortens pull-in time of industrial control relay or solenoid from normal 16 ms to 5 ms. With switch open, Q2 is on and current flows through inductor L1 (which can be another relay like L2 with armature jammed open). Closing switch turns Q2 off and Q1 on, causing field of L1 to collapse and generate large voltage spike that is integrated by L2-R2 to give fast build-up of current through relay coil. D1 and R1 are optional, for protecting Q1 against collector-emitter breakdown while increasing delay slightly.—J. Gaon, Storage Coil Cuts Relay Pull-In Delay, *Electronics*, Aug. 3, 1970, p 74.

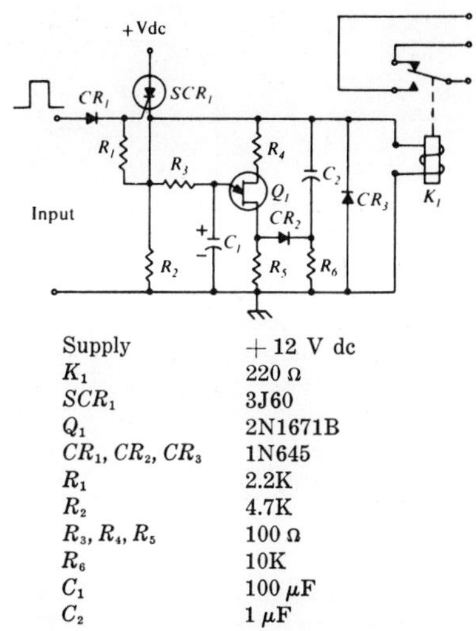

Supply	+ 12 V dc
K_1	220 Ω
SCR_1	3J60
Q_1	2N1671B
CR_1, CR_2, CR_3	1N645
R_1	2.2K
R_2	4.7K
R_3, R_4, R_5	100 Ω
R_6	10K
C_1	100 μF
C_2	1 μF

ONE-SHOT RELAY DRIVER—Will pull in relay for about 50 s out of every minute, with immunity to both positive and negative power supply transients. Initiating trigger pulse must be long enough for relay current through SCR1 to rise above its latching current. Ujt Q1 turns off scr when C1 has been charged through R3 to point where it discharges through Q1 and R5. Circuit was developed at Goddard Space Flight Center, and should be useful for general control applications.—"Selected Electronic Circuitry," NASA SP-5046, 1966, Government Printing Office, Washington, D.C., p 68.

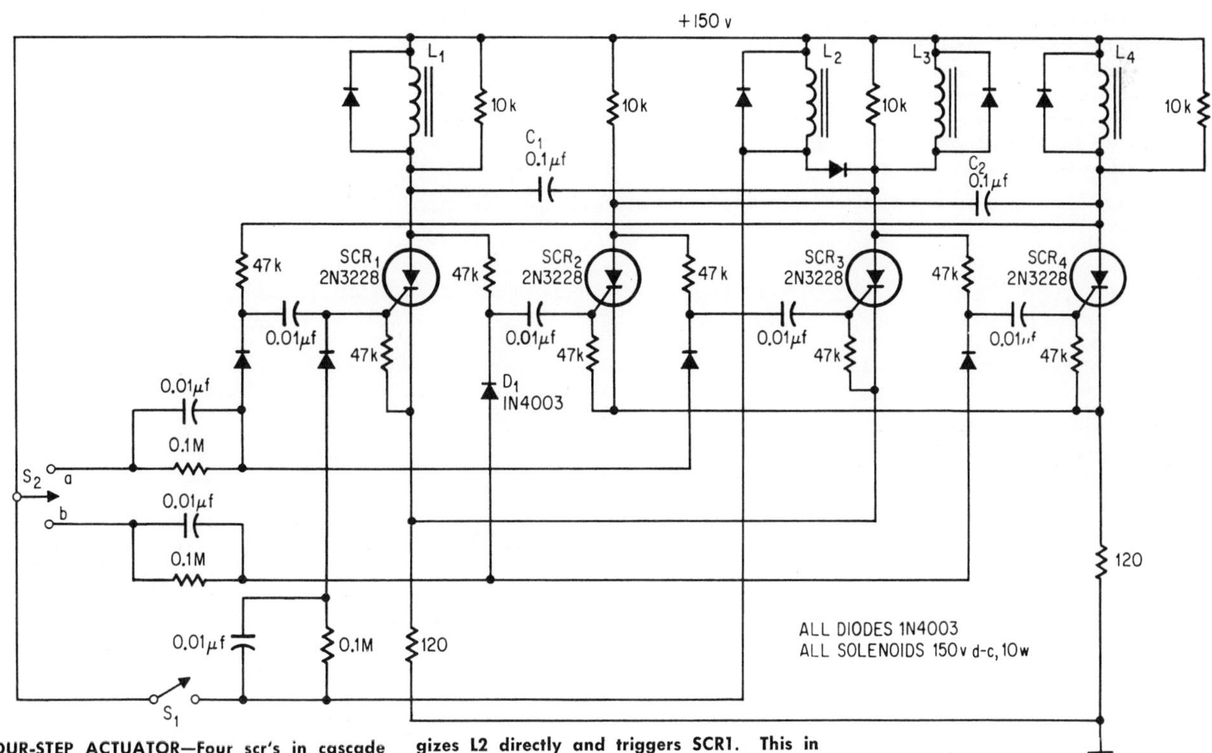

FOUR-STEP ACTUATOR—Four scr's in cascade serve in place of stepping relays to provide four-step actuating sequence for four solenoids controlling semiconductor bonding process. Closing momentary switch S1 energizes L2 directly and triggers SCR1. This in turn energizes L1. Remainder of sequence is then obtained by moving S2 alternately to positions b, a, b, a, and b. Continued operation of S2 then repeats entire cycle.—C. H. Harris, SCR Ring Circuit Replaces Stepping Relays, *Electronics*, July 10, 1967, p 80–81.

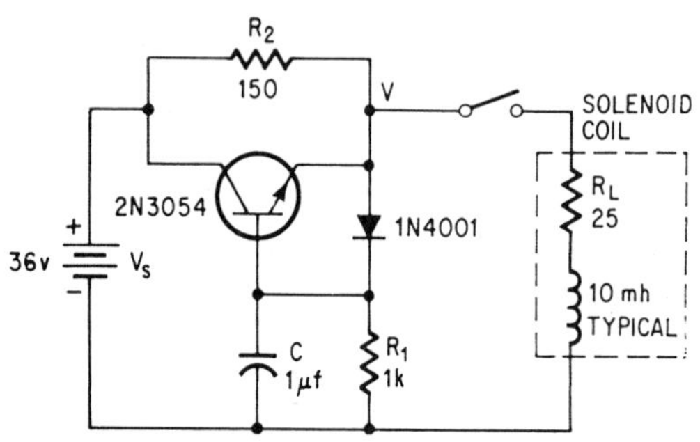

SPEEDING SOLENOID RECOVERY—Use of R-C network to control timing speeds recovery in circuits actuating solenoid-operating devices. Before operating solenoid, switch is opened so C charges to supply voltage. Closing switch makes C discharge through R1 and add to solenoid excitation current.—F. E. Mueller, Pick-Hold Coil Driver Recovers Quickly, *Electronics*, April 14, 1969, p 96–97.

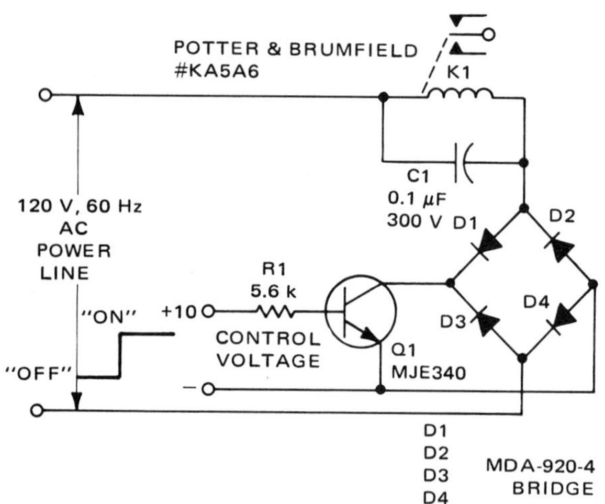

A-C RELAY CONTROL—Diode bridge provides d-c for transistor while passing a-c for operation of relay. C1 protects transistor from inductive voltage spikes of relay coil. One drawback is that control signal must be isolated from a-c power line. Control voltage source must provide 1.6 mA to base of transistor having gain of 10, to pull in relay coil requiring 16 mA.—"Semiconductor Power Circuits Handbook," Motorola, Phoenix, Ariz., 1968, p 6–38.

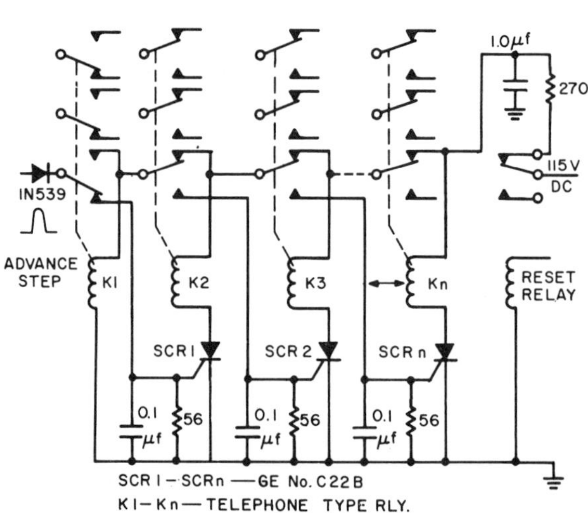

SCR STEPPING AND HOMING—Combination of telephone relays and scr's gives better reliability, faster stepping, and faster homing or resetting than conventional stepping switches.—E. Pacia, Relay Combination Improves Step Switching, Homing, *Electronic Design*, Oct. 26, 1964, p 52.

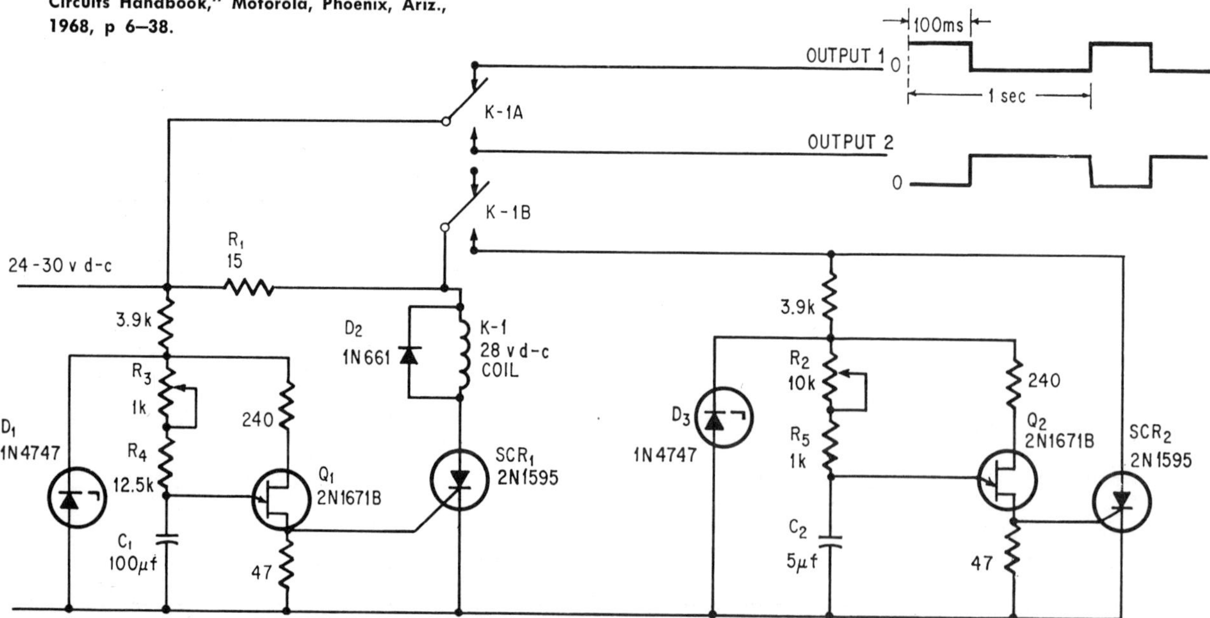

SLOW PULSER—Solid-state components and relay can stretch output pulses over range from 20 ms to one hour, depending on values used for C1 and R3-R4. Values shown give pulse width range of 50 to 150 ms at prr of 1 pps. D1 and D2 (20-V zeners) keep timing circuit voltage constant. Dpdt relay gives complementary outputs.—D. L. Pippen, Relay Actuator Produces One-Hour Pulses, *Electronics*, Nov. 13, 1967, p 100–101.

CHAPTER 73
Remote Control Circuits

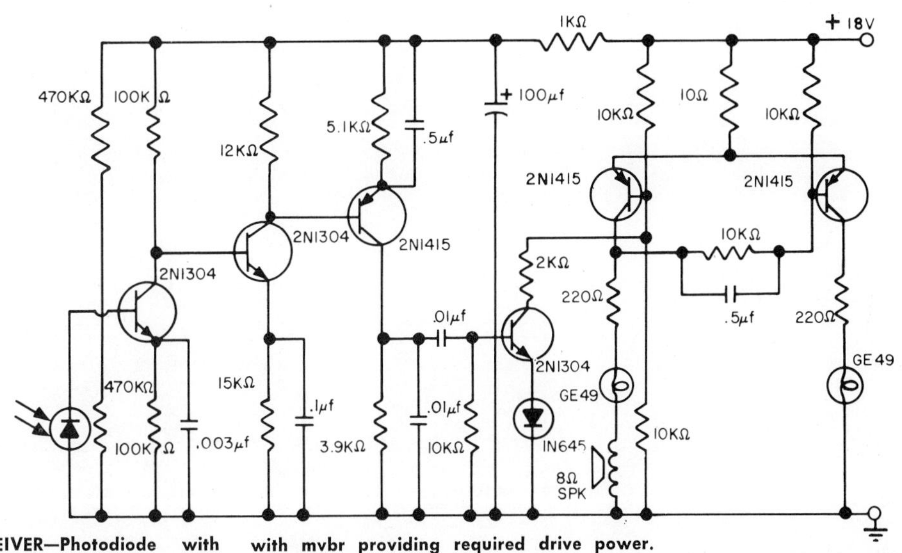

PULSED-LIGHT RECEIVER—Photodiode with simple lens picks up pulsed light from solid-state lamp up to 2 ft away, having one of four different pulsing rates. Speaker gives audible indication of tone being transmitted, with mvbr providing required drive power. Pilot lamps indicate, by intensity, frequency being transmitted. Alternatively, reed relays could be used to provide direct response to each signal. With infrared wavelength, visible ambient light does not affect performance.—L. M. Hertz, Solid State Lamps—Part II, General Electronic, Cleveland, Ohio, No. 3-0121, 1970, p 33.

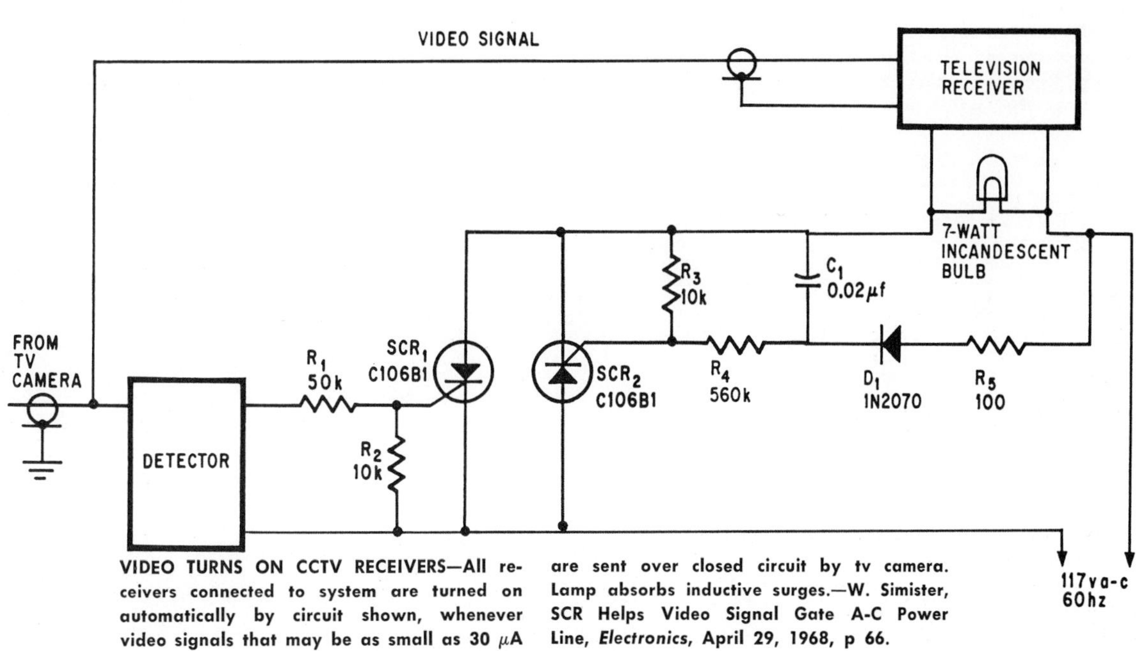

VIDEO TURNS ON CCTV RECEIVERS—All receivers connected to system are turned on automatically by circuit shown, whenever video signals that may be as small as 30 μA are sent over closed circuit by tv camera. Lamp absorbs inductive surges.—W. Simister, SCR Helps Video Signal Gate A-C Power Line, *Electronics*, April 29, 1968, p 66.

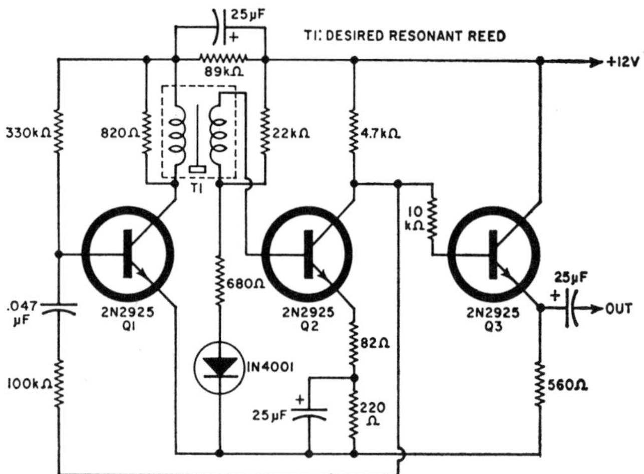

SELECTIVE-SIGNALING TONE GENERATOR—Can be used either with wire line or with modulator of radio transmitter, for radio remote control, selective CB or mobile radio communication, or for operating lamp or latching relay of frequency-selective receiver connected to wire line. Uses Motorola Minitone resonant-reed device capable of operating at any one of 200 preselected frequencies between 67 and 3,150 Hz. Reed unit is connected in feedback oscillator Q1-Q2. Emitter-follower Q3 matches high impedance of oscillator to load.—L. Solomon, Tone-Selective Signaling The New Look, *Electronics World*, Sept. 1967, p 88–90.

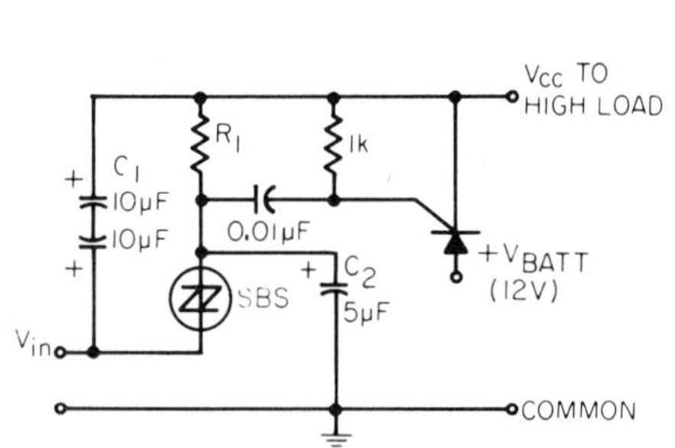

BILATERAL SBS TRIGGER—Provides high input impedance and draws negligible standby current, while providing reliable turn-on and turn-off of scr controlling heavy logic-system load. R1 must be large enough to couple substantial pulse to gate of scr but small enough for quick discharge of C1 and C2 for turn-off; good compromise is 1K. Scr type depends on load, while sbs can be D13E, MPT28, or MPT32. Can easily be driven by simple detector circuit such as Schmitt trigger. —C. H. Davis, Remote-Controlled Solid-State Switch, *EEE*, Nov. 1968, p 142 and 144.

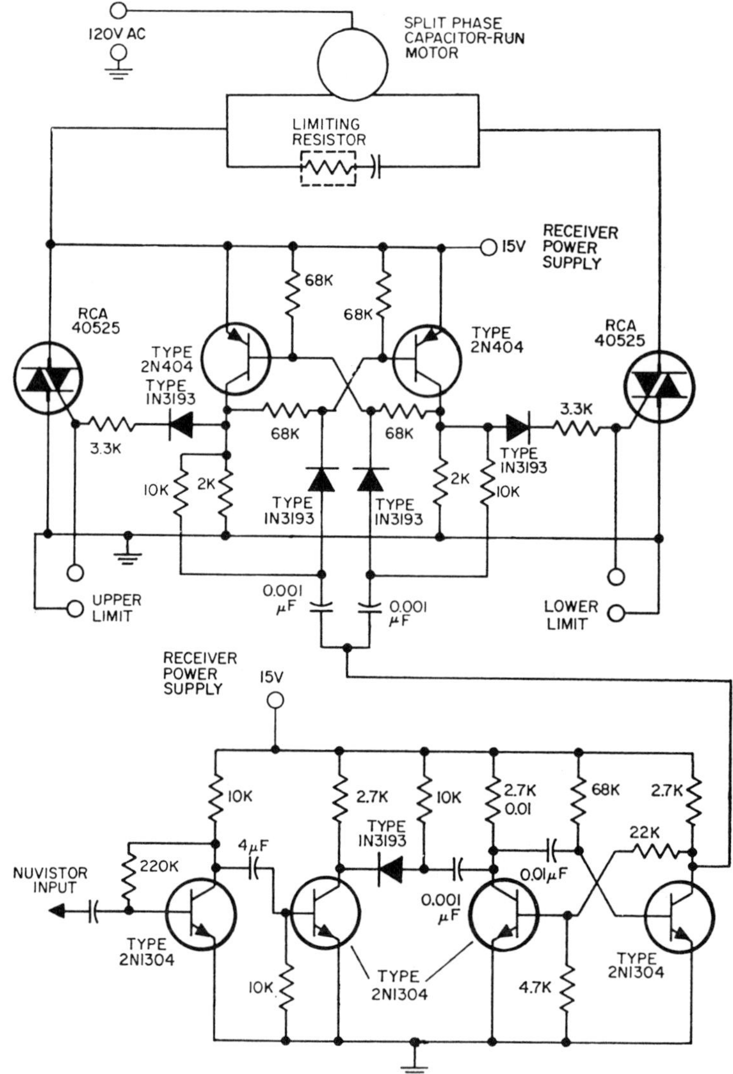

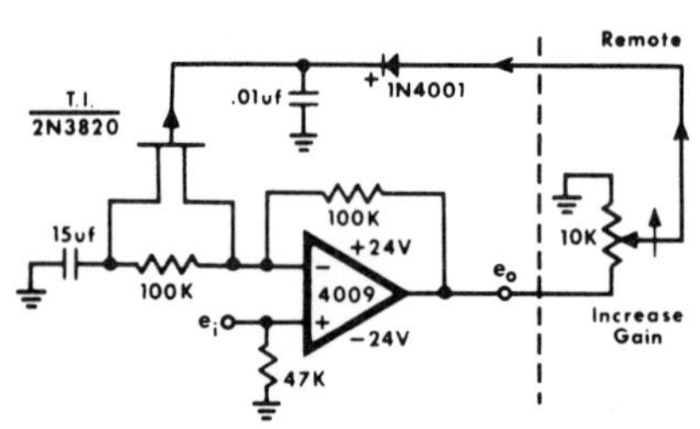

REMOTE AUDIO GAIN CONTROL—Requires only 10K pot at remote control location for adjusting gain of 20-dB audio compressor using IC opamp.—B. J. Losmandy, Operational Amplifier Application for Audio Systems, Opamp Labs, Los Angeles, Cal., 1968.

GARAGE-DOOR REVERSING CONTROL—Triacs eliminate arcing problems obtained with relays when reversing split-phase capacitor-run motor commonly used with radio-controlled garage door opener. Circuit includes time-delay mono mvbr. During door travel, transmitter keying will control motor direction independently of motor switches.—"Silicon Power Circuits Manual," RCA, Harrison, N.J., SP-51, p 252.

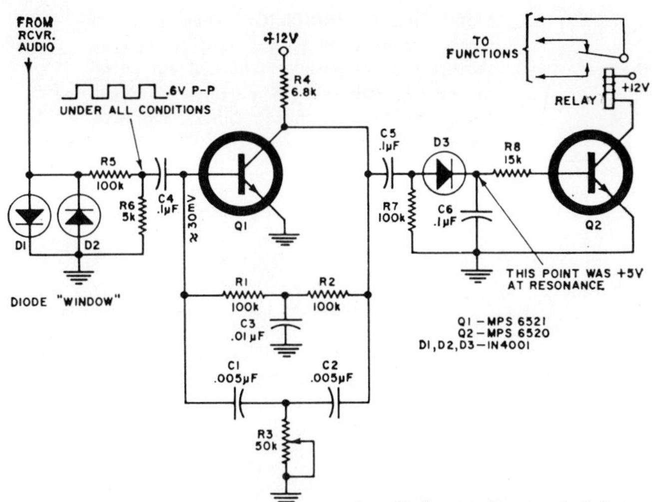

TWIN-T RESONANT AMPLIFIER—Low-power a-m transmitter on 27-MHz CB channel, modulated at 300, 400, and 500 Hz by twin-T oscillators, feeds superhet receiver of experimental radio remote-control system. Demodulated control signals are clipped to 0.6 V by diode window and fed to three twin-T resonant amplifiers, each tuned to one modulation frequency and driving relay (only one is shown). Reliability of system is good. —F. B. Maynard, Twin T's: Designs & Applications, *Electronics World*, Aug. 1968, p 35–37 and 64.

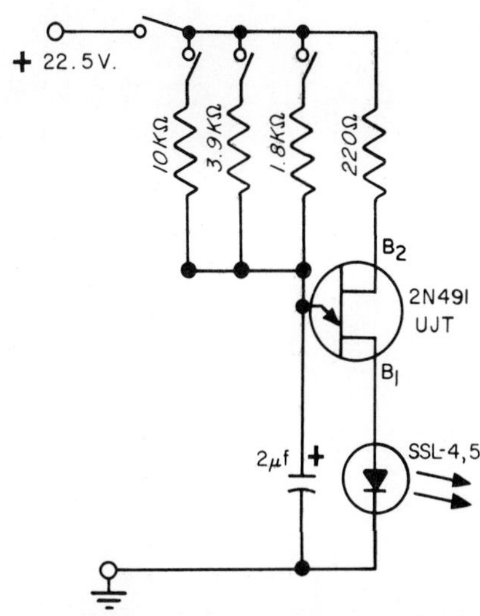

PULSED-LIGHT TRANSMITTER—Ujt oscillator pulses solid-state lamp to produce pulsed light beam for remote control. Range is about 2 ft when using simple lens over photodiode in receiver. Switches give choice of four pulse rates providing four different control functions in receiver. Supply voltage can be as low as 3 V, from pair of D flashlight cells, if low-voltage ujt is used.—L. M. Hertz, Solid State Lamps—Part II, General Electric, Cleveland, Ohio, No. 3-0121, 1970, p 32.

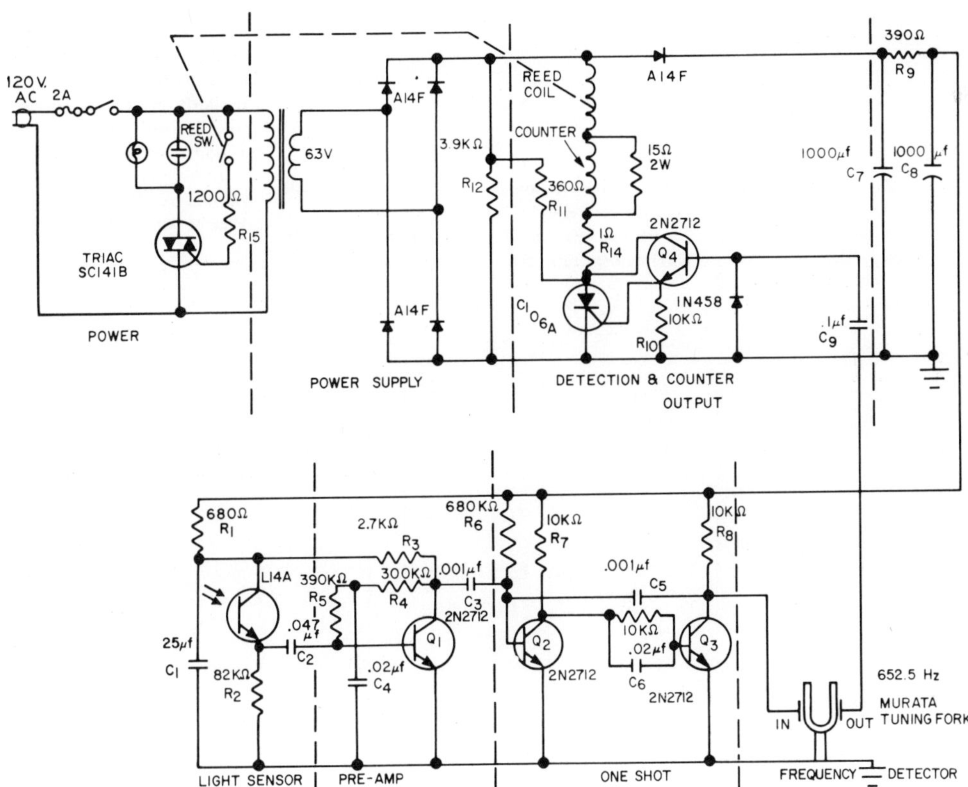

TUNED-RELAY RECEIVER—Silicon photodiode receives pulsed light beam in range of 300–1,200 pps from transmitter up to several hundred feet away. Q1 amplifies output and drives mvbr Q2-Q3 to stretch pulses to about 1 ms for driving tuning fork. When transmitted frequency corresponds to that of fork, fork output triggers gate of scr, to close reed switch and trigger triac that applies power to a-c receptacle for load up to 2 A. Additional channels are required if more than one control frequency is used.—L. M. Hertz, Solid State Lamps—Part II, General Electric, Cleveland, Ohio, No. 3-0121, 1970, p 35.

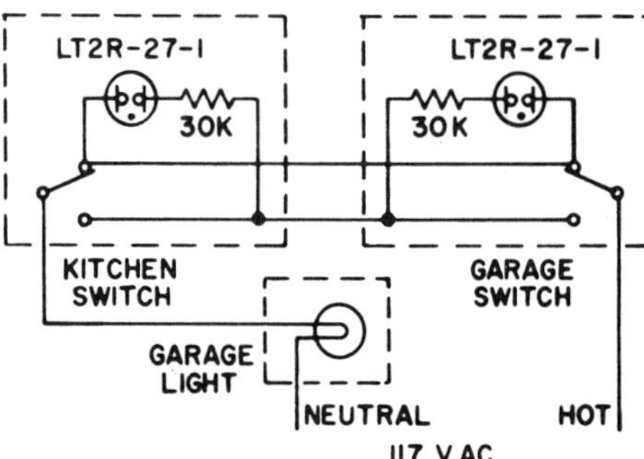

LAMP FAILURE INDICATOR—Neon glows if three-way switch in kitchen does not turn on garage light because it is burned out or removed.—E. Bauman, "Application of Neon Lamps and Gas Discharge Tubes," Signalite, Neptune, N.J., p 139.

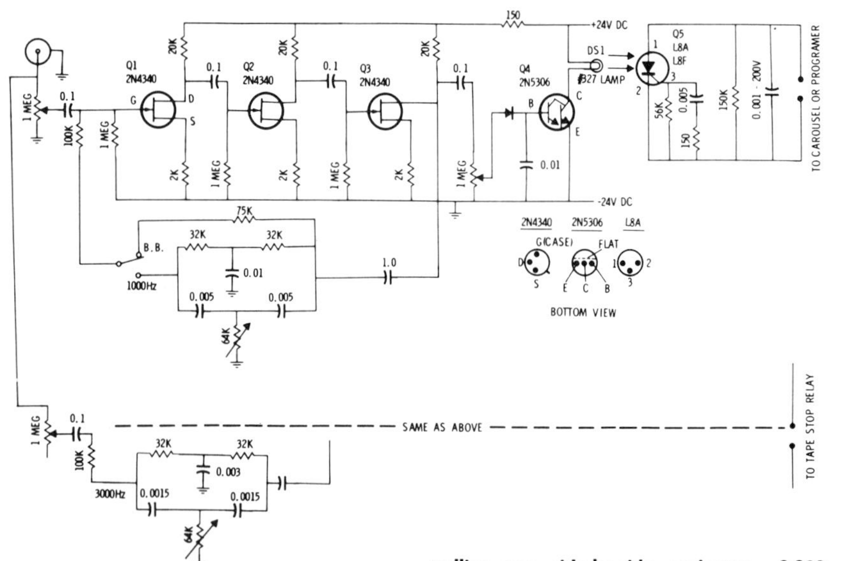

CASSETTE TONE COMMANDS—Dual-channel pulse circuit converts 1,000 and 3,200 Hz tone signals on second track of 150-mil stereo tape cassette to useful control commands, such as for advancing slide projector or controlling two side-by-side projectors. 3,200-Hz tone stops sound tape. Bridged-T network forms feedback loop that passes all frequencies except the one to which it is tuned.—W. Szabo, Control Commands, *A-V Communications*, Dec. 1969, p 6 and 31–33.

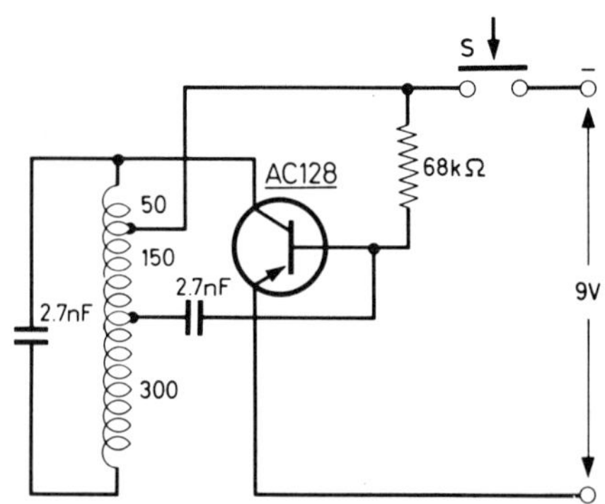

15-KHZ MAGNETIC DOOR OPENER—Developed to solve problem of radio-controlled garage doors that open when jokester drives past with transmitter in car, or photoelectric openers that are opened by boys with flashlights. Inductor wound on 12-mm rod of ferroxcube 4B 12 cm long serves as element of tuned circuit for Hartley oscillator and as magnetic antenna. Will operate in band from 10 to 100 kHz, permitting operation of two or more different systems close together. Control range is about 15 feet. Requires similarly tuned magnetic receiver and control actuator driving garage door motor.—J. van Oort, Brief Items of Interest, *Electronic Applications*, Philips, Pub. Dept., Elcoma Div., Eindhoven, The Netherlands, Vol. 27, No. 1, 1966–1967, p 38–40.

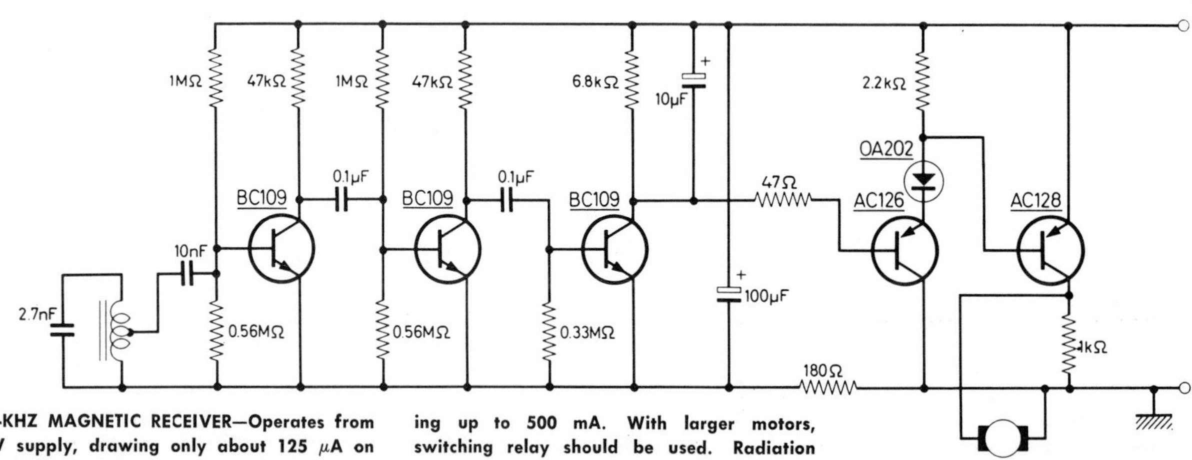

15-KHZ MAGNETIC RECEIVER—Operates from 3-V supply, drawing only about 125 μA on standby. Responds to 15-kHz magnetic radiation from single-tube transmitter up to 15 feet away, for remote control of garage-door opener having control actuator motor drawing up to 500 mA. With larger motors, switching relay should be used. Radiation is in form of alternating magnetic field, and is definitely not electromagnetic wave. Article covers possible sources of magnetic interference, such as stray fields from door-opening motor.—J. van Oort, Brief Items of Interest, *Electronic Applications*, Philips, Pub. Dept., Elcoma Div., Eindhoven, The Netherlands, Vol. 27, No. 1, 1966–1967, p 38–40.

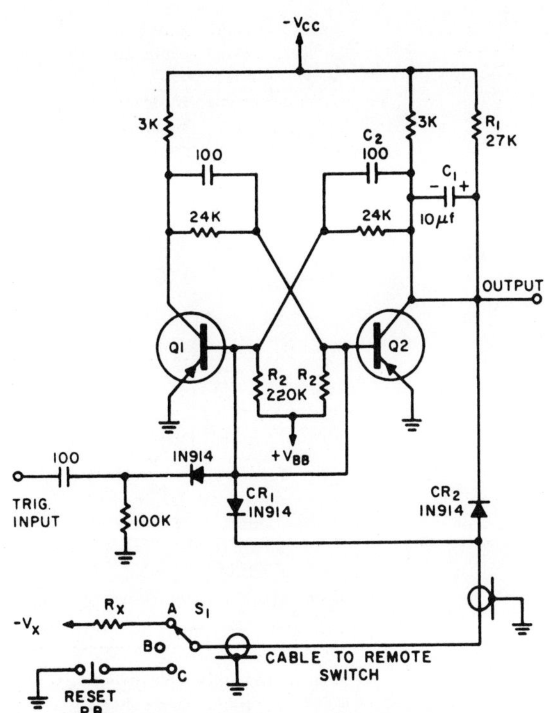

THREE-MODE REMOTE CONTROL—Single shielded wire going to remote control gives choice of three modes of operation: single-shot with minimum ON time; single-shot with ON time determined by C1 and R1; bistable operation with ON time determined by manual preset. Transistor types are not critical. —D. E. Campbell, Three-Mode Multivibrator Uses Single Control Wire, "400 Ideas for Design Selected from Electronic Design," Hayden Book Co., N.Y., 1964, p 192.

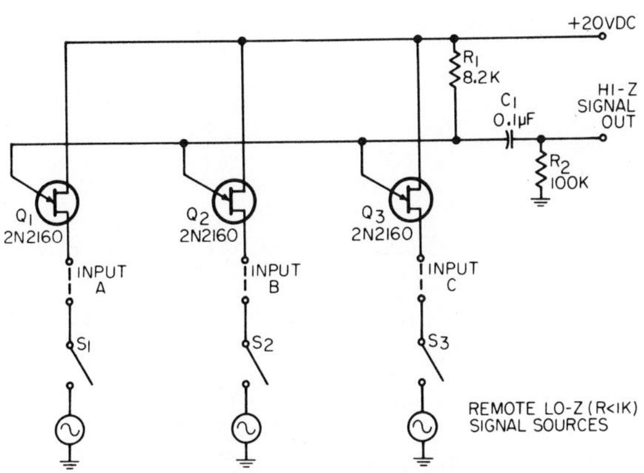

EXCLUSIVE-OR GATES FOR MIKES—Developed for paging and public address systems having many push-to-talk carbon microphones feeding common amplifier from different locations. When switch at any remote location is closed, corresponding ujt gate is triggered. Resulting emitter current makes emitter voltage stabilize below trigger level of other ujt stages, blocking all other mikes.—R. F. Sherwin, Remote-Controlled Exclusive OR Gate, *EEE*, Dec. 1966, p 119.

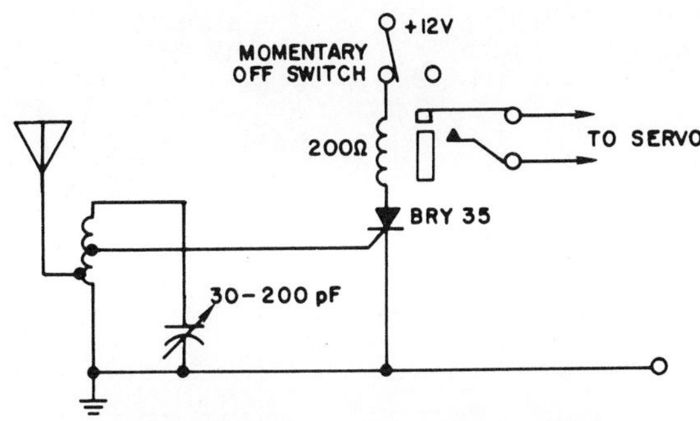

RADIO CONTROL FOR GARAGE DOOR—Simple receiver circuit requires only single scr in high-Q tuned antenna circuit. Signal input of only 30 µW, obtained from whip or wire antenna up to 100 feet from low-power transistor transmitter in auto, will trigger scr and pull in relay.—P. Antoniazzi, Inexpensive Radio-Controlled Door Opener Uses Only One SCR, *Electronic Design*, Nov. 8, 1969, p 109.

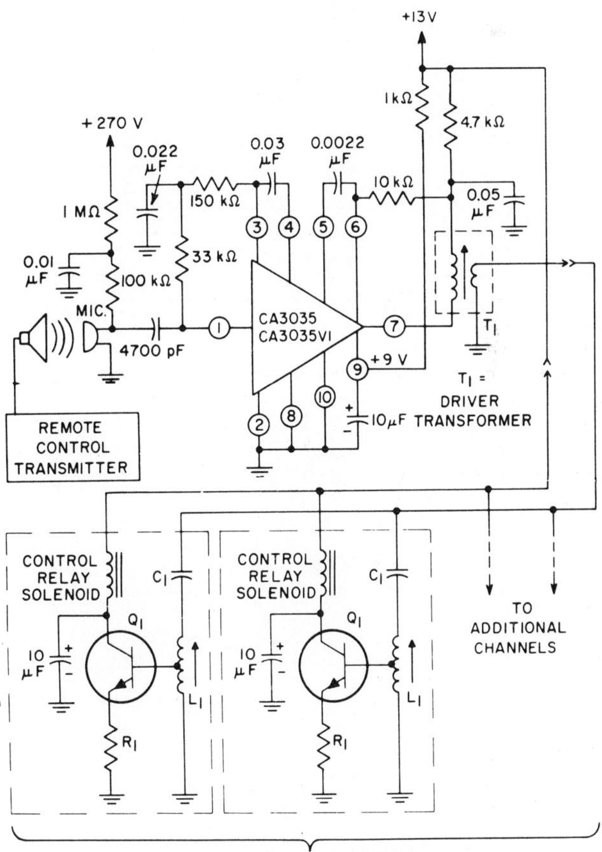

ULTRASONIC REMOTE CONTROL—40-kHz acoustic wave from remote ultrasonic transmitter is picked up by microphone and amplified by wideband IC amplifier driving frequency-sensitive control relay. Additional channels are tuned to different frequencies, above or below 40 kHz. May be used for remote tuning and control of color tv set.—"Linear Integrated Circuits," RCA, Harrison, N.J., IC-41, p 296.

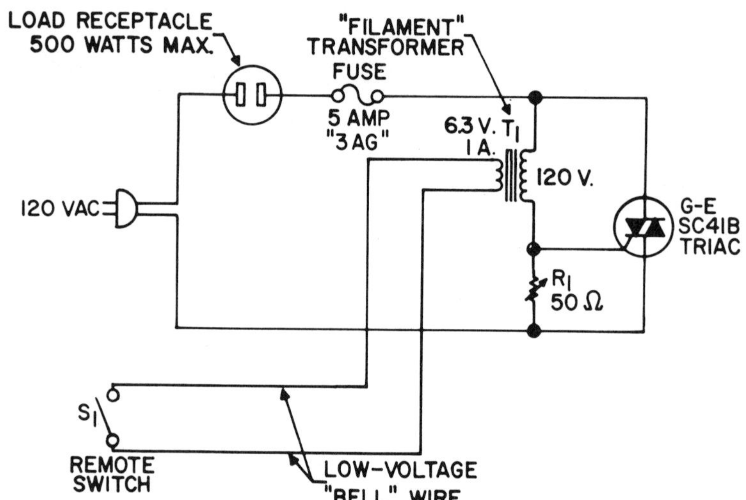

ISOLATED REMOTE SWITCH—Requires only bell wire, because switch simply shorts 6.3-V secondary of small filament transformer to make it saturate and thereby trigger triac on. Ideal for controlling outdoor light, lawn-sprinkling systems, irrigation pumps, and similar loads that may be at inconvenient locations.—F. W. Gutzwiller and E. K. Howell, Economy Power Semiconductor Applications, General Electric, Syracuse, N.Y., No. 671.1, 1965, p 9.

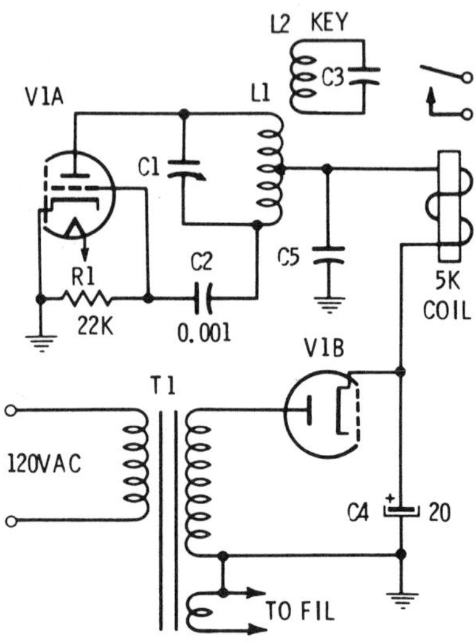

ELECTRONIC LOCK—Uses series-fed Hartley oscillator, adjusted to oscillate normally when key L3-C3 is removed. Triode V1A then draws only very low plate current and relay is open. When key is brought near oscillator tank circuit, it absorbs energy and loads oscillator, making its plate current rise and pull in relay that actuates electric door lock. To adjust, place key 0.5 in away from plate end of L1 and slowly adjust C1 until relay energizes. Relay will then drop out when key is removed. Key is small parallel resonant circuit having same frequency as L1-C1.—J. P. Shields, "Novel Electronic Circuits," H. W. Sams & Co., Indianapolis, Ind., 1968, p 83.

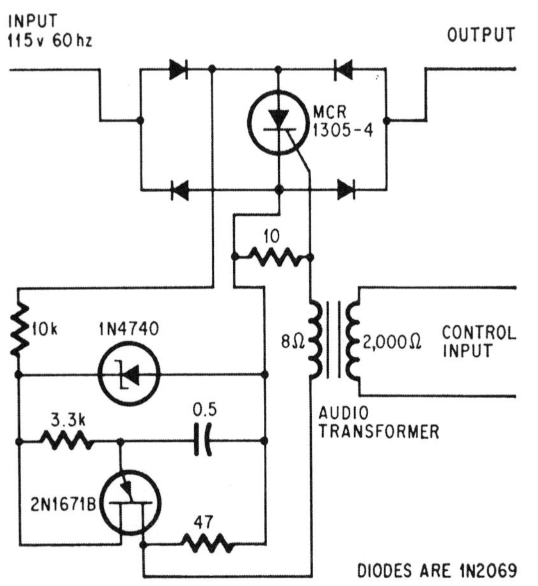

SOLID-STATE RELAY—Ujt produces pulse after each zero crossing of line voltage, but reactance of transformer prevents gating of pulses to scr when primary winding is open. When primary is shorted at remote control location, gating pulses trigger scr at start of each half-cycle, to give effect of closing switch between a-c line and output.—J. B. Johnson, Line-Operated Relay Uses Isolated Actuating Input, *Electronics*, Feb. 3, 1969, p 78.

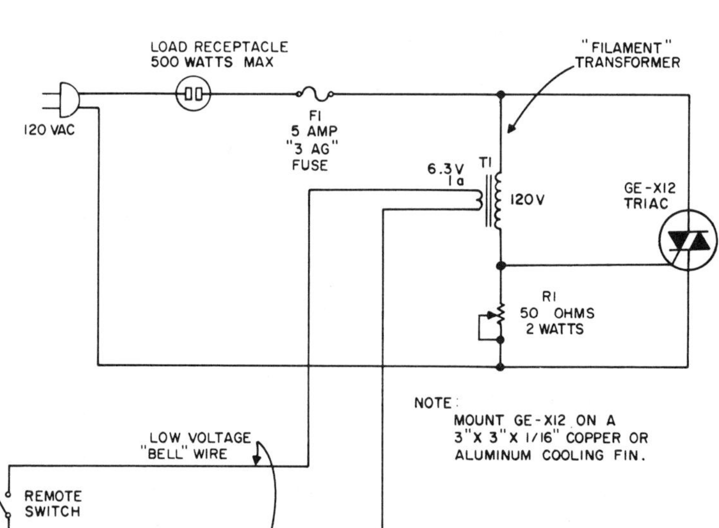

CONTROLLING 500 W WITH BELL WIRE—Closing remote switch shorts secondary of small filament transformer and triggers triac for turning on load. When triac conducts, it bypasses transformer primary and prevents burning it out. Will handle lamp or appliance loads up to 500 W.—"Hobby Manual," General Electric, Owensboro, Ky., 1965, p 162.

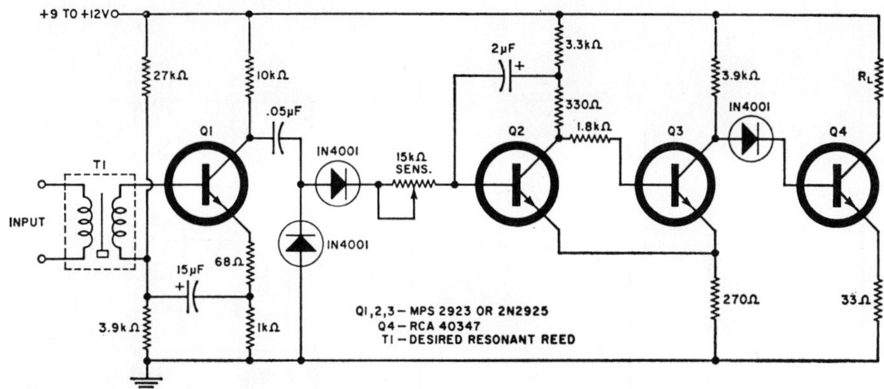

FREQUENCY-SELECTIVE RECEIVER—Uses Motorola Minitone resonant-reed device at input, tuned to same frequency between 67 and 3,150 Hz as in companion transmitter. Input can be from wire line or from audio output of radio receiver. Tone signal is amplified by Q1, detected in diodes, and used to activate Schmitt trigger Q2-Q3. This turns on Q4, to send current through load which can be latching relay, signal lamp, or other device.—L. Solomon, Tone-Selective Signaling The New Look, *Electronics World,* Sept. 1967, p 88–90.

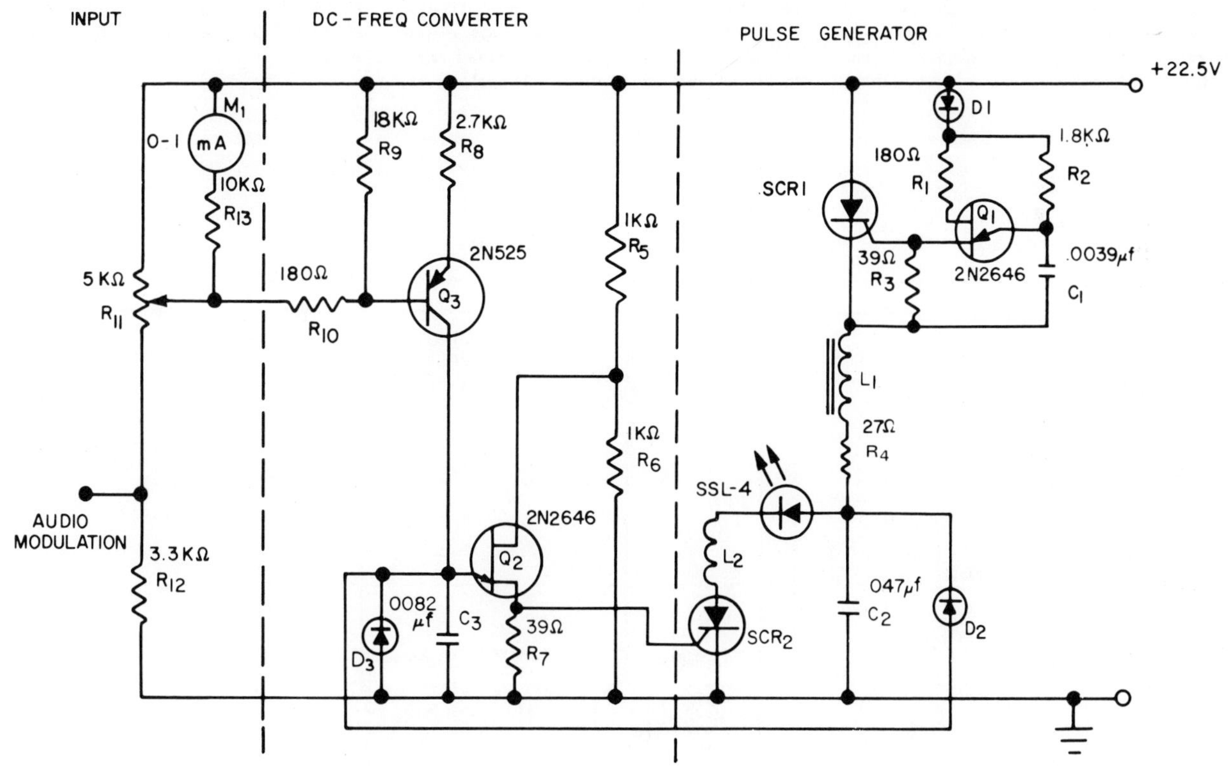

L_1 = 115μH, 60 turns #24 wire, Genelax Core G59N/30.1

L_2 = ≈ 1μH, 6 turns #26 wire, 3/4" dia. air core

D_1, D_2, and D_3 = glass signal diodes

OPTICAL F-M TRANSMITTER—Used to transmit analog information, with signal voltage being converted into pulse repetition rate that is adjustable from 50 Hz to 50,000 Hz by d-c control voltage. Pulses are 500 ns wide, with peaks of several amperes. Variations in received signal strength do not affect fidelity of transmitted signal. Pulse generator uses solid-state lamp and scr having actual switching time of only 40 ns, to give effective duty factor of about 0.025 at 50 kHz. Analog-frequency converter uses ujt Q2 controlled by adjustable constant-current source Q3. Audio information can be transmitted by frequency-modulating the transmitter. R11 then determines carrier frequency.—L. M. Hertz, Solid State Lamps—Part II, General Electric, Cleveland, Ohio, No. 3-0121, 1970, p 37.

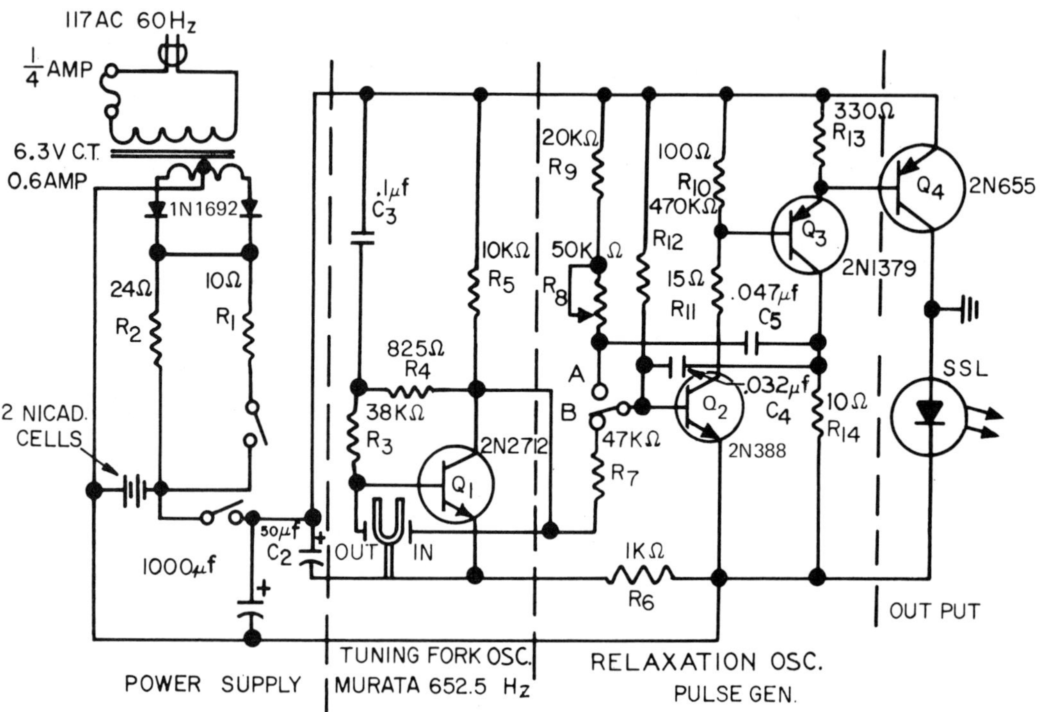

TUNED-RELAY TRANSMITTER—Operates from a-c line and drives solid-state lamp at pulsing rate corresponding to frequency of tuning fork used (switch at B) or at free-running frequency of relaxation oscillator Q2-Q3. R8 covers range of 300 to 1,200 pps. Used with receiver having appropriate tuned relay circuit for each transmitting channel.—L. M. Hertz, Solid State Lamps—Part II, General Electronic, Cleveland, Ohio, No. 3-0121, 1970, p 34.

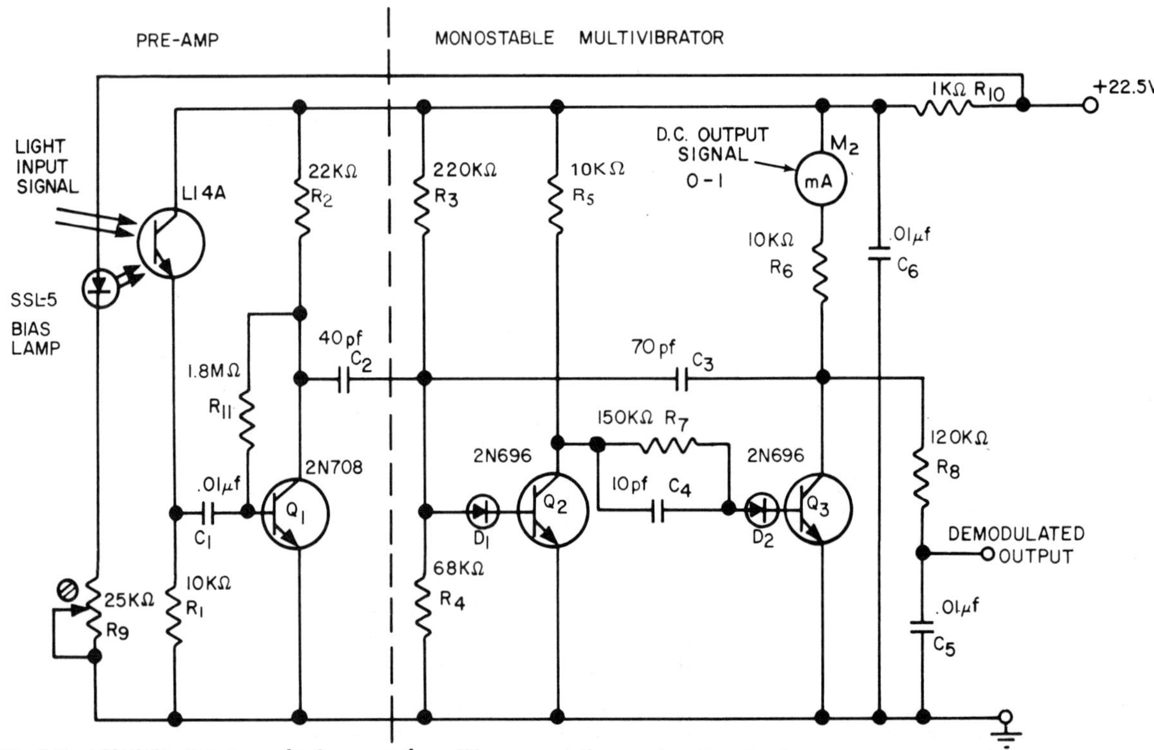

OPTICAL F-M RECEIVER—Detects pulse-frequency-modulated light beam and converts prr back to analog output. Mvbr Q2-Q3 generates one pulse for each detected light pulse. M2 averages these pulses for visual output, while d-c output is obtained across C5. System gives highly intelligible voice communication at maximum prr of 50 kHz and minimum of about 100 Hz.—L. M. Hertz, Solid State Lamps—Part II, General Electric, Cleveland, Ohio, No. 3-0121, p 38.

CHAPTER 74
Sampling Circuits

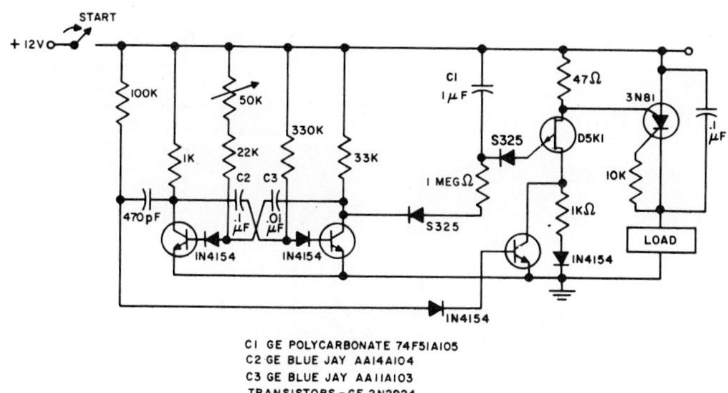

R-C MULTIPLICATION AND SAMPLING—Free-running mvbr with very low duty cycle applies timing voltage through diode S325 to 1-meg 1-μF R-C timing combination, to produce chopped exponential waveform like staircase. At end of each mvbr charging cycle, negative pulse is applied to base of sampling transistor through 470-pF capacitor and diode, to give about 10-μs sample period.—W. R. Spofford, Jr., Complementary Unijunction Transistor, General Electric, Syracuse, N.Y., No. 90.72, 1968, p 13.

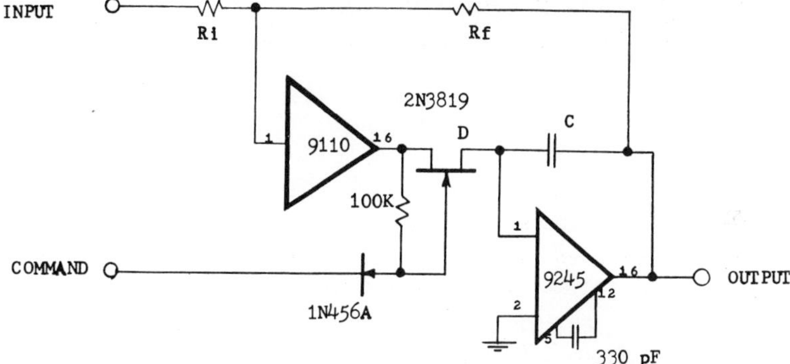

LONG HOLD—Command signal of 0 V initiates sampling, and −10 V gives hold. Report discusses frequency limitations of arrangement.—A Wide Band, Long Hold Sample and Hold Circuit, Optical Electronics, Tucson, Ariz., No. 10131.

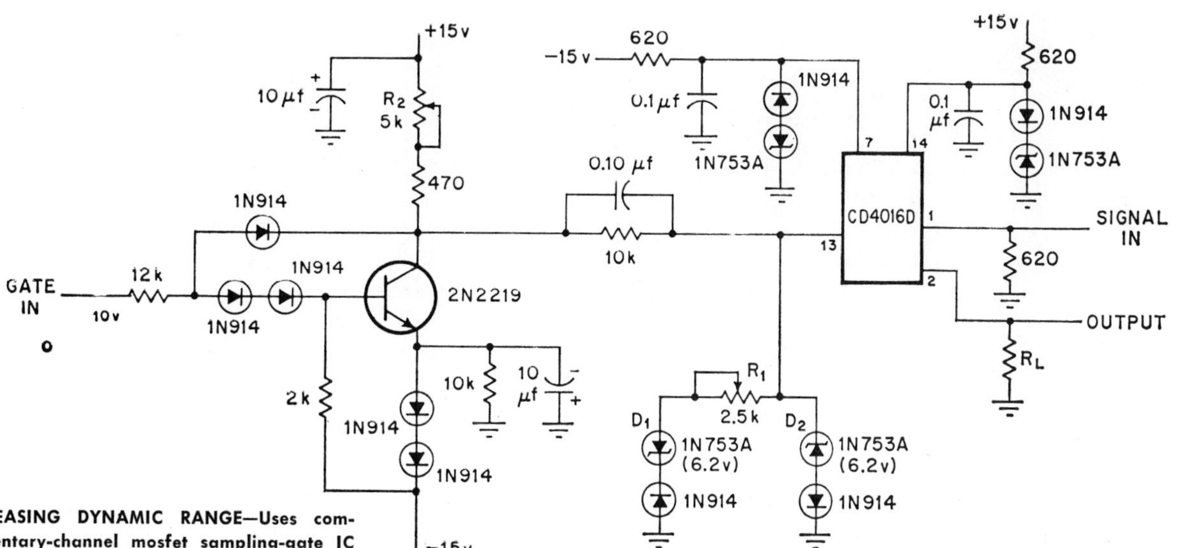

INCREASING DYNAMIC RANGE—Uses complementary-channel mosfet sampling-gate IC to increase dynamic range of sample-and-hold circuit. Keeps transient peaks in load 46 dB down from maximum gating amplitude. Zeners with series resistances soften sharp edges of drive waveform applied to IC, to reduce transients and thereby increase dynamic range of switch.—R. J. Turner, Zeners Cut Corners in MOS Gate Driver, *Electronics*, June 22, 1970, p 82.

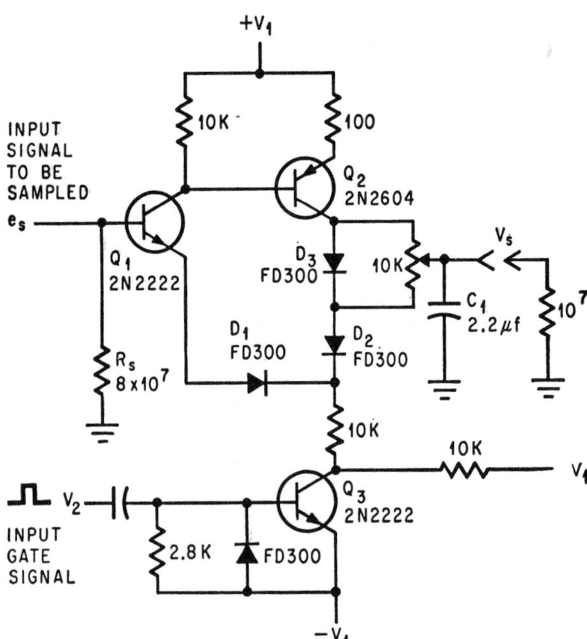

DATA SYSTEM PULSES—Will sample pulse input signal and hold for up to 1 min. Transistor beta of 100 gives signal transfer ratio of 10,000, making high-beta transistors unnecessary.—R. S. Cuikay, Circuit Samples A Signal, Holds It Up To 1 Minute, *Electronics*, Oct. 3, 1966, p 106–107.

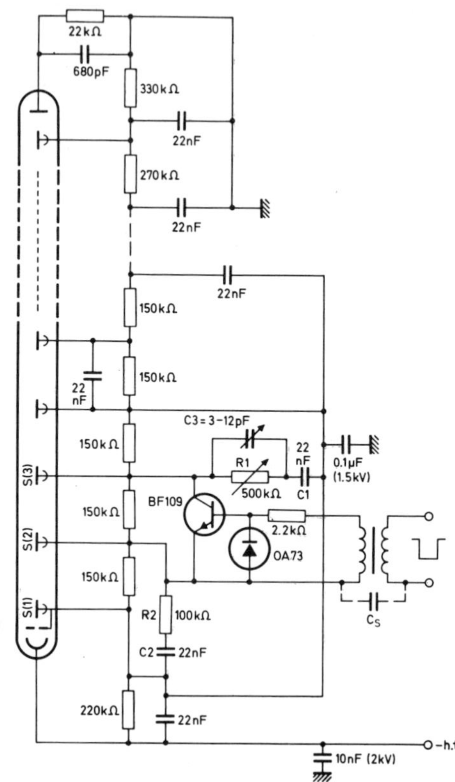

GATING PHOTOMULTIPLIER—Negative-going pulse applied through transformer makes transistor short bleeder resistor between dynodes S2 and S3, dropping voltage between them and reducing gain of photomultiplier by factor of about 100, which is usually enough for sampling applications such as are used in spectrometry.—J. M. Schonkeren, "Photomultipliers," Philips, Pub. Dept., Elcoma Div., Eindhoven, The Netherlands, 1970, p 99.

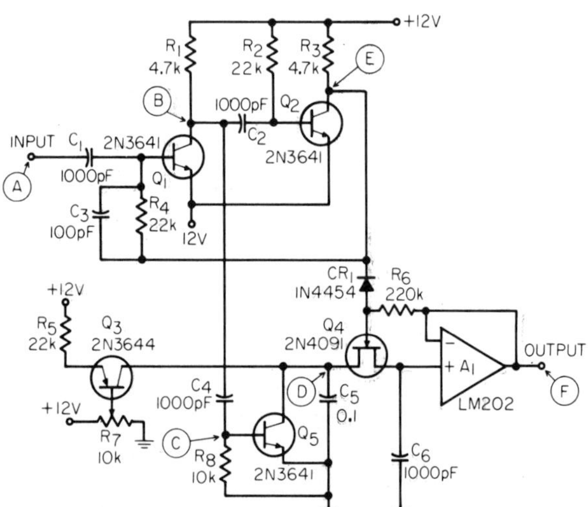

PERIOD-VOLTAGE CONVERTER—Allows sampling at rates approaching input frequency, without introducing excessive ripple. Instantaneous output voltage is proportional to input signal period or frequency. Consists of mono mvbr Q1-Q2, linear ramp generator Q3-Q5, and sample-and-hold circuit Q4-A1. Sample-hold allows accurate tracking of rapid changes in period, because each step is independent of preceding changes.—J. M. Kasson, Linear Period-to-Voltage Converter with Low Ripple, *EEE*, Jan. 1969, p 117–118.

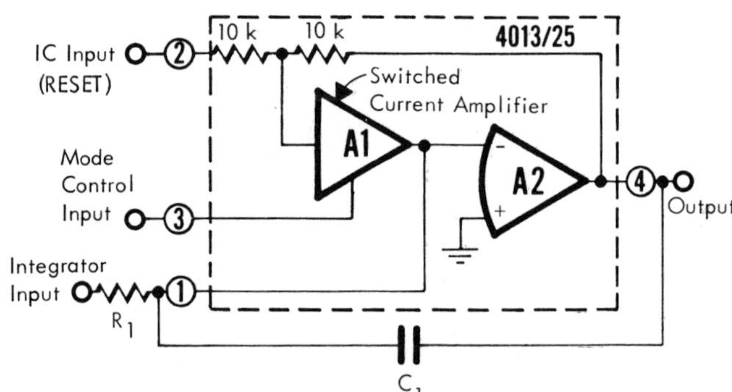

SWITCHED INTEGRATOR—Uses Burr-Brown 4013/25 sample-hold module, with input signal applied through external summing resistor R1 as shown. When switched current amplifier in module is gated off, input signal is integrated with integrator gain of 1/R1C1. In repetitive operation, initial value of time integral is set by IC (initial-condition) input voltage used for switching to reset mode.—Sample/Hold Modules, Burr-Brown Research, Tucson, Ariz., PDS-211, 1969.

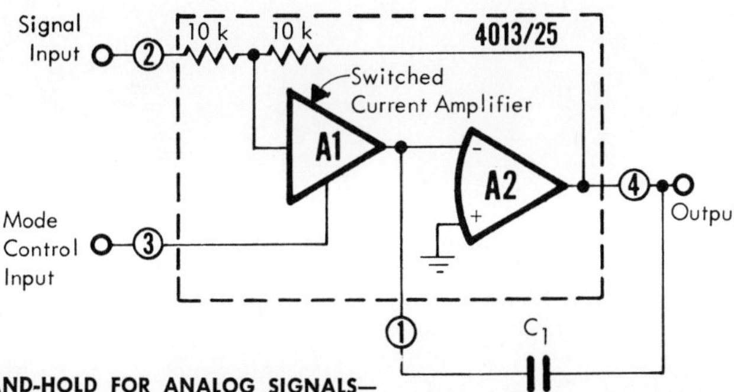

SAMPLE-AND-HOLD FOR ANALOG SIGNALS—Used to acquire and track analog input signal and hold its instantaneous value when commanded to do so by mode control logic input. Can be used in analog-digital converters, pulse amplitude detectors, measurement of time intervals, and conversion of pulse height to pulse width. C1 is holding capacitor, and should be low-leakage polystyrene.—Sample/Hold Modules, Burr-Brown Research, Tucson, Ariz., PDS-211, 1969.

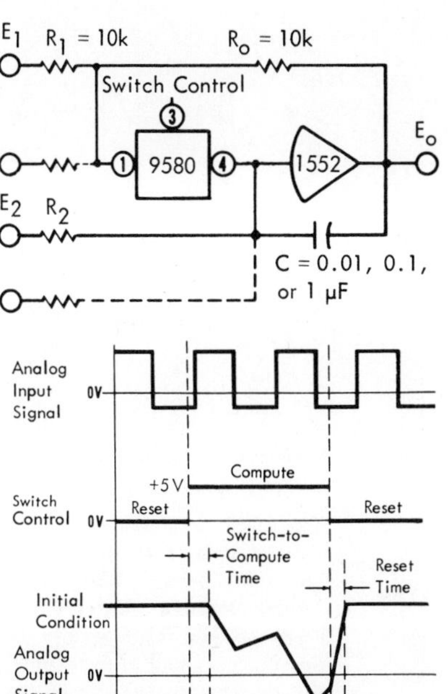

SWITCHED INTEGRATOR—Burr-Brown 9580 sample-hold electronic switch gives choice of reset and compute modes of operation for opamp.—Sample/Hold Electronic Switch, Burr-Brown Research, Tucson, Ariz., PDS-188A, 1968.

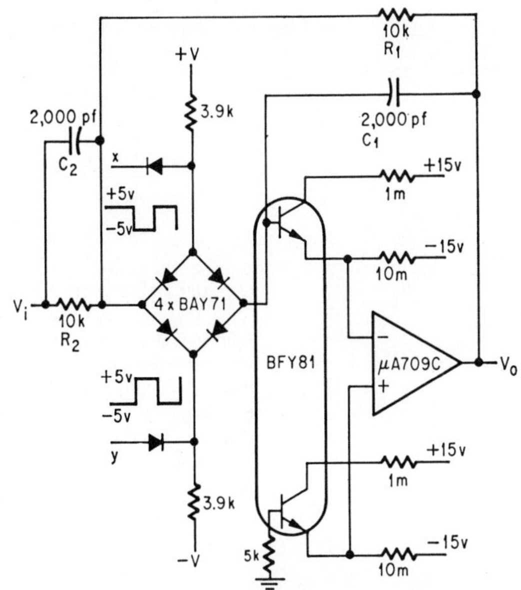

BETTER TRACKING—Accuracy of sample-and-hold circuit is increased by placing dual transistor at input of opamp to limit discharge current of feedback capacitor and thereby decrease holding error at output. Static and dynamic accuracy is better than 0.1% full scale, with a holding error of 1 to 2 mV, for input voltage range of 10 V for either polarity, frequencies from d-c to 1 kHz, and temperature range of 0 to 50 C. Circuit values shown give track and hold time of 200 μs.—G. Koch and U. Mocci, Dual Transistor Reduces Error of Track and Hold Circuit, *Electronics*, March 17, 1969, p 94–95.

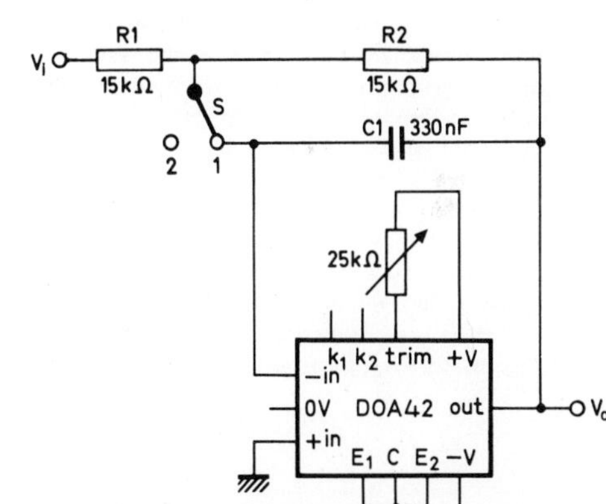

MEASURING MOMENTARY VALUE—Simple hold circuit using Philips DOA42 block charges R2-C1 network to hold information, after which switch is changed to position 2 so input signal can be removed.—Hold Circuit Using a DOA42 Block, Philips, Pub. Dept., Elcoma Div., Eindhoven, The Netherlands, No. 71.

SAMPLE-HOLD—Uses Burr-Brown 9580 sample-hold electronic switch to give choice of track and hold modes of operation with opamp. When 9580 is switched off by applying positive 5–15 V control signal, circuit switches from track mode to hold mode in about 200 ns.—Sample/Hold Electronic Switch, Burr-Brown Research, Tucson, Ariz., PDS-188A, 1968.

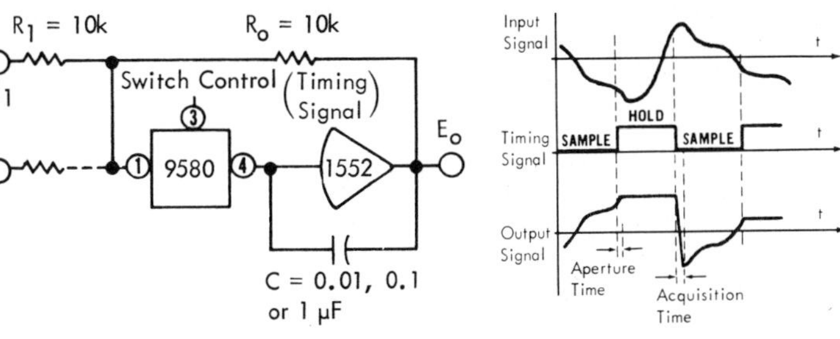

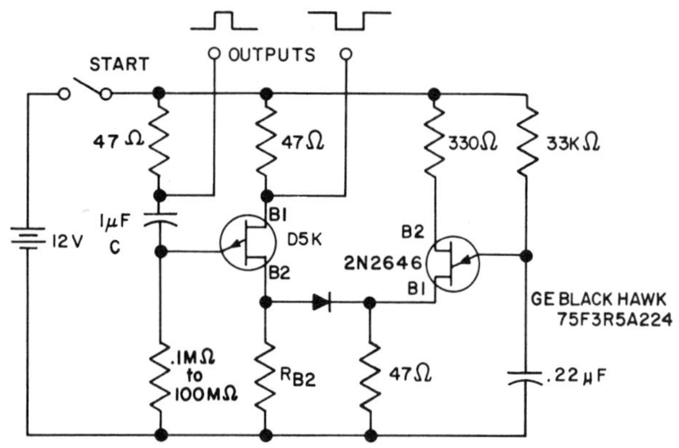

LOW-COST SAMPLER—Uses inexpensive ujt such as 2N2646 or D13T1 in oscillator configuration. When 0.22-μF capacitor discharges, voltage across 47-ohm resistor is lifted positive for few microseconds, back-biasing diode and allowing interbase voltage of complementary ujt D5K to reach its normal value.—W. R. Spofford, Jr., Complementary Unijunction Transistor, General Electric, Syracuse, N.Y., No. 90.72, 1968, p 12.

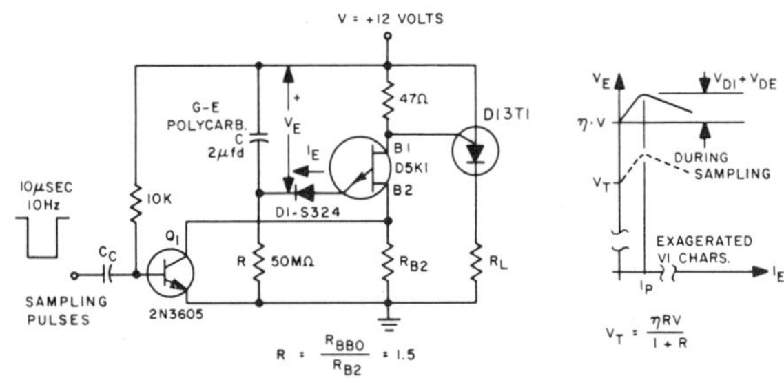

80-SEC TIMER WITH SAMPLING—Threshold sampling is achieved with complementary-ujt 80-s timer by turning Q1 off for 10 μs at 10-Hz rate with external sampling pulses. When capacitor voltage becomes large enough to fire the ujt, D13T1 programmable ujt is triggered into conduction.—W. R. Spofford, Jr., Complementary Unijunction Transistor, General Electric, Syracuse, N.Y., No. 90.72, 1968, p 12.

INTEGRATOR WITH SAMPLE & HOLD—Uses OEI Model 9186 uhf opamp having high slewing rate and very wide bandwidth at unity gain. In integrating mode, amplifier has integrating capacitor between output and inverting input, while noninverting input is at signal ground. During integrating mode, fet switches are on and not in circuit. When placed back in circuit and opened by sampling command input, output equals value at moment before switches were opened. For 20-V p-p swing, maximum frequency is 800 kHz. —A High Speed Integrator and Sample & Hold Circuit, Optical Electronics, Tucson, Ariz., No. 10079.

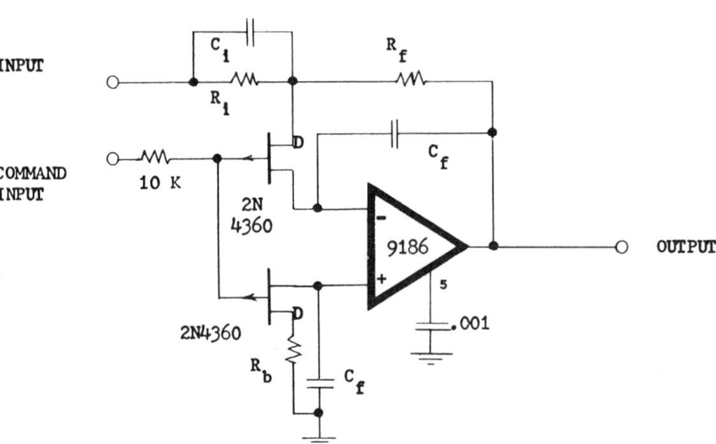

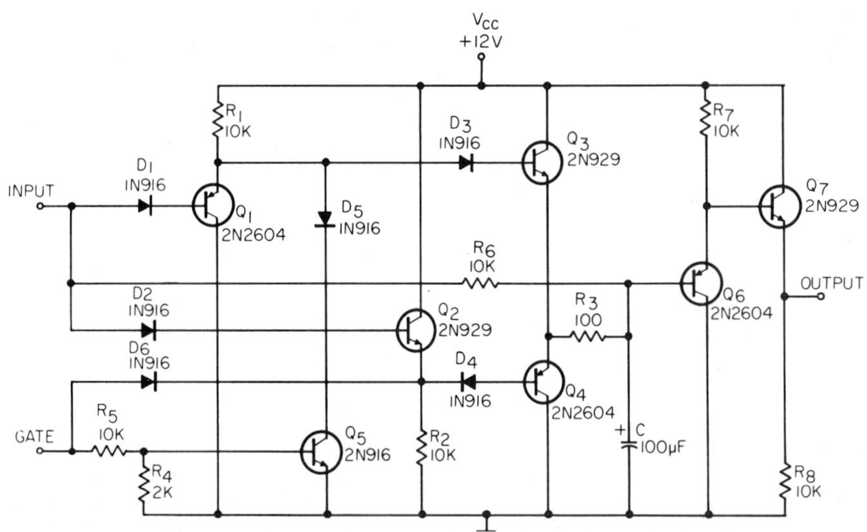

FILTER WITH SAMPLE-HOLD—Circuit functions as unity-gain amplifier having two different time constants that are selected by grounding or opening gate terminal, for use as gated low-pass filter operating in range of 0.1 to 1,000 Hz. Removing R6 converts it to sample-hold circuit functioning as amplifier when gate is grounded. When gate is opened, output is held at last voltage level. —R. S. Hughes, Gated Filter and Sample-Hold Circuit, *EEE*, Nov. 1966, p 154–155.

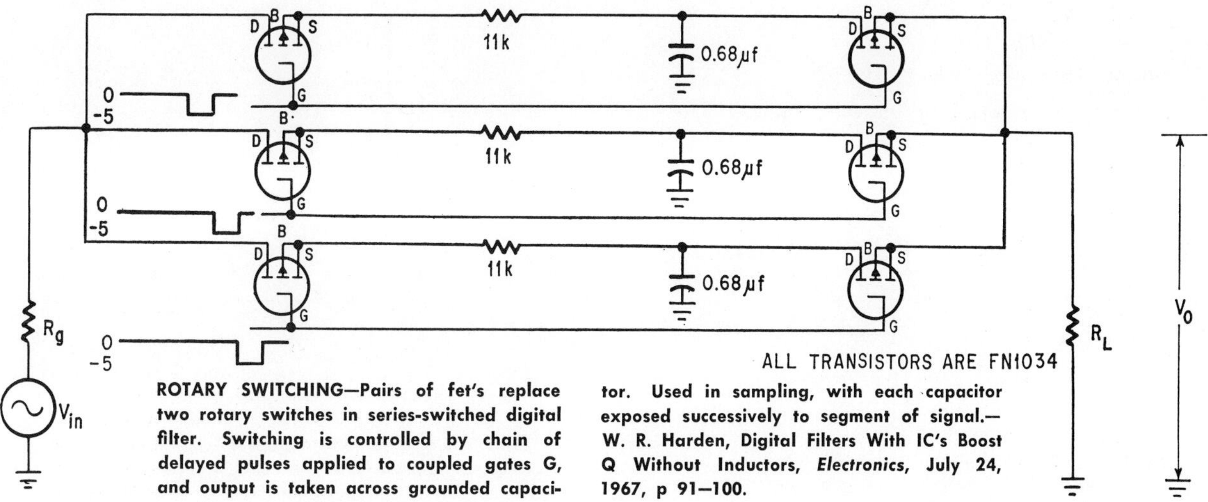

ROTARY SWITCHING—Pairs of fet's replace two rotary switches in series-switched digital filter. Switching is controlled by chain of delayed pulses applied to coupled gates G, and output is taken across grounded capacitor. Used in sampling, with each capacitor exposed successively to segment of signal.—W. R. Harden, Digital Filters With IC's Boost Q Without Inductors, *Electronics*, July 24, 1967, p 91–100.

LOAD-INDEPENDENT HOLDING—Opamp using super-gain transistors provides improved holding accuracy by minimizing error currents. Opamp buffers holding capacitor C1 to prevent it from being discharged by any output loading.—R. J. Widlar, Designing with Super-Beta Transistor Op-Amp ICs, *EEE*, Dec. 1969, p 70–73.

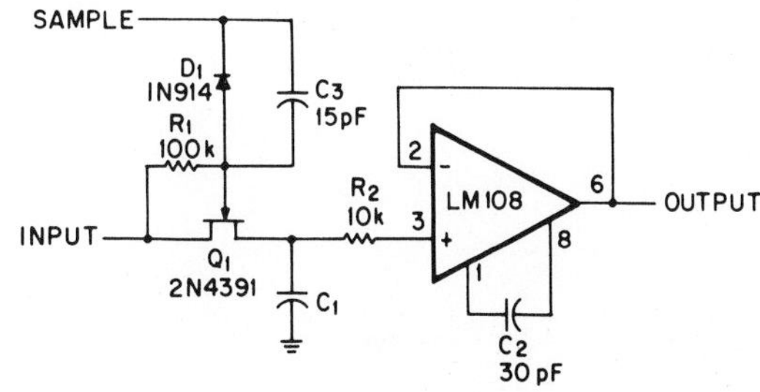

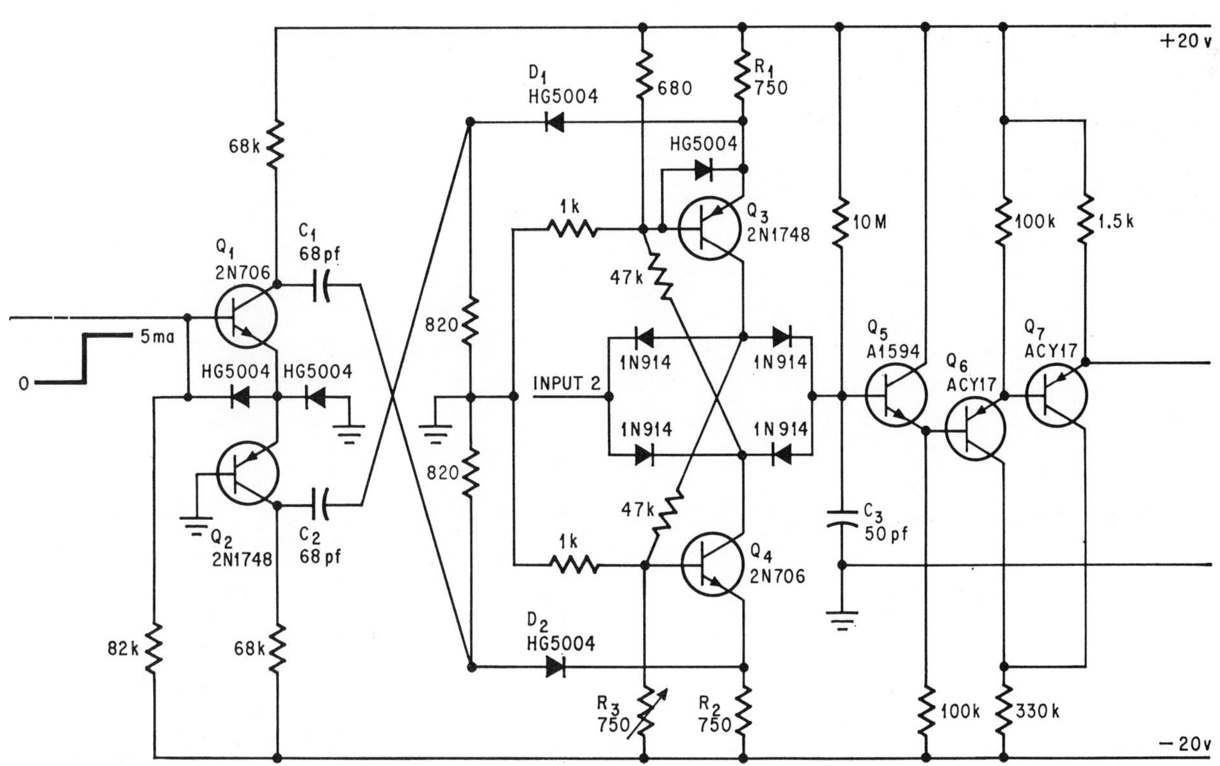

SAMPLING 10-V SIGNALS—Modification of conventional sampler uses balanced drive to diode bridge, in place of pulse transformer drive. Arrangement permits sampling of signal amplitudes comparable to power supply voltage. Ideal for progressive signal sampling, as in sampling oscilloscope.—D. J. Grover, Large-Signal Sampling Without a Transformer, *Electronics*, Nov. 27, 1967, p 80.

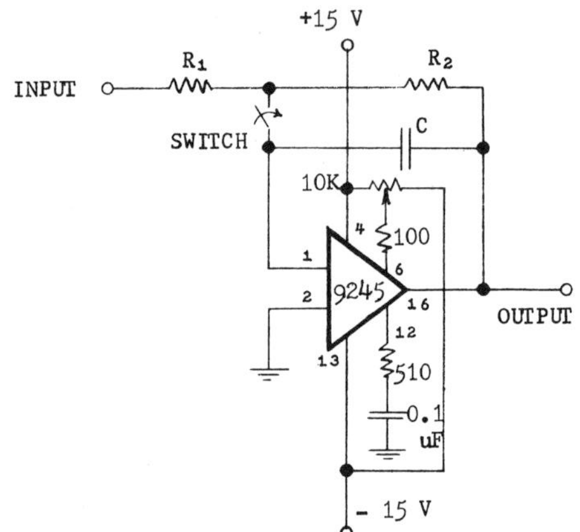

HIGH-SPEED SAMPLING & HOLD—When switch is opened, OEI Model 9245 opamp becomes unity-gain amplifier having same output voltage as that across C. When switch is closed, circuit is in sample mode and behaves as augmented integrator. If C is 150 pF, bandwidth for 3 dB down is 10 MHz.—The 9245 As A High Speed Sample and Hold, Optical Electronics, Tucson, Ariz., No. 10117.

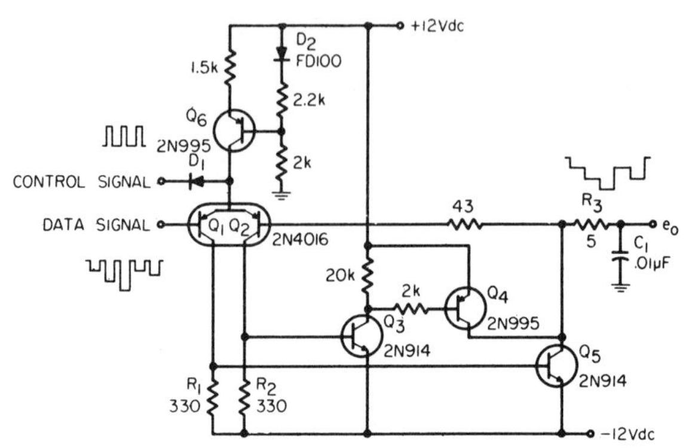

FASTER SAMPLE-HOLD—Matched transistors Q1-Q2 give low offset between sample data input and held output, to give 300-ns output response to step input level and 0.1% accuracy. Logic input applied to D1 controls state of circuit.—J. Downey, Sample-and-Hold Circuit is Fast Yet Accurate, *EEE*, March 1968, p 125.

FET BOXCAR SAMPLE-AND-HOLD—Will sample either d-c or a-c signals at repetition rates from 200 to 250 kHz, and store sample voltages having width of only 0.5 μs. Q1 and Q2 form cross-coupled series switch that conducts in both directions for transferring either increasing or decreasing input signals to glass storage capacitor during conduction. Gate input for fet's is −12 V switching pulse lasting 0.5 to 20 μs.—J. J. Contus, Boxcar Circuit Uses FETs, *EEE*, April 1967, p 136.

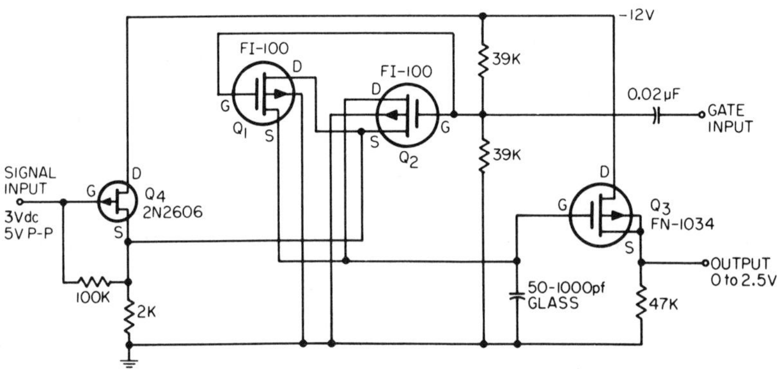

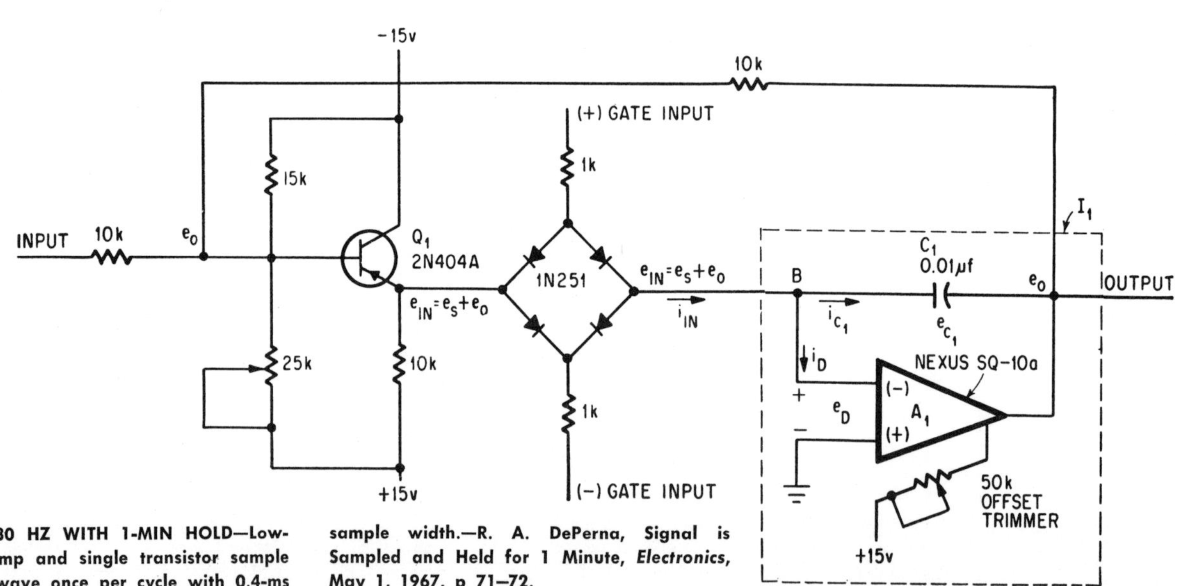

SAMPLING 30 HZ WITH 1-MIN HOLD—Low-cost IC opamp and single transistor sample 30-Hz sine wave once per cycle with 0.4-ms sample width.—R. A. DePerna, Signal is Sampled and Held for 1 Minute, *Electronics*, May 1, 1967, p 71–72.

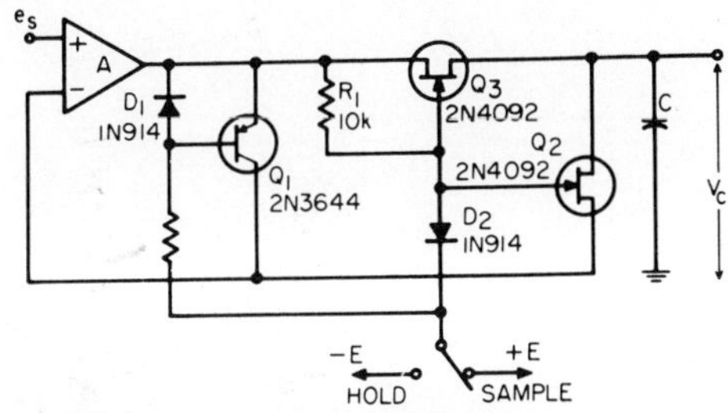

ERROR REDUCTION—Modification of conventional fet sample-and-hold circuit reduces errors caused by ON resistance of fet. During sampling interval, both fet's are on and Q1 is cut off. During hold interval, situation is reversed. With fet's inside feedback loop of high-gain opamp such as μA709C, ON resistance is reduced by open-loop gain, so charging speed is essentially limited only by output current capability of voltage follower. —I. Cohen and D. Clark, An Improved FET Sample-and-Hold Circuit, *EEE*, Sept. 1968, p 104 and 106.

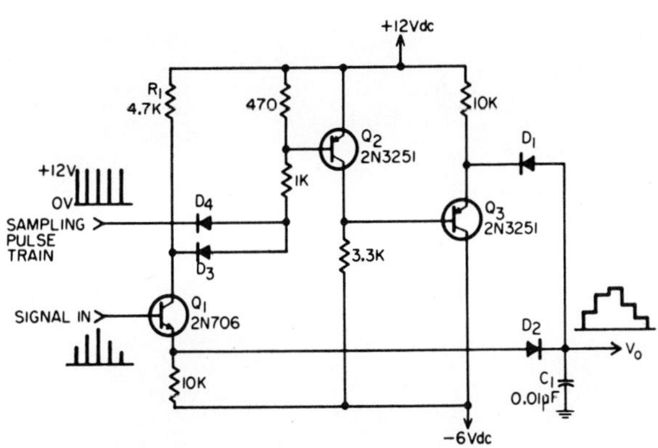

HIGH SPEED WITH SIMPLICITY—Charge and discharge cannot occur simultaneously in simplified circuit shown, and therefore no speed-inhibiting current-limiting resistor is needed. Sampling periods can be as short as 1 μs. Between pulses, sampling pulse train is at ground potential, holding Q2 in saturation. Article describes operation in detail.—B. Pearl, Sample-Hold Circuit, *EEE*, Dec. 1966, p 121–122.

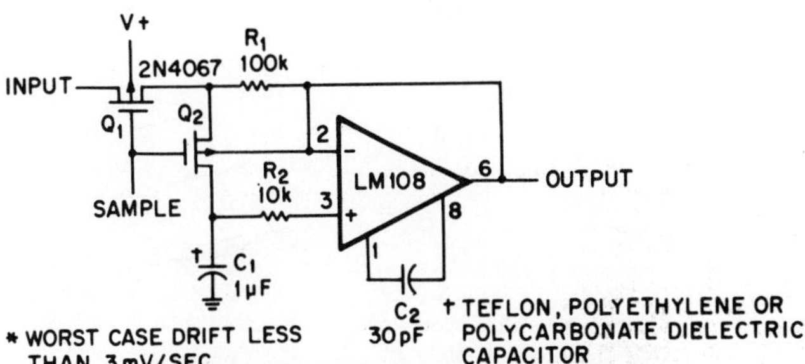

HIGH-ACCURACY HOLD—Error-producing leakage current across substrate-drain junction is routed to output of high-gain opamp through R1 to prevent it from contributing to residual error current that affects accuracy of sample-and-hold circuit. Hold capacitor must have low leakage and be free from dielectric polarization. For sample interval under 100 μs, use faster IC such as LM102A.—R. J. Widlar, Designing with Super-Beta Transistor Op-Amp ICs, *EEE*, Dec. 1969, p 70–73.

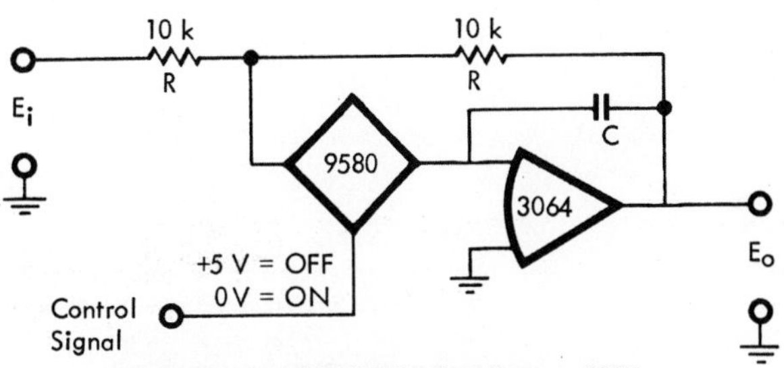

INVERTING SAMPLE-HOLD—Burr-Brown 3064 fet-input opamp module, used with 9580 switch having current amplification factor of 1,000, gives inverting unity-gain amplifier performance when switch is on and set to sample or track mode. Time constant of circuit is short.—Operational Amplifiers, Burr-Brown Research, Tucson, Ariz., LI-227, 1969, p 43.

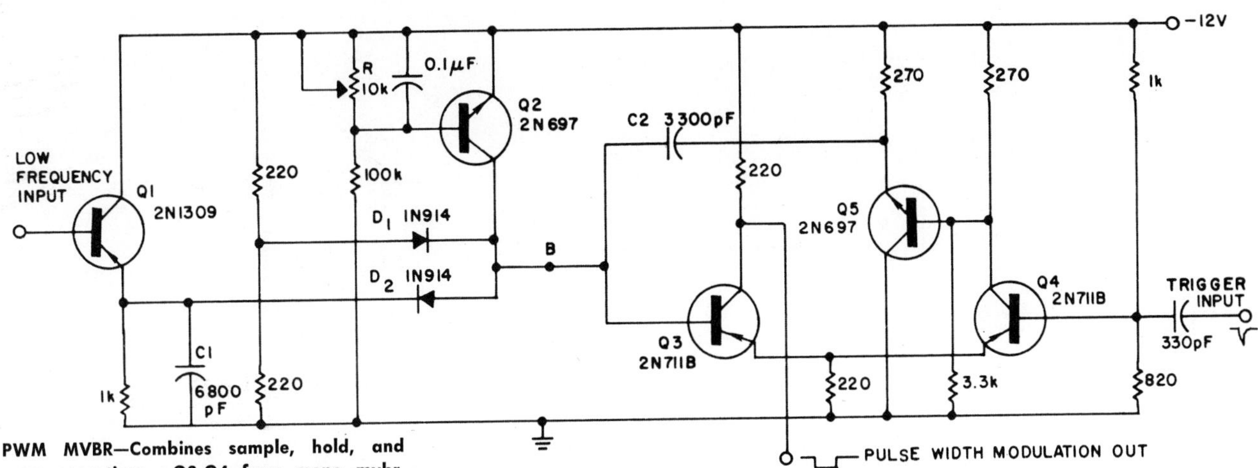

PWM MVBR—Combines sample, hold, and pwm operations. Q3-Q4 form mono mvbr, with C2 as charging capacitor. Positive peak of voltage at B is limited to instantaneous value of low-frequency input to achieve modulation. Maximum prr is 45 kHz and range of output pulse widths is 1 to 20 μs. Linearity is excellent.—A. Shah, Linear Pulse-Width Modulator Uses Monostable Multivibrator, *Electronic Design*, Nov. 8, 1969, p 103 and 105.

CHAPTER 75

Sawtooth Generator Circuits

UNIVERSAL SAWTOOTH—Converts 4-V p-p sine, square, or triangular waveform in range of 80 to 800 Hz to 0.3 V sawtooth at lower frequency and 1.5 V sawtooth at higher frequency. Diode can be any type, such as 1N457. Circuit is easily set up, even though not highly accurate.—C. Eddy, Simple Circuit Converts Any Waveform Into a Sawtooth, *Electronic Design*, Dec. 20, 1967, p 110.

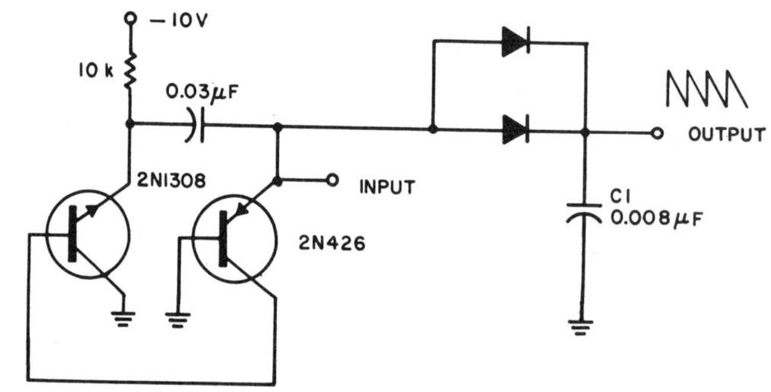

TRAPEZOIDAL VOLTAGE SWEEP—Transistor serves as switch for two wave-shaping networks, one shown by broken arrows and the other by solid arrows. When input pulse swings negative, transistor turns on and CC discharges over broken-arrow path. Output waveform is trapezoidal.—A. C. Gillie, "Pulse and Logic Circuits," McGraw-Hill, N.Y., 1968, p 277.

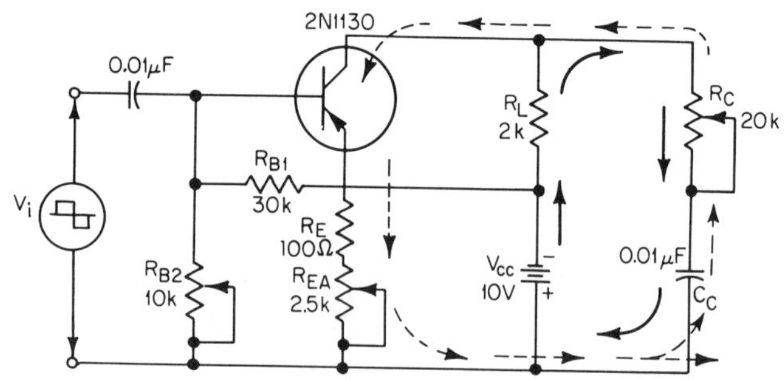

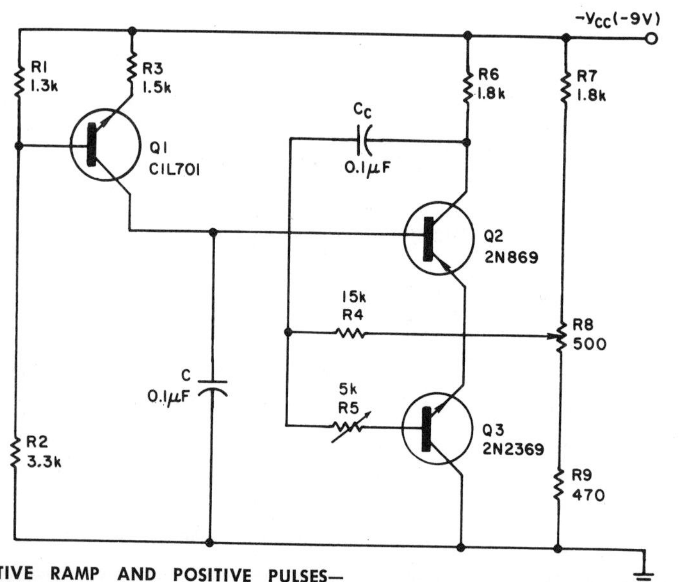

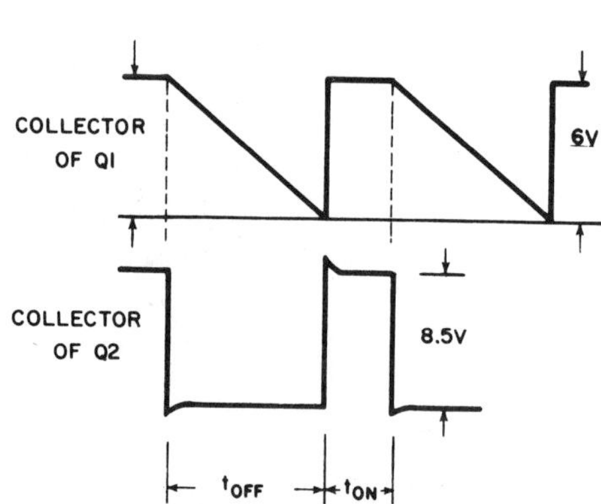

NEGATIVE RAMP AND POSITIVE PULSES—Provides 200-μs positive pulses with 15 ms OFF time for use in measuring transistor parameters, along with negative-going ramp having excellent linearity. Consumes very little power. Sawtooth can be as narrow as 1 μs, with ramp starting accurately at zero voltage and with no step. Pulses can also be as narrow as 1 μs. Q1 is constant-current source for emitter-coupled complementary pair Q2-Q3.—U. S. Singh, Circuit Generates Linear Ramp and Short Duty Cycle Pulses, *Electronic Design*, May 10, 1969, p 134.

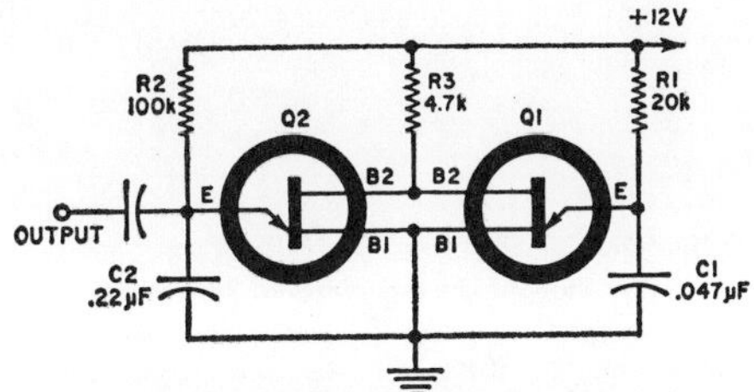

Q1,Q2—TIS43-TEXAS INSTRUMENTS UNIJUNCTION TRANSISTOR

IMPROVING LINEARITY—Instead of feeding timing capacitor from constant-current source, circuit uses two ujt sawtooth oscillators operating independently except for sharing common base-2 resistor R3. The two ujt's now fire in unison, with the fastest ujt determining repetition rate, which is about 500 Hz for values shown and 375-mV output signal. Increasing ratio of time constant R2C2 to R1C1 improves linearity.—F. H. Tooker, Improving Sawtooth Linearity, *Electronics World*, Feb. 1969, p 84.

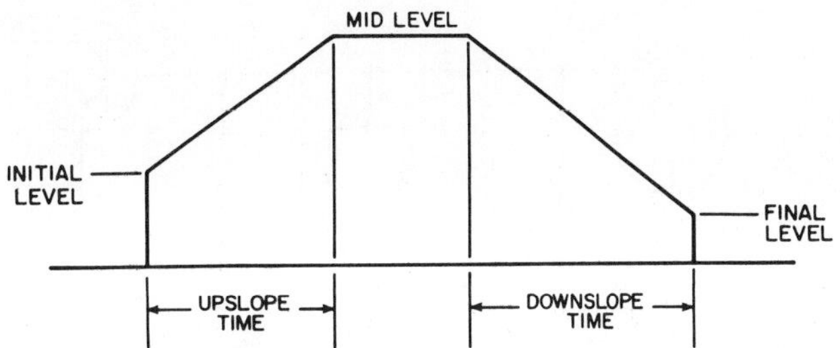

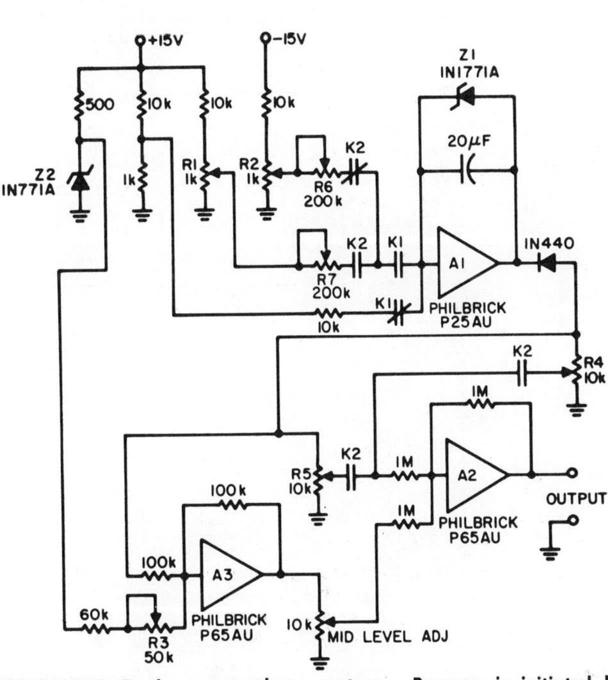

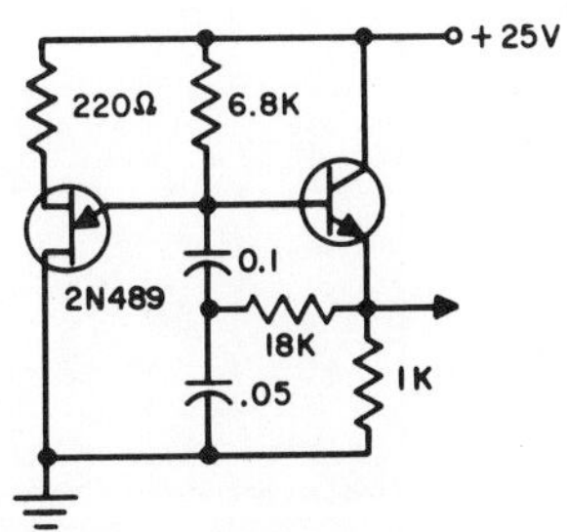

NONLINEARITY COMPENSATION—Addition of 18K-0.05 μF integrating network provides second-order compensation for nonlinearity of bootstrap sawtooth generator. Output stage can be any npn emitter-follower transistor.—T. P. Sylvan, The Unijunction Transistor Characteristics and Applications, General Electric, Syracuse, N.Y., No. 90.10, 1965, p 48.

SERVO CONTROLS RAMP—Produces ramp that rises from initial level to mid-level in independently adjustable time, remains at constant level for adjustable time, then drops to preset final level in adjustable downslope time, as required in many industrial control systems. Program is initiated by activating relay K1 and terminated by activating K2 (coils not shown) manually. R6 determines upslope time.—G. E. Cook, Servo Programmer Generates Linear On and Off Ramps, *Electronic Design*, Nov. 8, 1967, p 118 and 120.

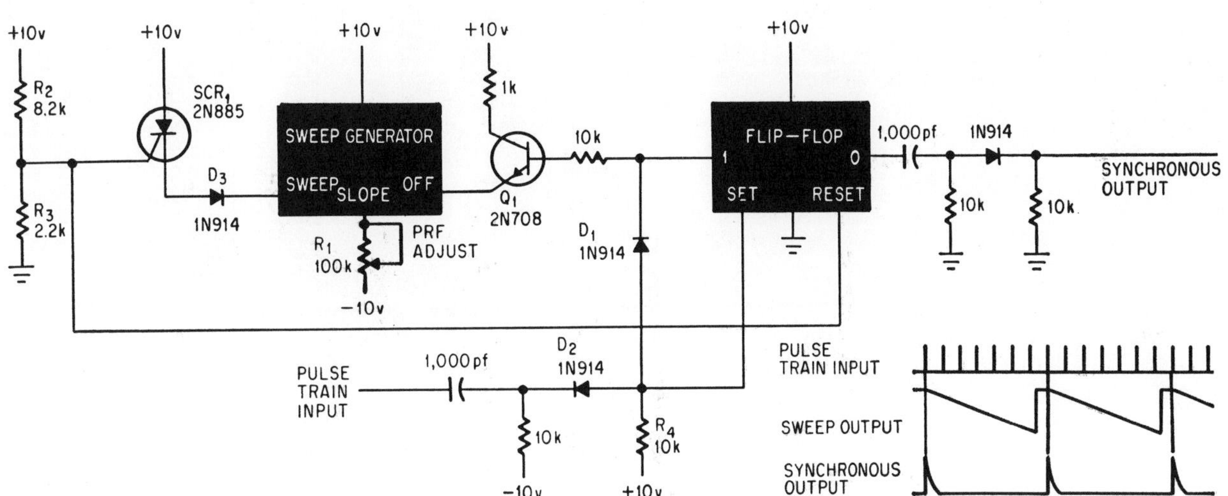

SWEEP IN FREQUENCY DIVIDER—Generates output pulses in synchronism with input pulse train, for pulse or digital systems. Permits using one variable-frequency generator in place of several fixed-frequency dividers. With values shown and 1-μF capacitor for C1 in linear sweep, output frequency can be varied from 10 to 1,000 Hz for input of 10 kHz. Input-to-output ratios can be as high as 1,000:1.—S. Weisman, One Transistor Sweeps Clean, *Electronics*, June 12, 1967, p 106–109.

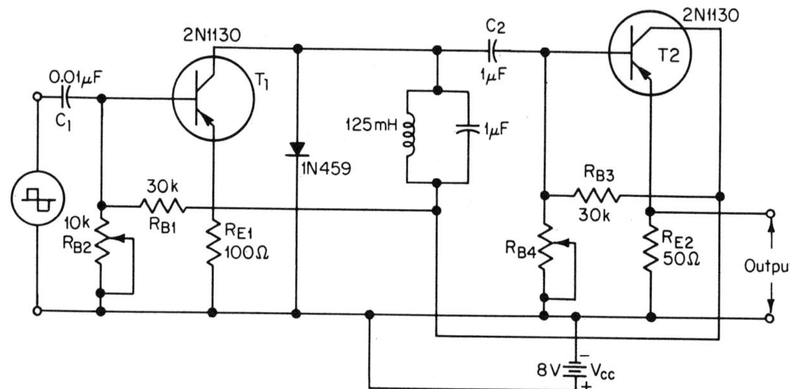

COMMON-COLLECTOR OUTPUT—Uses basic transistor current sweep coupled into class A common-collector amplifier serving also as buffer.—A. C. Gillie, "Pulse and Logic Circuits," McGraw-Hill, N.Y., 1968, p 273.

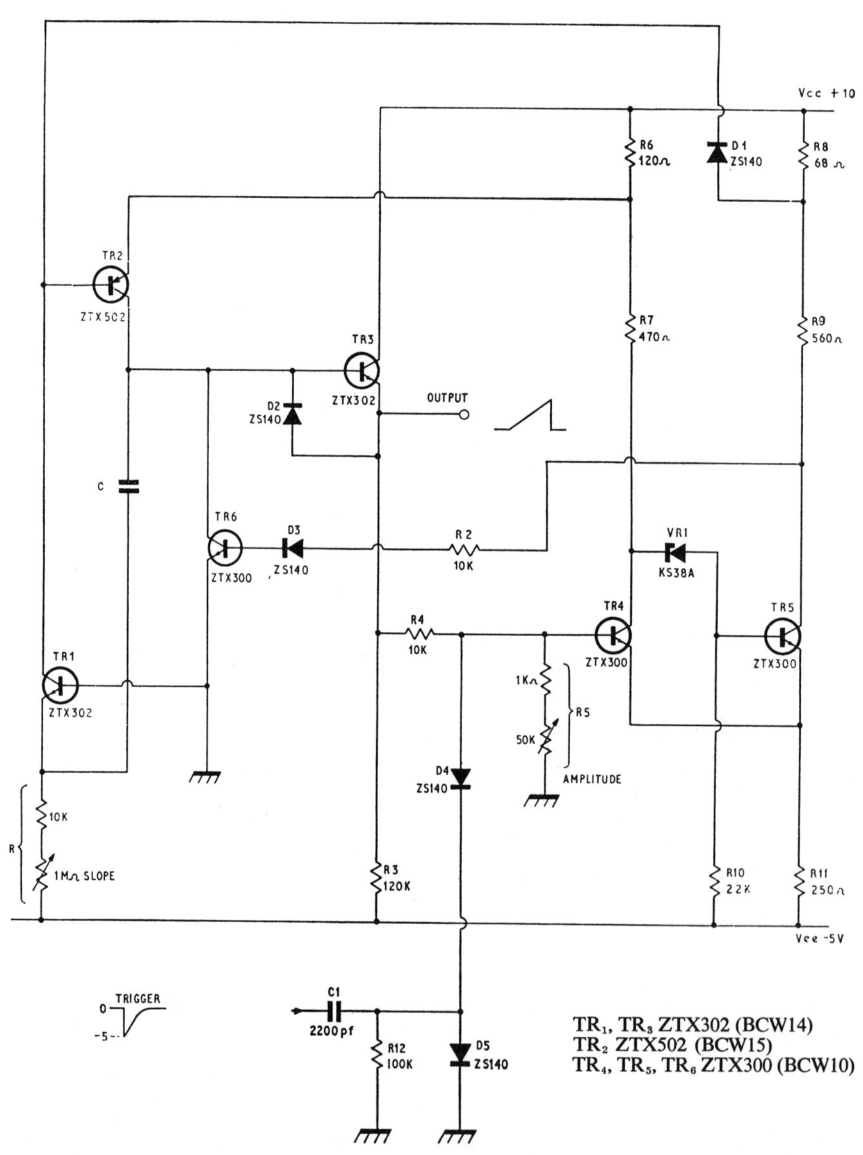

TR₁, TR₃ ZTX302 (BCW14)
TR₂ ZTX502 (BCW15)
TR₄, TR₅, TR₆ ZTX300 (BCW10)

1-MINUTE LINEAR RAMP—Provides adjustable ramp times up to 1 min and adjustable output amplitude up to 8 V. Separate discharge transistor gives rapid flyback and recovery. TR1 and TR2 form constant-current source, TR3 is buffer, and TR4-TR5 form Schmitt trigger. TR6 discharges C rapidly.—"E-Line Transistor Applications," Ferranti Ltd., Oldham, Lancs., England, 1969, p 24.

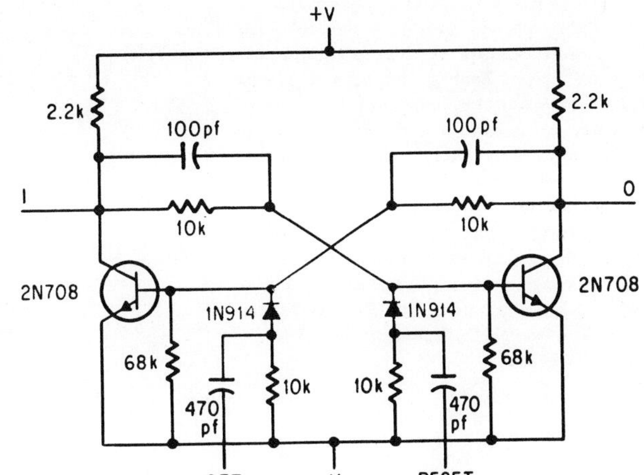

SWEEP-DRIVING FLIP-FLOP—Conventional flip-flop changes state from binary 1 to 0 when positive trigger is applied to set input, and reverses state when positive trigger is applied to reset input. Can be used to drive linear sweep circuit.—S. Weisman, One Transistor Sweeps Clean, *Electronics*, June 12, 1967, p 106–109.

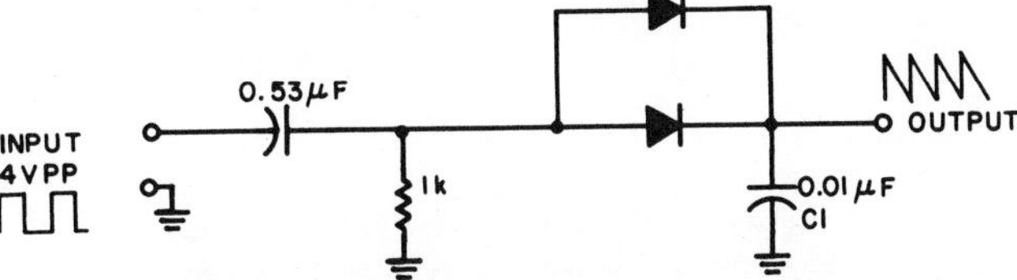

SQUARE TO SAWTOOTH—Two-diode circuit provides quick means of obtaining sawtooth from 80–800 Hz square wave. Accuracy is fair.—C. Eddy, Simple Circuit Converts Any Waveform Into a Sawtooth, *Electronic Design*, Dec. 20, 1967, p 110.

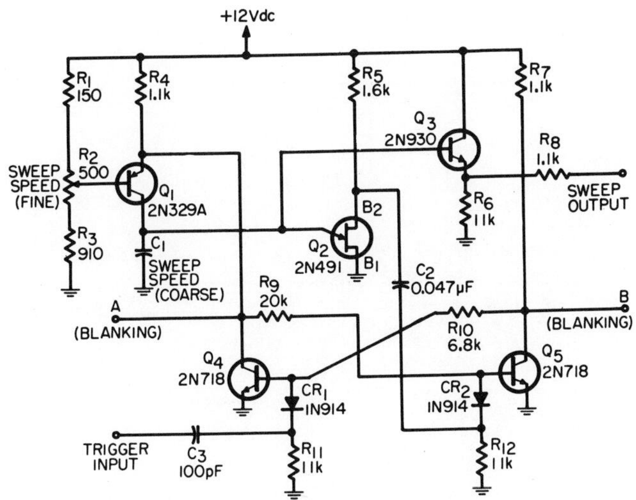

LINEAR RAMP—Changing value of coarse sweep speed capacitor C1 gives sweep frequencies from 0.1 to 500 Hz, along with positive and negative blanking pulses synchronized with output. Reliable triggering is achieved for sweep durations ranging from 2 μs to 10 s. Sweep output is 6 V p-p.—P. M. Salomon, Unijunction Transistor Simplifies Trigger Sweep Generator, *EEE*, March 1968, p 128–129.

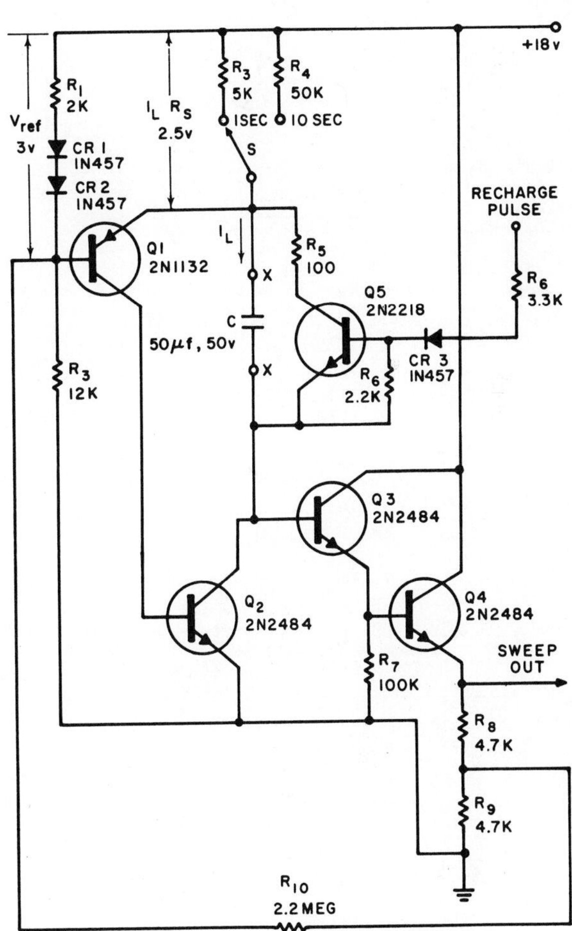

10-S SWEEP—Generates negative-going highly linear sweep with adjustable duration of from 1 to 10 s and sweep speed error under 0.5%. Polarity is easily changed to get positive-going sweep. Q1-Q2 charge C. Sweep output is buffered by Q3—Q4, and Q5 discharges C, which is polystyrene type.—D. Breslow, Infinite Z-out Current Source Generates Long, Linear Sweeps, *Electronic Design*, July 19, 1965, p 28–31.

VOLTAGE-FREQUENCY SWEEP—Circuit delivers sawtooth sweep waveform to horizontal input of cro, with linearity of sawtooth ramp assured by current-limiting diode, and sweep width determined by setting of R1. Center frequency of sweep depends on OEI Model 70 IC voltage-frequency transducer which delivers sinusoidal output whose frequency is directly proportional to d-c input voltage. Fet follower provides low output impedance for cro. Used in testing networks inserted in vertical feed from sweep generator to cro.—Sweep Generator Using a Voltage-To-Frequency Transducer, Optical Electronics, Tucson, Ariz., No. 10059.

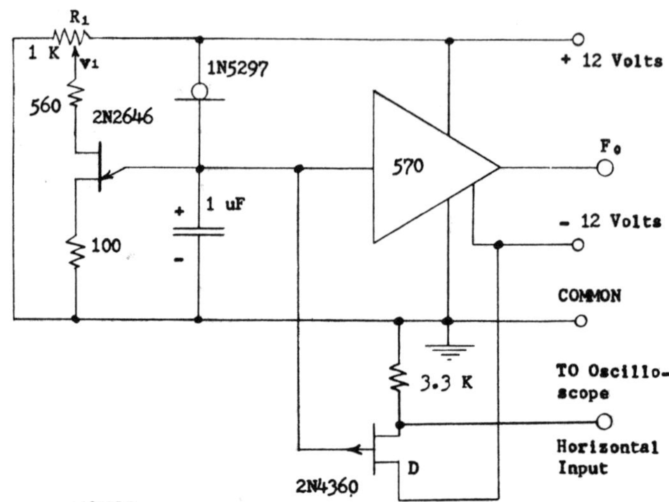

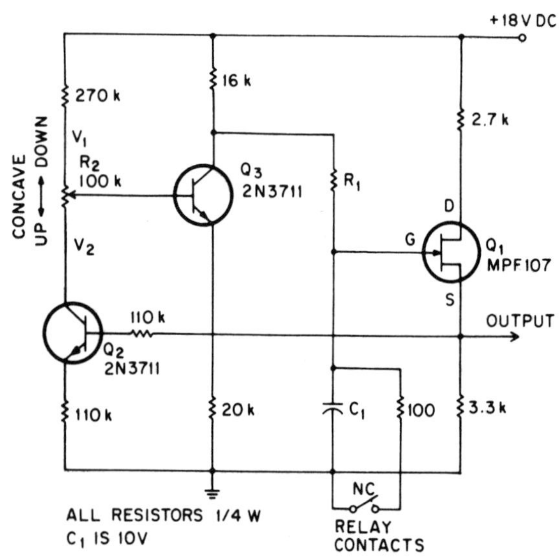

VERSATILE RAMP—R2 adjusts shape of ramp from concave upward through linear to concave downward. Different values for R1 and R2 give ramp durations ranging from 0.1 μs to several hours.—L. S. McLaughlin, Long Duration Variable Linearity Ramp Generator, *EEE*, Jan. 1970, p 127.

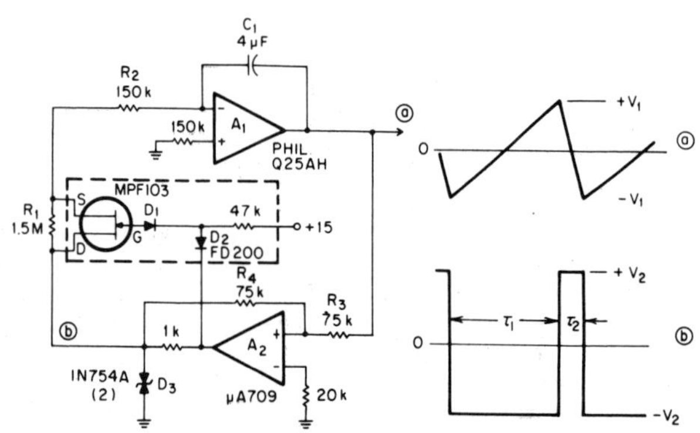

TRIANGULAR-SAWTOOTH CONVERTER—Triangular wave generated by opamps A1 and A2 is converted to sawtooth output by fet and two diodes connected as shown. Used to sweep voltage-controlled oscillator in phase-locked loop as part of automatic acquisition system. Output of sawtooth is symmetrical with respect to zero voltage.—E. F. Prozeller, FET Converts a Triangle Generator to a Sawtooth Generator, *EEE*, Dec. 1969, p 92–93.

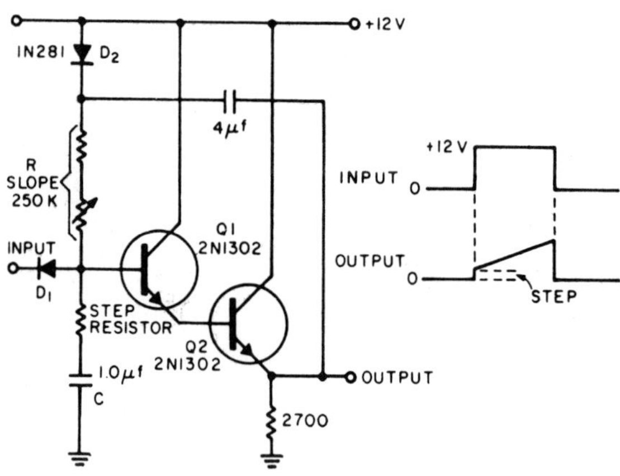

RAMP GENERATOR—Duration of rectangular initiating pulse determines width of highly linear ramp or sawtooth sweep generated by simple two-transistor circuit that is bootstrapped through blocking capacitor. Linearity of ramp is better than 0.25%.—J. Porter, Input Pulse Width Controls Simple Ramp Generator, "400 Ideas for Design Selected from Electronic Design," Hayden Book Co., N.Y., p 189.

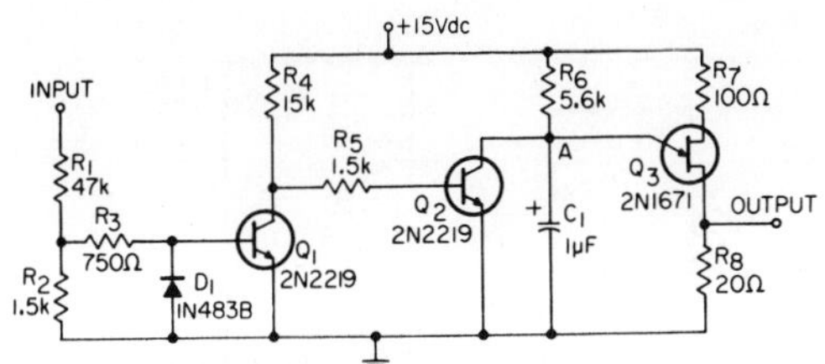

SYNC TO 60 HZ—Developed for scr control circuits requiring sawtooth generator synchronized with a-c line. Q1 and Q2 form switch that is periodically opened and closed under control of 115-V a-c voltage applied to input. When input voltage has peak value above 22 V, Q1 is turned on and Q2 off, allowing ujt oscillator Q3 to generate one output pulse for each cycle of line voltage. Applying positive full-wave-rectified line voltage to input gives one output pulse every 8.3 ms. If R6 is made variable, charging time of C1 can be varied to change time delay of output pulse with respect to zero crossing of power line, to control scr firing angle.—C. L. Wilson, Unijunction-Transistor Oscillator Locks to Line Frequency, *EEE*, Dec. 1967, p 93–94.

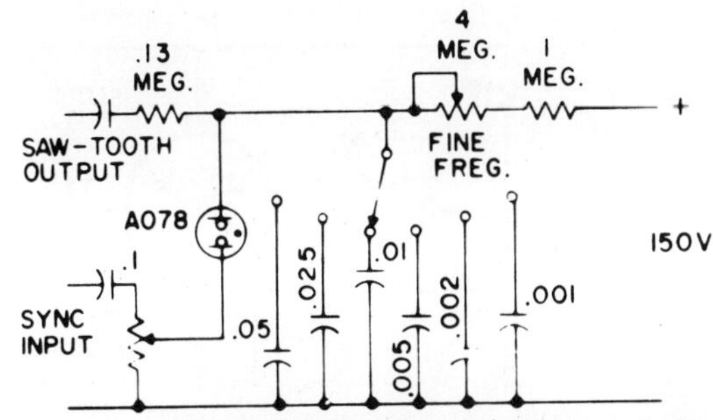

TIME-BASE VOLTAGE SOURCE—Covers range of 5 to 1,500 Hz for inexpensive moderately linear time bases. Used as horizontal sweep for small oscilloscopes.—E. Bauman, "Applications of Neon Lamps and Gas Discharge Tubes," Signalite, Neptune, N.J., p 34.

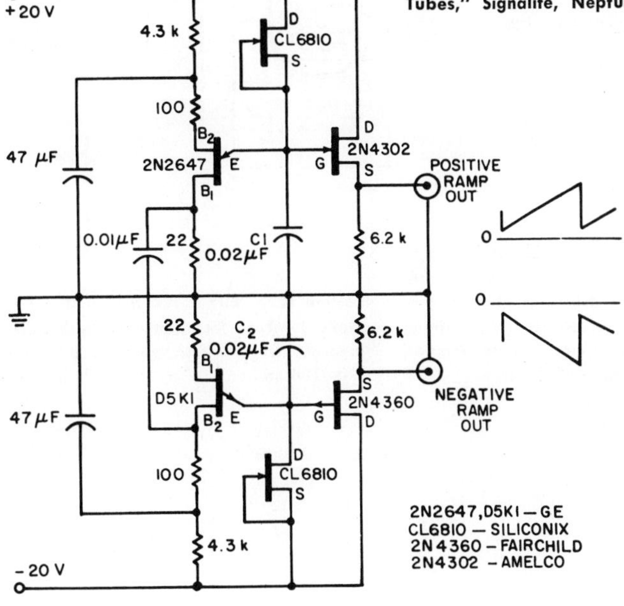

BIDIRECTIONAL RAMPS—Each ramp starts near 0 V and departs linearly, one in positive direction, and the other negative. Uses GE D5K1 complementary ujt and Siliconix CL6810 field-effect diodes to achieve symmetry.—H. Olson, Symmetrical Ramp Generator Uses New Devices, *Electronic Design*, Nov. 8, 1967, p 114.

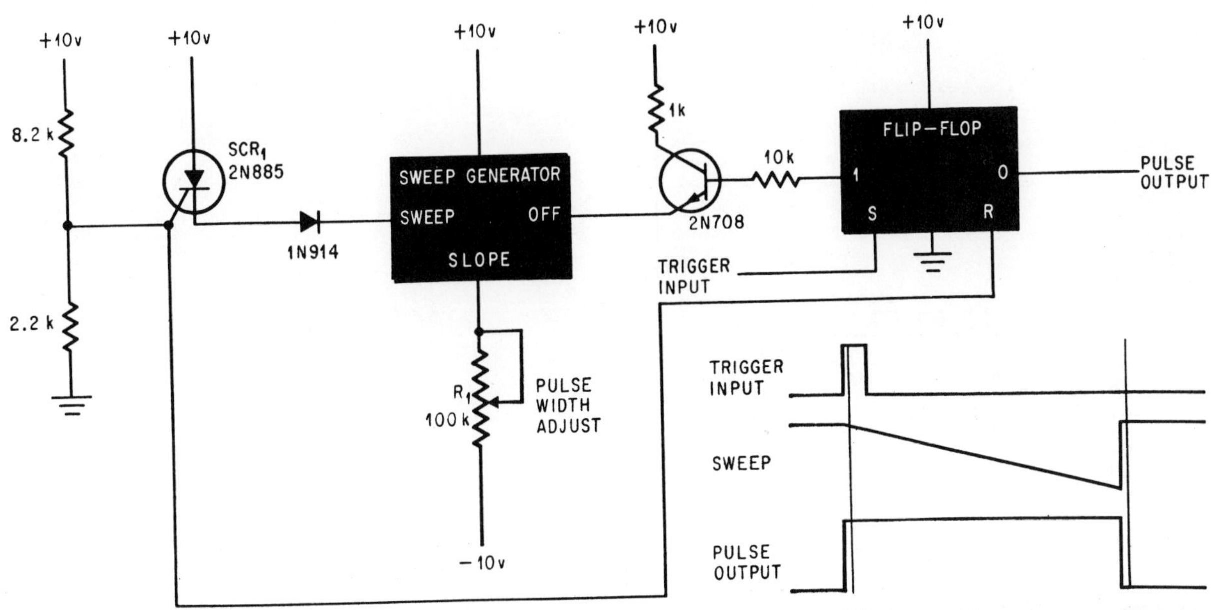

SWEEP GIVES VARIABLE-WIDTH PULSES—With calibrated multiturn linear pot for R1, and 1-μF charging capacitor in sweep generator, pulse width can be linearly changed from 1 to 100 ms. Circuits in boxes appear elsewhere in this chapter under headings LINEAR SWEEP and SWEEP-DRIVING FLIP-FLOP.—S. Weisman, One Transistor Sweeps Clean, *Electronics*, June 12, 1967, p 106–109.

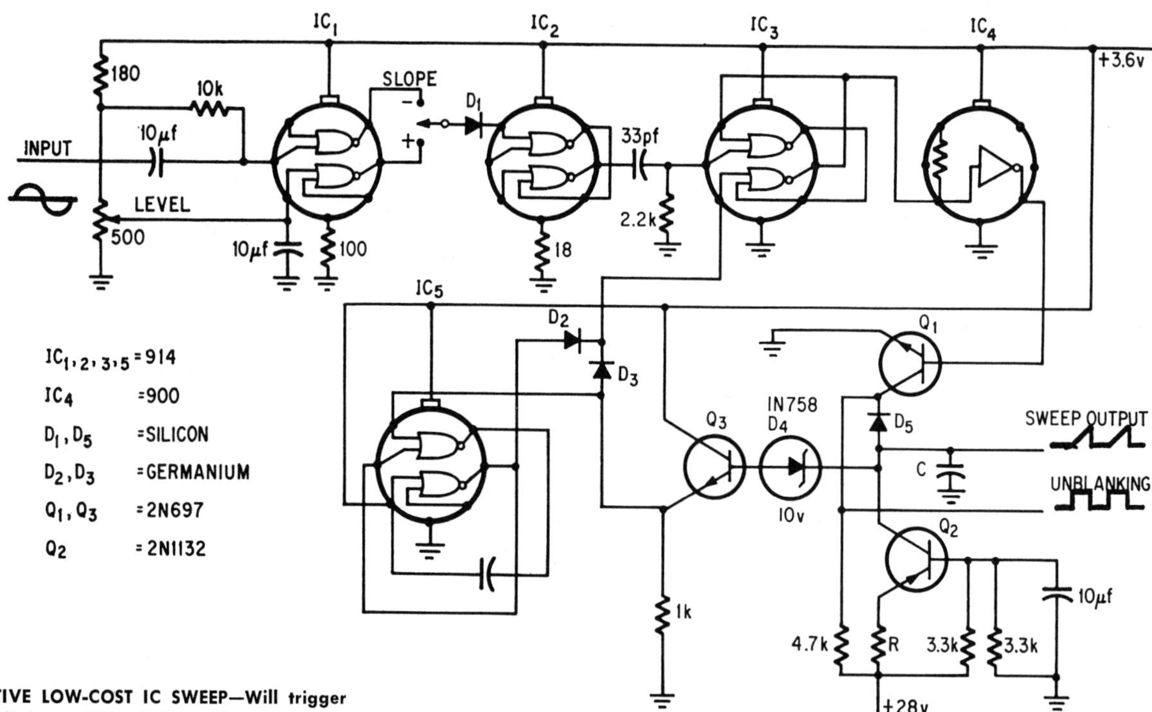

SENSITIVE LOW-COST IC SWEEP—Will trigger on as little as 200 mV from d-c to over 10 MHz. Input stage IC1 serves as preamp and phase inverter to allow selection of positive- or negative-slope triggering. Schmitt trigger IC2 supplies fast-rising positive pulse to R-S flip-flop IC3. Buffer IC4 drives Q1 at inputs above 1 MHz. Resultant sawtooth has good linearity, with sweep speed of 0.5 μs when C is 100 pF and R is 3K. When sawtooth reaches 10 V, zener breaks down and initiates retrace.—E. Feuer, Sweep Circuit Triggers On Only 200 Millivolts, *Electronics*, March 3, 1969, p 96–97.

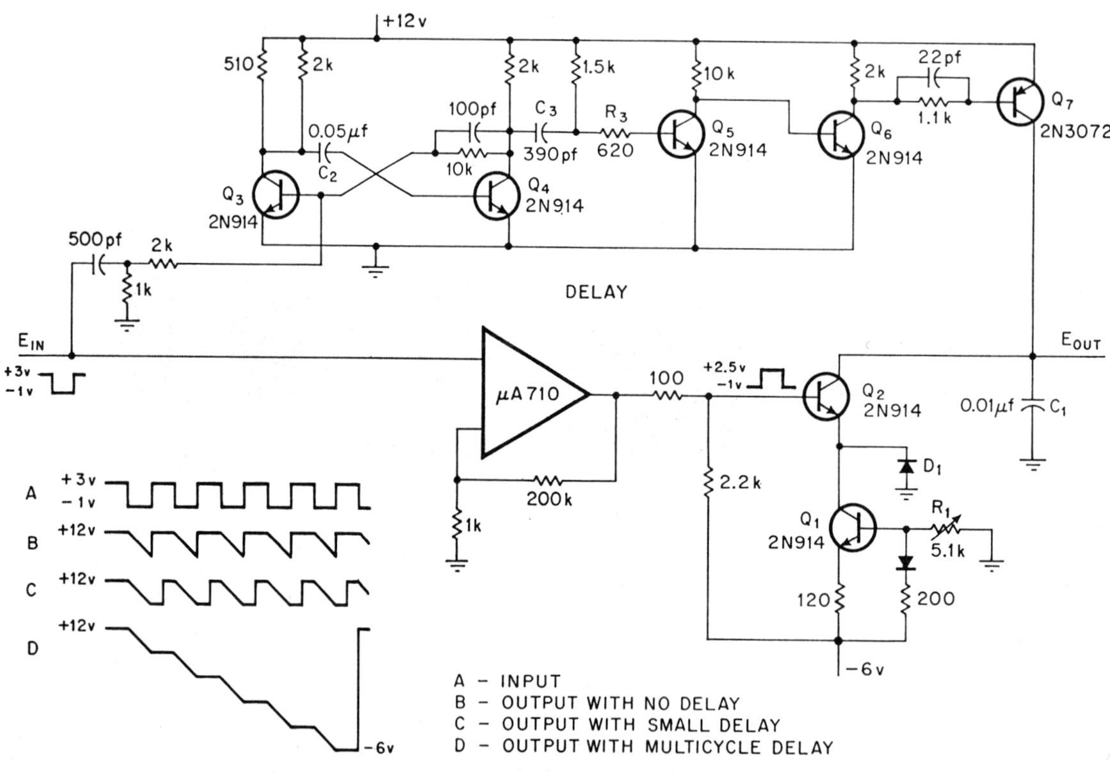

RAMP SLOPE CONTROL—Complex ramp function generator for multiple-axis cro scanning provides 50:1 range of slope adjustment for ramp segments without affecting their linearity. Ramp duration can be varied from several hundred ns to several hundred μs, by changing duration of input pulse. Uses constant-current generator Q1-Q2 for discharging C1 at rate set by R1, to control slope.—J. Downey, Capacitor Discharge Sets Shape of Ramp Function, *Electronics*, Dec. 8, 1969, p 90.

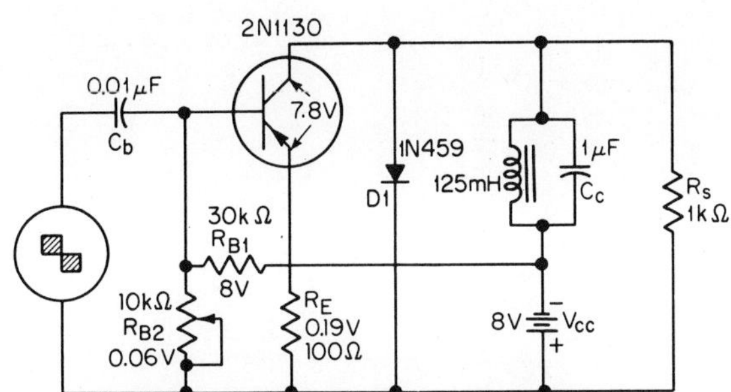

CURRENT SWEEP—Chief function of transistor is that of switch. When transistor is on, current flows from battery through inductor into collector. Current increases with maximum linearity at about 2,500 pps for values shown. Transistor opens during flyback time of sawtooth output. Book gives design procedure for obtaining maximum linearity.—A. C. Gillie, "Pulse and Logic Circuits," McGraw-Hill, N.Y., 1968, p 268.

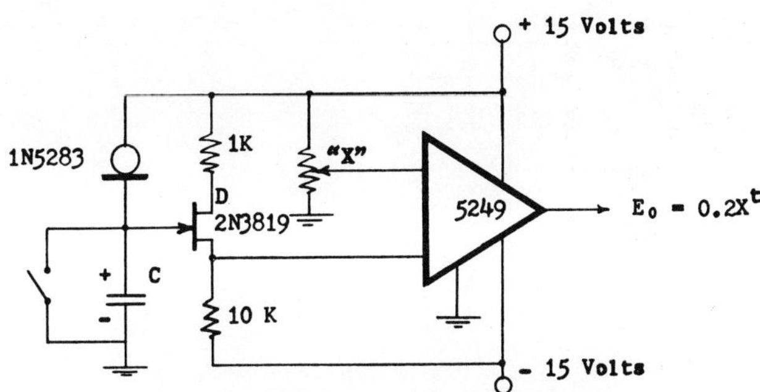

TIME RAMP—Generates ramp to simulate time as Y input, to give output voltage that is equal to constant multiplied by X input having time (Y) as exponent. Ramp begins when switch is opened and ends when switch is closed to discharge C. Switching transistor may be used instead of actual switch contacts.—Time as an Exponent, Optical Electronics, Tucson, Ariz., No. 10101.

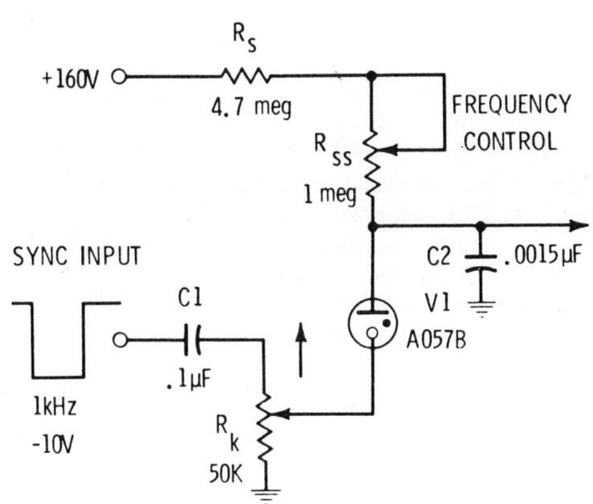

1-KHZ SYNCHRONIZED NEON—Adjust 50K control for proper synchronization with 50-μs input pulse.—W. G. Miller, "Using and Understanding Miniature Neon Lamps," H. W. Sams & Co., Indianapolis, Ind., 1969, p 41.

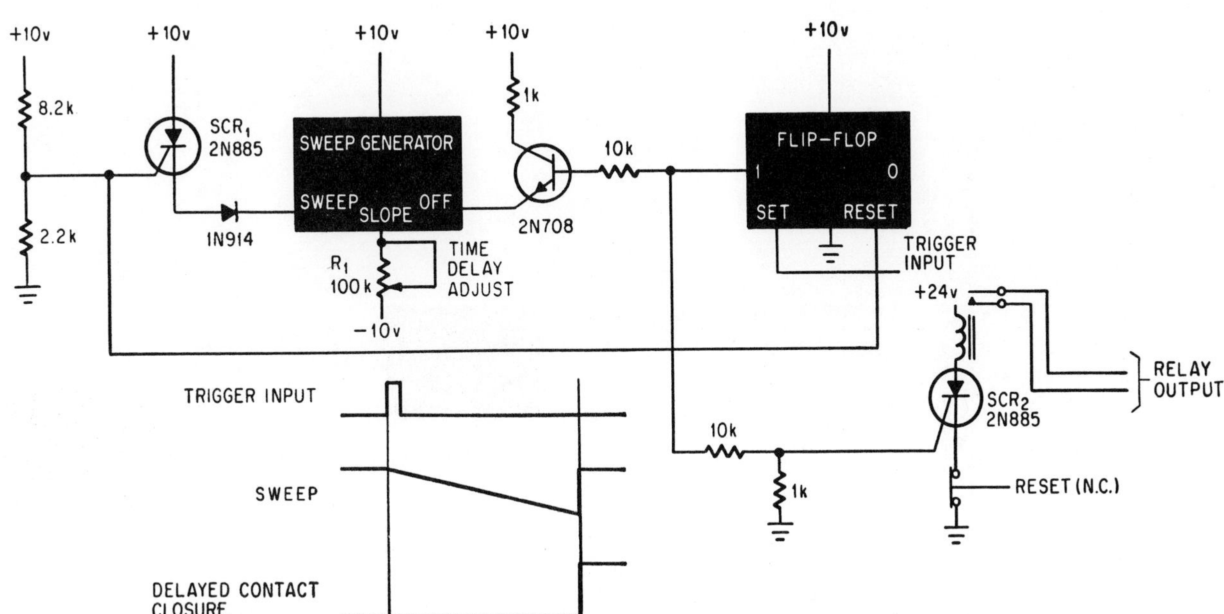

SWEEP CONTROLS RELAY TURN-ON TIME—Length of generated sweep determines turn-on time of time-delay relay with excellent repeatability. With values shown and 50-μF charging capacitor in sweep generator, relay delay can be varied from 50 ms to 5 s plus fixed relay turn-on-time.—S. Weisman, One Transistor Sweeps Clean, *Electronics*, June 12, 1967, p 106–109.

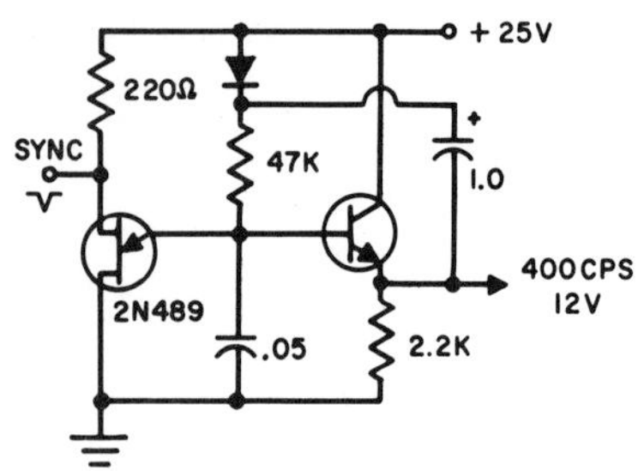

BOOTSTRAP WITH CAPACITOR FEEDBACK—Eliminates need for negative supply, makes frequency largely independent of supply voltage, and improves linearity of sawtooth output.—T. P. Sylvan, The Unijunction Transistor Characteristics and Applications, General Electric, Syracuse, N.Y., No. 90.10, 1965, p 48.

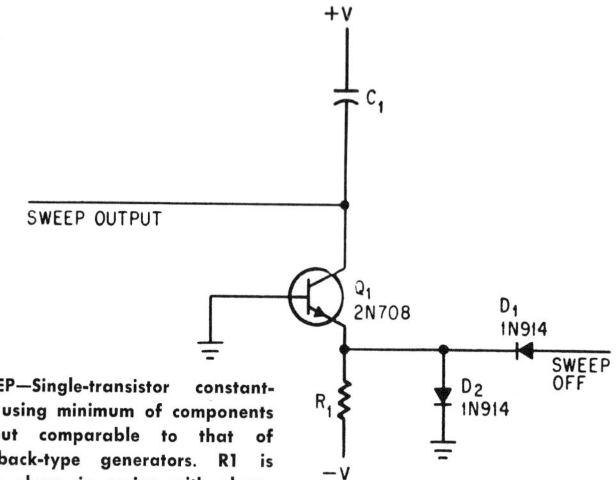

LINEAR SWEEP—Single-transistor constant-current sweep using minimum of components provides output comparable to that of complex feedback-type generators. R1 is typically 1,000 ohms, in series with slope-adjusting potentiometer of around 10K. Supply voltages can be 10 V. Article gives design equations and five examples of other circuits using this versatile basic sweep.—S. Weisman, One Transistor Sweeps Clean, *Electronics*, June 12, 1967, p 106–109.

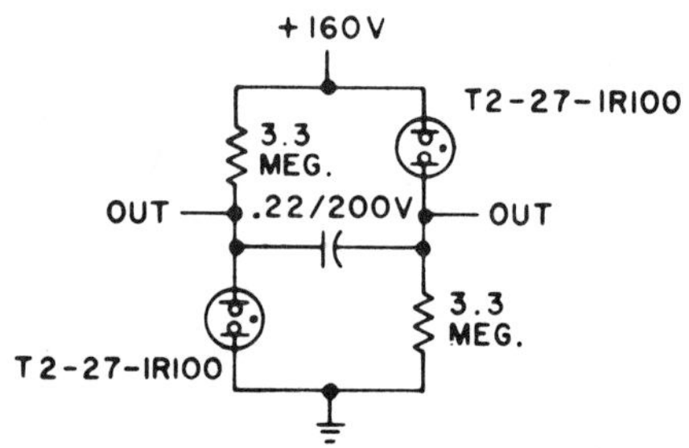

SAWTOOTH FROM TWO NEONS—Symmetrical output from dual-neon relaxation oscillator reduces power supply ripple and noise, and gives twice the voltage of single neon circuit.—E. Bauman, "Applications of Neon Lamps and Gas Discharge Tubes," Signalite, Neptune, N.J., p 36.

BOOTSTRAP WITH ZENER FEEDBACK—Arrangement improves linearity of ujt sawtooth generator that drives any npn emitter-follower output stage. Capacitor charging current is held constant over complete cycle. Output transistor also serves as driver for bootstrap circuit.—T. P. Sylvan, The Unijunction Transistor Characteristics and Applications, General Electric, Syracuse, N.Y., No. 90.10, 1965, p 48.

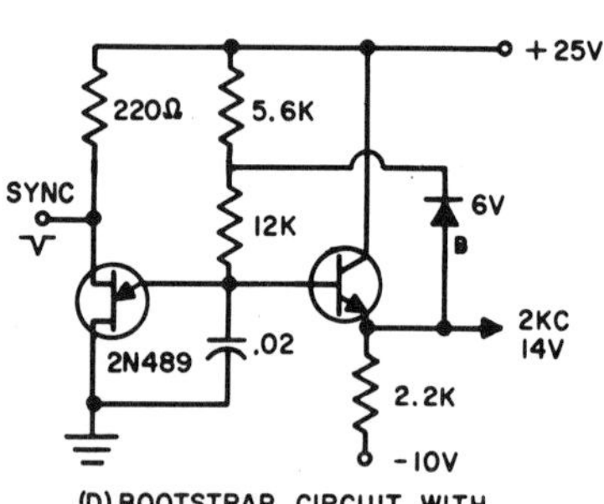

(D) BOOTSTRAP CIRCUIT WITH ZENER DIODE FEEDBACK

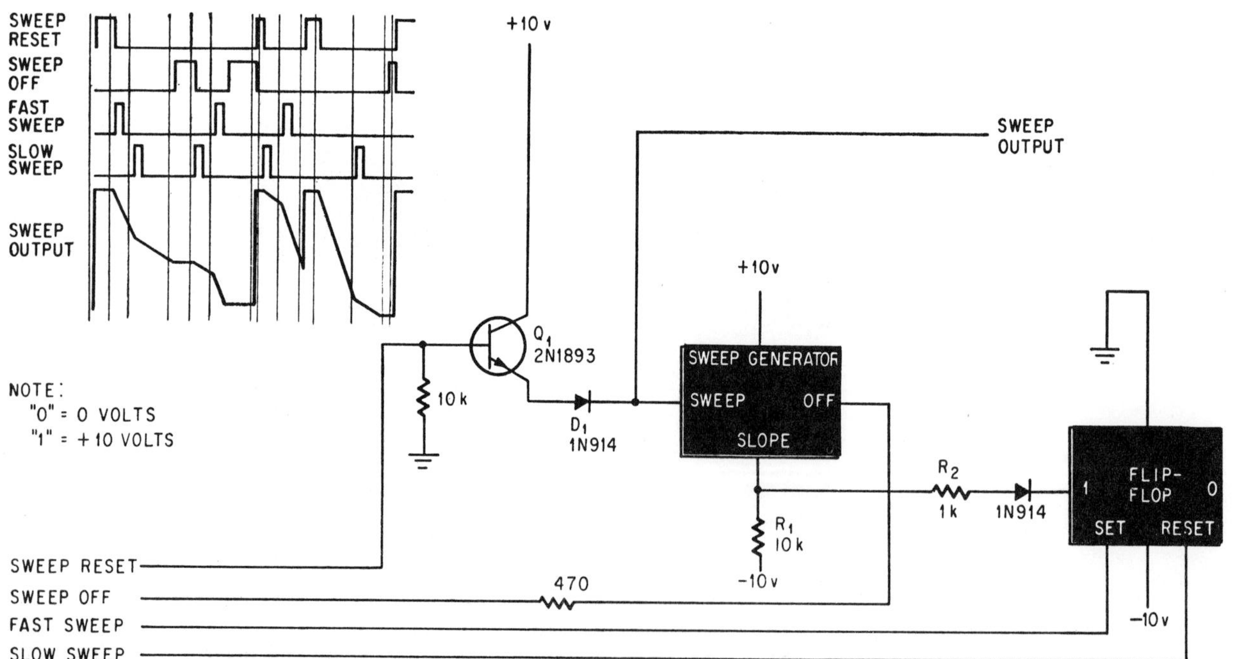

DIGITALLY CONTROLLED SWEEP—Digital signals can reset linear sweep, change its slope, or turn it off at any level. With 1-μF charging capacitor in sweep, slow sweep is 10 ms and fast sweep is 1 ms. Sweep slopes can be changed to form complex timing and control signals.—S. Weisman, One Transistor Sweeps Clean, *Electronics*, June 12, 1967, p 106–109.

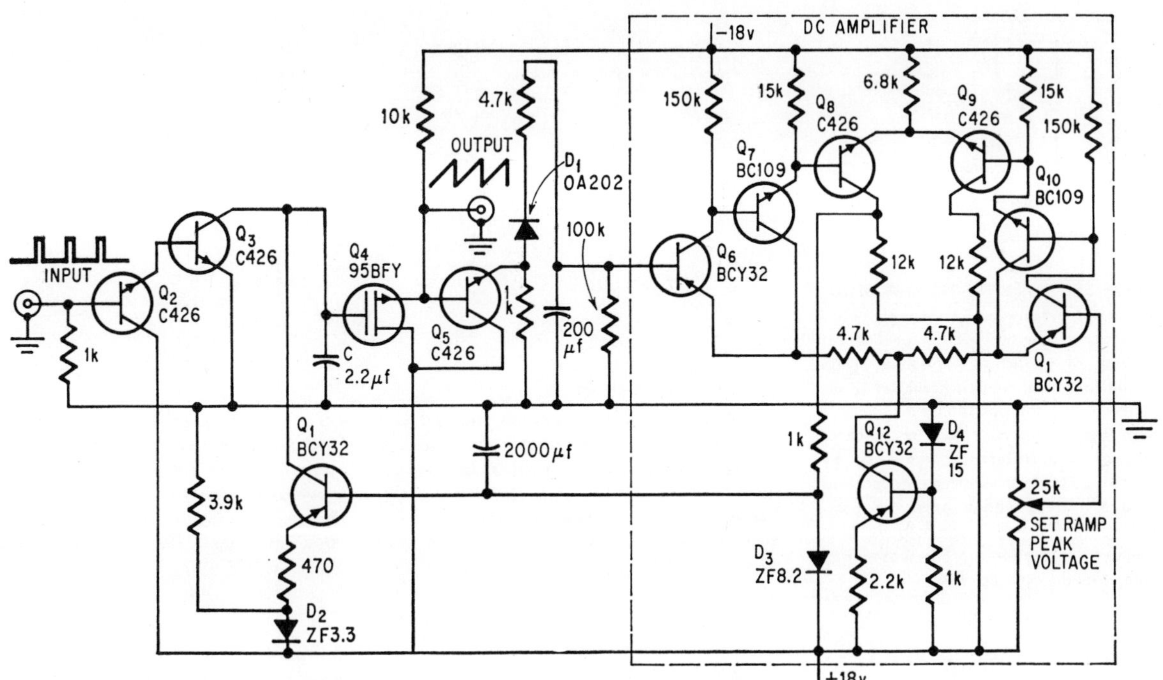

CONSTANT AMPLITUDE—Feedback amplifier compares peak voltage of ramp with reference set by 25K pot and uses error to control charging current. Ramp height is thus kept constant regardless of variations in trigger frequency. For values shown, frequency range is 10 Hz to 1 kHz for constant output within 5%. When combined with comparator set between 0 and 100% of ramp amplitude, can also serve as frequency-compensated phase delay.—P. R. Adby, Sawtooth Generator Delivers Constant Peak Voltage, *Electronics*, March 3, 1969, p 97.

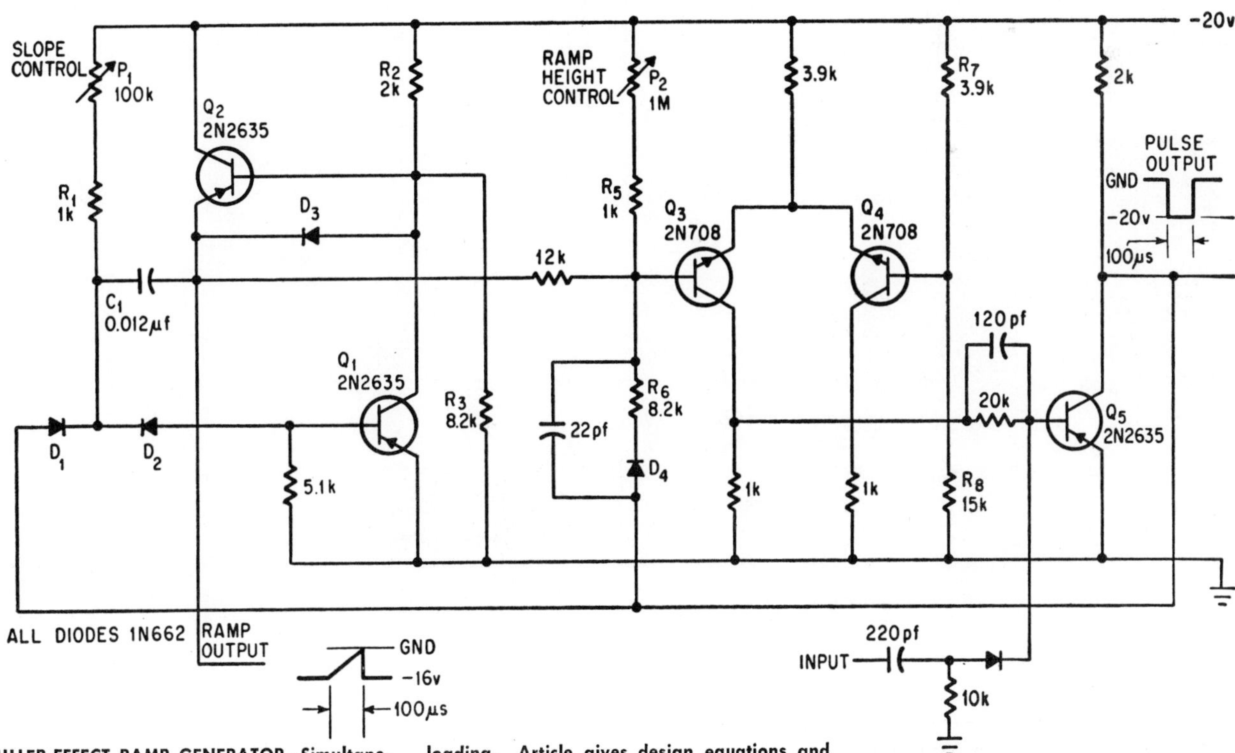

MILLER-EFFECT RAMP GENERATOR—Simultaneously generates train of positive-going waveforms and train of negative-going square waves. Ramp is linear to within 0.5%, requires no clipping, and is not distorted by loading. Article gives design equations and describes circuit operation in detail. Q1-Q2 are in Miller-effect ramp generator, and other transistors are in differential Schmitt trigger that can terminate ramp at any point, reset circuit, and put out gating pulses as byproduct.—G. Marosi, Gain-Multiplied Capacitance Generates Ramp Waveform, *Electronics*, March 6, 1967, p 130–131.

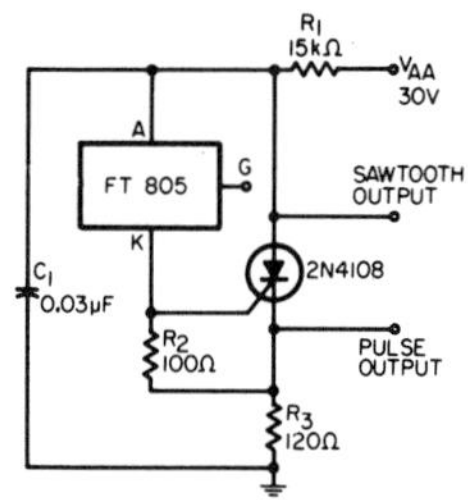

10 KHZ WITH REGENERATIVE TRIGGER DIODE—Allows use of relatively low supply voltages, to reduce circuit dissipation and lower voltage rating of capacitor. Fairchild FT805 trigger diode in scr relaxation oscillator gives high efficiency in comparison with circuits using three-layer triggers. May be synchronized with external reference frequency by feeding positive sync pulses directly to gate of trigger diode. Gives either pulse or sawtooth output.—M. Cottrell, Trigger-Diode Simplifies Efficient Generation of Sawtooths and Pulses, *EEE*, March 1968, p 130.

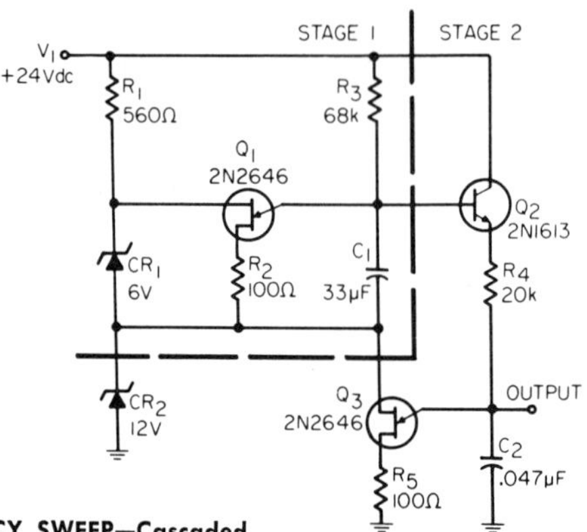

500–2,000 HZ FREQUENCY SWEEP—Cascaded ujt relaxation oscillators provide highly linear frequency sweep output that can be passed through narrow bandpass filter to produce short-duration signal. Q1 generates low-frequency sawtooth that controls higher-frequency sawtooth of Q3. Second stage must usually be at least 10 times frequency of first stage. First stage determines repetition rate and frequency range of swept output, while second stage determines amplitude of its generated higher-frequency sawtooth waveform.—R. Smith, Jr., Cascade UJT Oscillator Generates Linear Frequency Sweeps, *EEE*, April 1968, p 106–107.

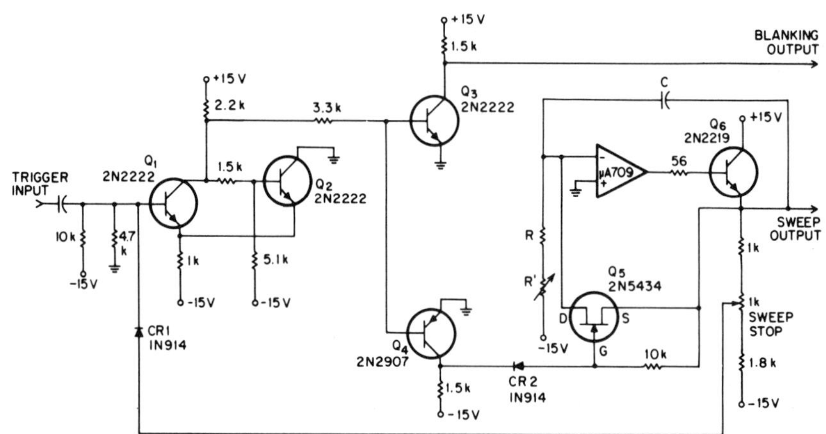

10-V LINEAR SWEEP—Combination of fet and μA709 opamp gives highly linear triggered sweep with very low d-c offset, along with blanking output for cro. Schmitt trigger at input drives Q3 and Q4 to provide unblanking output and to initiate sweep by unclamping fet Q5. Q6 is buffer for low-impedance load. Provides sweep speeds from 1 Hz to 100 kHz, depending on values of C, R, and R'.—D. A. Meyer, Triggered Sweep Features Low D-C Offset, *EEE*, Nov. 1969, p 106.

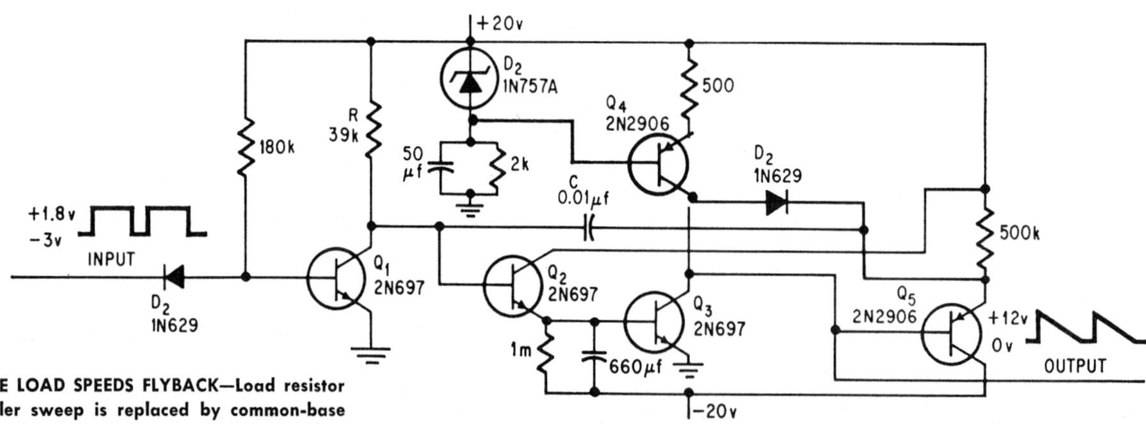

ACTIVE LOAD SPEEDS FLYBACK—Load resistor of Miller sweep is replaced by common-base transistor serving as active load, to reduce flyback time and improve linearity. Transistor acts as current source drawing only a few mA of collector current while providing megohms of dynamic impedance. Positive gating pulse makes Q4 charge C through D2 and switching transistor Q1. When pulse goes negative, Q3 is turned on and C discharges to start Miller rundown at collector of Q3.—D. K. Basu and B. Nag, Improved Miller Sweep Uses an Active Load, *Electronics*, March 31, 1969, p 86.

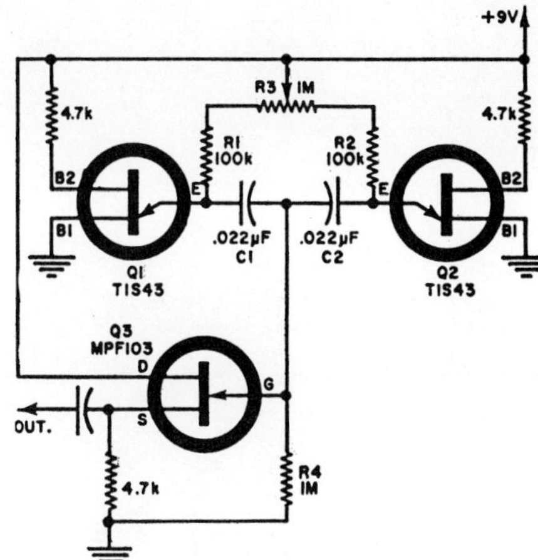

INDEPENDENTLY VARIABLE—Dual ujt multivibrator generates waveforms with two different repetition rates alternately when R3 is moved away from midpoint. Can be used as tone generator for electronic organ. If used as dual-rate horizontal sweep for oscilloscope, rectangular waveforms at base-2 of ujt's can drive electronic switches that apply the signals under observation alternately to vertical input of scope.—F. H. Tooker, Dual-Rate Sawtooth Generator, *Electronics World*, May 1969, p 74.

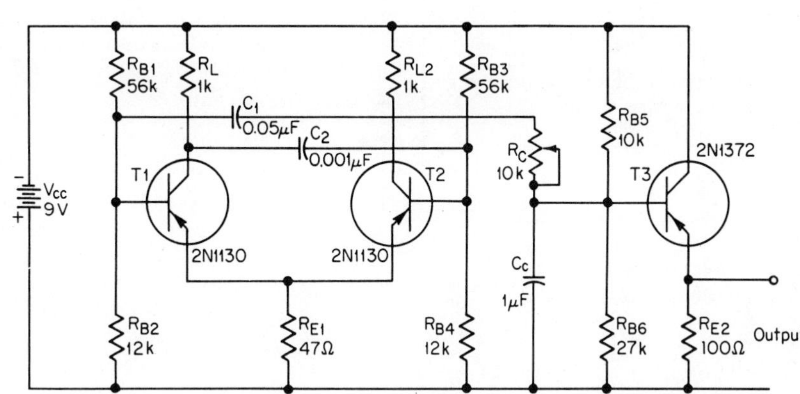

ASTABLE-MVBR SAWTOOTH—RC is adjusted until sawtooth waveform across CC has its most linear rise and fall. Common-collector amplifier T3 provides isolation between CC and output.—A. C. Gillie, "Pulse and Logic Circuits," McGraw-Hill, N.Y., 1968, p 280.

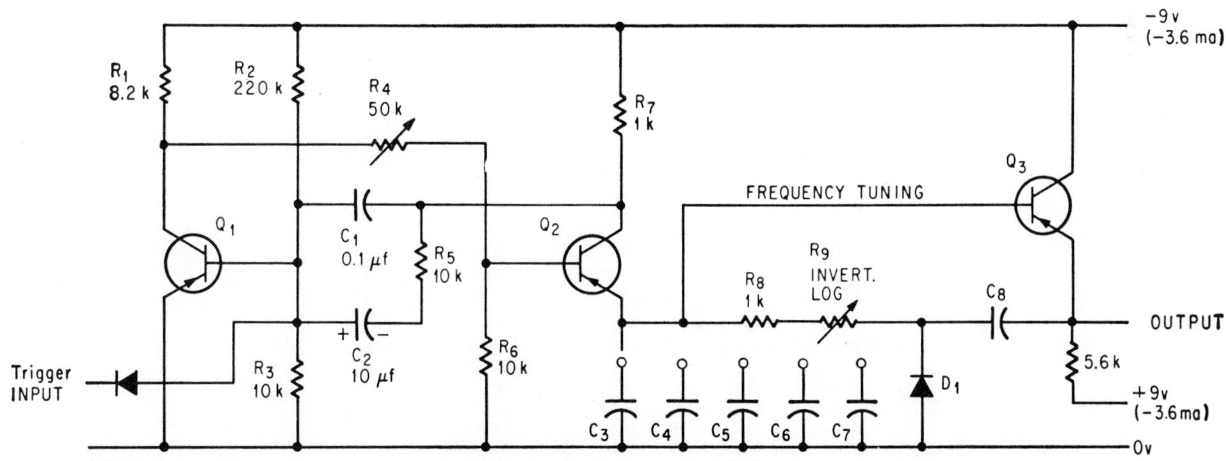

DRIVER FOR PORTABLE SCOPE—Covers 6 Hz to 450 kHz in 5 ranges, with good sawtooth slope linearity and constant amplitude. Trigger input must be 0.5 to 5 V rms. Transistors are AF117 germanium-alloy diffused. Free-running frequencies are determined by capacitor values: C3 = 8 μF for 6–48 Hz; C4 = 0.68 μF for 47–630 Hz; C5 = 0.068 μF for 470–5,900 Hz; C6 = 6,800 pF for 4.7–59 kHz; C7 = 560 pF for 50–450 kHz. C8 is large enough to remain almost fully charged over complete sweep cycle.—C. C. Hoo, Sawtooth Generator Drives Cathode-Ray Tube, *Electronics*, Sept. 19, 1966, p 124–125.

NOTE: To locate additional circuits in the category of this chapter, use the index at the back of this book. Check also the author's "Sourcebook of Electronic Circuits," published by McGraw-Hill in 1968.

CHAPTER 76
Servo Circuits

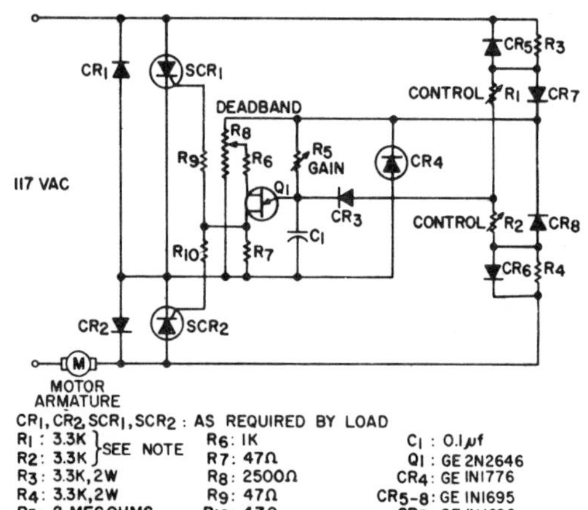

BALANCED-BRIDGE REVERSING SERVO—Phase-sensitive servo drive supplies reversible half-wave power to armature of small p-m or shunt motor. R1 can be GE B425B photoconductor, GE 1D301 thermistor, position-sensing pot, or output from control amplifier.—"SCR Manual," 4th Edition, General Electric, 1967, p 217–218.

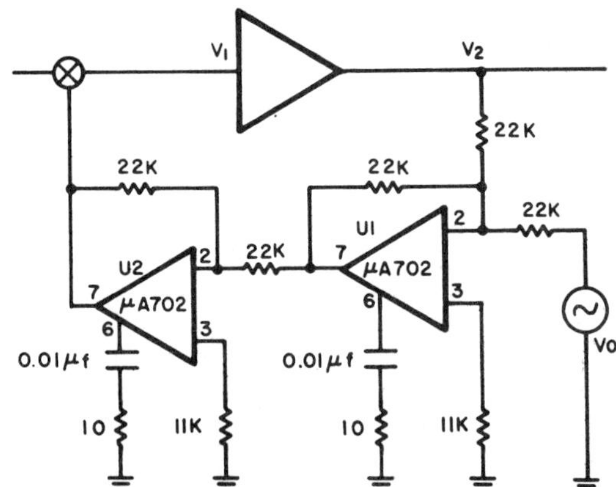

NYQUIST PLOT GENERATOR—Uses Fairchild IC opamps to insert disturbance in feedback path of closed-loop servo system to measure open-loop response in system that cannot be operated under open-loop conditions. Nyquist plot is then readily made.—R. W. Allington, The Integrated Operational Amplifier: A Versatile and Economical Circuit, "Microelectronic Design," Hayden Book Co., N.Y., 1966, p 189–194.

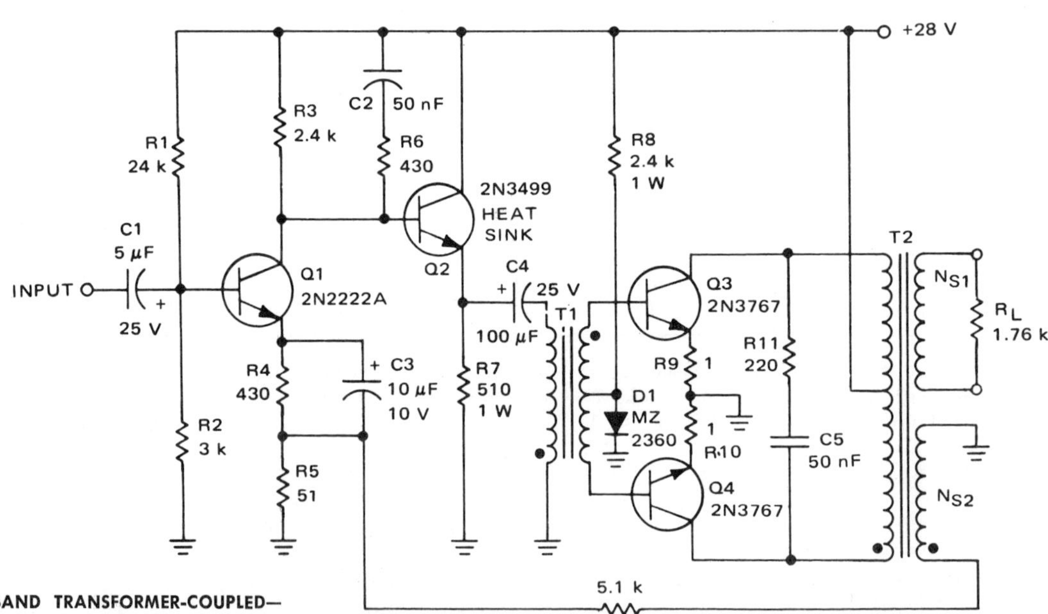

7.5-W WIDEBAND TRANSFORMER-COUPLED—Drives small a-c motor RL from a-c signal whose frequency may range from 50 to 5,000 Hz. Use of common-collector (emitter-follower) stage to provide low-source-impedance drive for transformer keeps phase shift below 10 deg over frequency range handled, to prevent instability. Feedback is derived from separate winding rather than from load or motor winding. Book gives transformer winding data.—"Semiconductor Power Circuits Handbook," Motorola, Phoenix, Ariz., 1968, p 5–11.

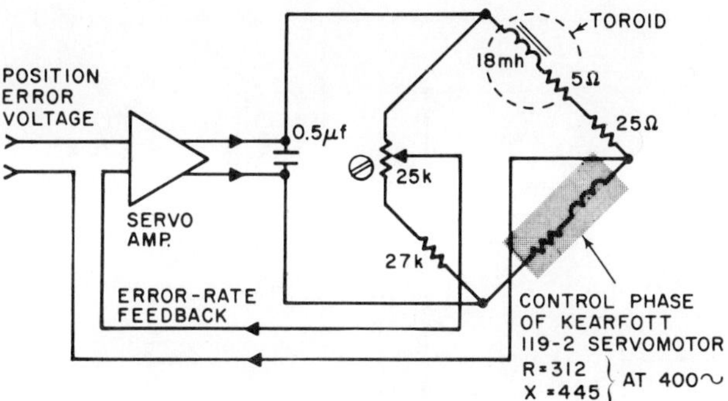

TOROID-BRIDGE TACHOMETER—Serves as inexpensive equivalent of tachometer generator in generating error-rate-feedback signals for servomotor loop. Bridge pot is adjusted for precise null with motor stalled. Circuit can be used only if there is no common connection from input of amplifier to output and if amplifier has sufficient gain and power output to compensate for bridge losses.—F. Close, Error-Rate Feedback Generation in Servomotor Handled by Toroid, *Electronic Design*, April 12, 1965, p 50.

6-W TRANSFORMERLESS SERVO—Suitable for driving control winding of 400-Hz two-phase size 15 servomotor. Class B push-pull output stage uses ZT1479 transistors. Other four transistors can be either ZT20 or ZT40. With bulky output and driver transformers eliminated, amplifier is compact as well as low in cost. Report includes design procedure.—6 Watt-400 c/s Transformerless Servo-Amplifier using Silicon Transistors, Ferranti Ltd., Oldham, Lancs., England, No. 13, 1965.

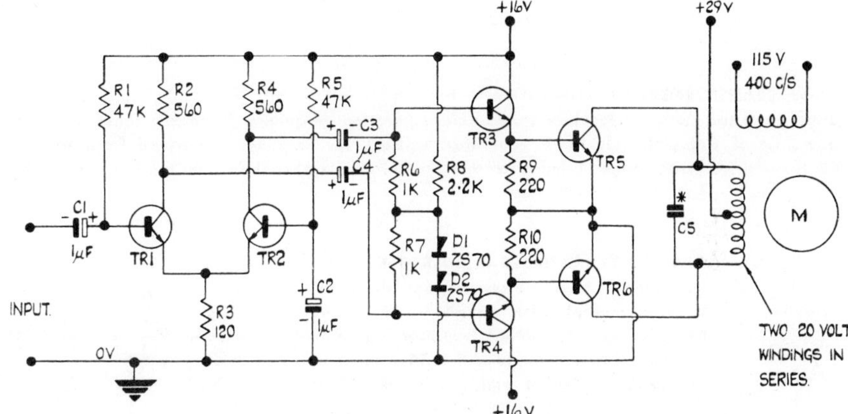

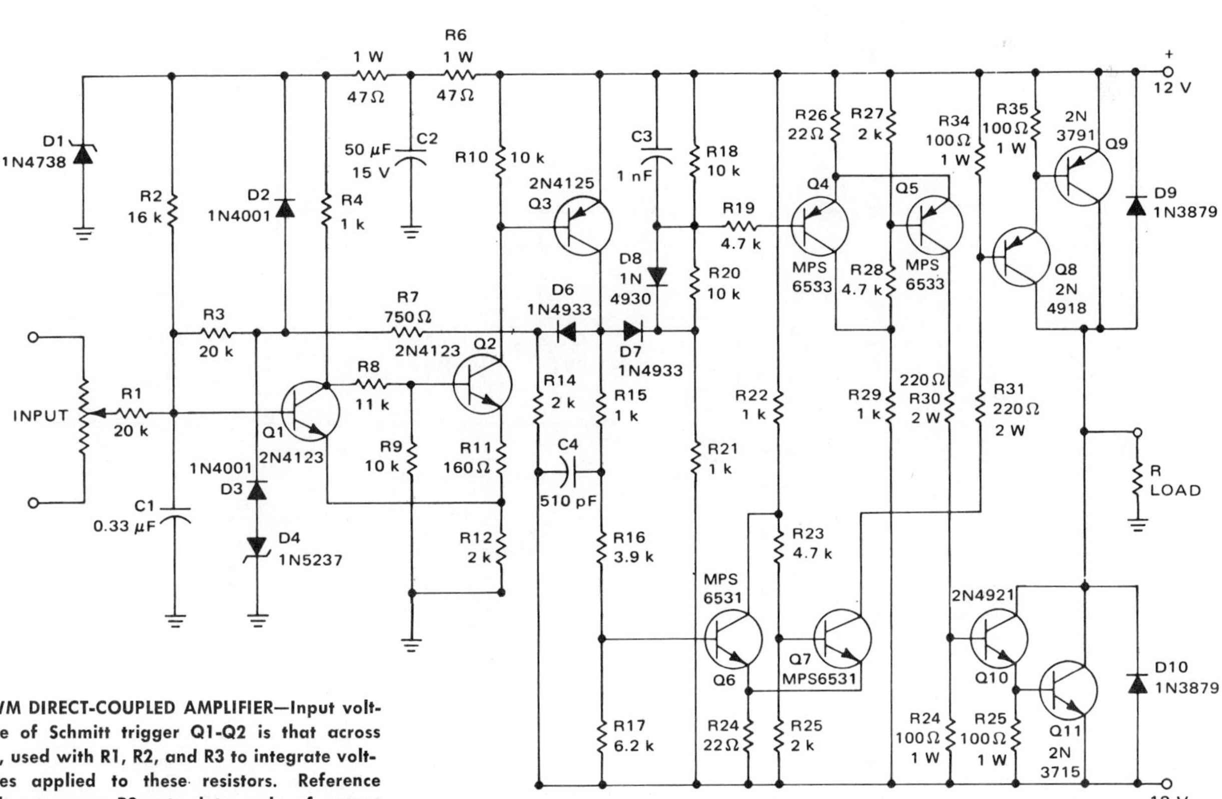

PWM DIRECT-COUPLED AMPLIFIER—Input voltage of Schmitt trigger Q1-Q2 is that across C1, used with R1, R2, and R3 to integrate voltages applied to these resistors. Reference voltage across R2 sets duty cycle of output waveform at 50% when there is no input. Schmitt drives signal-splitter Q3, which furnishes feedback voltage to input through R3, and feeds output drivers Q4-Q5 and Q6-Q7. —"Semiconductor Power Circuits Handbook," Motorola, Phoenix, Ariz., 1968, p 5–26.

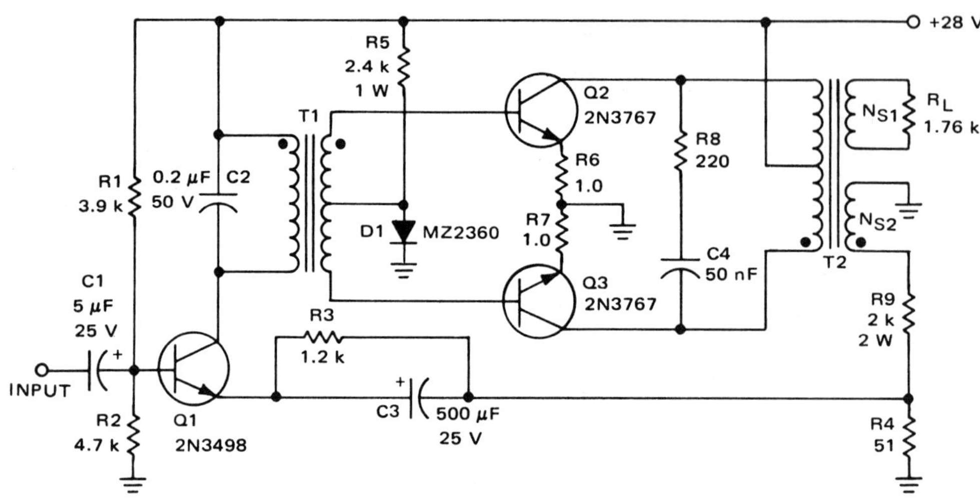

7.5-W TRANSFORMER-COUPLED—Designed to drive small a-c motors. Provides stable voltage gain of 100 with only three transistors. C2 tunes driver transformer primary to minimize phase shift, for applications where operating frequency is nearly constant. Feedback for amplifier is derived from separate winding rather than from load or motor winding. Book gives winding data for both transformers.—"Semiconductor Power Circuits Handbook," Motorola, Phoenix, Ariz., 1968, p 5–10.

OPAMP-FET MULTIPLIER-DIVIDER—Fet's serve as input and feedback resistors for IC opamp. Voltage multiplication range is 15:1 with fixed bias on fet at left, representing input resistor. Division range is 1:1/30 when bias of feedback fet at right is fixed. These values correspond to 30 dB of agc range, which is suitable for use as agc of servo error command. Input voltages for multiplying or dividing can be 0.1 to 1.5 V.—E. Hoelken, FET Feedback Configurations Provide Accurate Logic Functions, *Electronic Design*, Dec. 21, 1964, p 52–54.

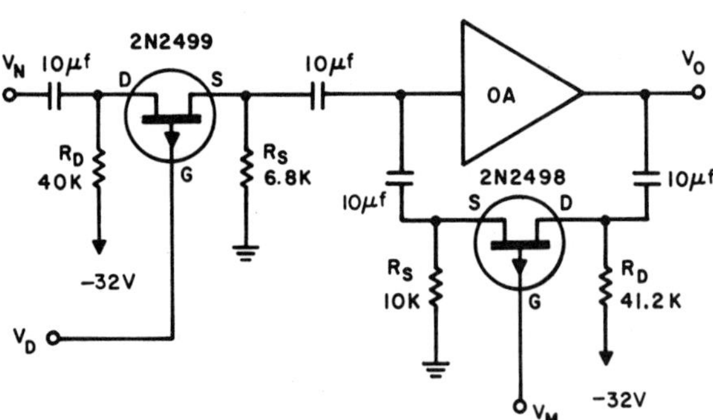

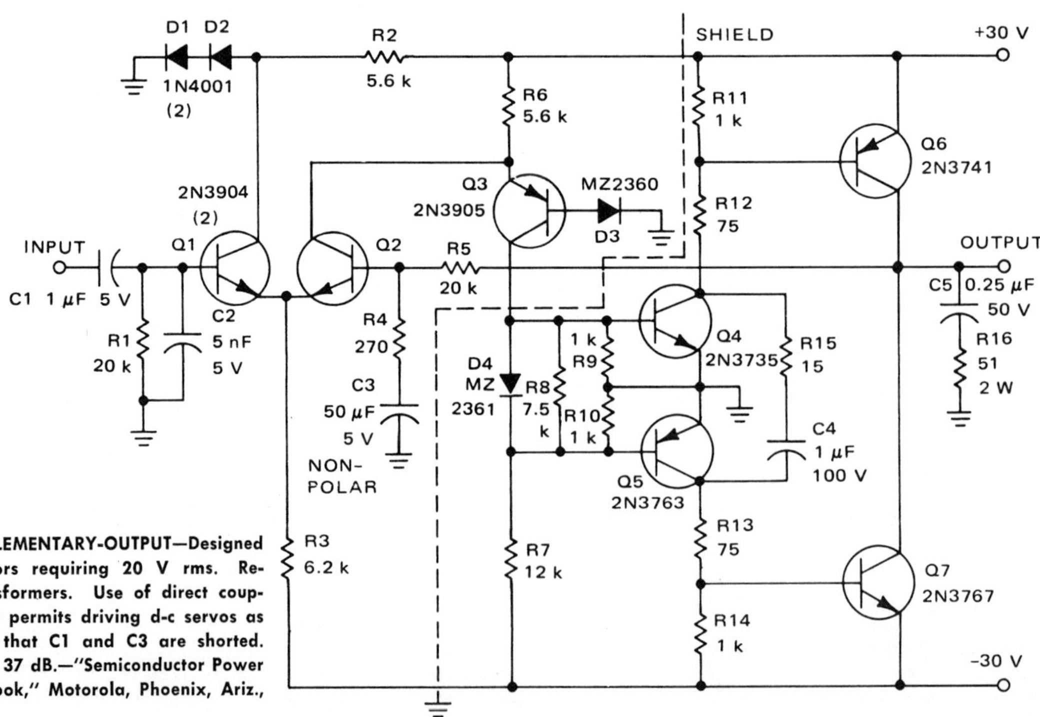

10-W COMPLEMENTARY-OUTPUT—Designed for servo motors requiring 20 V rms. Requires no transformers. Use of direct coupling throughout permits driving d-c servos as well, provided that C1 and C3 are shorted. Voltage gain is 37 dB.—"Semiconductor Power Circuits Handbook," Motorola, Phoenix, Ariz., 1968, p 5–15.

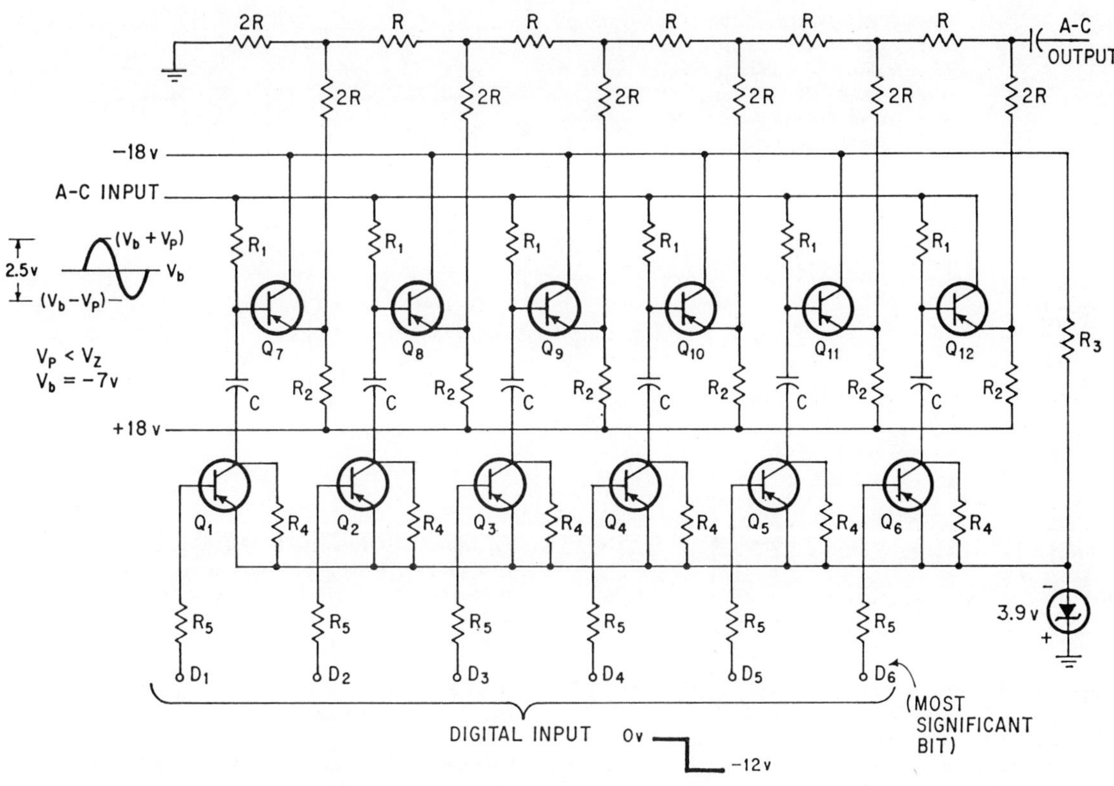

R_1 = 2.2k	R_4 = 1.0 m	C = 0.1μf
R_2 = 2.7k	R_5 = 5.6 k	$Q_1 - Q_{12}$ = 2N3644
R_3 = 1.5k	R = 1.0 k	FREQUENCY − 1 Mhz

LADDER-TYPE CONVERTER—Delivers a-c output with amplitude proportional to weight of set of binary inputs, for use in a-c servo system. Circuit can be made phase-sensitive by supplying most significant bit Q12 with a-c voltage 180 deg out of phase but with same amplitude and frequency as that used for other bits. This permits use of two's complement binary input code.—D. J. Gawlowicz and R. A. Fisher, Ladder Network Converts Binary Input to A-C Output, *Electronics*, July 7, 1969, p 106–107.

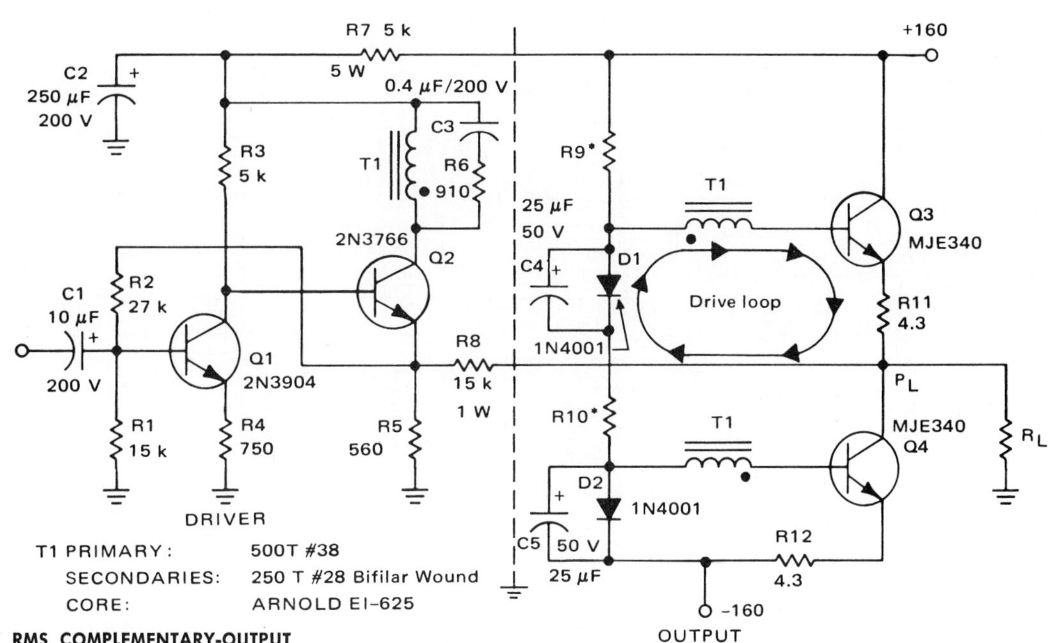

7.5-W 115-V RMS COMPLEMENTARY-OUTPUT—Uses high-voltage transistors to deliver high output voltage to load RL without using output transformer. This reduces phase-shift problems and permits operation from a-c line without power transformer. R9 and R10 should be adjusted so quiescent current of each output transistor does not exceed 15 mA at 100 C. Amplifier has good linearity up to rated output voltage. Frequency response is down only 1 dB from 95 to 2,000 Hz.—"Semiconductor Power Circuits Handbook," Motorola, Phoenix, Ariz., 1968, p 5–19.

VARIABLE COMMON-MODE LEVEL—With d-c servo amplifier shown, using Burr-Brown differential-input amplifier package, common-mode voltage will vary from −10 V to +10 V as servo follows input voltage. In this arrangement, common-mode rejection may be trimmed up with R for operation at a particular gain, but error from common-mode input cannot be trimmed out by adjusting offset voltage.—Instrument Amplifiers, Burr-Brown Research, Tucson, Ariz., PDS-207C, 1969.

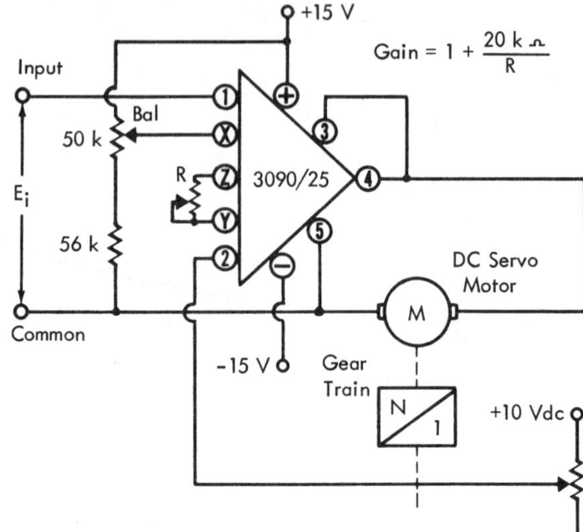

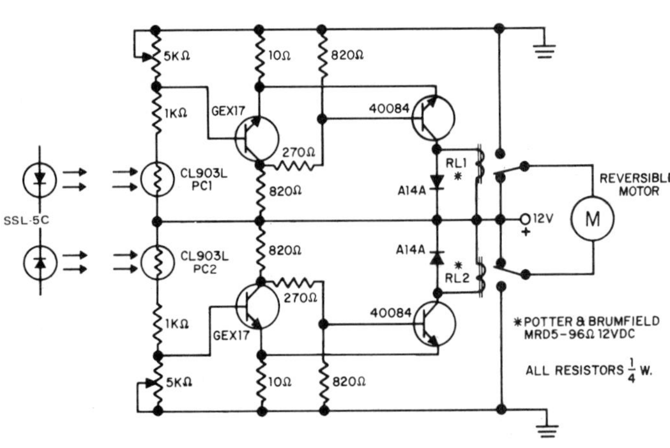

SSL CONTROL—Photocells in two Schmitt triggers coupled back-to-back are energized by solid-state lamps. Under steady-state conditions, both photocells are illuminated by lamps, relays are deenergized, and no voltage is applied to d-c motor. When light on either photocell is interrupted, corresponding relay pulls in and applies voltage to drive motor in one direction.—L. M. Hertz, Solid State Lamps—Part II, General Electric, Cleveland, Ohio, No. 3-0121, 1970, p 24.

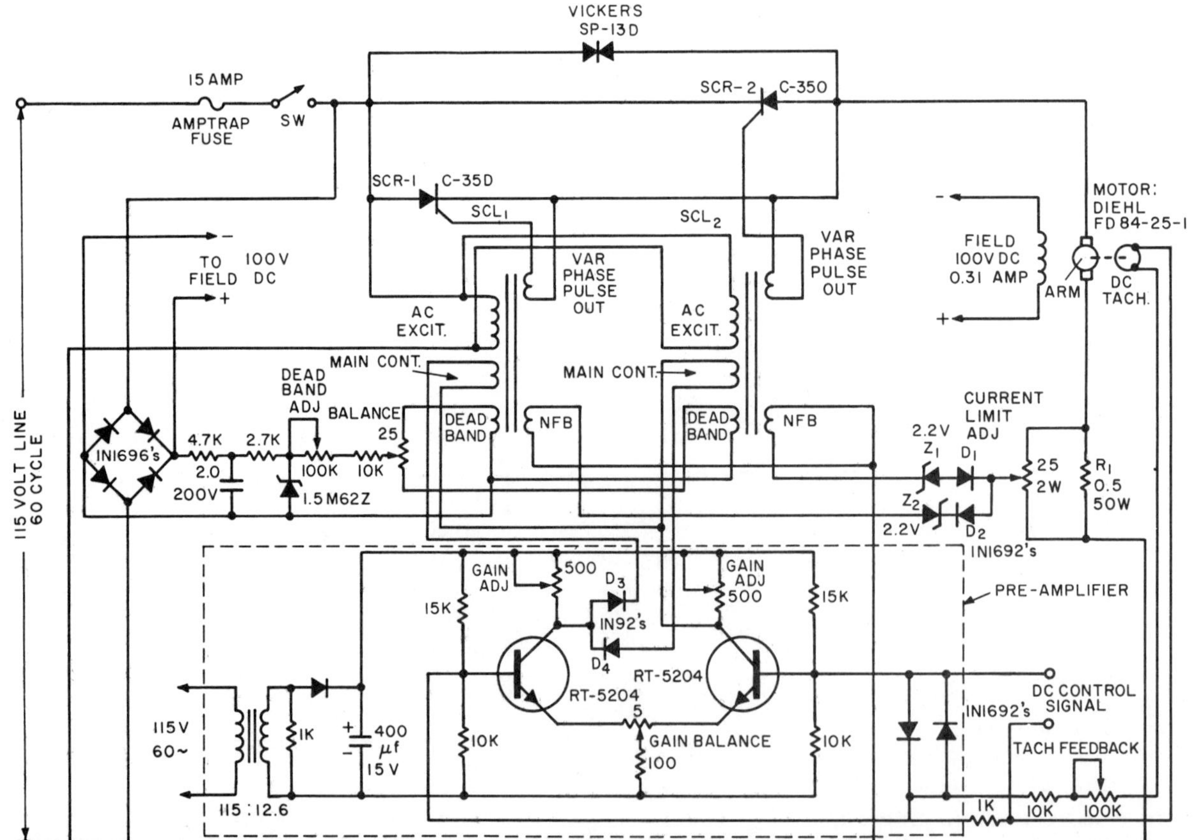

30 REVERSALS PER S—Pair of scr's can provide acceleration of d-c shunt-wound servomotor up to 5,300 radians per s and up to 30 complete reversals of armature current at 60 Hz (120 at 400 Hz). Article describes circuit operation in detail.—W. J. Brown and N. G. Muskovac, Compact Servoamp Has Fast Response, *Electronic Design*, Feb. 17, 1964, p 96–99.

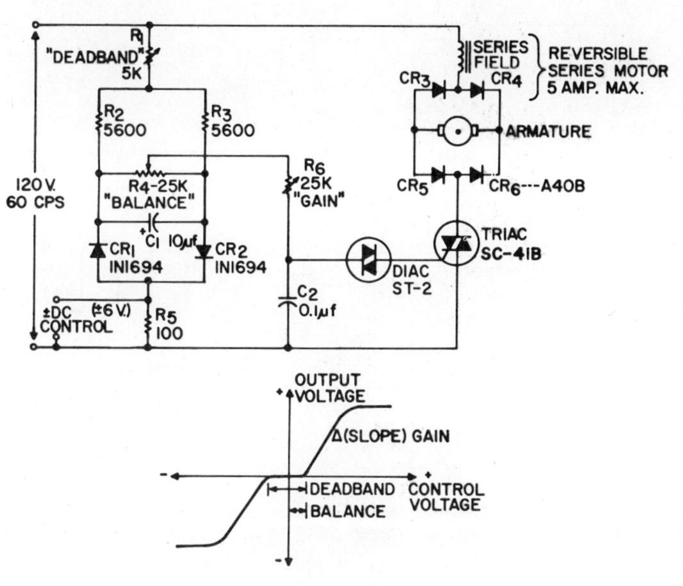

REVERSING DRIVE WITH D-C CONTROL—Positioning servo drive provides adjustment of balance, gain, and deadband. Polarity of 6-V d-c control signal determines direction of rotation. Mechanical control may be applied to balance control. Alternatively, pair of resistance transducers may be substituted for balance control, to give control either by light or temperature.—F. W. Gutzwiller and E. K. Howell, Economy Power Semiconductor Applications, General Electric, Syracuse, N.Y., No. 671.1, 1965, p 24.

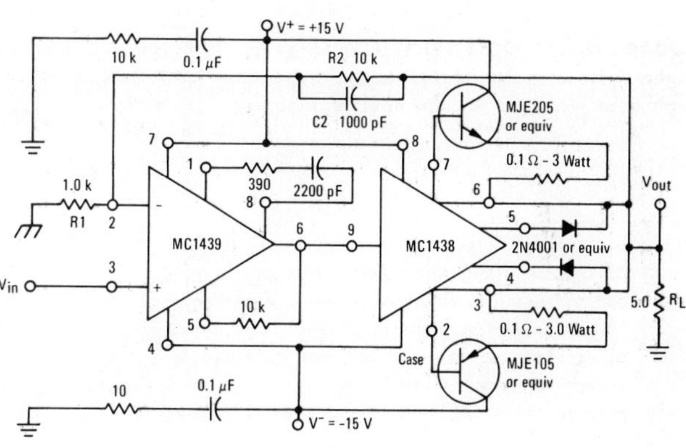

30-W SERVO AMPLIFIER—Uses Motorola amplifier providing 70 dB current gain and unity voltage gain, preceded by MC1439 opamp providing high voltage gain.—Power Booster MC1438R, Motorola, Phoenix, Ariz., ADI-14R1, 1969.

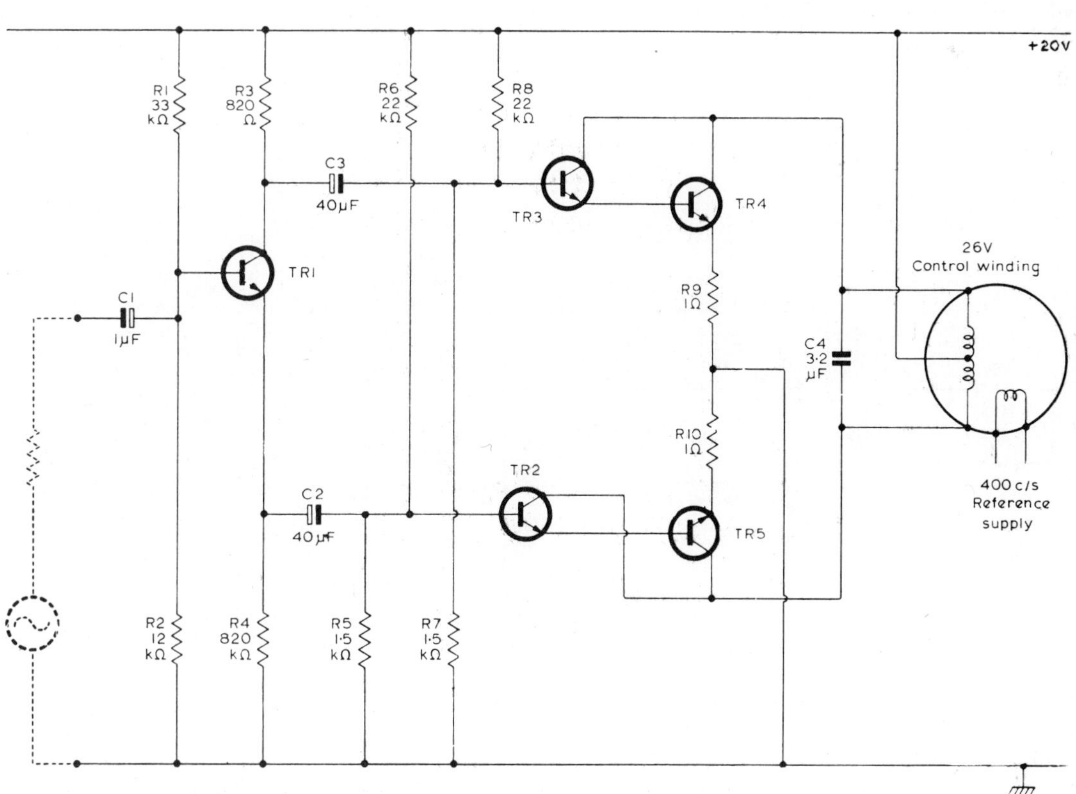

26-V 400-HZ DRIVE FOR 08, 10, AND 11 SERVOS—Provides 35 dB voltage gain when using BFY51 for TR1 and BFY52 for other transistors. Suitable for systems using velocity feedback, but not those depending on inherent viscous damping characteristics of motor.—Applications of the BFY50, BFY51 and BFY52, Philips, Pub. Dept., Elcoma Div., Eindhoven, The Netherlands, No. 428, 1965.

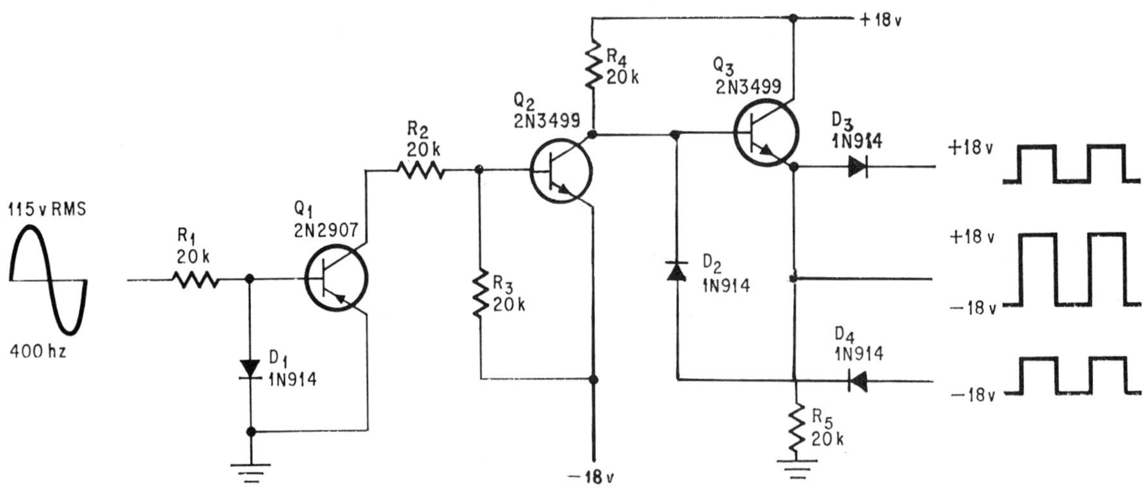

SQUARE WAVES FROM 400-HZ LINE—Provides highly accurate and stable frequency, with high peak voltage, for demodulating output of servo control amplifiers in ships and aircraft having 400-Hz power.—H. W. Candel, Sine Waves Become Square, With A Symmetrical Switch, *Electronics*, May 13, 1968, p 74.

DISCRIMINATOR—Gives linear changes in output voltage for changes in input duty cycle. Output is independent of amplitude of input pulses because Q1 and Q2 are operated in switching mode. Used in self-balancing servo loop in which R2 was pot geared to servomotor. Output voltage swings between fixed positive and negative voltages, with average value therefore depending on duty cycle.—P. Cutler, Pulse-Width Discriminator, *EEE*, Nov. 1966, p 152–153.

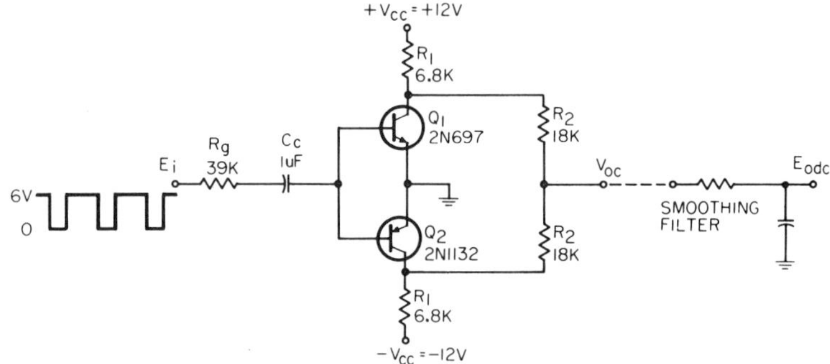

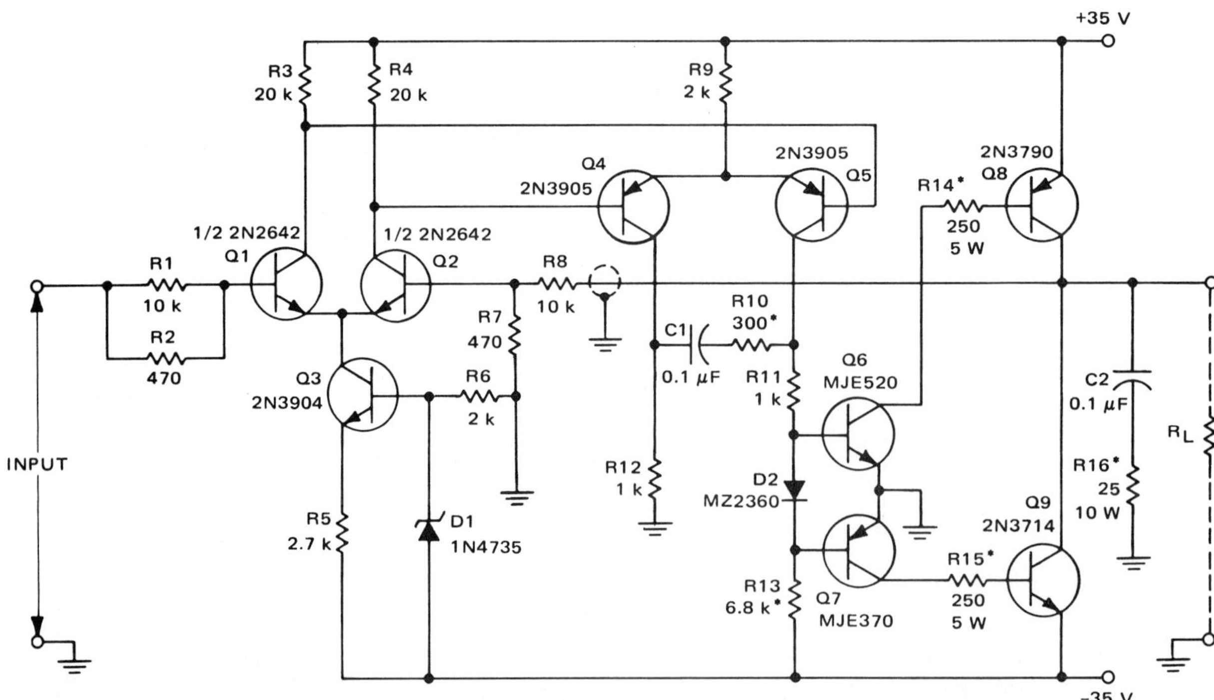

28-W 28-V D-C—Can drive 1-A load. Differential amplifier Q1-Q3 receives other input from amplifier output through R8, for negative feedback. Gain is about 22. Second stage, Q4-Q5, is differential-to-single-ended converter. Both driver and output stages use complementary-transistor connection.—"Semiconductor Power Circuits Handbook," Motorola, Phoenix, Ariz., 1968, p 5–23.

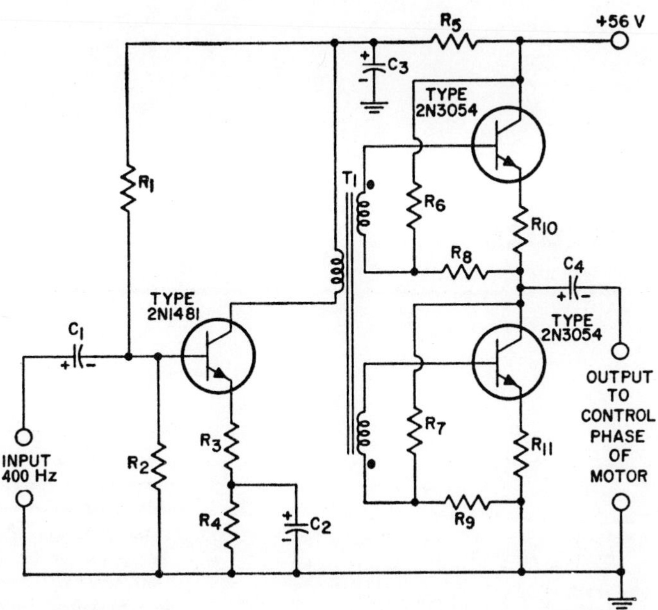

6-W 400-HZ AMPLIFIER—Upper transistor handles positive half-cycles of output signal and lower transistor handles negative half-cycles, so voltage swings are equal at motor. Values: R1 68K; R2 5.6K; R3 56; R4 560; R5 3.3K; R6-R7 18K; R8-R9 400; R10-R11 4; C1 10 μF; C2 47 μF; C3 20 μF; C4 500 μF; T1 1,500 turns primary and 225 turns each secondary bifilar wound.—"Transistor Manual," RCA, Harrison, N.J., SC-13, p 529.

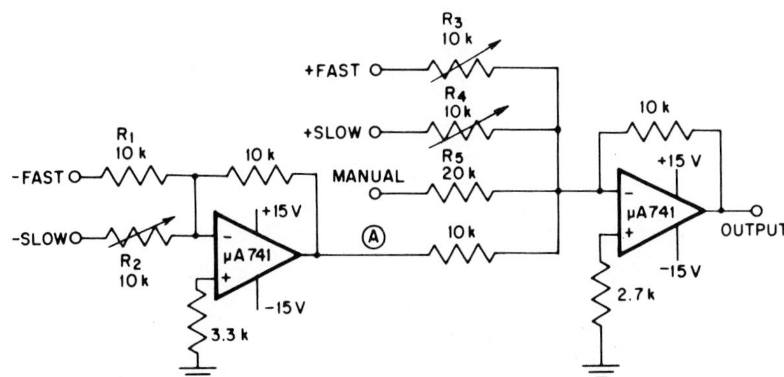

VELOCITY SERVO INTERFACE—Required when system must provide bidirectional rotation for both analog and digital inputs, with positive voltage providing drive in one direction and negative voltage in other direction. Combination of two opamps accepts either input logic levels from digital circuits or bipolar manual input such as from speed control, for either fast or slow motion in either direction. Manual input can be continuously variable from −15 V to +15 V, while other four inputs take 5-V logic. Output ranges from −10 V to +10 V.—J. E. McAlister, Bipolar Analog/Digital Interface for Servos, *EEE*, July 1970, p 85–86.

NOTE: To locate additional circuits in the category of this chapter, use the index at the back of this book. Check also the author's "Sourcebook of Electronic Circuits," published by McGraw-Hill in 1968.

CHAPTER 77
Shift Register Circuits

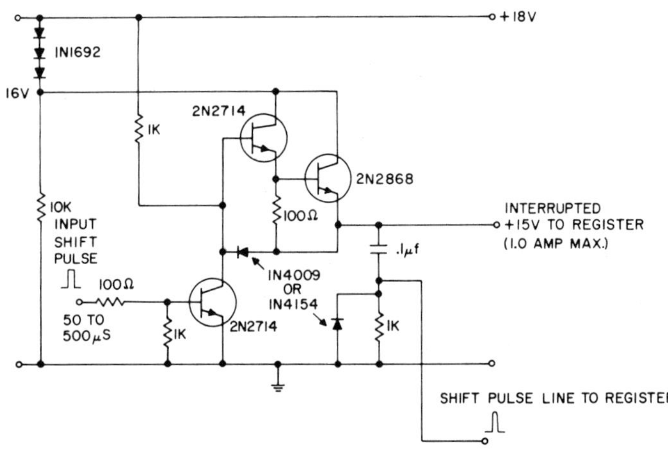

DARLINGTON DRIVER—Shift pulse input saturates lower 2N2714, depriving Darlington combination (above it) of base drive. Resulting negative pulse on 15-V line is differentiated to give desired positive output trigger pulse at its trailing edge, for driving shift register. Required 16-V power supply is synthesized from 18 V by using 1N1692 rectifiers.—Planar Silicon Controlled Switch 3N84/3N85, General Electric, Syracuse, N.Y., No. 65.18, 1964.

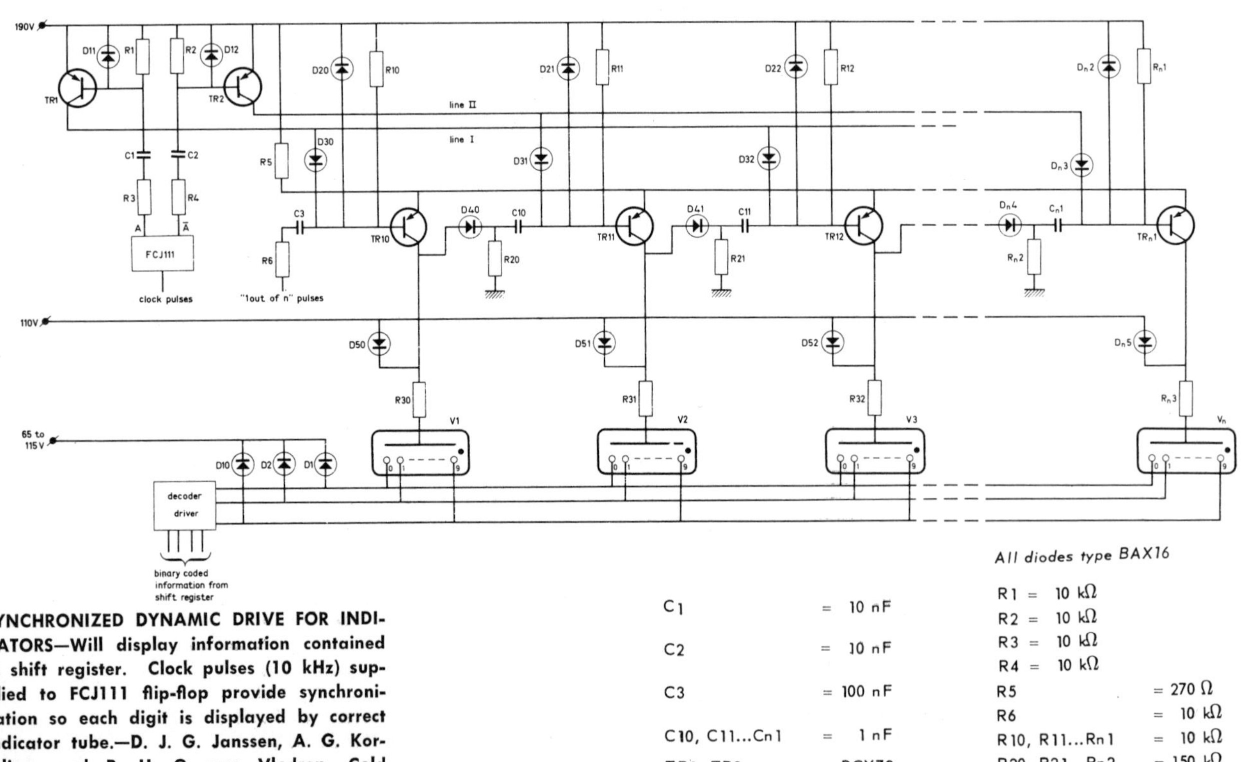

SYNCHRONIZED DYNAMIC DRIVE FOR INDICATORS—Will display information contained in shift register. Clock pulses (10 kHz) supplied to FCJ111 flip-flop provide synchronization so each digit is displayed by correct indicator tube.—D. J. G. Janssen, A. G. Korteling, and P. H. G. van Vlodrop, Cold Cathode Numerical Indicator Tubes, Philips, Pub. Dept., Elcoma Div., Eindhoven, The Netherlands, No. 327, 1968.

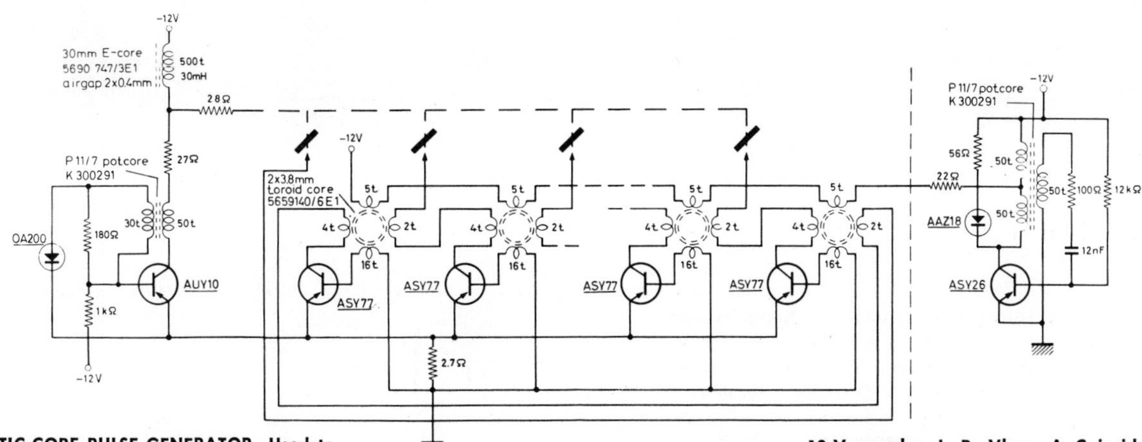

MAGNETIC-CORE PULSE GENERATOR—Used to supply 12-μs 3-mA current pulses to vertical wires in shift register. Rise time of 0.15 μs is independent of number of cores to be driven. Each transistor is part of triggered blocking oscillator using square-loop ferrite cores as transformers. Circuit requires only 12-V supply.—J. P. Vlam, A Coincident-Current Magnetic-Core Shift Register, Philips, Pub. Dept., Elcoma Div., Eindhoven, The Netherlands, No. 825, 1965.

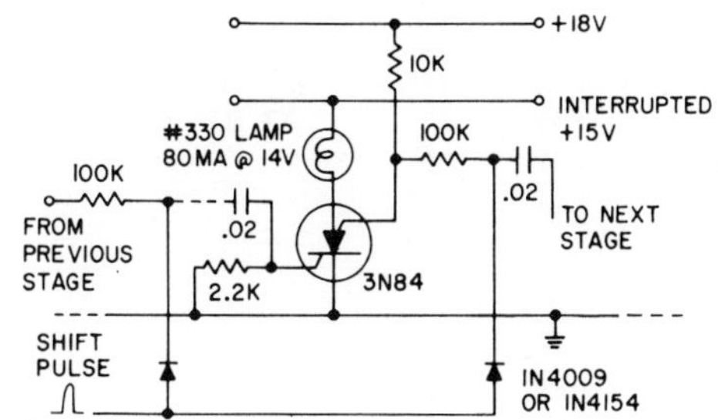

BASIC SCS STAGE—Planar scs gives immunity to voltage transients without affecting triggering sensitivity or transient response time. Shift pulse from driver should be less than 15 V. Anode supply is interrupted prior to each shift pulse to turn off all stages. Stored capacitor charge determines which stages will be retriggered.—Planar Silicon Controlled Switch 3N84/3N85, General Electric, Syracuse, N.Y., No. 65.18, 1964.

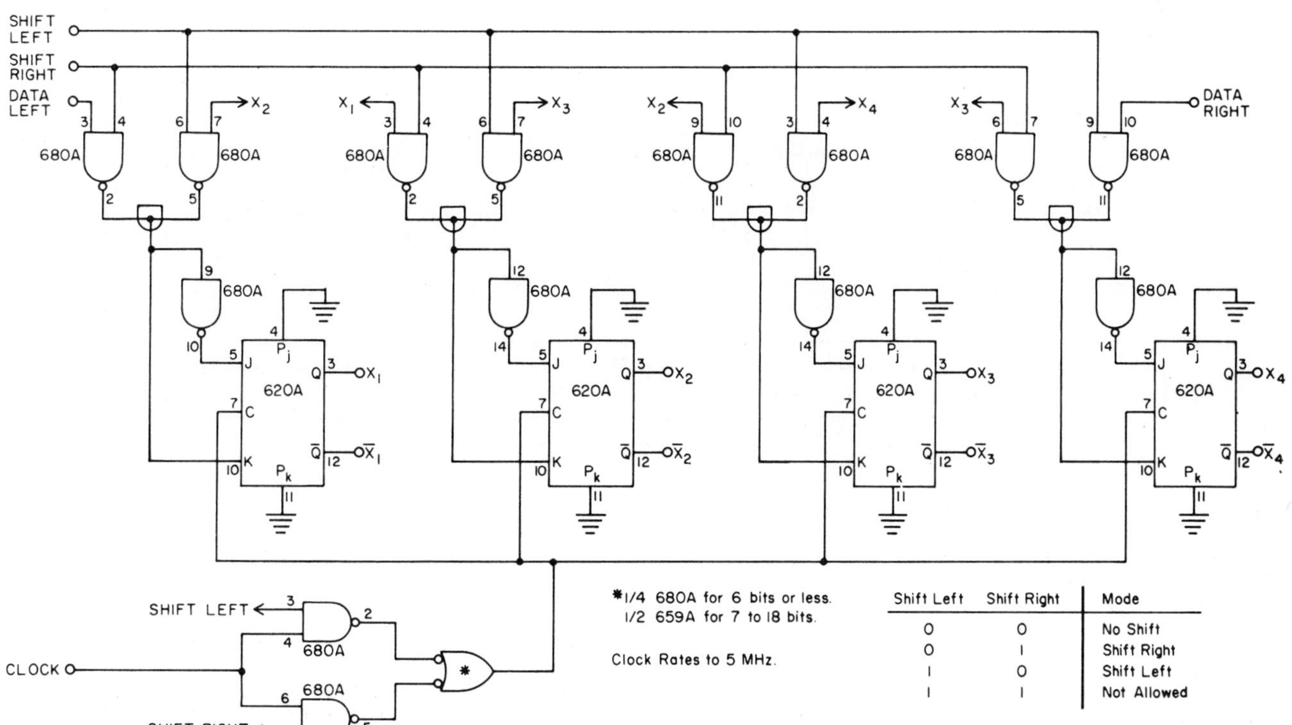

*1/4 680A for 6 bits or less.
1/2 659A for 7 to 18 bits.

Clock Rates to 5 MHz.

Shift Left	Shift Right	Mode
0	0	No Shift
0	1	Shift Right
1	0	Shift Left
1	1	Not Allowed

SERIAL-ENTRY BINARY—Used for storing and transferring binary numbers in or out in either direction (left-right) one at a time, with direction depending on which shift line is high at clock time. Uses Signetics IC gates and J-K binary IC elements. Will operate at clock rates up to 5 MHz.—SP/ST600-Series Design Data and Applications, Signetics, Sunnyvale, Cal., 1966, AN108.

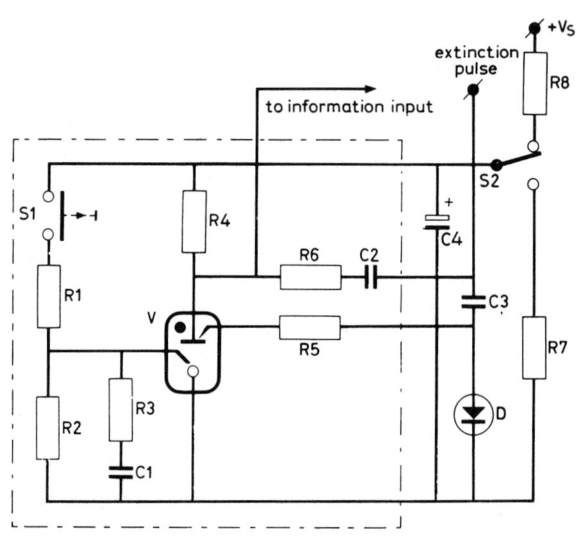

TRIGGER FOR RUNNING TEXT DISPLAY—Used for writing information into shift register having neon trigger tubes serving also as lamps for running-text display. Function of S1 is normally performed by punched paper tape reader containing text for display.—J. G. M. Thaens and P. H. G. van Vlodrop, Running Text Display with Cold-Cathode Trigger Tubes, *Electronic Applications*, Philips, Pub. Dept., Elcoma Div., Eindhoven, The Netherlands, Vol. 27, No. 3, 1966–1967, p 92–102.

R_1	100 kΩ, $\frac{1}{4}$ W ± 5%	R_8	4.7 kΩ, 1 W ± 5%
R_2	2.2 MΩ, $\frac{1}{4}$ W ± 10%	C_1	2.2 nF ± 10%
R_3	10 kΩ, $\frac{1}{8}$ W ± 5%	C_2	2.2 nF ± 10%
R_4	82 kΩ, $\frac{1}{2}$ W ± 5%	C_3	220 nF ± 10%
R_5	10 MΩ, $\frac{1}{8}$ W ± 10%	C_4	64 μF ± 20%
R_6	22 kΩ, $\frac{1}{8}$ W ± 5%	D	BYX10
R_7	3.3 kΩ, 1 W ± 5%	V	ZC1050

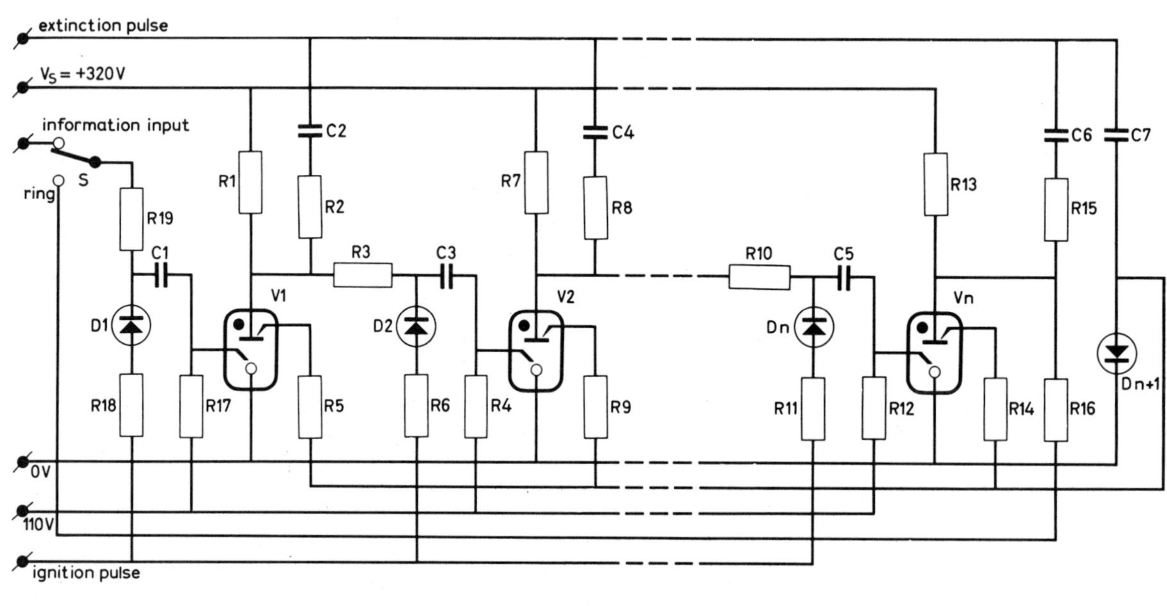

R_1, R_7, R_{13}	82 kΩ, $\frac{1}{2}$ W,	C_1 - C_6	2.2 nF	± 15%
R_2, R_8, R_{15}	22 kΩ, $\frac{1}{8}$ W,	C_7	470 nF	± 15%
R_3, R_{10}, R_{19}, R_4, R_{12}, R_{17}	1 MΩ, $\frac{1}{4}$ W,	D_1 - D_{n+1}	BYX10	
		V_1 - V_n	ZC1050	
R_5, R_9, R_{14}	10 MΩ, $\frac{1}{8}$ W ± 10%			
R_6, R_{11}, R_{18}	10 kΩ, $\frac{1}{8}$ W,			
R_{16}	100 kΩ, $\frac{1}{4}$ W,			

SHIFT REGISTER FOR RUNNING TEXT—Used to activate one of seven rows of neon-filled trigger tubes on which moving letters are formed in 5-by-7 matrix. Neons serve also as switching elements V1-Vn of shift register, because ZC1050 neon trigger has pure molybdenum cathode and very high light output. Other advantages are high switching speed, complete lack of afterglow, and guaranteed minimum life of 10,000 hours. Size of matrix is limited only by budget; seven rows are minimum for readable letters. Article gives all circuits and construction details.—J. G. M. Thaens and P. H. G. van Vlodrop, Running Text Display with Cold-Cathode Trigger Tubes, *Electronic Applications*, Philips, Pub. Dept., Elcoma Div., Eindhoven, The Netherlands, Vol. 27, No. 3, 1966–1967, p 92–102.

5-KHZ WITH UP TO 10 SCS STAGES—Shift pulse at input turns off all scs's. Trailing edge of turnoff pulse is differentiated for turning on appropriate stages. Will easily handle up to ten stages.—Planar Silicon Controlled Switch 3N81/3N82, General Electric, Syracuse, N.Y., No. 65.16, 1964.

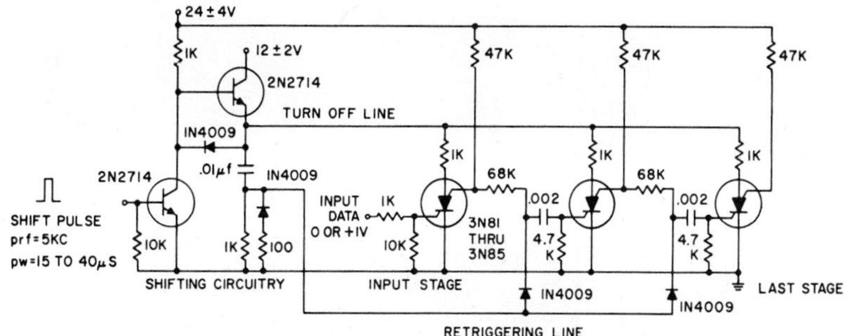

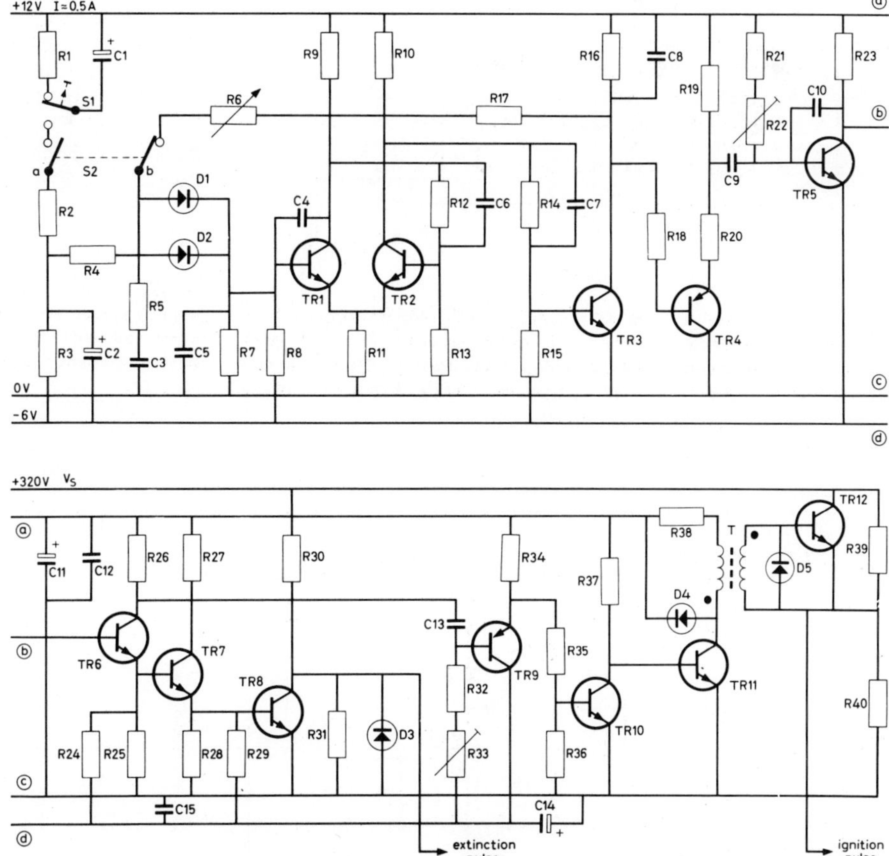

Transformer T: H20 core; secondary: 25 turns 0.35 mm diameter enamelled copper wire; primary: 100 turns 0.28 mm diameter enamelled copper wire wound on top of and insulated from the secondary.

R_1	5.6 kΩ, $\frac{1}{8}$ W	R_{15}	22 kΩ, $\frac{1}{8}$ W	R_{29}	1 kΩ, $\frac{1}{4}$ W	C_1	2.5 μF electrolytic
R_2	27 Ω, $\frac{1}{4}$ W	R_{16}	2.2 kΩ, $\frac{1}{4}$ W	R_{30}	3.9 kΩ. 16 W	C_2	1 μF electrolytic
R_3	10 kΩ, $\frac{1}{8}$ W	R_{17}	12 kΩ, $\frac{1}{8}$ W	R_{31}	10 kΩ, 16 W	C_3	4.4 μF polyester
R_4	10 kΩ, $\frac{1}{8}$ W	R_{18}	10 kΩ, $\frac{1}{8}$ W	R_{32}	10 kΩ, $\frac{1}{8}$ W	C_4	2.2 nF
R_5	470 Ω, $\frac{1}{8}$ W	R_{19}	470 Ω, $\frac{1}{4}$ W	R_{33}	5 kΩ, $\frac{1}{4}$ W pot.	C_5	12 nF
R_6	100 kΩ, $\frac{1}{4}$ W pot.	R_{20}	560 Ω, $\frac{1}{8}$ W	R_{34}	1.5 kΩ, $\frac{1}{4}$ W	C_6	220 pF
R_7	470 kΩ, $\frac{1}{8}$ W	R_{21}	10 kΩ, $\frac{1}{8}$ W	R_{35}	3.3 kΩ, $\frac{1}{8}$ W	C_7	330 pF
R_8	270 kΩ, $\frac{1}{8}$ W	R_{22}	10 kΩ, $\frac{1}{4}$ W pot.	R_{36}	1.5 kΩ, $\frac{1}{8}$ W	C_8	8.2 nF
R_9	1.5 kΩ, $\frac{1}{4}$ W	R_{23}	1 kΩ, $\frac{1}{4}$ W	R_{37}	330 Ω, $\frac{1}{2}$ W	C_9	220 nF
R_{10}	1.5 kΩ, $\frac{1}{4}$ W	R_{24}	6.8 kΩ, $\frac{1}{8}$ W	R_{38}	33 Ω, 8 W	C_{10}	3.3 NF
R_{11}	220 Ω, $\frac{1}{8}$ W	R_{25}	4.7 kΩ, $\frac{1}{8}$ W	R_{39}	39 kΩ, 5.5 W	C_{11}	1000 μF electrolytic
R_{12}	15 kΩ, $\frac{1}{8}$ W	R_{26}	560 Ω, $\frac{1}{2}$ W		in parallel with	C_{12}	3.3 nF
R_{13}	22 kΩ, $\frac{1}{8}$ W	R_{27}	27 Ω, 2 W		68 kΩ, 1 W	C_{13}	8.2 nF polyester
R_{14}	15 kΩ, $\frac{1}{8}$ W	R_{28}	1 kΩ, $\frac{1}{4}$ W	R_{40}	15 kΩ, 5.5 W	C_{14}	40 μF electrolytic
						C_{15}	3.3 nF

SHIFT REGISTER DRIVER FOR RUNNING TEXT—Generates extinction and ignition pulses for driving shift register using neon trigger tubes that serve also as lamps for running-text display. With switch S2a closed, each operation of S1 makes Schmitt trigger TR1-TR2 produce one positive-going pulse at collector of TR2. When S2b is closed, this output pulse is amplified and inverted by TR3 and fed back to base of TR1, making circuit astable at repetition frequency adjustable by R6 from 8 to 90 Hz. Article describes circuit operation in detail. Values shown are for display having seven rows with 100 tubes each.—J. G. M. Thaens and P. H. G. van Vlodrop, Running Text Display with Cold-Cathode Trigger Tubes, *Electronic Applications*, Philips, Pub. Dept., Elcoma Div., Eindhoven, The Netherlands, Vol. 27, No. 3, 1966–1967, p 92–102.

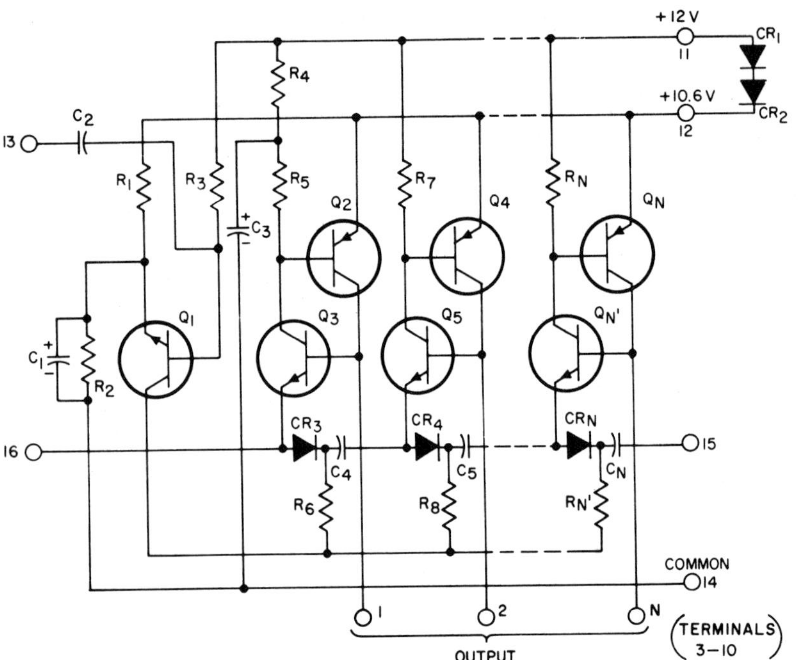

C_1 = 100 microfarads, 10 volts, electrolytic
$C_2\ C_4\ C_5\ C_N$ = 0.05 microfarad, 50 volts or greater
C_3 = 10 microfarads, 15 volts, electrolytic
$CR_1\ CR_2\ CR_N$ = silicon diode, type 1N270
$Q_1\ Q_3\ Q_5\ Q_{N'}$ = transistor, RCA SK3005
$Q_2 Q_4 Q_N$ = transistor, RCA SK3010
$R_1\ R_7\ R_N$ = 1000 ohms, 1/2 watt, 10%
R_2 = 47 ohms, 1/2 watt, 10%
R_3 = 5600 ohms, 1/2 watt, 10%
$R_4 R_5$ = 470 ohms, 1/2 watt, 10%
$R_6 R_8 R_{N'}$ = 270 ohms, 1/2 watt, 10%

TEN-STAGE CIRCUIT—Requires 2-V negative pulse at terminal 13 to change register to next stage. Required 10.6-V d-c supply is obtained from two diodes connected in series to 12-V supply. Each register stage is basically two-transistor regenerative switch using npn and pnp transistors; if either starts to conduct, both are quickly driven into saturation by regenerative action. Load connected to each output terminal should be under 1,000 ohms and draw less than 200 mA.—"Hobby Circuits Manual," RCA, Harrison, N.J., HM-90, p 56.

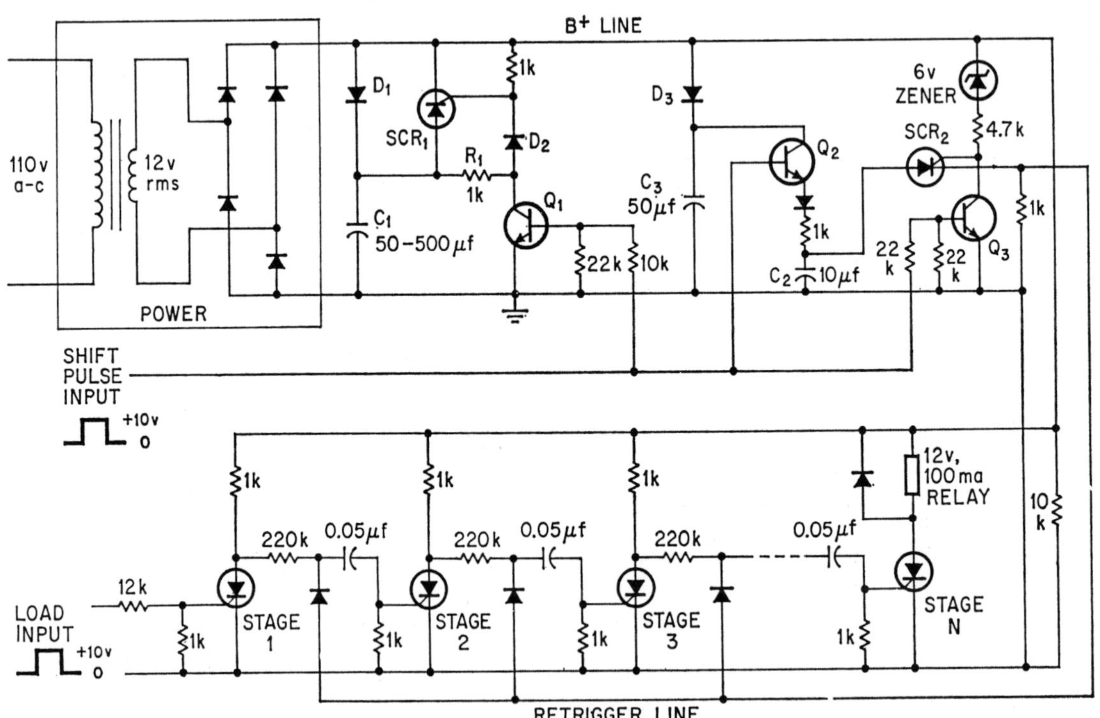

NOISE REJECTION—Can be used near factory production lines where electrical noise would cause false triggering of conventional shift registers if used to record data on components passed or rejected by automatic testing machine. For 60-Hz line, maximum shift rate is 120-Hz power-supply ripple frequency. Higher shift rate can be obtained with higher line frequency if 0.05-μF scr coupling capacitors are reduced in value.—J. G. Silverman, SCR Shift Register Can Take a Lot of Noise, *Electronics*, June 23, 1969, p 104–105.

REGENERATIVE-SWITCH REGISTER—Each shift register stage may be made regenerative by connecting points A and A'. Circuit can readily be adapted for other output current levels than 40-mA value obtained with 12 V for E1 and 9 V for E2. Values in parentheses will give output level of 3 A with 27 V for E1 and 24 V for E2. With regenerative connection, may be used as ring counter. Can have any number of stages.—"Transistor Manual," RCA, Harrison, N.J., SC-13, p 530.

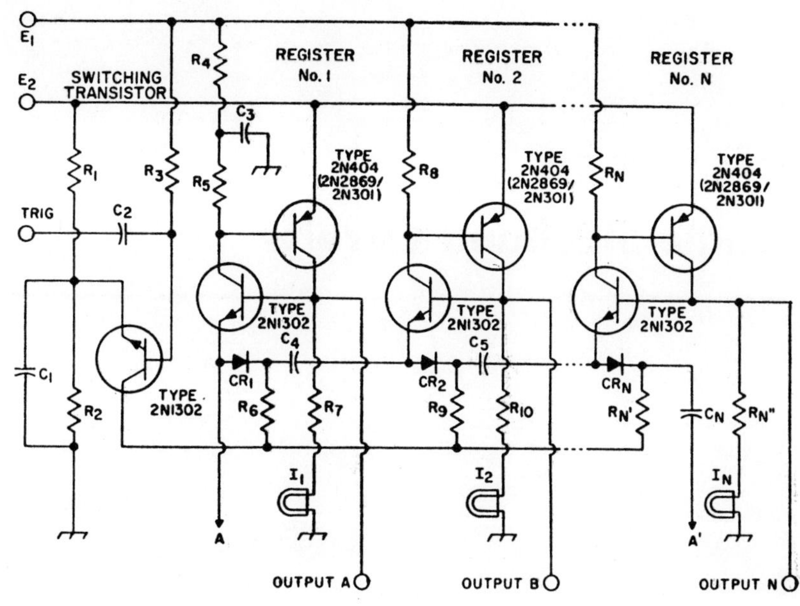

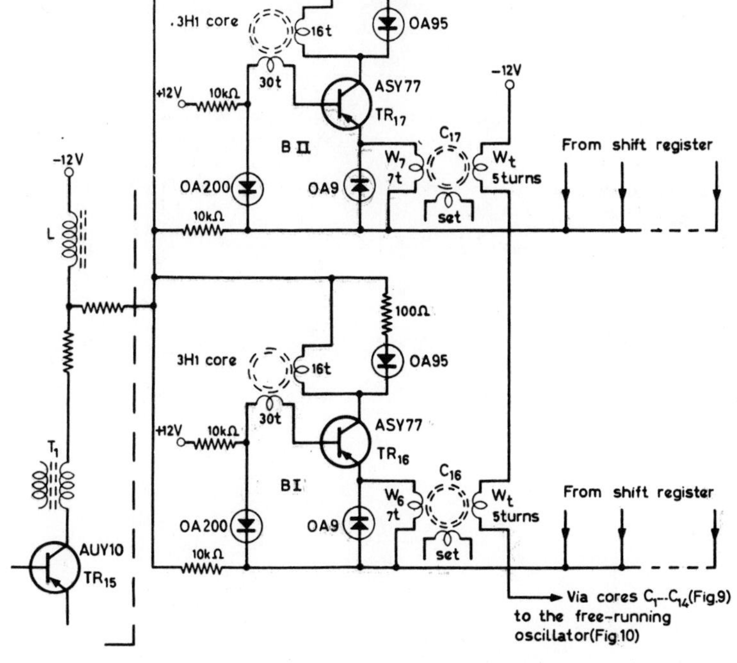

MAGNETIC-CORE SHIFT REGISTER—Used for storing information in desk calculators. Contents of magnetic cores are shifted sequentially by means of coincidence of two currents. Requires only one core per bit. Operates in low-speed region, involving add or subtract time of about 10 ms and multiply or divide time of 100 ms. Blocking oscillators TR16 and TR17 serve as switches triggered by pulses from shift register.—J. P. Vlam, A Coincident-Current Magnetic-Core Shift Register, Philips, Pub. Dept., Elcoma Div., Eindhoven, The Netherlands, No. 825, 1965.

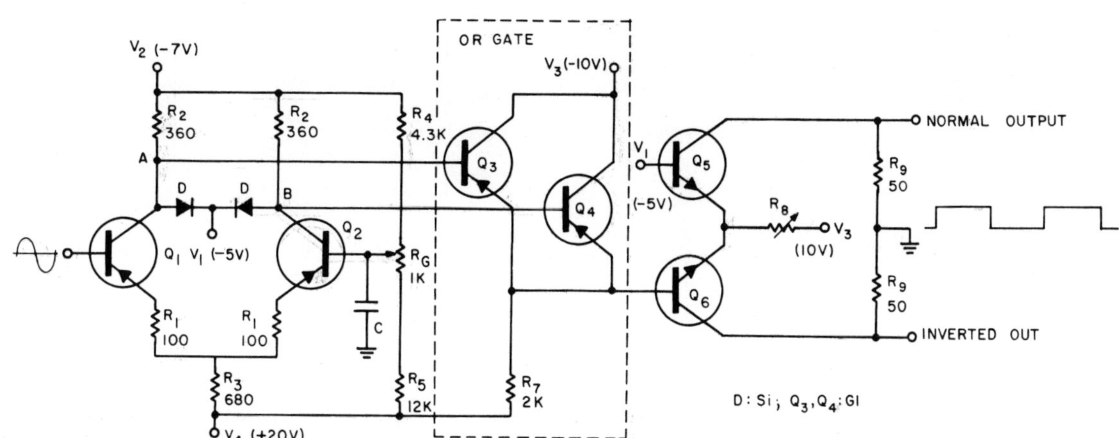

SHIFT REGISTER TESTER—Square-wave generator provides two separate waveforms, one representing information to be stored, and the other representing writing pulses, for testing register at its maximum clock rate. Transistors can be 2N797 for npn and 2N976 for pnp.—P. Maestrini, Generator Tests Register At Maximum Clock Rates, *Electronic Design*, Oct. 12, 1964, p 74–75.

CHAPTER 78
Single-Sideband Circuits

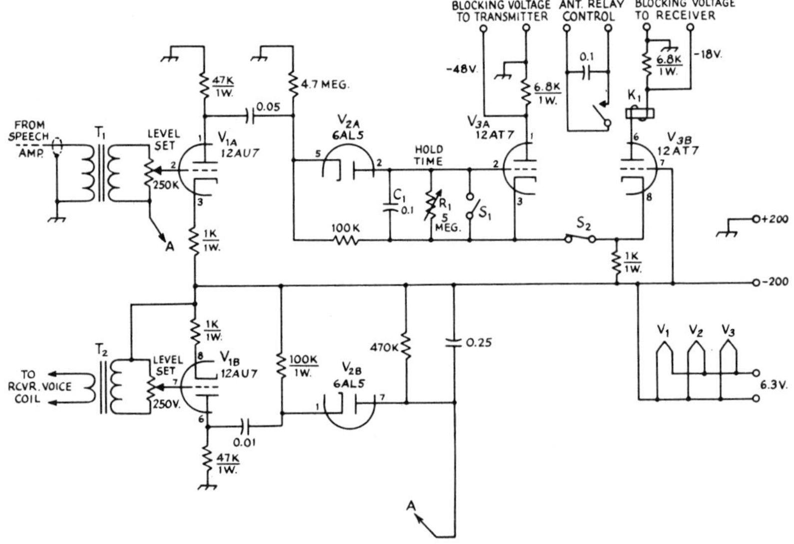

VOICE-CONTROLLED BREAK-IN—Provides VOX operation along with positive anti-trip for ssb receiver. Receiver audio voltage, taken from voice coil, is applied to circuit through T2 which may be almost any low-power tube to voice-coil transformer. Interstage transformer T1 is not critical. Book gives construction and adjustment details.—L. O. Leigh, Universal Voice-Control Circuit, "Single Sideband for the Radio Amateur," ARRL, Newington, Conn., 1965, p 231–232.

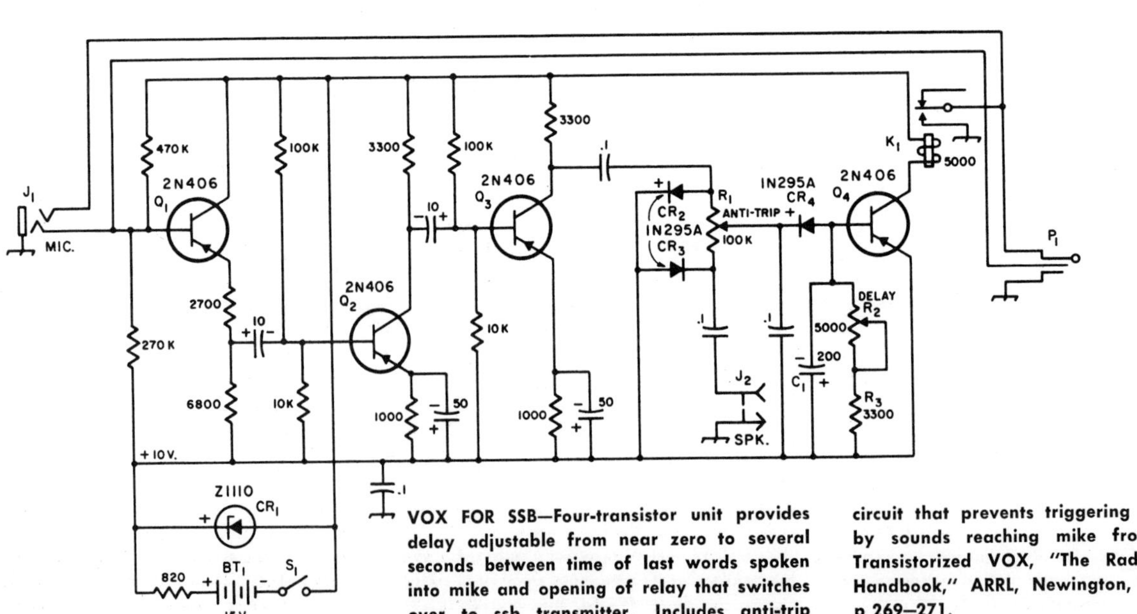

VOX FOR SSB—Four-transistor unit provides delay adjustable from near zero to several seconds between time of last words spoken into mike and opening of relay that switches over to ssb transmitter. Includes anti-trip circuit that prevents triggering of VOX unit by sounds reaching mike from speaker.—Transistorized VOX, "The Radio Amateur's Handbook," ARRL, Newington, Conn., 1969, p 269–271.

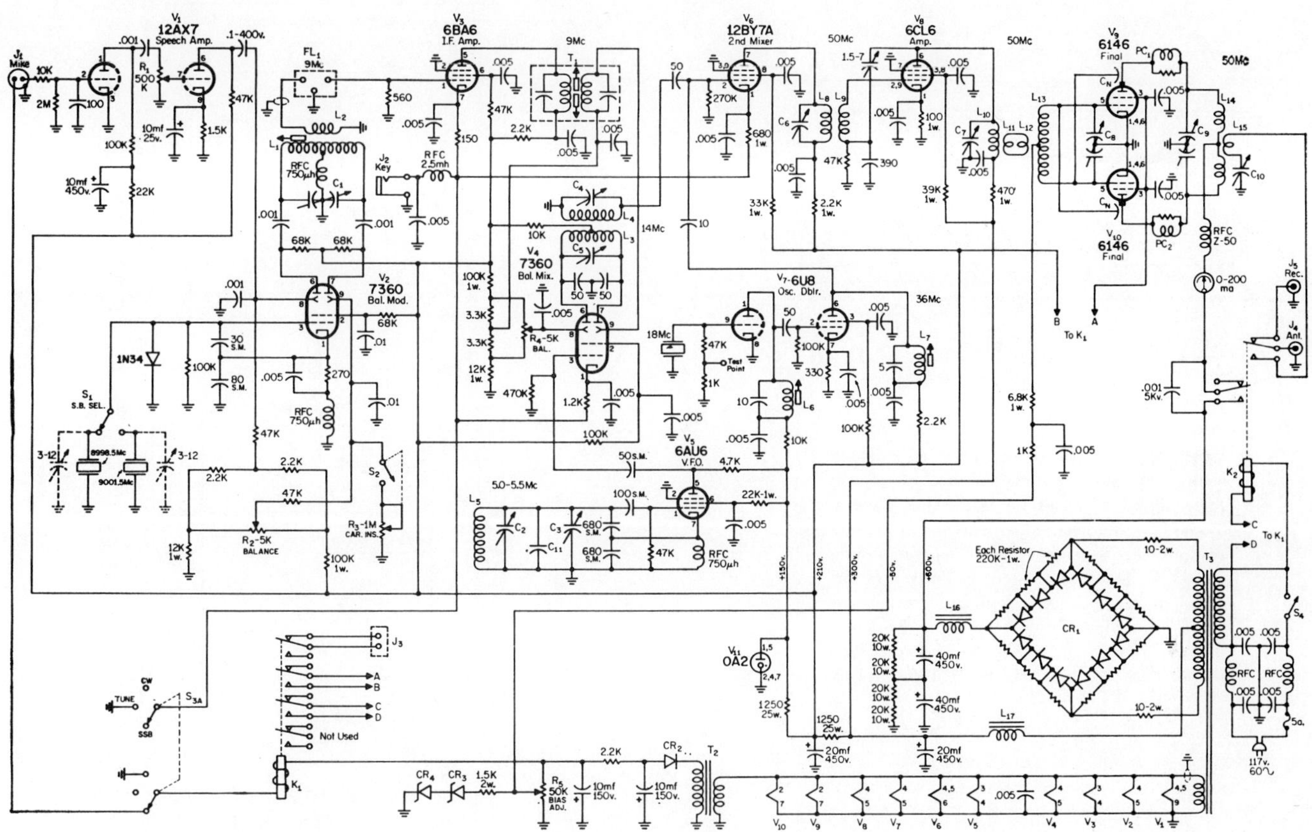

6-METER SSB TRANSMITTER—Complete self-contained transmitter is designed to produce only 50-MHz (6-meter) ssb signal, eliminating need for band-changing switches. Uses push-to-talk switch on mike. Article gives complete circuit description and construction details.—C. Johnson, A Six Meter S. S. B. Transmitter, CQ, May 1965, p 26–31 and 104.

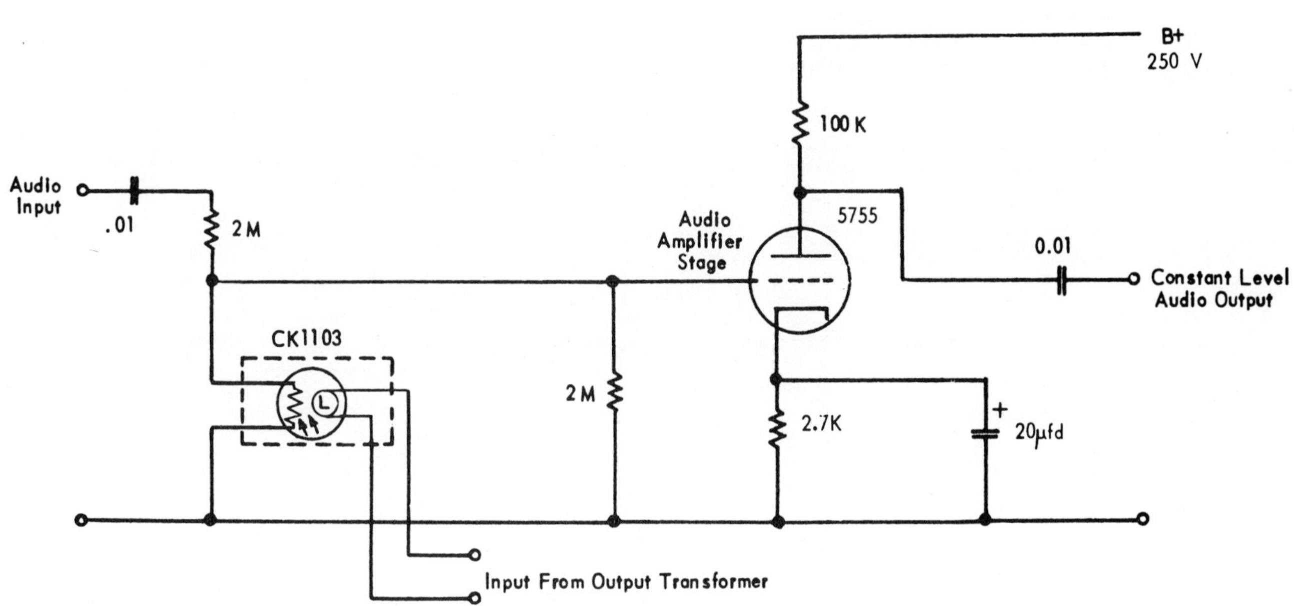

RAYSISTOR AVC CONTROL—Particularly useful in ssb suppressed-carrier receivers where normal avc will not operate because there is no carrier when there is no modulation. Audio output of receiver is fed into light source of optoelectronic device, to vary resistance of photocell used in place of normal volume control. Has fast ON action (10 ms) and slow OFF action (800 ms), which is ideal for ssb receiver. For remote control, lamp may be energized by d-c voltage. Gives greater than 60 dB control range, for photocell resistance change from 200 ohms to 2 meg.—Raysistor Optoelectronic Devices, Raytheon, Quincy, Mass., 1967, p 10–11.

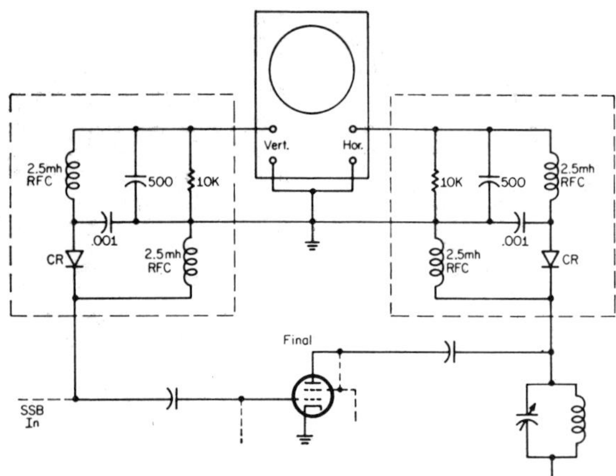

MONITOR—Two envelope detectors shielded from each other permit monitoring of ssb voice signal or two-tone test signal on cro. Diodes are matched RCA 1N445B. Diagonal straight line on screen for voice modulation means no distortion. Input to horizontal terminal of cro may be taken from any linear stage preceding final amplifier.—"Electronic Circuits Handbook," Vol. II, Cowan Pub. Corp., Port Washington, N.Y., 1966, p 52.

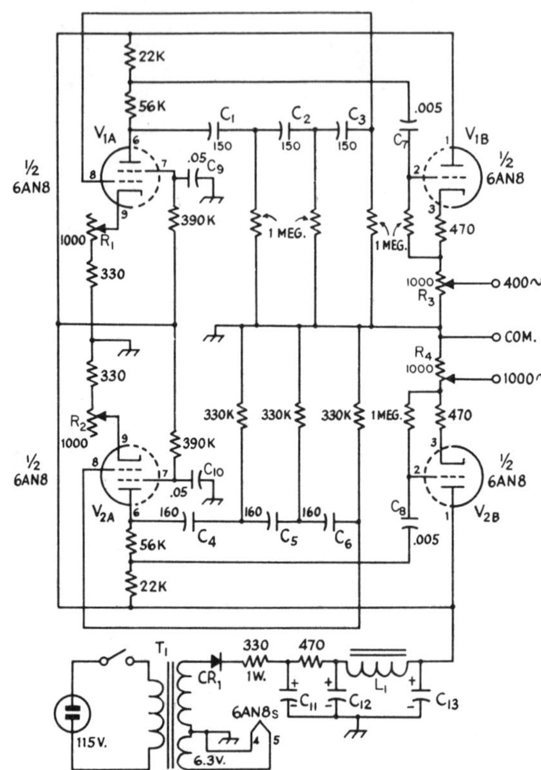

TWO-TONE AUDIO—Provides choice of two different audio frequencies in range of 250 to 2,000 Hz with good waveform, as required for ssb transmitter testing. CR1 is 75-mA selenium rectifier and L1 is 5 H at 50 mA. C11 and C12 are 120 μF; C13 is 40 μF.—R. F. Tschannen, Two-Tone Test Generator, "Single Sideband for the Radio Amateur," ARRL, Newington, Conn., 1965, p 204–206.

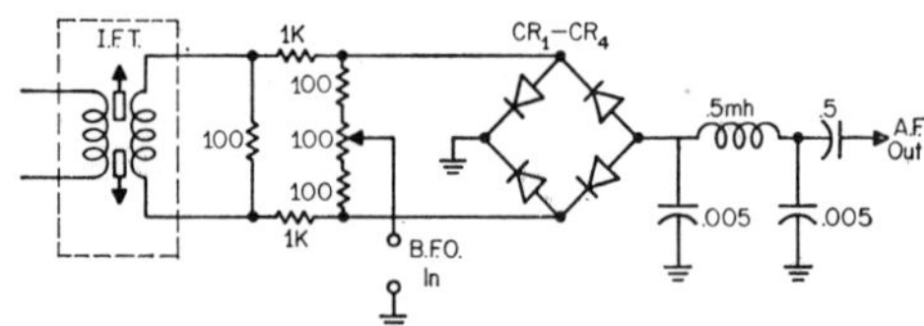

SSB RING DEMODULATOR—Diodes can be 1N78B or any other having low front-back resistance. Performance is excellent if bfo signal injected through i-f transformer is clean and stable sine wave.—C. J. Schauers, SSB Ring Demodulator, CQ, June 1965, p 73.

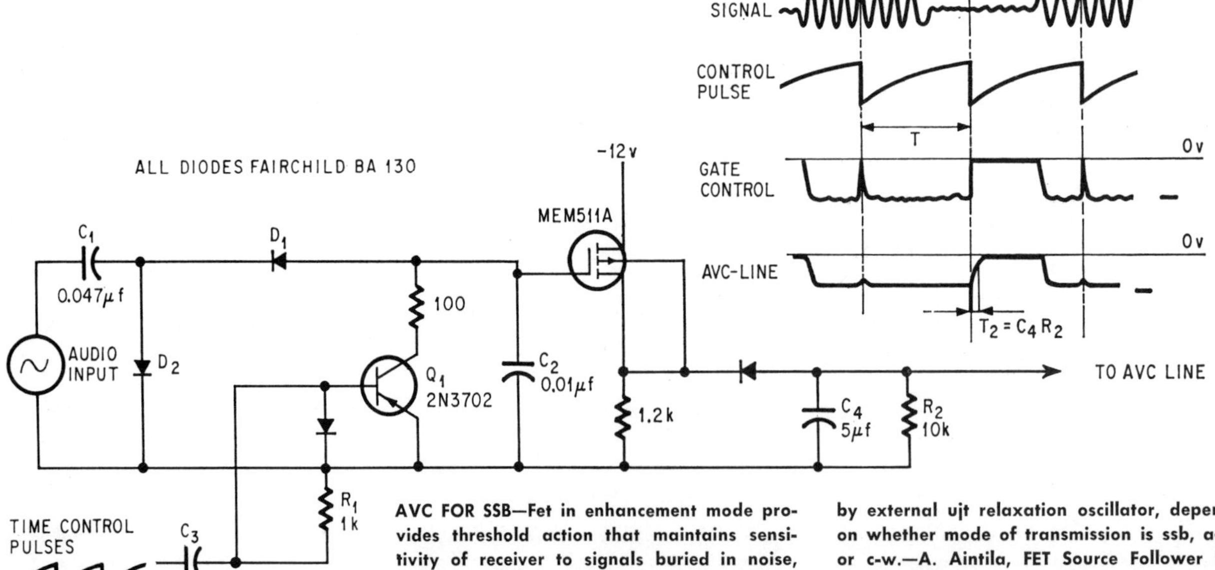

AVC FOR SSB—Fet in enhancement mode provides threshold action that maintains sensitivity of receiver to signals buried in noise, with fast rise time required for avc. Optimum repetition frequency of time-control pulses that determine avc speed, generated by external ujt relaxation oscillator, depends on whether mode of transmission is ssb, a-m, or c-w.—A. Aintila, FET Source Follower Enhances Single-Sideband, *Electronics*, Sept. 18, 1967, p 106–107.

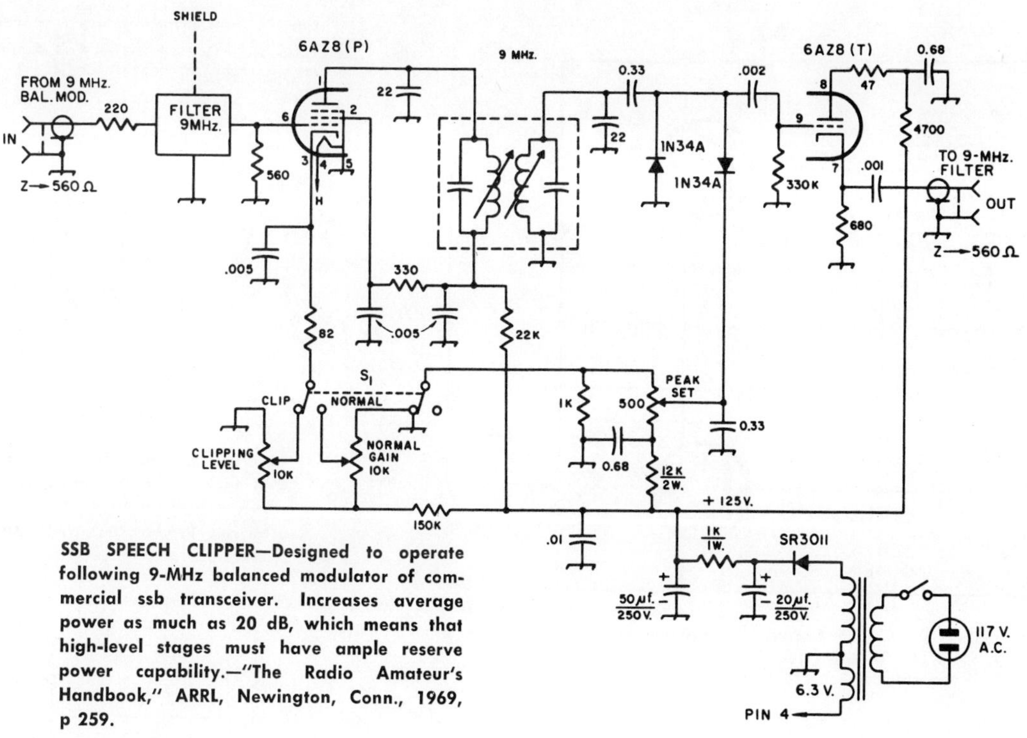

SSB SPEECH CLIPPER—Designed to operate following 9-MHz balanced modulator of commercial ssb transceiver. Increases average power as much as 20 dB, which means that high-level stages must have ample reserve power capability.—"The Radio Amateur's Handbook," ARRL, Newington, Conn., 1969, p 259.

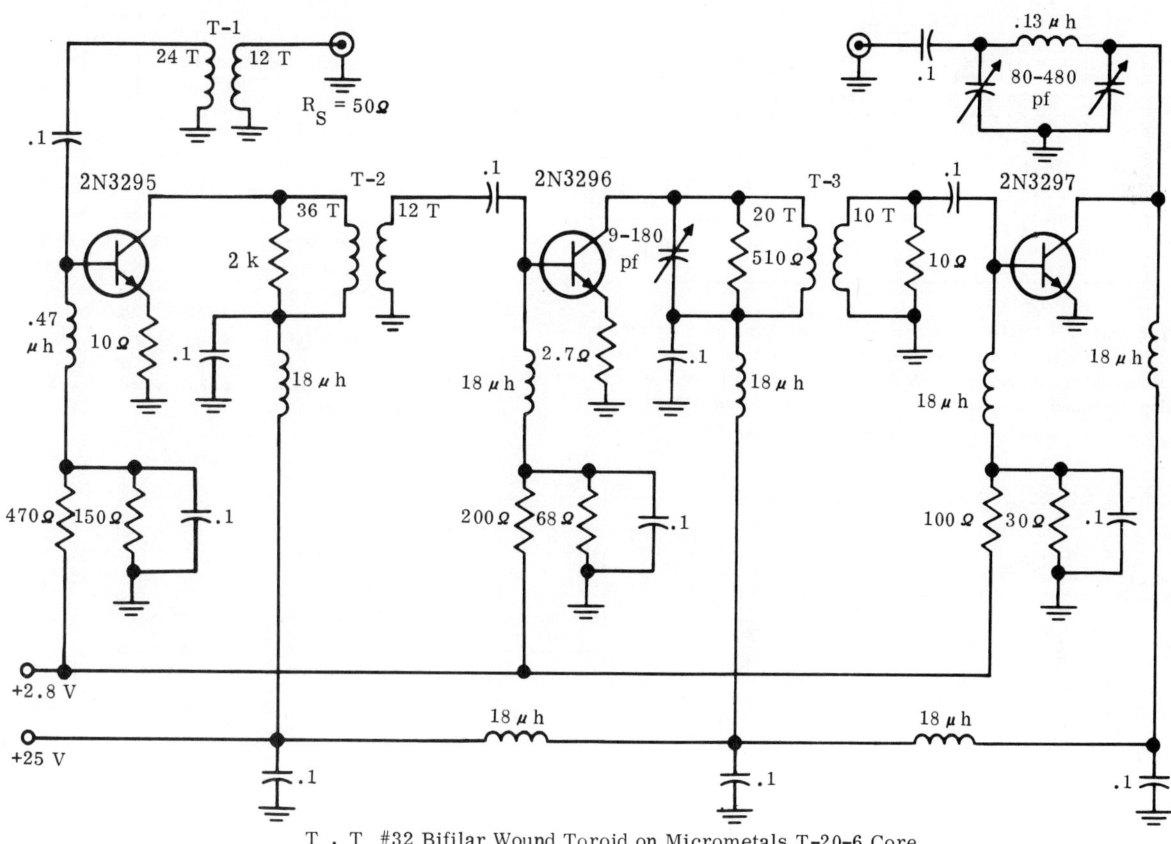

10-W 30-MHZ SSB—Requires only three transistors to give overall power gain of 35 dB for ssb operation. On two-tone test, all odd-order distortion products are more than 30 dB down from reference level. Unbypassed resistors in emitters of first two stages provide current feedback for stability.—"Circuits Manual," Motorola, Phoenix, Ariz., 1965, p 12-3-2.

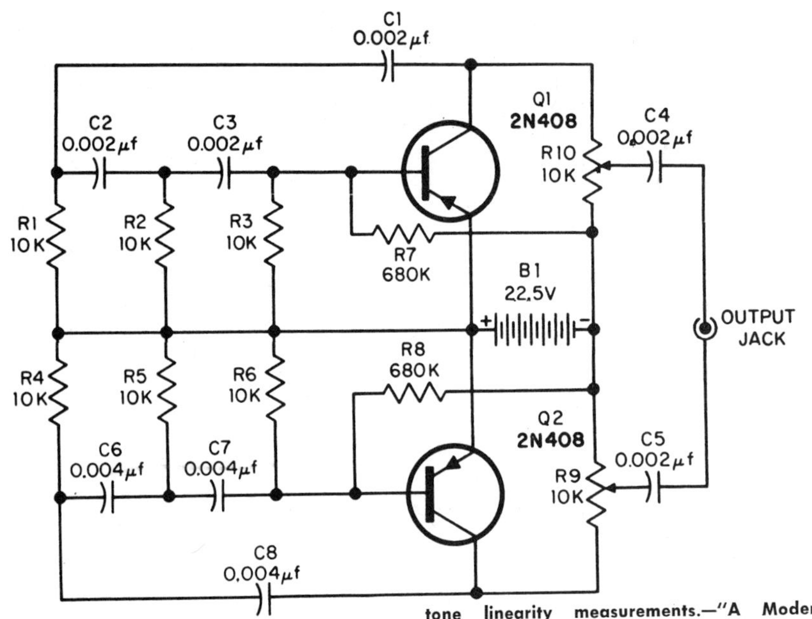

TWO-TONE SSB TEST OSCILLATOR—Output can be fed into ssb generator to make two-tone linearity measurements.—"A Modern Transistor Workbook," Radio Shack, Boston, Mass., 1965, p 11.

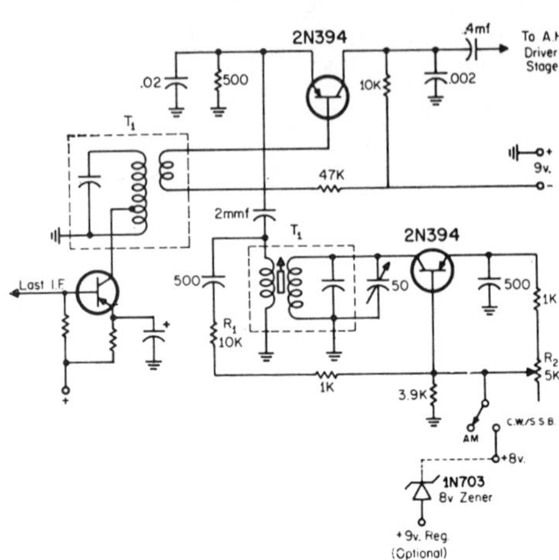

PRODUCT DETECTOR—Circuit works equally well on c-w and ssb. By switching out bfo, works on a-m as well.—C. J. Schauers, Transistorized Product Detector, CQ, Nov. 1964, p 113.

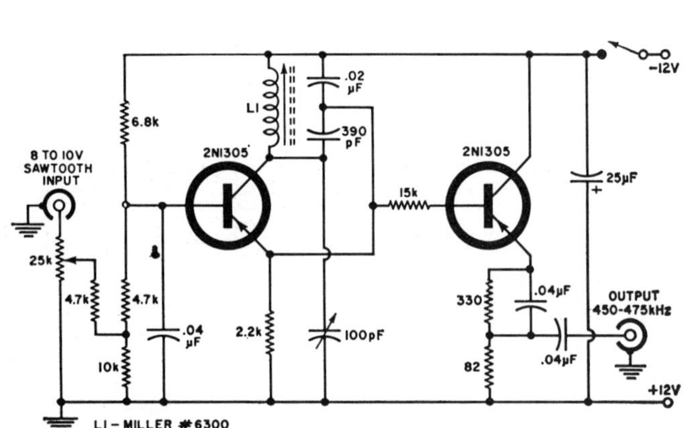

TEST SWEEP FOR SSB FILTER—Gives sweep range of about 25 kHz for sawtooth input of about 8 V peak from any scope. Designed for checking passband characteristics of crystal sideband filter between 460 and 466 kHz. —R. A. Genaille, Ferrite Coil and Crystal Sideband Filter, *Electronics World*, June 1967, p 46–47 and 80–81.

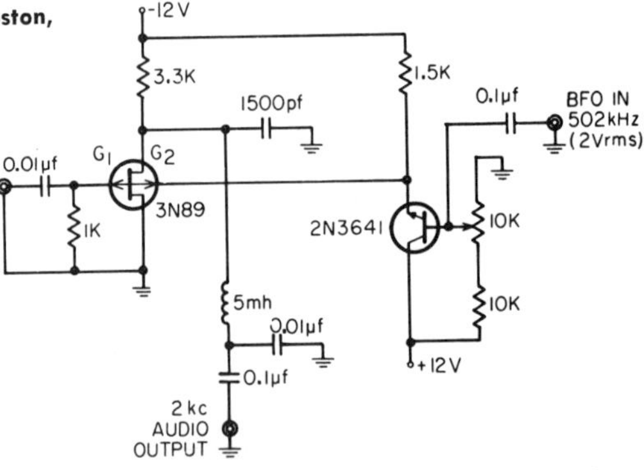

FET TETRODE PRODUCT DETECTOR—When 500-kHz i-f signal is fed into one gate of fet and beat-frequency oscillator voltage into other oscillator, output current is proportional to product of the two voltages over wide dynamic range. 2N3641 transistor isolates bfo from fet and provides proper bias for fet. Can be used in ssb receivers.—H. Olson, Product Detector Uses FET Tetrode, *EEE*, Sept. 1966, p 146.

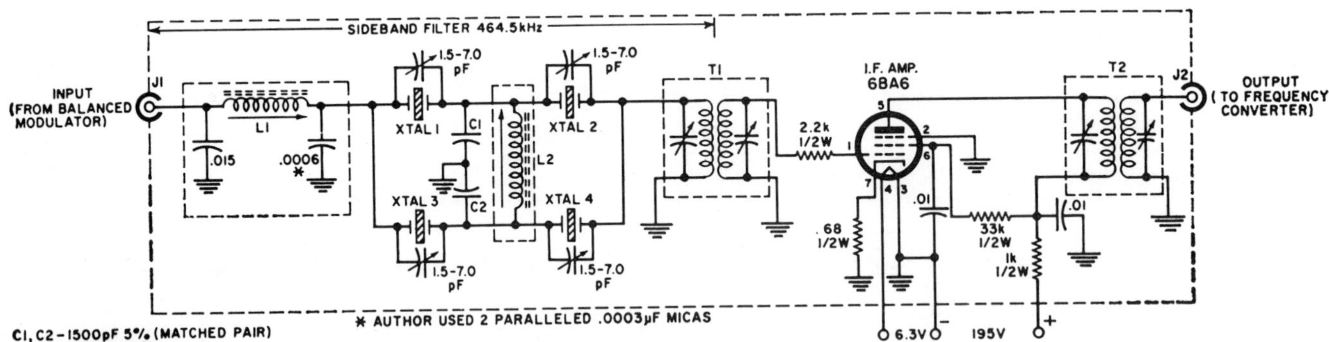

C1, C2 – 1500pF 5% (MATCHED PAIR)
J1, J2 – PHONO JACK
L1, L2 – HIGH-"Q" FERRITE ANTENNA COIL (MILLER #6300)
T1 – 450-475kHz, I.F. TRANSFORMER (MILLER #112-C1)
T2 – " " " " " (" #112-C4)
XTAL 1, XTAL 2 – 465.277kHz, FT-241-A CRYSTAL, CHANNEL 335, MATCHED PAIR (TEXAS CRYSTALS)
XTAL 3, XTAL 4 – 462.963kHz, " " " , " 50 , " " (" ")

SSB CRYSTAL FILTER—Uses four easily obtainable quartz crystals uniquely combined with ordinary ferrite antenna coils to select one sideband. Filter can serve as starting point for building ssb transmitter. Frequency separation of about 2.3 kHz between pairs of crystals gives bandwidth of about 2.9 kHz for reasonable voice quality. Consists of two cascaded half-lattice crystal-filter sections arranged for low-impedance input and high-impedance output to i-f stage. Article gives construction and alignment details.—R. A. Genaille, Ferrite Coil and Crystal Sideband Filter, *Electronics World*, June 1967, p 46–47 and 80–81.

CHAPTER 79

Square-Wave Generator Circuits

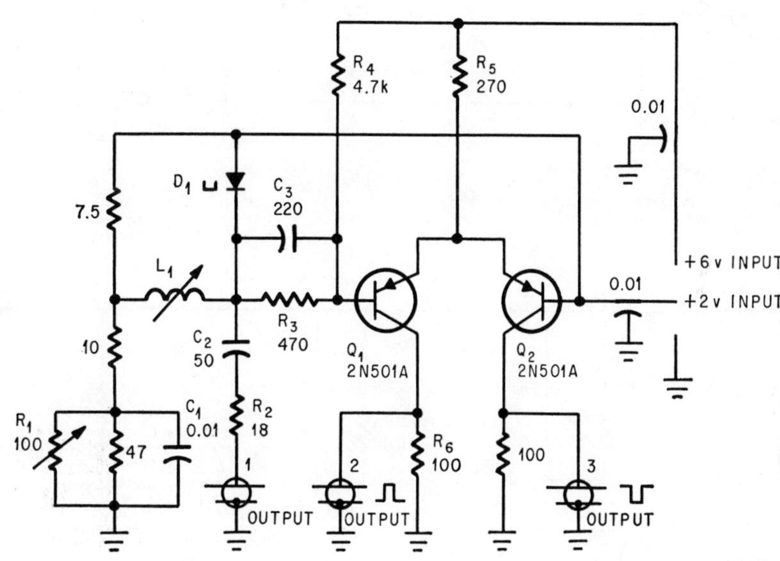

FLIP-FLOP TESTER—Provides positive or negative square-wave pulses at repetition rates up to 50 MHz for testing fast flip-flops, using gallium arsenide tunnel diode D1 (similar to RCA 40062) as relaxation oscillator. L1 controls frequency; at 0.5 μH, prf is 25 MHz. R1 changes ratio of pulse width to repetition period. Output terminal 1 gives positive and negative pulses in sequence, while terminals 2 and 3 give polarities shown. For 2-V supply, output pulse is 1.8 V and output impedance 100 ohms, for feeding into 100-ohm coax.—O. A. Horna, Bipolar Pulse Generator Tests Fast Flip-Flops, *Electronics*, Dec. 12, 1966, p 109.

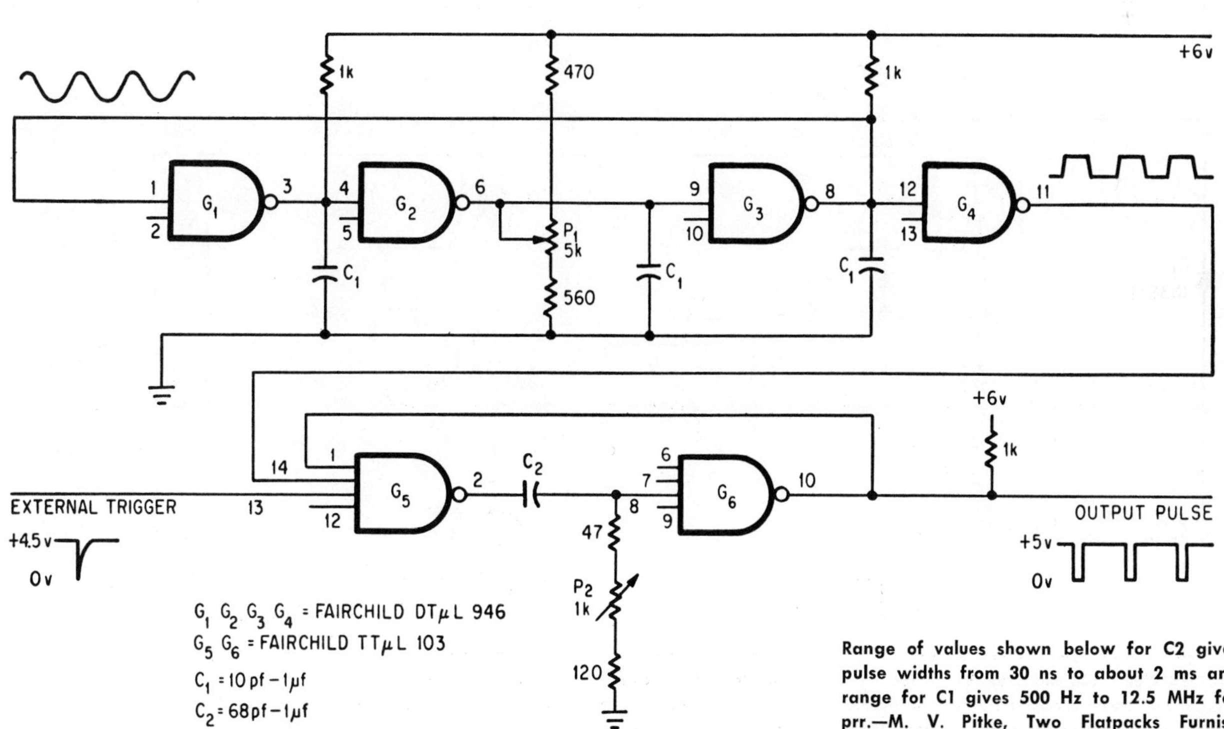

VARIABLE WIDTH AND PRR WITH IC'S—Push-pull oscillator G1-G2-G3 establishes pulse repetition rate of monostable mvbr G5-G6. G4 shapes output to desired pulse waveform. Range of values shown below for C2 gives pulse widths from 30 ns to about 2 ms and range for C1 gives 500 Hz to 12.5 MHz for prr.—M. V. Pitke, Two Flatpacks Furnish Pulses for IC Testing, *Electronics*, June 26, 1967, p 107–108.

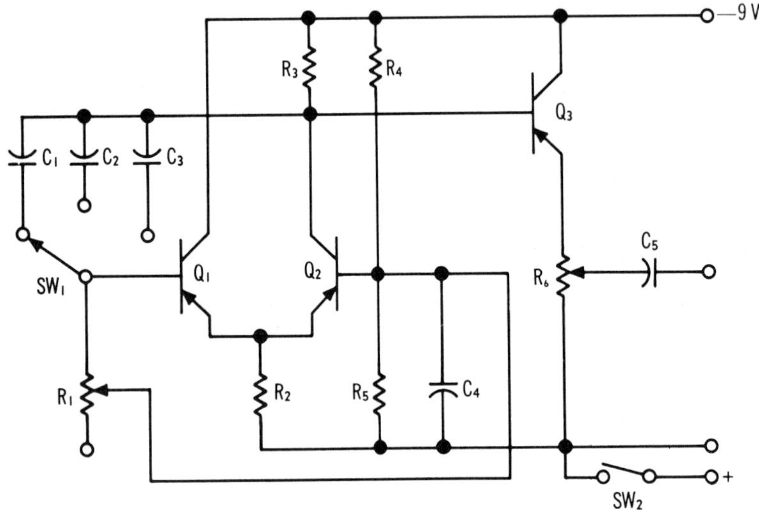

7.5—20,000 HZ SQUARE-WAVE—Economical and self-contained unit for general audio testing. Covers a-f spectrum in three ranges. Article gives construction details. Parts values are: R1 25K; R2 1.2K; R3 2.4K; R4–R5 3K; R6 2.5K; C1 1 μF; C2 0.1 μF; C3 0.01 μF; C4 5 μF; C5 0.25 μF; Q1-Q2 HEP253; Q3 HEP254.—"Solid State Projects Manual," 2nd Edition, Motorola, Phoenix, Ariz., 1968, p 27–32.

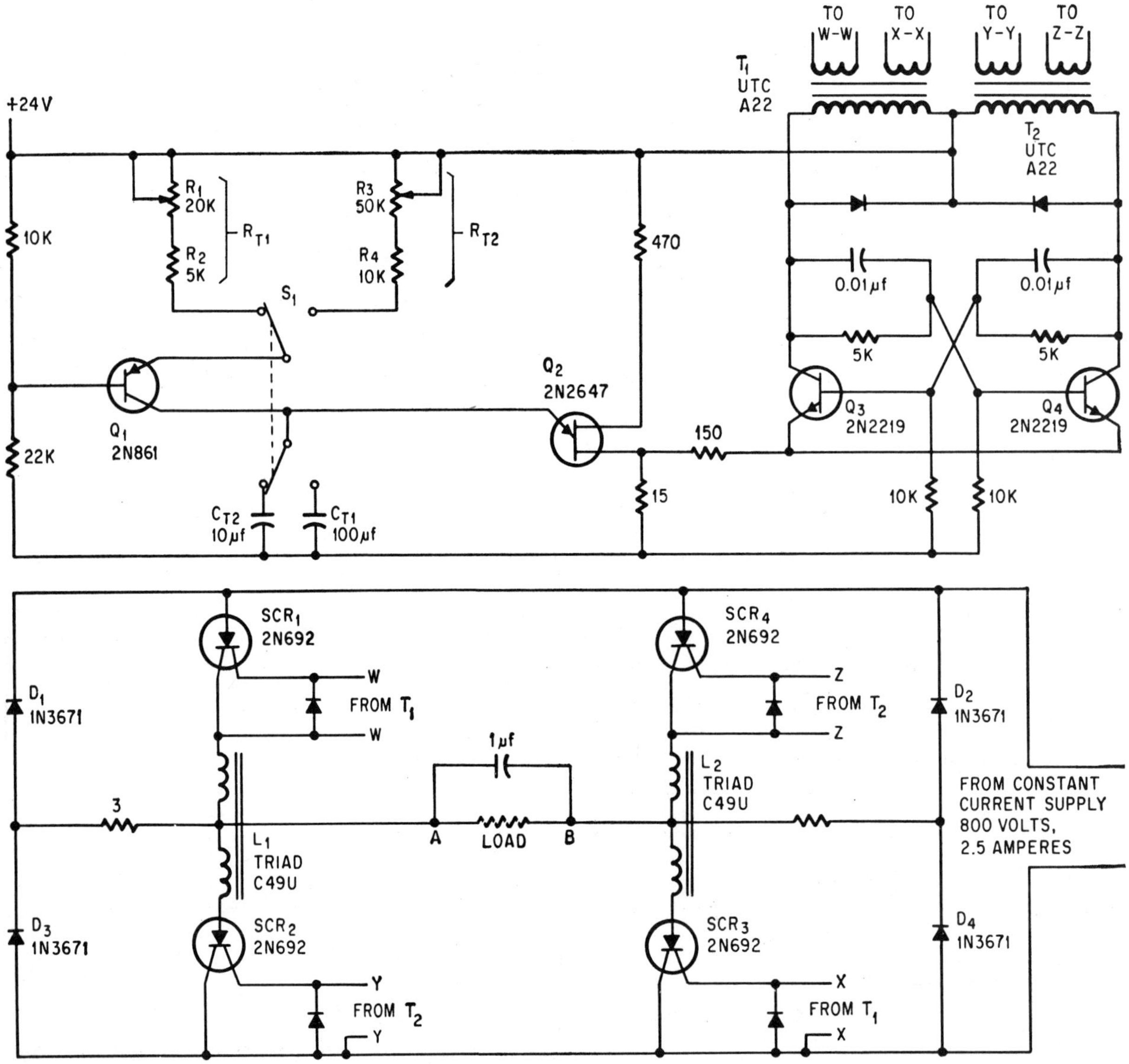

HIGH-POWER SQUARE WAVES—Used for measuring earth conductivity in geophysical applications, for which square waves of 0.1 to 4 Hz are usually required. Frequency can be boosted to 100 Hz by changing timing capacitors, but circuit losses become severe above this value. Uses bridge inverter to provide bipolar square wave, eliminating need for center-tapped constant-current supply. Transformer connections in upper circuit go to scr's in lower circuit.—S. I. Gaytan, Low-Frequency Oscillator Supplies High Pulse Power, *Electronics*, Oct. 17, 1966, p 90–91.

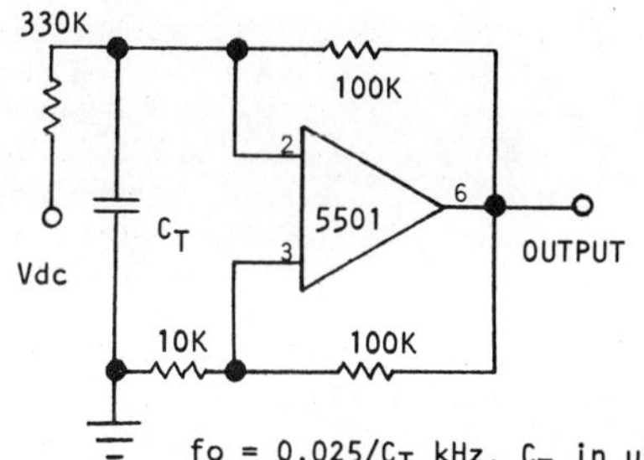

PWM—Analog comparator chip connected as shown functions as flexible square-wave oscillator having good frequency stability, with stable duty cycle and pulse-width modulator capability. Positive feedback causes output to be at either +10 or −10 V when power is applied, charging CT until pin 2 voltage equals pin 3, when 5501 changes state to begin cycle again.—Applying the Model 5501 Monolithic Analog Comparator, Optical Electronics, Tucson, Ariz., No. 10147.

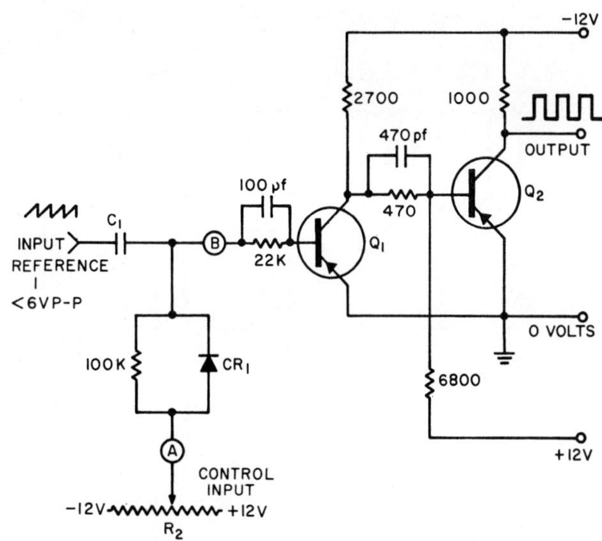

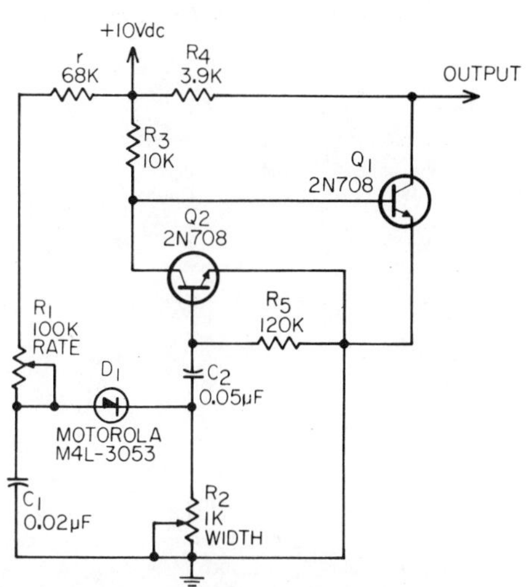

1–5 KHZ ADJUSTABLE-WIDTH—Four-layer diode D1 breaks down at threshold voltage of about 10 V, to give simple relaxation oscillator for generating pulses adjustable in width from 300 ns to 3 μs. Can be packaged in less than 0.5 cu in. Cost of components is about $10. Rise time is about 100 ns, but 2N4137 transistors will bring it below 20 ns.—G. B. Jordan, Pulse Generator with Variable Rate and Width, *EEE*, Feb. 1967, p 145–146.

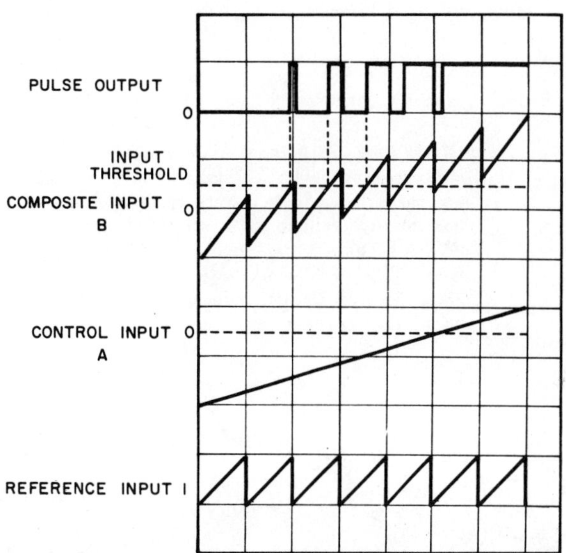

0–100% DUTY CYCLE—Standard clamp circuit using CR1, followed by conventional two-stage d-c amplifier Q1-Q2, gives infinitely adjustable pulse-width generator. Reference and control inputs, added at point B, make Q1 fire and produce output pulse whenever sum of voltages exceeds input threshold of Q1. Input may have any waveform. Transistor types are not critical.—T. Hart, Generator Permits Infinite Pulse Width Variation, *Electronic Design*, June 22, 1964, p 69–71.

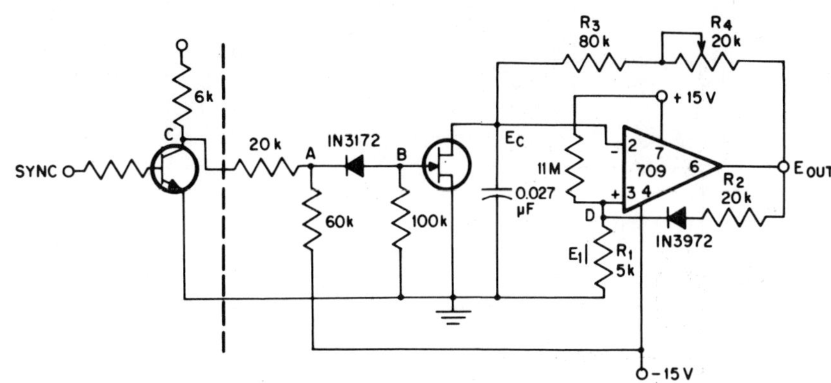

1-KHZ SYNCHRONIZED TO 60 HZ—Output shifts regularly between positive and negative saturation to give 50% duty cycle at frequency determined by voltage divider and R-C time constant. If output is in positive saturation when sync pulse arrives, it stays positive. If output is in negative saturation, sync pulse makes it switch to positive saturation. To sync at higher frequencies, change opamp to μA702 or μA710. Fet is 2N3792.—M. R. Utenick, FET and IC Make Syncable Oscillator, *EEE*, July 1969, p 105–106.

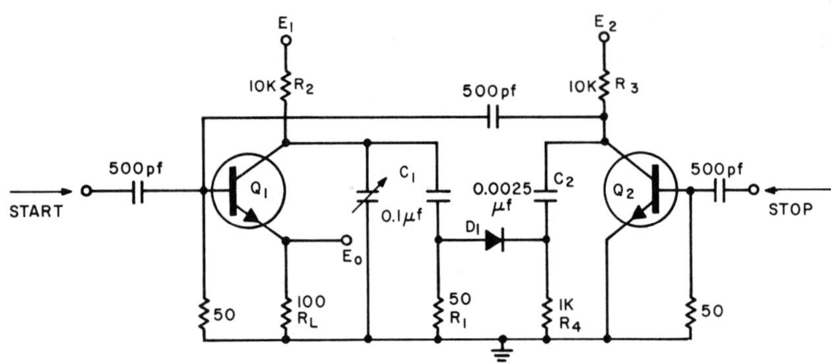

VARIABLE-WIDTH AVALANCHE PULSES—Uses two NS1110 avalanche transistors and two trigger inputs, one for start of rectangular output pulse and other for end of pulse. Pulse width is thus continuously adjustable by changing time interval between triggers, from a few ns to over 1 μs. Rise and fall times are about 2 ns.—B. H. Bell, Avalanche Circuits Are More Versatile Than You Think, *Electronic Design*, June 8, 1964, p 56–63.

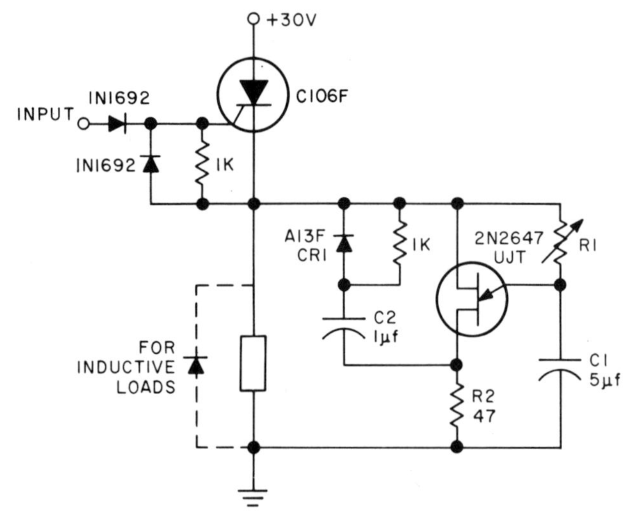

UJT-SCR ONE-SHOT—Input pulse triggers scr and energizes load. Voltage drop across load energizes ujt timer. When ujt fires after time interval, voltage pulse across R2 turns off scr to give single square-wave output pulse.—D. R. Grafham, Using Low Current SCR's, General Electric, Syracuse, N.Y., No. 200.19, 1967, p 26.

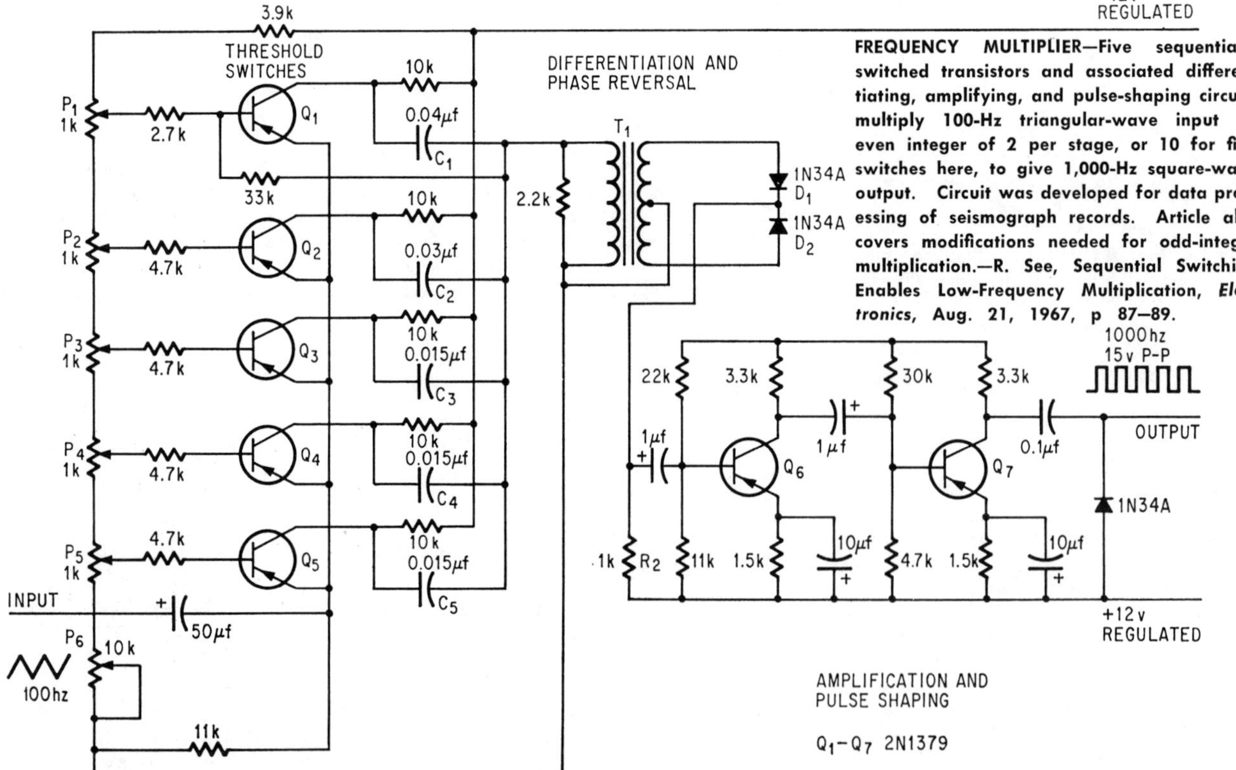

FREQUENCY MULTIPLIER—Five sequentially switched transistors and associated differentiating, amplifying, and pulse-shaping circuits multiply 100-Hz triangular-wave input by even integer of 2 per stage, or 10 for five switches here, to give 1,000-Hz square-wave output. Circuit was developed for data processing of seismograph records. Article also covers modifications needed for odd-integer multiplication.—R. See, Sequential Switching Enables Low-Frequency Multiplication, *Electronics*, Aug. 21, 1967, p 87–89.

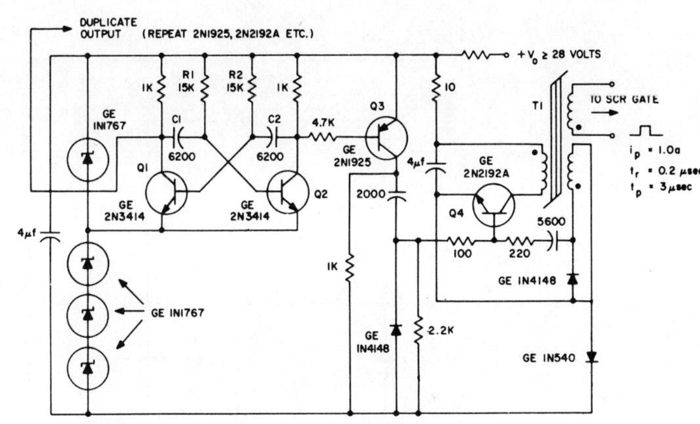

MVBR-DRIVEN BLOCKING OSCILLATOR—Produces rectangular gate pulses up to 1 A, for triggering thyristors in inverters, pulse modulators, and other circuits requiring fast turn-on.—"SCR Manual," 4th Edition, General Electric, 1967, p 85.

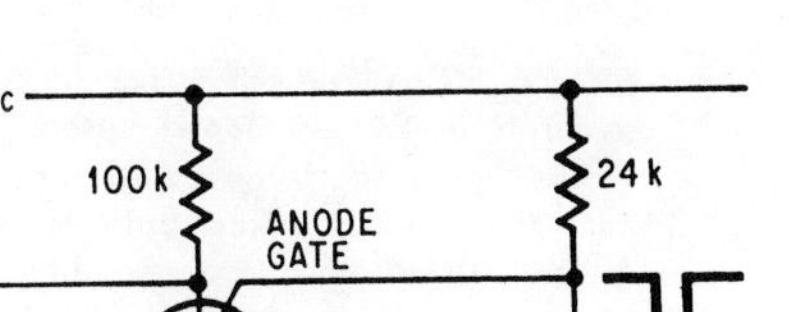

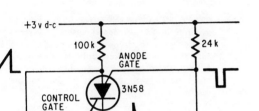

SCS RELAXATION OSCILLATOR—Consumes less power than ujt, operates at levels as low as 2 V, and produces more powerful output pulse with sharpened leading and falling edges. Frequency is 1 kHz and rise time about 60 ns.—J. S. Hayhurst, SCS Outperforms UJT in Relaxation Oscillator, *Electronics*, Sept. 16, 1968, p 100.

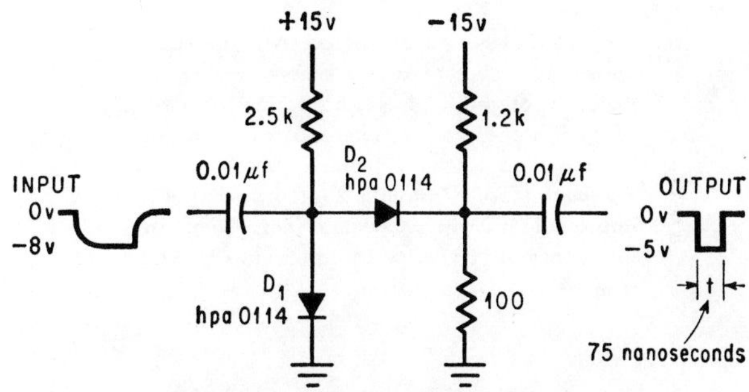

NANOSECOND PULSES WITH STEP RECOVERY DIODES—Pulse width is determined by difference in storage times of two diodes, which varies little with temperature, so width remains constant from −55 to 80 deg C. Pulse width may be varied from 1 to 1,000 ns by changing forward bias current.—L. St. Marie, Fast Pulse Generator is Temperature Stable, *Electronics*, Feb. 6, 1967, p 70–71.

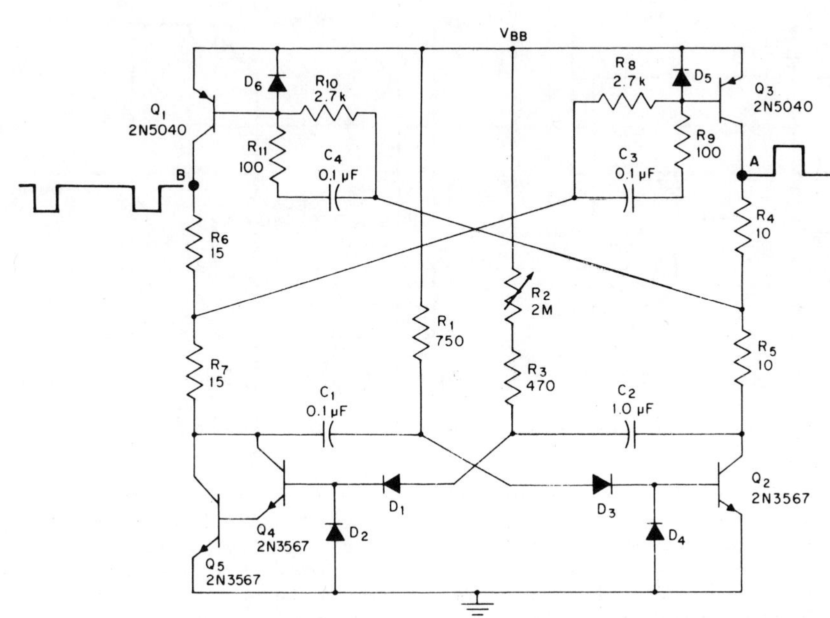

30,000:1 PERIOD-TO-PULSE RATIO—Used for generating fast-rise pulse or train of pulses with very narrow width in comparison with total period. If R1 is variable, can be used as astable, monostable, or bistable mvbr. Q1 and Q2 are simultaneously in either on or off state, with other three transistors always in opposite state to Q1-Q2. For values shown, pulse width is 50 μs, rise time 200 ns, fall time 20 ns, and periods ranging from 500 μs to 1.5 s depending on setting of R2.—D. R. Matthews, Ultralow-Duty-Cycle Pulser, *EEE*, March 1970, p 129.

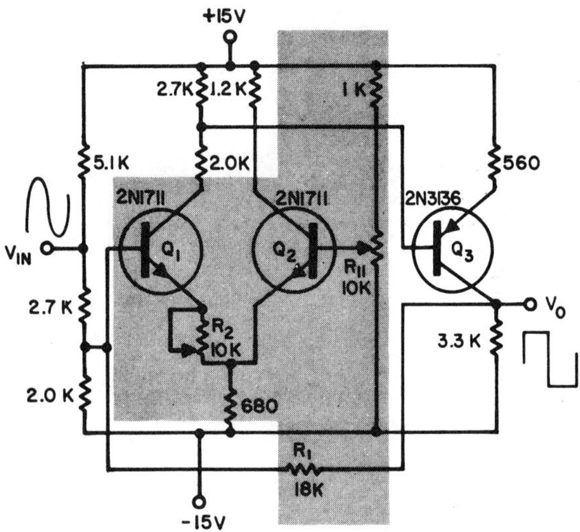

TEMPERATURE-STABLE SQUARE WAVES—Converts sine waves to square waves, with good isolation of output from input and excellent trigger stability for temperature changes. Shaded area covers differential amplifier and feedback loop. Output is 25 V p-p.—B. Pearl, Improved Squaring Circuit is Less Temperature Sensitive, *Electronic Design*, July 19, 1965, p 40–41.

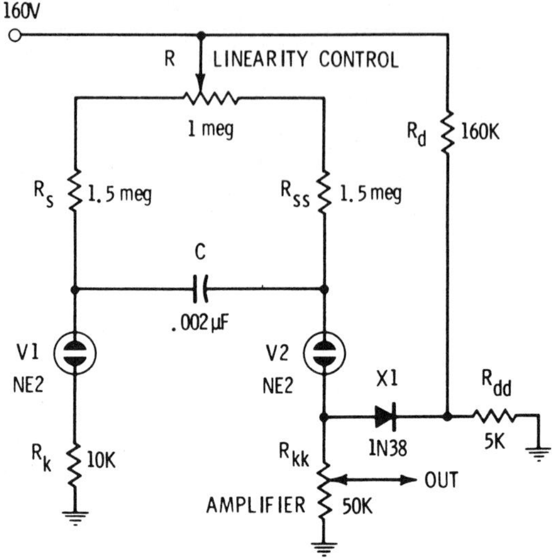

500-HZ SQUARE-WAVE—Uses neon mvbr to generate 0–4 C p-p sloped square wave, and diode clipper to straighten its top. Linearity control is used to adjust pulse width.—W. G. Miller, "Using and Understanding Miniature Neon Lamps," H. W. Sams & Co., Indianapolis, Ind., 1969, p 45.

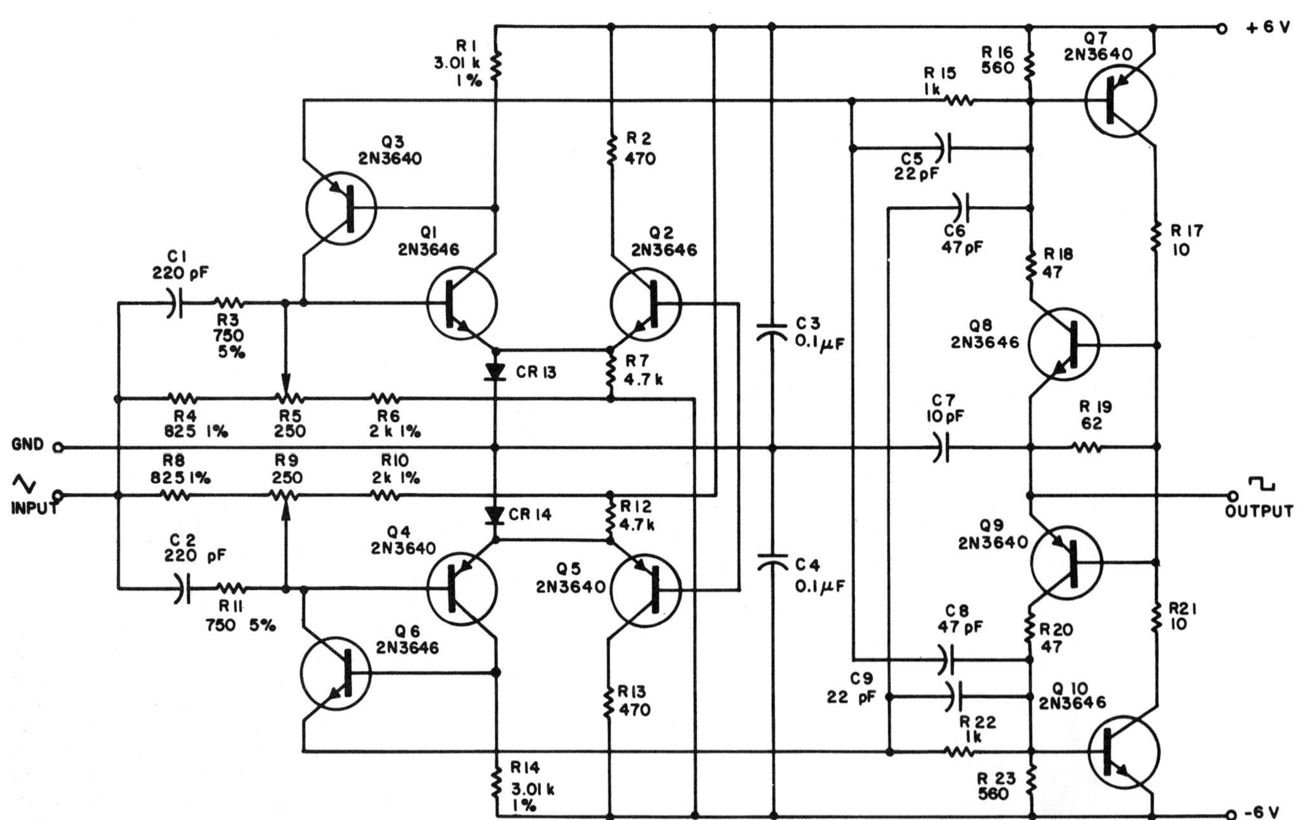

10-V P-P SQUARE WAVES—Provides excellent isolation between input and output over passband of d-c to 1 MHz, with less than 0.1 dB variation in output magnitude over frequency range. Rise time is 5 ns. Output is +5 V for input of +2.5 V and −5 V for input of −2.5 V. Output currents are 16 to 21 mA. Q7-Q10 form bistable regenerative output switch driven by hysteresis switch Q1-Q6. Q1-Q2 form comparator for negative hysteresis level. Dividers in bases of Q1 and Q4 set precise firing levels for Q3 and Q6.—J. F. Foster, Bistable DC-Coupled Switch Has 5-Nanosecond Rise Time, *Electronic Design*, Nov. 8, 1967, p 120.

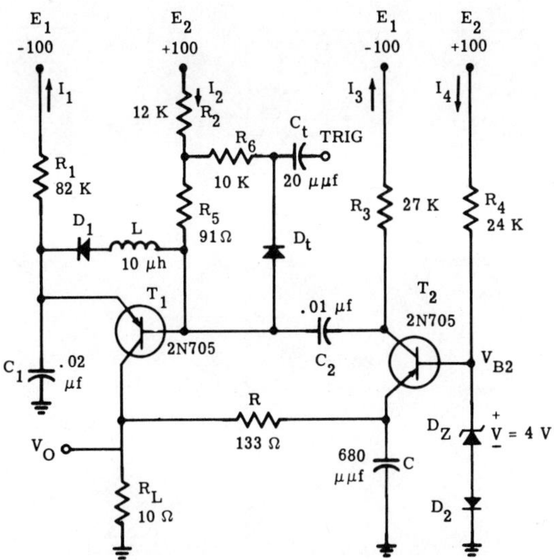

HIGH-CURRENT PULSES—Gives square-wave output waveform with amplitude of 5 V and width of about 200 ns at 0.5 A. Recovery time limits maximum repetition rate to range of 40 to 140 kHz, depending on permissible reduction in pulse amplitude.—"High Speed Switching Transistor Handbook," Motorola, Phoenix, Ariz., 1969, p 300.

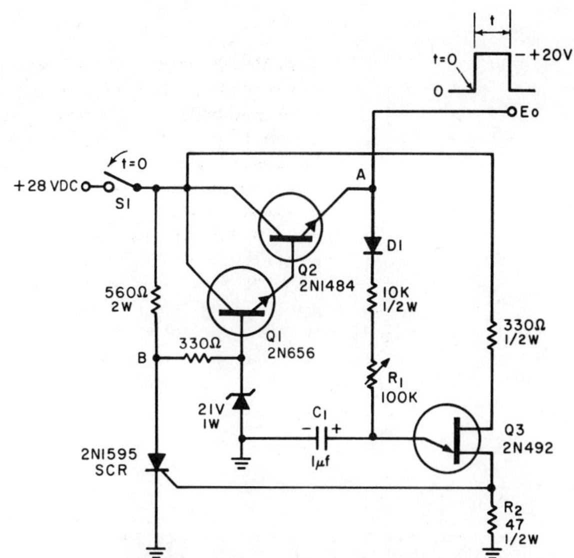

ADJUSTABLE PULSE WIDTH—R1 and C1 determine width of square-wave output independently of load. Values shown give 20-V pulse at 1 A, adjustable from 100 μs to 10 ms. Uses series regulator in combination with ujt time delay Q3.—G. E. Bloom, Time-Adjustable Pulse Generator Combines Unijunction, Zener, SCR, *Electronic Design*, May 25, 1964, p 68.

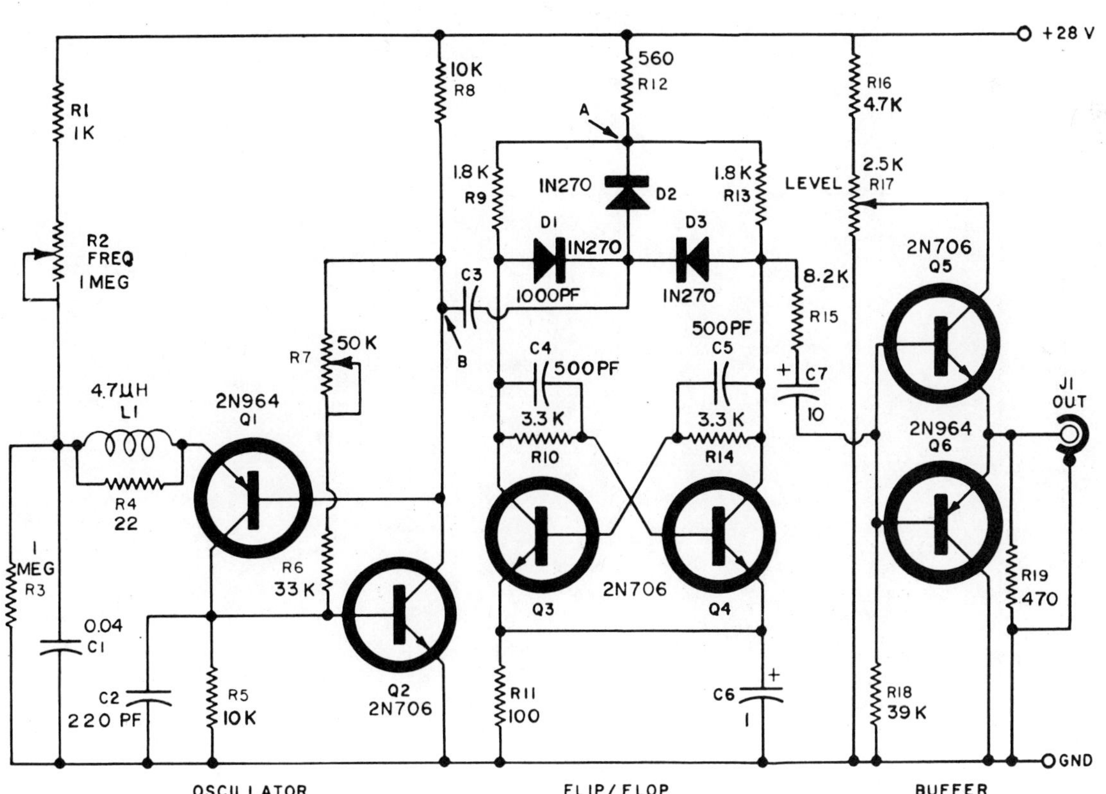

20–20,000-HZ SQUARE WAVES—Covers range with single-turn frequency control. Relaxation oscillator Q1-Q2 is adjustable over 1,000:1 with R7, to cover audio band without range switch. Triggered flip-flop Q3-Q4 serves as frequency divider for 40–40,000-Hz output of oscillator, while creating ideal square waves. Power supply should be zener-stabilized.—C. J. Ulrick, High-Quality Square-Wave Generator, *Electronics World*, Nov. 1966, p 43 and 82.

GUARANTEED SINGLE PULSE—Schmitt trigger and amplifier produce one and only one pulse when pushbutton is pressed, regardless of contact bounce. S1 is held down until C1 has charged to about 5 V, Schmitt has flipped, and lamp indicator has come on. When S1 is released, C1 starts discharging; when below 5 V, Schmitt flips again, lamp goes out, C2 starts charging through R8, and Q3 generates 26-V negative output pulse.—G. Demjanenko, Push-Button Single-Pulse Generator Is More Dependable, *Electronic Design*, Aug. 3, 1964, p 43.

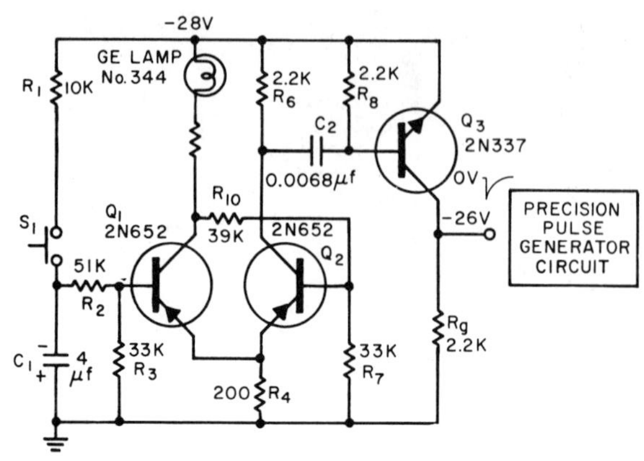

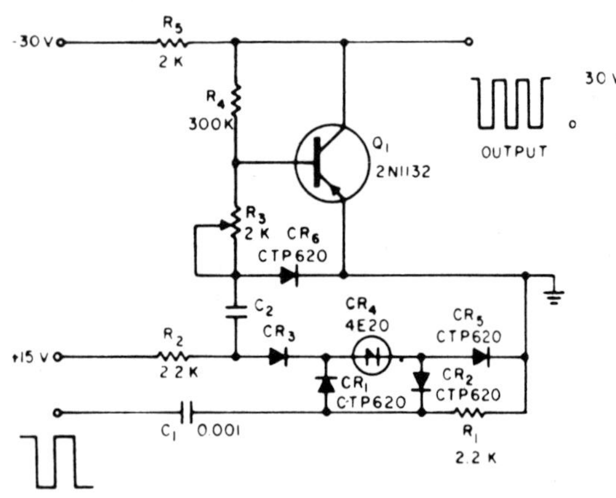

DOUBLING SQUARE WAVES—With 25-kHz 30-V p-p square-wave input, output is 50-kHz square wave of same amplitude, with better than 100-ns rise and fall times. Value of C2 depends on frequency; for 20-kHz input, use 0.02 μF.—C. R. See, Square-Wave Doubler Uses Four-Layer Diode, "400 Ideas for Design Selected from Electronic Design," Hayden Book Co., N.Y., 1964, p 155.

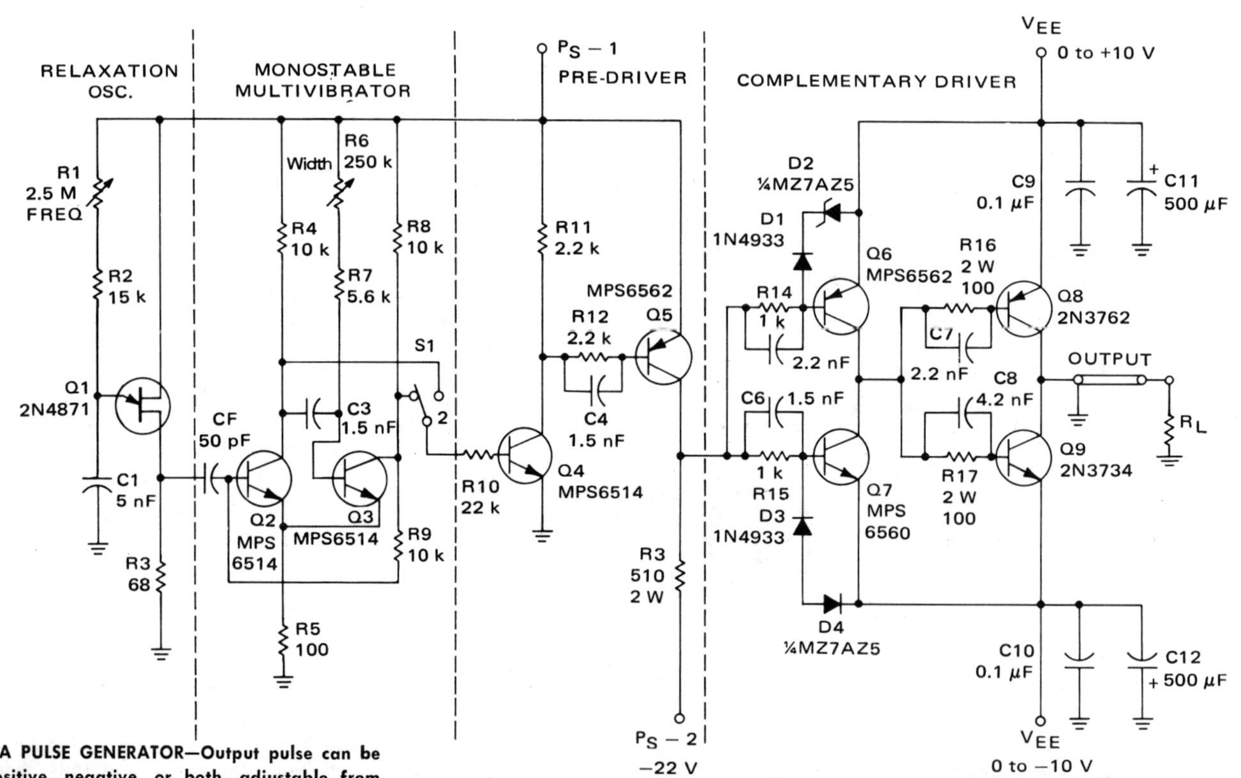

1-A PULSE GENERATOR—Output pulse can be positive, negative, or both, adjustable from zero to 10 V maximum, for maximum output of 20 V p-p at 1 A. Pulse width and frequency adjustments are provided. S1 inverts output pulse. Rise and fall times are 10 ns. —"Semiconductor Power Circuits Handbook," Motorola, Phoenix, Ariz., 1968, p 6–32.

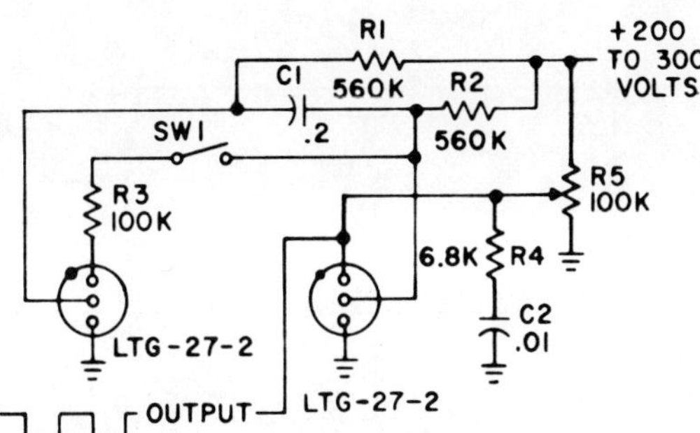

50-HZ SQUARE-WAVE—Uses three-element neon lamps. Closing SW1 makes cycle self-completing.—E. Bauman, "Applications of Neon Lamps and Gas Discharge Tubes," Signalite, Neptune, N.J., p 37.

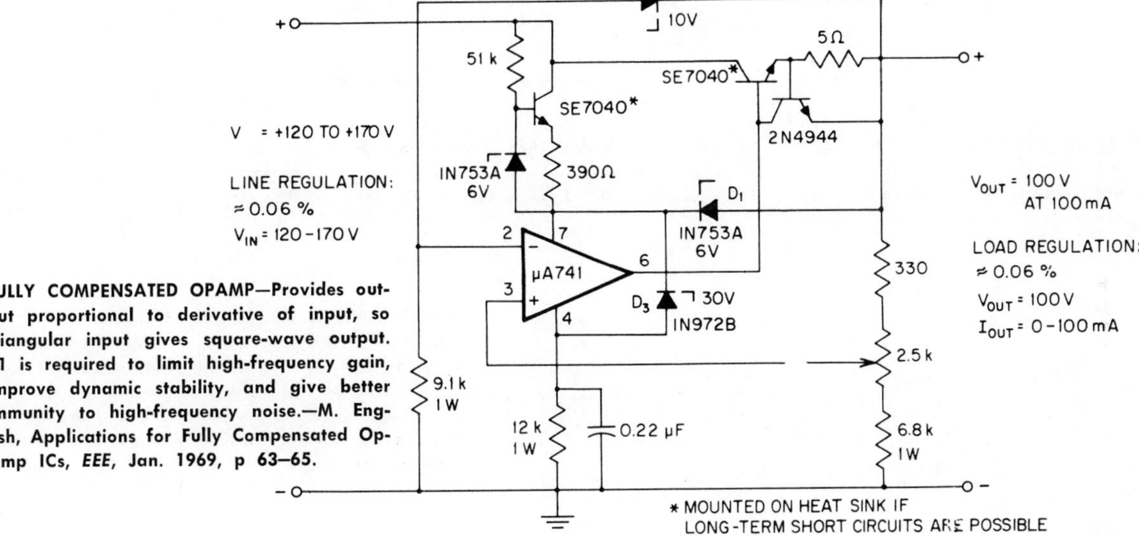

FULLY COMPENSATED OPAMP—Provides output proportional to derivative of input, so triangular input gives square-wave output. R1 is required to limit high-frequency gain, improve dynamic stability, and give better immunity to high-frequency noise.—M. English, Applications for Fully Compensated Op-Amp ICs, *EEE*, Jan. 1969, p 63–65.

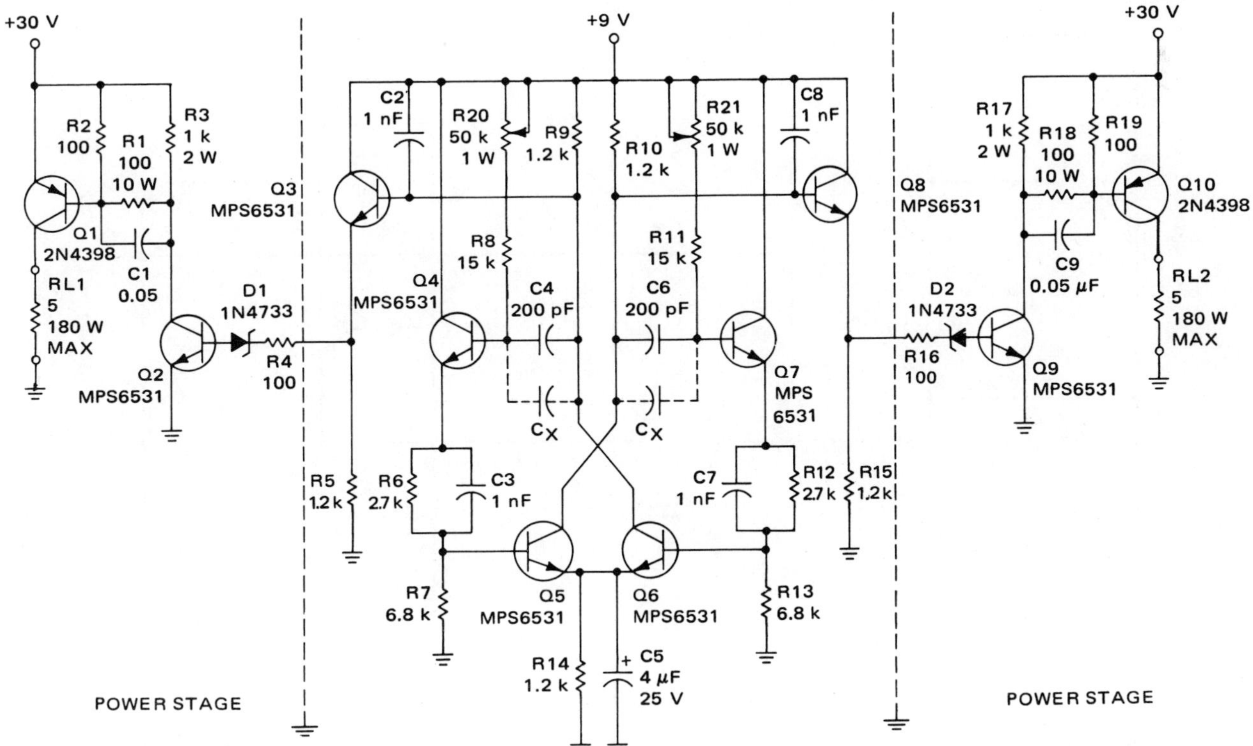

ADJUSTABLE 6-A PULSE GENERATOR—Astable mvbr Q5-Q6 has independent controls for on and off times of rectangular pulses, over ranges that can be increased by increasing values of capacitors CX across C4 and C6. Pulse generator drives two power stages capable of furnishing 6 A to 5-ohm load.—"Semiconductor Power Circuits Handbook," Motorola, Phoenix, Ariz., 1968, p 6–29.

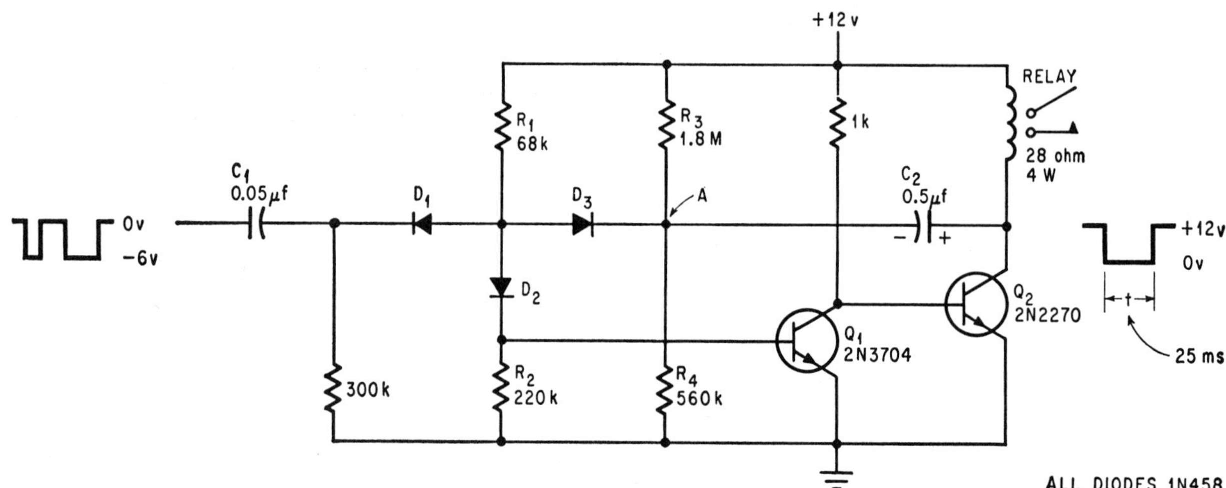

SIMPLE PULSE STRETCHER—Generates 25-ms output pulse for driving 4-W relay momentarily, independently of amplitude or duration of input pulse. Eliminates transistor stage normally required for pulse stretching. To adjust ON time of relay, replace R2 with pot.—K. Wahl, Constant Relay On-Time for Any Input Pulse, *Electronics*, March 6, 1967, p 133.

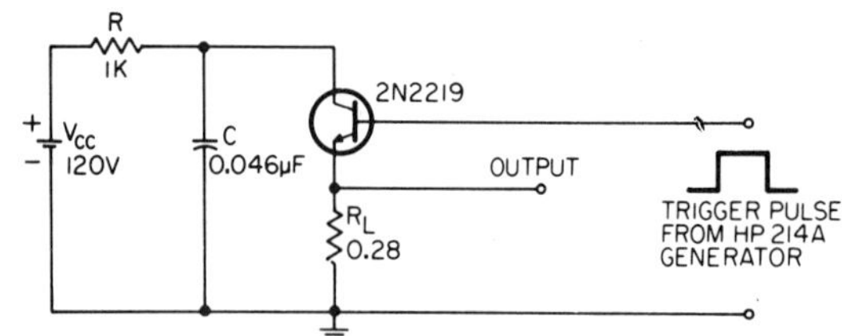

30-A PEAK PULSES AT 130 KHZ—Transistor is driven into second breakdown, to give 40-ns pulses at 5 A, with generating cycle completed before thermal buildup becomes excessive. Rise time of output pulse is less than 10 ns.—E. B. Hakim, Variable-Voltage Current Sink, *EEE*, March 1967, p 166–167.

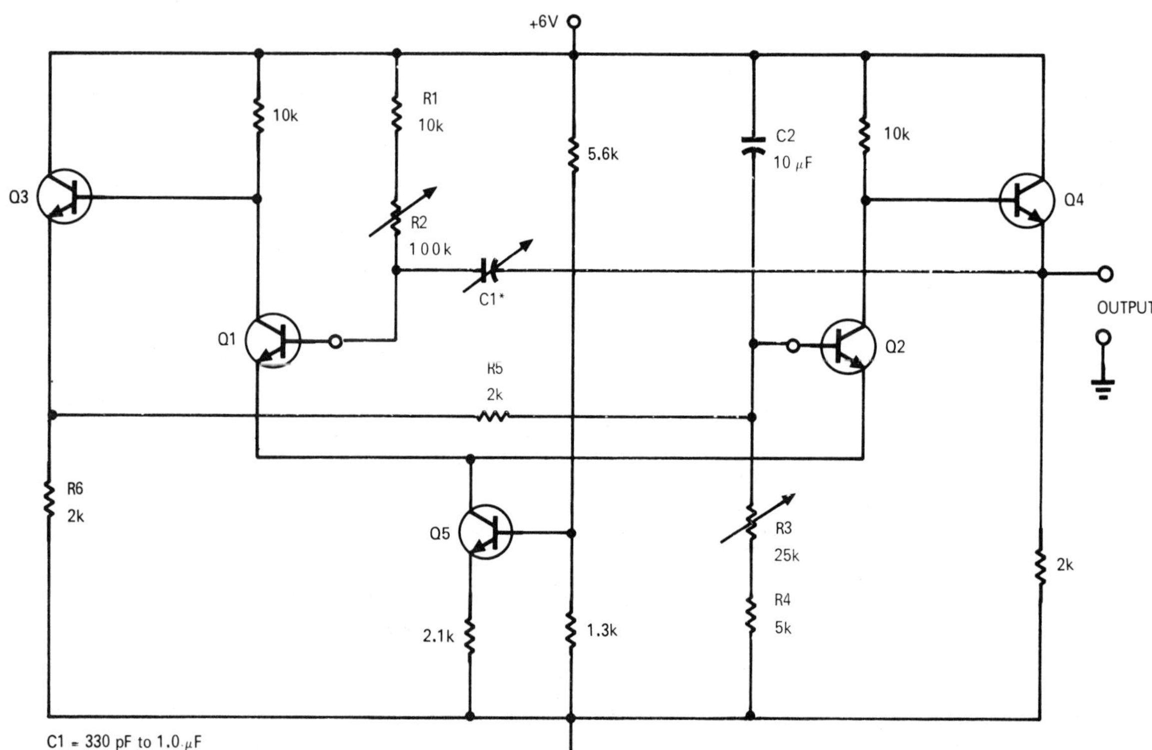

C1 = 330 pF to 1.0 μF

300 KHZ FOR $4—Addition of five resistors (R1-R5) and two capacitors (C1-C2) to μA730C IC differential amplifier gives inexpensive general-purpose pulse generator having frequency range extending to 300 kHz. Pulse rise and fall times are both under 200 ns. Output pulses are easily adjusted to switch above, below, or precisely at ground. Differential amplifier operates as current-mode switch in astable mvbr configuration. C1 determines frequency range, while R2 varies prr over 6:1 ratio.—C. Brogado, Converted Diff Amp Generates Pulses, *EDN*, June 15, 1970, p 57.

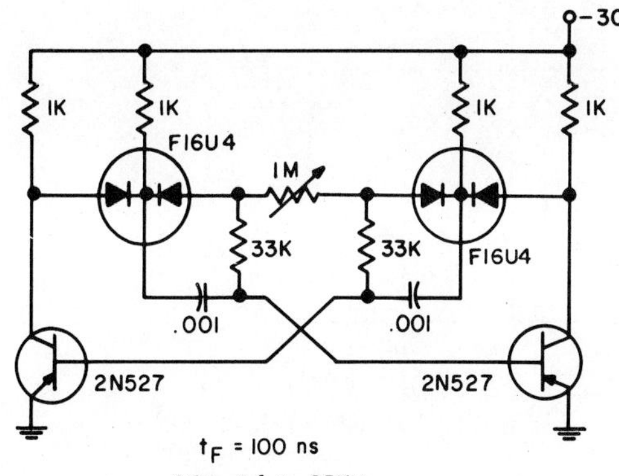

4–25 KHZ SQUARE-WAVE GENERATOR—Uses dual diodes having common cathodes. Provides excellent output waveform.—W. R. Spofford, Jr., Practical Circuit Applications for The New F16U Dual Diode, General Electric, Syracuse, N.Y., No. 90.53, 1965.

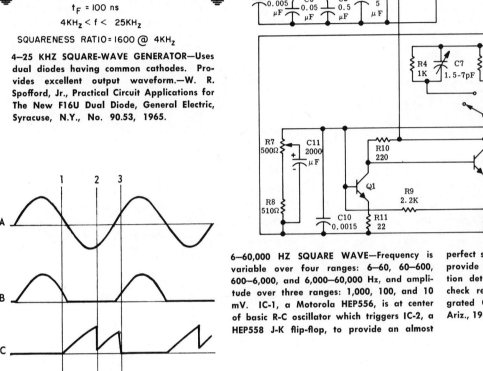

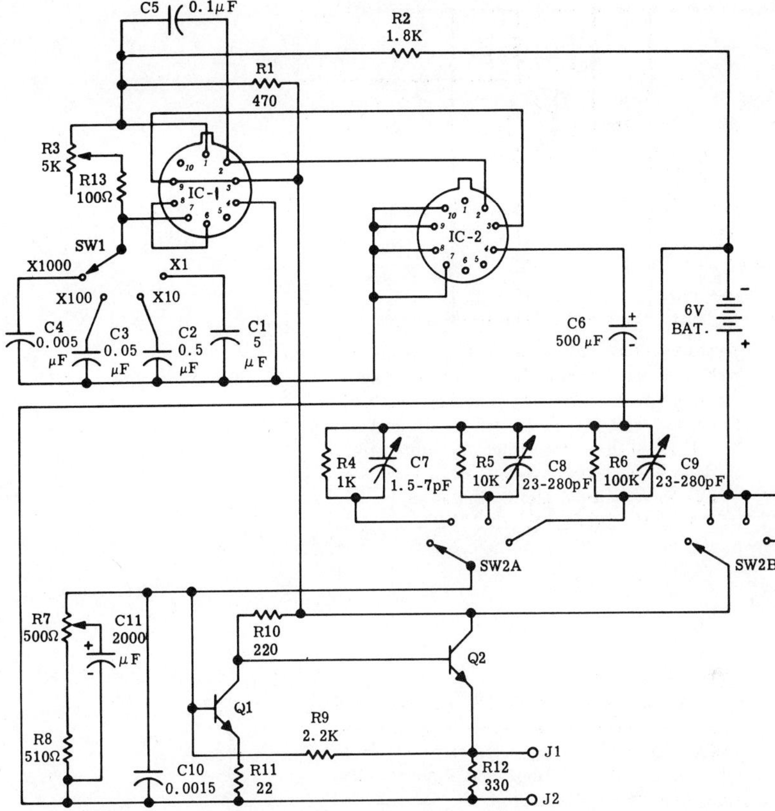

6–60,000 HZ SQUARE WAVE—Frequency is variable over four ranges: 6–60, 60–600, 600–6,000, and 6,000–60,000 Hz, and amplitude over three ranges: 1,000, 100, and 10 mV. IC-1, a Motorola HEP556, is at center of basic R-C oscillator which triggers IC-2, a HEP558 J-K flip-flop, to provide an almost perfect square wave. Two HEP50 transistors provide amplification. Article gives construction details. Designed for use with cro to check response of audio equipment.—"Integrated Circuit Projects," Motorola, Phoenix, Ariz., 1966, p 46–62.

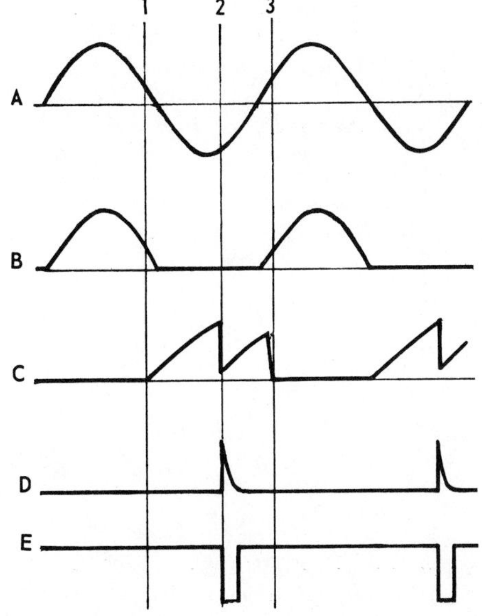

1. Q1 turns off.
2. Q2 fires (C1 is not fully discharged).
3. Q1 turns on before Q2 can fire again. (C1 is fully discharged)

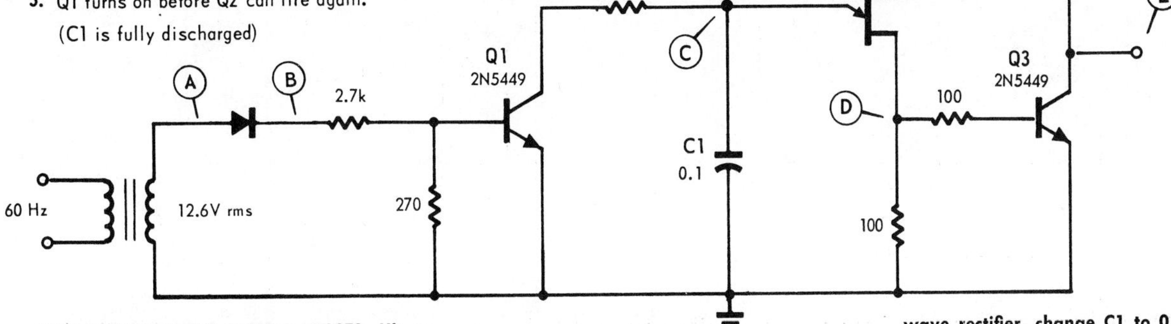

LINE-SYNCHRONIZED TIMING PULSES—Ujt oscillator Q2 generates sharp and clean 60-Hz timing pulse virtually unaffected by noise and transients on line. Only extremely severe noise on line may cause output pulse train to skip a beat. Invert output to obtain positive pulse. For 120-Hz output, use full-wave rectifier, change C1 to 0.05, and adjust bias resistors controlling Q1.—B. Heniford, UJT Generates Useful Timing Pulses, *EDN*, March 15, 1970, p 87–88.

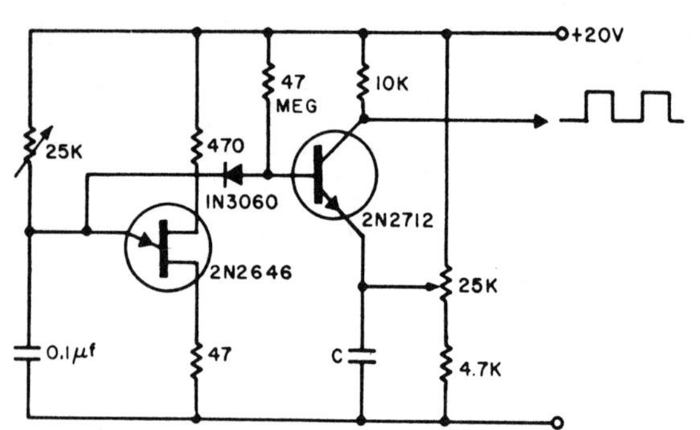

TWO-CONTROL UJT—Two pots provide control of frequency and duty cycle of square-wave output. Value of C affects rise and fall times, and can be between 0.01 and 50 μF.—J. H. Phelps, Unijunction Generator Has Variable Square-Wave Output, "400 Ideas for Design Selected from Electronic Design," Hayden Book Co., N.Y., 1964, p 191.

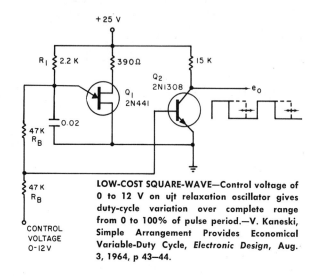

+25 V
R1 2.2 K
390Ω
15 K
Q2 2N1308
e0
Q1 2N441
0.02
47K RB
47 K RB
CONTROL VOLTAGE 0-12 V

LOW-COST SQUARE-WAVE—Control voltage of 0 to 12 V on ujt relaxation oscillator gives duty-cycle variation over complete range from 0 to 100% of pulse period.—V. Kaneski, Simple Arrangement Provides Economical Variable-Duty Cycle, *Electronic Design*, Aug. 3, 1964, p 43–44.

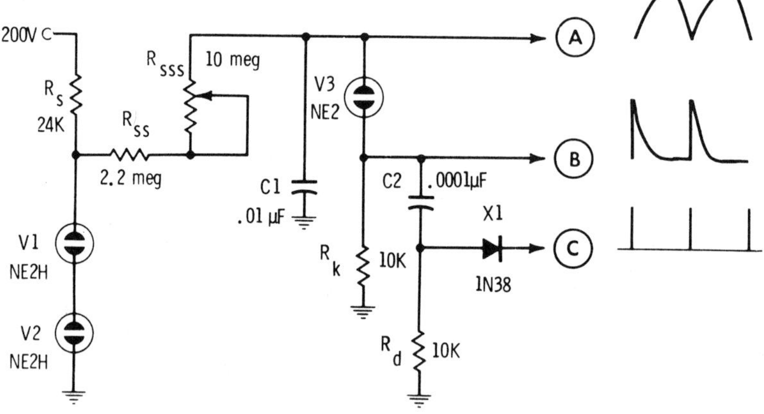

40–180 HZ MULTIPLE OUTPUTS—Consists of neon regulated power supply and neon oscillator. Positive 1-μs pulse is available at C.—W. G. Miller, "Using and Understanding Miniature Neon Lamps," H. W. Sams & Co., Indianapolis, Ind., 1969, p 40.

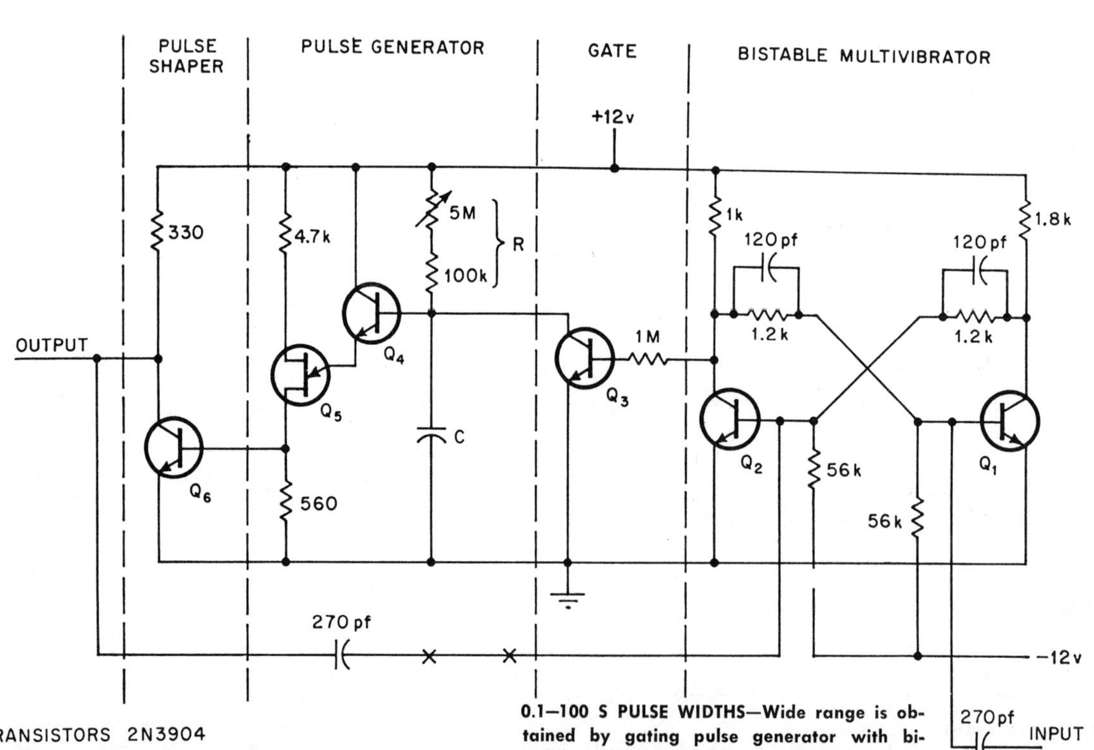

ALL TRANSISTORS 2N3904
UNIJUNCTION TRANSISTOR 2N1671B
FOR C = 6 μf, SWITCHING TIME = 1 − 30 SECONDS

0.1–100 S PULSE WIDTHS—Wide range is obtained by gating pulse generator with bistable mvbr.—S. Bell, One-Shot Generates Wide Range of Periods, *Electronics*, May 11, 1970, p 102.

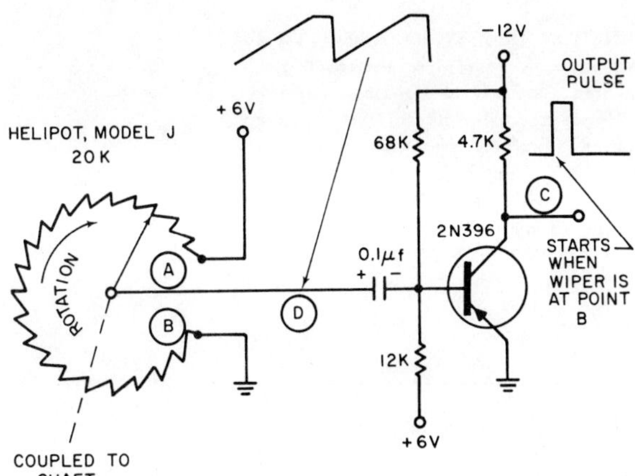

SHAFT ZERO-REFERENCE PULSE—Output pulse is generated when shaft of 360-deg pot is at zero. Leading edge of pulse coincides with position B of wiper arm. Applicable only to unidirectional drive, as by digital motor. Repeatability of pulse position is within 13.5 min of arc. Output pulse width is about 10 µs. Capacitor is charged during clockwise rotation from B to A. Charge is held until wiper arm crosses gap to B, then discharged to drive transistor into saturation and create output pulse.—W. E. Milroy, Shaft-Position Generator Provides Zero Reference, *Electronic Design*, March 15, 1965, p 64–65.

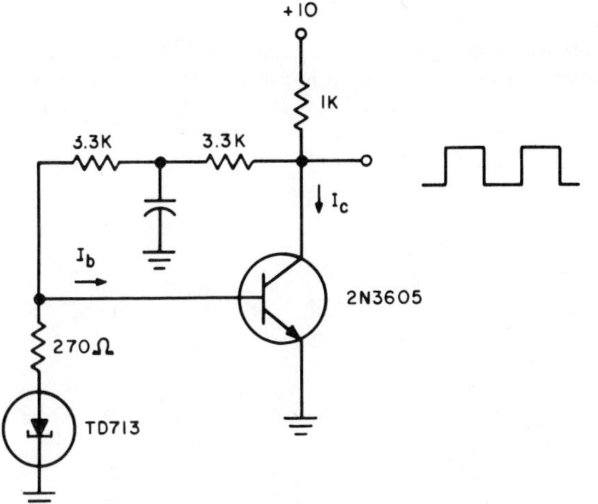

TUNNEL-DIODE ASTABLE—Simple free-running (astable) oscillator generates clean square wave. Frequency is determined by value of charging capacitor used.—W. R. Spofford, Jr., Applications For The New Low Cost TD 700 Series Tunnel Diodes, General Electric, Syracuse, N.Y., No. 90.66, 1967, p 9.

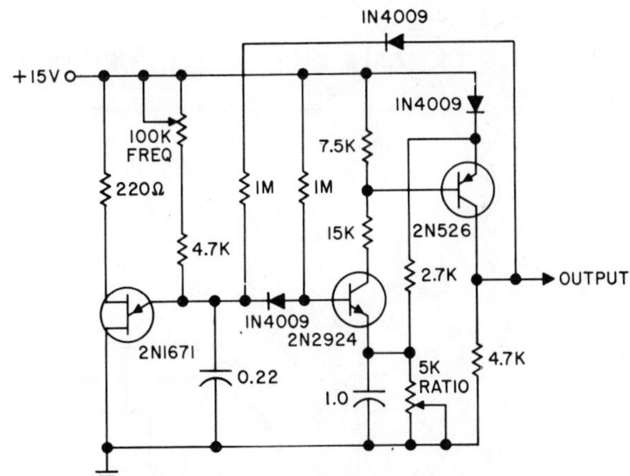

VARIABLE FREQUENCY AND DUTY CYCLE—Frequency range is 60 to 1,000 Hz, adjustable independently of 0–100% duty cycle range. Conventional ujt sawtooth followed by two transistors provides positive-going output, with rise and fall times about 1/500th of period of oscillation.—"Unijunction Circuit Hints," General Electric, Syracuse, N.Y., Fig. 7.

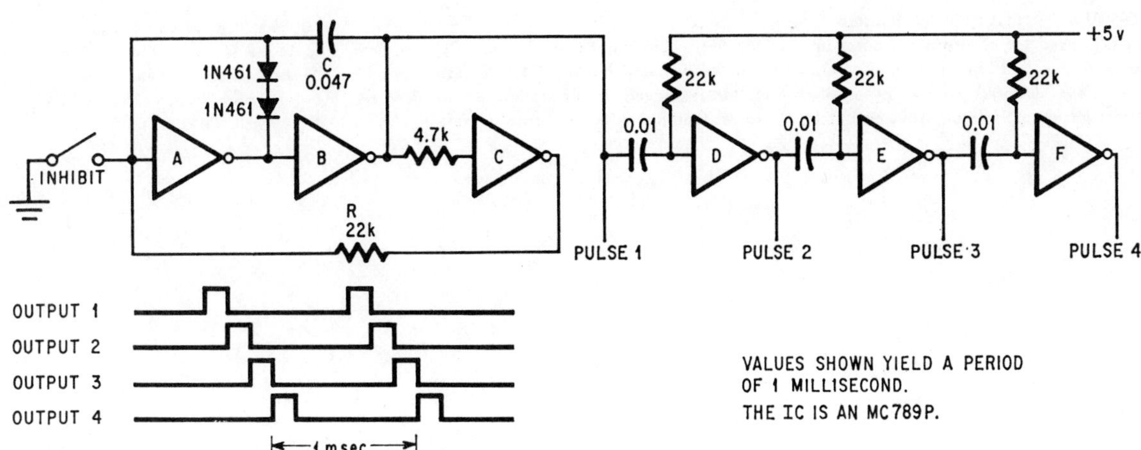

FOUR-PULSE SEQUENCE—Low-cost RTL hex-inverter IC delivers repeated sequence of four pulses, with equal or independently adjustable pulse widths. IC inverters A, B, and C form basic pulse generator. Inverters D, E, and F generate their pulses sequentially, with duration of each depending on RC network at inverter input. For values shown, duty cycle is 20%, leaving dead period before start of next four-pulse train. Pulse frequency can be up to a few MHz. Adding more hex-inverters increases number of pulses in train.—F. Cupp, 4-Pulse Sequence Generator Built With 1 Hex-Inverter, *Electronics*, Feb. 3, 1969, p 79–80.

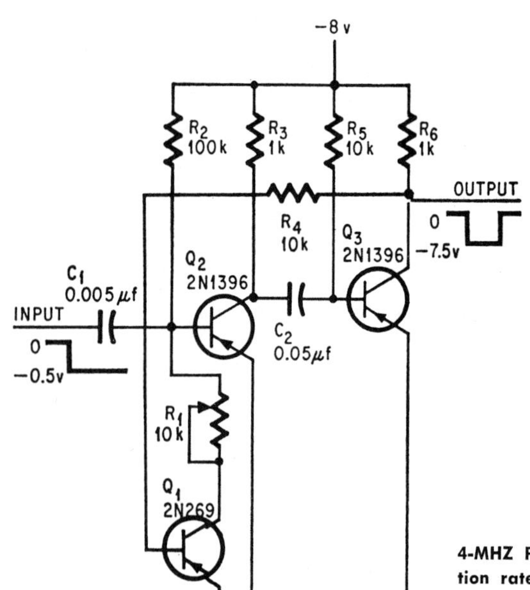

STEP-FUNCTION TRIGGERING—Adding Q1 to feedback loop of mono mvbr permits triggering by step function, to generate variable-width trigger pulse for digital system. Step function is obtained from shaft encoder. Negative 0.5 V input step gives 7.5-V output pulse 0.25 μs wide.—R. J. Hoss, Pulse Generator Triggered by a Step Function, *Electronics*, March 31, 1969, p 87–88.

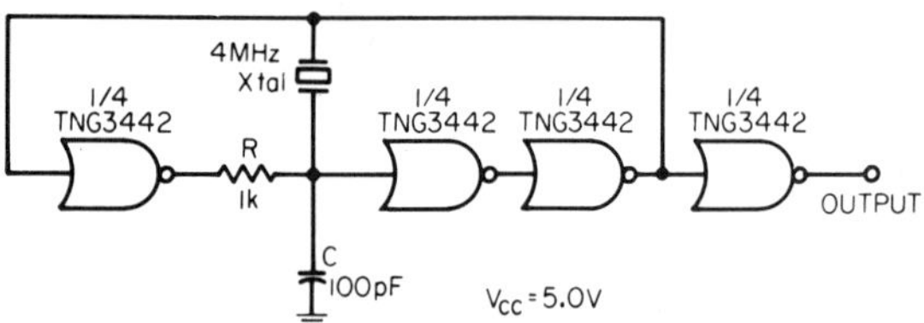

4-MHZ PULSE TRAIN—Crystal controls repetition rate and R-C network determines pulse width in square-wave generator using quad two-input gate. Square input to first gate can be used for stop-start control. Will operate with crystals from 10 kHz to 10 MHz. Stability is better than 0.02% within temperature range of IC.—K. Yu, Crystal Controls Rep Rate of Simple IC Pulse Generator, *EEE*, Jan. 1968, p 116–117.

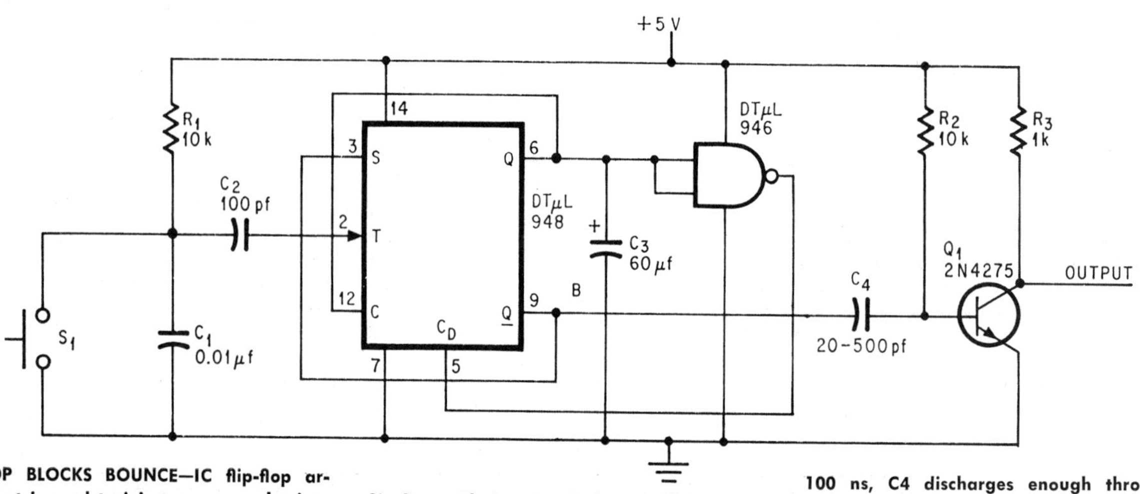

FLIP-FLOP BLOCKS BOUNCE—IC flip-flop arrangement is used to inject narrow pulse into equipment under test by closing S1 manually. Spurious voltages caused by contact bounce in switch are isolated from output by flip-flop. Closing S1 discharges C1, triggering flip-flop and biasing Q1 into cutoff so collector is moved from ground up to 5 V to form leading edge of output pulse. After 100 ns, C4 discharges enough through R2 to make Q1 saturate and form falling edge of pulse.—L. V. Hendricks, Flip-Flop Isolates Pulse From Switch Bounce, *Electronics*, Aug. 19, 1968, p 84–85.

NOTE: To locate additional circuits in the category of this chapter, use the index at the back of this book. Check also the author's "Sourcebook of Electronic Circuits," published by McGraw-Hill in 1968.

CHAPTER 80
Switching Circuits

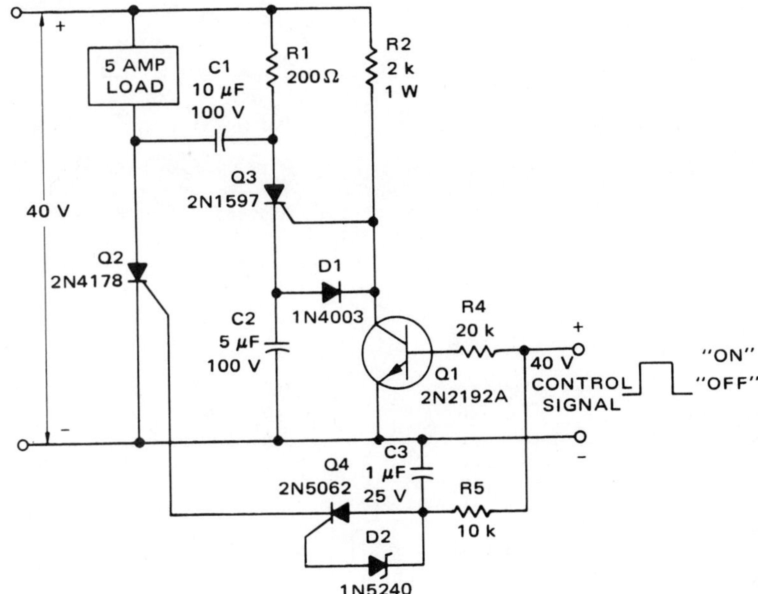

SCR STATIC D-C SWITCH—Control circuit turns on Q2 and load when control signal is applied. When signal is removed, Q2 opens and turns off load.—"Semiconductor Power Circuits Handbook," Motorola, Phoenix, Ariz., 1968, p 4–12.

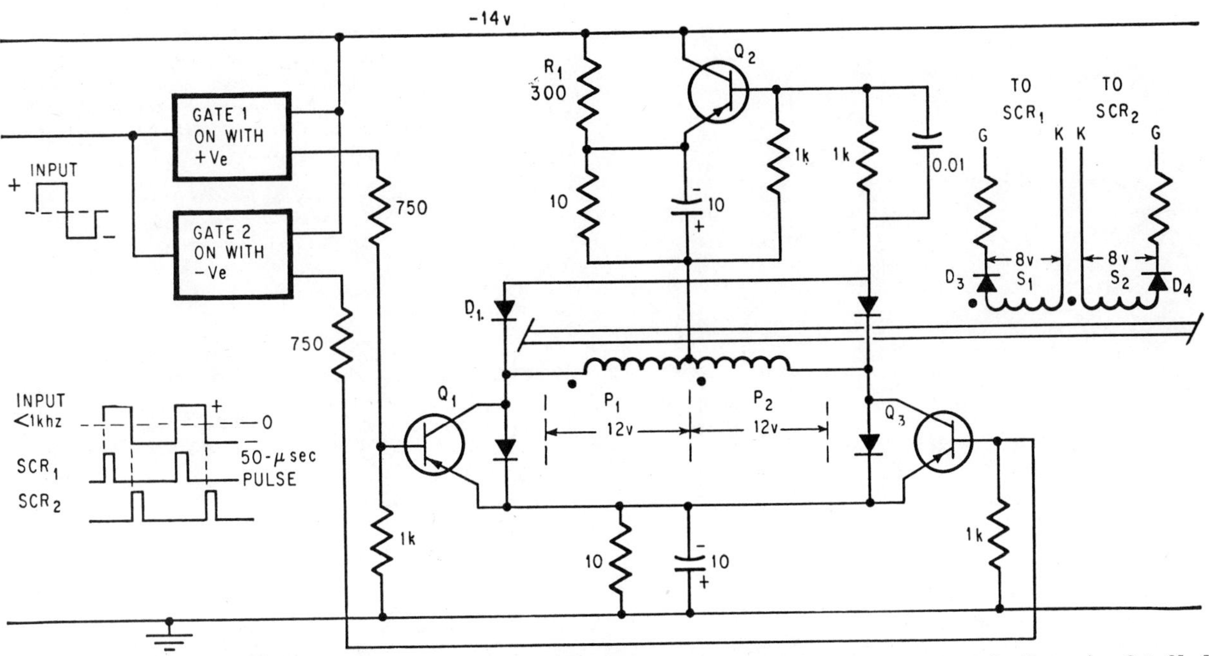

SYMMETRICAL ALTERNATE FIRING OF SCR'S—High-power firing pulses are alternated between pair of scr's by three-transistor pulse circuit, with timing of pulses controlled by low-power rectangular-wave input. Circuit delivers exact pulse to one scr, stalls until next half-cycle, and then delivers identical pulse to other scr.—B. McConnell, Pulse Circuit Fires Scr Pair, *Electronics*, Oct. 31, 1966, p 71.

IC-TRIAC ZERO-VOLTAGE POWER SWITCH—Circuit provides for shifting triac gate pulse in time to ensure reliable latching with small load. Triac used should latch at minimum load current of 4.2 A. Table gives component values required for four different values of minimum load current and 120-V a-c supply.—R. W. Fox, Low Power Zero Voltage Switching Using the PA42A, General Electric, Syracuse, N.Y., No. 201.22, 1969.

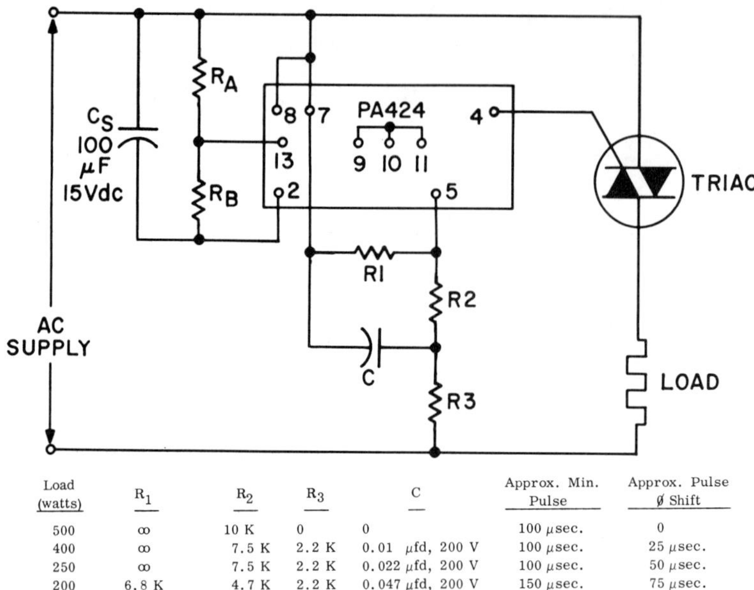

Load (watts)	R_1	R_2	R_3	C	Approx. Min. Pulse	Approx. Pulse ø Shift
500	∞	10 K	0	0	100 μsec.	0
400	∞	7.5 K	2.2 K	0.01 μfd, 200 V	100 μsec.	25 μsec.
250	∞	7.5 K	2.2 K	0.022 μfd, 200 V	100 μsec.	50 μsec.
200	6.8 K	4.7 K	2.2 K	0.047 μfd, 200 V	150 μsec.	75 μsec.

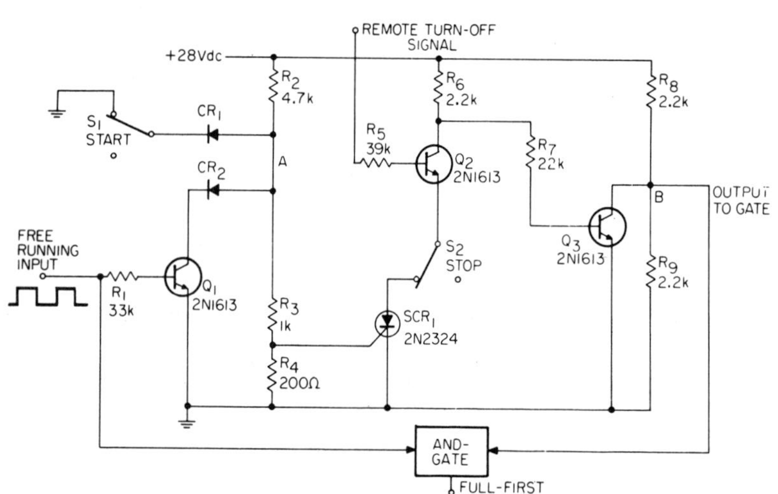

FIRST-PULSE PRESERVER—Switches free-running signal to load without interrupting first pulse, regardles of instant when start switch is actuated. Input square waves should be about 5 V p-p and wider than 50 μs. Frequency range is from near zero to about 1 kHz.—D. E. Manners, Switching Circuit Ensures Full First Pulse, *EEE*, Nov. 1967, p 126 and 128.

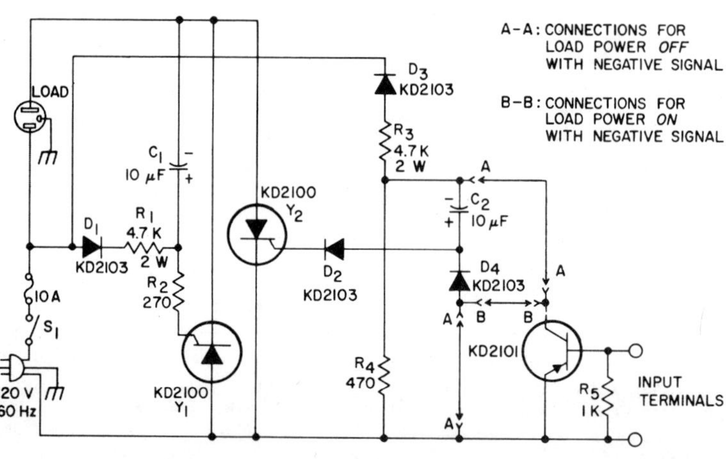

1-KW AUTOMATIC SYNCHRONOUS SWITCH—Either negative or positive 1-mA d-c input signal, depending on connections at AA and BB, applies power to load at next point in instantaneous line voltage that is low enough to prevent rfi generation.—"Silicon Controlled Rectifier Experimenter's Manual," RCA, Harrison, N.J., 1967, p 95.

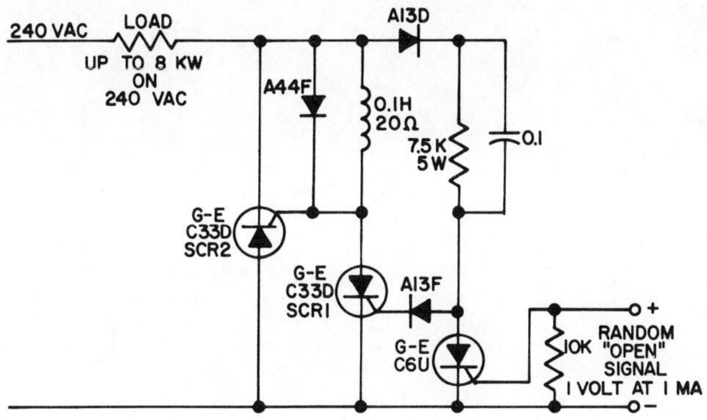

8-KW SYNCHRONOUS A-C SWITCH—In absence of switch-opening signal, scr's deliver full power to load, in full cycles and therefore with minimum rfi. Ideal for applications where magnetizing inrush current to transformers and motors causes nuisance fuse blowing, or where sensitive test equipment must be operated near switch location.—F. W. Gutzwiller and E. K. Howell, Economy Power Semiconductor Applications, General Electric, Syracuse, N.Y., No. 671.1, 1965, p 10.

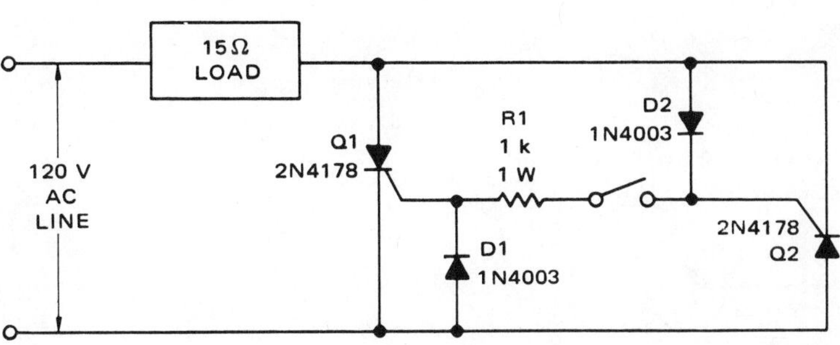

SCR STATIC A-C CONTACTOR—Small switch serves as static contactor for turning on one scr during positive half-cycles and other scr during negative half-cycles. When switch is opened, scr's remove load from line.—"Semiconductor Power Circuits Handbook," Motorola, Phoenix, Ariz., 1968, p 4–9.

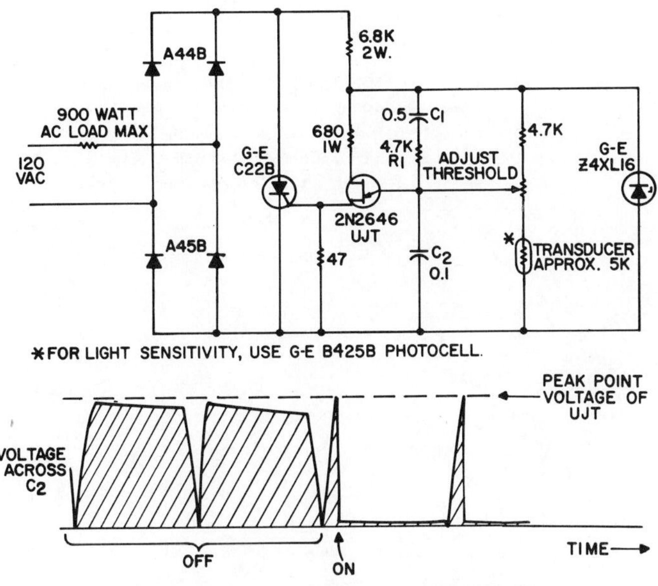

SNAP-ACTION A-C THRESHOLD SWITCH—R1 and C1 determine spread between pickup and dropout of a-c load up to 900 W. Can be used for temperature control, lighting control, and other applications, depending on type of transducer used.—F. W. Gutzwiller and E. K. Howell, Economy Power Semiconductor Applications, General Electric, Syracuse, N.Y., No. 671.1, 1965, p 10.

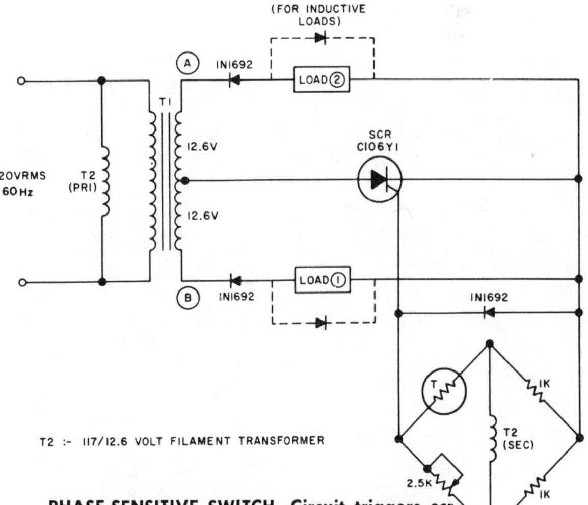

PHASE-SENSITIVE SWITCH—Circuit triggers scr for either direction of bridge unbalance, but transformer and steering diodes determine which of the two loads comes on for particular direction of unbalance. At balance, both loads are off. Ideal for monitoring or warning systems, where loads can be lamps labeled HIGH and LOW, relays providing corrective action, etc. Sensor may be photocell instead of thermistor shown.—D. R. Grafham, Using Low Current SCR's, General Electric, Syracuse, N.Y., No. 200.19, 1967, p 31.

HYBRID LADDER SWITCH—Trim value is 4 ohms in first three bits, and accuracy well within 1 mV. Has been used in 11-bit analog-digital converter, and time-shared as 9-bit successive-approximation 200-kHz analog-digital converter.—C. R. Luebke, Ladder Switch, *EDN*, Sept. 1, 1969, p 76.

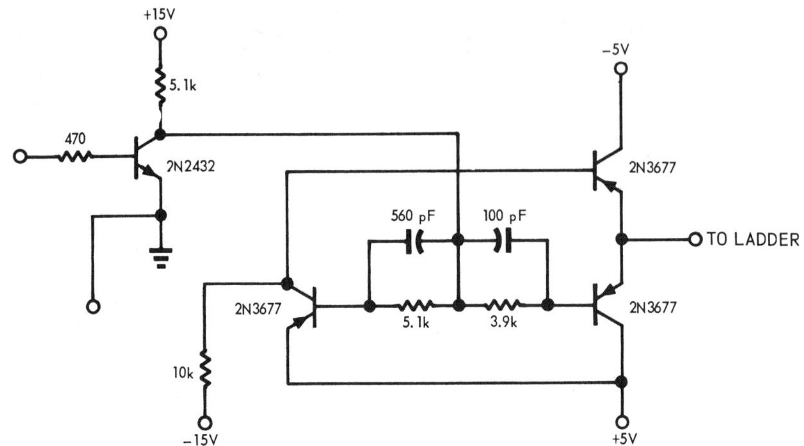

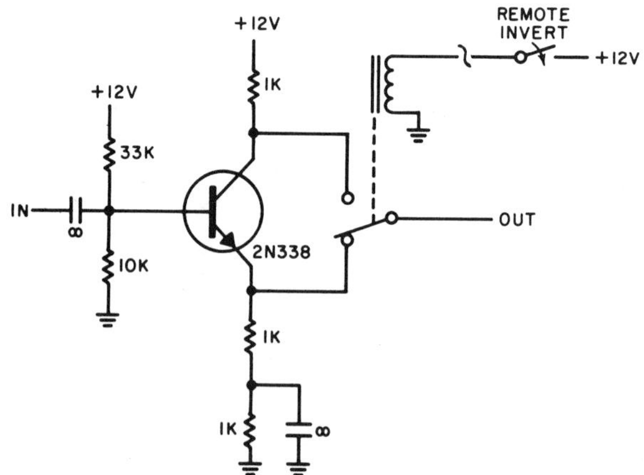

REMOTE-CONTROL PHASE SELECTOR—Relay and unity-gain transistor amplifier permit selection of a-c signal or 180-deg phase-inverted version while minimizing system noise of long signal paths.—M. I. Neidich, Remote Switching Technique Reduces System Noise, *Electronic Design*, Feb. 15, 1965, p 78–79.

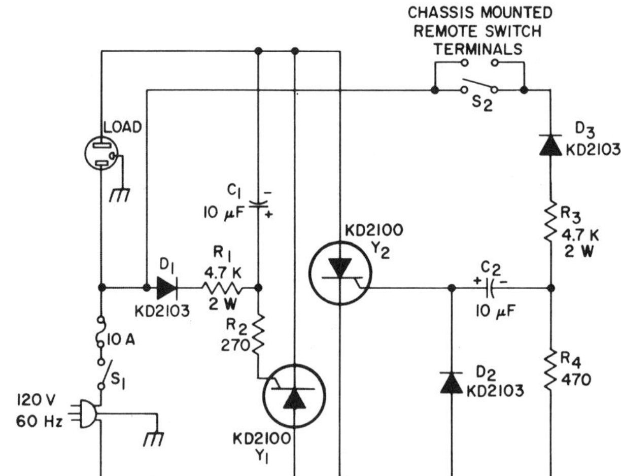

1-KW SYNCHRONOUS SWITCH—Provides switching without generation of rfi, using low-current switch S2 which may be remotely located.—"Silicon Controlled Rectifier Experimenter's Manual," RCA, Harrison, N.J., 1967, p 93.

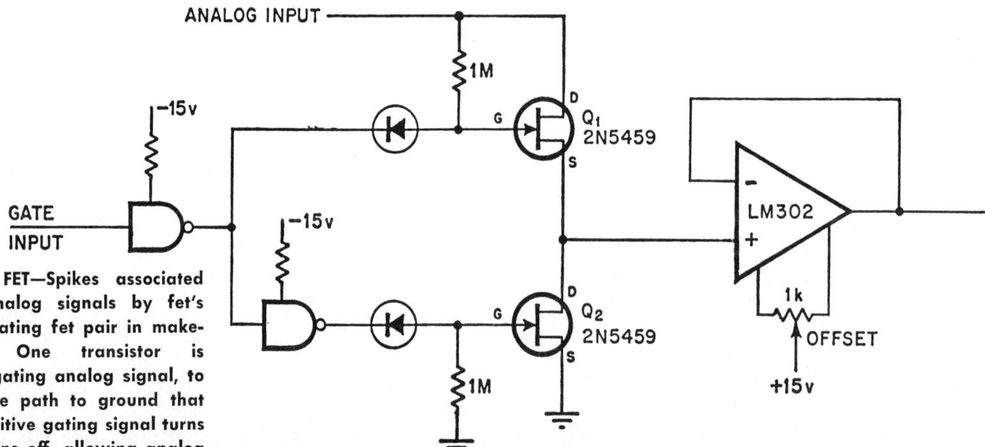

MAKE-BEFORE-BREAK FET—Spikes associated with switching of analog signals by fet's are overcome by operating fet pair in make-before-break mode. One transistor is switched on prior to gating analog signal, to provide low-impedance path to ground that minimizes spikes. Positive gating signal turns on Q1 while Q2 remains off, allowing analog signal to be transmitted through opamp to output. Negative gating signal opens analog switch by turning on Q2 before turning off Q1.—L. F. Halio, Make-Before-Break Mode Improves FET Switch, *Electronics*, April 27, 1970, p 90.

1-KW STATIC SWITCH—Operates from a-c line and provides 120 V d-c for 1,000-W load. Control signal applied to reed switch will turn load on or off in one cycle. Designed for applications having high duty cycle, such as motor controls for machine tools and conveyors, welding controls, battery chargers, temperature controls, and process controls.—F. W. Gutzwiller and E. K. Howell, Economy Power Semiconductor Applications, General Electric, Syracuse, N.Y., No. 671.1, 1965, p 6.

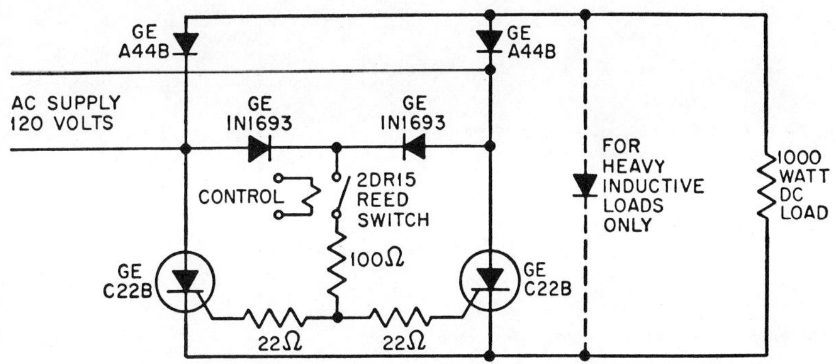

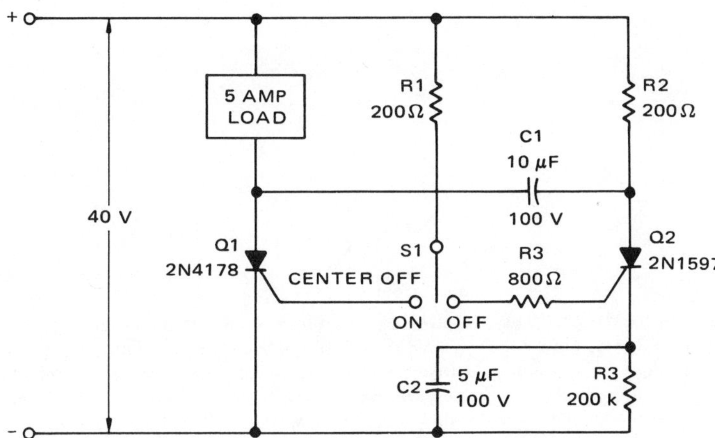

SCR STATIC D-C CONTACTOR—Requires only momentary contact of spring-loaded spdt switch for turning on or turning off 5-A d-c load. Once scr Q1 is turned on by gate current through R1, gate drive is no longer required and switch can be released. When switch is pushed to OFF position, scr Q2 receives gate current and comes on. C1 then discharges and turns Q1 off. C2 then charges to supply voltage and turns Q2 off. Q2 is much smaller than Q1 because it is used to commutate Q1 off.—"Semiconductor Power Circuits Handbook," Motorola, Phoenix, Ariz., 1968, p 4–11.

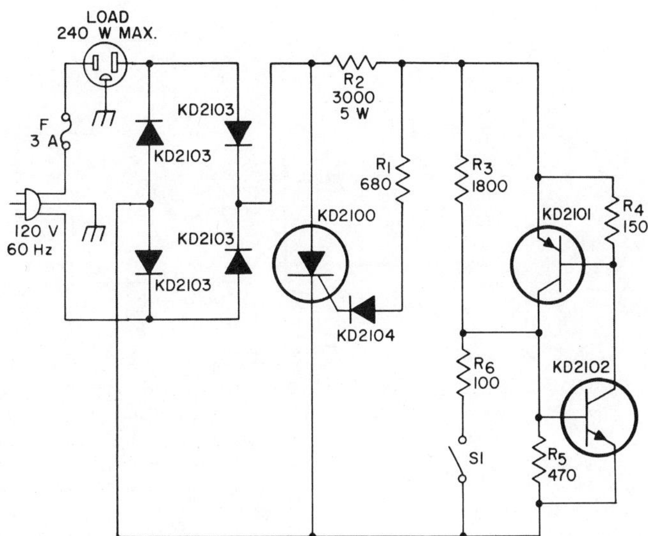

SYNCHRONOUS SWITCH—Prevents rfi by applying power to a-c loads up to 24 W only at near-zero points in a-c cycle. Triggering of scr occurs at 6.5 V. Regenerative-transistor switch triggers at 2.8 V with S1 open and 13.5 V with S1 closed. With S1 open, switch therefore conducts and blocks scr so load is off. When S1 is closed, scr conducts if supply voltage at that instant is less than 13.5 V, to apply power safely to load without rfi. If supply voltage is above 13.5 V, scr stays off for remainder of that input half-cycle, and is triggered only when voltage reaches 6.5 V on succeeding half-cycles.—"Silicon Controlled Rectifier Experimenter's Manual," RCA, Harrison, N.J., 1967, p 90.

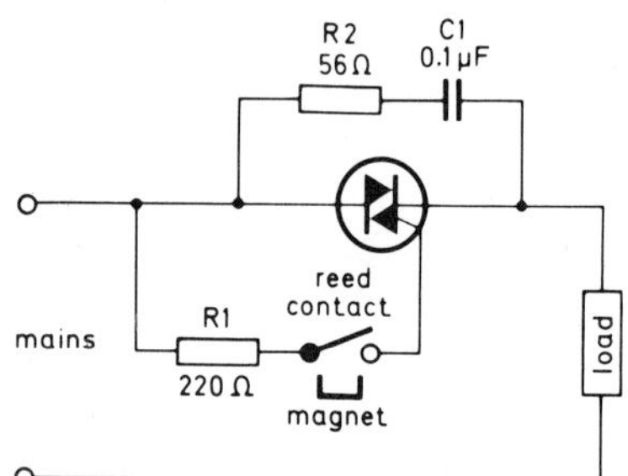

STATIC POWER SWITCH—Long-life reed relay serves as simple trigger for triac control of single-phase a-c load. Hermetic sealing of relay permits use in presence of gasoline vapor or in lines having explosive gases. Value of R1 in ohms should be about equal to a-c line voltage in volts, to give gate current of about 1 A for triac. R2 and C1 suppress transients.—Triacs—Operation and Use, Philips, Pub. Dept., Elcoma Div., Eindhoven, The Netherlands, No. 17, 1969.

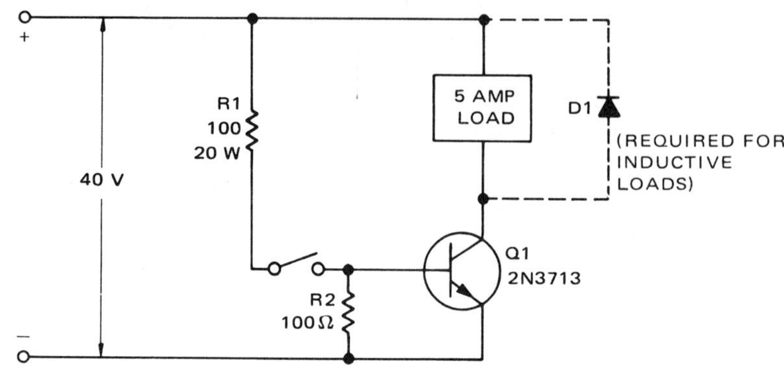

TRANSISTOR STATIC D-C CONTACTOR—Small switch, which can be remote from load, turns on transistor Q1 when closed. Will handle d-c loads up to 5 A.—"Semiconductor Power Circuits Handbook," Motorola, Phoenix, Ariz., 1968, p 4—11.

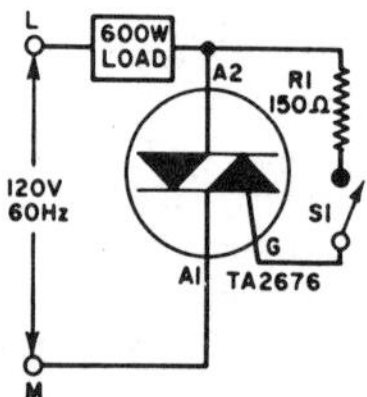

TRIAC FOR A-C LOADS—Power line triggers gated bidirectional controlled rectifier when S1 is closed. When S1 is opened, triac will cut off at next zero crossover of a-c line and remain off until S1 is again closed.—A. Harris, Semiconductor Switching of Low-Power Circuits, *Electronics World*, June 1967, p 33—35.

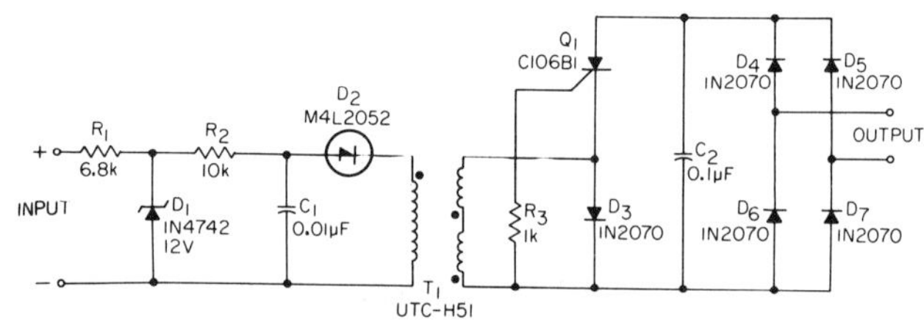

SIGNAL-POWERED SWITCH—D-c control voltage above 9.3 V at input turns on four-layer breakover diode D2 in simple relaxation oscillator circuit that induces train of pulses in secondary of T1, to gate scr on and apply power to load up to 1.5 A that scr places across a-c line. Pulse train ensures almost full firing of scr during each 60-Hz a-c cycle. Pulse transformer isolates voltage sensor from load. May be used to control alarm horn, lamp, or a-c relay.—P. A. Lajoie, Signal-Powered D-C Voltage Sensor Controls A-C Loads, *EEE*, Jan. 1968, p 117—118.

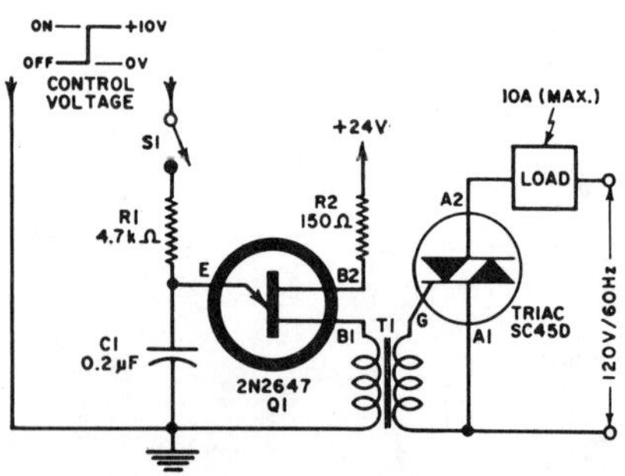

ISOLATED CONTROL—Transformer provides isolation of control circuit from a-c load. Closing S1 starts relaxation oscillator Q1 which operates in range of 600 to 6,000 Hz. First pulse of each half-cycle of a-c line causes triac to saturate for remainder of that half-cycle. Triac cuts off momentarily at first zero crossover of a-c line, but is triggered on again by the first pulse received from Q1 after the next half-cycle begins.—A. Harris, Semiconductor Switching of Low-Power Circuits, *Electronics World*, June 1967, p 33—35.

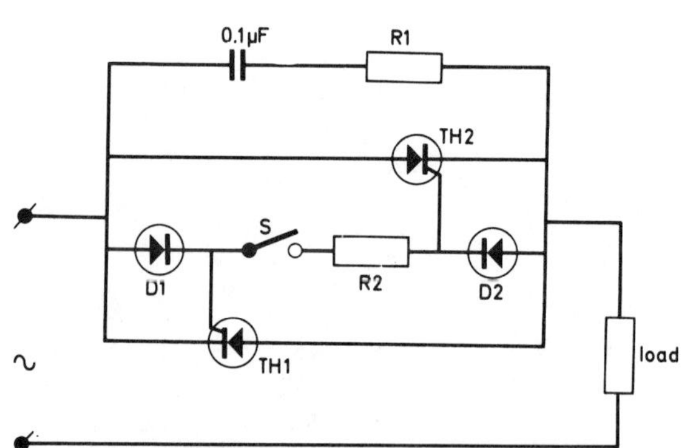

A-C STATIC CONTACTOR—Will give millions of operations silently, with minimum rfi and extremely low control power. Uses thyristors TH1 and TH2 connected in antiparallel, for handling load rated between about 0.5 and 35 kW; thus, for 25 A rms loads current, operating on 220 V a-c line, thyristor can be Philips BTX81-300R. Both diodes can be BA145, BY126, BYX10, or similar types. For 220-V line, R1 is 56 and R2 is 220; for 115-V line, R1 is 39 and R2 is 120. Switch may be reed-type, microswitch, or thermostat contact. —A. C. Static Contactor, Philips, Pub. Dept., Elcoma Div., Eindhoven, The Netherlands, No. 20, 1968.

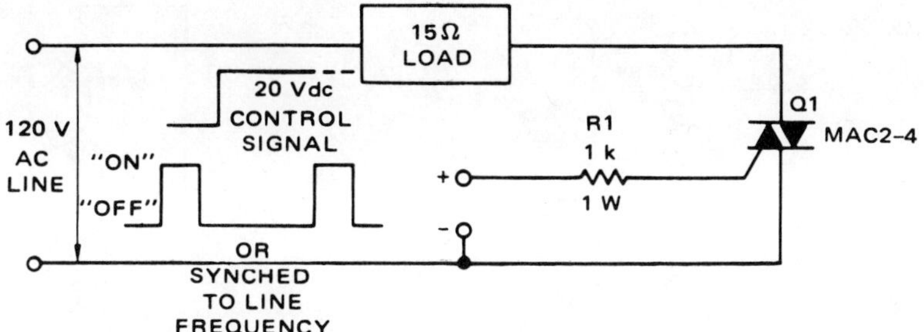

TRIAC A-C STATIC SWITCH—Triac remains on until control signal is removed, and turns off when current next drops to zero. Will handle reactive as well as resistive loads on 60-Hz a-c line.—"Semiconductor Power Circuits Handbook," Motorola, Phoenix, Ariz., 1968, p 4–8.

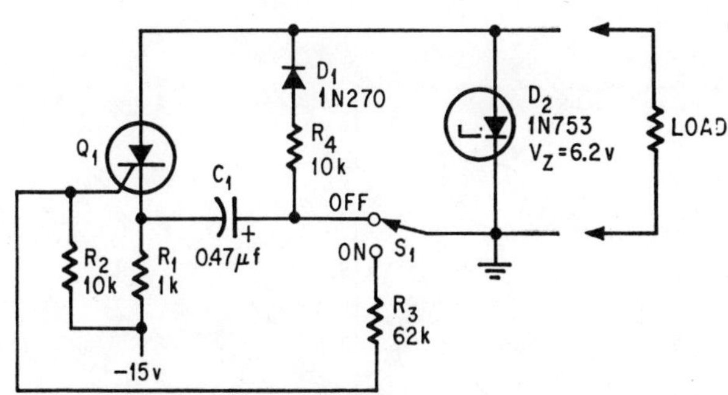

BOUNCE ELIMINATOR—Turning on scr Q1 simultaneously with closing of switch eliminates false triggering signal or noise caused by contact bounce. Scr consumes no quiescent power.—R. A. Wilson, SCR Takes Bounce Out of Switching, *Electronics*, Oct. 30, 1967, p 69.

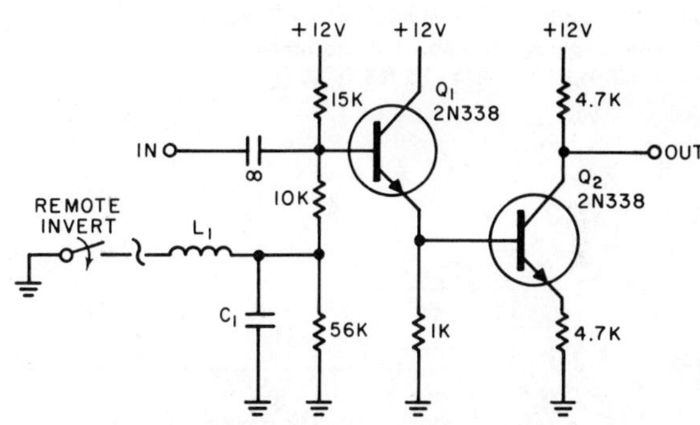

PHASE SELECTOR WITHOUT RELAY—Two-transistor circuit permits remote selection of a-c signal or 180-deg phase-inverted version without use of relay. When inversion is desired, switch is closed.—M. I. Neidich, Remote Switching Technique Reduces System Noise, *Electronic Design*, Feb. 15, 1965, p 78–79.

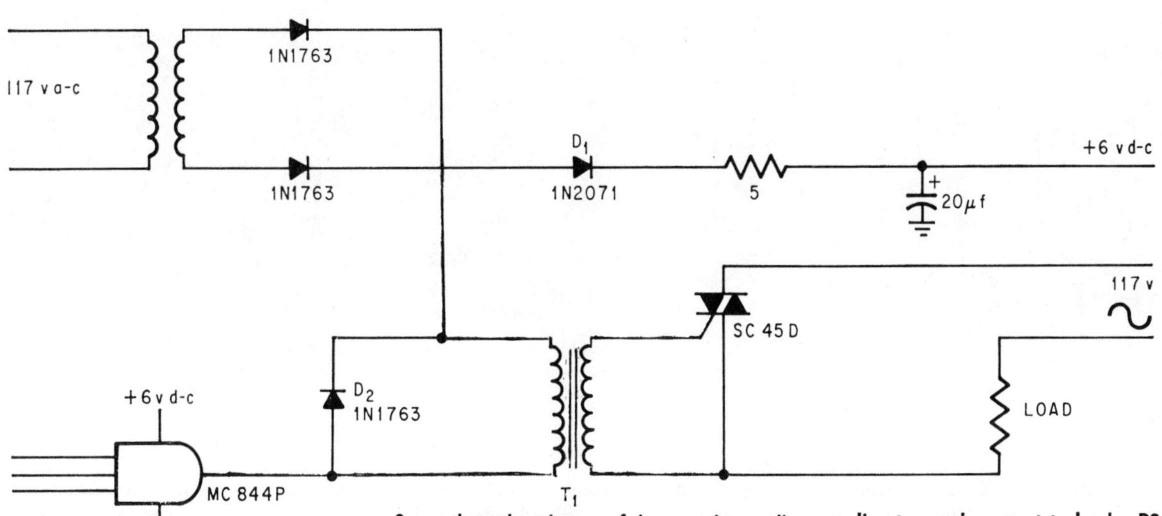

A-C CONTROL WITH GATE—When IC is gated on by three simultaneous inputs, current flows through primary of inexpensive audio transformer, inducing same half-wave rectified voltage in secondary for triggering triac into conduction every half-cycle and allowing a-c line to supply current to load. D2 shunts inductive spikes.—G. V. Wintress, IC Gate Controls Triac with Audio Transformer, *Electronics*, Aug. 5, 1968, p 106.

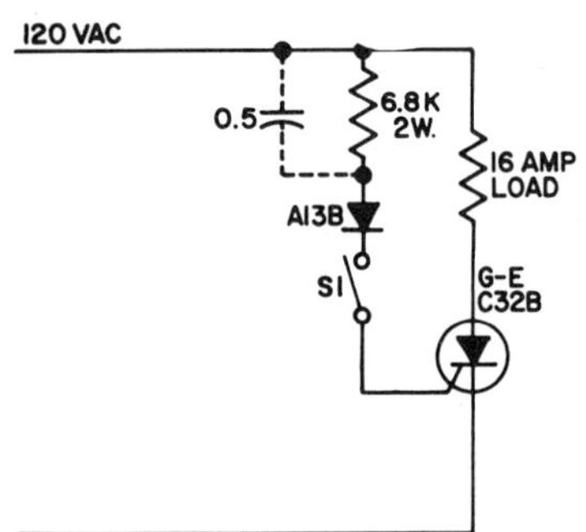

HALF-WAVE NORMALLY OPEN—Static power switch can be used for heater loads, limit switches, and other applications requiring switching of half-wave a-c power. Closing switch S1 fires scr and energizes load.—F. W. Gutzwiller and E. K. Howell, Economy Power Semiconductor Applications, General Electric, Syracuse, N.Y., No. 671.1, 1965, p 6.

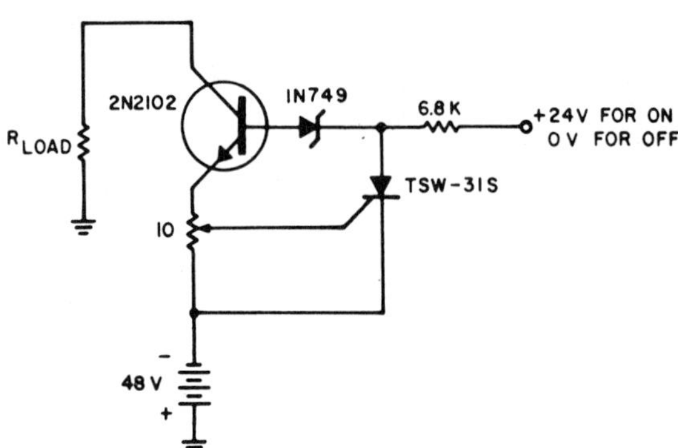

FAST-ACTING SCR—Simple scr circuit breaker operates in less than 2 μs to interrupt load current at any desired value between 100 and 300 mA as set by 10-ohm pot.—J. A. Means, SCR Circuit Breaker Has Fast Operation, "400 Ideas for Design Selected from Electronic Design," Hayden Book Co., N.Y., 1964, p 220.

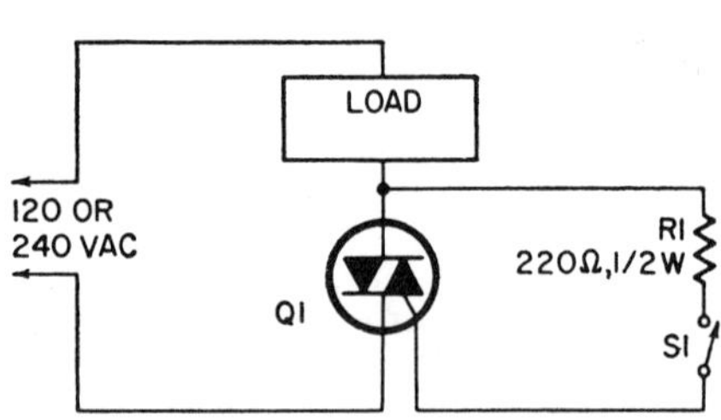

SELF-TRIGGERED TRIAC—When switch S1 is closed, triac is triggered on just after start of each half-cycle (at about 6 V). S1 may be relay contact, but must withstand full line voltage. Load can be up to 6 A. Use RCA 40429 for 120 V and 40430 for 240 V.—R. M. Marston, 20 Triac Circuits, *Radio-Electronics*, June 1970, p 51–53 and 97.

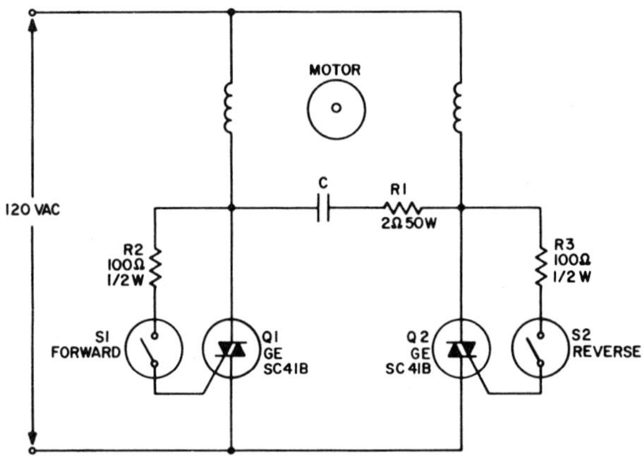

TRIAC AS STATIC REVERSING SWITCH—Pair of triacs serves as static switch, in place of contactors, for reversing-type psc motor, to provide rapid-response reversal. S1 and S2 can be reed switches, or triacs can be gated by other means. With appropriate firing circuit, arrangement can serve as motor overtemperature control that senses motor winding temperature directly.—"SCR Manual," 4th Edition, General Electric, 1967, p 222.

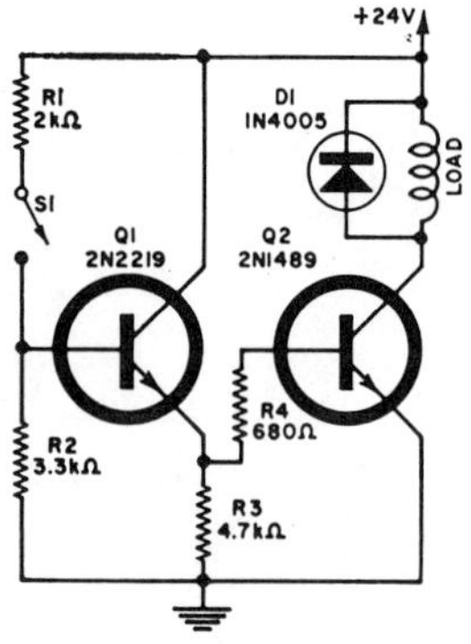

SOLENOID DRIVER—Will switch loads up to 5 A. Diode D1 protects Q2 by suppressing voltage transient developed when inductive load is de-energized.—A. Harris, Semiconductor Switching of Low-Power Circuits, *Electronics World*, June 1967, p 33–35.

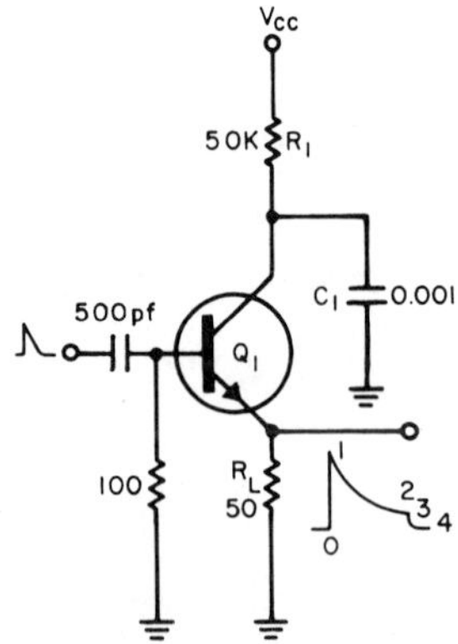

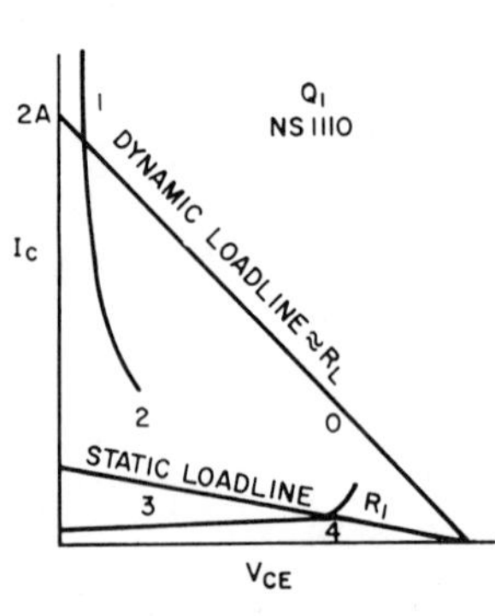

BASIC AVALANCHE—Can be used with any appropriate avalanche transistor meeting load requirements. Values shown are for NS1110, having load lines at right. C1 supplies rush of current for avalanche between point 0 and 1, but must be recharged between points 3 and 4 before circuit is ready for another avalanche. Can be used in pulse generators and voltage comparators.—B. H. Bell, Avalanche Circuits Are More Versatile Than You Think, *Electronic Design*, June 8, 1964, p 56–63.

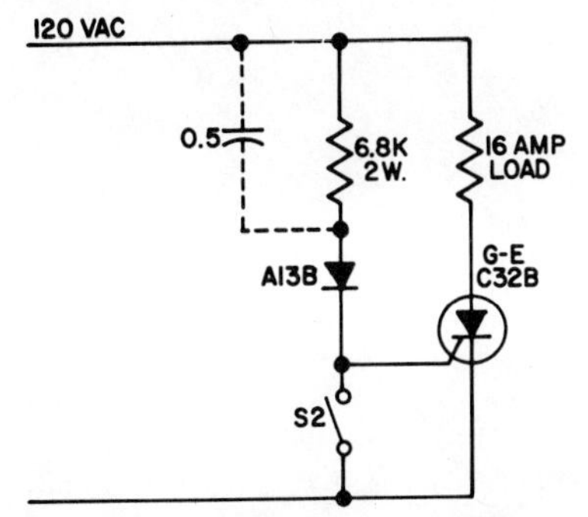

HALF-WAVE NORMALLY CLOSED—When switch is open, scr and load are energized. Closing of switch shorts out trigger to gate and opens scr, turning off load.—F. W. Gutzwiller and E. K. Howell, Economy Power Semiconductor Applications, General Electric, Syracuse, N.Y., No. 671.1, 1965, p 6.

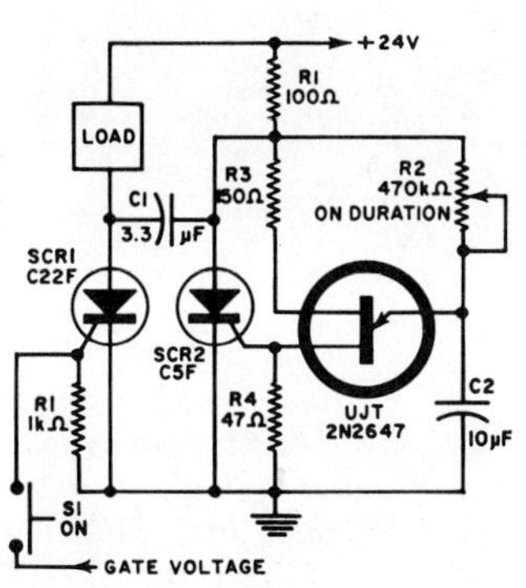

TIMING SWITCH—Actuating S1 gates SCR1 on and energizes load, while commutating capacitor C1 charges through SCR1 and R1. Relaxation oscillator UJT produces one cycle of oscillation under this condition, duration of which is determined by setting of R2. At end of cycle, SCR2 is gated on, UJT is disabled, and SCR1 turned off.—A. Harris, Semiconductor Switching of Low-Power Circuits, *Electronics World*, June 1967, p 33–35.

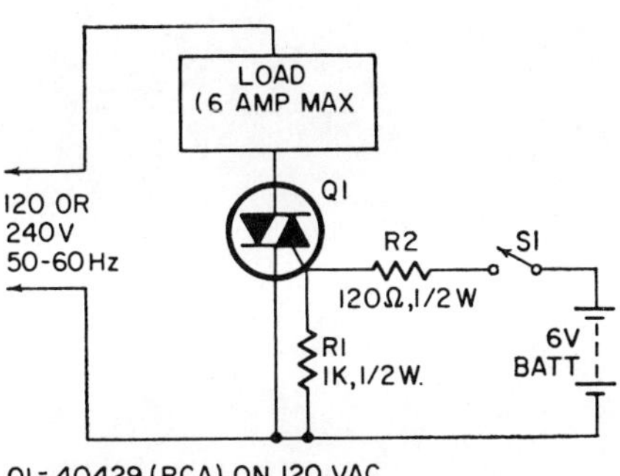

BASIC TRIAC SWITCH—Switch S1 handles only about 40 mA in triggering triac that carries 6-A load current. For 120 V a-c, use RCA 40429; for 240 V, use 40430. Will handle surge currents of cold incandescent lamps.—R. M. Marston, 20 Triac Circuits, *Radio-Electronics*, June 1970, p 51–53 and 97.

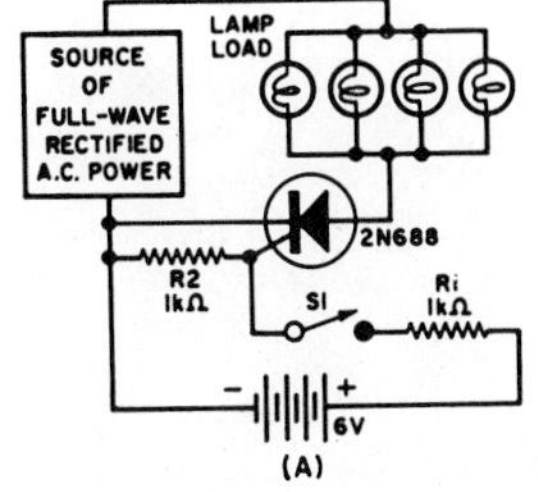

LAMP DRIVER—Gate drive of only 3 V at 40 mA on scr will handle lamp load of 35 A, provided lamp power source is full-wave rectified a-c, without filtering. When lamps are to be turned off, S1 is opened, and lamps are de-energized at next return of d-c waveform to zero.—A. Harris, Semiconductor Switching of Low-Power Circuits, *Electronics World*, June 1967, p 33–35.

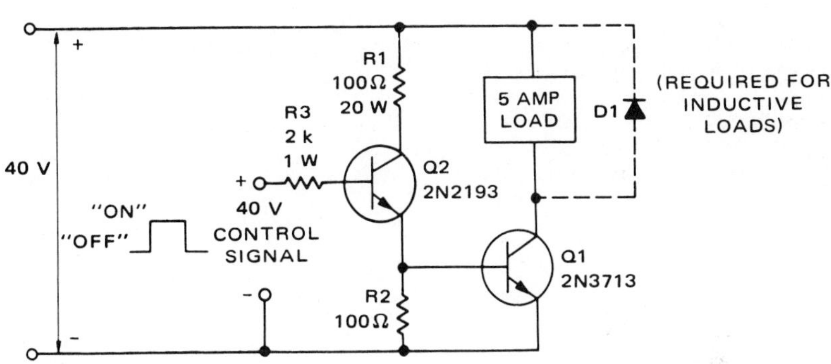

TRANSISTOR STATIC D-C SWITCH—Load is on only while control signal is present to turn on both transistors.—"Semiconductor Power Circuits Handbook," Motorola, Phoenix, Ariz., 1968, p 4–12.

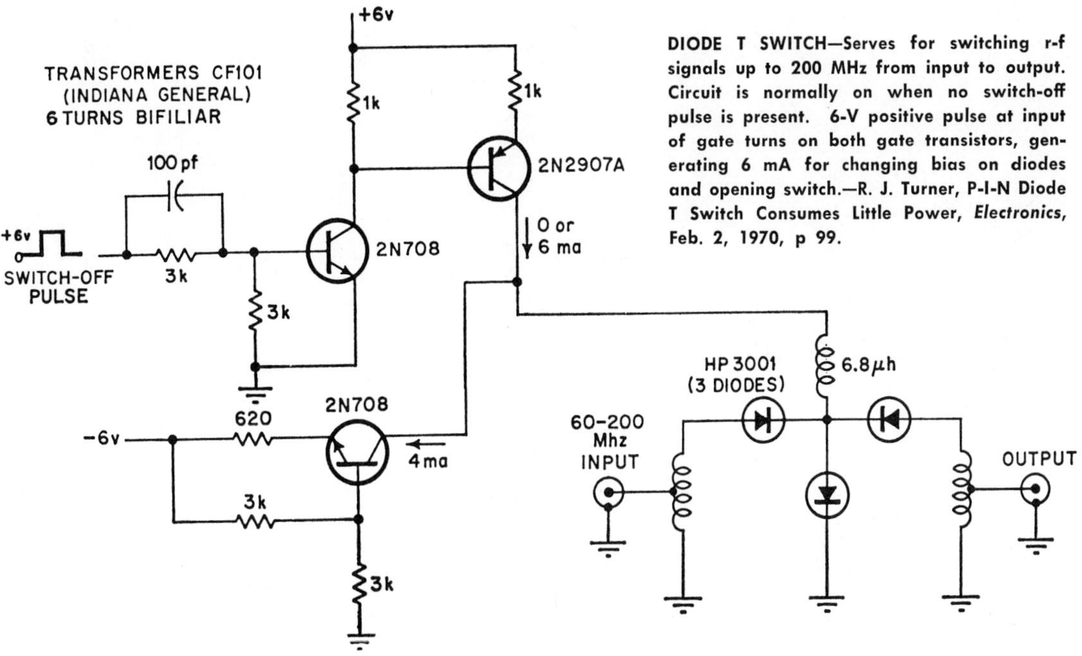

DIODE T SWITCH—Serves for switching r-f signals up to 200 MHz from input to output. Circuit is normally on when no switch-off pulse is present. 6-V positive pulse at input of gate turns on both gate transistors, generating 6 mA for changing bias on diodes and opening switch.—R. J. Turner, P-I-N Diode T Switch Consumes Little Power, *Electronics*, Feb. 2, 1970, p 99.

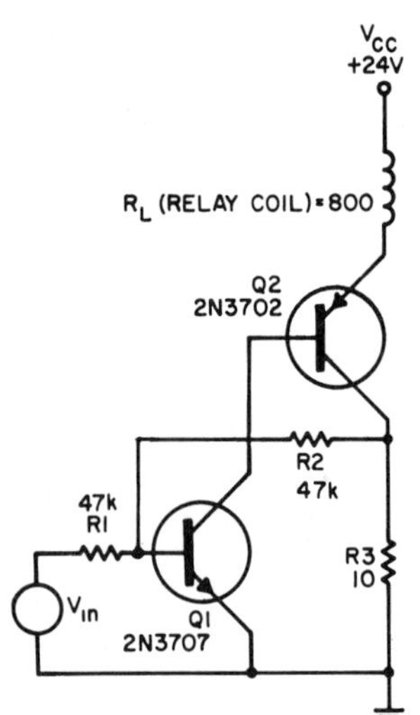

SNAP-ACTION SWITCH—Used for on-off control of relay or other load. Complementary silicon transistors behave like Schmitt trigger, with both turning on for 1.4 V d-c at input, and turning off at 1.1 V. When off, current drain is zero. If input is voltage drop across sensor, circuit may be used as simple and reliable temperature, photoelectric, or other control.—A. Anzani, On-Off Solid-State Switch Is Simple and Inexpensive, *Electronic Design*, Sept. 27, 1967, p 70.

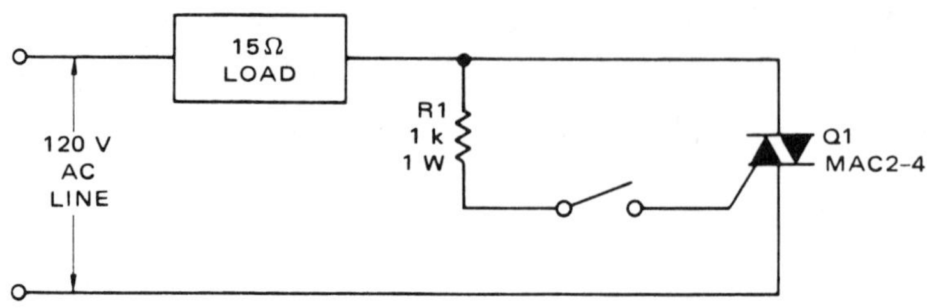

TRIAC STATIC A-C CONTACTOR—Small switch applies gate current to triac, to close load circuit. When switch is open, triac turns off when current next drops to zero. Will handle reactive and resistive loads.—"Semiconductor Power Circuits Handbook," Motorola, Phoenix, Ariz., 1968, p 4–9.

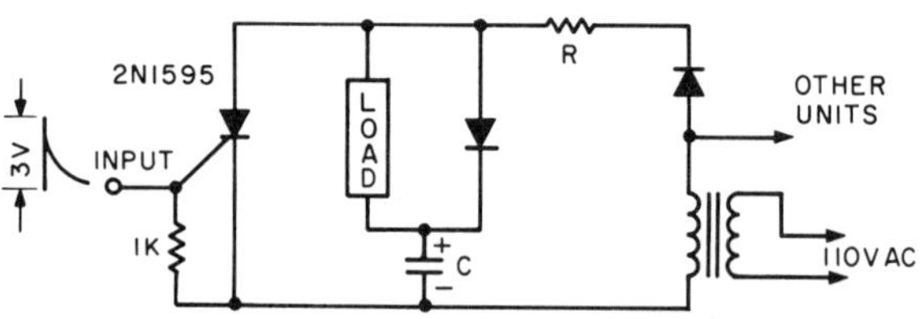

UNIVERSAL SCR DRIVER—Used to drive 20-channel operations recorder having pen deflection coils operating from 24-V d-c source. When scr is fired by input pulse, C discharges through load and charging current source is clamped. Value of C is determined by load inductance; typical value is 100 μF. R is usually 50 ohms, chosen to give fast recharging of C.—J. Gray, Jr., SCR Circuit a Versatile Driver of Many Loads, *Electronic Design*, April 13, 1964, p 74.

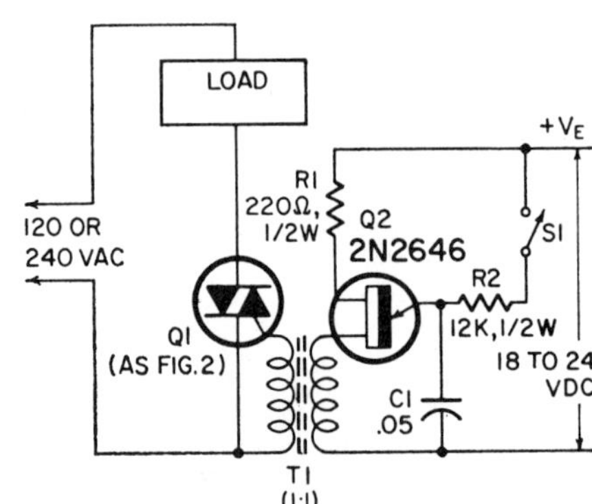

UJT-TRIGGERED TRIAC—When S1 is closed, ujt oscillator applies continuous train of trigger pulses to gate of triac Q1 through isolating transformer T1. With trigger at 2 kHz, triac is triggered on very shortly after start of each 60-Hz half-cycle, for full-wave control. Switch handles only 2 mA, and can be replaced by transistor driven by any type of transducer. Use RCA 40429 triac for 120 V and 40430 for 240 V.—R. M. Marston, 20 Triac Circuits, *Radio-Electronics*, June 1970, p 51–53 and 97.

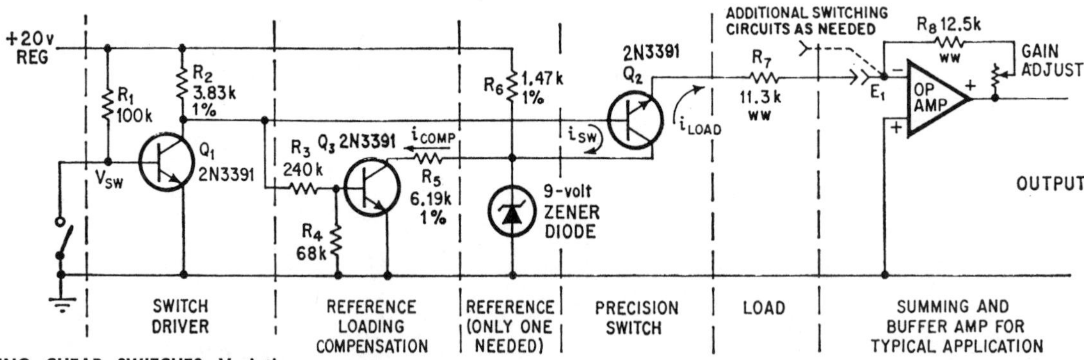

OVERCOMING CHEAP SWITCHES—Variations of up to 1,000 ohms in contact resistance of cheap switches have no effect on operation of circuit, in which Q2 connected in inverted mode acts as precision low-contact-resistance switch. Designed for applying precision reference voltage from 9-V zener to IC opamp.—G. R. Latham 4th, Inverted Transistor Switches Precision D-C Voltage, *Electronics*, Aug. 4, 1969, p 92–93.

CHAPTER 81
Staircase Generator Circuits

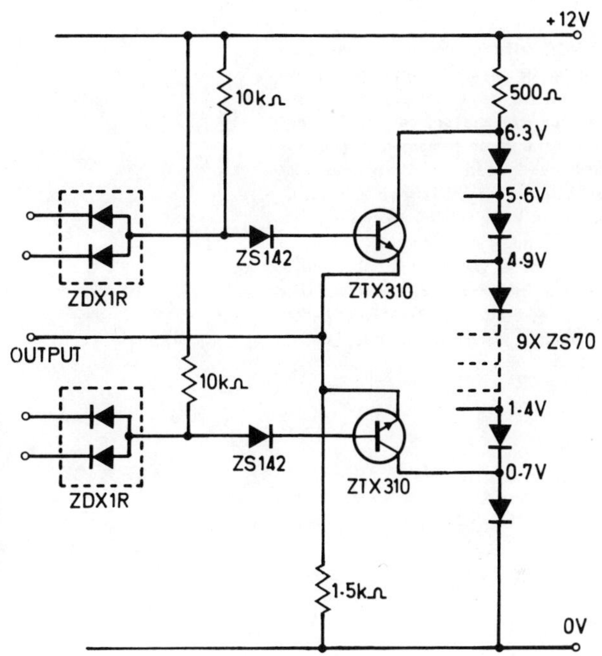

EQUAL STEPS—Reference chain of forward-biased diodes gives known equal steps of voltage, when reference points are connected sequentially to common load by switching transistors. Johnson decade counter is used with diode decoding to provide sequential switching.—"E-Line Transistor Applications," Ferranti Ltd., Oldham, Lancs., England, 1969, p 21.

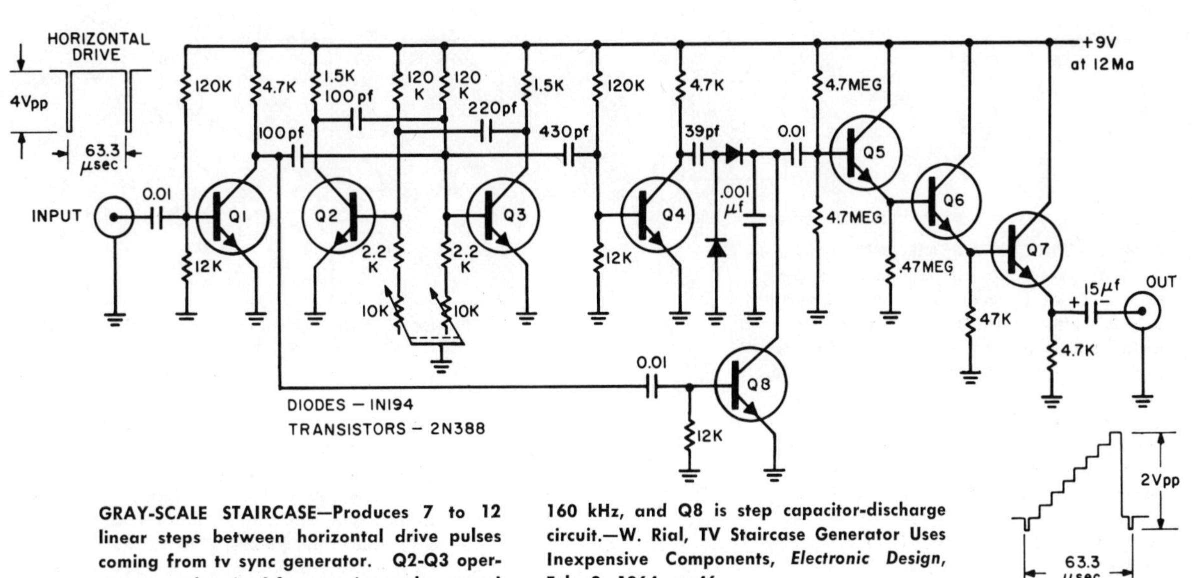

GRAY-SCALE STAIRCASE—Produces 7 to 12 linear steps between horizontal drive pulses coming from tv sync generator. Q2-Q3 operate as synchronized free-running mvbr around 160 kHz, and Q8 is step capacitor-discharge circuit.—W. Rial, TV Staircase Generator Uses Inexpensive Components, *Electronic Design*, Feb. 3, 1964, p 46.

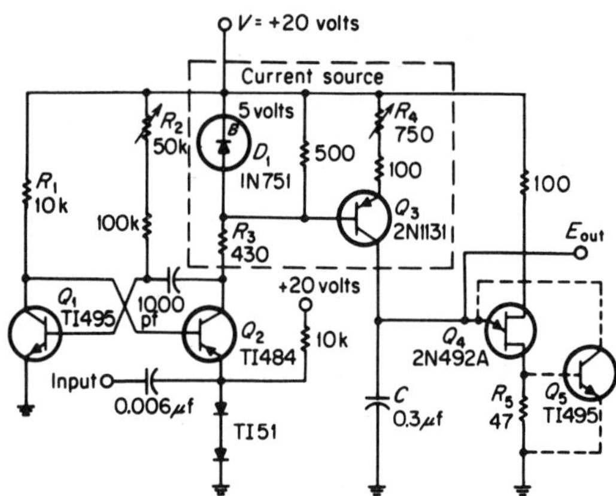

UJT STAIRCASE WITH COUNTER—Will operate at inputs up to 10 kHz. Negative input pulse triggers Q2 on for period set by R2, to furnish drive for current source Q3-D1 that charges C. At end of period, C discharges slowly until next negative pulse arrives. R4 determines height of each voltage step on C. When voltage is high enough to fire ujt Q4, C discharges and cycle repeats. Addition of Q5 discharges C faster, to double maximum operating frequency.—B. Crawford and R. T. Dean, The Unijunction Transistor in Relaxation Circuits, *Electro-Technology*, March 1964, p 40–45.

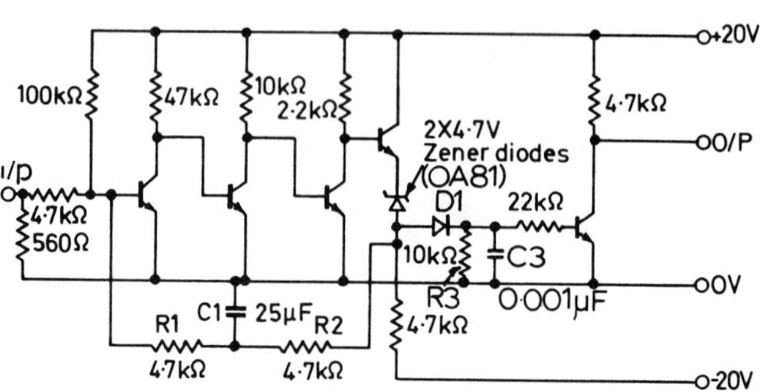

EQUAL-STEP LINEAR—Produces linear staircase voltage waveform for ultrasonic image converter using switching matrix and pulse techniques for reproducing object image on array of 100 transducer elements.—S. O. Harrold, Solid State Ultrasonic Camera, *Ultrasonics*, April 1969, p 95–101.

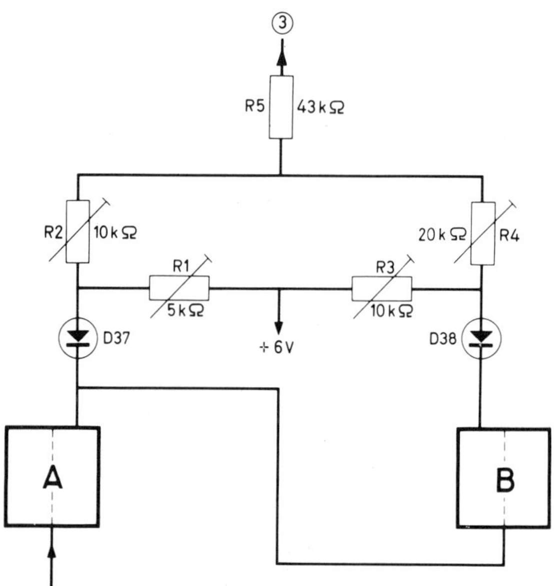

ROW-SELECTING STAIRCASE GENERATOR—Used in figure-8 bar matrix numerical display to step down crt beam one line and return it to left after every 12 generated characters. Circuit makes use of clock pulses (250 kHz) and control logic levels, as described in article. Flip-flops A and B give four possible output conditions, one for each row of characters displayed. Potentiometers adjust spacing between rows. Diodes are BAX13.—A. P. Tanis, Numerical Display with Bar Matrix Character Generator, *Electronic Applications*, Philips, Pub. Dept., Elcoma Div., Eindhoven, The Netherlands, Vol. 27, No. 2, 1966–1967, p 73–83.

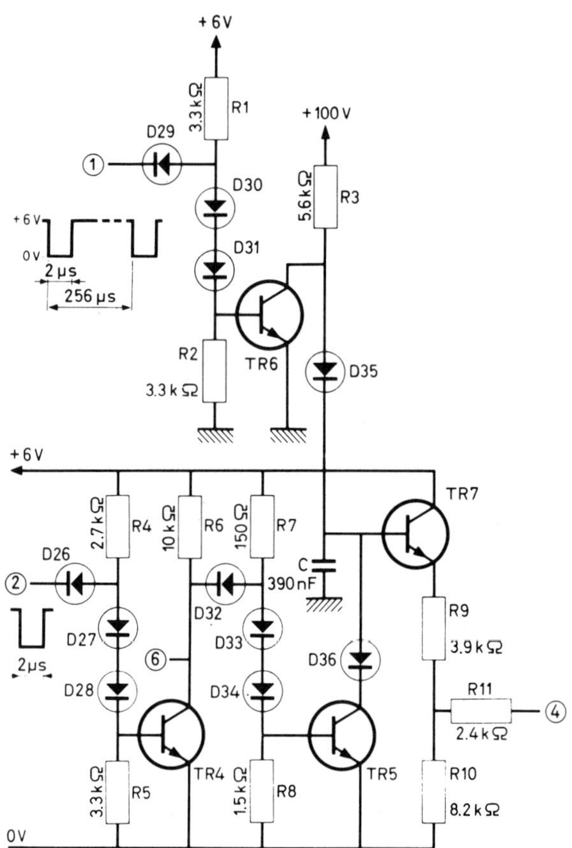

COLUMN-SELECTING STAIRCASE GENERATOR—Used in figure-8 bar matrix numerical display to shift crt beam one place to right after formation of each character. Sequence of gates identifies end of each character and triggers generator for producing next step of staircase. All transistors are BSX20 and all diodes BAX13.—A. P. Tanis, Numerical Display with Bar Matrix Character Generator, *Electronic Applications*, Philips, Pub. Dept., Elcoma Div., Eindhoven, The Netherlands, Vol. 27, No. 2, 1966–1967, p 73–83.

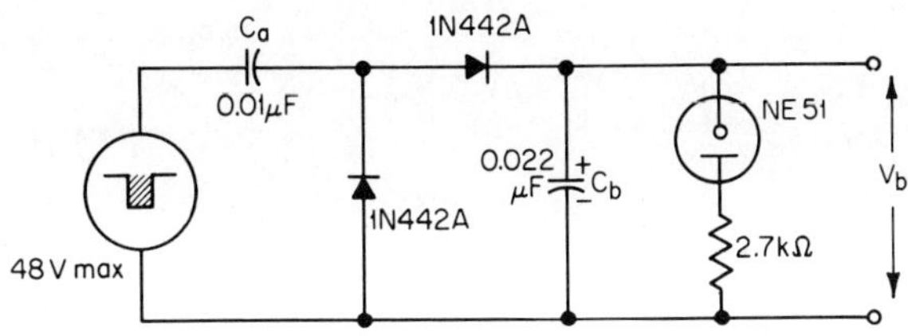

FOUR-STEP STAIRCASE—With neon lamp shown, firing at about 42 V, negative input pulse slightly greater than this value will require four chargings of Ca-Cb for series of four steps, with lamp firing on edge of fifth step to discharge capacitors and initiate new staircase.—A. C. Gillie, "Pulse and Logic Circuits," McGraw-Hill, N.Y., 1968, p 266.

THREE-TRANSISTOR LINEARIZING BOOTSTRAP—Used with staircase generator (not shown) to give essentially constant increase in pulse voltage increments, so corners of steps are on straight line. Solid arrows show path by which Cd discharges, and broken arrows show its charging path. T3 acts as switch. For optimum linearity, value of Cc in μF should be changed for each frequency band, as follows: 200–500 pps—1; 500–1,000—0.5; 1–20 kpps—0.1; 20–50—0.01; 50–100—0.001.—A. C. Gillie, "Pulse and Logic Circuits," McGraw-Hill, N.Y., 1968, p 292.

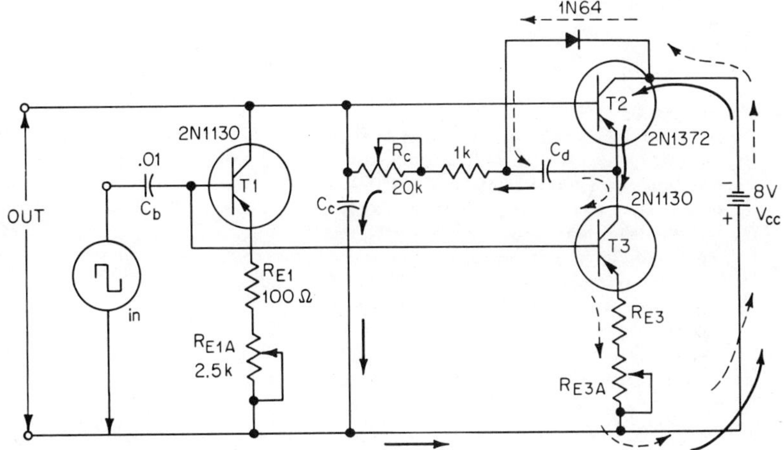

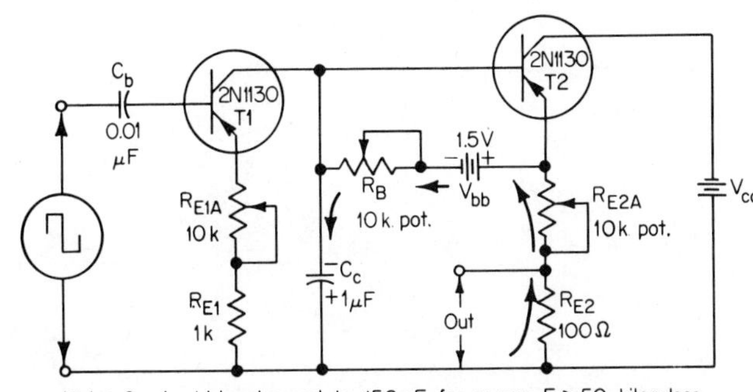

Note: C_b should be changed to 150 pF for sweep F > 50 kilopulses

TWO-TRANSISTOR LINEARIZING BOOTSTRAP—Used with staircase generator (not shown) to give essentially constant increase in pulse voltage increments, so corners of steps are on straight line. Depends on variable voltage feedback from amplifier whose voltage gain is unity. Maximum sweep-period time varies with battery voltage, for which typical value is 10 V.—A. C. Gillie, "Pulse and Logic Circuits," McGraw-Hill, N.Y., 1968, p 289.

ONE-SHOT LINEARIZING BOOTSTRAP—Used with staircase generator to give equal increments, so corners of steps are on straight line. Solid arrows show path for Cf charging current; final value of this capacitor is best determined empirically while observing output waveform on scope.—A. C. Gillie, "Pulse and Logic Circuits," McGraw-Hill, N.Y., 1968, p 294.

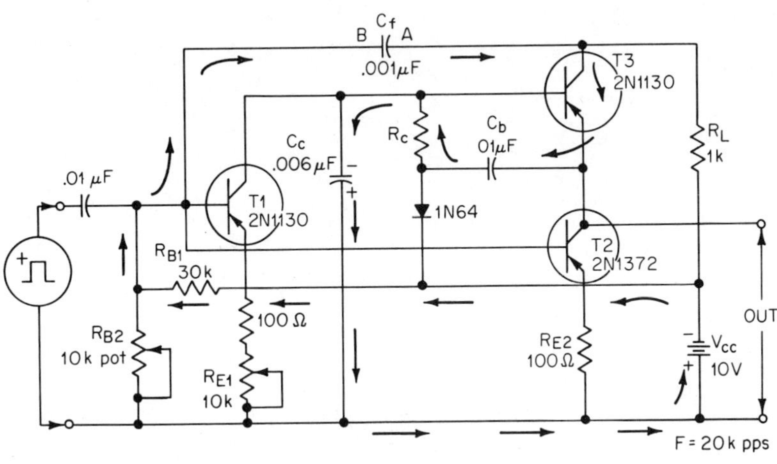

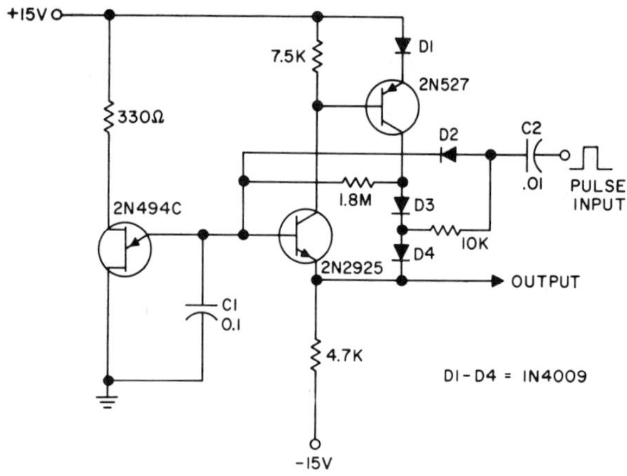

WIDE FREQUENCY RANGE—Npn-pnp emitter-follower output circuit gives high input impedance and low output impedance, to reduce droop in output voltage between pulses. Npn transistor bias is effectively bootstrapped on output, as also is diode-capacitor pump. Steps per cycle depend on ratio of C1 to C2 and amplitude of input pulse; for values shown, 12-V input gives 10 steps.—"Unijunction Circuit Hints," General Electric, Syracuse, N.Y., Fig. 6.

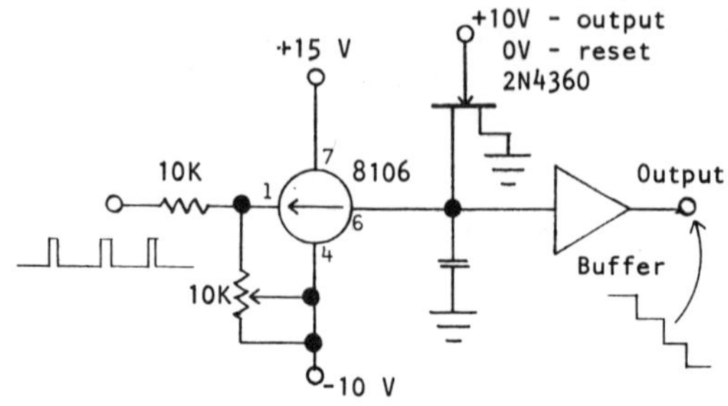

PULSE TRAIN GIVES STAIRCASE—Each input pulse produces current pulse at output of 8106 for charging capacitor in such a way that capacitor voltage increases linearly with each pulse to give staircase. Fet source follower or low-bias-current buffer amplifier must be used to isolate capacitor from low-impedance loads. For repetitive staircase, output voltage level is sampled and used to trigger fet switch that discharges capacitor. Staircase then builds up again from zero to same negative level.—Applying the Model 8106 Monolithic Precision Current Source, Optical Electronics, Tucson, Ariz., No. 10168.

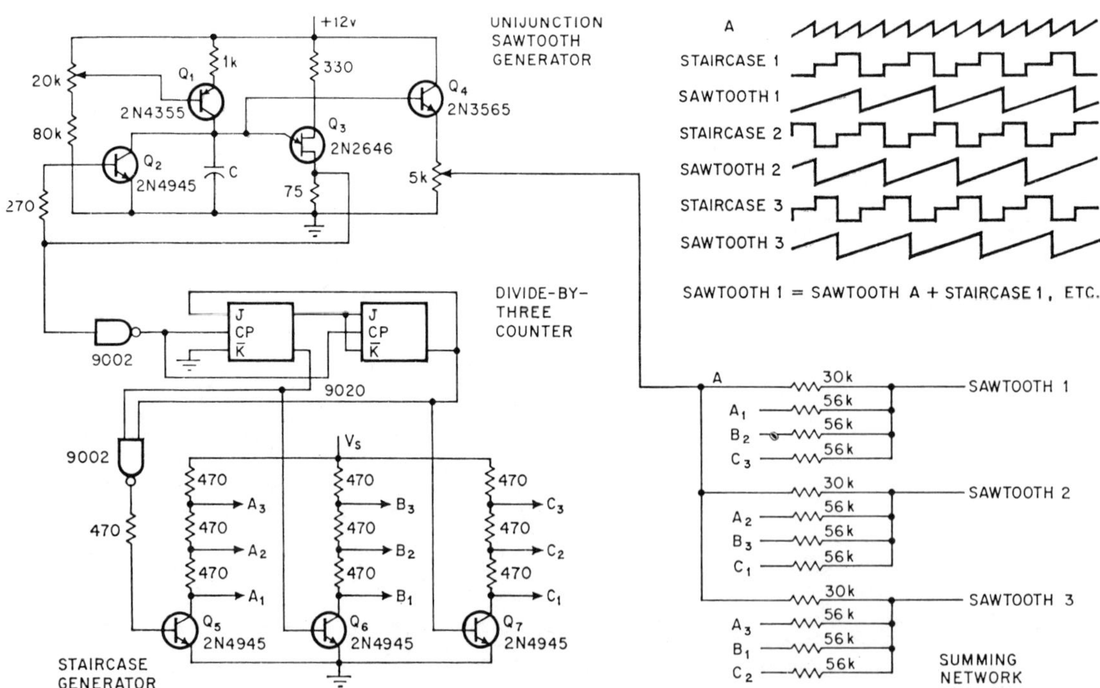

THREE-OUTPUT SAWTOOTH—Combined analog and digital circuit generates staircase whose equal-amplitude steps are added algebraically to ramps of sawtooth generator, for generating long sequential sawtooths in synchronism for crt displays, sweep circuits, and character generators. When ujt fires, counter starts and its outputs switch on Q5, Q6, and Q7 sequentially. Any number of sequential sawtooths may be produced.—E. G. Breeze, A Staircase and a Ramp Yield Multiple Sawtooths, *Electronics*, March 2, 1970, p 105.

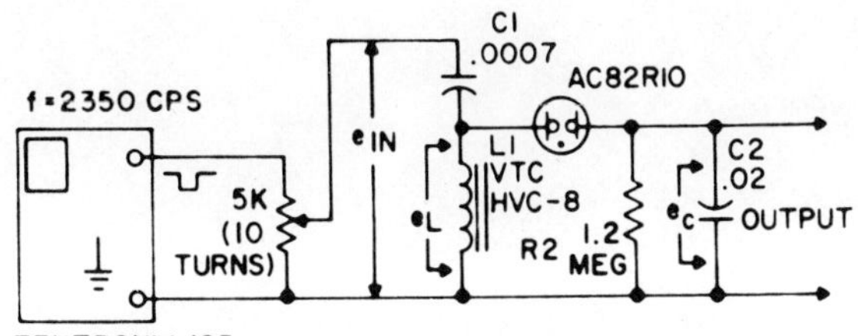

NEON STAIRCASE—Less complex than similar circuits not using neons. May also be used as frequency divider. When input voltage of 54 V is introduced, 3 steps appear across C2. Reducing amplitude of square wave by varying 5K pot increases number of steps. Below 40 V, circuit operates as frequency divider separating out odd pulses.—E. Bauman, "Applications of Neon Lamps and Gas Discharge Tubes," Signalite, Neptune, N.J., p 44–48.

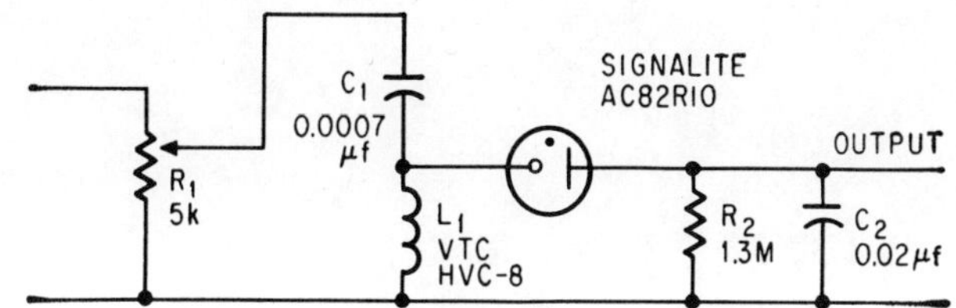

DUAL-FUNCTION NEON—Provides both frequency and voltage division with minimum components. In one mode, circuit divides input voltage into equal steps. In second mode, it acts as frequency divider in separating odd-numbered pulses in input train, eliminating need for decoding logic in binary systems. Mode of operation is determined by range of peak-to-peak input voltage; 32 to 40 gives frequency division, and 44 to 54 gives staircase generation with 4 to 13 steps. —A. B. Cistola, Neon Tube Staircase Generator Performs Two Jobs, *Electronics*, Dec. 26, 1966, p 74–75.

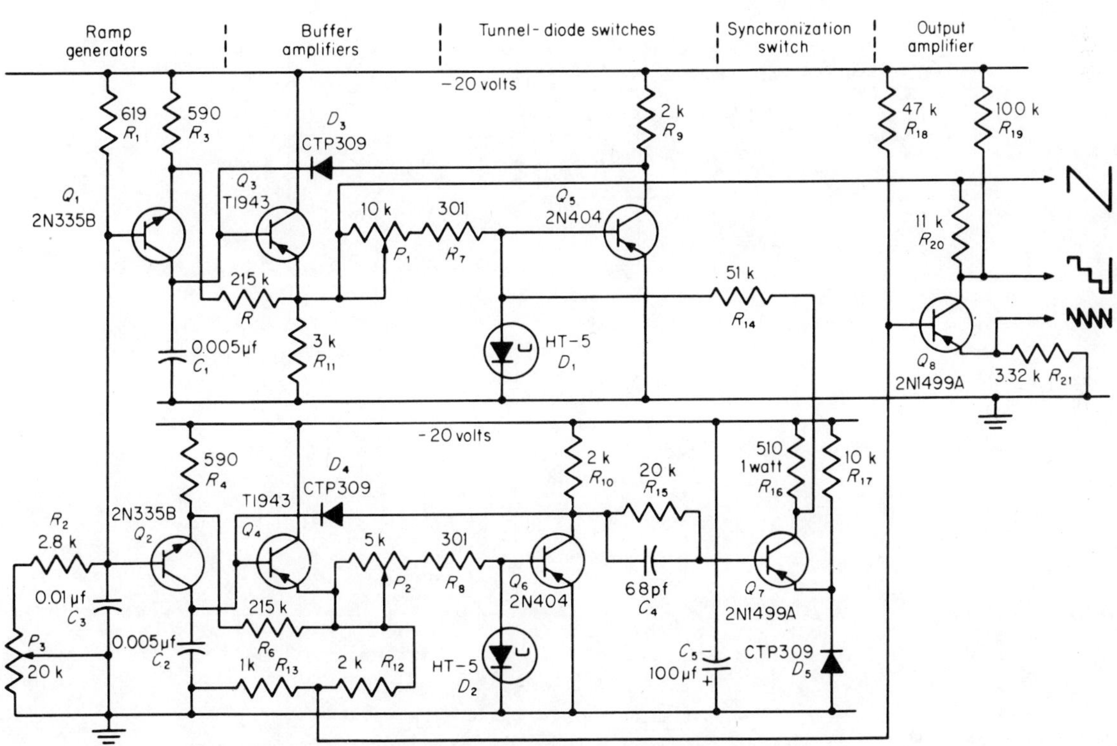

1-MHZ TUNNEL-DIODE—Maximum amplitude of long ramp is 10 V, with duration variable between 20 μs and 2 ms. Steps are equal.—T. Mollinga, Tunnel-Diode Applications, *Electro-Technology*, Sept. 1964, p 48–53.

NOTE: To locate additional circuits in the category of this chapter, use the index at the back of this book. Check also the author's "Sourcebook of Electronic Circuits," published by McGraw-Hill in 1968.

CHAPTER 82
Tachometer Circuits

	No. of Cylinders		
	4	6	8
C1 in mfd for 2-Cycle Engine	0.33	0.22	0.15
C1 in mfd for 4-Cycle Engine	0.68	0.47	0.33

PRECISION TACHOMETER—Designed for 12-V negative-ground ignition system. Counts number of times distributor points close per minute, to give rpm. Uses 500-μA meter movement calibrated linearly in rpm. Zener X11, rated 8.2 V at 1 W, prevents battery and generator fluctuations from affecting accuracy.—"Hobby Manual," General Electric, Owensboro, Ky., 1965, p 56.

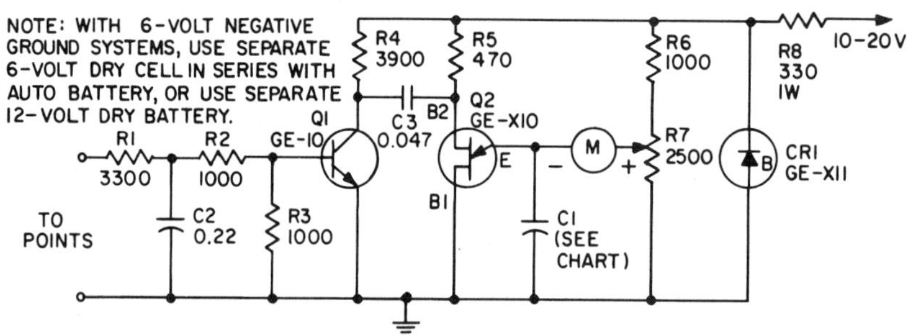

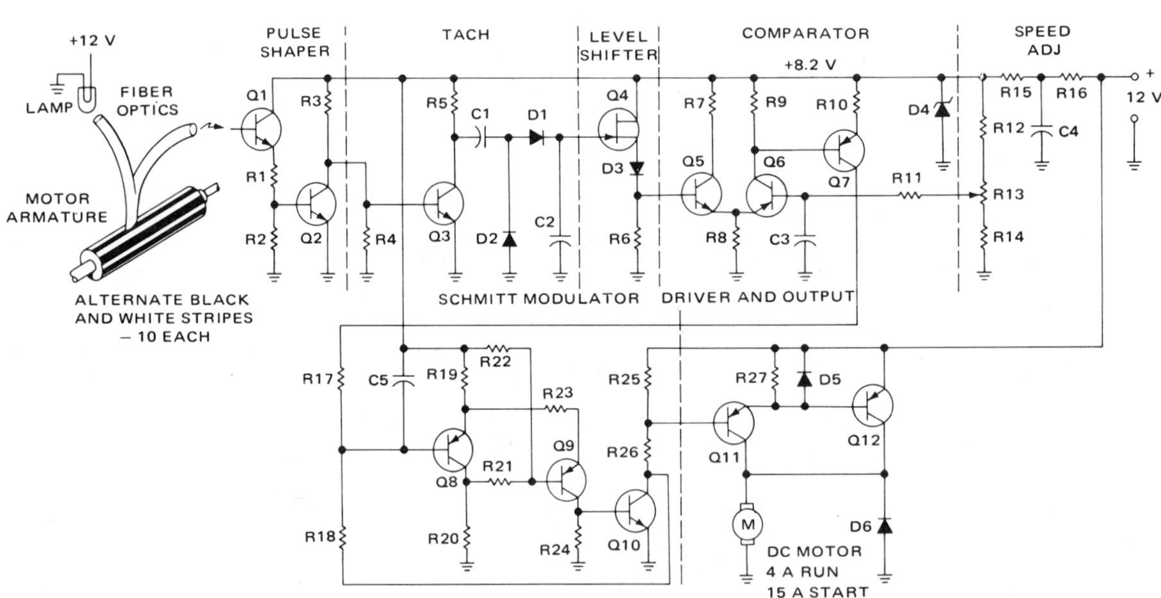

OPTICAL-FEEDBACK CONTROL—Armature of motor was painted with 20 alternating black and white stripes, and fiber optic system used to transmit reflected light to phototransistor Q1, to give chopping at frequency determined by speed of motor. Phototransistor output feeds through pulse shaper to tachometer circuit whose d-c output is proportional to input frequency and hence motor speed. Differential amplifier in comparator compares voltage from speed control R13 with output of tachometer level shifter and delivers error voltage for control of pulse width modulator (Schmitt) Q8-Q9 that drives motor through Darlington power amplifier Q11-Q12. Speed regulation is excellent.—"Semiconductor Power Circuits Handbook," Motorola, Phoenix, Ariz., 1968, p 1—33.

P-M MOTOR SPEED—Counter-emf of permanent-magnet motor charges C1 between power pulses. Voltage across C1, equal to open-circuit counter-emf and proportional to motor speed, is read out on d-c voltmeter. Measuring circuit ignores resistance drop of load current.—J. B. Tiedemann, Permanent-Magnet Motor Measures Its Own Speed, *Electronics*, May 29, 1967, p 84–85.

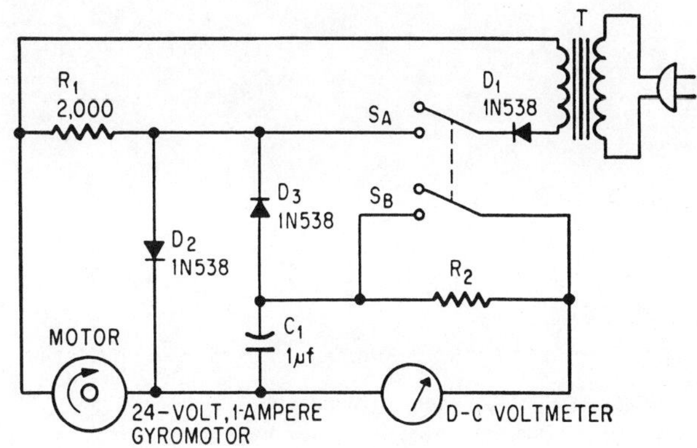

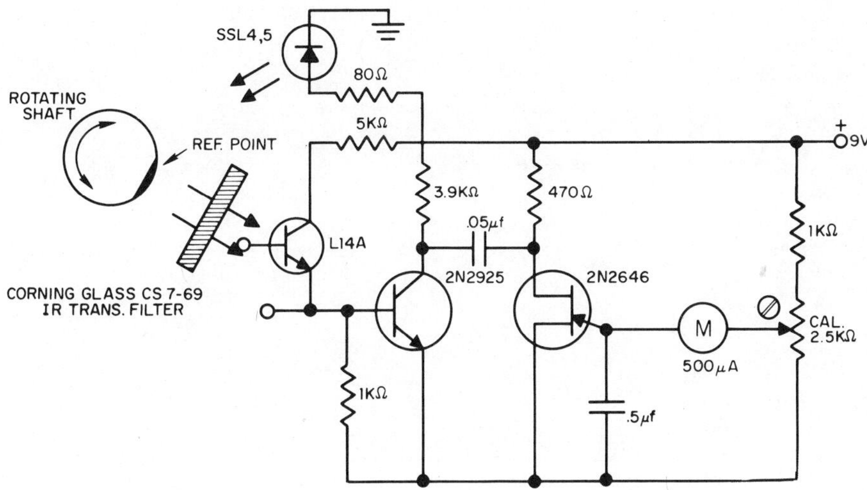

OPTICAL TACHOMETER—Dab of white paint on rotating shaft reflects light to L14A phototransistor when illuminated by solid-state lamp. Filter excludes ambient illumination that might falsely trigger L14A. Circuit converts light pulses to proportional current values indicated on microammeter calibrated in rpm. Will measure speeds as low as 60 rpm.—L. M. Hertz, Solid State Lamps—Part II, General Electric, Nela Park, Cleveland, Ohio, No. 3-0121, 1970, p 23.

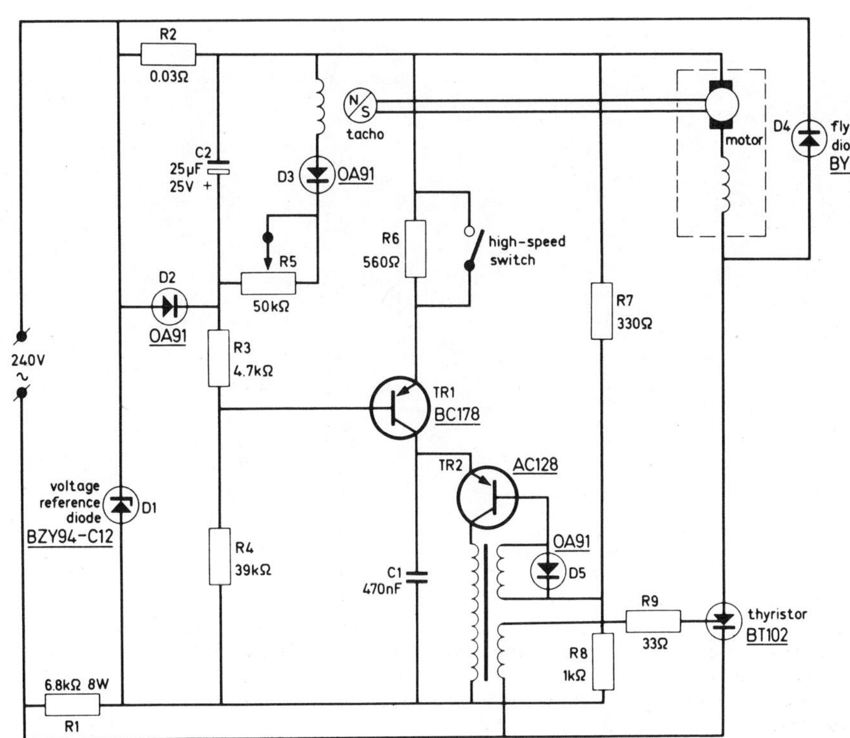

TACHOMETER-FEEDBACK CONTROL OF LARGE FHP MOTOR—Philips BT102 thyristor makes smooth, continuous speed control economical for larger fractional-horsepower motors such as are used in automatic washing machines. Ceramic magnetic material mounted on motor shaft induces pulses in adjacent coil to give tachometer feedback for stabilizing speed against variations in load. Thyristor is triggered by blocking oscillator at point in each half-cycle corresponding to setting of speed control R5, to give 30:1 speed range.—Series Motor Speed Control Systems with Tachometer, Philips, Pub. Dept., Elcoma Div., Eindhoven, The Netherlands, Application No. 6, 1968.

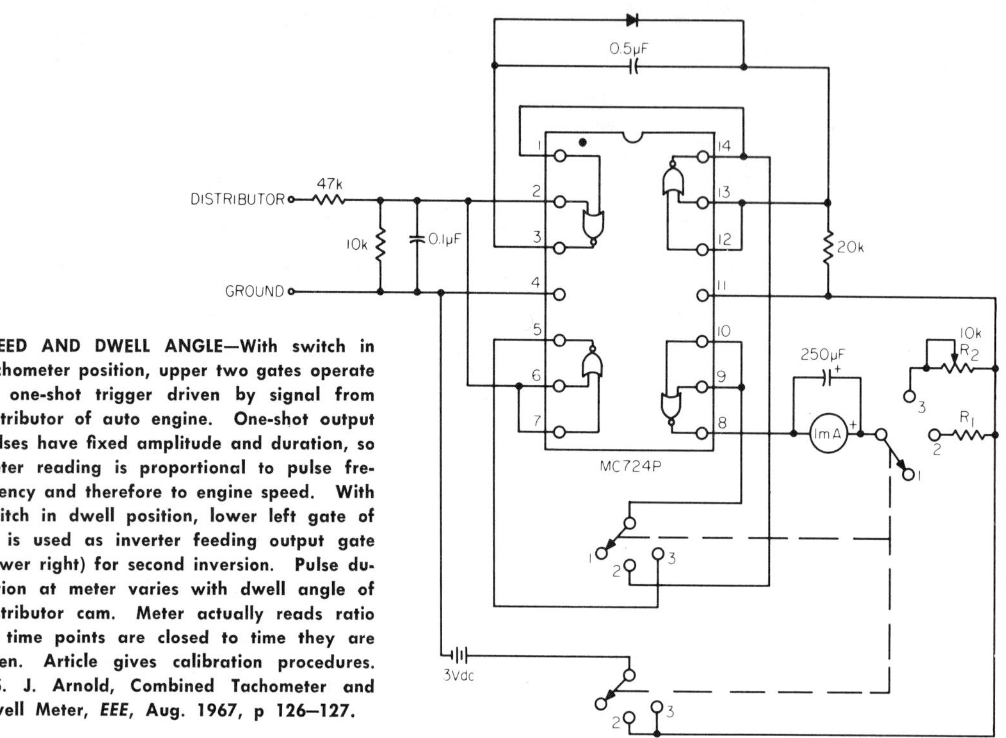

SWITCH POSITIONS: 1-OFF, 2-TACH, 3-DWELL

SPEED AND DWELL ANGLE—With switch in tachometer position, upper two gates operate as one-shot trigger driven by signal from distributor of auto engine. One-shot output pulses have fixed amplitude and duration, so meter reading is proportional to pulse frequency and therefore to engine speed. With switch in dwell position, lower left gate of IC is used as inverter feeding output gate (lower right) for second inversion. Pulse duration at meter varies with dwell angle of distributor cam. Meter actually reads ratio of time points are closed to time they are open. Article gives calibration procedures. —S. J. Arnold, Combined Tachometer and Dwell Meter, *EEE*, Aug. 1967, p 126–127.

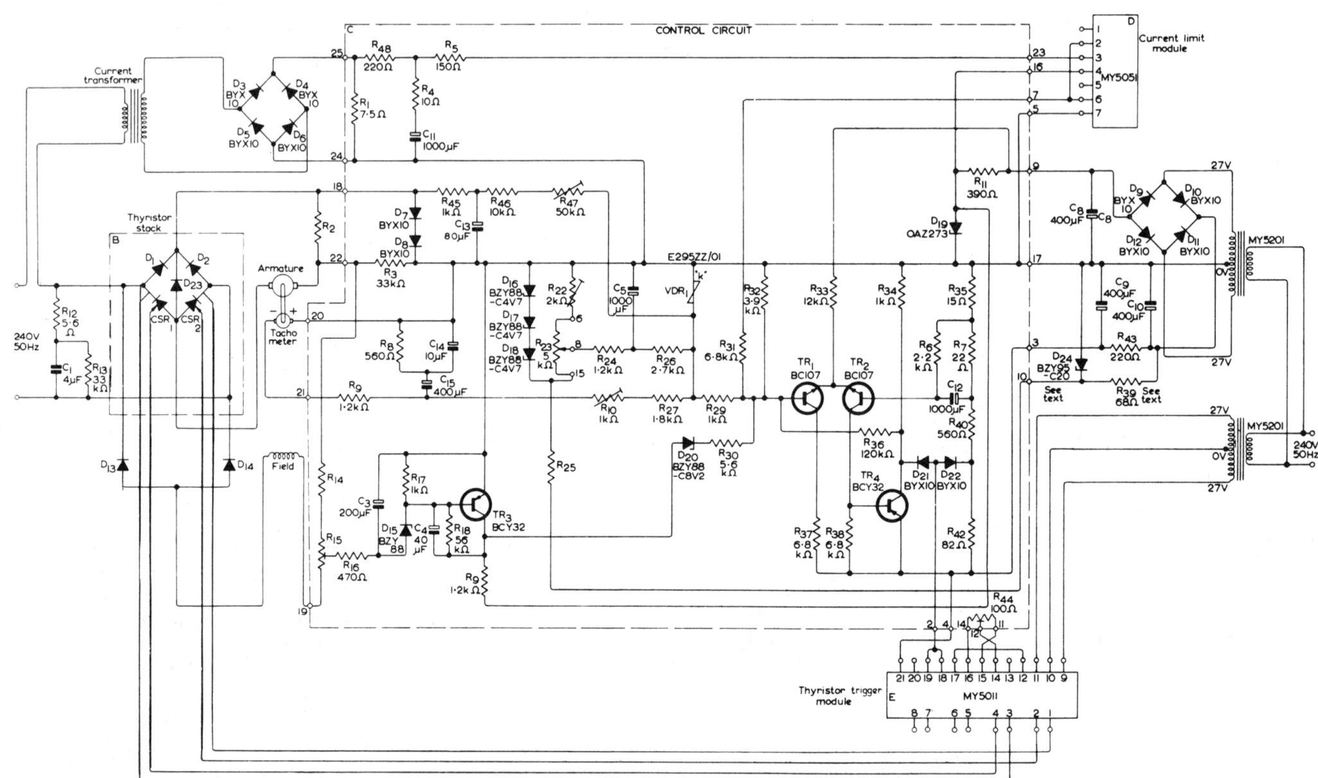

TACHOMETER SPEED CONTROL—Error amplifier uses balanced input to reduce drift caused by temperature or supply voltage changes. Controls 5-hp d-c shunt motor operating from a-c line. Speed regulation is better than 1% at full speed from full load down to 20% load. Report gives design equations. D13 and D14 are Mullard BYX-22-800 or others to suit field current. B is Mullard thyristor stack, D is Mullard MY5051 current-limiting module, and E is Mullard MY5011 trigger module.—J. Merrett, Thyristor Speed Control Circuit Design for D. C. Shunt Motors Supplied from A. C. Mains, Philips, Pub. Dept., Elcoma Div., Eindhoven, The Netherlands, No. 438, 1967.

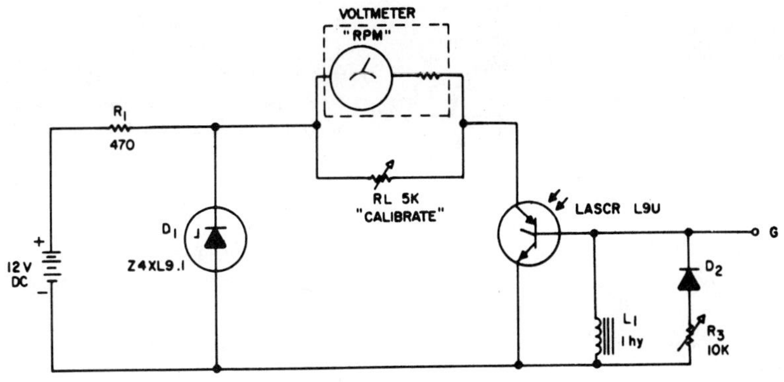

LASCR OPTICAL TACHOMETER—Trigger pulses may be either light on lascr or electrical pulses at G. Average anode current of lascr is proportional to repetition rate of pulses, permitting calibration of voltmeter in rpm.—E. K. Howell, The Light Activated SCR, General Electric, Syracuse, N.Y., No. 200.34, 1965.

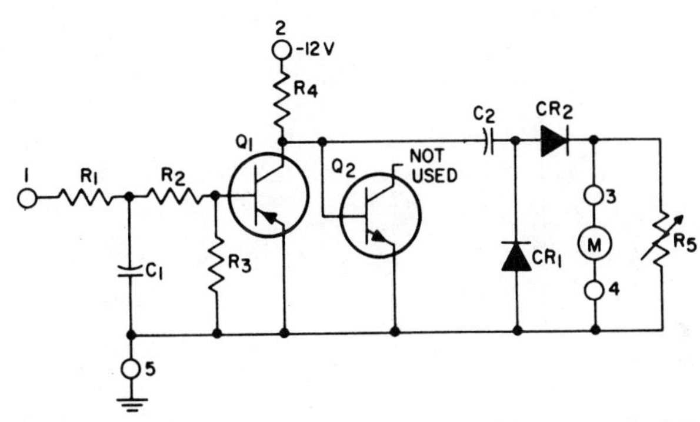

POSITIVE-GROUND TACHOMETER—For auto engines having positive terminal of 12-V battery grounded to frame. Meter specified gives full-scale reading of about 10,000 rpm when pulses from distributor points are applied to terminal 1.—"Hobby Circuits Manual," RCA, Harrison, N.J., HM-90, p 111.

C_1 = 1 microfarad, 50 volts or greater
C_2 = 0.5 microfarad, 50 volts or greater
CR_1CR_2 = silicon rectifier, RCA SK3030
M = milliammeter, 0 to 1 milliampere range (see text)
Q_1 = transistor RCA SK3025 for positive ground, RCA SK3020 for negative ground
Q_2 = transistor, RCA SK3020
R_1 = 22,000 ohms, 1/2 watt, 10%
R_2 = 220 ohms, 1/2 watt, 10%
R_3 = 1500 ohms, 1/2 watt, 10%
R_4 = 330 ohms, 1/2 watt, 10%
R_5 = potentiometer, 1000 ohms, trimmer type, linear taper

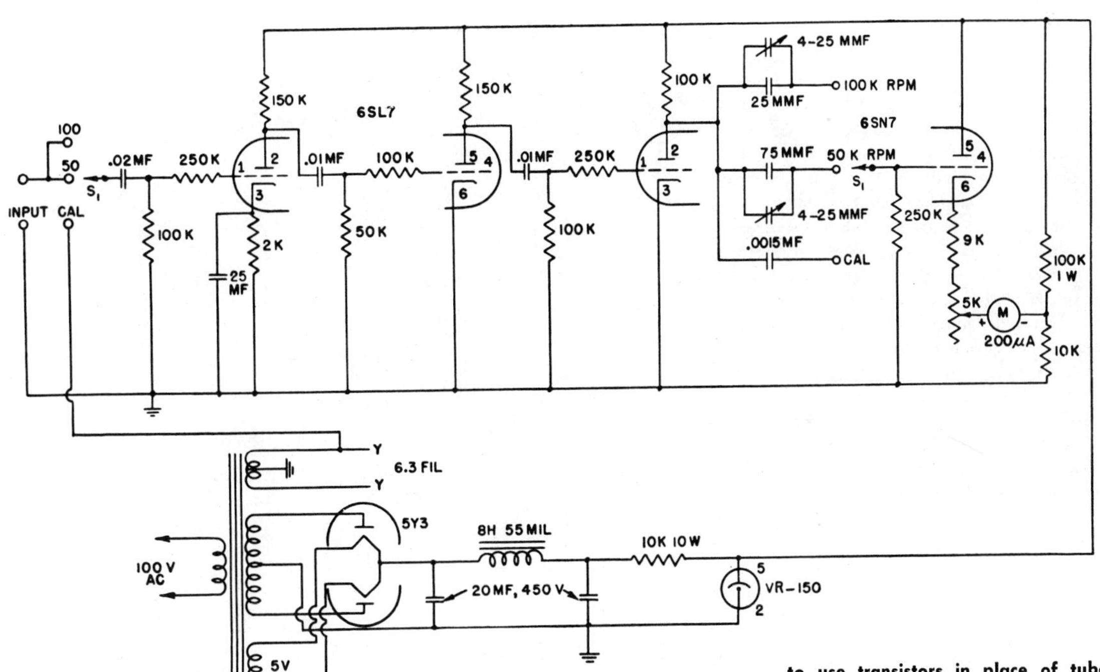

TACHOMETER FOR MISSILE FUZE GENERATOR—Circuit shown was most satisfactory of large number developed during World War II for measuring rotational speeds of generators used in proximity fuzes. Consists of amplifier, wave clipper, and vtvm reading average voltage across R-C network (proportional to speed). Can readily be adapted to use transistors in place of tubes.—A. V. Astin, Editor, "Radio Proximity Fuzes For Fin-Stabilized Missiles," Div. 4, NDRC, Vol. I, 1946 (available from Clearinghouse, Springfield, Va.), p 295.

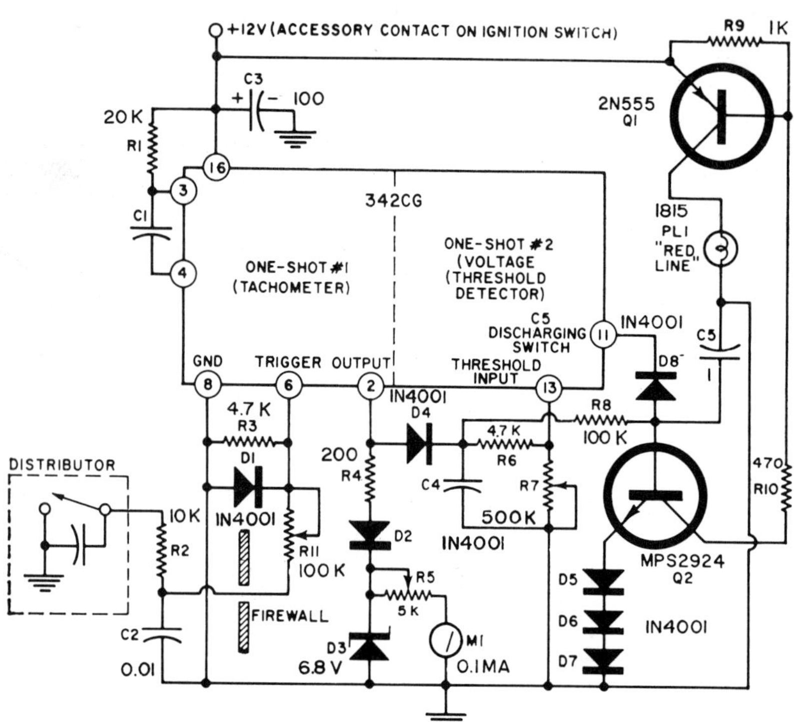

SHIFT-INDICATING TACHOMETER—Circuit turns on red warning lamp at pretetermined engine rpm value to tell driver to shift gears. Eliminates need for watching pointer of tachometer. Built around integrated circuit having two identical one-shot multivibrators. Can be calibrated with audio oscillator.—R. A. Hirschfeld, IC Engine Tachometer and "Red Line" Indicator, *Electronics World*, May 1967, p 37–39.

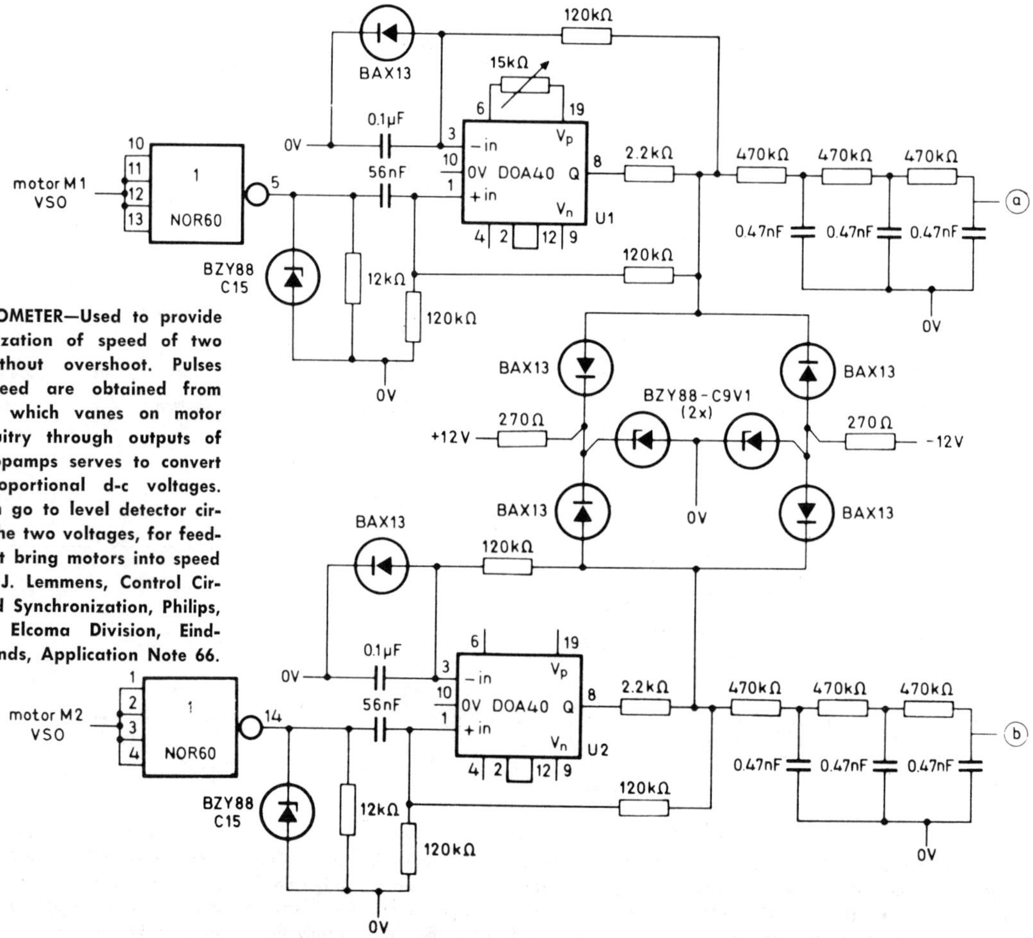

TWO-MOTOR TACHOMETER—Used to provide very fast synchronization of speed of two electric motors without overshoot. Pulses proportional to speed are obtained from coils (VSO) thrugh which vanes on motor shafts move. Circuitry through outputs of Philips DOA40 IC opamps serves to convert pulse rates to proportional d-c voltages. Points a and b then go to level detector circuit that compares the two voltages, for feeding logic circuits that bring motors into speed synchronization.—L. J. Lemmens, Control Circuit for Motor Speed Synchronization, Philips, Publications Dept., Elcoma Division, Eindhoven, The Netherlands, Application Note 66.

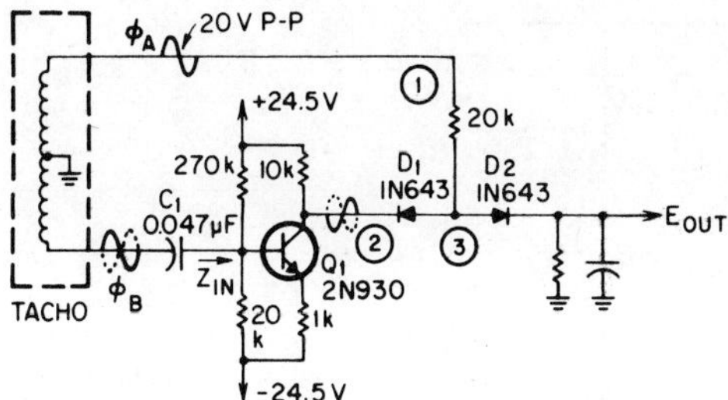

A-C TACH—Circuit detects whether there is 90-deg lead or lag between phases of two-phase tachometer, and can be used with peak detector and suitable threshold circuit to provide two discrete output logic levels that indicate direction of rotation.—T. B. Hooker, Phase Indicator for AC Tachometer, *EEE*, May 1969, p 118.

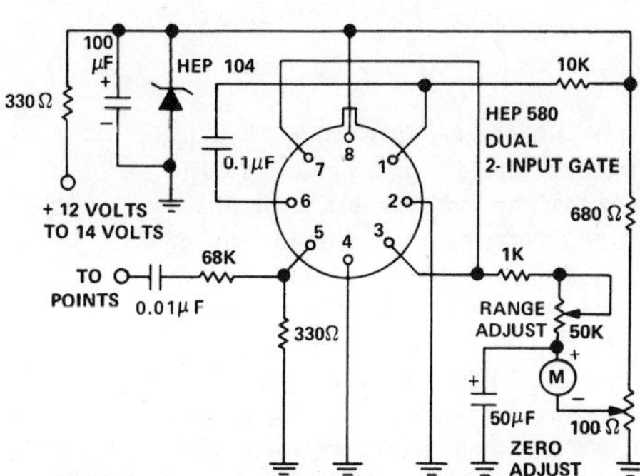

PRECISION IC TACHOMETER—Easily adjustable for different ranges and number of cylinders. Calibrating instructions are given.—"Tips on Using IC's," HMA-32, Motorola, Phoenix, Ariz., 1968.

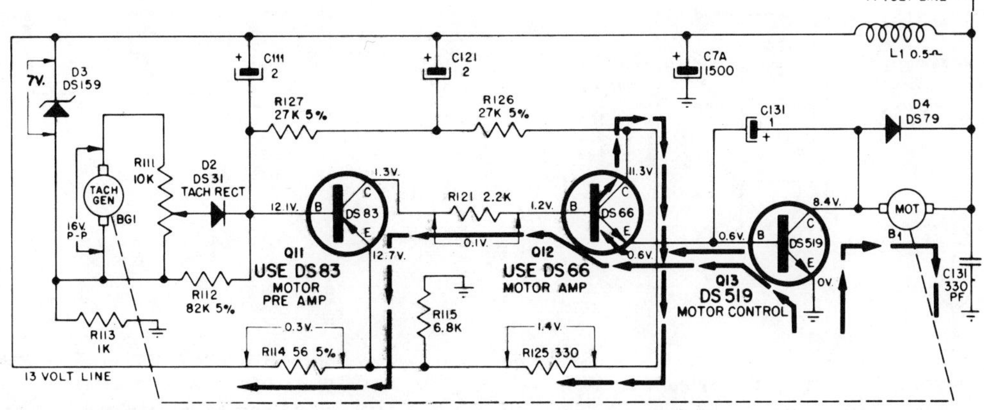

TAPE PLAYER SPEED CONTROL—Tachometer on shaft of drive motor produces a-c voltage directly proportional to speed. Tachometer output is applied to speed control pot, then rectified and resulting d-c voltage applied to three-transistor d-c amplifier that changes voltage across motor as required to give desired speed.—New Motor Speed Control Circuit and Inverted Cam Mechanism, Delco Radio, Kokomo, Ind., Bulletin 6D-1970-1, Supplement No. 3, 1969, p G-19.

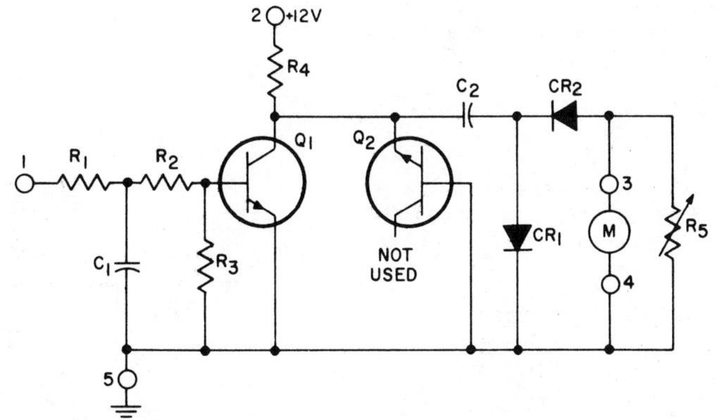

NEGATIVE-GROUND TACHOMETER—Used to indicate speed in rpm of auto engines having 12-V storage battery with negative terminal grounded to frame. Pulses from distributor points are applied to terminal 1 to turn Q1 on and off as points open and close. Meter deflection is proportional to rate of closing. Q2 acts as zener to make circuit insensitive to voltage variations. R5 is used when calibrating tachometer. Meter specified will have full-scale reading of 8,000 to 10,000 rpm.—"Hobby Circuits Manual," RCA, Harrison, N.J., HM-90, p 111.

C_1 = 1 microfarad, 50 volts or greater
C_2 = 0.5 microfarad, 50 volts or greater
CR_1CR_2 = silicon rectifier, RCA SK3030
M = milliammeter, 0 to 1 milliampere range (see text)
Q_1 = transistor RCA SK3025 for positive ground, RCA SK3020 for negative ground
Q_2 = transistor, RCA SK3020
R_1 = 22,000 ohms, 1/2 watt, 10%
R_2 = 220 ohms, 1/2 watt, 10%
R_3 = 1500 ohms, 1/2 watt, 10%
R_4 = 330 ohms, 1/2 watt, 10%
R_5 = potentiometer, 1000 ohms, trimmer type, linear taper

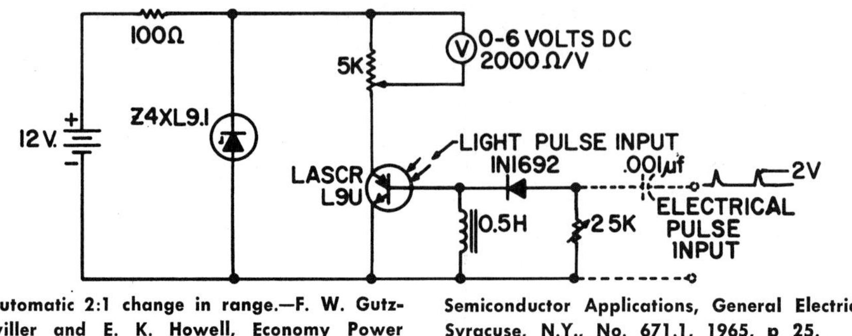

LASCR TACHOMETER—Light-activated scr serves as low-current gate-turnoff switch, triggered either by light or electrical pulse. Meter reading depends on repetition rate of triggering pulses. Voltmeter should be set for full-scale deflection when trigger rate is high enough so average current and peak current of scr are equal. Further increase in trigger rate then gives pulse-skipping or frequency-dividing action in which lascr conducts only on alternate pulses. This gives automatic 2:1 change in range.—F. W. Gutzwiller and E. K. Howell, Economy Power Semiconductor Applications, General Electric, Syracuse, N.Y., No. 671.1, 1965, p 25.

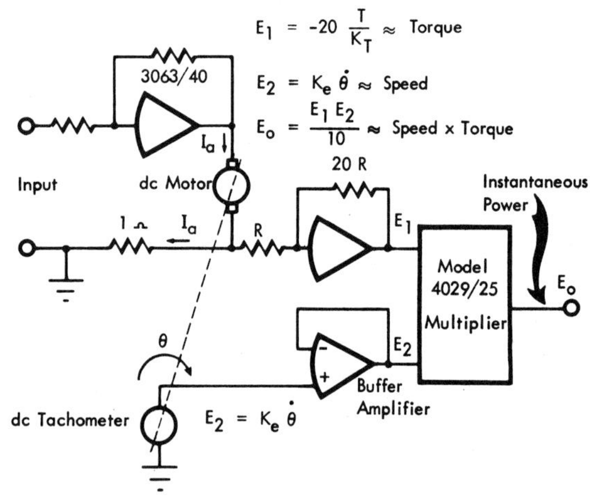

MOTOR SPEED-TORQUE PRODUCT—Uses Burr-Brown 4029/25 quarter-square multiplier-divider to give instantaneous product of motor speed and torque, as required for measuring instantaneous output power. D-c tachometer on motor shaft gives speed in electrical form, and current through p-m d-c servomotor serves as other input because it is linearily proportional to torque. Article gives relevant equations.—Quarter-Square Multiplier/Dividers, Burr-Brown Research, Tucson, Ariz., PDS-201C, 1969, p 7.

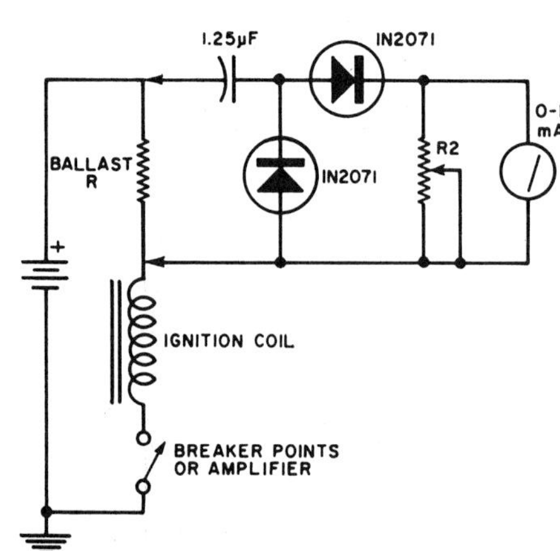

BALLAST-RESISTOR DRIVE FOR TACHOMETER—Clean voltage pulse of 4 to 12 V is available from 1-ohm ballast resistor used in every 12-V automotive ignition system, in form of length of resistance wire connected between ignition switch and positive terminal of ignition coil. Value of calibration potentiometer R2 depends on meter used. Circuit eliminates transient errors, so linearity is limited only by that of meter used.—R. L. Carroll, New Approach to Engine Tachometers, *Electronics World*, Sept. 1967, p 71.

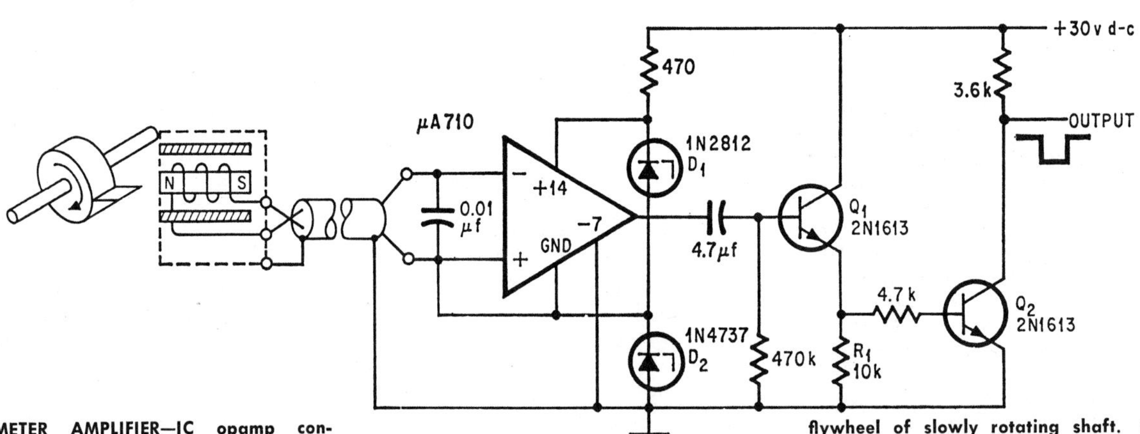

TACHOMETER AMPLIFIER—IC opamp connected for gain of 1,000 delivers pulse capable of driving Q1 into saturation, as required for emitter-follower Q2 to produce 30-V negative output pulse. Input is voltage induced in relay coil by triangular magnet on flywheel of slowly rotating shaft. Core of coil is Alnico magnet.—G. D. Morant, Op Amp Boosts Pick-up Voltage, *Electronics*, Aug. 5, 1968, p 108.

CHAPTER 83
Telemetry Circuits

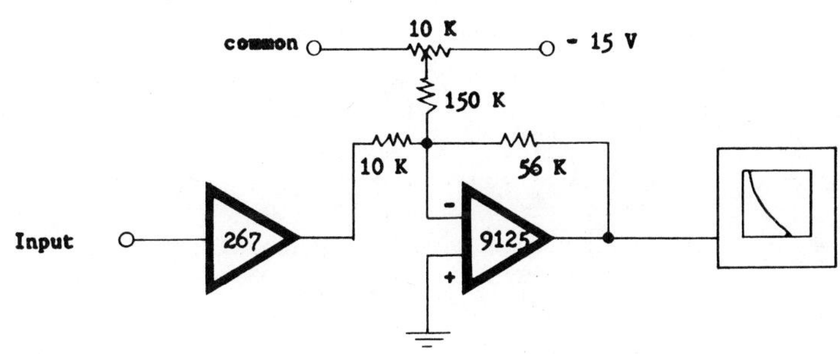

STRIP-CHART DRIVE—May be used also with X-Y and T-Y recorders. Values shown are for 1 V full-scale. For telemetry systems requiring 5 V full-scale, increase feedback resistor to 270K plus 10K in series. Uses OEI Model 267 logamp to drive opamp. System accuracy is within 2%.—Using Low Cost Logarithmic Amplifiers in Data Recording, Optical Electronics, Tuscon, Ariz., No. 10080.

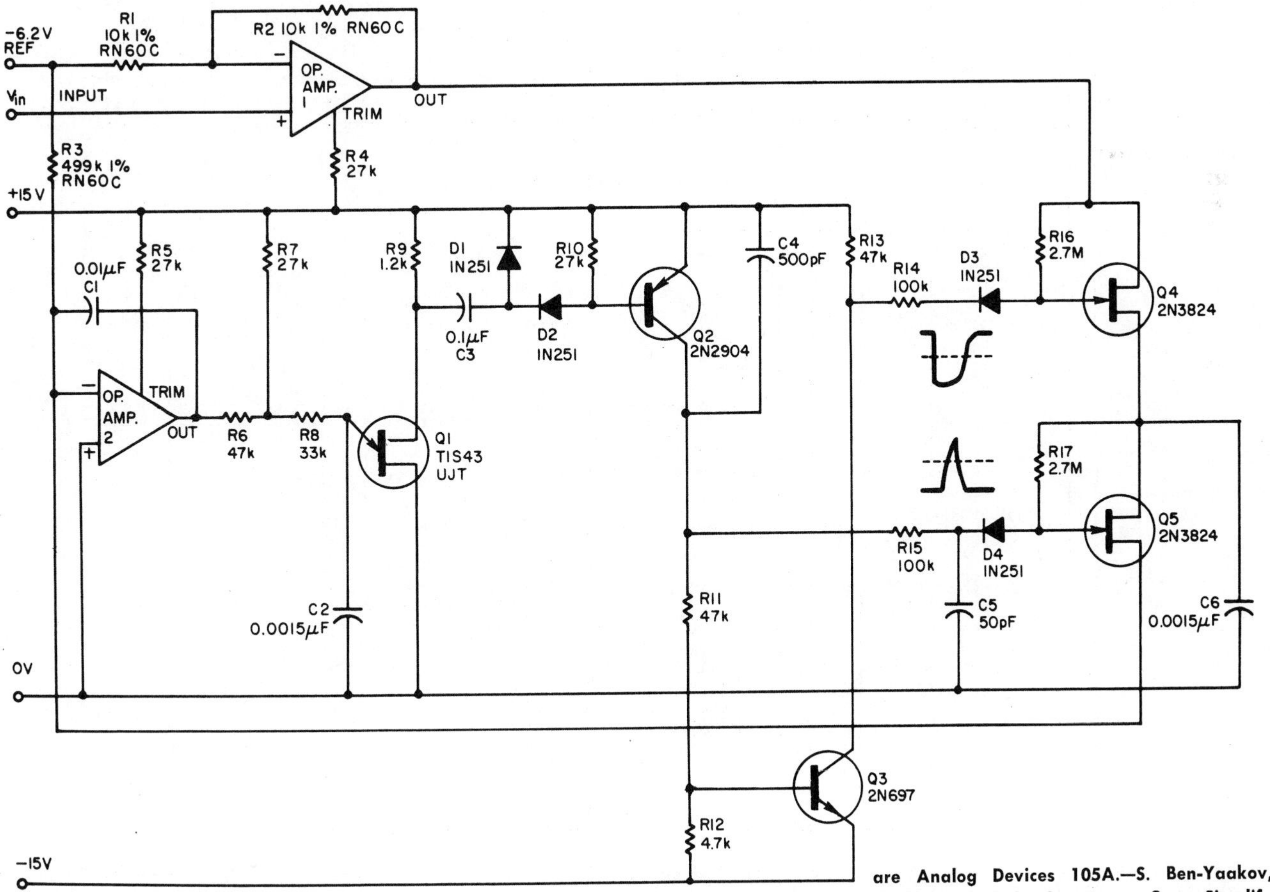

ANALOG-PERIOD CONVERTER—Converts input voltage to sawtooth whose period is linear function of input voltage over input signal range of −1 V to +1 V. With opamp (serving as summing amplifier) omitted, circuit is analog-frequency converter. Opamps are Analog Devices 105A.—S. Ben-Yaakov, Analog-To-Period Converter Can Simplify Telemetry Systems, *Electronic Design*, Aug. 16, 1969, p 240 and 242.

IC RECEIVER—Sinusoidal input from telemetry transforming media goes to Model 571 IC frequency-to-voltage transducer, and resulting logarithmically compressed signal is converted back to original data voltage input in Model 326 antilogarithmic amplifier.—A Wide Dynamic Range Telemetry System, Optical Electronics, Tucson, Ariz., No. 10062.

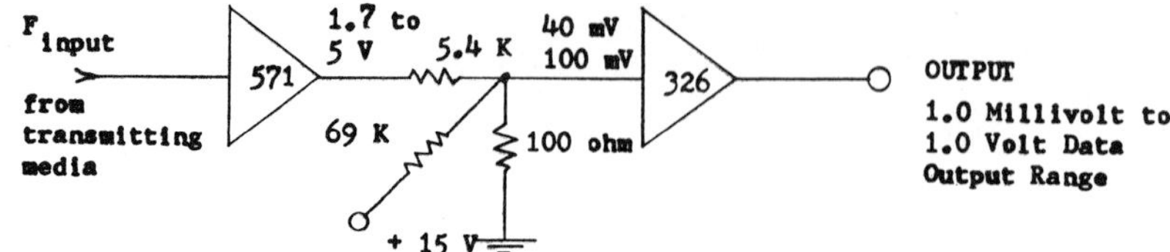

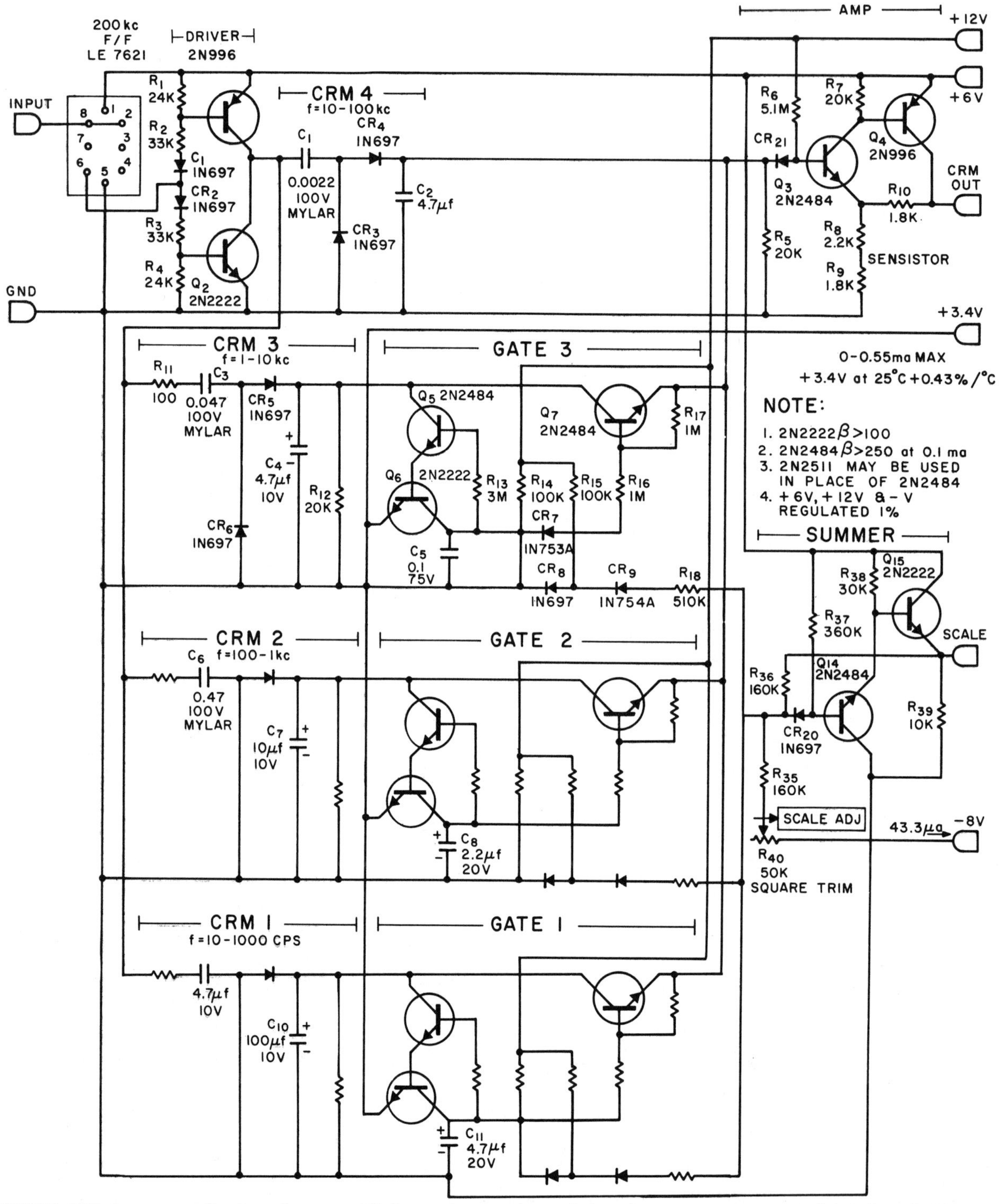

NOTE:
1. 2N2222 β>100
2. 2N2484 β>250 at 0.1 ma
3. 2N2511 MAY BE USED IN PLACE OF 2N2484
4. +6V, +12V & -V REGULATED 1%

FOUR-DECADE CRM—Improves utilization of two telemetry channels. One channel is switched from one count-rate meter (CRM) to next as input rate changes, while other channel indicates which meter is being read out. Eliminates decrease in resolution that would occur if one rate meter covered entire range. Circuit consumes little power and is unaffected by wide temperature swings. Decade inputs are connected in parallel, while outputs are paralleled through OR gates so only highest is read out into telemetry system. Frequency coverage is 10 pps to 100 kHz.—S. Thomas, N-Decade Count-Rate Meter, *Electronic Design*, March 15, 1965, p 34–39.

REGENERATIVE SWITCH—Removes sine-wave carrier in f-m/f-m telemetry, leaving only required pulse modulation waveform for use in digital circuits. Values shown are for 20-kHz carrier and digital transfer rate of 2.5 kHz. Filter in feedback circuit keeps hysteresis low.—W. S. Silbert, Regenerative Switch Demodulates Sinusoid, "400 Ideas for Design Selected from Electronic Design," Hayden Book Co., N.Y., 1964, p 195–196.

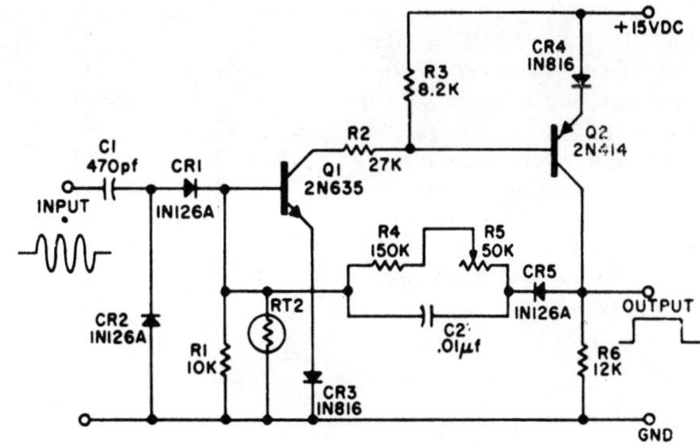

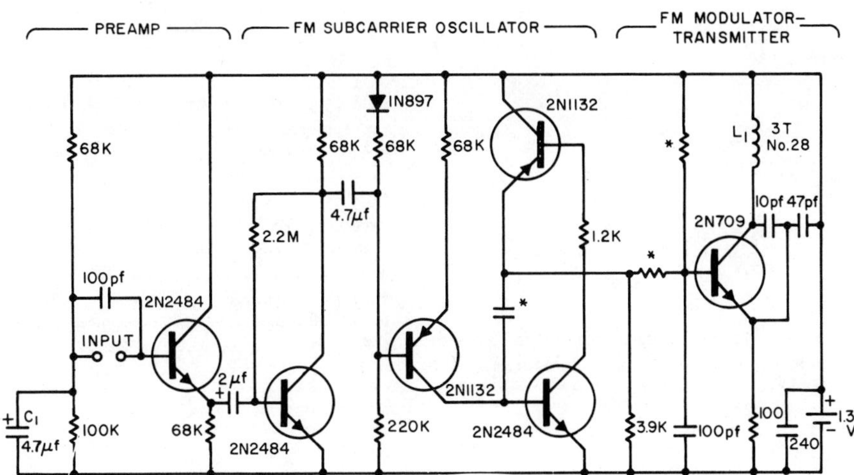

BIOPOTENTIALS—F-m telemetry circuit has 20-meg input impedance for nerve signals and 0.5–120 Hz response. Used in research for measuring signals along various paths linking retina of eye with brain. Values of asterisked components depend on desired battery life and transmitting range.—D. Harnar, Bio-Engineering Scores Wider Successes, *Electronic Design*, Dec. 21, 1964, p 6–9.

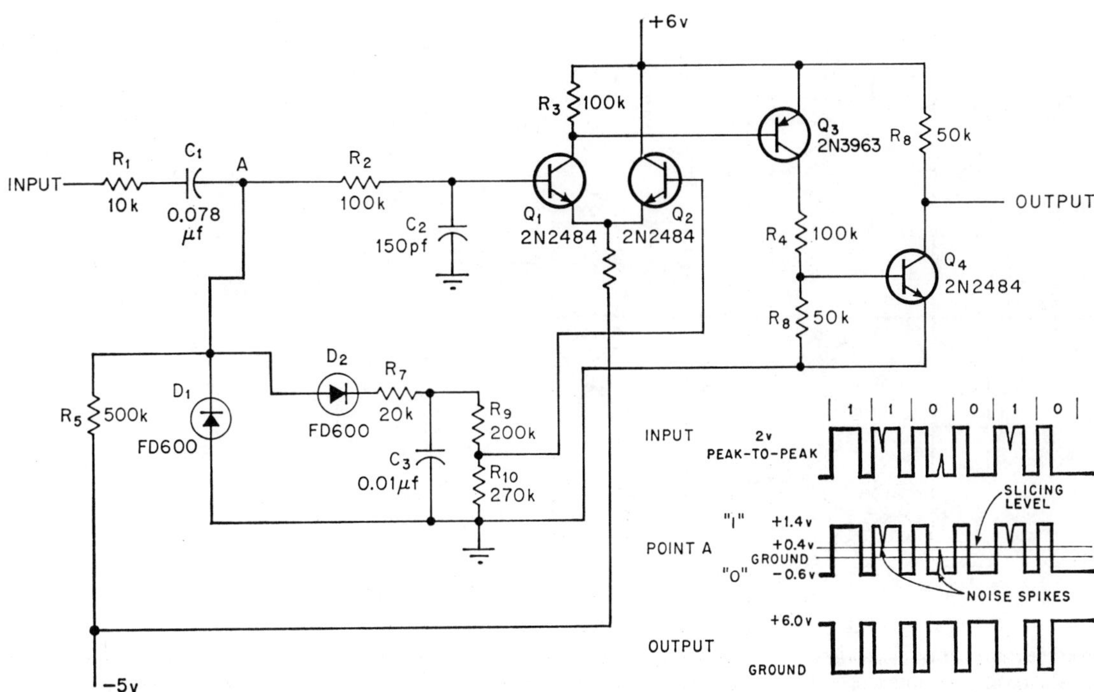

NOISE SUPPRESSOR—Provides 8-dB improvement in signal-to-noise ratio for 4-kHz input signals by driving output to full value whenever input varies from its nominal level by only few millivolts.—J. Schlageter, Telemetry Signal Conditioner Centers Its Slicing Level, *Electronics*, June 8, 1970, p 97.

LIZARD TEMPERATURE TELEMETER—Tiny pulsed Hartley oscillator operating at low duty cycle has average battery drain of 110 μA, giving transmitting life of 130 days with 350 mA-hr mercury cell. Pulse rate is controlled by temperature-sensing resistor R1. Transmitted signal has narrow bandwidth in range of 0.5 to 2 MHz.—H. Spencer, Thermally Stable Telemeter for Thermoregulation Studies, *Science*, Aug. 1968, p 574–575.

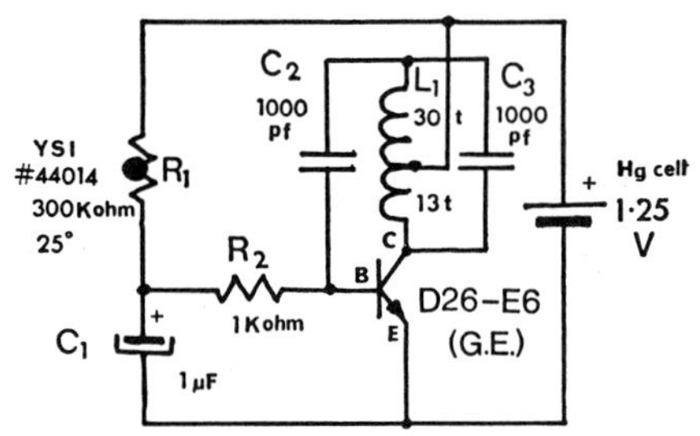

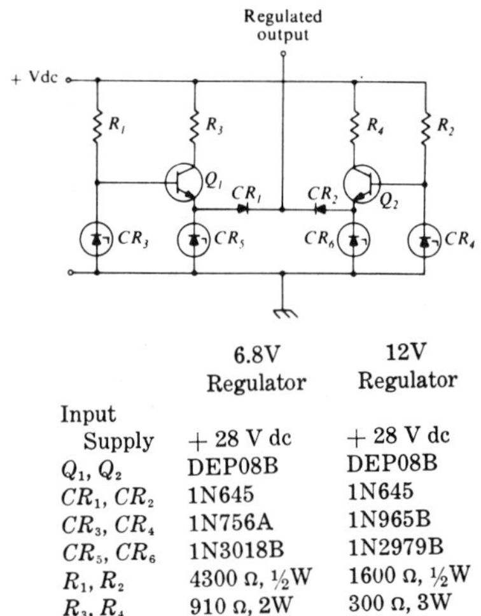

	6.8V Regulator	12V Regulator
Input Supply	+ 28 V dc	+ 28 V dc
Q_1, Q_2	DEP08B	DEP08B
CR_1, CR_2	1N645	1N645
CR_3, CR_4	1N756A	1N965B
CR_5, CR_6	1N3018B	1N2979B
R_1, R_2	4300 Ω, ½W	1600 Ω, ½W
R_3, R_4	910 Ω, 2W	300 Ω, 3W

FAIL-SAFE DESIGN—Achieves high reliability through redundancy. Regulated output remains constant if any single component fails or if one of many combinations of multiple failures occurs, with no excessive voltages on circuit. Intended for power supplies at relay stations, satellite equipment, and remote unattended communication and data telemetry stations.—"Selected Electronic Circuitry," NASA SP-5046, 1966, Government Printing Office, Washington, D.C., p 36.

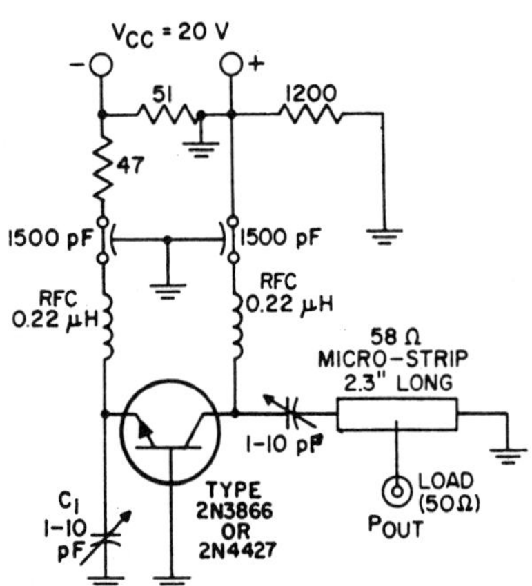

500-MHZ MICROSTRIPLINE OSCILLATOR—Provides 1 W when operating from 20-V d-c supply, for use as telemetering transmitter, radiosonde, artillery fuze, beacon, or remote sensor. Taps on output stripline can provide matching to wide range of loads.—"Silicon Power Circuits Manual," RCA, Harrison, N.J., SP-51, p 346.

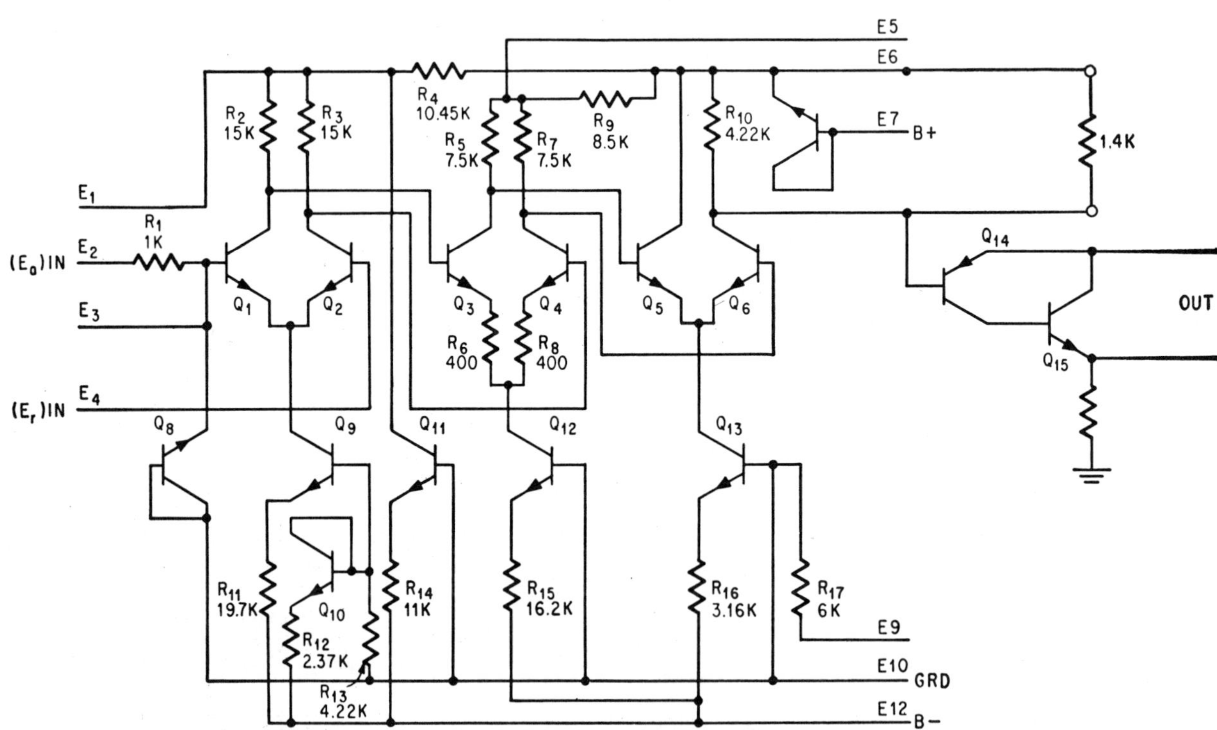

DIFFERENTIAL COMPARATOR—Combination of custom monolithic IC and outboarded level shift resolves signal differences in telemetry system and provides linear output level indicating which of two input voltages is greater. IC uses three cascaded direct-coupled differential amplifier stages working into single-ended output. External 1.4K load resistor and pnp level-shift stage Q14-Q15 help maintain minimum overall gain of 15,000. Article describes other TRW custom IC's used in same system.—D. P. Schulz and D. J. Dooley, Integrating Space Telemetry Systems with Compatible Thin Films on Silicon, *Electronics*, June 26, 1967, p 111–122.

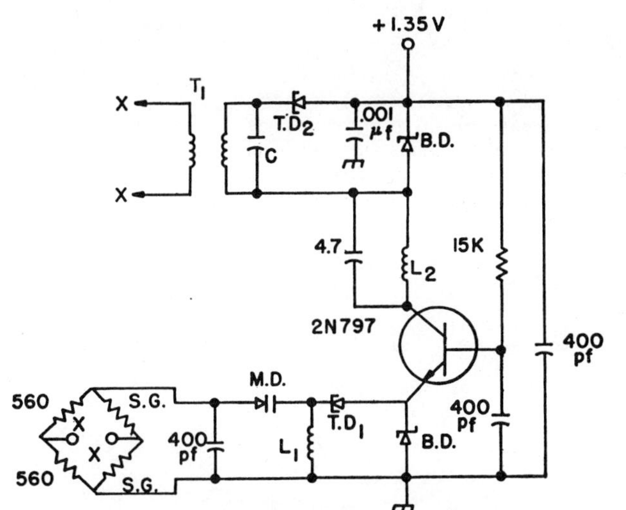

22-KHZ IMPLANT TRANSMITTER—Used to monitor intestinal pressures in animals. Strain gages (in bridge) are sutured to small intestine, and degree of balance of bridge arm is used to modulate subcarrier that in turn modulates carrier oscillator. Signal is picked up by f-m receiver having subcarrier filter, a-m detector, and recorder.—W. H. Ko and M. R. Neuman, Implant Biotelemetry and Microelectronics, *Science*, April 1967, p 351–360.

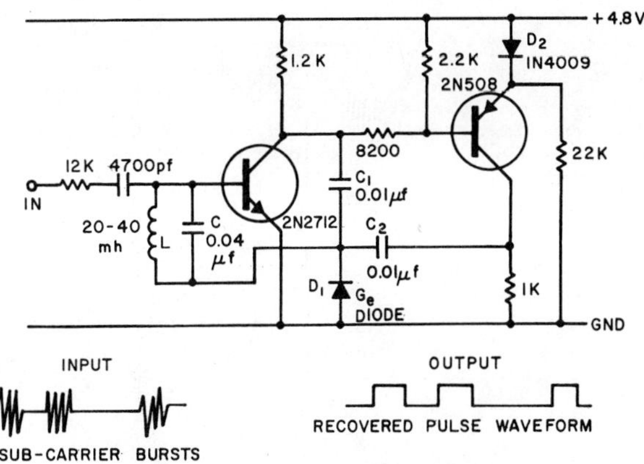

4-KHZ SUBCARRIER BURST REGENERATION—Frequency-selective L-C input network with 100-Hz passband recognizes only desired pulse modulation of 4-kHz subcarrier. Circuit delivers clean regenerated pulse. D2 provides 0.5-V threshold against noise pulses. —J. H. Phelps, Selective Circuit Provides High Pulse Regeneration, *Electronic Design*, March 16, 1964, p 103.

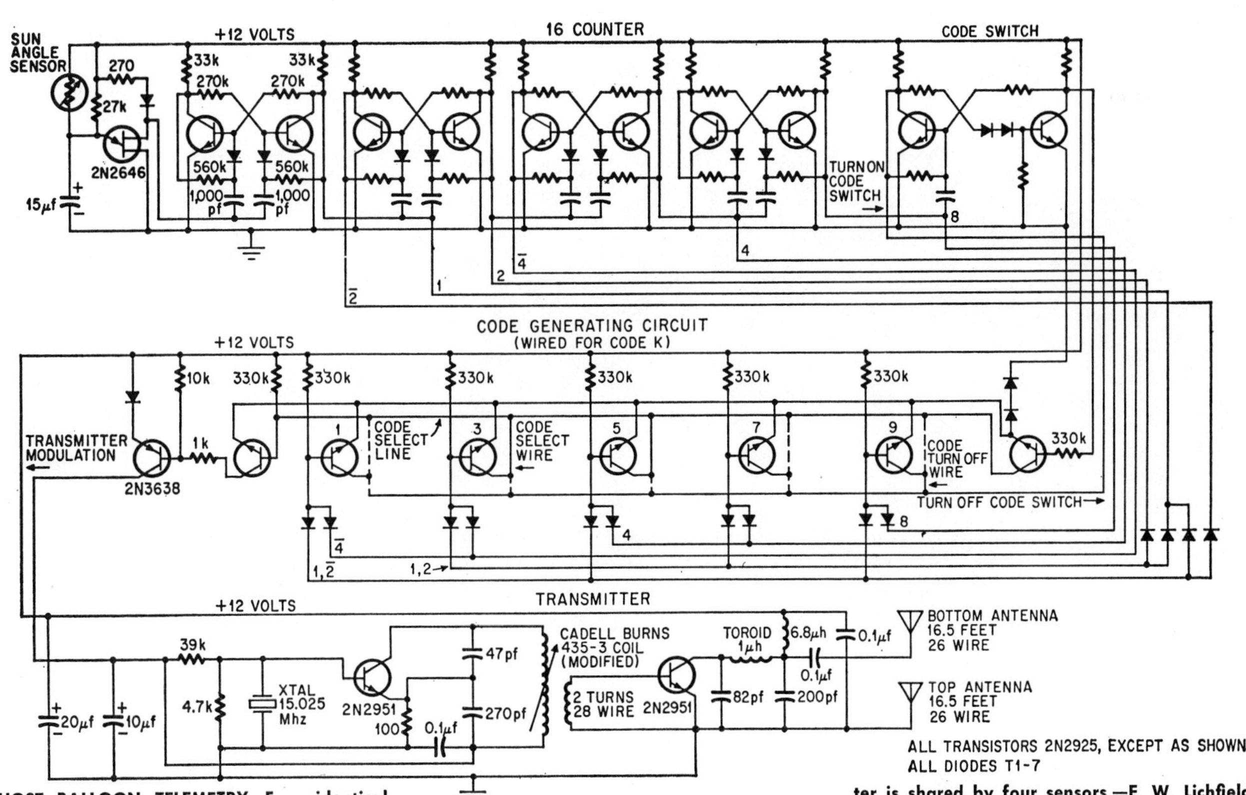

GHOST BALLOON TELEMETRY—Four identical flip-flops in 16-counter, five NAND gates, and mvbr switch serve as code generating and repeating circuits for Project GHOST (Global HOrizontal Sounding Technique). Circuit operates on maximum power of 150 mA at 12 V generated by solar-cell panel. Transmitter is shared by four sensors.—E. W. Lichfield and R. W. Frykman, Ghost Balloons Riding the Skies Will Report the World's Weather, *Electronics*, No. 28, 1966, p 98–106.

1,000-MHZ LUMPED-CONSTANT OSCILLATOR—Simple circuit delivers 0.5 W at 700 to 1,000 MHz, for use as low-power transmitter in telemetry and other applications.—"Silicon Power Circuits Manual," RCA, Harrison, N.J., SP-51, p 347.

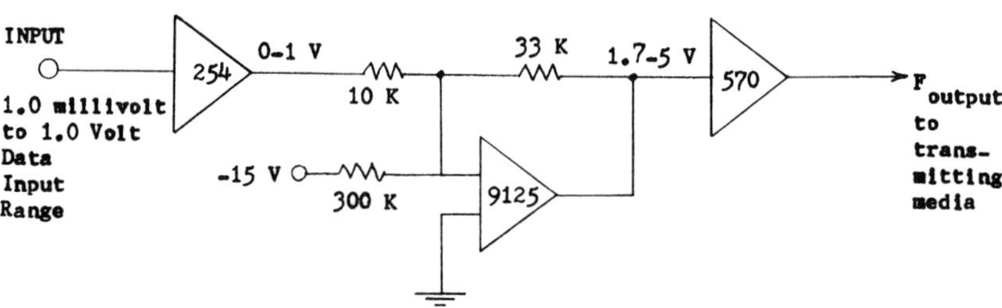

THREE-IC TRANSMITTER—Input signal is compressed in OEI Model 254 IC logamp and resulting signal with 3:1 dynamic range fed to OEI Model 570 voltage-to-frequency IC transducer to give proportional sinusoidal output for transmitting over telephone lines, a-m or f-m radio link, laser beam, or light beam. Model 9125 opamp establishes proper voltage levels for 570. Upper limit of frequency response is 1 kHz.—A Wide Dynamic Range Telemetry System, Optical Electronics, Tucson, Ariz., No. 10062.

NOTE: To locate additional circuits in the category of this chapter, use the index at the back of this book. Check also the author's "Sourcebook of Electronic Circuits," published by McGraw-Hill in 1968.

CHAPTER 84
Telephone Circuits

MANUAL PHONE PATCH—Prevents tripping of transmitter at wrong time, with resultant doubling and need for repeats during excitement of carrying on radio conversation from remote telephone. Parts values are not critical, except for transformers that must provide required impedance match.—G. L. Erland, A Junk Box Phone Patch, CQ, Oct. 1969, p 47–48.

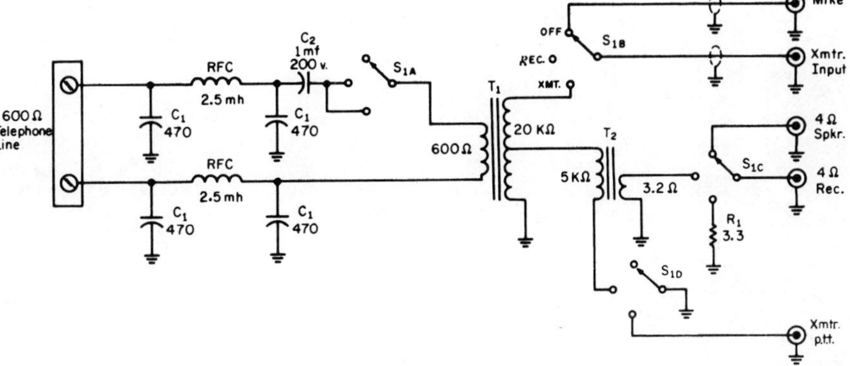

PHONE-PATCH TIMER—High-accuracy circuit can be set to produce speaker beep and warning light flash at any rate from one per second to one every 12 minutes. Can be set as 10-minute reminder for identifying amateur radio call, 3-minute reminder for long-distance phone calls, and as beep generator required by law for recording phone conversations. Reset switch may be used at any time to initiate new timing interval.—J. Ouellette, The Ten Minute Minder, CQ, May 1965, p 60.

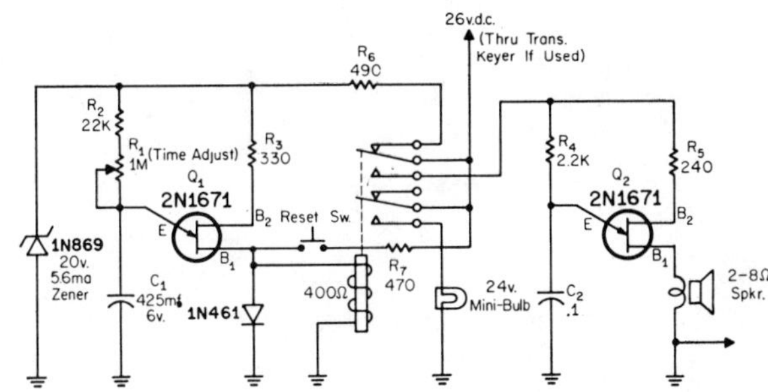

R-C LINE EQUALIZER—Eliminates bulky inductors when transmitting data over phone lines. Circuit is easy to align to attenuation characteristics of given line. Used for transmitting 50-kilobit data in which waveform has frequency components from 10 to 70,000 Hz. Article gives equalizer transfer function equation and Bode plot.—A. R. Campbell, Line Equalizer Uses Active RC Network, *Electronic Design*, Feb. 1, 1969, p 74 and 76.

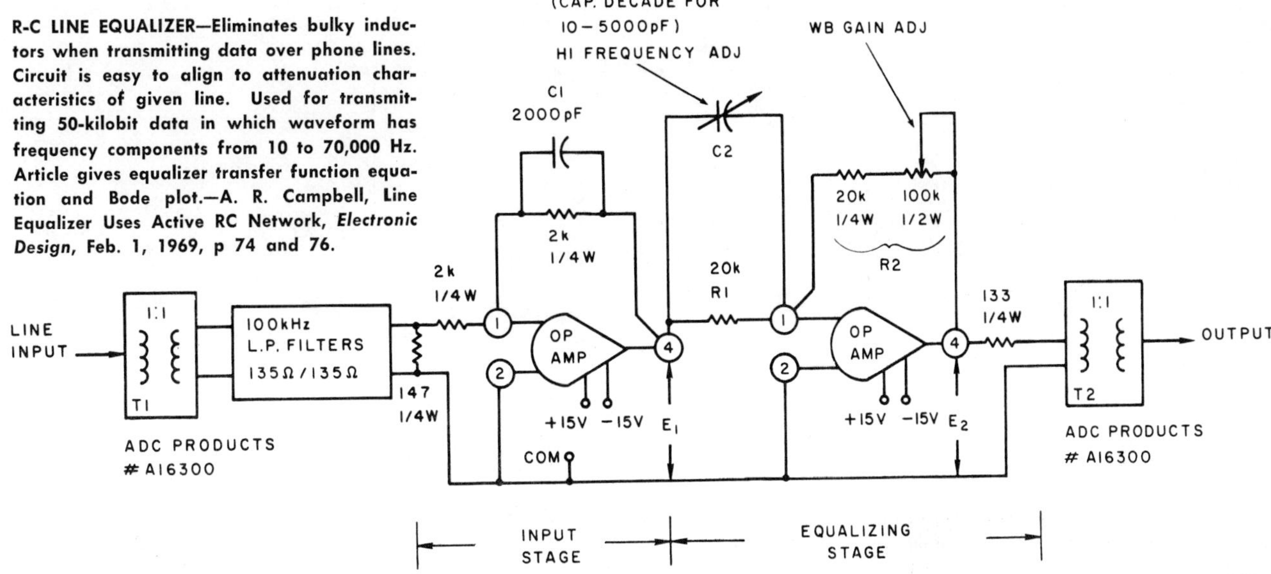

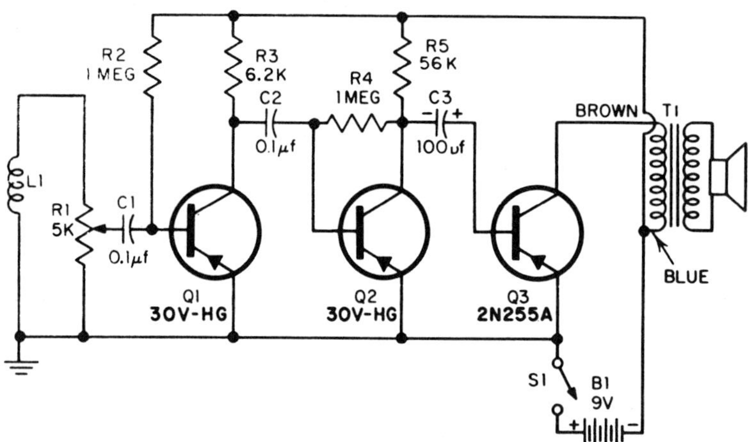

TELEPHONE AMPLIFIER—Used for listening to both sides of telephone conversation on loudspeaker. L1 is commercial induction coil made for telephone pickup, placed near telephone set or telephone line (Radio Shack No. 44-533). T1 is transistor audio output transformer with 500-ohm primary and 8-ohm secondary, driving small 8-ohm speaker.—"A Modern Transistor Workbook," Radio Shack, Boston, Mass., 1965, p 24.

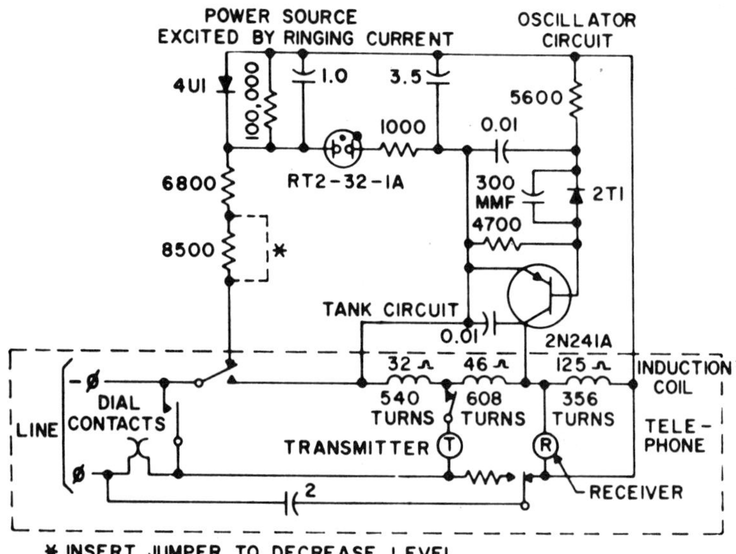

SOLID-STATE TONE RINGER—Used in Ericfon one-piece telephone to give pleasant warbling tone instead of nerve-jangling sound of standard bell. Ringing 20-Hz voltage rectified by power source is applied to transistor oscillator via neon lamp. Oscillator produces sine-wave output of variable amplitude which causes diaphragm of receiver to vibrate, generating tone.—E. Bauman, "Applications of Neon Lamps and Gas Discharge Tubes," Signalite, Neptune, N.J., p 98.

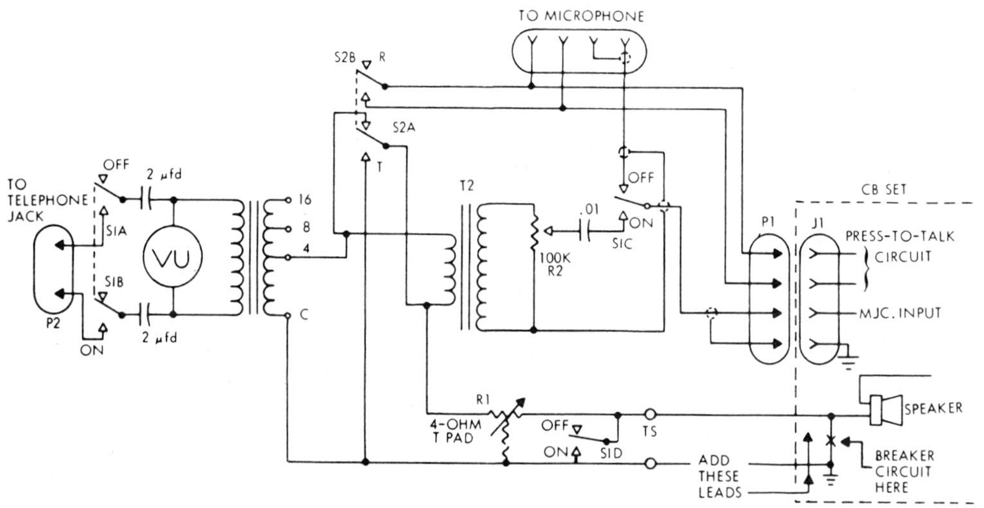

CB PHONE PATCH—Can be connected to telephone line through telephone jack, or through protective network furnished by telephone company. If person at distant telephone is called conventionally by phone and switch S1 is closed, that person can transmit and receive over station equipment connected to phone patch.—Phone Patch, *CB Magazine*, July 1969, p 16, 34–36, and 38.

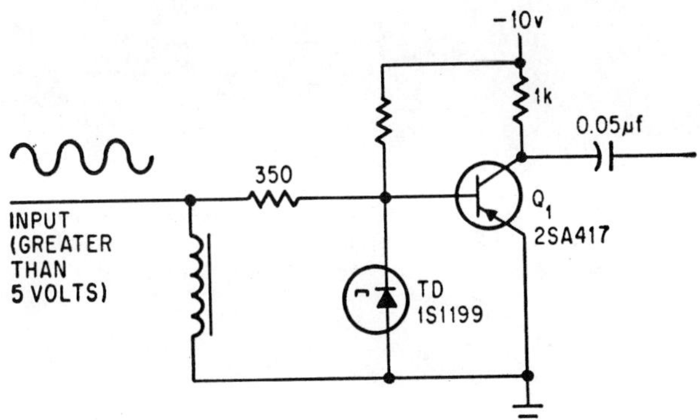

TUNNEL-DIODE PCM SHAPER—Similar to Schmitt trigger, but simpler, more stable, and requires less power. Operation is monostable. Used in Japanese PCM-24 telephone system.—H. Inose and H. Fujisaki, Japanese Stay with PCM to Meet Mushrooming Growth in Telephony, *Electronics*, Dec. 12, 1966, p 134–147.

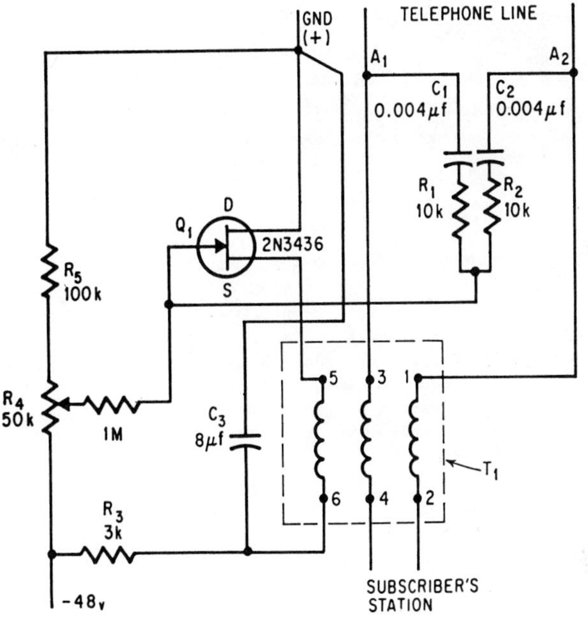

PHONE NOISE CANCELLER—Feedback circuit shown is inserted in telephone line at subscriber's location to cancel large noise voltages induced by power lines. Circuit senses, amplifies, and reintroduces these longitudinal noise voltages 180 deg out of phase to give cancellation.—R. G. Stoneman, Feedback Eliminates Noise in Telephone Circuit, *Electronics*, Nov. 27, 1967, p 82.

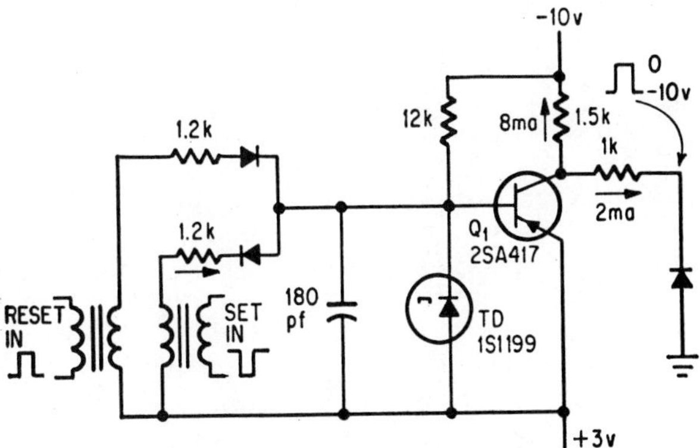

PCM SWITCHING—Transistor-tunnel diode combination provides high-speed switching along with memory, in Japanese PCM-24 telephone system in which speech signals are sampled 8,000 times a second. A set signal switches tunnel diode to high-voltage state, where it remains after set pulse is removed. Reset signal switches diode to low-voltage state, where it remains after reset pulse is removed. —H. Inose and H. Fujisaki, Japanese Stay with PCM to Meet Mushrooming Growth in Telephony, *Electronics*, Dec. 12, 1966, p 134–147.

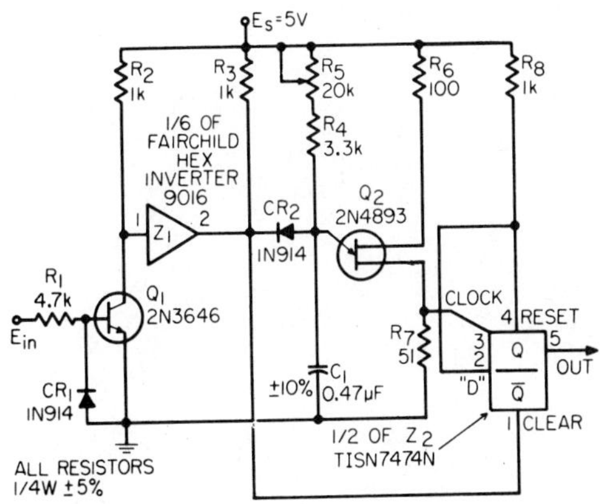

DATAPHONE CARRIER DELAY—Gives adjustable delay of up to 9 ms for leading edge of input pulse when carrier-detect line from Dataphone comes on, to avoid noise that normally appears during first 4 ms due to line deflections. Advantages are low cost, noise immunity, and ability to provide delays up to several seconds without need for large capacitors.—D. J. Duffy, Delayed-Action Data Receiver, *EEE*, Oct. 1968, p 127–128.

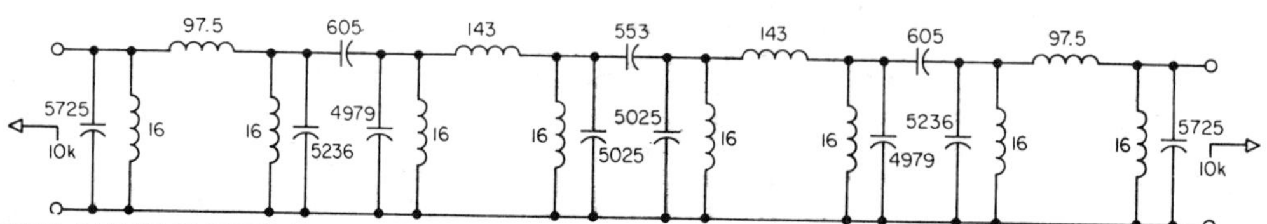

16–20 KHZ CHANNEL BANDPASS FILTER—Designed with coupled resonator units. Inductances are in mH and capacitances in pF. Maximum reflection coefficient is 0.15 over equal-ripple passband of 16.2 to 19.5 kHz. Gyration resistances are 4K.—H. J. Orchard and D. F. Sheahan, Inductorless Bandpass Filters, *IEEE Journal of Solid-State Circuits*, June 1970, p 108–118.

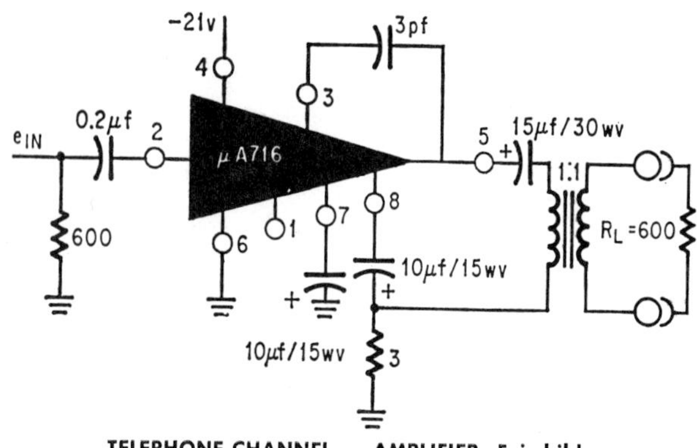

TELEPHONE-CHANNEL AMPLIFIER—Fairchild μA716 low-distortion IC opamp matches 600-ohm line impedance and provides flat frequency response over channel bandwidth of 0.1 to 3.2 kHz. Output is 13 dBm. Article contains 13 other IC opamp application circuits.—J. F. Gifford and M. Markkula, Linear IC's: Part 5, Ins and Outs of Op Amps, *Electronics*, Nov. 27, 1967, p 84–93.

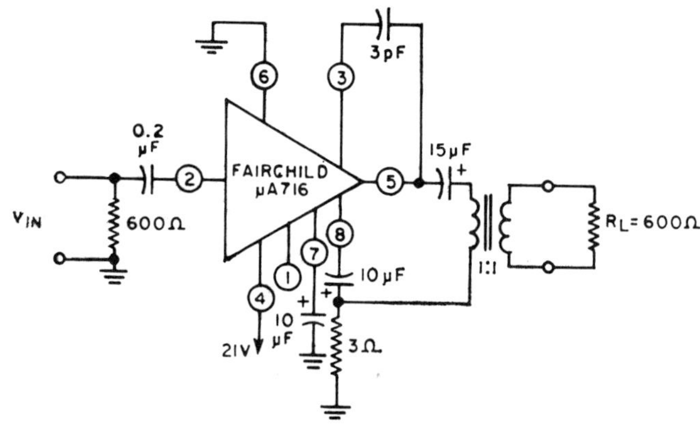

TELEPHONE-CHANNEL IC AMPLIFIER—Provides 40 dB gain with less than 0.1% distortion. Output noise level is minus 75 dBm over any 4,000-Hz bandwidth.—D. E. Lancaster, Audio Integrated Circuits—What's Available?, *Electronics World*, Oct. 1967, p 34–36.

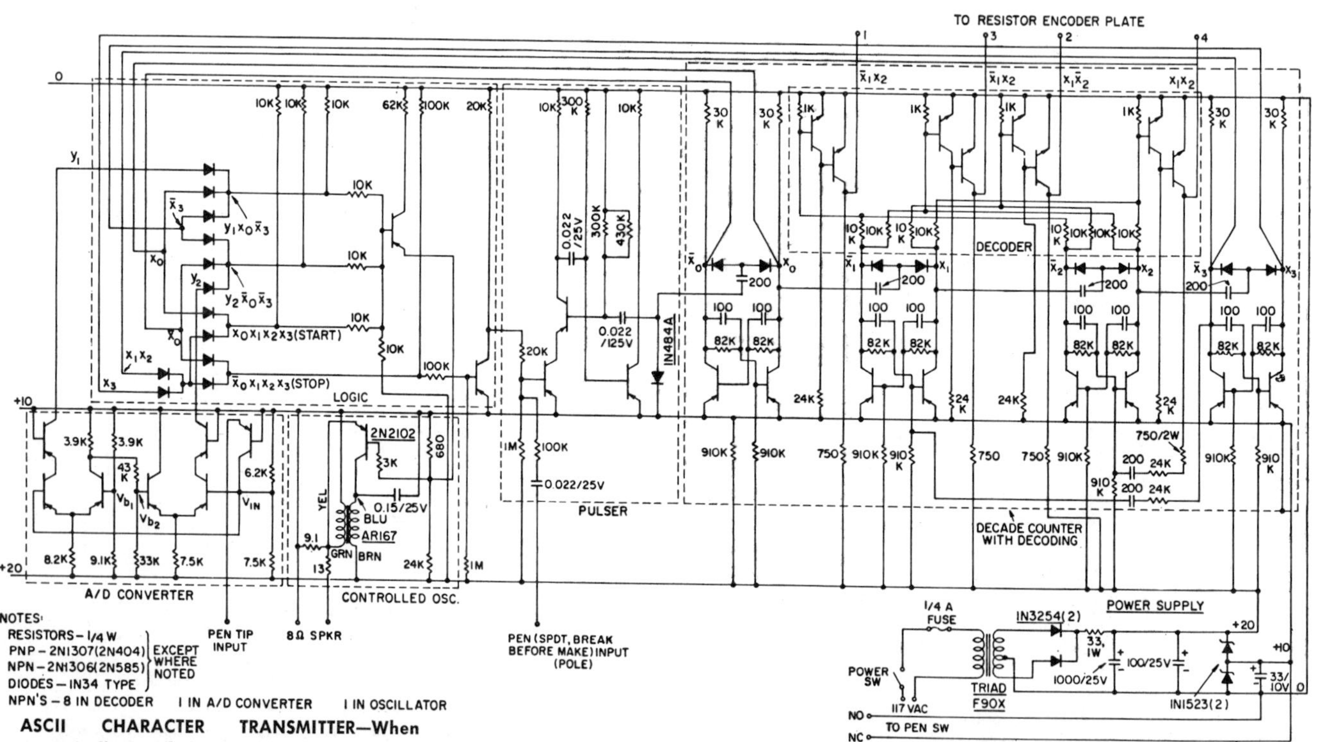

ASCII CHARACTER TRANSMITTER—When acoustically coupled to conventional handset, generates coded tone sequences for 128 alphanumeric characters when user dials remote machine and inputs message by pointing at symbols on keyboard with hand-held selection pen in hunt-and-peck fashion. Tone sequences correspond to those generated by most Teletype-Dataphone terminals in typical time-sharing systems. Pen closes conductive path and at same time has pressure-actuated switch that advances counter.—M. H. Lewin, Portable Electronic Keyboard for Computer Input by Telephone, *IEEE Transactions on Electronic Computers*, June 1967, p 332–334.

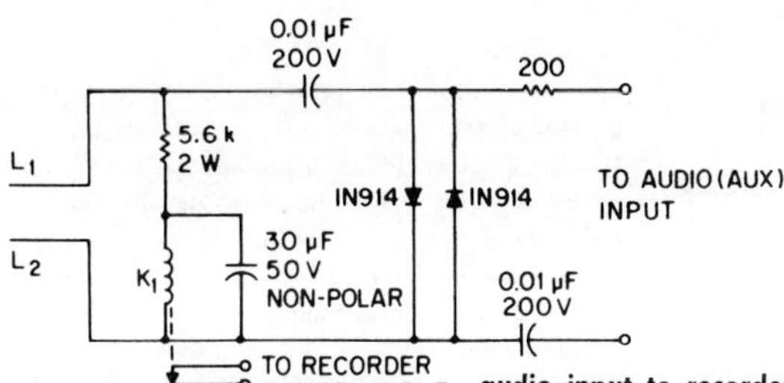

AUTOMATIC RECORDER—Requires connection to telephone input wires L1-L2, which are normally 48 V d-c. When phone is on hook, this voltage energizes relay K1 and keeps recorder switch contacts open. Combination of relay and series resistor must be well above 2K to prevent off-hook indication. Ringing voltage of 90 V at 20 Hz is blocked out of audio input to recorder by IN914 diode pair and kept out of relay coil by 30-µF capacitor. When receiver is lifted, varistor in phone drops L1-L2 voltage to about 6 V d-c, and relay drops out for starting recorder and recording both sides of conversation. Relay can be Sigma 65F1A or equivalent 24 V d-c unit.—H. Metz, Automatic Telephone Recorder, *EEE*, July 1970, p 85.

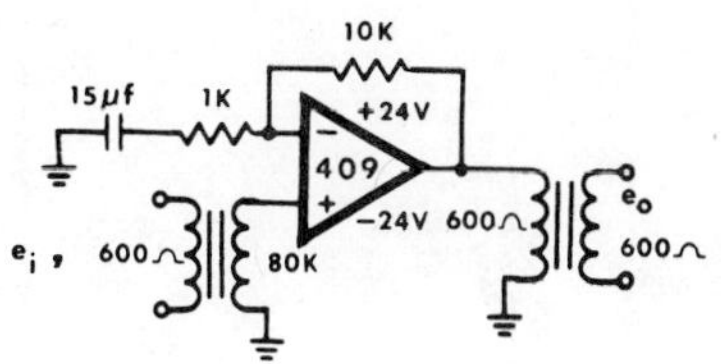

LINE AMPLIFIER—Provides gain of 100 (40 dB) when inserted in 600-ohm telephone line. Output across secondary of line transformer is 22 dBm. Uses model 409 IC opamp. With 150-ohm primary in output transformer, output level goes up to 30 dBm.—B. J. Losmandy, Operational Amplifier Application for Audio Systems, Opamp Labs, Los Angeles, Cal., 1968.

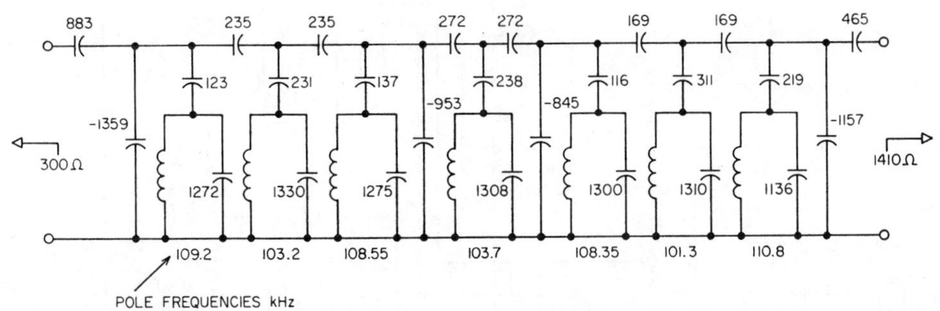

104–108 KHZ CHANNEL BANDPASS FILTER—Used in multiplex telephony. Designed with grounded inductors that are all 1.523 mH, and negative capacitors whose values are given in pF. Gives maximum reflection coefficient of 0.1 over equal-ripple passband from 104.5 to 107.85 kHz. All gyration resistances are 1.8K (Riordan gyrator). Supply voltages of 10 V positive and negative were used for opamps in both gyrators and negative-capacitance circuits that simulate components shown.—H. J. Orchard and D. F. Sheahan, Inductorless Bandpass Filters, *IEEE Journal of Solid-State Circuits*, June 1970, p 108–118.

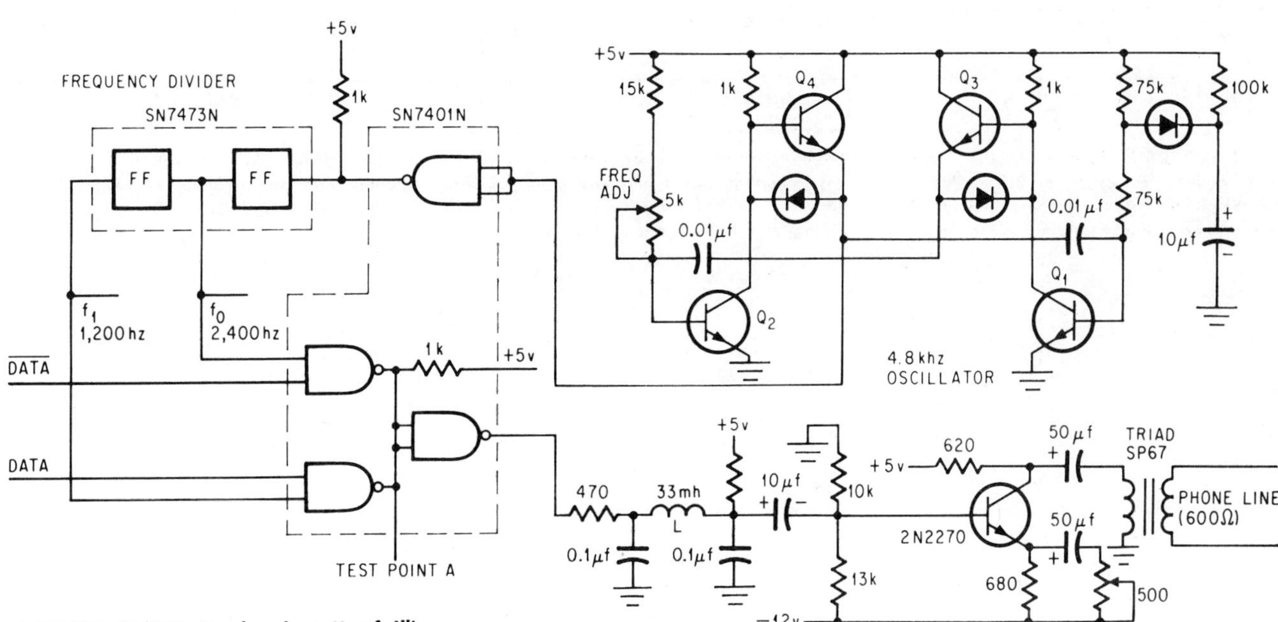

1,200-BPS MODEM—Developed at U. of Illinois for Plato (Programmed Logic for Automatic Teaching Operations) system. Input signal from phone line, consisting of two cycles of 2.4-kHz sine wave for binary 0 and one cycle of 1.2 kHz for binary 1, is converted back to digital form by limiting amplifier and integrator-comparator whose threshold is set so that only the 1 pulses, twice as wide as 0 pulses, rise above threshold. Resulting 1 pulse turns on data flip-flop, while 0 pulse turns it off, to restore digital equivalent of transmitted data.—J. Stifle and M. Johnson, Design Pruning Trims Costs of Data Modem, *Electronics*, July 20, 1970, p 99–101.

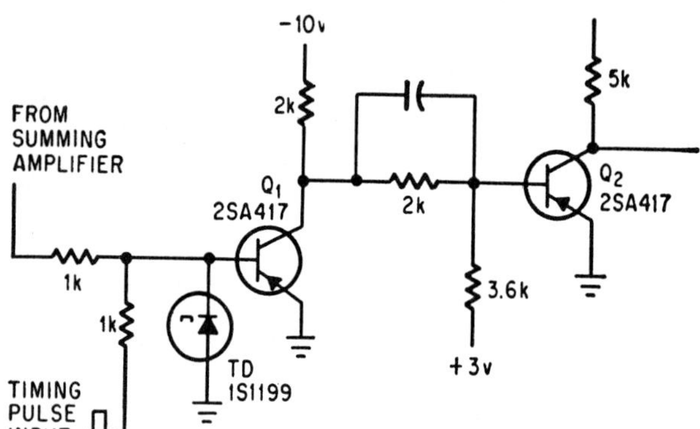

COMPARATOR WITH AND GATE—Used in feedback encoder for Japanese PCM-24 telephone system, for comparing amplitudes of pulses created by sampling speech signals 8,000 times per second. Input must be above specified level and timing pulse present to get pulsed output.—H. Inose and H. Fujisaki, Japanese Stay with PCM to Meet Mushrooming Growth in Telephony, *Electronics*, Dec. 12, 1966, p 134–147.

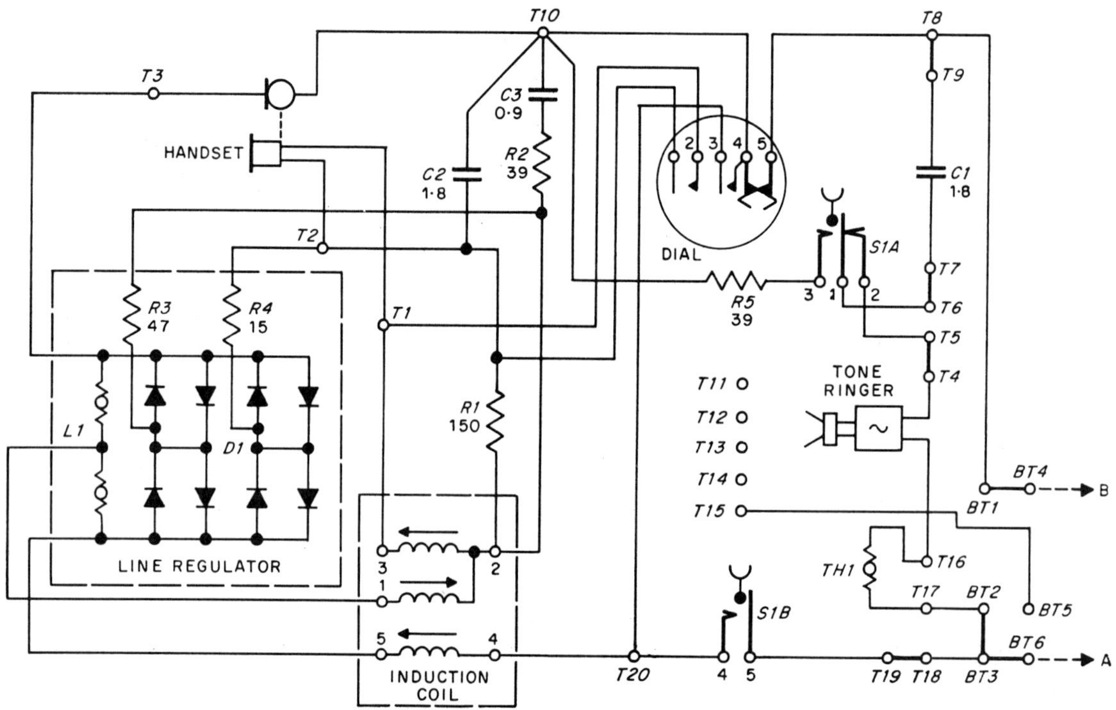

TELEPHONE TRANSMISSION CIRCUIT—Used in new handset developed for British Post Office telephone system. Includes highly effective automatic line regulator. Tone ringer is single-transistor oscillator, giving more pleasant tone than harsh magneto bell. C2 and R5 serve as dial spark-quench circuit, eliminating unwetted cradle switch contacts from speech circuit.—J. S. P. Roberton and A. C. Beadle, Deltaphone, *Electrical Communication*, 42:2, 1967, p 212–218.

NOTE: To locate additional circuits in the category of this chapter, use the index at the back of this book. Check also the author's "Sourcebook of Electronic Circuits," published by McGraw-Hill in 1968.

CHAPTER 85
Television Circuits—Black-and-White

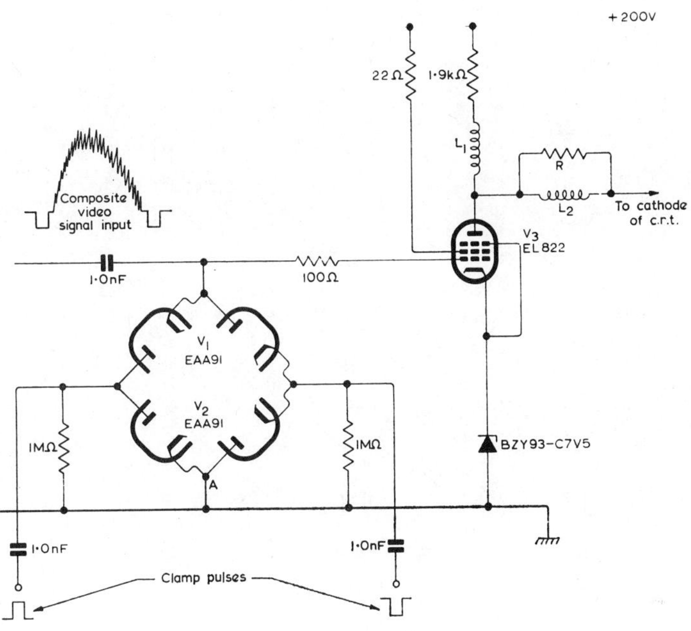

VIDEO AMPLIFIER WITH ZENER BIAS—Voltage regulator diode in cathode circuit of pentode makes constant black level more readily obtainable and gives higher gain because it introduces no degeneration. Without cathode degeneration, however, there is no selfcompensation for tube aging.—Voltage Regulator (Zener) Diodes, Philips, Pub. Dept., Elcoma Div., Eindhoven, The Netherlands, Application Book, p 59.

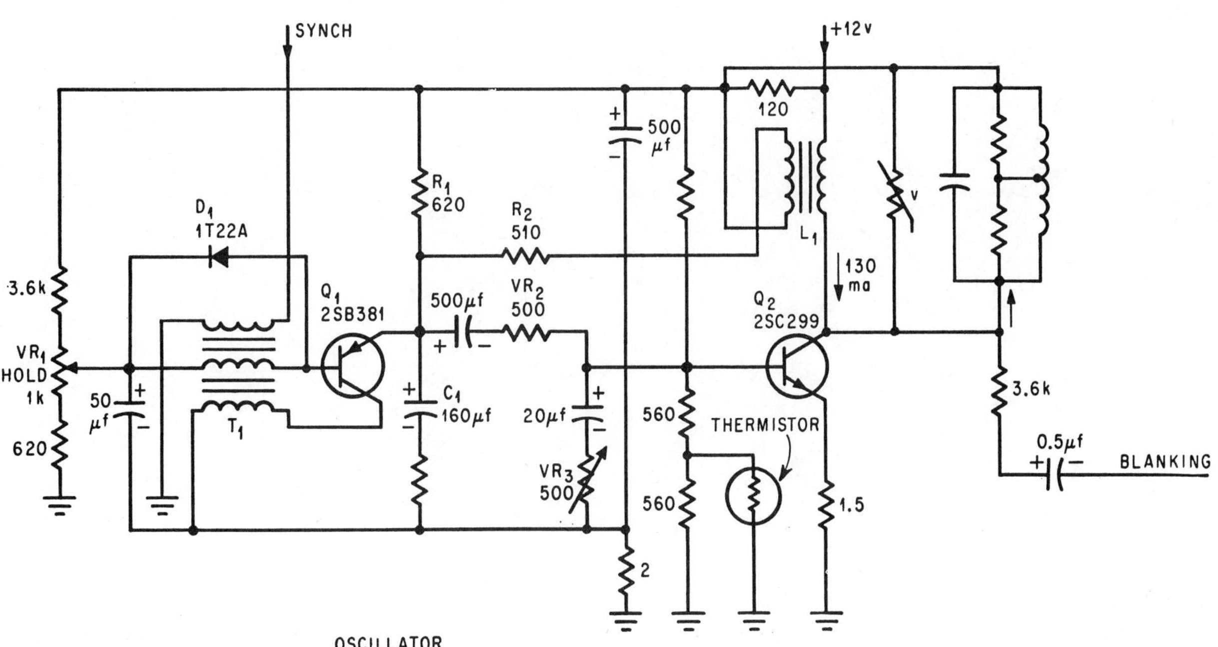

TWO-TRANSISTOR VERTICAL DEFLECTION—Number of components is minimized with circuit version used in Sony model 700U 7-inch portable tv. Blocking oscillator Q1 periodically discharges C1, which is charged through R1 to generate vertical sawtooth sweep voltage.—Careful Sweep Design Cuts Power Drain and Cost, *Electronics*, Nov. 14, 1966, p 167–169.

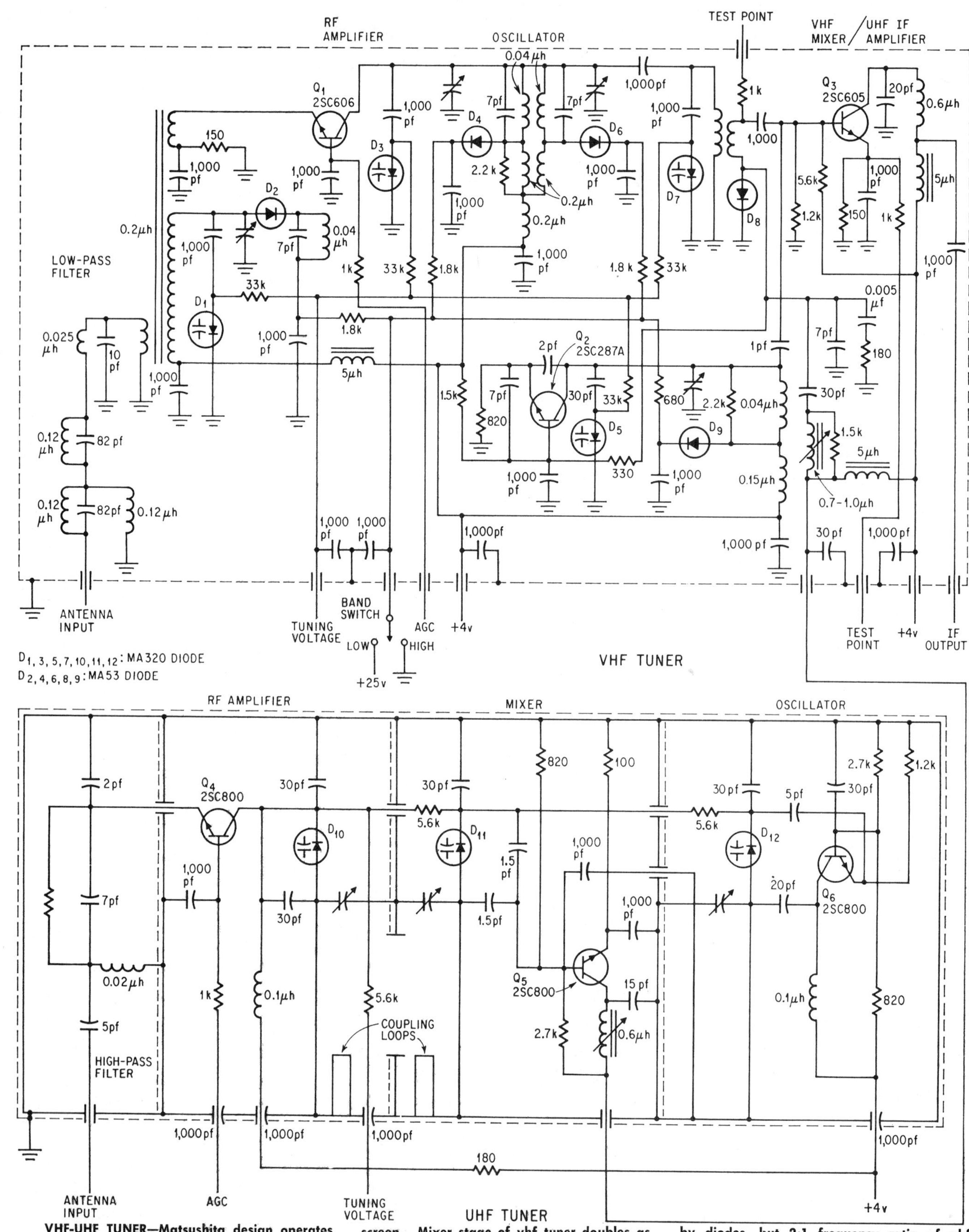

VHF-UHF TUNER—Matsushita design operates from 5-V battery and requires only single combination vhf/uhf antenna. Used in receiver drawing only 1.35 W from set of penlight batteries and having 1.5-inch-diagonal screen. Mixer stage of vhf tuner doubles as i-f amplifier in uhf mode. Uses electronic tuning through variable-capacitance diodes, fixed inductors, and switching diodes. Vhf 4:1 frequency ratio requires coil switching by diodes, but 2:1 frequency ratio of uhf band is handled without switching.—R. Sasaki and K. Uno, Low-Power Design is Heart of Penlight-Powered Mini-Tv, *Electronics*, June 8, 1970, p 106–113.

CATV DISTRIBUTION AMPLIFIER—Uses power fet made by Crystalonics, to give excellent stability with 2 W output up to several hundred megahertz for community antenna tv distribution systems.—J. Tamosaitis, The Power FET, *Electronics World*, June 1969, p 34–35 and 82.

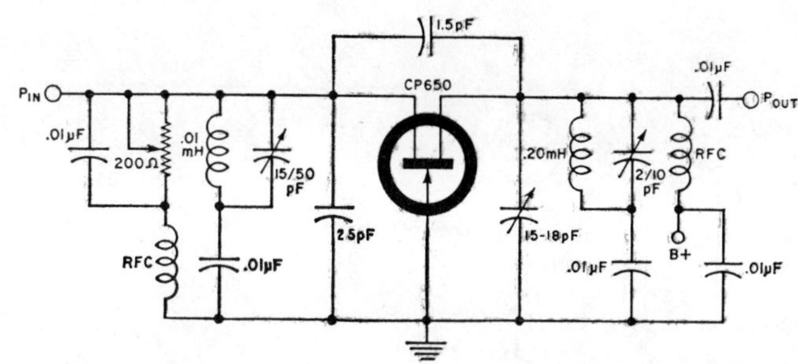

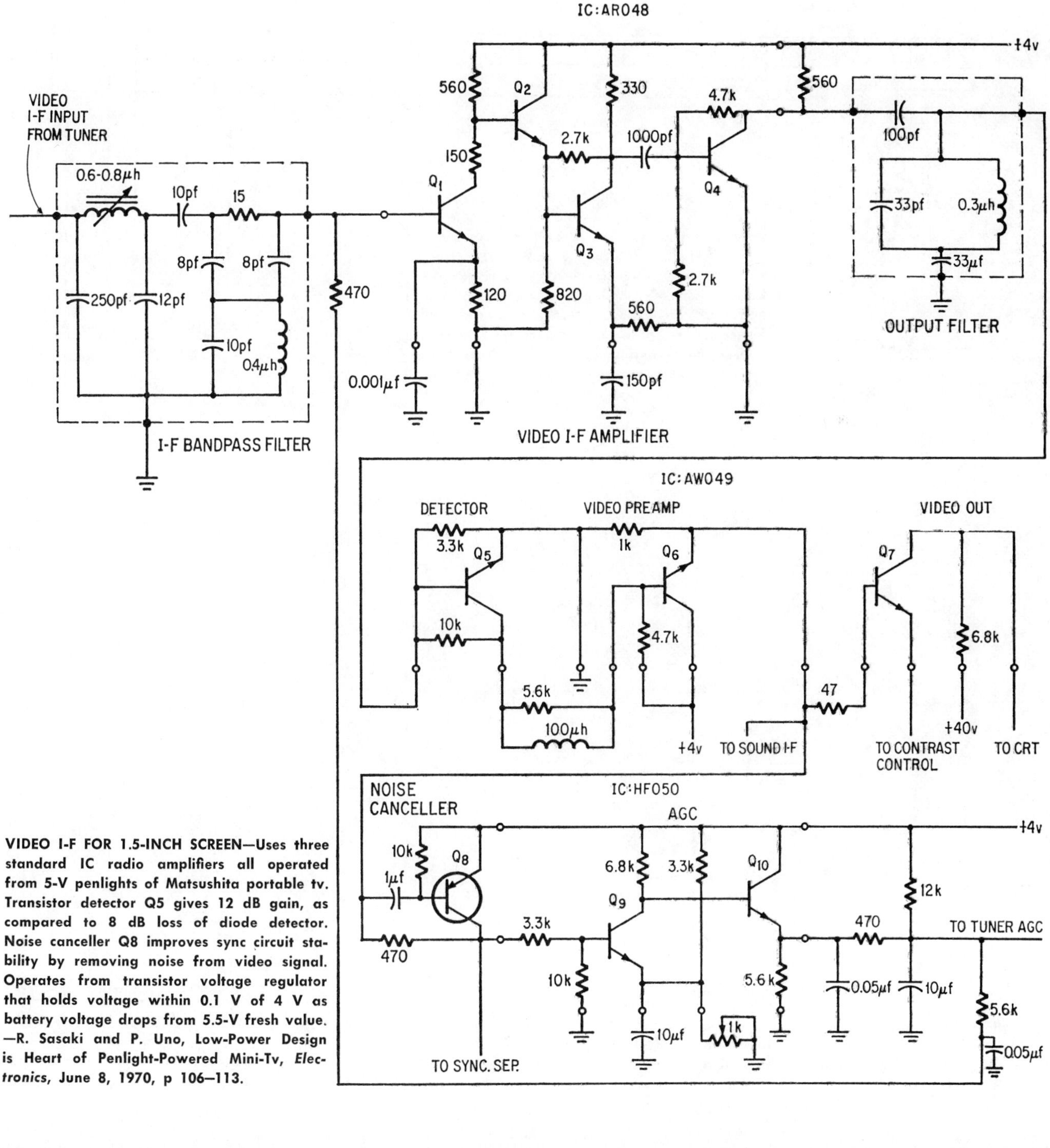

IC:AR048

VIDEO I-F INPUT FROM TUNER

I-F BANDPASS FILTER

VIDEO I-F AMPLIFIER

OUTPUT FILTER

+4v

IC:AW049

DETECTOR

VIDEO PREAMP

VIDEO OUT

+4v TO SOUND I-F

+40v

TO CONTRAST CONTROL

TO CRT

NOISE CANCELLER

IC:HF050

AGC

TO TUNER AGC

TO SYNC. SEP.

VIDEO I-F FOR 1.5-INCH SCREEN—Uses three standard IC radio amplifiers all operated from 5-V penlights of Matsushita portable tv. Transistor detector Q5 gives 12 dB gain, as compared to 8 dB loss of diode detector. Noise canceller Q8 improves sync circuit stability by removing noise from video signal. Operates from transistor voltage regulator that holds voltage within 0.1 V of 4 V as battery voltage drops from 5.5-V fresh value. —R. Sasaki and P. Uno, Low-Power Design is Heart of Penlight-Powered Mini-Tv, *Electronics*, June 8, 1970, p 106–113.

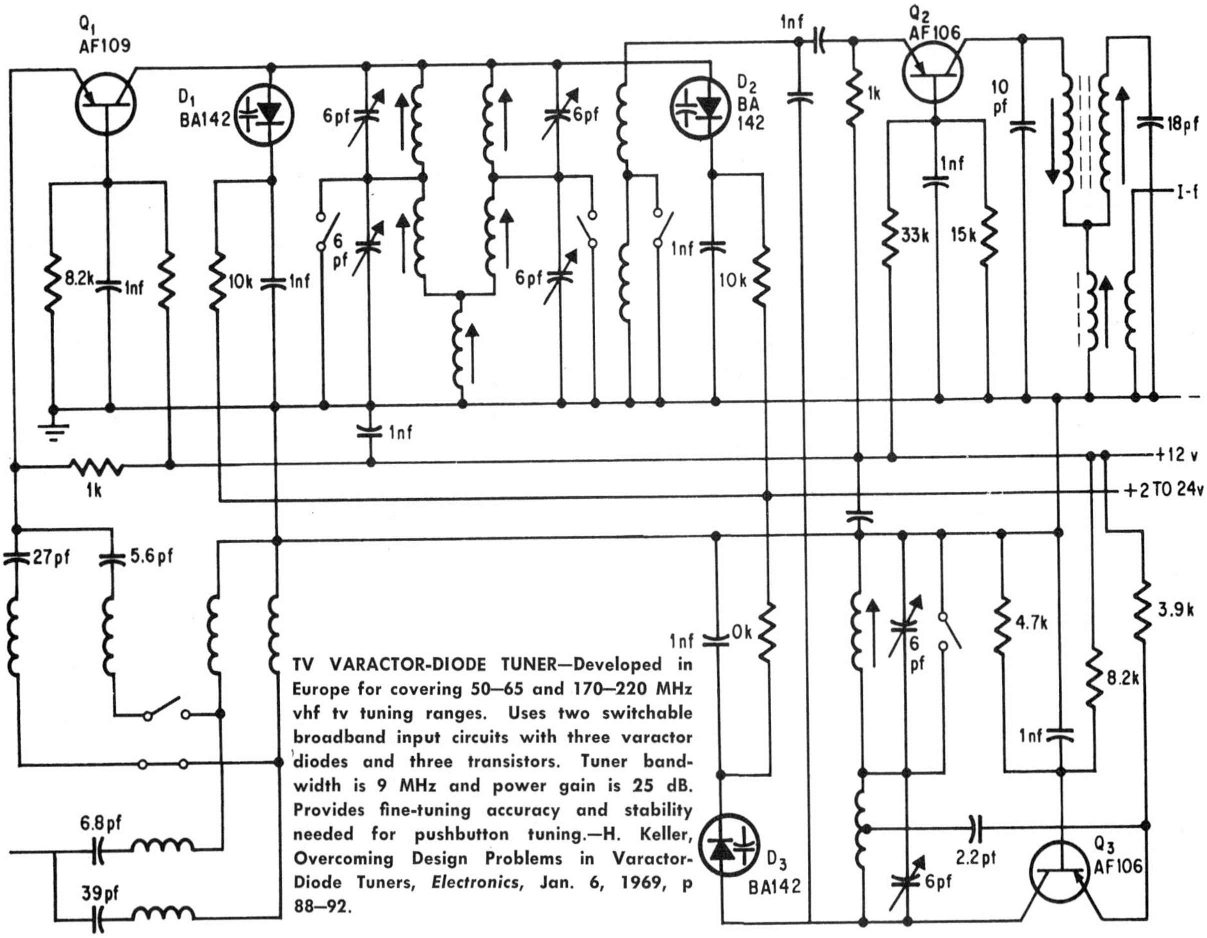

TV VARACTOR-DIODE TUNER—Developed in Europe for covering 50–65 and 170–220 MHz vhf tv tuning ranges. Uses two switchable broadband input circuits with three varactor diodes and three transistors. Tuner bandwidth is 9 MHz and power gain is 25 dB. Provides fine-tuning accuracy and stability needed for pushbutton tuning.—H. Keller, Overcoming Design Problems in Varactor-Diode Tuners, *Electronics*, Jan. 6, 1969, p 88–92.

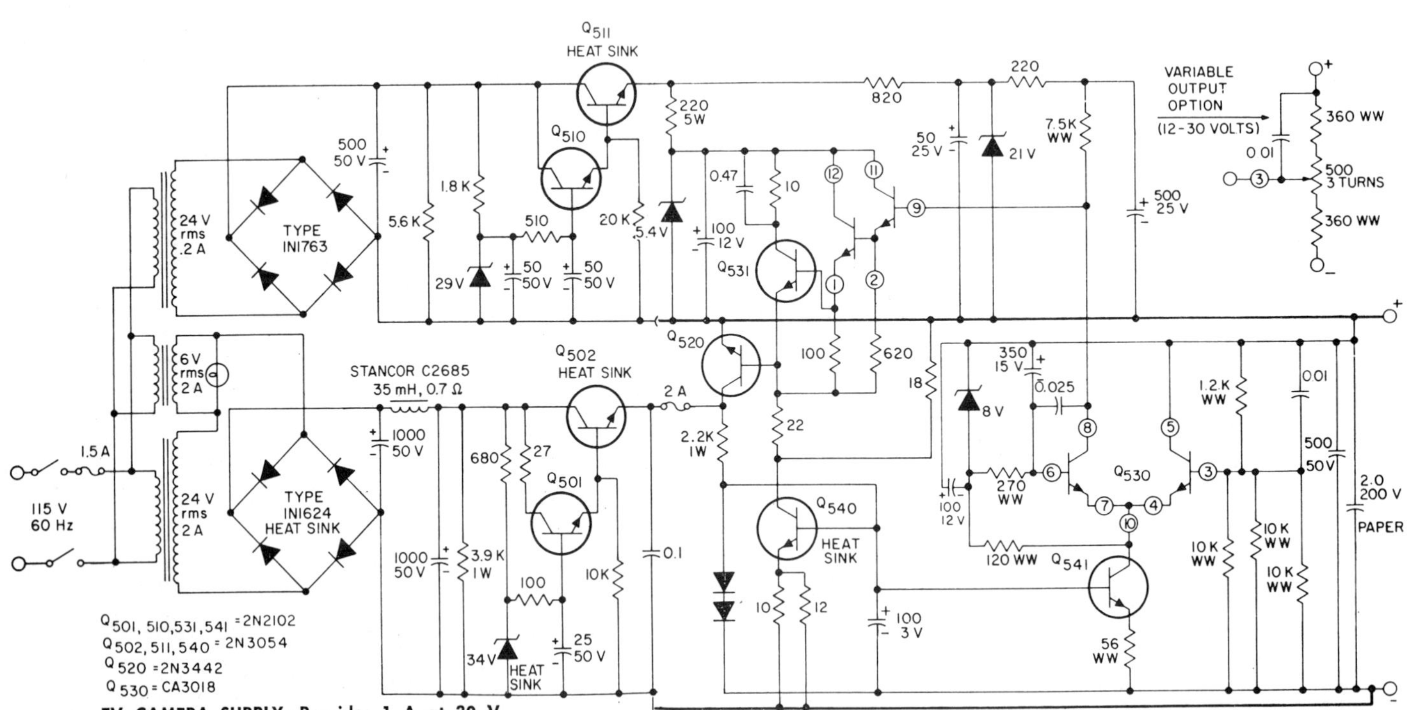

TV CAMERA SUPPLY—Provides 1 A at 30 V with 0.005% load regulation, for vertical deflection service. Noise and ripple are more than 100 dB down p-p, and line regulation is better than 0.01% for 10% change in a-c line voltage. Q530 is CA3018 IC differential amplifier which drives 2N3422 series regulator Q520. Transistors Q510 and Q511 form additional regulator stage needed for good line isolation while providing power for matching and driving network, and serving as decoupled reference for amplifier load resistor.—O. H. Shade, Jr., Stable Solid-State Vertical Deflection for High-Definition Television Systems, *RCA Review*, March 1970, p 120–147.

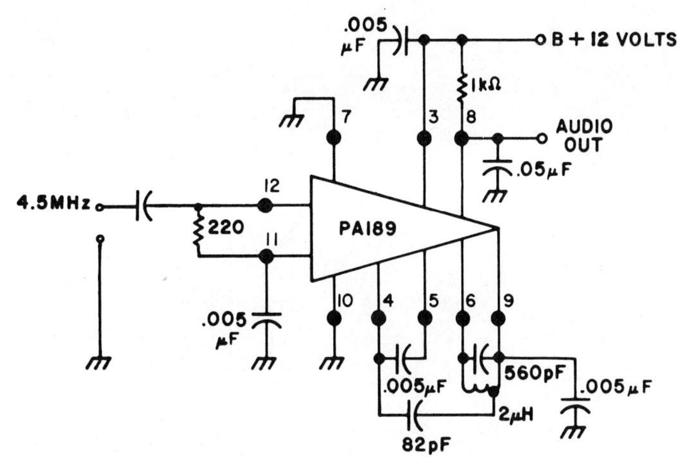

IC QUADRATURE DETECTOR—PA189 linear IC i-f amplifier is used here as quadrature-detector type of f-m discriminator for b-w tv. Arrangement is more economical than ratio detector but has about 10 dB less a-m rejection.—E. L. Haas and D. J. Hubbard, Linear Integrated Circuits in a TV Sound System, General Electric, Syracuse, N.Y., No. 90.74, 1968.

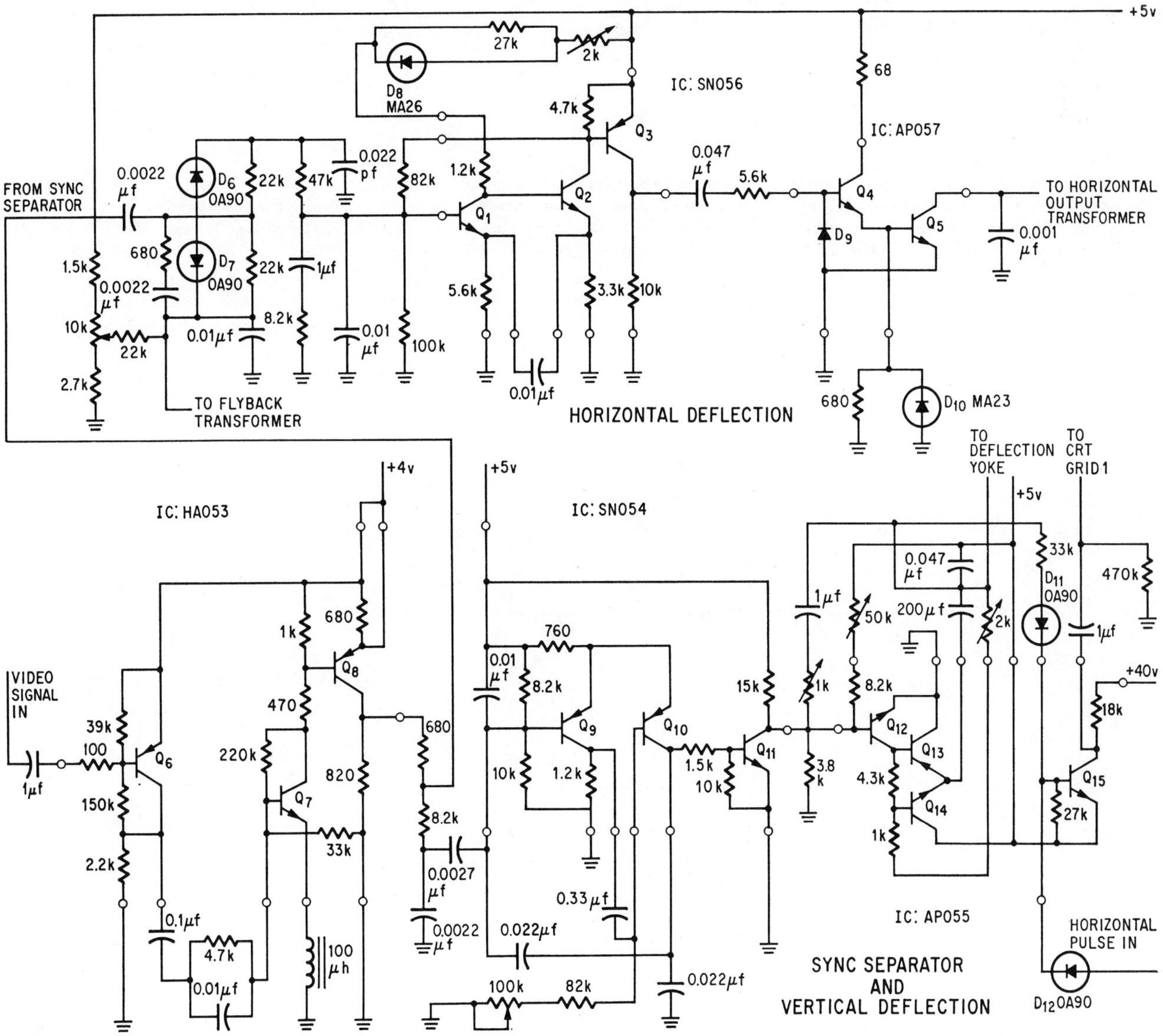

HORIZONTAL DEFLECTION

SYNC SEPARATOR AND VERTICAL DEFLECTION

DEFLECTION WITH 5-V SUPPLY—Used in Matsushita 1.5-inch-diagonal tv operating from 5-V penlight batteries. Both IC oscillators use emitter-coupled multivibrators, with afc required only for horizontal oscillator voltage. As battery voltage drops with age, deflection amplitude and high voltage fall proportionally; since required deflection amplitude is inversely proportional to high voltage, raster width still fills screen but brightness decreases.—R. Sasaki and K. Uno, Low-Power Design is Heart of Penlight-Powered Mini-Tv, *Electronics*, June 8, 1970, p 106–113.

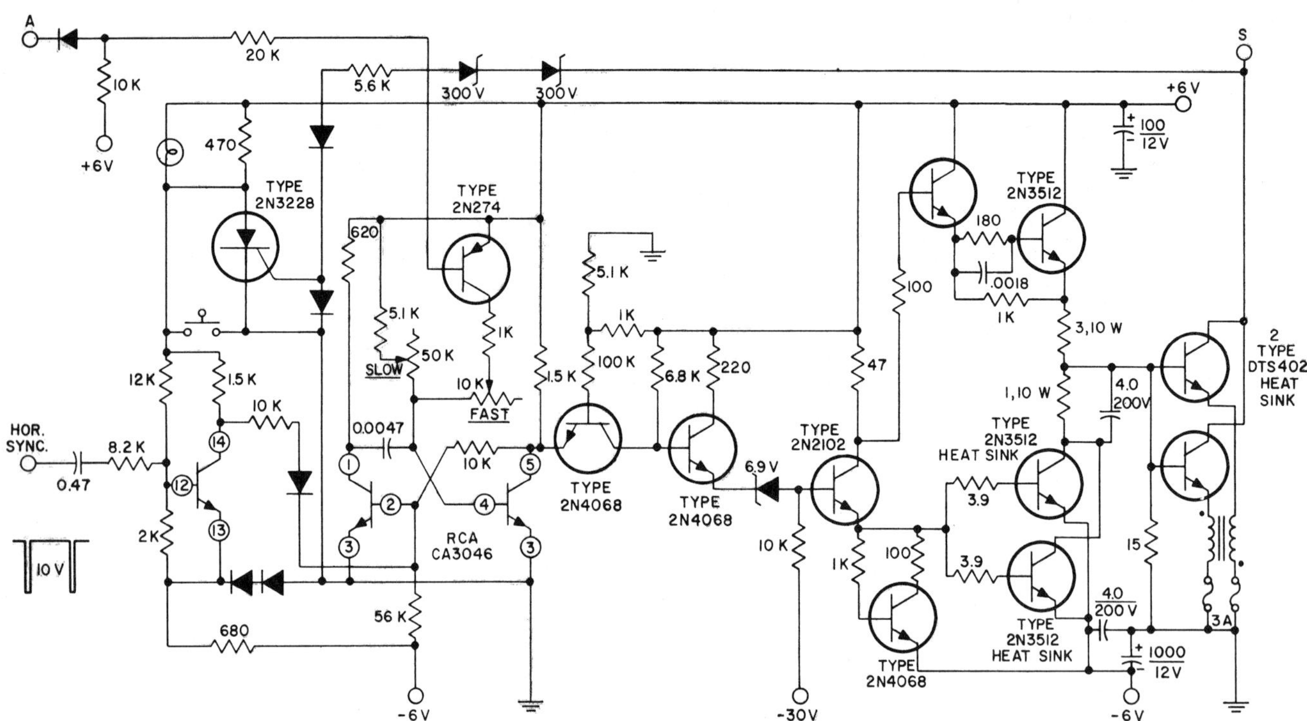

HORIZONTAL DRIVE—Circuit includes drive-waveform controls, switch circuits, and horizontal drive approaching ideal in stability and linearity, for use in high-definition 4,000-line tv system. Developed for use with 4.5-inch return-beam vidicon camera. Terminal S goes to horizontal ramp generator, and terminal A goes to horizontal switching circuit.—O. H. Schade, Jr., Linear Solid-State Horizontal-Deflection Circuit For High-Definition Television Systems, *RCA Review*, March 1970, p 148–170.

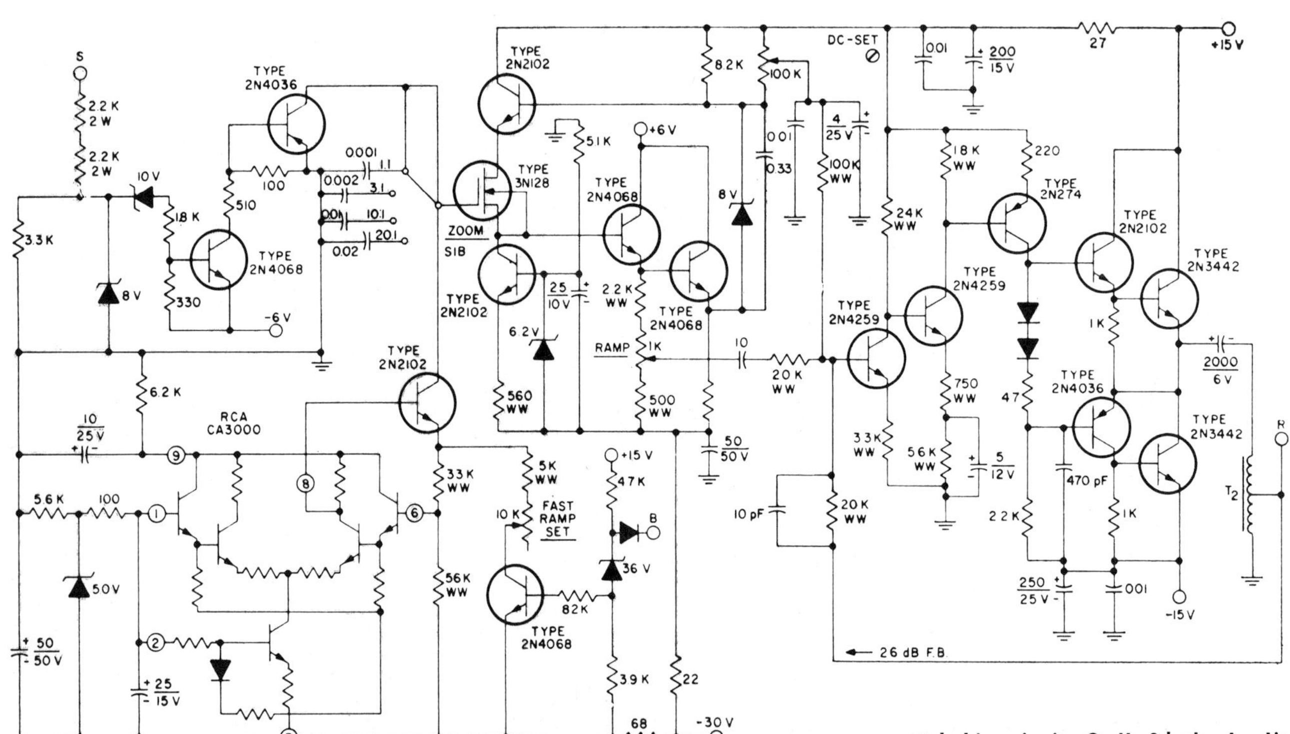

HORIZONTAL RAMP GENERATOR—Provides superior stability and linearity for 4.5-inch return-beam vidicon camera of 4,000-line television system. Operates at 1 MHz. Ramp output at R goes to horizontal switching circuit. Terminal S at upper left goes to horizontal drive circuit.—O. H. Schade, Jr., Linear Solid-State Horizontal-Deflection Circuit For High-Definition Television Systems, *RCA Review*, March 1970, p 148–170.

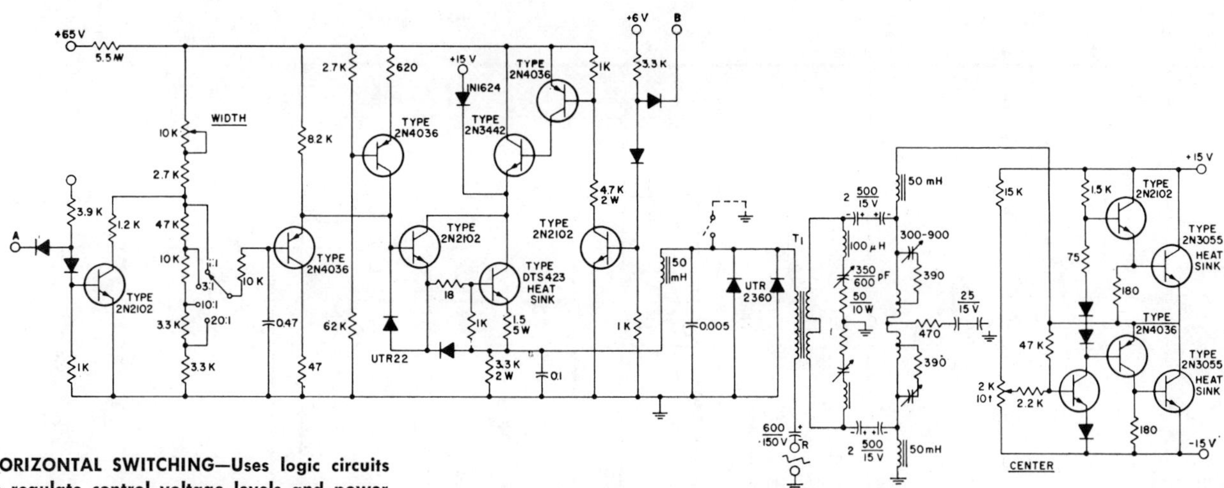

HORIZONTAL SWITCHING—Uses logic circuits to regulate control voltage levels and power supplies, as required for fast and slow scans in 4.5-inch return-beam vidicon camera of high-definition 4,000-line tv system. Terminal A goes to horizontal drive circuit, and terminal B goes to horizontal ramp generator. —O. H. Schade, Jr., Linear Solid-State Horizontal-Deflection Circuit For High-Definition Television Systems, *RCA Review*, March 1970, p 148–170.

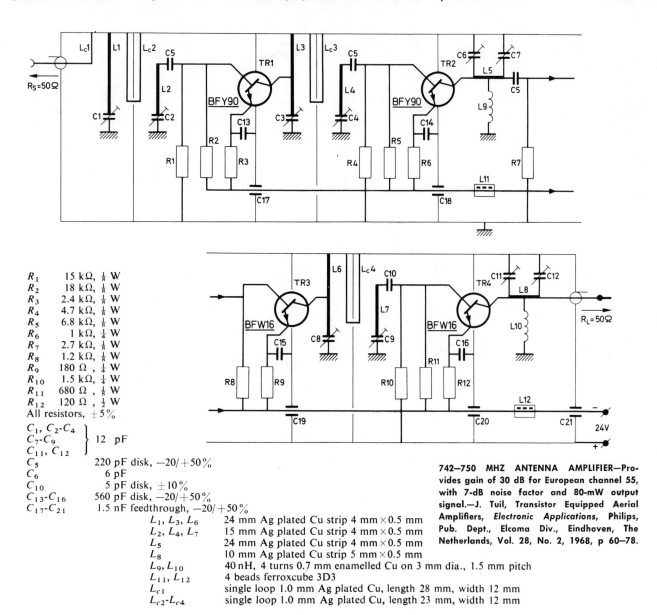

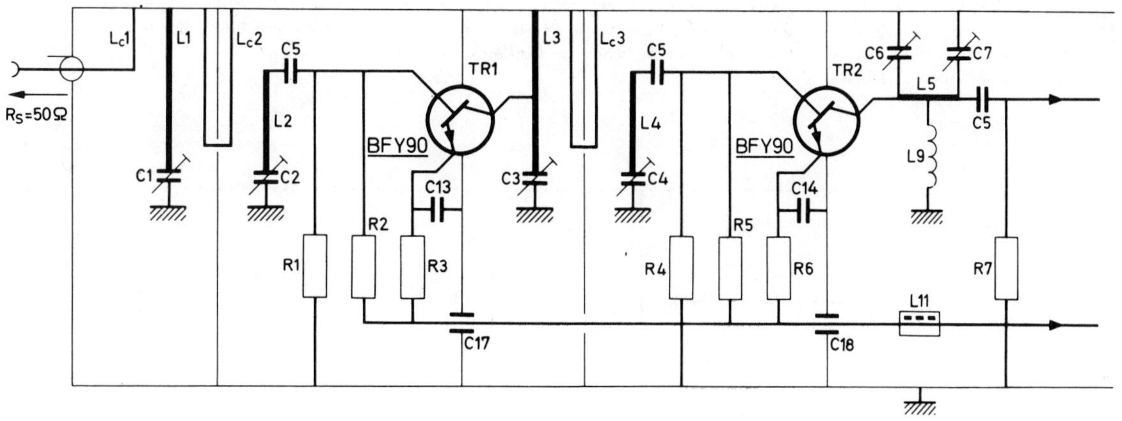

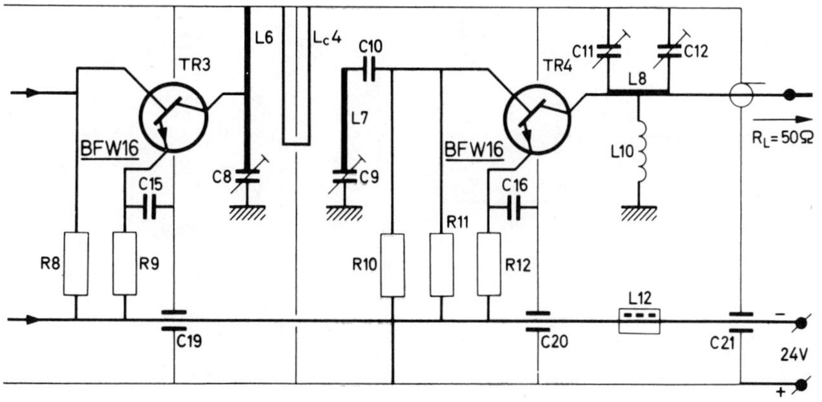

R_1 15 kΩ, $\frac{1}{8}$ W
R_2 18 kΩ, $\frac{1}{8}$ W
R_3 2.4 kΩ, $\frac{1}{8}$ W
R_4 4.7 kΩ, $\frac{1}{8}$ W
R_5 6.8 kΩ, $\frac{1}{8}$ W
R_6 1 kΩ, $\frac{1}{4}$ W
R_7 2.7 kΩ, $\frac{1}{8}$ W
R_8 1.2 kΩ, $\frac{1}{8}$ W
R_9 180 Ω, $\frac{1}{4}$ W
R_{10} 1.5 kΩ, $\frac{1}{4}$ W
R_{11} 680 Ω, $\frac{1}{8}$ W
R_{12} 120 Ω, $\frac{1}{2}$ W
All resistors, ±5%
C_1, C_2-C_4, C_7-C_9, C_{11}, C_{12} 12 pF
C_5 220 pF disk, −20/+50%
C_6 6 pF
C_{10} 5 pF disk, ±10%
C_{13}-C_{16} 560 pF disk, −20/+50%
C_{17}-C_{21} 1.5 nF feedthrough, −20/+50%
L_1, L_3, L_6 24 mm Ag plated Cu strip 4 mm×0.5 mm
L_2, L_4, L_7 15 mm Ag plated Cu strip 4 mm×0.5 mm
L_5 24 mm Ag plated Cu strip 4 mm×0.5 mm
L_8 10 mm Ag plated Cu strip 5 mm×0.5 mm
L_9, L_{10} 40 nH, 4 turns 0.7 mm enamelled Cu on 3 mm dia., 1.5 mm pitch
L_{11}, L_{12} 4 beads ferroxcube 3D3
L_{c1} single loop 1.0 mm Ag plated Cu, length 28 mm, width 12 mm
L_{c2}-L_{c4} single loop 1.0 mm Ag plated Cu, length 23 mm, width 12 mm

742–750 MHZ ANTENNA AMPLIFIER—Provides gain of 30 dB for European channel 55, with 7-dB noise factor and 80-mW output signal.—J. Tuil, Transistor Equipped Aerial Amplifiers, *Electronic Applications*, Philips, Pub. Dept., Elcoma Div., Eindhoven, The Netherlands, Vol. 28, No. 2, 1968, p 60–78.

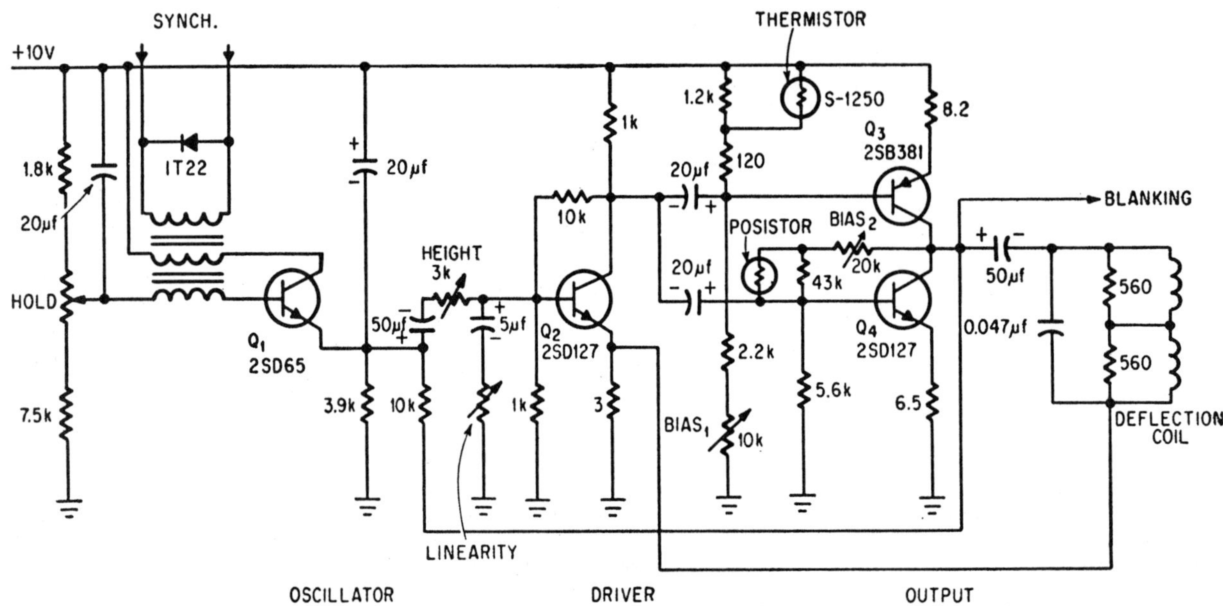

LOW-DRAIN VERTICAL SWEEP—Design goal for 4-inch Sony 4-20UW battery-operated portable tv was reduction of battery drain. Combination of four transistors used as shown gives deflection current of 134 mA p-p with only 20 mA d-c. Power drain is thus less than half that of more conventional class A circuit.—Careful Sweep Design Cuts Power Drain and Cost, *Electronics*, Nov. 14, 1966, p 167–169.

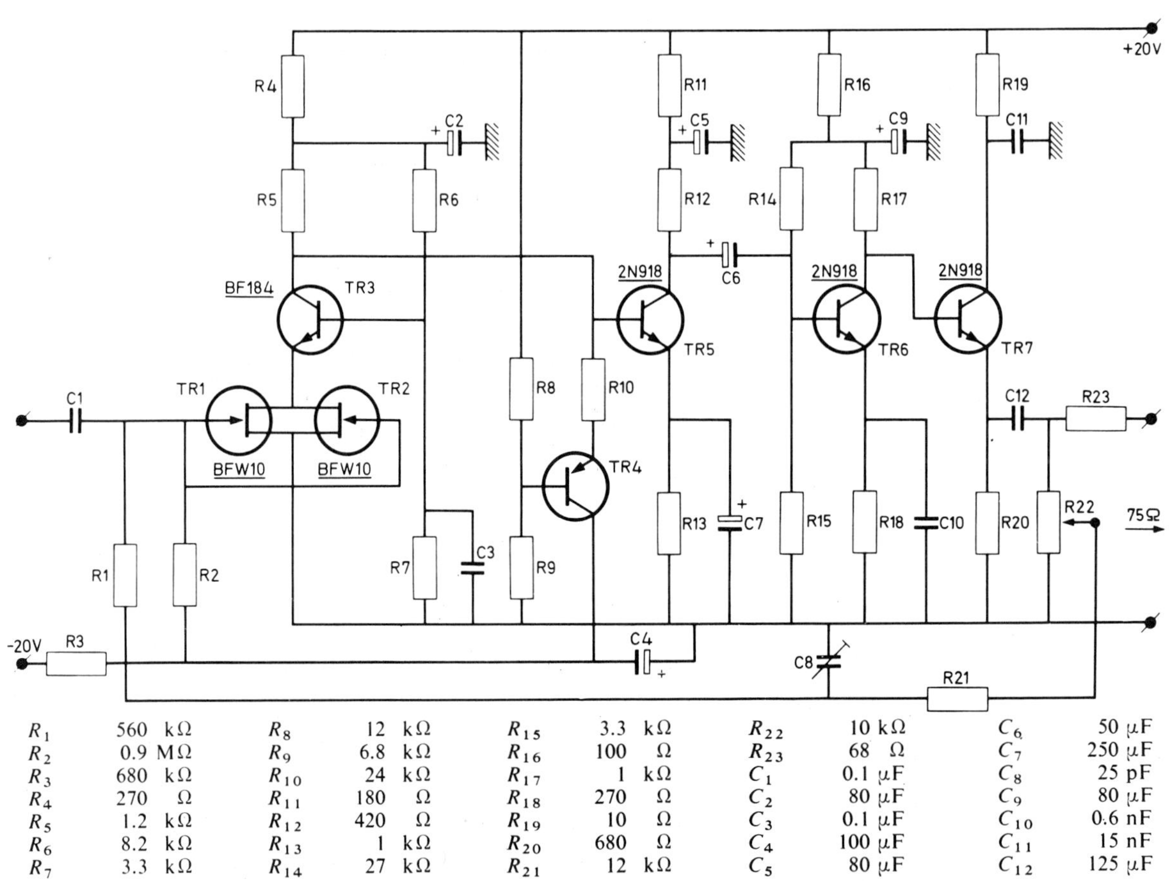

R_1	560 kΩ	R_8	12 kΩ	R_{15}	3.3 kΩ	R_{22}	10 kΩ	C_6	50 μF
R_2	0.9 MΩ	R_9	6.8 kΩ	R_{16}	100 Ω	R_{23}	68 Ω	C_7	250 μF
R_3	680 kΩ	R_{10}	24 kΩ	R_{17}	1 kΩ	C_1	0.1 μF	C_8	25 pF
R_4	270 Ω	R_{11}	180 Ω	R_{18}	270 Ω	C_2	80 μF	C_9	80 μF
R_5	1.2 kΩ	R_{12}	420 Ω	R_{19}	10 Ω	C_3	0.1 μF	C_{10}	0.6 nF
R_6	8.2 kΩ	R_{13}	1 kΩ	R_{20}	680 Ω	C_4	100 μF	C_{11}	15 nF
R_7	3.3 kΩ	R_{14}	27 kΩ	R_{21}	12 kΩ	C_5	80 μF	C_{12}	125 μF

PLUMBICON PREAMP—Circuit shows complete preamp for b-w tv camera tube such as Plumbicon. Frequency response is substantially flat to 5.5 MHz. Two fet stages in parallel in input stage give required low noise figure. Circuit makes use of frequency-dependent feedback. Miller effect in input stage is avoided by using TR3 in cascode with parallel fet's.—B. Overgoor, A Camera Tube Amplifier with FET Input, *Electronic Applications*, Philips, Pub. Dept., Elcoma Div., Eindhoven, The Netherlands, Vol. 28, No. 4, 1968, p 155–159.

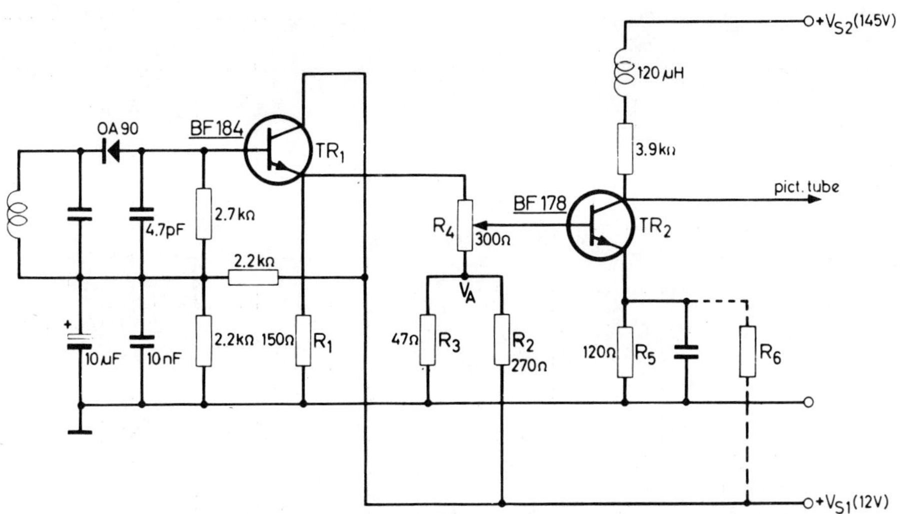

BASE-CIRCUIT CONTRAST CONTROL—R2 and R3 keep black level constant while contrast is controlled with R4. Video signal is distorted at maximum setting of contrast pot, but distortion can be cleared up by turning back the control.—A. Cense, The N-P-N Silicon Planar Transistor BF178 in a Video Amplifier, Philips, Pub. Dept., Elcoma Div., Eindhoven, The Netherlands, No. 251, 1966.

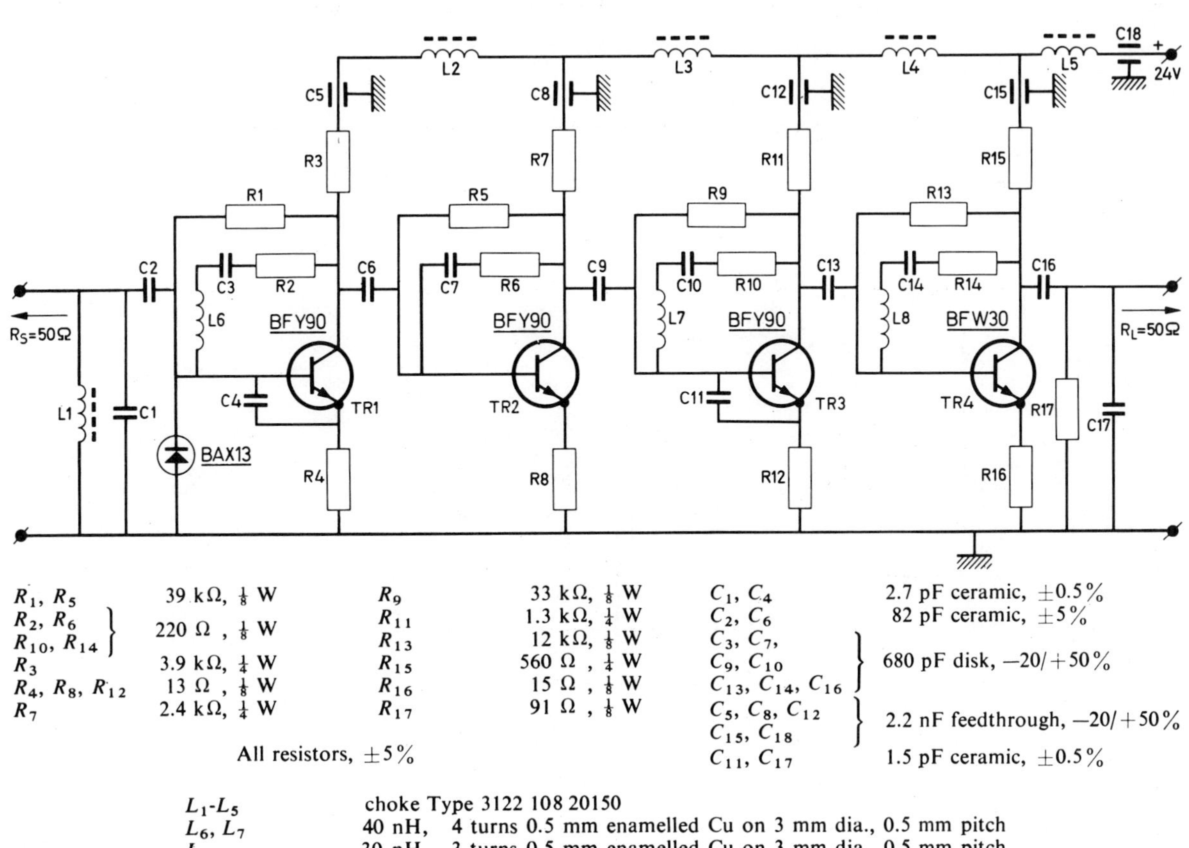

R_1, R_5	39 kΩ, $\frac{1}{8}$ W	R_9	33 kΩ, $\frac{1}{8}$ W	C_1, C_4	2.7 pF ceramic, ±0.5%
R_2, R_6, R_{10}, R_{14}	220 Ω, $\frac{1}{8}$ W	R_{11}	1.3 kΩ, $\frac{1}{4}$ W	C_2, C_6	82 pF ceramic, ±5%
R_3	3.9 kΩ, $\frac{1}{4}$ W	R_{13}	12 kΩ, $\frac{1}{8}$ W	C_3, C_7, C_9, C_{10}, C_{13}, C_{14}, C_{16}	680 pF disk, −20/+50%
R_4, R_8, R_{12}	13 Ω, $\frac{1}{8}$ W	R_{15}	560 Ω, $\frac{1}{4}$ W	C_5, C_8, C_{12}, C_{15}, C_{18}	2.2 nF feedthrough, −20/+50%
R_7	2.4 kΩ, $\frac{1}{4}$ W	R_{16}	15 Ω, $\frac{1}{8}$ W	C_{11}, C_{17}	1.5 pF ceramic, ±0.5%
		R_{17}	91 Ω, $\frac{1}{8}$ W		

All resistors, ±5%

L_1-L_5	choke Type 3122 108 20150
L_6, L_7	40 nH, 4 turns 0.5 mm enamelled Cu on 3 mm dia., 0.5 mm pitch
L_8	30 nH, 3 turns 0.5 mm enamelled Cu on 3 mm dia., 0.5 mm pitch

FOUR-STAGE 40–860 MHZ ANTENNA AMPLIFIER—Provides gain of 26 dB and 70-mV output per signal over entire European television band, with noise factor of 6.9 to 10 dB. Inductor shunting input terminals dissipates static charges accumulated on antenna, to protect transistors from damage by sudden discharge. Further protection is provided by BAX13 diode connecting base of input transistor to ground.—J. Tuil, Transistor Equipped Aerial Amplifiers, *Electronic Applications*, Philips, Pub. Dept., Elcoma Div., Eindhoven, The Netherlands, Vol. 28, No. 2, 1968, p 60–78.

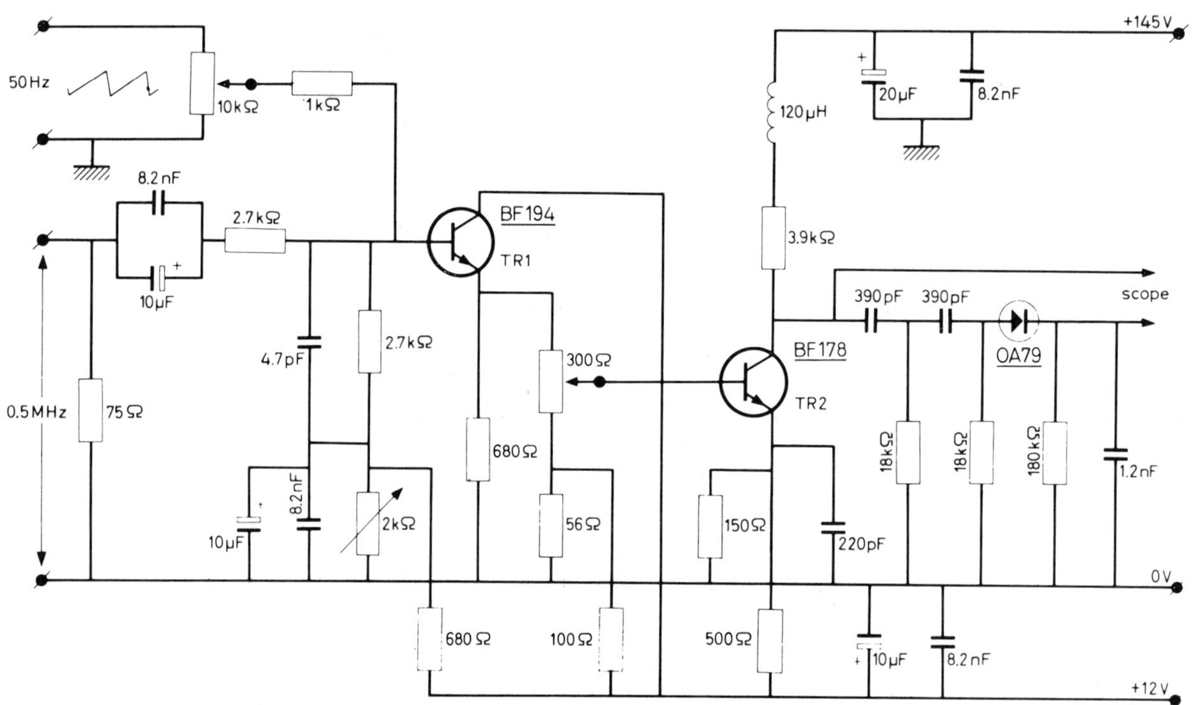

MEASURING VIDEO AMPLIFIER LINEARITY—Connections are shown for showing gain and collector voltage simultaneously on screen of dual-trace cro. One input is 50-Hz sawtooth with sufficient amplitude to drive output stage from cutoff to knee. Other input is 0.5-MHz sine wave with 10 mV p-p amplitude.—A. Cense, Recent Developments in Circuits and Transistors for Television Receivers, *Electronic Applications*, Philips, Pub. Dept., Elcoma Div., Eindhoven, The Netherlands, Vol. 27, No. 2, 1966–1967, p 41–52.

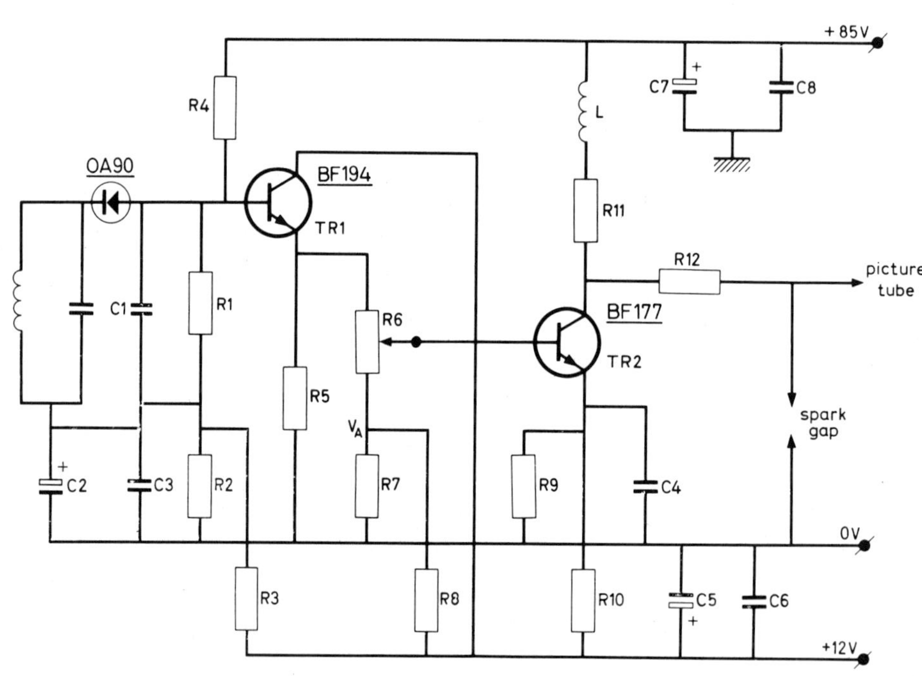

Fig. 3. Circuit diagram of the video output amplifier.

R_1	2.7 kΩ, ¼ W	R_5	470 Ω, ¼ W	R_9	180 Ω, ¼ W	C_1	4.7 pF, 500 V	C_5	10 μF, 16 V
R_2	1.2 kΩ, ¼ W	R_6	300 Ω, pot.	R_{10}	820 Ω, ¼ W	C_2	10 μF, 16 V	C_6	6.8 nF, 500 V
R_3	1 kΩ, ¼ W	R_7	47 Ω, ½ W	R_{11}	4.7 kΩ, 5.5 W	C_3	6.8 nF, 500 V	C_7	20 μF, 250 V
R_4	390 kΩ, ¼ W	R_8	120 Ω, 1 W	R_{12}	1.5 kΩ, 1 W	C_4	180 pF, 500 V	C_8	6.8 nF, 500 V

625-LINE VIDEO AMPLIFIER—Uses two direct-coupled stages to drive 11-inch picture tube. Bandwidth is at least 4 MHz for 3-dB down at all settings of contrast control. Output voltage (black-to-white) is 50 V and gain is 30. Black level is independent of contrast control or picture content.—A. Cense, Recent Developments in Circuits and Transistors for Television Receivers, *Electronic Applications*, Philips, Pub. Dept., Elcoma Div., Eindhoven, The Netherlands, Vol. 27, No. 3, 1966–1967, p 85–91.

SYNC SEPARATOR FOR MONITOR—Works equally well on standard or closed-circuit signals in television monitor. Depends on coincidence of vertical sync signals and non-coincidence of horizontal sync signals in coincidence circuit. Gives improved vertical resolution, accurate interlace, and noncritical vertical hold adjustments.—H. F. Stearns, Delay-Line Sync Separator Improves Video Resolution, *Electronic Design*, Nov. 22, 1965, p 60.

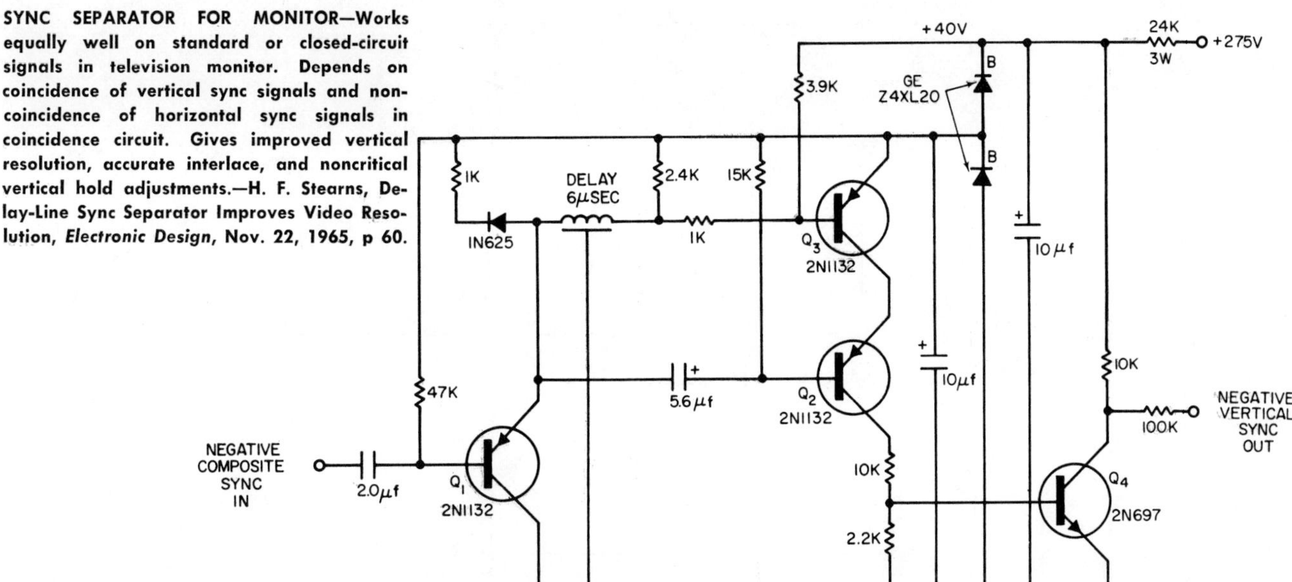

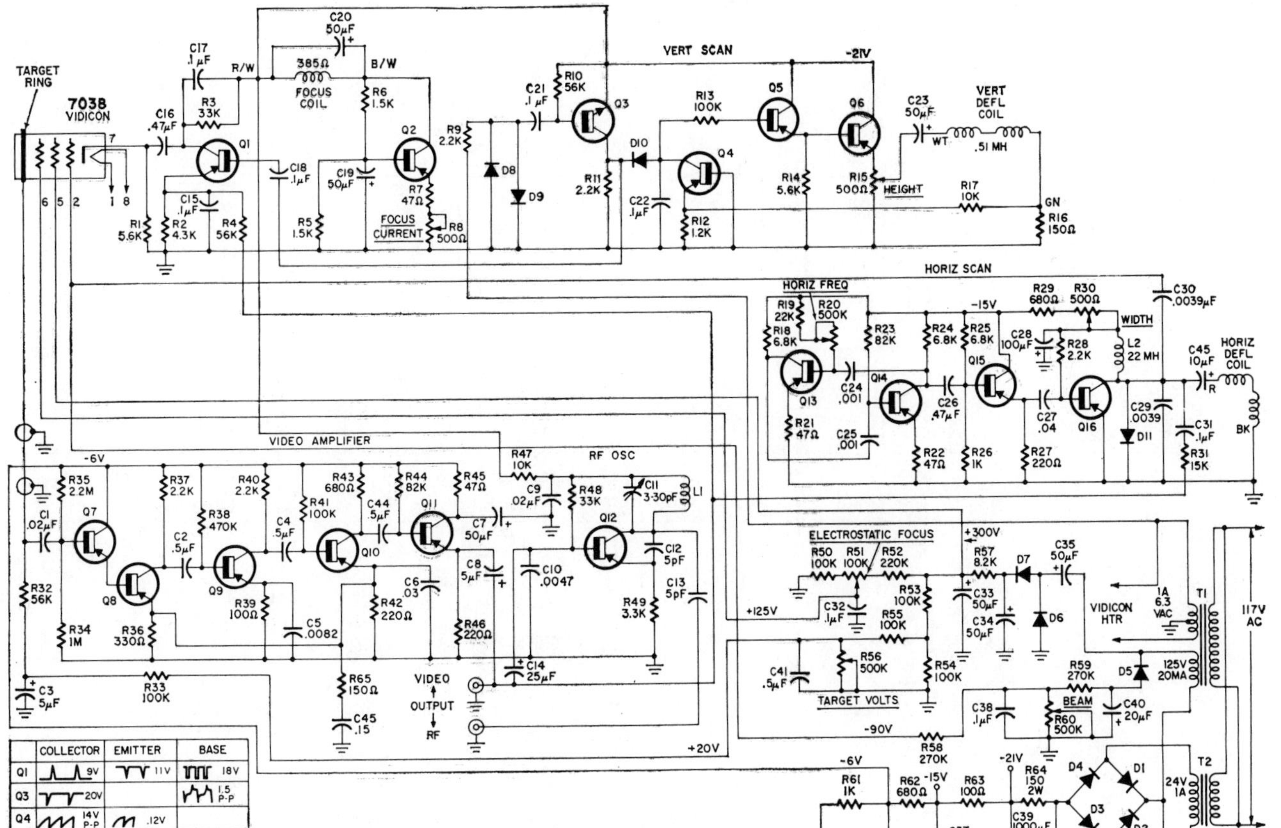

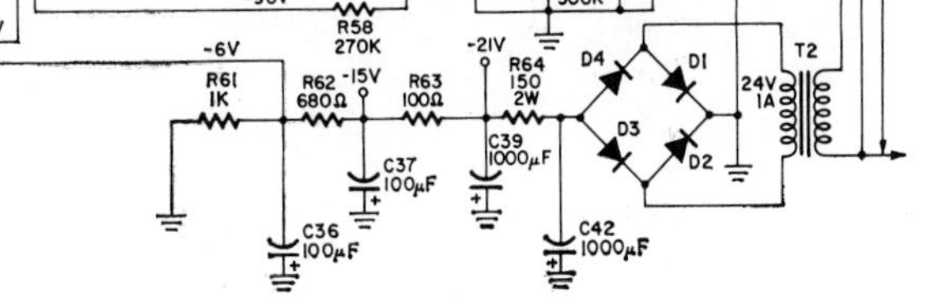

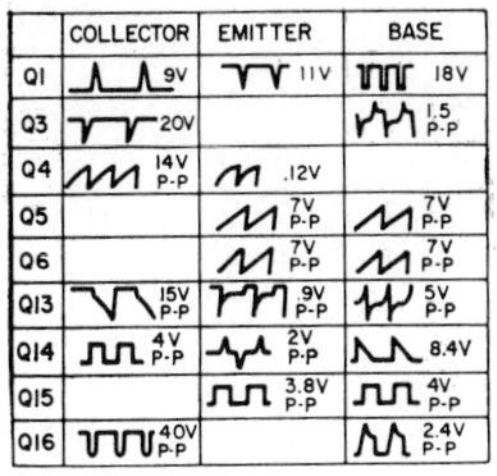

	COLLECTOR	EMITTER	BASE
Q1	9V	11V	18V
Q3	20V		1.5 P-P
Q4	14V P-P	.12V	
Q5		7V P-P	7V P-P
Q6		7V P-P	7V P-P
Q13	15V P-P	9V P-P	5V P-P
Q14	4V P-P	2V P-P	8.4V
Q15		3.8V P-P	4V P-P
Q16	40V P-P		2.4V P-P

CAMERA FOR HOME RECEIVER—Has both r-f and video signal outputs, for connecting directly to antenna terminals of set, or can be used with video line amplifier to drive video tape recorder or ham tv transmitter. Article gives construction details and sources for yoke and focus coils. Alternative vidicon having higher sensitivity is 7735A. Diodes D1-D7 are GE-504; D8-D11 1N60; Q1-Q2, Q6-Q13 2N3638; Q3 2N2926; Q4-Q5, Q14-Q16 SA599. With short whip antenna connected to output of oscillator, camera will transmit picture to tv set about 50 ft away. —G. Davis, Jr., Build All-Transistor TV Camera for $100, *Radio-Electronics*, July 1969, p 23–26 and 92.

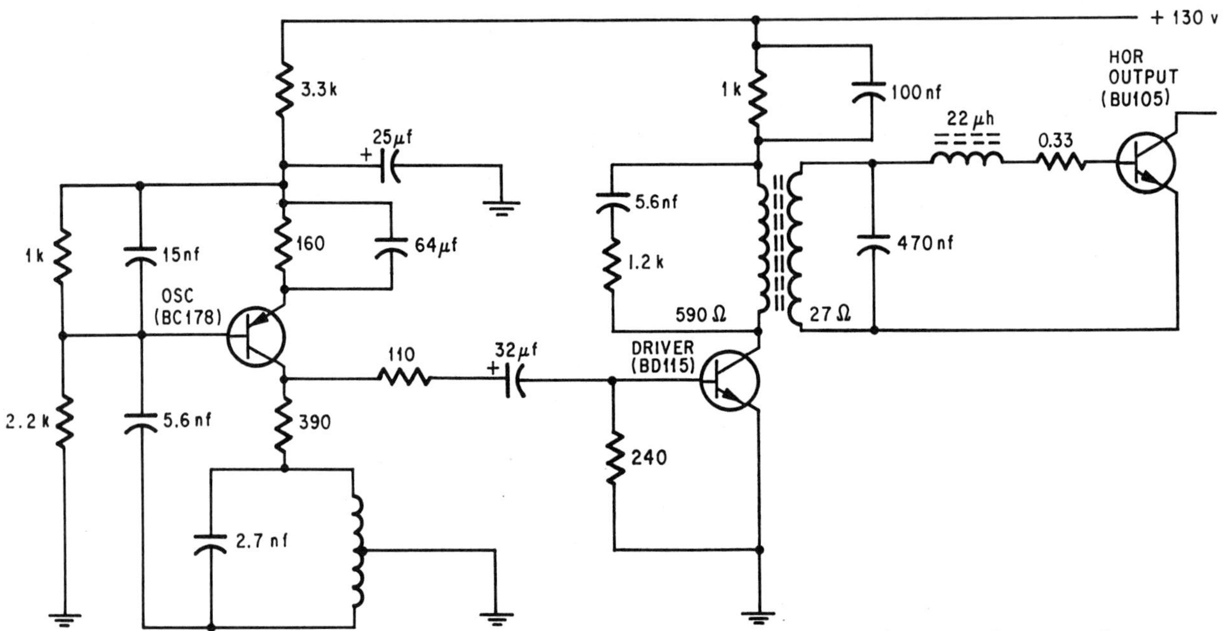

ALL-TRANSISTOR HORIZONTAL SYSTEM—Developed for 23-inch Philips tv sets. Oscillator should have frequency adjustment. Output stage is designed so it cannot be damaged by sudden failure of oscillator or driver. Article gives step-by-step procedure for designing all-transistor large-screen tv.—W. Hetterscheid, All-Solid State Design Overtakes Large-Screen Monochrome TV Sets, *Electronics*, June 24, 1968, p 104–111.

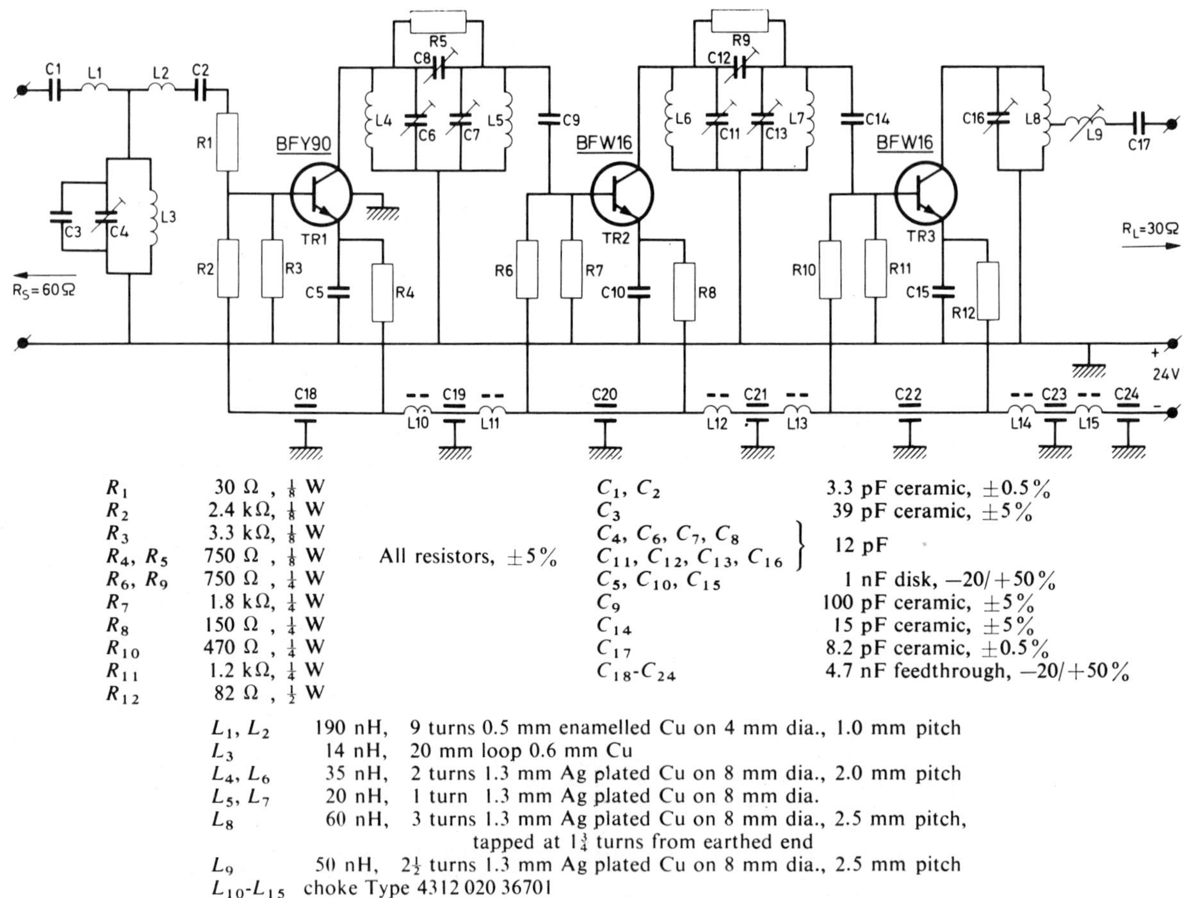

R_1	30 Ω, $\frac{1}{8}$ W		C_1, C_2	3.3 pF ceramic, ±0.5%
R_2	2.4 kΩ, $\frac{1}{8}$ W		C_3	39 pF ceramic, ±5%
R_3	3.3 kΩ, $\frac{1}{8}$ W		C_4, C_6, C_7, C_8 / C_{11}, C_{12}, C_{13}, C_{16}	12 pF
R_4, R_5	750 Ω, $\frac{1}{8}$ W	All resistors, ±5%		
R_6, R_9	750 Ω, $\frac{1}{4}$ W		C_5, C_{10}, C_{15}	1 nF disk, −20/+50%
R_7	1.8 kΩ, $\frac{1}{4}$ W		C_9	100 pF ceramic, ±5%
R_8	150 Ω, $\frac{1}{4}$ W		C_{14}	15 pF ceramic, ±5%
R_{10}	470 Ω, $\frac{1}{4}$ W		C_{17}	8.2 pF ceramic, ±0.5%
R_{11}	1.2 kΩ, $\frac{1}{4}$ W		C_{18}-C_{24}	4.7 nF feedthrough, −20/+50%
R_{12}	82 Ω, $\frac{1}{2}$ W			

L_1, L_2	190 nH,	9 turns 0.5 mm enamelled Cu on 4 mm dia., 1.0 mm pitch
L_3	14 nH,	20 mm loop 0.6 mm Cu
L_4, L_6	35 nH,	2 turns 1.3 mm Ag plated Cu on 8 mm dia., 2.0 mm pitch
L_5, L_7	20 nH,	1 turn 1.3 mm Ag plated Cu on 8 mm dia.
L_8	60 nH,	3 turns 1.3 mm Ag plated Cu on 8 mm dia., 2.5 mm pitch, tapped at $1\frac{3}{4}$ turns from earthed end
L_9	50 nH,	$2\frac{1}{2}$ turns 1.3 mm Ag plated Cu on 8 mm dia., 2.5 mm pitch
L_{10}-L_{15}		choke Type 4312 020 36701

174–230 MHZ ANTENNA AMPLIFIER—Provides gain of 39 dB for European band III, with noise factor of 6.2 to 6.7 dB and 10-mW output per signal. Article gives alignment instructions.—J. Tuil, Transistor Equipped Aerial Amplifiers, *Electronic Applications*, Philips, Pub. Dept., Elcoma Div., Eindhoven, The Netherlands, Vol. 28, No. 2, 1968, p 60–73.

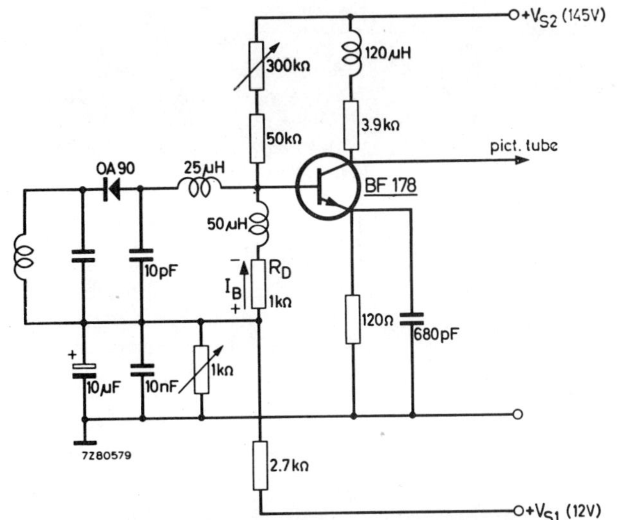

SINGLE-STAGE VIDEO AMPLIFIER—Silicon planar transistor supplies sufficient drive for all large-screen picture tubes. Circuit values are for European 625-line system. One drawback is inability of video detector to operate at low input levels because high base current flows through detector load resistor RD and causes reverse voltage for detector diode, with resulting distortion in peak white signal. Another problem is insufficient bandwidth.—A. Cense, The N-P-N Silicon Planar Transistor BF178 in a Video Amplifier, Philips, Pub. Dept., Elcoma Div., Eindhoven, The Netherlands, No. 251, 1966.

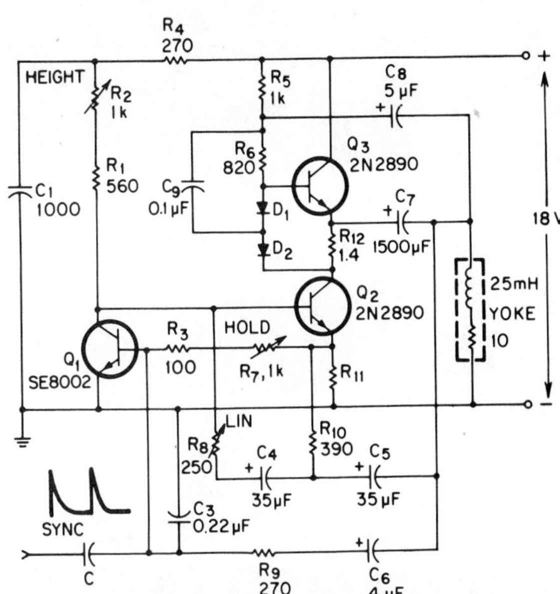

CHOKELESS VERTICAL SWEEP—Efficiency of chokeless vertical deflection circuit for small-screen b-w tv is improved by resonating yoke with capacitor and isolating yoke for that portion of retrace pulse which exceeds B+. Generates yoke current of 0.6 A p-p in 25-mH 10-ohm yoke from 18-V supply. Retrace time is 1.35 ms.—J. M. Tucker, Higher-Efficiency Chokeless Vertical Sweep, *EEE*, July 1969, p 106.

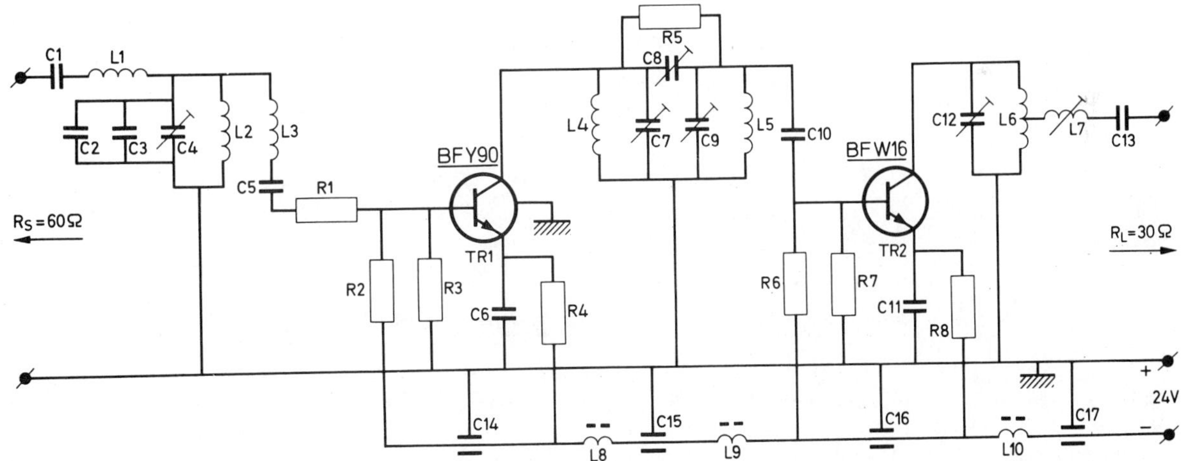

R_1	27 Ω, $\frac{1}{8}$ W	C_1, C_5	6.8 pF ceramic, ±0.5%
R_2	2.2 kΩ, $\frac{1}{8}$ W	C_2	10 pF ceramic, ±0.5%
R_3	1.5 kΩ, $\frac{1}{8}$ W	C_3	100 pF ceramic, ±5%
R_4	1 kΩ, $\frac{1}{8}$ W	C_4, C_7, C_8, C_9, C_{12}	12 pF
R_5	7.5 kΩ, $\frac{1}{8}$ W	C_6, C_{11}	4.7 nF disk, −20/+50%
R_6	470 Ω, $\frac{1}{4}$ W	C_{10}	15 pF ceramic, ±5%
R_7	1.2 kΩ, $\frac{1}{4}$ W	C_{13}	22 pF ceramic, ±5%
R_8	82 Ω, $\frac{1}{2}$ W	C_{14}-C_{17}	4.7 nF feedthrough, −20/+50%

All resistors, ±5%

L_1, L_3	380 nH,	14 turns 0.5 mm enamelled Cu on 4 mm dia., 0.5 mm pitch
L_2	28 nH,	2 turns 1.0 mm enamelled Cu on 4 mm dia., 2.5 mm pitch
L_4, L_5	135 nH,	5 turns 1.3 mm Ag plated Cu on 8 mm dia., 2.5 mm pitch
L_6	135 nH,	5 turns 1.3 mm Ag plated Cu on 8 mm dia., 2.5 mm pitch, tapped 2½ turns from earthed end
L_7	70 nH,	2 turns 1.3 mm Ag plated Cu on 8 mm dia., 2.0 mm pitch
L_8-L_{10}	choke Type 4312 020 36701	

87.5–108 MHZ ANTENNA AMPLIFIER—Provides gain of 43 dB for European band II, with noise factor of 6 to 6.5 dB and 25-mW output per signal. Article gives alignment information.—J. Tuil, Transistor Equipped Aerial Amplifiers, *Electronic Applications*, Philips, Pub. Dept., Elcoma Div., Eindhoven, The Netherlands, Vol. 28, No. 2, 1968, p 60–78.

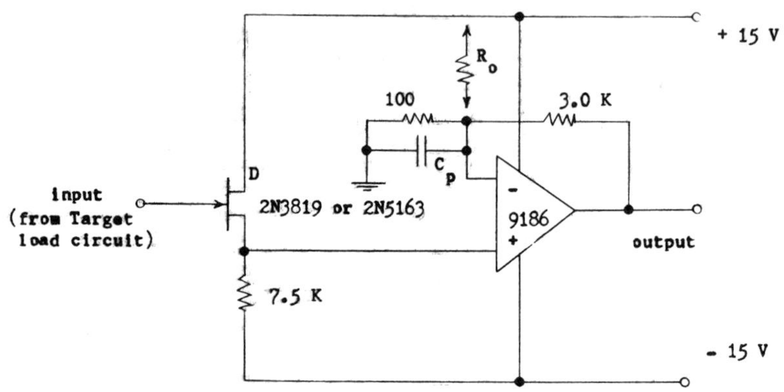

VIDICON PREAMP—Input fet is used as source follower to provide impedance buffering for wide range of vidicon target loading circuits. High open-loop gain of 1,000 for opamp and 1-MHz bandwidth make arrangement ideal for video amplifiers requiring high-frequency peaking and low noise.—A Video Pre-Amplifier for Use With a Vidicon, Optical Electronics, Tucson, Ariz., No. 10089.

VERTICAL BLANKING CIRCUIT—With terminals 4, 5, and 6 connected to field (vertical) output stage, circuit generates suitable blanking pulse for feeding directly to emitter of video output transistor in small-screen battery-operated tv receiver. Diode clips initial peak of flyback voltage.—A. H. Nillesen, Field Deflection Circuit for Tiny-Vision Receivers, Philips, Pub. Dept., Elcoma Div., Eindhoven, The Netherlands, No. 256, 1967.

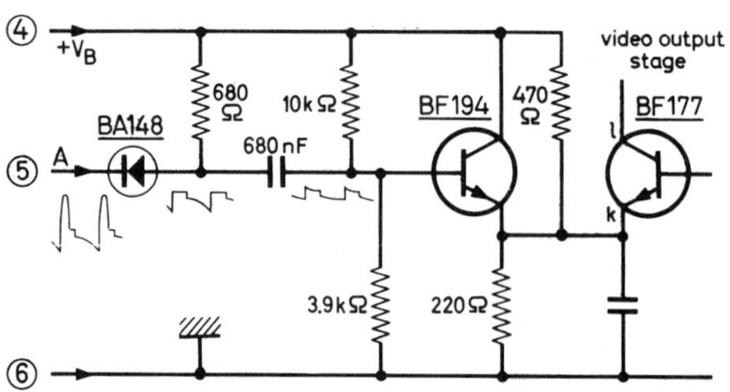

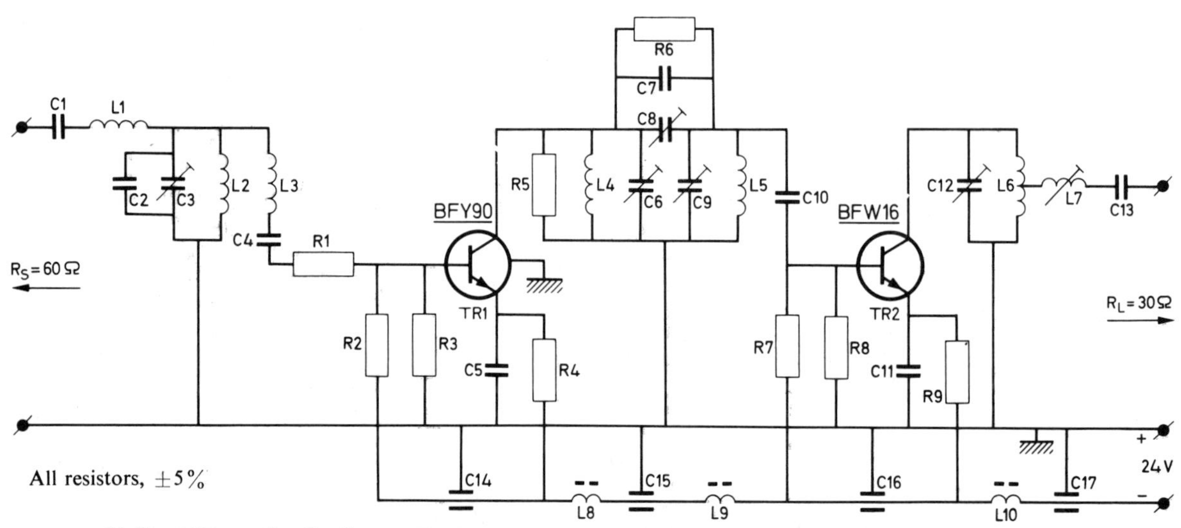

R_1	10 Ω, $\frac{1}{8}$ W	C_1, C_4, C_7	12 pF ceramic, ±5%
R_2	2.2 kΩ, $\frac{1}{8}$ W	C_2	10 pF ceramic, ±0.5%
R_3	1.5 kΩ, $\frac{1}{8}$ W	C_3, C_6, C_8	12 pF
R_4, R_5	1 kΩ, $\frac{1}{8}$ W	C_9, C_{12}	
R_6	750 Ω, $\frac{1}{8}$ W	C_5, C_{11}	4.7 nF disk, −20/+50%
R_7	470 Ω, $\frac{1}{4}$ W	C_{10}	82 pF ceramic, ±5%
R_8	1.2 kΩ, $\frac{1}{4}$ W	C_{13}	56 pF ceramic, ±5%
R_9	82 Ω, $\frac{1}{2}$ W	C_{14}-C_{17}	4.7 nF feedthrough, −20/+50%

L_1, L_3	500 nH,	21 turns 0.5 mm enamelled Cu on 4 mm dia., 0.5 mm pitch
L_2	200 nH,	13 turns 1.0 mm enamelled Cu on 4 mm dia., 1.5 mm pitch
L_4	200 nH,	8 turns 1.0 mm enamelled Cu on 8 mm dia., 1,5 mm pitch
L_5	85 nH,	4 turns 1.0 mm enamelled Cu on 8 mm dia., 2.5 mm pitch
L_6	240 nH,	11 turns 1.0 mm enamelled Cu on 8 mm dia., 2.0 mm pitch, tapped 4½ turns from earthed end
L_7	75 nH,	3 turns 1 mm enamelled Cu on 8 mm dia., 2.0 mm pitch,
L_8-L_{10}	choke Type 4312 020 36701	

47–68 MHZ ANTENNA AMPLIFIER—Provides gain of 52 dB for European band I, with noise factor of 6 to 6.5 db and 10-mW output per signal. Article gives alignment information.—J. Tuil, Transistor Equipped Aerial Amplifiers, *Electronic Applications*, Philips, Pub. Dept., Elcoma Div., Eindhoven, The Netherlands, Vol. 28, No. 2, 1968, p 60–78.

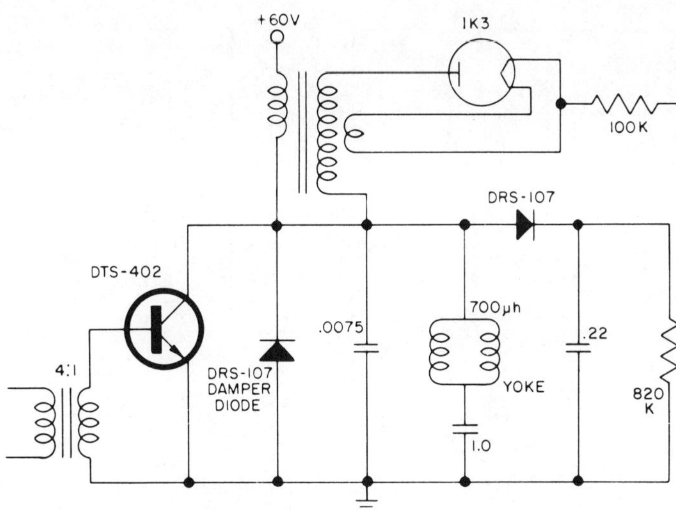

HORIZONTAL OUTPUT—Uses silicon power transistor designed especially for operation from 60-V supply in horizontal deflection stage of large-screen monochrome tv set.—Video Horizontal and Vertical Output Transistor Pair, Delco Radio, Kokomo, Ind., DTS-401 DTS-402, 1968.

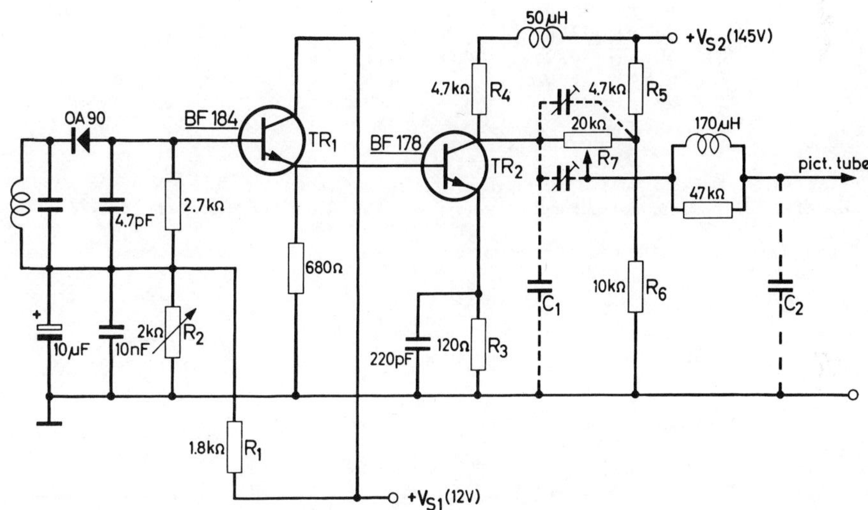

VIDEO WITH CONTRAST CONTROL—Shows method of applying contrast control in collector circuit of video output transistor. R5 and R6 provide constant black level during contrast control. Report discusses design problems, including that of capacitance introduced by long wires going from contrast pot at front of set to video amplifier. Total value of C1 and C2 is about 30 pF.—A. Cense, The N-P-N Silicon Planar Transistor BF178 in a Video Amplifier, Philips, Pub. Dept., Elcoma Div., Eindhoven, The Netherlands, No. 251, 1966.

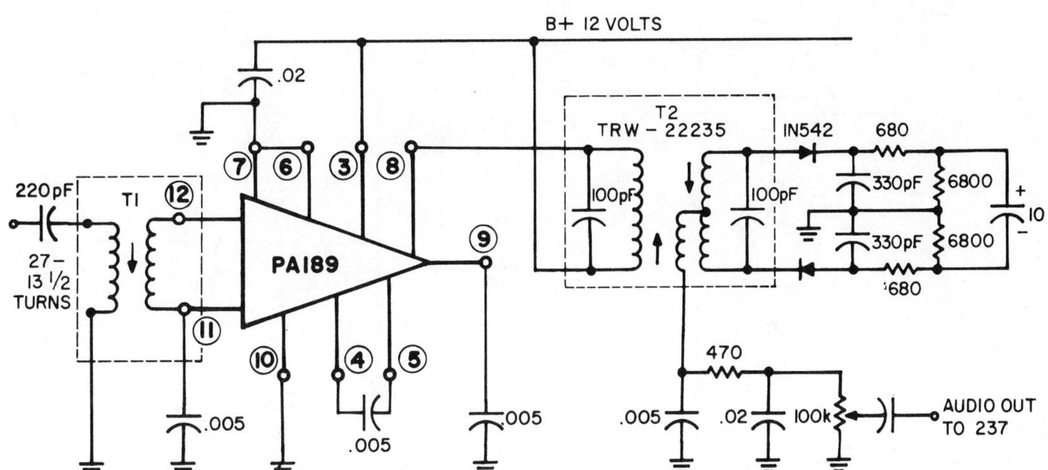

IC I-F AND RATIO DETECTOR—PA189 linear IC with external components shown gives good a-m rejection and very high gain along with bandwidth of at least 50 kHz. I-f value is 4.5 MHz. Sensitivity is 200 μV for 3 dB limiting.—E. L. Haas and D. J. Hubbard, Linear Integrated Circuits in a TV Sound System, General Electric Co., Syracuse, N.Y., Application Note 90.74, 6/68.

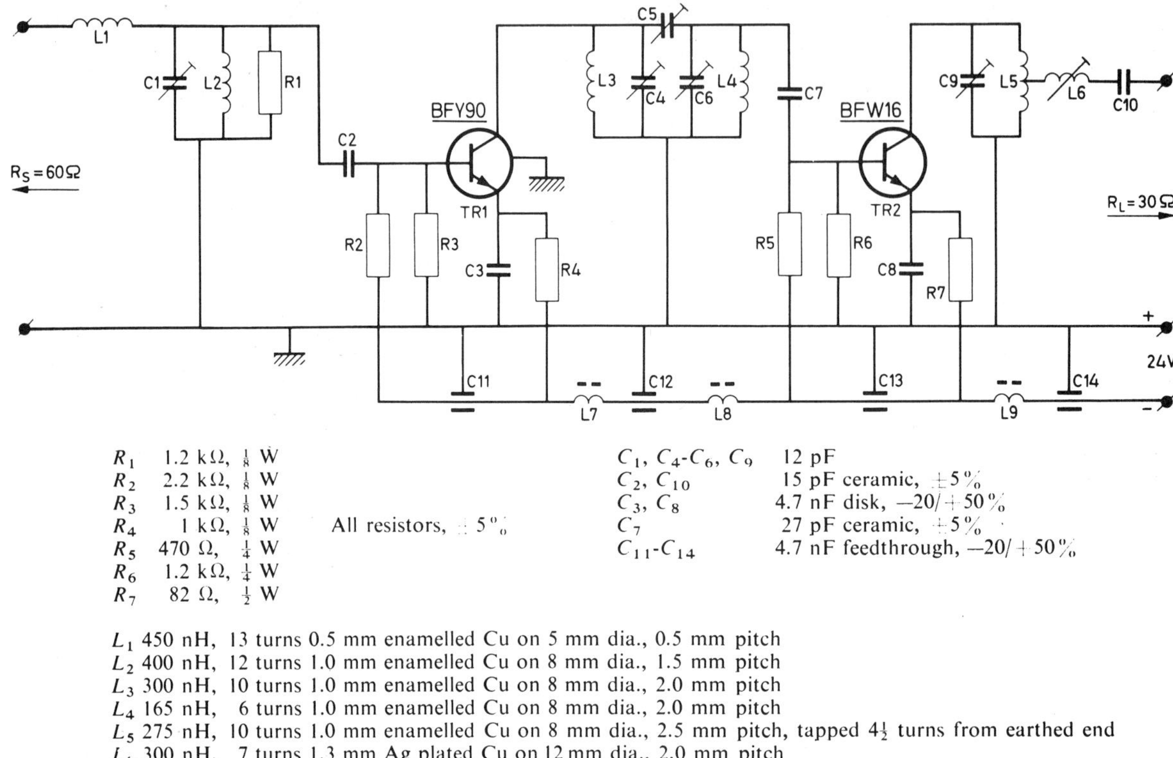

R_1	1.2 kΩ, $\frac{1}{8}$ W	C_1, C_4-C_6, C_9	12 pF
R_2	2.2 kΩ, $\frac{1}{8}$ W	C_2, C_{10}	15 pF ceramic, ±5%
R_3	1.5 kΩ, $\frac{1}{8}$ W	C_3, C_8	4.7 nF disk, −20/+50%
R_4	1 kΩ, $\frac{1}{8}$ W	C_7	27 pF ceramic, ±5%
R_5	470 Ω, $\frac{1}{4}$ W	C_{11}-C_{14}	4.7 nF feedthrough, −20/+50%
R_6	1.2 kΩ, $\frac{1}{4}$ W		
R_7	82 Ω, $\frac{1}{2}$ W		

All resistors, ±5%

L_1 450 nH, 13 turns 0.5 mm enamelled Cu on 5 mm dia., 0.5 mm pitch
L_2 400 nH, 12 turns 1.0 mm enamelled Cu on 8 mm dia., 1.5 mm pitch
L_3 300 nH, 10 turns 1.0 mm enamelled Cu on 8 mm dia., 2.0 mm pitch
L_4 165 nH, 6 turns 1.0 mm enamelled Cu on 8 mm dia., 2.0 mm pitch
L_5 275 nH, 10 turns 1.0 mm enamelled Cu on 8 mm dia., 2.5 mm pitch, tapped 4½ turns from earthed end
L_6 300 nH, 7 turns 1.3 mm Ag plated Cu on 12 mm dia., 2.0 mm pitch
L_7-L_9 choke Type 4312 020 36701

61–68 MHZ ANTENNA AMPLIFIER—Provides gain of 50 dB for European channel 4, with 7-dB noise factor and 150-mW output signal. —J. Tuil, Transistor Equipped Aerial Amplifiers, *Electronic Applications*, Philips, Pub. Dept., Elcoma Div., Eindhoven, The Netherlands, Vol. 28, No. 2, 1968, p 60–78.

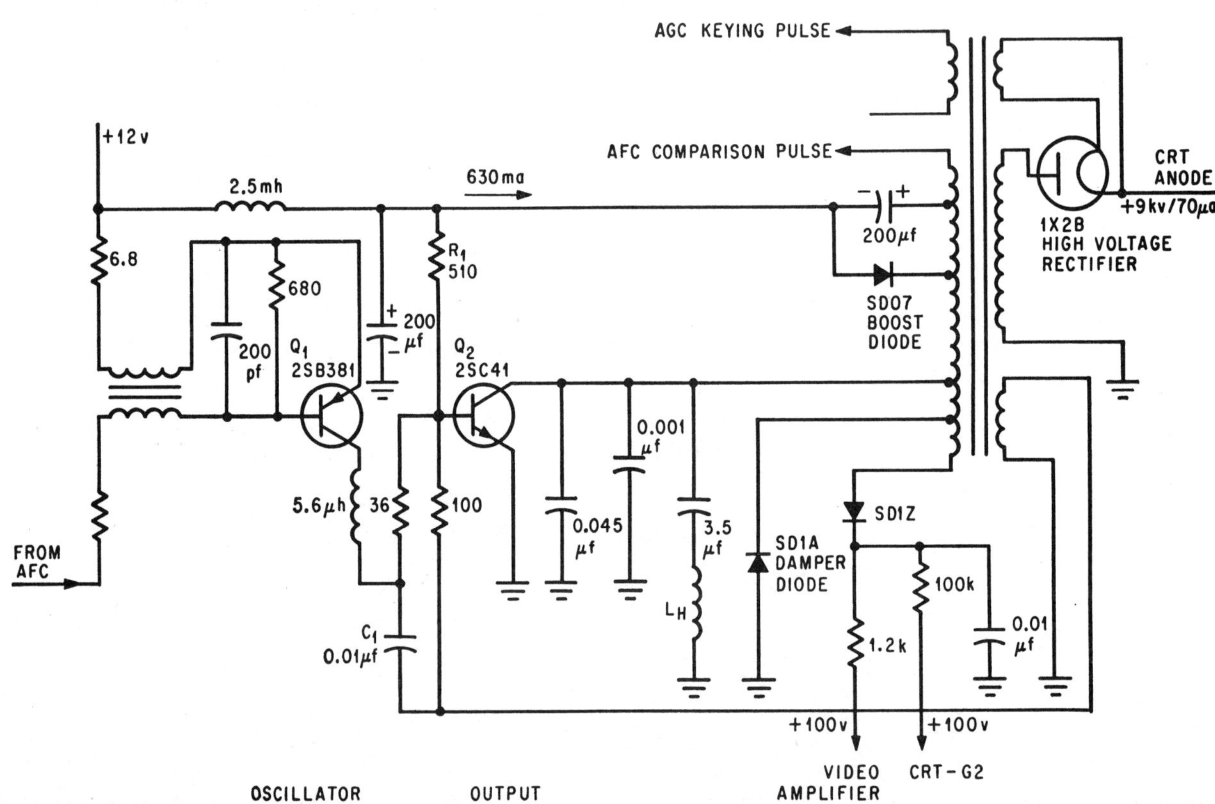

TWO-TRANSISTOR HORIZONTAL SWEEP—Used in Sony 7-inch 700U portable tv. Tertiary winding on flyback transformer provides positive feedback to base of Q2 to offset gain lost through omission of driver stage. Total power consumption of horizontal output stage is only 9.5 W. Sweep Eliminates Driver Stage, *Electronics*, Nov. 14, 1966, p 169–171.

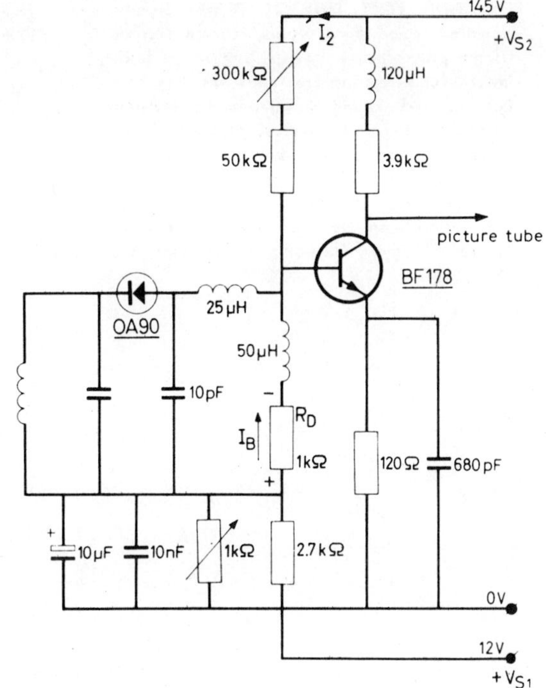

SINGLE-STAGE VIDEO AMPLIFIER—Provides bandwidth of 4.5 MHz at 3-dB-down points and 80 V black-to-white output voltage for typical large-screen picture tube such as A59-11W in European 625-line tv receiver. Transistor is direct-coupled to video detector circuit. Contrast control is in base circuit, where it places no restrictions on circuit layout or wiring, and does not affect either bandwidth or transient response.—A. Cense, Recent Developments in Circuits and Transistors for Television Receivers, *Electronic Applications*, Philips, Pub. Dept., Elcoma Div., Eindhoven, The Netherlands, Vol. 27, No. 2, 1966–1967, p 41–52.

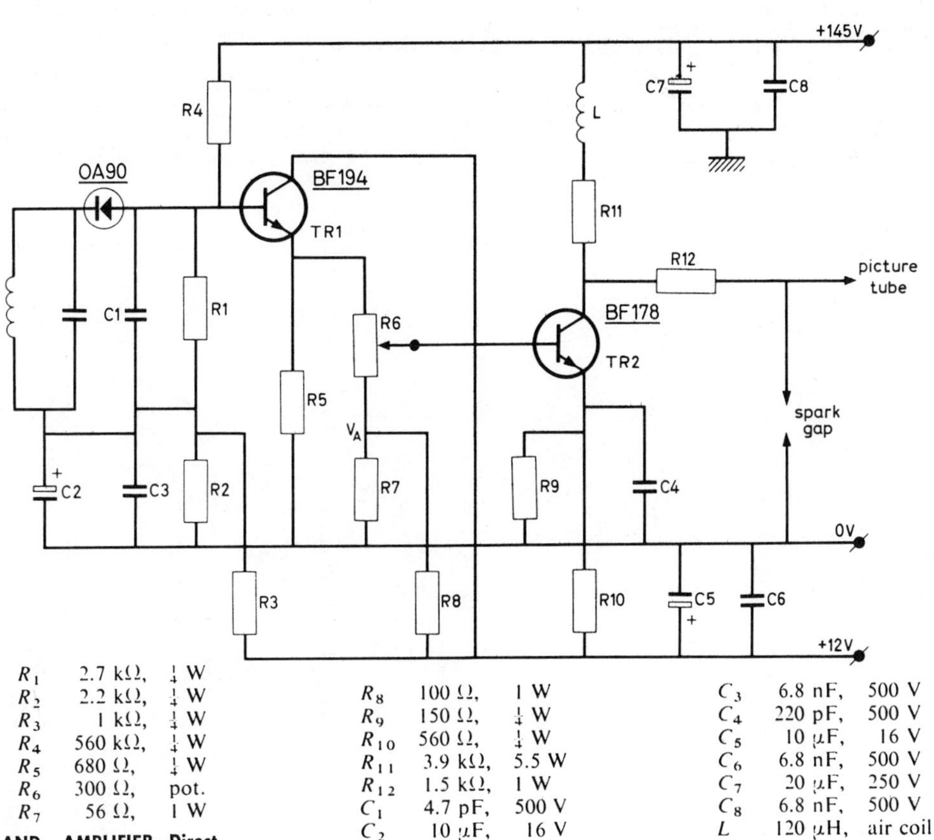

R_1	2.7 kΩ,	¼ W
R_2	2.2 kΩ,	¼ W
R_3	1 kΩ,	¼ W
R_4	560 kΩ,	¼ W
R_5	680 Ω,	¼ W
R_6	300 Ω,	pot.
R_7	56 Ω,	1 W
R_8	100 Ω,	1 W
R_9	150 Ω,	¼ W
R_{10}	560 Ω,	¼ W
R_{11}	3.9 kΩ,	5.5 W
R_{12}	1.5 kΩ,	1 W
C_1	4.7 pF,	500 V
C_2	10 μF,	16 V
C_3	6.8 nF,	500 V
C_4	220 pF,	500 V
C_5	10 μF,	16 V
C_6	6.8 nF,	500 V
C_7	20 μF,	250 V
C_8	6.8 nF,	500 V
L	120 μH,	air coil

VIDEO DETECTOR AND AMPLIFIER—Direct coupling is used throughout to keep black level constant and independent of picture content in European large-screen 625-line tv receiver. Collector circuit compensation is used in first video amplifier stage to provide required bandwidth. Spark gap protects transistors from high-voltage spikes appearing at picture-tube cathode as result of flashovers. Maximum breakdown voltage of spark gap is 3,000 V.—A. Cense, Recent Developments in Circuits and Transistors for Television Receivers, *Electronic Applications*, Philips, Pub. Dept., Elcoma Div., Eindhoven, The Netherlands, Vol. 27, No. 2, 1966–1967, p 41–52.

SELECTING FIRST LINE OF FRAME—Signal-powered coincidence gate delivers output trigger only when pulses are present at both inputs, for triggering cro coincident with first field of each frame in interlaced television scanning system. Overcomes problem of delayed time base in cro that may lock onto first or second field pulse at random because it cannot distinguish between them.—O. Harper, Coincidence Gate Generates First Field Reference Trigger, *Electronic Design*, Sept. 27, 1967, p 66.

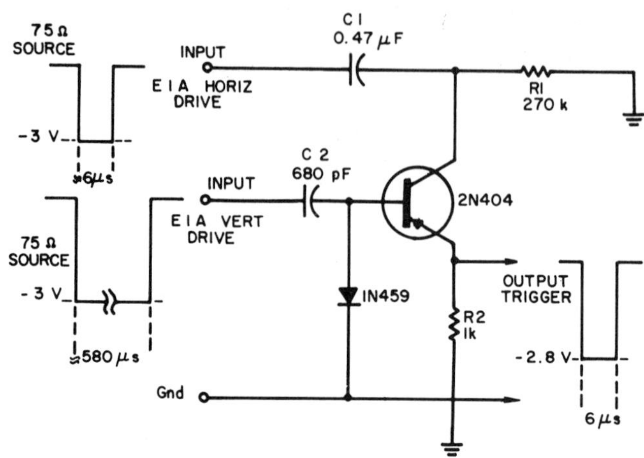

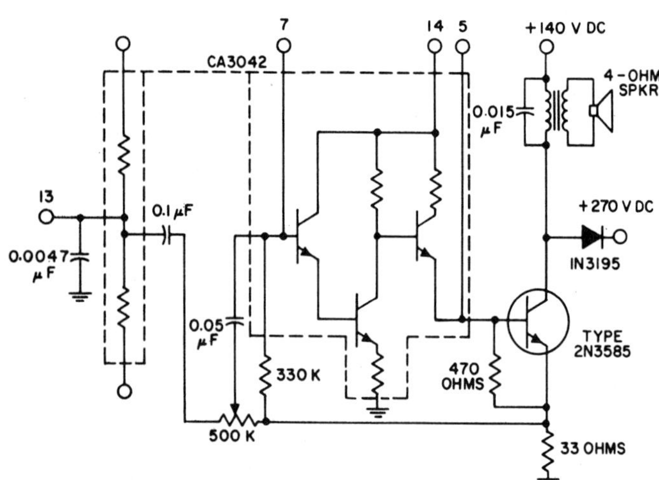

FEEDBACK VOLUME CONTROL—Used with CA3042 IC to cut production costs through use of smaller coupling capacitors. Delivers 2 W audio power output at 7 kHz maximum deviation from 4.5-MHz carrier.—L. Kaplan, Feedback-Type Volume-Control Circuits for RCA-CA3041 and CA3042 Integrated Circuits, RCA, Harrison, N.J., No. ICAN-5841, 1968.

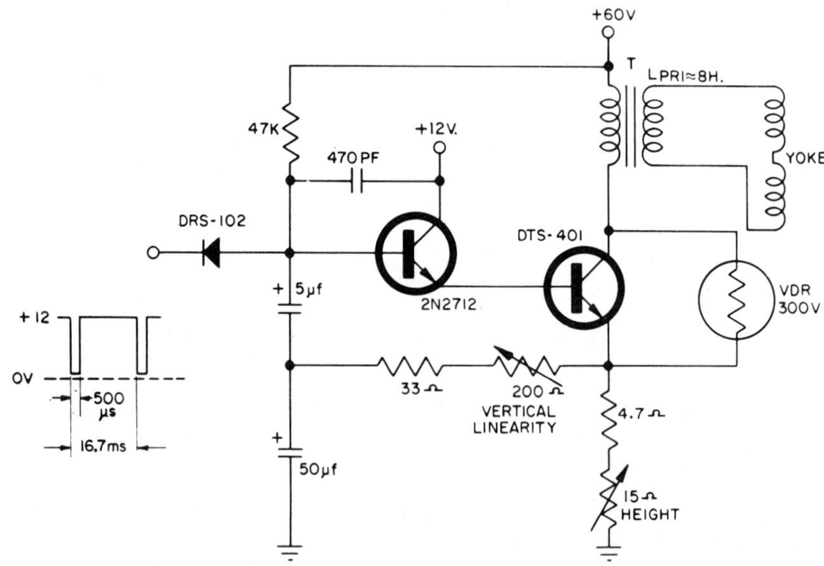

VERTICAL OUTPUT—Uses silicon power transistor designed especially for operation from 60-V supply in vertical deflection stage. Has good gain linearity.—Video Horizontal and Vertical Output Transistor Pair, Delco Radio, Kokomo, Ind., DTS-401 DTS-402, 1968.

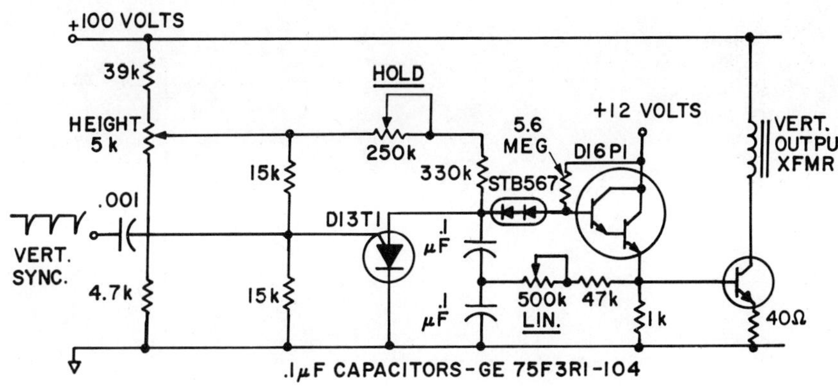

SOLID-STATE VERTICAL DEFLECTION—Uses D13T1 programmable ujt as relaxation oscillator operating at 60-Hz sweep rate, with synchronization by 4-V negative pulses. D16P1 high-gain Darlington drives output power transistor, and multipellet diode provides d-c level shifting. Bootstrap feedback through 500K improves linearity.—W. R. Spofford, Jr., The D13T—A Programmable Unijunction Transistor, General Electric, Syracuse, N.Y., No. 90.70, 11/67, p 10.

PHOTOMULTIPLIER AMPLIFIER FOR FLYING-SPOT SCANNER—Used for detecting high-frequency modulated light from flying-spot scanners used for slide reproduction in television studios. For color slides, three identical amplifiers are required. Photomultiplier shown will handle bandwidth from d-c to 100 MHz, but XP1210 will go up to 350 MHz.—J. M. Schonkeren, "Photomultipliers," Philips, Pub. Dept., Elcoma Div., Eindhoven, The Netherlands, 1970, p 102.

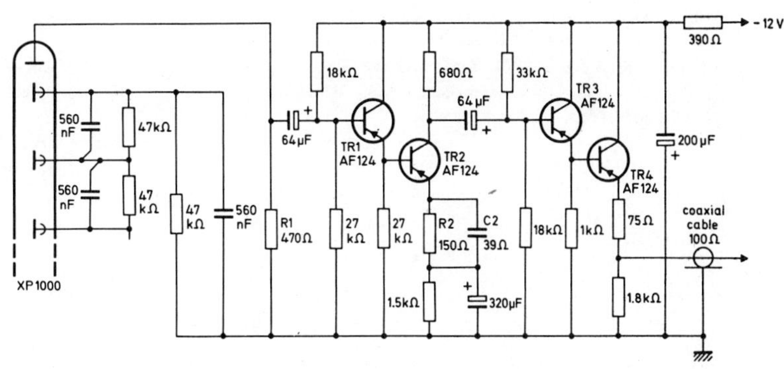

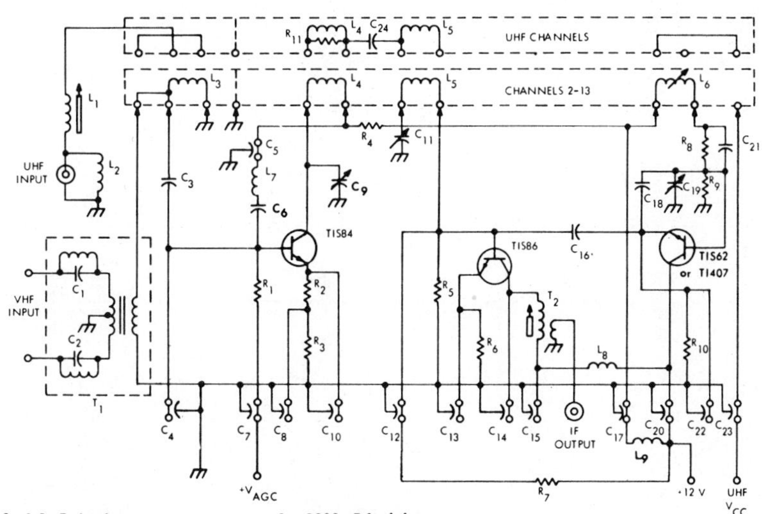

- C_1: 47 pF
- C_2: 47 pF
- C_3: 8.2 pF
- C_4: 1.8 pF feed-thru
- C_5: 30 pF feed-thru
- C_6: 0.68 pF
- C_7: 1000 pF feed-thru
- C_8: 1000 pF feed-thru
- C_9: 2-8 pF air trimmer
- C_{10}: 39 pF feed-thru
- C_{11}: 2-8 pF air trimmer
- C_{12}: 30 pF feed-thru
- C_{13}: 1000 pF feed-thru
- C_{14}: 10 pF feed-thru
- C_{15}: 1000 pF feed-thru
- C_{16}: 3.6 pF
- C_{17}: 1000 pF feed-thru
- C_{18}: 5.6 pF
- C_{19}: 0.5-3 pF air trimmer
- C_{20}: 1000 pF feed-thru
- C_{21}: 5.6 pF
- C_{22}: 2.5 pF feed-thru
- C_{23}: 1000 pF feed-thru
- C_{24}: 5.6 pF

RESISTORS (1/2 W, ten percent)

- R_1: 1 kΩ
- R_2: 15 Ω
- R_3: 560 Ω
- R_4: 390 Ω
- R_5: 1.2 kΩ
- R_6: 220 Ω
- R_7: 10 kΩ
- R_8: 5.6 kΩ
- R_9: 10 kΩ
- R_{10}: 1 kΩ
- R_{11}: 10 kΩ

INDUCTORS

- L_1: UHF matching coil
- L_2: UHF matching coil
- L_3: as required per channel
- L_4: as required per channel
- L_5: as required per channel
- L_6: as required per channel
- L_7: neutralizing coil
- L_8: RFC
- L_9: RFC

VHF TUNER—Uses npn planar silicon transistors. Power gain ranges from 39 dB for channel 2 to 35 dB for channel 13. Noise figure ranges from 5.5 to 6.2 dB, i-f rejection from 55 to 84 dB, and image rejection from 66 to 88 dB. T1 is balun assembly, including i-f traps, and T2 is i-f output transformer.—Preferred Semiconductors and Components, Texas Instruments, Dallas, Texas, Bulletin CC101, 1968, p 1039.

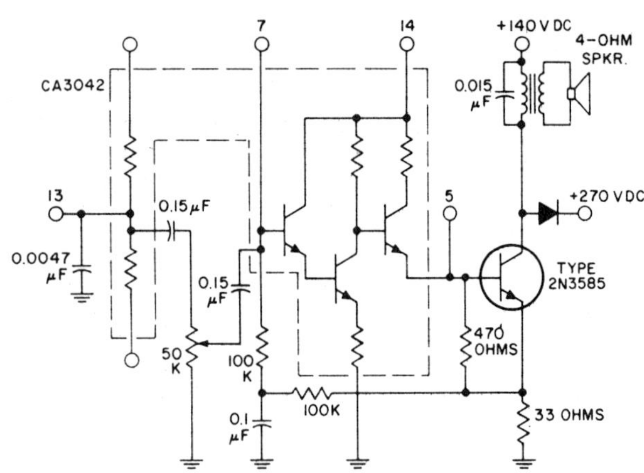

VOLUME CONTROL WITH IC—Circuit illustrates method of using conventional volume control with IC audio amplifier for tv sound. —L. Kaplan, Feedback-Type Volume-Control Circuits for RCA-CA3041 and CA3042 Integrated Circuits, RCA, Harrison, N.J., No. ICAN-5841, 1968.

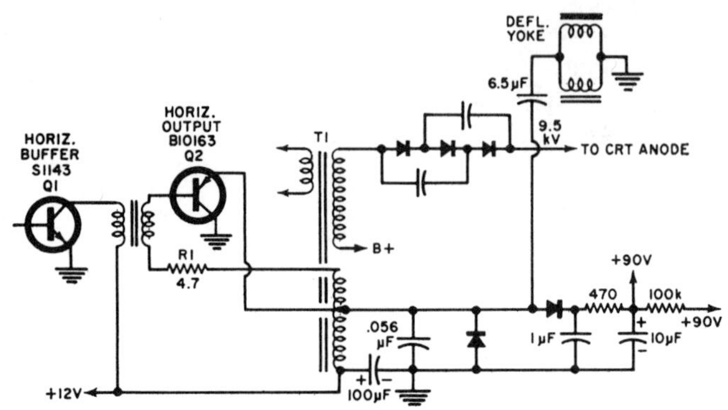

HORIZONTAL OUTPUT WITH B+ AND HV SUPPLIES—High-voltage rectifier circuit of G-E Model TA 9-inch tv uses conventional three-rectifier two-capacitor voltage-doubler with unique method of operation. With 5-kV positive pulse from T1, first and third rectifiers act in effect as peak detectors during retrace, and middle rectifier conducts during trace time. Result is maximum output of about 9.5 kV.—W. H. Buchsbaum, Line-Operated Transistor TV Sets: G-E, *Electronics World*, Oct. 1966, p 29 and 70.

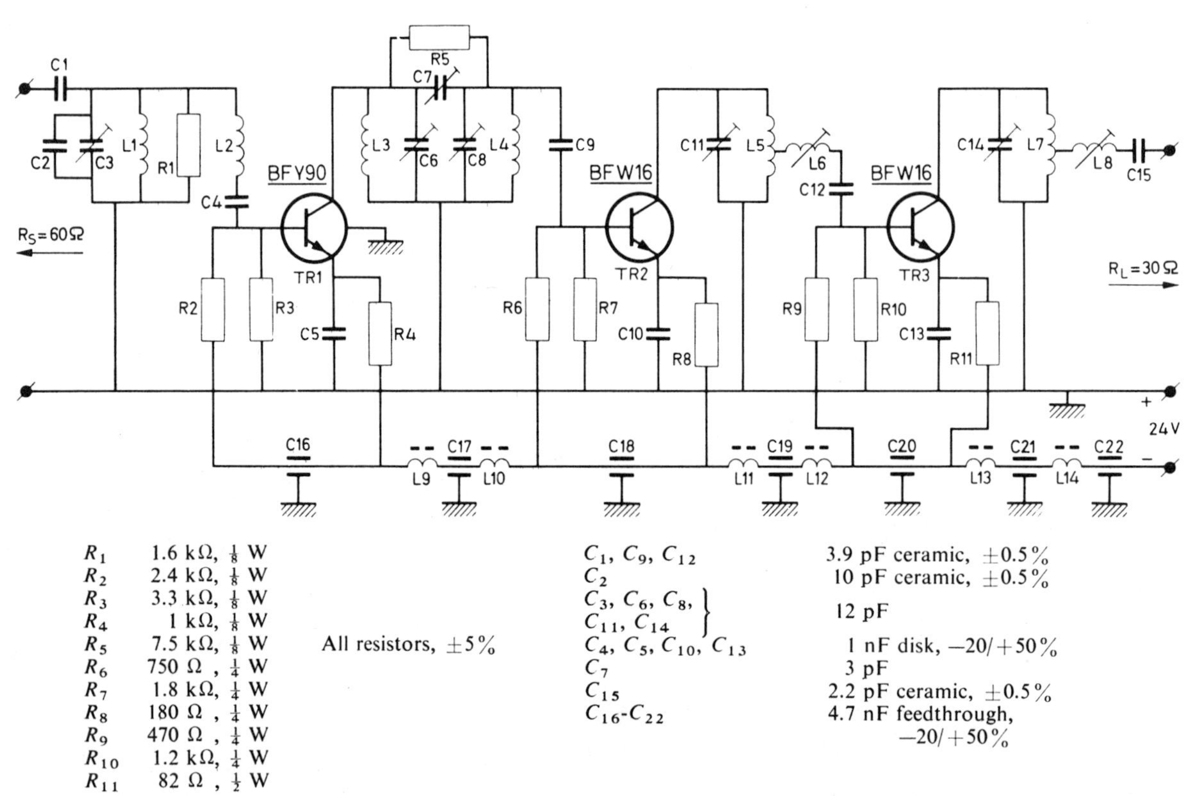

R_1	1.6 kΩ, $\frac{1}{8}$ W	
R_2	2.4 kΩ, $\frac{1}{8}$ W	
R_3	3.3 kΩ, $\frac{1}{8}$ W	
R_4	1 kΩ, $\frac{1}{8}$ W	
R_5	7.5 kΩ, $\frac{1}{8}$ W	All resistors, ±5%
R_6	750 Ω, $\frac{1}{4}$ W	
R_7	1.8 kΩ, $\frac{1}{4}$ W	
R_8	180 Ω, $\frac{1}{4}$ W	
R_9	470 Ω, $\frac{1}{4}$ W	
R_{10}	1.2 kΩ, $\frac{1}{4}$ W	
R_{11}	82 Ω, $\frac{1}{2}$ W	

C_1, C_9, C_{12}	3.9 pF ceramic, ±0.5%
C_2	10 pF ceramic, ±0.5%
C_3, C_6, C_8, C_{11}, C_{14}	12 pF
C_4, C_5, C_{10}, C_{13}	1 nF disk, −20/+50%
C_7	3 pF
C_{15}	2.2 pF ceramic, ±0.5%
C_{16}-C_{22}	4.7 nF feedthrough, −20/+50%

L_1, L_3, L_4	35 nH,	2 turns 1.3 mm Ag plated Cu on 8 mm dia., 2.0 mm pitch
L_2	120 nH,	$5\frac{1}{2}$ turns 1.3 mm Ag plated Cu on 8 mm dia., 2.0 mm pitch
L_5	35 nH,	2 turns 1.3 mm Ag plated Cu on 8 mm dia., 2.0 mm pitch, tapped 3/4 turn from earthed end
L_6	100 nH,	$4\frac{1}{2}$ turns 1.3 mm Ag plated Cu on 8 mm dia., 2.0 mm pitch
L_7	60 nH,	3 turns 1.3 mm Ag plated Cu on 8 mm dia., 2.5 mm pitch, tapped 3/4 turn from earthed end
L_8	165 nH,	$5\frac{1}{2}$ turns 1.3 mm Ag plated Cu on 11 mm dia., 2.0 mm pitch
L_9-L_{14}	choke Type 4312 020 36701	

202–209 MHZ ANTENNA AMPLIFIER—Provides gain of 44 dB for European channel 9, with 6.3-dB noise factor and 150-mW output signal.—J. Tuil, Transistor Equipped Aerial Amplifiers, *Electronic Applications*, Philips, Pub. Dept., Elcoma Div., Eindhoven, The Netherlands, Vol. 28, No. 2, 1968, p 60–78.

PENLIGHT REGULATOR—Holds output constant within 0.1 V as 5.5-V penlight supply for 1.5-inch Matsushita portable tv ages down to 4 V.—R. Sasaki and K. Uno, Low-Power Design is Heart of Penlight-Powered Mini-Tv, *Electronics*, June 8, 1970, p 106–113.

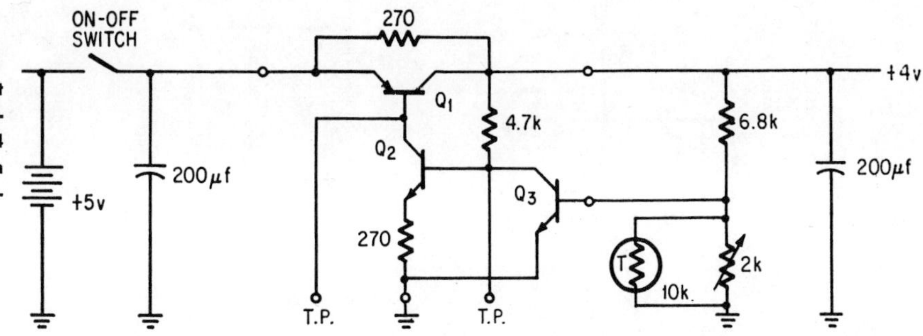

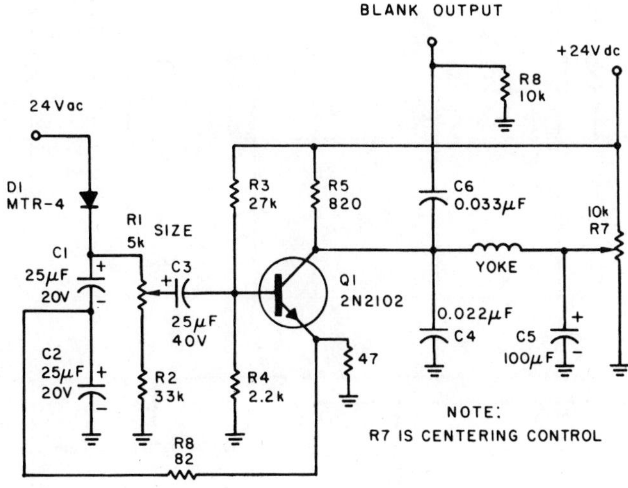

LINE-LOCKED VERTICAL SWEEP—A-c input at 24 V is applied to half-wave rectifier-filter delivering nearly linear line-locked vertical sawtooth that is amplified by Q1 for driving deflection yoke. R7 and C5 set d-c reference for centering control. Blank output may be used to trigger sync and cathode-blanking functions of camera.—J. M. Meacham, TV-Camera Vertical Sweep Produced by Filter Ripple, *Electronic Design*, Feb. 1, 1969, p 72.

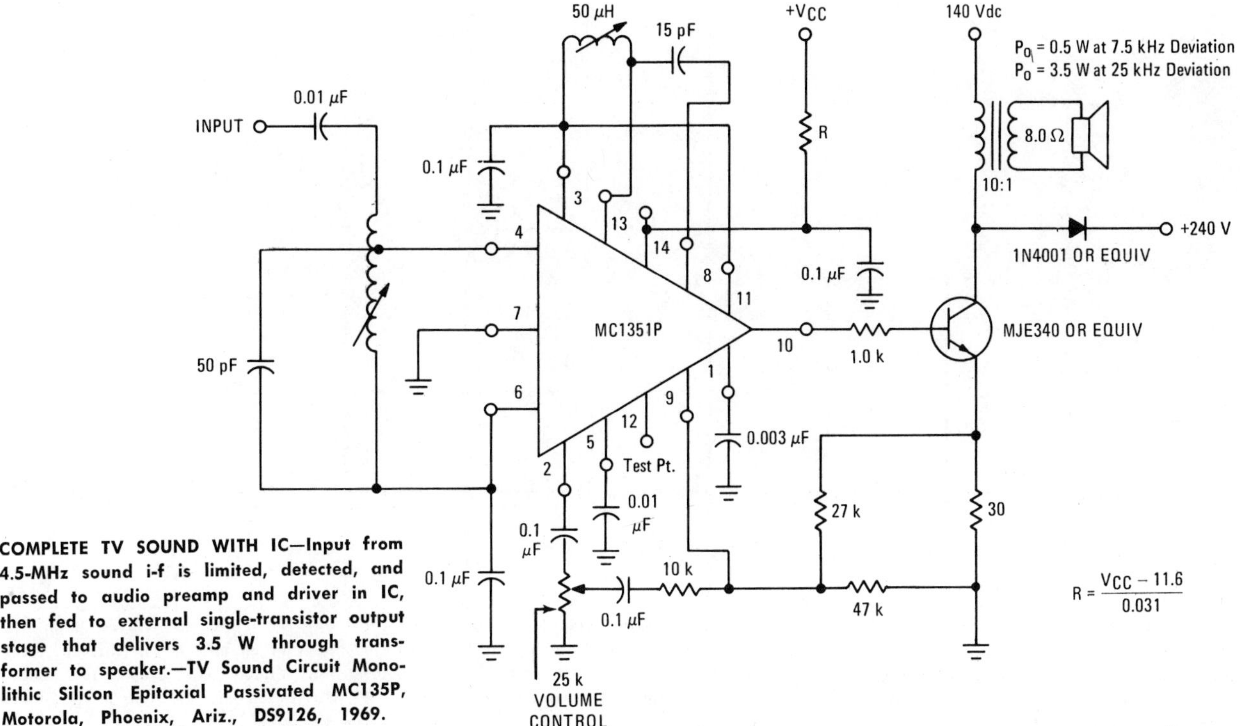

COMPLETE TV SOUND WITH IC—Input from 4.5-MHz sound i-f is limited, detected, and passed to audio preamp and driver in IC, then fed to external single-transistor output stage that delivers 3.5 W through transformer to speaker.—TV Sound Circuit Monolithic Silicon Epitaxial Passivated MC135P, Motorola, Phoenix, Ariz., DS9126, 1969.

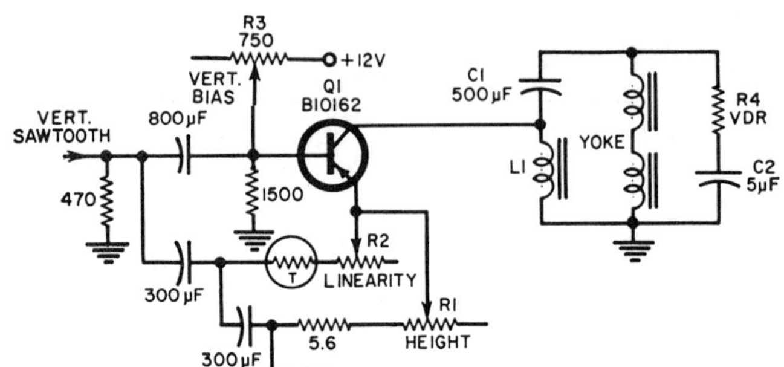

CONSTANT-HEIGHT VERTICAL OUTPUT—Voltage-dependent resistor R4 and C2 are shunted across deflection yoke to maintain constant height despite output voltage variations in G-E Model TA 9-inch portable tv.—W. H. Buchsbaum, Line-Operated Transistor TV Sets: G-E, *Electronics World*, Oct. 1966, p 29 and 70.

HORIZONTAL DEFLECTION—Addition of Q2 to output driver stage eliminates need for power transformer and high-voltage transistors in Siemens AG tv developed for 250-V European a-c line voltages. Q2 switches rectified 250-V supply to deflection circuit during flyback interval, when voltage across yoke is at peak. Winding n3 is on T2. Arrangement also gives low-level d-c for vertical deflection and audio stages; control voltage properly applied to Q2 keeps this source stable even for 20-W power drain. Use standard 300-V transistors.—Add One (Electronics Abroad), *Electronics*, Feb. 19, 1968, p 238.

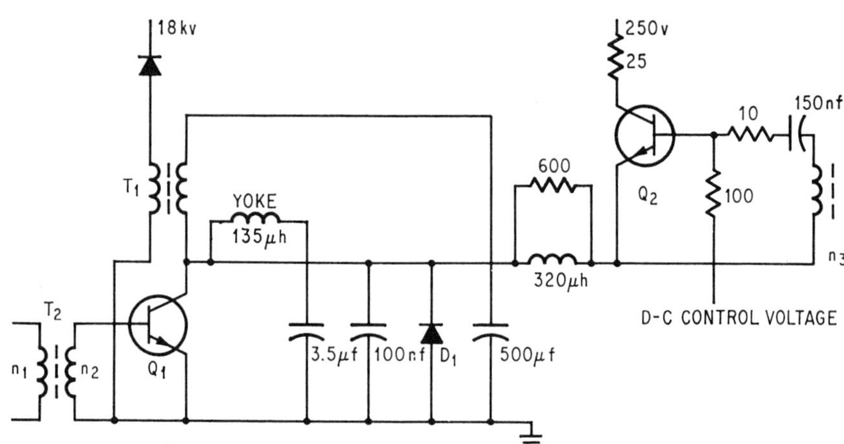

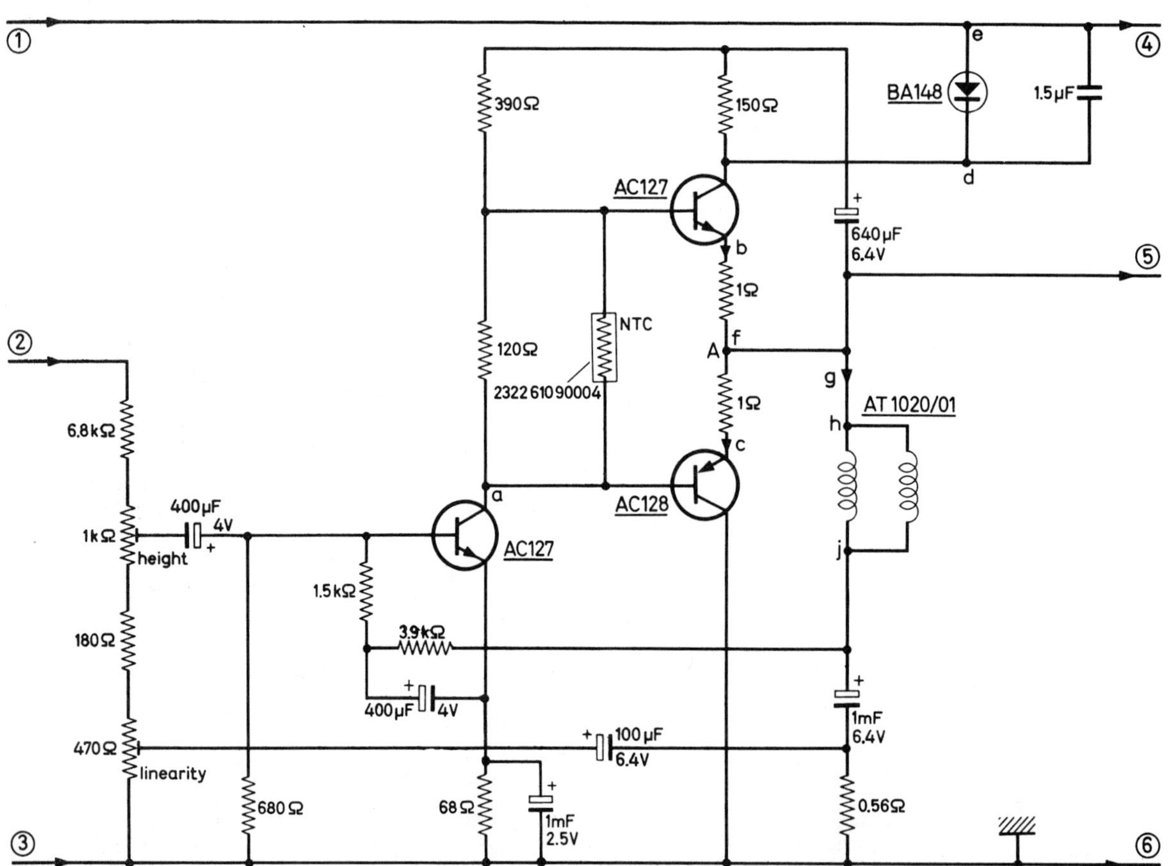

TINY-VISION FIELD OUTPUT STAGE AND DRIVER—Terminals 1, 2, and 3 come from field oscillator of small-screen battery-operated tv receiver, and terminals 4, 5, and 6 go to blanking circuit that supplies suitable blanking pulse during retrace. Circuit design minimizes current drain by using two medium-power transistors in complementary connection, without usual transformer. Output stage consumes only 1.1 W. Use of both d-c and a-c feedback to driver simplifies adjustment of circuit.—A. H. Nillesen, Field Deflection Circuit for Tiny-Vision Receivers, Philips, Pub. Dept., Elcoma Div., Eindhoven, The Netherlands, No. 256, 1967.

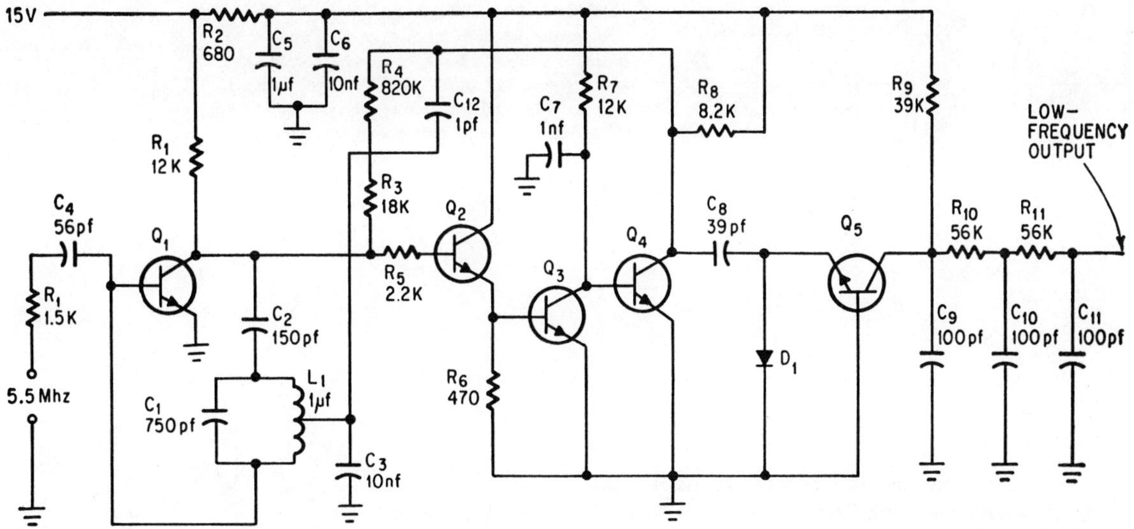

NO-COIL IC FOR TV SOUND I-F—Only coil used in Standard Elektrik Lorenz IC monolithic chip is in mixer, and requires no adjustment. Designed for standard 5.5-MHz European f-m intercarrier frequency, converted to sound i-f of about 250 kHz in mixer. Hartley oscillator can deviate 150 kHz without affecting mixer performance, so fixed coil can be used. Overall gain is about 60 dB from 50 to 450 kHz, with 12 V output for about 7-mV input.—Electronics Abroad—West Germany—Uncoiled, *Electronics*, Oct. 17, 1966, p 223.

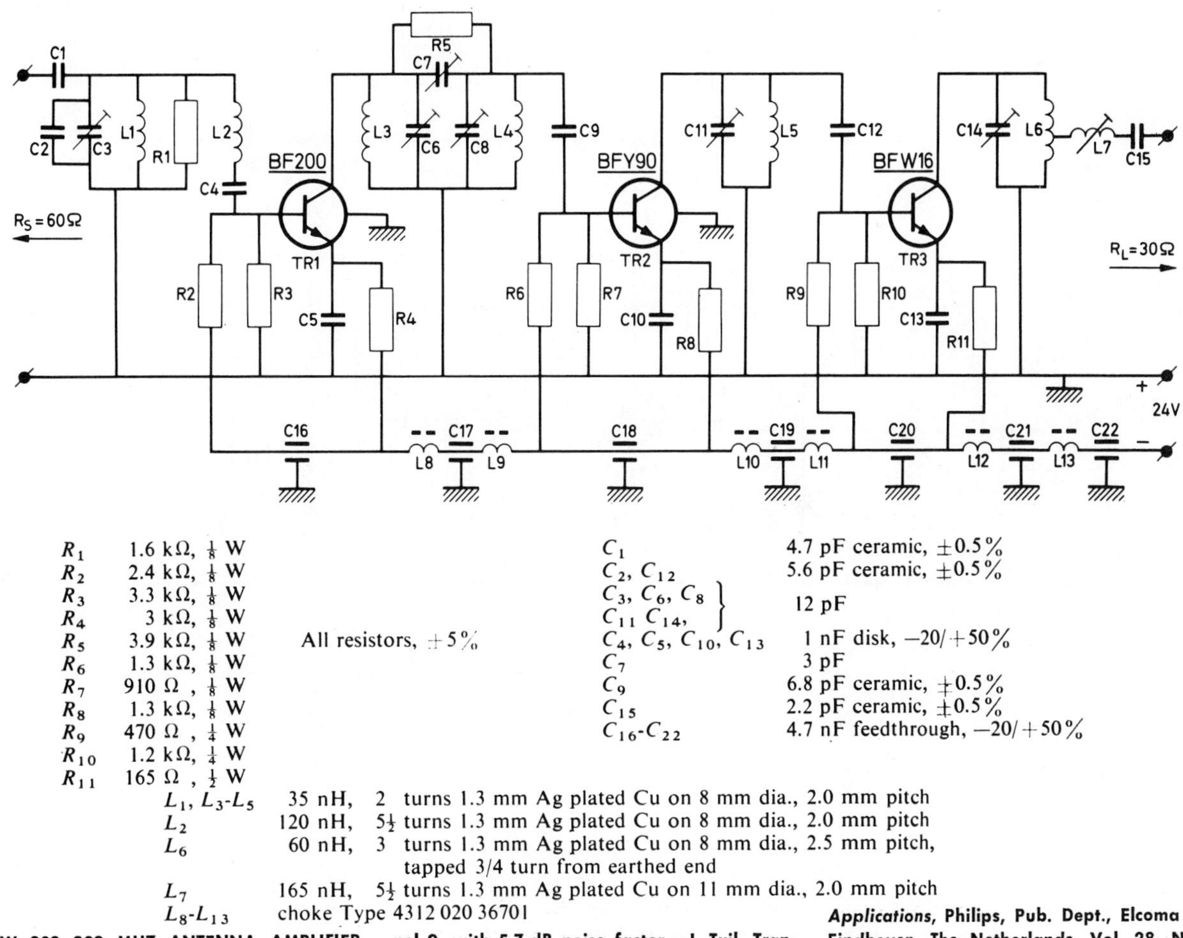

R_1	1.6 kΩ, $\frac{1}{8}$ W	
R_2	2.4 kΩ, $\frac{1}{8}$ W	
R_3	3.3 kΩ, $\frac{1}{8}$ W	
R_4	3 kΩ, $\frac{1}{8}$ W	
R_5	3.9 kΩ, $\frac{1}{8}$ W	All resistors, $\pm 5\%$
R_6	1.3 kΩ, $\frac{1}{8}$ W	
R_7	910 Ω, $\frac{1}{8}$ W	
R_8	1.3 kΩ, $\frac{1}{4}$ W	
R_9	470 Ω, $\frac{1}{4}$ W	
R_{10}	1.2 kΩ, $\frac{1}{4}$ W	
R_{11}	165 Ω, $\frac{1}{2}$ W	

C_1	4.7 pF ceramic, $\pm 0.5\%$
C_2, C_{12}	5.6 pF ceramic, $\pm 0.5\%$
C_3, C_6, C_8, C_{11} C_{14},	12 pF
C_4, C_5, C_{10}, C_{13}	1 nF disk, $-20/+50\%$
C_7	3 pF
C_9	6.8 pF ceramic, $\pm 0.5\%$
C_{15}	2.2 pF ceramic, $\pm 0.5\%$
C_{16}-C_{22}	4.7 nF feedthrough, $-20/+50\%$

L_1, L_3-L_5	35 nH,	2 turns 1.3 mm Ag plated Cu on 8 mm dia., 2.0 mm pitch
L_2	120 nH,	$5\frac{1}{2}$ turns 1.3 mm Ag plated Cu on 8 mm dia., 2.0 mm pitch
L_6	60 nH,	3 turns 1.3 mm Ag plated Cu on 8 mm dia., 2.5 mm pitch, tapped 3/4 turn from earthed end
L_7	165 nH,	$5\frac{1}{2}$ turns 1.3 mm Ag plated Cu on 11 mm dia., 2.0 mm pitch
L_8-L_{13}	choke Type 4312 020 36701	

60-MW 202–209 MHZ ANTENNA AMPLIFIER—Provides gain of 48 dB for European channel 9, with 5.7-dB noise factor.—J. Tuil, Transistor Equipped Aerial Amplifiers, *Electronic Applications*, Philips, Pub. Dept., Elcoma Div., Eindhoven, The Netherlands, Vol. 28, No. 2, 1968, p 60–78.

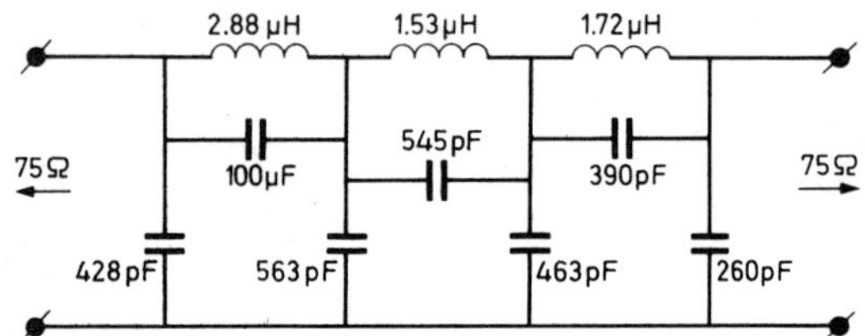

LOW-PASS FOR NOISE ABOVE 5.5 MHZ—Used after preamp of television camera to suppress noise above desired bandwidth, which peaks at about 8 MHz and extends beyond 12 MHZ.—B. Overgoor, A Camera Tube Amplifier with FET Input, *Electronic Applications*, Philips, Pub. Dept., Elcoma Div., Eindhoven, The Netherlands, Vol. 28, No. 4, 1968, p 155–159.

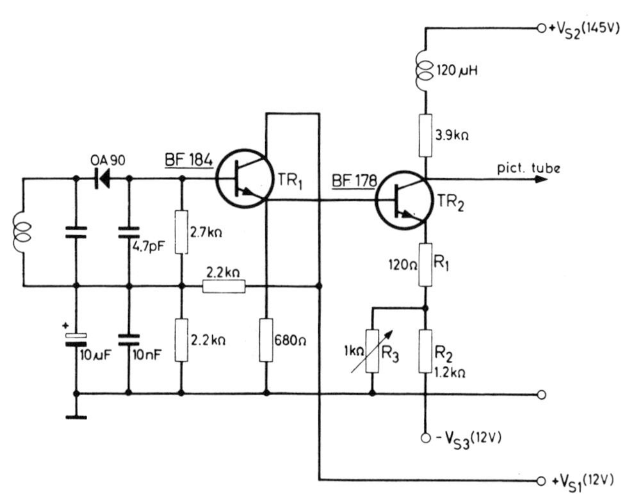

EMITTER-CIRCUIT CONTRAST CONTROL—Control R3 is here located in emitter lead of video output stage of two-stage video amplifier. One advantage is that long leads may be used between contrast pot and video amplifier without affecting performance. R2 and negative supply voltage together hold black level constant during contrast control. —A. Cense, The N-P-N Silicon Planar Transistor BF178 in a Video Amplifier, Philips, Pub. Dept., Elcoma Div., Eindhoven, The Netherlands, No. 251, 1966.

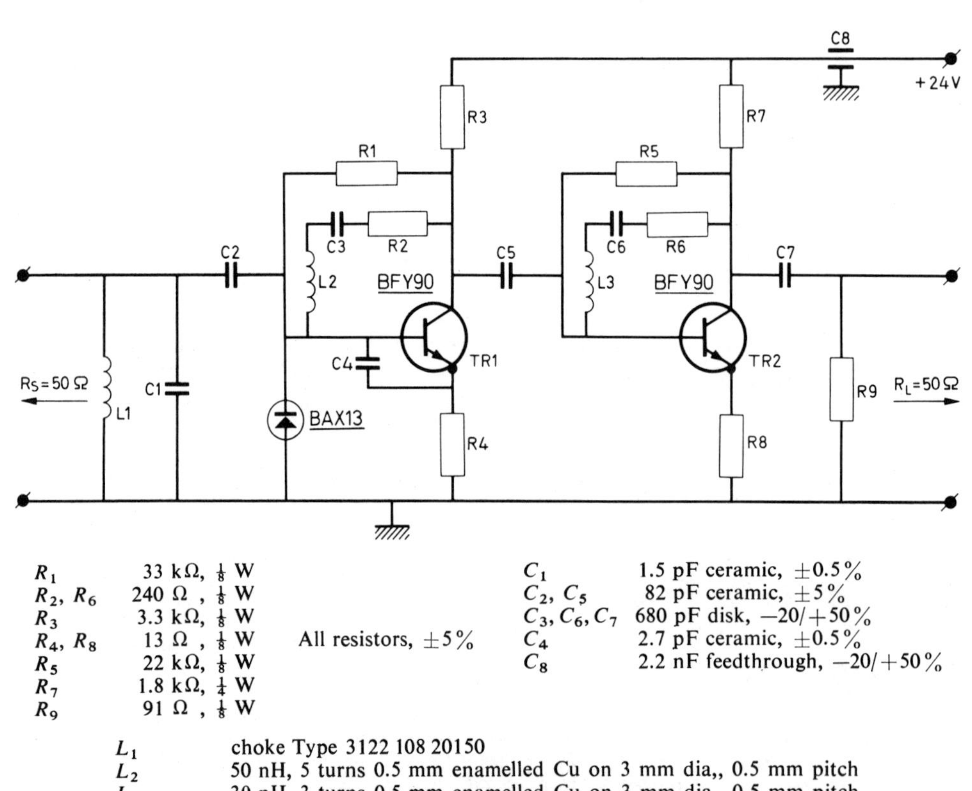

R_1	33 kΩ, ⅛ W		C_1	1.5 pF ceramic, ±0.5%
R_2, R_6	240 Ω , ⅛ W		C_2, C_5	82 pF ceramic, ±5%
R_3	3.3 kΩ, ⅛ W		C_3, C_6, C_7	680 pF disk, –20/+50%
R_4, R_8	13 Ω , ⅛ W	All resistors, ±5%	C_4	2.7 pF ceramic, ±0.5%
R_5	22 kΩ, ⅛ W		C_8	2.2 nF feedthrough, –20/+50%
R_7	1.8 kΩ, ¼ W			
R_9	91 Ω , ⅛ W			

L_1	choke Type 3122 108 20150
L_2	50 nH, 5 turns 0.5 mm enamelled Cu on 3 mm dia,, 0.5 mm pitch
L_3	30 nH, 3 turns 0.5 mm enamelled Cu on 3 mm dia., 0.5 mm pitch

40–860 MHZ ANTENNA AMPLIFIER—Provides gain of 13.5 dB for 30-mW output per signal over entire European television band, with noise factor of 6.3 to 10 dB. Uses transistors having very high transition frequency and very low feedback capacitance, for common-emitter configuration.—J. Tuil, Transistor Equipped Aerial Amplifiers, *Electronic Applications*, Philips, Pub. Dept., Elcoma Div., Eindhoven, The Netherlands, Vol. 28, No. 2, 1968, p 60–78.

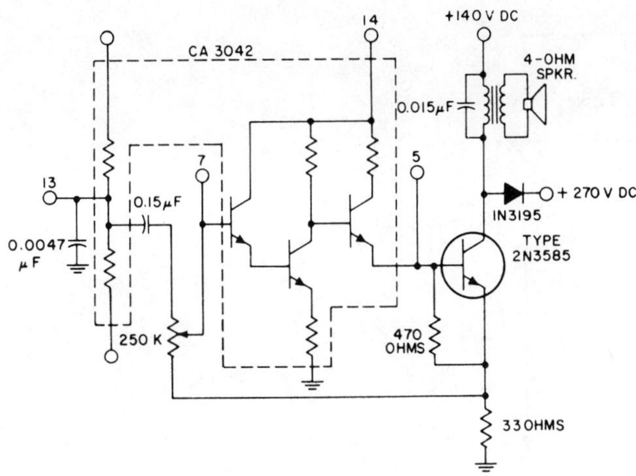

LOW-COST FEEDBACK VOLUME CONTROL—Uses minimum number of components with CA3042 IC. Although steady-state current flows through volume control, it is limited to about 1.5 μA under worst-case conditions.—L. Kaplan, Feedback-Type Volume-Control Circuits for RCA-CA3041 and CA3042 Integrated Circuits, RCA, Harrison, N.J., No. ICAN-5841, 1968.

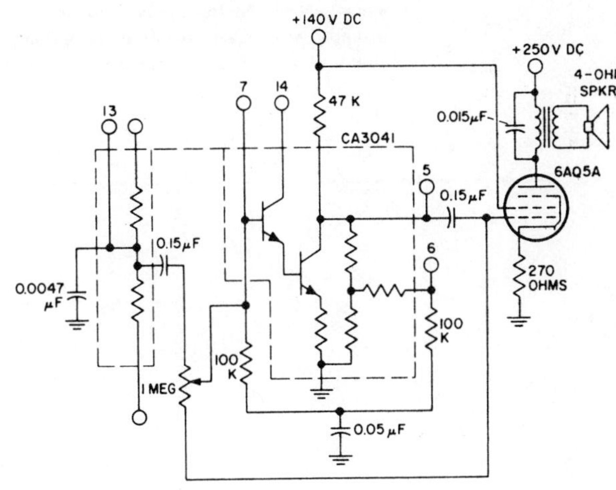

FEEDBACK VOLUME CONTROL—Used with CA3041 IC to increase power output and gain over that obtained with conventional losser type of control. At 4.5 MHz, circuit provides 1 W power output at 8.5 kHz deviation.—L. Kaplan, Feedback-Type Volume-Control Circuits for RCA-CA3041 and CA3042 Integrated Circuits, RCA, Harrison, N.J., No. ICAN-5841, 1968.

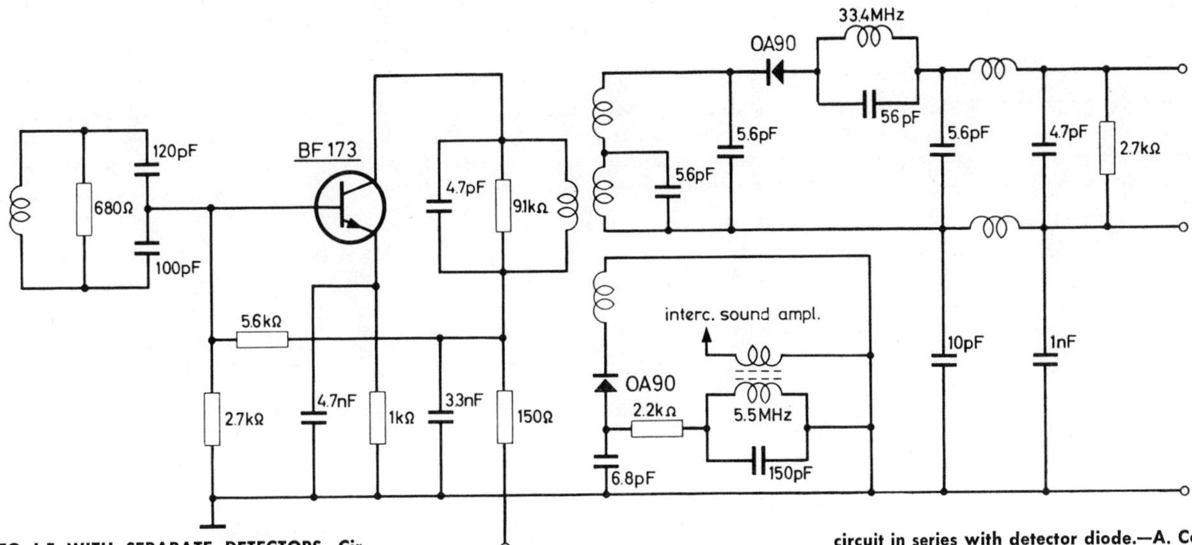

VIDEO I-F WITH SEPARATE DETECTORS—Circuit shows how separate intercarrier sound detector can be used with video output stage of European 625-line tv receiver, for compatibility with color programs. Video and intercarrier signals have separate takeoffs, so sound carrier can be heavily suppressed in video detector by 33.4-MHz parallel tuned circuit in series with detector diode.—A. Cense, The N-P-N Silicon Planar Transistor BF178 in a Video Amplifier, Philips, Pub. Dept., Elcoma Div., Eindhoven, The Netherlands, No. 251, 1966.

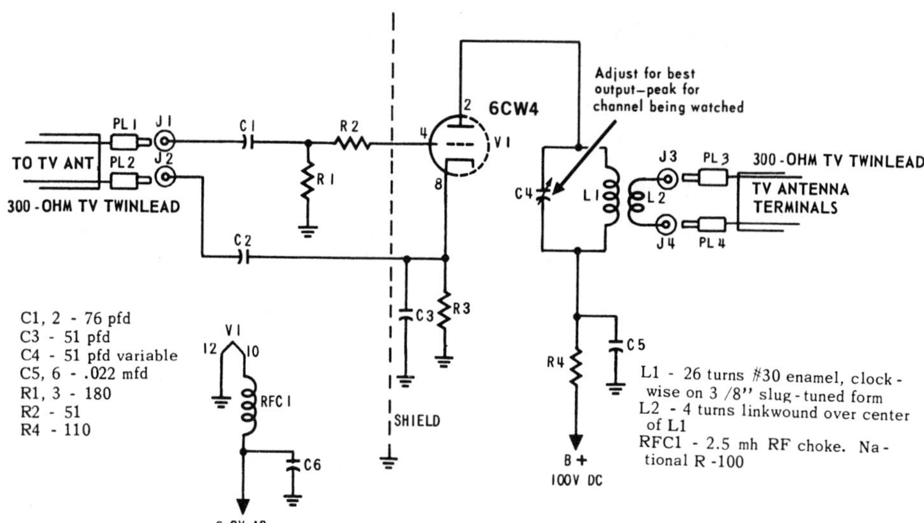

TV SIGNAL BOOSTER—Can be inserted in 300-ohm twinlead at back of set, to boost signal strength of weaker signals in reception area. Parts at left of broken shield line must be shielded from rest of circuit to eliminate undesirable interference and hash.—R. M. Brown, "104 Simple One-Tube Projects," Tab Books, Blue Ridge Summit, Pa., 1969, p 168.

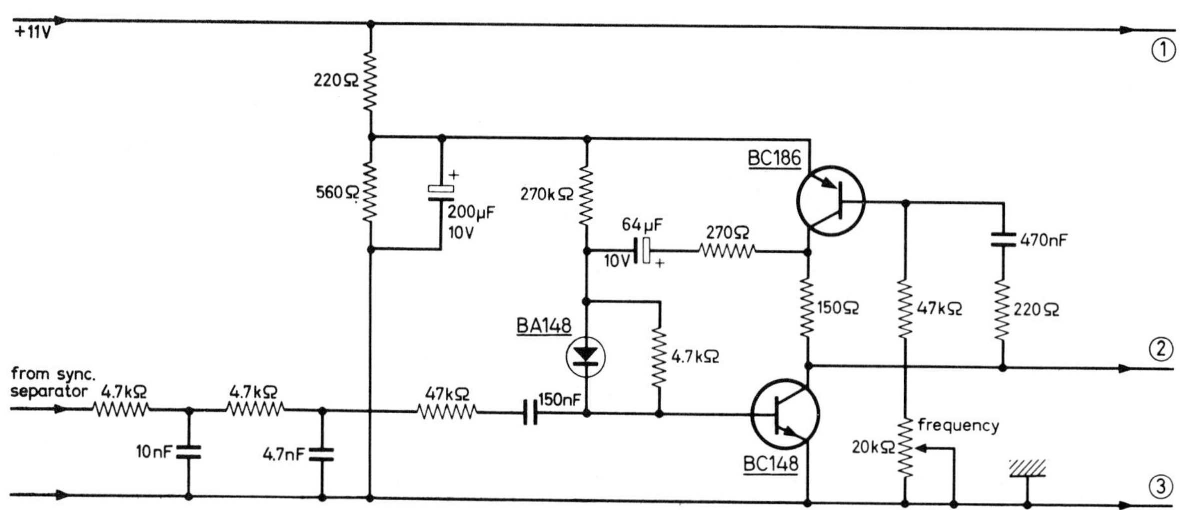

TINY-VISION FIELD OSCILLATOR—Makes use of Miller integrator principle to generate sawtooth voltage having sufficient amplitude to meet requirements of small-screen battery-operated tv receiver. Terminals 1, 2, and 3 go to field output stage. Report describes operation of oscillator in detail.—A. H. Nillesen, Field Deflection Circuit for Tiny-Vision Receivers, Philips, Pub. Dept., Elcoma Div., Eindhoven, The Netherlands, No. 256, 1967.

NOTE: To locate additional circuits in the category of this chapter, use the index at the back of this book. Check also the author's "Sourcebook of Electronic Circuits," published by McGraw-Hill in 1968.

CHAPTER 86
Television Circuits—Color

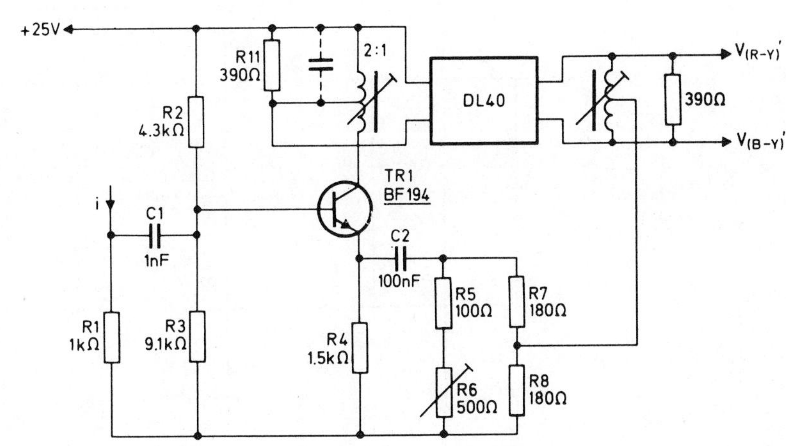

MATRIX FOR CHROMINANCE SIGNAL—Chrominance signal is fed to base of delay line driver transistor TR1. Uses Philips DL40 delay line having nominal frequency of 4.433619 MHz and phase delay of 63.943 μs. Output of delay line is balanced with 2:1 stepdown transformer to simplify addition of delayed and undelayed signals.—C. A. M. Sidler, Pal Matrix Circuits Using Delay Line DL40, Philips, Pub. Dept., Elcoma Div., Eindhoven, The Netherlands, Application Note 88, 1970.

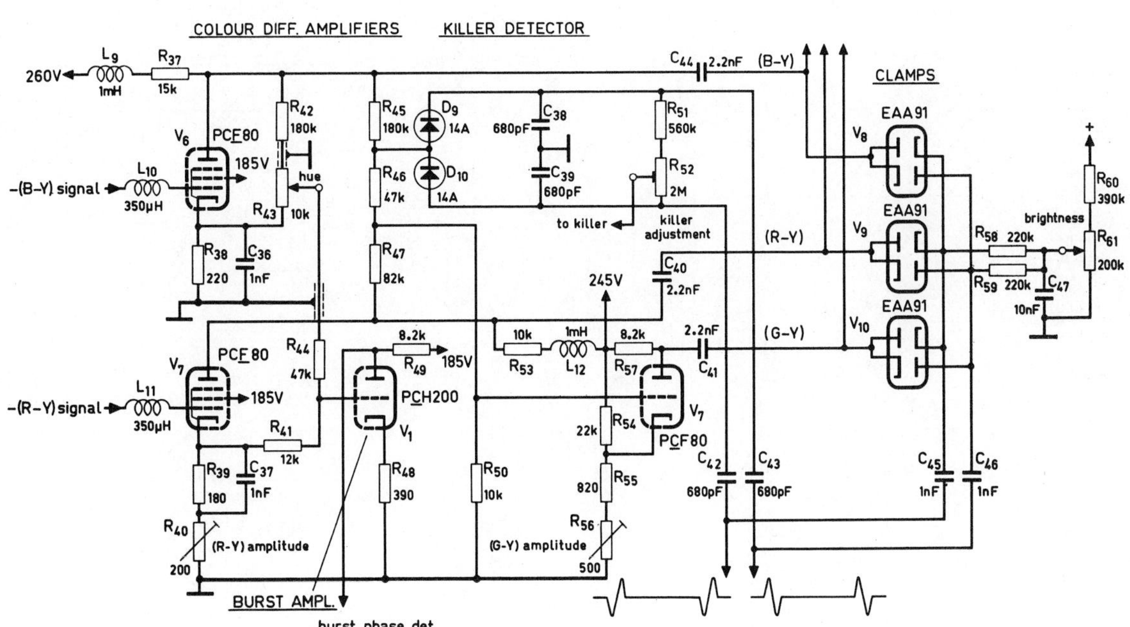

COLOR DIFFERENCE AMPLIFIER—Color difference signals are applied to control grids of pentodes for amplification and adjustment of gain in accordance with NTSC specifications. Double-diode circuit is used for killer detection, in G—Y matrix circuit branch going to anode of B—Y amplifier. This diode circuit detects negative-going burst in B—Y signal. Double-diode clamp at output of each color difference amplifier gives same clamping level for all three signals, with brightness control changing all levels simultaneously.—A. Boekhorst and W. Graat, Chrominance Circuits for N. T. S. C. Colour Television Receivers, Philips, Pub. Dept., Elcoma Div., Eindhoven, The Netherlands, No. 234, 1966.

X-RAY HOLD-DOWN—Used in Zenith 1970 television receivers to provide automatic protection against excessive x-ray emission from high-voltage power supply. Circuit limits horizontal, drive voltage to about 27 kV regardless of line voltage and load. Also provides protection if voltage regulator fails or is removed from socket.—Consumer Hazards: How They Can Be Fixed, *Electronics*, Aug. 3, 1970, p 62–67.

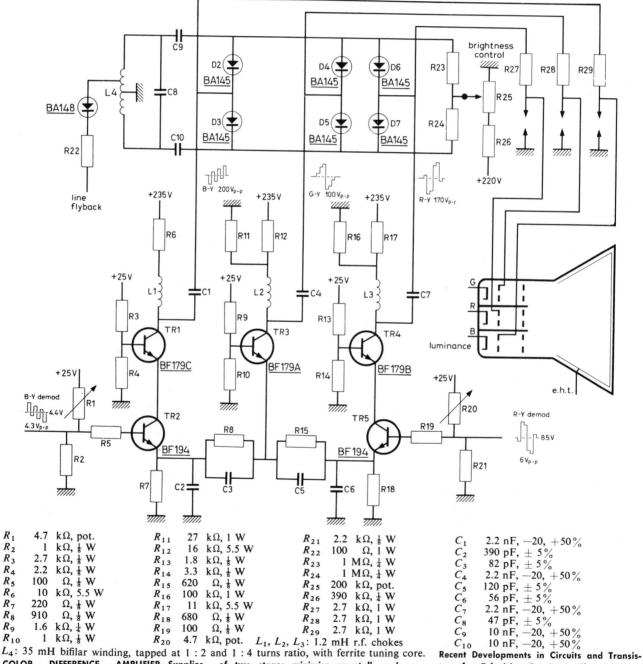

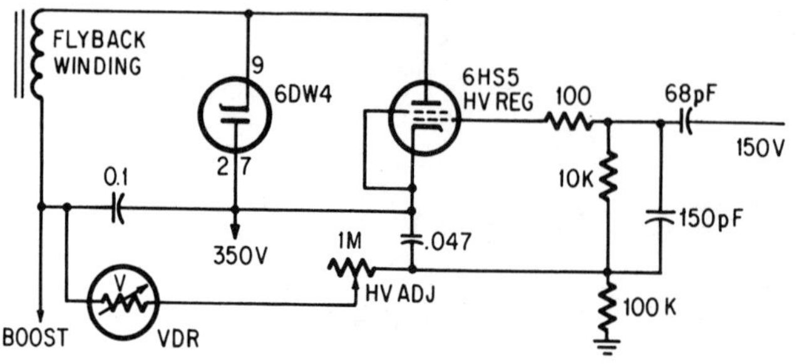

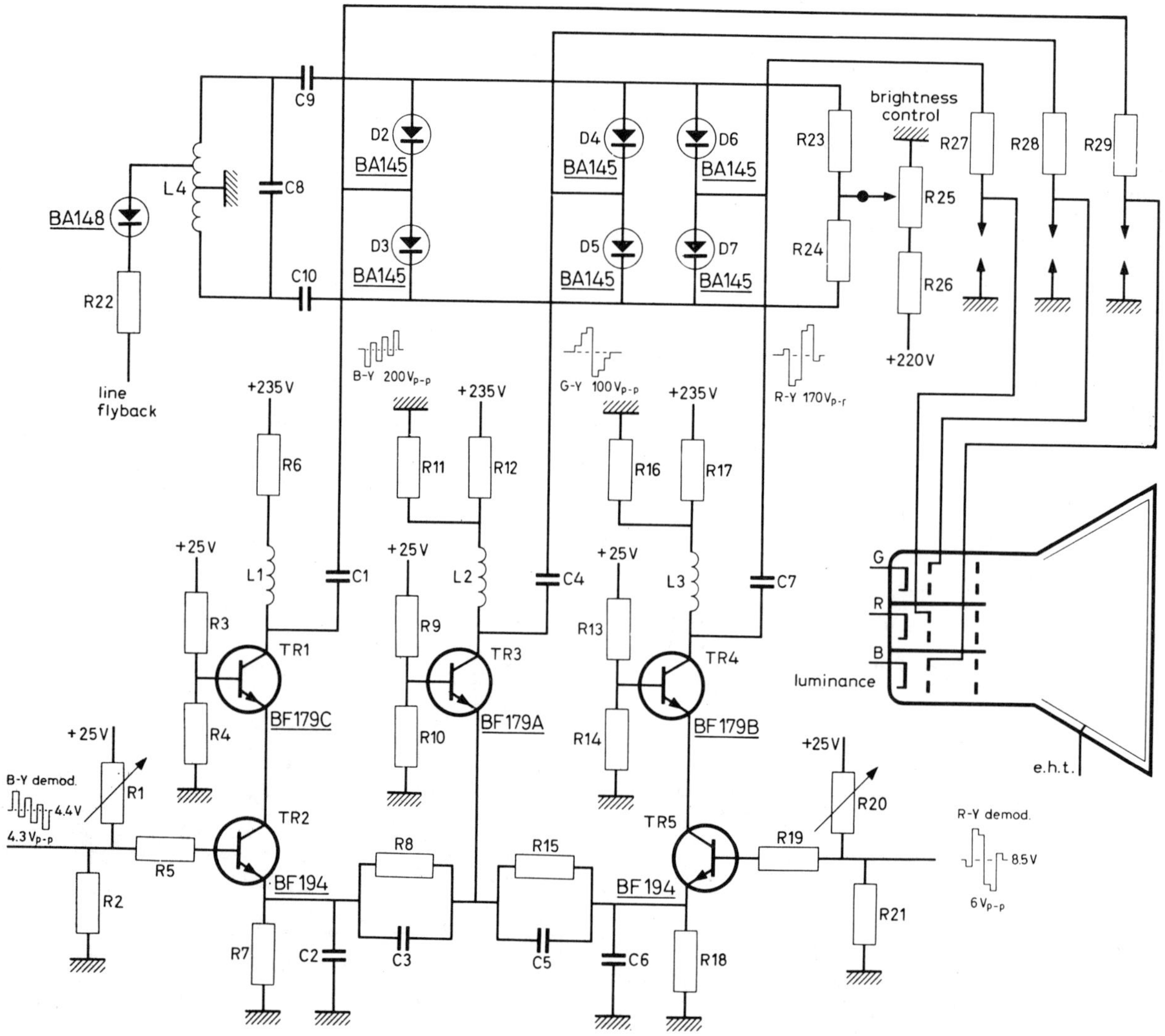

R_1 4.7 kΩ, pot.
R_2 1 kΩ, $\frac{1}{8}$ W
R_3 2.7 kΩ, $\frac{1}{8}$ W
R_4 2.2 kΩ, $\frac{1}{8}$ W
R_5 100 Ω, $\frac{1}{8}$ W
R_6 10 kΩ, 5.5 W
R_7 220 Ω, $\frac{1}{8}$ W
R_8 910 Ω, $\frac{1}{8}$ W
R_9 1.6 kΩ, $\frac{1}{4}$ W
R_{10} 1 kΩ, $\frac{1}{8}$ W

R_{11} 27 kΩ, 1 W
R_{12} 16 kΩ, 5.5 W
R_{13} 1.8 kΩ, $\frac{1}{8}$ W
R_{14} 3.3 kΩ, $\frac{1}{8}$ W
R_{15} 620 Ω, $\frac{1}{8}$ W
R_{16} 100 kΩ, 1 W
R_{17} 11 kΩ, 5.5 W
R_{18} 680 Ω, $\frac{1}{4}$ W
R_{19} 100 Ω, $\frac{1}{8}$ W
R_{20} 4.7 kΩ, pot.

R_{21} 2.2 kΩ, $\frac{1}{8}$ W
R_{22} 100 Ω, 1 W
R_{23} 1 MΩ, $\frac{1}{4}$ W
R_{24} 1 MΩ, $\frac{1}{4}$ W
R_{25} 200 kΩ, pot.
R_{26} 390 kΩ, $\frac{1}{4}$ W
R_{27} 2.7 kΩ, 1 W
R_{28} 2.7 kΩ, 1 W
R_{29} 2.7 kΩ, 1 W

C_1 2.2 nF, −20, +50%
C_2 390 pF, ± 5%
C_3 82 pF, ± 5%
C_4 2.2 nF, −20, +50%
C_5 120 pF, ± 5%
C_6 56 pF, ± 5%
C_7 2.2 nF, −20, +50%
C_8 47 pF, ± 5%
C_9 10 nF, −20, +50%
C_{10} 10 nF, −20, +50%

L_1, L_2, L_3: 1.2 mH r.f. chokes
L_4: 35 mH bifilar winding, tapped at 1 : 2 and 1 : 4 turns ratio, with ferrite tuning core.

COLOR DIFFERENCE AMPLIFIER—Supplies drive voltages required by each of three electron guns in typical 25-inch shadow-mask color picture tube. Cascode arrangements of two stages minimize crosstalk and ensure maximum bandwidth. Article covers circuit design in detail. Spark gaps protect against flashovers in picture tube.—A. Cense, Recent Developments in Circuits and Transistors for Television Receivers, *Electronic Applications*, Philips, Pub. Dept., Elcoma Div., Eindhoven, The Netherlands, Vol. 27, No. 4, 1966–1967, p 147–154.

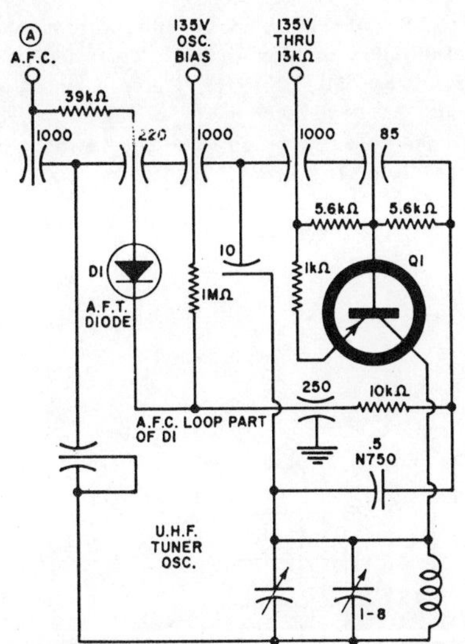

MAGNAVOX AFT TUNER—Shows how control voltage derived from video i-f is applied to diode that controls transistor oscillator of uhf tuner to achieve automatic fine tuning. Complete circuit is given in Magnavox 1968 top-of-line color tv service manuals.—F. H. Belt, Inside the 1968 Color Sets, *Electronics World*, Jan. 1968, p 41–45 and 72–75.

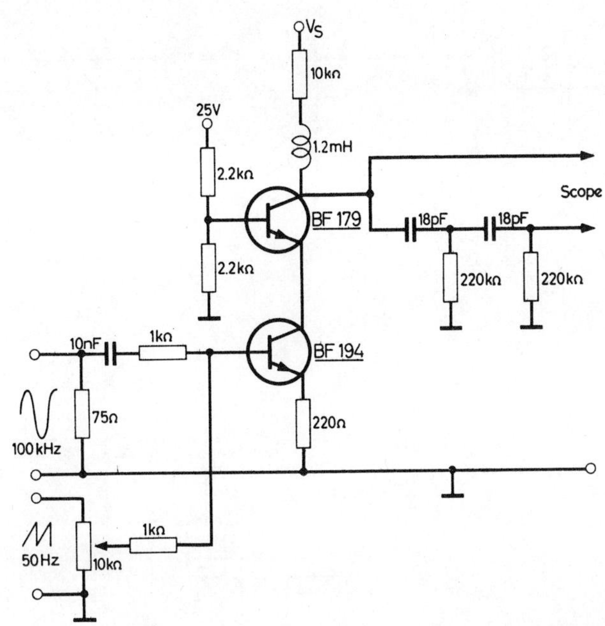

COLOR DIFFERENCE LINEARITY—Circuit for checking linearity of cascaded-transistor color difference amplifier applies two signals to input of amplifier—50-Hz sawtooth with amplitude that drives output stage from cutoff to knee, and 100-kHz sine wave with amplitude of 10 mV p-p. Differentiating network at output of amplifier suppresses sawtooth and applies 100-kHz signal to dual-trace scope, with other trace showing voltage swing at collector of output stage.—A. Cense, Colour Difference Amplifiers Using the N-P-N Silicon Planar Package 40822, Philips, Pub. Dept., Elcoma Div., Eindhoven, The Netherlands, 1966.

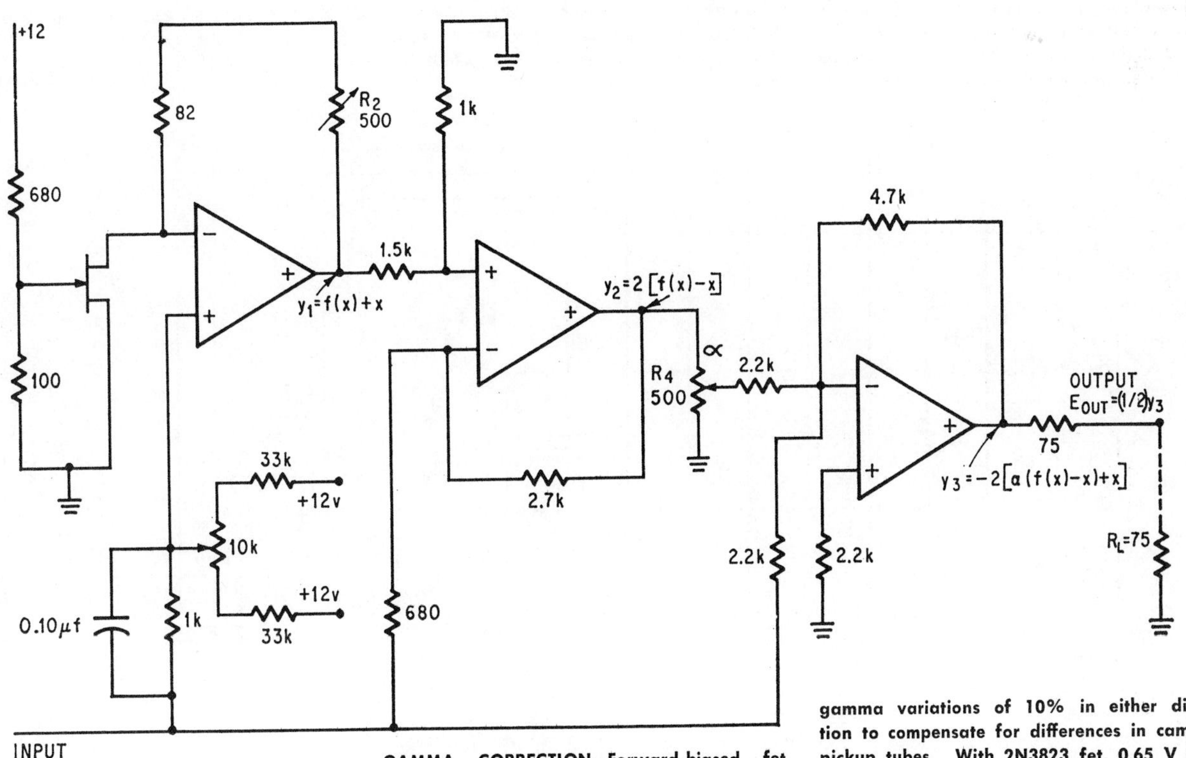

GAMMA CORRECTION—Forward-biased fet followed by three opamps compensates for nonlinearity of gamma in color or black-and-white tv camera circuit and also provides temperature stability. Single pot provides gamma variations of 10% in either direction to compensate for differences in camera pickup tubes. With 2N3823 fet, 0.65 V forward bias is used. Choice of opamp is not critical.—R. Williams, Linearity Corrector Does Double Duty, *Electronics*, June 9, 1969, p 110–113.

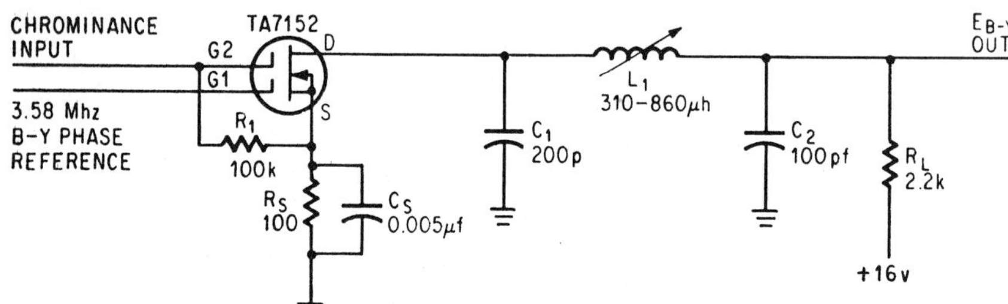

COLOR DEMODULATOR—With chrominance information applied to gate 2 of dual-gate transistor and 3.58-MHz reference signal on gate 1, demodulation is accomplished by synchronous detection.—Outlook Bright for Dual-Gate Transistors, *Electronics*, July 10, 1967, p 141–142.

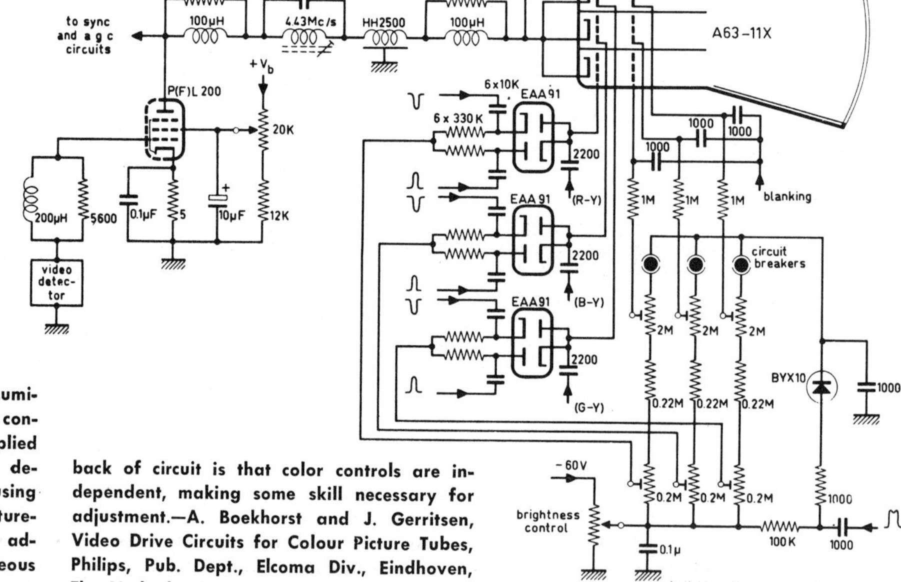

EQUAL CATHODE DRIVES FOR GUNS—Luminance amplifier is pentode with contrast control in screen grid circuit. Agc is supplied to anode, to permit grounding of video detector. Symmetrical clamp circuit using double-diode is connected to each picture-tube control grid. Clamping levels are adjusted individually to obtain simultaneous spot cutoff for all three guns. One drawback of circuit is that color controls are independent, making some skill necessary for adjustment.—A. Boekhorst and J. Gerritsen, Video Drive Circuits for Colour Picture Tubes, Philips, Pub. Dept., Elcoma Div., Eindhoven, The Netherlands, No. 233, 1965.

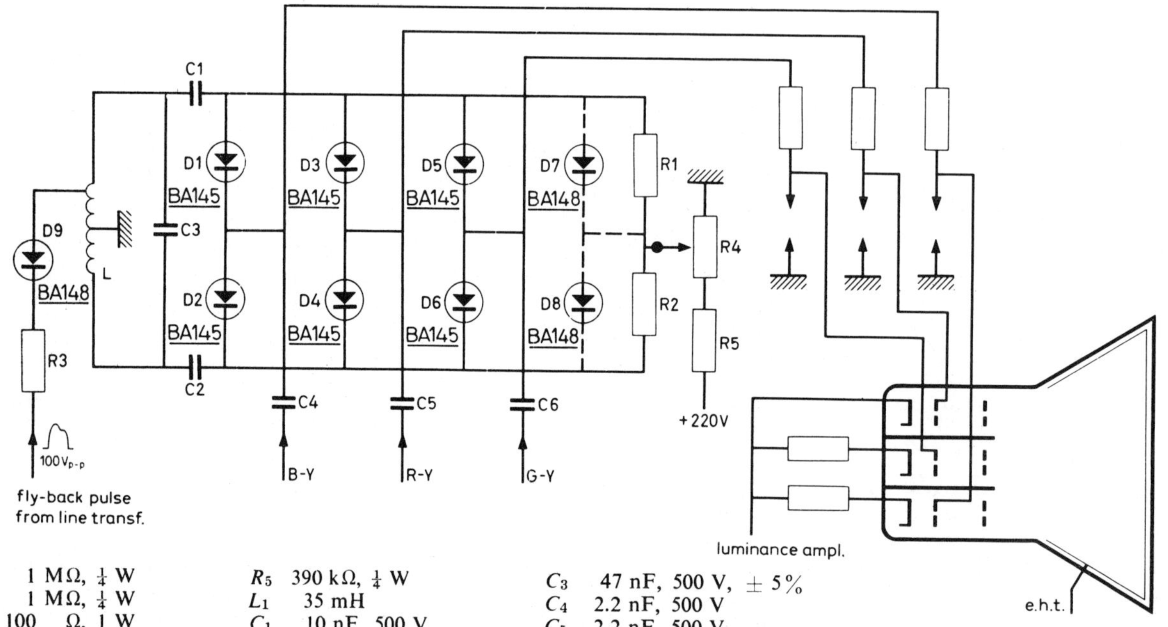

R_1	1 MΩ, ¼ W	R_5	390 kΩ, ¼ W	C_3	47 nF, 500 V, ± 5%
R_2	1 MΩ, ¼ W	L_1	35 mH	C_4	2.2 nF, 500 V
R_3	100 Ω, 1 W	C_1	10 nF, 500 V	C_5	2.2 nF, 500 V
R_4	220 kΩ, potentiometer	C_2	10 nF, 500 V	C_6	2.2 nF, 500 V

SYNCHRONOUS CLAMP—Used for restoring equal direct voltage levels to three color difference signals. Brightness control R4 establishes reference voltage to which clamping diodes are returned.—A. Cense, Recent Developments in Circuits and Transistors for Television Receivers, *Electronic Applications*, Philips, Pub. Dept., Elcoma Div., Eindhoven, The Netherlands, Vol. 28, No. 1, 1968, p 22–28.

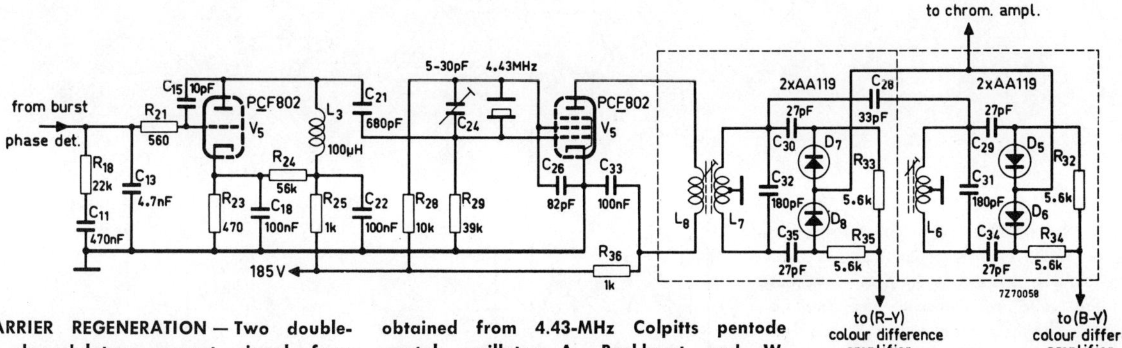

SUBCARRIER REGENERATION—Two double-diode demodulators convert signal from chrominance amplifier into R—Y and B—Y signals. Required subcarrier voltages are obtained from 4.43-MHz Colpitts pentode crystal oscillator.—A. Boekhorst and W. Graat, Chrominance Circuits for N. T. S. C. Colour Television Receivers, Philips, Pub. Dept., Elcoma Div., Eindhoven, The Netherlands, No. 234, 1966.

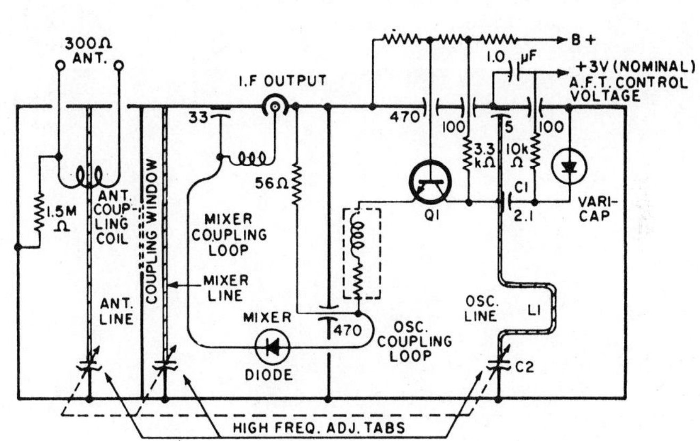

UHF TUNER WITH AFT—Zenith version uses transistor as oscillator, with Varicap receiving correction voltage from control discriminator fed by third i-f, to provide automatic fine tuning for color programs.—F. H. Belt, Inside the 1968 Color Sets, *Electronics World*, Jan. 1968, p 41–45 and 72–75.

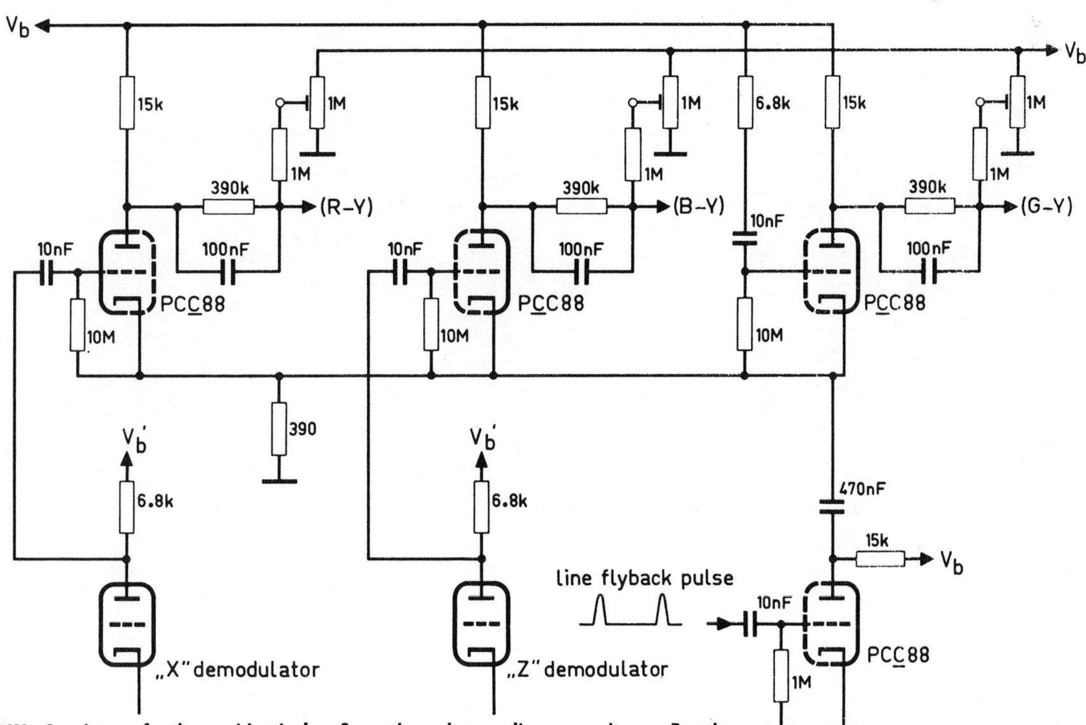

X-Z MATRIX—Consists of three identical color difference amplifiers operating with common cathode resistor, with X and Z signals applied to grids of two triode amplifiers through coupling capacitors. Requires d-c coupling to picture tube, because clamping is impracticable.—A. Boekhorst and W. Graat, Chrominance Circuits for N. T. S. C. Colour Television Receivers, Philips, Pub. Dept., Elcoma Div., Eindhoven, The Netherlands, No. 234, 1966.

AUXILIARY HORIZONTAL OUTPUT—Pentode stage is stabilized against line voltage variations, to keep picture width from changing with line voltage. Transistor d-c amplifier, with zener holding emitter at 9 V, has sufficiently high gain to provide stabilization and completely compensate for aging of tube or transistor. Stage is modulated to provide East-West raster correction, with modulation such that deflection current is about 13% less at top and bottom of picture than at center.—C. J. Boers, Circuits for 110 Degree Colour TV Picture Tube, Philips, Pub. Dept., Elcoma Div., Eindhoven, The Netherlands, No. 261, 1969.

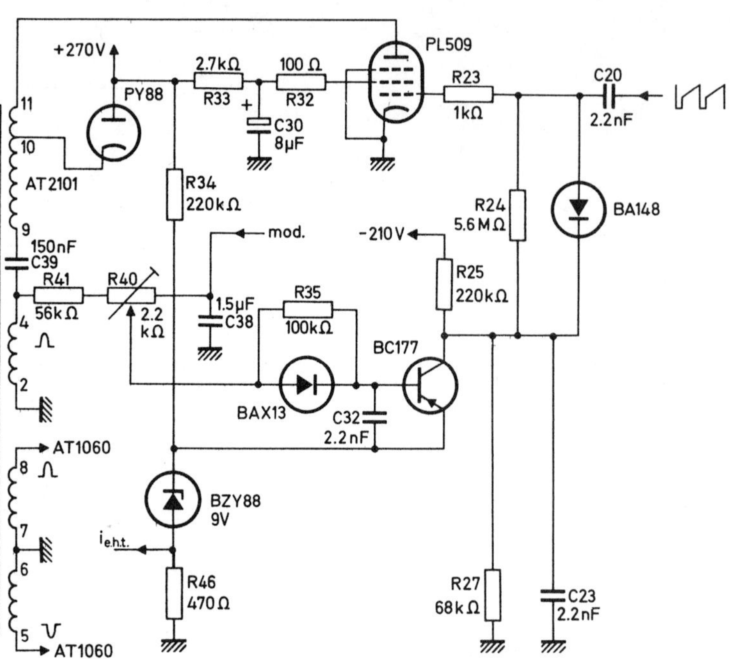

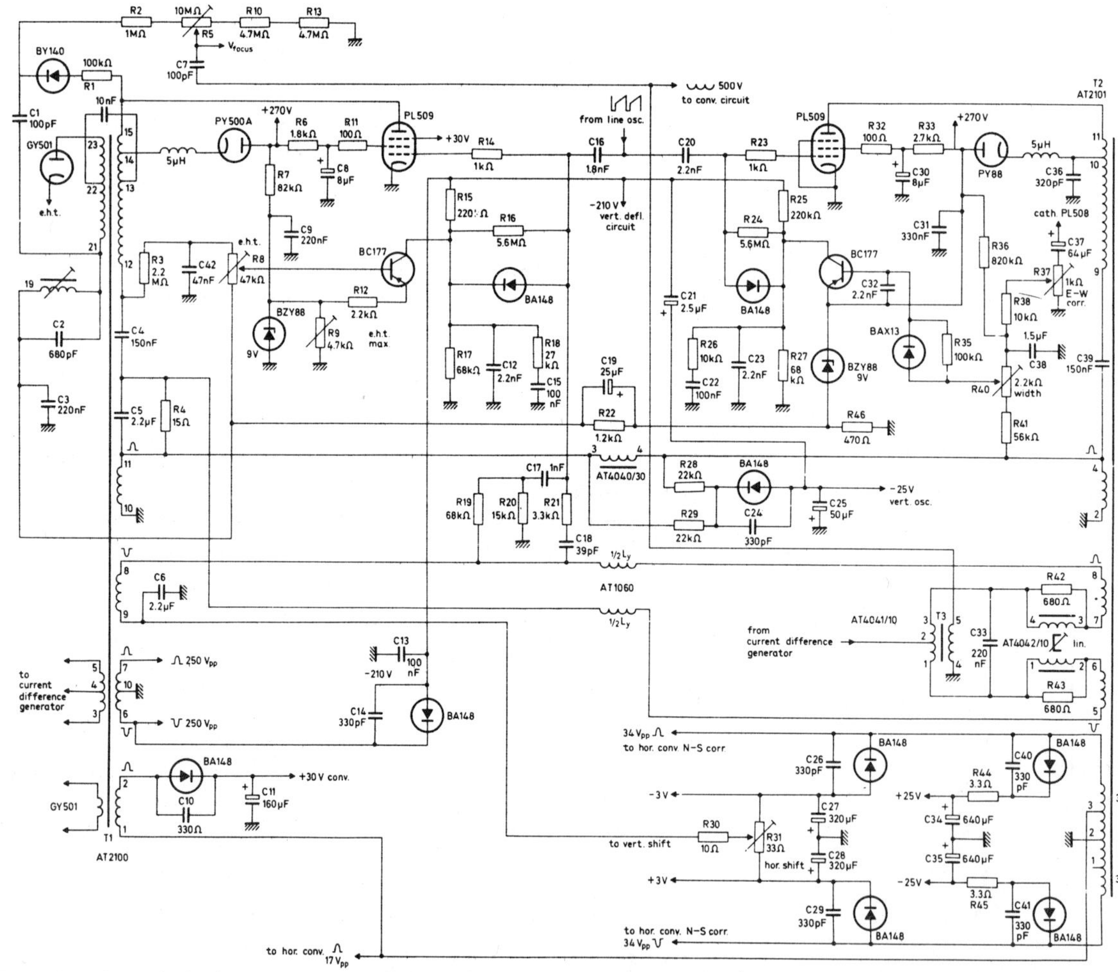

COMPLETE HORIZONTAL DEFLECTION—Includes main stage at left which supplies extra high voltage for 110-deg color picture tube, power for difference current drive, and half of deflection power. Stages at right supply power for shift circuits and other half of deflection power, with modulation to provide East-West master correction.—C. J. Boers, Circuits for 110 Degree Colour TV Picture Tube, Philips, Pub. Dept., Elcoma Div., Eindhoven, The Netherlands, No. 261, 1969.

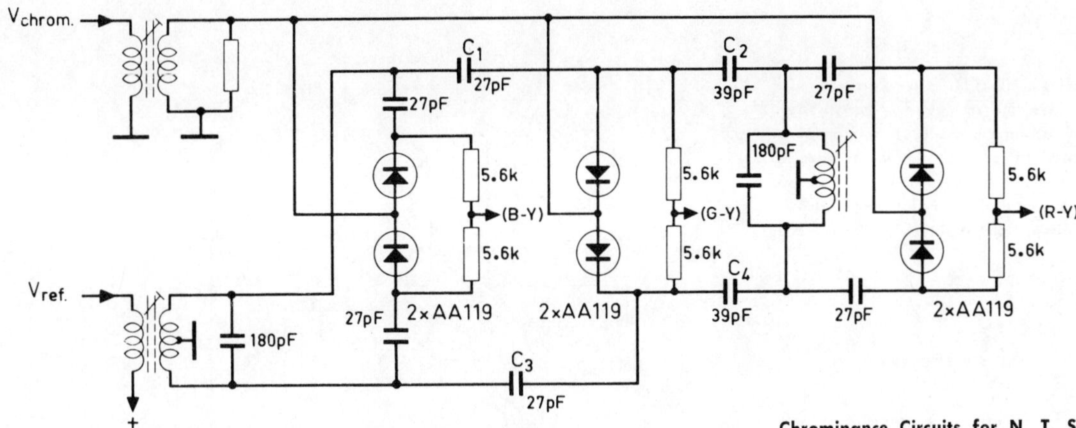

THREE DEMODULATORS—Individual demodulators for R — Y, B — Y, and G — Y stages give greater design flexibility. Resulting color difference signals can be applied to three completely independent color difference amplifiers.—A. Boekhorst and W. Graat, Chrominance Circuits for N. T. S. C. Colour Television Receivers, Philips, Pub. Dept., Elcoma Div., Eindhoven, The Netherlands, No. 234, 1966.

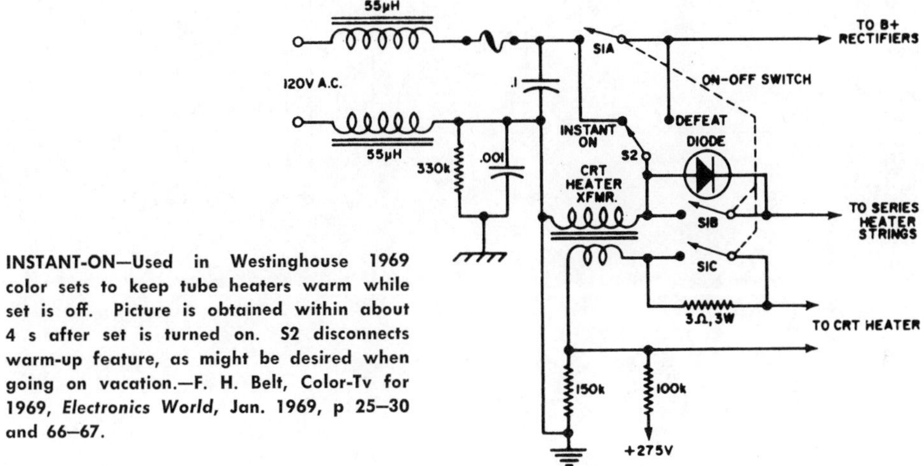

INSTANT-ON—Used in Westinghouse 1969 color sets to keep tube heaters warm while set is off. Picture is obtained within about 4 s after set is turned on. S2 disconnects warm-up feature, as might be desired when going on vacation.—F. H. Belt, Color-Tv for 1969, *Electronics World*, Jan. 1969, p 25–30 and 66–67.

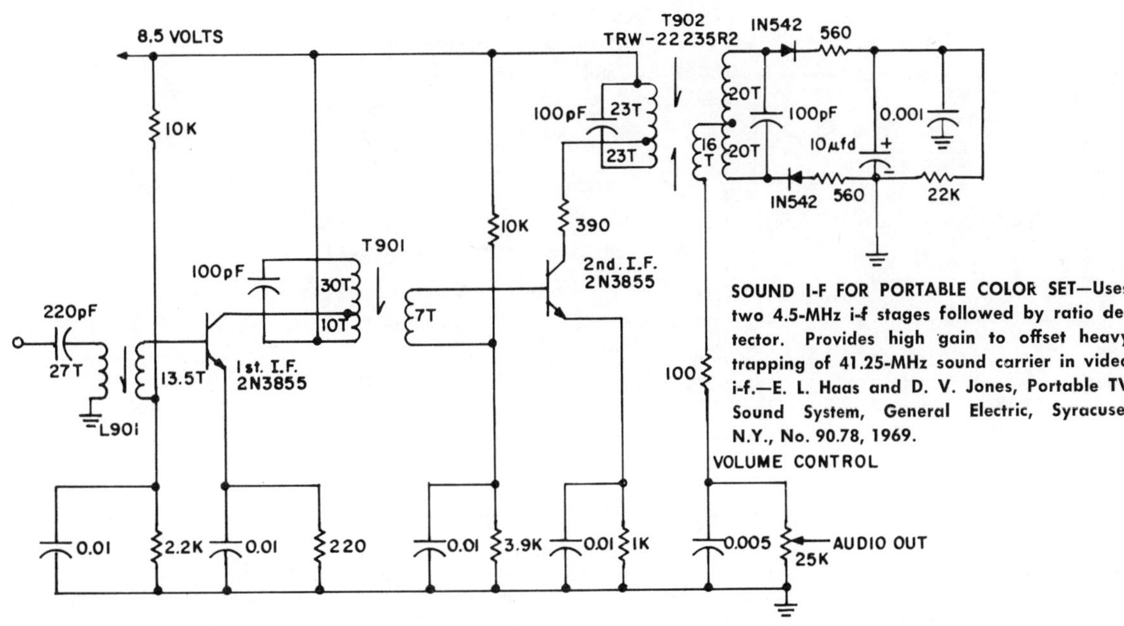

SOUND I-F FOR PORTABLE COLOR SET—Uses two 4.5-MHz i-f stages followed by ratio detector. Provides high gain to offset heavy trapping of 41.25-MHz sound carrier in video i-f.—E. L. Haas and D. V. Jones, Portable TV Sound System, General Electric, Syracuse, N.Y., No. 90.78, 1969.

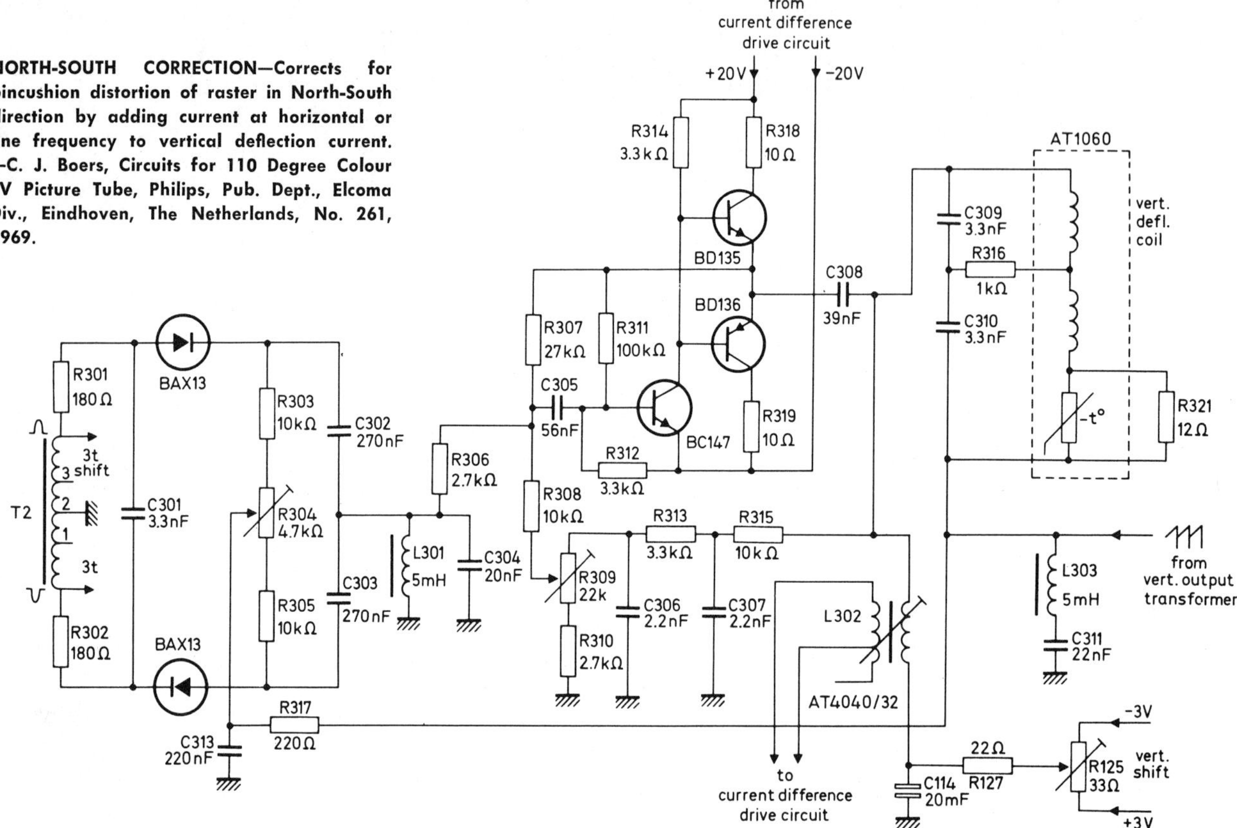

NORTH-SOUTH CORRECTION—Corrects for pincushion distortion of raster in North-South direction by adding current at horizontal or line frequency to vertical deflection current. —C. J. Boers, Circuits for 110 Degree Colour TV Picture Tube, Philips, Pub. Dept., Elcoma Div., Eindhoven, The Netherlands, No. 261, 1969.

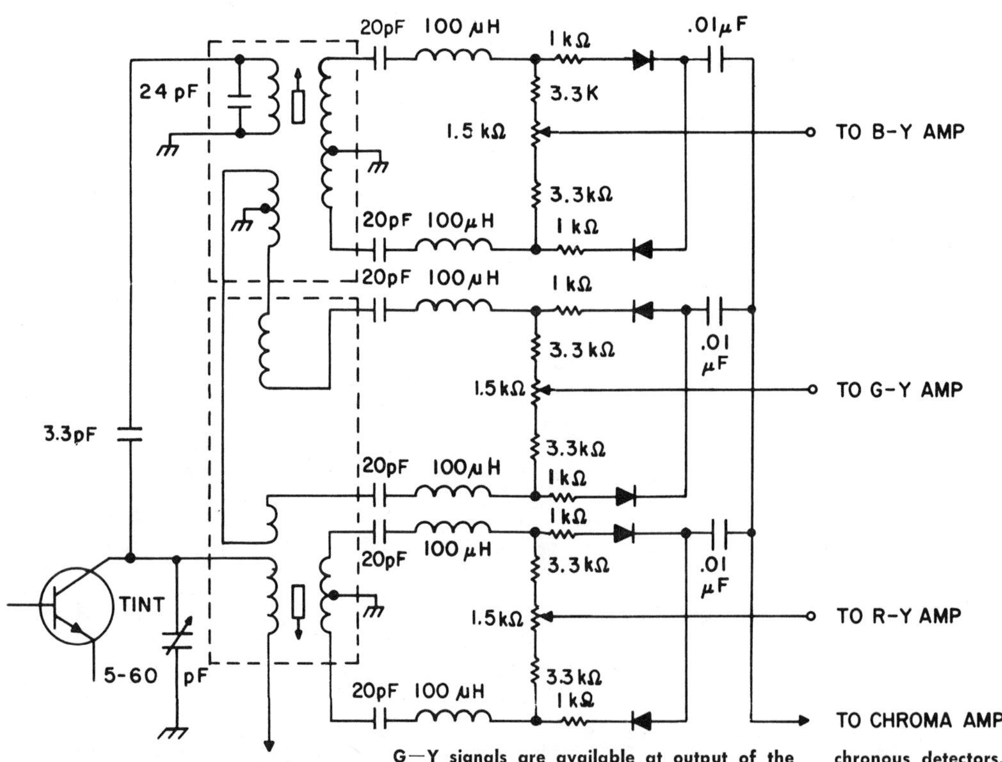

TRANSFORMER MATRIXING—Demodulation transformer (dashed boxes) performs matrixing function, such that R—Y, B—Y, and G—Y signals are available at output of the three synchronous detectors. Both secondary windings and the tertiary winding are center-tapped to maintain a-c balance in synchronous detectors.—O. A. Kolody, Simplified Transistor Color TV Processing Circuitry, General Electric, Syracuse, N.Y., No. 90.63, 1969.

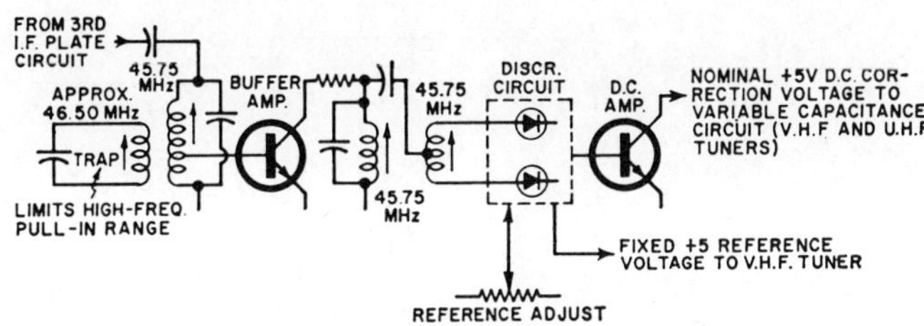

RCA AFT CONTROL—Takes signal from 3rd i-f and converts it to d-c correction voltage of up to 5 V for correcting fine tuning of tuner in RCA CTC-28 chassis. Complete version of this simplified circuit is given in RCA service manual.—F. H. Belt, Inside the 1968 Color Sets, *Electronics World*, Jan. 1968, p 41–45 and 72–75.

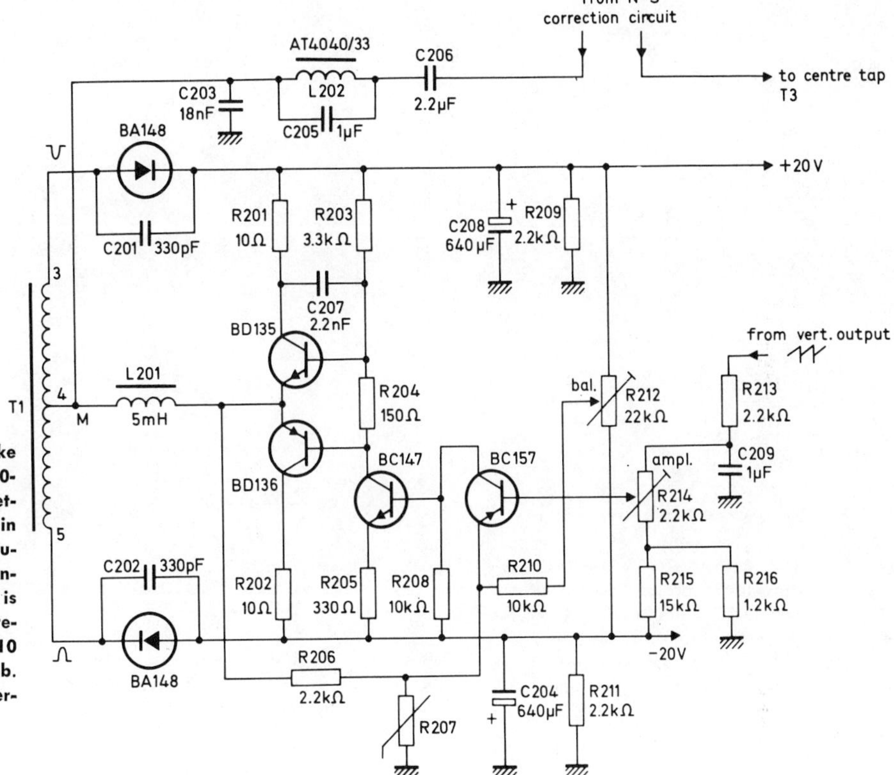

DIFFERENCE CURRENT DRIVE—Used to make beams converge in corners of picture on 110-deg color crt. Includes wave-shaping networks. Report describes circuit operation in detail. Field-frequency voltage that modulates difference current is supplied by transistor amplifier in which feedback loop is shunted to ground by voltage-dependent resistor R207.—C. J. Boers, Circuits for 110 Degree Colour TV Picture Tube, Philips, Pub. Dept., Elcoma Div., Eindhoven, The Netherlands, No. 261, 1969.

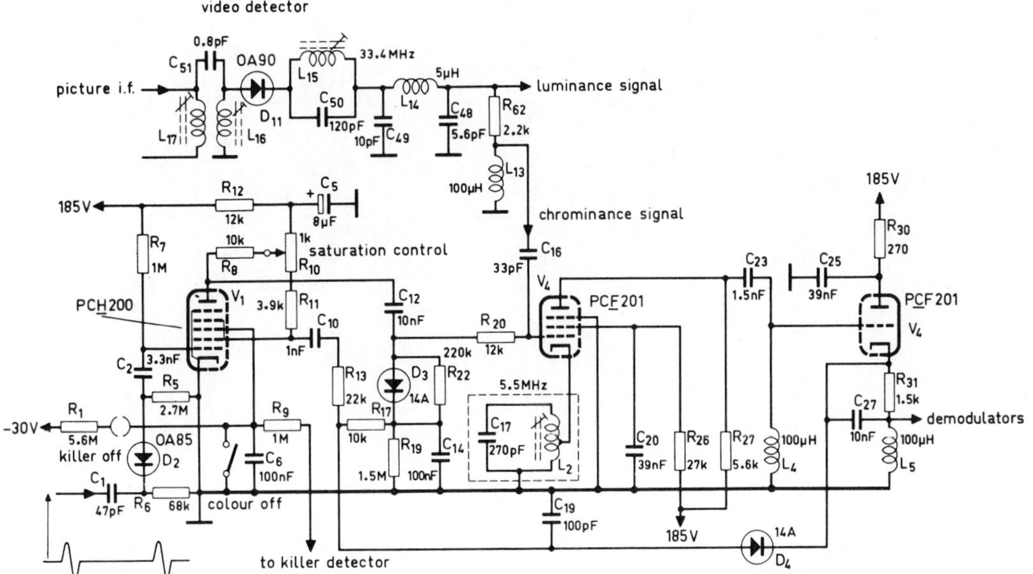

CHROMINANCE AMPLIFIER—Designed for use in NTSC color television receiver. Consists of gain-controlled pentode and triode cathode follower, with output going to two double-diode demodulators. Gain control is partly automatic, using burst amplitude as reference (obtained by burst amplitude detector D4).—A. Boekhorst and W. Graat, Chrominance Circuits for N. T. S. C. Colour Television Receivers, Philips, Pub. Dept., Elcoma Div., Eindhoven, The Netherlands, No. 234, 1966.

GRAY-SCALE TRACKING—Helps chroma gain to follow the settings of contrast control in Hoffman 1968 color sets. Complete circuit can be found in Hoffman 1968 tv service manuals.—F. H. Belt, Inside the 1968 Color Sets, *Electronics World*, Jan. 1968, p 41–45 and 72–75.

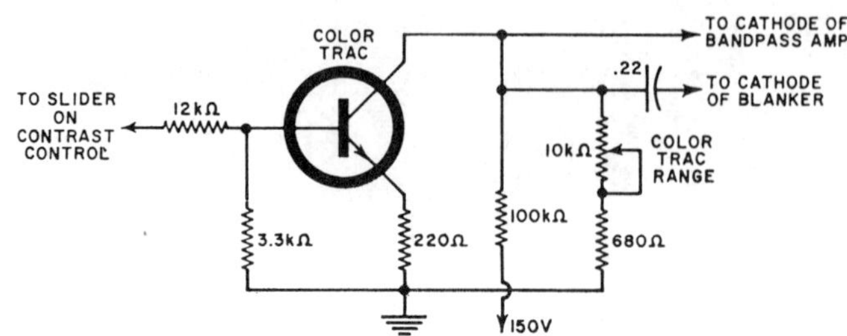

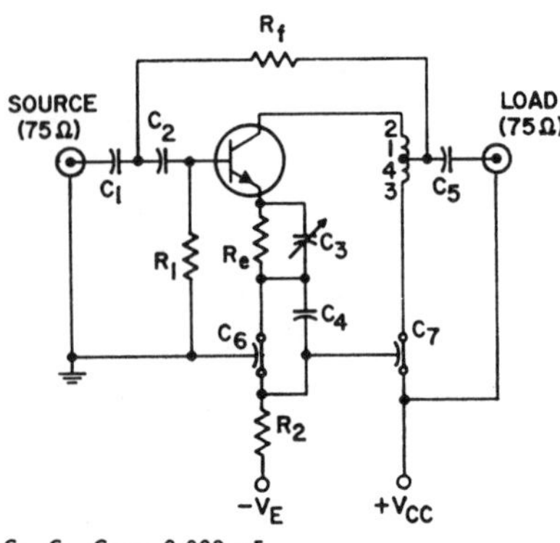

C_1, C_2, C_5 = 0.002 μF
C_3 = 8-60 pF, Arco 404 or equiv.
C_4 = 0.03 μF
C_6, C_7 = 1500 pF
R_1 = 390 ohms, ½ watt
R_2 = 330 ohms, 1 watt
R_e = 6.8 ohms, ½ watt
R_f = 200 ohms, ½ watt
T = 4-turn bifilar winding, 3/16″ ID, No. 30 wire; Core: G.I. material Q_1 or equiv.

54–216 MHZ WIDEBAND CATV—Uses single 2N5109 transistor to provide gain of 12 dB. Suitable for CATV applications. Uses ferrite-toroid wideband transformer with 4:1 impedance ratio at output to transform 75-ohm load into 300-ohm collector load.—"Silicon Power Circuits Manual," RCA, Harrison, N.J., SP-51, p 342.

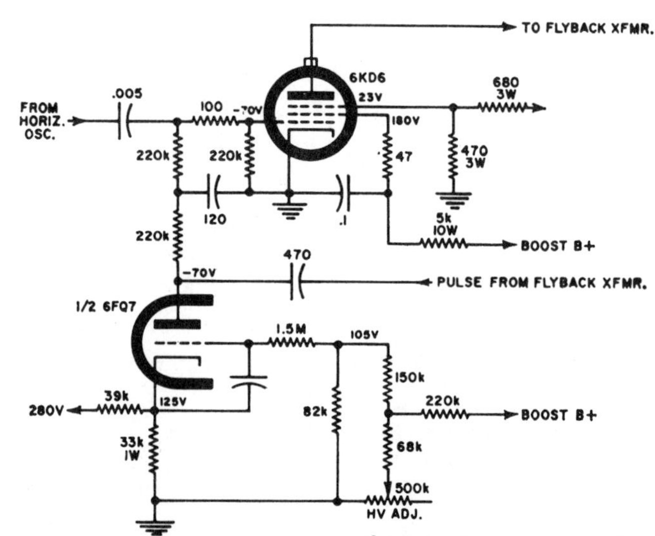

PULSE H-V REGULATOR—Used in Olympic CTC-31 color set to keep high voltage below level of dangerous x-rays. Keying pulse from flyback transformer is applied to anode of triode, to produce negative d-c voltage that increases with pulse amplitude and thereby counteracts increase in high voltage.—F. H. Belt, Color-Tv for 1969, *Electronics World*, Jan. 1969, p 25–30 and 66–67.

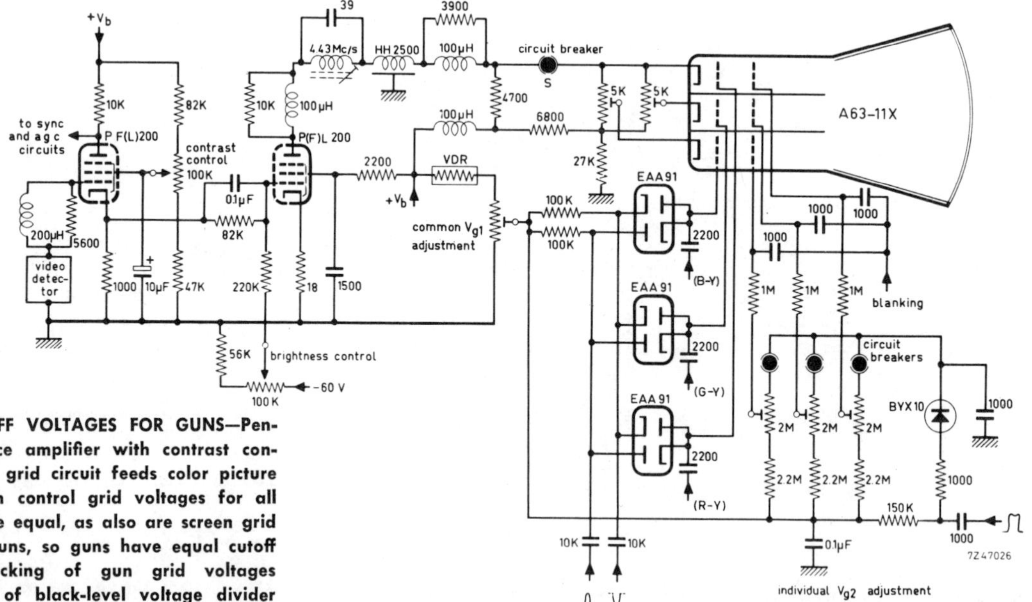

EQUAL CUTOFF VOLTAGES FOR GUNS—Pentode luminance amplifier with contrast control in screen grid circuit feeds color picture tube in which control grid voltages for all three guns are equal, as also are screen grid voltages of guns, so guns have equal cutoff voltages. Tracking of gun grid voltages with voltage of black-level voltage divider is obtained by means of voltage-dependent resistor VDR. Complexity of circuit and limited brightness control range are chief drawbacks.—A. Boekhorst and J. Gerritsen, Video Drive Circuits for Colour Picture Tubes, Philips, Pub. Dept., Elcoma Div., Eindhoven, The Netherlands, No. 233, 1965.

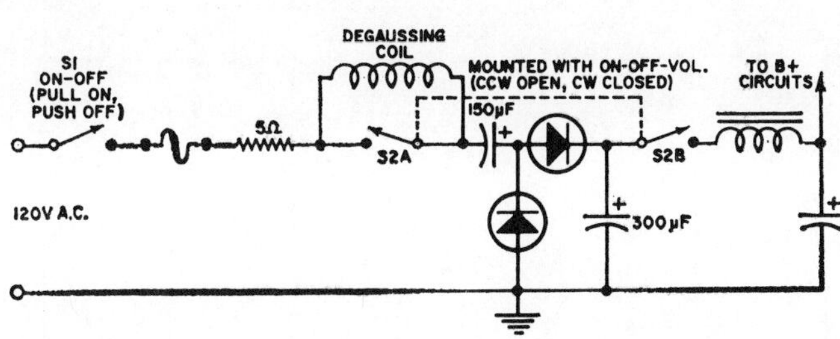

MANUAL DEGAUSSING—Used in Philco 19-FT20 color tv. Normally, switches S2 are closed and degaussing coil is shorted out. For degaussing, volume control is turned further counterclockwise after set is turned off, to open sections of S2. Set is then turned on by pulling outward on volume-control shaft. Coil then degausses crt for few seconds, until voltage-doubler capacitors at right have charged. Volume control is then rotated clockwise to close S2.—F. H. Belt, Color-Tv for 1969, *Electronics World*, Jan. 1969, p 25–30 and 66–67.

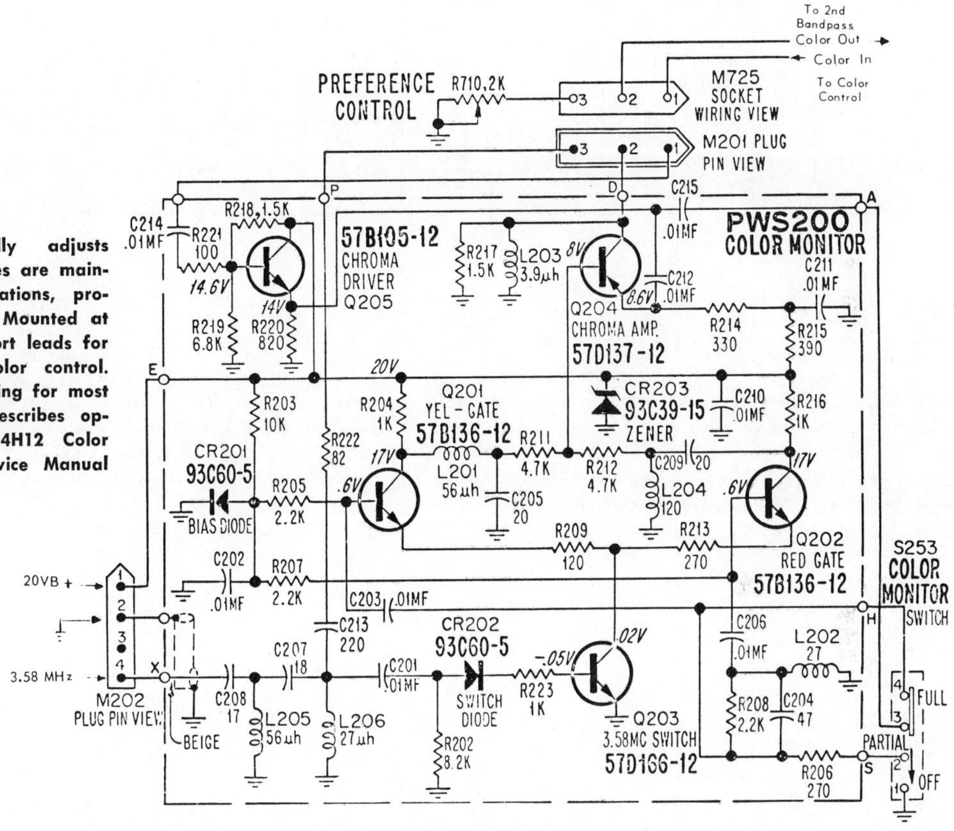

COLOR MONITOR—Automatically adjusts color signal so correct flesh tones are maintained during switching of stations, programs, tv cameras, or scenes. Mounted at rear of vhf tuner, to permit short leads for picking up color signal at color control. Preference control permits adjusting for most pleasing flesh tone. Manual describes operation of circuit in detail.—14H12 Color Television Chassis, Admiral Service Manual Supplement S1062N, 1970.

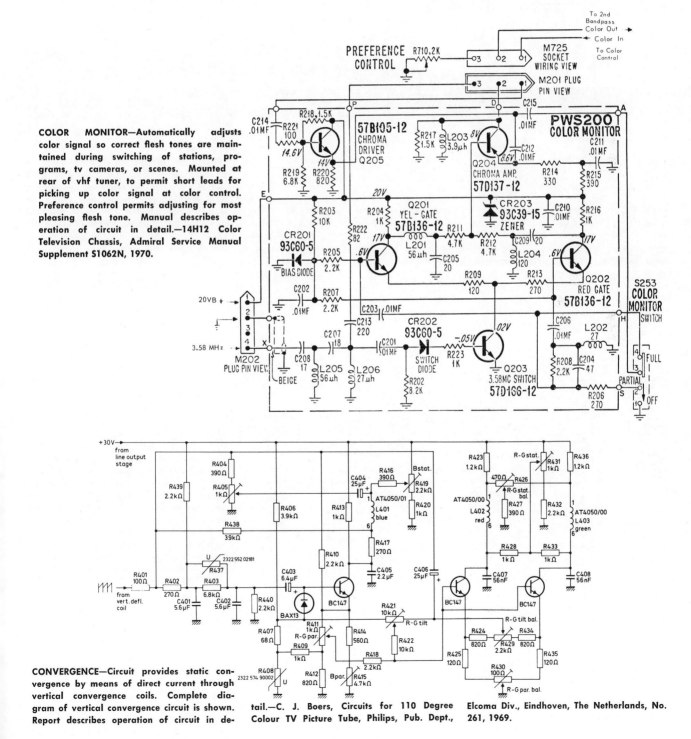

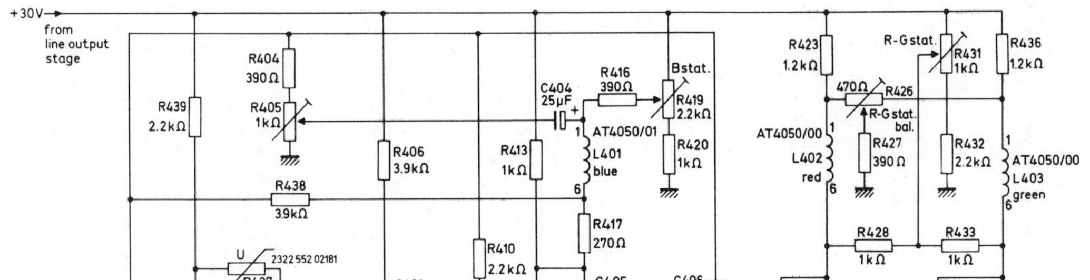

CONVERGENCE—Circuit provides static convergence by means of direct current through vertical convergence coils. Complete diagram of vertical convergence circuit is shown. Report describes operation of circuit in detail.—C. J. Boers, Circuits for 110 Degree Colour TV Picture Tube, Philips, Pub. Dept., Elcoma Div., Eindhoven, The Netherlands, No. 261, 1969.

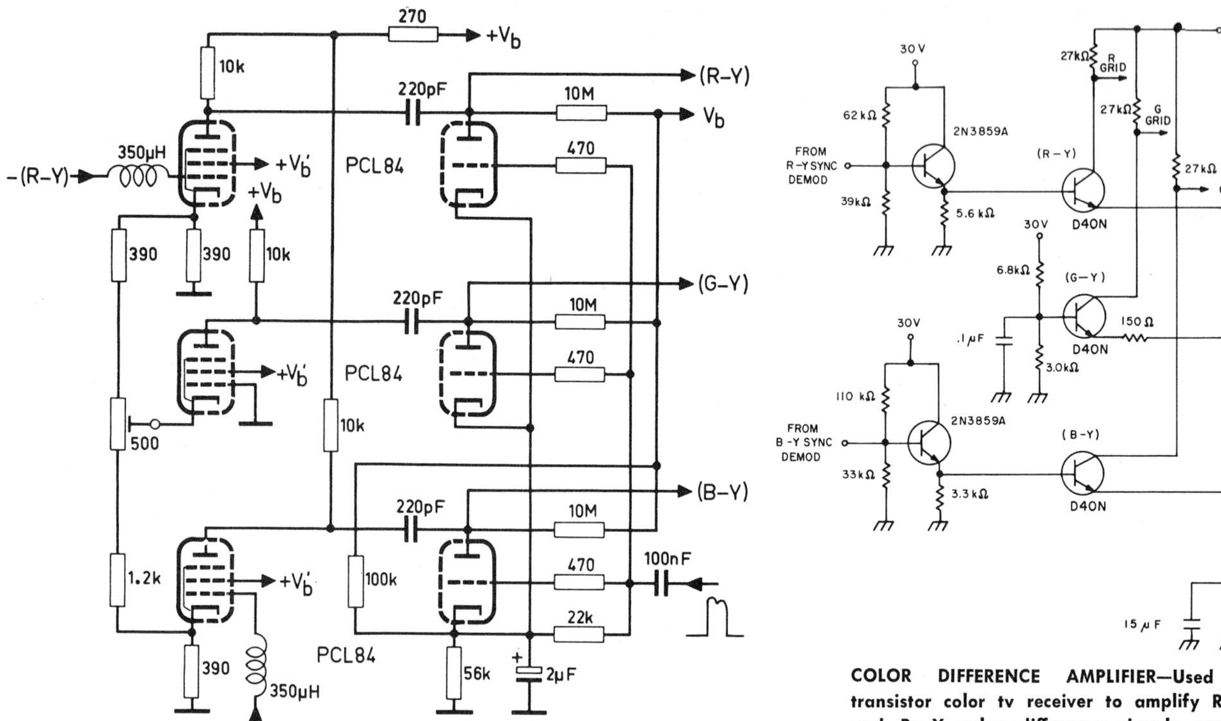

KEYED-DIODE CLAMPING—Color difference amplifier uses triodes as keyed diodes to provide asymmetrical clamping of color difference signals. Requires that blanking be applied to chrominance amplifier during flyback time.—A. Boekhorst and W. Graat, Chrominance Circuits for N. T. S. C. Colour Television Receivers, Philips, Pub. Dept., Elcoma Div., Eindhoven, The Netherlands, No. 234, 1966.

COLOR DIFFERENCE AMPLIFIER—Used in transistor color tv receiver to amplify R—Y and B—Y color difference signals coming from synchronous detectors and matrix the signals to get required G—Y color difference signal.—O. A. Kolody, Simplified Transistor Color TV Processing Circuitry, General Electric, Syracuse, N.Y., No. 90.63, 1969.

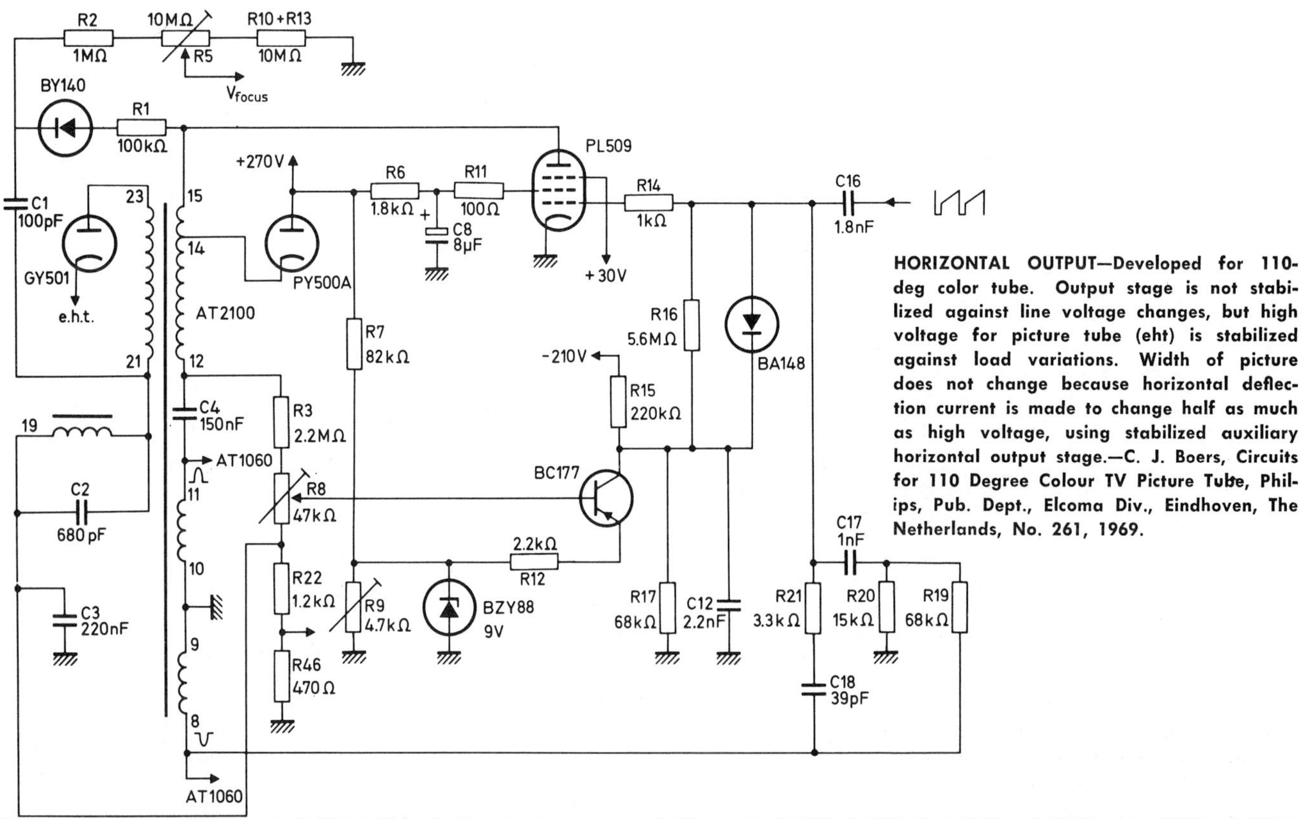

HORIZONTAL OUTPUT—Developed for 110-deg color tube. Output stage is not stabilized against line voltage changes, but high voltage for picture tube (eht) is stabilized against load variations. Width of picture does not change because horizontal deflection current is made to change half as much as high voltage, using stabilized auxiliary horizontal output stage.—C. J. Boers, Circuits for 110 Degree Colour TV Picture Tube, Philips, Pub. Dept., Elcoma Div., Eindhoven, The Netherlands, No. 261, 1969.

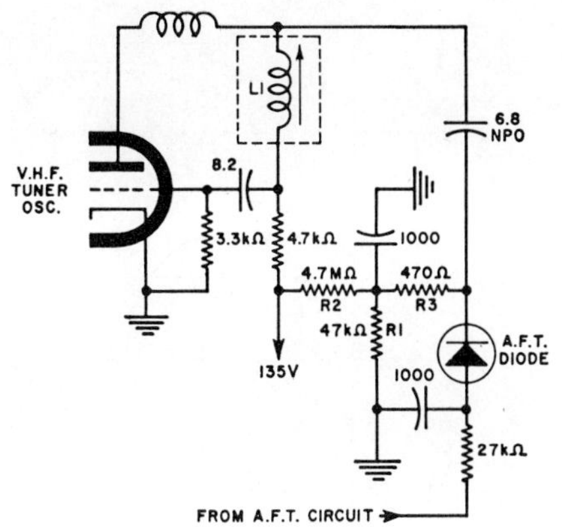

MAGNAVOX VHF AFT TUNER—Automatic fine tuning voltage derived from 3rd video i-f is applied to semiconductor diode that controls tuned circuit of triode oscillator. Complete circuit is given in Magnavox 1968 color tv service manuals.—F. H. Belt, Inside the 1968 Color Sets, *Electronics World*, Jan. 1968, p 41–45 and 72–75.

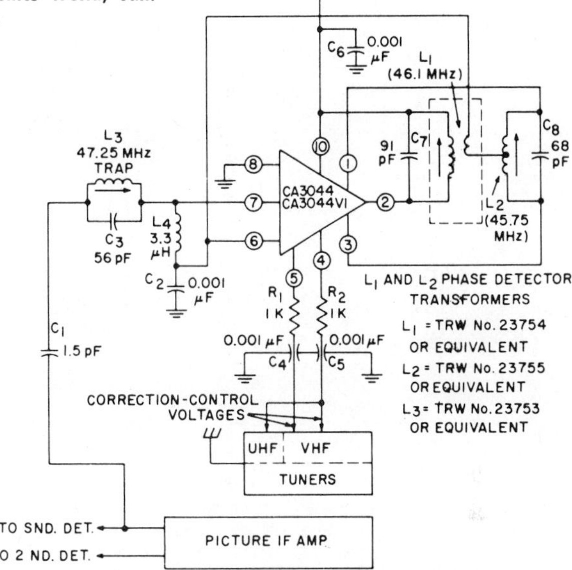

COLOR AFT SYSTEM—Uses RCA special-function IC to provide accurate tuning reference. System locks on picture-carrier i-f and holds tuner oscillator within 25 kHz of picture carrier to give high-quality picture at all times. Report describes operation and gives performance graphs.—W. M. Austin, H. M. Kleinman, and J. Sundburg, Application of the RCA-CA3044 and CA3044V1 Integrated Circuits in Automatic-Fine-Tuning Systems, RCA, Harrison, N.J., ICAN-5831, 1968.

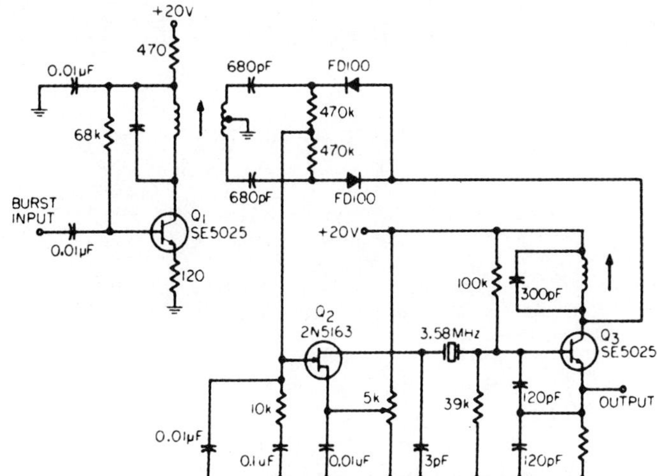

3.58-MHZ PHASE-LOCKED OSCILLATOR—Voltage-dependent resistance characteristic of fet is used to vary effective tuning capacitance of crystal subcarrier oscillator for color tv. Permits fine adjustment of oscillator frequency to give accurate control of picture tint.—N. P. Doyle, FET Controls Crystal Oscillator, *EEE*, Aug. 1968, p 136–137.

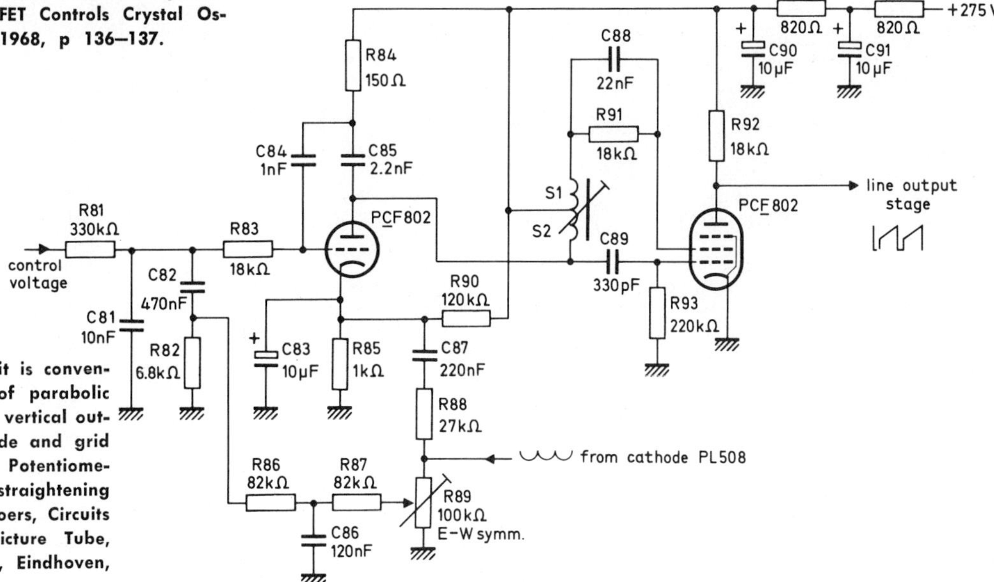

HORIZONTAL OSCILLATOR—Circuit is conventional except that small part of parabolic voltage derived from cathode of vertical output tube PL508 is fed to cathode and grid both in PCF802 reactance tube. Potentiometer R89 can then be used for straightening vertical lines in picture.—C. J. Boers, Circuits for 110 Degree Colour TV Picture Tube, Philips, Pub. Dept., Elcoma Div., Eindhoven, The Netherlands, No. 261, 1969.

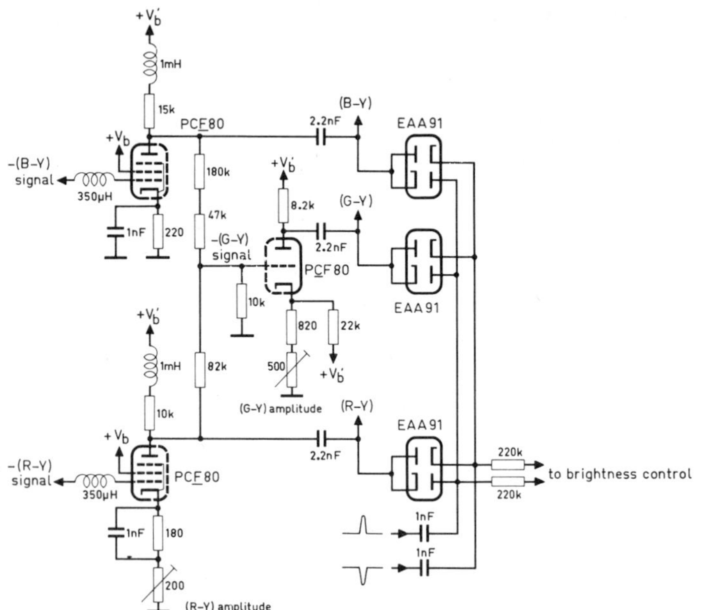

SYMMETRICAL CLAMPING—Chief advantage of circuit is immunity to noise, making blanking unnecessary.—A. Boekhorst and W. Graat, Chrominance Circuits for N. T. S. C. Colour Television Receivers, Philips, Pub. Dept., Elcoma Div., Eindhoven, The Netherlands, No. 234, 1966.

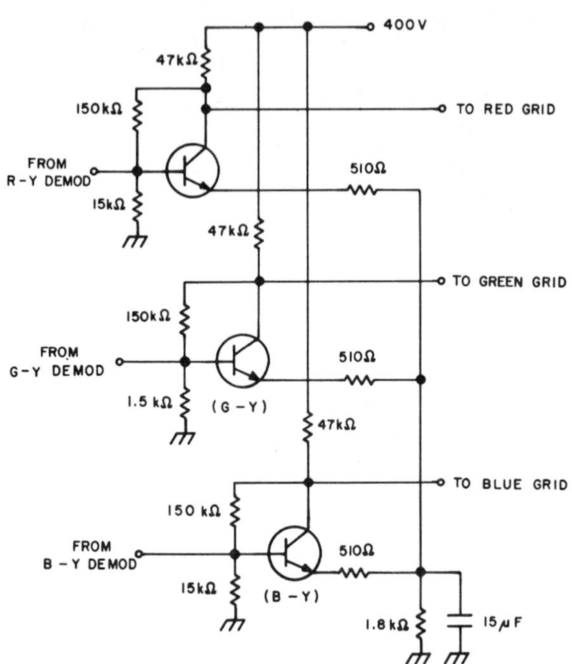

COLOR DIFFERENCE AMPLIFIER—Nonmatrixing amplifiers use D40N transistors. Input impedance of G—Y transistor is 1,000 ohms and that of other transistor is 6,000 ohms, to provide different voltage levels required for driving picture tube.—O. A. Kolody, Simplified Transistor Color TV Processing Circuitry, General Electric, Syracuse, N.Y., No. 90.63, 1969.

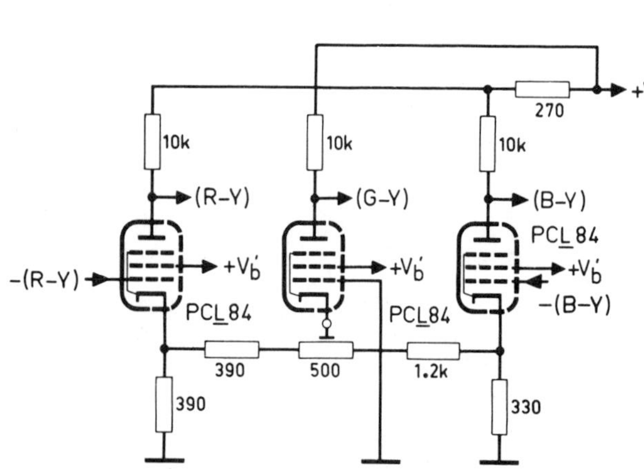

G—Y CATHODE MATRIX—Crosstalk between R—Y and B—Y amplifiers is a few percent, but offsetting advantage is that eventual hum on anode voltages of these stages is not phase-inverted on G—Y amplifier anode. Pentodes are used throughout to provide required gain.—A. Boekhorst and W. Graat, Chrominance Circuits for N. T. S. C. Colour Television Receivers, Philips, Pub. Dept., Elcoma Div., Eindhoven, The Netherlands, No. 234, 1966.

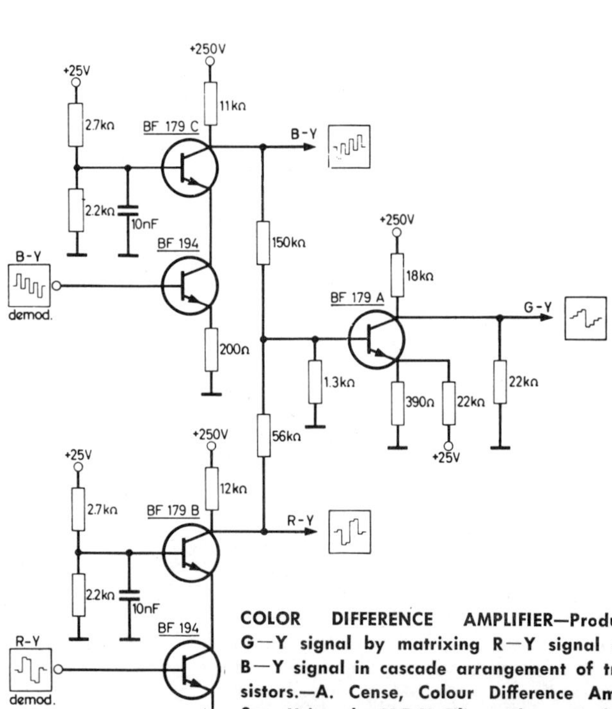

COLOR DIFFERENCE AMPLIFIER—Produces G—Y signal by matrixing R—Y signal and B—Y signal in cascade arrangement of transistors.—A. Cense, Colour Difference Amplifiers Using the N-P-N Silicon Planar Package 40822, Philips, Pub. Dept., Elcoma Div., Eindhoven, The Netherlands, 1966.

DOUBLE-DIODE DEMODULATOR—Used for phase demodulation of chrominance signals. Desired signal provides output voltages with equal phases from both diode circuits, to give color difference signal at junction of load resistors. Provides no gain, but has efficiency of about 80% with load values shown.—A. Boekhorst and W. Graat, Chrominance Circuits for N. T. S. C. Colour Television Receivers, Philips, Pub. Dept., Elcoma Div., Eindhoven, The Netherlands, No. 234, 1966.

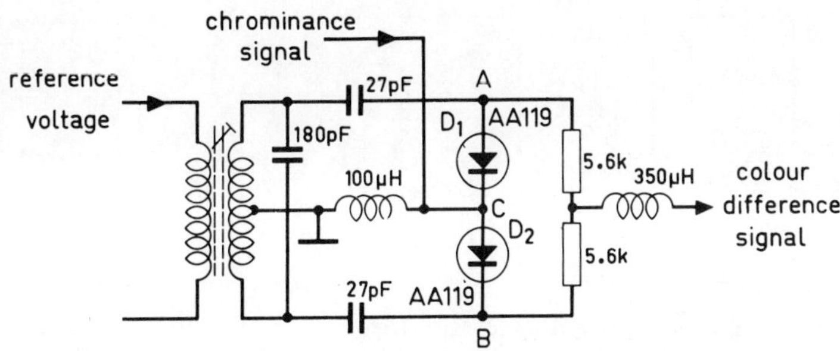

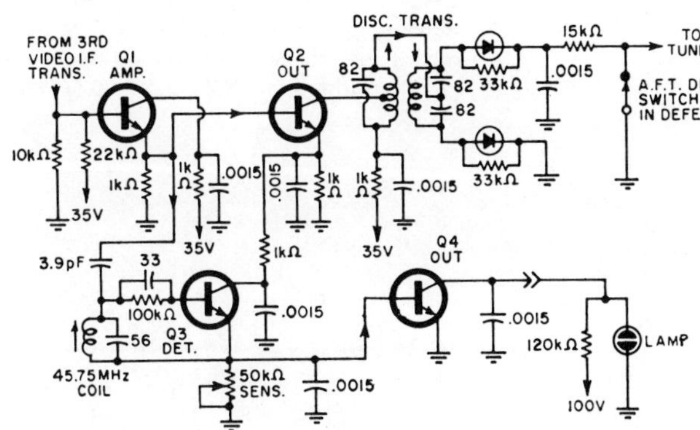

MOTOROLA AFT CONTROL—Takes signal from 3rd i-f and converts it to d-c automatic fine tuning voltage for tuner of color set. Includes neon-lamp indicator circuit to indicate when fine tuning needs manual adjustment. Complete circuit is given in service manuals for 1968 Motorola color sets.—F. H. Belt, Inside the 1968 Color Sets, *Electronics World*, Jan. 1968, p 41–45 and 72–75.

BURST PHASE DETECTOR—Demodulated R—Y color difference signal, in which burst is zero if phase of burst is correctly received, is amplified by triode V1, fed to clamp V2 to reduce blanking level to zero, then applied to phase detector V3 to detect any deviation of burst from zero.—A. Boekhorst and W. Graat, Chrominance Circuits for N. T. S. C. Colour Television Receivers, Philips, Pub. Dept., Elcoma Div., Eindhoven, The Netherlands, No. 234, 1966.

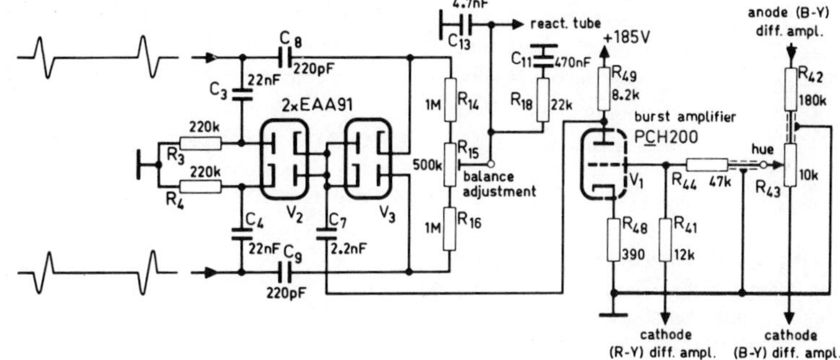

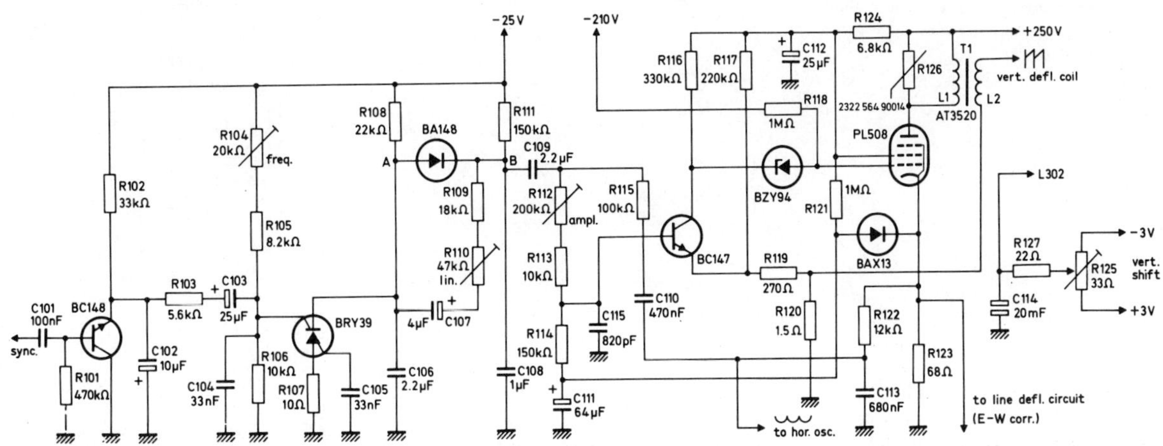

VERTICAL DEFLECTION—Sawtooth voltage is derived from synchronized relaxation oscillator using BRY39 scs. Sync signal is amplified by BC148 transistor before being applied to scs. Integrating network R122-C113 in cathode circuit of output pentode provides required S-correction of deflection current.—C. J. Boers, Circuits for 110 Degree Colour TV Picture Tube, Philips, Pub. Dept., Elcoma Div., Eindhoven, The Netherlands, No. 261, 1969.

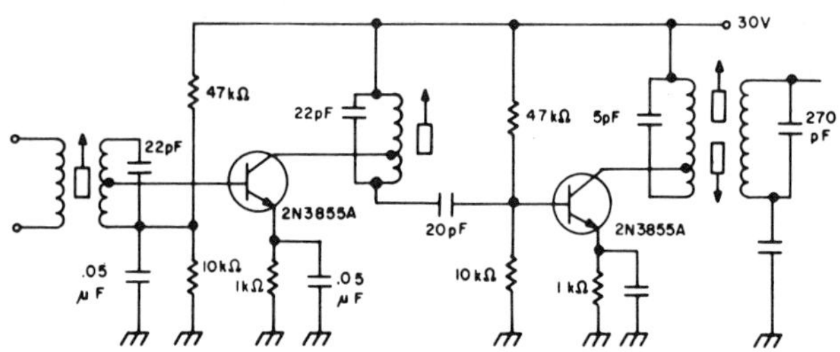

PEAKER FOR CHROMA BANDPASS AMPLIFIER—Simple a-c coupled peaker stage for transistor color tv receiver improves performance of chroma bandpass amplifier. No automatic color control is used on this stage.—O. A. Kolody, Simplified Transistor Color TV Processing Circuitry, General Electric, Syracuse, N.Y., No. 90.63, 1969.

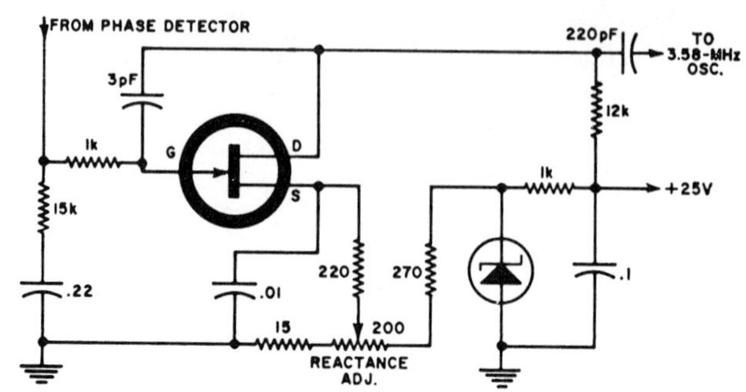

JFET 3.58-MHZ OSCILLATOR—Junction fet serves as reactance control for oscillator in chroma section of Admiral K10-2A 1969 color tv.—F. H. Belt, Color-Tv for 1969, *Electronics World*, Jan. 1969, p 25–30 and 66–67.

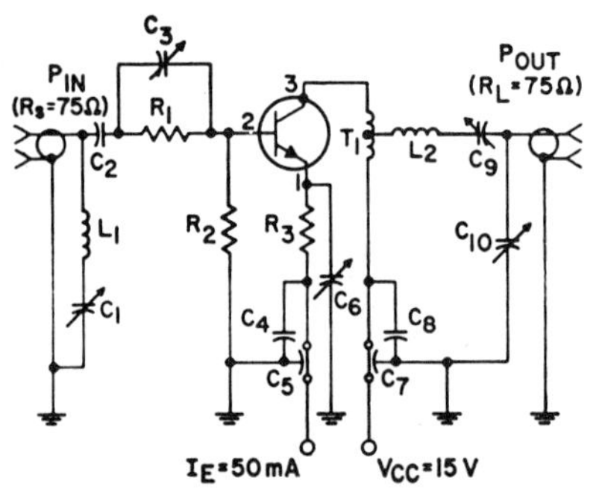

C_1 = 1.5 — 20 pF
C_2 = 0.002 pF
C_3 = 55 — 300 pF
C_4, C_8 = 0.02 pF
C_5, C_7 = 1000 pF
C_6 = 32 — 250 pF
C_9 = 7 — 100 pF
C_{10} = 8 — 60 pF
L_1 = 7 turns, 3/16" diameter, No. 26 wire
L_2 = 3 turns, 3/16" diameter, No. 26 wire
R_1 = 30 ohms
R_2 = 390 ohms
R_3 = 220 ohms
T = 4-turn bifilar winding, 3/16" ID; Core: G.I. material Q_1 or equiv.

54–216 MHZ CATV AMPLIFIER—Sophisticated wideband amplifier uses variety of matching, peaking, and feedback techniques to increase gain-bandwidth product. Provides minimum gain of 14 dB over entire band. Used in trunk line and bridger amplifiers usually having two to four stages, with tilt control generally incorporated only in second stage.—"Silicon Power Circuits Manual," RCA, Harrison, N.J., SP-51, p 342.

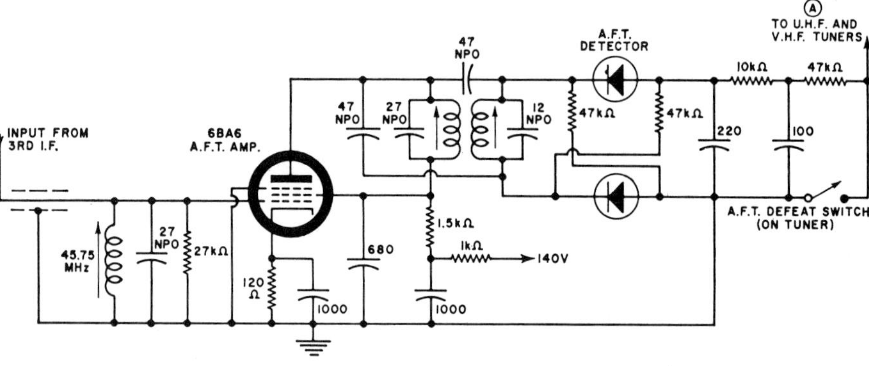

AUTOMATIC FINE TUNING—Used in Magnavox top-of-line sets to adjust tuner accurately so color burst is not lost. Article gives operating principle.—F. H. Belt, Inside the 1968 Color Sets, *Electronics World*, Jan. 1968, p 41–45 and 72–75.

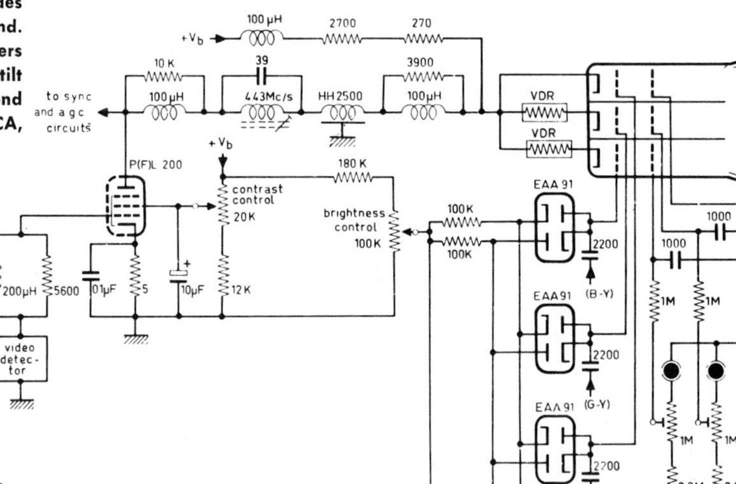

VDR FEEDBACK IN GUN CATHODES—Required drive ratio for guns is obtained by cathode feedback, with screen grid and control grid voltages being held equal. Brightness control varies both control grid and screen grid voltages by same amount, to avoid color shift. Circuit is simple in setup and adjustment. Gives good gray-scale tracking.—A. Boekhorst and J. Gerritsen, Video Drive Circuits for Colour Picture Tubes, Philips, Pub. Dept., Elcoma Div., Eindhoven, The Netherlands, No. 233, 1965.

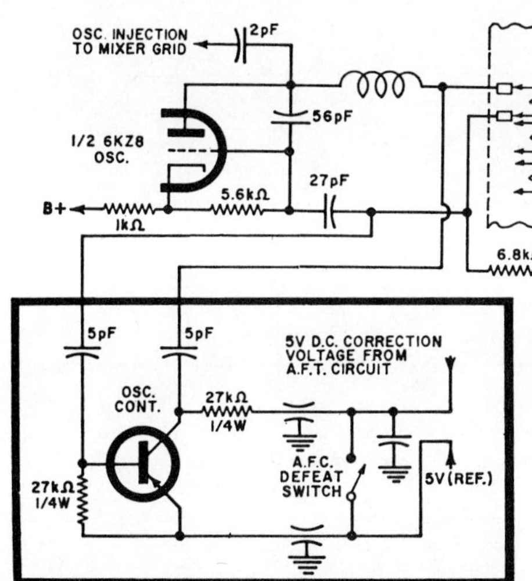

RCA AFT—Shows method of applying automatic fine tuning control voltage to oscillator control transistor in RCA KRK-131 vhf tuner. Complete circuit can be found in RCA service manual for CTC-28 color chassis. —F. H. Belt, Inside the 1968 Color Sets, *Electronics World*, Jan. 1968, p 41–45 and 72–75.

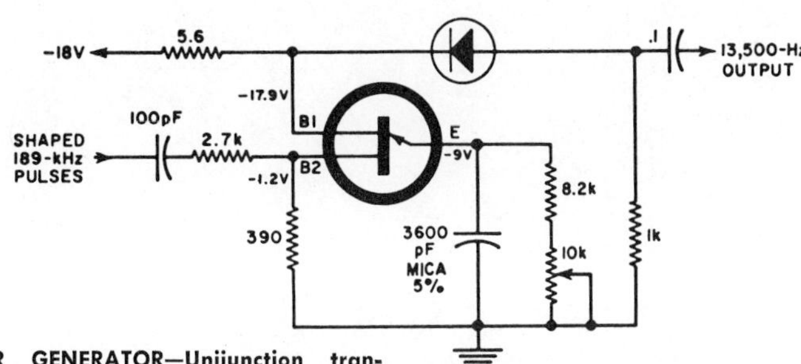

COLOR-BAR GENERATOR—Unijunction transistor serves as down-counter, triggered by every 14th pulse of its input, in B&K Model 1242 keyed-rainbow color generator. Diode aids stability and shapes output pulses for next stage. Generator uses total of four ujt's.—F. H. Belt, Color Generators Reach the Solid State, *Electronics World*, May 1968, p 25–29 and 64–65.

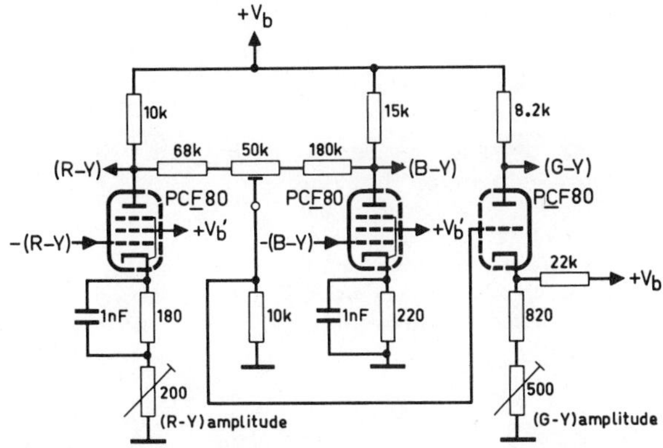

G—Y ANODE MATRIX—Provides two-phase pentode demodulation, with triode as phase inverter and amplifier for G—Y signal. Advantages include minimum crosstalk.—A. Boekhorst and W. Graat, Chrominance Circuits for N. T. S. C. Colour Television Receivers, Philips, Pub. Dept., Elcoma Div., Eindhoven, The Netherlands, No. 234, 1966.

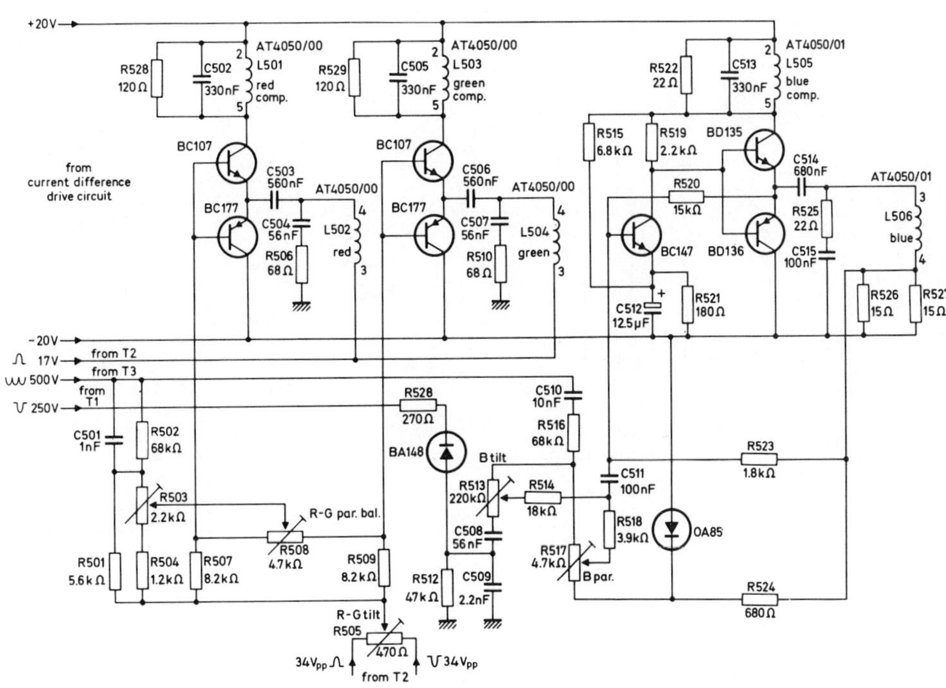

HORIZONTAL DYNAMIC CONVERGENCE—Complementary pair of emitter-followers is used for each convergence coil. Report describes operation of circuit and gives waveforms of horizonal convergence currents and fields.—C. J. Boers, Circuits for 110 Degree Colour TV Picture Tube, Philips, Pub. Dept., Elcoma Div., Eindhoven, The Netherlands, No. 261, 1969.

CHAPTER 87
Temperature Control Circuits

4-A SCR CONTROL FOR RELAY—Permits control of high-current loads plugged into load receptacle. R1 can be GE 1D303 thermistor having 1,000 ohms at 70 F, cadmium sulfide photocell, or other sensor. Relay can be 6-V d-c such as Potter & Brumfield PT11.—"Hobby Manual," General Electric, Owensboro, Ky., 1965, p 160.

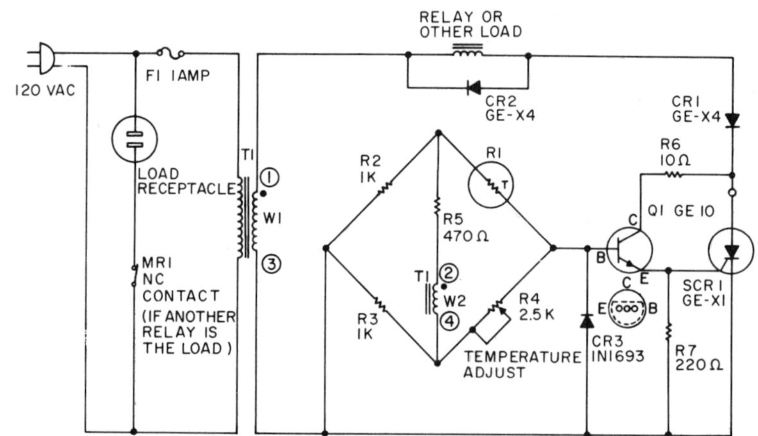

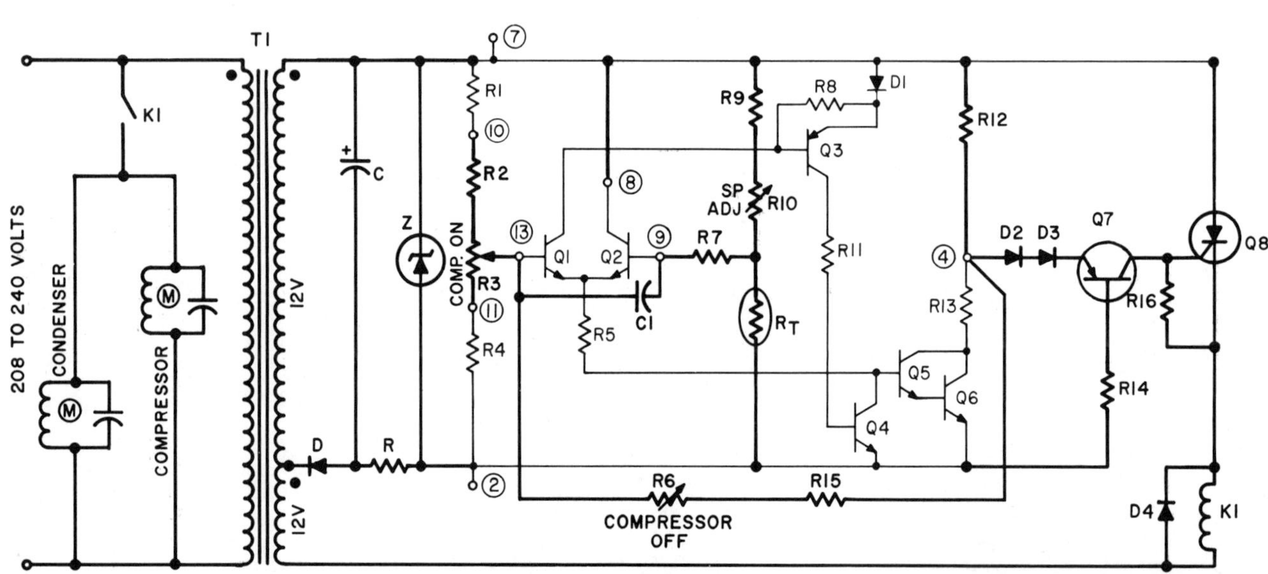

R_1, R_4, R_5, R_8, R_{11}, R_{13}	- in PA424
R_2, R_3, R_{16}	1K ohm
R_6	5 megohm
R_7	12K ohm
R_9	3.3K ohm
R_{10}	5K ohm
R_{12}	2.2K ohm
R_{14}	82K ohm
R_{15}	220K ohm
R_T	GE 2R114
R	120 ohm

C	- GE 43F9723AA9 250µfd 25V
C_1	- GE 75F1R5A103 .01µfd 50V
D_1	- in PA424
D, D_2, D_3, D_4	- GE A14F
Q_1 thru Q_6	- in PA424
Q_7	- GE D29A4
Q_8	- GE C106F
Z	- GE Z4XL12
K1	- 24V Coil; Contacts as req.
T1	220V PRI; 24V CT SEC; 25 WATT

AIR CONDITIONER CONTROL—Incorporates PA424 IC, shown in thin lines, and uses electromechanical relay to handle relatively high compressor surge current (60 A or higher) of larger units. Also controls condenser fan. Hysteresis of control is adjustable from 0.25 to 4 F with R6. Can be combined with heater control, for regulating room temperature under all weather conditions.—T. A. Penkalski, Better Room Conditioning via Solid State Controls, General Electric, Syracuse, N.Y., No. 200.51, 1967, p 6.

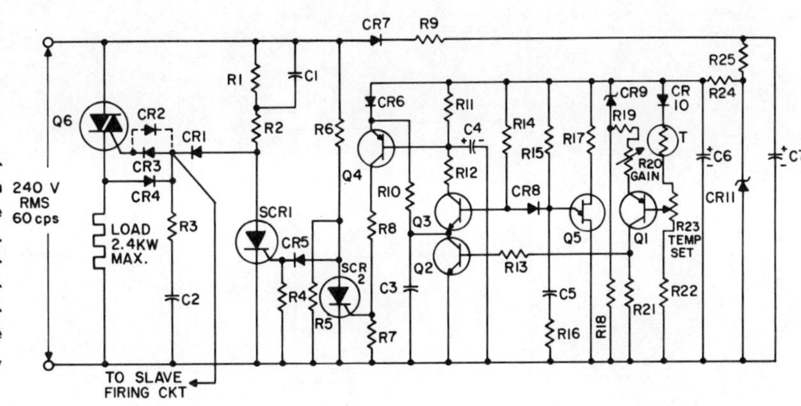

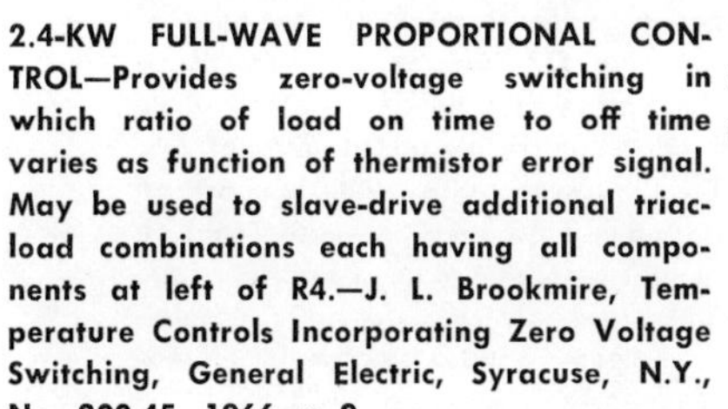

2.4-KW FULL-WAVE PROPORTIONAL CONTROL—Provides zero-voltage switching in which ratio of load on time to off time varies as function of thermistor error signal. May be used to slave-drive additional triac-load combinations each having all components at left of R4.—J. L. Brookmire, Temperature Controls Incorporating Zero Voltage Switching, General Electric, Syracuse, N.Y., No. 200.45, 1966, p 9.

CR1 - G.E. A13B - A14B
CR2 - G.E. A13F - A14F
CR3 - G.E. A13F - A14F
CR4 - G.E. A13F - A14F
CR5 - G.E. A13F - A14F
CR6 - G.E. 1N4009
CR7 - G.E. A13B - A14B
CR8 - G.E. 1N4009
CR9 - G.E. Z4XL6.2
CR10 - G.E. 1N4009
CR11 - G.E. Z4XL16
R1 - 3K, 10W
R2 - 56, 1W

R3 - 470, 1W
R4 - 1K
R5 - 15K, 1W
R6 - 15K, 2W
R7 - 1K
R8 - 4.7K
R9 - 6.8K, 5W
R10 - 22K
R11 - 22K
R12 - 22K
R13 - 12K
R14 - 1MEG
R15 - 1MEG

R16 - 100
R17 - 220
R18 - 6.8K
R19 - 1K
R20 - 10K POT
R21 - 10K
R22 - 4.7K
R23 - 10K POT
R24 - 47
R25 - 150
C1 - 0.82 UF, 20%, 400 VDC
C2 - 0.47 UF, 20%, 400 VDC
C3, C5 - 1 UF, 10%, 15 VDC (MYLAR OR LOW LEAKAGE TYPE)

C4 - 3 UF, 20 WVDC
C6 - 100 UF, 20 WVDC
C7 - 500 UF, 25 WVDC
Q1, Q4 - 2N3638 (Fairchild)
Q2, Q3 - G.E. 2N2923
T - 5K THERMISTOR AT OPERATING TEMPERATURE } G.E. TYPE 2H502 - 5K AT 25°C.
Q5 - G.E. 2N2646
SCR1 - G.E. C5DX280
SCR2 - G.E. C6B OR C106B
Q6 - TRIAC - G. E. SC45D - 10 AMP
G. E. SC40D - 6 AMP

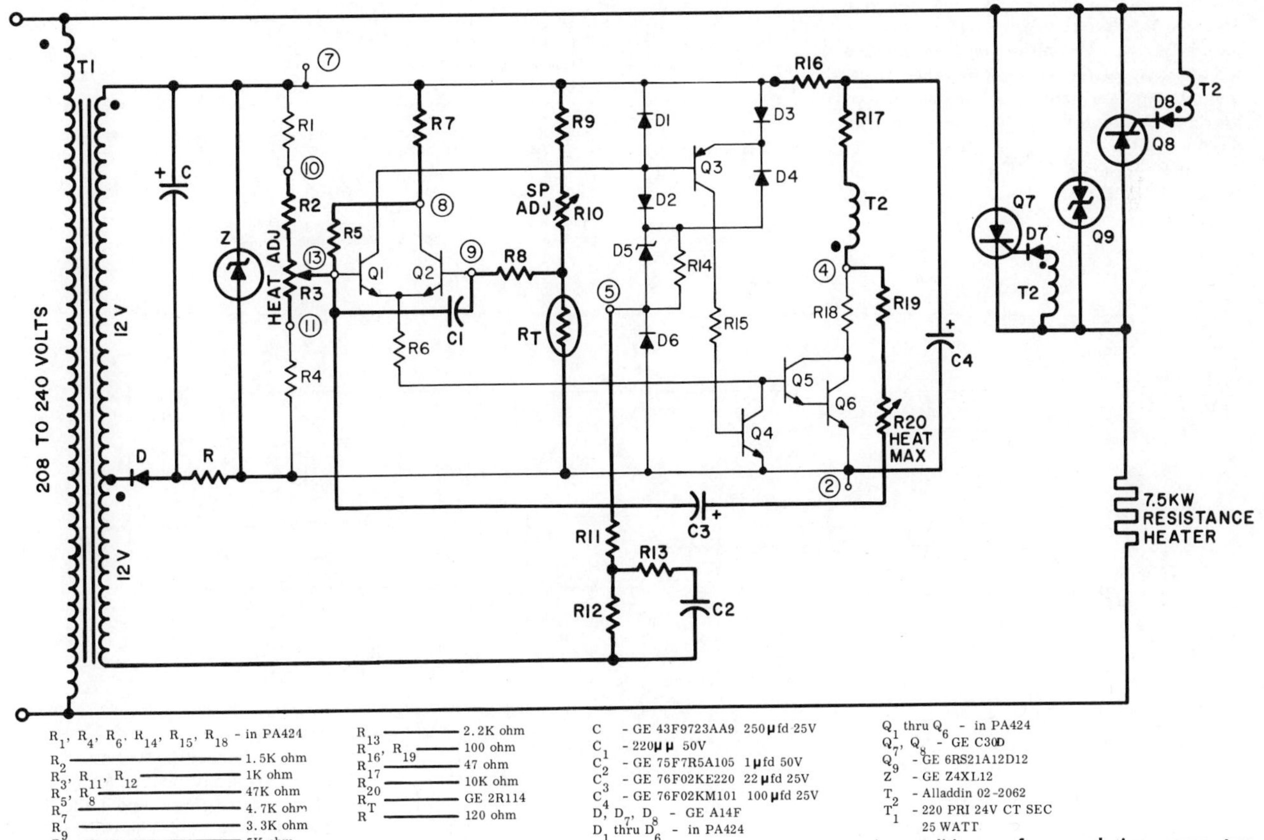

IC PROPORTIONAL FOR 7.5-KW HEATER—Uses inverse parallel scr combination Q7-Q8 operating from a-c line, with triggering circuit operated from low-voltage secondary of transformer. This isolates thermostat from high-voltage power line. Components in General Electric PA424 IC are shown in thin lines. Can be combined with control for air conditioner, for regulating room temperature under all weather conditions.—T. A. Penkalski, Better Room Conditioning via Solid State Controls, General Electric, Syracuse, N.Y., No. 200.51, 1967, p 5.

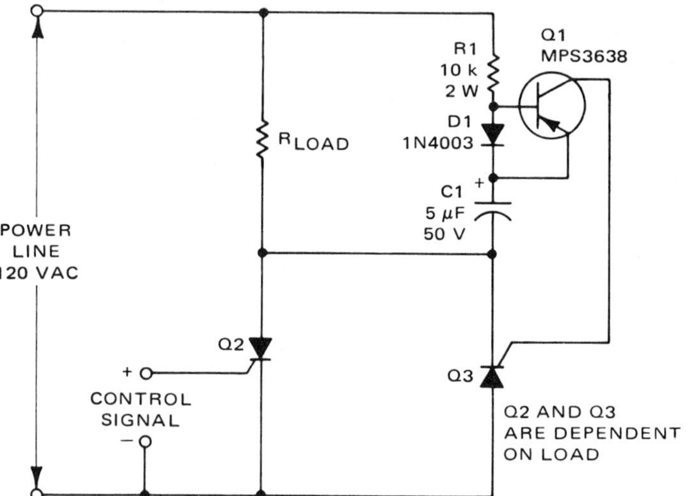

SCR SLAVE—Slave circuit Q1-Q3, added to half-wave control scr Q2, gives full-wave control. Each time Q2 turns on, it feeds single power pulse through Q1 to gate of scr Q3, making Q3 turn on and pass load current for half-cycle following that in which Q2 was on. Control signal at gate of Q2, either d-c or power pulse, will thus act on both Q2 and Q3 to give full-wave control. If control pulse is synchronized with a-c line, switching occurs only at zero point.—"Semiconductor Power Circuits Handbook," Motorola, Phoenix, Ariz., 1968, p 6–13.

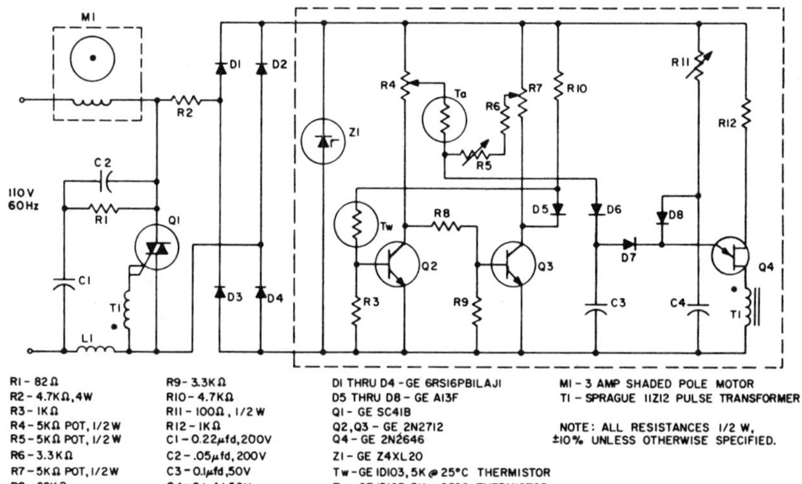

3-A BLOWER CONTROL—Phase-controlled blower regulates temperature produced by external heat source. May be used in systems having single blower for regulating both room heating and cooling. Room temperature is monitored by feedback thermistor Ta. Feedback signal is compared in ujt error detector with reference R5, and resulting error fed to triac Q1 which supplies power to blower motor. Thermistor Tw and flip-flop Q2-Q3 sense water temperature when water is used either for heating or cooling. Circuit provides rfi suppression. Will maintain temperature within 3% of thermistor resistance for 10% variation in line voltage.—"SCR Manual," 4th Edition, General Electric, 1967, p 287–288.

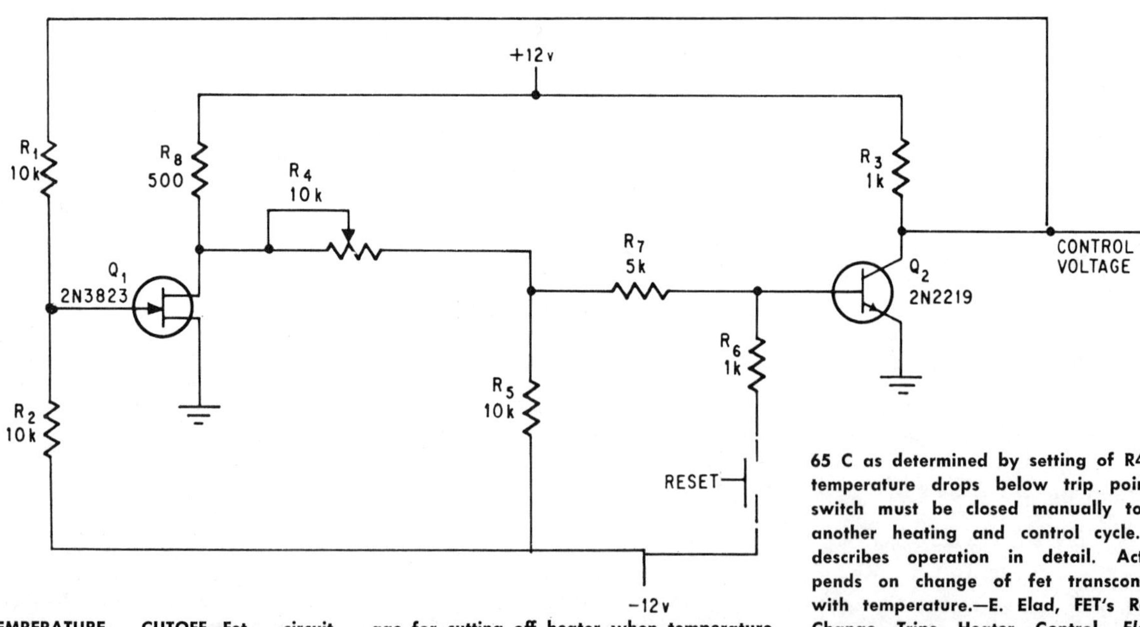

HIGH-TEMPERATURE CUTOFF—Fet circuit placed in heat chamber provides control voltage for cutting off heater when temperature reaches desired maximum between 35 and 65 C as determined by setting of R4. After temperature drops below trip point, reset switch must be closed manually to initiate another heating and control cycle. Article describes operation in detail. Action depends on change of fet transconductance with temperature.—E. Elad, FET's Resistance Change Trips Heater Control, *Electronics*, April 29, 1968, p 65–66.

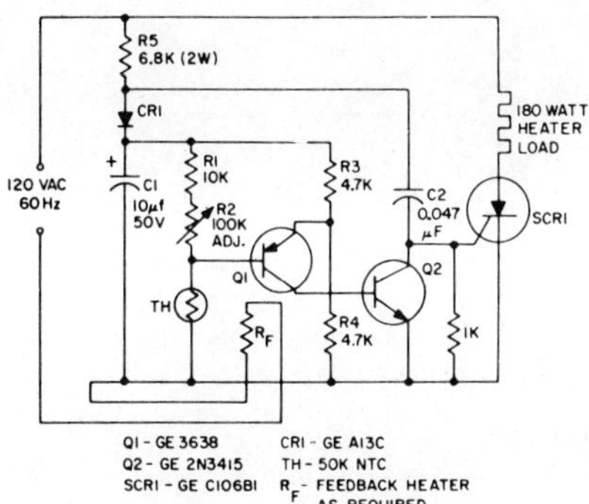

HALF-WAVE ZERO-VOLTAGE SWITCHING—Duplicates function of bimetallic switch normally used in electric blankets. Scr is fired either at beginning of alternate half-cycles or biased off completely. On-off cycle repeats at rate determined by room temperature, so ON time increases when temperature is low. Switching at zero voltage minimizes rfi, eliminating need for filter.—"SCR Manual," 4th Edition, General Electric, 1967, p 149–150.

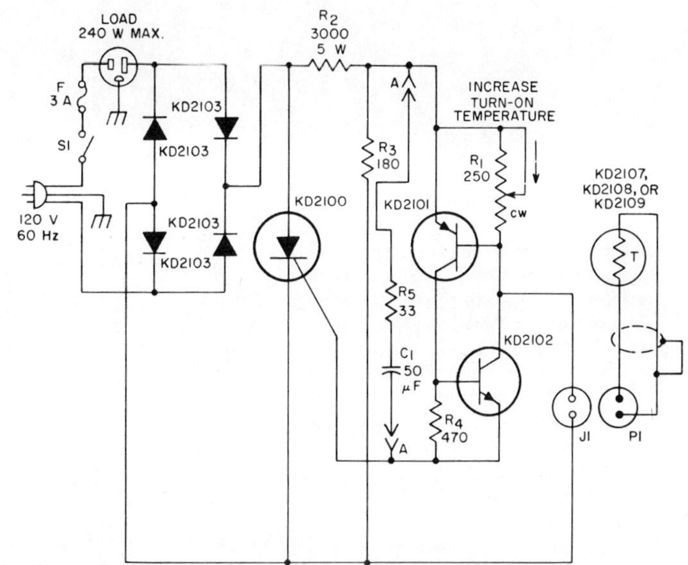

240-W COOLING CONTROL—When thermistor T senses that temperature is above that called for by setting of R1, transistor switch and scr are retriggered early in each succeeding half-cycle of a-c input to give full-wave current through cooling fan or other load, without rfi. Optional latching circuit R5-C1 would, if used, keep fan on until line switch S1 is opened.—"Silicon Controlled Rectifier Experimenter's Manual," RCA, Harrison, N.J., 1967, p 110.

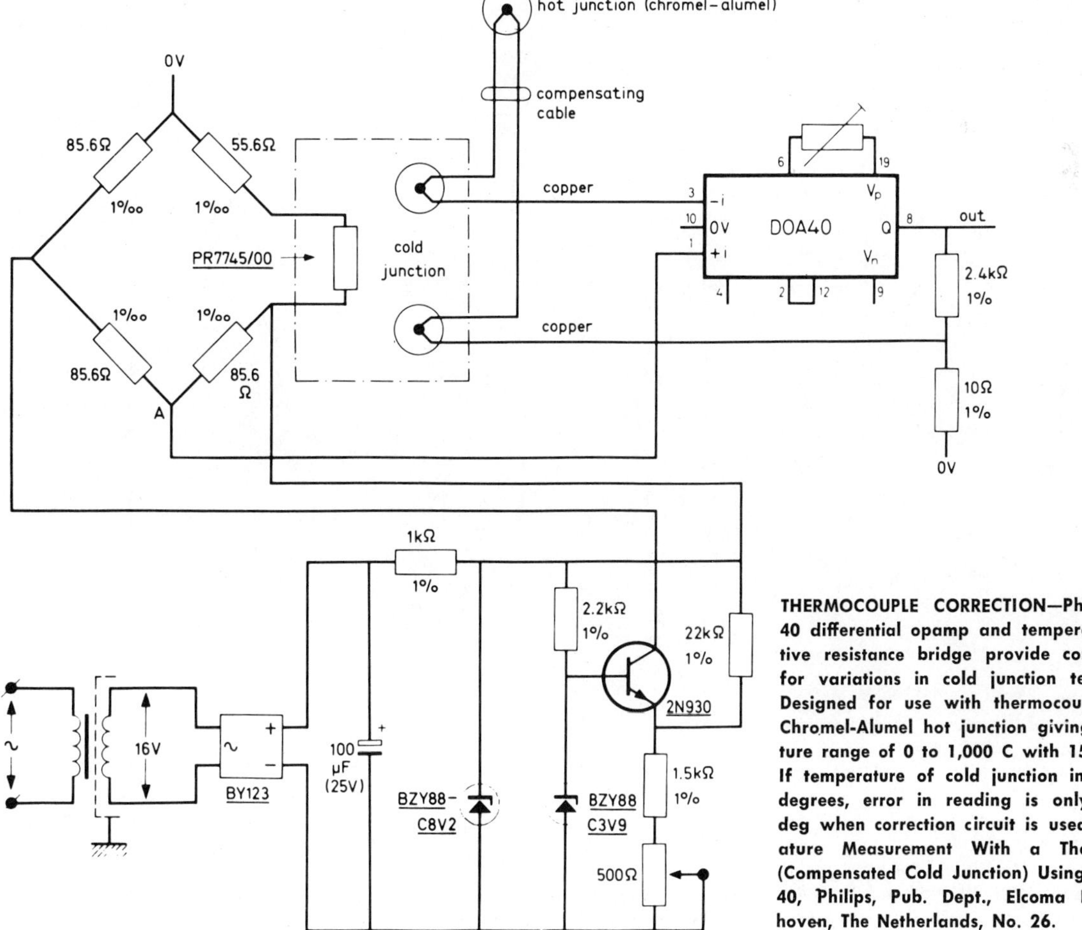

THERMOCOUPLE CORRECTION—Philips DOA-40 differential opamp and temperature-sensitive resistance bridge provide compensation for variations in cold junction temperature. Designed for use with thermocouple having Chromel-Alumel hot junction giving temperature range of 0 to 1,000 C with 15-V supply. If temperature of cold junction increases 80 degrees, error in reading is only about 6 deg when correction circuit is used.—Temperature Measurement With a Thermocouple (Compensated Cold Junction) Using the DOA-40, Philips, Pub. Dept., Elcoma Div., Eindhoven, The Netherlands, No. 26.

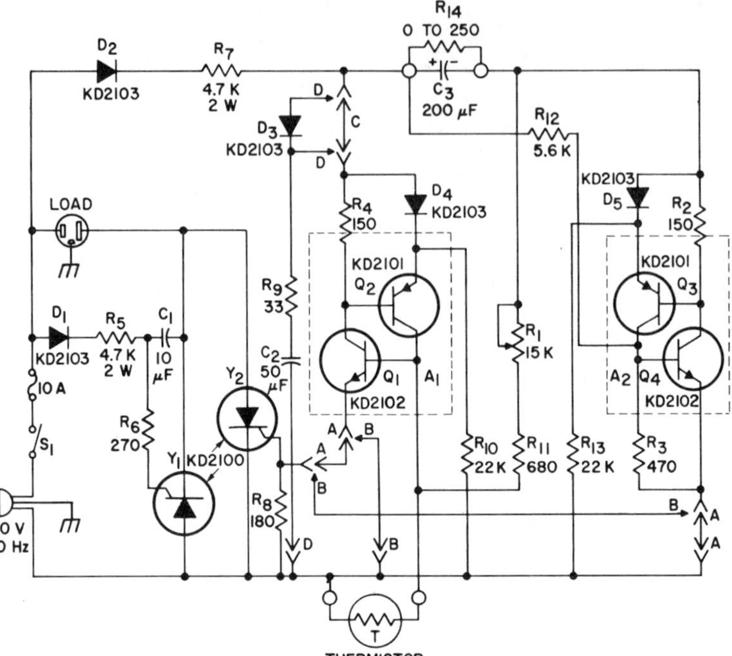

MULTIPURPOSE TEMPERATURE CONTROL—Different combinations of wiring give choice of operating methods. With wiring A, load is turned off when temperature increases, for heating applications. Wiring B gives opposite effect, for cooling applications. With wiring C, circuit does not lock in either mode. Wiring D will latch control in either mode, depending on whether used with A or B. With D, R14 and C3 should be removed and replaced by jumper.—"Silicon Controlled Rectifier Experimenter's Manual," RCA, Harrison, N.J., 1967, p 117.

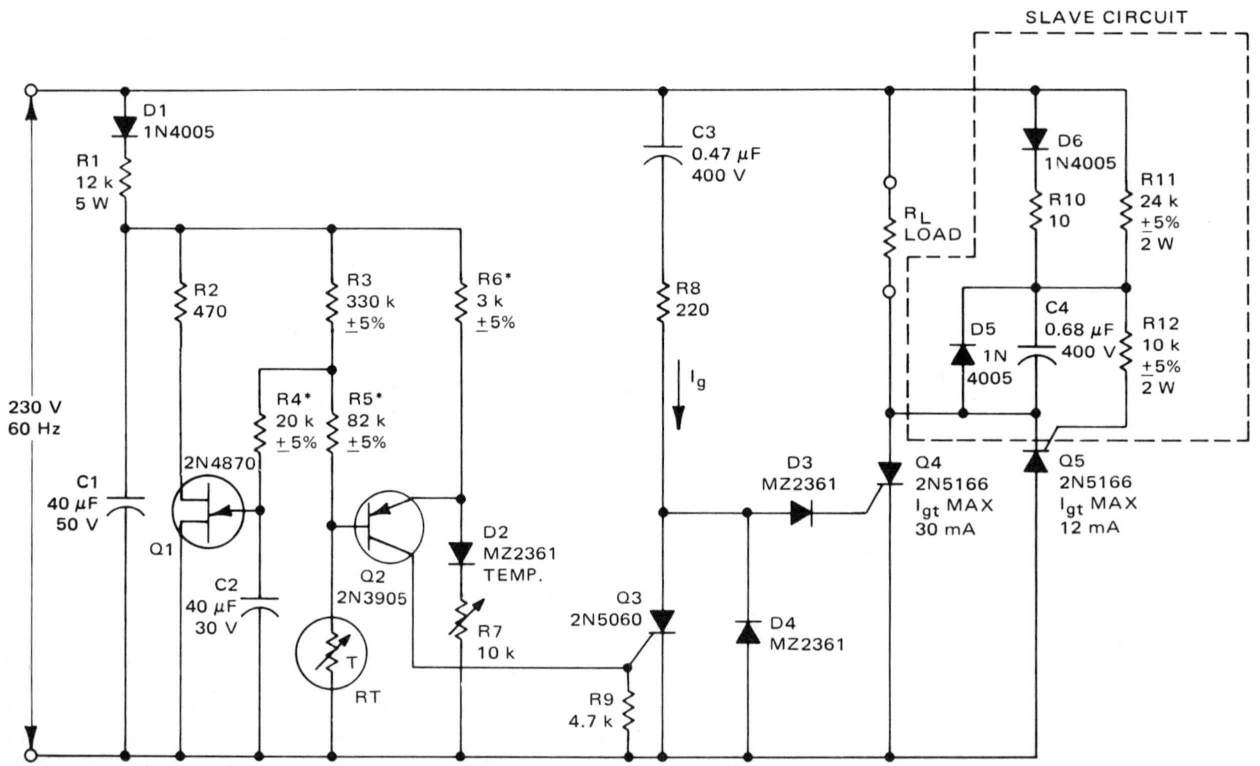

*LOW TEMP. COEFFICIENT
FENWELL QR51J1 100 k THERMISTOR

4-KW MODULATED-SCR CONTROL WITH ZERO-POINT SWITCHING—Designed for 230-V a-c line operation. Each time master scr Q4 applies positive half-cycle of power to load, it energizes slave circuit that fires Q5 and applies following negative half-cycle of power to load. Modulation involves dividing line frequency into 12-cycle groups and applying 1 to 12 cycles of each group to load, for modulation in 8% steps from 0 to 100% duty cycle. C2 controls number of cycles per group. Intended primarily for industrial applications where separate transformers are available for supplying banks of heaters, because switching of load power on and off at 6 Hz may cause undesirable flickering of incandescent lamps connected to same line.—"Semiconductor Power Circuits Handbook," Motorola, Phoenix, Ariz., 1968, p 6–8.

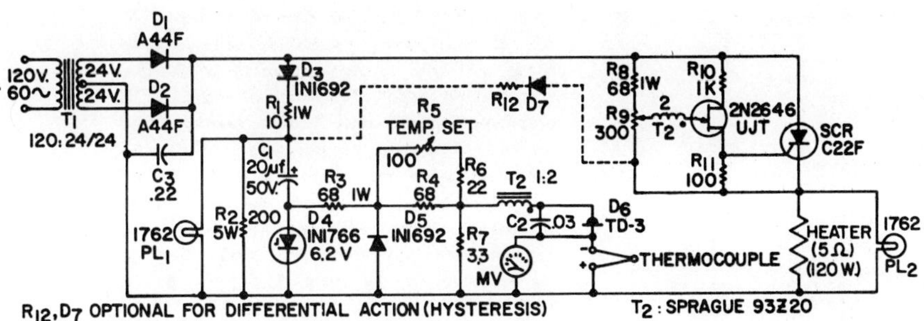

CONTROLLING HEATER AT 800 F—Tunnel diode compares output of thermocouple with reference voltage appearing only at beginning of each half-cycle. When tunnel diode switches, pulse is applied to ujt operating in latching mode, for triggering scr at beginning of each half-cycle. Will hold temperature within 20 F of 800 F set point.—F. W. Gutzwiller and E. K. Howell, Economy Power Semiconductor Applications, General Electric, Syracuse, N.Y., No. 671.1, 1965, p 11.

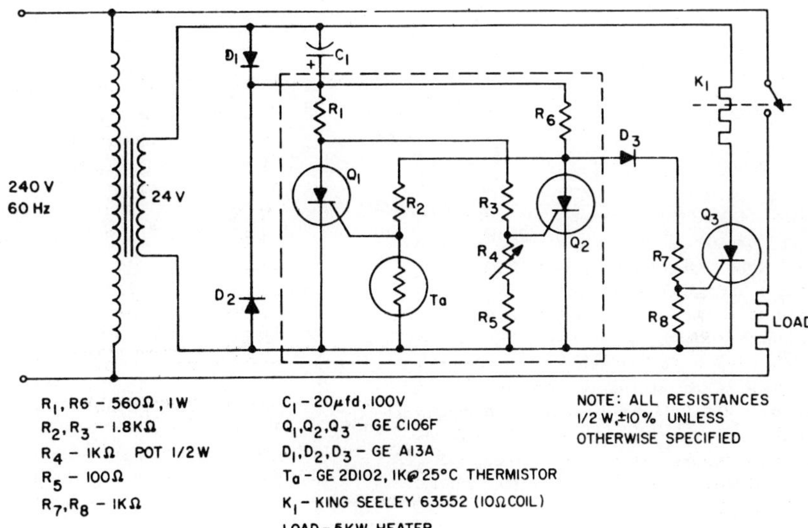

5-KW ON-OFF—Uses half-wave zero-voltage switching to control low-power hot-wire relay that in turn switches large heater or other load operating directly across power line. Feedback element, reference, and error detector (in dashed block) regulate within 0.2% of thermistor resistance over 10% variation in line voltage.—"SCR Manual," 4th Edition, General Electric, 1967, p 281–282.

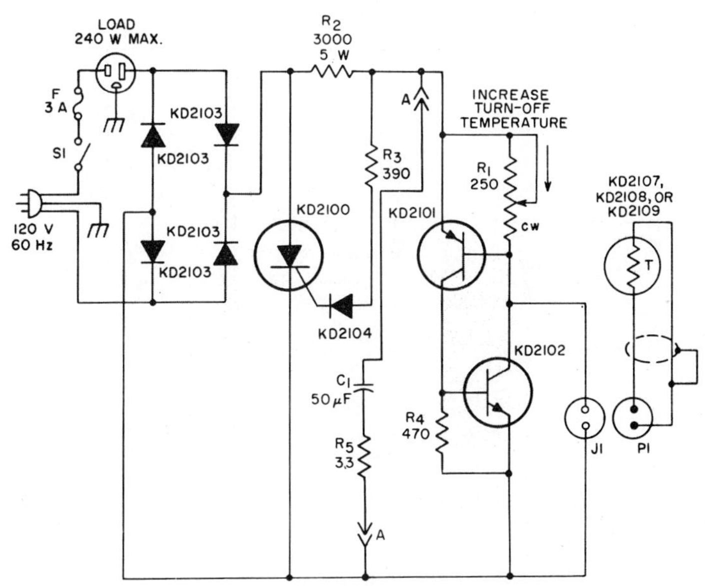

240-W HEATER CONTROL—When thermistor T senses that temperature is below that called for by setting of R1, transistor switch and scr are retriggered early in each succeeding half-cycle of a-c input to give full-wave current through load, without rfi. Optional latching circuit R5-C1 would, if used, keep heater on until line switch S1 is opened.—"Silicon Controlled Rectifier Experimenter's Manual," RCA, Harrison, N.J., 1967, p 113.

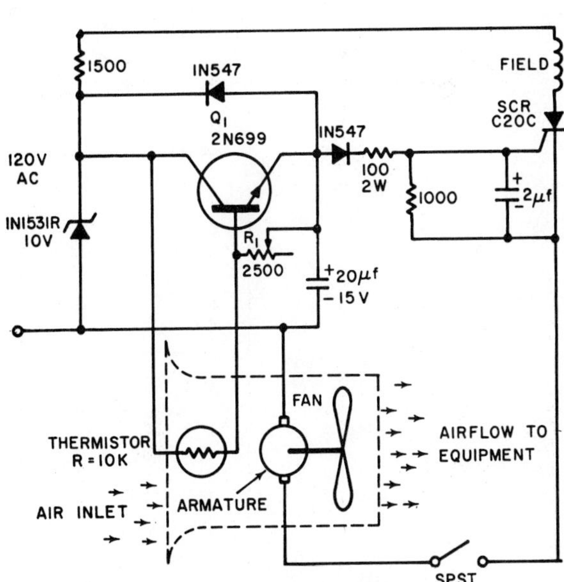

COOLING FAN CONTROL—Maintains equipment at preselected temperature by adjusting volume of cooling air with fan motor speed control circuit, to compensate for variations in air inlet temperature as sensed by thermistor. Temperature variation of about 10 C will change speed of universal motor linearly from standstill to full speed.—H. B. Opladen, Control Circuit Maintains Constant Operating Temperature, *Electronic Design*, Oct. 26, 1964, p 55–56.

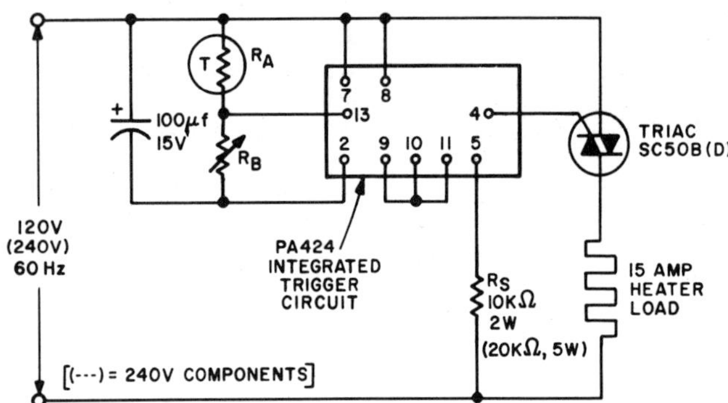

15-A IC-TRIAC HEATER CONTROL—Uses PA-424 IC zero-voltage switching trigger combined with triac to give equivalent of thermostat having differential of less than 0.2 F, response time of only a few seconds, and no rfi. Controlled temperature must fluctuate in order to operate switch, and resultant hunting may be unacceptable for some applications.—E. K. Howell, Integrated Circuits for Sophisticated, Low Cost AC Power Control, General Electric, Syracuse, N.Y., No. 671.9, 1968, p 23.

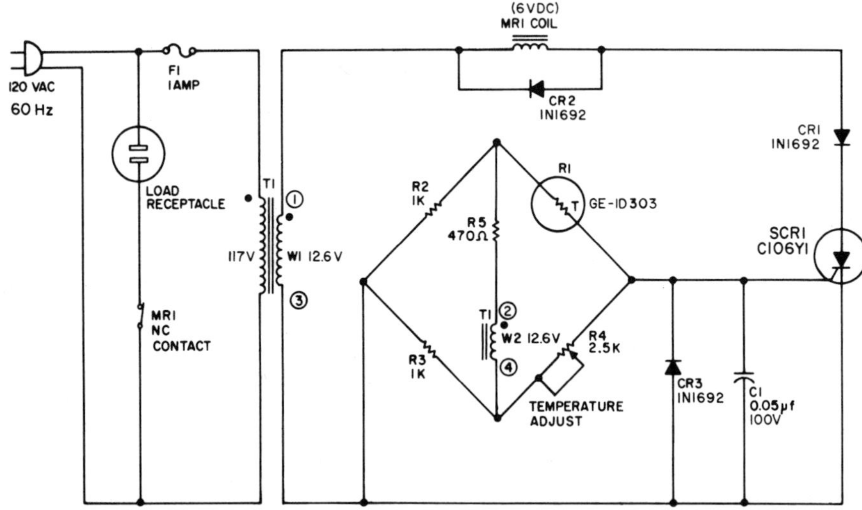

BATH CONTROL—Low-cost thermistor-operated controller is ideal for molten lead and other fluid baths, soldering irons, temperature ovens, and other heat loads. May also be used to control cooling system such as fan or air conditioner, by connecting load to normally open contact on relay or by reversing connections to secondary winding W2 in bridge. Will hold temperature within 1 deg of desired value in range of 20 to 150 F.—D. R. Grafham, Using Low Current SCR's, General Electric, Syracuse, N.Y., No. 200.19, 1967, p 30.

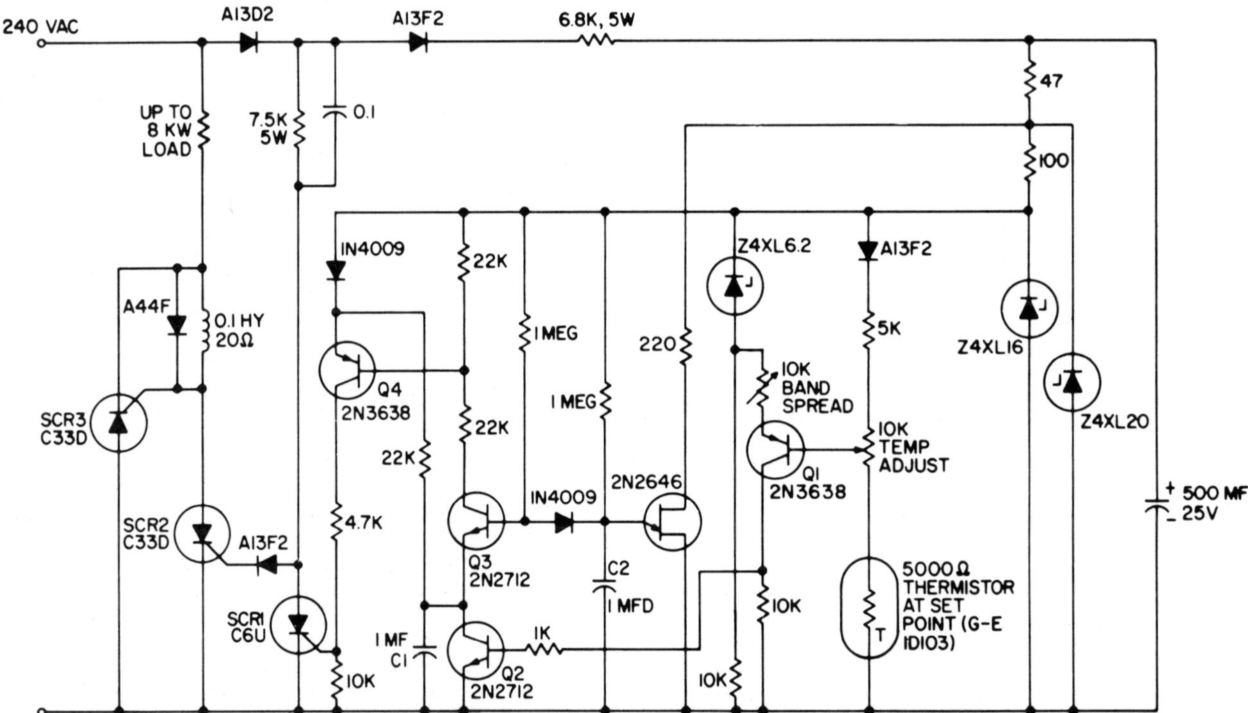

PROPORTIONAL CONTROL WITH 8-KW SYNCHRONOUS A-C SWITCH—Under control of thermistor, heater is switched on and off in whole number of cycles, thereby eliminating rfi and making r-f filters unnecessary. High-gain control circuit, consisting of thermistor in bridge followed by error-signal amplifier Q1-Q2 driving SCR2 and SCR3 through Q3, Q4, and SCR1, maintains temperature of system within 1 F of set point.—F. W. Gutzwiller and E. K. Howell, Economy Power Semiconductor Applications, General Electric, Syracuse, N.Y., No. 671.1, 1965, p 11.

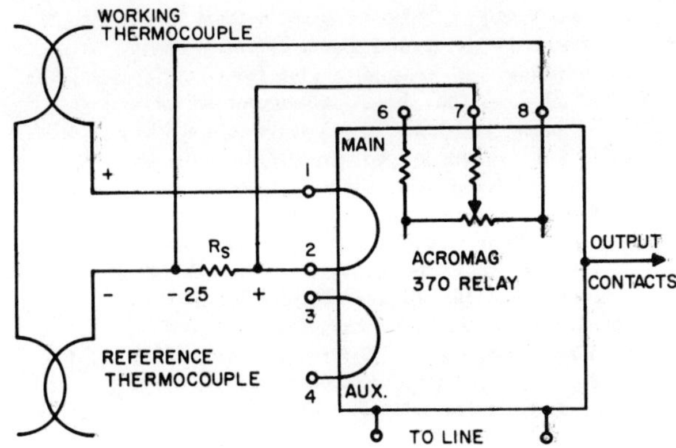

THERMOCOUPLE-DRIVEN CONTROLLER—Low-level solid-state relay serves as inexpensive trip control that responds to voltage difference between thermocouples in range of 0–50 mV. Arrangement is particularly useful when ambient temperature is fairly constant.—Microvolt DC Relay Makes Inexpensive Thermocouple Trip, *Electronic Design*, Nov. 29, 1965, p 81.

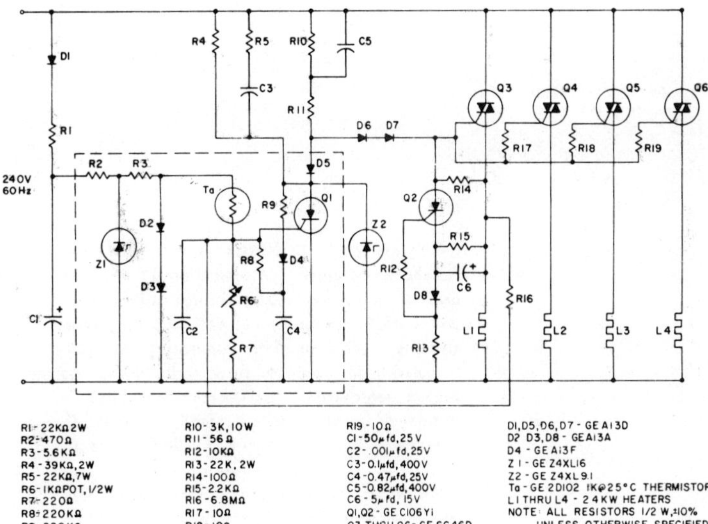

9.6-KW ZERO-VOLTAGE SWITCHING—Provides either proportional or on-off control of four 2.4-kW heaters, using master triac Q3 and three slaved triacs Q4-Q5-Q6. Control circuit, in dashed block, consisting of feedback element, reference, and error detector, has regulating accuracy of 0.5% of thermistor resistance for 10% variation in line voltage.—"SCR Manual," 4th Edition, General Electric, 1967, p 280–281.

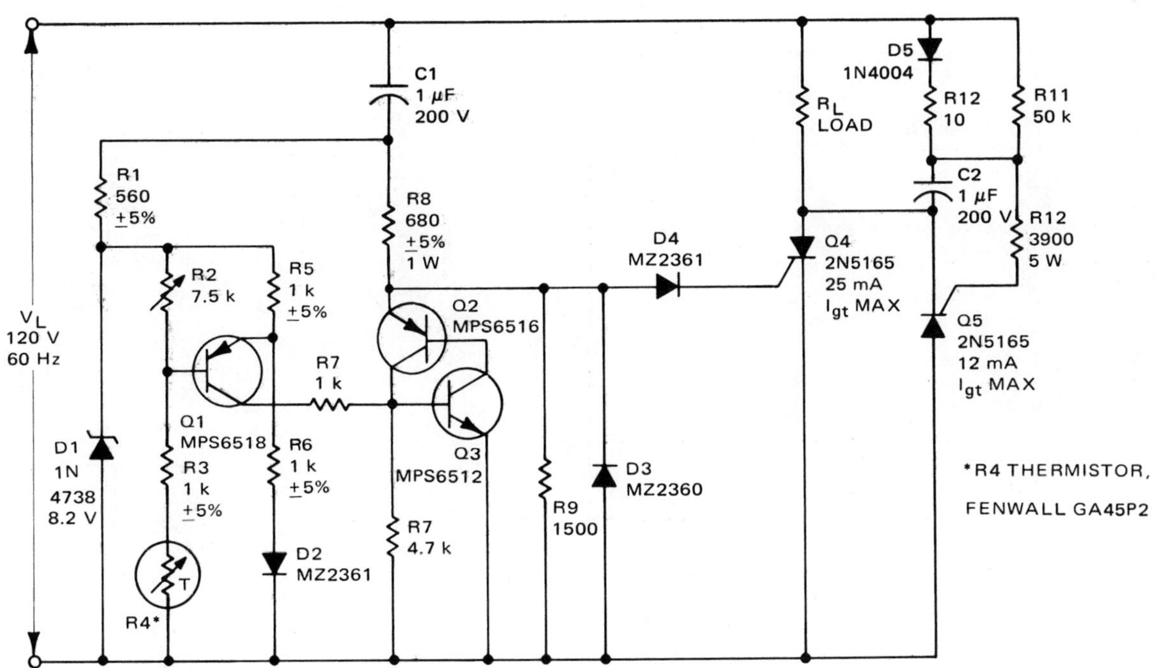

2-KW CONTROL WITH ZERO-POINT SWITCHING—Cycling rate is controlled by temperature, so it will overshoot slightly because of time lag between heat source, surface being controlled, and thermistor R4. Cycling rate can be made slow enough, such as once per minute, so it will not cause objectionable blinking of lights or changes in tv picture size when heater is switched on and off without proportional control.—"Semiconductor Power Circuits Handbook," Motorola, Phoenix, Ariz., 1968, p 6–11.

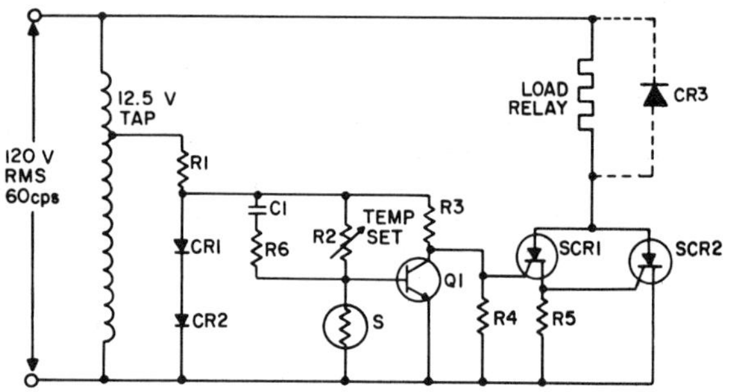

R1 - 28 OHMS, 4W
CR1 - CR2 - G.E. A13F - A14F
R2 - 250 OHM POT.
S - < 1 OHM THRU 100 OHMS
R3 - 1K
R4 - 1K
R6 - 1K
R5 - 1K
LOAD - 12 WATTS TESTED (RESISTIVE)

Q1 - G.E. 2N3390, 2N3391 OR LOWER GAIN TYPES SUCH AS 2N2925 OR 2N2711 SERIES.
SCR1 - G.E. C106B } C6B MAY BE SUBSTITUTED
SCR2 - G.E. C106B }

HALF-WAVE CONTROL WITH 1-OHM SENSOR—Uses pulse and pedestal zero-voltage switching, with sensors ranging from fraction of ohm to 100 ohms. Differential is 0.5% of sensor resistance at set temperature. C1 is not needed in this circuit, but may be required when using different type of transformer, to give some differentiation for more zero-voltage switching action. Circuit is best for resistive loads because it is not entirely free from rfi. Diode CR3 (A13B) is not needed if load is thermal relay.—J. L. Brookmire, Temperature Controls Incorporating Zero Voltage Switching, General Electric, Syracuse, N.Y., No. 200.45, 1966, p 5.

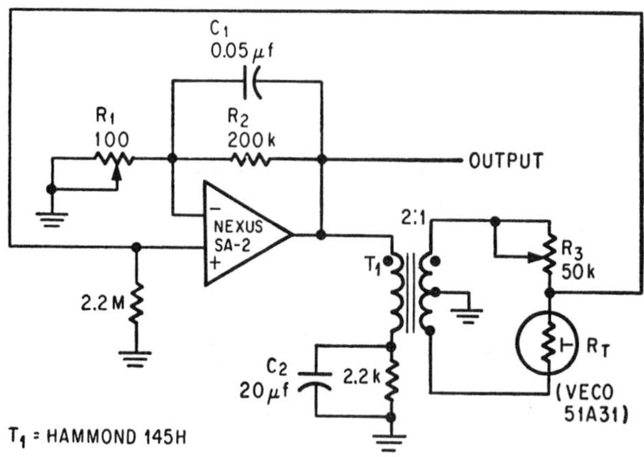

PROPORTIONAL CONTROL WITH OPAMP—Feedback between IC operational amplifier and temperature-sensing bridge gives proportional temperature control and long-term stability. With amplifier operating as 100-Hz oscillator, output power increases as sensed temperature decreases. Response is obtained to changes as small as 0.01 C. Thermistor used as sensor is 100K at 25 C. Article gives design equation.—H. D. Valliant, Exact Temperature Control With Operational Amplifier, *Electronics*, April 3, 1967, p 97–98.

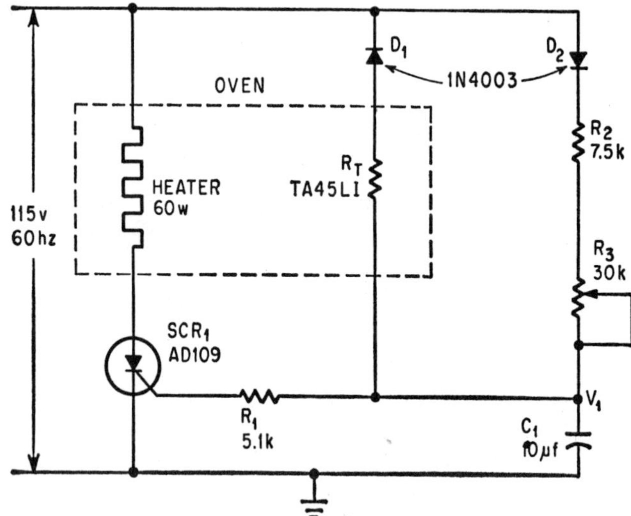

SCR OVEN CONTROL—Circuit varies charge on capacitor to control firing angle of scr. This, in turn, controls the time that current flows through heating coil, for regulation of oven temperature. Potentiometer R3 adjusts temperature control point.—D. E. La Plante, Scr Triggered by Capacitor Lowers Cost of Oven Control, *Electronics*, Nov. 28, 1966, p 83–84.

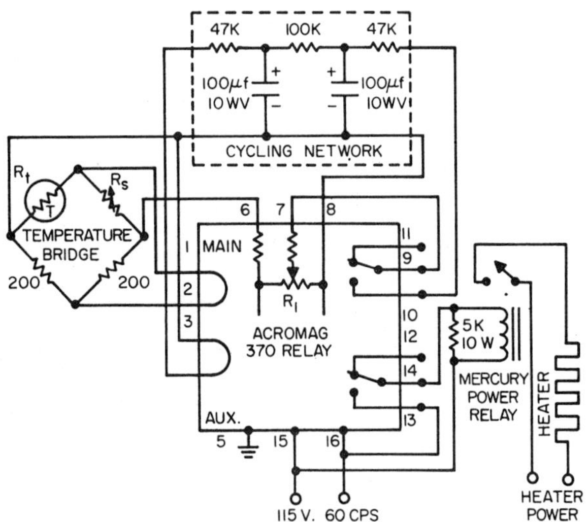

RESPONDS TO 0.02 C CHANGE—Bridge circuit feeding ultrasensitive solid-state relay serves as precision temperature controller for small oven. Rs is adjusted to equal thermistor resistance at desired set-point temperature, which is from 350 ohms at 50 C to 70 ohms at 100 C.—Ultrasensitive Relay Forms Precise Temperature Controller, *Electronic Design*, Nov. 29, 1965, p 76.

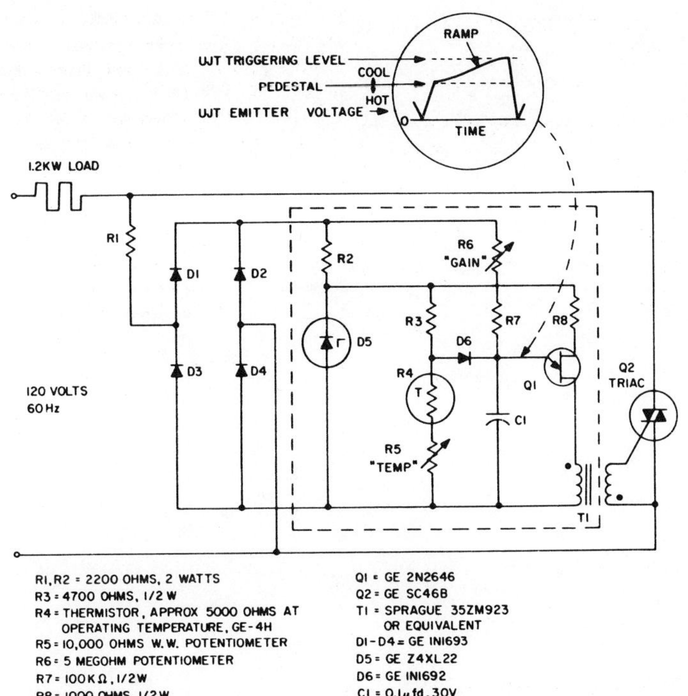

1.2-KW REGULATOR—Phase-controlled precision temperature regulator uses cosine-modified ramp-and-pedestal phase control. Triac supplies full-wave phase-controlled a-c power to heater load. Feedback-circuit thermistor R4 senses temperature for comparison with R5 reference signal in ujt error detector, to control turn-on of triac. Will control temperature to within 2% of thermistor resistance despite 10% variation in line voltage.—"SCR Manual," 4th Edition, General Electric, 1967, p 278–279.

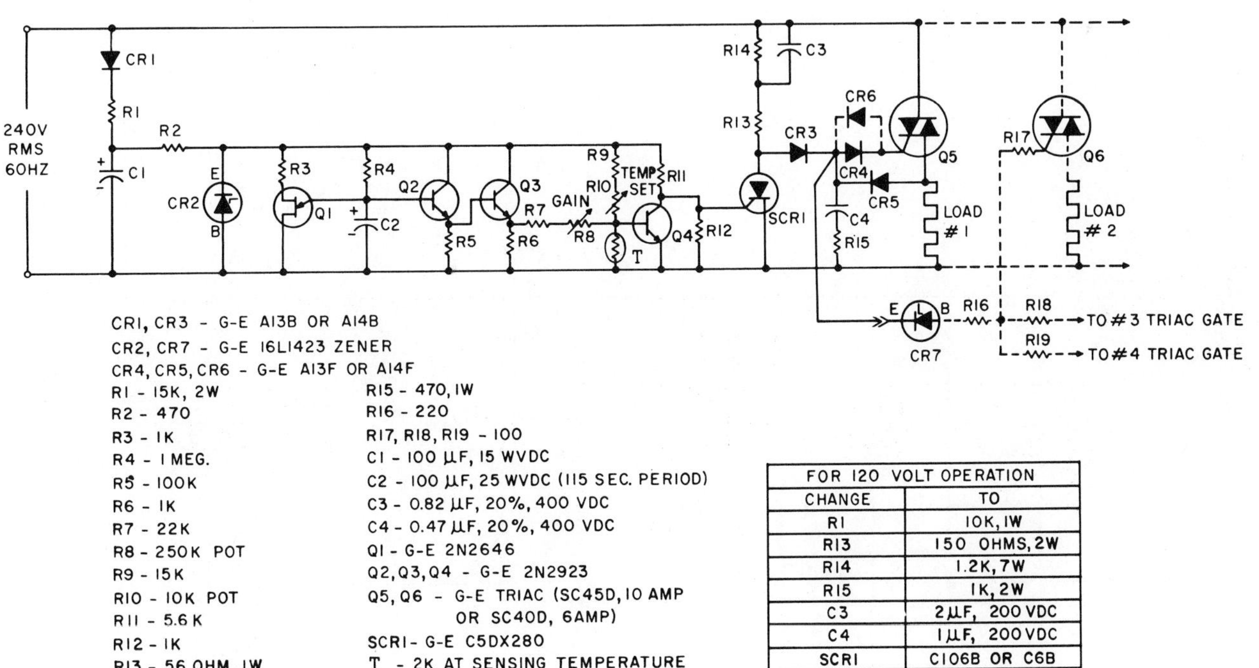

FOR 120 VOLT OPERATION	
CHANGE	TO
R1	10K, 1W
R13	150 OHMS, 2W
R14	1.2K, 7W
R15	1K, 2W
C3	2 μF, 200 VDC
C4	1 μF, 200 VDC
SCR1	C106B OR C6B
Q5, Q6	SC40B OR SC45B

PROPORTIONAL CONTROL WITH RFI SUPPRESSION—Precision control for convection baseboard heating systems and combined central air conditioning and electric heating systems has manually adjustable gain control. At low gain, spread is 21 F from full on to off for load power, and only 2 F for high gain. Load can be over 10 kW. Cycling period (ON plus OFF time) may be changed in steps from 1 to 115 s by changing value of C2; that shown is for 115 s. Circuit includes free-running sawtooth generator Q1-Q2-Q3 whose period of oscillation is determined by C2 and R4. Dashed lines show method of slave-driving additional triacs.—J. L. Brookmire, Proportional Zero Voltage Switching Temperature Control, General Electric, Syracuse, N.Y., No. 201.20, 1966.

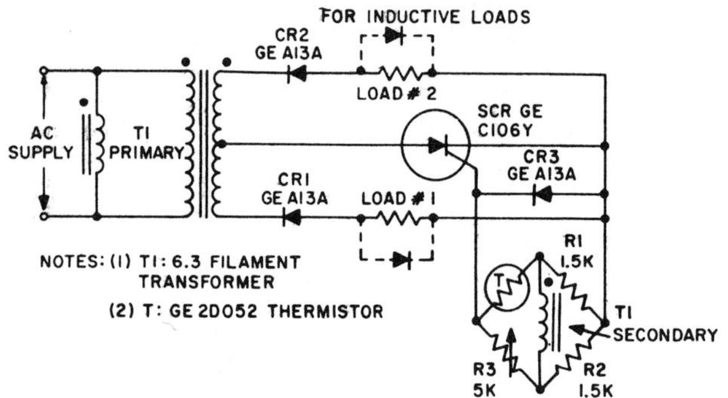

DUAL-OUTPUT MONITOR—Can be used to drive lamps or relays responding to both high and low temperatures. Secondary of T1 is connected inside bridge (lower right). When bridge is balanced, its a-c output is zero and scr receives no gate signal. If bridge is unbalanced by raising or lowering ambient temperature of thermistor T, a-c voltage will appear across gate-cathode of scr, in phase with a-c supply for load-1 current and 180 deg out of phase for load-2 current. Circuit responds to temperature changes of 1 to 2 C.—"SCR Manual," 4th Edition, General Electric, 1967, p 167–168.

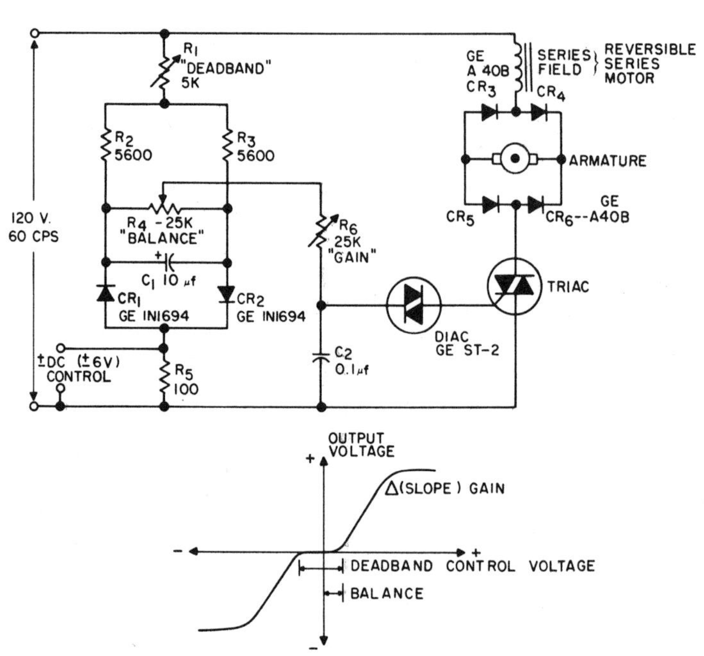

10-KW CLIMATE-CONTROLLED HEATER—When temperature drops below reference level determined by setting of 5K rheostat, left-hand 2N3417 transistor of differential input stage conducts more and turns on 2N3251 to give faster pulsing of 2N489 ujt. As a result, triac is triggered more often through output transistor and transformer, to increase heater load current.—D. Cooper, SCR's and Triacs—the Revolution Continues, *Electronics World*, Aug. 1968, p 25–28.

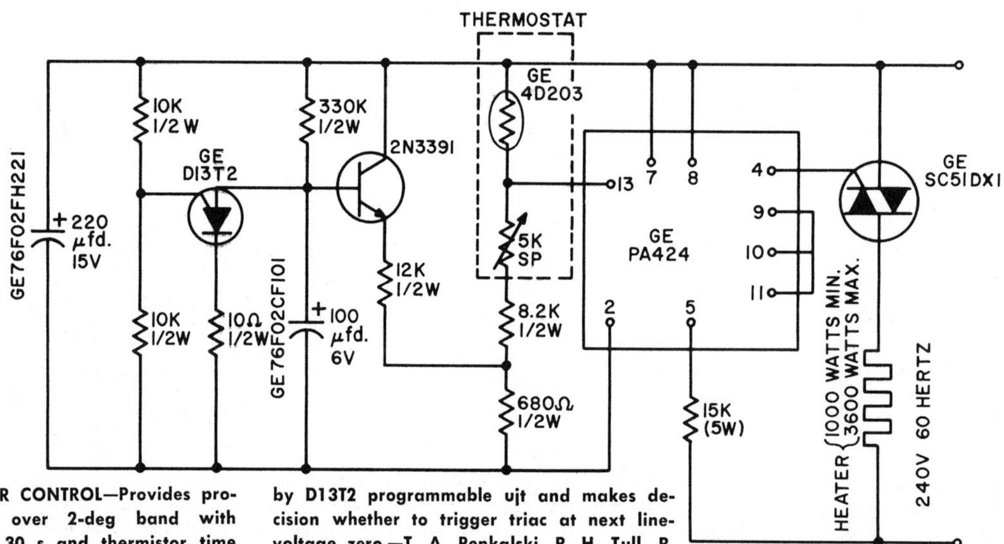

3,600-W IC HEATER CONTROL—Provides proportional control over 2-deg band with repetition rate of 30 s and thermistor time constant of 19 s. IC compares thermostat information with reference sawtooth generated by D13T2 programmable ujt and makes decision whether to trigger triac at next line-voltage zero.—T. A. Penkalski, R. H. Tull, R. C. Cape, Optimum Solid State Control Parameters for Improved Performance of In-Space Electric Heating Systems, General Electric, Syracuse, N.Y., No. 671.12, 1968, p 53.

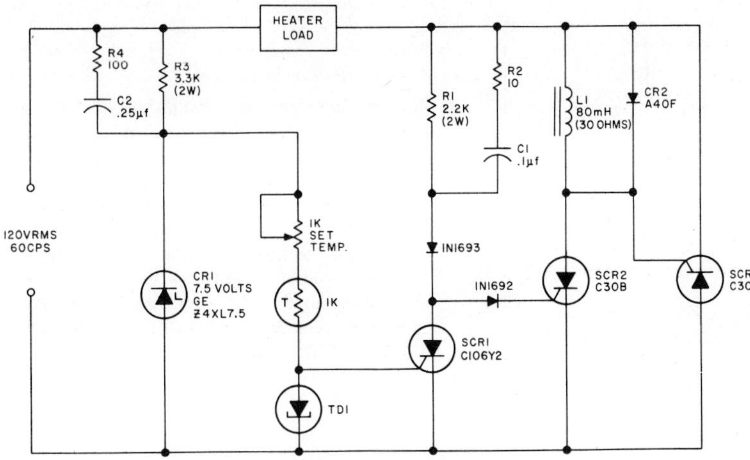

PRECISION 1.5-KW HEATER CONTROL—Will maintain load temperature within 1 F of set point. Thermistor should be about 1K at set point. Article describes circuit operation. —D. R. Grafham, Using Low Current SCR's, General Electric, Syracuse, N.Y., No. 200.19, 1967, p 34.

SHADED-POLE BLOWER MOTOR CONTROL—Arrangement shown is for heating applications requiring sophisticated ramp-and-pedestal system having high control gain, for shaded-pole or psc motors, in response to thermistor. When used to control cooling coil temperature of air conditioner to prevent freeze-up, R5 and R6 should be interchanged. Thermistor R6 should be somewhere between 3,000 and 5,000 ohms at temperature desired. R5 should be set to provide full-on control at desired upper temperature limit, and R3 then set for full-off or zero-speed condition at desired lower-temperature limit of R6. Circuit includes r-f noise suppression.—"SCR Manual," 4th Edition, General Electric, 1967, p 220–221.

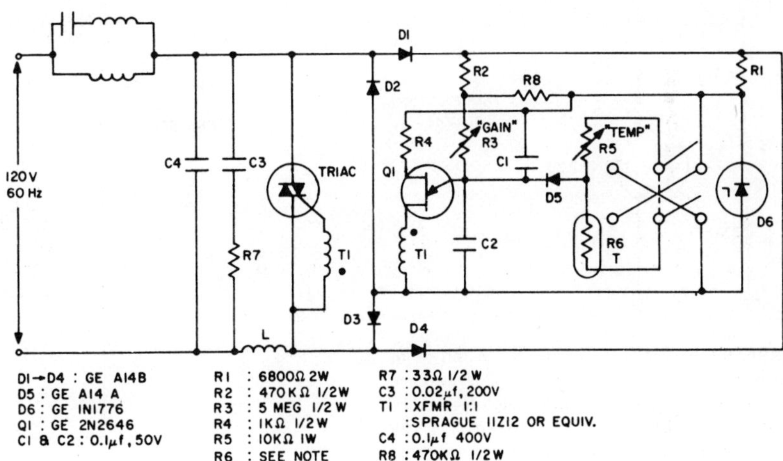

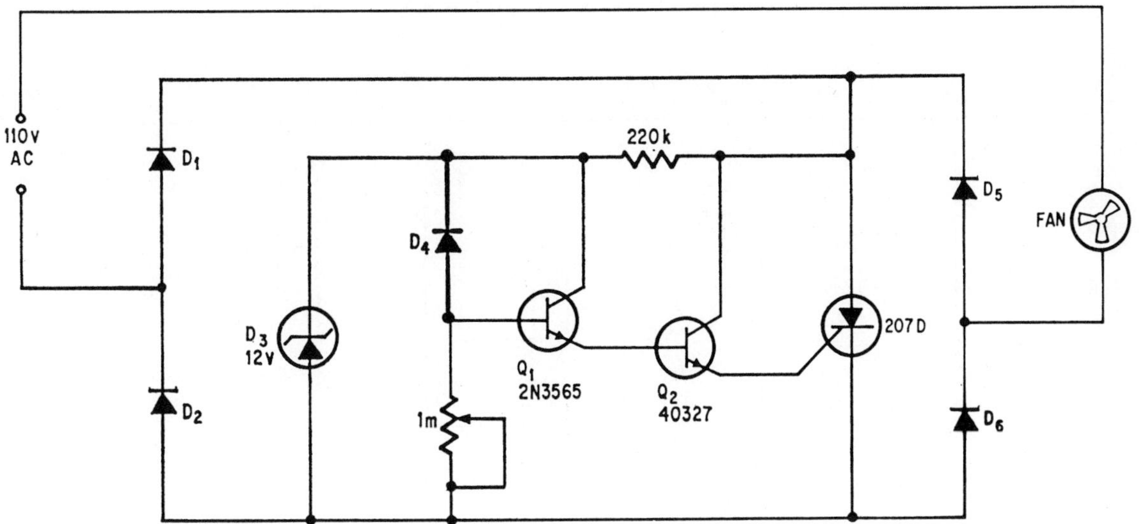

COOLING FAN CONTROL—Ordinary series-connected a-c fan in simple speed-control circuit holds temperature of condensed mercury in high-voltage thyratron within 0.5 C of constant temperature. Germanium diode D4, glued to outside of tube in condensed mercury region, serves as sensor. Temperature-dependent reverse current of diode, regulated by 1-meg pot, is amplified by Q1-Q2 to vary firing angle of scr and change speed of fan.—Y. Alon and M. Jonas, Diode Controls Speed of Fan That Cools a Thyratron, *Electronics*, Jan. 6, 1969, p 95.

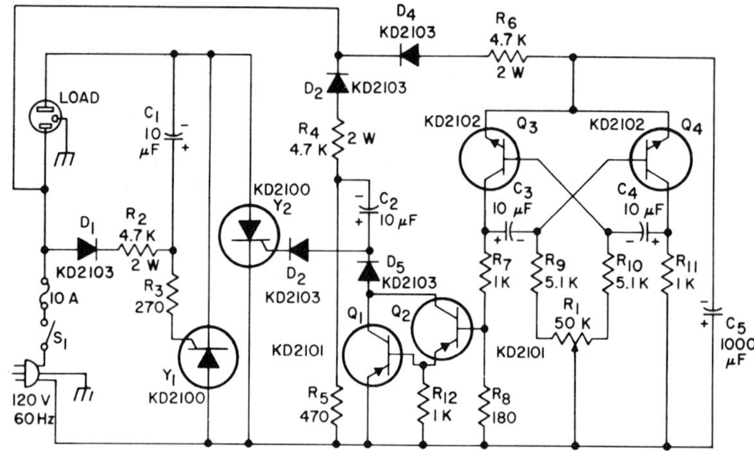

COFFEE WARMER—R1 is adjusted manually to give desired ratio of conducting to nonconducting time of load, over conduction range of 5 to 95%, with switching occurring only when input a-c voltage passes through zero point. Circuit is excellent for electric coffee pots, electric blankets, soldering irons, and other heater loads up to 1 kW. Does not produce rfi.—"Silicon Controlled Rectifier Experimenter's Manual," RCA, Harrison, N.J., 1967, p 130.

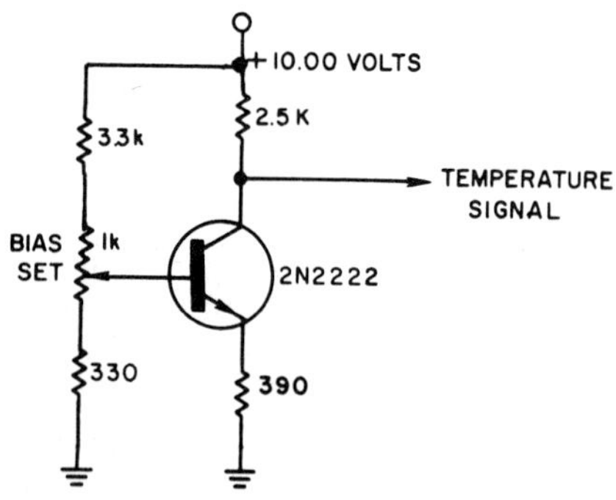

TRANSISTOR SENSOR—Single transistor, with collector connected to case for fast response to thermal changes, provides high-level output with linearity of 1% from −40 to +125 C.—J. M. Loe, Linear Temperature Sensor Uses Only a Single Transistor, *Electronic Design*, Feb. 15, 1970, p 86 and 88.

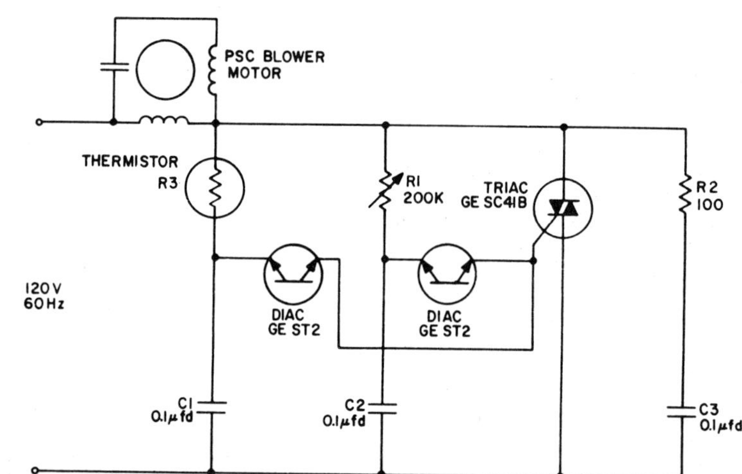

FURNACE BLOWER CONTROL—Thermistor R3 responds to changes in air temperature to control a-c power supplied to blower induction motor. R1 and its phase control network set minimum blower speed, to provide continuous air circulation and maintain lubrication of motor bearings.—"SCR Manual," 4th Edition, General Electric, 1967, p 219–220.

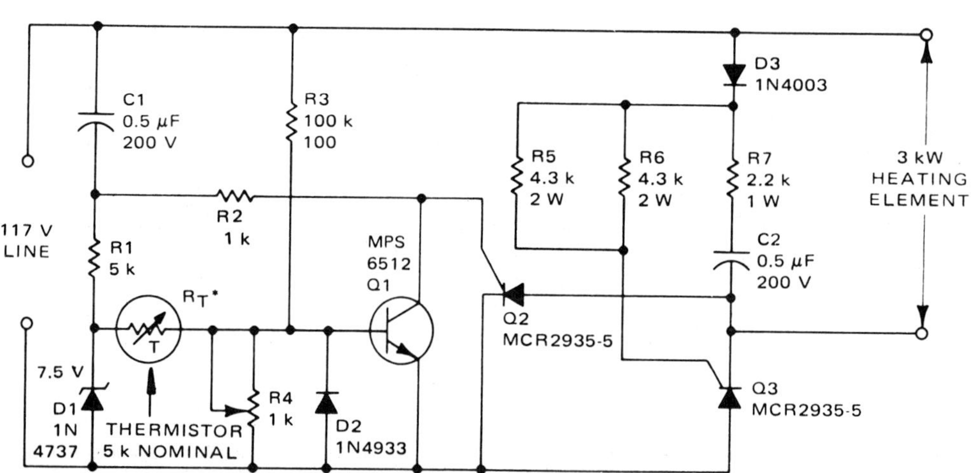

*Thermistor, 5 k nominal. Mount in proximity of heated area.

3-KW CONTROL WITH ZERO-POINT SWITCHING—Load switching is done only at zero point of a-c line voltage, to prevent electromagnetic interference. Power is applied to load in full cycles.—"Semiconductor Power Circuits Handbook," Motorola, Phoenix, Ariz., 1968, p 6–6.

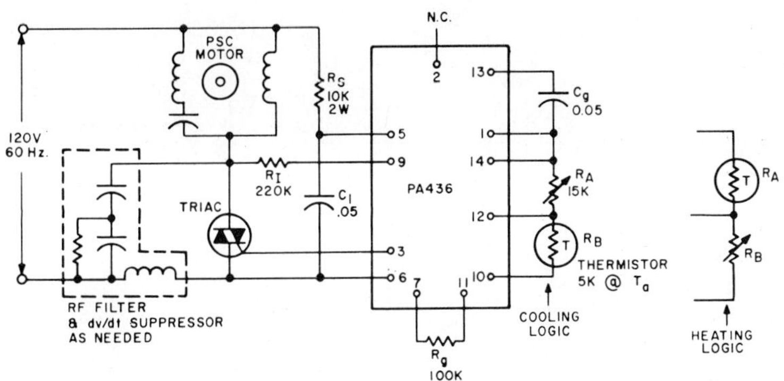

IC BLOWER CONTROL—Uses PA436 phase-control IC with triac to drive psc blower or fan motor. Cooling application is shown. For room-heating fan, thermistor and RA are reversed as at right so increase in temperature will reduce fan speed. Triac should match motor rating.—E. K. Howell, Applications of the PA436 Monolithic Integrated Phase-Control Trigger Circuit, General Electric, Syracuse, N.Y., No. 671.9, 1968, p 12.

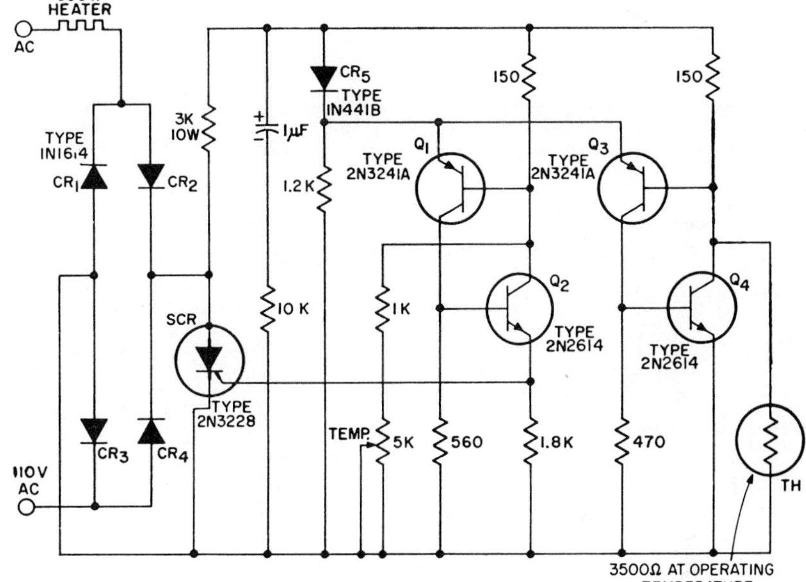

HALF-WAVE SCR 600-W HEATER CONTROL—Regulates temperature within 0.2 C, using single scr in rectifier bridge.—"Silicon Power Circuits Manual," RCA, Harrison, N.J., SP-51, p 254.

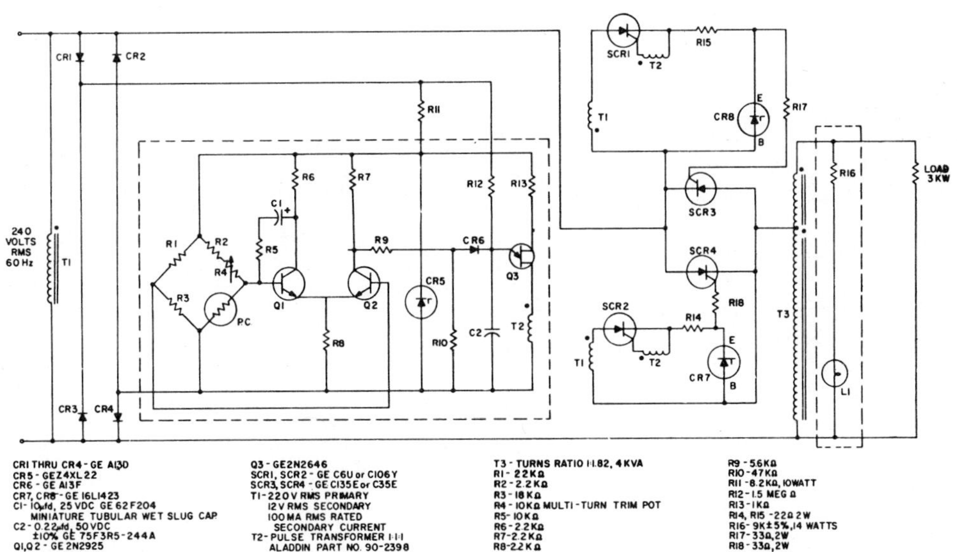

3-KW PHASE-CONTROLLED—Regulates rms value of unfiltered phase-controlled voltage across heater or other resistive load. Lamp in parallel with load, shining on photocell, provides required long averaging time constant. Stability against voltage and temperature variations is achieved with differential amplifier and ujt, ramp-and-pedestal phase-control, and ujt working with scr's.—"SCR Manual," 4th Edition, General Electric, 1967, p 282–283.

HIGH-GAIN IC PROPORTIONAL CONTROL—Uses PA424 IC zero-voltage switching trigger fed by thermistor in external circuit that provides narrow, adjustable proportional band that makes heater power proportional to error of measured temperature from set point. SC50B (triac) and 15-A heater load are connected between a-c lines 1 and 2, with triac gate going to terminal 4 (not shown) of IC. Gives precise and stable control of temperature. Article describes circuit operation in detail.—E. K. Howell, Integrated Circuits for Sophisticated, Low Cost AC Power Control, General Electric, Syracuse, N.Y., No. 671.9, 1968, p 23.

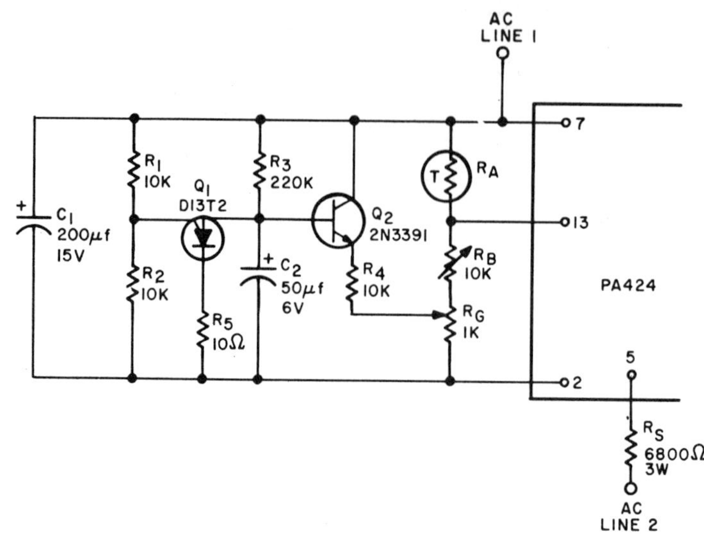

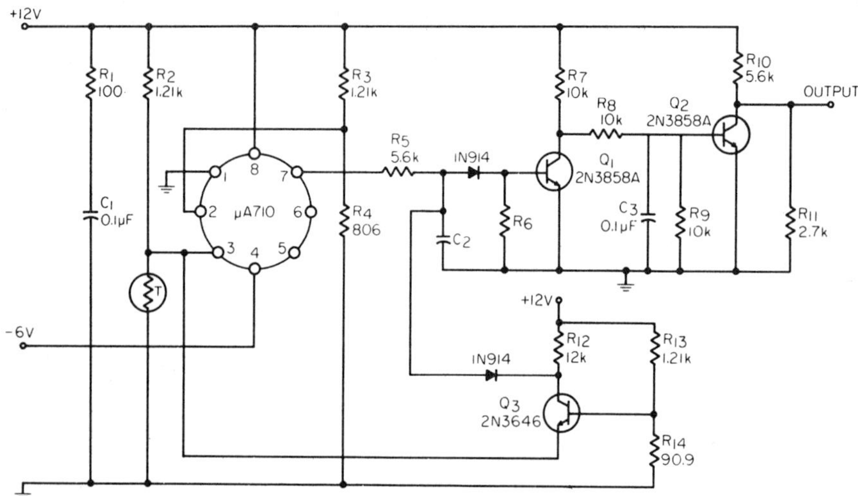

FAIL-SAFE THERMOMETER—Circuit delivers output pulse conventionally when temperature at PTC thermistor T reaches predetermined critical value, and in addition gives output pulse if thermistor opens or shorts. In either case, output pulse shuts down associated industrial control system. Circuit is capable of distinguishing between shorted thermistor and one having 30 ohms resistance. IC operates as differential comparator. —G. J. Granieri, Fail-Safe Temperature Sensor, *EEE*, Sept. 1967, p 132–133.

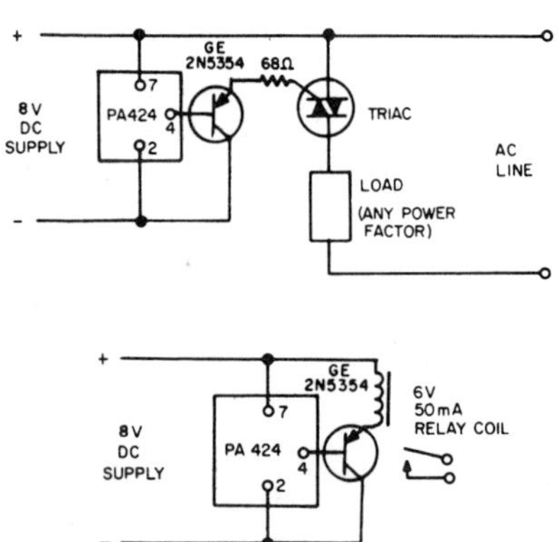

IC ZERO-VOLTAGE SWITCH—Can be used for temperature control, driving relay from 8-V d-c source. For larger loads, transistor can be used to trigger triac. Integrated circuit here acts as combination threshold detector and trigger circuit. Applications include photoelectric and heater control.—Integrated Circuit Zero Voltage Switch PA424, General Electric, Syracuse, N.Y., No. 85.21, 3/69.

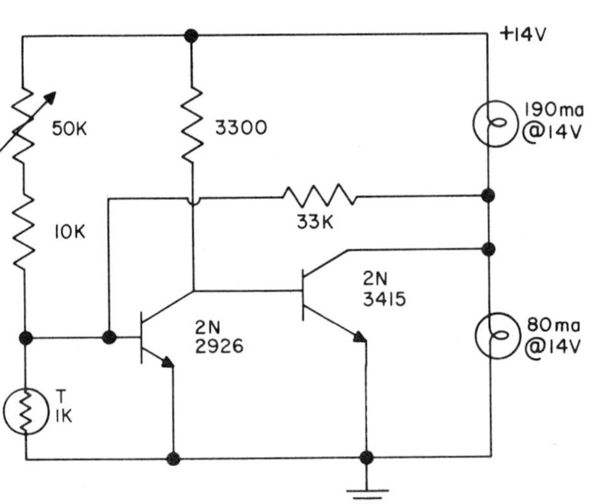

AIR-CONDITIONER MONITOR—Bottom lamp is on at low temperatures, and top lamp when temperature rises above set point. Cost of all parts required is under $1.—R. M. Muth, Digital Circuits with Visual Readouts, General Electric, Syracuse, N.Y., No. 671.3, 1966, p 9.

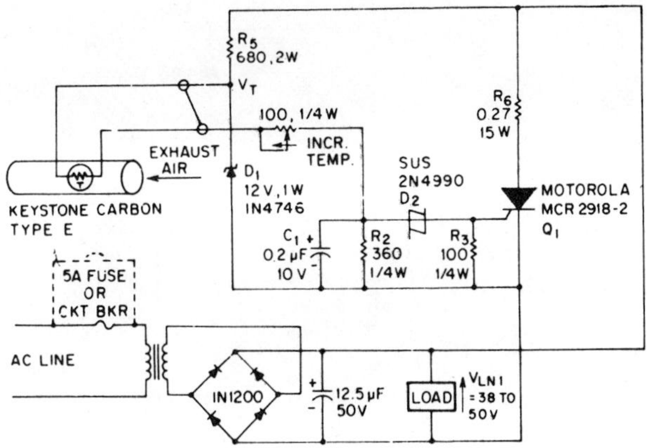

AIR TEMPERATURE AND VELOCITY—Used to sense overheating of power supply. If ambient temperature exceeds predetermined limit for combination of exhaust air or if forced air cooling supply fails, scr fires and blows fuse or opens circuit breaker.—H. Green, Thermistor Circuit Senses Air Temperature and Velocity, *EEE*, March 1969, p 124 and 126.

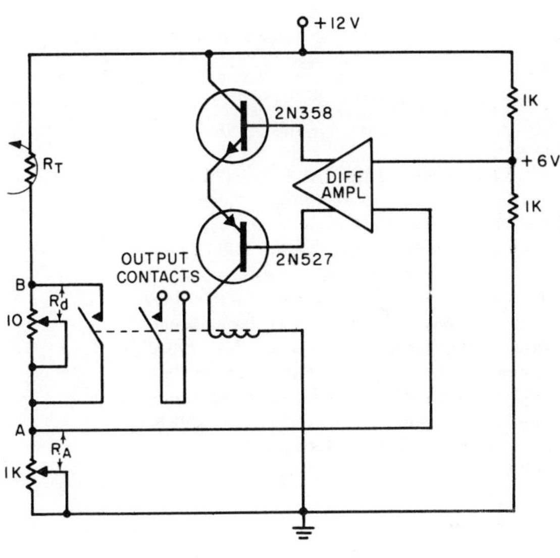

ADJUSTABLE DEAD ZONE—Uses IC differential amplifier in bridge with two transistors for on-off temperature control having excellent stability at set value. Voltage gain of IC should be above 20,000, and output impedance about 1K. Stability can be improved still more by using platinum resistance thermometer in place of temperature-sensitive resistor RT. Rd sets dead zone.—L. R. Long, Adjustable Dead Zone Improves Temperature-Controller Stability, *Electronic Design*, July 6, 1964, p 52.

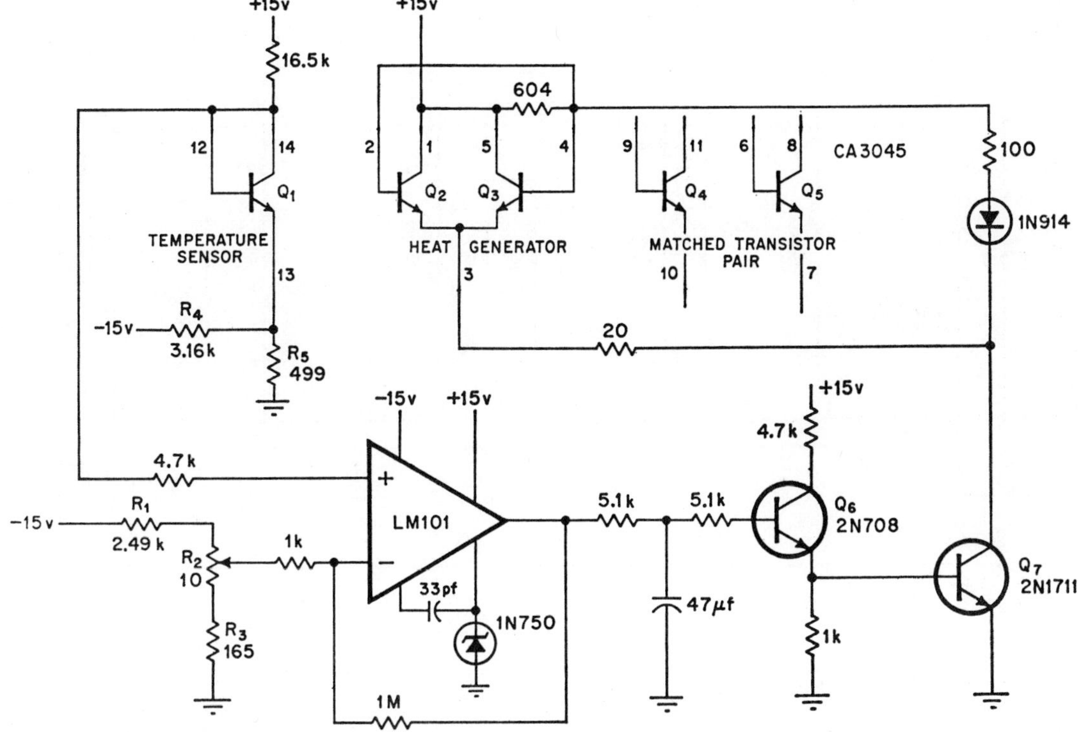

SUBSTRATE TEMPERATURE CONTROL—Q1 serves as temperature sensor and Q2-Q3 as heater for holding Q4-Q5 at desired ambient temperature to hold input offset voltage of matched pair below 5 mV over 300-MHz bandwidth.—D. P. DeAngelis and M. Palumbo, Regulator Holds Temperature of Chip's Substrate Constant, *Electronics*, Feb. 2, 1970, p 100.

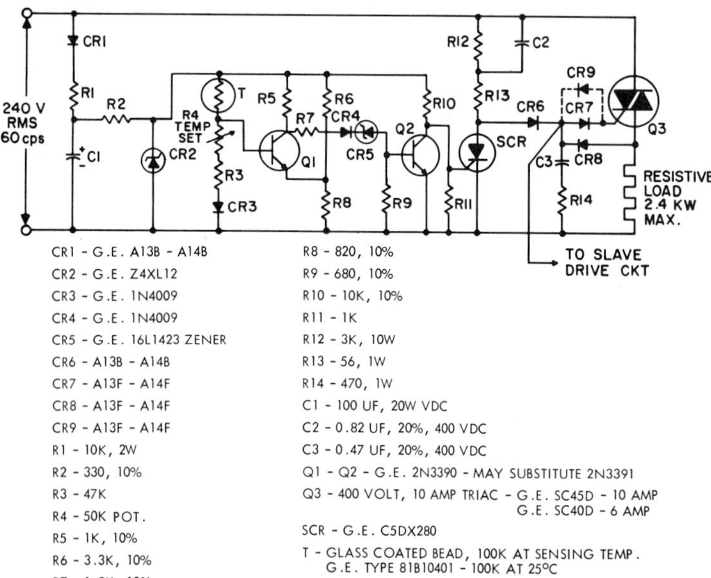

HIGH-PRECISION FULL-WAVE SEMIPROPORTIONAL—Provides zero-voltage switching. May be used to slave-drive additional triac-load combinations each having all components at right of R11. CR9 may be omitted if only one triac is being driven. Differential is 0.1 F above and below set temperature. Article gives changes required for 120-V operation, at which differential is better than twice as good.—J. L. Brookmire, Temperature Controls Incorporating Zero Voltage Switching, General Electric, Syracuse, N.Y., No. 200.45, 1966, p 6.

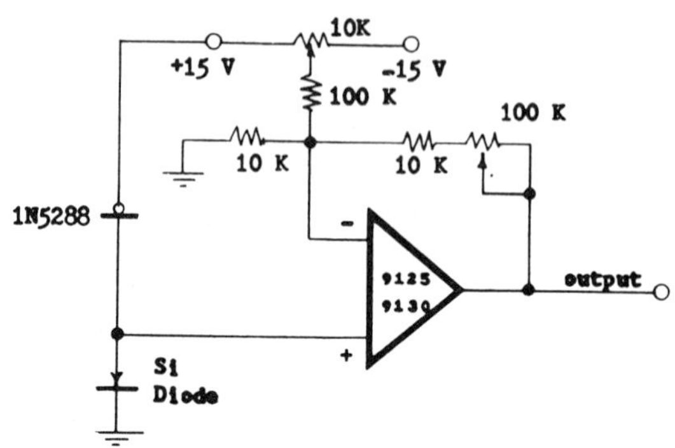

INDUSTRIAL THERMOMETER—Temperature-sensing silicon junction diode, driven by 1N5288 current-limiting diode giving true constant-current operation, drives panel meter through OEI Model 9125 opamp. Sensing diode should be on probe using shielded cable. Temperature coefficient of diode is −1.5 to −2 mV per deg C, which remains constant over wide range of temperatures. Can be calibrated in water-ice slurry and in boiling water.—Two Electronic Thermometers for Medical/Industrial Use, Optical Electronics, Tucson, Ariz., No. 10075.

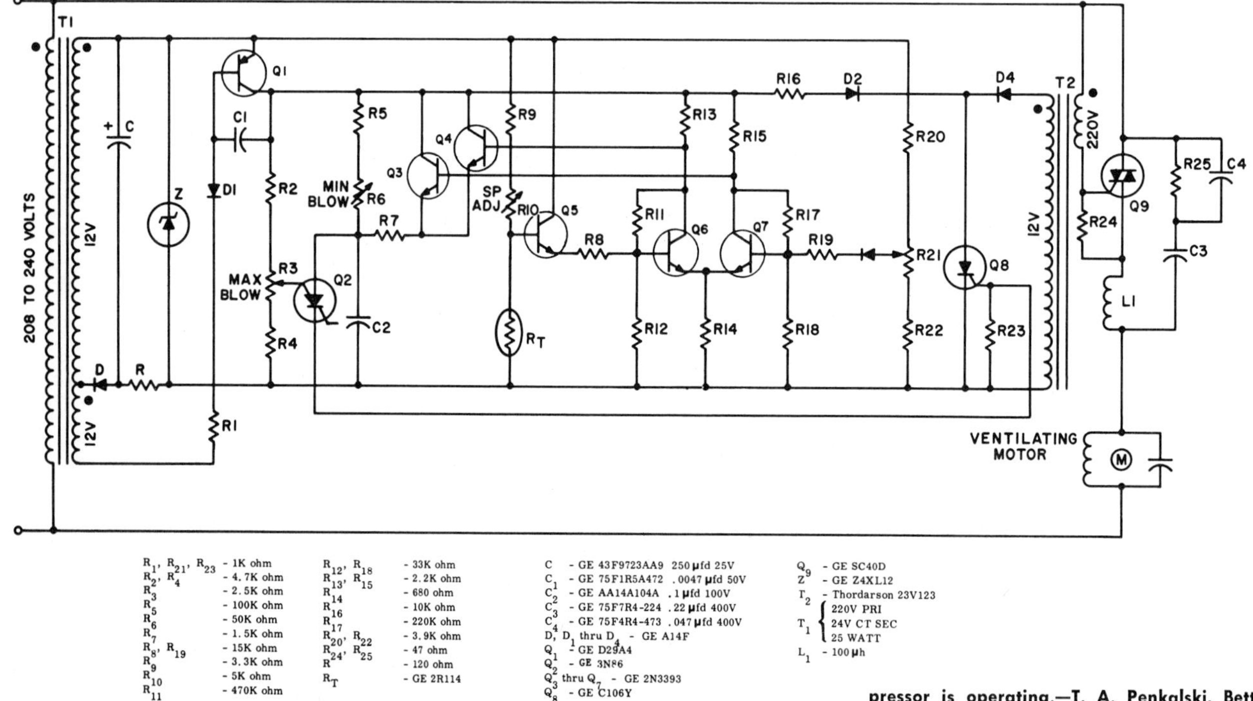

BLOWER CONTROL—Provides proportional motor speed control with rfi suppression circuit. Blower speed is increased for temperature deviations either above or below set point, because central control determines independently whether heater or cooling compressor is operating.—T. A. Penkalski, Better Room Conditioning via Solid State Controls, General Electric, Syracuse, N.Y., No. 200.51, 1967, p 10.

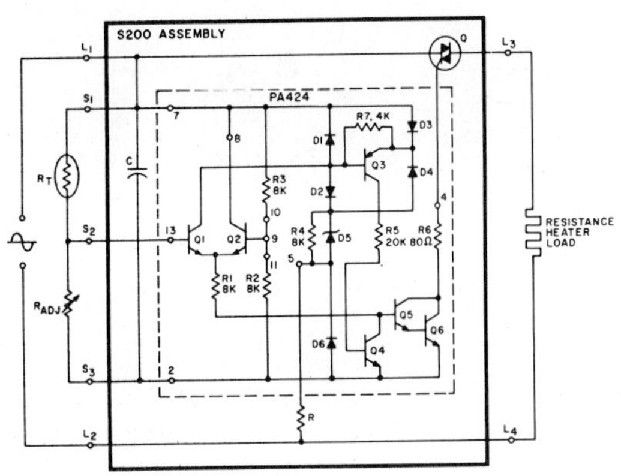

IC ZERO-VOLTAGE SWITCH—Gives on-off control of heater load with only 0.2 F differential when used with solid-state thermostat consisting of thermistor RT and set-point potentiometer in series. Triac Q turns off at end of each half-cycle and removes power from heater, to provide zero-voltage switching of heater. With appropriate triac rating, IC can control heater loads from 500 to 4,150 W on supply voltages up to 277 V a-c.—T. A. Penkalski, Better Room Conditioning via Solid State Controls, General Electric, Syracuse, N.Y., No. 200.51, 1967, p 4.

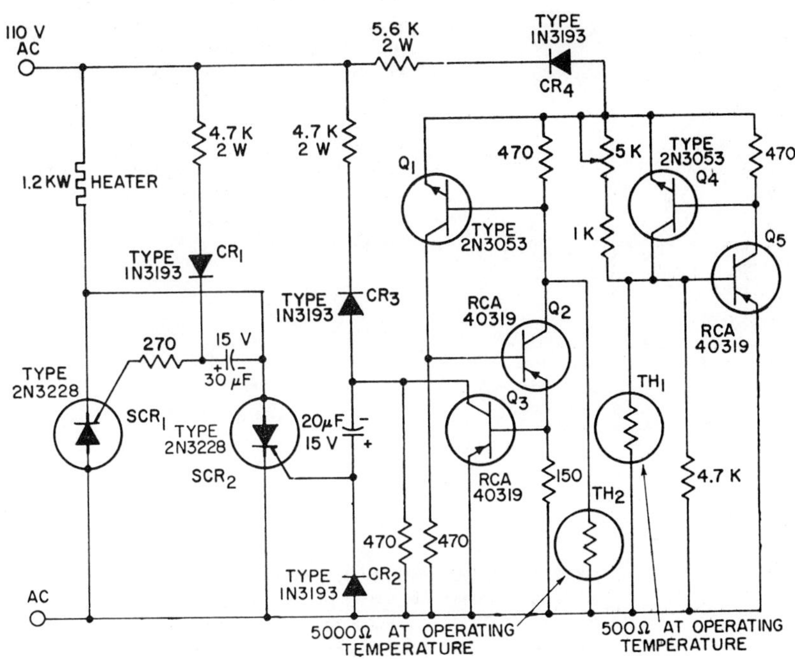

FULL-WAVE 1.2-KW ZERO-SWITCHING—Uses anticipation-type control with two thermistors as sensors. Book describes operation in detail.—"Silicon Power Circuits Manual," RCA, Harrison, N.J., SP-51, p 255.

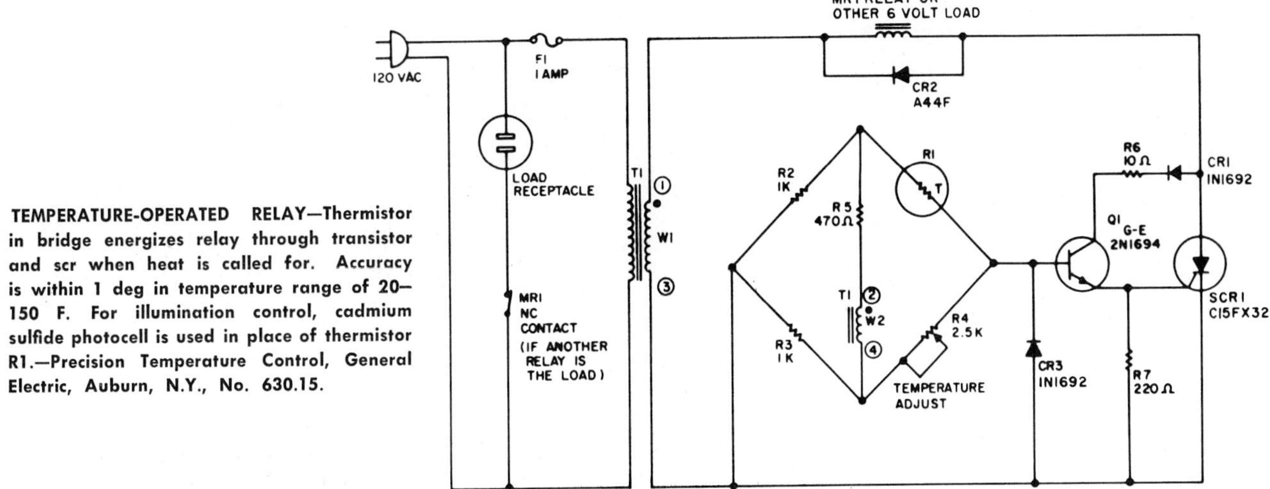

TEMPERATURE-OPERATED RELAY—Thermistor in bridge energizes relay through transistor and scr when heat is called for. Accuracy is within 1 deg in temperature range of 20–150 F. For illumination control, cadmium sulfide photocell is used in place of thermistor R1.—Precision Temperature Control, General Electric, Auburn, N.Y., No. 630.15.

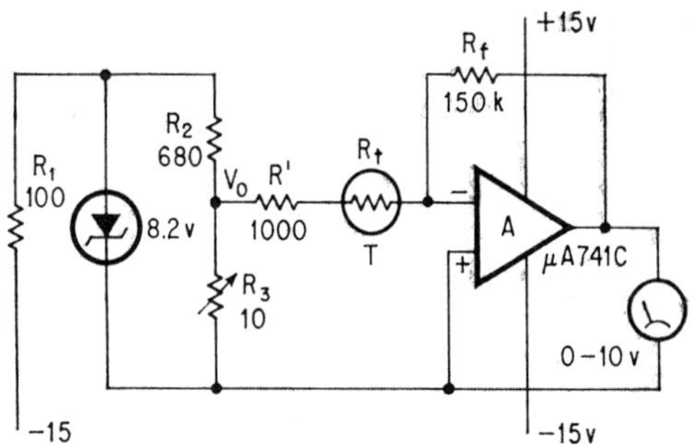

CORRECTING THERMISTOR LINEARITY—Combining opamp and zener with thermistor boosts output voltage 150 times without exceeding submilliwatt rating of thermistor, and makes output voltage true linear function of temperature over range of −20 C to 70 C if R' is made equal to thermistor resistance at center of desired temperature range. R3 is adjusted so Vo is −0.067 V.—J. M. Nemchik and R. J. Fritsch, Circuit Improves Thermistor's Linearity and Boosts Output, *Electronics*, June 9, 1969, p 99–100.

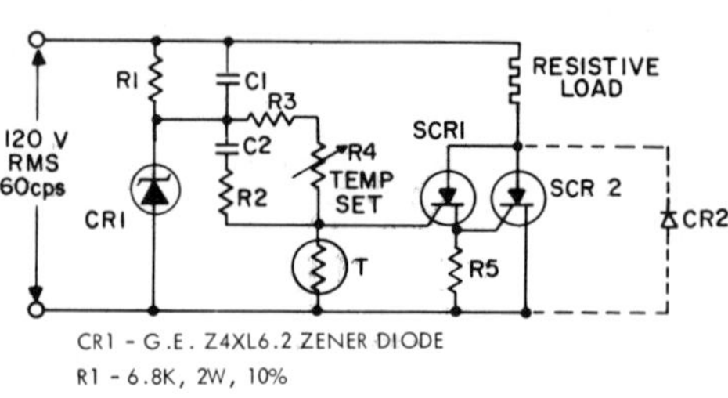

CR1 - G.E. Z4XL6.2 ZENER DIODE
R1 - 6.8K, 2W, 10%
C1 - 0.22 UF, 10%, 200 VDC
C2 - 0.33 UF, 10%, 10 VDC
R2 - 4.7K,
(R3 - R4) - TOTAL RESISTANCE ≈ 1.25K
SCR1 - G.E. C106B OR G.E. C6B
R5 - 100 OHMS
SCR 2 - G.E. C20B
T - 100 OHM THERMISTOR AT SENSING TEMPERATURE. CAN BE GLASS COATED BEAD OR HIGHER DISSIPATION TYPES. MAY USE G.E. TYPE 3D054 (100 OHMS@25°C).

HALF-WAVE CONTROL—Uses pulse and pedestal zero-voltage switching. Voltage is applied to load for all of each negative half-cycle, while positive half-cycles are switched on and off in semiproportional manner as called for by thermistor T. Sensing differential is 0.25 F above and below set point. Zero-voltage switching action eliminates need for rfi filtering.—J. L. Brookmire, Temperature Controls Incorporating Zero Voltage Switching, General Electric, Syracuse, N.Y., No. 200.45, 1966, p 4.

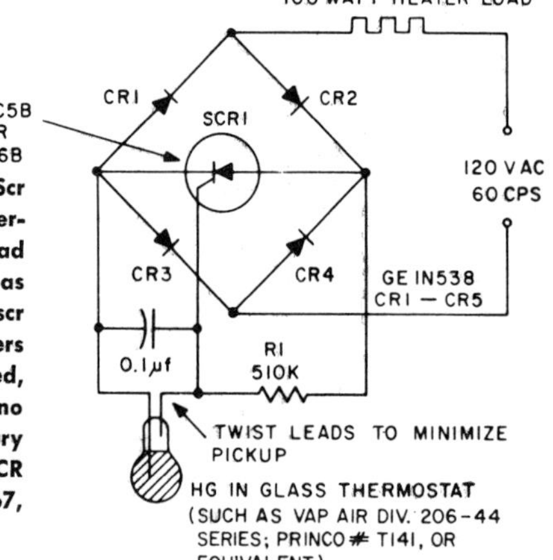

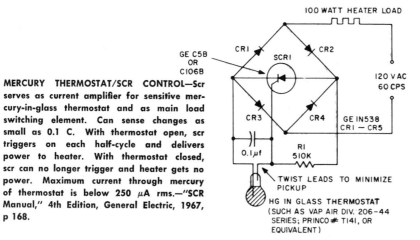

MERCURY THERMOSTAT/SCR CONTROL—Scr serves as current amplifier for sensitive mercury-in-glass thermostat and as main load switching element. Can sense changes as small as 0.1 C. With thermostat open, scr triggers on each half-cycle and delivers power to heater. With thermostat closed, scr can no longer trigger and heater gets no power. Maximum current through mercury of thermostat is below 250 μA rms.—"SCR Manual," 4th Edition, General Electric, 1967, p 168.

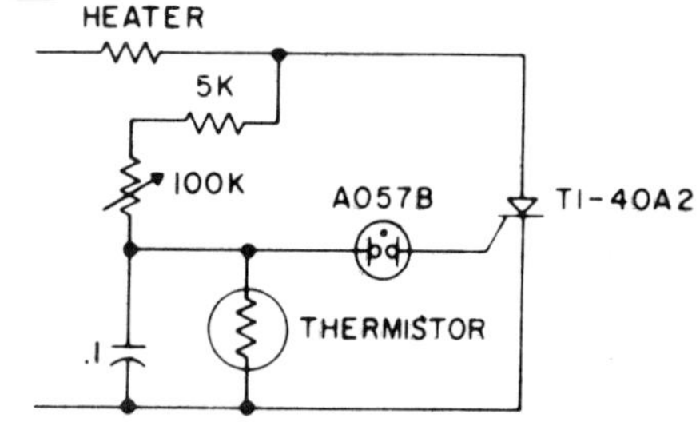

NEON-TRIGGERED SCR—High-resistance thermistor determines amount of power delivered to heater. Desired temperature is set with 100K pot.—E. Bauman, "Applications of Neon Lamps and Gas Discharge Tubes," Signalite, Neptune, N.J., p 124.

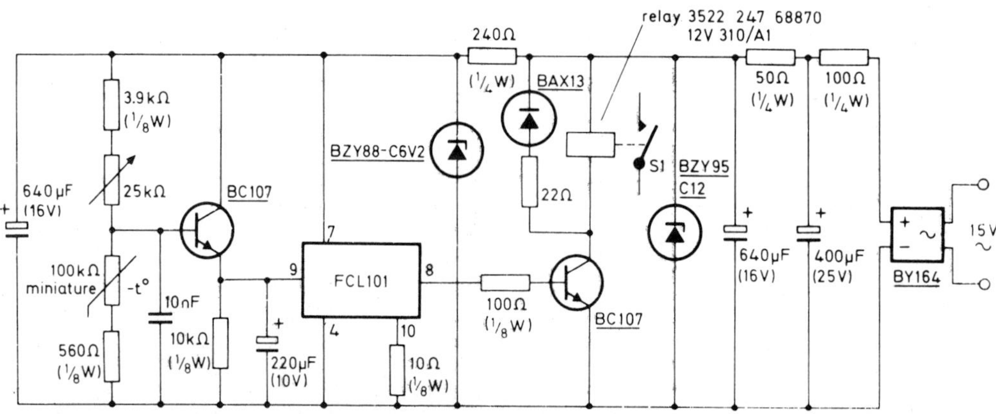

100–300 C PRECISION ON-OFF CONTROL—Although electrical precision with thermistor sensor and FCL101 IC level detector is better than 0.5 deg C, actual overall precision depends on thermal time constant of object being heated, and is generally about 2 deg C for range covered.—Triacs—Operation and Use, Philips, Pub. Dept., Elcoma Div., Eindhoven, The Netherlands, No. 17, 1969.

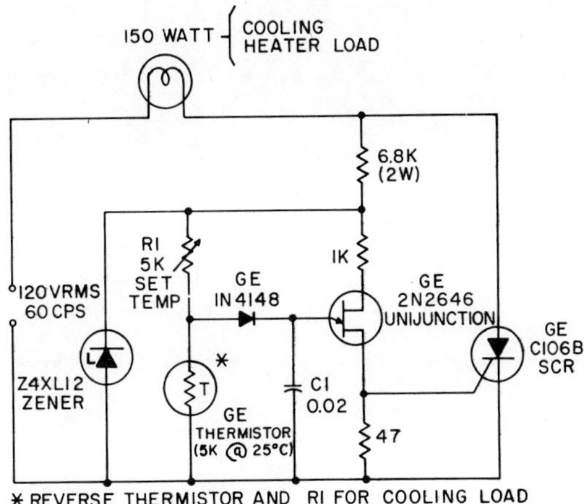

PHOTODEVELOPER HEATER CONTROL—Ujt-scr circuit varies power steplessly to 150-W heater in response to thermistor in liquid bath.—D. R. Grafham, Precision Temperature Controller, General Electric, Syracuse, N.Y., No. 201.9, 1965.

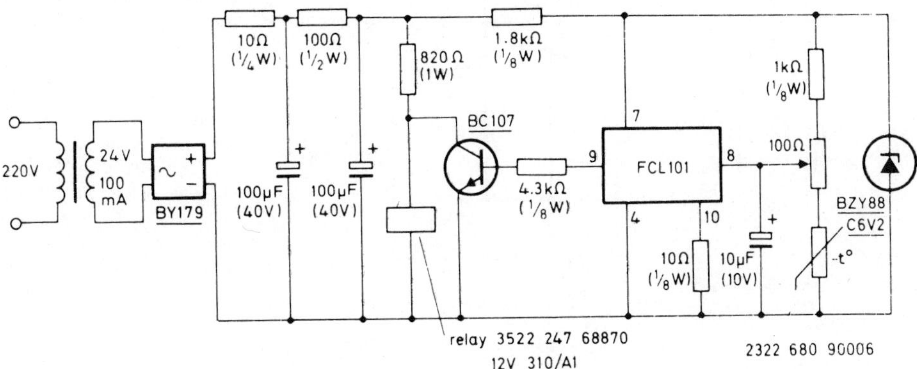

ON-OFF TRIAC TRIGGERING CONTROL—Suitable for range of 30 to 45 deg C. Uses thermistor with positive temperature coefficient of resistance, to actuate relay through FCL101 level detector and transistor.—Triacs—Operation and Use, Philips, Pub. Dept., Elcoma Div., Eindhoven, The Netherlands, No. 17, 1969.

NOTE: To locate additional circuits in the category of this chapter, use the index at the back of this book. Check also the author's "Sourcebook of Electronic Circuits," published by McGraw-Hill in 1968.

CHAPTER 88
Test Circuits

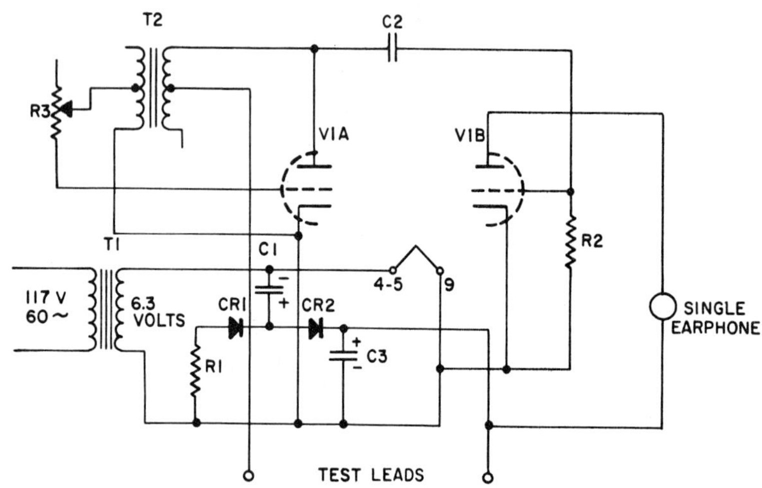

6-V VERSION OF CONTINUITY TESTER—Produces tone in earphone when continuity exists between points in circuit to which test leads are touched. Reversing test leads will tell whether path contains electrolytic, because for one polarity tone will die away in few seconds; for resistive path, tone is same loudness for both polarities. Tone changes with resistance of measured path, giving rough indication of amount of resistance; measuring assortment of known resistance values will show how tone changes. Parts values are not critical: C1 and C3 25 μF; C2 0.005 μF; CR1-CR2 1N34AS; R1 150; R2 470K; R3 250K; T1 6.3 V 0.3 A filament transformer; T2 any audio interstage transformer; V1 almost any twin-triode such as 12AX7, 12AT7, or 12AU7.—"Hobby Manual," General Electric, Owensboro, Ky., 1965, p 175.

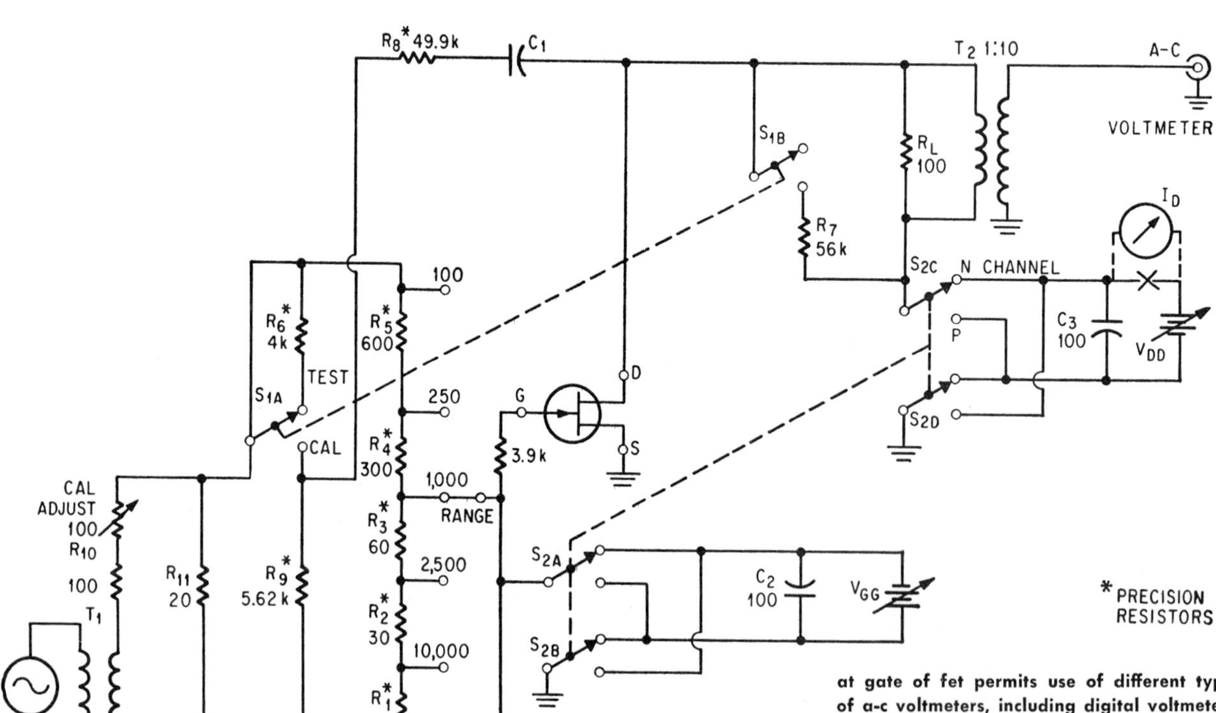

FET TESTER—Measures broad range of transconductance values, even under abnormal bias conditions. Automatically compensates for most sources of errors. Range switch at gate of fet permits use of different types of a-c voltmeters, including digital voltmeters, for reading transconductance values. Article gives design equations and detailed calibration and test procedures.—C. D. Todd, Taking the Measure of FET Transconductance, *Electronics*, April 3, 1967, p 88–92.

SCR-TRANSISTOR TESTER—Simple circuit turns on lower DEVICE S/C lamp to indicate that solid-state device under test is short-circuited. Good device turns on only upper lamp. Other fault conditions turn both lamps on or leave both off. Practically any junction diodes can be used in test circuit. Not recommended for devices having less than 12 V collector-base voltage, peak collector current less than 100 mA, or dissipation below 50 mW.—D. Wadsworth, Go/No-Go Tester Checks SCRs, NPN and PNP Transistors, *Electronic Design*, June 6, 1968, p 112.

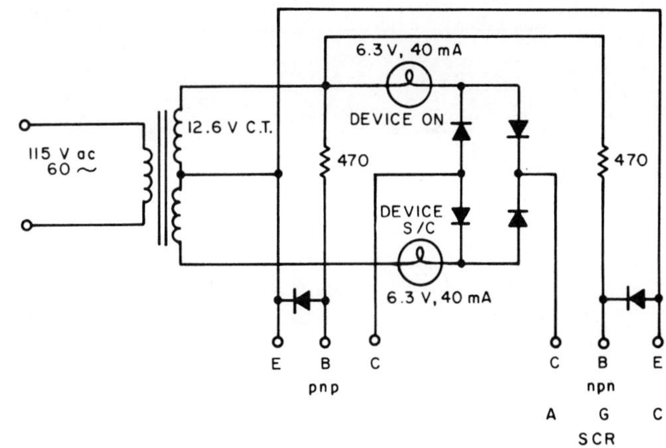

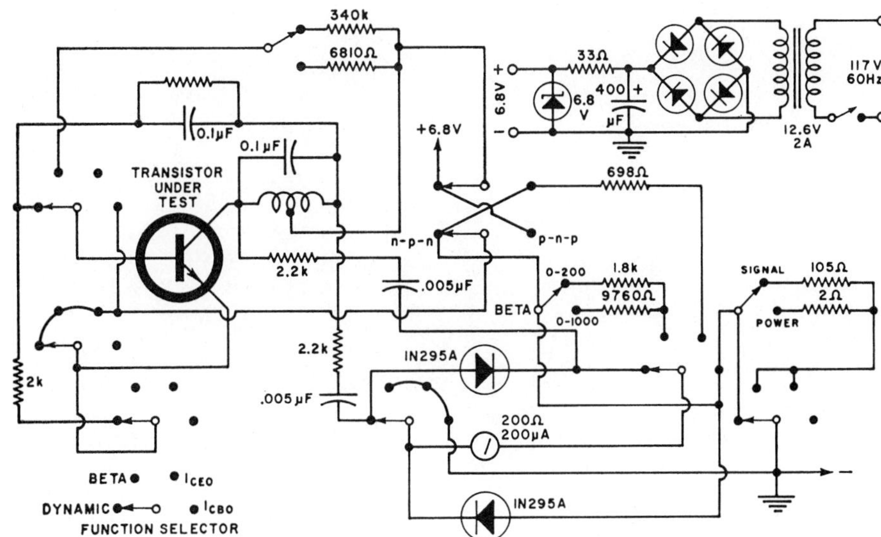

TRANSISTOR ANALYZER—Checks both power and signal transistors without removal from circuits. Identifies npn or pnp, as well as lead connections. Reads d-c gain directly. Measures collector-emitter and collector-base leakage currents.—Seco Model 260 Transistor Analyzer, *Electronics World*, Oct. 1967, p 76–77.

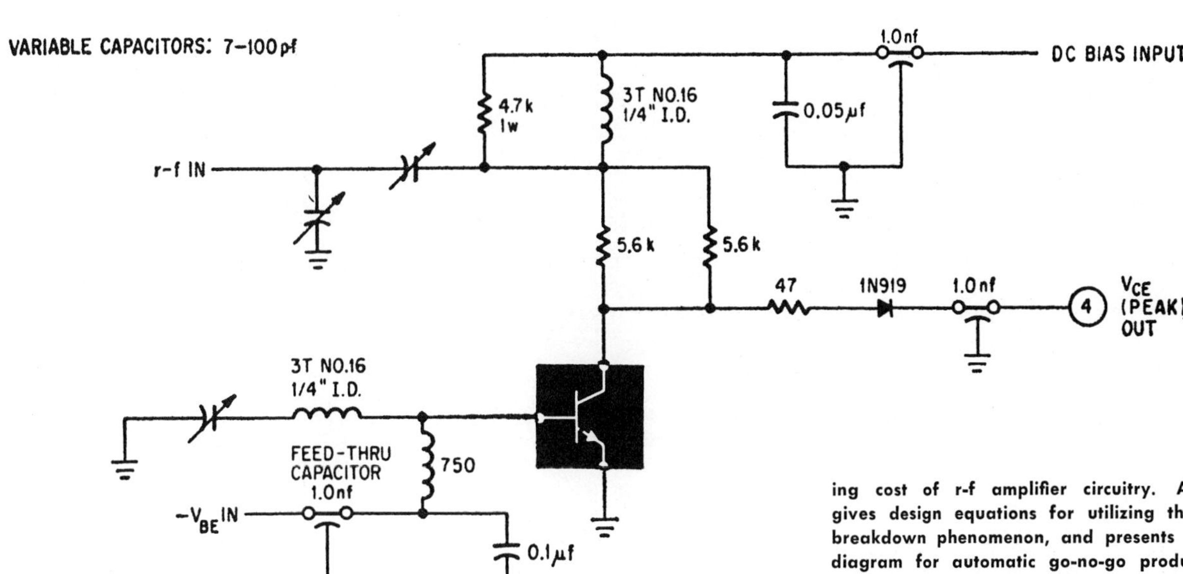

TRANSISTOR R-F BREAKDOWN TEST—Measures r-f breakdown voltage while transistor is operated above its specified alpha-cutoff frequency, using sine-wave r-f input. Once limit of transistor is determined, it can be operated at much higher frequencies, lowering cost of r-f amplifier circuitry. Article gives design equations for utilizing this r-f breakdown phenomenon, and presents block diagram for automatic go-no-go production setup for making r-f breakdwn test in 30 ms per transistor.—P. Schiff, R-F Breakdown Phenomenon Improves the Voltage Capability of a Transistor, *Electronics*, June 12, 1967, p 97–101.

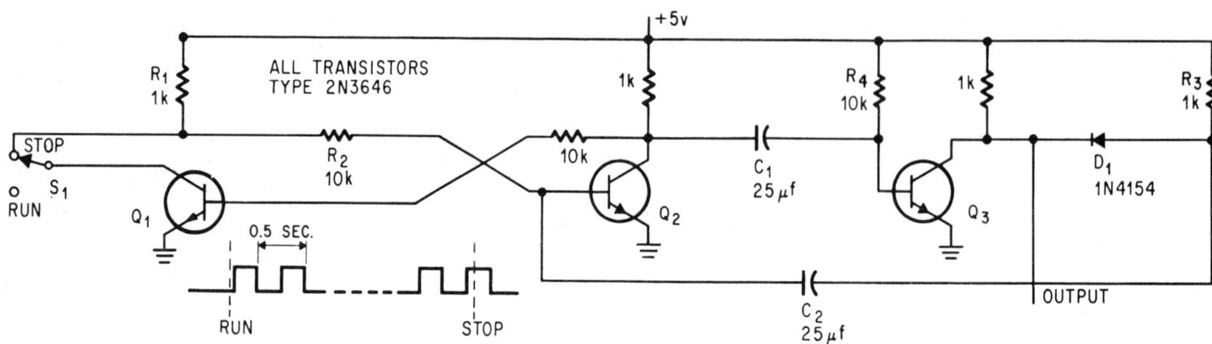

2-HZ CHECKOUT—Extra transistor Q2 in low-speed oscillator permits checking of digital circuits at 2 Hz, slow enough so operator can watch logic operate visual indicator, with no risk of false output because of contact bounce in switch or because oscillator is switched off in middle of cycle. Q1 keeps oscillator running until cycle is ended.—P. T. Rux, Oscillator Waits for Switch to Quiet Down, *Electronics*, Nov. 13, 1967, p 103.

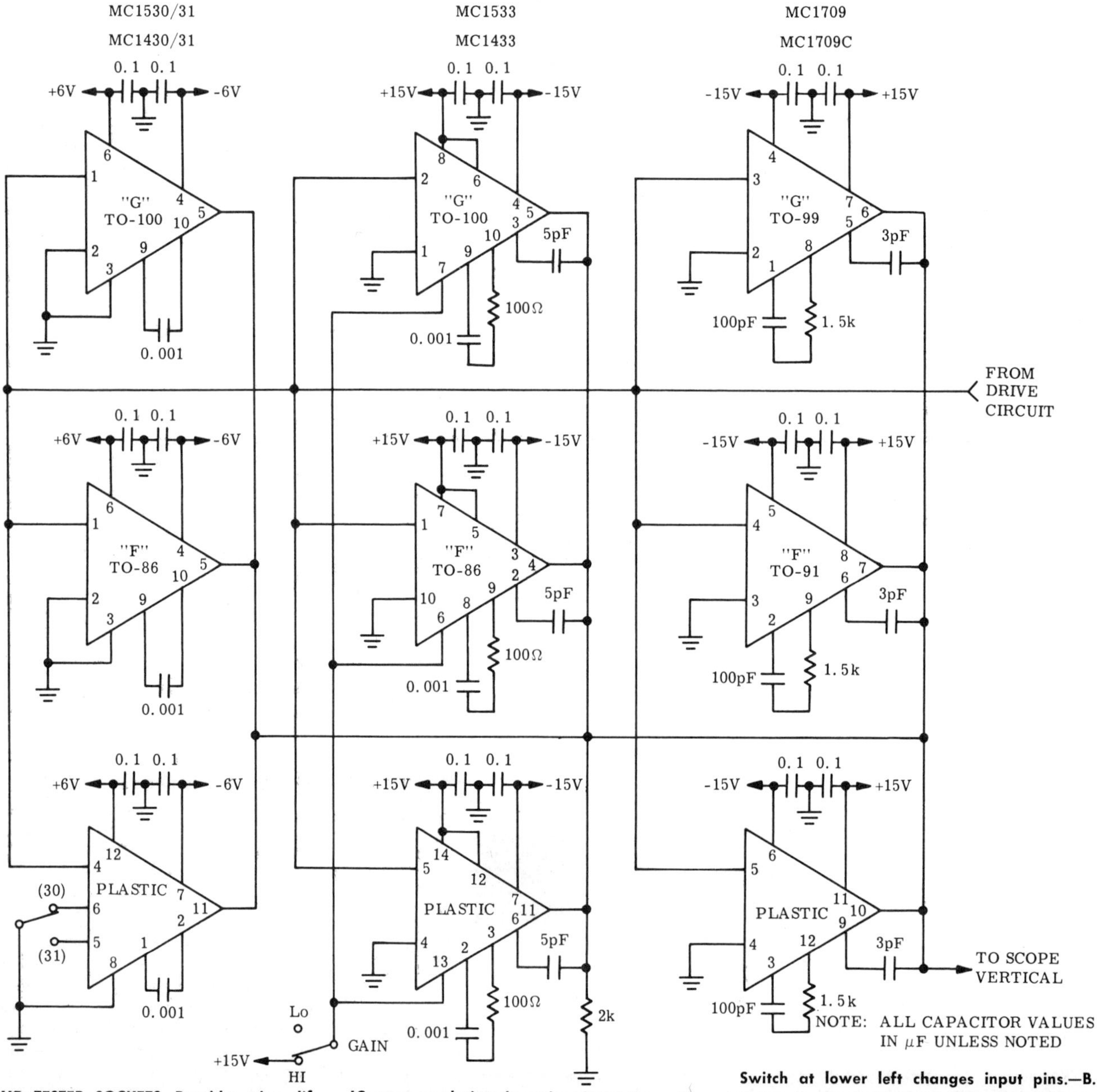

MC1530/31 MC1430/31 — MC1533 MC1433 — MC1709 MC1709C

FROM DRIVE CIRCUIT

TO SCOPE VERTICAL

NOTE: ALL CAPACITOR VALUES IN μF UNLESS NOTED

OPAMP TESTER SOCKETS—Provides nine different sockets for testing commonest types of IC opamps during incoming inspection. Requires power supply and drive circuit. Switch at lower left changes input pins.—B. Botos, An Operational Amplifier Tester, Motorola, Phoenix, Ariz., No. AN-400, 1967.

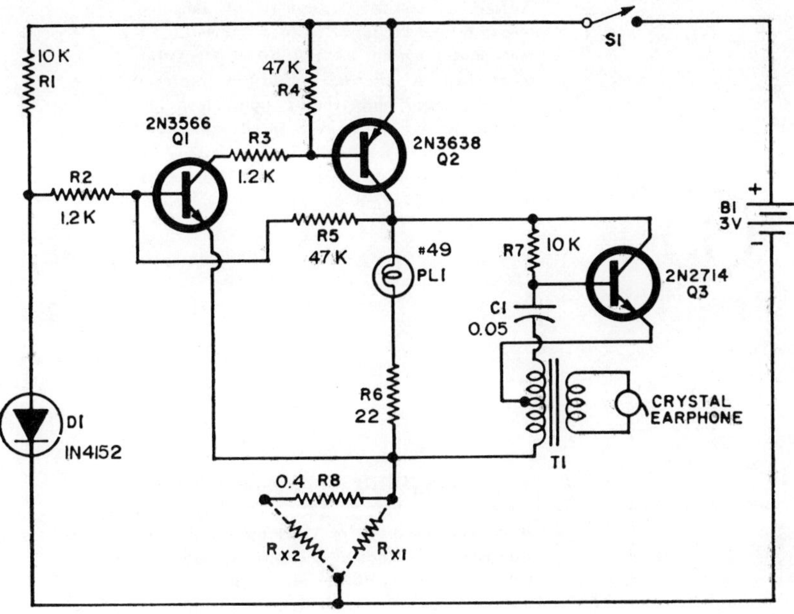

CONTINUITY TESTER—Gives reliable indication of continuity down to 0.1 ohm on go/no-go lamp or by tone in earphone, with no risk of damage to sensitive transistors and integrated circuits. R8 should be about 0.1 ohm less than maximum value for which continuity indication is desired. Use RX2 terminals for checking down to 0.1 ohm.—C. D. Todd, A Sub-Ohm Continuity Tester, *Electronics World*, Feb. 1969, p 78–80.

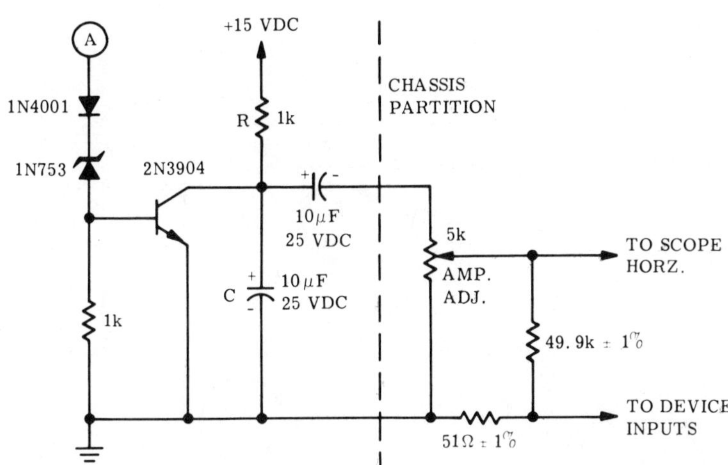

OPAMP TESTER—Includes drive circuit shown, providing horizontal sweep drive for standard X-Y scope, feed to input terminals of all nine opamp test sockets, and 60-Hz voltage at point A, obtained from secondary of power supply transformer. Developed as simple and inexpensive tester for use by customers in checking shipments of opamps. Cro display shows transfer function of opamp.—B. Botos, An Operational Amplifier Tester, Motorola, Phoenix, Ariz., No. AN-400, 1967.

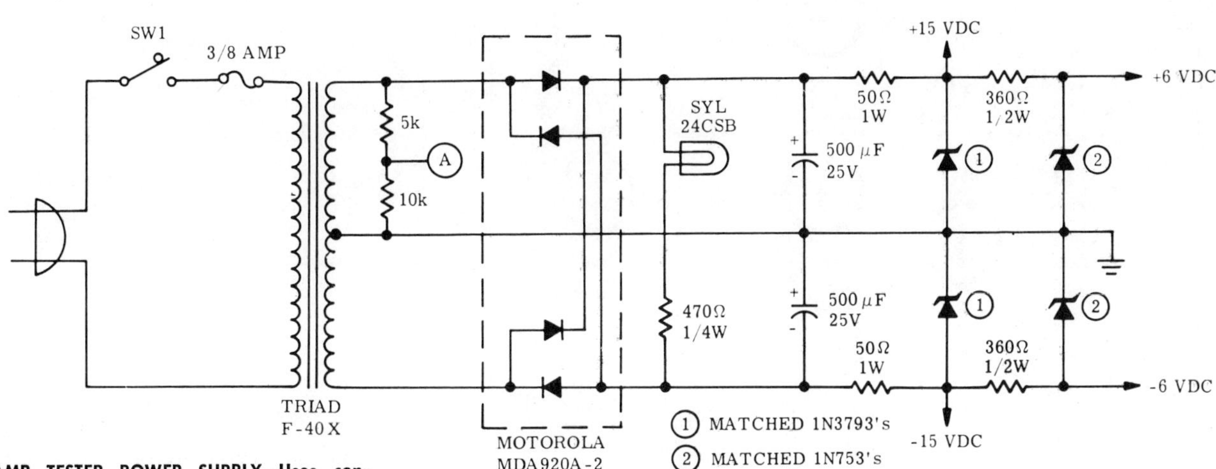

OPAMP TESTER POWER SUPPLY—Uses conventional shunt zener regulator, with pilot lamp bridged across filter capacitors as on-off indicator and as bleeder for capacitor charge after power is turned off.—B. Botos, An Operational Amplifier Tester, Motorola, Phoenix, Ariz., No. AN-400, 1967.

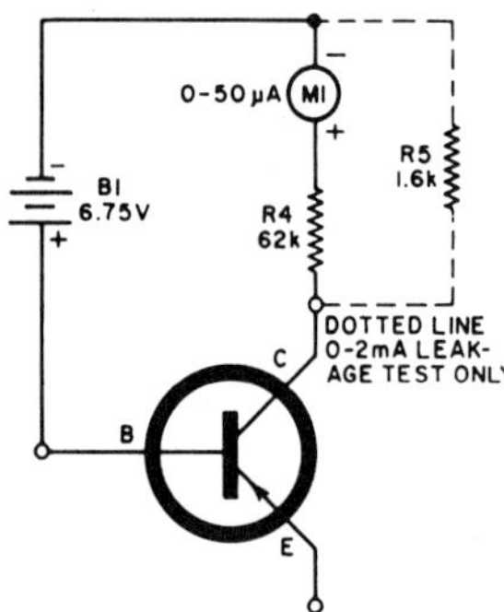

TRANSISTOR LEAKAGE—Basic circuit measures reverse-biased collector-to-base current. R4 limits meter current to 100 μA if transistor under test is shorted. Used in battery-powered tester that checks gain, leakage, and breakdown voltage of small-signal and power transistors. Also checks diodes.—M. J. Moss, Versatile Transistor Tester, *Electronics World*, Aug. 1967, p 56–58.

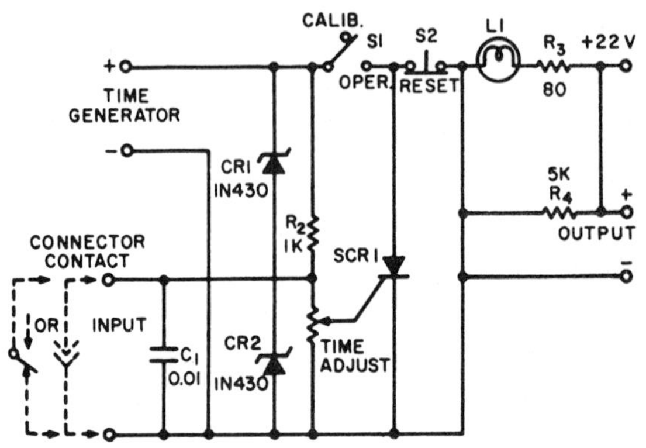

CONTACT-CHATTER TESTER—Immunity of scr to noise excitation makes it far superior to conventional thyratron in discontinuity tester used for monitoring circuit interruptions in 10-μs range. Once scr conducts and turns on indicator lamp, S2 must be opened momentarily to reset circuit.—J. A. Ray, Discontinuity Tester is Insensitive to Noise, "400 Ideas for Design Selected from Electronic Design," Hayden Book Co., N.Y., 1964, p 152.

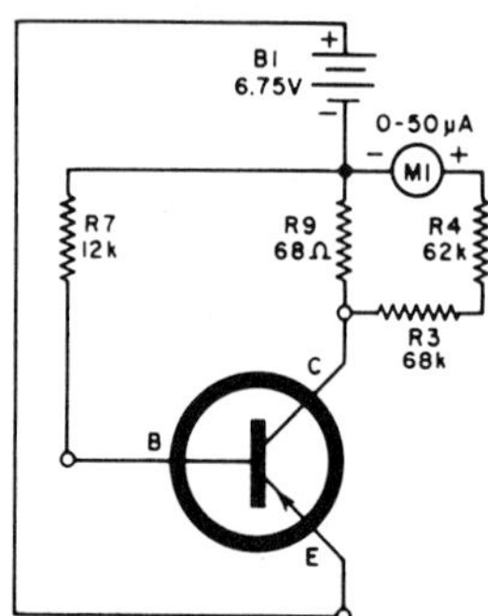

POWER TRANSISTOR GAIN—Basic test circuit for measuring beta or gain, using higher collector current than for checking small-signal transistors so higher leakage currents of power transistors do not mask true measurement. Collector current is set at 50 mA, corresponding to beta of 100.—M. J. Moss, Versatile Transistor Tester, *Electronics World*, Aug. 1967, p 56–58.

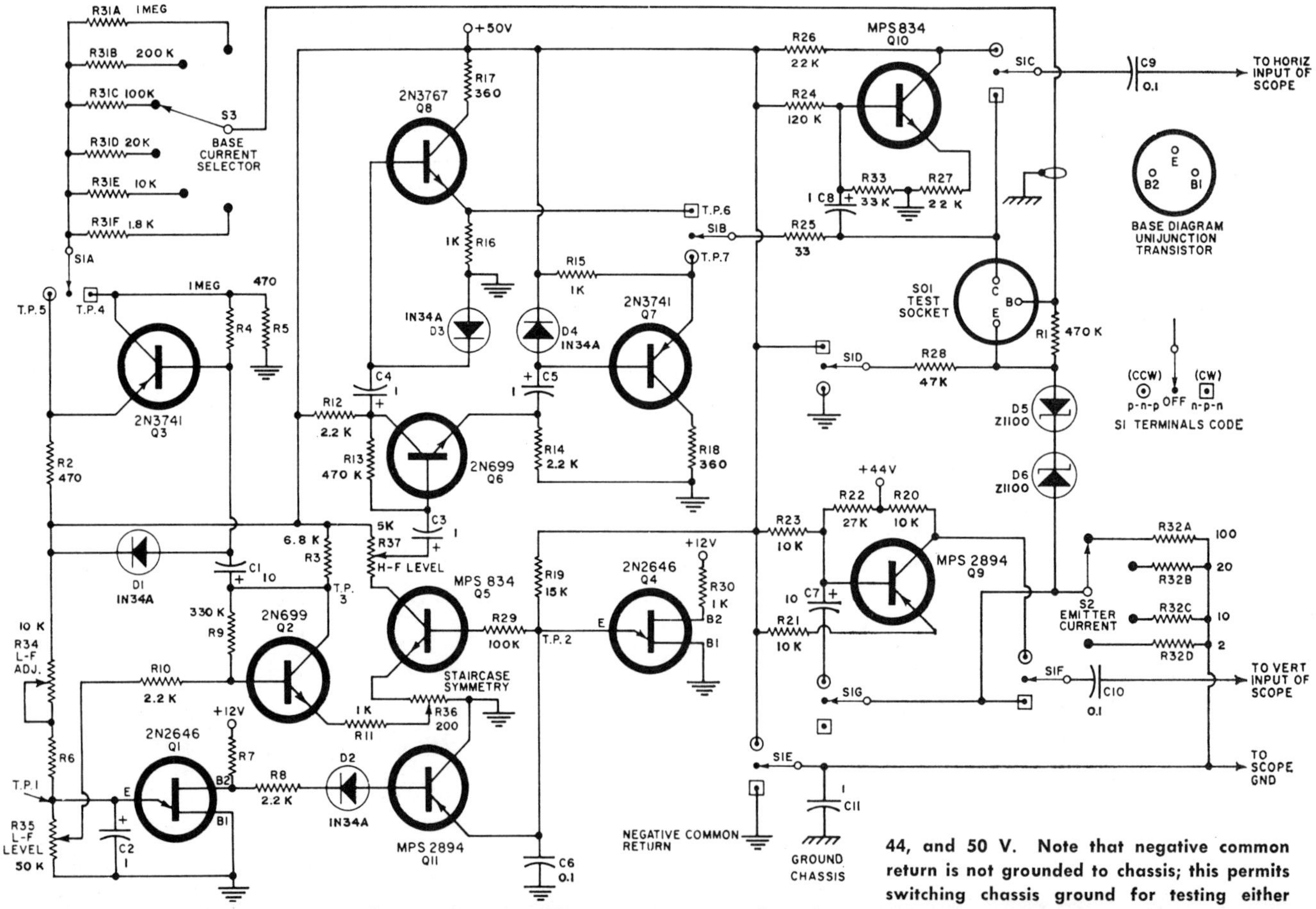

TRANSISTOR CURVE TRACER—Generates family of characteristic curves for display on scope, as aid to solution of transistor circuit design problems. Parts cost is less than $50. Construction details are given. Requires regulated power supply providing 12, 44, and 50 V. Note that negative common return is not grounded to chassis; this permits switching chassis ground for testing either pnp or npn transistors.—M. Chan, Transistor Curve Tracer, *Electronics World*, Jan. 1968, p 55–58, 60, and 66.

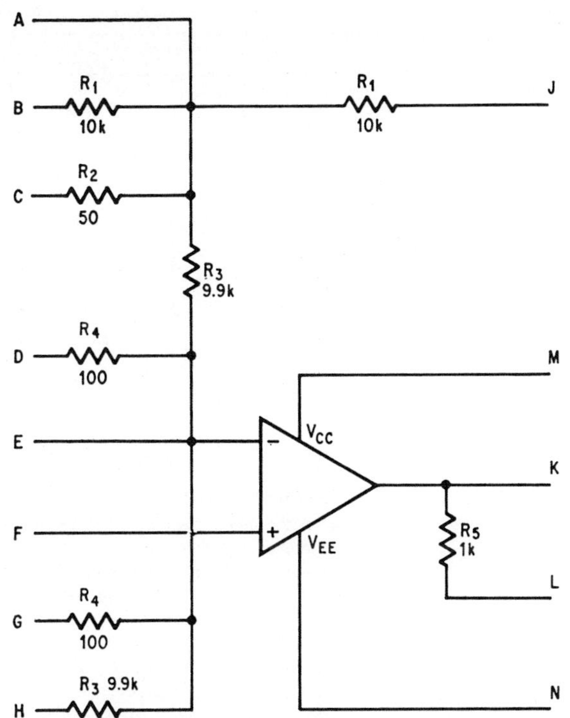

AUTOMATIC OPAMP TESTER—Simple, versatile interface fixture circuit shown permits checking of opamps and other linear circuits with automatic testers designed primarily for digital IC's. Opamp is connected through pins E and F, and receives power from pins M and N, while K and L are output lines. Resistor values must be adjusted for opamp under test; those shown are for Amelco 809. Article gives setup and measurement procedures.—R. McIntyre, Adapter Lets Digital IC Tester Check on Operational Amplifiers, *Electronics*, July 21, 1969, p 94–96.

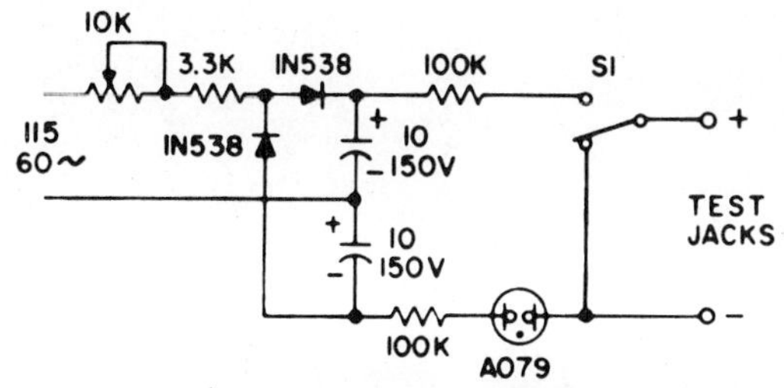

CAPACITOR LEAKAGE—Blinking neon lamp with S1 closed indicates capacitor connected to test jacks is leaking.—E. Bauman, "Applications of Neon Lamps and Gas Discharge Tubes," Signalite, Neptune, N.J., p 150.

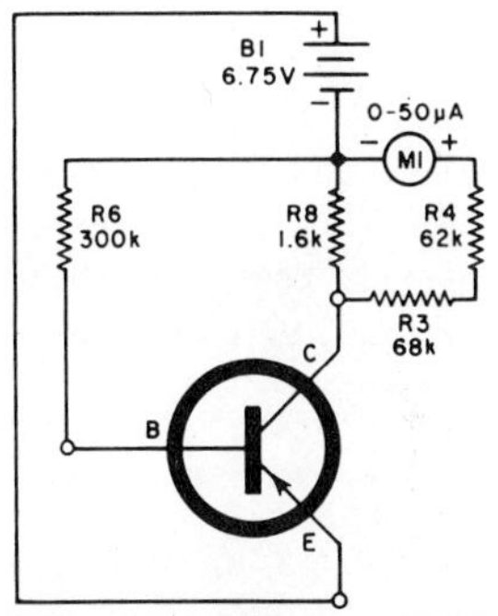

SMALL-SIGNAL TRANSISTOR CURRENT GAIN—Basic circuit for measuring current gain of pnp transistor uses base current of about 20 μA. Used in battery-powered tester that checks gain, leakage, and breakdown voltage of small-signal and power transistors. Also checks diodes.—M. J. Moss, Versatile Transistor Tester, *Electronics World*, Aug. 1967, p 56–58.

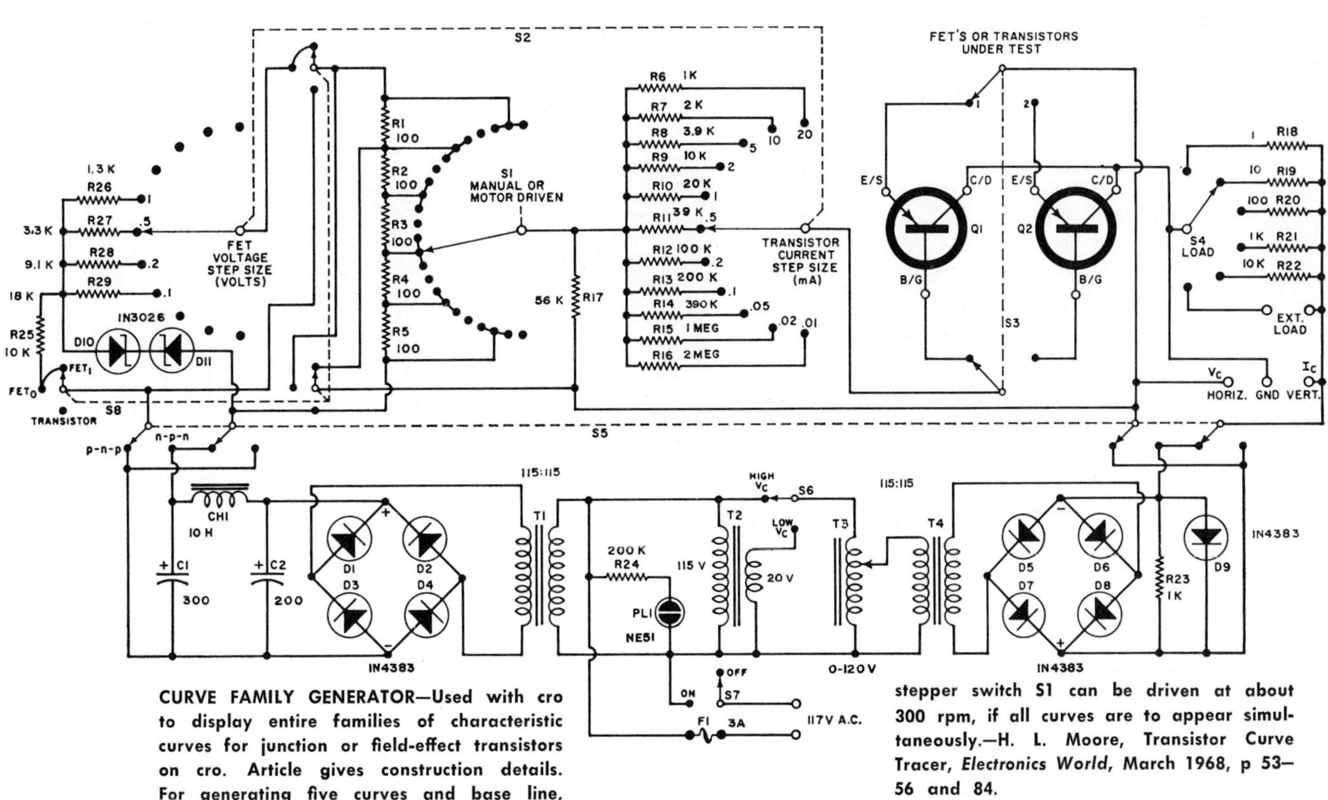

CURVE FAMILY GENERATOR—Used with cro to display entire families of characteristic curves for junction or field-effect transistors on cro. Article gives construction details. For generating five curves and base line, stepper switch S1 can be driven at about 300 rpm, if all curves are to appear simultaneously.—H. L. Moore, Transistor Curve Tracer, *Electronics World*, March 1968, p 53–56 and 84.

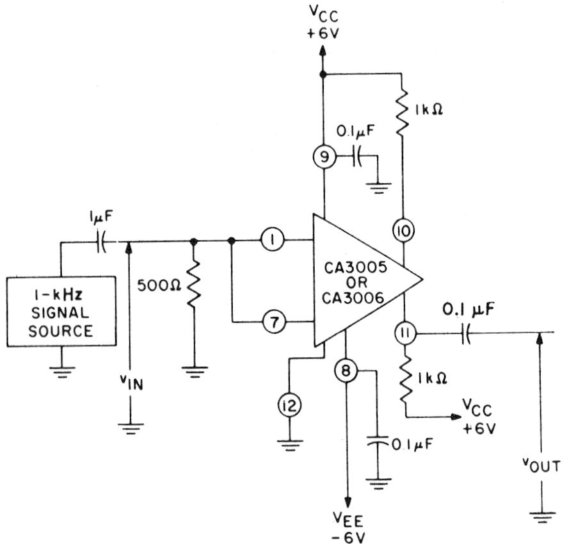

IC R-F AMPLIFIER TESTER—Determines single-ended common-mode gain of IC r-f amplifier at 1 kHz. With variable-frequency signal source, test can be made over entire useful frequency range.—"Linear Integrated Circuits," RCA, Harrison, N.J., IC-41, p 200.

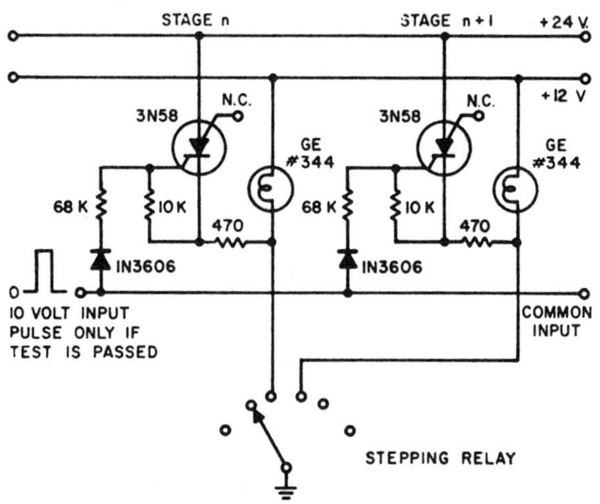

INDICATORS FOR SEQUENCE TESTER—Scr and lamp for each position of stepper relay provide visual indication of passed tests and indicate position of stepper. All lamps are reset by opening 24-V supply for few seconds. Lamp is ON at stepper position, but stays ON only if passed-test pulse arrives and turns on scr before stepper moves to next position.—E. Pacia, Visual Readout for Tester Uses Silicon-Controlled Switch, "400 Ideas for Design Selected from Electronic Design," Hayden Book Co., N.Y., 1964, p 146–147.

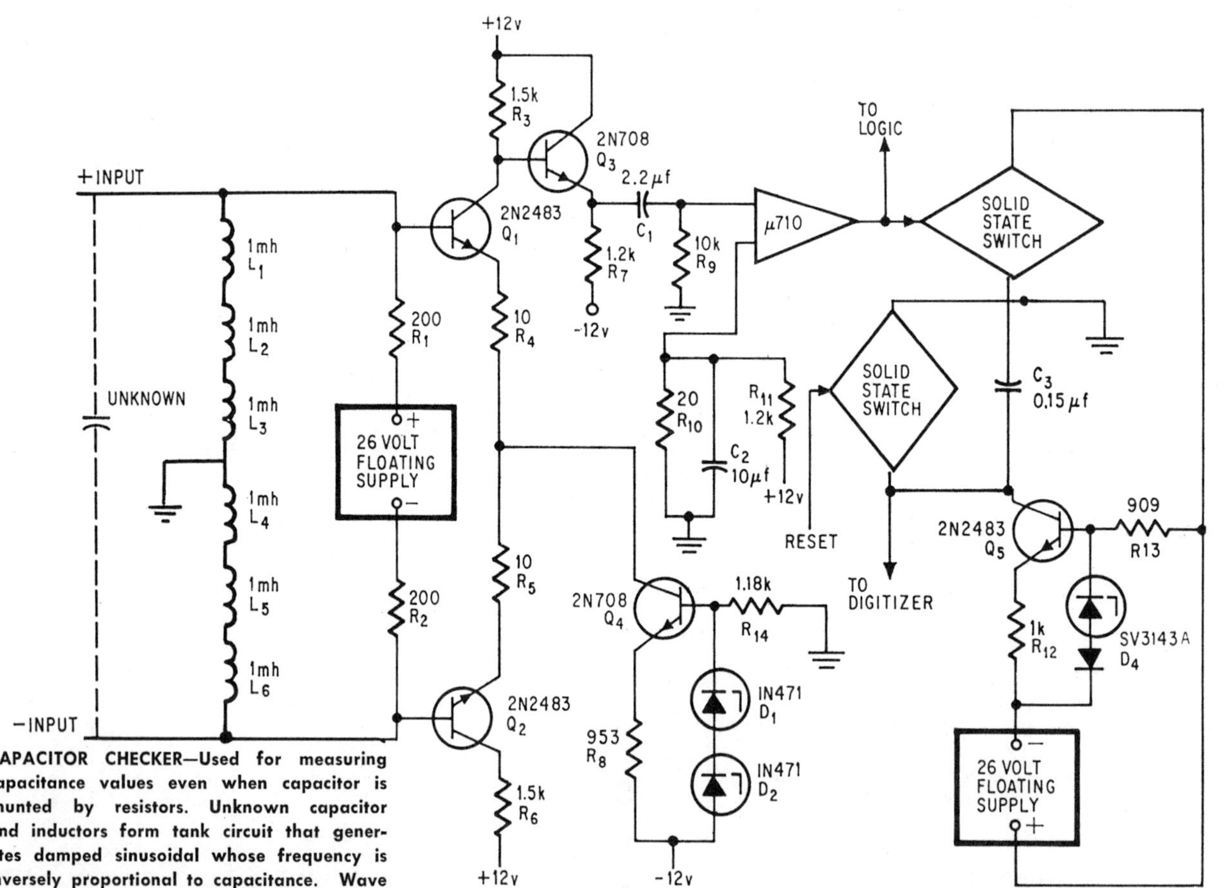

CAPACITOR CHECKER—Used for measuring capacitance values even when capacitor is shunted by resistors. Unknown capacitor and inductors form tank circuit that generates damped sinusoidal whose frequency is inversely proportional to capacitance. Wave is amplified by differential amplifier Q1-Q2 and squared by IC differential comparator whose output turns on solid-state switch for duration of first pulse. This initiates charging of C3 for first quarter-cycle to give voltage proportional to pulse width and to capacitance, for reading with digitizer.—C. H. Ristad, Resonance Effects Yield In-Circuit Capacitance Checks, *Electronics*, Oct. 14, 1968, p 119–120.

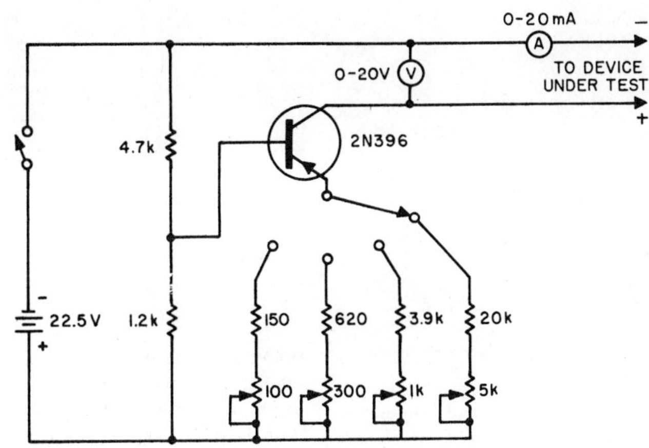

ZENER TESTER—Permits quick check of zener voltage and current characteristics of unmarked zener diodes. Can also be used to check forward voltage drop across diodes. Adjust variable resistors until desired values of current (0.2, 1, 5, and 20 mA) flow through milliammeter. Use heat sink with transistor.—G. V. Pallottino, Simple Zener-Diode Tester Uses Single Transistor, *Electronic Design*, Oct. 25, 1967, p 140.

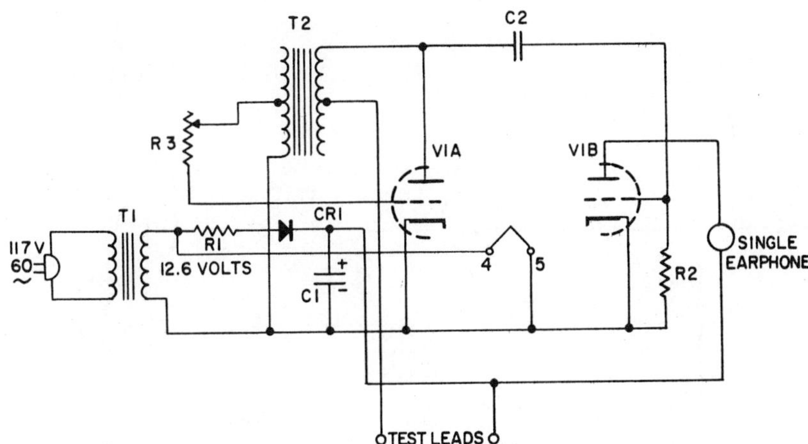

AURAL CONTINUITY TESTER—Continuity is indicated by tone in earphone, eliminating need for watching meter. Sends only very small current through circuit under test, minimizing damage to components under test. None of parts are critical; V1 can be almost any twin-triode having 12.6-V filament, such as 12AX7, 12 AT7, or 12AU7. T2 is any interstage audio transformer. Values are: C1 25 μF; C2 0.005 μF; CR1 1N34AS; R1 150; R2 470K; R3 250K. R3 adjusts tone; if not heard, reverse connections to one winding of T2.—"Hobby Manual," General Electric, Owensboro, Ky., Second Edition, 1965, p 174.

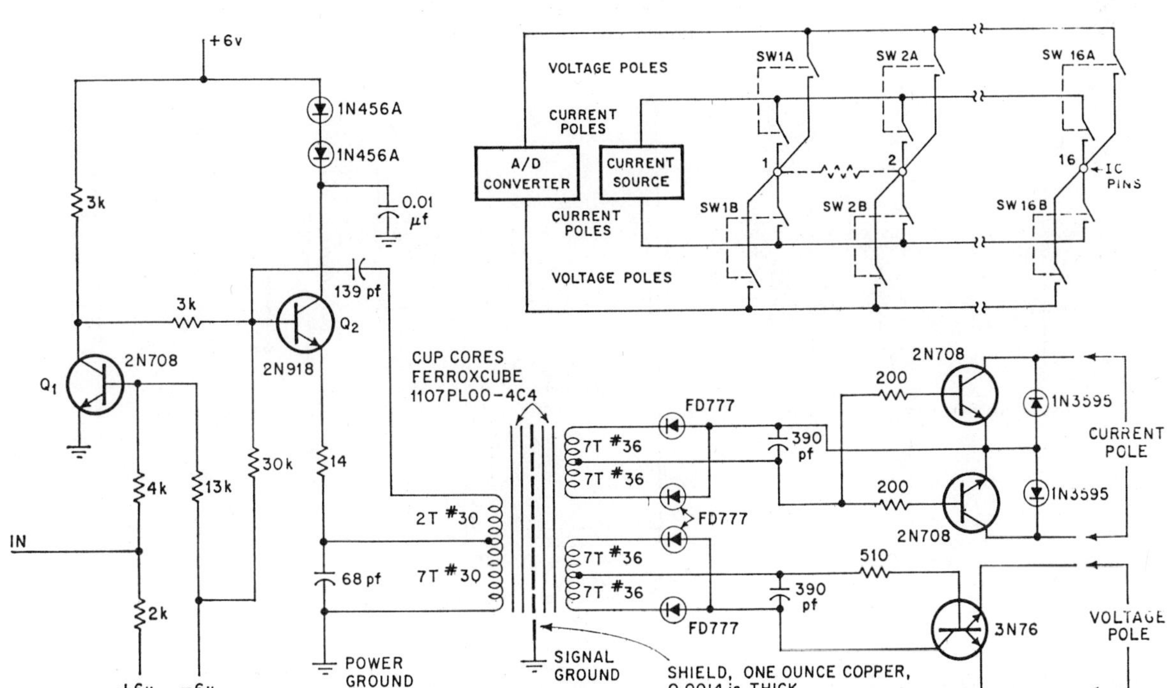

FOUR-WIRE RESISTANCE CHECKER—Used in computer-controlled component testing in which voltage or current drive is applied to component under test and appropriate meter is connected. 14-MHz Hartley Q2 turns on current and voltage switches in about 2 μs. Transformer provides isolation between switch control and measurement circuit grounds for four-wire resistance measurements.—C. H. Ristad, Switched Oscillator Controls Four-Wire Resistance Checks, *Electronics*, July 6, 1970, p 78.

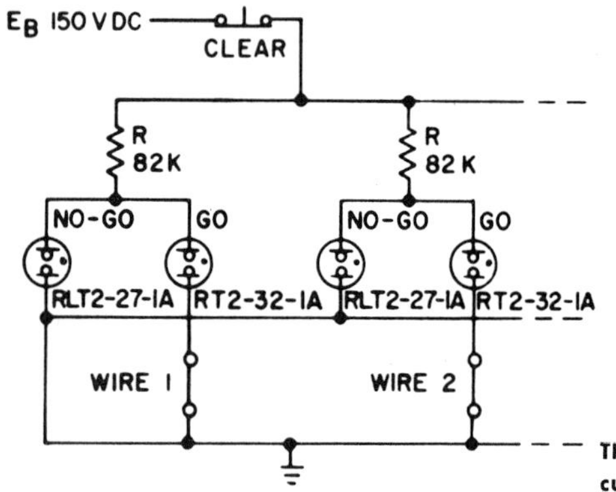

NEON CABLE TESTER—Simple and economical tester for one or more wires uses neon lamps with different firing potentials. NO-GO lamp glows only when cable under test is open.—E. Bauman, "Applications of Neon Lamps and Gas Discharge Tubes," Signalite, Neptune, N.J., p 142.

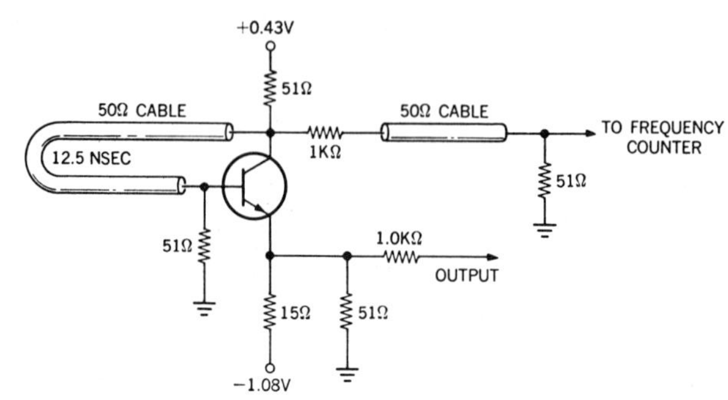

TRANSISTOR CHIP TESTER—Variation of circulating loop test is used to check switching speed of transistor chips before committing them to ASLT module for IBM 360/91 computer. Transistor drives itself on and off at rate determined by sum of its turn-on and turn-off delays and electrical length of cable in ns, according to equation given in article. Frequency counter is used to count number of switching operations and thereby determine switching speed.—R. F. Sechler, A. R. Strube, and J. R. Turnbull, ASLT Circuit Design, *IBM Journal*, Jan. 1967, p 74–85.

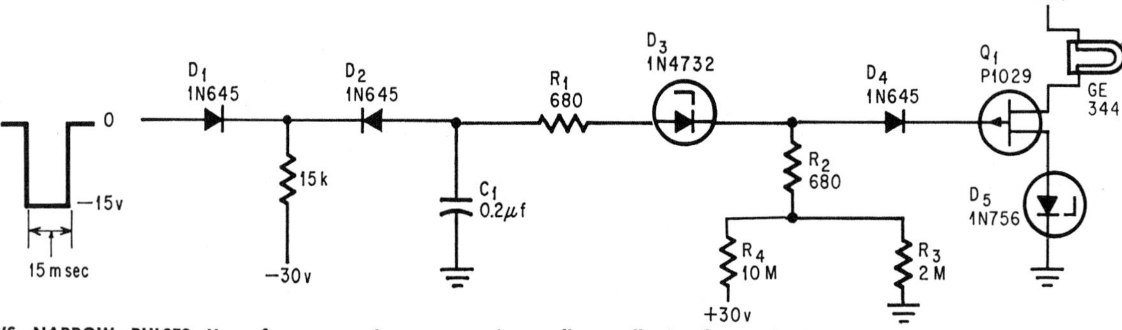

LAMP SHOWS NARROW PULSES—Uses fet, gated into conduction while 15-ms pulse at test point in radar receiver is slowly discharged, to hold indicator lamp on for 180 ms. Lamp system is equally as effective for troubleshooting pulse circuits as more expensive oscilloscope systems. Can also be used for testing color tv and f-m multiplex circuits.—W. A. Magee, Stretching Video Pulse Keeps Indicator On, *Electronics*, March 4, 1968, p 90.

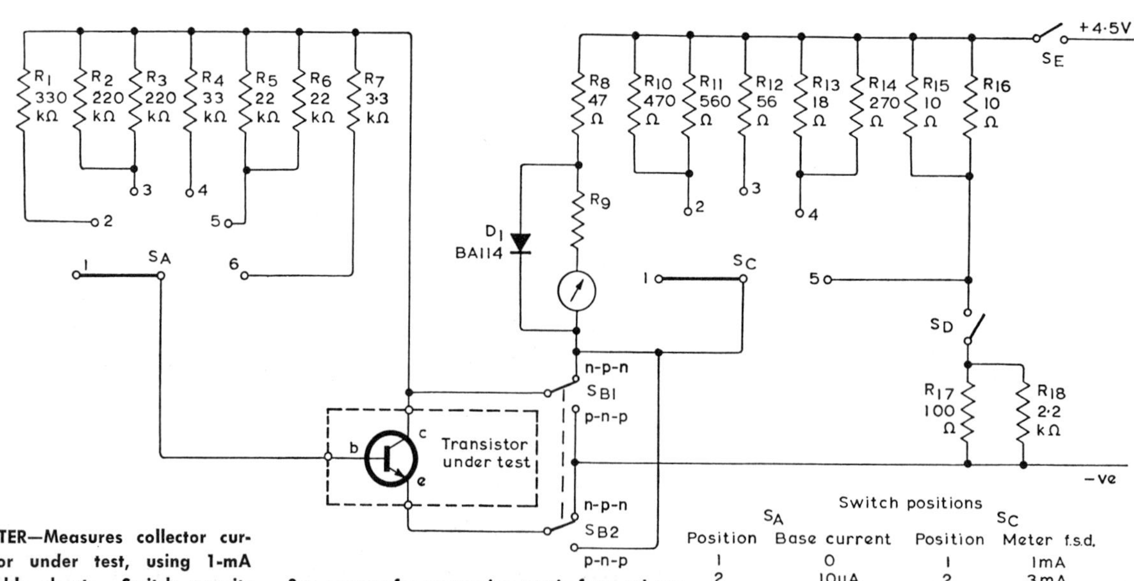

Switch positions

S_A Position	Base current	S_C Position	Meter f.s.d.
1	0	1	1mA
2	10μA	2	3mA
3	30μA	3	10mA
4	100uA	4	30mA
5	300μA	5	100mA
6	1mA		

TRANSISTOR TESTER—Measures collector current of transistor under test, using 1-mA meter with suitable shunts. Switch permits measurement of collector-emitter reverse leakage current while base current of transistor is zero. Switch SA gives choice of five ranges for measuring static forward current transfer ratio.—"Transistor Audio and Radio Circuits," Mullard Ltd., London, 1969, p 180.

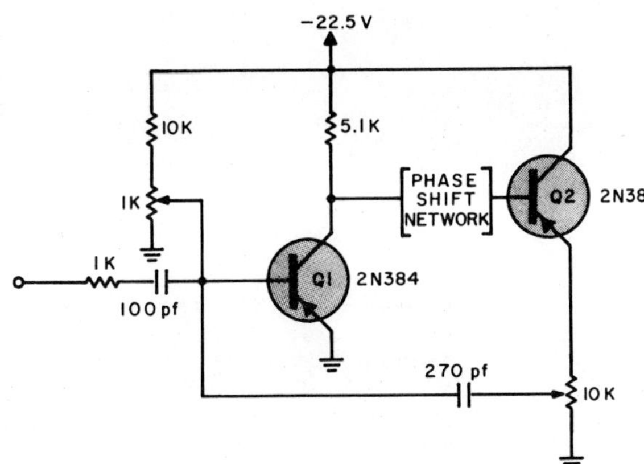

PHASE-SHIFT NETWORK TESTER—Simple amplifier serves for evaluation of distributed-parameter networks for i-f tuned amplifiers. —I. F. Barditch, Adapting Conventional VHF Equipment to Molecular Electronics, *Electronic Design*, Feb. 17, 1964, p 44–51.

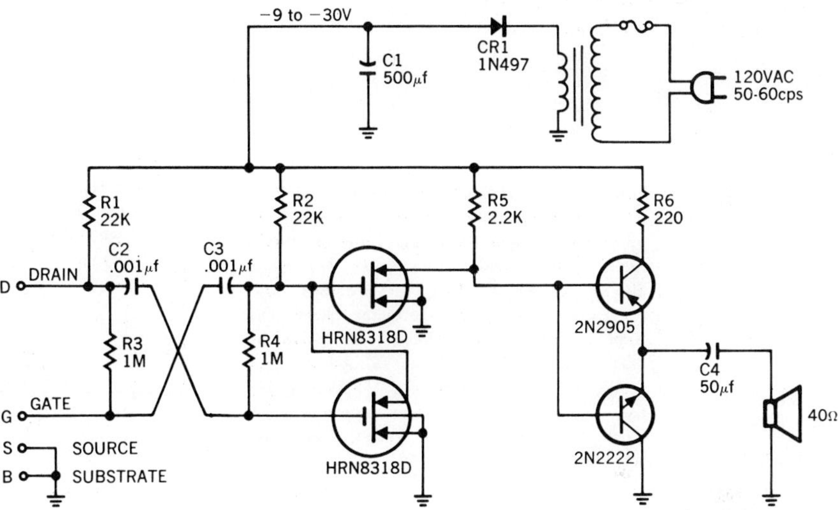

GO-NO-GO FET TESTER—Produces audible tone when good fet is properly inserted in test terminals at left. Fet under test serves as half of low-frequency mvbr, with lower fet of tester as other half. Upper fet serves as buffer for complementary-transistor output stage. May be used on fet production line to verify connections and operation before final encapsulation.—C. R. Perkins, "Application of MOSFET Devices to Electronic Circuits," Hughes, Newport Beach, Cal., 1968, p 2.

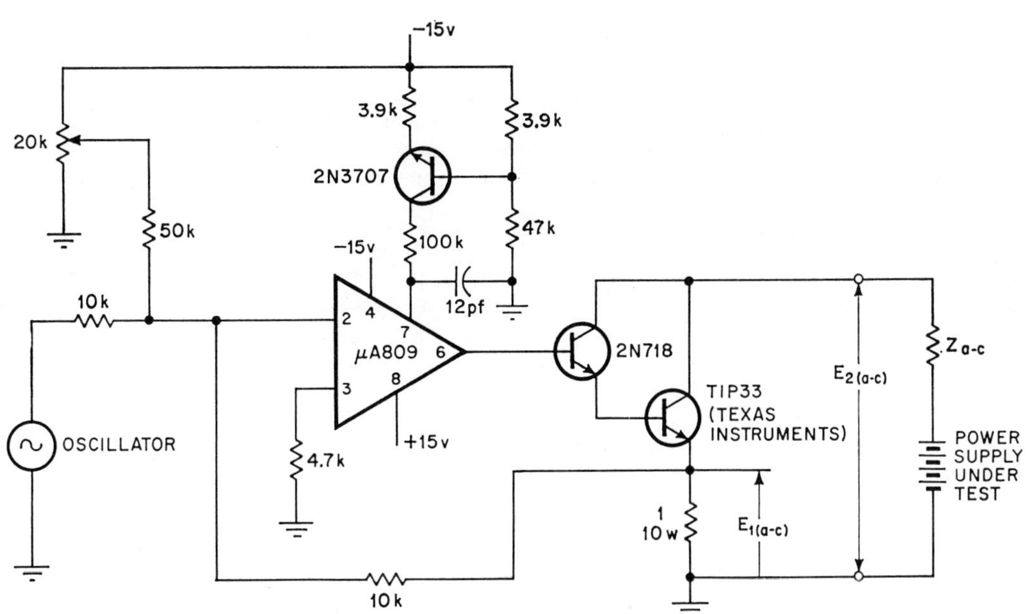

REGULATOR TESTER—Measures dynamic output impedance of regulated power supply, using high-gain feedback amplifier that accurately sets a-c load current at frequencies up to 500 kHz. A-c component from oscillator and d-c component from pot are fed into opamp. Transistor circuit connected to pin 7 improves high-frequency large-signal response without lowering gain appreciably.—R. D. Guyton, A Dynamic Load Tester for Regulated Power Supplies, *Electronics*, Feb. 2, 1970, p 98.

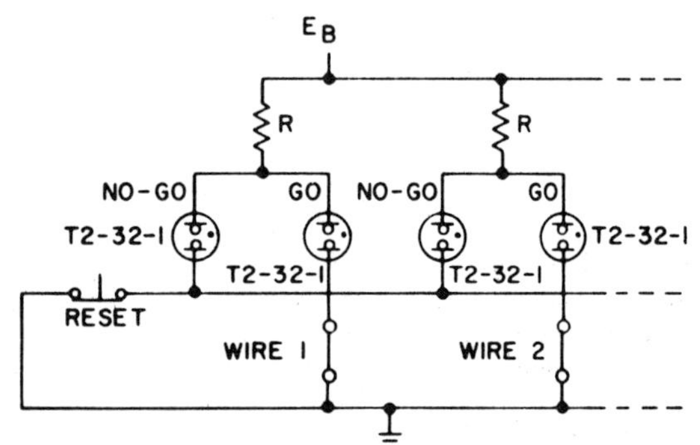

NEON HARNESS TESTER—Compact and inexpensive neon flip-flop circuit continuously monitors each individual wire in cable harness. Resistor values depend on E; for 250 V, R is 220K.—E. Bauman, "Applications of Neon Lamps and Gas Discharge Tubes," Signalite, Neptune, N.J., p 142.

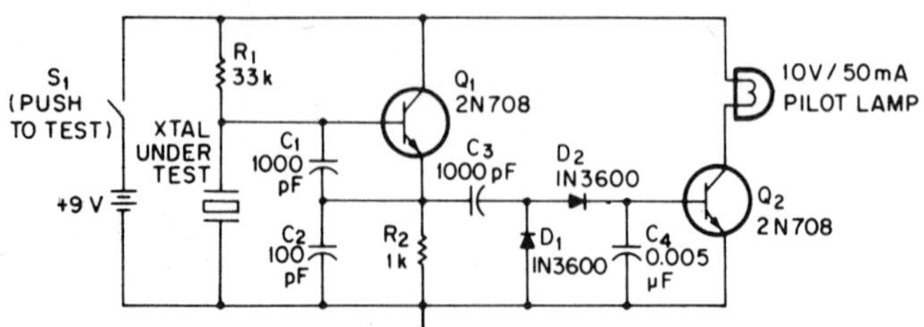

CRYSTAL TESTER—Will check any crystal in range of 3.5 to 90 MHz almost instantly. Crystal is inserted in test socket and switch S1 pushed. If crystal is good, untuned Colpitts oscillator goes into oscillation, and its output signal is rectified to turn on Q2 and pilot lamp.—M. Kaufman, Self-Contained Crystal Tester, *EEE*, July 1970, p 84.

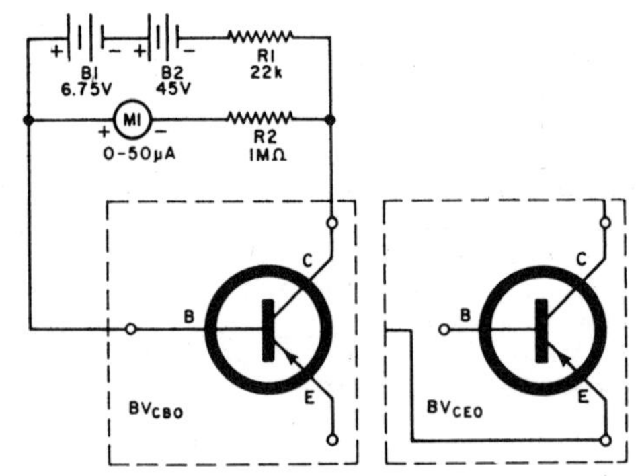

TRANSISTOR BREAKDOWN—Same circuit can be used to measure collector breakdown to emitter with base open and collector breakdown to base with emitter open, for up to 50 V breakdown. This test provides data for deciding if given transistor should be used in high-voltage circuit. Can also be used to measure breakdown voltage of zener diode, and for determining whether given transistor is germanium or silicon.—M. J. Moss, Versatile Transistor Tester, *Electronics World*, Aug. 1967, p 56–58.

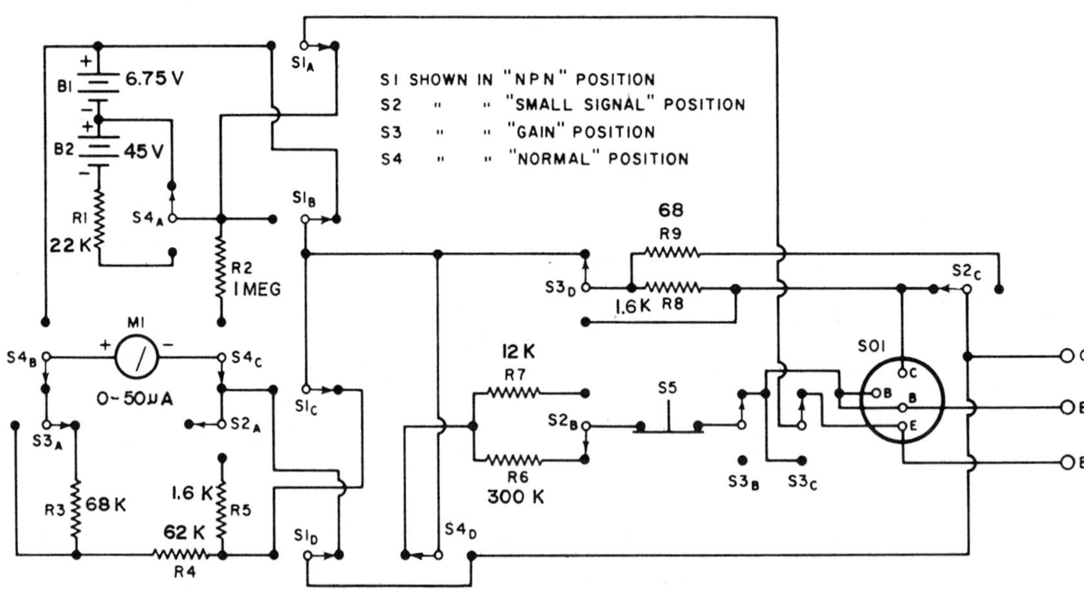

TRANSISTOR/DIODE TESTER—Circuit features simplicity of operation and lack of critical adjustments, for checking gain, leakage, and breakdown voltage of small-signal and power transistors. No on-off switch is needed for battery supply, so tester is ready for instant use. Circuit design makes it virtually impossible to damage either meter or transistor under test even if switches are set wrong. Also makes zener breakdown tests. Article gives operating instructions, along with changes needed to use 100-μA meter.—M. J. Moss, Versatile Transistor Tester, *Electronics World*, Aug. 1967, p 56–58.

SURPLUS-CRYSTAL CHECKER—Provides quick performance check of used or surplus crystals often available for as little as 10 cents each. Tube circuit operating from a-c line will oscillate for crystals throughout 2–30 MHz range and for fundamental crystals in 200–500 kHz range. (Transistor equivalent was extremely critical as to frequency.) Good crystal gives meter reading of 0.3 to 1 mA, while bad crystals read below 0.2 mA. Checker is easily calibrated with a few good crystals.—E. H. Marriner, The Crystal Checker, CQ, July 1964, p 30–31.

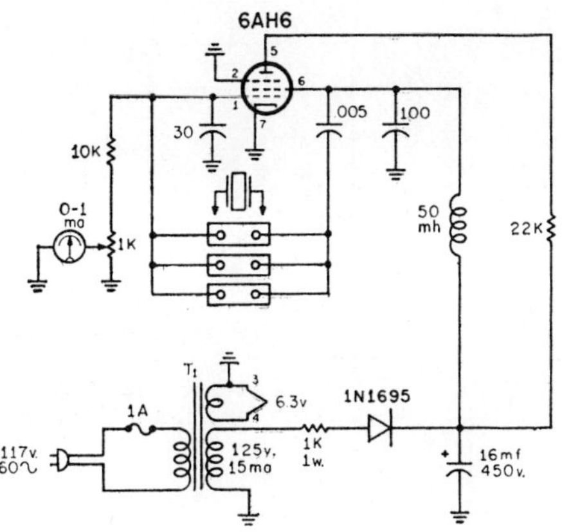

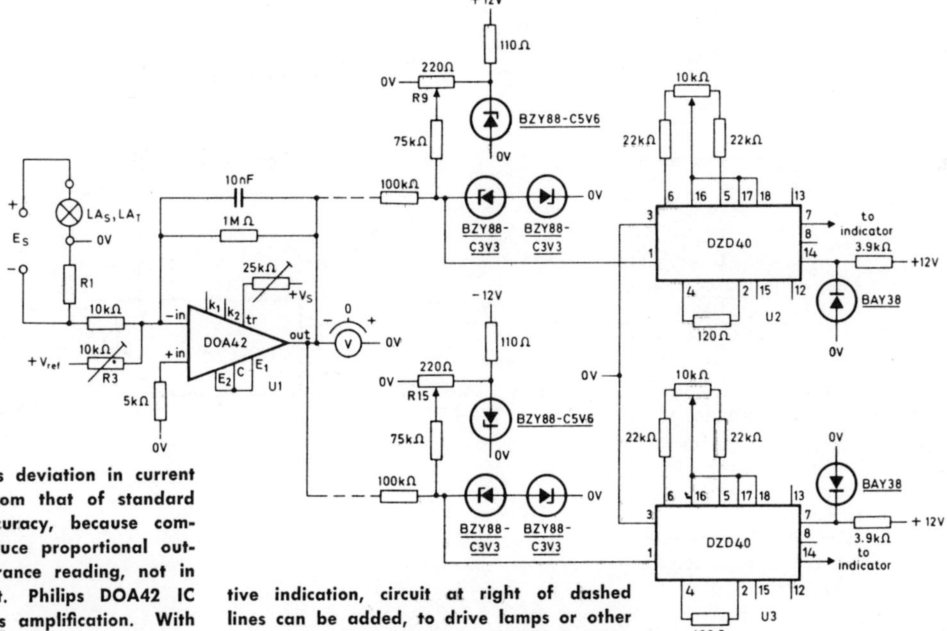

LAMP TESTER—Measures deviation in current of lamp under test from that of standard lamp. Gives high accuracy, because component variations produce proportional output error only in tolerance reading, not in total measured current. Philips DOA42 IC opamp gives 100 times amplification. With standard lamp LAs in circuit, either R3 or Vref is adjusted for zero output of opamp as indicated by zero-center voltmeter. Lamp testing can now be carried out. For positive indication, circuit at right of dashed lines can be added, to drive lamps or other indicators showing that lamp is outside upper or lower tolerance limits determined by 10K pots connected to DZD40 Philips IC zero detectors.—P. Havas, Measurement of Deviation from Standard Using A DOA42 Circuit Block, Philips, Pub. Dept., Elcoma Div., Eindhoven, The Netherlands, No. 83.

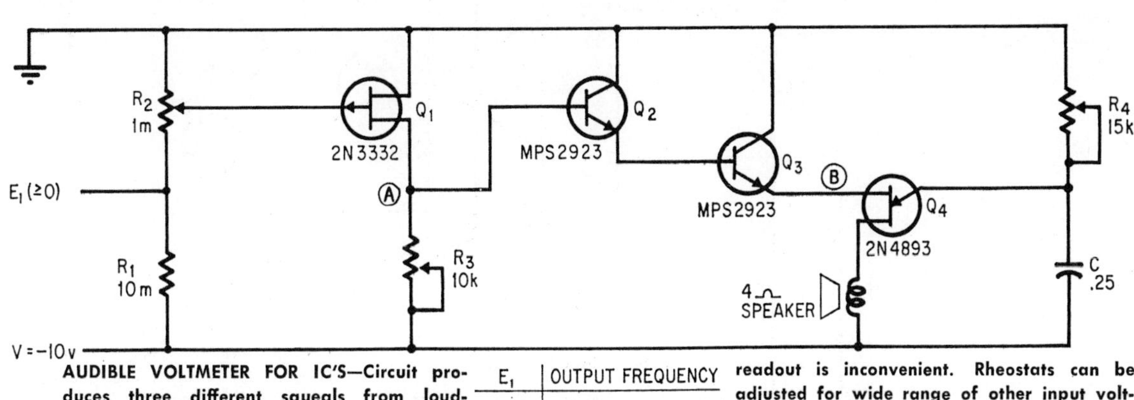

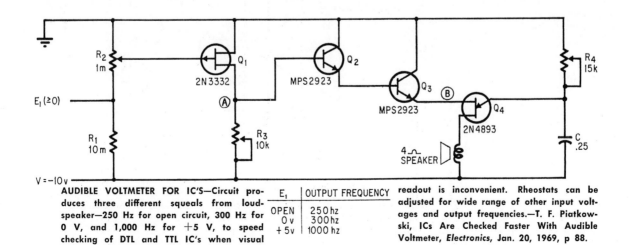

AUDIBLE VOLTMETER FOR IC'S—Circuit produces three different squeals from loudspeaker—250 Hz for open circuit, 300 Hz for 0 V, and 1,000 Hz for +5 V, to speed checking of DTL and TTL IC's when visual readout is inconvenient. Rheostats can be adjusted for wide range of other input voltages and output frequencies.—T. F. Piatkowski, ICs Are Checked Faster With Audible Voltmeter, *Electronics*, Jan. 20, 1969, p 88.

E_1	OUTPUT FREQUENCY
OPEN	250hz
0 v	300hz
+5v	1000 hz

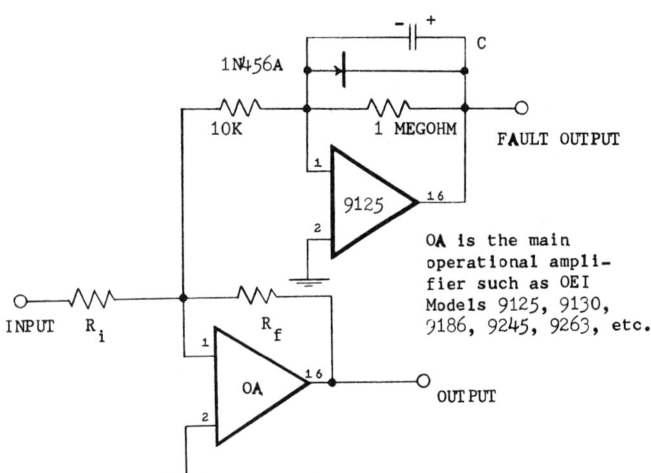

OPAMP FAULT DETECTOR—Senses and indicates presence of signal at inverting input of opamp. Detection takes place in another opamp connected in polar integrator circuit, to give positive d-c voltage as indication of fault output. Can be used to drive indicator lamp, reset analog computer, or stop process under control. Choose value of C for desired R-C time constant with 1-meg feedback resistor. 1 μF gives 1 s. Values of Ri and Rf depend on opamp OA under test.—An Operational Amplifier Fault Detector, Optical Electronics, Tucson, Ariz., No. 10168.

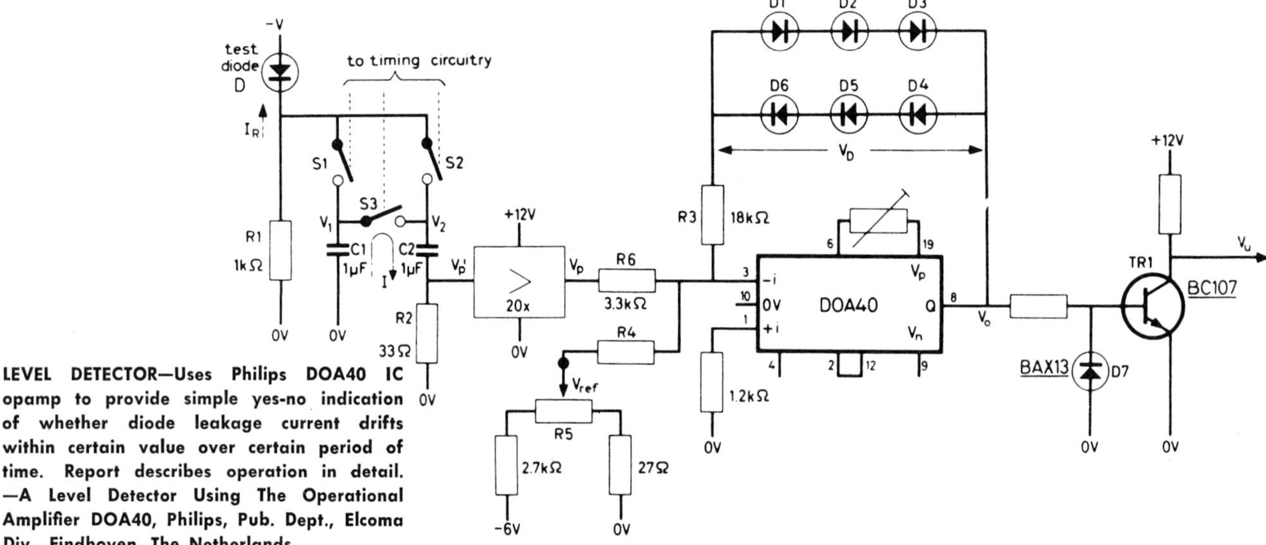

LEVEL DETECTOR—Uses Philips DOA40 IC opamp to provide simple yes-no indication of whether diode leakage current drifts within certain value over certain period of time. Report describes operation in detail. —A Level Detector Using The Operational Amplifier DOA40, Philips, Pub. Dept., Elcoma Div., Eindhoven, The Netherlands.

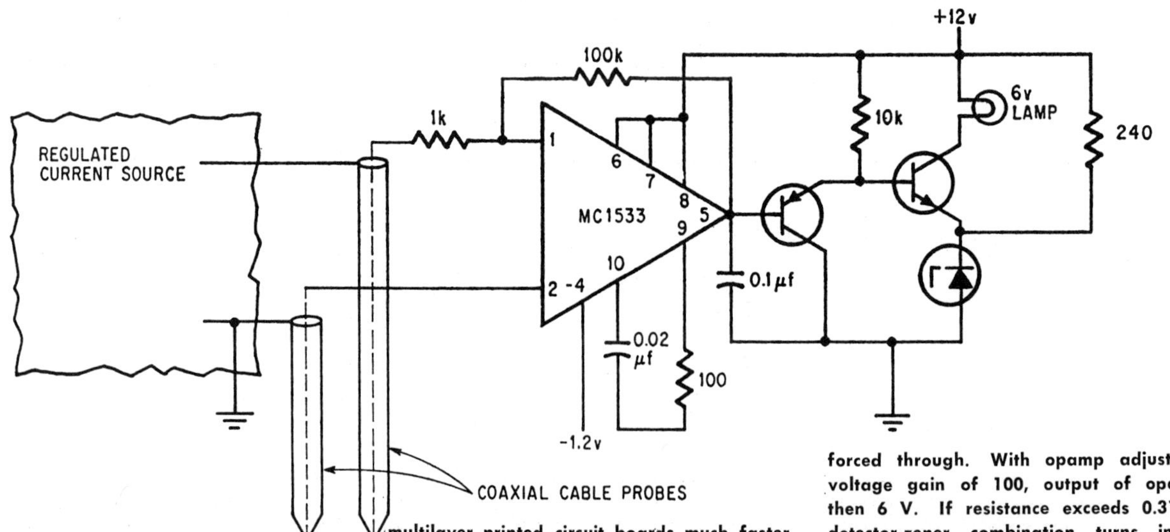

WIRING CHECKER—IC opamp followed by two-transistor detector with indicator lamp checks resistance of critical conductor runs on multilayer printed circuit boards much faster than with digital ohmmeter. Maximum permissible resistance is 0.3 ohm, which gives voltage drop of 0.06 V when 200 mA is forced through. With opamp adjusted for voltage gain of 100, output of opamp is then 6 V. If resistance exceeds 0.31 ohm, detector-zener combination turns indicator lamp off.—D. Haggan, Tester Measures Resistance of Multilayer P-C Boards, *Electronics*, Sept. 16, 1968, p 100–101.

TRANSISTOR-DIODE-SCR TESTER—Measures leakage current and d-c current gain (beta) of transistors, indicates open or shorted junctions via lamp, indicates whether scr will conduct when current is furnished to gate and will turn off when voltage is removed, and checks for opens or shorts in diodes. Q1 and Q2 should have beta over 20. Article gives construction and calibration procedures.—M. Gross, Semiconductor Test Set, *Electronics World*, Nov. 1967, p 74–76.

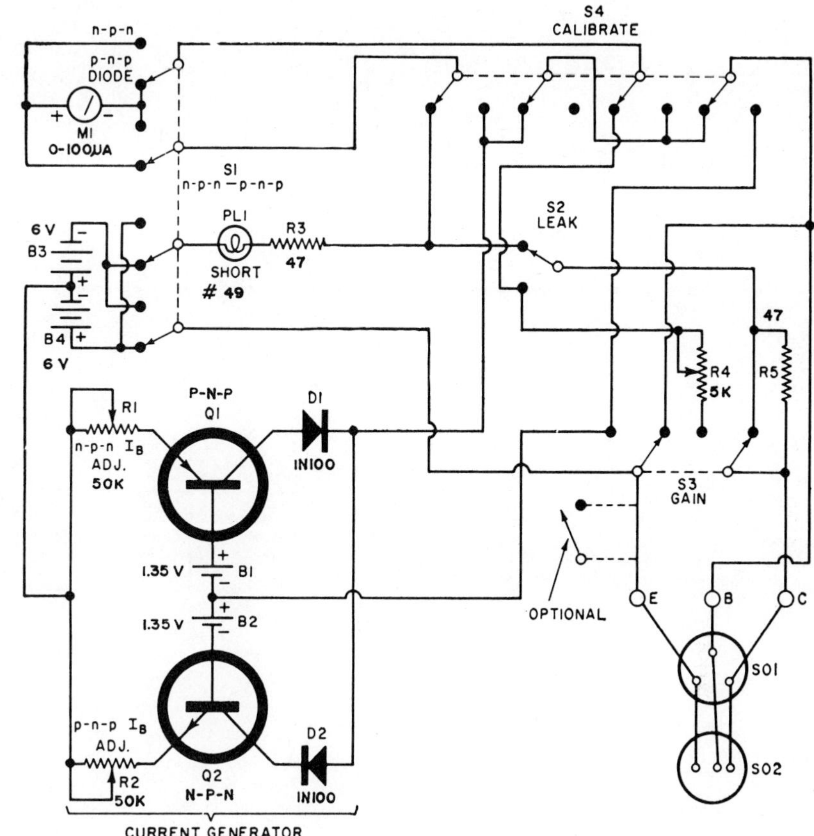

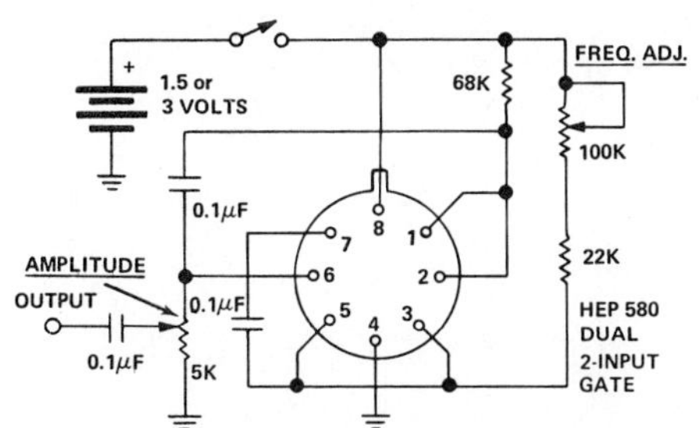

SIGNAL INJECTOR—Helps locate defective r-f or audio stage in radio or tv testing. Square-wave output is variable from 200 to 2,000 Hz, with amplitude adjustable from 0 to 1 V.—"Tips on Using IC's," Motorola, Phoenix, Ariz., HMA-32, 1968.

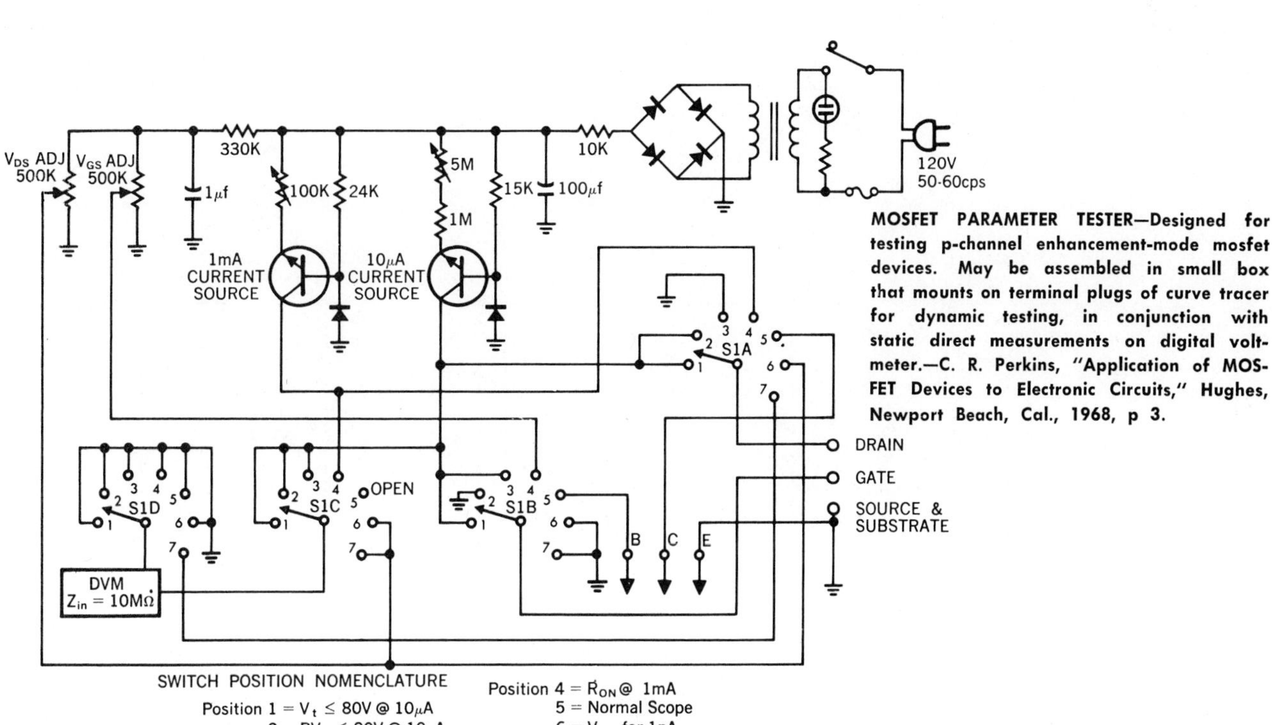

MOSFET PARAMETER TESTER—Designed for testing p-channel enhancement-mode mosfet devices. May be assembled in small box that mounts on terminal plugs of curve tracer for dynamic testing, in conjunction with static direct measurements on digital voltmeter.—C. R. Perkins, "Application of MOSFET Devices to Electronic Circuits," Hughes, Newport Beach, Cal., 1968, p 3.

SWITCH POSITION NOMENCLATURE

Position 1 = $V_t \leq 80V$ @ 10μA
2 = $BV_D \leq 80V$ @ 10μA
3 = $BV_G \leq 80V$ @ 10μA
Position 4 = R_{ON} @ 1mA
5 = Normal Scope
6 = V_{DS} for 1nA
7 = 1nA Adj Monitor

CHAPTER 89
Timer Circuits

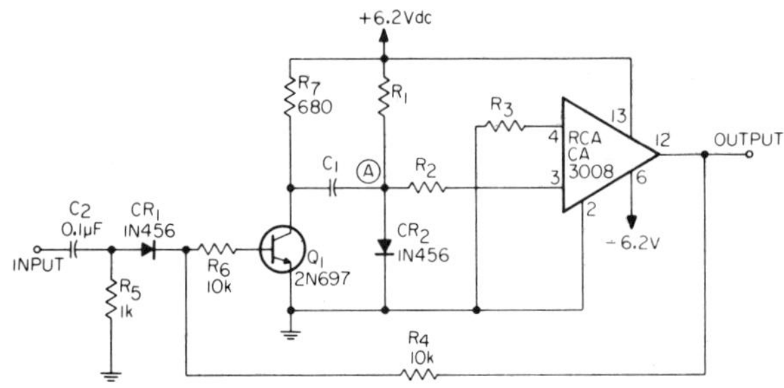

VARIABLE-DELAY ONE-SHOT—With C1 0.22 μF, R1 47–547K, and R2 and R3 10K, range of delay times is 7 to 80 ms. With C1 10 μF and other values same, range is 0.4–4 s. May also be used as countdown circuit or one-shot driving 1K load. IC opamp contributes to high performance. Input trigger should be greater than 2.5 V p-p, with 5-μs rise time and at least 10-μs pulse width.—W. R. Walters, IC Opamp Improves Stability of Monostable Multivibrator, *EEE*, Dec. 1967, p 92–93.

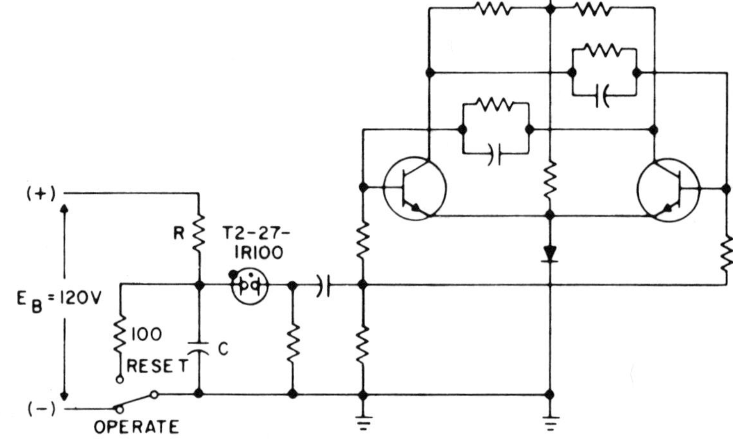

NEON-OPERATED FLIP-FLOP—Peak voltage and duration of driver pulse from neon are determined by value of capacitor between neon lamp and flip-flop. Book has nomograph (p 31) for determing values of R and C to give desired time.—E. Bauman, "Applications of Neon Lamps and Gas Discharge Tubes," Signalite, Neptune, N.J., p 61.

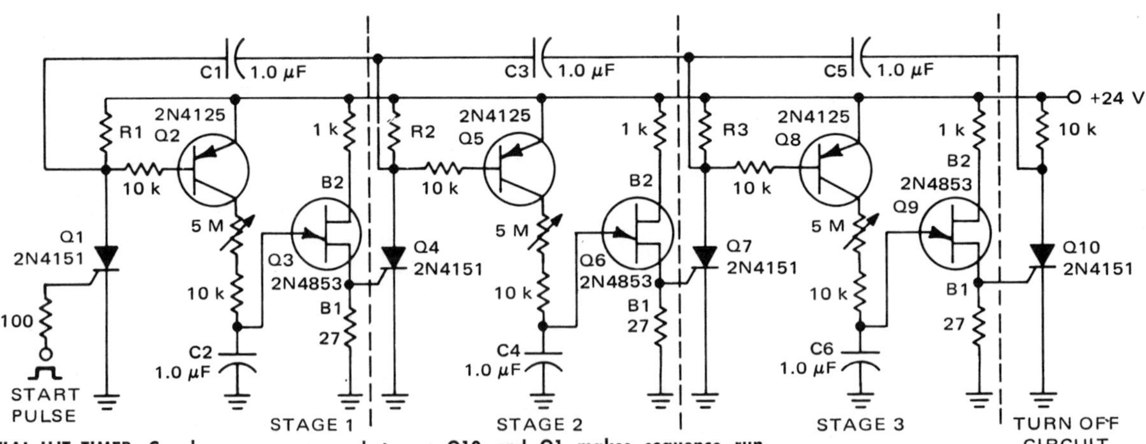

SEQUENTIAL UJT TIMER—Can have any number of stages. Output pulse from each stage follows that of previous stage by adjustable interval. Q10 serves only to turn off scr in last stage (Q7). Addition of timing circuit between Q10 and Q1 makes sequence run continuously. Delay time of each stage can be anywhere between 10 ms and 5 s, set by 5-meg pot. R1, R2, and R3 can be relays or other types of loads for scr's; if output pulses are desired from scr gates, these resistors should be 100 ohms.—"Semiconductor Power Circuits Handbook," Motorola, Phoenix, Ariz., 1968, p 6–27.

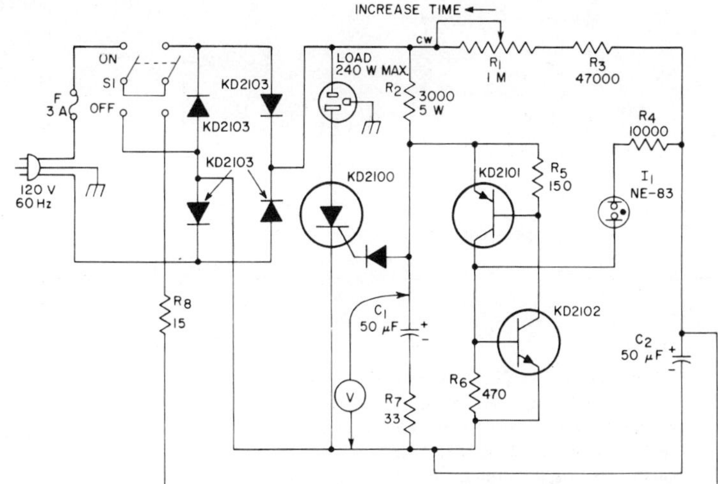

5–120 S TIMER FOR 240 W—Provides controlled on time for enlargers, house or garage lights, and universal motors, with automatic turn-off at end of interval by single scr in series with load.—"Silicon Controlled Rectifier Experimenter's Manual," RCA, Harrison, N.J., 1967, p 62.

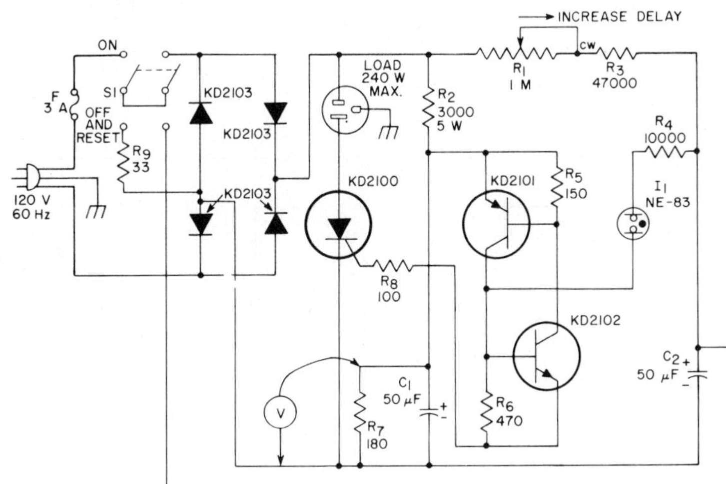

5–300 S TIMER FOR 240 W—Timing capacitor C2 gives maximum delay of 2 min before applying power with values shown, but larger capacitor will increase delay to 5 min. In addition to lamp, heater, and motor applications, can be used to turn on alarm at end of desired time interval such as for signaling 1-min limit of thinking time in chess or bridge game.—"Silicon Controlled Rectifier Experimenter's Manual," RCA, Harrison, N.J., 1967, p 66.

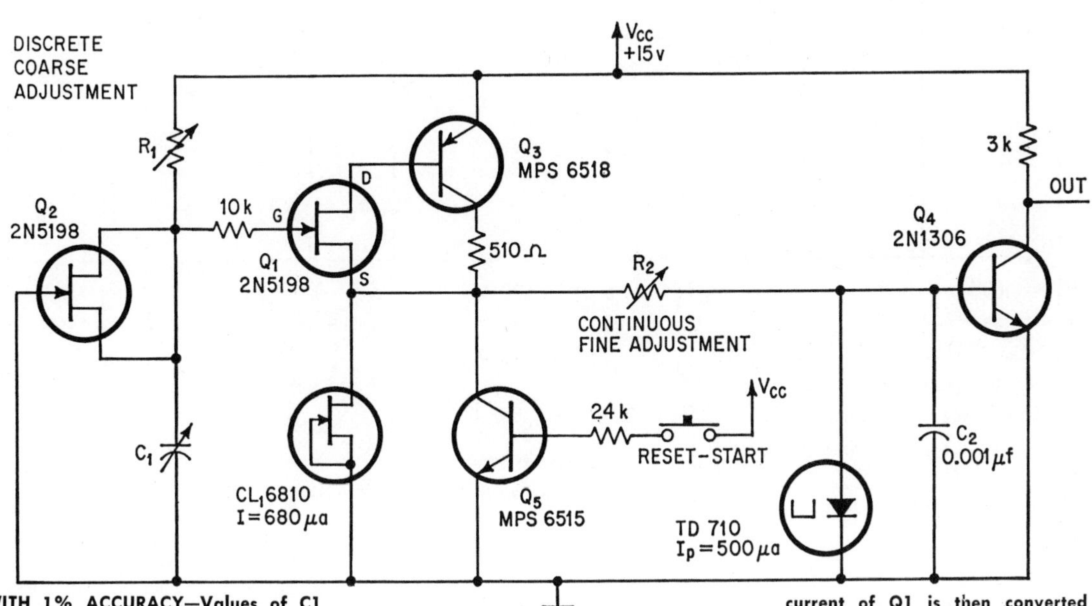

30 HR WITH 1% ACCURACY—Values of C1 and R2 have maximum effect on interval between input and output signals; 30-hr delay is obtained with 28K for R2 and 1 μF for C1. For 70-min delay, R1 is 100 billion ohms, R2 is 18K, and C1 is 0.1 μF. Circuit can also be used to measure small currents such as fet gate leakage currents in picoampere region, by removing R1 and Q2; leakage current of Q1 is then converted into time delay. With feedback from output to reset input, circuit can be used as current-frequency converter.—G. Black and K. C. Smith, BIFET Circuit Yields Time Delays Up to 30 Hours, *Electronics*, May 26, 1969, p 94.

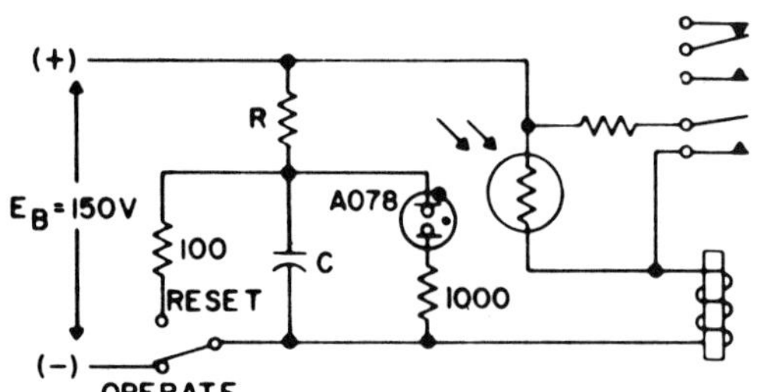

NEON-OPERATED PHOTOCELL—Light from neon reduces resistance of cadmium sulfide or cadmium selenide photocell, permitting relay to lock up. Book has nomograph (p 31) for determining values of R and C to give desired time.—E. Bauman, "Applications of Neon Lamps and Gas Discharge Tubes," Signalite, Neptune, N.J., p 59.

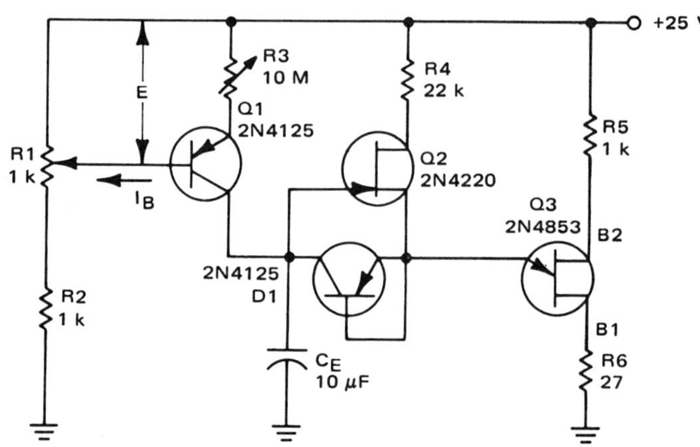

10-HR FET TIMER—Circuit is basically ujt sawtooth oscillator, in which conventional charging resistor for CE is replaced by current source Q1-R1-R2-R3. For timing accuracy of 10%, voltage supply must have 2.5% regulation. Book analyzes sources of error in timing.—"Semiconductor Power Circuits Handbook," Motorola, Phoenix, Ariz., 1968, p 6–24.

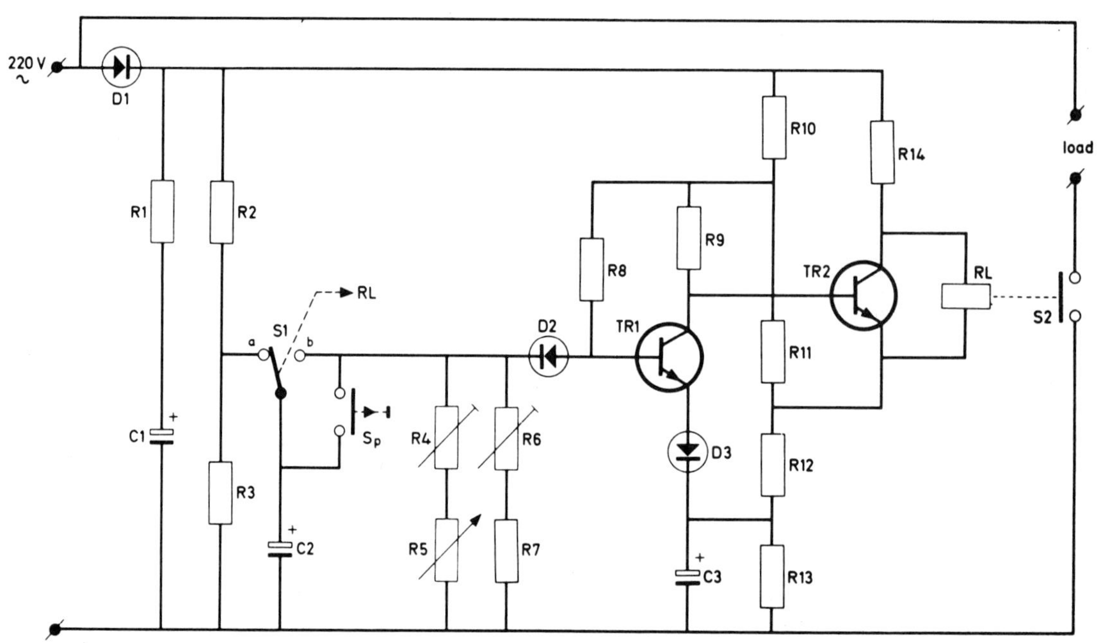

R_1 = 100 Ω; ¼ W
R_2 = 56 kΩ; 5.5 W
R_3 = 4.7 kΩ; ¼ W
R_4 = 20 kΩ; potentiometer
R_5 = 2 MΩ; potentiometer
R_6 = 2 MΩ; potentiometer
R_7 = 3.3 MΩ; ¼ W
R_8 = 2.7 MΩ; ¼ W
R_9 = 56 kΩ; ¼ W
R_{10} = 220 kΩ; 1 W
R_{11} = 4.7 kΩ; ¼ W
R_{12} = 120 Ω; ¼ W
R_{13} = 1.2 kΩ; ¼ W
R_{14} = 39 kΩ; 5.5 W

C_1 = 8 μF – 500 V
C_2 = 800 μF – 40 V (2222 060 17801)
C_3 = 5 μF – 16 V

RL = relay 35 V – 7 mA

D_1 = BYX10 or BY100
D_2 = OA200 or OA202
D_3 = OA202

TR_1 = BC147
TR_2 = BC147

HIGH-ACCURACY 20-MIN DELAY—Energizes relay with high reproducibility at end of delay interval that is continuously adjustable up to 20 min with R5. Setting of R4 determines minimum time and R6 maximum time. Operates from 220-V a-c line through half-wave rectifier D1, with relay connected to handle a-c load.—Transistorized Timers, Philips, Pub. Dept., Elcoma Div., Eindhoven, The Netherlands, No. 443, 1968.

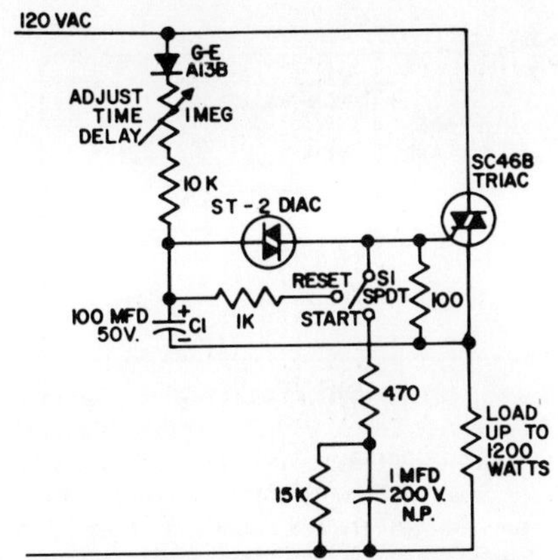

1-MINUTE DELAY FOR 1,200 W—Static a-c time delay, adjustable up to 1 min, handles inductive or resistive load. Simplicity of triac a-c latch is combined with low cost of diac triggering. For industrial and commercial control applications requiring delayed switching on of load and quick reset.—F. W. Gutzwiller and E. K. Howell, Economy Power Semiconductor Applications, General Electric, Syracuse, N.Y., No. 671.1, 1965, p 9.

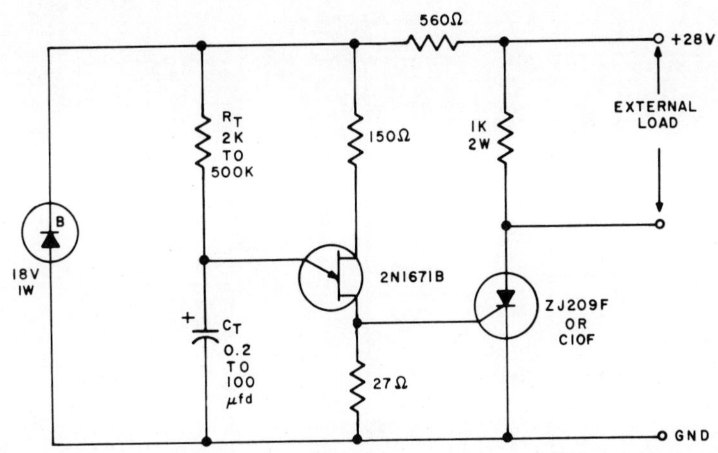

PRECISION UJT DELAY—Range of values indicated for RT and CT gives time delays from 0.4 ms to 1 minute. Load current is limited only by rating of scr. If RT is precision calibrated potentiometer such as Helipot, delay can be set accurately over wide range after one initial calibration.—T. P. Sylvan, The Unijunction Transistor Characteristics and Applications, General Electric, Syracuse, N.Y., No. 90.10, 1965, p 77.

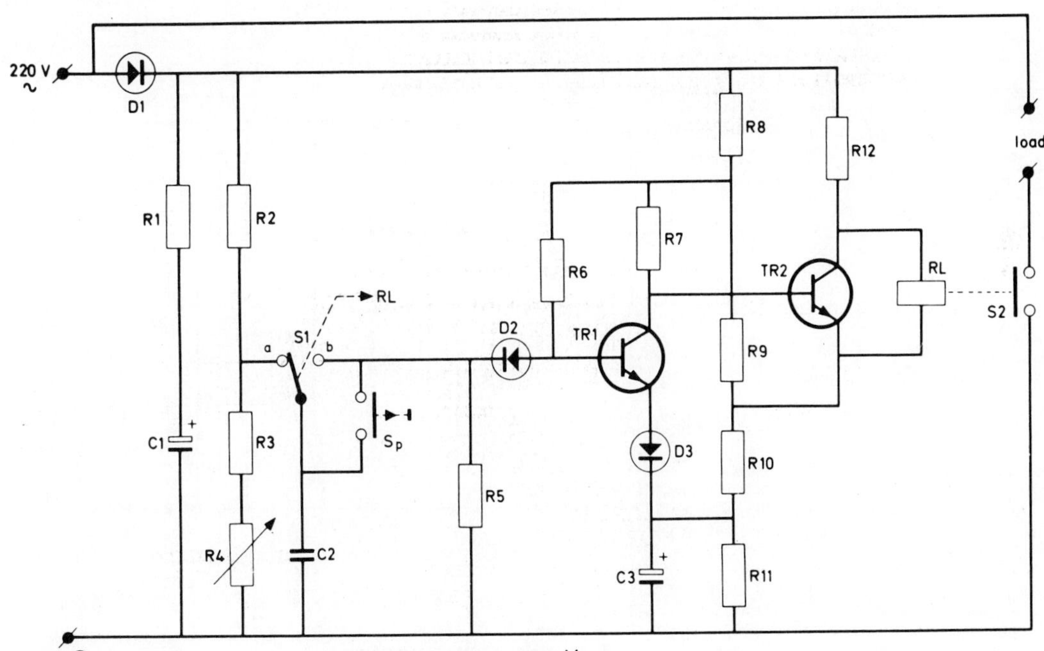

R_1 = 100 Ω; ¼ W
R_2 = 47 kΩ; 5.5 W
R_3 = 18 kΩ; 1 W
R_4 = 100 kΩ; potentiometer
R_5 = 27 MΩ; ¼ W
R_6 = 2.7 MΩ; ¼ W
R_7 = 56 kΩ; ¼ W
R_8 = 150 kΩ; 1 W
R_9 = 3.9 kΩ; ¼ W
R_{10} = 120 Ω; ¼ W
R_{11} = 10 kΩ; 1 W
R_{12} = 33 kΩ; 5.5 W

C_1 = 8 μF – 500 V
C_2 = 2×2.2 μF – 260 V
C_3 = 0.56 μF – 160 V

RL = relay 35 V – 7 mA

D_1 = BYX10 or BY100
D_2 = OA202
D_3 = OA202

TR_1 = BC147
TR_2 = BC147

2-MINUTE TIMER—Uses foil-dielectric timing capacitor having extremely small leakage current and narrow tolerances, to eliminate need for preadjustment of time. Switching time is adjusted by varying initial capacitor voltage with R4.—Transistorized Timers, Philips, Pub. Dept., Elcoma Div., Eindhoven, The Netherlands, No. 443, 1968.

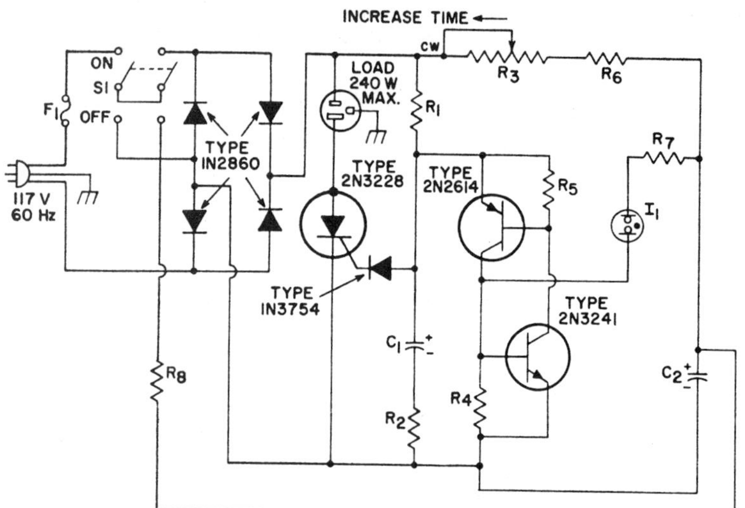

5–120 S TURN-ON TIMER FOR 240 W—Will turn off enlarger, heater, lamp, or universal motor after time interval determined by setting of R3, when S1 is set at ON position. OFF position of S1 serves to discharge timing capacitor C2 so circuit is reset. Values: R1 3K; R2 33; R3 1 meg; R4 470; R5 150; R6 47K; R7 10K; R8 15; C1-C2 50 μF; F1 3AG; I1 NE-83.—"Transistor Manual," RCA, Harrison, N.J., SC-13, p 524.

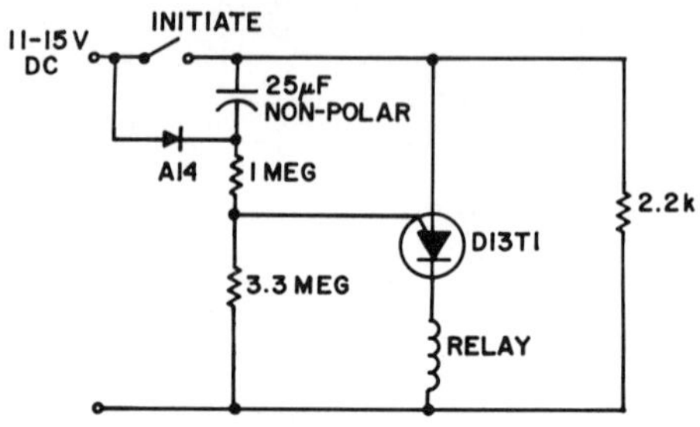

60-S DELAY WITH D13T1—Single programmable ujt serves both as sensitive time-delay element and as switch for applying power to load. When circuit is energized, capacitor charges to full supply voltage. When INITIATE switch is closed, diode side of capacitor raises to twice supply voltage, and capacitor discharges through resistors until gate of D13T1 becomes forward-biased and ujt turns on, applying power to relay. Delay is independent of supply voltage, in range of 40 to 60 s.—W. R. Spofford, Jr., The D13T—A Programmable Unijunction Transistor, General Electric, Syracuse, N.Y., No. 90.70, 1967, p 12.

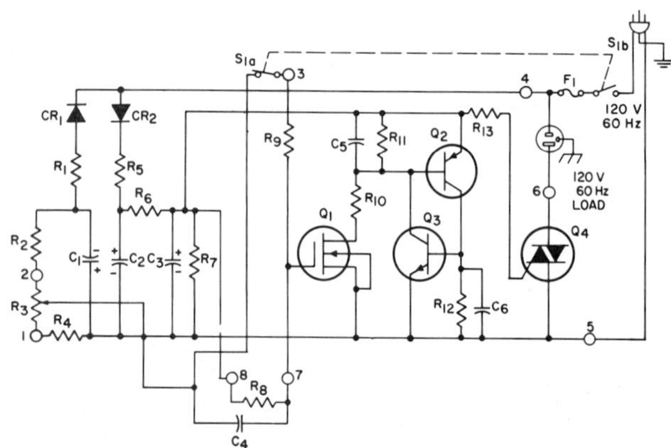

C1 = 10 microfarads, 200 volts, electrolytic
C2 = 10 microfarads, 200 volts, electrolytic
C3 = 50 microfarads, 15 volts, electrolytic
C4 = 4 microfarads, see text
C5 C6 = 0.01 microfarad, 25 volts or greater, 10%
CR1 CR2 = silicon rectifier, RCA SK3031
F1 = fuse, size depends on expected load
Q1 = MOS field-effect transistor, type 3N128
Q2 = transistor, RCA SK3005
Q3 = transistor, RCA SK3020
Q4 = triac, RCA 40503 or RCA 40429 (the RCA 40429 may be used with Wakefield No. NC401K or equivalent heat sink.)
R1 R5 = 100 ohms, 1/2 watt, 10%
R2 = 15,000 ohms, 1/2 watt, 10%
R3 = potentiometer, 10,000 ohms, linear taper
R4 = 1000 ohms, 1/2 watt, 10%
R6 = 3000 ohms, 5 watts, 10%
R7 = 390 ohms, 1/2 watt, 10%
R8 = 4.7 megohms, 1/2 watt, 10%, see text
R9 = 5.6 ohms, 1/2 watt, 10%
R10 = 3900 ohms, 1/2 watt, 10%
R11 = 150 ohms, 1/2 watt, 10%
R12 R13 = 470 ohms, 1/2 watt, 10%
S1 = switch, 125 volts, double-pole, double-throw, capable of handling the expected load.

UNIVERSAL TIMER—Turns electrical device off after predetermined interval determined by setting of R3. With 40503 triac, will handle loads up to 3.3 A. With 40429 triac, load without sink can be 2.7 A and up to 6 A with sink. For wider range of time periods, provisions can be made to switch in different values for R8 or C4.—"Hobby Circuits Manual," RCA, Harrison, N.J., HM-90, p 75.

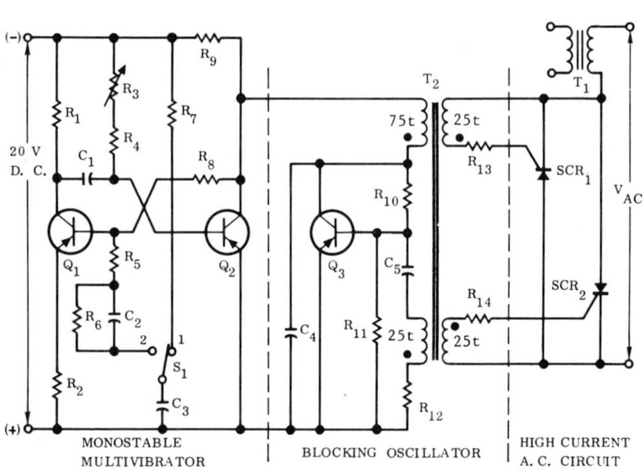

R_1 - 1.2 KΩ	R_9 - 180Ω	C_3 - 0.5 μfd	T_1 - Weld trans.
R_2 - 300Ω	R_{10} - 68 KΩ	C_4 - 240 μμfd	T_2 - Arnold Core #4T5651D1 turns as indicated on sketch above.
R_3 - 1 KΩ	R_{11} - 10 KΩ	C_5 - 0.01 μfd	
R_4 - 3 KΩ	R_{12} - 100Ω	Q_1 - 2N650	
R_5 - 240Ω	R_{13} - 10Ω	Q_2 - 2N650	
R_6 - 3 KΩ	R_{14} - 10Ω	Q_3 - 2N651	
R_7 - 5.1 KΩ	C_1 - 50 μfd	SCR_1 - 2N2577	
R_8 - 5.1 KΩ	C_2 - 0.1 μfd	SCR_2 - 2N2577	

A-C BURST WELDER—Controls time duration at which a-c line voltage is applied to welding transformer T1, over range of 20 ms to 1 s. 10-kHz blocking oscillator produces 2-μs trigger pulses for scr's under control of mono mvbr.—"Circuits Manual," Motorola, Phoenix, Ariz., 1965, p 9-4-3.

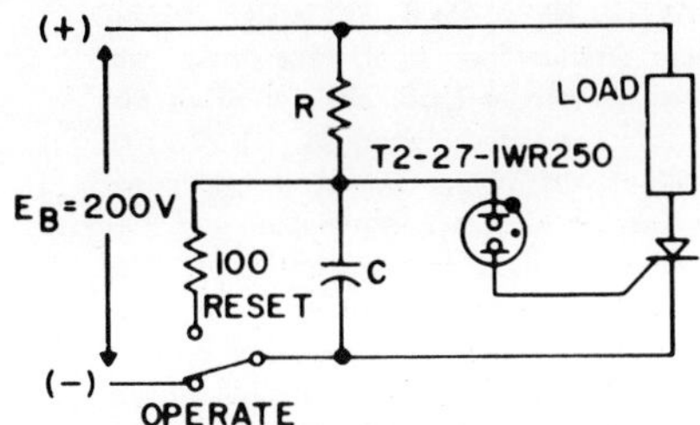

NEON-OPERATED SCR—Output from neon operates scr until circuit is reset. Book has nomograph (p 31) for determining values of R and C to give desired time.—E. Bauman, "Applications of Neon Lamps and Gas Discharge Tubes," Signalite, Neptune, N.J., p 60.

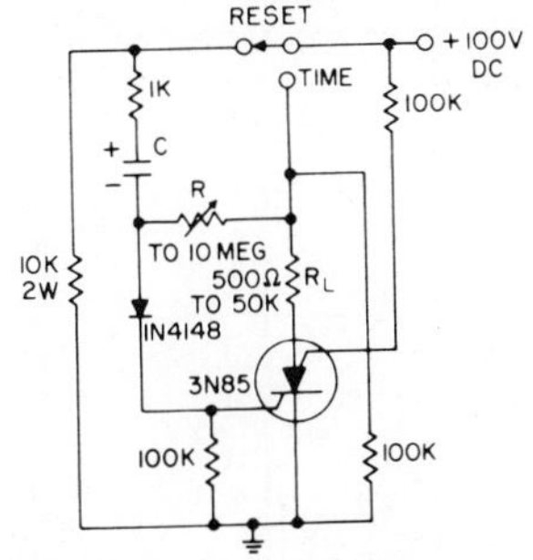

SCS TIMER—Load current begins about 0.5 RC after switch is set to TIME, and continues until switch is reset.—Planar Silicon Controlled Switch 3N84/3N85, General Electric, Syracuse, N.Y., No. 65.18, 1964.

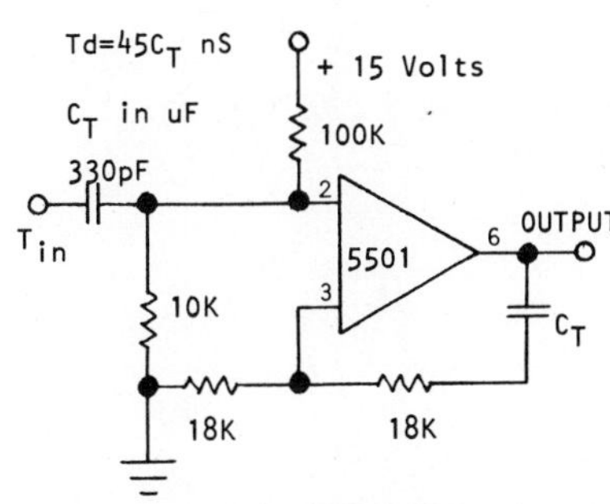

MICROSECONDS TO MINUTES—Comparator IC connected as shown behaves as one-shot delay in which value of CT determines timing interval. Output is normally at −10 V. Negative input trigger pulse makes output switch to +10 V and hold at that level until charge on CT drops to point where pin 3 of IC is less positive than pin 2; output then reverts to −10 V. Circuit has good noise immunity.—Applying the Model 5501 Monolithic Analog Comparator, Optical Electronics, Tucson, Ariz., No. 10147.

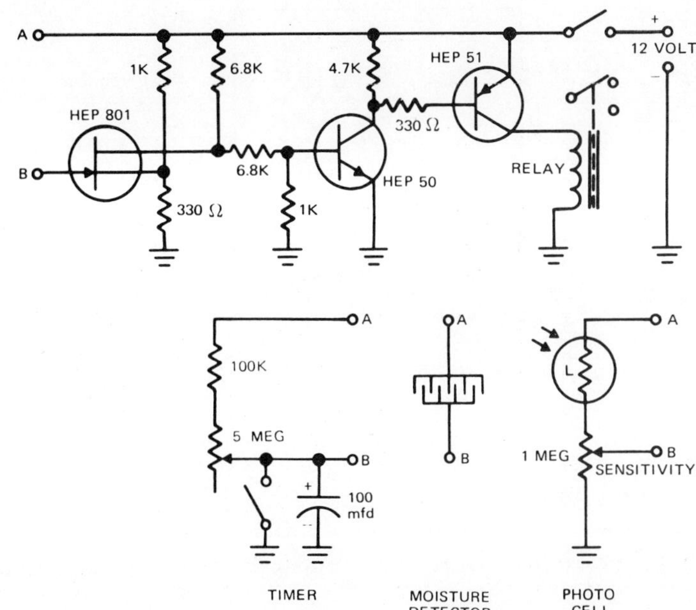

FET TIMER—Range is 5–50 s with values shown for timer input to terminals A-B. By substituting network of wires spaced 1/16" apart between A-B, circuit operates as moisture detector. With photocell, circuit becomes light-activated relay.—"Tips on FET's," Motorola, Phoenix, Ariz., HMA-33, 1969.

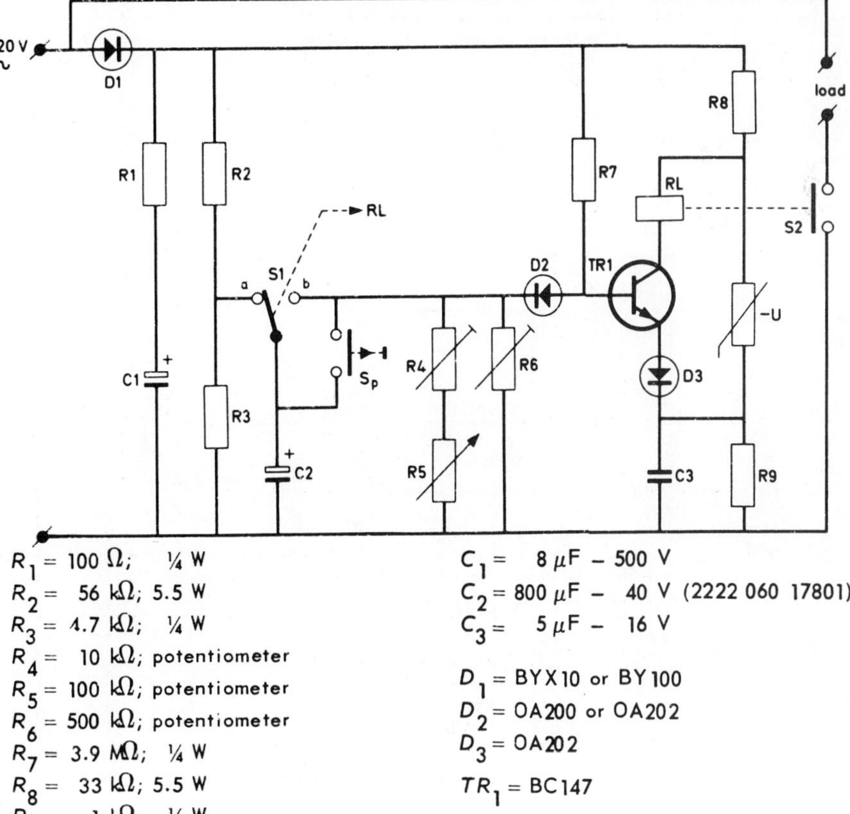

R_1 = 100 Ω; ¼ W
R_2 = 56 kΩ; 5.5 W
R_3 = 4.7 kΩ; ¼ W
R_4 = 10 kΩ; potentiometer
R_5 = 100 kΩ; potentiometer
R_6 = 500 kΩ; potentiometer
R_7 = 3.9 MΩ; ¼ W
R_8 = 33 kΩ; 5.5 W
R_9 = 1 kΩ; ¼ W
V.D.R. = 2322 552 02321

C_1 = 8 μF − 500 V
C_2 = 800 μF − 40 V (2222 060 17801)
C_3 = 5 μF − 16 V

D_1 = BYX10 or BY100
D_2 = OA200 or OA202
D_3 = OA202

TR_1 = BC147

RL = relay 35 V − 7 mA

1-MIN TIMER—Interval before relay is energized can be adjusted for delay up to 1 min. Uses voltage-dependent resistor to stabilize voltage across R9, eliminating need for excessively high bleeder current.—Transistorized Timers, Philips, Pub. Dept., Elcoma Div., Eindhoven, The Netherlands, No. 443, 1968.

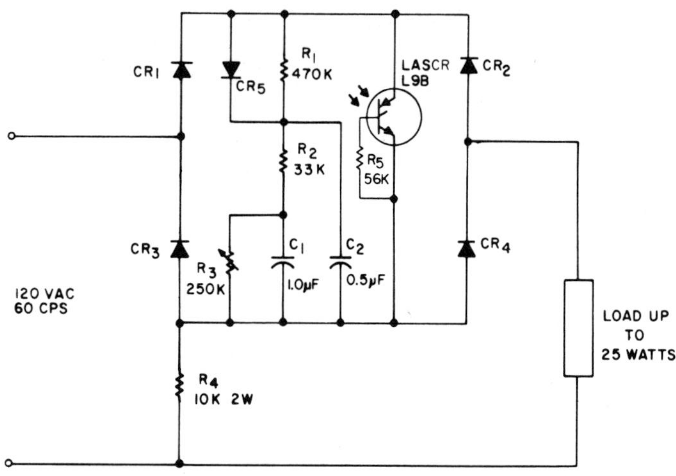

FLASH-ACTIVATED LASCR TURN-OFF DELAY—Random impulse of light fires lascr, applying full current to load, and initiating discharge of capacitors through R1-R3 and lascr. When discharge current drops below holding current of lascr, it goes off and cuts load current at next line current zero. Decreasing R3 reduces time that lascr stays on. During conduction, full sine wave is applied to load, with very little harmonic distortion, so rfi is negligible. Useful for driving lamps, solenoids, small motors, and other devices up to 25 W, particularly with optical programmer. Will turn on at any part of cycle, but go off only at zero.—E. K. Howell, The Light Activated SCR, General Electric, Syracuse, N.Y., No. 200.34, 1965.

6-MINUTE UJT—Simple two-ujt circuit provides 6-min delay that is accurate within 2% from −10 to 70 C. R4 provides fine adjustment of delay. Oscillator Q1 charges C2 at rate of one pulse per minute until voltage across C2 exceeds firing point of Q2.—G. E. Huffman, Unijunction Circuit Gives Long Time Delay, *Electronic Design*, Feb. 17, 1964, p 92–93.

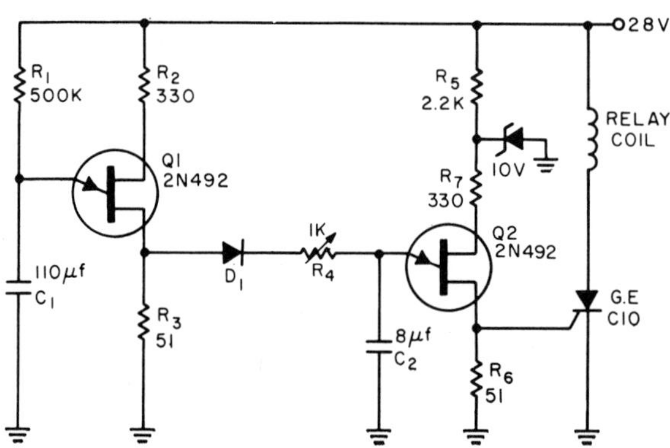

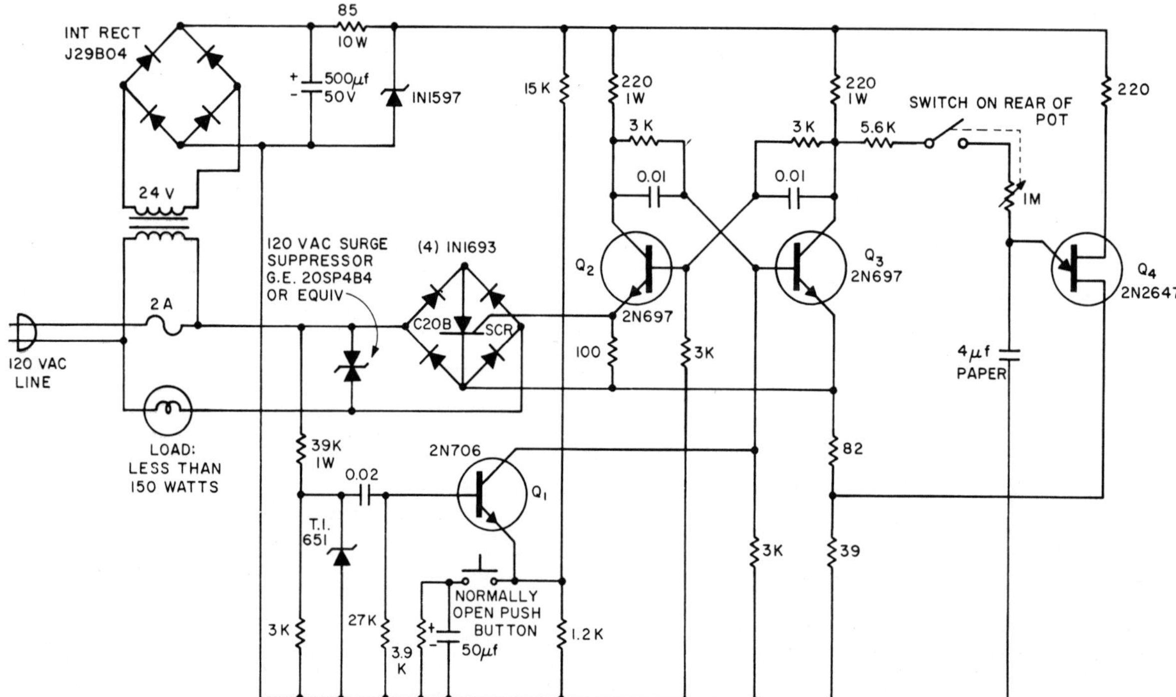

2 HZ TO 5 S—Accuracy is ideal for photographic work. Uses scr to gate diode bridge that drives ujt Q4 through binary Q2-Q3. Q1 acts as AND gate to eliminate starting ambiguity. Timing range can be extended by using larger timing capacitors. When switch on rear of pot is open, timer is bypassed for focusing.—R. A. Kawcyn, Solid-State Timer Expands Time Interval Range, *Electronic Design*, Aug. 31, 1964, p 46 and 48.

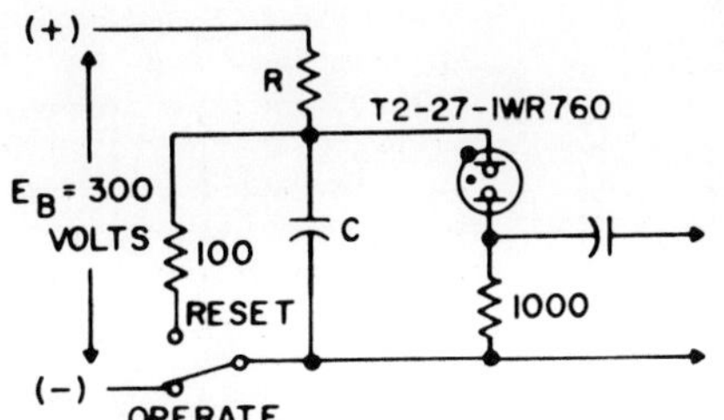

NEON TIMER—Output is positive-going pulse of at least 100 V. Duration is determined by value of capacitor before output. Book has nomograph (p 31) for determining values of R and C to give desired time delay.—E. Bauman, "Applications of Neon Lamps and Gas Discharge Tubes," Signalite, Neptune, N.J., p 61.

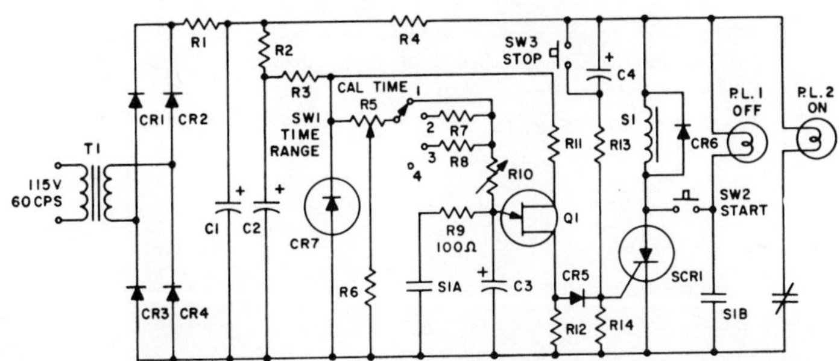

R1 - 2Ω, 1 WATT
R2, R3 - 330Ω, 1/2 WATT
R4 - 35Ω, 5 WATT
R5 - 2.5K, LINEAR POT
R6 - 25K, 1/2 WATT
R7 - 100K, 1/2%, 1/2 WATT
R8 - 200K, 1/2%, 1/2 WATT
R9 - 10Ω, 1/2 WATT
R10 - 100K, 10 TURN HELIPOT
R11 - 150Ω, 1/2 WATT
R12 - 18Ω, 1/2 WATT
R13 - 1.2K, 2 WATT
R14 - 100Ω, 1/2 WATT
C1 - 500μFD, 50V
C2 - 100μ FD, 50V
C3 - 100μFD, 20V TANTALUM
C4 - 10μFD, 50V
SCR1 - GE C15F OR C11F
CR1 - CR6 - G E A13A
CR7 - 18V, 10% 1 WATT ZENER
Q1 - GE 2N1671B
S1 - GE CR2791G122A4 4PDT RELAY
PL1, PL2 - GE 1447, 24V LAMP
T1 - 115V/25V 1A TRANSFORMER

0.25–10.25 S—Uses pushbutton initiation of timing sequence, with relay output. Timing interval is determined by setting of precision 10-turn Helipot R10, in increments of 0.01 s. Minimum value of 0.25 s is due to series resistance of time calibration pot R5. SW1 adds 100K series resistance R7 to extend time range by 10 s, and 200K for 20 s. In position 4, SW1 opens timing resistor circuit to give on-off control. Absolute timing accuracy is 0.5% after initial calibration, and repeatability is 0.05%.—"SCR Manual," 4th Edition, General Electric, 1967, p 164–165.

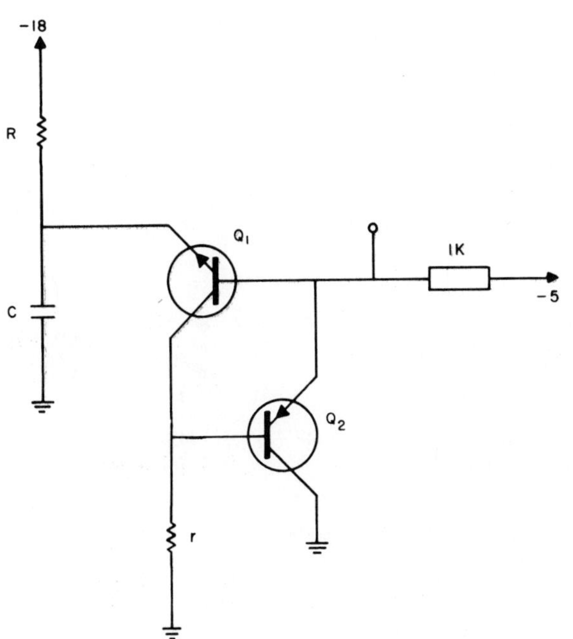

HALF AN HOUR—Inexpensive modification of astable mvbr permits use of relatively small values of C to produce time delays up to 30 min. Component values are determined by delay time t = RC and R = 10 r. R can be 30 meg or more. Q1 is 2N1308 and Q2 is 2N1309.—J. L. Johansen, Modified Astable Multivibrator Produces Very Long Time Delay, *Electronic Design*, May 10, 1965, p 48–49.

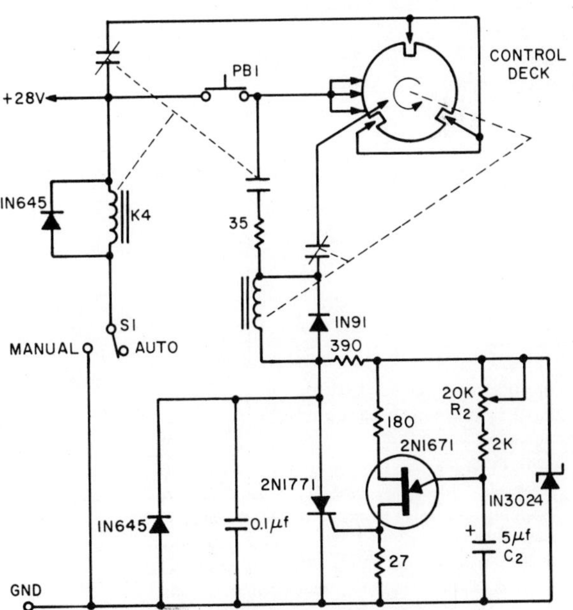

20–200 MS FOR STEPPER—R2 controls amount of delay between closing of pushbutton and stepping of 7-A rotary selector switch to next position, when circuit switch S1 is in position shown for automatic homing. Selector switch sequences additional positions until home position is reached. In manual mode, pushbutton sequences selector one position for each closure.—E. G. McCoy, Adjustable Time Delay For Rotary Switches, *Electronic Design*, April 13, 1964, p 72–73.

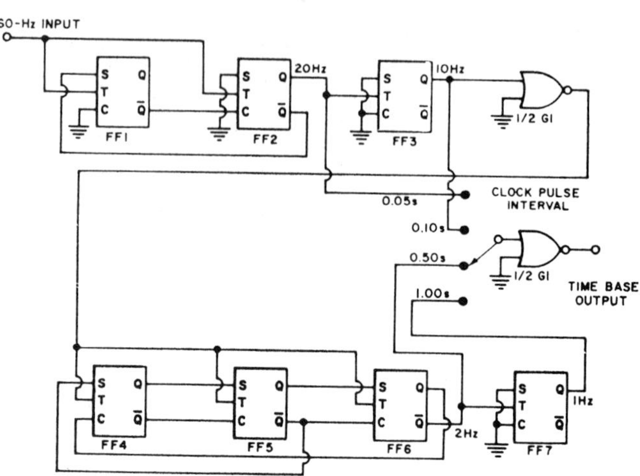

FOUR RANGES TO 15 S—Use of Fairchild RTμL 9923 JK flip-flops and RTμL 9914 dual two-input gates dramatically simplifies construction by experimenters of IC interval timer that would otherwise require 211 transistors and 271 resistors. Time-base generator arrangement shown provides accurately spaced clock pulses when enabled by control section, for counting during duration of event being timed, in four ranges covering 0.05 to 15 s.—D. L. Steinbach, A Digital IC Timer, *Electronics World*, May 1969, p 48–50.

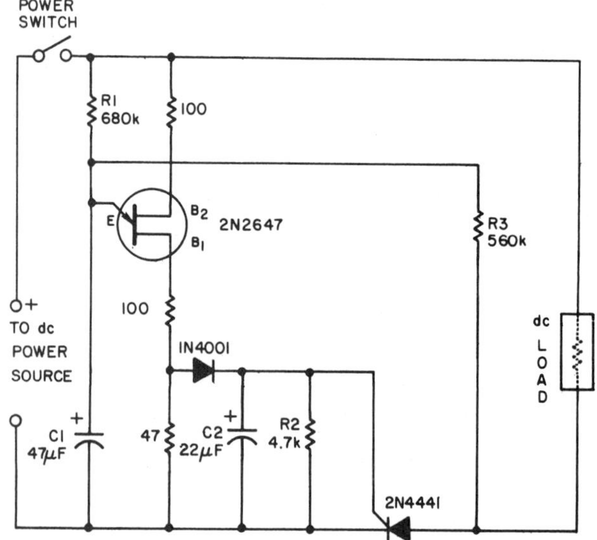

DOUBLE DELAY—Provides adjustable turn-on delay of up to 30 s after power is applied, controlled by R1-C1, and turn-off delay controlled by R2-C2. Circuit is immune to power interruptions up to several ms and will not reset for them. Operates from 12 to 36 V d-c.—G. W. Vest, Timing Circuit Has Independent Turn-On and Turn-Off Delays, *Electronic Design*, Aug. 16, 1969, p 238.

SEQUENCED TIMER—Versatile ujt-scr arrangement, operating from 24 V d-c, may have as many stages as are required, each with preset timing or transducer-triggered time intervals. Ideal for automatic starting and stopping controls, vending machines, process control, traffic control, and other sequence programmer applications. Handles loads up to 1 A, such as heater, lamps, motors, and relays.—F. W. Gutzwiller and E. K. Howell, Economy Power Semiconductor Applications, General Electric, Syracuse, N.Y., No. 671.1, 1965, p 5.

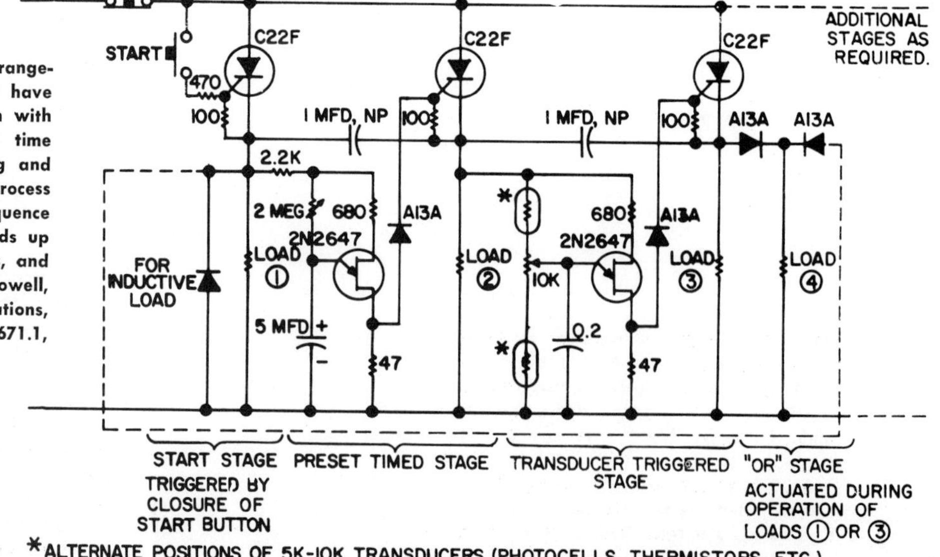

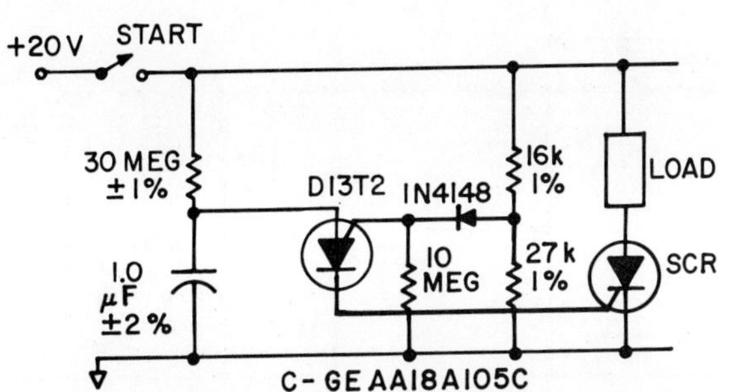

30 S WITH D13T2—Programmable ujt provides 30-s delay after switch is closed, before scr turns on and applies power to load. With tolerances shown for components, calibration is unnecessary.—W. R. Spofford, Jr., The D13T—A Programmable Unijunction Transistor, General Electric, Syracuse, N.Y., No. 90.70, 1967, p 11.

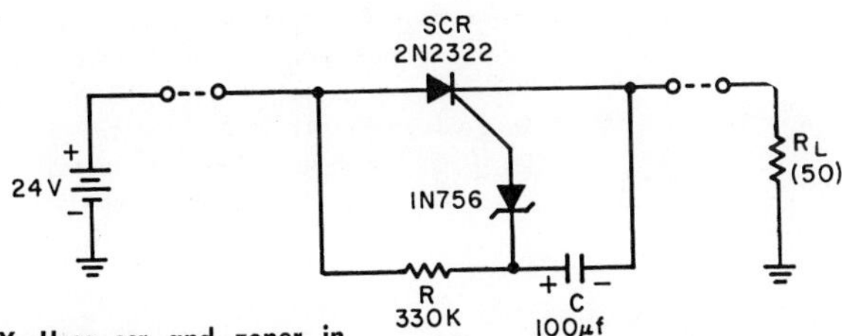

10-S POWER DELAY—Uses scr and zener in place of relay to apply power to 500-mA load 10 s after 24-V battery is switched on. Values of R, C, and zener can be changed to give different delay.—J. A. Means, SCR and Zener Diode Provide Time Delay, *Electronic Design*, March 30, 1964, p 73–75.

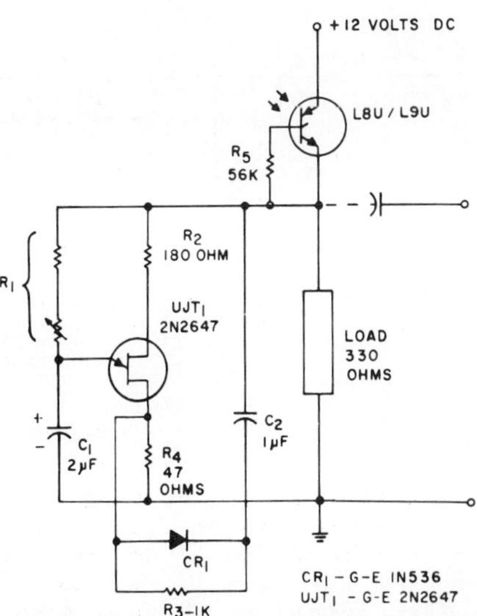

LASCR VARIABLE-PULSE-WIDTH TURN-OFF DELAY—Incident light triggers lascr and applies power to load. Voltage drop across load activates ujt timing-turn-off circuit, with delay determined by R1, C1, and ujt, to turn off load in interval of up to several seconds.—E. K. Howell, The Light Activated SCR, General Electric, Syracuse, N.Y., No. 200.34, 1965.

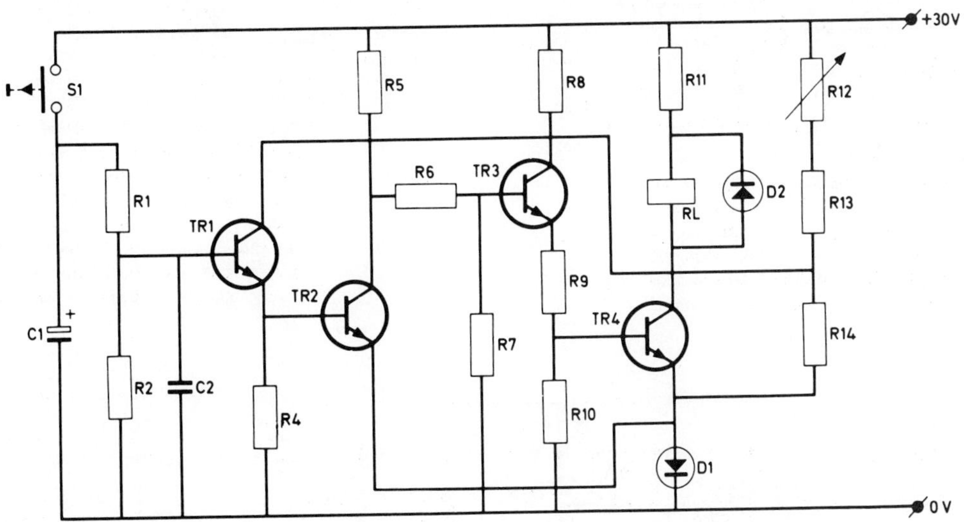

R_1 = 390 kΩ; 1/8 W
R_2 = 560 kΩ 1/8 W
R_4 = 6.8 kΩ; 1/8 W
R_5 = 12 kΩ; 1/8 W
R_6 = 5.6 kΩ 1/8 W
R_7 = 4.7 kΩ 1/8 W
R_8 = 1.2 kΩ; 1/4 W
R_9 = 270 Ω; 1/8 W
R_{10} = 270 Ω; 1/8 W
R_{11} = 10 Ω; 1 W
R_{12} = 1 kΩ; potentiometer
R_{13} = 330 Ω; 5.5 W
R_{14} = 33 Ω; 1/4 W
C_1 = 800 μF; 40 V (2222 060 17801)
C_2 = 100 nF;
RL = relay 24 V – 300 mA
TR_1 = BC147
TR_2 = BC147
TR_3 = AC127
TR_4 = AC127
D_1 = BY100
D_2 = OA200

14-MIN TIMER—Operates from 30-V d-c supply and energizes relay after 14-min delay.—Transistorized Timers, Philips, Pub. Dept., Elcoma Div., Eindhoven, The Netherlands, No. 443, 1968.

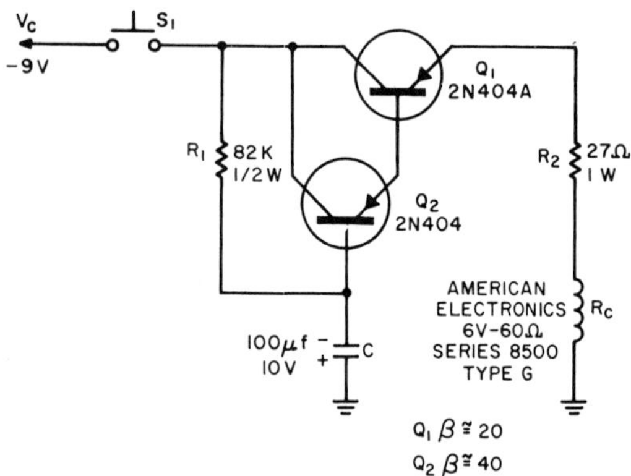

COST-CUTTING RELAY DELAY—Darlington connection of transistors gives time delay of 8 s for relay pull-in with values shown. With larger values of C, delay can be several minutes. For still greater delays, use higher-beta transistors and higher-resistance relay coil. Article gives delay equation.—M. Leopold and A. L. Plevy, Relay Arrangement Increases Time Delay—Reduces Cost, *Electronic Design*, Dec. 21, 1964, p 55–56.

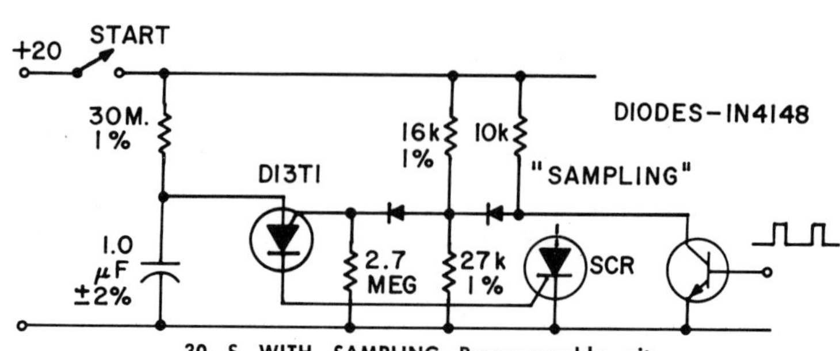

30 S WITH SAMPLING—Programmable ujt provides 30-s delay after switch is closed, before scr turns on and applies power to load that is connected between anode of scr and +20 V. Both diodes are 1N4148; right-hand diode serves with 10K resistor and sampling transistor to apply external 1-kHz pulse train for modulating intrinsic standoff voltage once per ms to sample capacitor voltage during delay interval.—W. R. Spofford, Jr., The D13T—A Programmable Unijunction Transistor, General Electric, Syracuse, N.Y., No. 90.70, 1967, p 11.

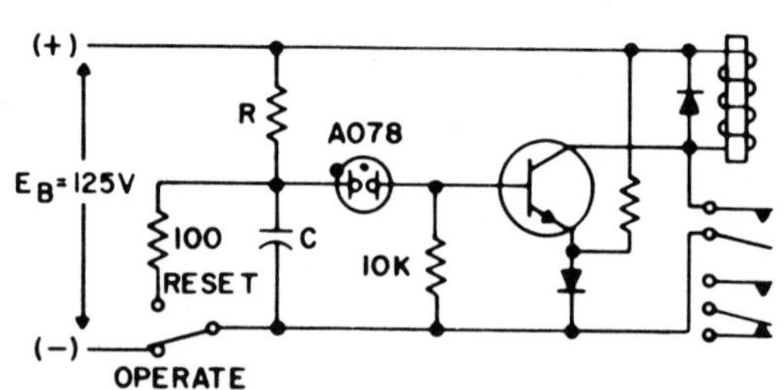

NEON-OPERATED TRANSISTOR—Output from neon operates transistor which pulls in relay. Book has nomograph (p 31) for determining values of R and C to give desired time.—E. Bauman, "Applications of Neon Lamps and Gas Discharge Tubes," Signalite, Neptune, N.J., p 60.

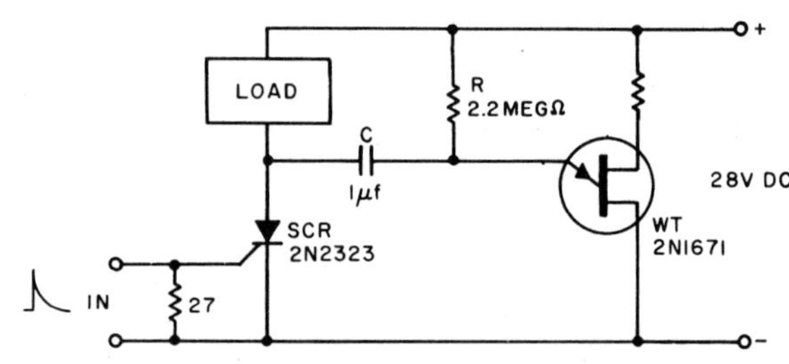

PULSE-TRIGGERED 4-S TIMER—Can be triggered by pulse as short as a few microseconds, to apply power to load for time duration determined by RC time constant. Inductive load requires clamping, along with parallel resistor to facilitate triggering.—A. Balint, SCR and UJT Form Simple Precision Timer, *Electronic Design*, Sept. 14, 1964, p 76.

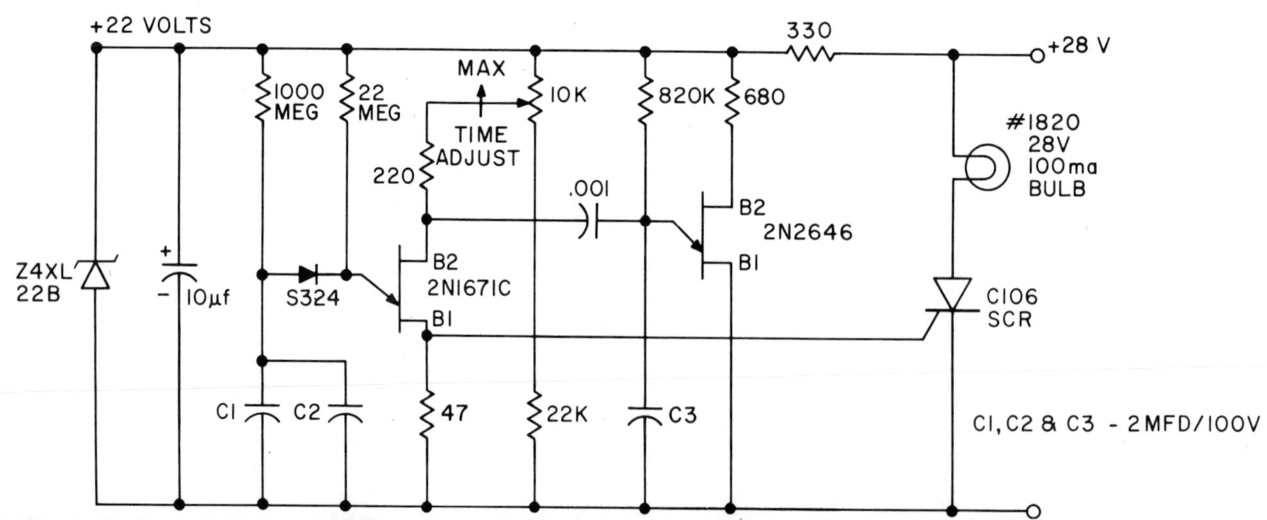

45-MIN TIMER—Gives long and adjustable time delays without using tantalum or electrolytic capacitors. Uses low-cost 2N2646 ujt to apply sampling pulse to base 2 of other ujt, thereby reducing required trigger current by 1,000:1 or more.—D. V. Jones, Semiconductor Timers and Low Frequency Oscillators, General Electric, Syracuse, N.Y., No. 671.3, 1966, p 15.

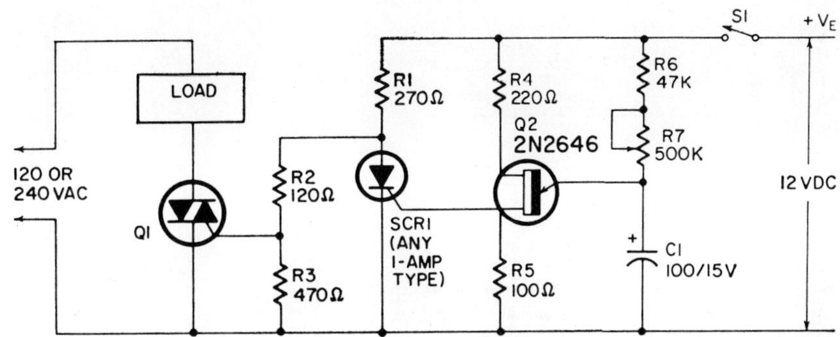

8–80 S TURN-OFF DELAY—Closing S1 makes triac turn on and handle up to 6 A load current. After interval determined by setting of R7, ujt fires and delivers trigger pulse that turns on scr and makes it self-latch. This breaks drive to triac gate and triac turns off. Circuit is reset by opening S1 briefly. Use RCA 40429 triac for 120 V and 40430 for 240 V.—R. M. Marston, 20 Triac Circuits, *Radio-Electronics*, June 1970, p 51–53 and 97.

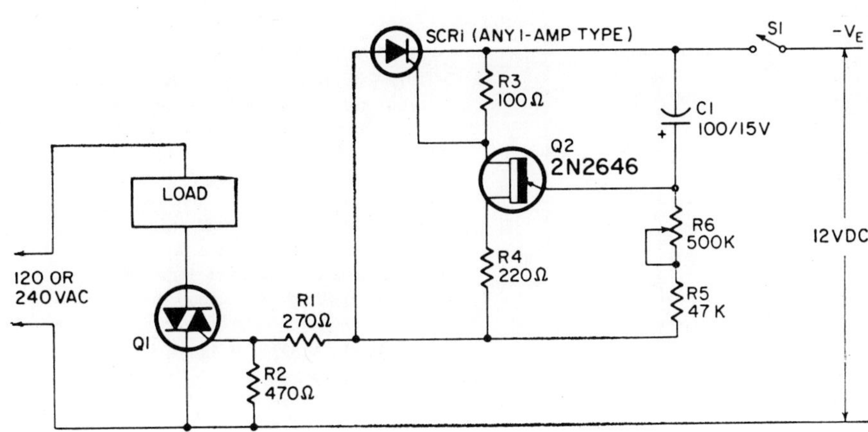

8–80 S DELAYED TURN-ON—R6 determines interval between closing of S1 and turning on of triac Q1 by ujt and scr. Triac then remains on as long as S1 is closed. Use RCA 40429 triac for 120 V and 40430 for 240 V.—R. M. Marston, 20 Triac Circuits, *Radio-Electronics*, June 1970, p 51–53 and 97.

INTERVAL TIMER FOR 3-A D-C LOAD—Timing cycle is initiated by low-level (minimum of 1 V) 5-μs pulse applied to terminal A, which turns on scr CS-1 to supply power to load. Simultaneously, CS-2 is turned off and C2 begins charging through R2, R3, and R4. Zener minimizes timing error. When charge reaches 7.5 V, Z1 conducts and makes CS-2 fire, 1 s after initiating pulse, to turn off CS-1 and remove power from load. D1 and R3 discharge C2 rapidly, to keep recycle time under 1 ms.—Interval Timer for High Level Output, Solid State Products, Salem, Mass., No. 1.

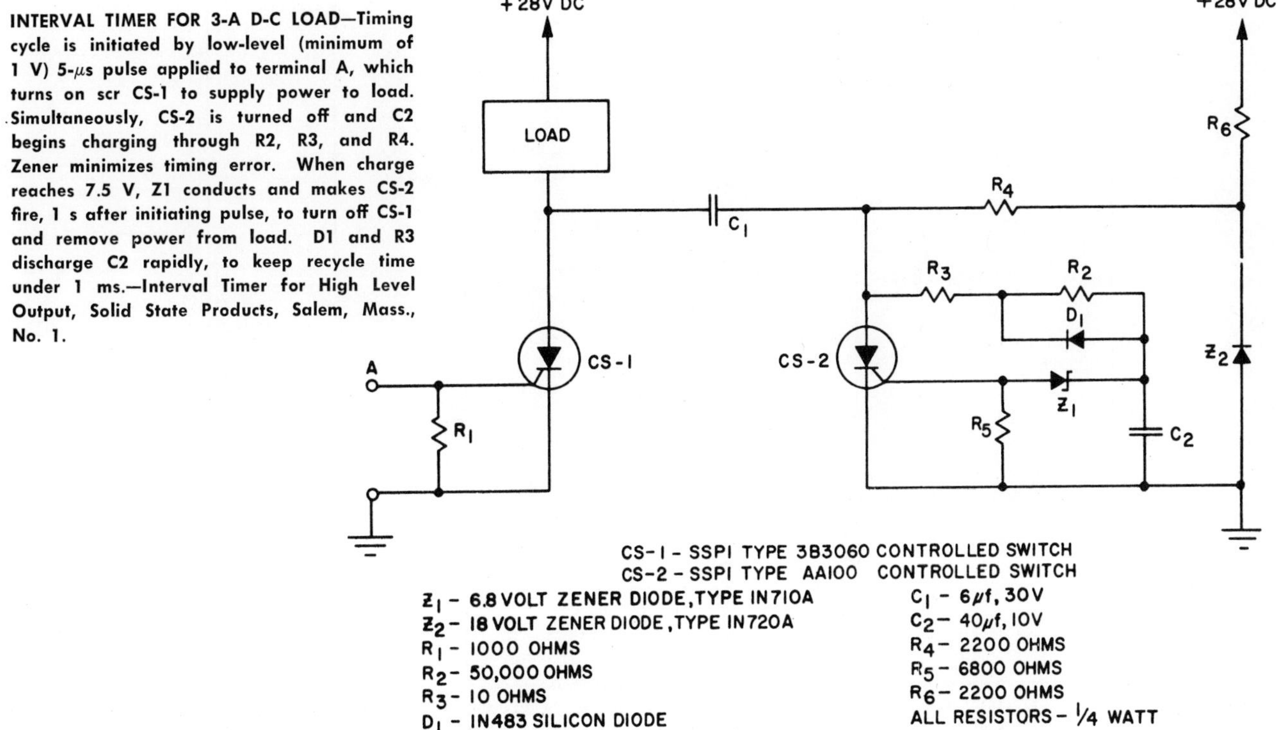

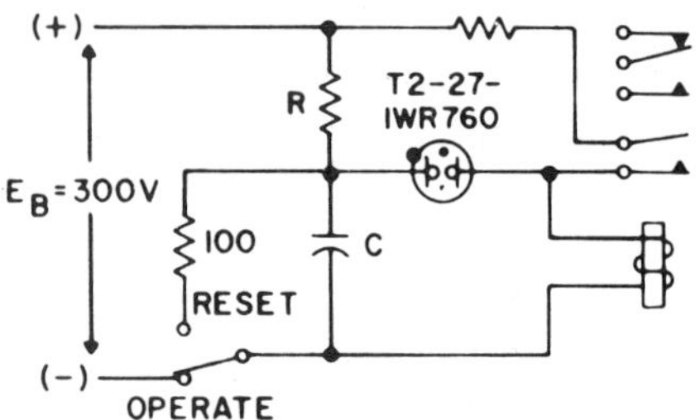

NEON TIMER—Relay latches when capacitor charges to breakdown voltage of lamp. Book has nomograph (p 31) for determining values of R and C to give desired time.—E. Bauman, "Applications of Neon Lamps and Gas Discharge Tubes," Signalite, Neptune, N.J., p 58.

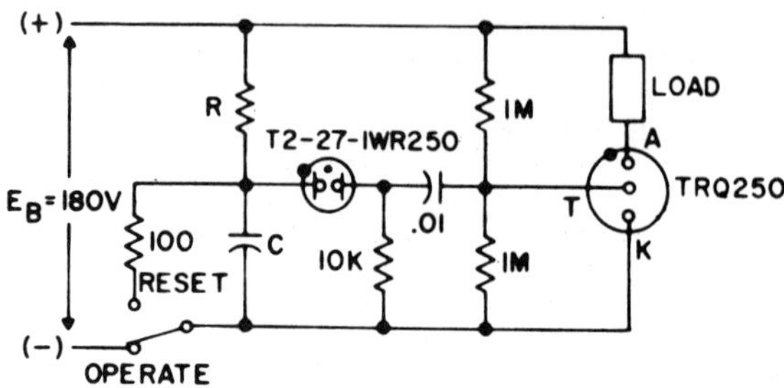

NEON-PULSED THYRATRON—Output pulse from neon causes thyratron to ignite and remain on until circuit is reset. Handles ½-W load. Book has nomograph (p 31) for determining values of R and C to give desired time.—E. Bauman, "Applications of Neon Lamps and Gas Discharge Tubes," Signalite, Neptune, N.J., p 59.

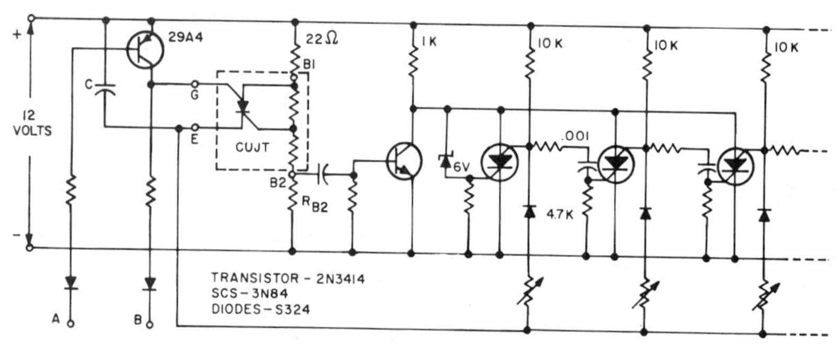

SEQUENTIAL TIMER—RC timer is driven from scs ring counter at right. Only one scs is on at a time, with successive timer output pulses at B2 advancing ON stage to right. Time interval is adjustable for each scs stage. Timer itself uses four-lead complementary ujt such as 3N81 (dashed box), which can be inhibited from firing by applying appropriate voltages to terminals A and B.—W. R. Spofford, Jr., Complementary Unijunction Transistor, General Electric, Syracuse, N.Y., No. 90.72, 1968, p 14.

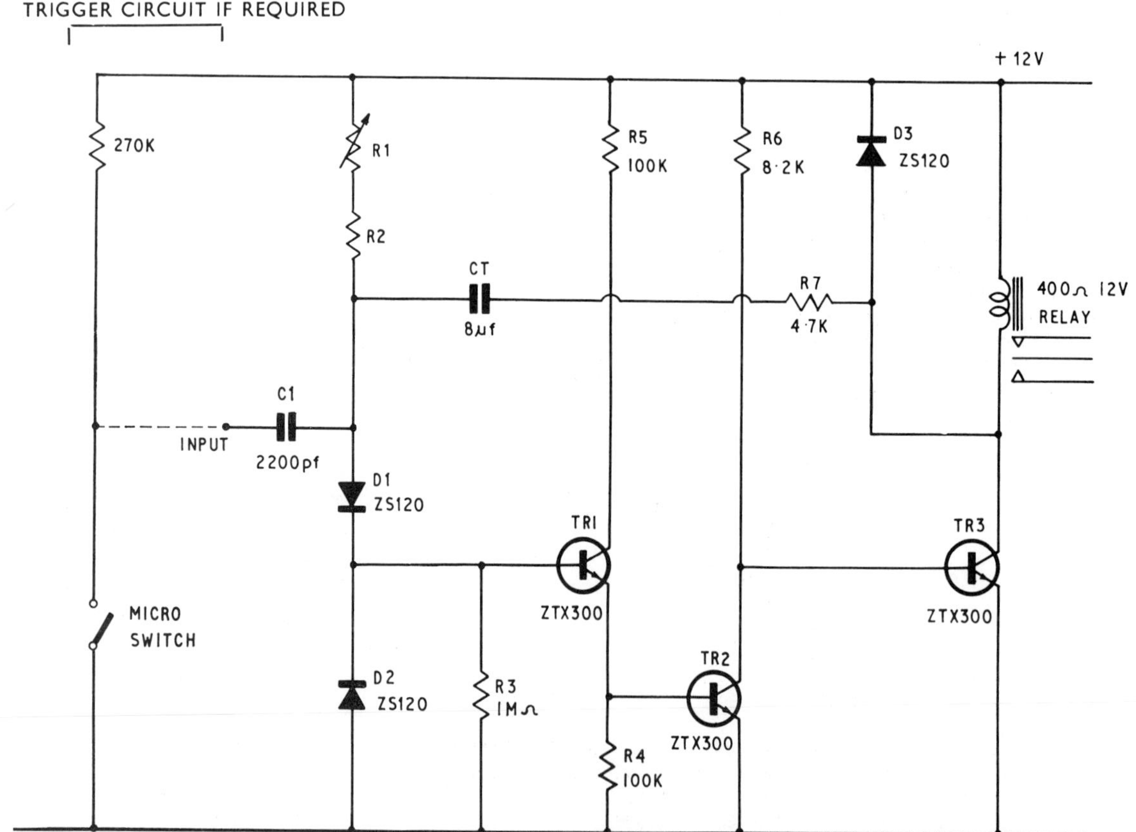

PROCESS TIMER—Holds relay closed for time interval adjustable between 1 and 10 s after timing action is initiated by negative input pulse from external circuitry or by simple microswitch. For range of 1 to 10 s, R2 is 200K and R1 is 2-meg pot.—E-Line Transistor Applications, Ferranti Ltd., Oldham, Lancs., England, 1969, p 40.

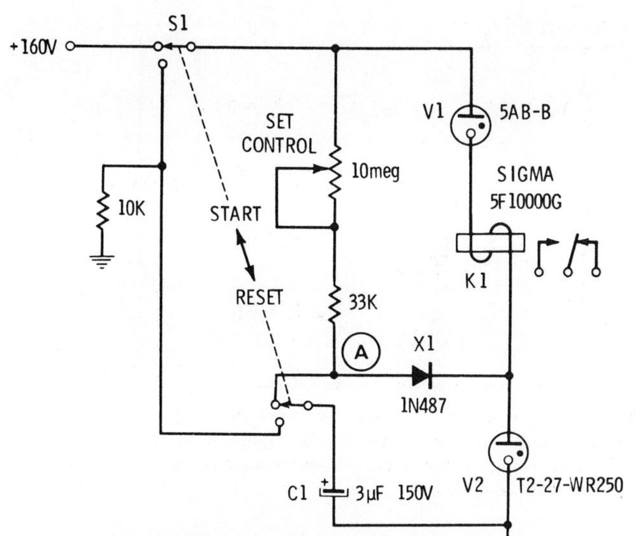

0.1—25 S NEON TIMER—Gives wide range of delays for relay operation after power is applied with S1. Power must be removed with S1 to release relay after it pulls in.—W. G. Miller, "Using and Understanding Miniature Neon Lamps," Howard W. Sams & Co., Indianapolis, Ind., 1969, p 72.

R5
+28V
CR2
EXTERNAL LOAD
RI
R2
R3
QI
CRI
SCRI
CI
R4
GND

RI - 2.2K, I/2 WATT
R2 - IK TO 500K LINEAR POT
R3 - 150Ω, I/2 WATT
R4 - 27, Ω, I/2 WATT
R5 - 560Ω, 2 WATT
CI - 0.2 TO 100 MFD, 15V
SCRI - GE C22F OR CIIF
CRI - 18V, 10%, I WATT ZENER, IN1776
CR2 - GE A13A
QI - GE 2N1671B

UJT-SCR DELAY—Simple, versatile, and accurate circuit applies power to load at predetermined interval after initiating signal is applied. Timing is initiated either by applying supply voltage or opening shorting contact across C1. Delay depends on values of R1, R2, and C1. For reset, scr must be turned off by momentarily shorting it or by opening d-c supply.—"SCR Manual," 4th Edition, General Electric, 1967, p 163—164.

VERSATILE TIMER—Easily assembled one-transistor circuit pulls in relay when switch S1 is closed, charging C1 to battery supply voltage. C1 then discharges and turns on Q1, which pulls in relay. Circuit stays in this condition until C1 is discharged below saturation level of Q1, as determined by setting of R3, to turn off Q1 and release relay. Gives choice of intervals from 10 to 100 s, and even greater timing range if values of R1 and C1 are changed. No on-off switch is required in battery circuit, because leakage through transistor when it is off is only about 1 µA. Can be used for enlarger control in dark room or for delay in turning off garage light.—"Calectro Handbook," GC Electronics, Rockford, Ill., FR-69-C, p 45.

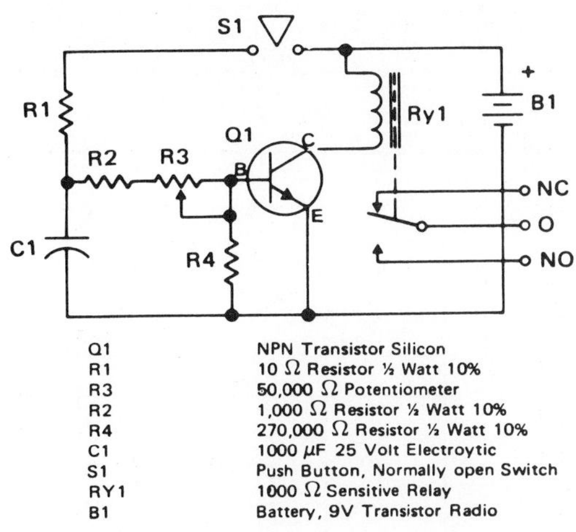

Q1	NPN Transistor Silicon
R1	10 Ω Resistor ½ Watt 10%
R3	50,000 Ω Potentiometer
R2	1,000 Ω Resistor ½ Watt 10%
R4	270,000 Ω Resistor ½ Watt 10%
C1	1000 µF 25 Volt Electroytic
S1	Push Button, Normally open Switch
RY1	1000 Ω Sensitive Relay
B1	Battery, 9V Transistor Radio

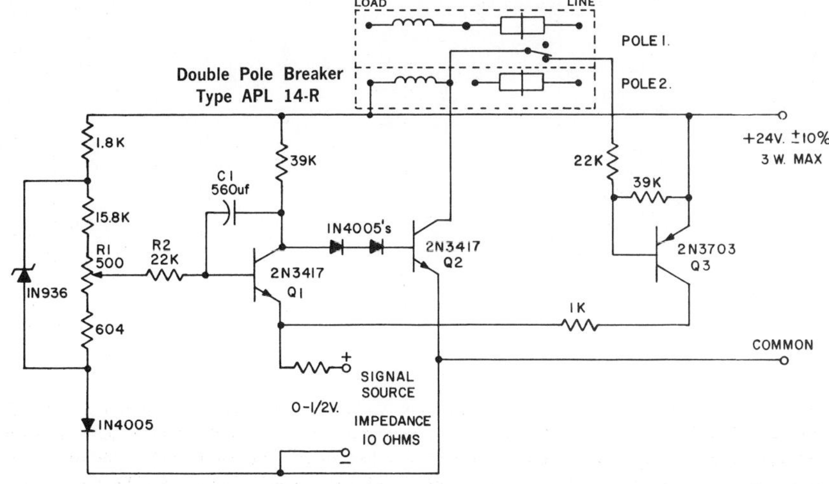

DOUBLE-THRESHOLD DELAY—Allows adjustable time delay that responds to average (not rms) value of an overload, with essentially zero delay above adjustable limit. R1 determines first threshold, while C1 and R2 determine time delay. With 560 µF for C1, there is no tripping of Airpax APL14-R double-pole breaker (dashed box) at 100% load, delay of about 20 s at 150% load, 5 s at 200% load, and minimum delay of about 0.01 s beyond 240% load.—Double Threshold Time Delay (Airpax ad), *Electronics*, Dec. 9, 1968, p 156.

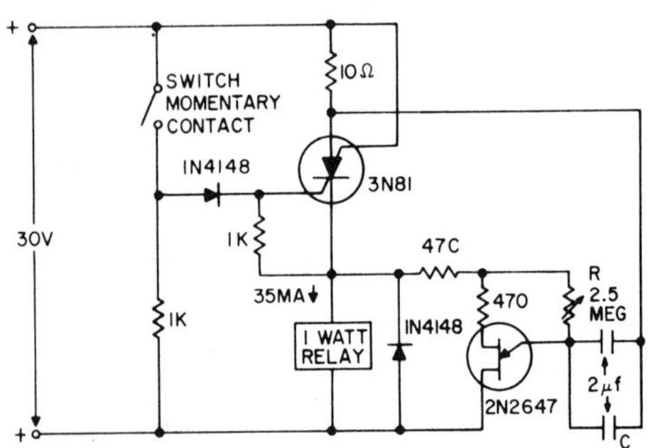

10-S SCS—Positive pulse to gate of 3N81 scs triggers it on, for supplying power to relay load and ujt timing circuit. At completion of timing interval based on RC, negative pulse is applied to anode of scs to turn it off.—Planar Silicon Controlled Switch 3N81/3N82, General Electric, Syracuse, N.Y., No. 65.16, 1964.

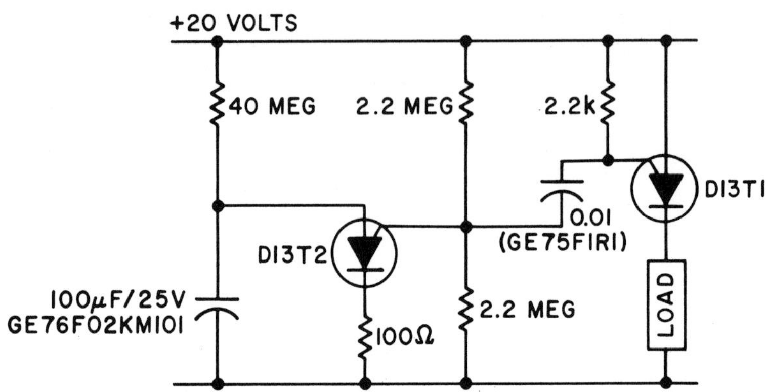

LONG DELAY WITH D13T2—At end of timing interval, D13T2 produces sharp negative pulse for triggering D13T1 programmable ujt acting as thyristor for controlling load current.—W. R. Spofford, Jr., The D13T—A Programmable Unijunction Transistor, General Electric, Syracuse, N.Y., No. 90.70, 1967, p 12.

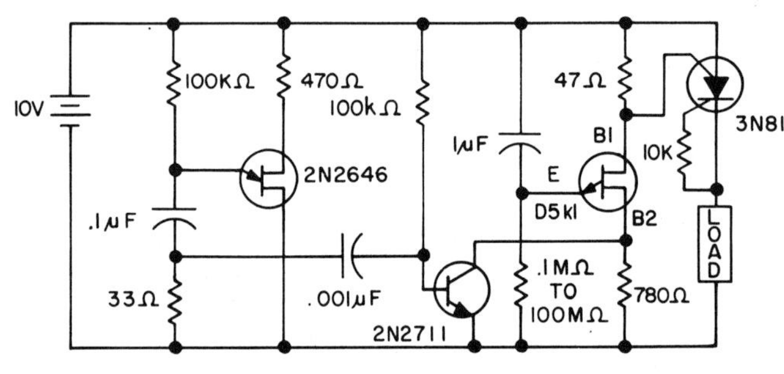

0.1–90 S—Timing interval starts when power is applied, and stops when voltage is applied to load. Ujt operates as oscillator that pulses base 2 of D5K1 complementary ujt for triggering of 3N81 scs. Chief advantage of circuit is use of larger timing resistor and smaller timing capacitor than in conventional timers.—Silicon Complementary Unijunction Transistor D5K1, General Electric, Syracuse, N.Y., No. 60.15, 1967.

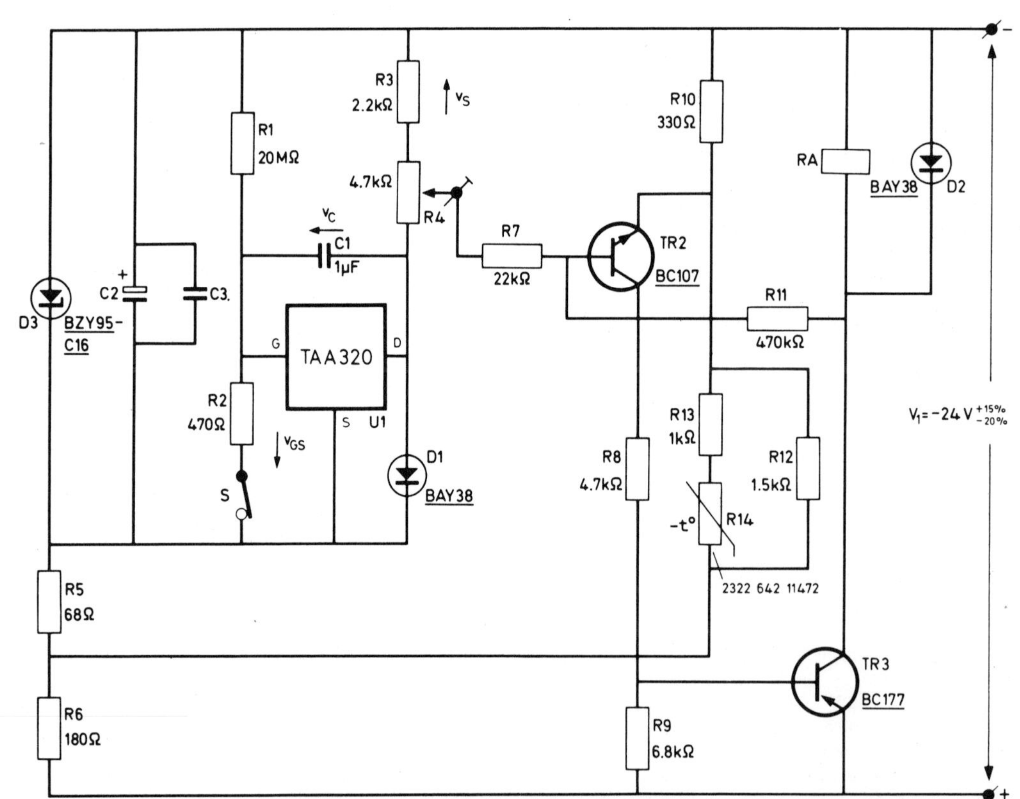

HIGH-ACCURACY ADJUSTABLE TIMER—Provides adjustable delay after switch S is closed, before relay RA is energized. Includes temperature compensation with R14, along with voltage stabilization, to minimize time terror. Actual timer is Miller integrator that includes IC, with zener reference voltage. Report includes mathematical analysis of performance.—The TAA320 Integrated Circuit Used in Long Delay Time Switches, Philips, Pub. Dept., Elcoma Div., Eindhoven, The Netherlands, No. 447, 1969.

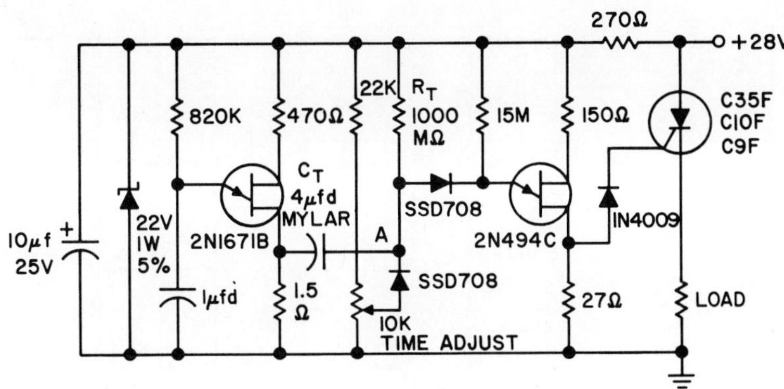

UP TO 1 HR—Requires only low-leakage 4-μF mylar capacitor for time delays up to 1 hr because effective firing current is reduced by factor of 1,000. Voltage on timing capacitor CT is periodically sampled by sampling pulse generated by 2-Hz ujt relaxation oscillator.—"Unijunction Circuit Hints," General Electric, Syracuse, N.Y., Fig. 9.

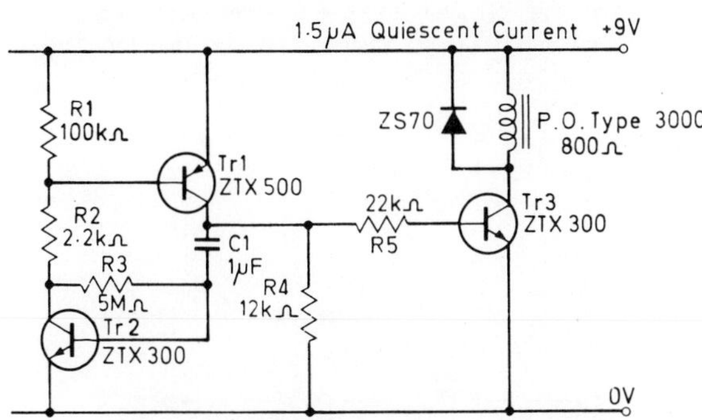

SELF-REPEATING TIMER—C1 is charged quickly almost to 9 V through resistors and first two transistors. When it approaches full charge, charging current drops and both transistors turn off. Capacitor then discharges through R3, giving 5-s delay. When base voltage of TR2 rises above emitter voltage, TR1 and TR2 turn on and process repeats. Positive pulse is applied to TR3 every 5 s as TR1 turns on, turning on TR3 and energizing relay. —E-Line Transistor Applications, Ferranti Ltd., Oldham, Lancs., England, 1969, p 48.

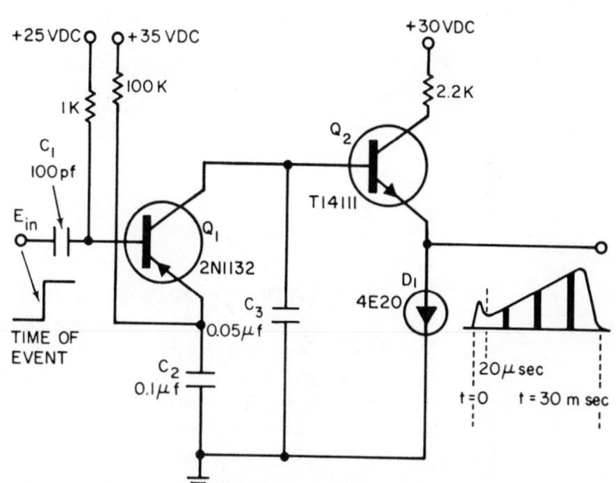

TIME OF OCCURRENCE—Simple two-stage transistor circuit with Shockley diode gives highly precise timing of start of event. For values shown, three samples of input waveform are taken at predetermined intervals to establish slope and base line, from which exact time of initiation of input signal can be computed.—L. M. Germain, Occurrence Generator Uses Shockley Diode, *Electronic Design*, Nov. 22, 1965, p 64.

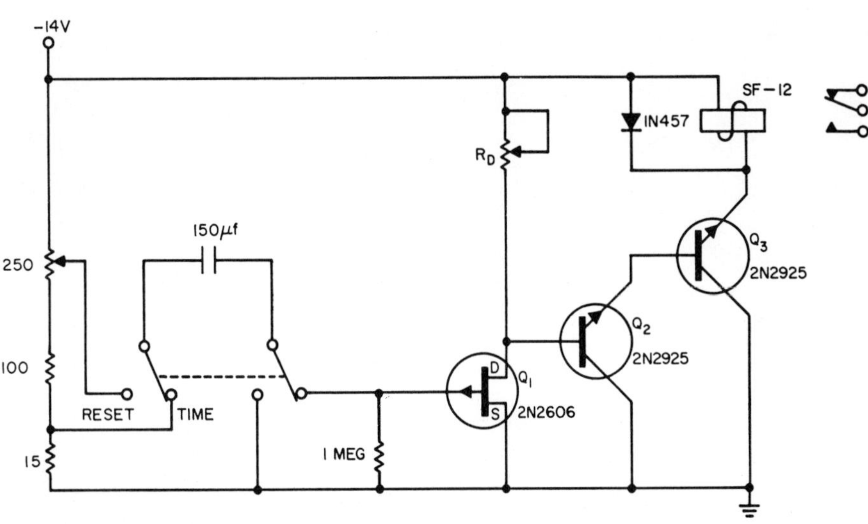

BASIC FET TIMER—Circuit shown, covered in Siliconix application note, has near-zero temperature coefficient. Charge and discharge time of R-C tank determines period of timer above 90 s. For shorter periods, use of junction fet's operating as constant sources with linear charging rates is recommended. Regenerative circuitry is added to provide on-off timing.—FETs for Timers, *Electronic Design*, Nov. 8, 1965, p 94.

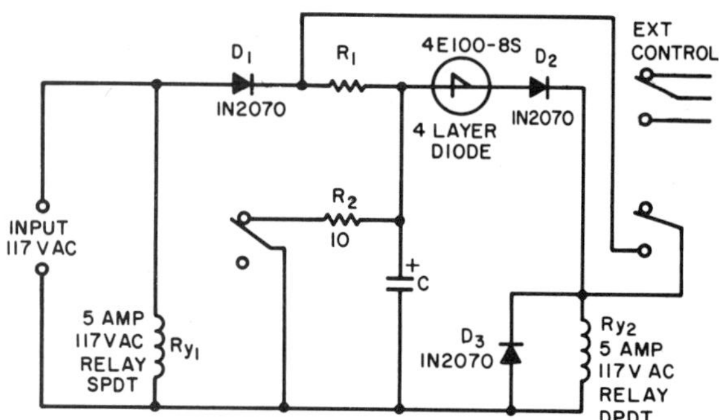

VARIABLE DELAY WITH INSTANT RESET—Shockley diode in series with relay provides instant reset for time delays from fraction of second to several minutes. For typical 5-A a-c relay, C should be above 1 μF.—B. Evans, Four-Layer Diode Provides Time Delay with Instant Reset, *Electronic Design*, March 29, 1965, p 33–34.

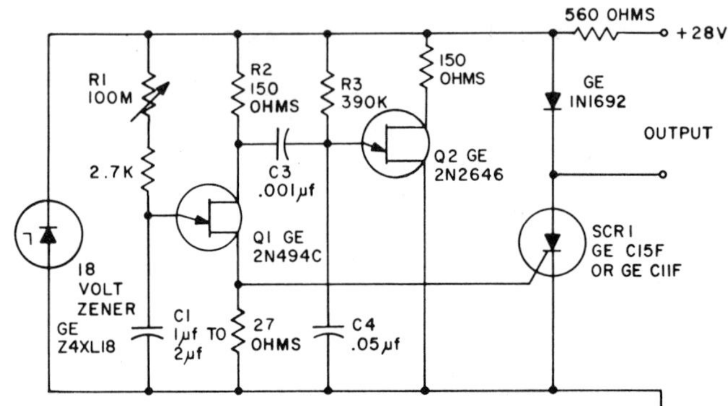

0.3 MS–3 MIN—C1 is stable low-leakage paper or mylar capacitor. Peak-point requirement of timing ujt Q1 is reduced up to 1,000 times by pulsing its upper base with 0.75-V negative pulse derived from free-running oscillator Q2. If R1 is 2,000 meg and C1 2-μF mylar, circuit gives stable time delays of over 1 hr.—"SCR Manual," 4th Edition, General Electric, 1967, p 165–166.

SELF-DESTRUCTION FOR FUZES—Used in T-5 antiaircraft battery-powered fuze for 4.5-inch M-8 rocket, to explode fuze from 6 to 11 s after missile was launched, if it had not been triggered by proximity to enemy aircraft, to preclude explosion on ground approach over friendly territory after miss. Delay circuit connects to grid of thyratron and uses NE23 neon tube along with R-C components. Small amount of radioactive material on neon tube keeps neon sufficiently ionized to minimize variations in striking voltage. When delay circuit trips thyratron, 1.5-μF capacitor discharges through armed (switch closed) detonator.—A. V. Astin, Editor, "Radio Proximity Fuzes for Fin-Stabilized Missiles," Div. 4, NDRC, Vol. I, 1946 (available from Clearinghouse, Springfield, Va.), p 131.

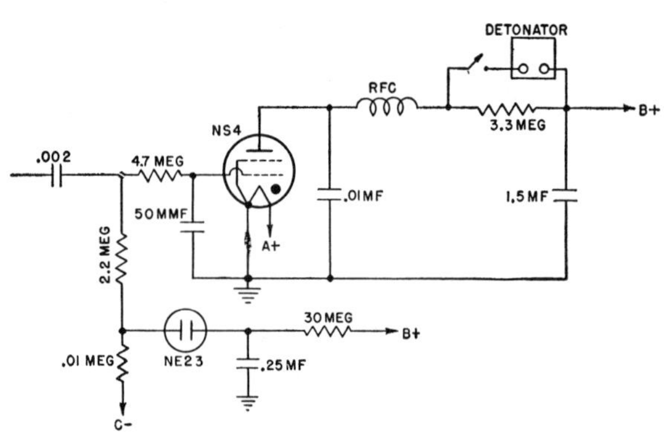

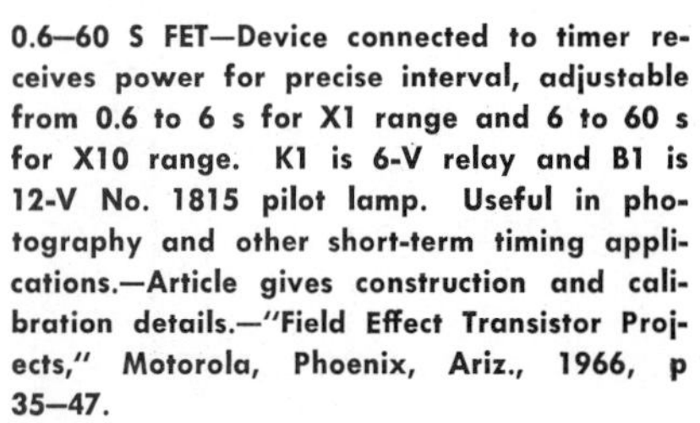

0.6–60 S FET—Device connected to timer receives power for precise interval, adjustable from 0.6 to 6 s for X1 range and 6 to 60 s for X10 range. K1 is 6-V relay and B1 is 12-V No. 1815 pilot lamp. Useful in photography and other short-term timing applications.—Article gives construction and calibration details.—"Field Effect Transistor Projects," Motorola, Phoenix, Ariz., 1966, p 35–47.

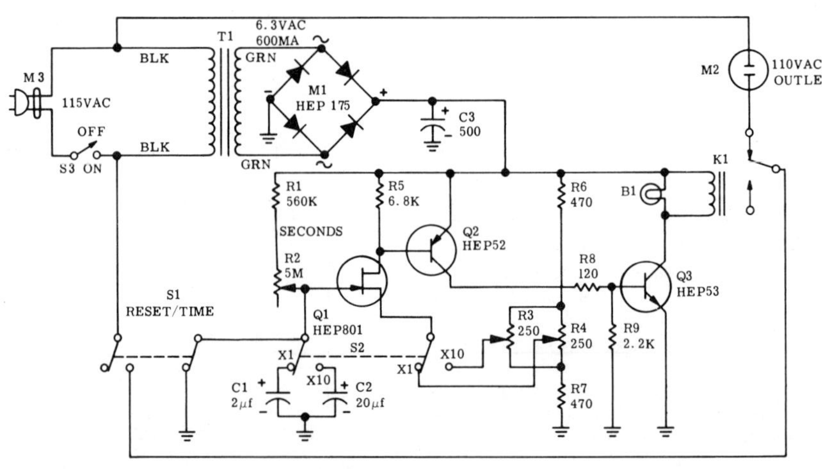

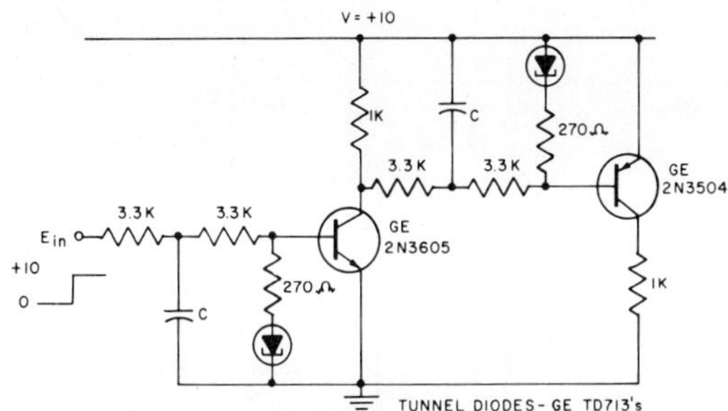

CASCADED TUNNEL-DIODE TIME DELAY—Two identical time delay stages are cascaded. When current threshold of first tunnel diode is reached while capacitor is charging, this diode switches into high-voltage state and turns on first transistor, to initiate similar timing action for second stage. Time delay equations are given in article.—W. R. Spofford, Jr., Applications For The New Low Cost TD 700 Series Tunnel Diodes, General Electric, Syracuse, N.Y., No. 90.66, 1967, p 8.

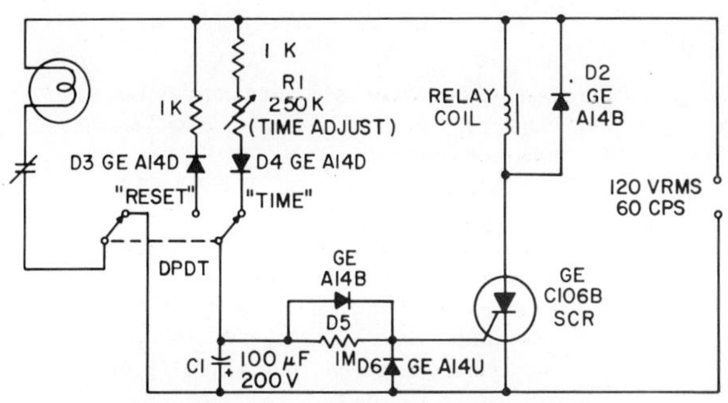

GARAGE-LIGHT TURN-OFF DELAY—Simple timing circuit gives adjustable delay of 0.01 to 60 s before light is turned off by relay after actuation of switch. Can also be used as timer for enlarger.—D. R. Grafham, Time-Delay Relay, General Electric, Syracuse, N.Y., No. 201.11, 1967.

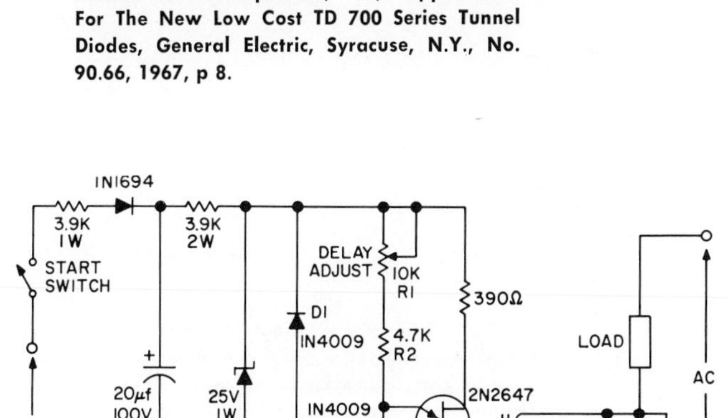

1-S A-C TIME DELAY—Requires only single ujt, oscillating much higher than a-c line frequency so switching of scr's is practically from full on to full off. Time delay is determined by (R1 + R2)(C1 + C2). For greater delay, increase C2.—"Unijunction Circuit Hints," General Electric, Syracuse, N.Y., Fig. 10.

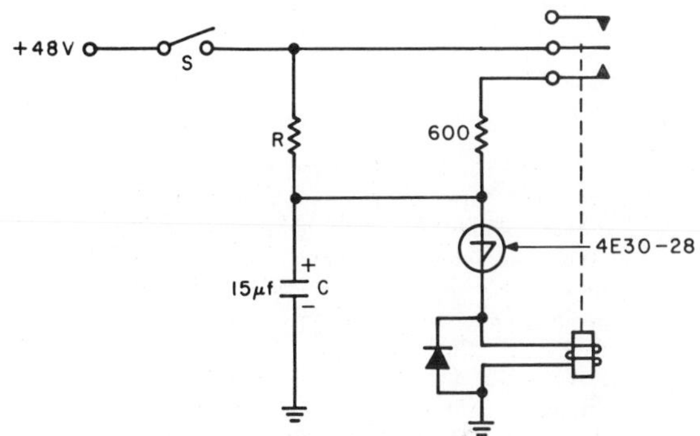

10 MS TO 10 MIN—Four-layer diode acts as self-latching pnpn switch that closes (fires) when C charges to firing voltage through R. Delay time in seconds is 0.000006R, or 10 min if R is 100 meg. Relay remains energized until S is opened.—J. McNellis, PNPN Switch Affords Wide Range Time Delay, *Electronic Design*, March 2, 1964, p 65–66.

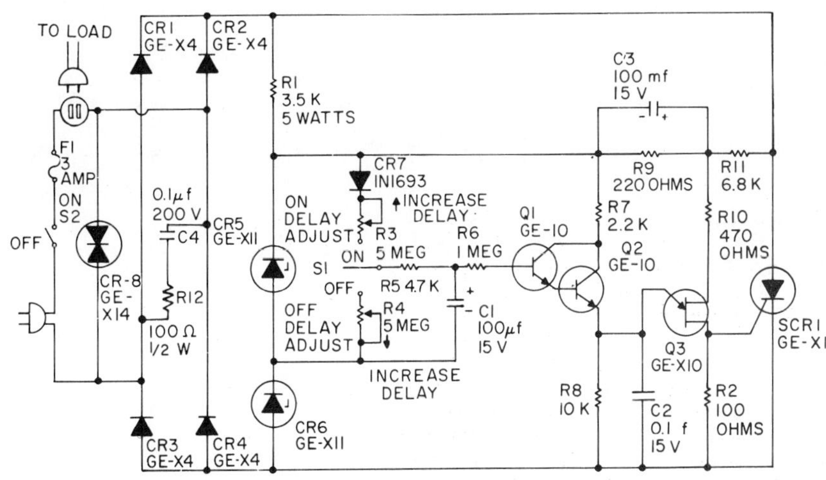

500-W 10-MIN DELAY—Will turn off soldering iron or clothes-pressing iron after adjustable delay of up to 10 min after weight of iron in holder closes S1. This keeps iron warm and ready for use within delay interval while eliminating fire hazard of forgetting to turn it off when leaving. Can also be used for delayed turn-off of garage or porch lights, or for turning on lamp or appliance after similarly adjustable delay.—"Hobby Manual," General Electric, Owensboro, Ky., 1965, p 142.

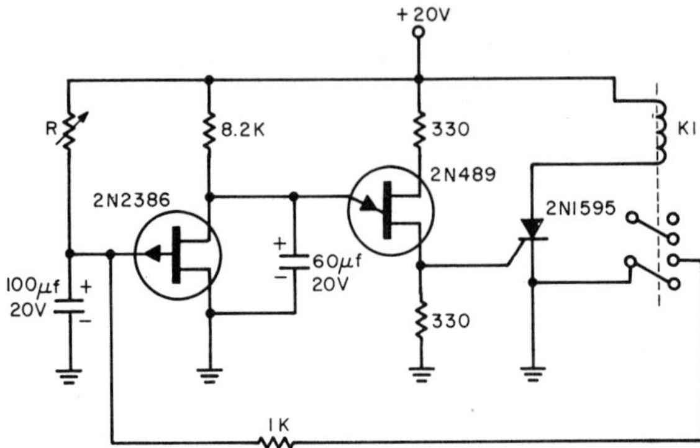

1–60 MIN WITH 5% ACCURACY—Fet follower, ujt, and scr provide adjustable time intervals, determined by R, for recycling intervals of 5 to 10 min. R can be 12-position rotary switch having 12 values of R ranging from 350K to 20 meg. Value of T in minutes is approximately equal to 2.86 times value of R in megohms.—E. B. Croson, Solid-State Timer Improves Recycling Accuracy, *Electronic Design*, July 6, 1964, p 51–52.

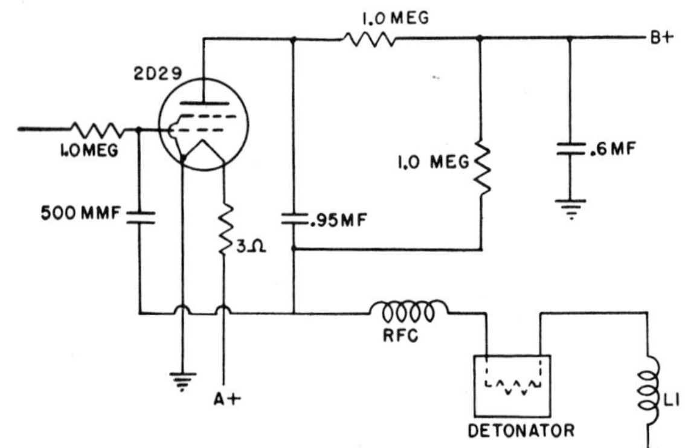

R-C ARMING OF FUZE—Used in T-171 radio proximity fuze for trench mortar shells to provide additional delay in electric arming after mechanical arming has occurred. Time delays up to 8 s can be obtained, depending upon size of arming resistor between anode of 2D29 thyratron and B supply. Fuze cannot be tripped by input signal to thyratron until 0.95-μF detonator firing capacitor has been fully charged by delay circuit after mechanical arming.—A. V. Astin, Editor, "Radio Proximity Fuzes for Fin-Stabilized Missiles," Div. 4, NDRC, Vol. I, 1946 (available from Clearinghouse, Springfield, Va.), p 125–130.

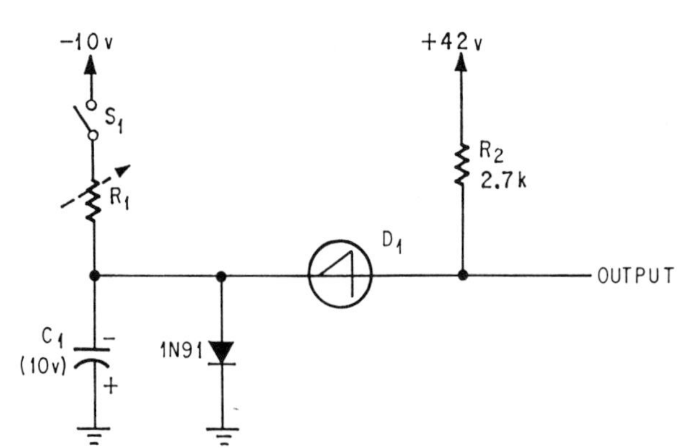

TIME STRETCHER—Modification of Shockley diode delay eliminates need for large capacitor to give delays up to 30 min. When anode of D1 is tied to 42-V supply, C1 needs to supply only remaining 8 V of 50-V breakdown voltage of D1. R1 can be as large as necessary to give desired R1C1 time constant, and C1 proportionally small. D1 is 4E50.—A. L. Plevy, Time Delay Stretched With New Bias Scheme, *Electronics*, Oct. 30, 1967, p 72.

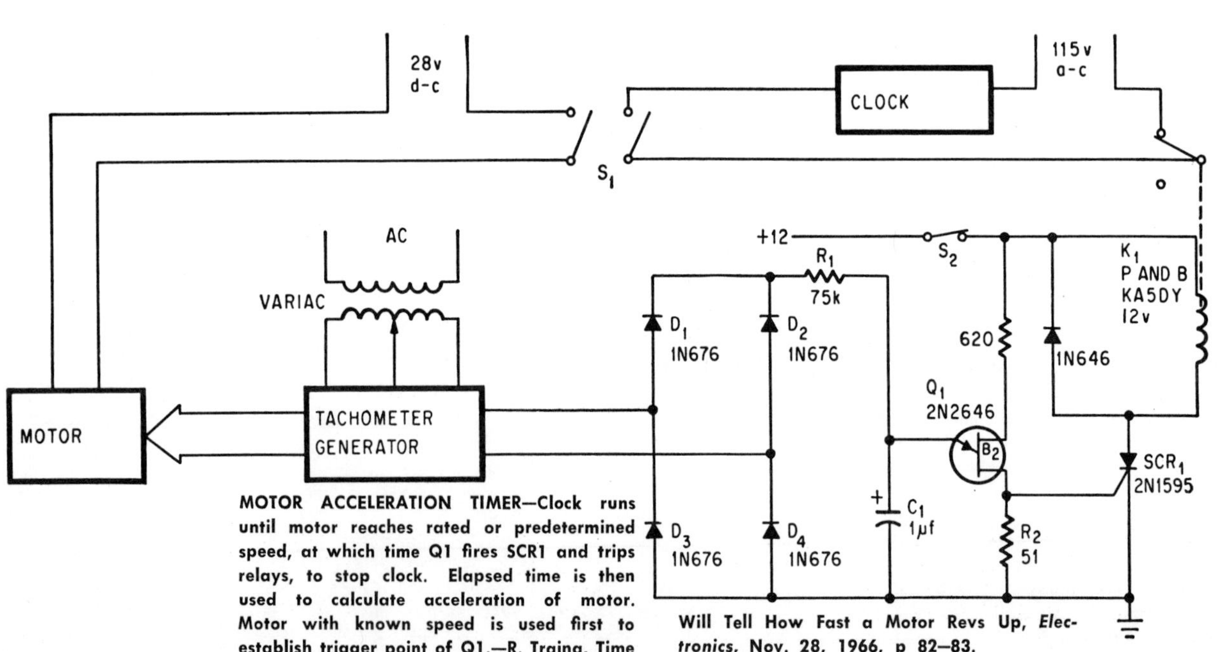

MOTOR ACCELERATION TIMER—Clock runs until motor reaches rated or predetermined speed, at which time Q1 fires SCR1 and trips relays, to stop clock. Elapsed time is then used to calculate acceleration of motor. Motor with known speed is used first to establish trigger point of Q1.—R. Traina, Time Will Tell How Fast a Motor Revs Up, *Electronics*, Nov. 28, 1966, p 82–83.

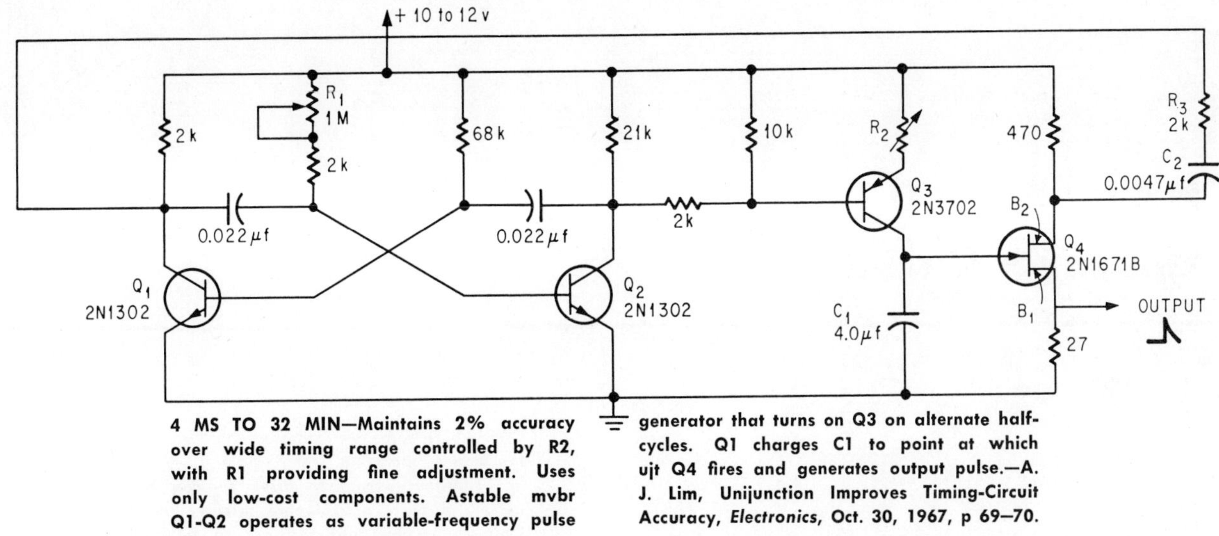

4 MS TO 32 MIN—Maintains 2% accuracy over wide timing range controlled by R2, with R1 providing fine adjustment. Uses only low-cost components. Astable mvbr Q1-Q2 operates as variable-frequency pulse generator that turns on Q3 on alternate half-cycles. Q1 charges C1 to point at which ujt Q4 fires and generates output pulse.—A. J. Lim, Unijunction Improves Timing-Circuit Accuracy, *Electronics*, Oct. 30, 1967, p 69–70.

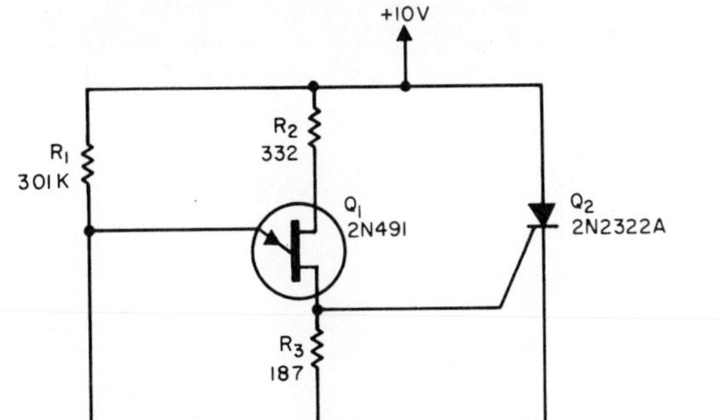

40-S POWER-SWITCH DELAY—Modified ujt trigger Q1 provides delay up to 40 s, depending on values of R1 and C1, after 10-V source voltage is applied, before firing scr Q2 to apply power to load. Scr then remains on until 10-V source voltage is removed. Temperature range is −30 to 100 C.—A. M. Hildebrandt, SCR and UJT Form Time-Delay Switch, *Electronic Design*, Sept. 13, 1965, p 82–83.

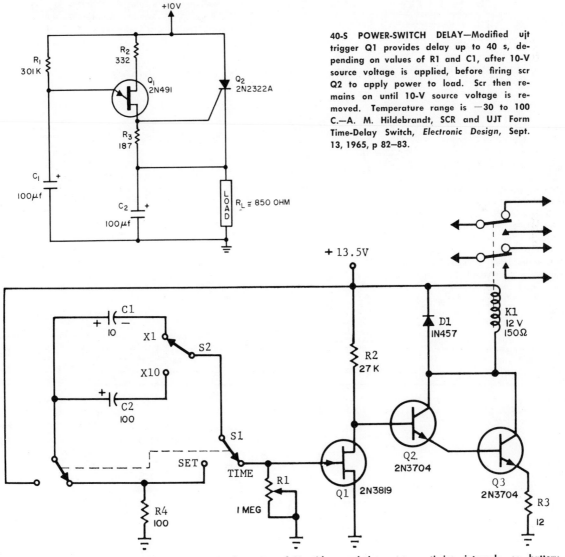

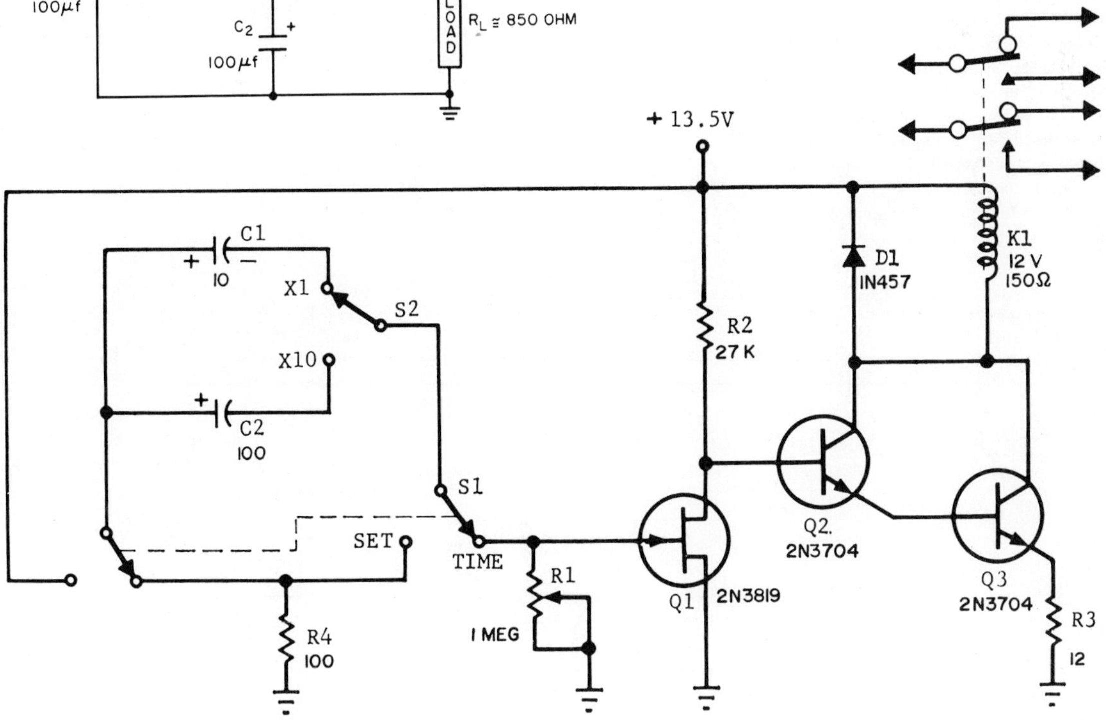

1 S TO 5 MIN—Potentiometer R1 in fet circuit determines time delay before relay pulls in after S1 is moved to TIME position. Darlington-connected transistors provide additional power amplification to ensure fast pull-in of relay. Use of S2 with second timing capacitor C2 increases versatility by providing two timing ranges. Maximum current drain is only 75 mA during actual timing interval, dropping to 0.5 mA between timing intervals, so battery supply can be used.—G. L. Jackson, Wide-Range Electronic Timer, *Electronics World*, Nov. 1967, p 56–57.

CHAPTER 90
Transceiver Circuits

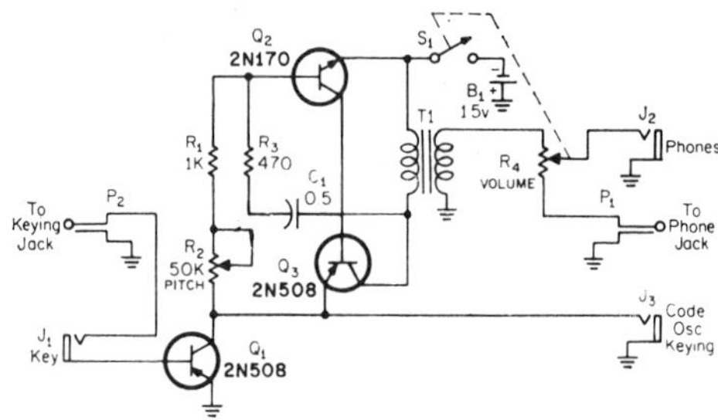

C-W MONITOR—Self-contained three-transistor circuit operating from single 1.5-V cell has sufficient output to drive speaker connected in place of 100-ohm primary of T1. Only connections required are to terminals of transceiver keying jack. May also be used as code-practice oscillator.—A. D'Onofrio and P. Stark, A C. W. Monitor for Grid-Block Keyed Transceivers, CQ, April 1965, p 62–63.

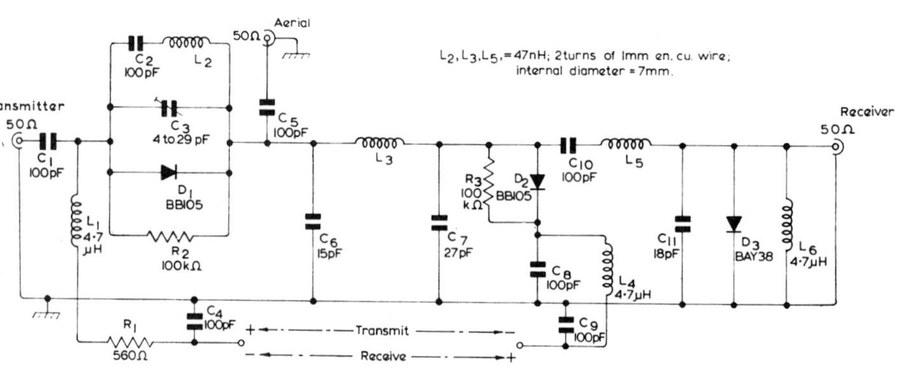

165-MHZ T-R SWITCH—Developed for mobile application having transmitter power of 12 W. Switching is done by BB105 variable-capacitance diode. During reception, D1 and D2 are reverse-biased and present high-Q capacitance. When transmitter is operating, these diodes are forward-biased and present only small resistance. Bias voltage is 13.8 V, with polarity being reversed to change from transmit to receive.—J. M. Siemensma, Electronic Aerial Switch for Mobile Transceivers, *Mullard Technical Communications*, Jan. 1968, p 30–31.

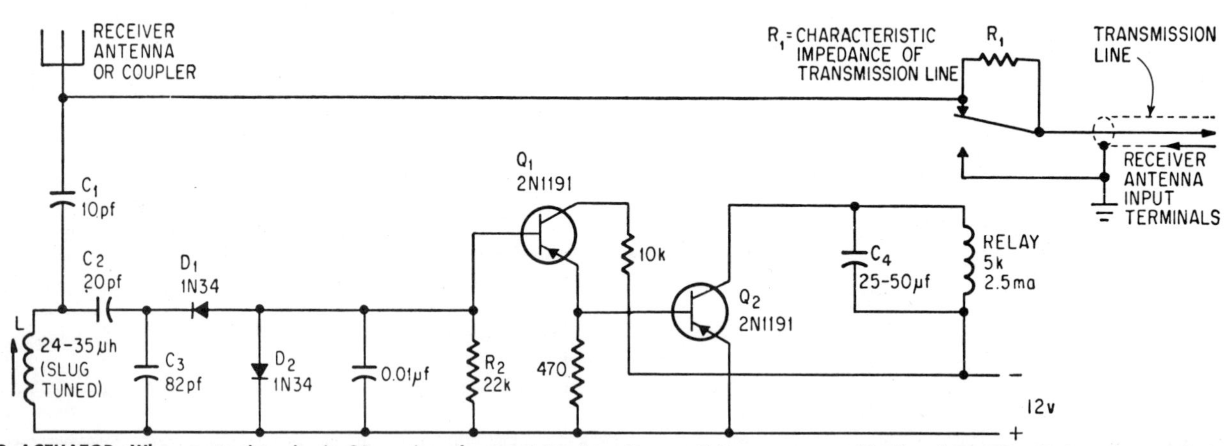

T/R ACTUATOR—When protection circuit Q1-Q2 is actuated by r-f signal exceeding 1 V at predetermined frequency, relay is pulled in to ground transmission line going to receiver, to terminate receiving antenna in its characteristic impedance. This protects input stage of receiver, without using expensive coaxial relays and disabling circuits. Circuit can be made to operate at other r-f signal levels by changing ratios C2:C3 and R2:470. K. C. Morton, R-f Signals Actuate Transmit-Receive Switch, *Electronics*, June 12, 1967, p 103–104.

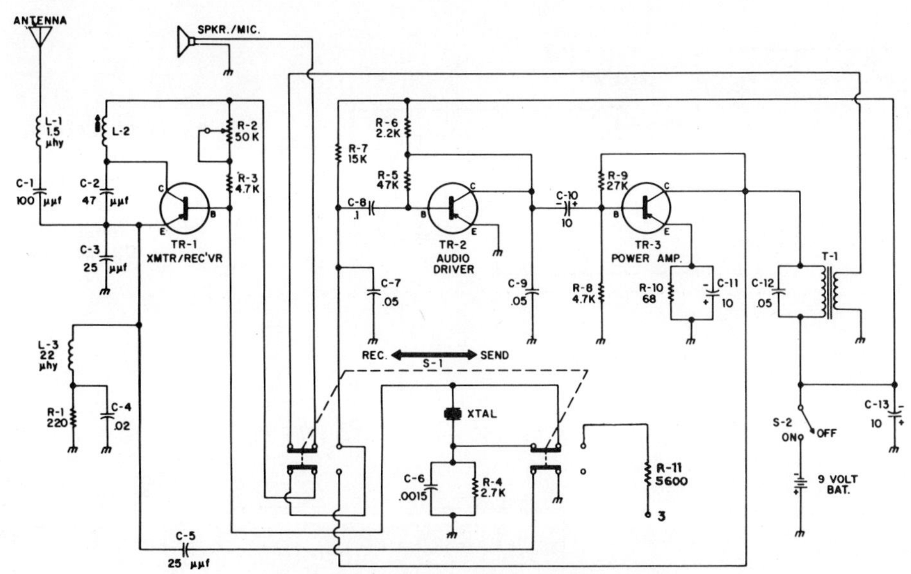

50-MC CONVERSION FROM CB—Requires only addition of R-11 to parts furnished with low-priced CB kit, for short-range communication (0.5 to 3 miles, depending on fixed station) in 6-meter amateur band. Book gives changes required in coils and crystals.—E. C. Pienkowski, Converting the Knight C-100 CB Transceiver to 50 Mc, "The Mobile Manual for Radio Amateurs," ARRL, Newington, Conn., 1968, p 218–219.

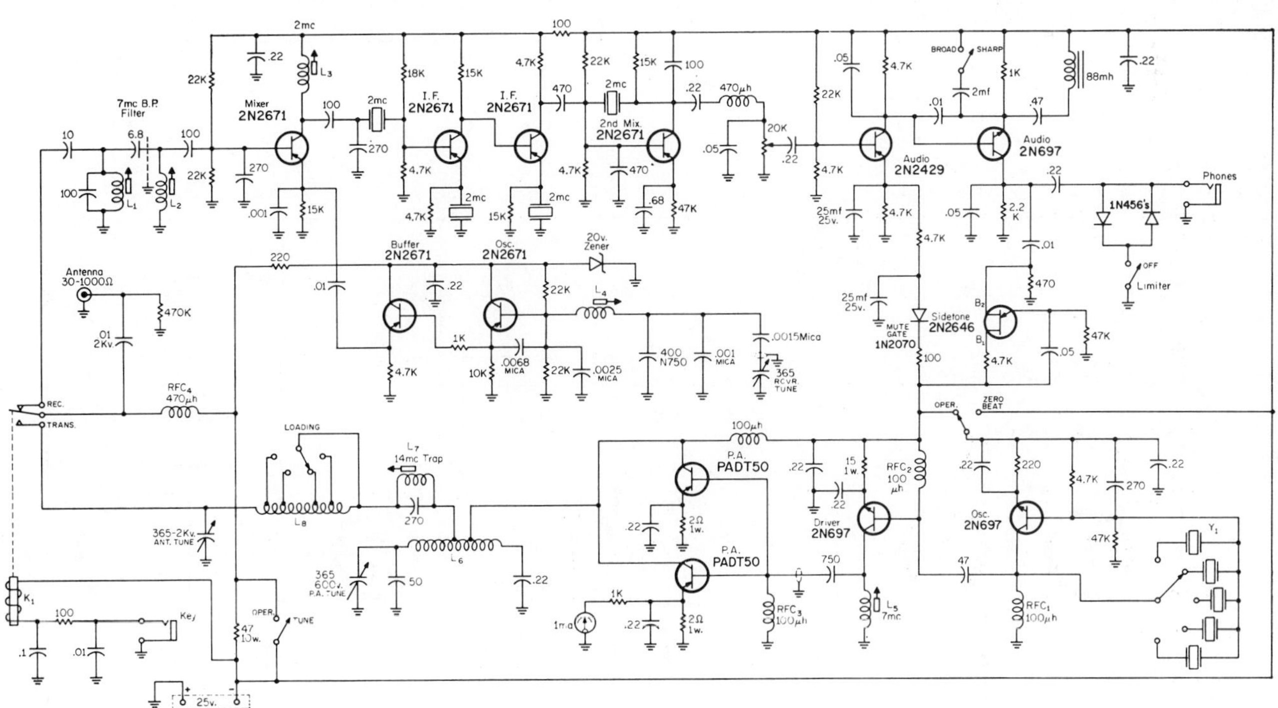

40-METER C-W TRANSCEIVER—Receiver section has sensitivity of 0.1 μV and transmitter has output of 23 W, operating from 28 V d-c supply. Receiver is single-conversion superhet with no r-f stage but with two tuned circuits ahead of mixer to form 7-MHz bandpass filter. Oscillator is zener regulated to reduce warmup or temperature drift at 5 MHz. I-f value is 2.105 MHz. Second detector is single-transistor oscillator-mixer followed by two direct-coupled audio stages having muting, side-tone injection, and additional selectivity. Article describes operation of entire circuit and gives construction details. Can be operated on 20-meter and 80-meter amateur bands as well, simply by changing coils.—J. S. Hill, A Compact 40 Meter Transceiver, CQ, June 1966, p 22–27.

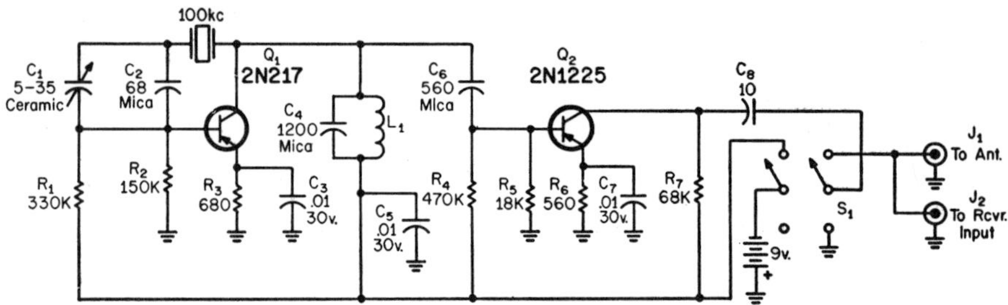

PORTABLE CALIBRATOR—Simple circuit can be used for checking frequency points in receiver or transmitter up to at least 150 MHz. Article gives construction details.—W. M. Scherer, Harmonic-Rich 100 Kc Crystal Calibrator, CQ, Dec. 1965, p 28–30.

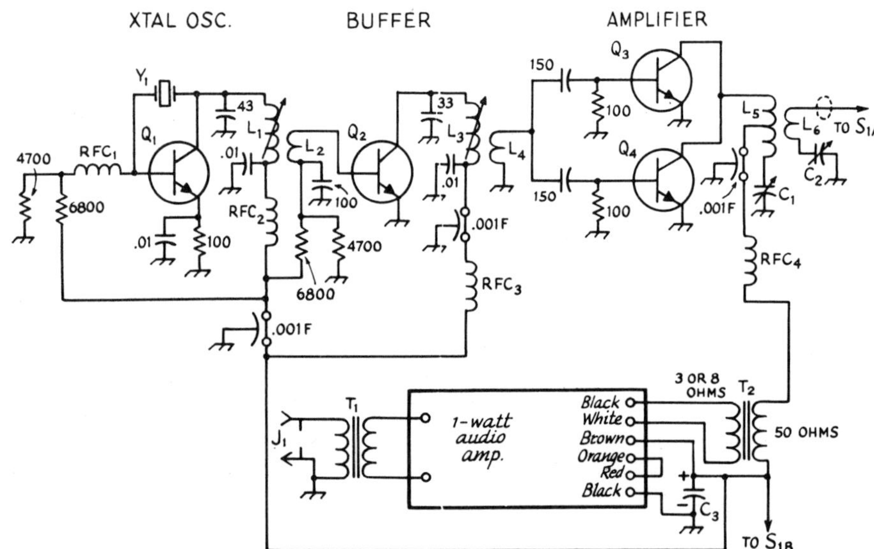

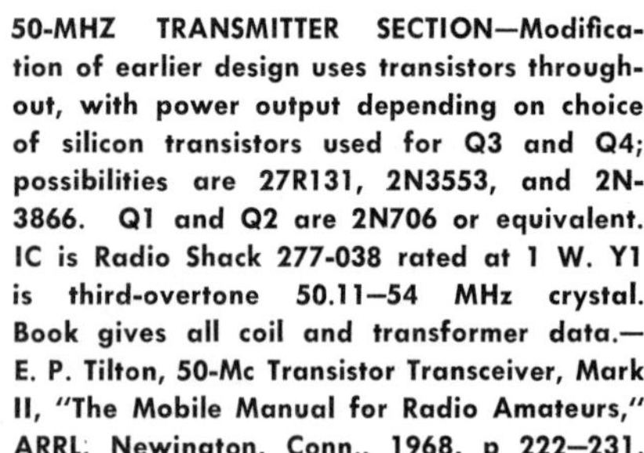
50-MHZ TRANSMITTER SECTION—Modification of earlier design uses transistors throughout, with power output depending on choice of silicon transistors used for Q3 and Q4; possibilities are 27R131, 2N3553, and 2N-3866. Q1 and Q2 are 2N706 or equivalent. IC is Radio Shack 277-038 rated at 1 W. Y1 is third-overtone 50.11–54 MHz crystal. Book gives all coil and transformer data.—E. P. Tilton, 50-Mc Transistor Transceiver, Mark II, "The Mobile Manual for Radio Amateurs," ARRL, Newington, Conn., 1968, p 222–231.

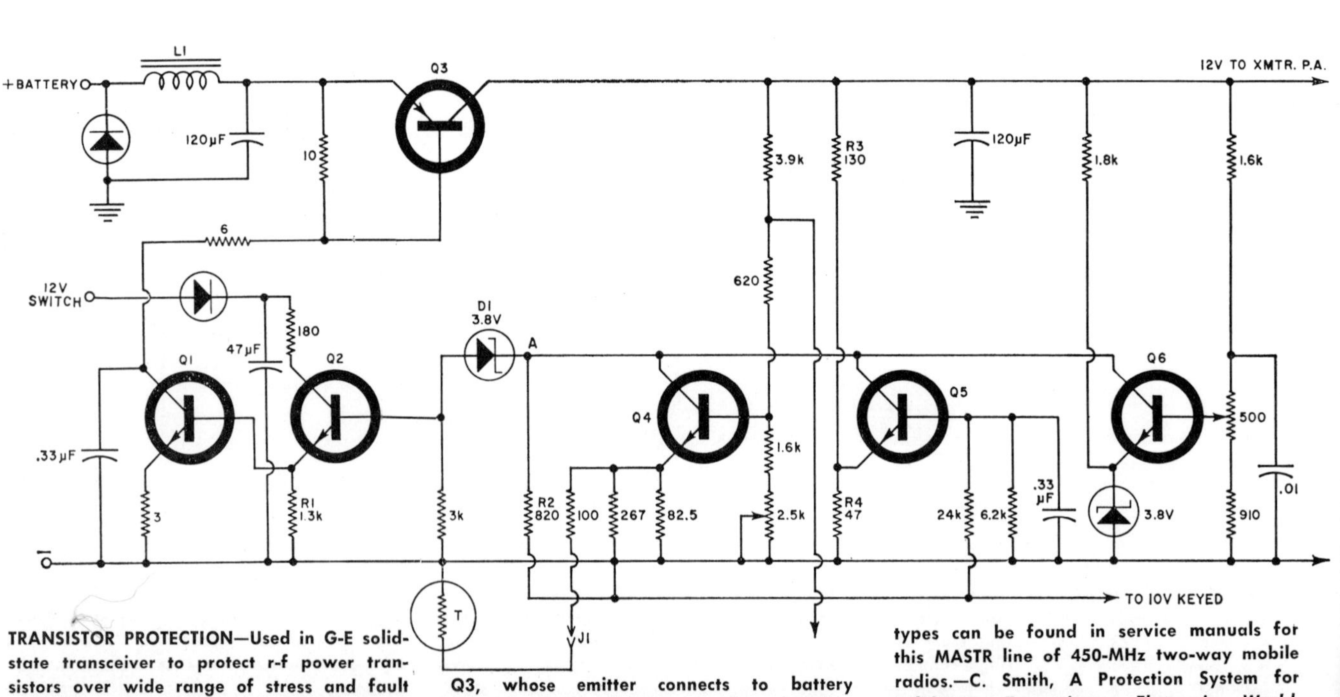

TRANSISTOR PROTECTION—Used in G-E solid-state transceiver to protect r-f power transistors over wide range of stress and fault conditions without affecting efficiency. High transmit current is carried and controlled by Q3, whose emitter connects to battery through L1 at all times. Article describes other protective actions in detail. Transistor types can be found in service manuals for this MASTR line of 450-MHz two-way mobile radios.—C. Smith, A Protection System for Solid-State Transmitters, *Electronics World*, Feb. 1969, p 38–39 and 77.

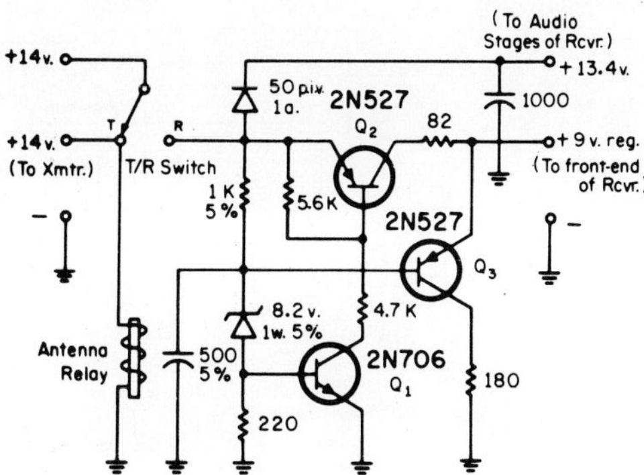

PROTECTING RECEIVER FRONT END—Circuit delays application of supply voltage to receiver section 0.6 s to prevent burnout of delicate transistors by residual radiation from turned-off transmitter.—R. Jayaraman, Delayed Switching for Transistor Receivers, CQ, Feb. 1970, p 39–40 and 98.

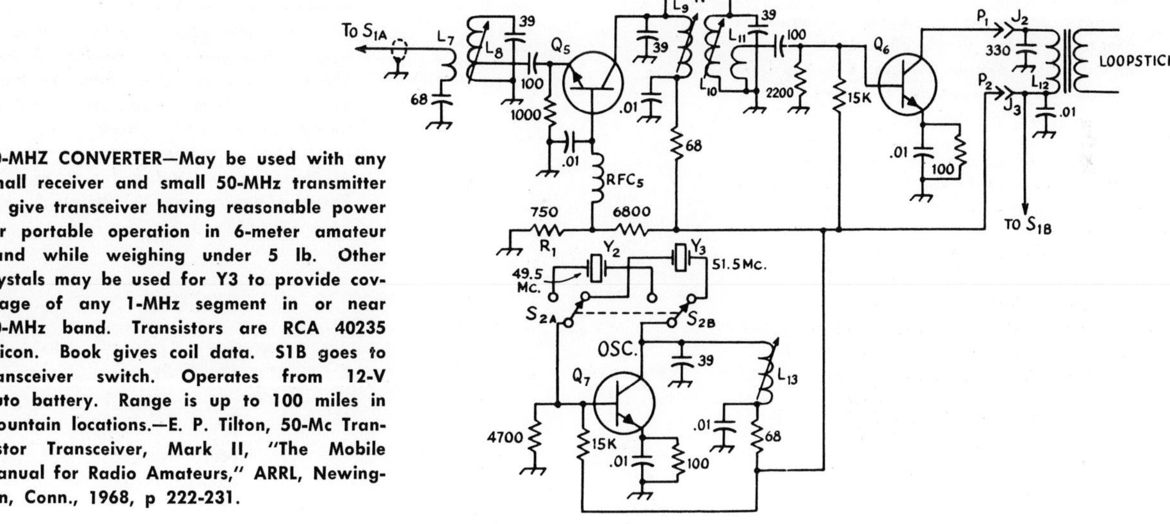

50-MHZ CONVERTER—May be used with any small receiver and small 50-MHz transmitter to give transceiver having reasonable power for portable operation in 6-meter amateur band while weighing under 5 lb. Other crystals may be used for Y3 to provide coverage of any 1-MHz segment in or near 50-MHz band. Transistors are RCA 40235 silicon. Book gives coil data. S1B goes to transceiver switch. Operates from 12-V auto battery. Range is up to 100 miles in mountain locations.—E. P. Tilton, 50-Mc Transistor Transceiver, Mark II, "The Mobile Manual for Radio Amateurs," ARRL, Newington, Conn., 1968, p 222-231.

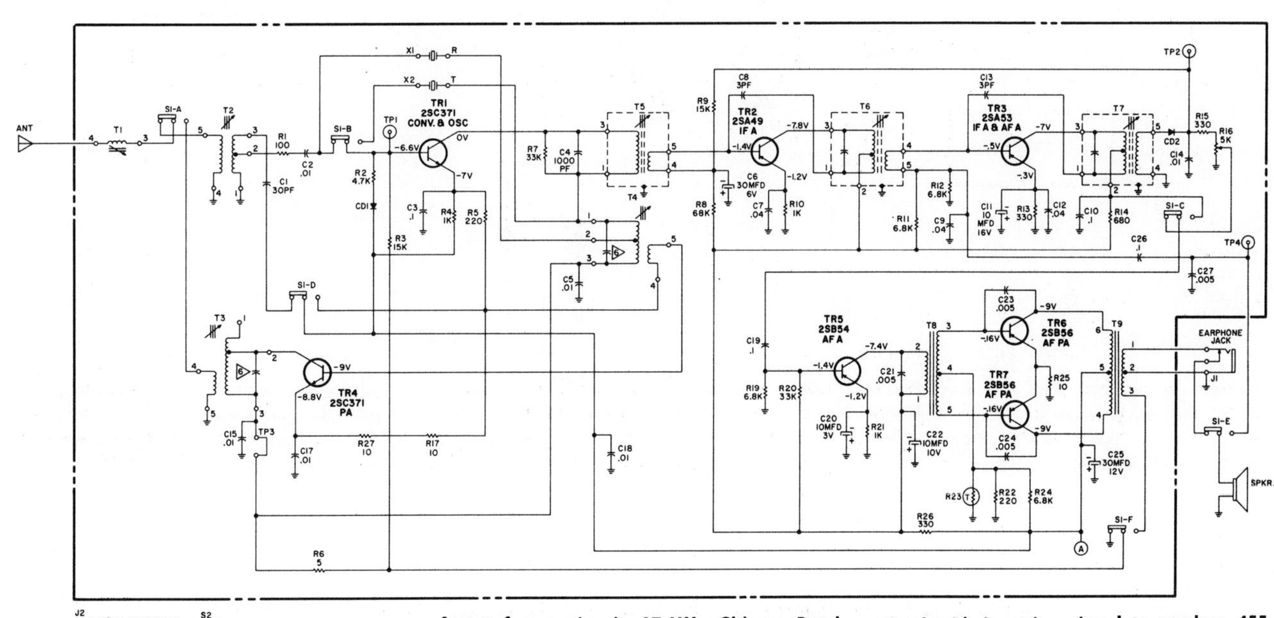

CB TRANSCEIVER—Seven-transistor portable transmitter-receiver operates on any of 22 different frequencies in 27-MHz Citizens Band, depending on crystal used in transmitting. When receiving, unit operates like a-m radio except that intermediate frequency is determined by separate crystal whose output is mixed with incoming signal to produce 455-kHz i-f signal. Talk-receive switch S1 is shown in receive position.—1R1007 Citizens Band Transceiver, Magnavox Service Manual 6299, Fort Wayne, Ind., 1970.

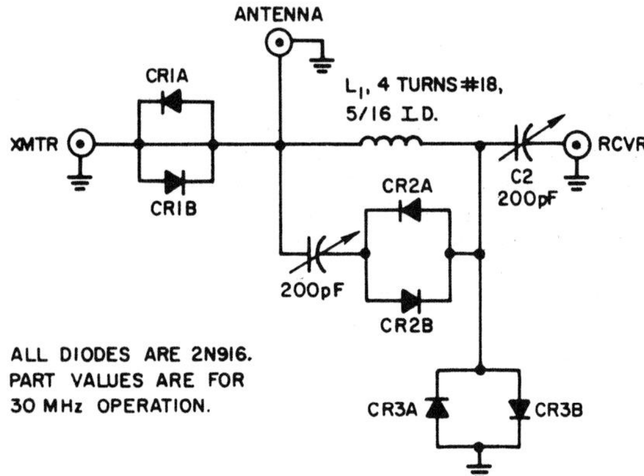

ALL DIODES ARE 2N916. PART VALUES ARE FOR 30 MHz OPERATION.

10–50 MHZ DUPLEXER—All diodes conduct in transmit mode, and none conduct in receive mode, to give simple and low-cost transmit-receive switch requiring no external bias supplies or switching signals. Isolation is greater than 26 dB for 30-V peak signal.—R. Van Sickle, Simple Duplexer Requires Only Inexpensive Components, *Electronic Design,* July 5, 1969, p 80.

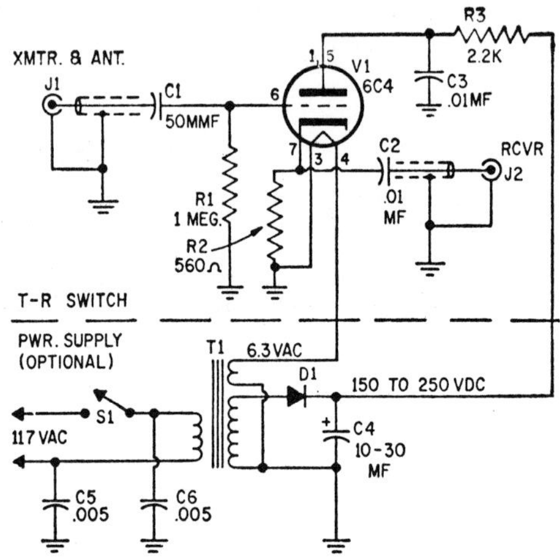

TRANSMIT-RECEIVE SWITCH—Permits instant break-in during pauses in amateur c-w transmissions. Eliminates need for antenna relay, because transmitter is connected all the time. Similarly, receiver is operating all the time, permitting monitoring of station interference during transmissions. Book gives complete construction and operation data.—M. Lincoln, All-Electronic T-R Switch for Hams, "Bench-Tested Communications Projects," Hayden Book Co., N.Y., p 22–25.

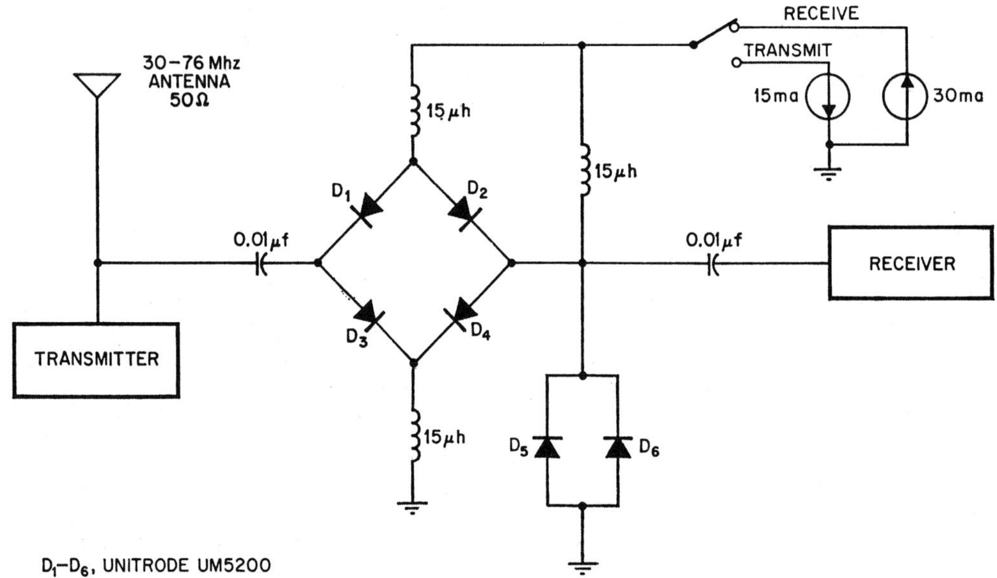

D1–D6, UNITRODE UM5200

BRIDGE T-R SWITCH—With switch in RECEIVE position shown, current of 30 mA from constant-current source flows through diode bridge, forward-biasing diodes at 1.2 V. Receiver is then connected to antenna through 1.2 ohms. With switch in TRANSMIT position, D5 and D6 conduct, grounding receiver input, while bridge diodes are reverse-biased and open-circuited, so transmitter is ungrounded and feeding antenna.—P. V. Wanek, Transmit-Receive Switch Exceeds 60-dB Isolation, *Electronics,* Aug. 18, 1969, p 93.

NOTE: To locate additional circuits in the category of this chapter, use the index at the back of this book. Check also the author's "Sourcebook of Electronic Circuits," published by McGraw-Hill in 1968.

CHAPTER 91
Transmitter Circuits

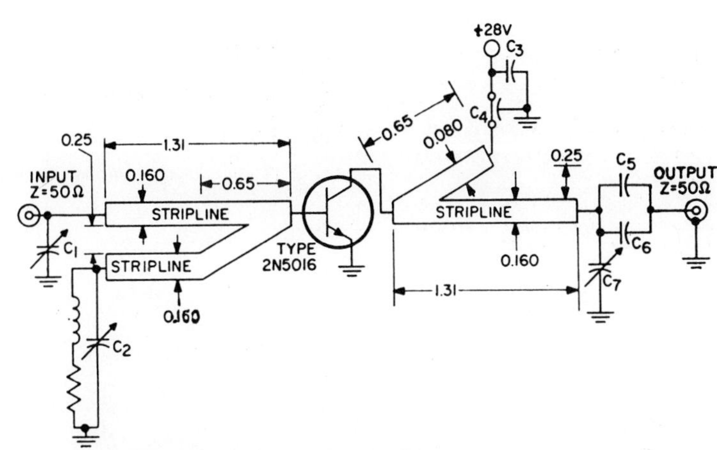

400-MHZ MICROSTRIPLINE AMPLIFIER—Delivers 15 W to 50-ohm line. Correct bias is obtained without d-c blocking, as long as d-c impedance of source is above 50 ohms.—"Silicon Power Circuits Manual," RCA, Harrison, N.J., SP-51, p 349.

C_1, C_2, C_7 = trimmer capacitor, 2 to 18 pF, Amperex HT10A/218 or equiv.
C_3 = 0.03 μF, ceramic disc
C_4 = 470 pF, feedthru, Allen Bradley FA5C or equiv.
C_5, C_6 = 0.005 μF, ceramic disc

R_1 = 5.1 ohms, 0.5 watt, carbon
Notes:
1. Broad = 1/16" Teflon board (ε = 2.6), Budd Co. Polychem Div., Grade 108T, 1 oz, double-clad copper, or equiv.
2. Dimensions in inches.

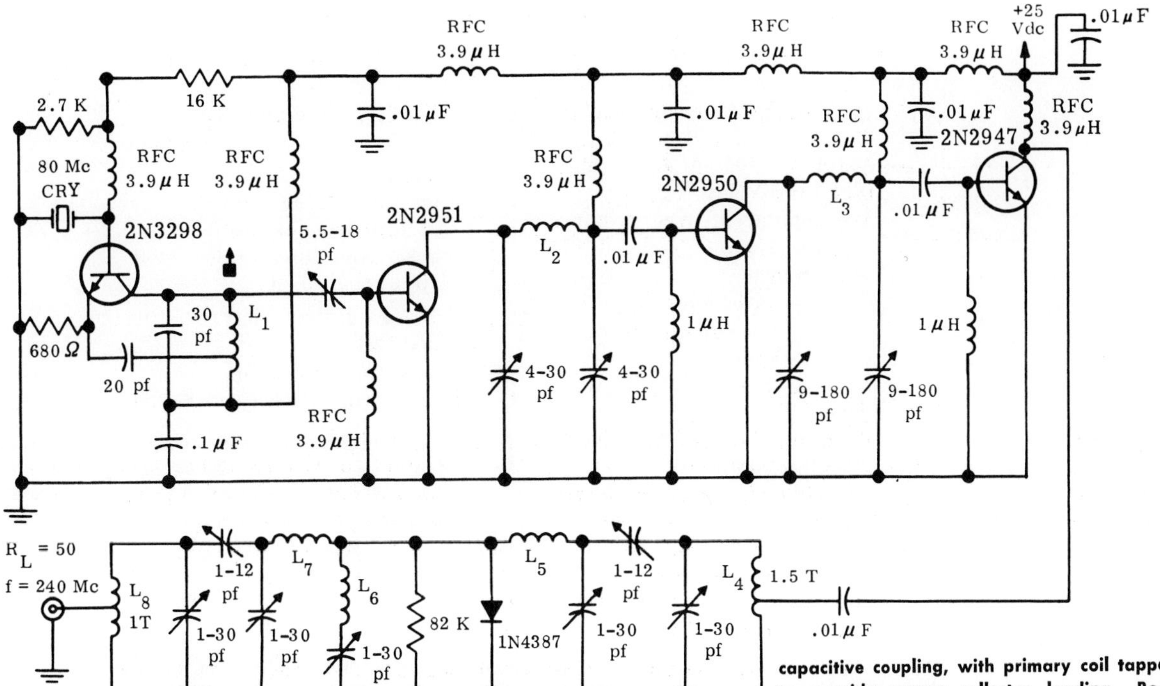

8-W 240-MHZ C-W—Output stage is varactor tripler that consists basically of three tuned circuits. Output circuit is double-tuned to 240 MHz using capacitive coupling. Idler circuit is series-tuned to 160 MHz. Input circuit is double-tuned to 80 MHz and uses capacitive coupling, with primary coil tapped to provide proper collector loading. Book gives winding data for all coils.—"Circuits Manual," Motorola, Phoenix, Ariz., 1965, p 12-8-2.

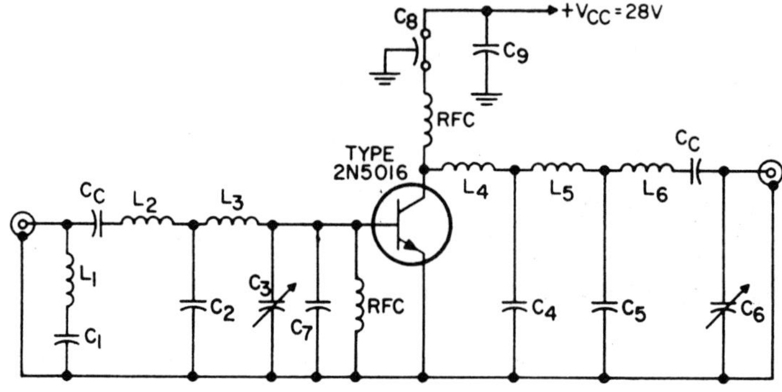

225–400 MHZ POWER AMPLIFIER—Uses low-pass L-C ladder networks for impedance transformation. With 6 W drive, provides 17 W output power across entire band with total output variation of 0.5 dB.—"Silicon Power Circuits Manual," RCA, Harrison, N.J., SP-51, p 350.

C_c = 2000 pF
C_1, C_8 = 7.5 pF
C_2 = 10 pF
C_3 = 1.5 to 30 pF (Johanson type or equiv.)
C_4 = 26.5 pF
C_5 = 17.5 pF
C_7 = 26.5 pF
L_1 = 4.5 nH
L_2 = 14 nH (includes inductance of input coupling capacitor C_c)
L_3 = 8.5 nH
L_4 = 5.6 nH
L_5 = 10 nH
L_6 = 19.5 nH (includes inductance of output coupling capacitor C_c)

Note:
All fixed components measured at 400 MHz

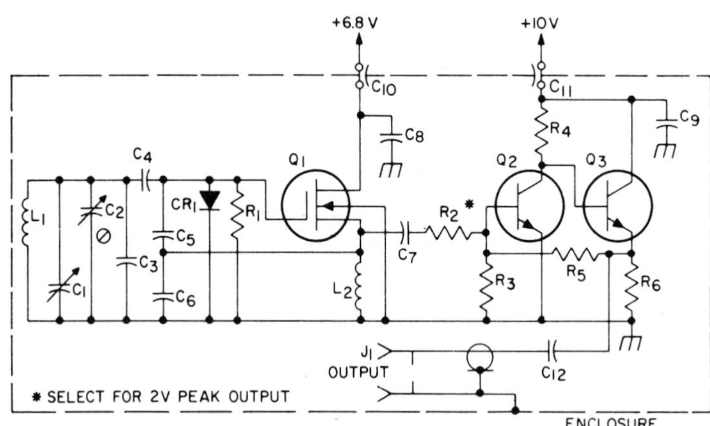

C_1 = variable capacitor, high-quality, double-bearing type, Miller 23100 or 23050 or equivalent (See Table VII for value)
C_2 = 25-picofarad air-type trimmer capcitor; Hammarlund APC-25 or equivalent
C_3 C_4 C_5 C_6 = silver mica capacitors, 300 volts (See Table VII for values)
C_7 = 2200 picofarads, 300 volts, silver mica
C_8 = 0.05 picofarad, 50 volts or greater, ceramic disc
C_9 = 0.1 picofarad, 50 volts or greater, ceramic disc
C_{10} C_{11} = 1500 picofarads, 500 volts, feedthrough type
C_{12} = 0.025 microfarad, 50 volts or greater, ceramic disc
CR_1 = silicon rectifier, type 1N914
J_1 = coaxial connector, chassis-mount vhf type
L_1 = (See Table VII for values)
L_2 = 2.5 millihenries, minature rf choke, iron core, Millen J300-2500 or equivalent
Q_1 = MOS field effect transistor, type 3N128
Q_2 = transistor, RCA 40245
Q_3 = transistor, RCA SK3020
R_1 = 22,000 ohms, 1/2 watt, 10%
R_2 = 12,000 to 47,000 ohms, 1/2 watt, 10%; select for 2-volt peak output
R_3 = 12,000 ohms, 1/2 watt, 10%
R_4 = 820 ohms, 1/2 watt, 10%
R_5 = 47,000 ohms, 1/2 watt, 10%
R_6 = 240 ohms, 1/2 watt, 10%

VFO—Variable-frequency oscillator is basically Colpitts type, covering 1.75 to 9 MHz in five ranges each having different values for L1 and C1-C6. Each range is bandspread over almost all of tuning dial, for accurate calibration and resettability. Can be used with fixed or mobile amateur radio transmitter. Book gives construction details and values for all ranges.—"Hobby Circuits Manual," RCA, Harrison, N.J., HM-90, p 144.

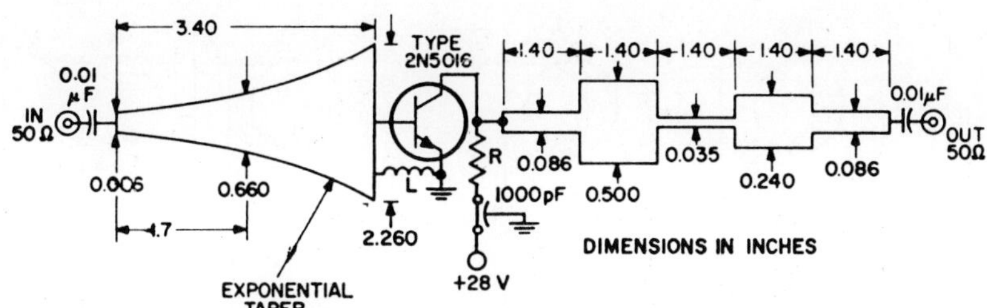

200–400 MHZ MICROSTRIPLINE AMPLIFIER—With 5 W drive, delivers 15 W across entire band with less than 1.5 dB output variation.—"Silicon Power Circuits Manual," RCA, Harrison, N.J., SP-51, p 349.

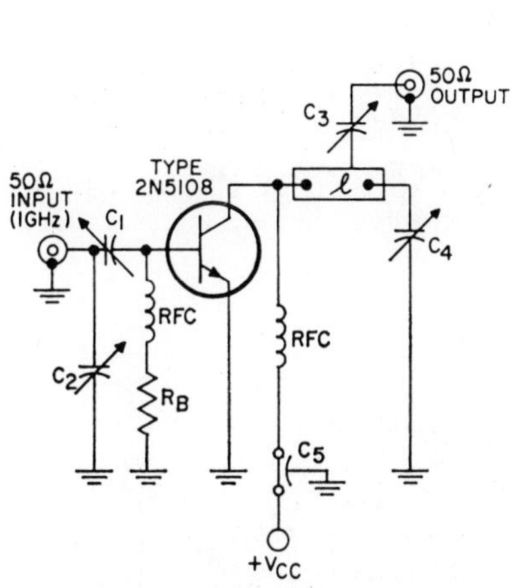

C_1, C_2, C_3, C_4 = Variable capacitor, 0.3 to 3.5 pF, Johanson piston type or equiv.
C_5 = 420 pF, feedthru
l = As described in text
R_B = 2.7 ohms, ¼ W
RFC = 0.1 μH

1-GHZ 1-W AMPLIFIER—Emitter is directly connected to ground plane of stripline circuit board. Power gain is 6 dB.—"Silicon Power Circuits Manual," RCA, Harrison, N.J., SP-51, p 361.

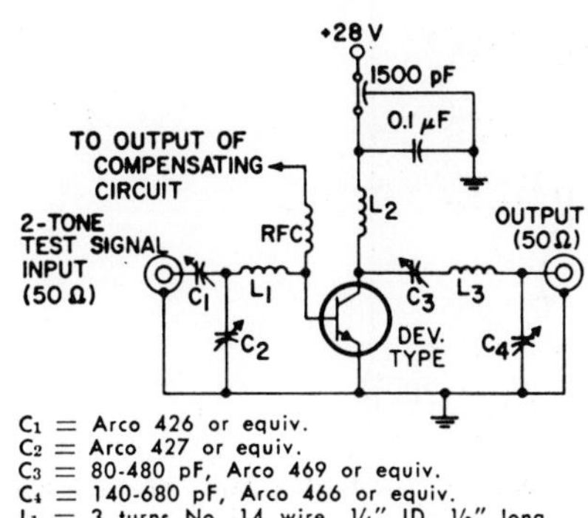

C_1 = Arco 426 or equiv.
C_2 = Arco 427 or equiv.
C_3 = 80-480 pF, Arco 469 or equiv.
C_4 = 140-680 pF, Arco 466 or equiv.
L_1 = 3 turns No. 14 wire, ¼" ID, ½" long
L_2 = 3 turns No. 10 wire, ½" ID, ⅜" long
L_3 = 3-½ turns No. 10 wire, ⅝" ID, ½" long

30-MHZ NARROW-BAND 100-W AMPLIFIER—Developed for use with 28-V mobile radio supply. Uses RCA SSB developmental transistor.—"Silicon Power Circuits Manual," RCA, Harrison, N.J., SP-51, p 320.

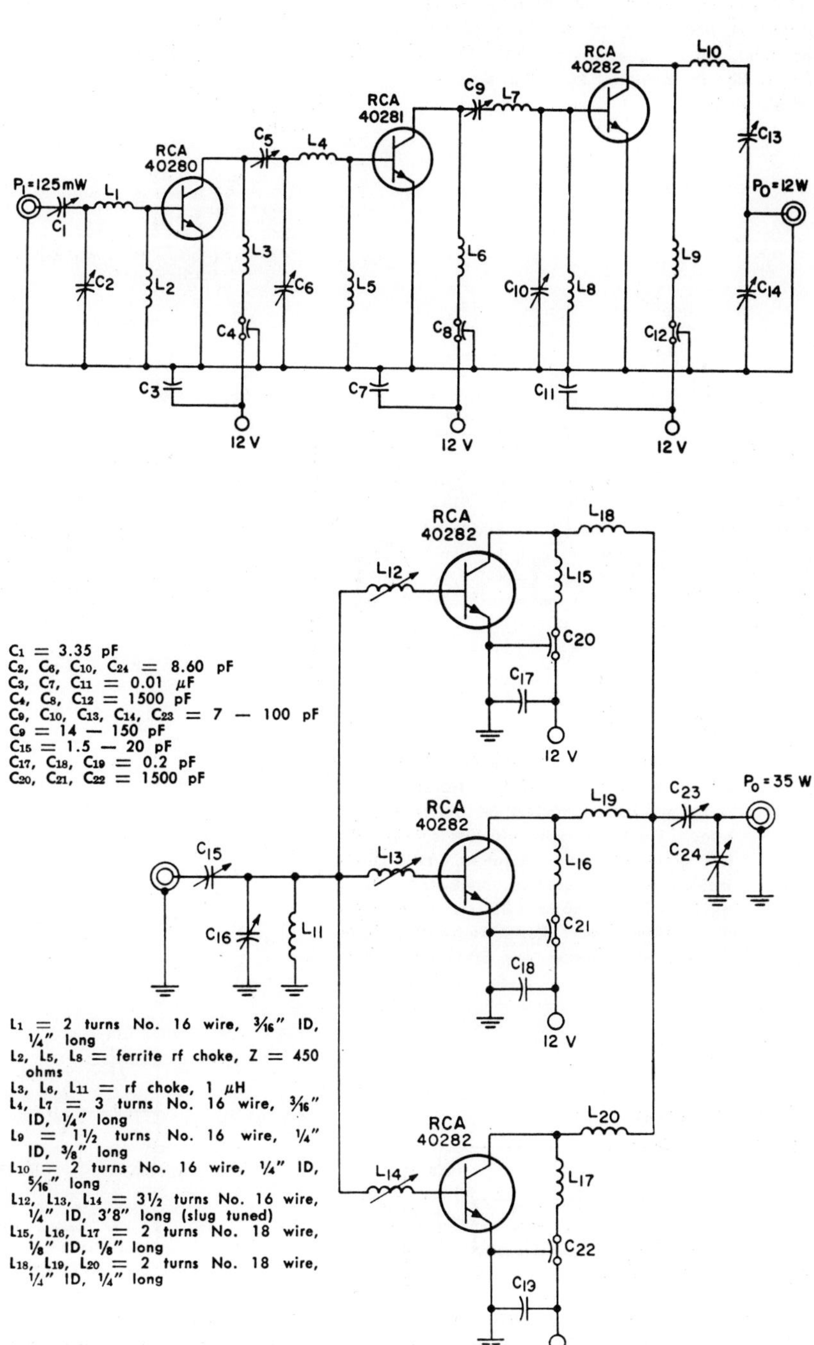

C_1 = 3.35 pF
C_2, C_6, C_{10}, C_{24} = 8.60 pF
C_3, C_7, C_{11} = 0.01 μF
C_4, C_8, C_{12} = 1500 pF
C_9, C_{10}, C_{13}, C_{14}, C_{23} = 7 — 100 pF
C_9 = 14 — 150 pF
C_{15} = 1.5 — 20 pF
C_{17}, C_{18}, C_{19} = 0.2 pF
C_{20}, C_{21}, C_{22} = 1500 pF

L_1 = 2 turns No. 16 wire, 3/16" ID, ¼" long
L_2, L_5, L_8 = ferrite rf choke, Z = 450 ohms
L_3, L_6, L_{11} = rf choke, 1 μH
L_4, L_7 = 3 turns No. 16 wire, 3/16" ID, ¼" long
L_9 = 1½ turns No. 16 wire, ¼" ID, ⅜" long
L_{10} = 2 turns No. 16 wire, ¼" ID, 5/16" long
L_{12}, L_{13}, L_{14} = 3½ turns No. 16 wire, ¼" ID, 3'8" long (slug tuned)
L_{15}, L_{16}, L_{17} = 2 turns No. 18 wire, ⅛" ID, ⅛" long
L_{18}, L_{19}, L_{20} = 2 turns No. 18 wire, ¼" ID, ¼" long

175-MHZ 35-W POWER AMPLIFIER—Incorporates matching networks and techniques for avoiding low-frequency oscillation when operating from 12-V battery for mobile radio application.—"Silicon Power Circuits Manual," RCA, Harrison, N.J., SP-51, p 309.

27-MHZ CB TRANSMITTER—Straightforward design consists of modulator and transmitter. Number of tuning components is minimized. One section of double-pi network is peaked for maximum output, and the other is adjusted to limit of 5 W d-c input to final amplifier, as required by FCC.—"Silicon Power Circuits Manual," RCA, Harrison, N.J., SP-51, p 304.

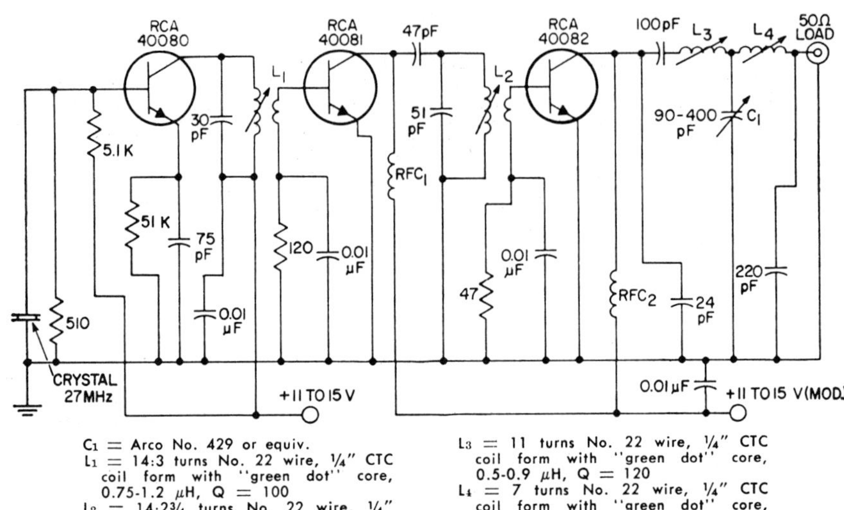

C_1 = Arco No. 429 or equiv.
L_1 = 14:3 turns No. 22 wire, ¼" CTC coil form with "green dot" core, 0.75-1.2 μH, Q = 100
L_2 = 14:2¾ turns No. 22 wire, ¼" CTC coil form with "green dott' core, 0.75-1.2 μH, Q = 100
L_3 = 11 turns No. 22 wire, ¼" CTC coil form with "green dot" core, 0.5-0.9 μH, Q = 120
L_4 = 7 turns No. 22 wire, ¼" CTC coil form with "green dot" core, 0.21-0.34 μH, Q = 140
RFC_1, RFC_2 = 15 μH, Miller No. 4624 or equiv.

5 0
TRIGGER IN
TO MODULATOR
CR2
R1 56K
R2 100K
620K R3
Q2
C1 100μf
CR1
Q1
R4 75K
+24
-70
-12

60-S TRANSMITTER WARM-UP—Allows filaments in pulse-modulated transmitter to warm up before modulation pulses are applied. Transistor types are not critical. Article gives time delay equation. With silicon transistors and tantalum capacitors, circuit operates from −55 to +85C.—E. Rosenbaum, Sixty-Second Timer Allows Transmitter Warm-Up, *Electronic Design*, Jan. 20, 1964, p 82.

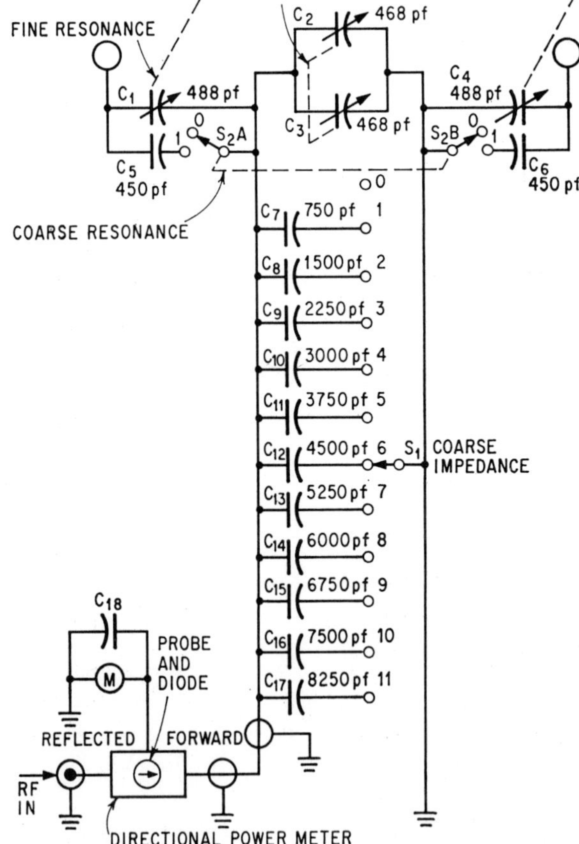

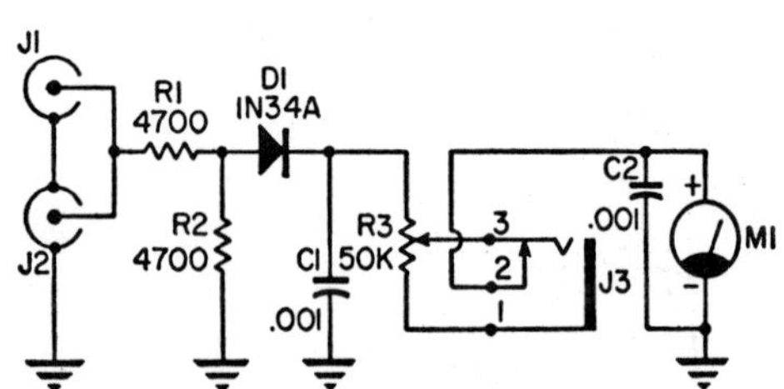

CITIZENS BAND TUNING MONITOR—Miniature illuminated S meter M1 peaks when CB transmitter has good modulation and is tuned for maximum r-f output. Monitor can be permanently connected to transmission line. Book gives construction details.—H. Friedman, CB Tuning Monitor, "Bench-Tested Communications Projects," Hayden Book Co., N.Y., p 48–50.

MATCHING VERTICAL LOOP—Depends on switching of low-loss fixed mica capacitors and variable air-dielectric capacitors instead of customary taps or links. High-impedance, low-value capacitor is divided into two equal sections to provide close balance with respect to ground and thereby permit higher voltages. Used with equilateral octagonal portable vertical loop antenna having 5-foot sides, in jungle locations where minimum height of conventional long-wire, dipole, or rhombic antenna would have to be at least 40 feet for comparable performance. Will work in ham bands if military-quality capacitors can be obtained.—K. H. Patterson, Down-To-Earth Army Antenna, *Electronics*, Aug. 21, 1967, p 111–114.

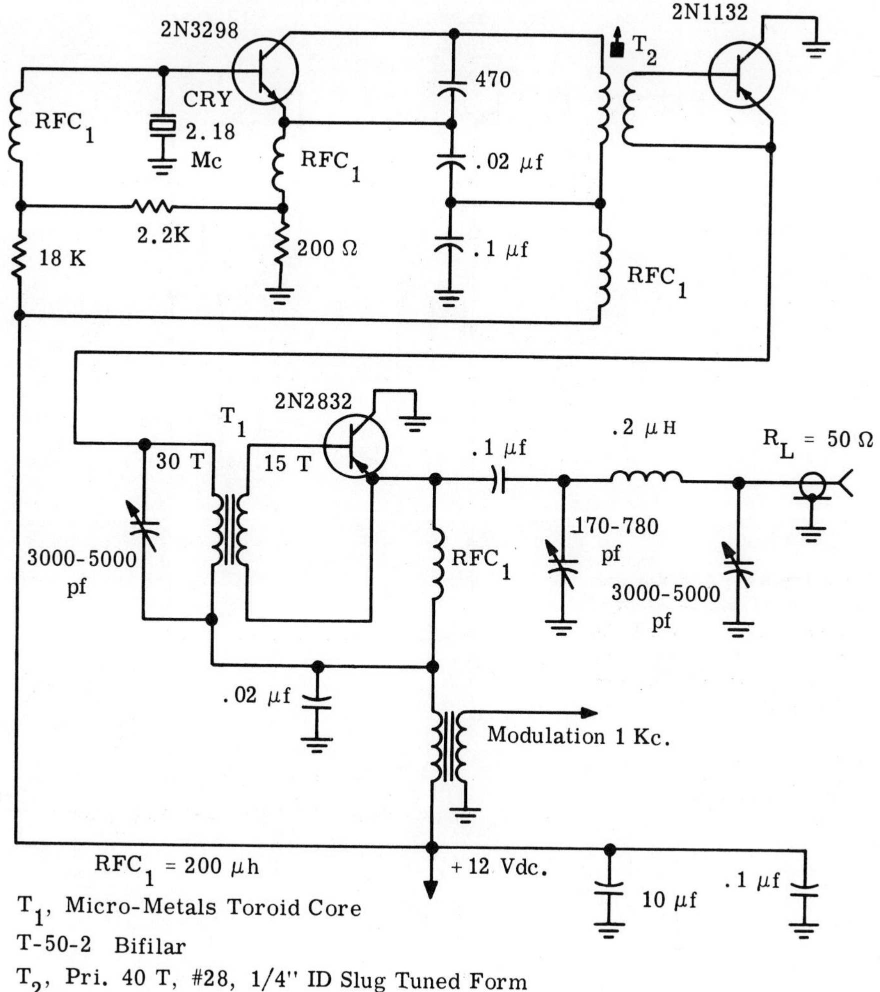

20 W AT 2.18 MHz—Designed for marine-band radiotelephone use. Consists of crystal oscillator, driver, and output stage. Requires 7-W modulation power from 10-ohm source. —"Circuits Manual," Motorola, Phoenix, Ariz., 1965, p 12-1-2.

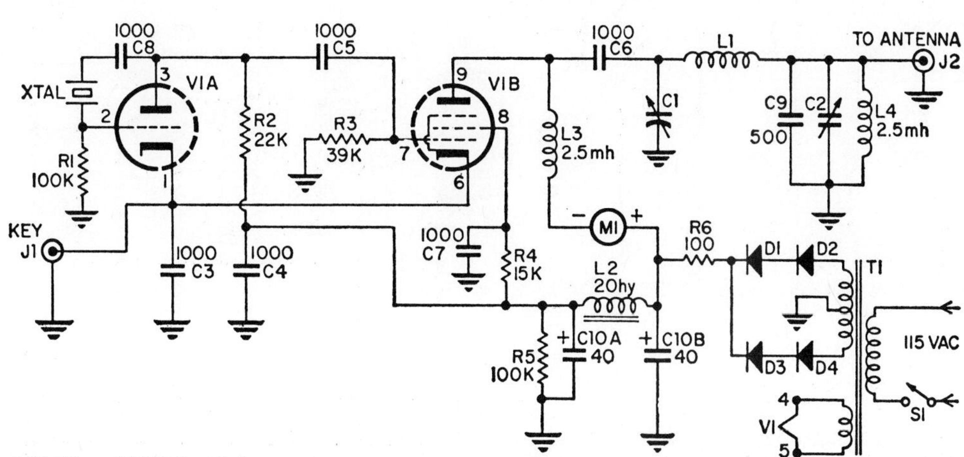

5-W ONE-TUBE C-W—Uses 6AW8-A triode-pentode. Can be operated on 160, 80, 40, and 20 meter bands, by using appropriate crystal frequency and appropriate plug-in coils for L1. Diodes D1-D4 are 750-mA 400-piv silicon. C1 is 10—365 μμF and C2 is 100—580 μμF mica trimmer. Book gives complete construction details.—E. N. Noll, One-Tube 5-Watter, "Bench-Tested Communications Projects," Hayden Book Co., N.Y., p 31—33.

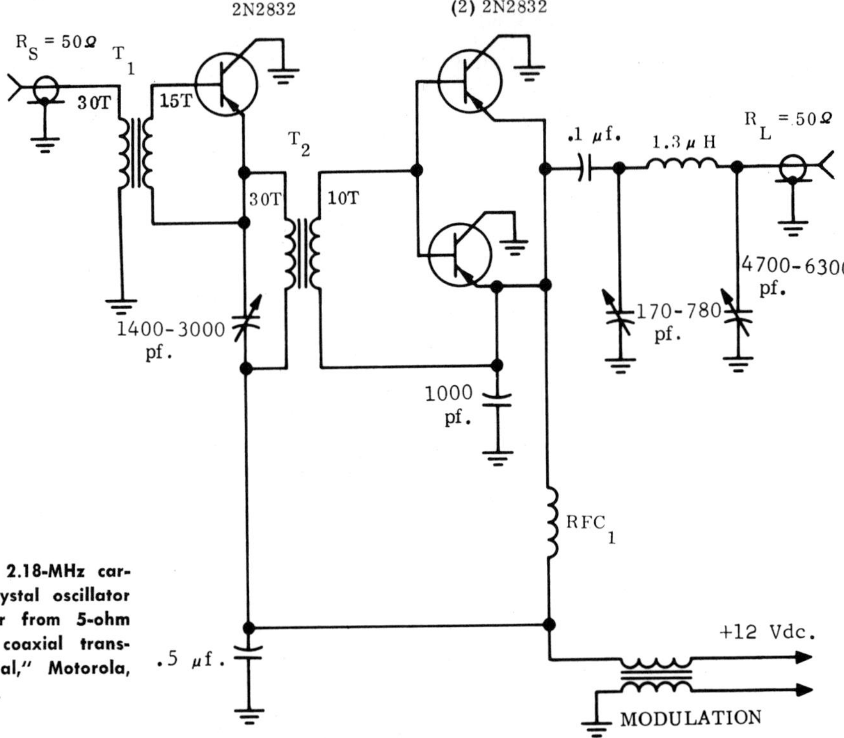

40 W at 2.18 MHZ—Requires 2.18-MHz carrier signal from standard crystal oscillator and 18-W modulation power from 5-ohm source. Feeds into 50-ohm coaxial transmission line.—"Circuits Manual," Motorola, Phoenix, Ariz., 1965, p 12-1-4.

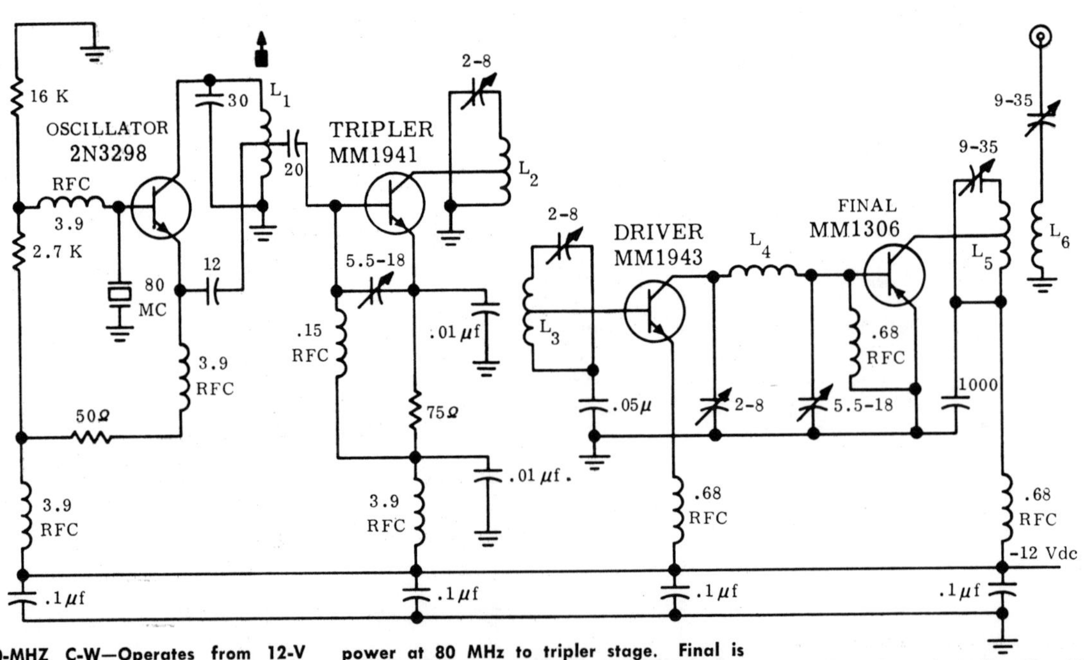

0.5-W 240-MHZ C-W—Operates from 12-V storage battery with total current drain of 180 mA. Oscillator is common-base crystal-controlled Hartley delivering about 15 mW of power at 80 MHz to tripler stage. Final is zero-biased class C loaded by double-tuned close-coupled transformer with impedances ranging from 25 to 100 ohms. Book gives winding data for all coils.—"Circuits Manual," Motorola, Phoenix, Ariz., 1965, p 12-7-2.

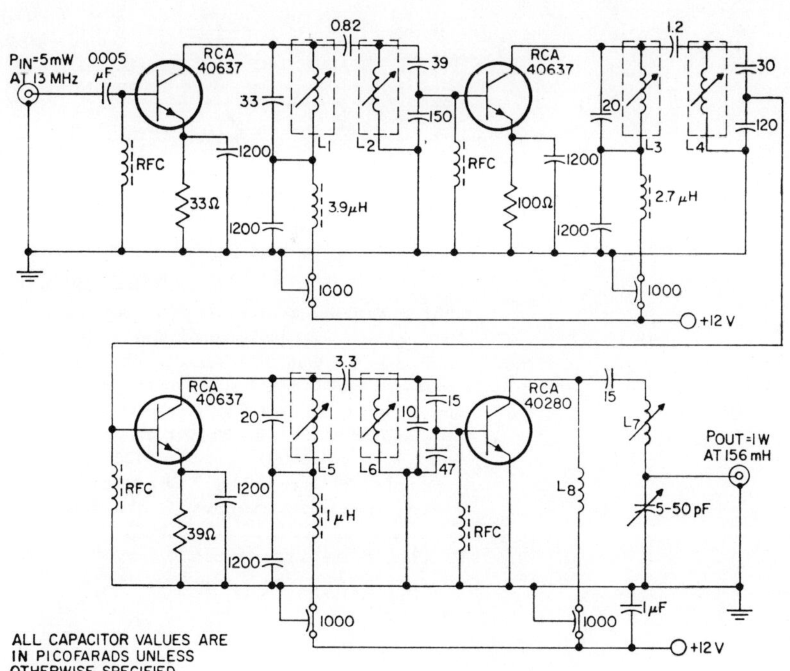

156–174 MHZ MARINE-BAND MULTIPLIER-AMPLIFIER—Delivers 1 W to antenna (maximum power specified by FCC for harbor communications). Can be operated anywhere in band without retuning, simply by changing crystal frequency of exciter section (not shown). Consists of three frequency multiplier stages using 40637 transistors, followed by power amplifier stage.—"Silicon Power Circuits Manual," RCA, Harrison, N.J., SP-51, p 297.

L_1, L_2 = 10½ turns No. 22 enamel wire, closewound, 10/32" slug tuned coil forms 15/64" OD, shield can ½" x ½" x 1"; slug = carbonyl S.F. or equiv.
L_3, L_4 = 4½ turns No. 22 enamel wire, closewound, 10/32" slug tuned coil forms 15/64" OD, shield can ½" x ½" x 1"; slug = carbonyl S.F. or equiv.
L_5, L_6 = 1½ turns No. 20 B.T., ¼" long, closewound, 10/32" slug tuned coil forms 15/64" OD, shield can ½" x ½" x 1"; slug-carbonyl S.F. or equiv.
L_7 = 2½ turns No. 20 B.T., ¼" long, closewound, 10/32" slug tuned coil forms 15/64" OD, shield can ½" x ½" x 1"; slug = carbonyl S.F. or equiv.
L_8 = 2 turns No. 20 B.T., 3/16" D, 3/16" long
RFC = 4 turns No. 30 enamel wire, ferrite bead, Ferroxcube No. 56-590-65/4B or equiv.

50 W AT 50 MHZ—Operates from 12-V auto storage battery, using three transistors in parallel and three chokes per stage for transient suppression.—"Silicon Power Circuits Manual," RCA, Harrison, N.J., SP-51, p 307.

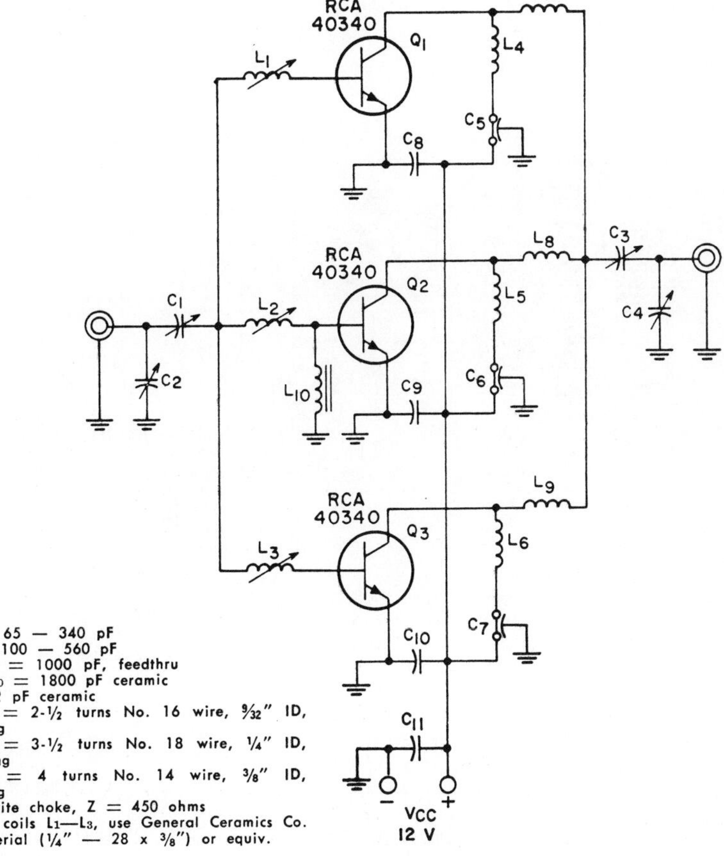

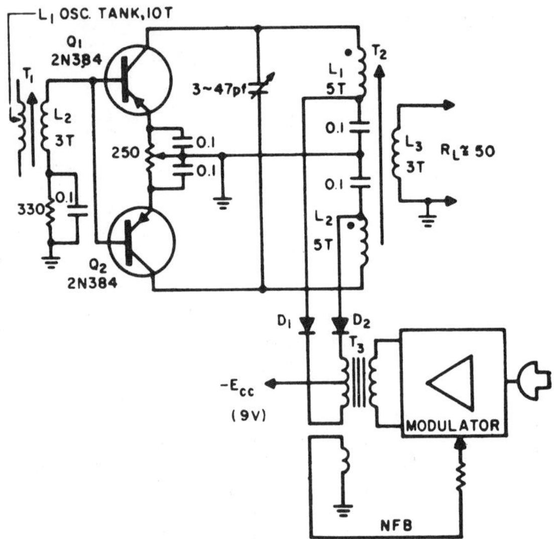

DOUBLE-SIDEBAND CB—Parallel-fed push-pull transistor output stage suppresses carrier of Citizens Band transmitter, giving greater operating range. Used in 100-mW 11-meter transceiver.—L. E. Geisler, Transistor Transmitter Has High-Level DSB Modulation, "400 Ideas for Design Selected from Electronic Design," Hayden Book Co., N.Y., 1964, p 30.

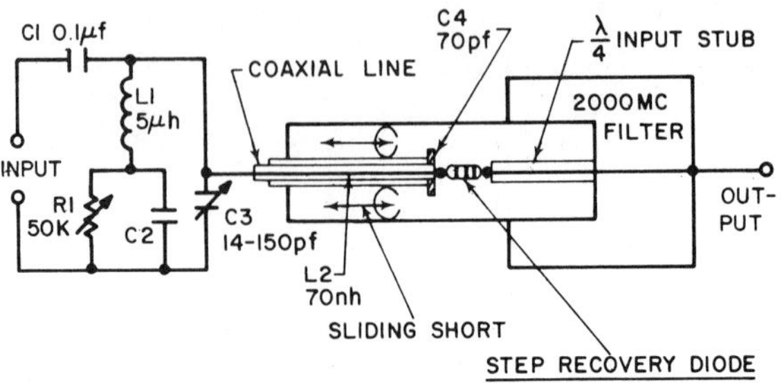

S-BAND MULTIPLIER—Use of step recovery diode gives efficiency greater than 10%, which is better than with varactor diode as frequency multiplier. Article gives circuit design criteria. Output filter is six-resonator interdigital structure with 20-MHz bandwidth and 2-dB insertion loss. Input of 100 MHz is multiplied 20 times to give 2 GHz output.—R. Hall, Harmonic Generators: Is the Step Recovery Diode Best?, *Electronic Design*, Jan. 18, 1965, p 28—33.

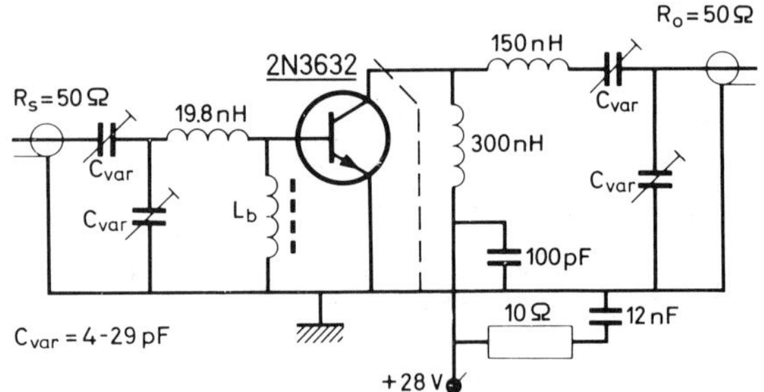

175-MHZ POWER AMPLIFIER—Circuit is example of design procedure for optimizing input and output matching networks for r-f power transistor. Maximum power output is 13.5 W. Causes and cures for spurious oscillations are covered. Appendix gives derivations of design equations.—J. Mulder, On the Design of Transistor R. F. Power Amplifiers, *Electronic Applications*, Philips, Pub. Dept., Elcoma Div., Eindhoven, The Netherlands, Vol. 27, No. 4, 1966—1967, p 155—171.

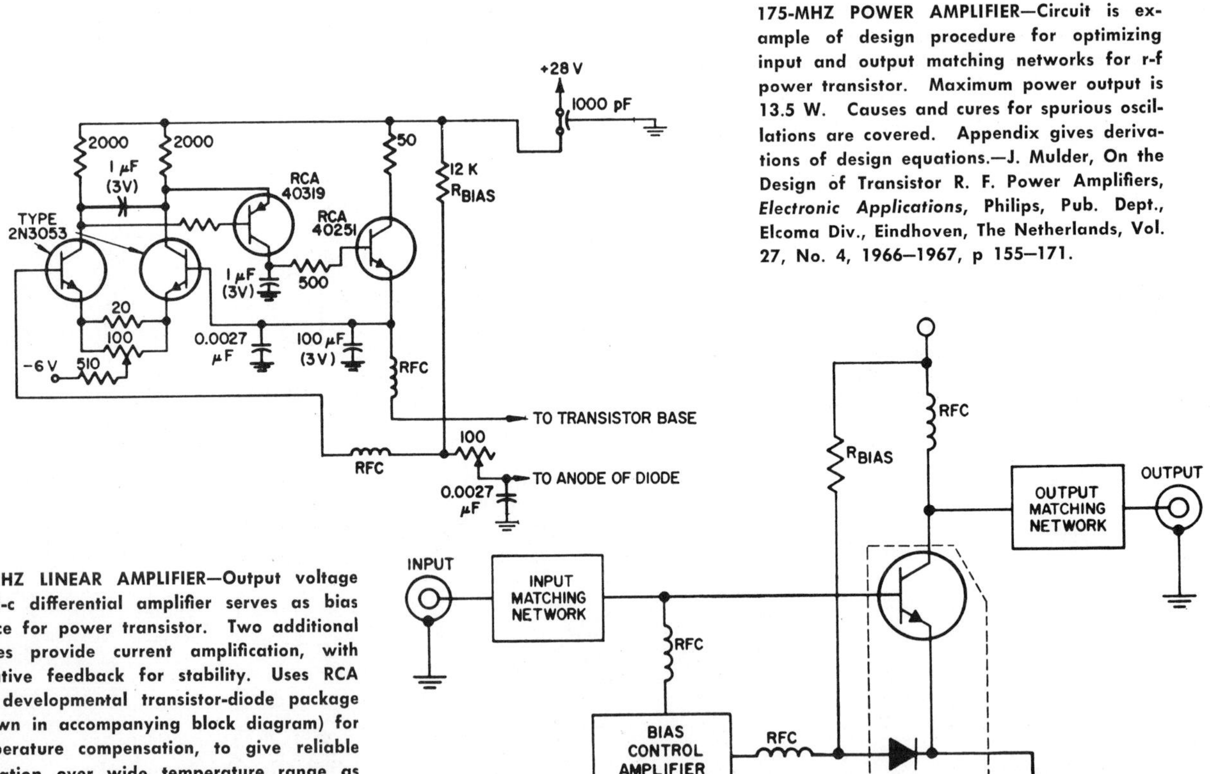

30-MHZ LINEAR AMPLIFIER—Output voltage of d-c differential amplifier serves as bias source for power transistor. Two additional stages provide current amplification, with negative feedback for stability. Uses RCA SSB developmental transistor-diode package (shown in accompanying block diagram) for temperature compensation, to give reliable operation over wide temperature range as class AB amplifier.—"Silicon Power Circuits Manual," RCA, Harrison, N.J., SP-51, p 318.

2–30 MHZ LINEAR POWER AMPLIFIER—Wideband amplifier has power gain of over 40 dB and delivers 5 W pep output for 28-V mobile applications.—"Silicon Power Circuits Manual," RCA, Harrison, N.J., SP-51, p 321.

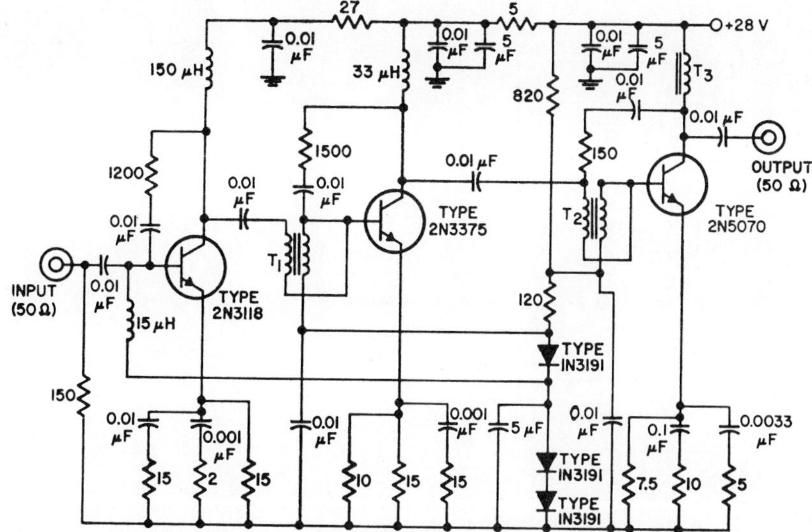

T_1, T_2 = 18 turns twisted pair. No. 28 enamel wire on Q_1 CF 102 form

T_3 = 50 turns No. 30 enamel wire on CF 102 Q_1 form

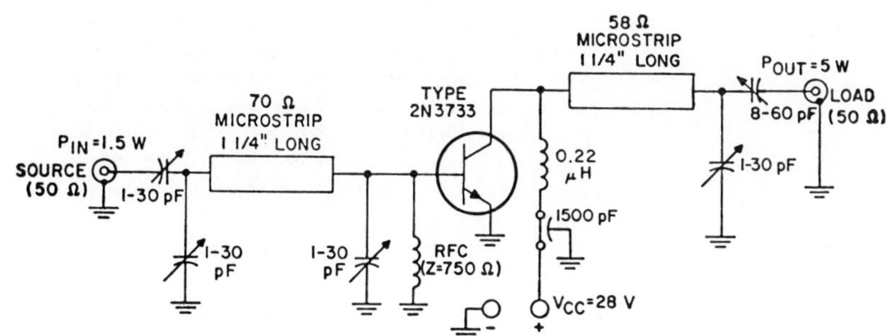

375-MHZ STRIPLINE AMPLIFIER—Delivers 5 W for military a-m voice communication systems. Transmission-line elements are constructed from 1/32-inch Teflon fiberglass microstrip board. Ferrite choke in transistor base return provides low-frequency stability.—"Silicon Power Circuits Manual," RCA, Harrison, N.J., SP-51, p 347.

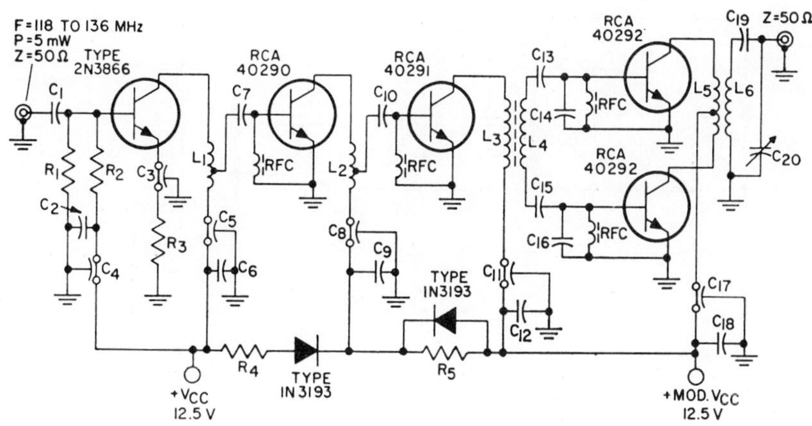

118–136 MHZ AIRCRAFT RADIO TRANSMITTER—Requires no retuning for band coverage. Push-pull output stage delivers 40 W pep. All stages are amplitude-modulated.—"Silicon Power Circuits Manual," RCA, Harrison, N.J., SP-51, p 329.

C_1 = 330 pF, Arco S.M. or equiv.
C_2 = 0.005 μF, ceramic
C_3, C_4, C_5, C_8, C_{11}, C_{17} = 1000 pF, feedthru
C_6, C_9, C_{12}, C_{18} = 0.05 μF, ceramic
C_7 = 50 pF, 5%, Arco S.M., or equiv.
C_{10}, C_{13}, C_{15} = 82 pF, 5%, Arco S.M., or equiv.
C_{14}, C_{16}, C_{19} = 150 pF, 5%, Arco S.M., or equiv.
C_{20} = Variable capacitor, 8-to-60 pF, Arco 404 or equiv.
L_1 = 7 turns No. 22 wire, 13/64" ID, 9/16" long, tapped at 1.5 turns
L_2 = 5½ turns No. 22 wire, 13/64" ID, close wound, tapped at 2 turns
L_3 = 6 turns No. 22 wire, 13/64" ID, interwind with L_4 on IRN-9 core material
L_4 = 4 turns No. 22 wire, 13/64" ID, interwind with L_3 on IRN-9 core material
L_5 = 5 turns No. 22 wire, 13/64" ID, center-tapped, interwind with L_6
L_6 = 5 turns No. 22 wire, 13/64" ID, interwind with L_5
RFC = 1 turn No. 28 wire, ferrite bead, Ferroxcube No. 56-590-65/4B or equiv.

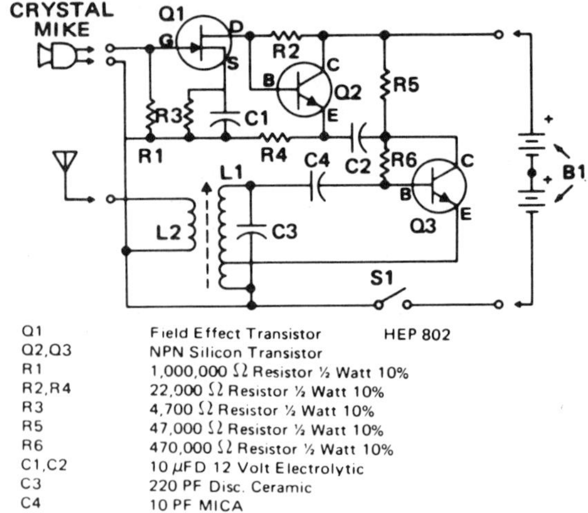

CRYSTAL MIKE
Q1
G
D
S
R2
B
C
Q2
E
R5
R3
C1
R1
R4
C4
C2
R6
C
B
Q3
E
L1
L2
C3
S1
B1
Q1 Field Effect Transistor HEP 802
Q2,Q3 NPN Silicon Transistor
R1 1,000,000 Ω Resistor ½ Watt 10%
R2,R4 22,000 Ω Resistor ½ Watt 10%
R3 4,700 Ω Resistor ½ Watt 10%
R5 47,000 Ω Resistor ½ Watt 10%
R6 470,000 Ω Resistor ½ Watt 10%
C1,C2 10 μFD 12 Volt Electrolytic
C3 220 PF Disc. Ceramic
C4 10 PF MICA

A-M WIRELESS TRANSMITTER—High impedance of fet input stage of audio amplifier provides proper match with crystal mike. Driver Q2 modulates Hartley oscillator Q2 for feeding short antenna wire connected to four turns of hookup wire wound around adjustable ferrite antenna coil L1. Operates from two 9-V transistor radio batteries in series. Tune a-m radio to quiet spot, then adjust L1 until voice at mike is picked up. Range is one or two rooms in home.—"Calectro Handbook," GC Electronics, Rockford, Ill., FR-69-C, p 46.

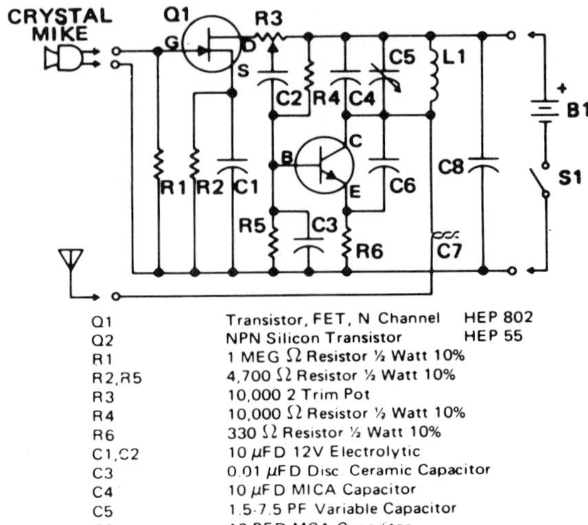

CRYSTAL MIKE
Q1
G
D
S
R3
C5
L1
C2
R4
C4
B1
B
C
E
R1
R2
C1
C6
C8
S1
R5
C3
R6
C7
Q1 Transistor, FET, N Channel HEP 802
Q2 NPN Silicon Transistor HEP 55
R1 1 MEG Ω Resistor ½ Watt 10%
R2,R5 4,700 Ω Resistor ½ Watt 10%
R3 10,000 2 Trim Pot
R4 10,000 Ω Resistor ½ Watt 10%
R6 330 Ω Resistor ½ Watt 10%
C1,C2 10 μFD 12V Electrolytic
C3 0.01 μFD Disc Ceramic Capacitor
C4 10 μFD MICA Capacitor
C5 1.5-7.5 PF Variable Capacitor
C6 10 PFD MCA Capacitor

F-M WIRELESS TRANSMITTER—High impedance of fet input stage of audio amplifier provides proper match with crystal mike. Q1 frequency-modulates single-transistor oscillator tunable over 88—108 MHz f-m band. L1 is four turns of wire wound on pencil and spaced half-inch apart. C7 is two short pieces of insulated wire twisted together, C8 is 0.01-μF disc capacitor, and B1 is 9-V transistor radio battery. Normal setting of modulation control R3 is mid-position. Tune f-m receiver to quiet spot, then adjust C5 until voice at mike is heard.—"Calectro Handbook," GC Electronics, Rockford, Ill., FR-69-C, p 46.

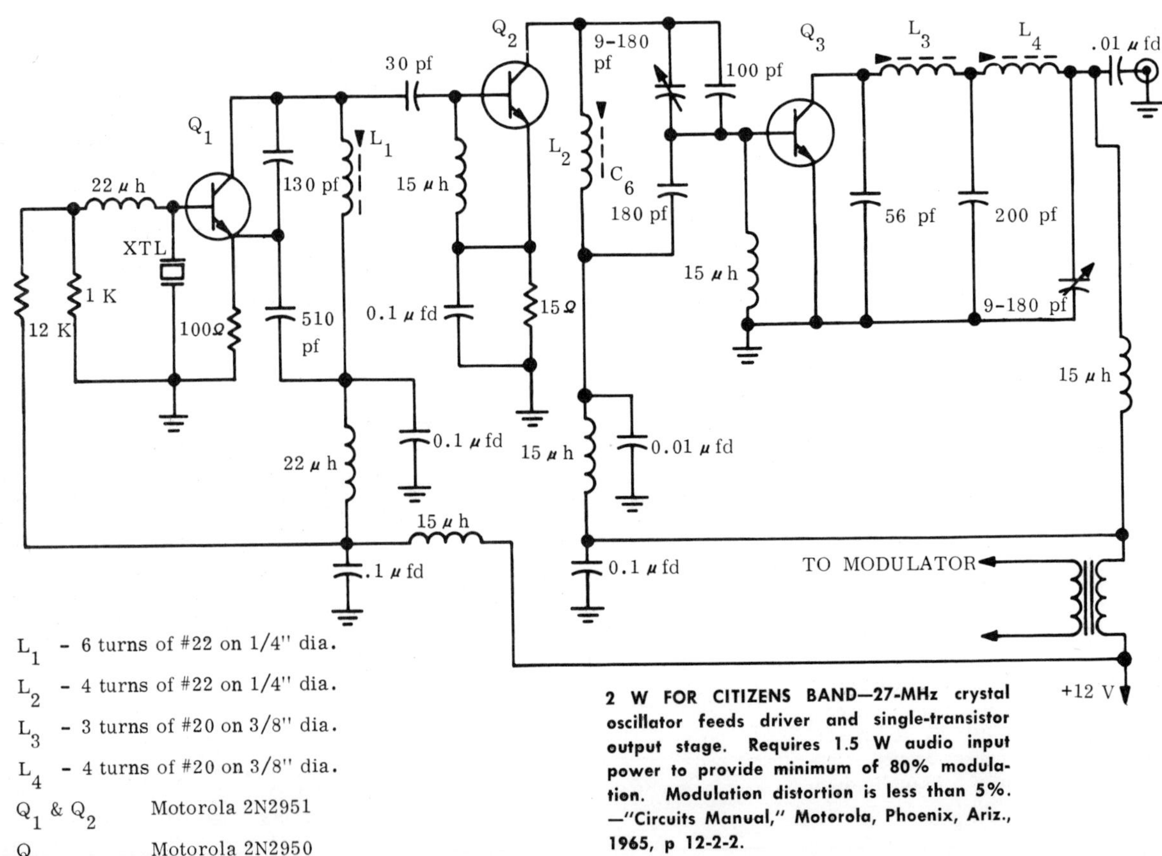

2 W FOR CITIZENS BAND—27-MHz crystal oscillator feeds driver and single-transistor output stage. Requires 1.5 W audio input power to provide minimum of 80% modulation. Modulation distortion is less than 5%. —"Circuits Manual," Motorola, Phoenix, Ariz., 1965, p 12-2-2.

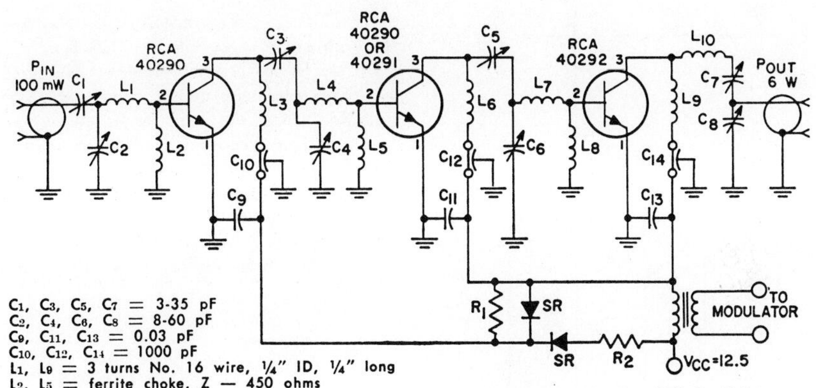

C_1, C_3, C_5, C_7 = 3-35 pF
C_2, C_4, C_6, C_8 = 8-60 pF
C_9, C_{11}, C_{13} = 0.03 pF
C_{10}, C_{12}, C_{14} = 1000 pF
L_1, L_9 = 3 turns No. 16 wire, 1/4" ID, 1/4" long
L_2, L_5 = ferrite choke, Z — 450 ohms
L_3 = rf choke, 1.5 μH
L_4, L_7 = 4 turns No. 16 wire, 1/4" ID, 3/8" long
L_6 = rf choke, 1.0 μH
L_8 = wire-wound resistor, R = 2.4 ohms
L_{10} = 5 turns No. 16 wire, 3/8" ID, 1/2" long
R_1 = 220 ohms
R_2 = 180 ohms
SR = IN2858A

35-MHZ 6-W NARROW-BAND A-M TRANSMITTER—Modulator requires 6 W audio power, because transmitter has total of 12 W d-c input power from 12-V mobile storage battery. Developed for aircraft radio applications.—"Silicon Power Circuits Manual," RCA, Harrison, N.J., SP-51, p 327.

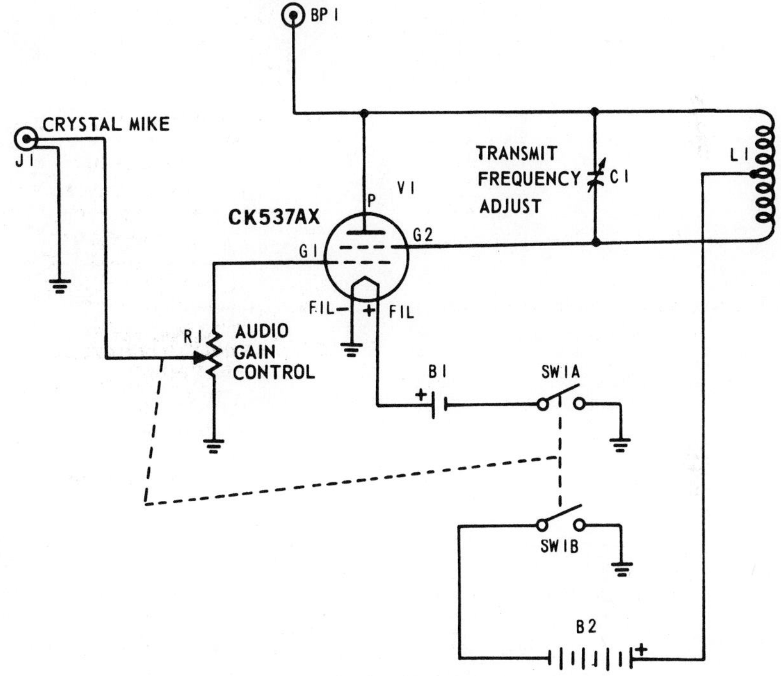

A-M WIRELESS MIKE—Can be operated legally if antenna is no longer than 10 ft. Tune radio to dead spot, then adjust C1 and R1 until voice at mike is heard. Use 1.25-V dry cell for B1 and 45-V or 90-V battery for V2. C1 is 150 pF, R1 750K, and L1 205 turns No. 24 enamel on 3/8-inch coil form.—R. M. Brown, "104 Simple One-Tube Projects," Tab Books, Blue Ridge Summit, Pa., 1969, p 102.

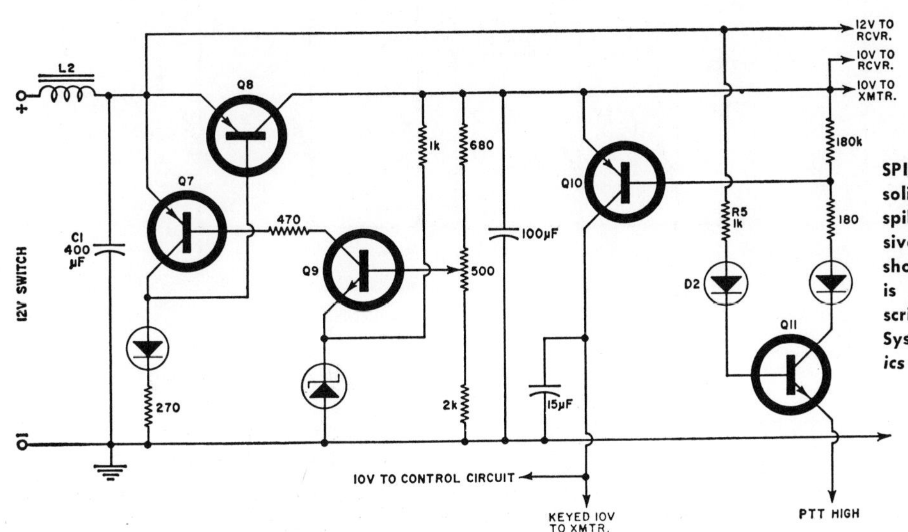

SPIKE REGULATOR—Used in G-E 450-MHz solid-state mobile radio to suppress voltage spikes caused by antenna mismatch, excessive temperature, high input voltage, or short on 12-V transmitter supply. Regulator is part of complete protection system described in article.—C. Smith, A Protection System for Solid-State Transmitters, *Electronics World*, Feb. 1969, p 38–39 and 77.

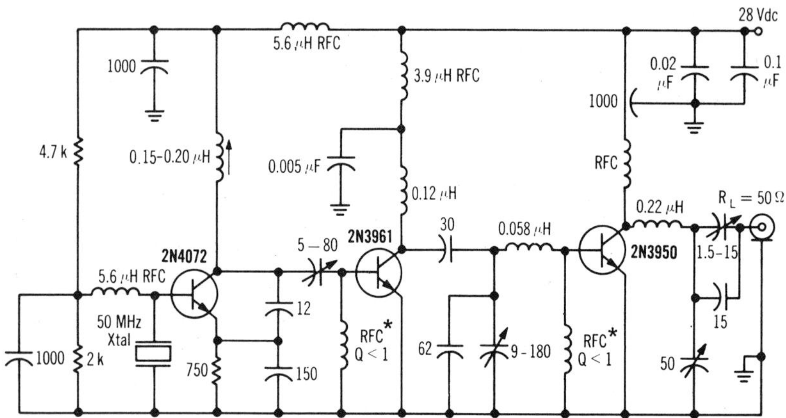

50-W 50-MHZ THREE-TRANSISTOR—Uses only three stages, one of which is low-level Colpitts crystal oscillator. Provides continuous power output, with 27 dB combined power gain for driver and final stages. Provisions for keying or frequency modulation may be added. Report gives design approach for optimizing performance of each stage. Circuit is suitable only for f-m or c-w, not a-m. —R. C. Hejhall, A 50 Watt 50 MHz Solid-State Transmitter, Motorola, Phoenix, Ariz., AN-246, 1967.

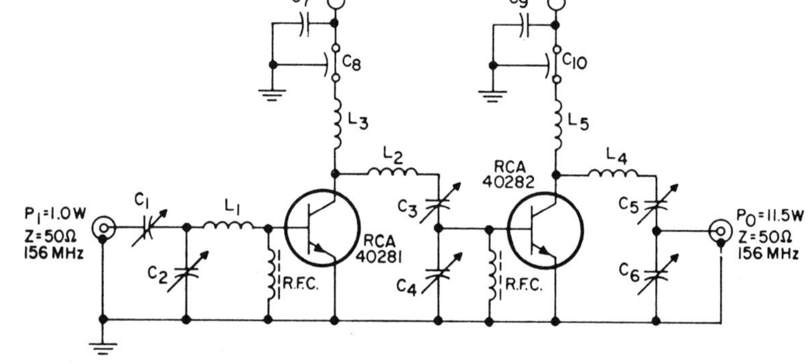

156–174 MHz MARINE-BAND POWER AMPLIFIER—With 1-W f-m power applied to input of driver, output stage delivers over 10 W to 50-ohm transmission line.—"Silicon Power Circuits Manual," RCA, Harrison, N.J., SP-51, p 298.

C_1, C_2, C_3, C_4, C_5, C_6, = Arco 404 or equiv.
C_7, C_9 = 0.022 μF, 25 V
C_8, C_{10} = 1000 pF, ceramic standoff
L_1, L_5 = 1 turn No. 20 wire, 1/4" ID, 3/32" long

L_2, L_3 = 1 1/2 turns No. 20 wire, 1/4" ID, 3/32" long
L_4 = 2 turns No. 18 wire, 1/4" ID, 5/16" long
RFC = 4 turns No. 30 wire, ferrite bead Ferroxcube No. 56-590-65/4B or equiv.

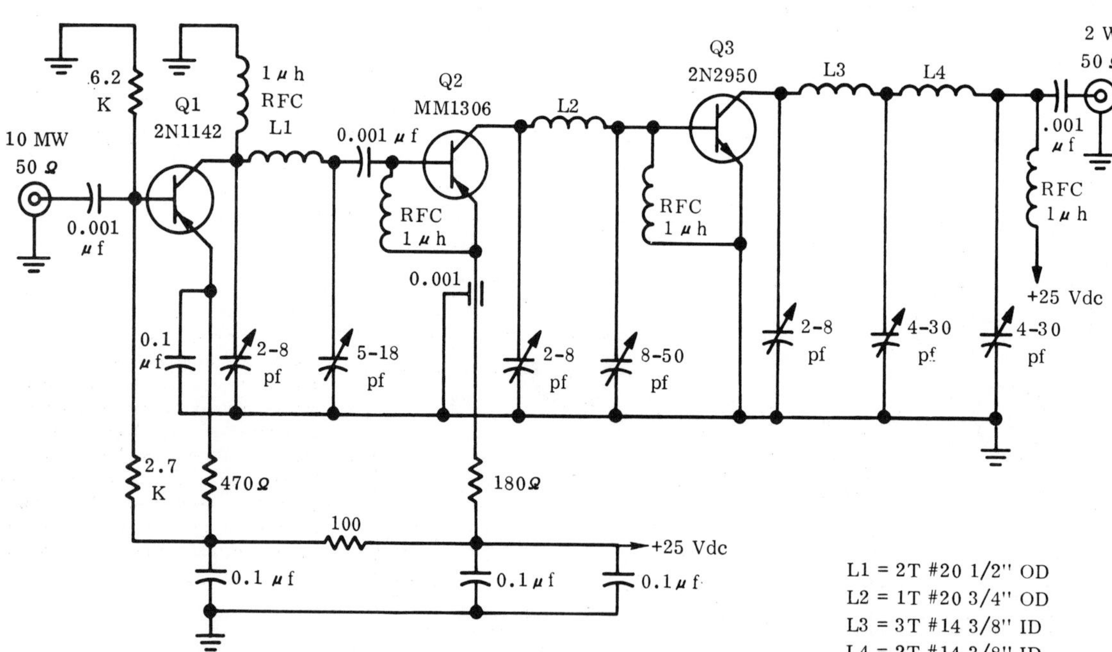

L1 = 2T #20 1/2" OD
L2 = 1T #20 3/4" OD
L3 = 3T #14 3/8" ID
L4 = 2T #14 3/8" ID

2-W 160-MHZ DRIVER AND FINAL—Three-transistor output circuit provides overall gain of 23 dB. Q1 operates class A and provides fair stability without neutralization. R-f choke that provides zero bias for Q2 should be as small as possible electrically to minimize possibility of circuit oscillation at some lower frequency.—"Circuits Manual," Motorola, Phoenix, Ariz., 1965, p 12-6-2.

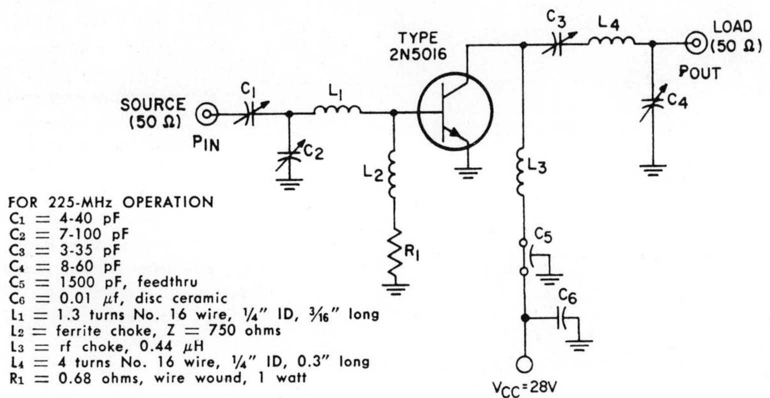

400-MHZ POWER AMPLIFIER—Delivers over 15 W at 400 MHz and over 20 W at 225 MHz. T network matches 3-ohm input impedance of transistor to 50-ohm source impedance, and pi network matches output to 50-ohm load.—"Silicon Power Circuits Manual," RCA, Harrison, N.J., SP-51, p 348.

FOR 400-MHz OPERATION
C_1, C_3 = 1.5-20 pF
C_2, C_4 = 3-35 pF
C_5 = 1000 pF, feedthru
C_6 = 0.01 μF, disc ceramic
L_1 = 1.3 turns No. 16 wire, 1/4" ID, 1/4" long
L_2 = ferrite choke, 2 = 750 ohms (or 0.12-pH choke)
L_3 = rf choke, 0.13 μH
L_4 = 3 turns 1/32" x 1/8" copper ribbon, 3/16" ID, 1/2" long
R_1 = 0.68 ohms, wire wound, 1 watt

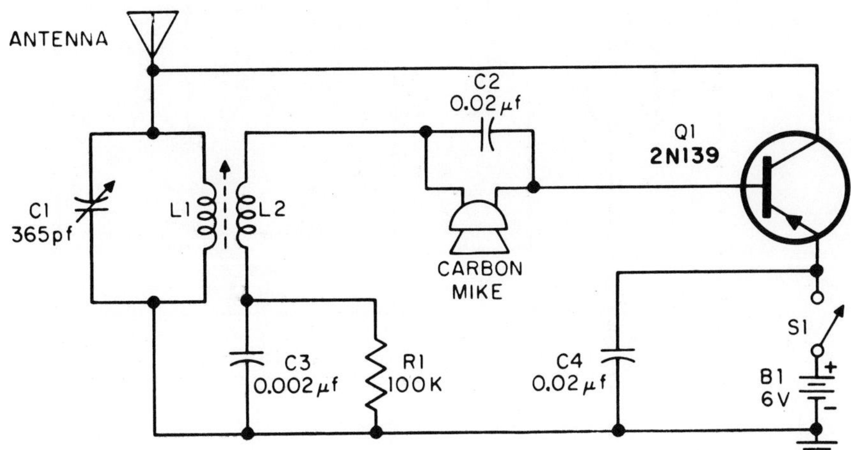

WIRELESS MIKE—Tune to dead spot at low end of a-m broadcast-band receiver. Antenna length is limited to 10 ft by law. If not heard, try reversing connections to L2. L1 is No. 7/41 Belden Litz wire wound closely in single layer to within 1/4 inch of ends of 7-inch by 0.33-inch ferrite rod. L2 is 35 turns of No. 24 enameled wire wound directly over L1.—"A Modern Transistor Workbook," Radio Shack, Boston, Mass., 1965, p 13.

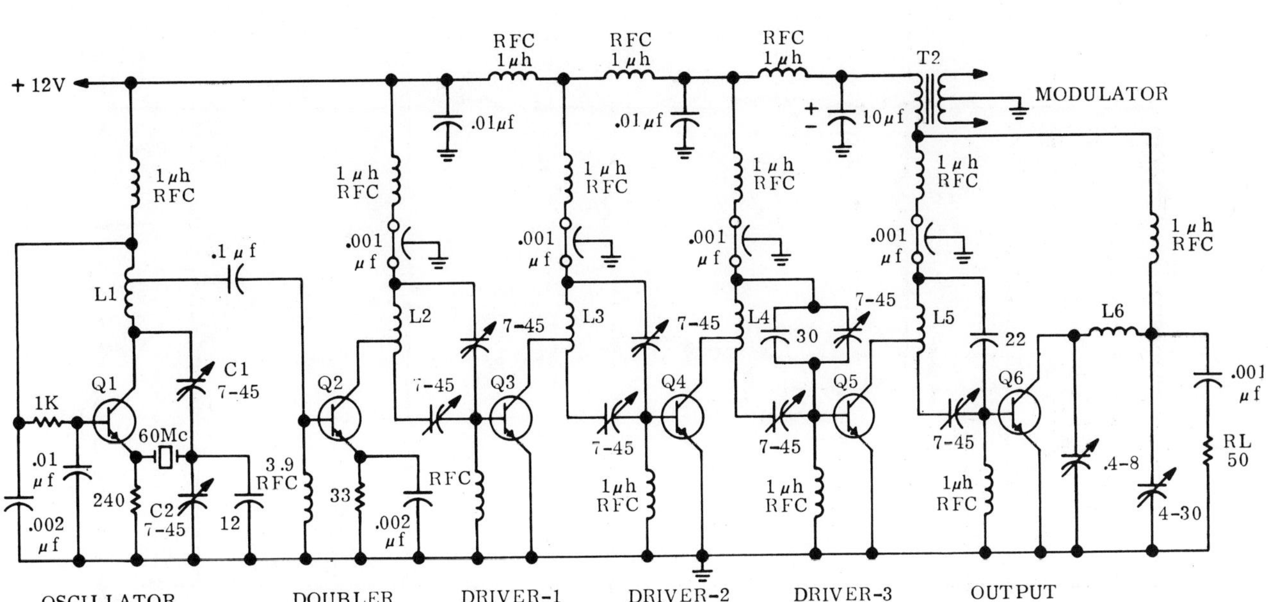

1.5-W 120-MHZ AIRCRAFT—Uses 60-MHz crystal oscillator to feed frequency-doubling amplifier stage Q2. Both driver and output stages are collector-modulated in order to obtain 100% modulation. Q5 and Q6 are 2N2950 and all other transistors are 2N2951. Book gives coil-winding data.—"Circuits Manual," Motorola, Phoenix, Ariz., 1965, p 12-5-2.

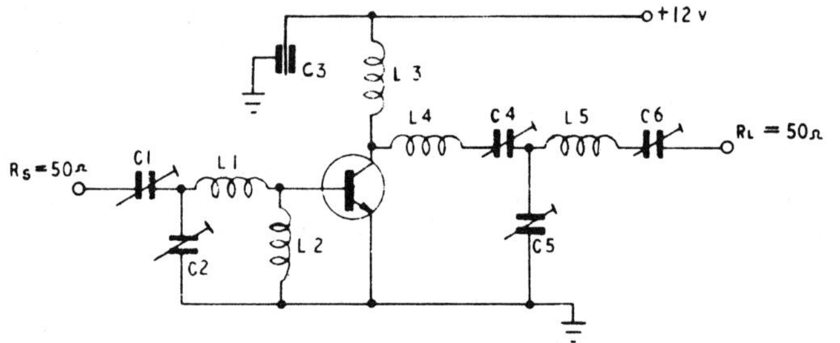

C_1, C_2, C_4 - C_6	3 - 30pF trimmer
C_3	1500pF feedthrough
L_1	4T, 6.3mm I.D. 1.2mm T.C.W. 10mm long
L_2	0.47μH Cambion Choke type 3640-13-2
L_3	0.15μH Cambion Choke type 3640-1-2
L_4, L_5	0.22μH Cambion Choke type 3640-5-2

150-MHZ NARROW-BAND OUTPUT STAGE—For use in battery-operated portable transmitter where good gain and high efficiency are important. Uses ZT3866 uhf transistor in switching mode. Second harmonic suppression is excellent. Current drain is 155 mA. Report gives design equations.—A Low Power High Efficiency Output Stage Using ZT3866 Transistors, Ferranti Ltd., Oldham, Lancs., England, Application Note 37, Dec. 1968.

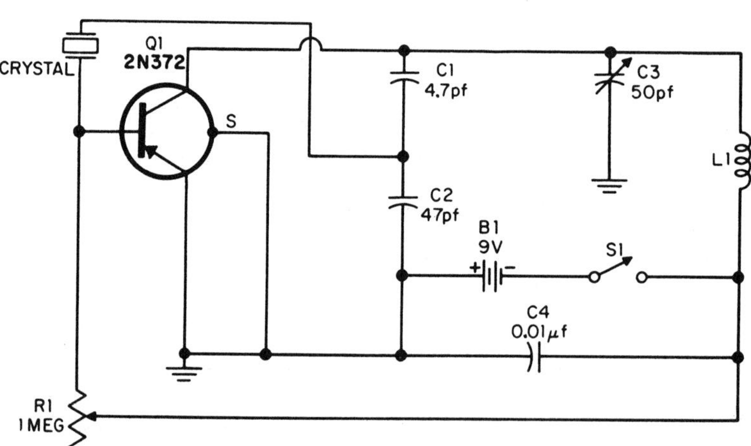

CB CHANNEL LOCATOR—When third-overtone Citizens-Band crystal for desired channel is inserted in oscillator, L1 will radiate that frequency to receiver for quick location of that channel. Adjust R1 initially, without crystal, until milliammeter in series with battery shows 0.2 mA, then insert crystal and adjust C3 for maximum signal at receiver. L1 is B&W 3003.—"A Modern Transistor Workbook,". Radio Shack, Boston, Mass., 1965, p 17.

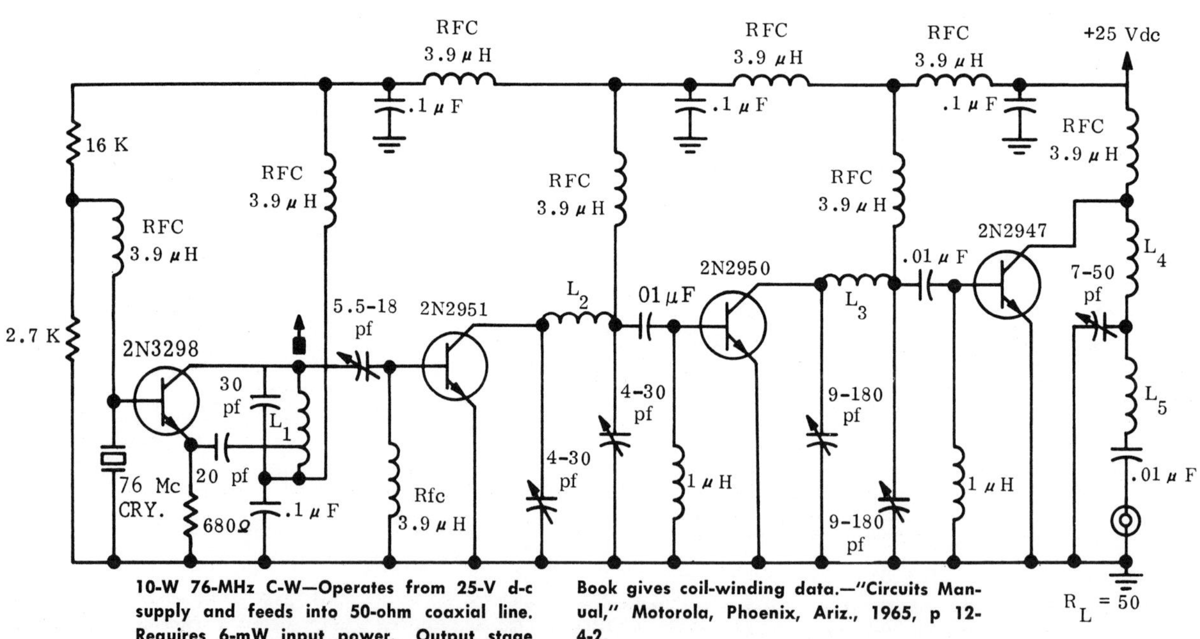

10-W 76-MHz C-W—Operates from 25-V d-c supply and feeds into 50-ohm coaxial line. Requires 6-mW input power. Output stage draws 600 mA and driver stages 166 mA. Book gives coil-winding data.—"Circuits Manual," Motorola, Phoenix, Ariz., 1965, p 12-4-2.

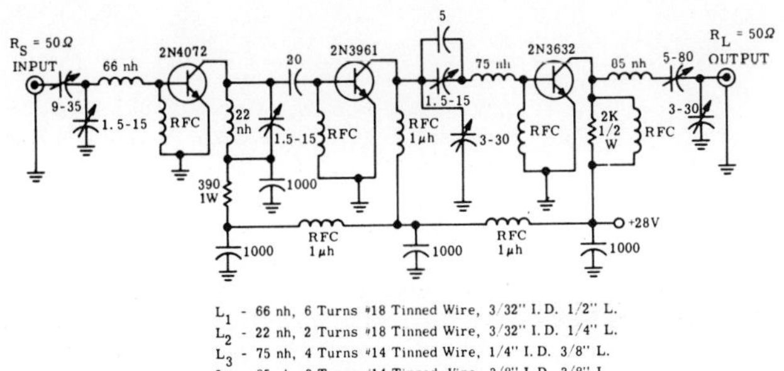

15 W at 160 MHZ—Provides 30.5 dB power gain with only three transistor stages. Report shows how input-output admittance data in network design is used to optimize performance of each stage. Addition of appropriate oscillator, buffer, and multiplier stages would give complete f-m or c-w transmitter. Not intended for a-m operation. Requires 13-mW power input.—R. Hejhall, A 160 MHz 15-Watt Solid-State Power Amplifier, Motorola, Phoenix, Ariz., AN-214, 1967.

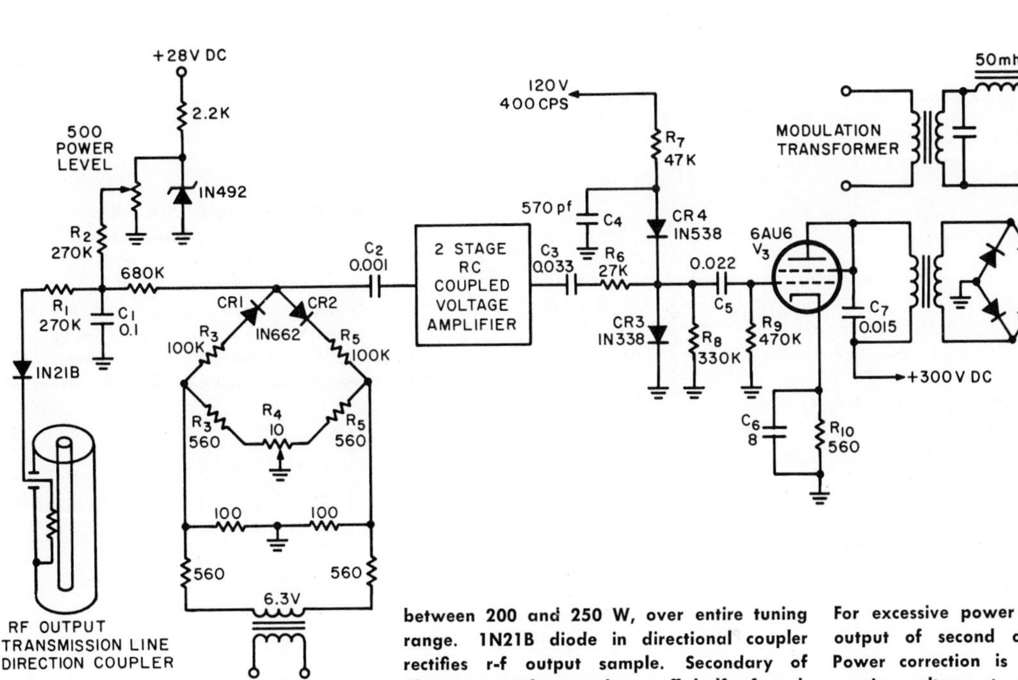

R-F POWER OUTPUT CONTROL—Used in servo-tuned a-m fsk 225–399.95 MHz transmitter to maintain power within 10% of present value, between 200 and 250 W, over entire tuning range. 1N21B diode in directional coupler rectifies r-f output sample. Secondary of filament transformer chops off half of each input cycle at 400-Hz rate. CR3 and CR4 form second chopper—a shunt gate that alternately blocks and passes when input error signal is positive to indicate low power. For excessive power (negative error signal), output of second chopper drops to zero. Power correction is made automatically by varying voltage at screen of 4CX250B driver over range of 50 to 120 V.—J. H. Davis and B. van Sutphin, Automatic Carrier-Level System Controls 250-Watt Transmitter, *Electronic Design*, March 16, 1964, p 78–81.

NOTE: To locate additional circuits in the category of this chapter, use the index at the back of this book. Check also the author's "Sourcebook of Electronic Circuits," published by McGraw-Hill in 1968.

CHAPTER 92
Triangular-Wave Generator Circuits

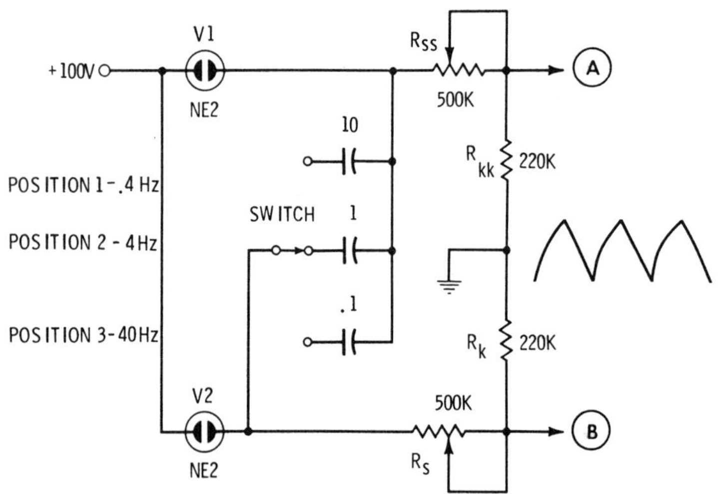

LOW-FREQUENCY TRIANGULAR-PULSE NEON—May be used as time base for any slow-scan device requiring equal trace and retrace time. 500K controls may be ganged for frequency control, or isolated for linearity adjustment.—W. G. Miller, "Using and Understanding Miniature Neon Lamps," H. W. Sams & Co., Indianapolis, Ind., 1969, p 47.

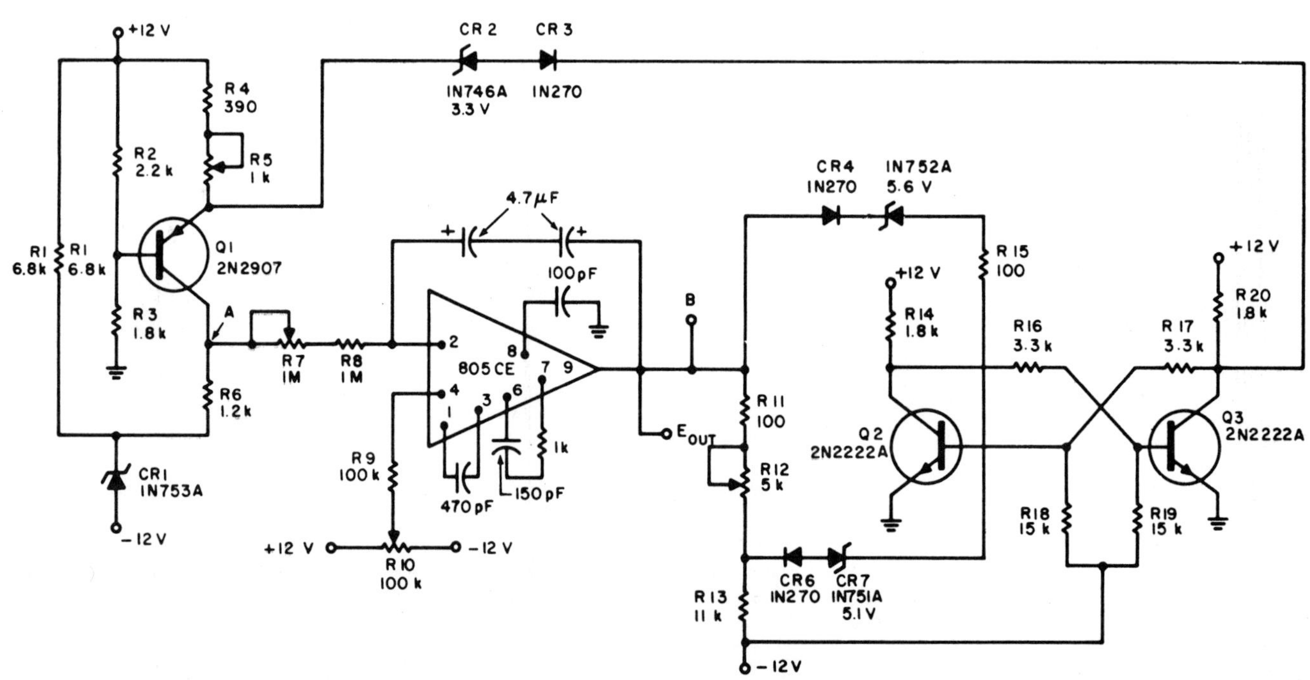

SUBAUDIO TRIANGULAR WAVES—With values shown, output can be adjusted down to 0.05 Hz with R7. Wave shape is good.—N. M. Nekomoto, LF Triangular Wave Generator Has Just a Few Components, *Electronic Design*, Nov. 22, 1967, p 105.

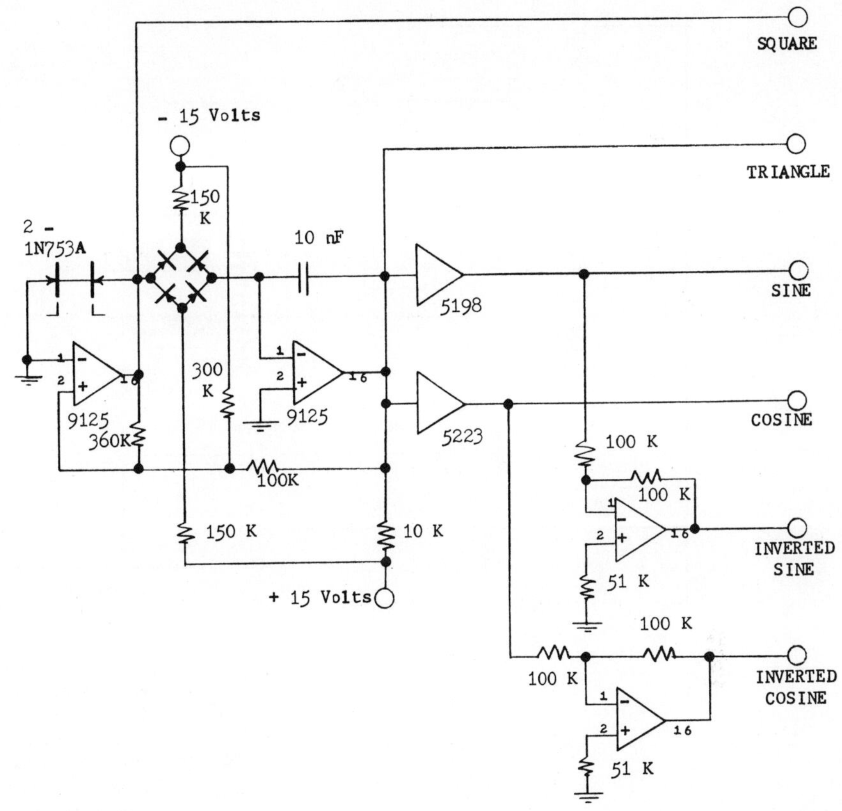

UNIVERSAL WAVEFORM GENERATOR—Combination of six OEI IC modules provides choice of six different output waveforms, with frequency determined by 10-nF capacitor and 150K resistors in oscillator using first 9125 opamp as switch with hysteresis and second as integrator driven by current having polarity determined by switch and diode bridge. All waveforms are symmetrical about common output except triangle. Diodes are 1N914 or similar.—A Square/Triangle/Sine/Cosine Waveform Generator, Optical Electronics, Tucson, Ariz., No. 10116.

SQUARE
- 15 Volts
150 K
TRIANGLE
2 -
1N753A
10 nF
SINE
5198
9125
300 K
9125
COSINE
5223
360K
100K
100 K
100 K
150 K
10 K
INVERTED SINE
+ 15 Volts
51 K
100 K
100 K
INVERTED COSINE
51 K

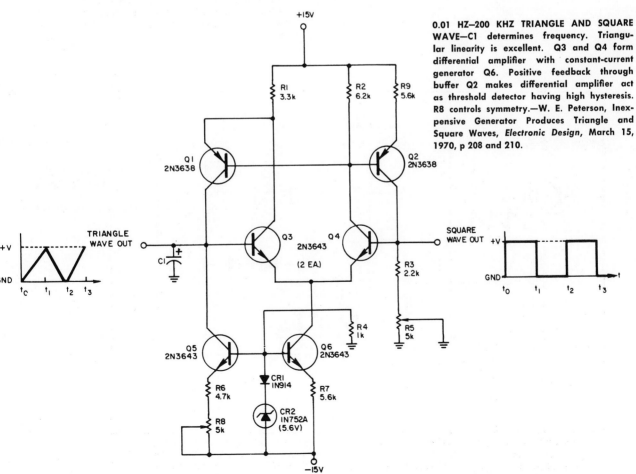

0.01 HZ–200 KHZ TRIANGLE AND SQUARE WAVE—C1 determines frequency. Triangular linearity is excellent. Q3 and Q4 form differential amplifier with constant-current generator Q6. Positive feedback through buffer Q2 makes differential amplifier act as threshold detector having high hysteresis. R8 controls symmetry.—W. E. Peterson, Inexpensive Generator Produces Triangle and Square Waves, *Electronic Design*, March 15, 1970, p 208 and 210.

+V
GND
t_0 t_1 t_2 t_3

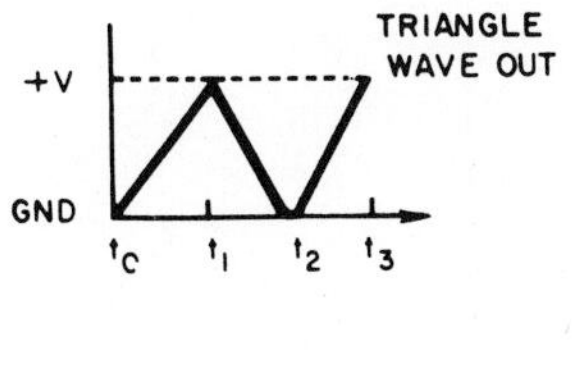

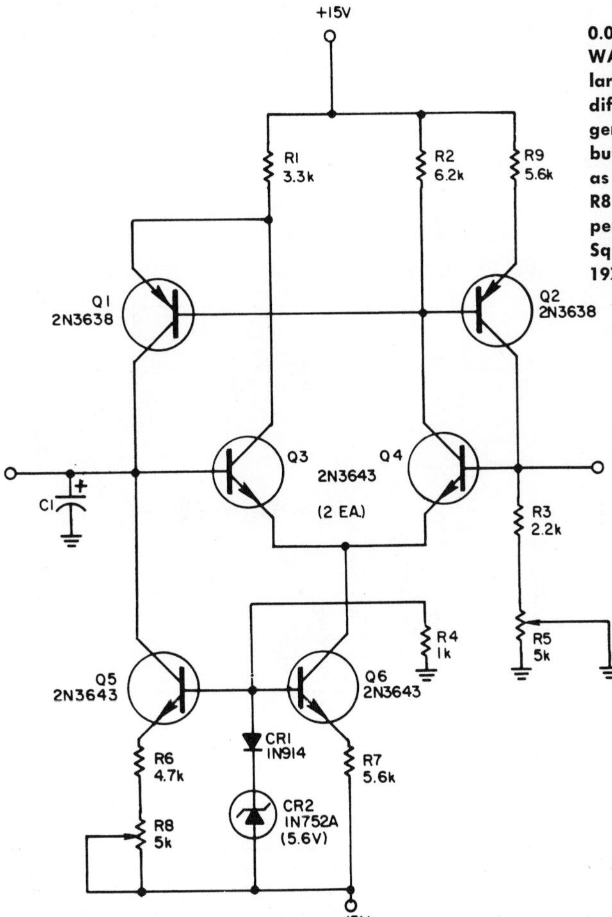

+15V
R1 3.3k
R2 6.2k
R9 5.6k
Q1 2N3638
Q2 2N3638
TRIANGLE WAVE OUT
C1
Q3
Q4
2N3643
(2 EA)
SQUARE WAVE OUT
R3 2.2k
R4 1k
R5 5k
Q5 2N3643
Q6 2N3643
CR1 1N914
R6 4.7k
R7 5.6k
CR2 1N752A (5.6V)
R8 5k
−15V

+V
GND
t_0 t_1 t_2 t_3
t

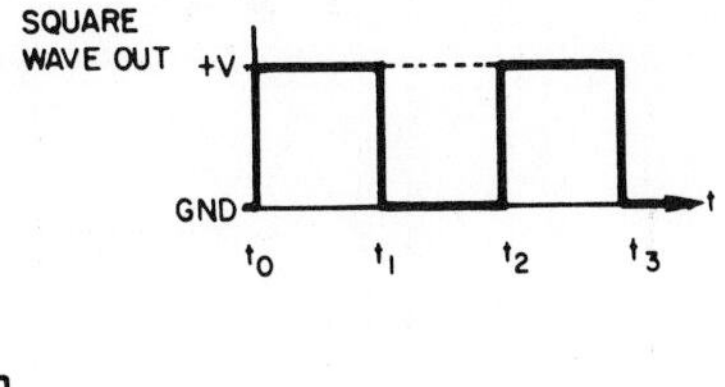

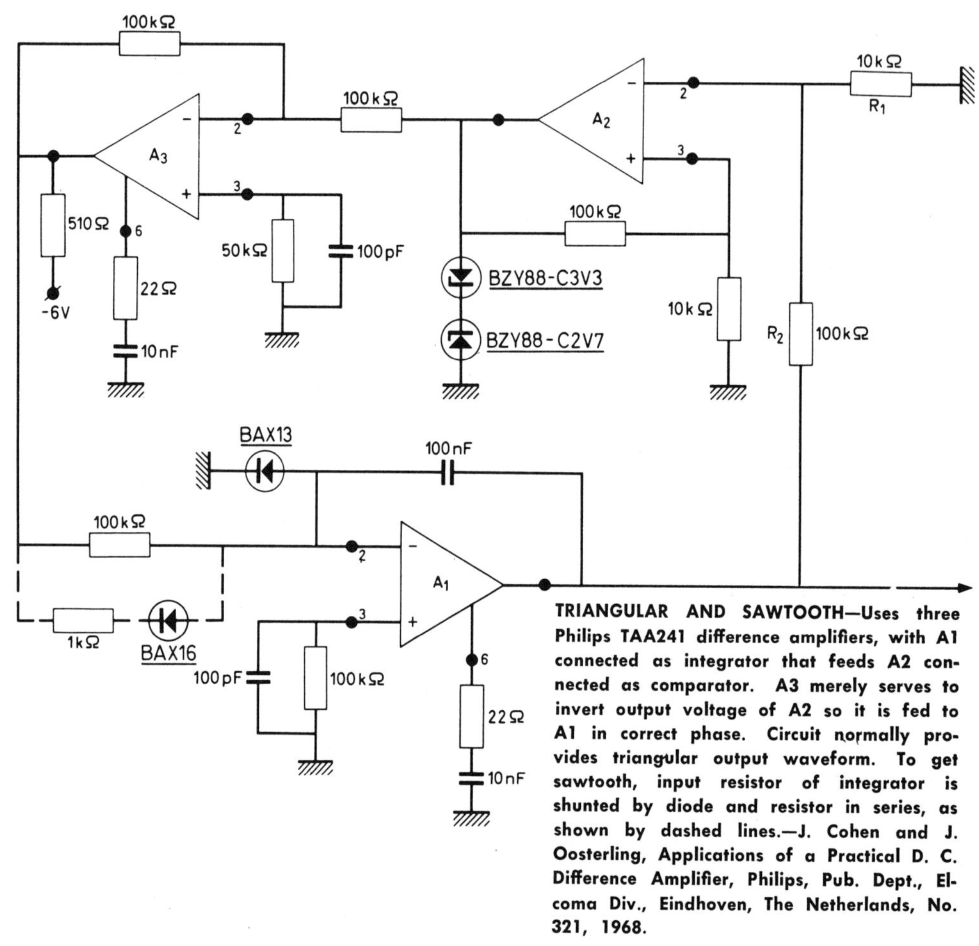

TRIANGULAR AND SAWTOOTH—Uses three Philips TAA241 difference amplifiers, with A1 connected as integrator that feeds A2 connected as comparator. A3 merely serves to invert output voltage of A2 so it is fed to A1 in correct phase. Circuit normally provides triangular output waveform. To get sawtooth, input resistor of integrator is shunted by diode and resistor in series, as shown by dashed lines.—J. Cohen and J. Oosterling, Applications of a Practical D. C. Difference Amplifier, Philips, Pub. Dept., Elcoma Div., Eindhoven, The Netherlands, No. 321, 1968.

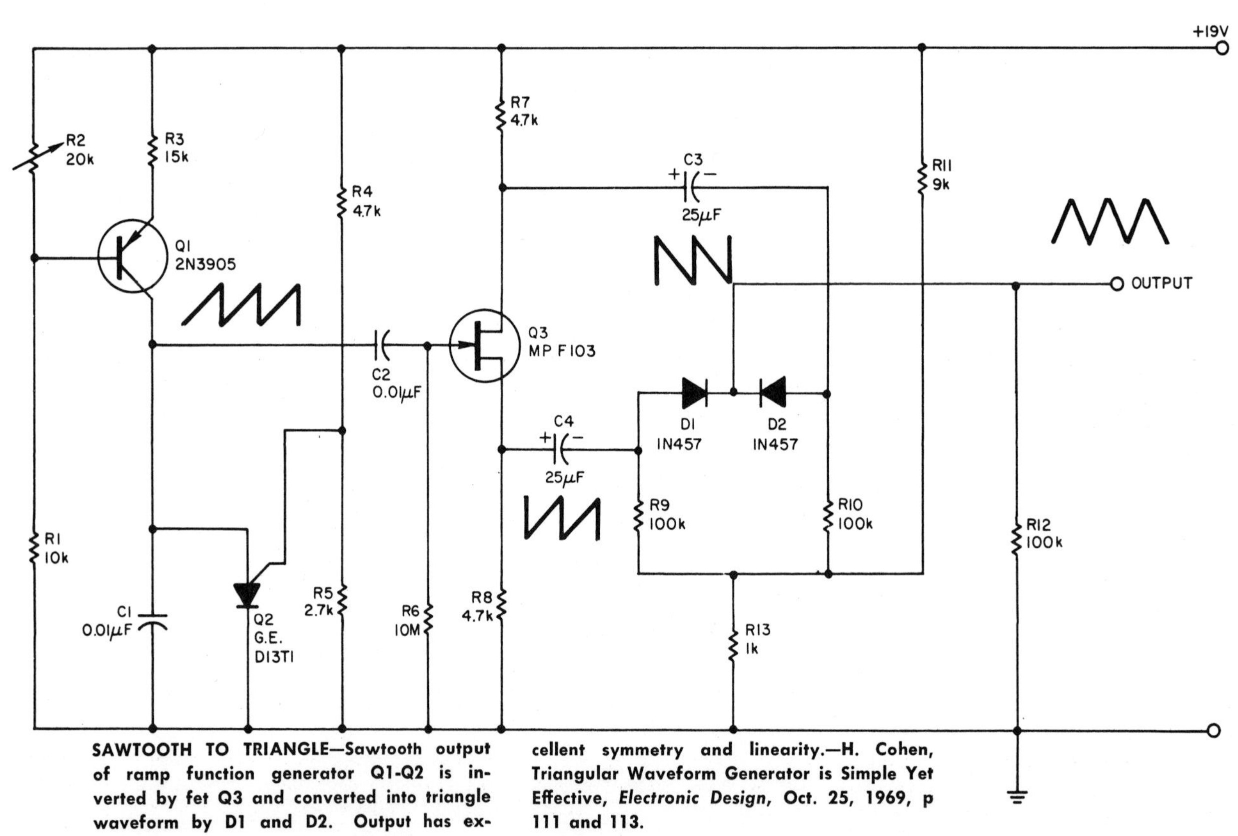

SAWTOOTH TO TRIANGLE—Sawtooth output of ramp function generator Q1-Q2 is inverted by fet Q3 and converted into triangle waveform by D1 and D2. Output has excellent symmetry and linearity.—H. Cohen, Triangular Waveform Generator is Simple Yet Effective, *Electronic Design*, Oct. 25, 1969, p 111 and 113.

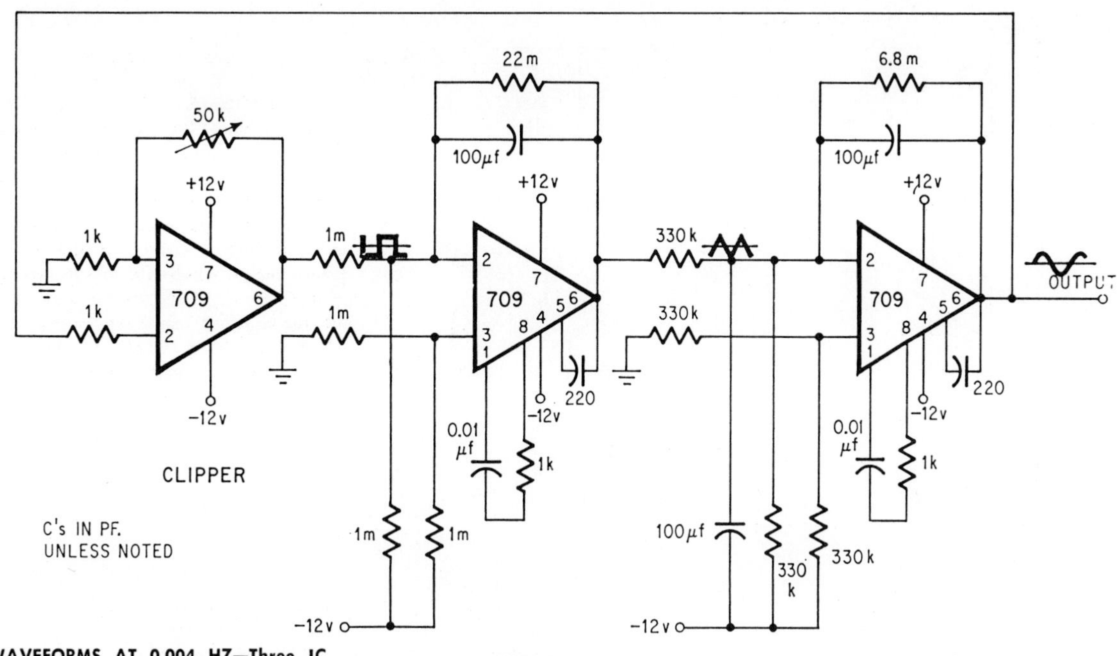

THREE WAVEFORMS AT 0.004 HZ—Three IC opamps, connected as clipper and two inverters, give choice of square-wave, triangular-wave, and parabolic waveform approximating sine wave, for universal subaudio generator. Pot controls output amplitude.—A. D. Delagrange, Low Frequency Waveform Generator Uses 3 Op Amps, *Electronics*, April 14, 1969, p 98.

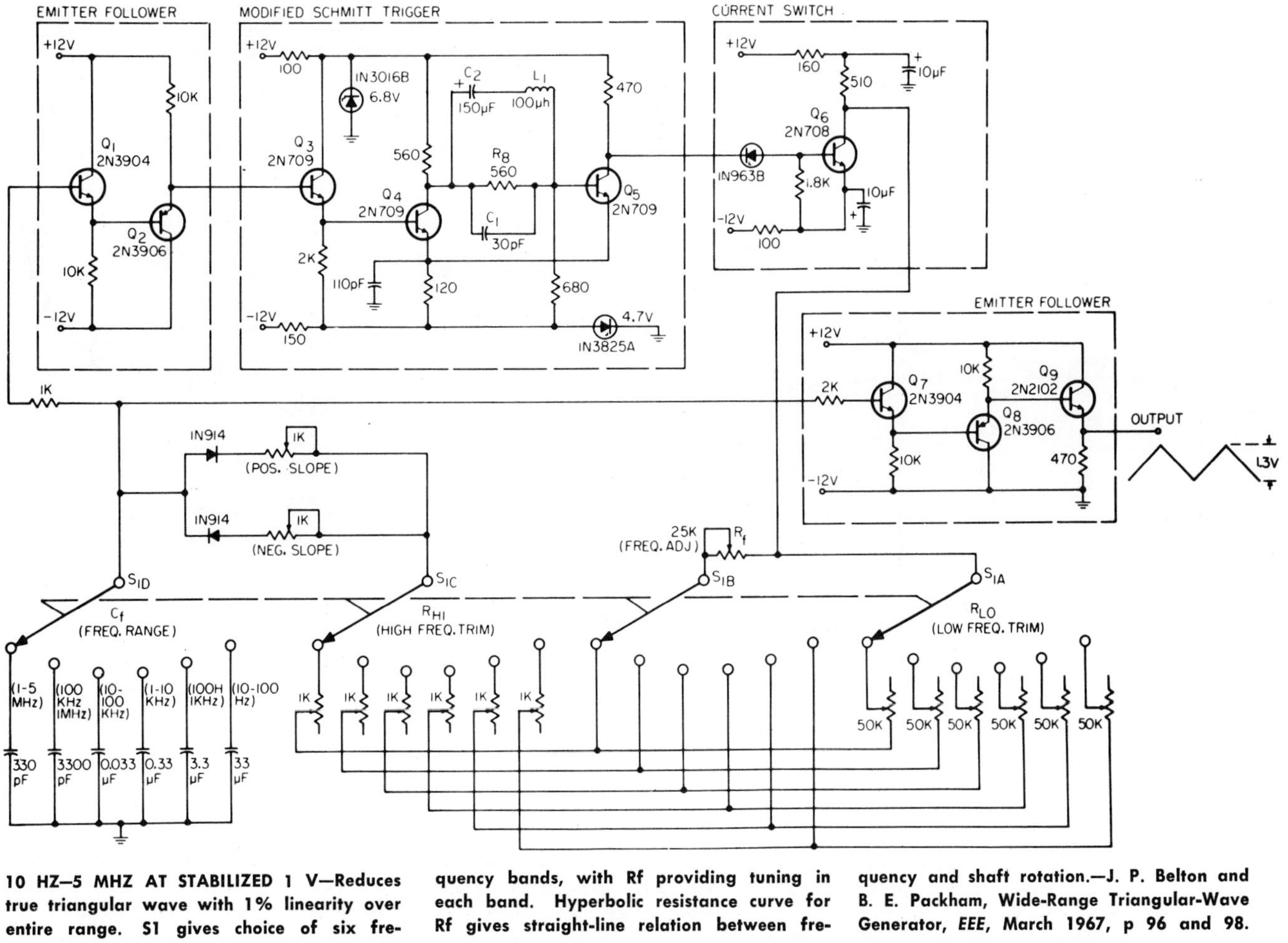

10 HZ–5 MHZ AT STABILIZED 1 V—Reduces true triangular wave with 1% linearity over entire range. S1 gives choice of six frequency bands, with Rf providing tuning in each band. Hyperbolic resistance curve for Rf gives straight-line relation between frequency and shaft rotation.—J. P. Belton and B. E. Packham, Wide-Range Triangular-Wave Generator, *EEE*, March 1967, p 96 and 98.

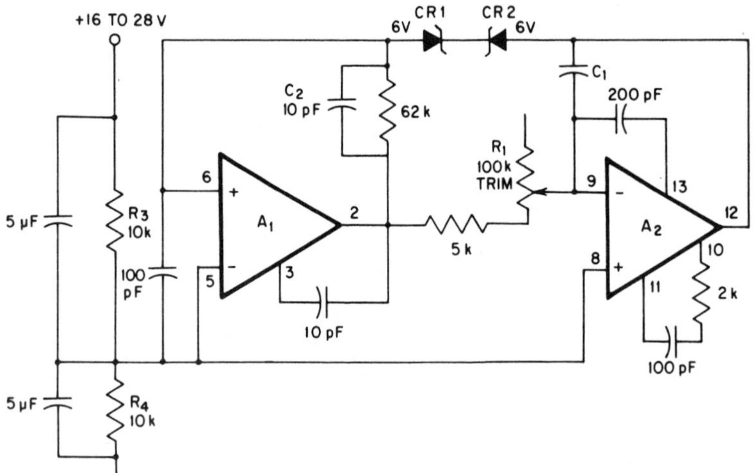

TRIANGLE-SQUARE WITH ONE IC—Uses Burroughs dual 1709 opamp package MC-1437P, with opamp A1 serving as level-detecting switching amplifier for generating square waves, and opamp A2 connected as integrator for generating triangular waves with excellent linearity. C1 determines frequency range, which is 8 to 120 kHz for 500 pF and 400 to 10,000 Hz for 0.01 μF. Output has constant amplitude to over 50 kHz.—J. F. Kingsbury, Single IC Forms Wide-Range Triangle/Square-Wave Generator, *EEE*, Oct. 1969, p 109–110.

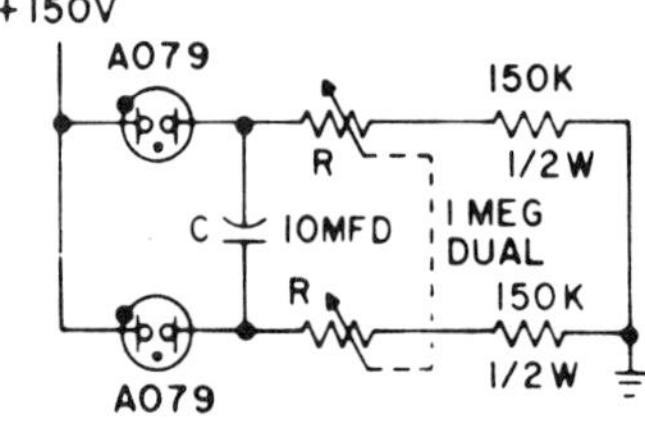

0.005–0.5 HZ TRIANGULAR—Upper frequency limit of dual astable low-subaudio oscillator is set by ionization time of neons. Lower frequency depends on leakage resistance of C, which should be high-quality paper or mylar.—E. Bauman, "Applications of Neon Lamps and Gas Discharge Tubes," Signalite, Neptune, N.J., p 37.

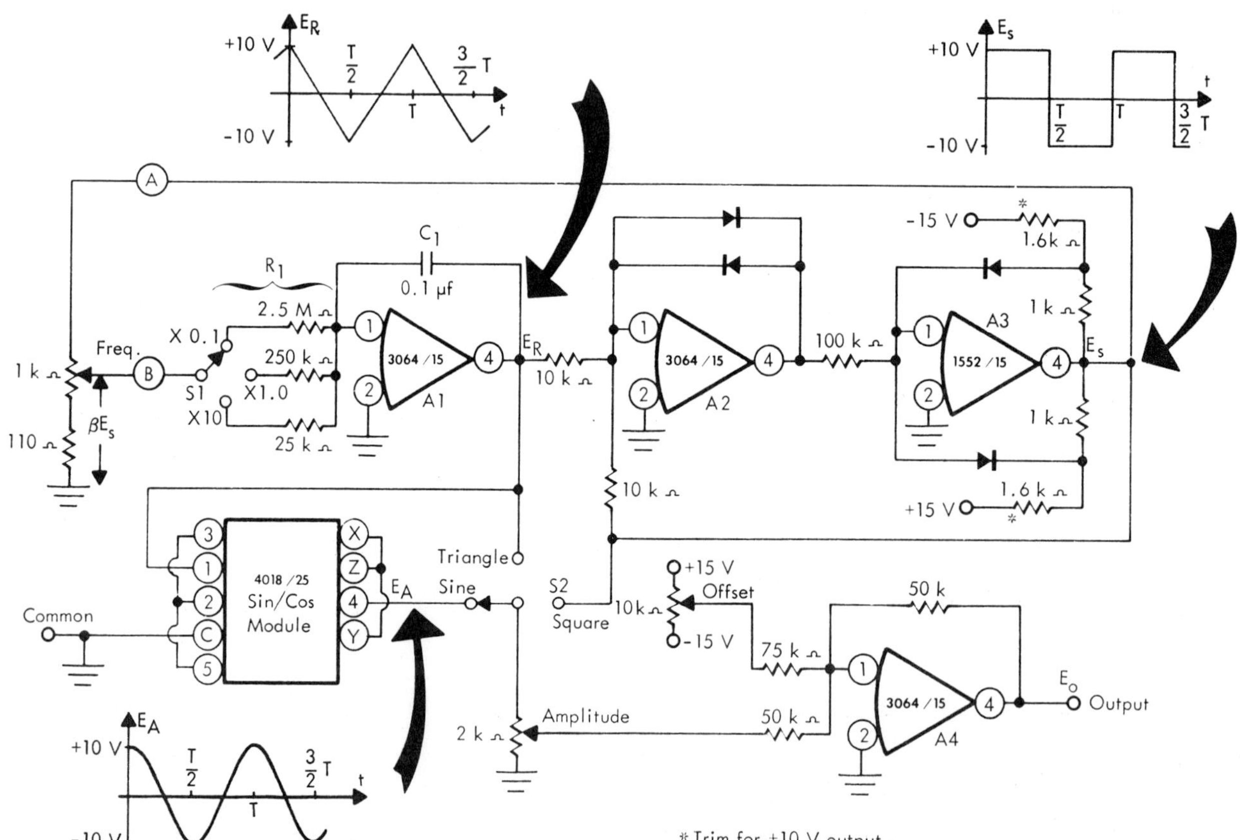

0.1–100 HZ SINE-SQUARE-TRIANGULAR—Combination of opamps with Burr-Brown 4018-25 sine-cosine module gives accurate and stable low-frequency function generator having choice of three output waveforms, as required for testing electrical or hydraulic servos, low-pass active filters, and other low-frequency devices. Adjustments of frequency, amplitude, and offset are independent.—Sine/Cosine Function Generator, Burr-Brown Research, Tucson, Ariz., PDS-210, 1968, p 6.

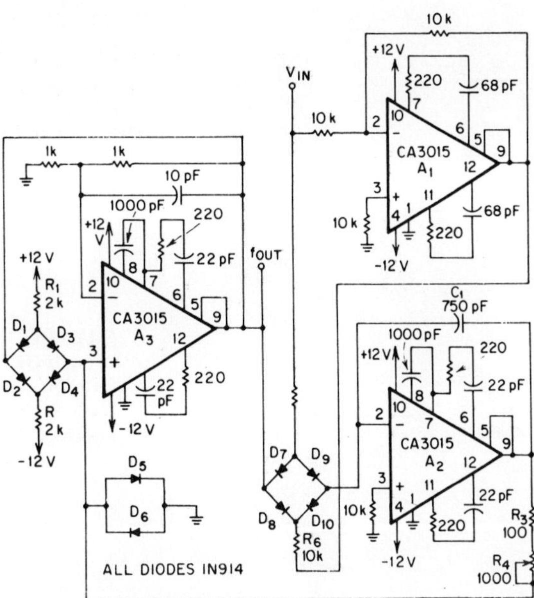

40–70 KHZ TRIANGULAR AND SQUARE WAVES—Output frequency range of almost one octave is covered by control voltages of 4 to 7 V d-c with better than 0.5% linearity. C1 determines nominal center frequency, with values from 2 μF to 60 pF giving frequencies from 30 Hz to 750 kHz respectively. Produces triangular wave at output of opamp A2 (terminal 9 of A2) and square wave at output of A3. Amplitude of square wave is 3 V p-p and rise time 100 ns.—D. M. Stewart, Linear VCO Generates Sawtooth and Square Waveforms, *EEE*, March 1969, p 86.

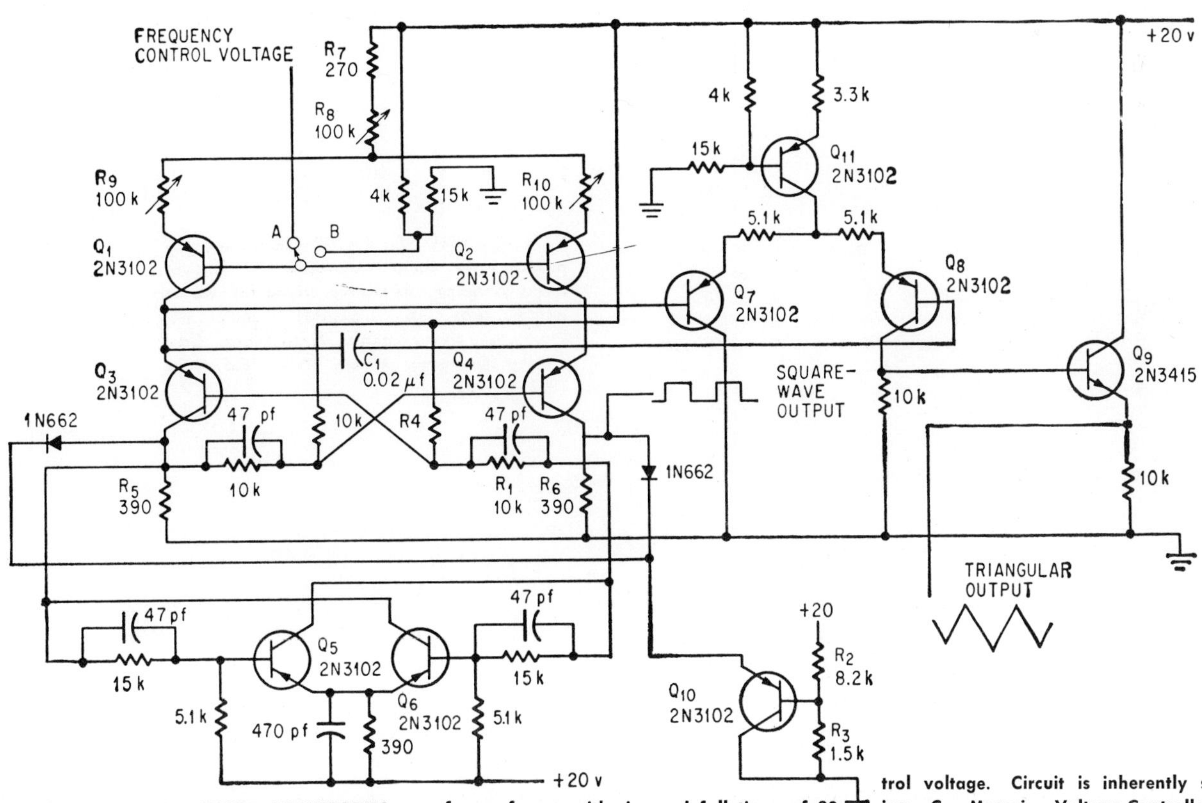

TRIANGULAR AND SQUARE WAVEFORMS—D-c amplifier Q7-Q8-Q9-Q11 added to modified astable mvbr Q1-Q2-Q5-Q6 gives choice of waveforms, with rise and fall times of 80 ns. Both outputs can be linearly varied over frequency range of 25 to 1 by external control voltage. Circuit is inherently self-starting.—C. Marosi, Voltage-Controlled Multi Produces Triangular Output, *Electronics*, Oct. 31, 1966, p 72–73.

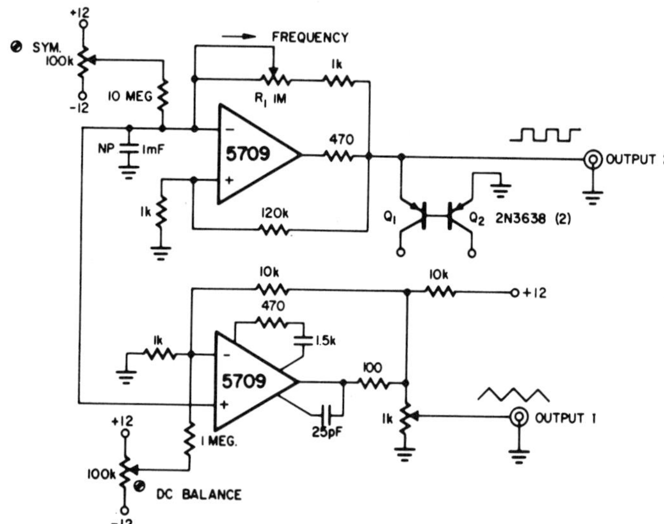

TRIANGLE OR SQUARE-WAVE—Gives choice of outputs. Symmetry is better than 1% from 30 Hz to 25 kHz. R1 should be log taper.—"Linear Applications," Signetics, Sunnyvale, Cal.

VOLTAGE SWEEP GENERATOR—Input pulse must be negative. Frequency range is 5,000 to 10,000 pps with values shown for CC, going down to minimum of 500 pps for 2 μF and up to maximum of 200,000 pps for 0.001 μF. Output waveform is constant-voltage triangular.—A. C. Gillie, "Pulse and Logic Circuits," McGraw-Hill, N.Y., 1968, p 274.

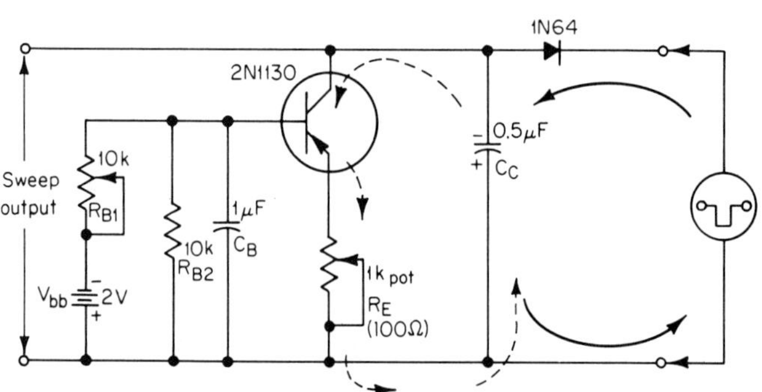

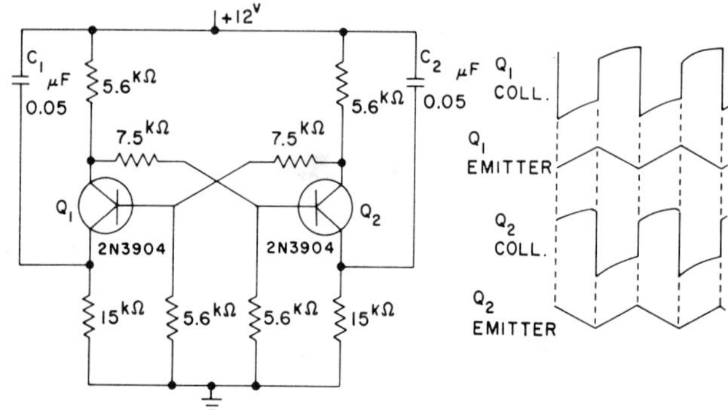

NEW TRIANGLE GENERATOR—Modification of astable mvbr, using two resistors in place of direct coupling, generates triangular waves automatically at transistor emitters.—S. Chang, A New Astable Multivibrator Generating Triangular Waves, *Proc. IEEE*, June 1968, p 1103.

NOTE: To locate additional circuits in the category of this chapter, use the index at the back of this book. Check also the author's "Sourcebook of Electronic Circuits," published by McGraw-Hill in 1968.

CHAPTER 93
Trigger Circuits

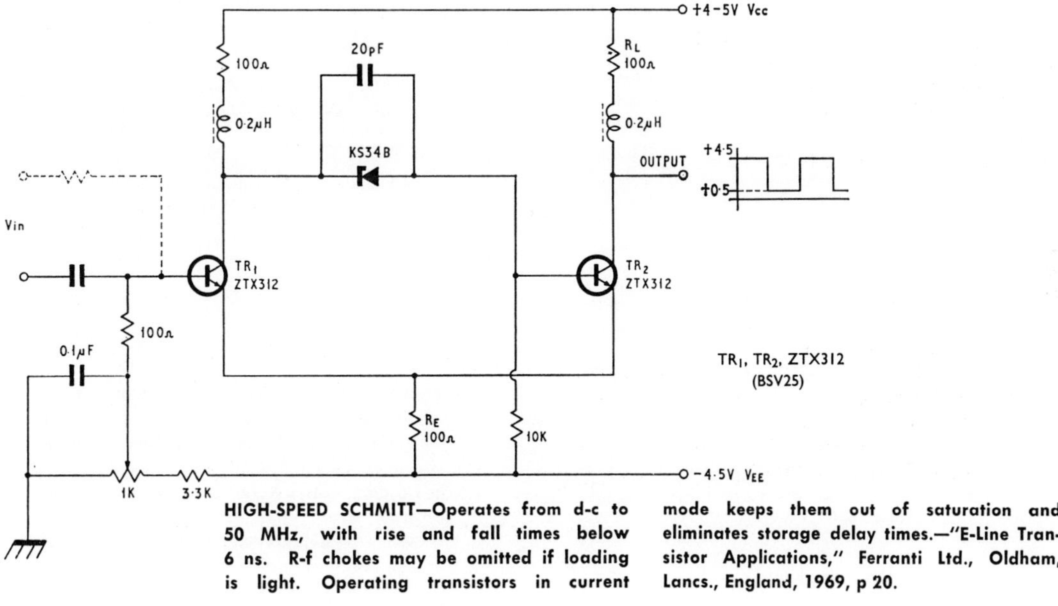

HIGH-SPEED SCHMITT—Operates from d-c to 50 MHz, with rise and fall times below 6 ns. R-f chokes may be omitted if loading is light. Operating transistors in current mode keeps them out of saturation and eliminates storage delay times.—"E-Line Transistor Applications," Ferranti Ltd., Oldham, Lancs., England, 1969, p 20.

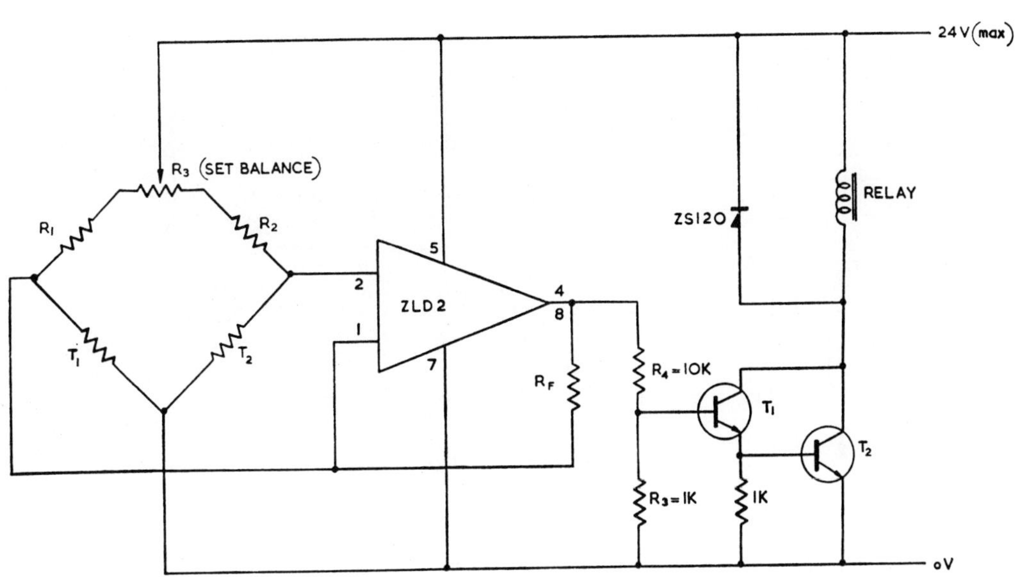

TRIGGER PREVENTS RELAY CHATTER—Two transistors are inserted between IC differential amplifier and relay to introduce enough trigger action to prevent chatter of relay when input is changing very slowly, as when comparing temperatures at two different locations with thermistors T1 and T2 in bridge circuit. Bridge resistors R1 and R2 should have low temperature coefficients. Value of feedback resistor RF is determined by maximum hysteresis that can be tolerated. —Microlin Amplifiers ZLD2S and ZLD2T, Ferranti Ltd., Oldham, Lancs., England, Report 11, 1967, p 13.

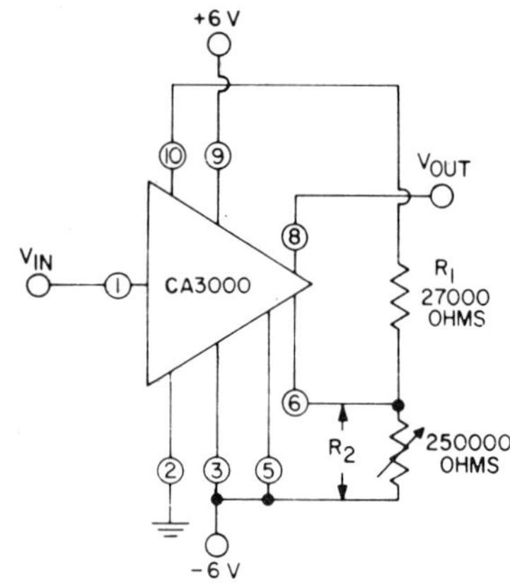

IC SCHMITT—Only two resistors need be added to IC d-c amplifier to give stable and predictable operation as Schmitt trigger. Book gives design equations.—"Linear Integrated Circuits," RCA, Harrison, N.J., IC-41, p 129.

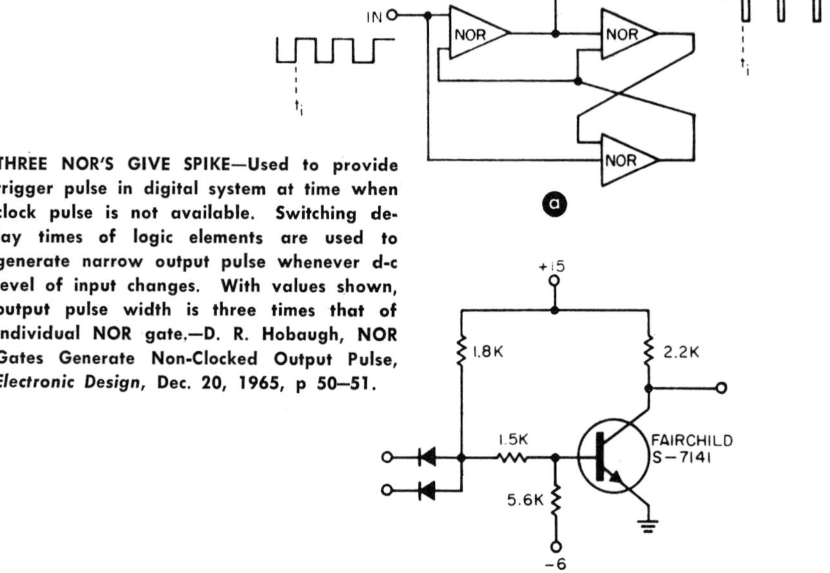

THREE NOR'S GIVE SPIKE—Used to provide trigger pulse in digital system at time when clock pulse is not available. Switching delay times of logic elements are used to generate narrow output pulse whenever d-c level of input changes. With values shown, output pulse width is three times that of individual NOR gate.—D. R. Hobaugh, NOR Gates Generate Non-Clocked Output Pulse, *Electronic Design*, Dec. 20, 1965, p 50–51.

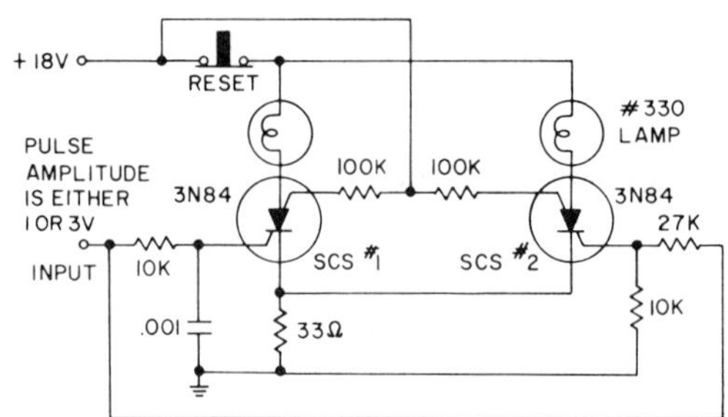

VOLTAGE-LEVEL INDICATOR LAMPS—Pulse amplitude of 1 V triggers SCS-1 and turns on associated incandescent lamp without affecting other lamp. 3-V pulse is delayed by R-C integrating network for SCS-1 and therefore triggers SCS-2 first. This raises common emitter voltage, preventing SCS-1 from triggering, so only right-hand lamp comes on to indicate presence of 3-V pulse.—Planar Silicon Controlled Switch 3N84/3N85, General Electric, Syracuse, N.Y., No. 65.18, 1964.

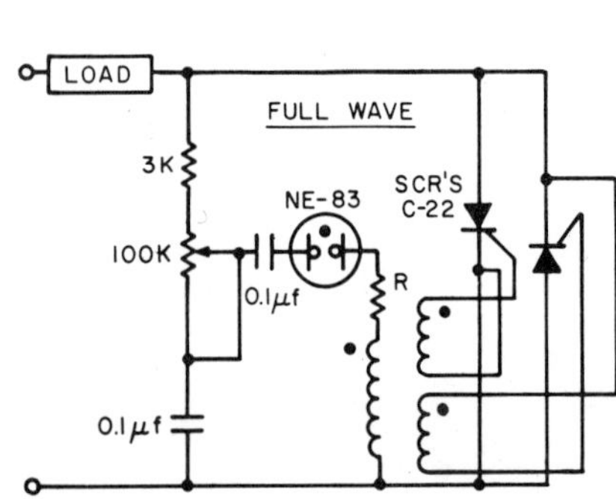

FULL-WAVE NEON—Neon provides triggering of scr when voltage across the two capacitors reaches its breakdown voltage in range of 60 to 100 V. Will control scr from full off up to 95% of total rms load voltage. Pulse transformer fires scrs alternately. Neon gives visual indication that one of scrs is receiving triggering pulse.—C. R. Dougherty, Neon Trigger Circuits for SCR's, *Electronic Design*, Jan. 6, 1964, p 78.

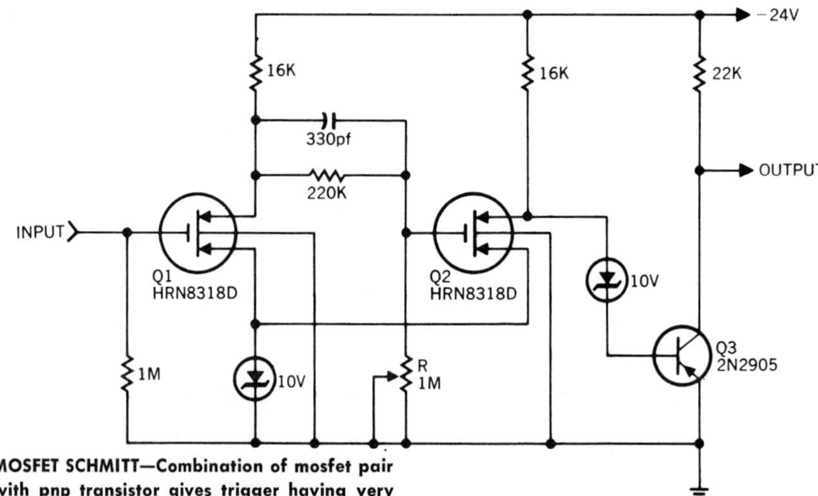

MOSFET SCHMITT—Combination of mosfet pair with pnp transistor gives trigger having very high input impedance, low output impedance, and good temperature stability. Zeners used for generating reference voltage and shifting level can be changed to allow for different detection levels. Adjust R so Q1 is nonconducting and Q2 is fully on; input signal about 3 V more negative than zener reference voltage will then operate trigger.—C. R. Perkins, "Application of MOSFET Devices to Electronic Circuits," Hughes, Newport Beach, Cal., 1968, p 34.

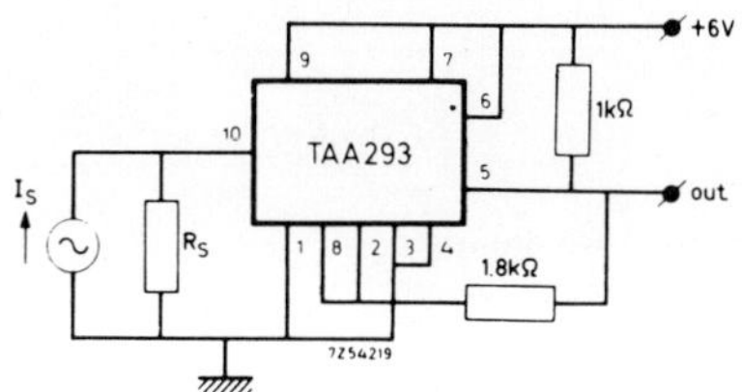

CURRENT-OPERATED SCHMITT IC—Uses Philips TAA293 general-purpose amplifier. With zero input current, output is about 4 V. At about 26 μA input, circuit switches to low state.—The TAA293 as a Schmitt Trigger and Multivibrator, Philips, Pub. Dept., Elcoma Div., Eindhoven, The Netherlands, No. 25, 1968.

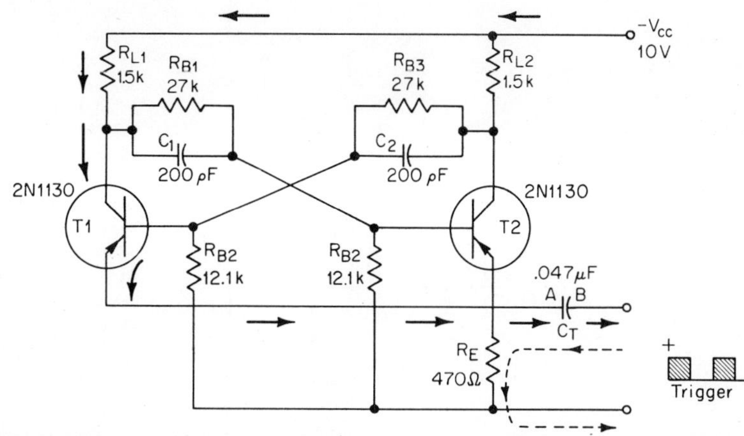

EMITTER-TRIGGERED MVBR—Circuit is basically emitter-triggered flip-flop, developed for use with ring counters, shift registers, and other counters. Often called complemented flip-flop. Most effective at lower trigger frequencies. Book gives design criteria and equations.—A. C. Gillie, "Pulse and Logic Circuits," McGraw-Hill, N.Y., 1968, p 238.

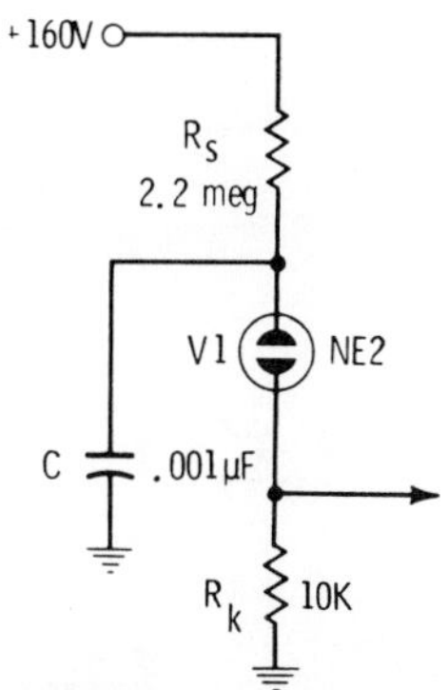

2,400-HZ NEON—Trigger pulse reaches maximum amplitude of 5 V p-p in less than 10 μs. Value of 10K resistor may be varied for different pulse height.—W. G. Miller, "Using and Understanding Miniature Neon Lamps," H. W. Sams & Co., Indianapolis, Ind., 1969, p 40.

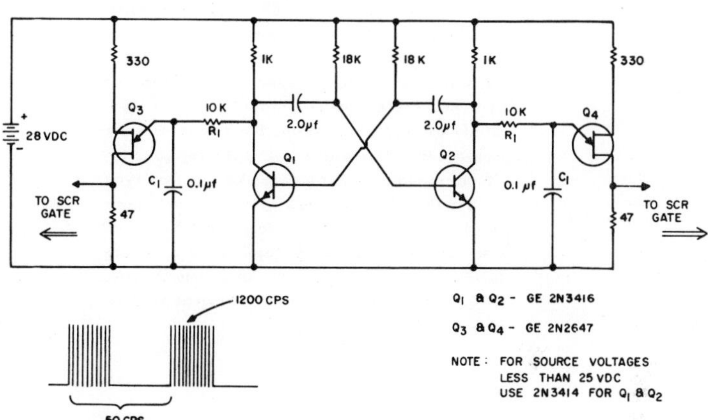

PULSE TRAIN GENERATOR—Used to maintain triggering of scr during major portion or all of conduction period. Transistor mvbr provides alternate driving voltages to ujt oscillators. Pulse frequency within train of pulses is determined by R1C1 time constant, and is 1,200 Hz for values shown. Frequency of flip-flop Q1-Q2 determines frequency of scr output.—J. C. Hey, Simple Circuits for Triggering SCR's Into Fast-Rising Load Currents, General Electric, Syracuse, N.Y., No. 200.41, 1965, p 6.

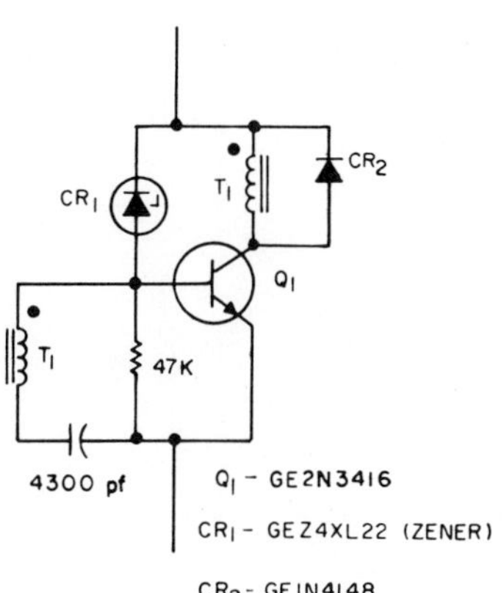

TRIGGER-DIODE EQUIVALENT—Developed for applications where driving voltage for trigger is too low for available trigger diodes. Uses low-cost components.—J. C. Hey, Simple Circuits for Triggering SCR's Into Fast-Rising Load Currents, General Electric, Syracuse, N.Y., No. 200.41, 1965, p 4.

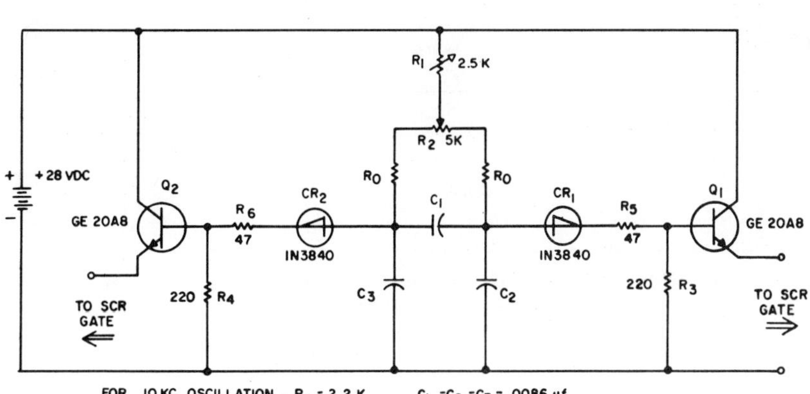

FLIP-FLOP TRIGGER FOR TWO SCR's—Provides alternate output pulses as required for two-scr inverter circuits. R1 adjusts frequency. R2 adjusts symmetry. Capacitors should be closely matched. Frequency of trigger pulses depends on value of resistors RO.—J. C. Hey, Simple Circuits for Triggering SCR's Into Fast-Rising Load Currents, General Electric, Syracuse, N.Y., No. 200.41, 1965, p 3.

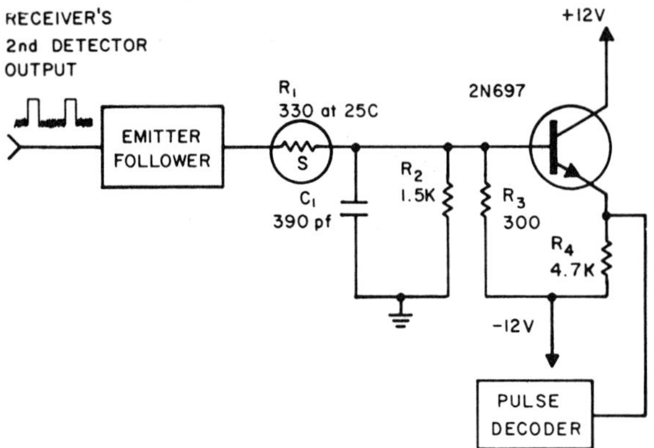

SUPPRESSING NOISE TRIGGERING—Insertion of low-pass filter at second detector output of pulse-decoding receiver, using temperature-sensing Sensistor as resistive element R1, improves trigger sensitivity by making bandwidth decrease with increasing temperature. At −40 C, 3-dB bandwidth is 3.9 MHz, as compared to 2.7 MHz at 50 C.—C. Samocki, Temperature Varies Bandwidth to Improve Trigger Sensitivity, *Electronic Design*, Jan. 4, 1965, p 77–78.

POSITIVE HALF-CYCLE SCR TRIGGER—When pushbutton switch SW is moved from 1 to 2, scr will trigger near beginning of next positive half-cycle and stay on only for balance of that half-cycle. Switch may be closed randomly at any time during the two preceding half-cycles. Scr will not trigger again until SW is opened and then reclosed. This type of one-shot logic is used in some test equipment supplies and for solenoid drives of electronic hammers and stapling guns, where load current must flow only for one half-cycle. —"SCR Manual," 4th Edition, General Electric, 1967, p 151–152.

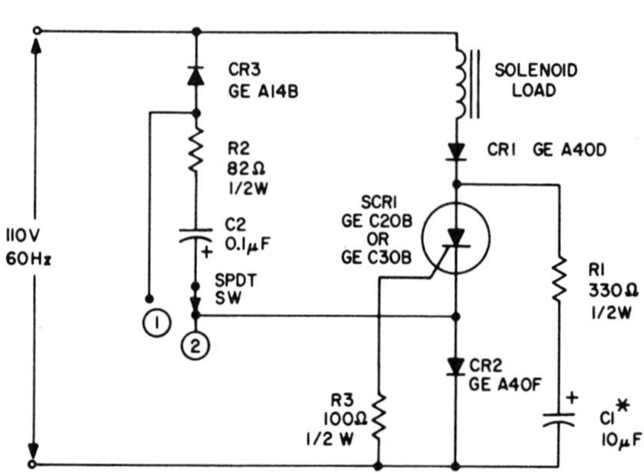

*TIME CONSTANT OF C1 R1 MAY NEED TAILORING DEPENDING ON HOLDING CURRENT OF SCR1.

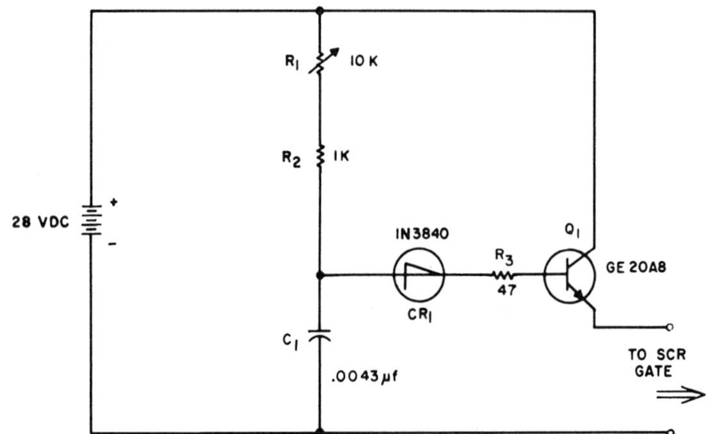

SIMPLE SCR TRIGGER—C1 charges through R1-R2 to 25-V breakover of1N3840 trigger diode, then discharges through diode into base of power transistor Q1 to make it produce high-current output pulse of about 20 V for applying to gate of scr as trigger. Stray circuit inductances must be minimized to give required current rise of 10 A per μs. Repetition rate of trigger pulses is adjusted with R1.—J. C. Hey, Simple Circuits for Triggering SCR's Into Fast-Rising Load Currents, General Electric, Syracuse, N.Y., No. 200.41, 1965, p 3.

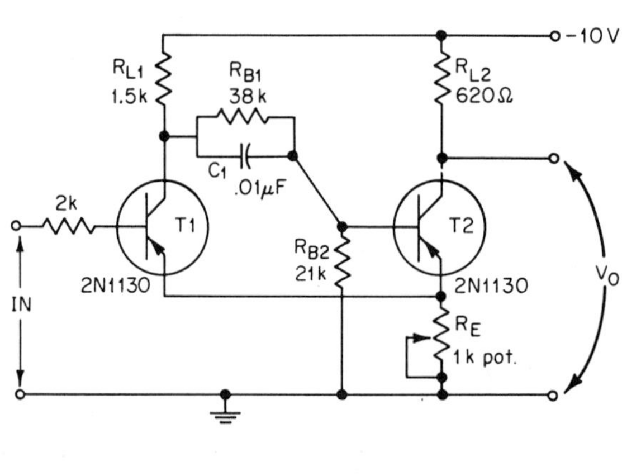

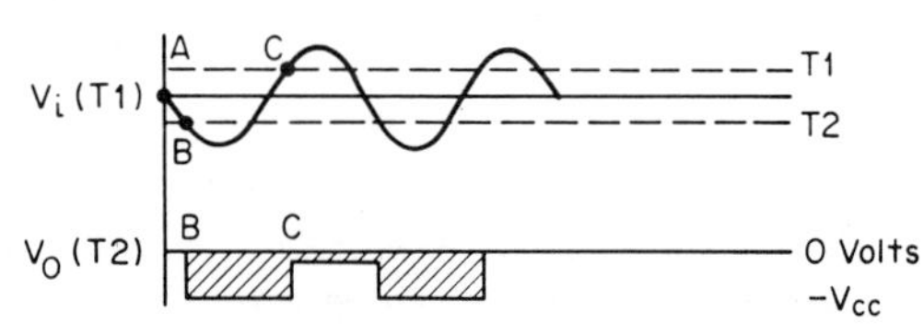

BASIC SCHMITT—Chief uses are converting sine wave into rectangular wave, reshaping distorted rectangular waves, and detecting presence of signals. Book gives design criteria.—A. C. Gillie, "Pulse and Logic Circuits," McGraw-Hill, N.Y., 1968, p 244.

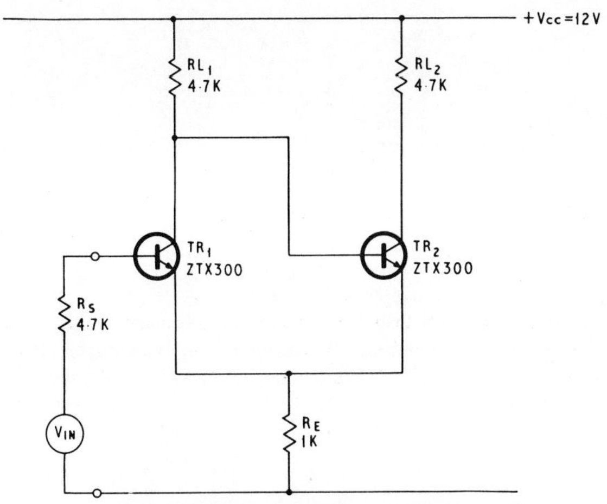

LEVEL-OPERATED SWITCH—Feedback through common emitter resistor of Schmitt trigger makes circuit switch rapidly from on to off and vice versa. Design equations are given. —"E-Line Transistor Applications," Ferranti Ltd., Oldham, Lancs., England, 1969, p 19.

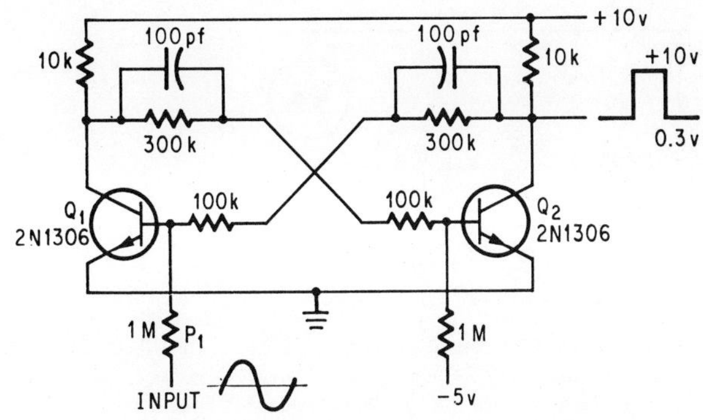

ADJUSTABLE HYSTERESIS—Potentiometer P1 at input of conventional flip-flop determines threshold level at which input signal turns Q1 on and Q1 off to generate output step. Ideal for generating square pulses from sine waves or for providing binary output from transducer. Setting of P1 also controls amount of hysteresis, for preventing chatter in trigger circuit as it changes state if 60-Hz hum is picked up by sensing transducer.—D. Schoon, Potentiometer Turns Flip-flop Into An Adjustable Trigger, *Electronics*, Sept. 4, 1967, p 95–96.

SPIKE GENERATOR—Simple capacitorless circuit differentiates leading edge of rectangular input pulse, to produce fixed-width triggering spikes about 16 ns wide. Can be built with RTL IC's.—G. A. May, Differentiating Pulse Former Requires No Capacitors, *Electronics*, May 1, 1967, p 70–71.

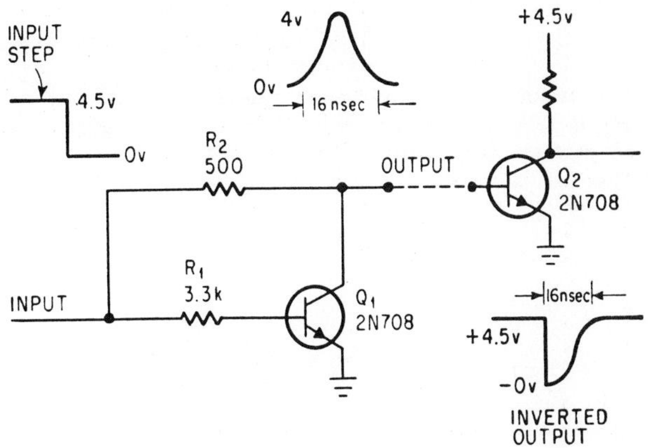

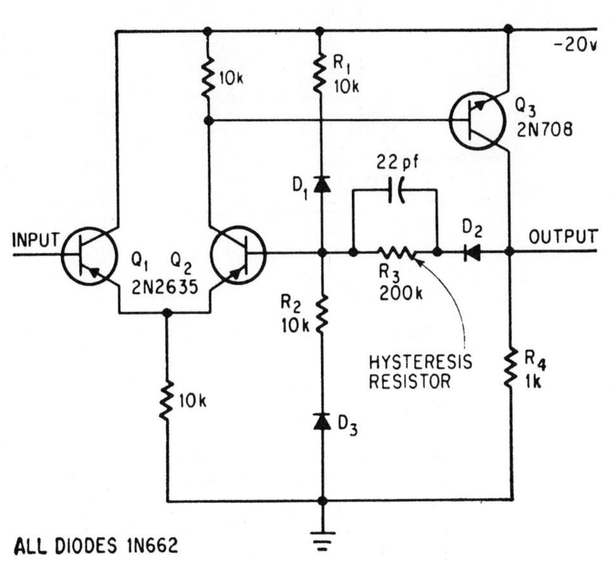

HIGH-IMPEDANCE SCHMITT—Input impedance is over 2,000 ohms, about 200 times greater than conventional Schmitt, as required for squaring low-power information signals. Trip points and hysteresis of circuit remain stable and predictable over wide temperature range. Q1 and Q2 form current-mode switch controlling Q3.—G. Marosi, Differential Schmitt Trigger with 200-K Input Impedance, *Electronics*, Jan. 23, 1967, p 90–91.

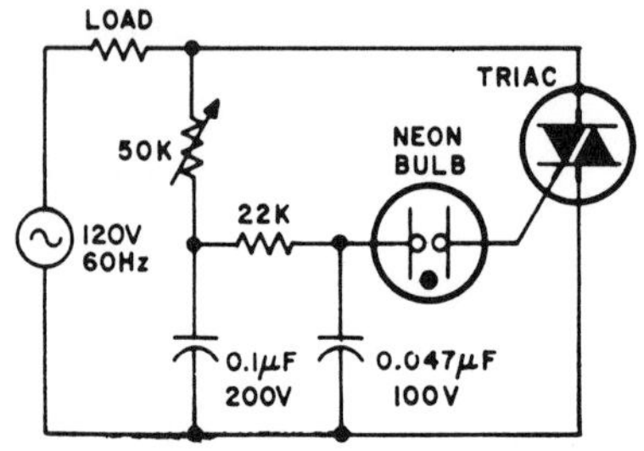

NEON TRIGGER FOR TRIAC—Choice of triac depends on load. For maximum precision of triggering, neon should be shielded against radiation.—"Silicon Power Circuits Manual," RCA, Harrison, N.J., SP-51, p 237.

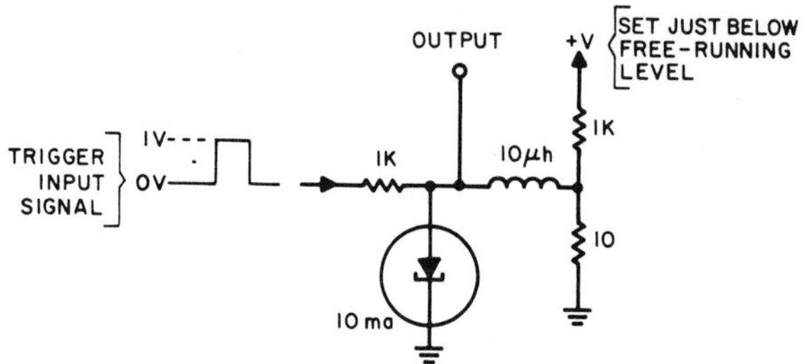

TUNNEL-DIODE TRIGGER—Simple one-shot mvbr is triggered by 1-V pulse. One drawback, however, is varying response to different trigger signals because of manner in which one-shot recovers triggering sensitivity. Article presents pseudo-Schmitt circuit that eliminates these uncertainties in trigger logic. —H. A. Zimmerman, Pseudo-Schmitt Eliminates Uncertainties in Trigger Logic, *Electronic Design*, Nov. 22, 1965, p 30–35.

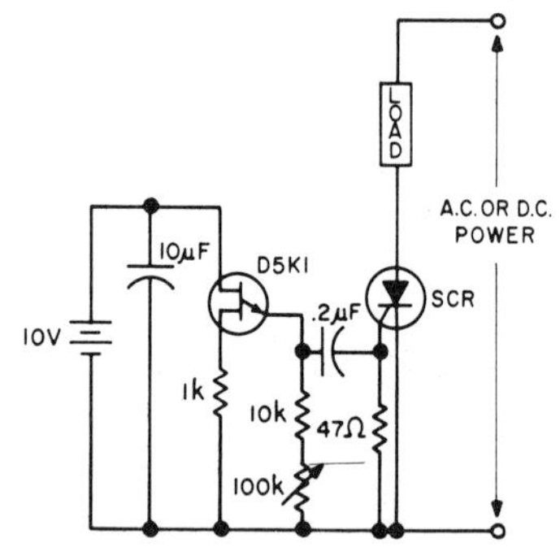

POSITIVE-SUPPLY UJT-SCR—Trigger current flows through 10-V supply, with 10-μF capacitor assuring low supply impedance and adequate trigger current. Choice of scr depends on load current.—Silicon Complementary Unijunction Transistor D5K1, General Electric, Syracuse, N.Y., No. 60.15, 1967.

EFFICIENT TRIGGER—Three parts minimize cost while giving good temperature stability, rapid switching, and efficient energy transfer. Utilizes reverse breakdown characteristic of emitter-base junction to set triggering level accurately. Ideal for use as thyristor gate-drive trigger in phase controls.—R. B. Hood, Transistor Breakdown Yields Inexpensive Thyristor Trigger, *Electronics*, Sept. 4, 1967, p 96.

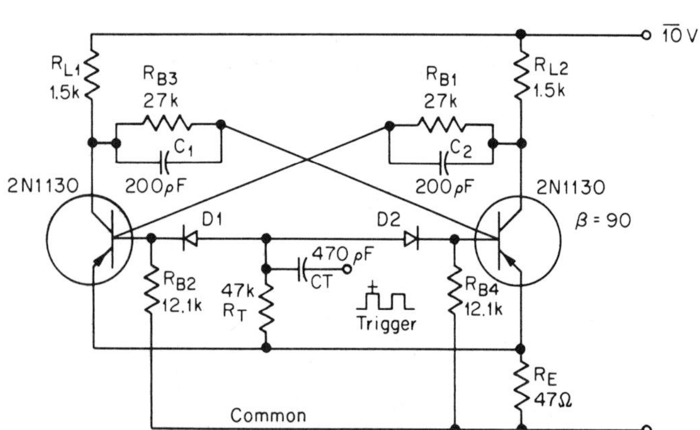

BASE-TRIGGERED FLIP-FLOP—Switching action occurs only on positive excursions of input trigger applied to base, so output frequency is half that of input to complemented flip-flop (4,000 pps for input of 8,000 pps with values shown), and circuit acts as frequency divider. —A. C. Gillie, "Pulse and Logic Circuits," McGraw-Hill, N.Y., 1968, p 240.

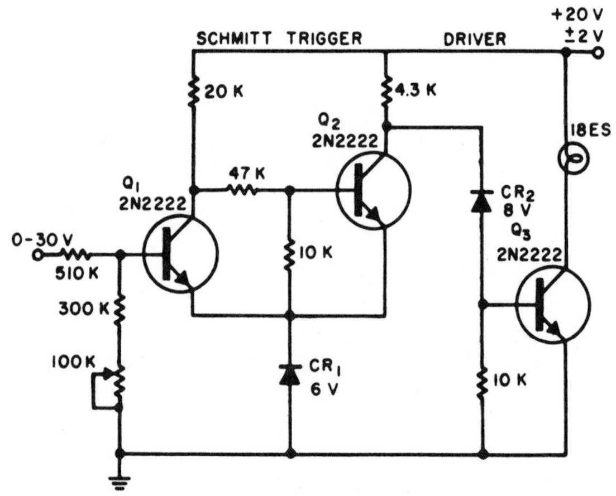

ZENER IMPROVES TRIGGERING ACCURACY—Replacement of feedback resistor with 6-V zener CR1 in Schmitt trigger narrows range between turn-on and turn-off voltages from 4 V to about 0.3 V.—R. E. Risely, Zener Diode Reduces Schmitt Trigger Hysteresis, "400 Ideas for Design Selected from Electronic Design," Hayden Book Co., N.Y., 1964, p 93.

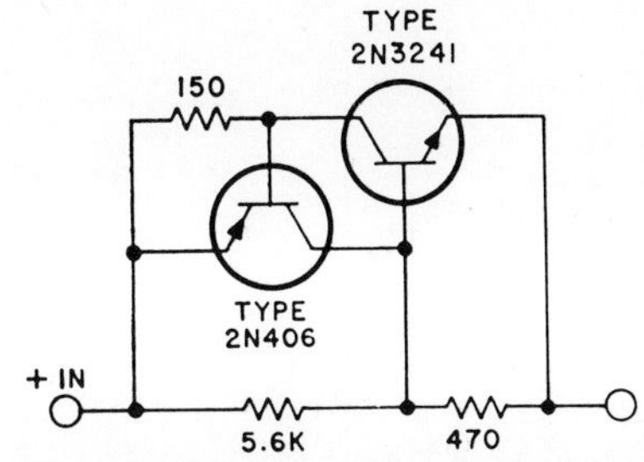

TWO TRANSISTORS EQUAL ONE DIODE—Regenerative action of circuit, when either transistor begins to conduct, causes switching comparable to avalanching in trigger diode. With proper biasing, circuit will trigger at 15 V or less.—"Silicon Power Circuits Manual," RCA, Harrison, N.J., SP-51, p 240.

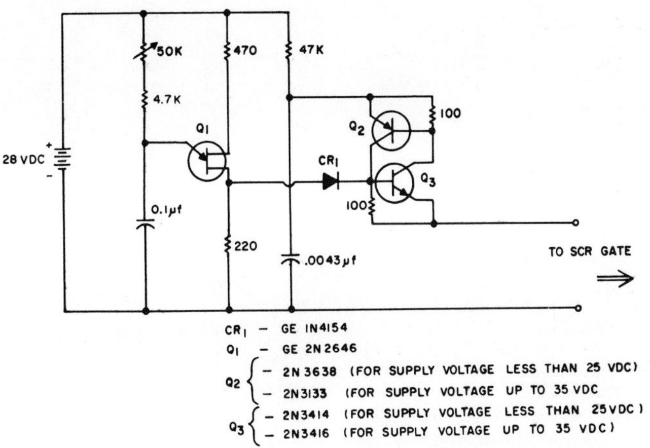

REGENERATIVE TRANSISTOR PAIR AS SCR TRIGGER—Can be used when trigger-circuit driving voltage is too low for available trigger diodes. Ujt Q1 provides external sync pulse at desired triggering frequency.—J. C. Hey, Simple Circuits for Triggering SCR's Into Fast-Rising Load Currents, General Electric, Syracuse, N.Y., No. 200.41, 1965, p 5.

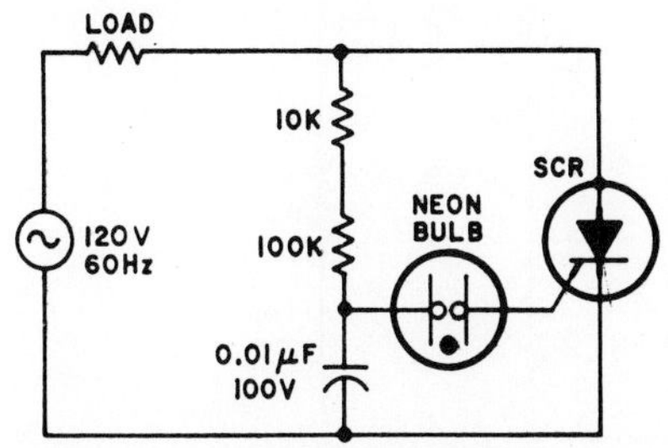

NEON TRIGGER FOR SCR—Possible drawback is effect of radiation on breakdown point of neon. For precise control, neon should be shielded or specially treated for radiation. Low cost and long life are offsetting advantages.—"Silicon Power Circuits Manual," RCA, Harrison, N.J., SP-51, p 237.

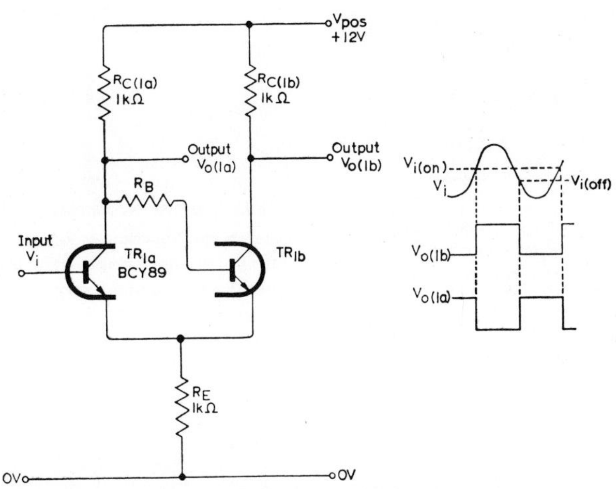

STABLE SCHMITT—Close thermal coupling of transistor pair results in trigger (input) voltages more stable over entire frequency range than separate transistors.—"Circuits Using Low-Drift Transistor Pairs," Philips, Pub. Dept., Elcoma Div., Eindhoven, The Netherlands, Application Book, 1968, p 25.

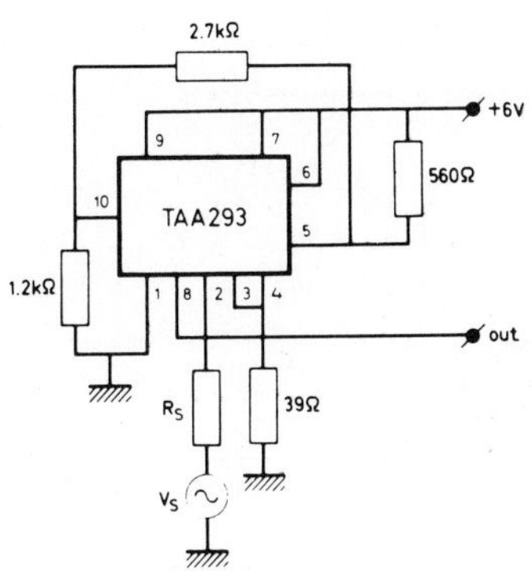

VOLTAGE-OPERATED SCHMITT IC—Uses Philips TAA293 general-purpose amplifier connected as emitter-coupled Schmitt followed by output amplifier. Output voltage is 5 to 6 V p-p depending on saturation voltage of output transistor. Rise time is about 200 ns and fall time 40 ns.—The TAA293 as a Schmitt Trigger and Multivibrator, Philips, Pub. Dept., Elcoma Div., Eindhoven, The Netherlands, No. 25, 1968.

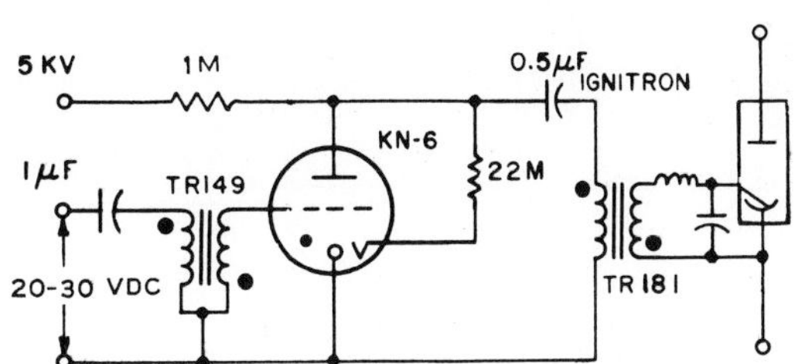

KRYTRON-TRIGGERED IGNITION—Four-element cold-cathode gas-filled switch tube produces high peak current for short duration through pulse transformer, for triggering industrial ignition.—Krytrons—Cold Cathode Switch Tubes, EG&G, Boston, Mass., KR-100, 1968.

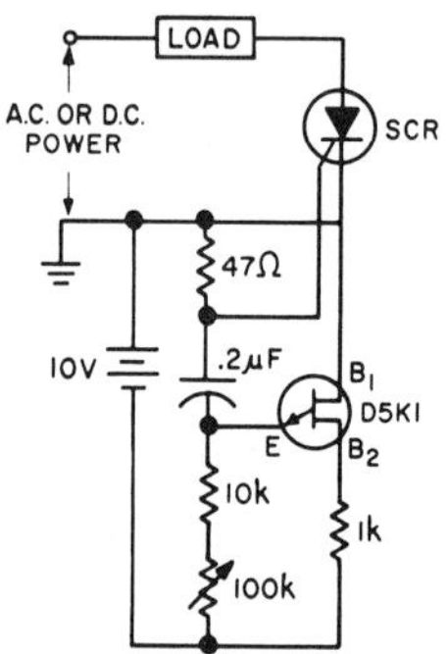

NEGATIVE-SUPPLY UJT-SCR—Complementary ujt makes triggering of scr easier than with positive supply. Choice of scr depends on load current.—Silicon Complementary Unijunction Transistor D5K1, General Electric, Syracuse, N.Y., No. 60.15, 1967.

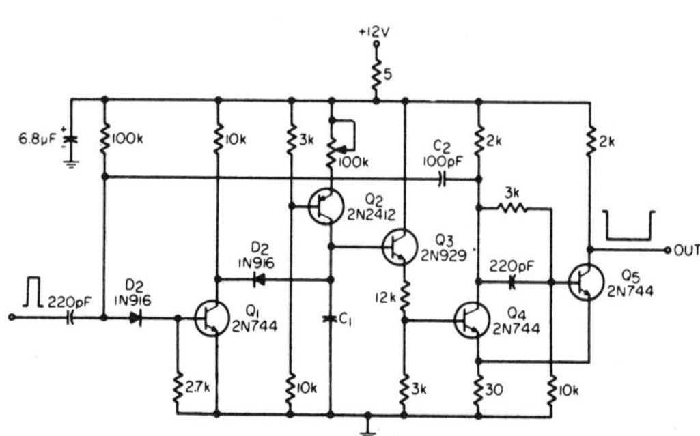

MULTI-SHOT TRIGGER—Period of output pulse depends on number of input trigger pulses occurring while circuit is active. Uses Schmitt trigger Q4-Q5. Article gives design equations.—R. S. Hughes, Multi-Shot Trigger Circuit, *EEE*, June 1967, p 138–139.

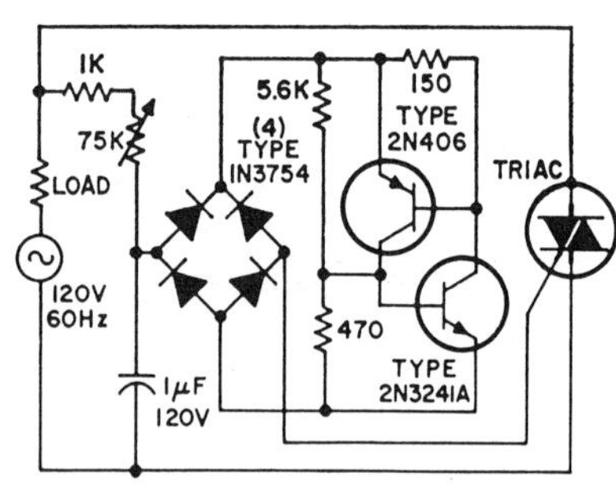

TWO-TRANSISTOR SCR TRIGGER—Two-transistor circuit, with regenerative action comparable to avalanching in trigger diode, can deliver trigger currents up to 1 A, more than enough for triggering all RCA thyristors. —"Silicon Power Circuits Manual," RCA, Harrison, N.J., SP-51, p 240.

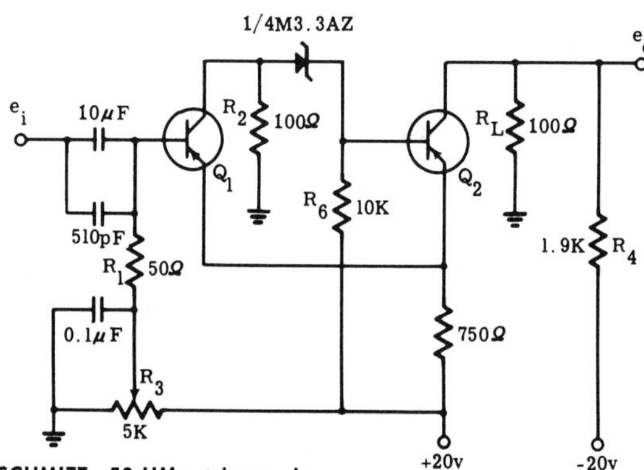

CURRENT-MODE SCHMITT—50-HMz trigger is inverter modification in which input reference voltage of one stage depends on collector voltage of preceding stage. Bias pot serves as sensitivity-symmetry control. R4 supplies constant current into 100-ohm output load, so output levels are shifted to +1 V and −1 V from levels of 0 and −2 V which would otherwise result. With 2N2258 transistors, rise and fall times are 2 and 3 ns respectively.—"High Speed Switching Transistor Handbook," Motorola, Phoenix, Ariz., 1969, p 283.

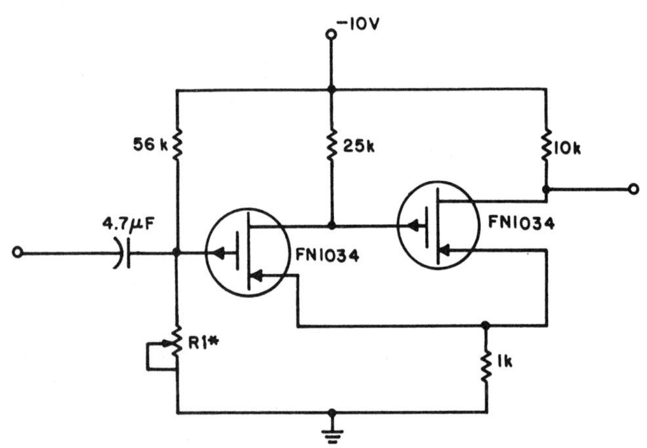

BETTER SCHMITT—Two mosfet's provide higher trigger speed, higher input inmpedance, and better temperature stability than transistor version. R1 sets trigger level in range from −2 V to +2 V.—S. Biren, Two MOS-FETs and Resistors Make Better Schmitt Trigger, *Electronic Design*, May 10, 1967, p 92.

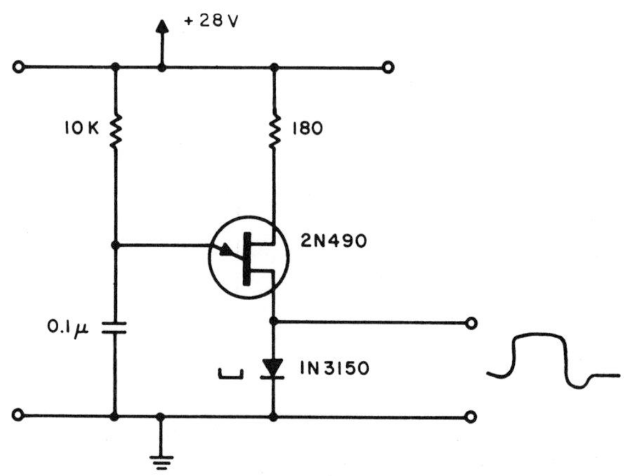

1-NS RISE TIME—Simple modification of ujt relaxation oscillator, driving tunnel diode, serves as fast trigger generator that can deliver high enough output current to simplify amplification and shaping of output waveform.—E. Elad, Tunnel Diode and UJT Produce Ultra-Fast Trigger Output, *Electronic Design*, June 7, 1965, p 40–41.

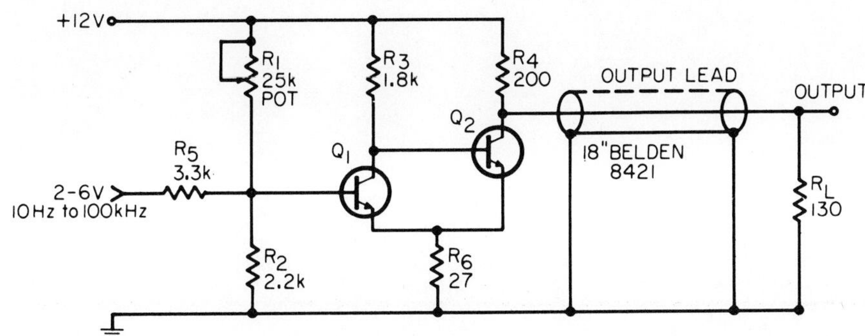

10 HZ—100 KHZ FAST-RISE SCHMITT—Requires no capacitors, and transistors may be low-cost types such as 2N4418, 2N4275, or MPS2369. Waveform is excellent at all frequencies without adjustment of component values, and both rise and fall times are less than 12 ns. May be used for sine-square wave conversion.—J. H. Cone, Simplified Schmitt Yields Fast Rise Time, *EEE*, April 1968, p 108.

HALF-WAVE NEON—Controls scr from full off up to 95% of half-wave rms output voltage. Closing switch applies full power. Neon also provides visual indication that scr is receiving triggering pulse.—C. R. Dougherty, Neon Trigger Circuits for SCR's, *Electronic Design*, Jan. 6, 1964, p. 78.

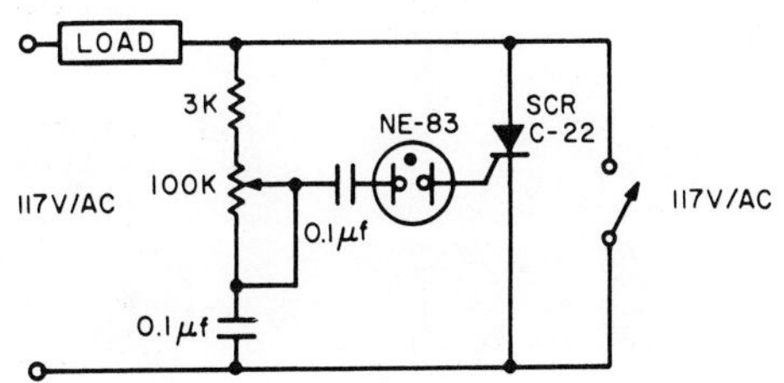

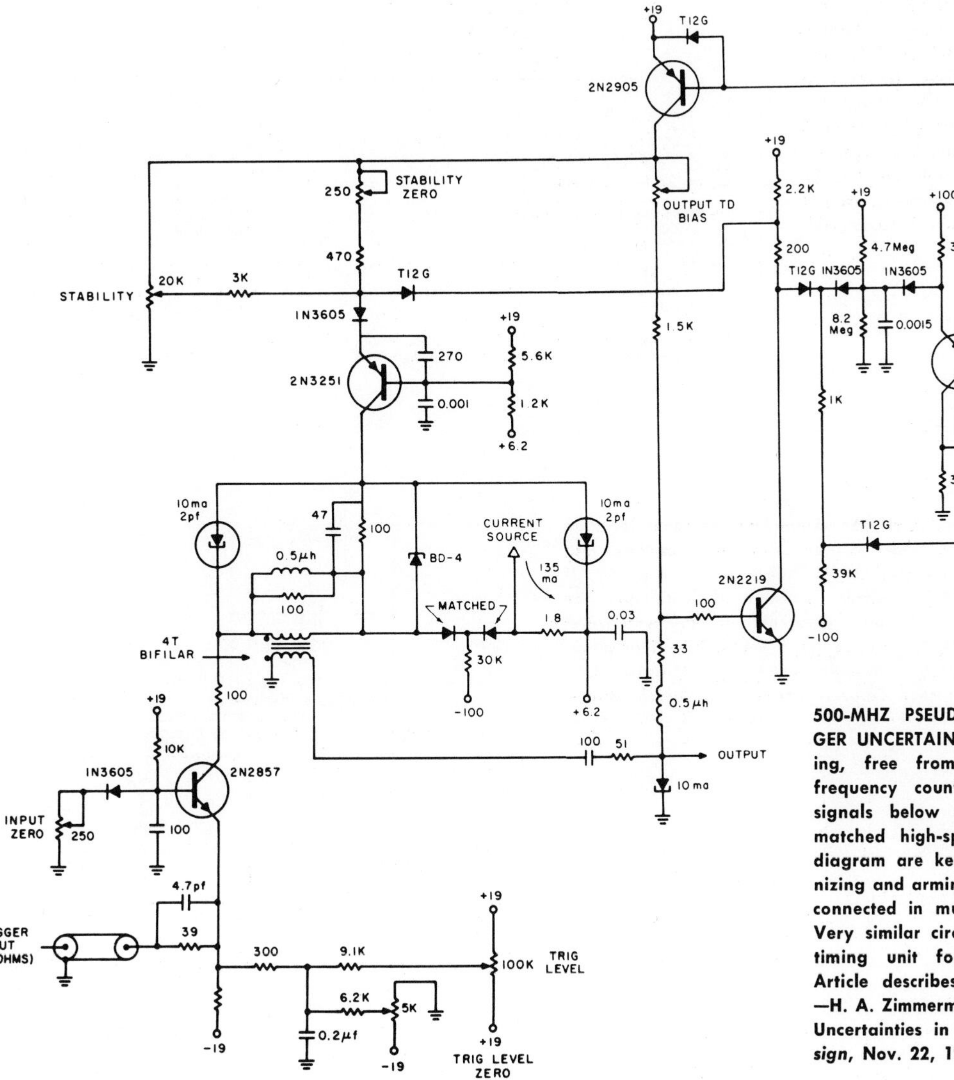

500-MHZ PSEUDO-SCHMITT WITHOUT TRIGGER UNCERTAINTY—Provides reliable triggering, free from input misrecognition and frequency countdown problems, for input signals below 5 mV. Tunnel diodes and matched high-speed diodes near center of diagram are key elements, providing recognizing and arming functions for multivibrators connected in multiple-feedback arrangement. Very similar circuit is used in Tektronix 5T3 timing unit for Type 661 sampling cro. Article describes circuit operation in detail. —H. A. Zimmerman, Pseudo-Schmitt Eliminates Uncertainties in Trigger Logic, *Electronic Design*, Nov. 22, 1965, p 30–32 and 34–35.

CHAPTER 94
Ultrasonic Circuits

1.5-W SONOBUOY TRANSMITTER—Used with underwater hydrophone to pick up sounds of enemy submarine. Crystal oscillator frequency is 165 MHz. Over-all efficiency is greater than 50% with 12–15 V battery supply. Final stage is straight-through class C amplifier using RCA developmental transistor; if power output of 0.5 W is sufficient, 2N4427 may be used instead.—"Silicon Power Circuits Manual," RCA, Harrison, N.J., SP-51, p 344.

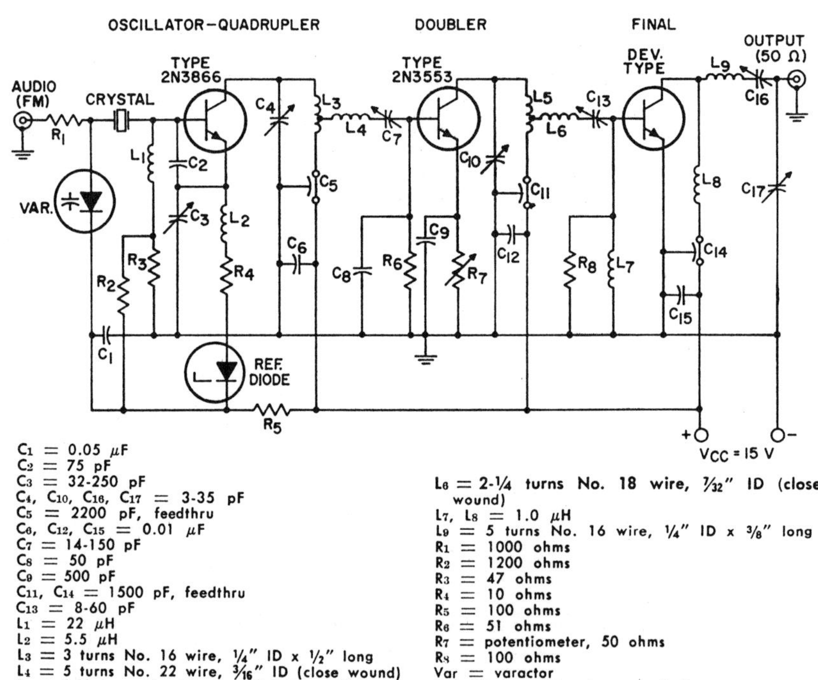

C_1 = 0.05 μF
C_2 = 75 pF
C_3 = 32-250 pF
C_4, C_{10}, C_{16}, C_{17} = 3-35 pF
C_5 = 2200 pF, feedthru
C_6, C_{12}, C_{15} = 0.01 μF
C_7 = 14-150 pF
C_8 = 50 pF
C_9 = 500 pF
C_{11}, C_{14} = 1500 pF, feedthru
C_{13} = 8-60 pF
L_1 = 22 μH
L_2 = 5.5 μH
L_3 = 3 turns No. 16 wire, 1/4" ID x 1/2" long
L_4 = 5 turns No. 22 wire, 3/16" ID (close wound)
L_5 = 2-1/4 turns No. 16 wire, 1/4" ID x 3/8" long
L_6 = 2-1/4 turns No. 18 wire, 7/32" ID (close wound)
L_7, L_8 = 1.0 μH
L_9 = 5 turns No. 16 wire, 1/4" ID x 3/8" long
R_1 = 1000 ohms
R_2 = 1200 ohms
R_3 = 47 ohms
R_4 = 10 ohms
R_5 = 100 ohms
R_6 = 51 ohms
R_7 = potentiometer, 50 ohms
R_8 = 100 ohms
Var = varactor
Ref. Diode = 12-volt zener diode

2-KHZ PINGER—Pulse from ujt timer turns on transistor that applies power to oscillator that generates 2-kHz pulse for transducer. If 100K resistor is replaced with pressure potentiometer, ping rate can vary with water depth. Transducer is double bilaminar piezoelectric ceramic unit.—F. Watlington, Unijunction Controls Oscillator in Simple Underwater Pinger, *Electronics*, Jan. 5, 1970, p 98.

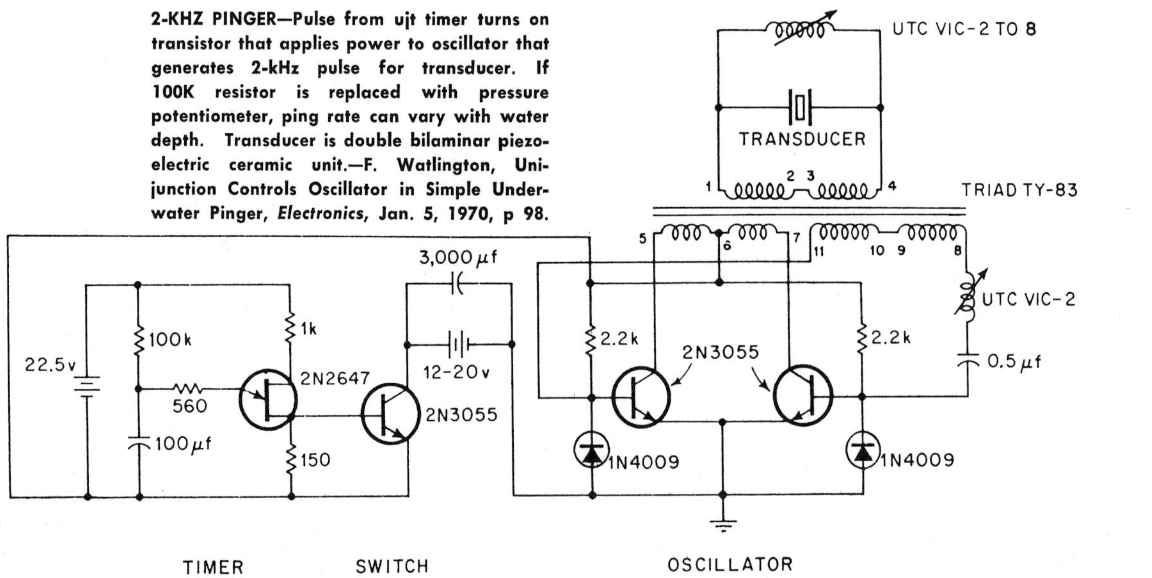

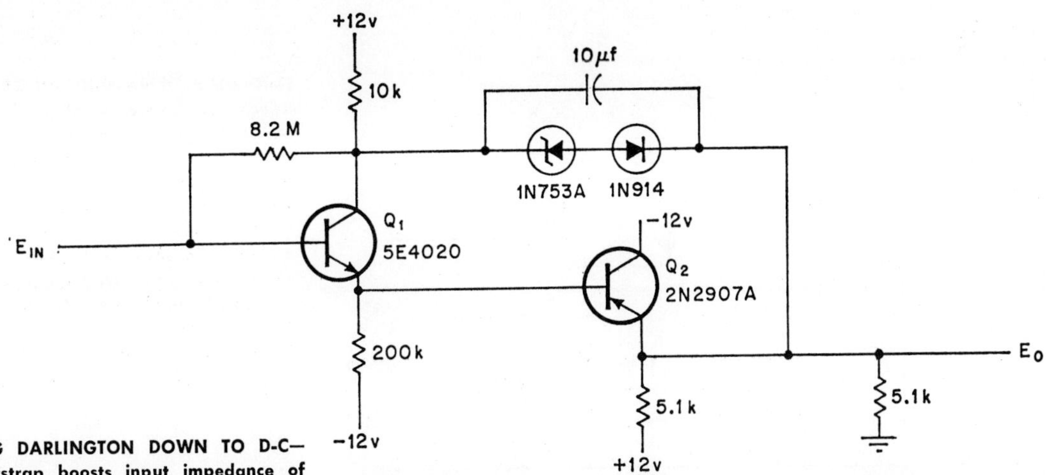

EXTENDING DARLINGTON DOWN TO D-C—Zener bootstrap boosts input impedance of Darlington to 30 meg and assures operation down to d-c signals. Useful as isolation amplifier for applications such as medical sensors and hydrophone transducers. If super-beta transistor such as MC1556 is used for Q1, input resistance is over 100 meg.—R. J. Turner, Zener in Bootstrap Extends Amplifier's Range to D-C, *Electronics*, March 16, 1970, p 88.

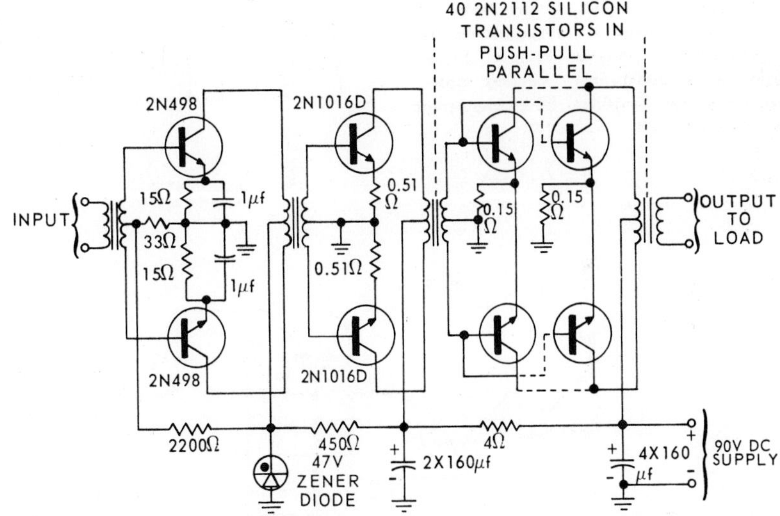

10-KW AMPLIFIER—All-transistor amplifier provides better than 50% efficiency in generating 10-kW pulses 250-ms wide with 10% duty cycle, over frequency range of 2 to 12 kHz. When driving crystal for ceramic transducers, tuning reactors are required for power factor correction so amplifier sees resistive load at transmitted frequency. Pulse-shaping network is necessary to prevent dangerous transients at start and finish of keying.—"Silicon Power Transistor Handbook," Westinghouse, Youngwood, Pa., p 6-6.

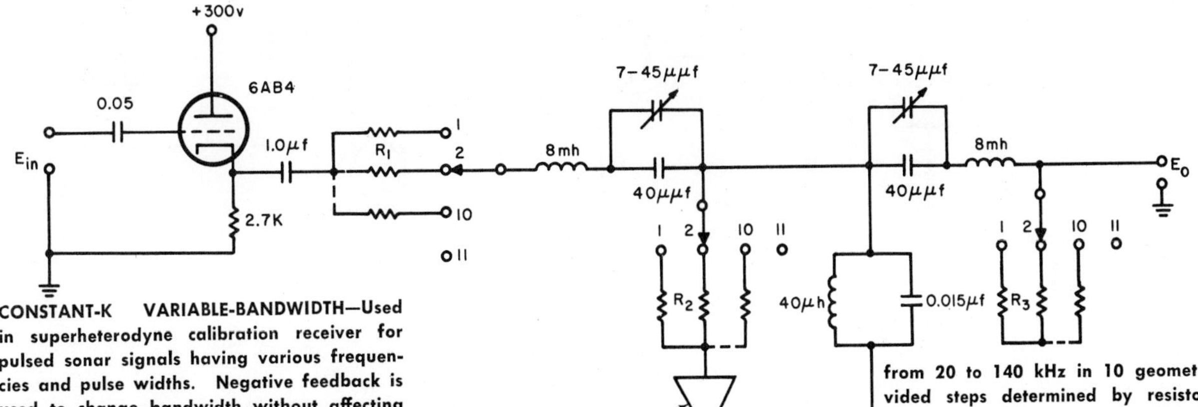

CONSTANT-K VARIABLE-BANDWIDTH—Used in superheterodyne calibration receiver for pulsed sonar signals having various frequencies and pulse widths. Negative feedback is used to change bandwidth without affecting gain of i-f amplifier. Article gives design equations. Values shown are for 200-kHz center frequency, with bandwidth varying from 20 to 140 kHz in 10 geometrically divided steps determined by resistor values.—G. E. Ott, Filter Amplifier Maintains Gain Over Wide Band, *Electronic Design*, Oct. 11, 1965, p 58–61.

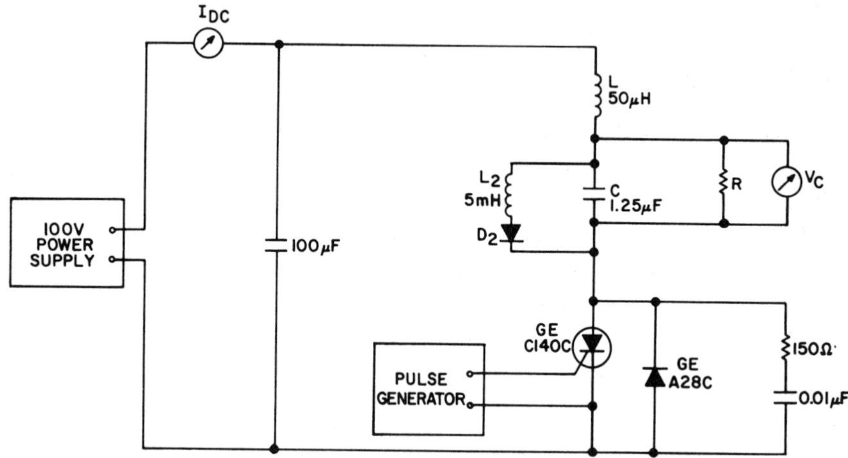

SINGLE-SCR ULTRASONIC INVERTER—Can be driven over frequency range of about 400 to 30,000 Hz by external pulse generator. For values shown, will deliver 500 W at 10,000 Hz from 100 V d-c for ultrasonic cleaning, welding, and mixing applications, induction heating, sonar, fluorescent-lamp dimmers, and d-c/d-c converters. Article gives complete design procedure for adapting circuit to any specific application.—N. Mapham, A Low-Cost, Ultrasonic-Frequency Inverter Using a Single SCR, General Electric, Syracuse, N.Y., No. 671.2, 1966, p 10.

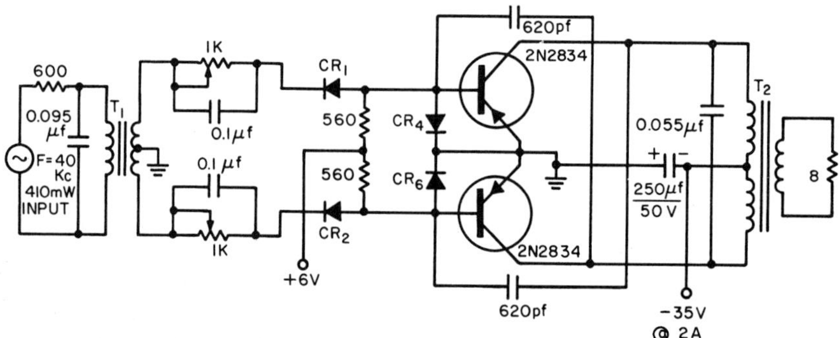

50 W AT 40 KHZ—Power transistors in tuned class C power amplifier achieve 88% efficiency. Can be used for ultrasonic cleaners and fathometers. Power gain is 21 dB. Article gives transformer winding data.—50-W Ultrasonic Amplifier, *Electronic Design*, March 2, 1964, p 58.

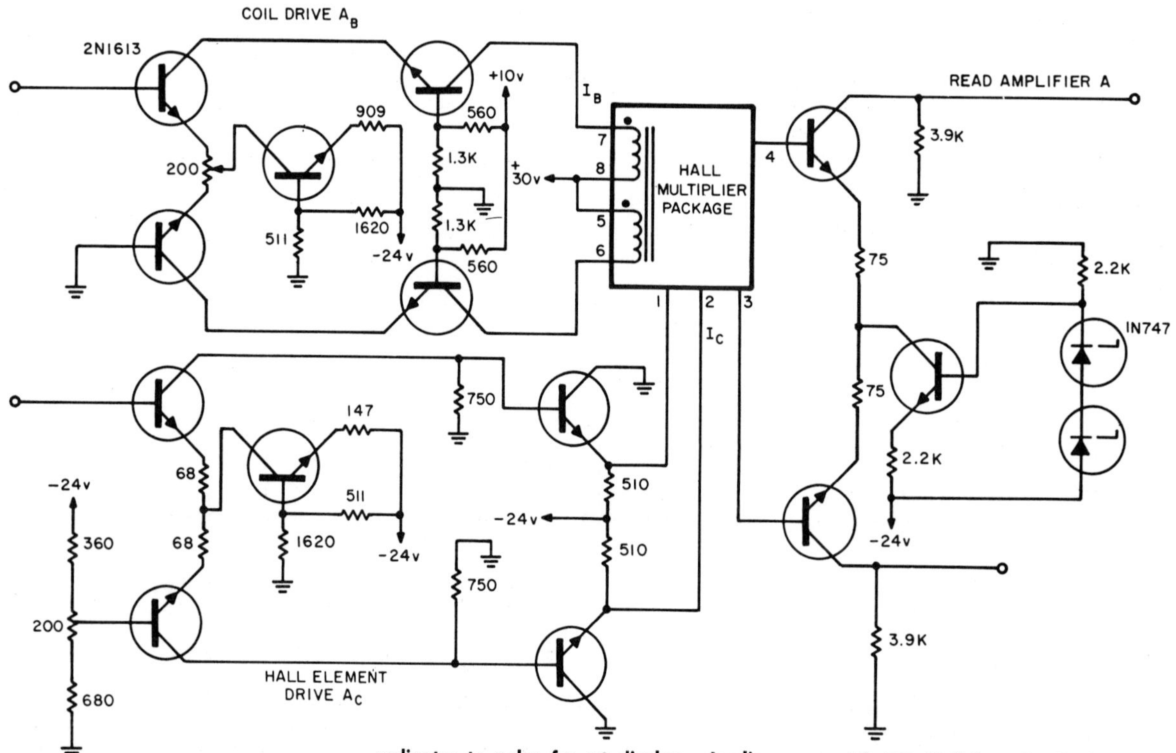

POLAR DISPLAY—Drive and read amplifier circuits shown are for Hall multiplier, two of which are used to transform rectangular coordinates to polar for crt display. Applications include direction-finding, sonar, and ppi radar systems. Both drives are differential amplifiers. Hall multiplier is Helipot model 700 Hallefex.—G. H. Smerage, Hall-Effect Multiplier Simplifies Polar Display, *Electronic Design*, March 29, 1965, p 24, 26, 28–29.

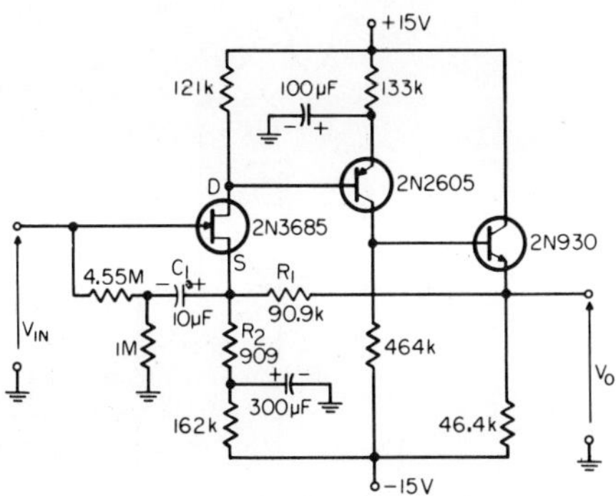

HYDROPHONE PREAMP—Low-noise circuit provides 40 dB gain from 10 to 10,000 Hz when used with 330-pF hydrophone.—W. F. Blodgett, Low-Noise Preamplifier Uses FET, *EEE*, May 1967, p 182.

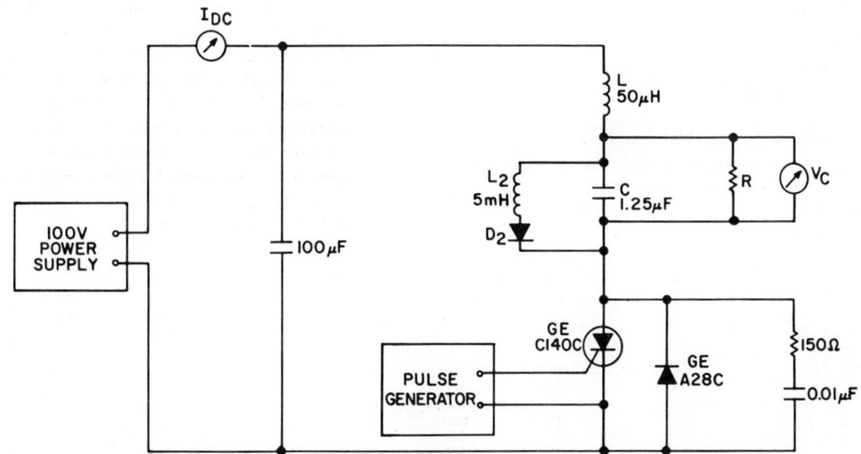

BASIC SOLID-STATE INVERTER—Can generate kilowatts of power over frequency range of 400 Hz to 30 kHz for ultrasonic and other applications, with good waveform and good regulation over wide range of loads and phase angles. Requires only single scr, minimizing cost of trigger circuitry. Can handle reactive loads. Applications include ultrasonic cleaning, mixing, and welding with either magnetostrictive or electrostrictive transducers, induction heating, sonar, d-c/d-c converters, regulated d-c power supplies, and high-frequency supplies for fluorescent lamps and fluorescent dimmers. Operates from 100–120 V d-c supply. Frequency is determined by external pulse generators. Article gives design procedure and equations. —N. Mapham, A Low Cost, Ultrasonic Frequency Inverter Using a Single SCR, General Electric, Syracuse, N.Y., No. 200.49, 1967, p 10.

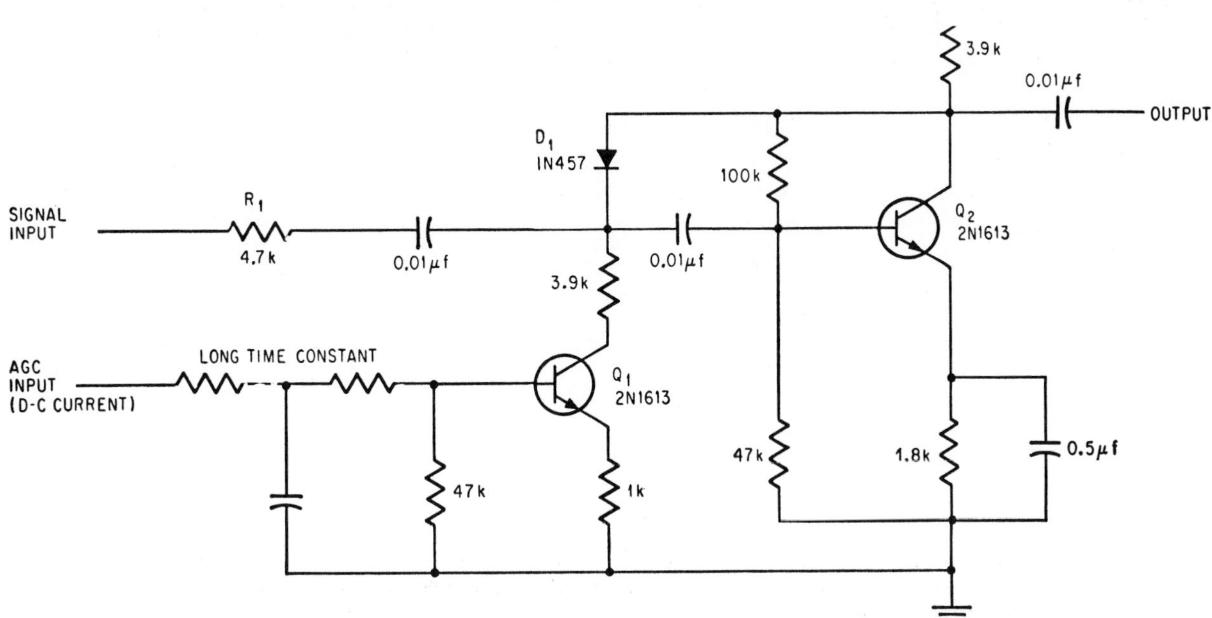

WIDE-RANGE AGC FOR SONAR—Accepts much greater range of input signal levels than conventional agc circuits while holding undistorted output between 0.5 and 1.5 V for inputs from 0.5 mV to 0.5 V. Frequency range is 20 Hz to 100 kHz. Designed for use in low-cost pleasure-craft sonar.—M. F. Feller, AGC Amplifier Handles 60-DB Range, *Electronics*, Nov. 28, 1966, p 81–82.

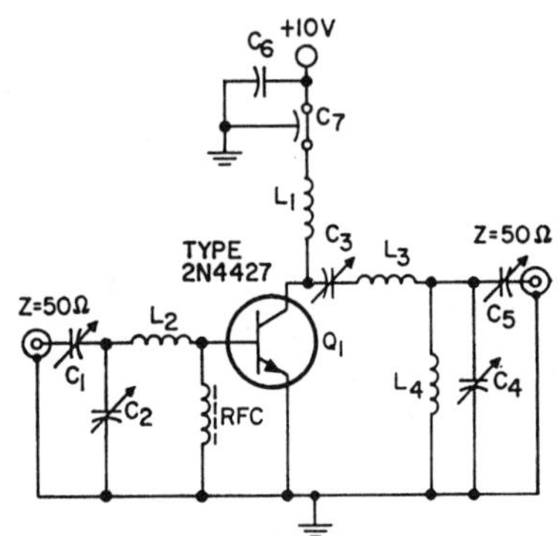

C_1, C_2, C_4, C_5 = 7-to-100 pF Arco 423 or equiv.
C_3 = 14-to-150 pF, Arco 424, or equiv.
C_6 = 0.01 μF, 50 V
C_7 = 1000 pF, feedthru
L_1 = 0.75 μH
L_2 = 1 turn No. 18 wire, 5/32" ID
L_3 = 1½ turns No. 18 wire, ¼" ID
L_4 = 1¼ turns No. 18 wire, 3/16" ID
RFC = 450 ohms, ferrite

175-MHZ SONOBUOY OUTPUT STAGE—Straight-through class C power output stage delivers 500 mW for 60 mW drive power.—"Silicon Power Circuits Manual," RCA, Harrison, N.J., SP-51, p 345.

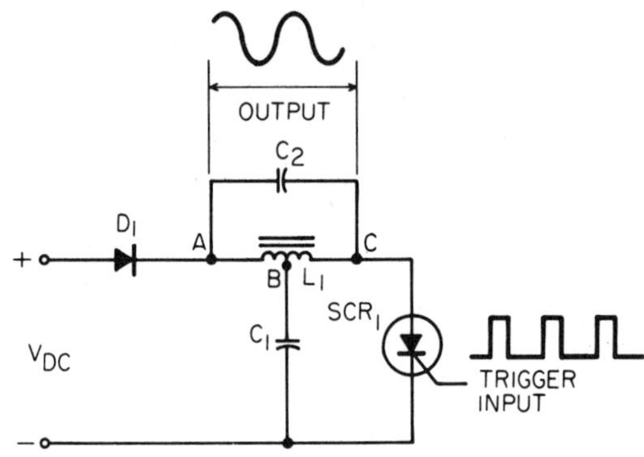

100 W AT 1–20 KHZ WITH SCR—Simple scr circuit has better than 90% efficiency in generating ultrasonic sine-wave output at frequency of input trigger which can be simple mvbr or ujt oscillator. If 60-Hz line voltage is used in place of d-c supply, will give bursts of ultrasonic power. Values of components are not critical, even though they determine operating frequency.—H. R. Camenzind, Seesaw Circuit Gives Sine-Wave Power, *EEE*, Dec. 1966, p 119–120.

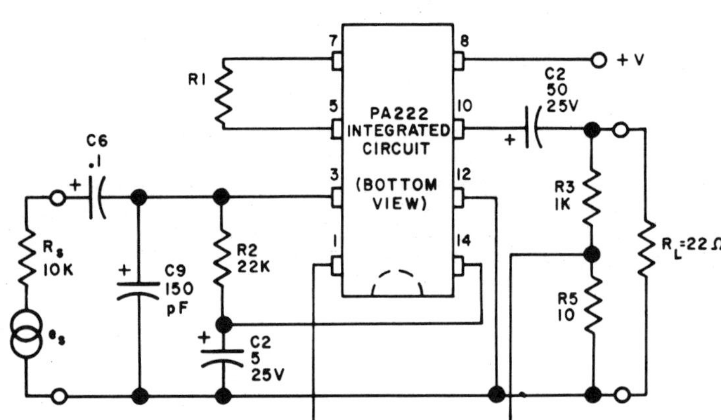

50–100,000 HZ IC AMPLIFIER—Input resistance is about 22K. Distortion level at output is 3% at about 1 W. R1 is selected to adjust no-signal current drain, and can be 68K, 100K, or 150K.—Integrated Circuit Audio Amplifier PA222, General Electric, Syracuse, N.Y., No. 85.20, 1967.

NOTE: To locate additional circuits in the category of this chapter, use the index at the back of this book. Check also the author's "Sourcebook of Electronic Circuits," published by McGraw-Hill in 1968.

CHAPTER 95
Video Circuits

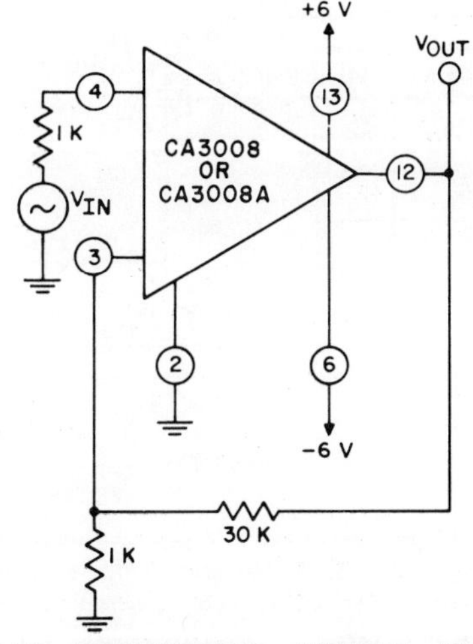

30-DB NONINVERTING WITHOUT PHASE COMPENSATION—IC opamp with only three external resistors provides flat response to 2 MHz, with gain then increasing to peak at 4.5 MHz before dropping down to zero above 10 MHz.—"Linear Integrated Circuits," RCA, Harrison, N.J., IC-41, p 247.

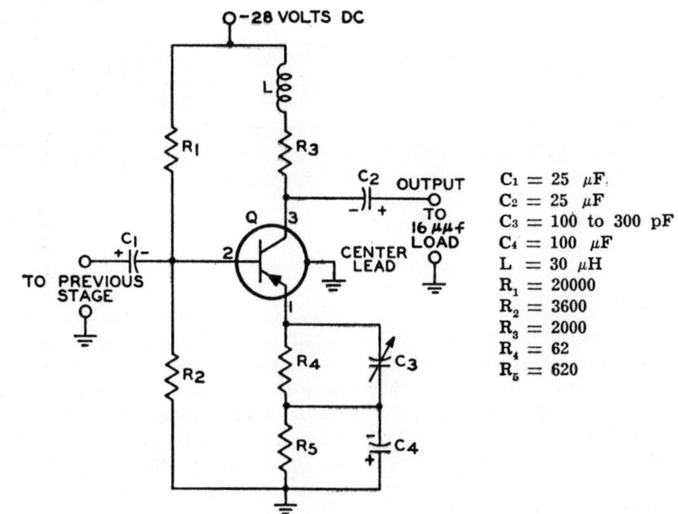

LOW-LEVEL VIDEO AMPLIFIER—Uses 2N274 pnp transistor having cutoff frequency of 30 MHz. At 12.5 MHz, input resistance is 150 ohms, output resistance 4,000 ohms, and power gain up to 27 dB.—"Transistor Manual," RCA, Harrison, N.J., SC-13, p 130.

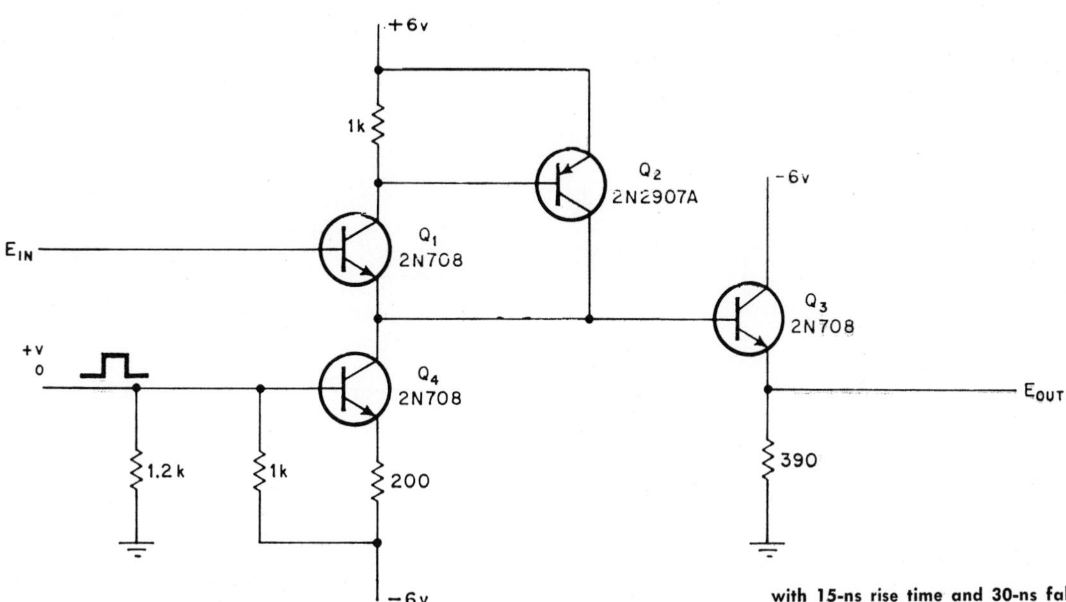

UNITY-GAIN BUFFER—Voltage gain is between 0.995 and 0.999 over entire temperature range of −30 to +160 F and input impedance is high, as required in radar video processors. Can be used to sample d-c level of integrator and transfer analog pulse to output decision circuits such as Schmitt trigger. Will handle input pulses with 15-ns rise time and 30-ns fall time. Q1 and Q2 cancel d-c offset at input.—R. J. Turner, Buffer Amp Provides Stability Over Wide Temperature Range, *Electronics*, Nov. 24, 1969, p 107.

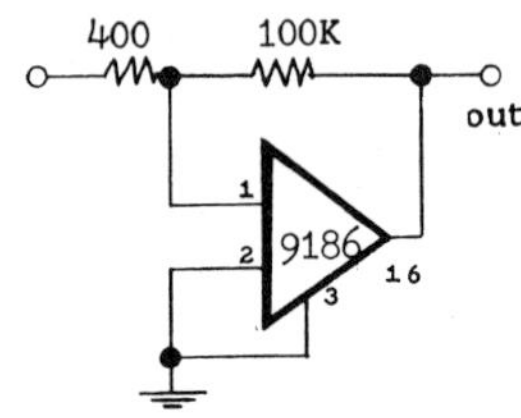

7-MHZ WITH 250 GAIN—OEI Model 9186 opamp in two-resistor configuration shows low noise and good stability without external phase compensation, with closed-loop gain level of 250 from d-c to 7 MHz.—Three Inverting Amplifiers Using the 9186, Optical Electronics, Tucson, Ariz., No. 10124.

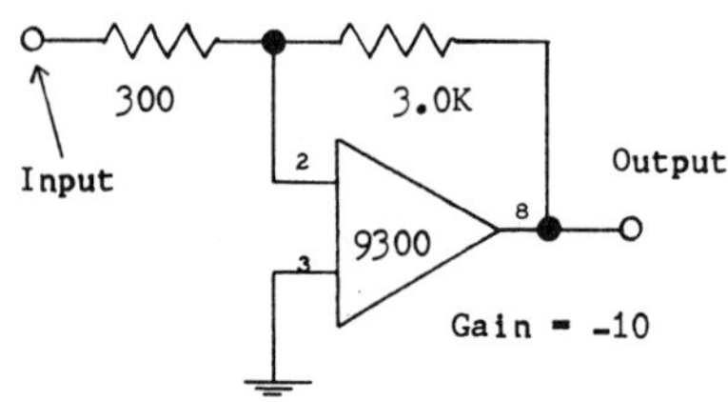

INVERTING WITH GAIN OF 10—Uses OEI 9300 opamp having 6 dB/octave rolloff up to 100 MHz. IC requires +6 V and −6V supplies. Rise and fall times are 30 ns for 1 V output. Use metal-film resistors to prevent overshoot and ringing.—Applying the Model 9300 Monolithic Operational Amplifier, Optical Electronics, Tucson, Ariz., No. 10134.

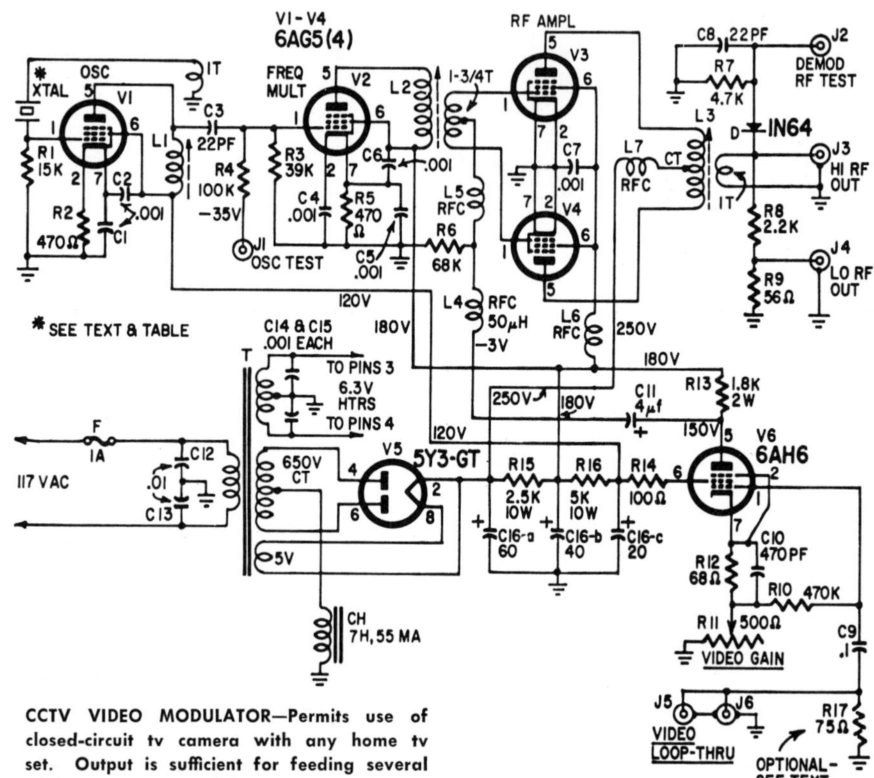

CCTV VIDEO MODULATOR—Permits use of closed-circuit tv camera with any home tv set. Output is sufficient for feeding several receivers over several hundred feet of coax cable. Article gives coil turns data and crystal frequency for each channel. For channel 10, use 48.312-MHz crystal, with 11 turns for L1, 4 for L2, and 5½ for L3. Camera should provide about 1 V p-p and negative-going sync.—E. T. Hansen, Build a Video Modulator for CCTV, *Radio-Electronics*, Jan. 1966, p 52–54.

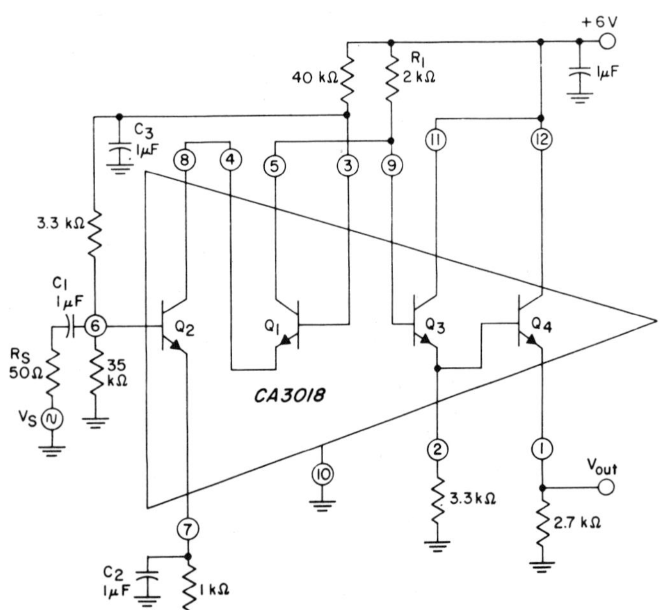

CASCODE VIDEO AMPLIFIER—Frequency response is flat within 3 dB between 6 kHz and 11 MHz, using four-transistor IC connected as shown. Mid-frequency voltage gain is 37 dB, and useful dynamic input range is 40 μV to 16.6 mV p-p.—"Linear Integrated Circuits," RCA, Harrison, N.J., IC-41, p 311.

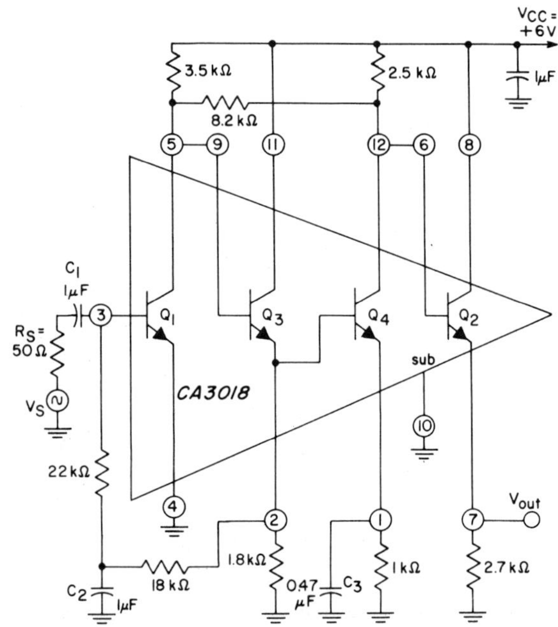

BROADBAND VIDEO AMPLIFIER—Uses CA3018 transistor IC array in two d-c coupled stages. Two feedback loops provide d-c stability. Frequency response is down 3 dB at 800 Hz and 32 MHz.—"Linear Integrated Circuits," RCA, Harrison, N.J., IC-41, p 309.

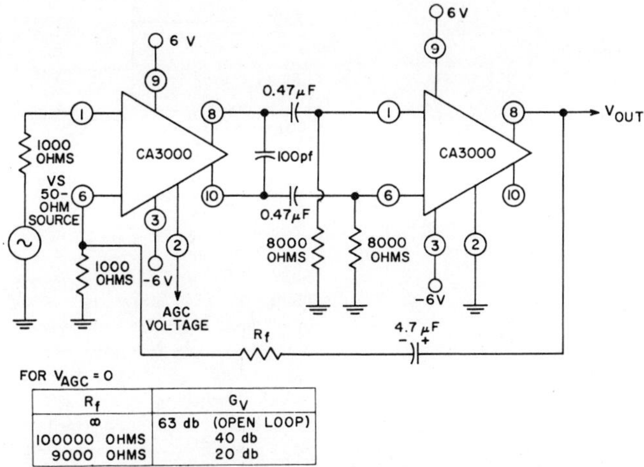

R_f	G_V
∞	63 db (OPEN LOOP)
100000 OHMS	40 db
9000 OHMS	20 db

CASCADED IC WITH FEEDBACK—With R-C coupling of two IC d-c amplifiers, open-loop mid-band gain is 63 dB, and bandpass is 18 Hz to 135 kHz. Under closed-loop conditions, bandpass is 0.13 Hz to 6.6 MHz for 20 dB gain.—"Linear Integrated Circuits," RCA, Harrison, N.J., IC-41, p 126.

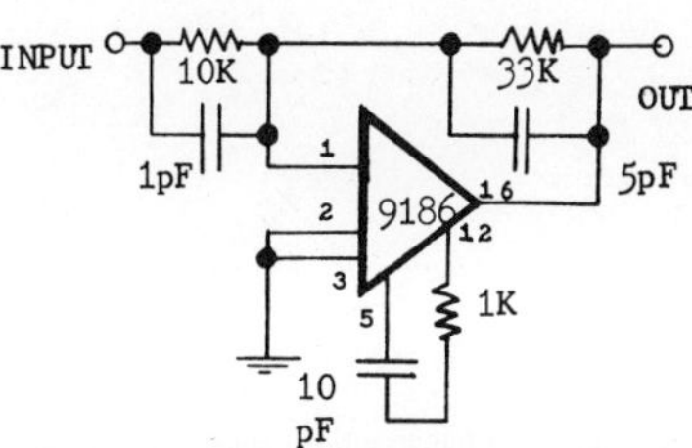

30-MHZ FAST-RISE AMPLIFIER—Provides gain of 3.3 and 7-ns rise time with OEI 9186 opamp.—Three Inverting Amplifiers Using the 9186, Optical Electronics, Tuscon, Ariz., No. 10124.

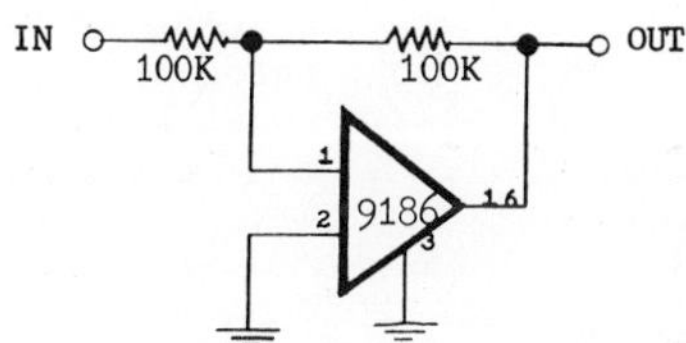

UNITY-GAIN BUFFER—Used as wide-band inverting amplifier having high input impedance, as required by vidicon, high-impedance transducer, and some detectors. With OEI 9186 opamp, provides unity gain up to 17 MHz.—Three Inverting Amplifiers Using the 9186, Optical Electronics, Tucson, Ariz., No. 10124.

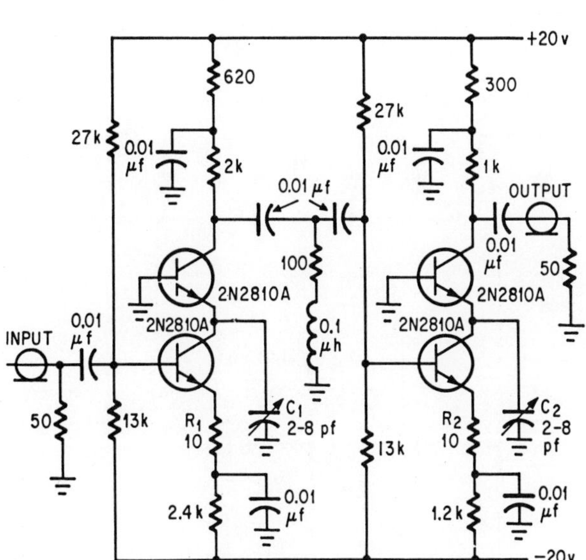

500-MHZ VIDEO—Variable capacitors C1 and C2 adjust bandwidth of two-stage cascode amplifier. Increased bandwidth is achieved by adding common-base transistor amplifier to single common-emitter stage having 50-ohm input; inductive component of common-base stage forms resonant rise in current to compensate for dropoff of other stage at high frequencies.—H. T. McAleer, Emitter Peaking Pushes Bandwidth to 500 MHz, *Electronics*, Sept. 4, 1967, p 96–97.

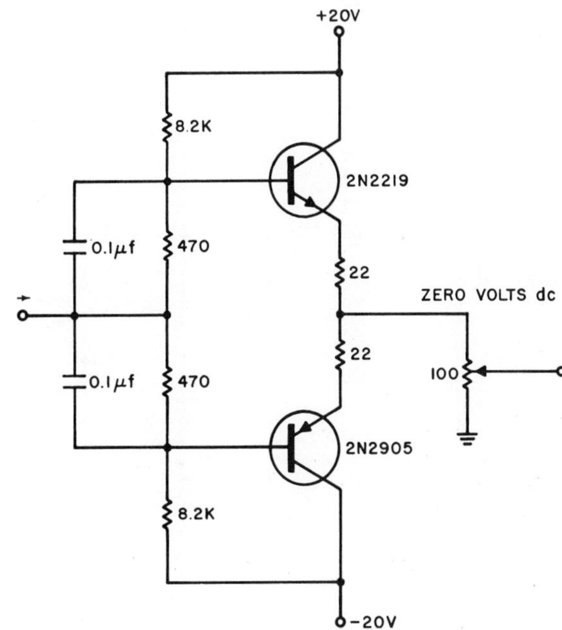

GAIN CONTROL—Push-pull emitter-follower provides high-level gain control of video signal while maintaining zero d-c voltage at output. Transistors must be balanced; common heat sink helps. Can be used to drive long cables, with signals up to 30 V p-p. —H. F. Stearns, Gain-Control Circuit Avoids D-C Shift, *Electronic Design*, Feb. 1, 1965, p 28.

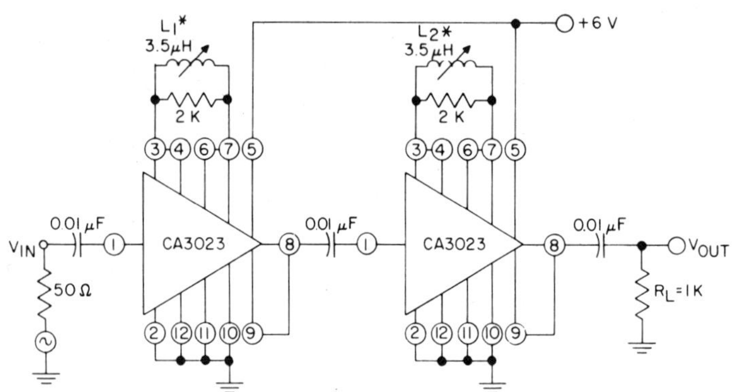

∗ SELF-RESONANT AT 28 MHz

28-MHZ LIMITER—Uses two IC video amplifiers to provide full limiting at input of 300 μV. Total gain is 61 dB, and bandwidth before limiting is 3.8 MHz.—"Linear Integrated Circuits," RCA, Harrison, N.J., IC-41, p 179.

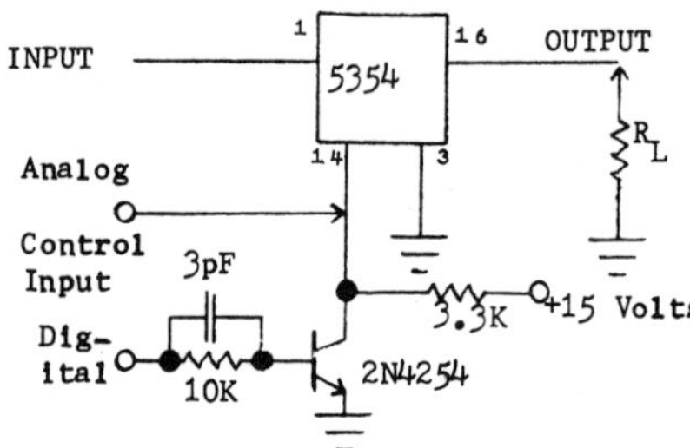

FAST SWITCH—OEI 5354 analog switch is basically spst, either on or off. Provides very high isolation at video frequencies, with sufficiently fast switching time to allow video switching during vertical retrace interval. Switching voltage is at analog levels of 0 and +10 V. For spdt switching, two 5354 switches are needed.—A Fast Video Switcher Using Analog Switches, Optical Electronics, Tucson, Ariz., No. 10171.

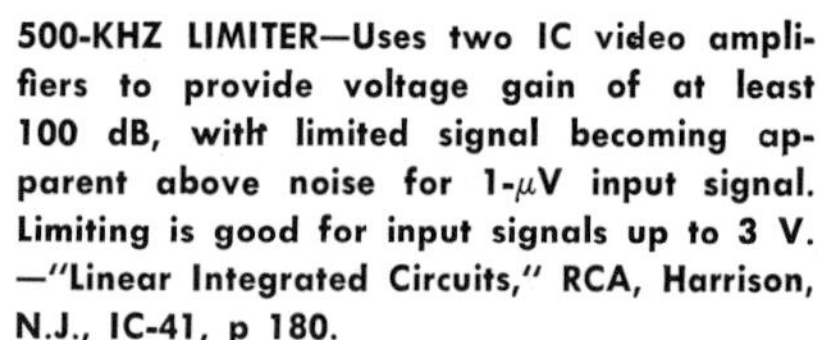

500-KHZ LIMITER—Uses two IC video amplifiers to provide voltage gain of at least 100 dB, with limited signal becoming apparent above noise for 1-μV input signal. Limiting is good for input signals up to 3 V. —"Linear Integrated Circuits," RCA, Harrison, N.J., IC-41, p 180.

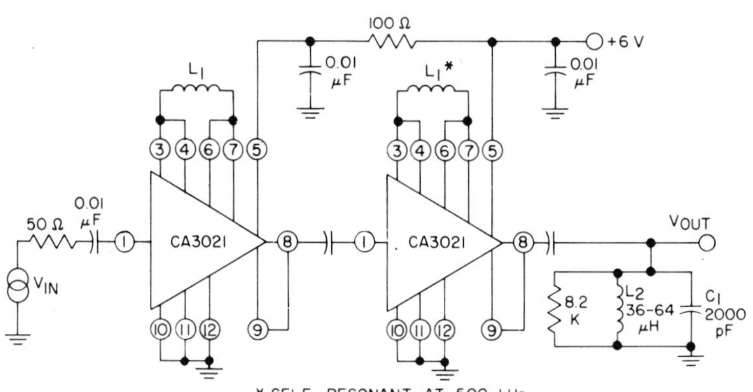

∗ SELF-RESONANT AT 500 kHz

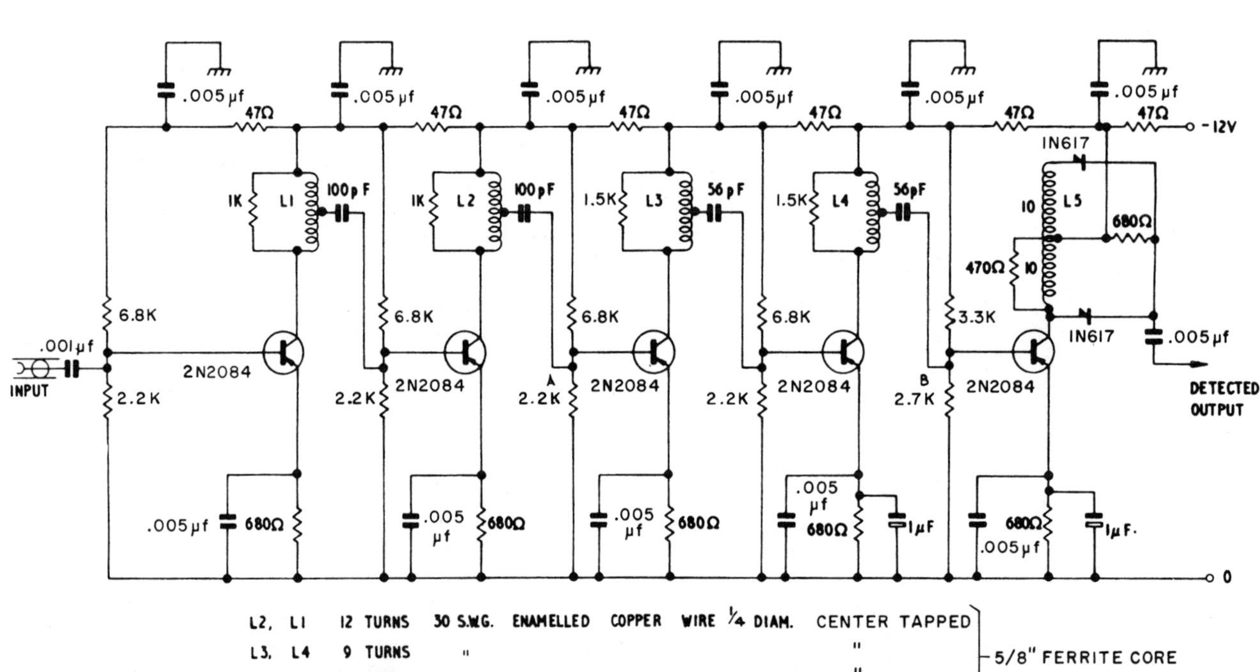

15-MHZ BANDWIDTH AT 30 MHZ—Stagger-tuned video amplifier with balanced detector has gain of 60 dB. Article gives detailed design procedure and instructions for alignment.—A 30 MC Wide Band Transistor Amplifier Using the 2N2084 Universal Transistor, Amperex Electronic Corp., Hicksville, L.I., N.Y., ALR-5621, 1964.

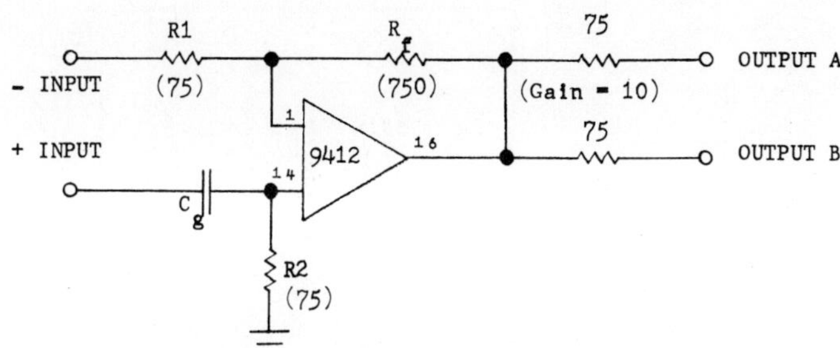

SINGLE-CHIP LINE DRIVER—Module contains high-level output stage and high-performance opamp in one package, for applications requiring low closed-loop gain (below 30). Will drive 50-ohm load at 10 V with either polarity, and may therefore be used to drive two cables with full output swing, or more if lower voltage is permissible. Use negative input if phase inversion is required. Either input may be d-c or a-c coupled.—A Video Amplifier/Line Driver, Optical Electronics, Tucson, Ariz., No. 10170.

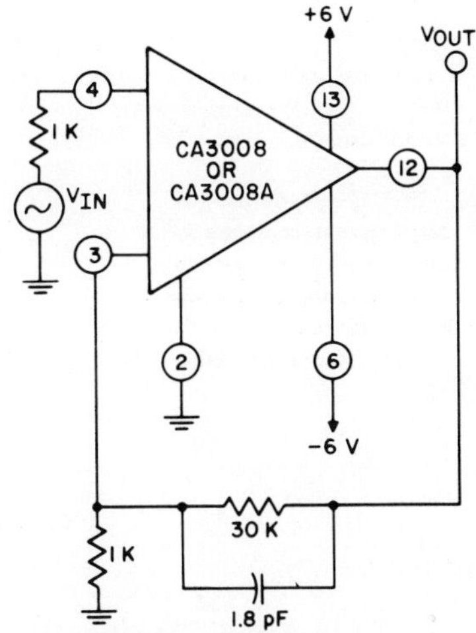

30-DB NONINVERTING WITH PHASE COMPENSATION—Use of 1.8-pF capacitor in parallel with feedback resistor of IC opamp gives flat response to about 3 MHz, with feedback ratio rolling off at slope of one for higher frequencies.—"Linear Integrated Circuits," RCA, Harrison, N.J., IC-41, p 247.

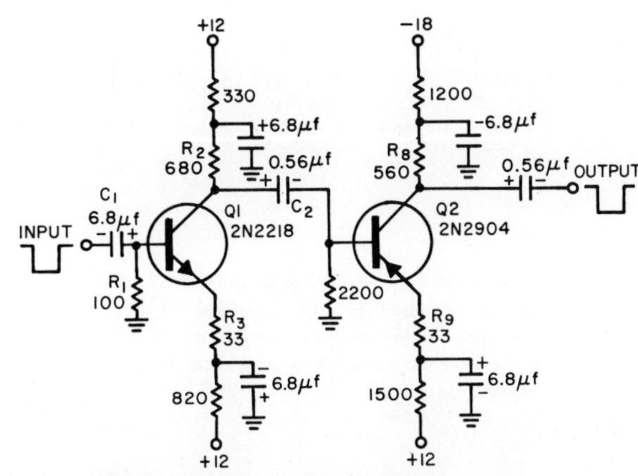

SELF-LIMITING—Use of complementary transistors in pulsed video amplifier provides compression without limiter diodes, for operation over wide dynamic range of input voltages, from 5 mV to 5 V. Can be used to drive Schmitt trigger for reshaping of pulses. —R. P. Fischi, Jr., Pulsed-Video Amplifier Limits Without Diodes, *Electronic Design*, April 13, 1964, p 68 and 70.

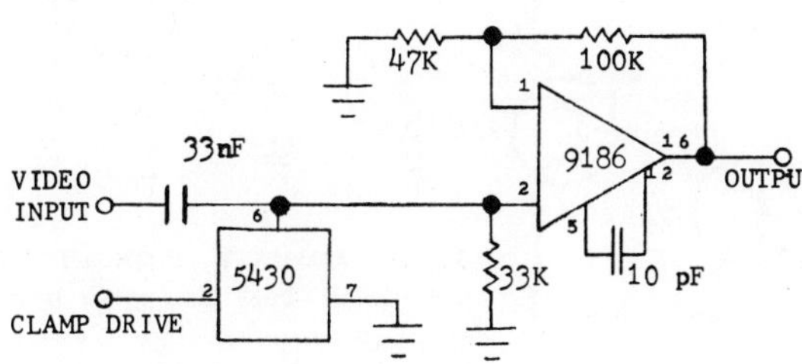

CLAMP AMPLIFIER—Used in cable tv circuits when hum level is so high that shaded horizontal bars appear in picture. Video is clamped during horizontal blanking interval, at known sync level. Clamping also restores d-c information. Clamping reduces hum amplitude as much as 6 dB per octave. Uses OEI 5430 spst analog switch.—A Video Clamp Amplifier, Optical Electronics, Tucson, Ariz., No. 10164.

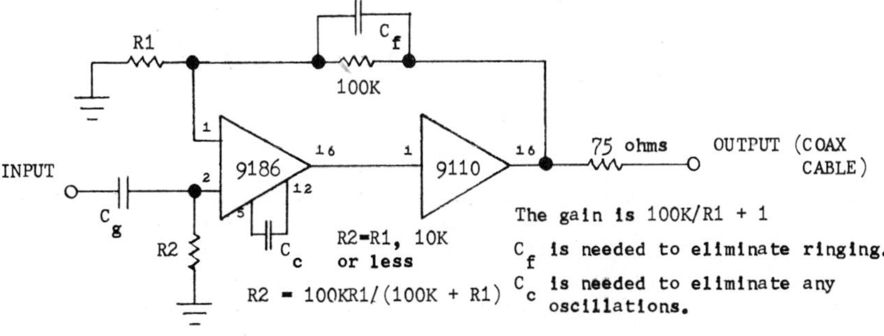

LINE DRIVER—Combination of 9186A opamp and 9110 current booster will drive 100-ohm load with up to 10 V of either polarity, at bandwidths up to 10 MHz. Slewing rate of opamp is 600 V per μs. Circuit is useful for gain levels up to 100 (40 dB).—A Video Amplifier/Line Driver, Optical Electronics, Tucson, Ariz., No. 10170.

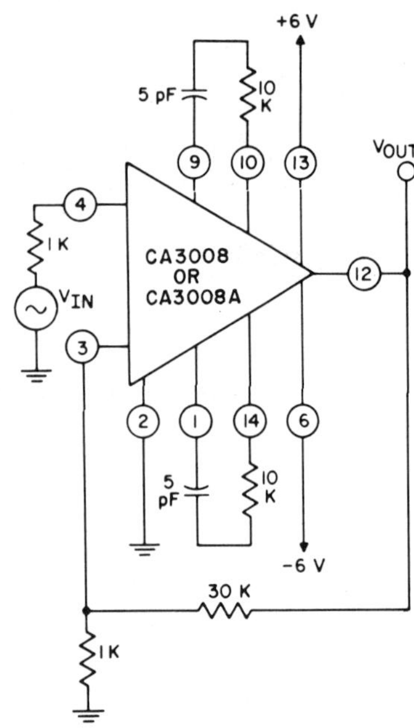

30-DB NONINVERTING—Phase compensation of IC opamp is provided by 5-pF capacitor in series with 10K. Used as video amplifier having flat closed-loop response up to about 3 MHz.—"Linear Integrated Circuits," RCA, Harrison, N.J., IC-41, p 246.

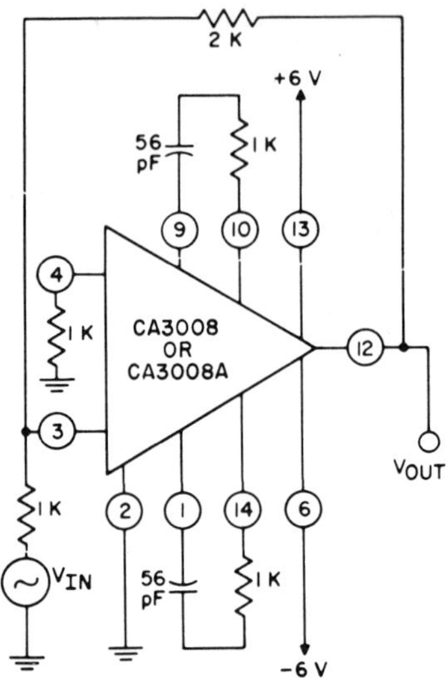

6-DB INVERTING IC OPAMP—Response of video amplifier with 56-pF phase-compensating capacitance is flat within 3 dB up to 5.6 MHz. Changing compensating capacitance to 33 pF increases 3-dB bandwidth to 11 MHz.—"Linear Integrated Circuits," RCA, Harrison, N.J., IC-41, p 248.

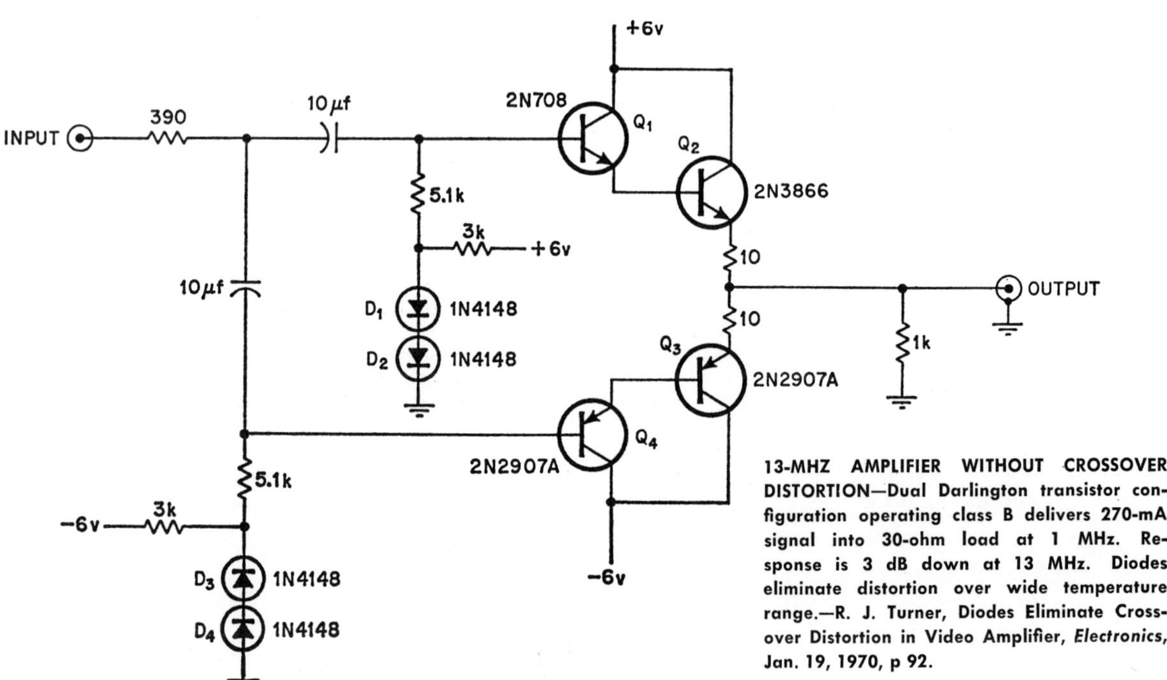

13-MHZ AMPLIFIER WITHOUT CROSSOVER DISTORTION—Dual Darlington transistor configuration operating class B delivers 270-mA signal into 30-ohm load at 1 MHz. Response is 3 dB down at 13 MHz. Diodes eliminate distortion over wide temperature range.—R. J. Turner, Diodes Eliminate Crossover Distortion in Video Amplifier, *Electronics*, Jan. 19, 1970, p 92.

NOTE: To locate additional circuits in the category of this chapter, use the index at the back of this book. Check also the author's "Sourcebook of Electronic Circuits," published by McGraw-Hill in 1968.

CHAPTER 96
Voltage-Controlled Oscillator Circuits

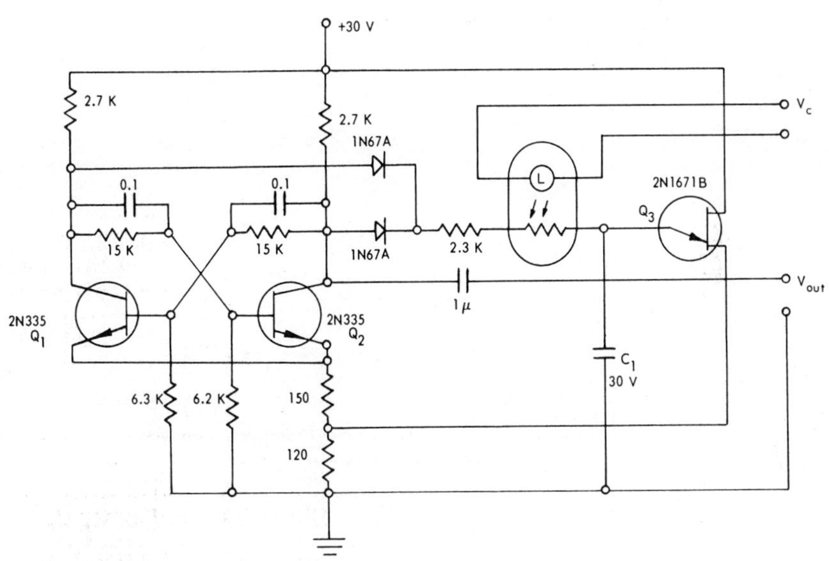

OPTOELECTRONIC VCO—Output frequency is proportional to d-c voltage applied to lamp terminals of Raysistor. Multivibrator is driven at half speed, to produce square wave at output terminals. Output frequency increases with lamp voltage. Oscillator is isolated from control voltage, permitting simple remote control of frequency.—Raysistor Optoelectronic Devices, Raytheon Components Division, Quincy, Mass., 1967, p 16.

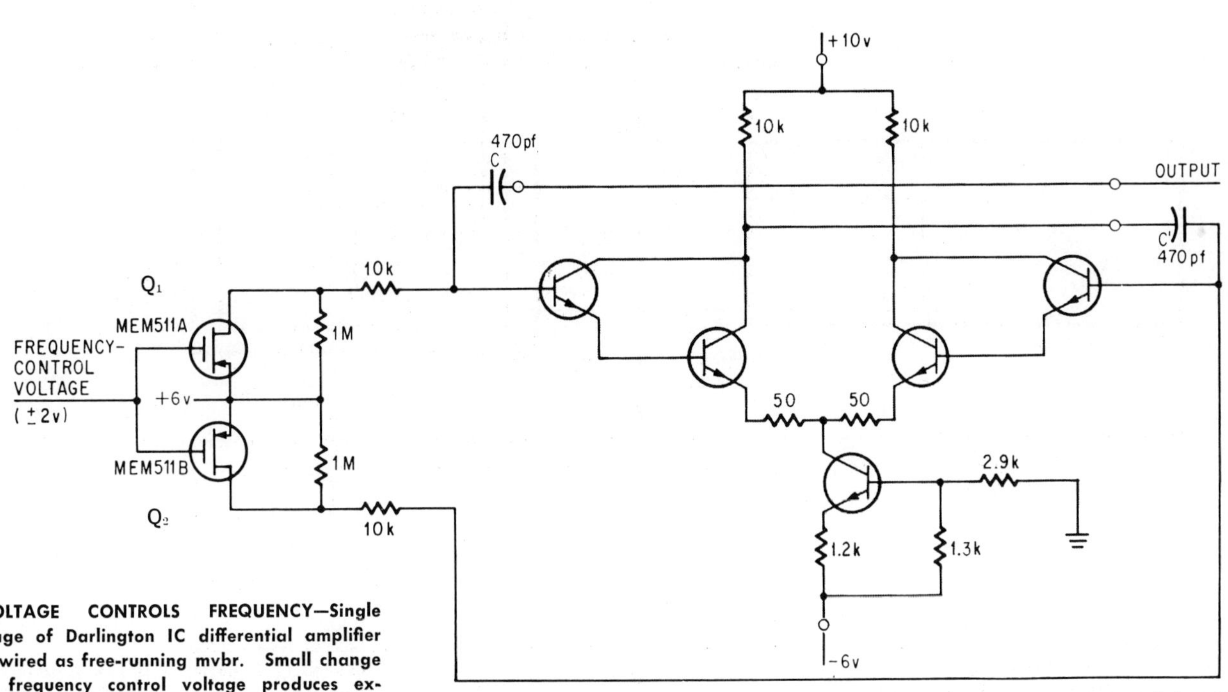

VOLTAGE CONTROLS FREQUENCY—Single stage of Darlington IC differential amplifier is wired as free-running mvbr. Small change in frequency control voltage produces extremely large frequency shift because input fet's act as voltage-variable resistors. Sensitivity is 40 kHz per volt, essentially independent of temperature.—F. G. Christiansen, Multivibrator Sensitivity Improved by MOS FET's, *Electronics*, Dec. 11, 1967, p 96.

100-KHZ VOLTAGE-CONTROLLED—Addition of two feedback loops to saturating-type mvbr Q3-Q4 gives voltage-controlled square-wave oscillator whose frequency is determined by the 10K emitter current sources, 3,600-pF capacitor, and collector voltage of Q3 with respect to ground. Q1-Q2 form integrating opamp that changes collector voltage of Q3 to control frequency.—Modified Multi Forms Voltage-Controlled Oscillator, *Electronic Design*, Oct. 11, 1965, p 68.

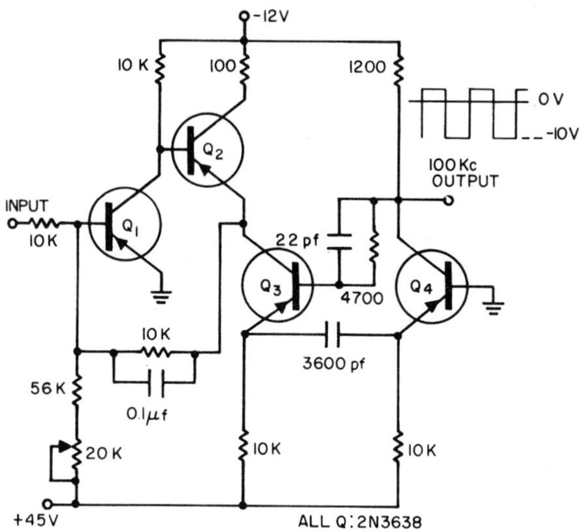

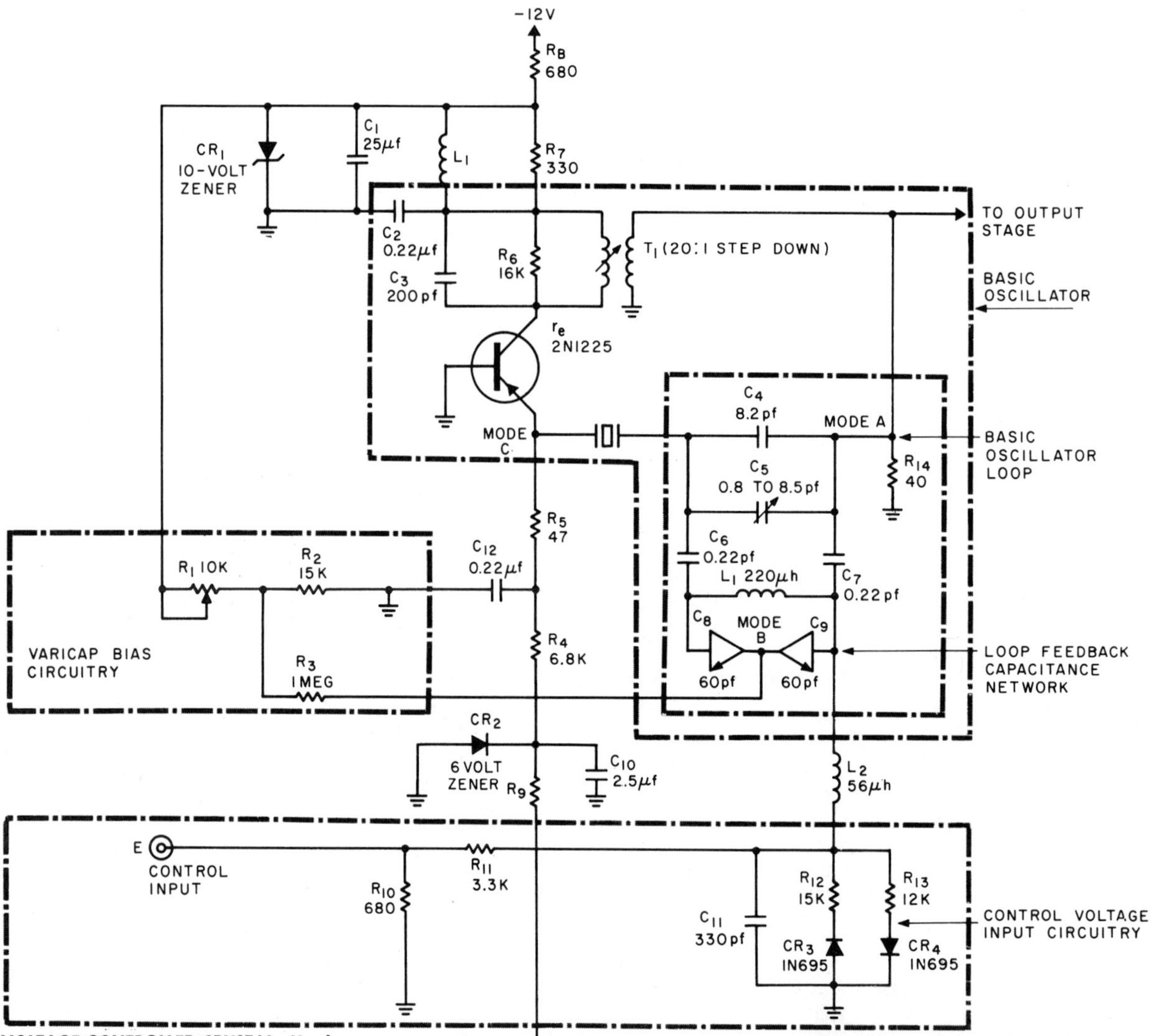

1-MHZ VOLTAGE-CONTROLLED CRYSTAL—Used as servo element in c-w tracking system. Article describes operation in detail and gives design procedure. Short-term stability can typically be 8 parts in one billion, and long-term drift as good as 2 parts in one million.—P. J. Boyle, A Design Approach to Transistorized Voltage-Controlled Crystal Oscillators, *Electronic Design*, March 2, 1964, p 22–24 and 26–27.

STEPPING MOTOR DRIVE—Produces sawtooth waveform over frequency range of 100,000:1 for d-c control voltage range of 0 to 5 V, as source of pulses for driving stepping motor in servo system. Upper frequency limit is about 250 Hz. Q1 discharges C at end of each timing period as set by R5.—W. F. Ball, Ultrawide-Range VCO Uses Op Amp and UJT, *Electronic Design*, Sept. 27, 1967, p 66 and 68.

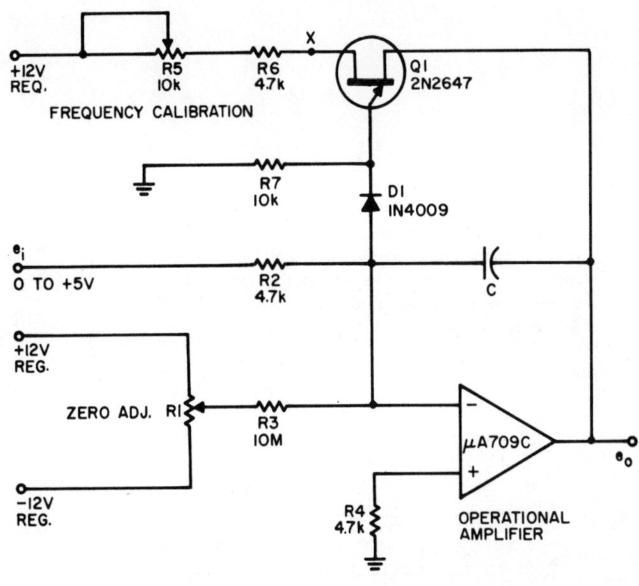

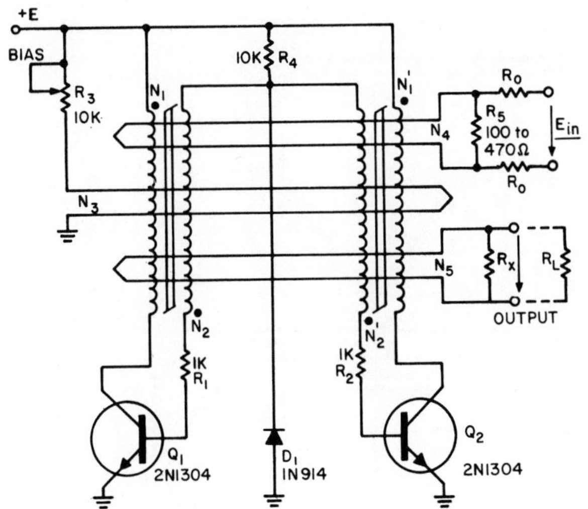

LINEAR VCO—Output frequency is proportional to input current or voltage within 1% for 15% deviation from given center frequency. Typical values for 10-V supply voltage and operation between 5 and 10 kHz, using Magnetics 50056-1D cores, are 350 to 500 turns for N4, 50 turns for N2 and N2', and 150 turns for other windings. Can be operated with balanced floating input and output. Has good rejection for common-mode signals.—M. W. Barth, Voltage Controlled Oscillator Provides Good Linearity, *Electronic Design*, Nov. 23, 1964, p 65–67.

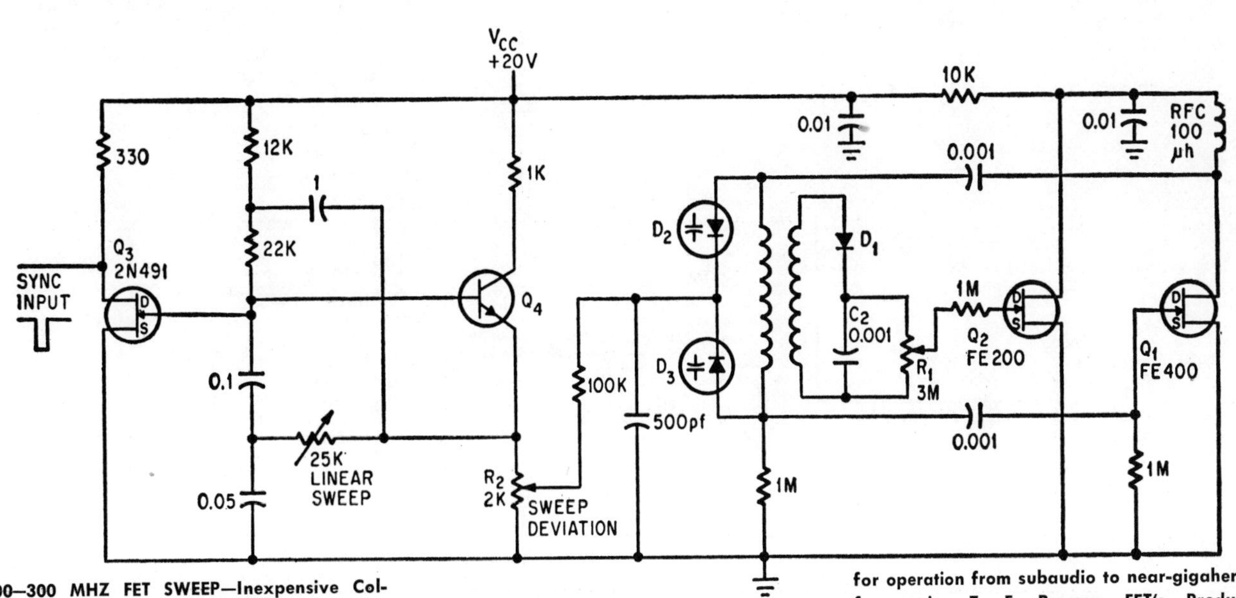

200–300 MHZ FET SWEEP—Inexpensive Colpitts oscillator uses voltage-variable capacitors D2 and D3 to change frequency of fet oscillator Q1-Q2. Sync input pulse initiates triangular output of Q3 for driving diodes through buffer Q4. Circuit can be designed for operation from subaudio to near-gigahertz frequencies.—T. F. Prosser, FET's Produce Stable Oscillators, *Electronics*, Oct. 3, 1966, p 102–103.

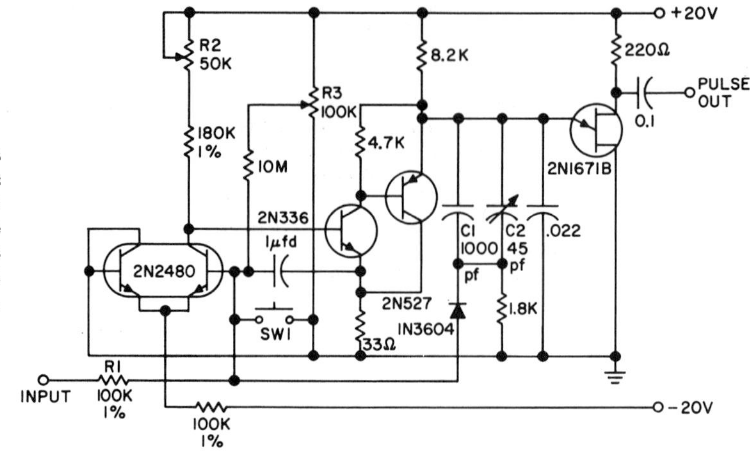

VOLTAGE-FREQUENCY—Output frequency is proportional to input voltage, with 1 V d-c input producing 1 kHz with better than 0.1% linearity. Input impedance is 100K. Article gives adjustment procedure. Supply voltages must be as stable as accuracy required. —Unijunction Circuit Hints, General Electric, Syracuse, N.Y., Fig. 11.

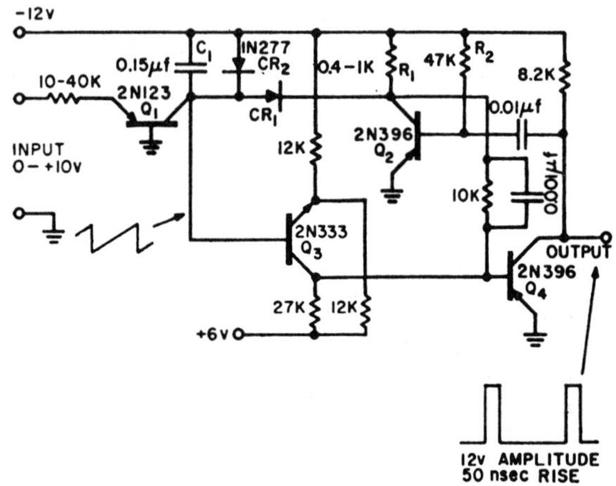

VOLTAGE-FREQUENCY CONVERTER—Produces pulse rate directly proportional to varying d-c input voltage, for driving digital motor of servo system. Frequency of output varies linearly from zero for no input to 300 Hz for 10 V input.—J. M. Howe, Transistorized Voltage-Frequency Converter Operates Linearly, "400 Ideas for Design Selected from Electronic Design," Hayden Book Co., N.Y., 1964, p 77.

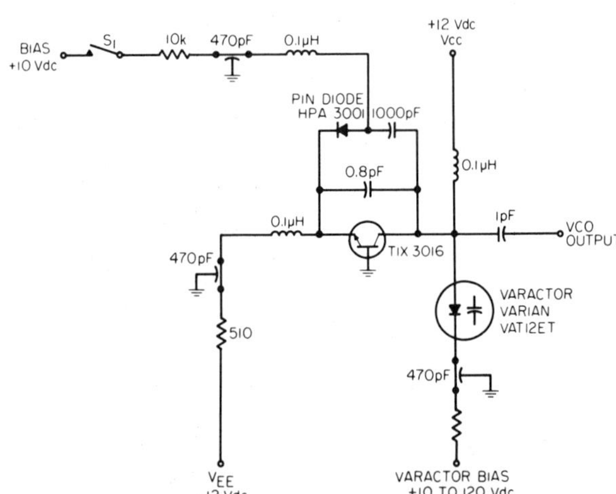

1,500-MHZ VCO—Tunable range is 500 MHz, and frequency drift less than 100 kHz after vco is turned off for 15 min. Useful when several vco's are used alternately to cover larger frequency range. Diode in feedback loop minimizes thermal effects.—A. Barone, PIN-Diode Turnoff for Microwave VCO, *EEE*, Sept. 1967, p 133–134.

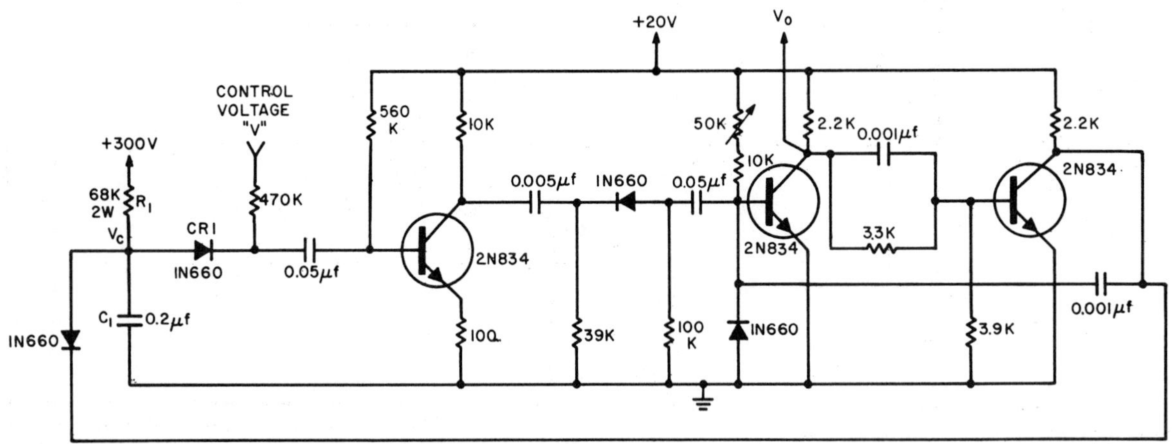

PULSE PERIOD CONTROL—Provides linear voltage control of pulse repetition period. Control range is about 4 to 45 V, with pulse period varying from about 0.2 to 2 ms. Comparator diode CR1 triggers mono mvbr through 2N834 amplifier.—B. Pearl, Comparator Circuit Controls Repetition Period Linearly, *Electronic Design*, June 22, 1964, p 66 and 68.

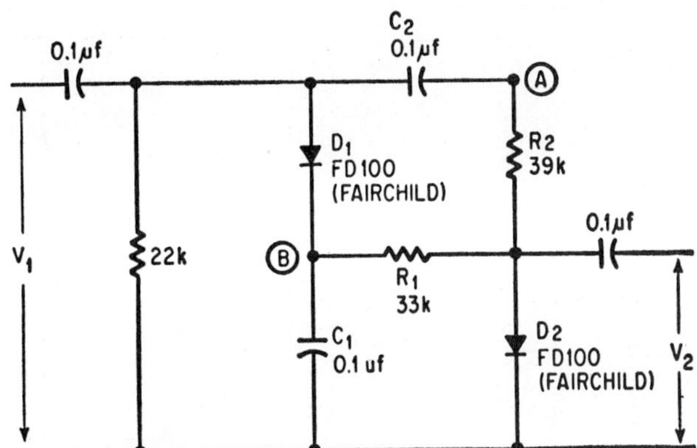

STABILIZING VCO—Output amplitude of voltage-controlled oscillator (V1) is stabilized over its frequency range by simple junction diode circuit that acts as nonlinear resistive divider whose output V2 varies inversely with input changes. Proper circuit operation is obtained when V2 is about 10 mV. Operation depends on the fact that dynamic resistance of junction diode varies inversely with input changes.—F. Giannazzi, Diode's Resistance Variation Stabilizes Signal Amplitudes, *Electronics*, June 26, 1967, p 107.

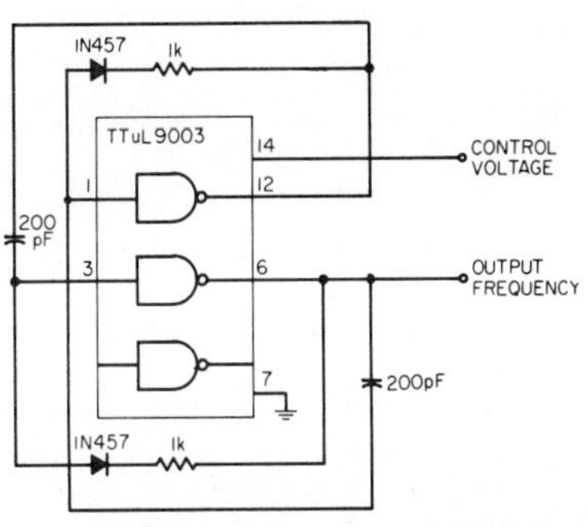

3–11 MHZ VCO WITH CROSS-COUPLED IC GATES—Linearity is better than 5% of full-scale frequency over entire control voltage range of 3.5 to 7 V d-c. Output waveform is square, with rise and fall times typically less than 5 ns. Output amplitude varies with control voltage, but this can be overcome by adding another gate or buffer.—I. Israely, Improved VCO Uses TTL IC, *EEE*, Sept. 1968, p 106–107.

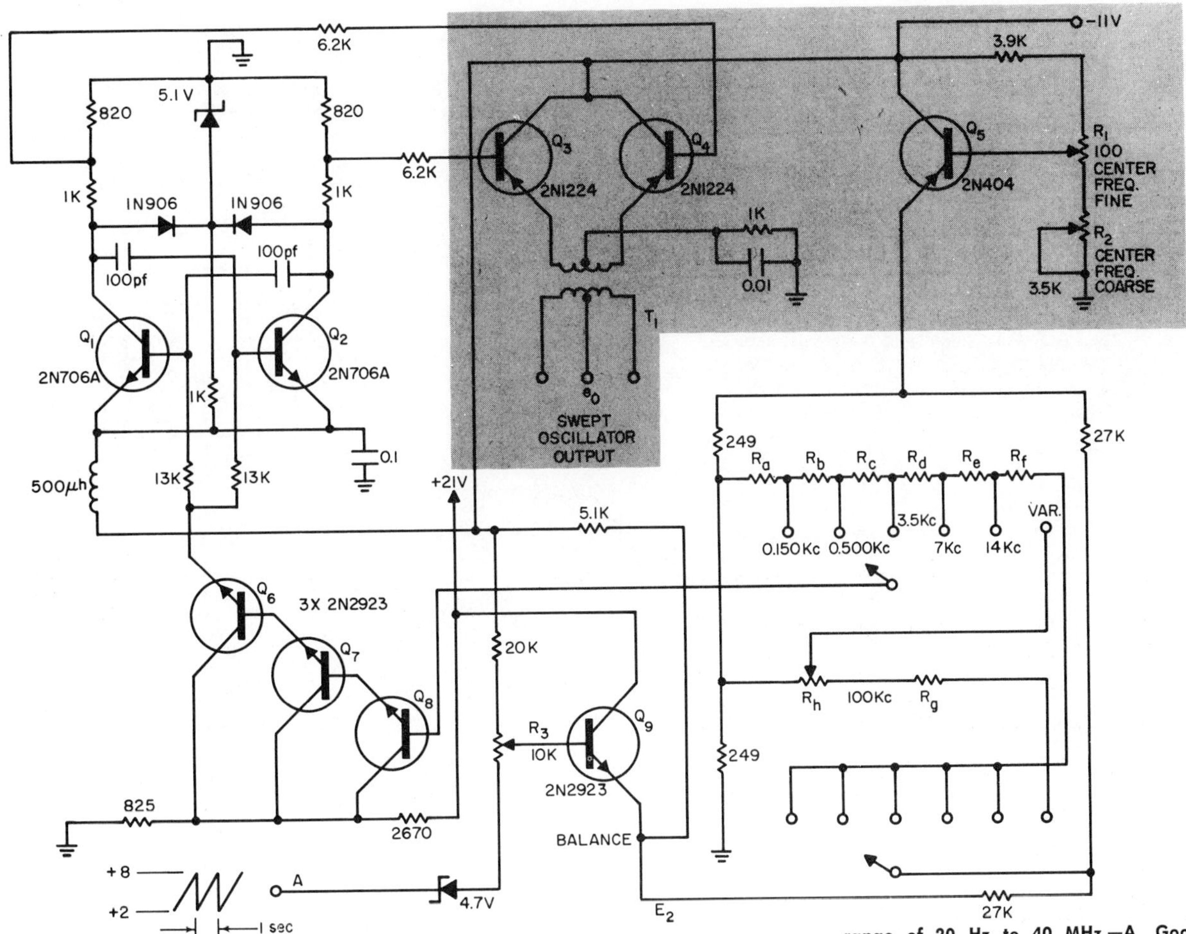

PANORAMIC-RECEIVER VCO—Balanced-bridge summing network at lower right makes center frequency of vco Q1-Q2 independent of modulation on signal. Article gives design equations. Oscillator has linear voltage-frequency characteristic over required receiver range of 20 Hz to 40 MHz.—A. Goodman, Improve VCO Frequency Control Via Balanced-Bridge Mixer, *Electronic Design*, Nov. 22, 1965, p 48 and 50–53.

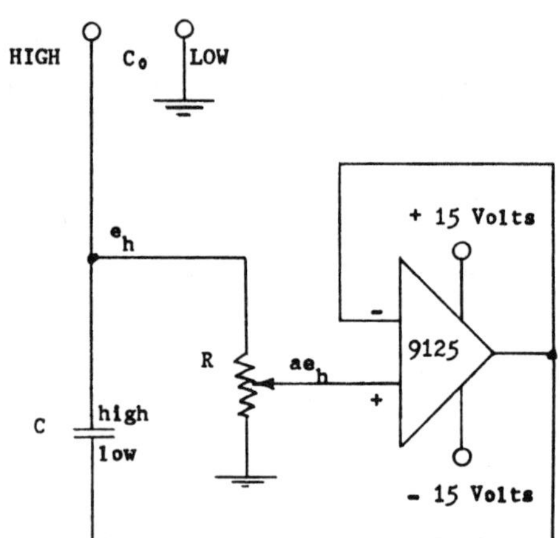

ELECTRONICALLY VARIABLE CAPACITOR—Gives output swing of over 100 kHz in voltage follower mode when using OEI opamp having unity-gain frequency of 60 MHz. Report gives detailed description of operation. Useful in voltage-controlled L-C and R-C oscillators and filters.—An Electronically Variable Capacitor, Optical Electronics, Tucson, Ariz., No. 10042.

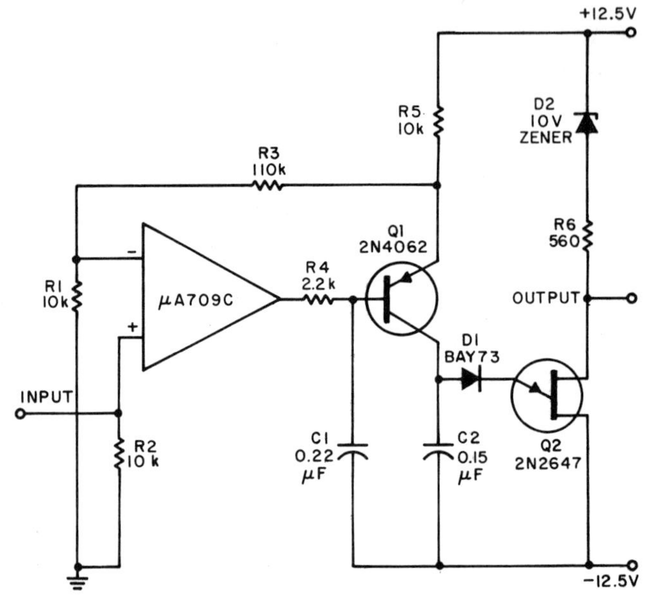

VOLTAGE-FREQUENCY CONVERTER—Linearity is better than 0.5% over frequency range of two decades produced by input signal range of 0 to 1 V d-c. Rate of charge of C2 in ujt oscillator Q2 varies linearly with input voltage.—S. G. Johnson, Voltage-To-Frequency Converter Built With One UJT Oscillator, *Electronic Design*, Dec. 6, 1967, p 122.

7-MHZ VCO USING TTL GATES—Low shunt capacitance of gates permits much higher upper frequency limit than is possible with cross-coupled transistors. Frequency can be increased or decreased 10% by varying input control voltage between +5 V and −5 V. Resistor values are chosen to bias gates at their turnover points, typically 1.4 to 2 V. Inverting gates are optional, but will improve wave shape and buffer output from external clock load.—A. C. Burley and A. V. Aellen, High-Frequency VCO Uses TTL Gates, *Electronic Design*, May 24, 1970, p 112 and 114.

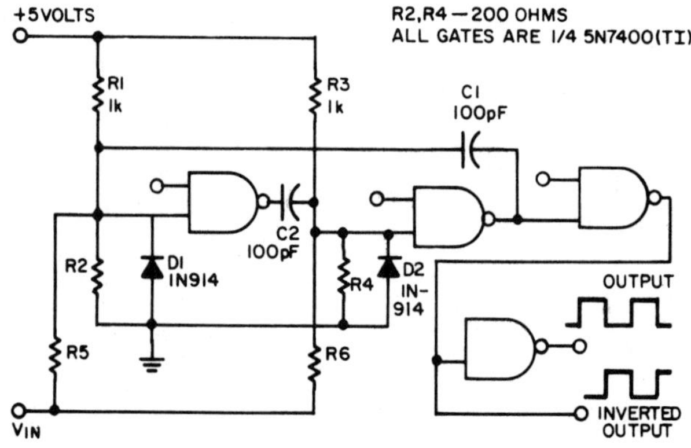

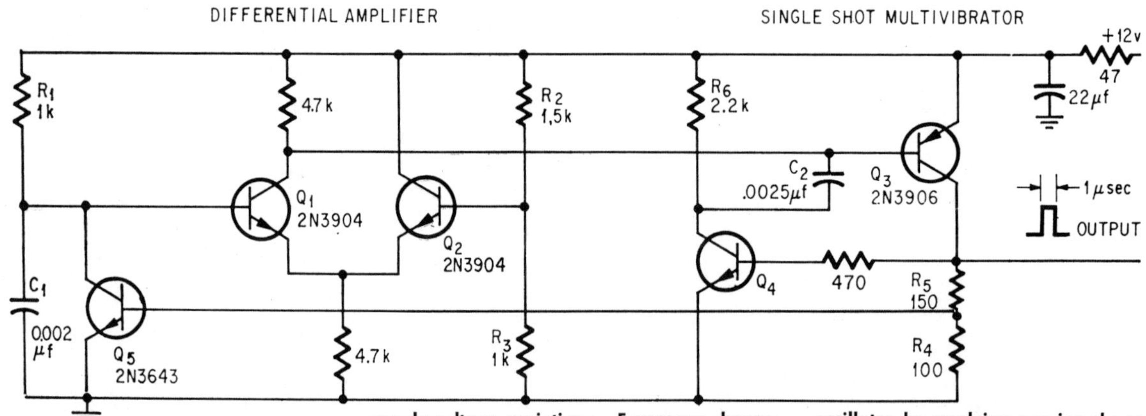

STABLE SQUARE-WAVE—Time constant R1C1 is essentially independent of temperature and supply-voltage variations. Frequency change is less than 1% for 30% supply-voltage change and temperature range of −25 to 100 C. Can be used as voltage-controlled oscillator by applying varying d-c voltage to base of Q2.—J. Kisslinger, Pulse Generator Is Supply And Temperature Independent, *Electronics*, May 27, 1968, p 106.

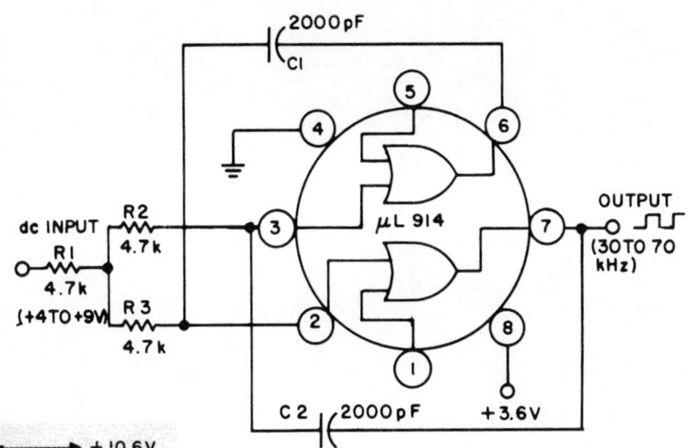

DUAL-GATE IC AS VCO—Total cost of parts is under $1. Gates are connected as free-running mvbr whose frequency is controlled over range of 30 to 70 kHz by d-c input control voltage of 4 to 9 V.—L. Toth, Voltage-Controlled Oscillator Uses Two Integrated Circuits, *Electronic Design*, Nov. 8, 1969, p 109.

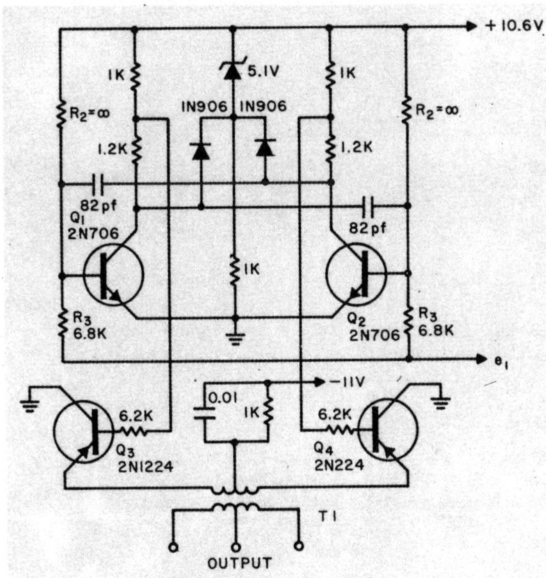

VOLTAGE-CONTROLLED 800 KHZ–1.7 MHZ—Serves as local sweep oscillator in superhet receiver used for signal analysis and/or signal identification. Provides greater linearity over wider bandwidth of modulation than conventional circuits. Uses mvbr operating from well-regulated power supply. Article gives design equations and performance graphs.—A. Goodman, Increasing the Band Range of a Voltage-Controlled Oscillator, *Electronic Design*, Sept. 28, 1964, p 28–35.

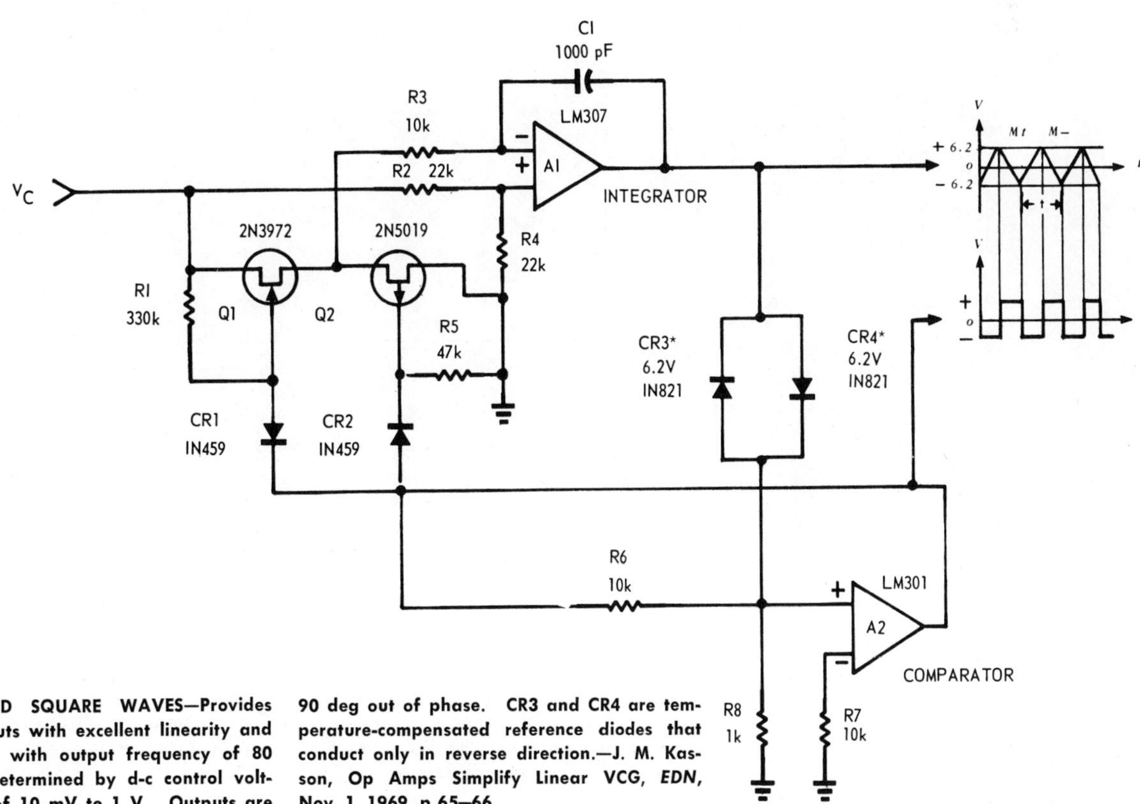

TRIANGLE AND SQUARE WAVES—Provides choice of outputs with excellent linearity and good stability, with output frequency of 80 to 8,000 Hz determined by d-c control voltage in range of 10 mV to 1 V. Outputs are 90 deg out of phase. CR3 and CR4 are temperature-compensated reference diodes that conduct only in reverse direction.—J. M. Kasson, Op Amps Simplify Linear VCG, *EDN*, Nov. 1, 1969, p 65–66.

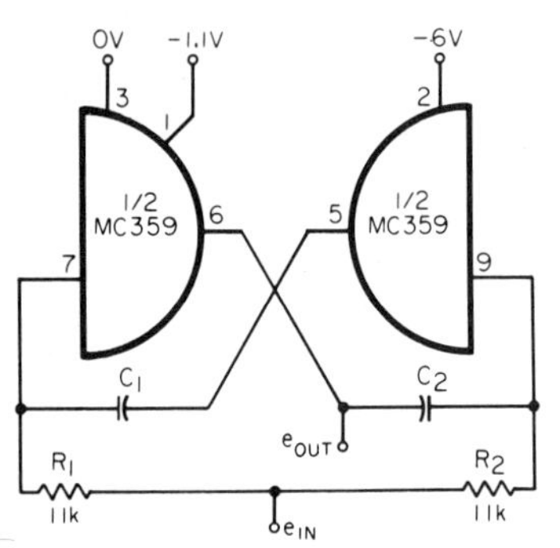

CROSS-COUPLED NOR GATES—Low-cost vco may be used as f-m generator, phase-lock loop reference, or analog-digital converter. IC gate connections form astable mvbr for which frequency is 0.5 Hz when C1 and C2 are 100 μF and control voltage is zero. With 10 μF for both capacitors, frequency is 6.3 Hz; 4,700 pF gives 20 kHz; 110 pF gives 757 kHz.—E. S. Donn, Wide Range VCO Uses IC, *EEE*, May 1967, p 182 and 184.

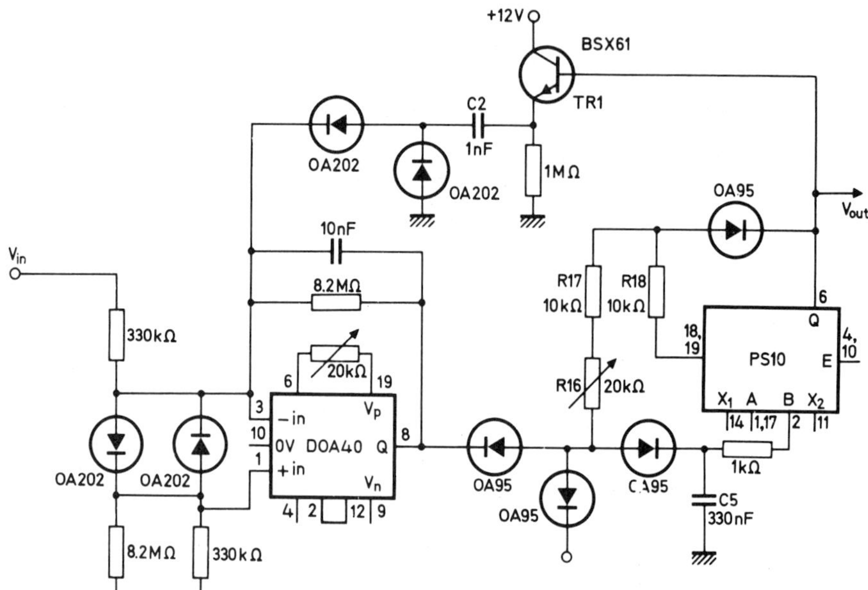

A/D CONVERTER DRIVES STEPPING MOTOR—Magnitude of analog input voltage determines period between output pulses, making number of output pulses per unit time proportional to magnitude of analog input signal. Uses Philips DOA40 opamp and PS10 gate to drive pulse generator.—O. Beate, Simple Analogue-to-Digital Converter, Philips, Pub. Dept., Elcoma Div., Eindhoven, The Netherlands, No. 68.

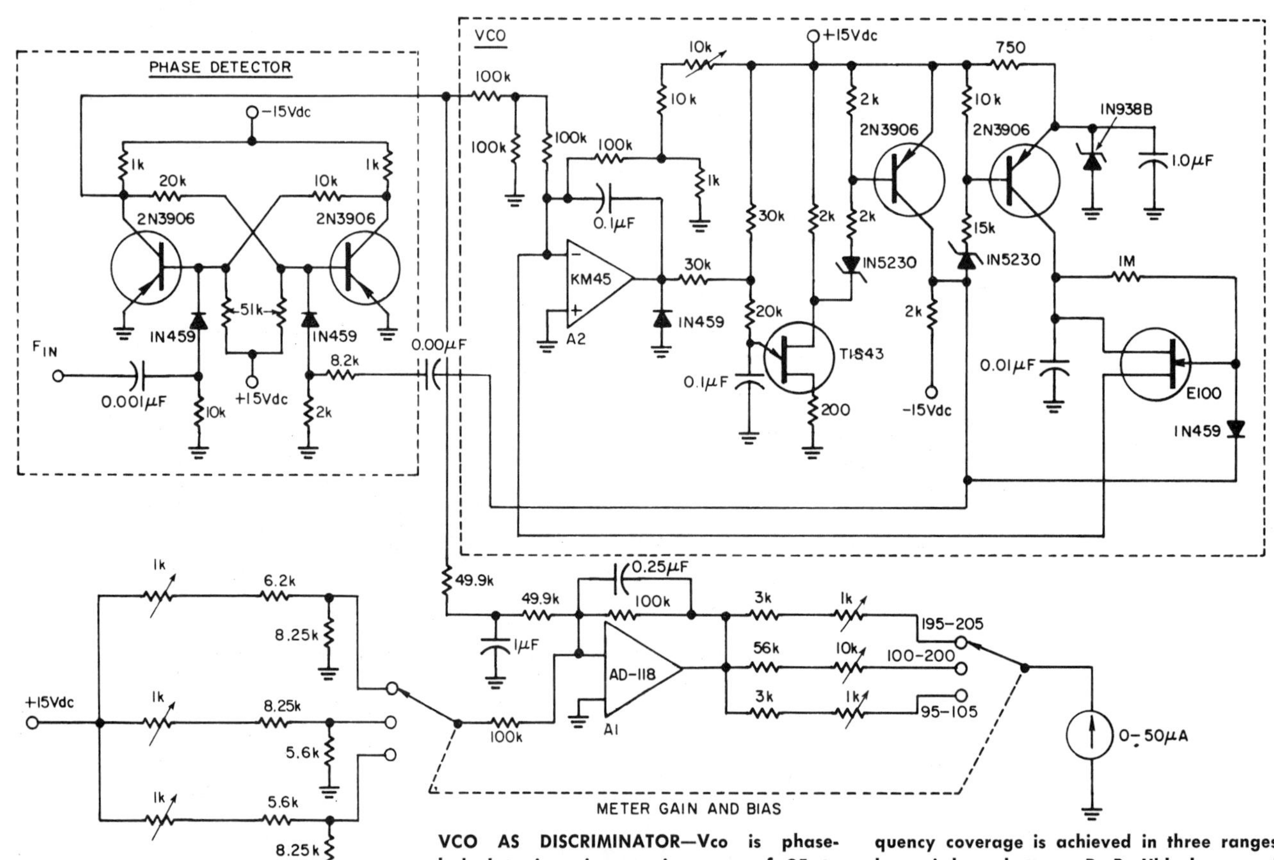

VCO AS DISCRIMINATOR—Vco is phase-locked to incoming prr in range of 95 to 205 Hz. Average value of phase-detector output varies linearly with phase angle over full 360-deg range. System is similar to that long used in f-m/f-m telemetry. Frequency coverage is achieved in three ranges by switch at bottom.—P. B. Uhlenhopp and L. G. Smeins, Try Using VCOs as Discriminators, *Electronic Design*, June 7, 1970, p 86–87.

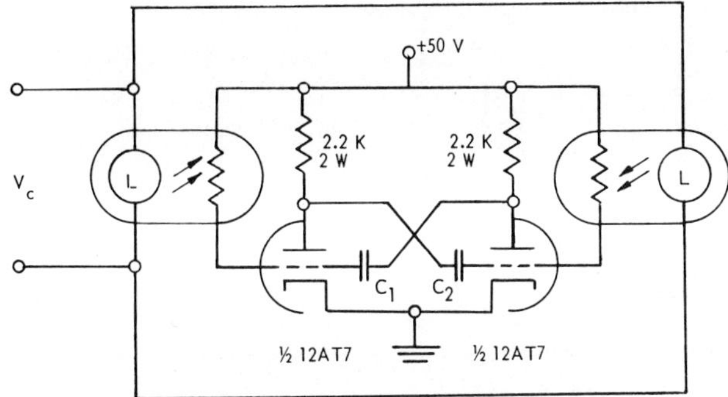

OPTOELECTRONIC VCO—Two Raysistors in grid circuits of anode-coupled mvbr, with lamps in parallel, provide frequency range of 5 to 5,000 Hz for d-c input control voltage range of 0.4 V. Raysistors can be Raytheon CK1102.—Raysistor Optoelectronic Devices, Raytheon Components Division, Quincy, Mass., 1967, p 18.

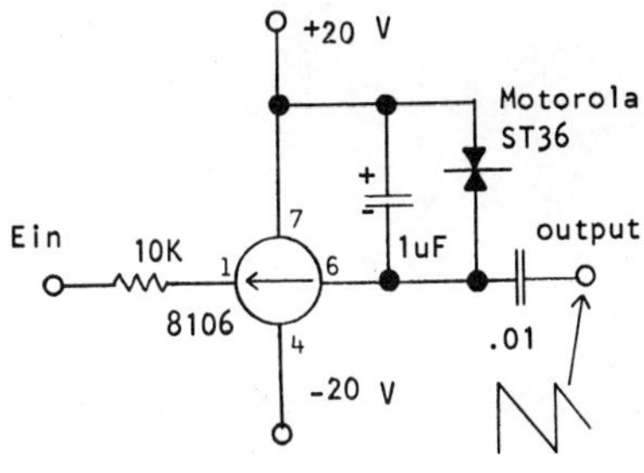

CURRENT SOURCE AS VCO—Current source charges capacitor linearly at rate determined by input voltage. Capacitor discharges when its voltage exceeds breakdown voltage of four-layer diode. Can be used as sweep circuit, with or without synchronization by external pulse. Linearity is better than 1% of full scale as voltage-frequency transducer below 1 kHz.—Applying the Model 8106 Monolithic Precision Current Source, Optical Electronics, Tucson, Ariz., No. 10168.

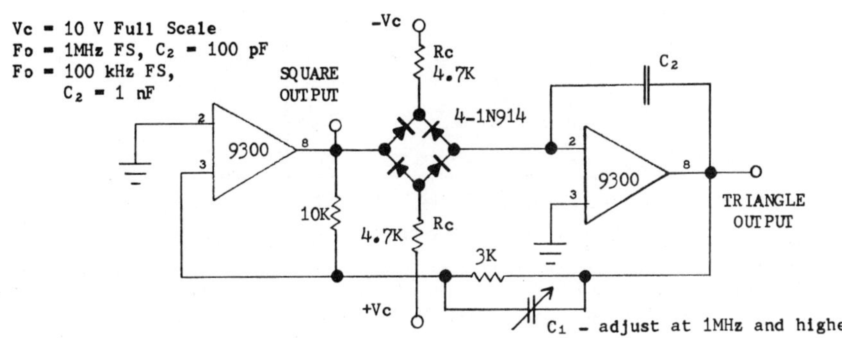

LINEAR VCO—Generates both square and sawtooth waveforms at frequency dependent on differential control voltage Vc having equal positive and negative levels. Control voltage is readily generated by signal itself and inverted signal of opamp such as OEI 9302.—Applying the Model 9300 Monolithic Operational Amplifier, Optical Electronics, Tucson, Ariz., No. 10134.

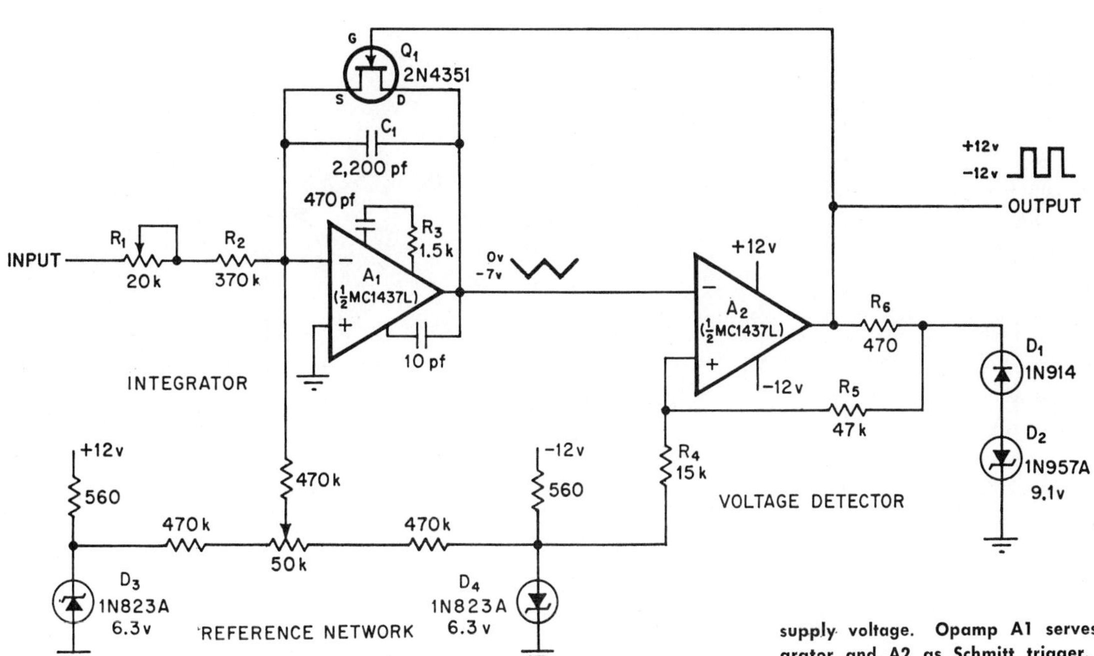

0–1 KHZ VCO—Increasing d-c input voltage from 0 to 5 V makes output frequency of voltage-controlled oscillator increase linearly from 0 to 1 kHz. Output frequency is stable within 0.1% for variations up to 15% in supply voltage. Opamp A1 serves as integrator and A2 as Schmitt trigger. Used in analog-digital converters.—D. J. Knowlton, Two OP Amps Simplify Design of Oscillator, *Electronics*, April 27, 1970, p 92.

CHAPTER 97
Voltage-Level Detector Circuits

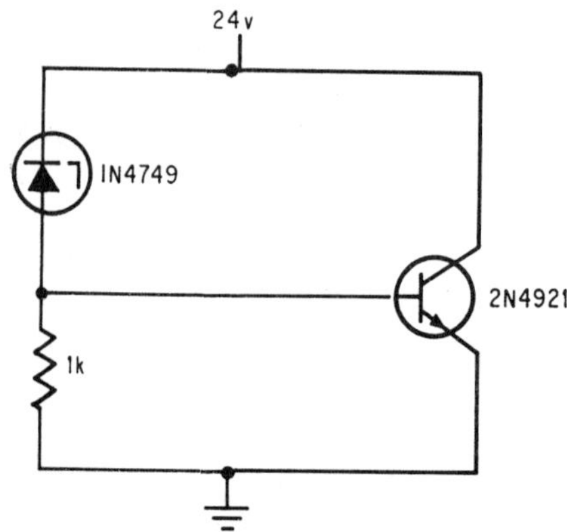

POWER ZENER—Zener conducts when supply voltage reaches 24 V, developing voltage across 1K resistor that turns on transistor. Resulting increased power is obtained at fraction of cost of power zener otherwise required.—J. O. Schroeder, Transistor Increases Zener's Power Capability, *Electronics*, Sept. 16, 1968, p 99–100.

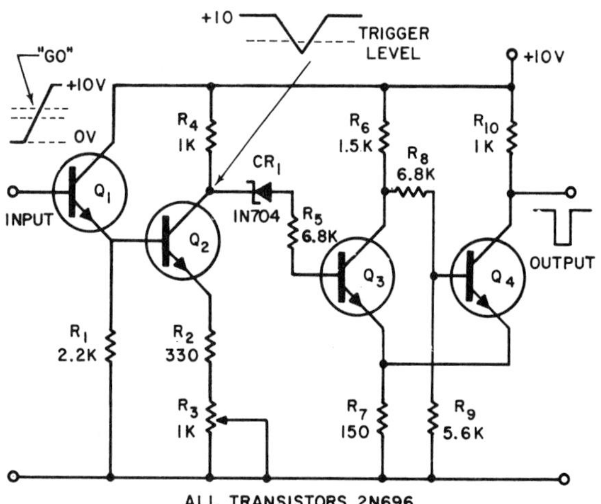

5.6–5.8 V GO-NO-GO—Provides voltage discrimination within 0.2-V passband for automatic testing. Only voltages within passband cause switching of Schmitt trigger. R3 controls width of passband. For other GO bands, input voltages should be applied to Q1 through suitable voltage dividers or zener diodes.—R. Vokoun, Voltage Level Discriminator Provides Go-No-Go Indication, *Electronic Design*, Nov. 23, 1964, p 67–69.

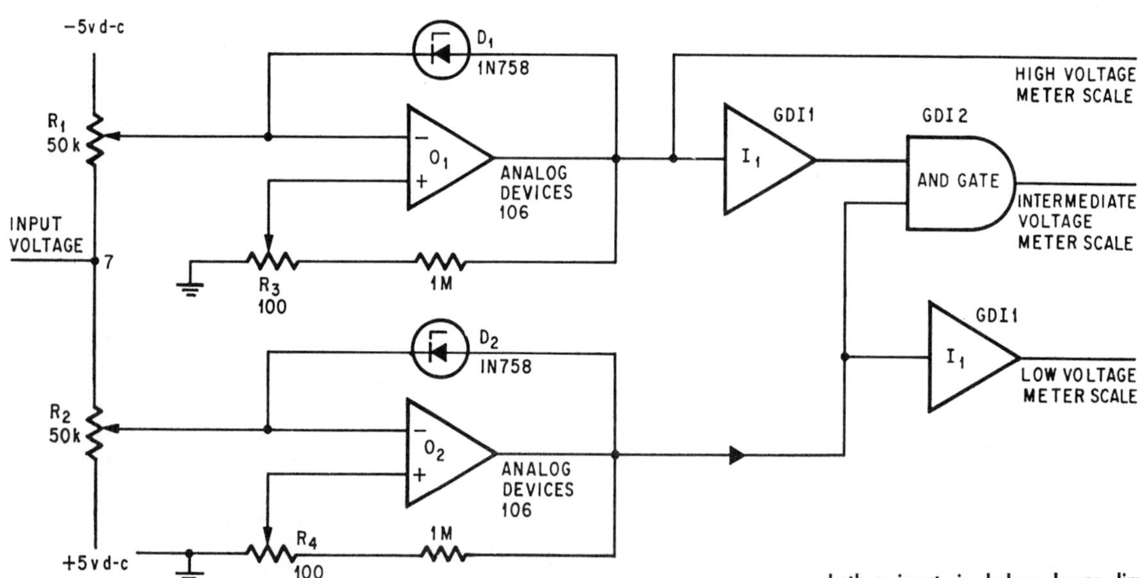

AUTOMATIC VOLTMETER—IC opamps and other standard logic circuits connected as shown give automatic three-range switching for voltage comparator. Voltage limits are independently adjustable. One output will indicate whether input is above upper limit, another will indicate whether input is between limits, and third output will indicate whether input is below lower limit. Any limit may be either positive or negative.—W. Ellermeyer, Voltage Comparator Is Made With Op Amps and Logic Gates, *Electronics*, July 8, 1968, p 91–92.

VOLTAGE-LEVEL DETECTOR—Differential amplifier has two stable states as in flip-flop, and changes state whenever d-c input level goes above preset reference level. With components shown, differential of only 100 mV with respect to reference will change state. —G. Richwell, Adjustable Level-Detector, *EEE*, Oct. 1966, p 139.

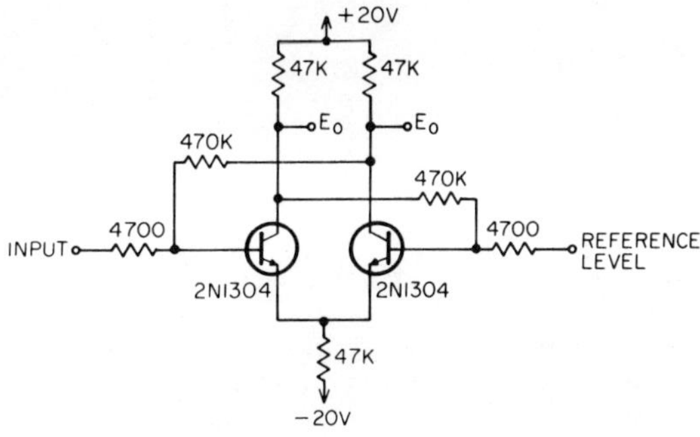

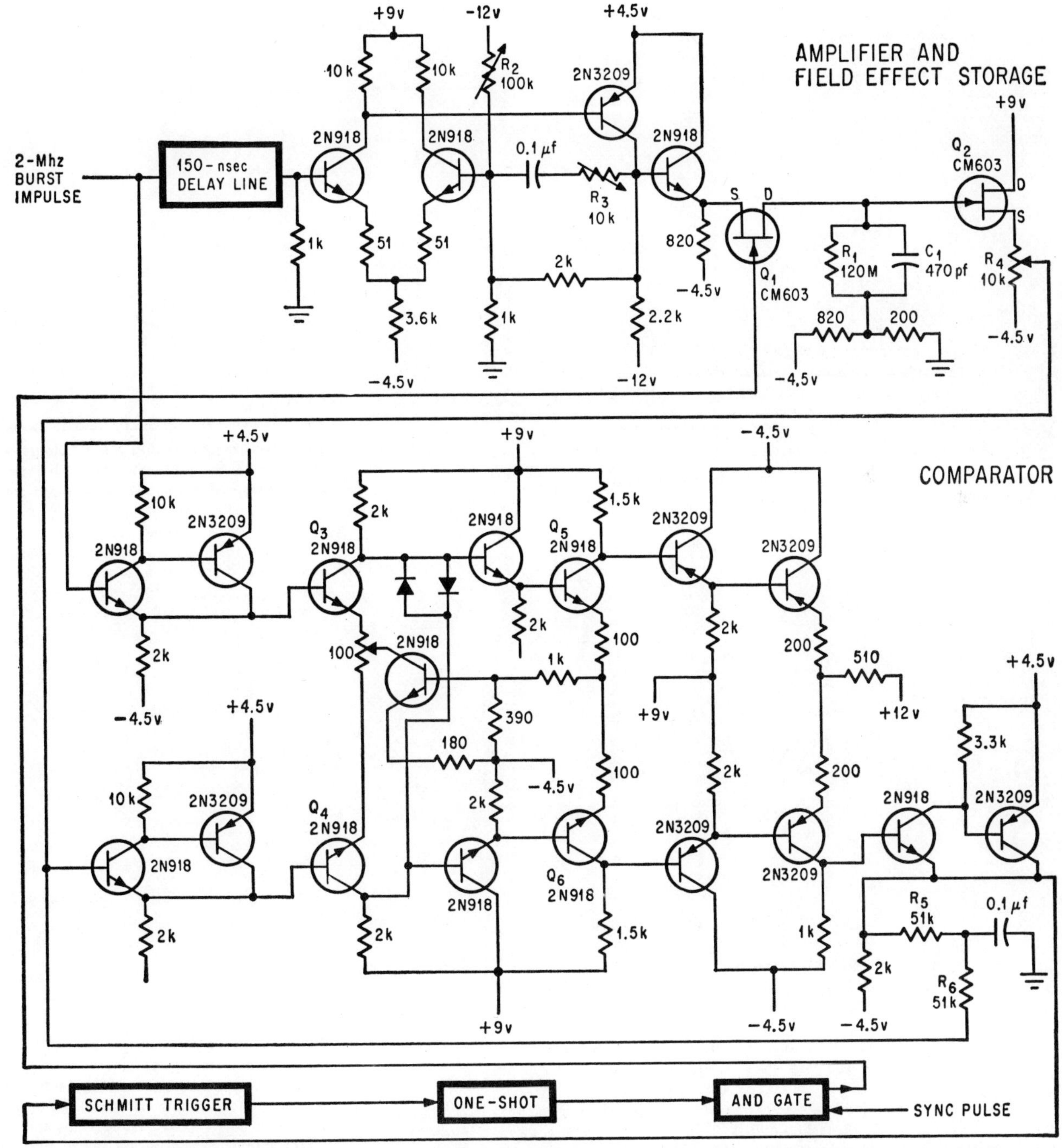

VIDEO BURST PEAK DETECTOR—Useful where position of peak in video signal is required, as for sampling time delay signals and for video, radar, and sonar equipment. Comparator circuit can sense highest peak of 2-MHz a-m burst to within 5 mV for peaks up to 1 V.—D. S. Greenstein, Detector Stores Peaks of Video Bursts, *Electronics*, Oct. 3, 1966, p 104–106.

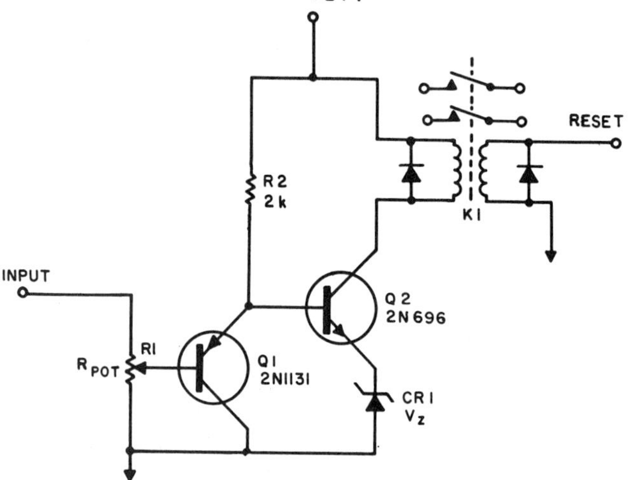

FAIL-SAFE VOLTAGE MONITOR—Operates latching relay when input voltage exceeds threshold level set by R1. For fail-safe application, relay contacts are connected to remove power from system or perform other required function. Transistors provide temperature compensation to improve accuracy. —M. Furukawa, Voltage-Sensing Circuit Is Temperature-Compensated, *Electronic Design*, May 10, 1967, p 90–91.

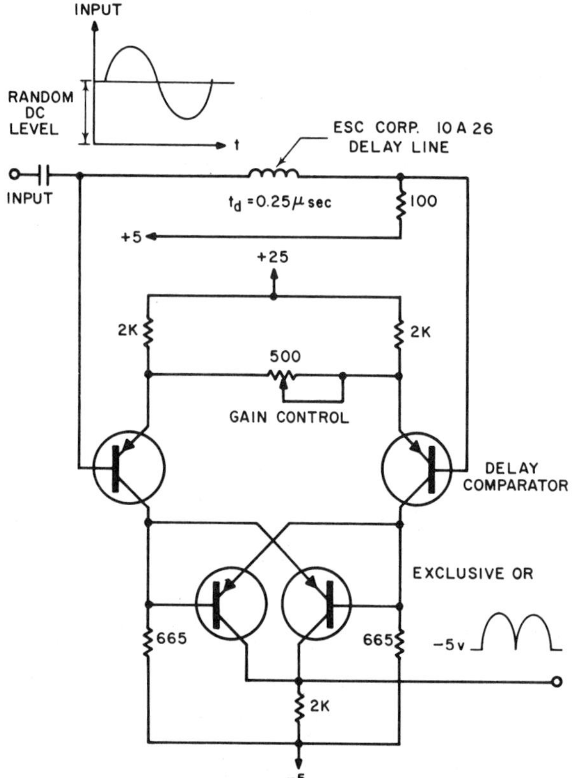

CORE PULSE-HEIGHT DETECTOR—Self-tracking detector is virtually independent of duty cycle, recovers core-memory outputs having random d-c component, and can detect signals in presence of noise frequencies that are one order of magnitude lower than signal. Will detect 200-ns pulse with rise time of 100 ns. Uses comparator method, by making comparison between each half-cycle preceding and following d-c level crossing. All transistors are 2N711.—R. T. Shevlin, Pulse-Height Detector Operates Independently of D-c Input Level, *Electronic Design*, March 29, 1965, p 32–33.

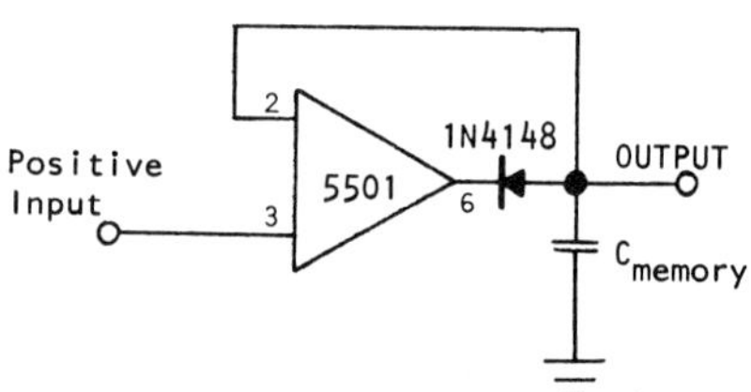

PEAK SENSE AND HOLD—IC analog comparator serves for comparing input voltage with that across memory capacitor. If input is greater than that of capacitor, output moves in positive direction to charge capacitor until it equals input voltage. 5501 then changes state and reverse-biases diode, isolating capacitor to hold value of input voltage.—Applying the Model 5501 Monolithic Analog Comparator, Optical Electronics, Tucson, Ariz., No. 10147.

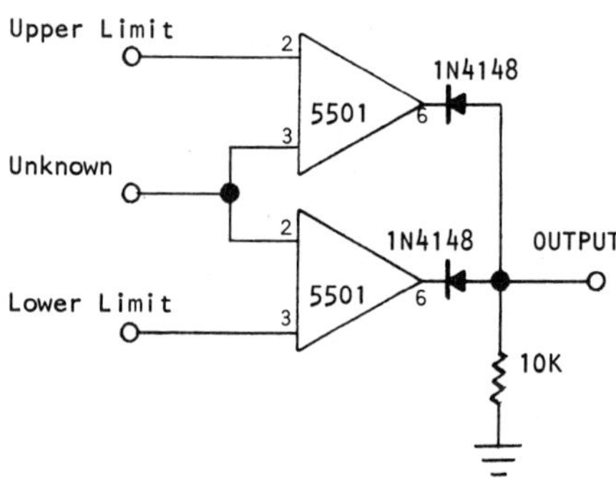

WINDOW DETECTOR—Uses two analog comparators to give zero output when unknown input voltage is within predetermined acceptable range or "window." Output is positive when unknown is beyond limits that are independently set.—Applying the Model 5501 Monolithic Analog Comparator, Optical Electronics, Tucson, Ariz., No. 10147.

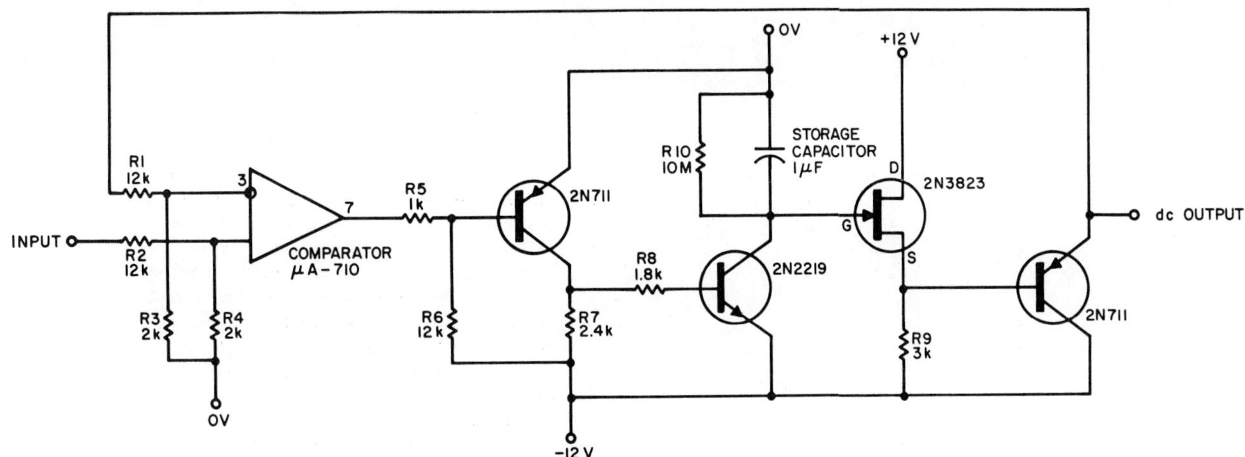

NARROW-PULSE PEAK SENSOR—Provides exact proportionality of d-c output to input signal peaks. Has low threshold, for response to very slight increases in peak amplitudes. Will handle pulses as narrow as 0.2 μs and duty cycle below 1% for repetitive signals. IC differential comparator samples peak and compares it with existing d-c output voltage, then drives level shifter controlling transistor switch that supplies current to storage capacitor that governs d-c output voltage.—W. C. Dillon, An Operational Peak Detector Captures Very Narrow Pulses, *Electronic Design*, Oct. 25, 1967, p 138 and 140.

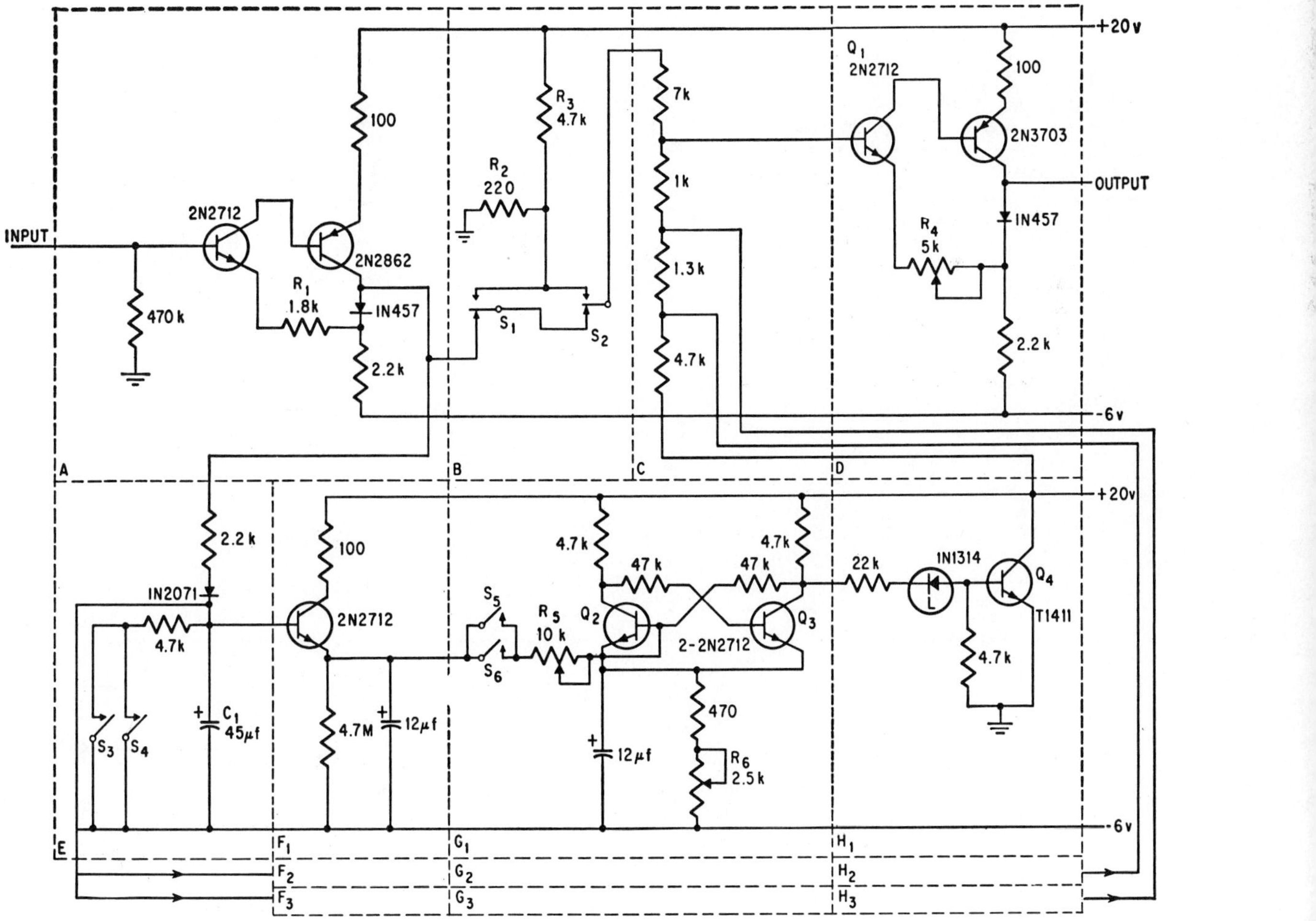

PEN RECORDER SCALE CHANGER—Although developed to operate with spectrometer that repetitively scans frequency band of light emissions in upper atmosphere, this low-cost scale changer can be used with other meters and recorders as well. Three ranges are provided, with automatic changing at end of scan when input during scan rises to 1 V, 2 V, and 4 V. Article gives operating details. Peak-level detector stage E drives three identical chains of F, G, and H stages, one for each scale factor. F stages provide impedance matching. G stages are flip-flops adjusted to switch at different input voltage levels. H stages operate as ground switches. —B. E. Bourne and R. L. Gattinger, Automatic Scale Changer Shifts Recorder Range, *Electronics*, May 15, 1967, p 95–97.

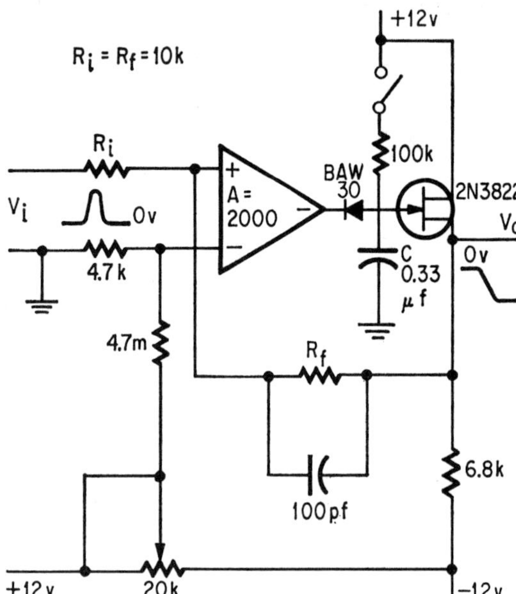

PEAK DETECTOR—Basic diode-capacitor peak detector accuracy is improved 1,000 times by adding fet and IC opamp. With nulling switch open and positive pulse at input, circuit acts as inverting amplifier. When downward transition of pulse begins, output is held constant at peak value because detector and source follower cannot follow change in polarity. To adjust output for zero offset with zero input voltage, close nulling switch and adjust 20K pot.—A. E. Vinatzer, High Accuracy Obtained from Peak Detector Using Op Amp, *Electronics*, March 17, 1969, p 94.

DETECTOR AND COUNTER—Circuit shown will detect envelope of bursts of high-frequency pulses in range of 1 kHz to 1 MHz if suitable component values are used. For those shown, upper limit for input prf is 1 kHz. If D1 is connected to point A instead of to +5 V, circuit becomes pulse counter that delivers output pulse after arrival of specified number of input pulses. After each circuit lock-up, 0.01-μF capacitor must be discharged manually or given time to discharge before input is reapplied.—K. Sheth, Pulse-Train Detector and Counter, *EEE*, Nov. 1966, p 156.

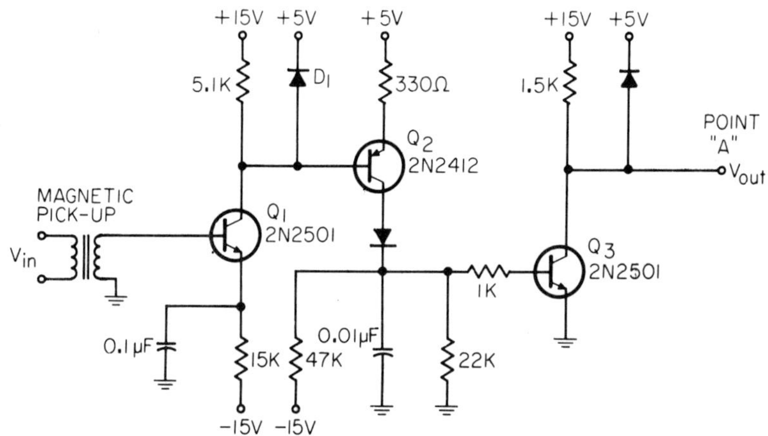

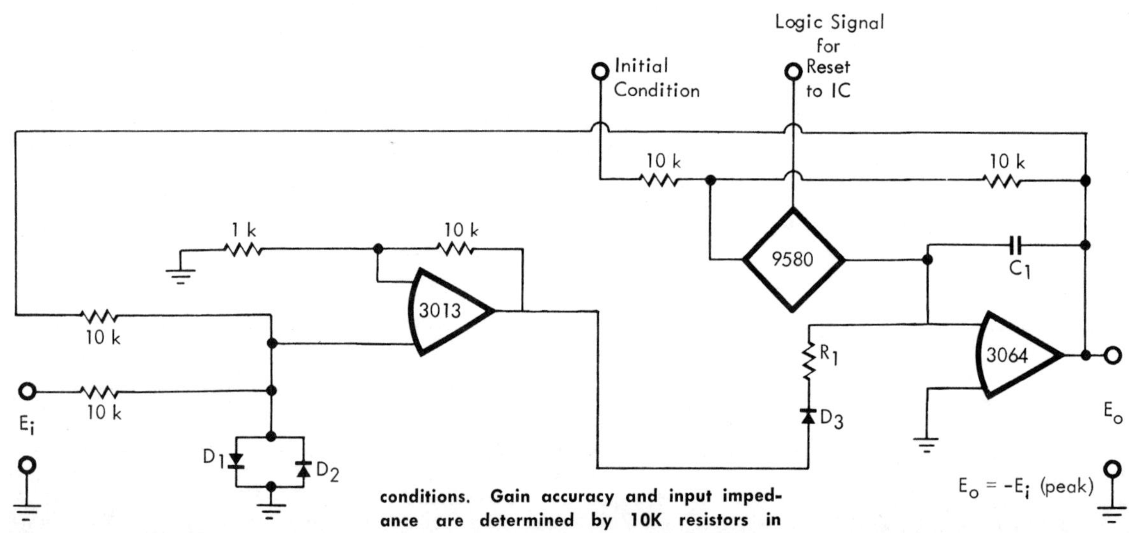

INVERTING PEAK DETECTOR—Uses Burr-Brown 9580 electronic switch and two opamps to provide high-speed reset to initial conditions. Gain accuracy and input impedance are determined by 10K resistors in summing network. Can reset to either negative or positive initial conditions, permitting use as peak detector even if some maxima are negative and some positive.—Operational Amplifiers, Burr-Brown Research, Tucson, Ariz., LI-327, 1969, p 43.

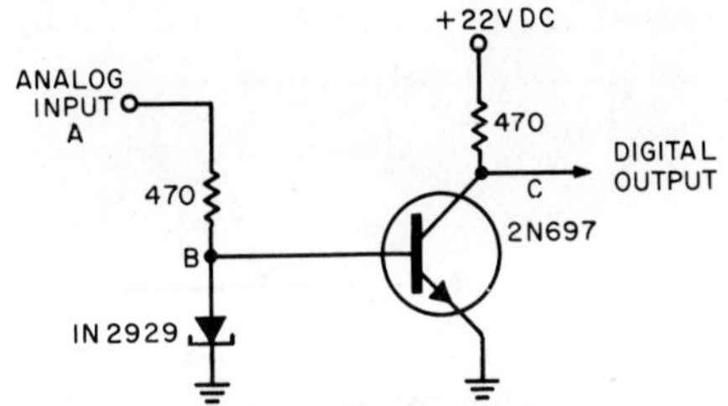

ANALOG VOLTAGE SENSOR—Action of positive-going analog input voltage on tunnel diode makes transistor saturate, at predetermined input point, so as to switch transistor on for positive halves of input signal cycles.—Tunnel Diode-Transistor Level Sensor (Circuit Digest), *Electronic Design*, March 2, 1964, p 58.

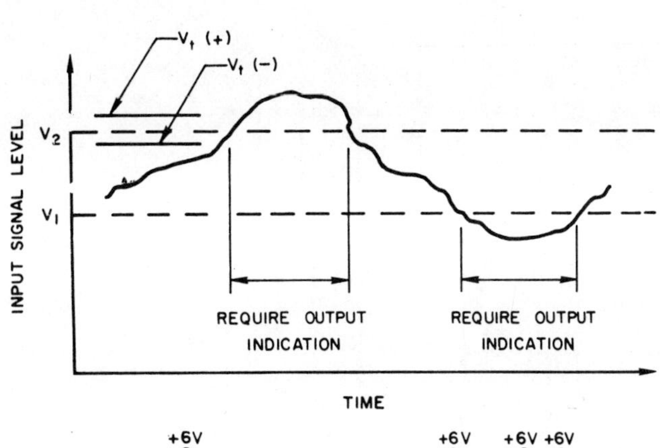

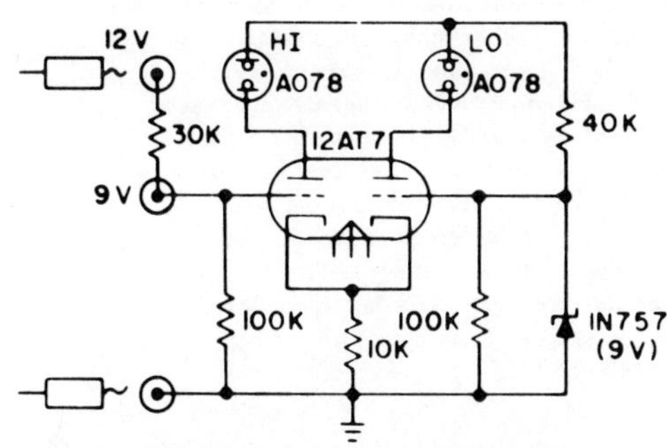

EQUAL VOLTAGE TEST—For balancing two voltage-divider points in production testing. Only 200-mV difference in either direction causes variation in illumination level of lamps. Any reference from zero to dissipation level of tube can be used instead of 9 V shown.—E. Bauman, "Applications of Neon Lamps and Gas Discharge Tubes," Signalite, Neptune, N.J., p 145.

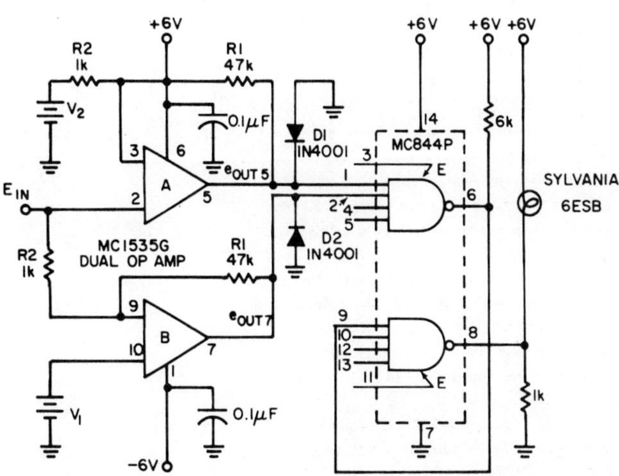

ENVELOPE DETECTOR—Pilot lamp is turned on when input signal voltage is above upper limit V2 or below lower limit V1. Amount of hysteresis about each limit is function of R1 and R2, and is 69 mV for limits of 2.5 V and 3.5 V.—K. Wolf, Signal-Level Envelope Detector Uses Dual Operational Amplifier, *Electronic Design*, Feb. 1, 1969, p 78 and 80.

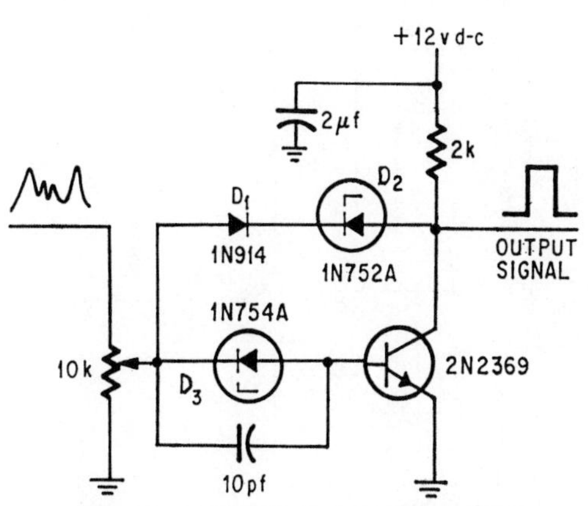

THRESHOLD DETECTOR—Zener diodes clamp collector of transistor at 0.5 V, just outside saturation region, to eliminate turnoff delay and thereby give faster rise and fall times, of order of 30 ns. Threshold value is independent of temperature if temperature coefficient of D1 is matched to D2 and that of D3 is matched to base-emitter junction of Q1. Potentiometer sets threshold level.—B. Fugit, Collector Clamping Improves Threshold Detector, *Electronics*, Sept. 30, 1968, p 81.

5 MV—10 V LEVEL DETECTOR—High-sensitivity voltage level detector, using only tunnel diode and two transistor switches, requires no diode limiters to protect from overload. To sample input, Q2 is turned off by sample pulse. Q1 will switch only if input signal is positive during sampling time. With minor changes, circuit can be used as transient detector or level comparator.—A. J. Welty, Tunnel-Diode Level Detector Is Ultra-Sensitive, *Electronic Design*, Jan. 4, 1965, p 73–74.

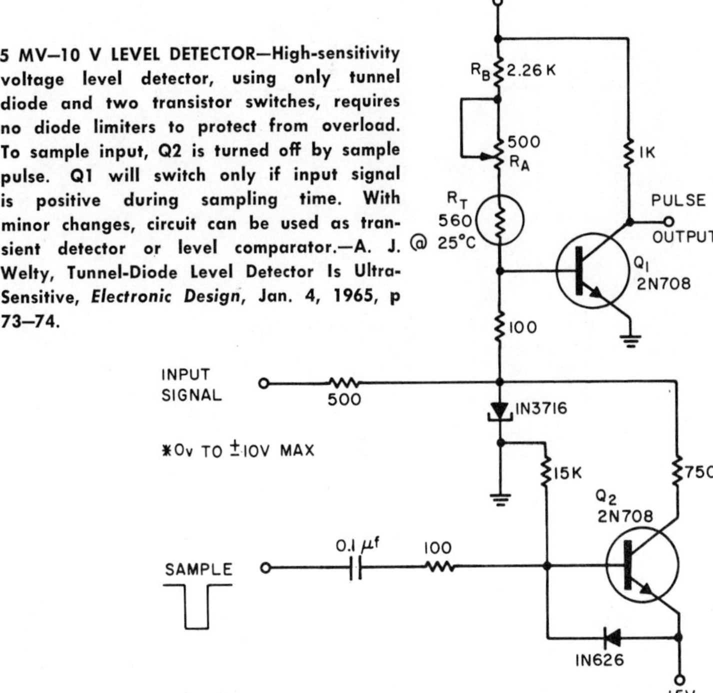

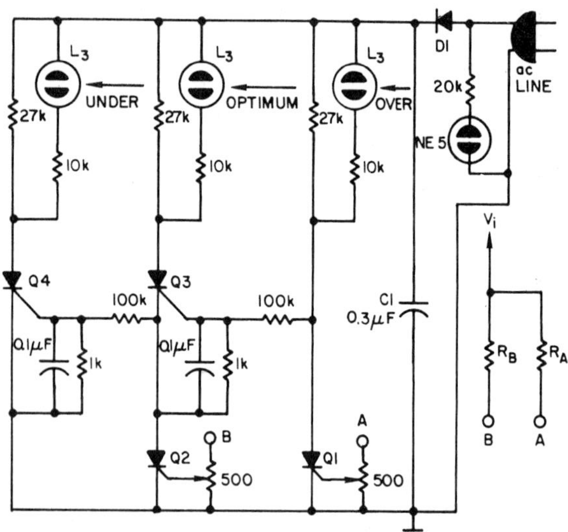

AMBIGUITY—Three-level voltage monitor automatically turns off lower-level indicator lamps when lamp at higher level is triggered, to eliminate ambiguity in display. Uses C106B1 scr's and any suitable neon lamps. If circuit is to monitor 100 V d-c to tolerance of 2 V, RA and RB are chosen to make Q1 and Q2 fire when Vi is 102 V and 98 V. Technique can be extended to more levels by adding more sections like middle one (Q2-Q3-L3).—A. Prokop, SCR Threshold Detector Eliminates Ambiguities, *Electronic Design*, Sept. 1, 1969, p 104 and 106.

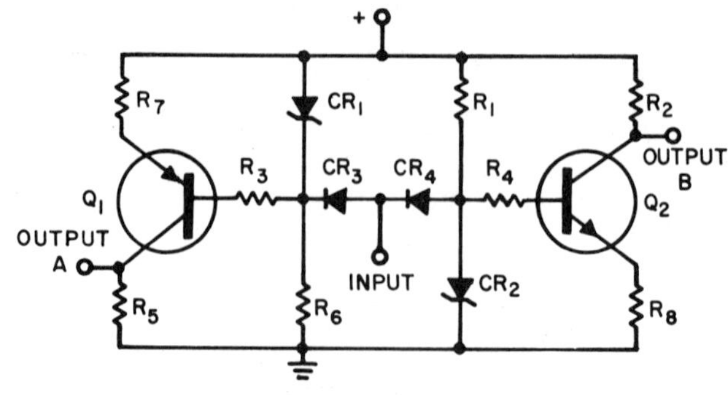

PULSE AMPLITUDE-POLARITY SORTER—Q1 detects positive input pulses and amplifies them sufficiently to drive several output circuits, while Q2 similarly detects and amplifies negative input pulses. Transistor types are not critical, as long as Q1 is pnp and Q2 is npn. Zenérs CR1 and CR2 are chosen to maintain associated transistors back-biased until incoming pulse makes transistors conduct. Other two diodes simply provide isolation. Signal-level adjustments are best made by using variable resistors for R1 and R6. Pulses of different levels can be sorted by using several circuits in parallel and adjusting each for different level. Other resistor values are not critical.—F. W. Kear, Pulse-Sorter Network Detects, Amplifies Bi-Polar Signals, *Electronic Design*, Aug. 30, 1965, p 48–49.

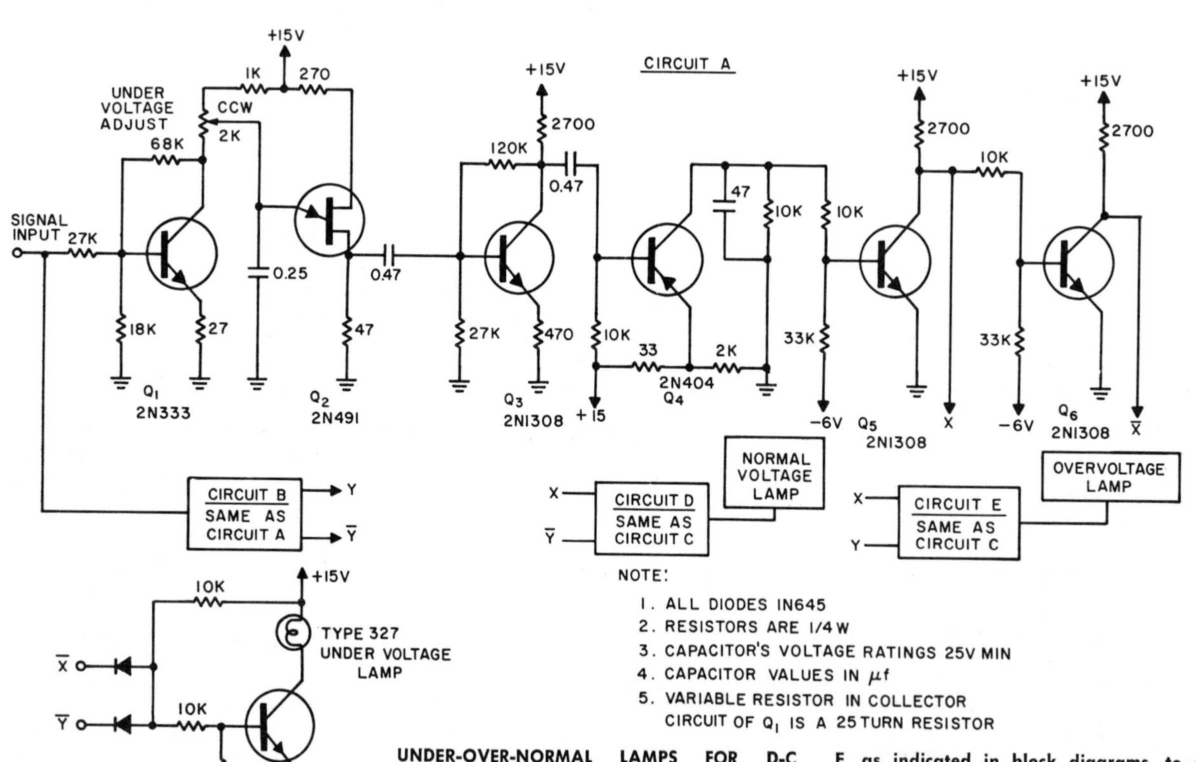

UNDER-OVER-NORMAL LAMPS FOR D-C VOLTAGE MONITOR—Range of operation is 0.5 V to 8 V for values given. Monitor uses two identical channels containing circuit A having six transistors. These two channels feed circuit C (lower left), D, and E, as indicated in block diagrams, to drive indicating lamps. Article describes operation of circuit.—G. W. Gault, Simple Voltage Monitor Increases Sensitivity, *Electronic Design*, Sept. 14, 1964, p 70.

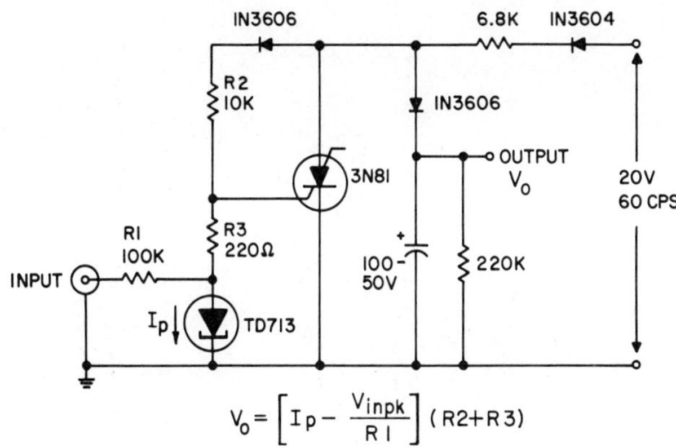

PEAK SENSING WITH TUNNEL DIODE—Used to measure peak voltage of waveform that repeats well above 60 times per second. 100-μF capacitor is charged by half-wave rectified 60-Hz voltage that also is applied to anode of scs 3N81. When input waveform brings tunnel diode to its peak point current, diode switches and turns on scs, terminating charging of capacitor. In negative half-cycle, capacitor discharges slightly but is recharged on next positive half-cycle. Output voltage is thus proportional to peak of input waveform.—W. R. Spofford, Jr., Applications For The New Low Cost TD700 Series Tunnel Diodes, General Electric, Syracuse, N.Y., No. 90.66, 3/67, p 10.

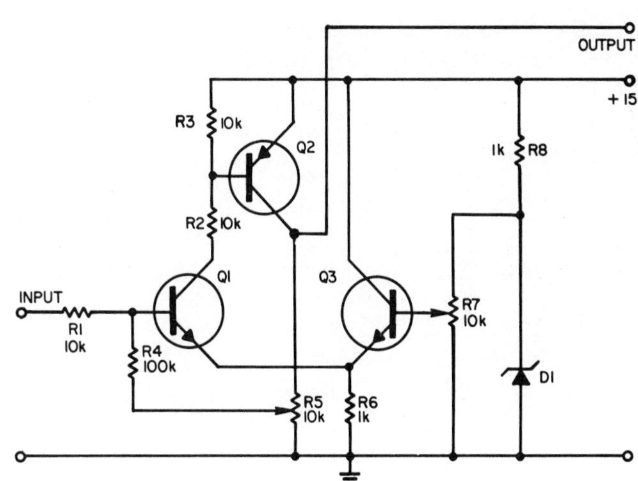

ADJUSTABLE HYSTERESIS—Differential comparator and zener provide independently adjustable voltage trip point and hysteresis. Q1 and Q3 can be 2N3904 or equivalent, Q2 2N3096 or equivalent, and D1 1N708. R7 varies reference level, for changing trip point from 0.7 V to 5 V, while R5 changes hysteresis.—R. Billon, Level Detector Has Independently Adjustable Hysteresis and Trip Point, *Electronic Design*, Oct. 11, 1967, p 98.

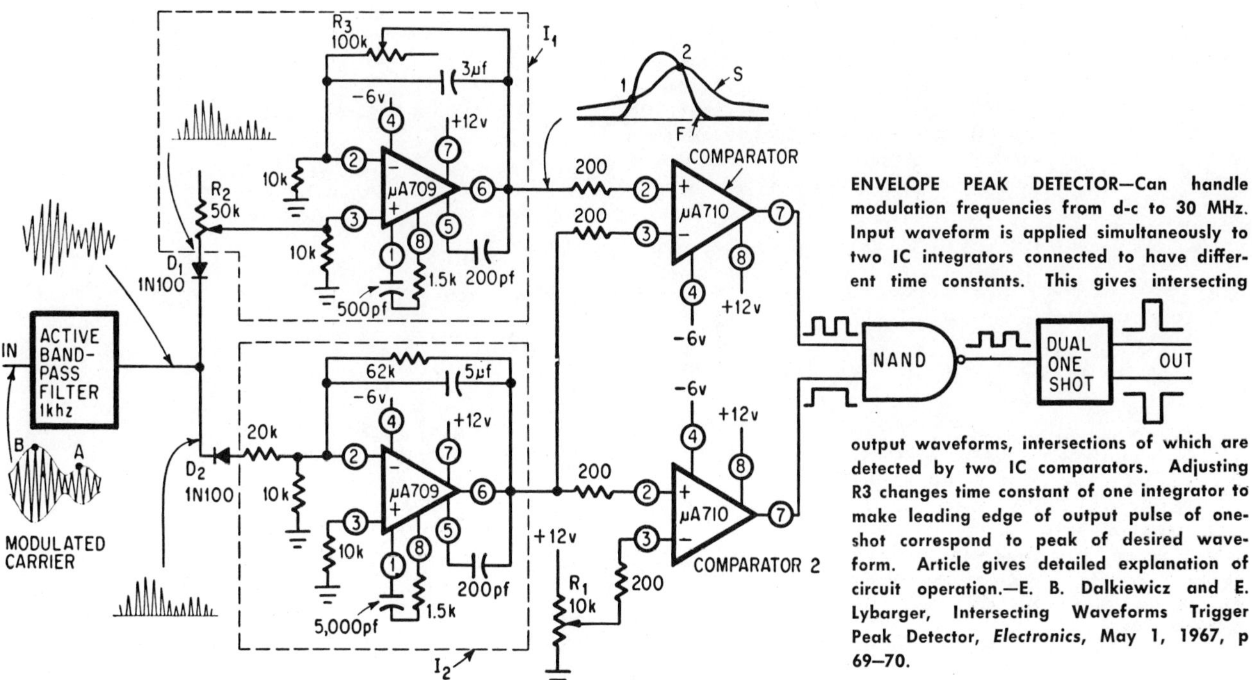

ENVELOPE PEAK DETECTOR—Can handle modulation frequencies from d-c to 30 MHz. Input waveform is applied simultaneously to two IC integrators connected to have different time constants. This gives intersecting output waveforms, intersections of which are detected by two IC comparators. Adjusting R3 changes time constant of one integrator to make leading edge of output pulse of one-shot correspond to peak of desired waveform. Article gives detailed explanation of circuit operation.—E. B. Dalkiewicz and E. Lybarger, Intersecting Waveforms Trigger Peak Detector, *Electronics*, May 1, 1967, p 69–70.

MULTIPLE-VOLTAGE MONITOR—Simple comparison amplifier and summing junction are used to compare junction voltage with reference voltage that is actually system ground or zero. Used for monitoring system having many power supplies with voltage levels of both polarities. Any change in one of monitored voltage levels will unbalance comparison amplifier and make warning lamp glow. Voltage measurements must then be made to identify defective supply. Sensing accuracy is 5%.—R. C. Gerdes, Voltage Sensor Monitors Multiple Power Supply Outputs, "400 Ideas for Design Selected from Electronic Design," Hayden Book Co., N.Y., 1964, p 216.

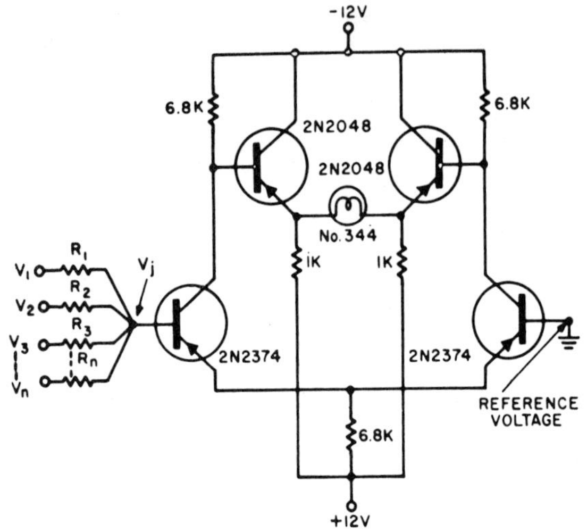

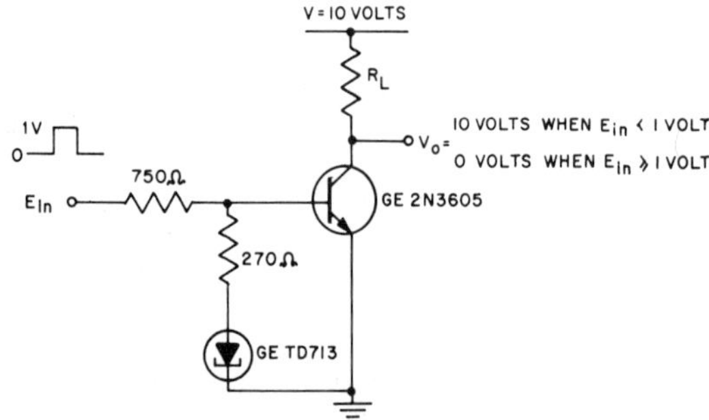

TUNNEL-DIODE LEVEL DETECTOR—Adjusting value of input resistor will make tunnel diode switch at any desired threshold voltage, and turn back off when input voltage is dropped to zero.—W. R. Spofford, Jr., Applications For The New Low Cost TD 700 Series Tunnel Diodes, General Electric, Syracuse, N.Y., No. 90.66, 1967, p 8.

LOGIC-LEVEL LAMP—Lamp lights when probe is touched to terminal having pulse amplitude or d-c level above 0.7 V. Speeds trouble-shooting of digital circuits by eliminating need to look at cro or meter. Lamp is mounted directly on probe. Light-emitting diodes such as HP5082-4400 in series with 470-ohm resistor may be used in place of lamp for faster response. Level detector Q1 triggers 1-ms mono mvbr Q2-Q3.—J. M. Firth, Go/No Go Circuit Gives Visual Indication of RTL Logic Level, *Electronic Design*, Feb. 15, 1970, p 88.

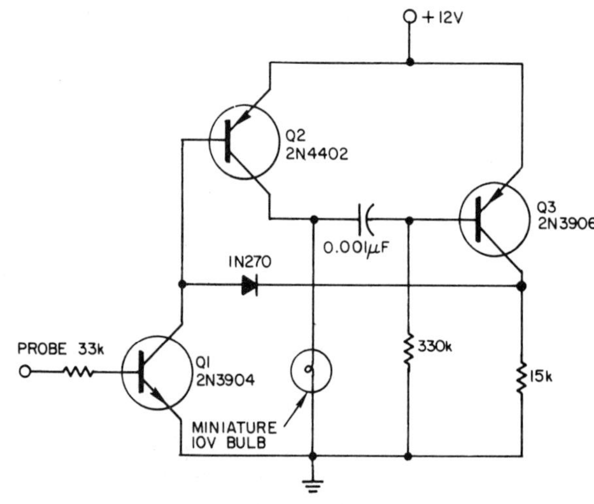

HOLDING PEAK VOLTAGE—Will hold peak voltage of short-duration analog signal for any required period up to several hundred ms. Permits use of pen recorders having slow response. Value of C1 determines holding period. First three transistors form combined Schmitt trigger and one-shot.—P. P. Tong, Peak-Hold Circuit, *EEE*, March 1967, p 164 and 166.

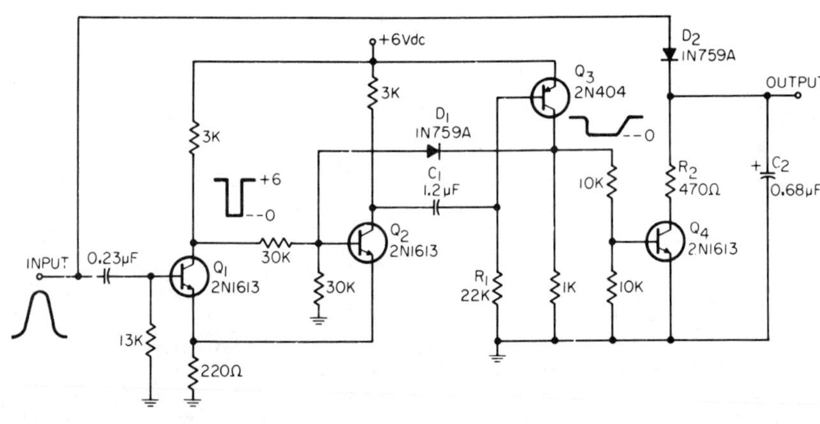

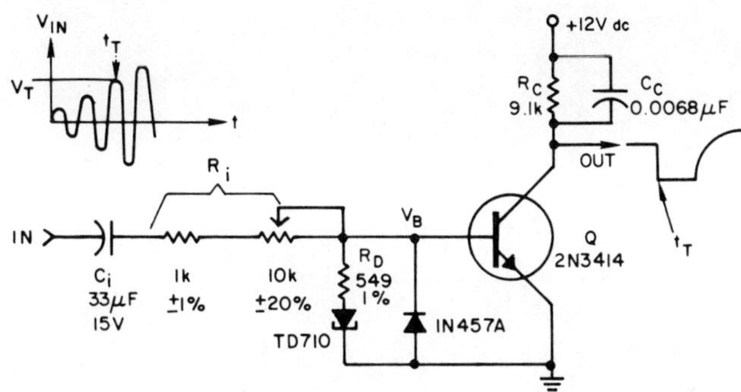

10-KHZ SINE-WAVE PEAK DETECTOR—Simple tunnel-diode threshold detector senses peak values exceeding preset level. Output voltage is near supply voltage while input is low, and drops to about zero when input exceeds threshold value controlled by setting of Ri.—D. B. Heckman, Sense Signal Levels with a Tunnel Diode, *Electronic Design*, Feb. 1, 1969, p 48–51.

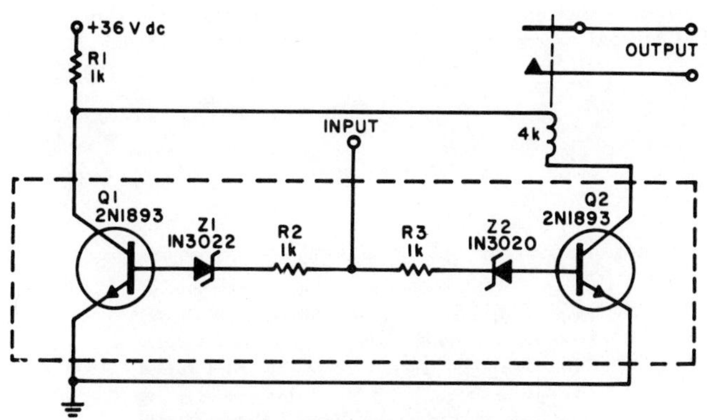

VOLTAGE LIMIT MONITOR—Relay contacts are closed as long as d-c input voltage is within specified limits. If voltage rises above limit, Q1 conducts and shorts out relay coil. If voltage drops below limit, both transistors cut off and relay drops out. Zeners determine voltage limits.—O. Tedenstig, Monitor DC Levels with a Simple Circuit, *Electronic Design*, June 6, 1968, p 110 and 112.

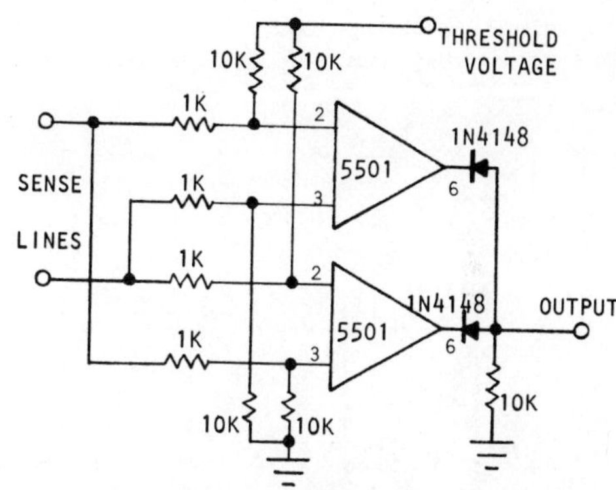

DUAL SENSE AMPLIFIER—Uses two 5501 analog comparators to indicate when any unbalance or voltage difference exists on two input lines. Output is positive regardless of which input line is more positive. Noise on lines does not cause false output indication.—Applying the Model 5501 Monolithic Analog Comparator, Optical Electronics, Tucson, Ariz., No. 10147.

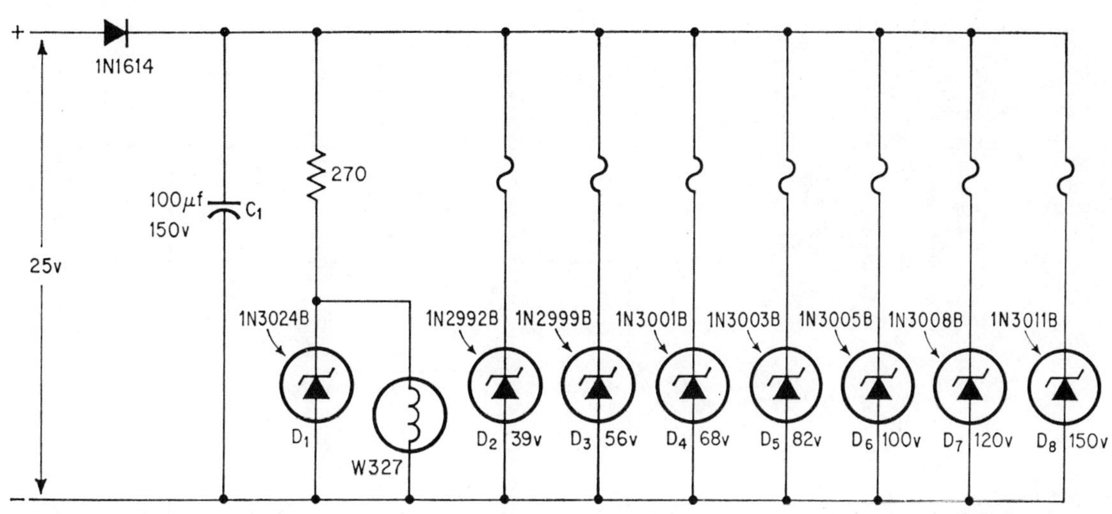

MONITORING POWER-LINE TRANSIENTS—Provides continuous surveillance of 28-V d-c supply line, storing approximate voltage magnitude of largest transient spike. Each zener is in series with sensitive 10-ohm 0.066-A instrument fuse, and each zener-fuse combination corresponds to detected voltage level about 5 V above zener breakdown voltage. Detection levels for zeners shown are 44, 61, 73, 87, 105, 125, and 155 V. 37-V spike on 28-V line means total peak of 65 V, which blows fuses for D2 and D3 because they avalanche into conduction. Operator then knows that spike was greater than 61 V but less than 73 V required to blow fuse for D4.—O. Pitzalis, Jr., Zener Circuit Detects Transients in Power Lines, *Electronics*, May 12, 1969, p 111.

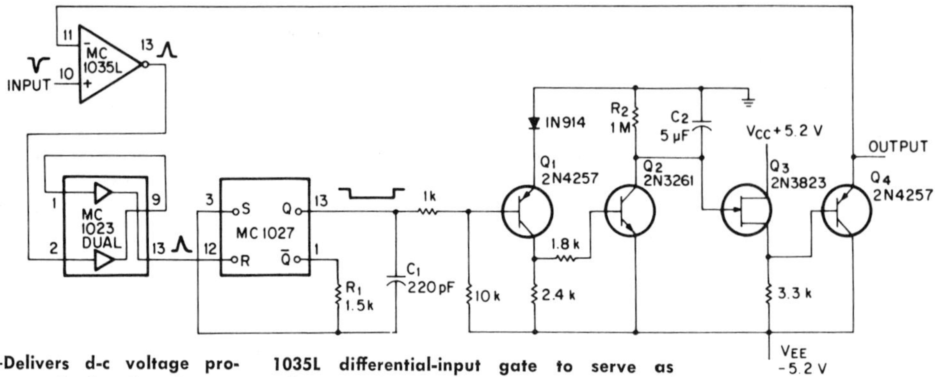

PEAK DETECTOR—Delivers d-c voltage proportional to peak amplitude of pulses as narrow as 10 ns. Negative output voltage, proportional to voltage across C2, is fed back to inverting input of Motorola MC-1035L differential-input gate to serve as arbitrary reference against which negative-going input pulse is compared. Reference rises with each input pulse until equilibrium is reached and C2 stops charging. Output is independent of pulse width.—M. J. Prickett, Peak Detector for Very Narrow Pulses, *EEE*, June 1970, p 92 and 94.

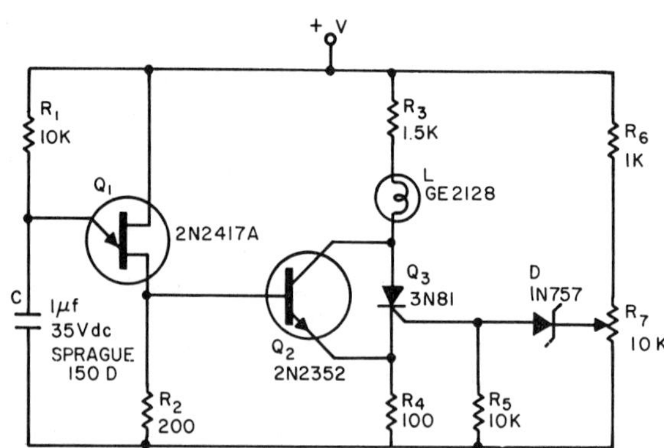

CURE FOR VOLTAGE-DROPPING HYSTERESIS—Use of ujt oscillator Q1 in voltage indicator overcomes hysteresis effect. Circuit will trigger off within 2% of desired level for triggering on, over wide temperature range. Supply voltage is 28 V. Lamp glows when voltage reaches desired level. If two circuits are used, with relays in place of lamps, they can be used to remove power whenever voltage goes above or below 2% of desired trigger level determined by R7.—J. V. Crowling, Solid-State Voltage Indicator Overcomes Hysteresis Problem, *Electronic Design*, Dec. 21, 1964, p 51–52.

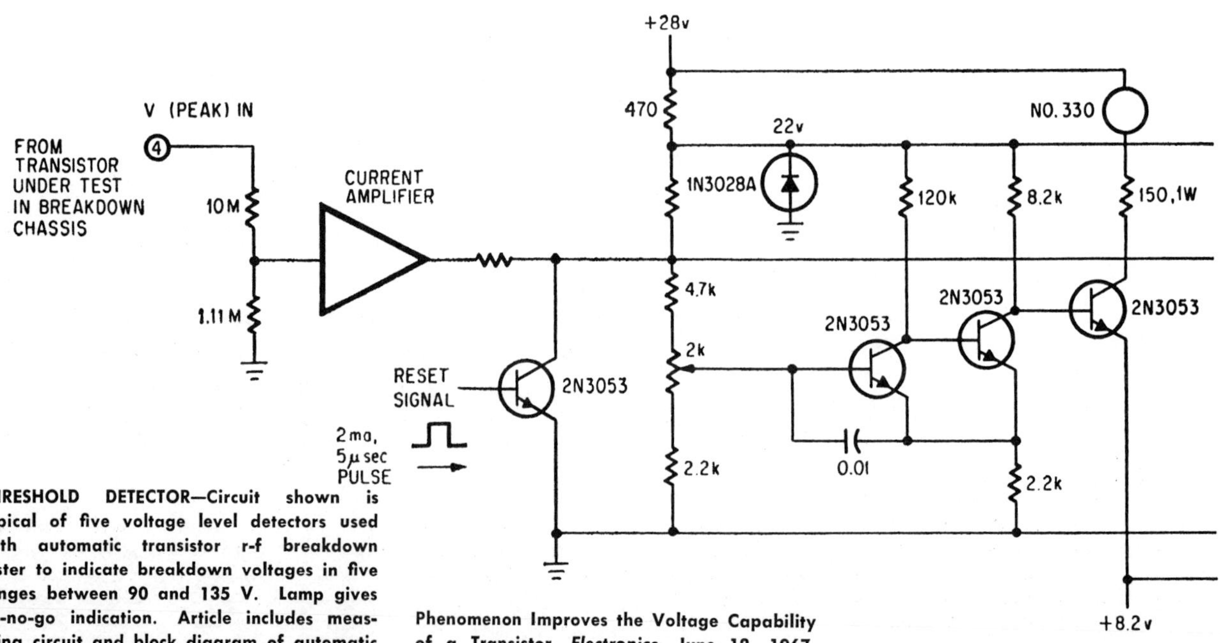

THRESHOLD DETECTOR—Circuit shown is typical of five voltage level detectors used with automatic transistor r-f breakdown tester to indicate breakdown voltages in five ranges between 90 and 135 V. Lamp gives go-no-go indication. Article includes measuring circuit and block diagram of automatic production tester.—P. Schiff, R-F Breakdown Phenomenon Improves the Voltage Capability of a Transistor, *Electronics*, June 12, 1967, p 97–101.

HYSTERESIS CIRCUIT DESIGN—Article gives mathematical procedure requiring calculation of only four resistor values to obtain desired upper and lower threshold points on hysteresis curve. Design approach assumes opamp input impedance is much larger than source impedance, and output impedance much smaller than load impedance, with amplifier switching state when differential input voltage is 0 V. Values shown are for 6.2 V upper threshold and −0.7 V lower threshold, with 3 V input required for switching amplifier from low to high state and 0.5 V for high to low state.—W. A. Cooke, A Simplified Design Approach for Hysteresis Circuits, *Electronics*, Nov. 10, 1969, p 106.

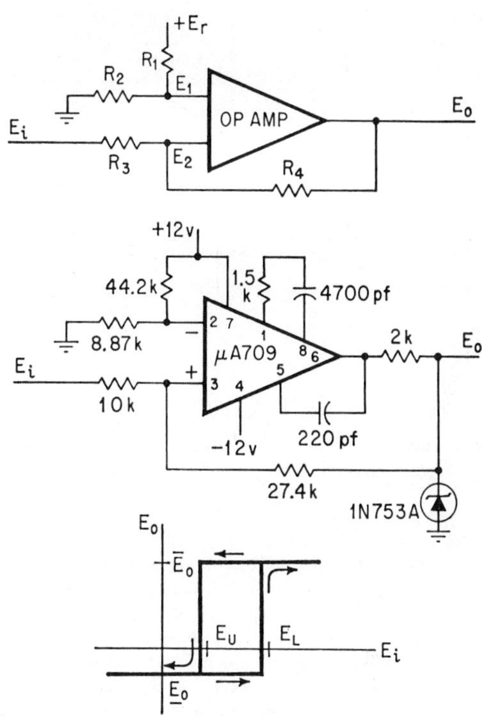

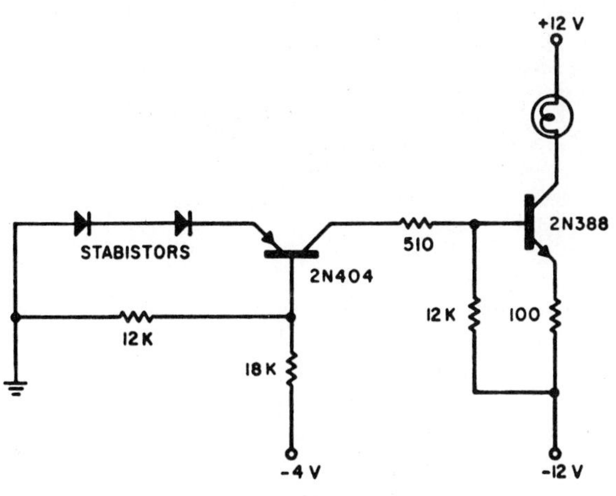

THREE-VOLTAGE MONITOR—Lamp glows only when all three supply voltages are present in typical pnp digital system having negative collector and clamp supplies, and positive bias supply. For npn system, use complementary version of circuit. Absence of any one voltage extinguishes lamp, giving true AND function. Stabistors provide tight control over error level of clamp voltage.—D. Chin, DC Presence Indicator Checks Three Voltages, "400 Ideas for Design Selected from Electronic Design," Hayden Book Co., N.Y., 1964, p 155.

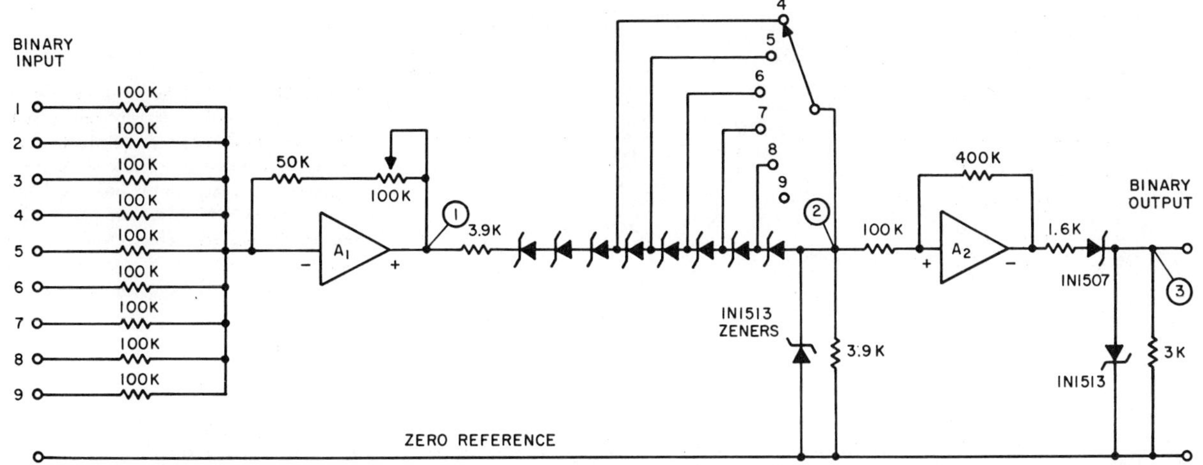

NINE-INPUT LEVEL DETECTOR—Simple opamp circuit with diode limiting serves in place of expensive binary logic. Binary output depends on whether each binary input is off (0 V for logical zero) or on (−11 V d-c for logical one). Output is binary one only when more than preselected number of inputs is one. Developed in connection with design of radio telescope.—W. Leroy Gahm, Binary Level Detector for Input Step-Voltages, *Electronic Design*, Oct. 26, 1964, p 50.

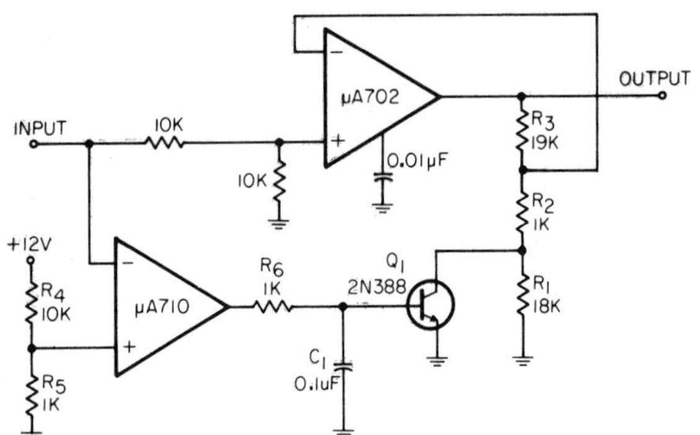

AUTOMATIC RANGE SELECTOR—Electronic range-changing switch for voltmeter uses two opamps to compare input voltage with fixed reference derived from divider R4-R5. With values shown, ranges provided are 0–1 V and 0–10 V full-scale. When input voltage exceeds first range, output of opamp μA710 goes negative and shuts off Q1, decreasing gain by factor of 10 for upper range. Isolation diode can be added to Q1 for driving scale indicator showing which range is in use.—C. Becklein, Automatic Scaling Circuit Uses ICs, *EEE*, Dec. 1966, p 118.

VOLTAGE SENSING—When input voltage to be sensed exceeds reference voltage applied by external source, ujt fires and produces output pulse that can be used to fire scr or other pulse-sensitive device. R1 adjusts trigger level. Trigger current required is less than 5 μA. Long-term voltage stability is 10 mV, and short-term is 1 mV.—T. P. Sylvan, The Unijunction Transistor Characteristics and Applications, General Electric, Syracuse, N.Y., No. 90.10, 1965, p 79.

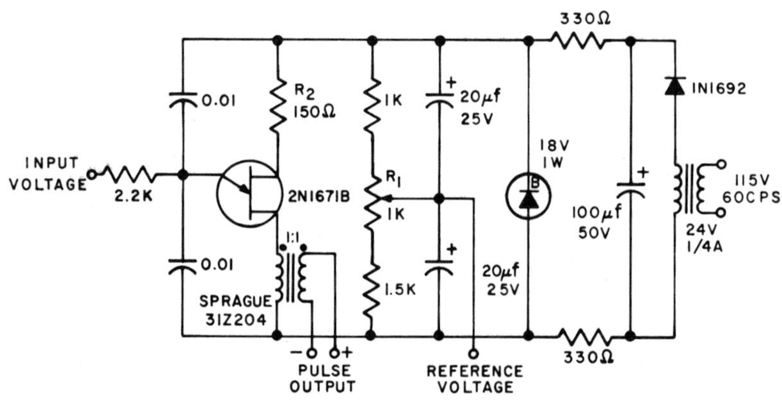

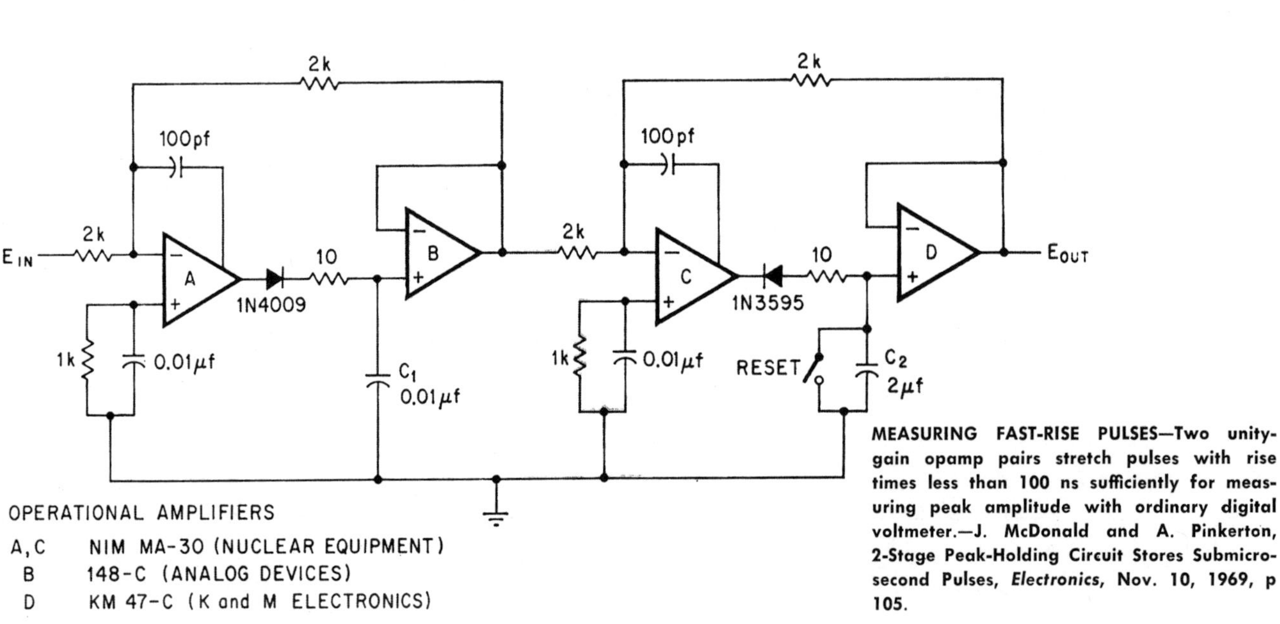

MEASURING FAST-RISE PULSES—Two unity-gain opamp pairs stretch pulses with rise times less than 100 ns sufficiently for measuring peak amplitude with ordinary digital voltmeter.—J. McDonald and A. Pinkerton, 2-Stage Peak-Holding Circuit Stores Submicrosecond Pulses, *Electronics*, Nov. 10, 1969, p 105.

NOTE: To locate additional circuits in the category of this chapter, use the index at the back of this book. Check also the author's "Sourcebook of Electronic Circuits," published by McGraw-Hill in 1968.

CHAPTER 98
Voltage Reference Circuits

5-V REFERENCE SUPPLY—Circuit actually gives highly stable 6.7 V, but this can be adjusted to exactly 5 V by R5 in precision-type output control circuit. Transistor Q4 serves as temperature-compensating voltage-regulator diode. Article gives construction and adjustment details.—C. D. Todd, Stable, Low-Cost Reference Power Supplies, *Electronics World*, Dec. 1967, p 39–41 and 79.

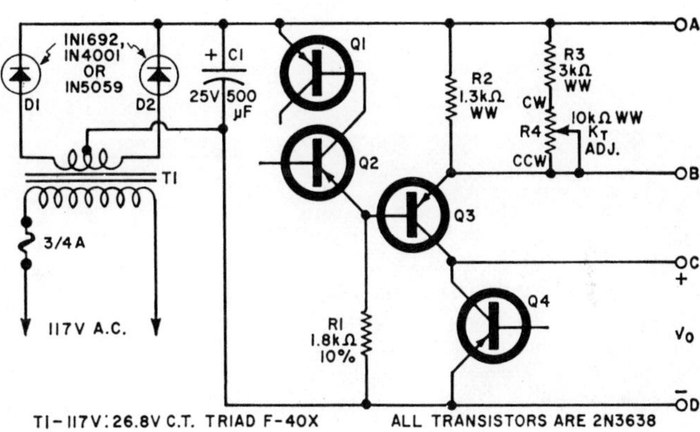

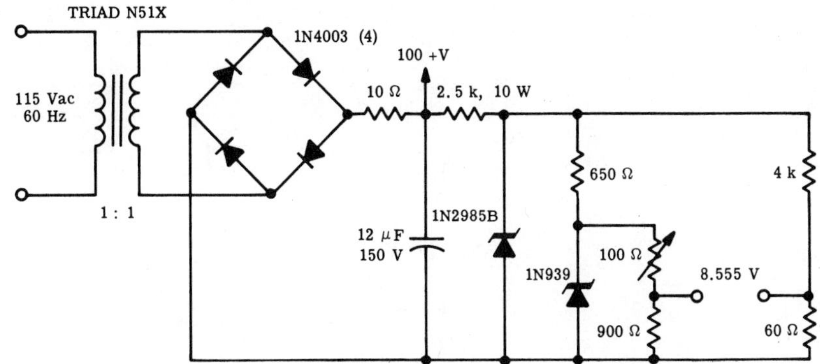

CASCADED ZENER REFERENCE—Provides reference voltage supply of 8.555 V, which changes only 0.0001% for 10% input voltage change. 1N2985B 22-V diode absorbs large changes in input, permitting operation of second diode over linear range.—"Zener Diode Handbook," Motorola, Phoenix, Ariz., 1967, p 6–19.

−4 KV BRIDGE REFERENCE—Diode bridge coupled to astable mvbr clamps random-frequency random-width digital input pulses to d-c level without distortion. Used to unblank crt where grid is biased at −4 kV below ground.—W. E. Peterson, D-c Restorer Clamps Random Pulses to a Reference, *Electronics*, July 7, 1969, p 106.

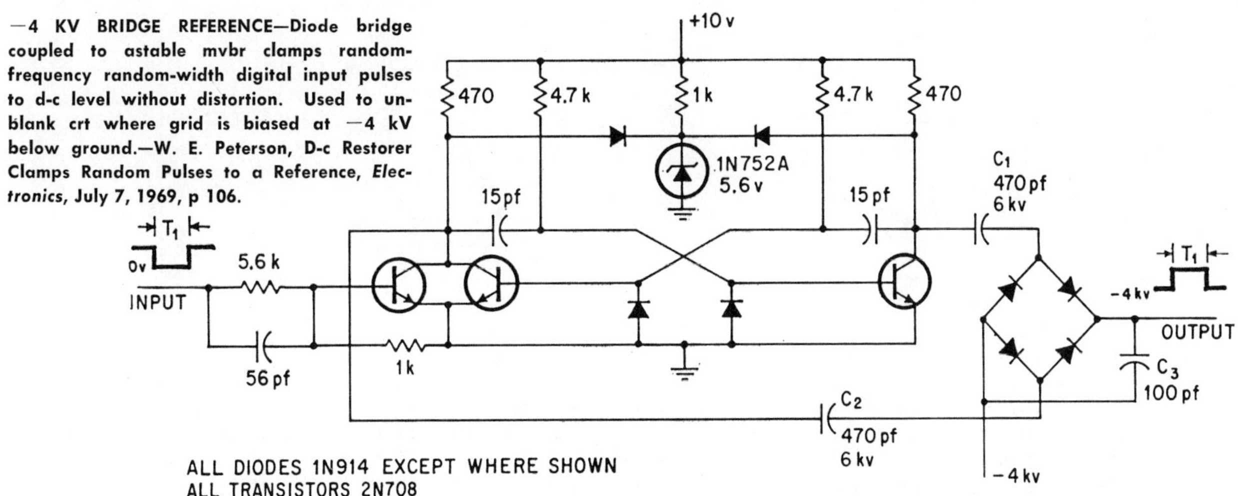

10-V REFERENCE SUPPLY—Provides constant voltage, independent of temperature, for calibrating lab or shop instruments and for monitoring very small voltage changes. Stability is achieved by using low-cost transistors as temperature-compensated voltage regulator diodes. Article gives construction and adjustment details, and chopper circuits for making a-c measurements.—C. D. Todd, Stable, Low-Cost Reference Power Supplies, *Electronics World*, Dec. 1967, p 39–41 and 79.

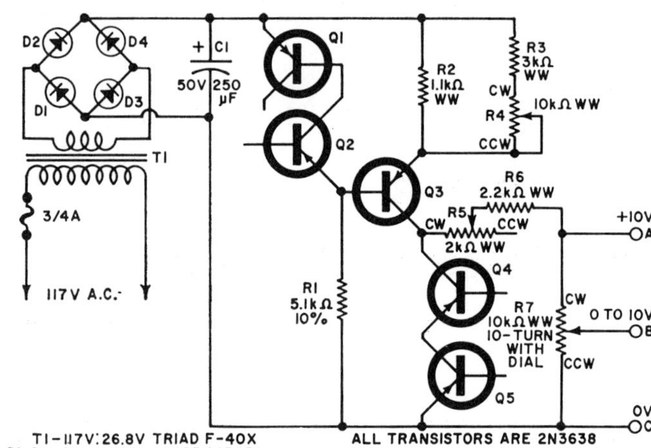

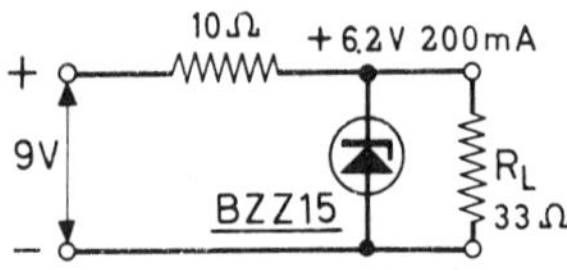

6.2 V D-C WITH POWER ZENER—Converts nonstabilized 9-V d-c supply to 6.2 V with stabilization factor of 50:1. Diode must be mounted on heat sink. Hum and ripple from source are attenuated in same ratio.—"Zener Diodes and Their Applications," Philips, Pub. Dept., Elcoma Div., Eindhoven, The Netherlands, No. 17, 1966.

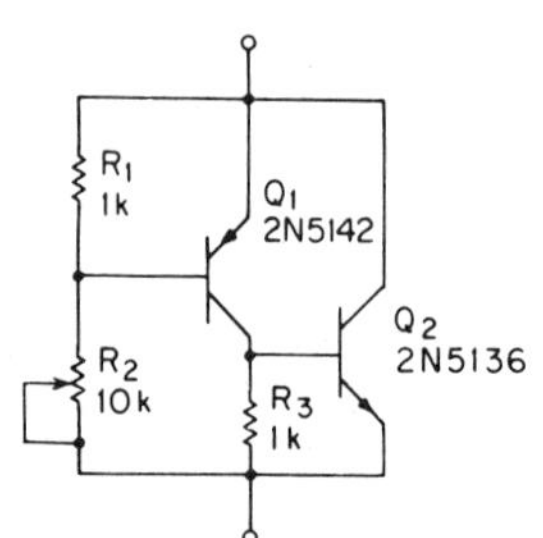

ADJUSTABLE ZENER—Performs functions of zener diode, with R2 determining operating voltage at any value above about 0.8 V. Impedance is maximum of 3 ohms below 5 V, where conventional zeners have considerably higher impedance and are not always readily available.—K. Karash, Adjustable, Low-Impedance Zener, *EEE*, March 1970, p 130.

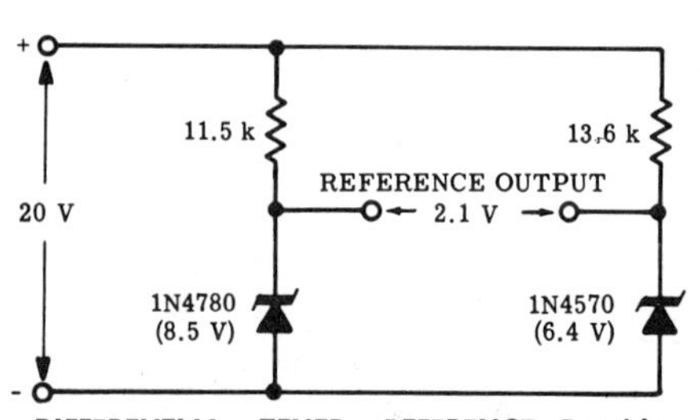

DIFFERENTIAL ZENER REFERENCE—Provides 2.1-V reference by utilizing difference between 8.5-V and 6.4-V zener references. Technique is particularly useful for temperature-compensated reference voltage sources. —"Zener Diode Handbook," Motorola, Phoenix, Ariz., 1967, p 6–19.

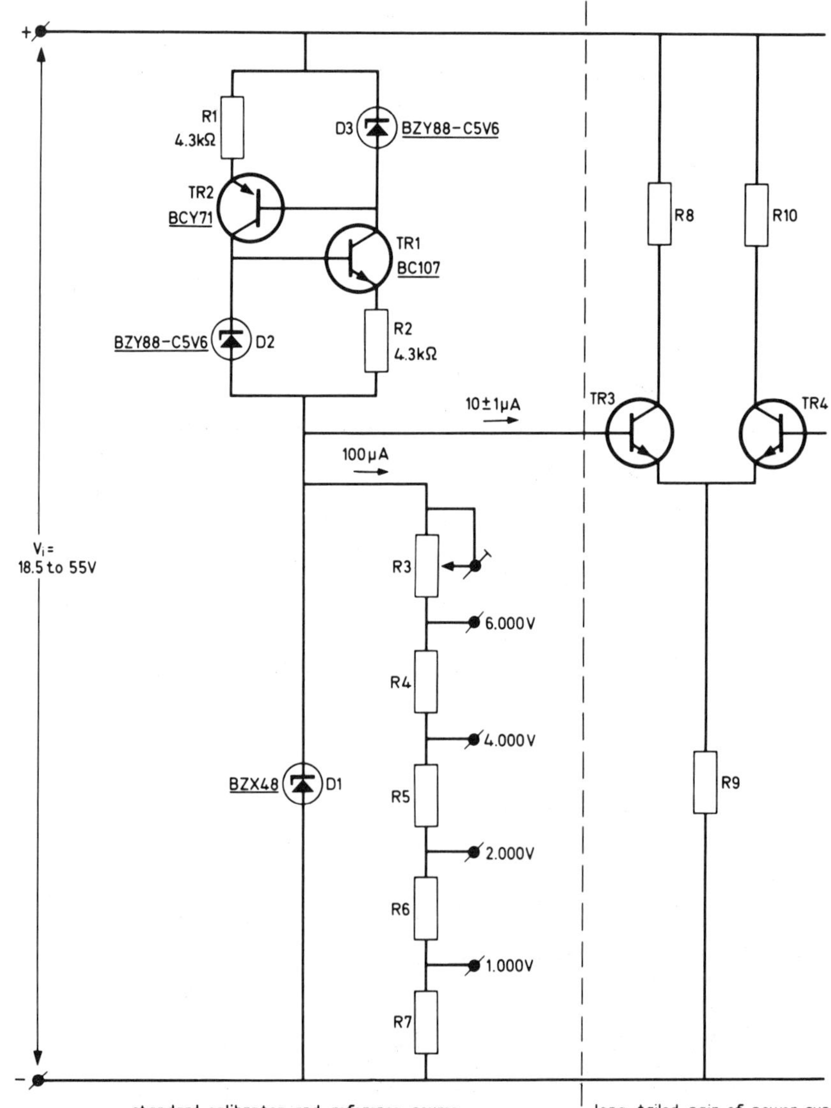

MULTIPLE-VOLTAGE REFERENCE SOURCE—Stabilizing circuit at left of dashed line, using zener D1 in series with two-transistor constant-current source, can be incorporated between differential amplifier and any supply between 18.5 and 55 V d-c, for excellent voltage and temperature stability. When D1 is changed, R3 can be adjusted to give same reference voltages and 6.5 V d-c across entire resistor string R3-R7.—High Stability Reference Diodes BZX47 Family, Philips, Pub. Dept., Elcoma Div., Eindhoven, The Netherlands, No. 331, 1968.

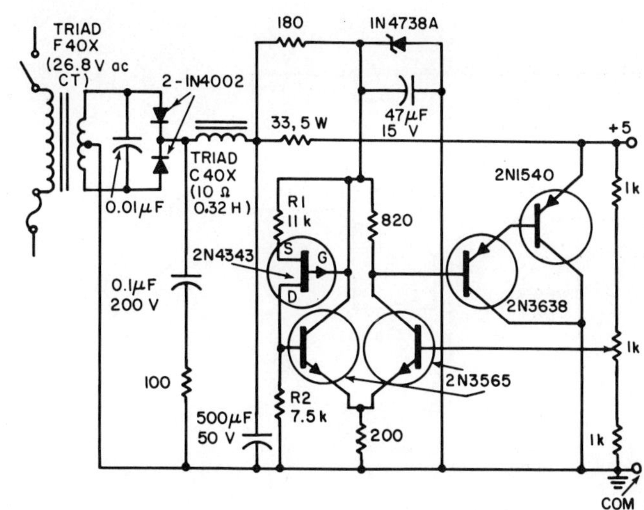

5-V FET REFERENCE—Use of p-channel 2N-4343 fet as constant-current source in combination with resistor gives much better temperature stability than convenional zener reference. Ouput impedance is below 0.1 ohm up to full load of 180 mA.—H. Olson, Stabilize Voltage Regulator by Replacing Zener with a FET, *Electronic Design*, Sept. 27, 1967, p 72 and 74.

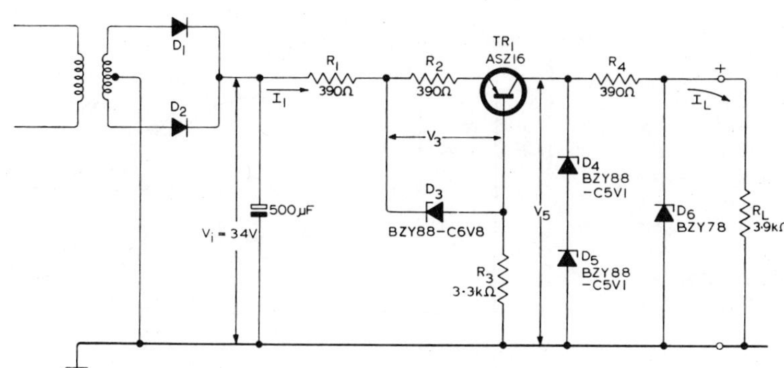

DIFFERENTIAL-AMPLIFIER SUPPLY—Provides highly stabilized output of about 5.3 V at 1.5 mA, as required by many differential amplifiers. Change of 20% in input voltage changes output less than 0.011%.—"Voltage Regulator (Zener) Diodes," Philips, Pub. Dept., Elcoma Div., Eindhoven, The Netherlands, Application Book, p 46.

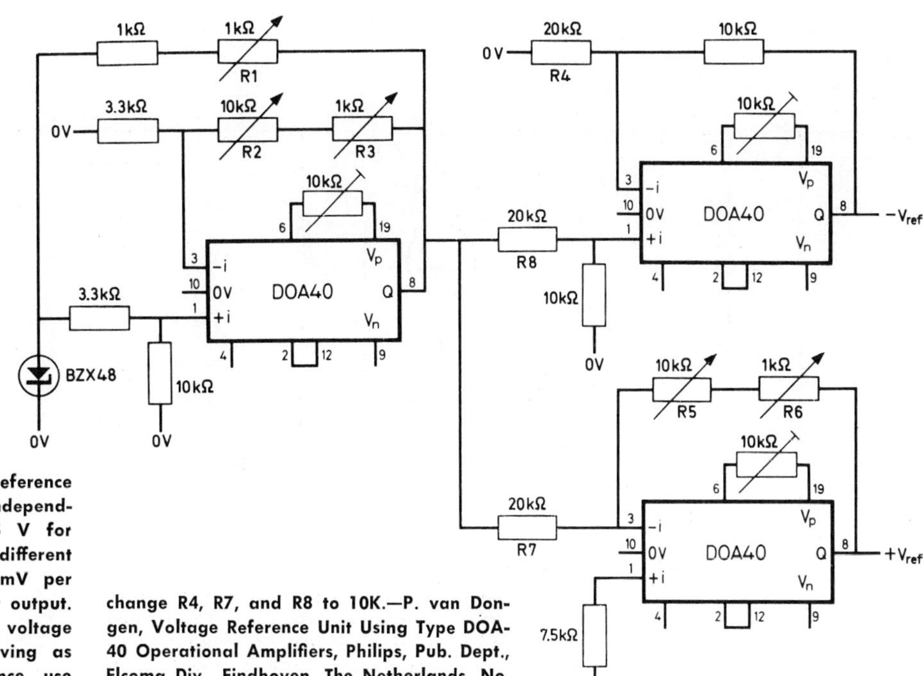

POSITIVE AND NEGATIVE 5 V—Reference voltages of opposite polarity are independently adjustable to same value, 5 V for resistor values shown, or 10 V with different values. Voltage drift is only 0.2 mV per deg C. Can deliver up to 5 mA per output. Uses three Philips DOA40 opamps as voltage comparators, with BZX48 zener serving as reference voltage. For 10 V reference, use 15-V positive and negative supplies and change R4, R7, and R8 to 10K.—P. van Dongen, Voltage Reference Unit Using Type DOA-40 Operational Amplifiers, Philips, Pub. Dept., Elcoma Div., Eindhoven, The Netherlands, No. 65.

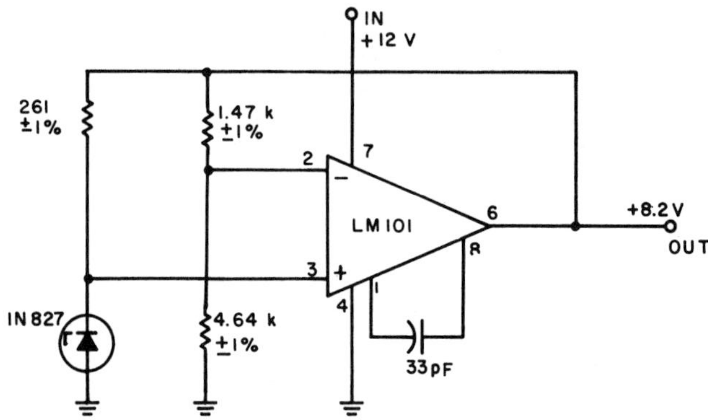

8.2 V D-C REFERENCE—Opamp and five components provide 0.01 mV per V d-c regulation for low-current applications (10 mA) such as for vco's in feedback loops and for precision digital-analog converters. Other output voltages are obtained by changing zener and resistor divider values.—F. R. Shirley and L. Vanderlosk, A Stable Voltage Reference Uses Only Six Components, *Electronic Design*, Jan. 18, 1968, p 128.

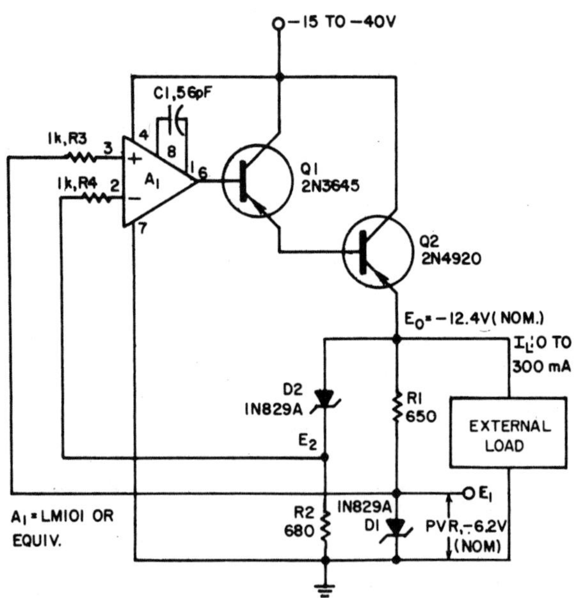

CONSTANT CURRENT FOR ZENER—Precision voltage obtained by sending constant current through temperature-compensated reference diode D1 is compared with voltage drop across R2 by differential amplifier A1. Amplifier adjusts its output to produce constant voltage drop across R2 for driving constant current through D2. Output voltage varies less than 2 mV for load currents of 0 to 300 mA and supply voltages of 15 to 40 V.—S. Miller, Precision Voltage Reference Combined with Voltage Regulator, *Electronic Design*, Sept. 1, 1969, p 102 and 104.

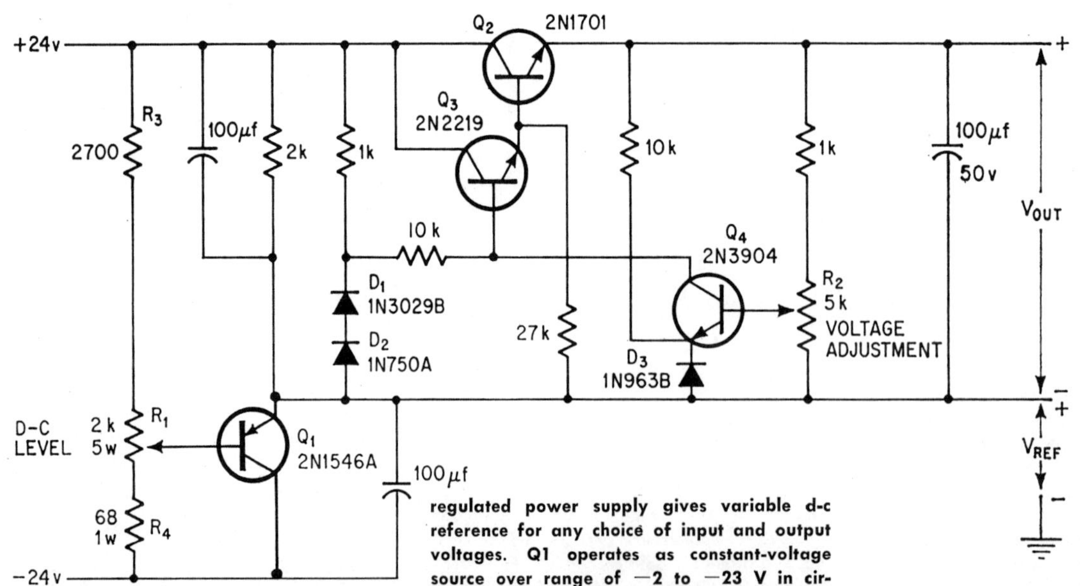

VARIABLE D-C REFERENCE—Addition of transistor Q1 to standard regulator circuit of regulated power supply gives variable d-c reference for any choice of input and output voltages. Q1 operates as constant-voltage source over range of −2 to −23 V in circuit shown, in which output voltage range is 15 to 24 V.—A. Steinman, Modified Regulator Yields Variable d-c Reference, *Electronics*, April 28, 1969, p 78.

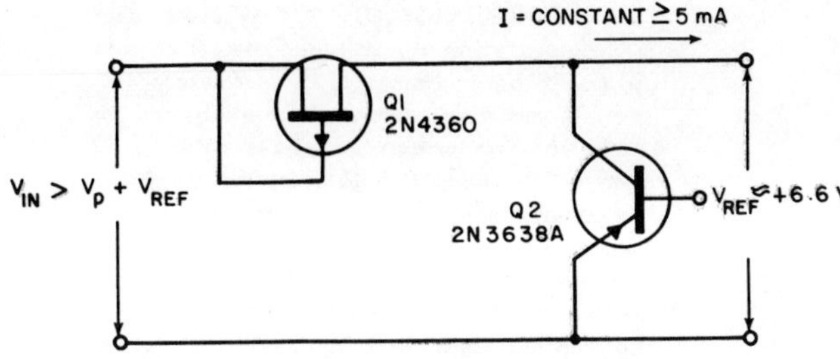

6 V AT 5 MA—Utilizes collector-emitter breakdown characteristic of bipolar transistor and constant-current property of junction fet to give low-cost reference source having output variation of only 3%.—E. J. Kennedy, Inexpensive 6-V Reference Is Also Temperature-Stable, *Electronic Design*, Nov. 8, 1967, p 112 and 114.

STANDARD-CELL REPLACEMENT — Provides constant output of about 4.5 V over temperature range of 30 to 60 C, is undamaged by intermittent short-circuits, and much more shock-resistant than Weston standard cell. D1-D6 are BZY88-C6V2 zeners and D7 is BZY88-C4V3. Values of R3 and R5 are determined by experiment as described in book. —"Voltage Regulator (Zener) Diodes," Philips, Pub. Dept., Elcoma Div., Eindhoven, The Netherlands, Application Book, p 26.

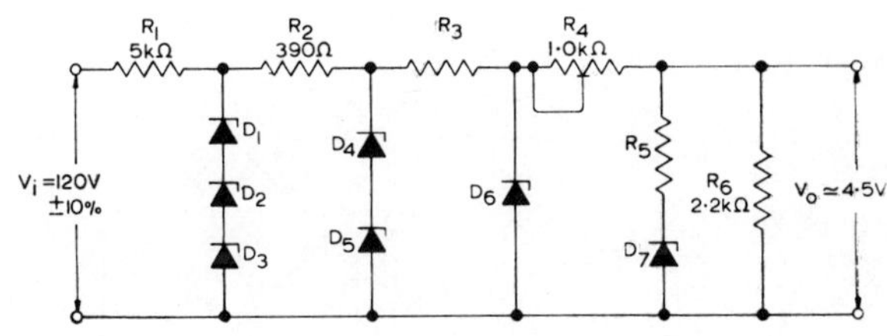

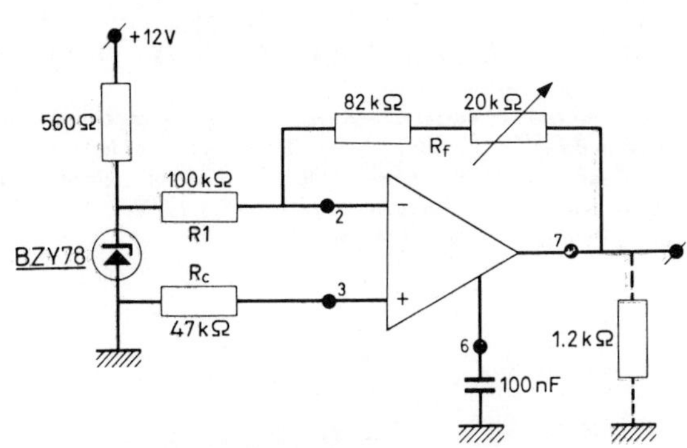

ADJUSTABLE REFERENCE—Uses Philips TAA-241 difference amplifier in circuit with 5.3 V zener. Can be adjusted to steady value close to −5 V with Rf. Rc provides compensation for bias current drift. Temperature drift of circuit is 0.5 mV per degree C. —J. Cohen and J. Oosterling, Applications of a Practical D. C. Difference Amplifier, Philips, Pub. Dept., Elcoma Div., Eindhoven, The Netherlands, No. 321, 1968.

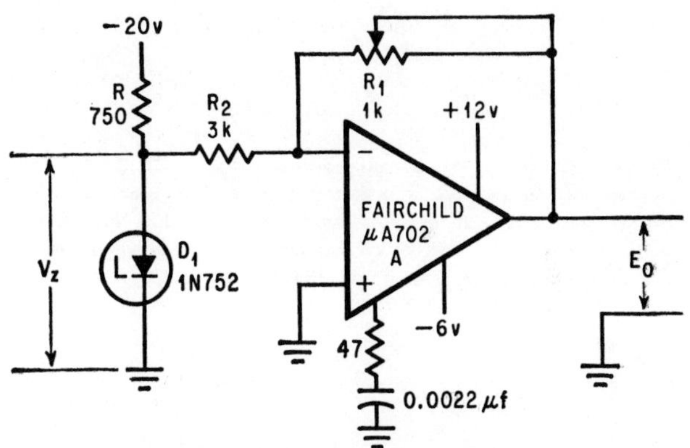

ADJUSTABLE REFERENCE VOLTAGE—IC op-amp and resistor divider translate zener diode reference to any desired precise voltage in range from −5 to +5 V, at low cost. Useful when required voltage reference is low, as for powering thermistor bridge. R1 adjusts reference voltage.—J. Althouse, IC Amplifier Provides Variable Reference Voltage, *Electronics*, Oct. 17, 1966, p 88.

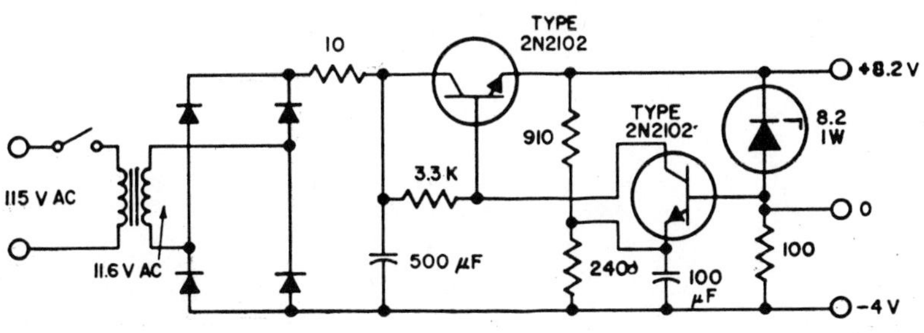

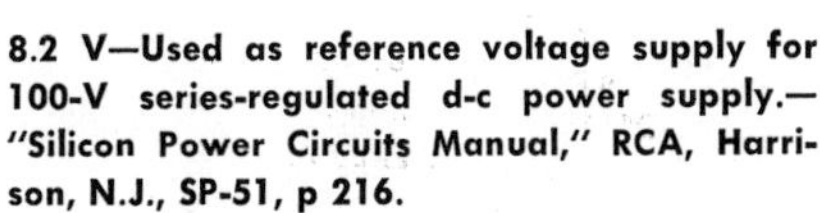
8.2 V—Used as reference voltage supply for 100-V series-regulated d-c power supply.—"Silicon Power Circuits Manual," RCA, Harrison, N.J., SP-51, p 216.

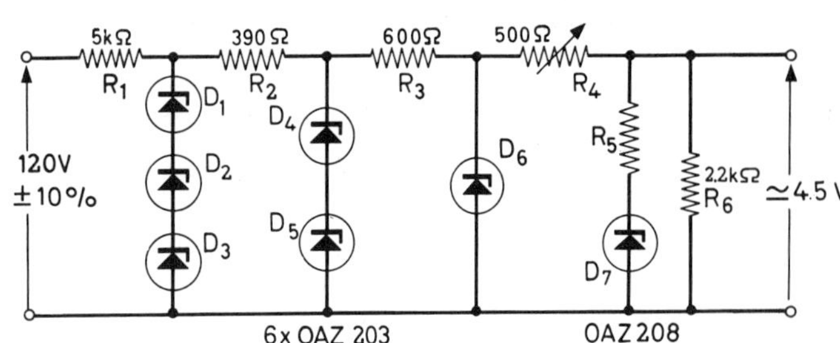

4.5-V ZENER SUBSTITUTE FOR WESTON CELL—Provides reference voltage between 4 and 6 V with better constancy than standard cell, despite a-c line voltage fluctuations up to 10% and temperature variations between 30 and 60 C. Supply voltage is first stabilized by shunt-regulated circuits connected in cascade. Final zener has opposite temperature coefficient to that of preceding diode, to eliminate effect of temperature.—S. T. Ho, Reference-Voltage Unit Equipped with Zener Diodes, *Electronic Applications*, Philips, Pub. Dept., Elcoma Div., Eindhoven, The Netherlands, Vol. 24, No. 4, 1963–1964, p 153–161.

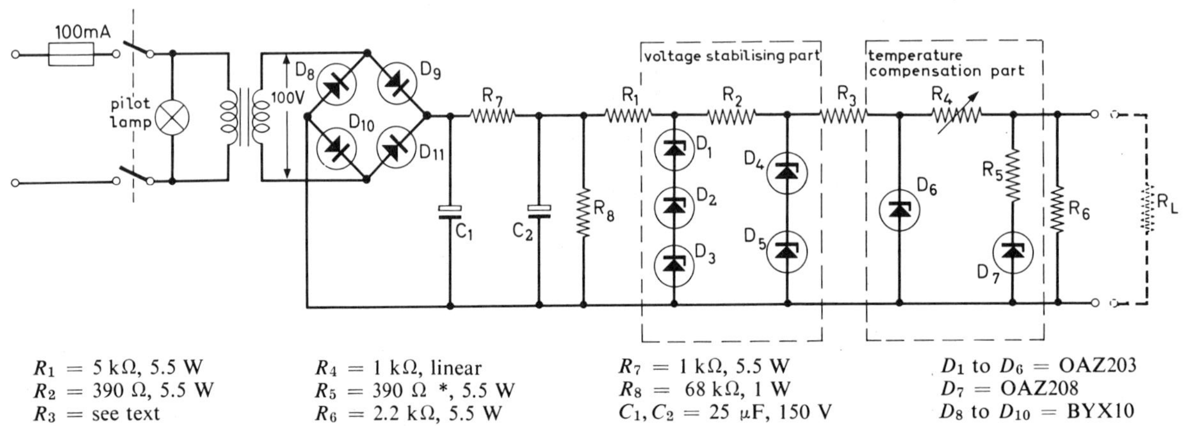

R_1 = 5 kΩ, 5.5 W
R_2 = 390 Ω, 5.5 W
R_3 = see text
R_4 = 1 kΩ, linear
R_5 = 390 Ω *, 5.5 W
R_6 = 2.2 kΩ, 5.5 W
R_7 = 1 kΩ, 5.5 W
R_8 = 68 kΩ, 1 W
C_1, C_2 = 25 μF, 150 V
D_1 to D_6 = OAZ203
D_7 = OAZ208
D_8 to D_{10} = BYX10

4–6 V SECONDARY STANDARD—Bridge rectifier across secondary of power-line transformer energizes zeners providing output voltage between 4 and 6 V, depending on components, having greater constancy than standard cells. Requires calibration against standard cell or equivalent-accuracy measuring instrument. Value of R5 is based on assumed permissible output voltage variation of 0.1 mV for 10% line voltage variation.—S. T. Ho, Reference-Voltage Unit Equipped with Zener Diodes, *Electronic Applications*, Philips, Pub. Dept., Elcoma Div., Eindhoven, The Netherlands, Vol. 24, No. 4, 1963–1964, p 153–161.

NOTE: To locate additional circuits in the category of this chapter, use the index at the back of this book. Check also the author's "Sourcebook of Electronic Circuits," published by McGraw-Hill in 1968.

CHAPTER 99
Zero-Voltage Detector Circuits

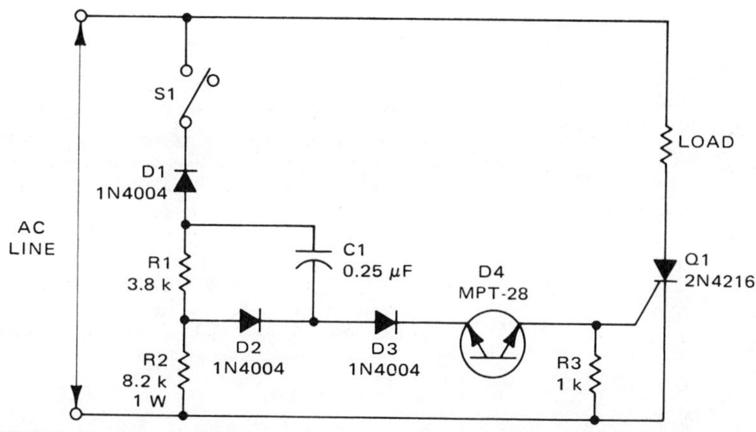

SENSITIVE-GATE SCR SWITCH—Zero-point switch ensures that control scr turns on at start of each positive alternation. If turned on later in cycle, voltage and current spikes produced could cause electromagnetic interference. Circuit actually oscillates near zero-crossing point and provides series of pulses to assure zero-point switching.—"Semiconductor Power Circuits Handbook," Motorola, Phoenix, Ariz., 1968, p 6–5.

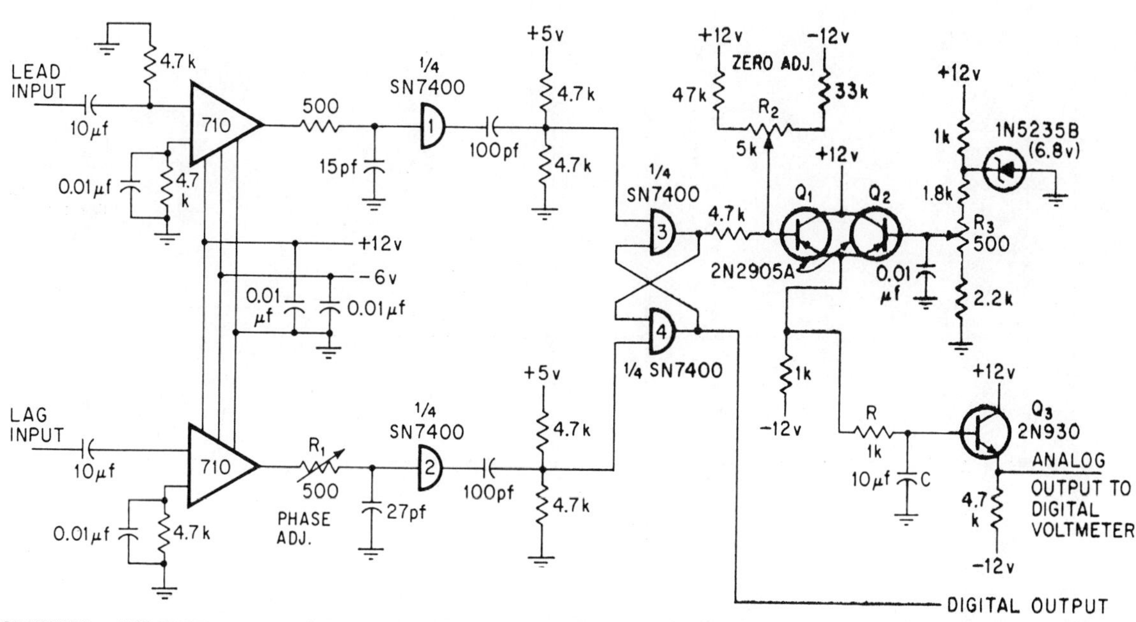

ZERO-CROSSING DETECTOR—Two voltage comparators and logic gate feed digital voltmeter to form digital-output phase comparator giving 1% accuracy at 1 MHz. Voltage comparators detect zero crossings of each input signal, for amplification by SN7400 TTL gate, differentiation, and setting of latch gates 3 and 4 for driving analog switch at duty cycle determined by phase relationship of input signals. D-c complement of resulting pulse train is applied to digital voltmeter. —R. H. Gruner, Phase Comparator Yields Digital Output, *Electronics*, Sept. 15, 1969, p 118.

RFI-FREE A-C SWITCH—Triacs close circuit only when line voltage is near zero and open it only when current is near zero, to minimize rfi. With S1 open, T1 fires at beginning of each a-c half-cycle and prevents T2 from firing. When S1 is closed, T1 commutates off at next zero crossing and R2 supplies gate current to T2 so it fires at beginning of each following half-cycle until S1 is opened.—W. B. Miles, Switch Your AC Loads at Zero Voltage or Current, *Electronic Design*, Sept. 13, 1967, p 128, 130, and 132.

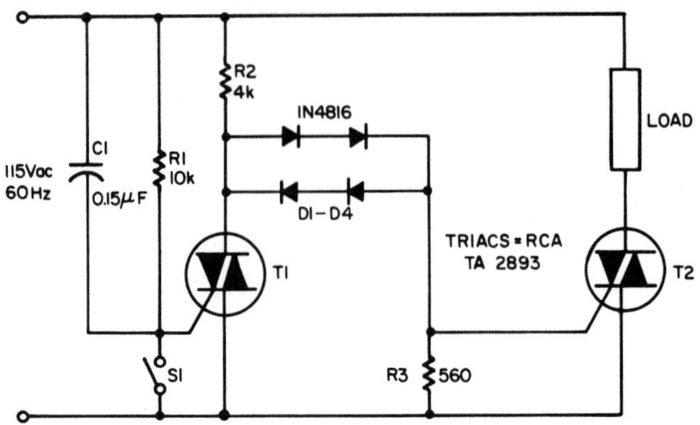

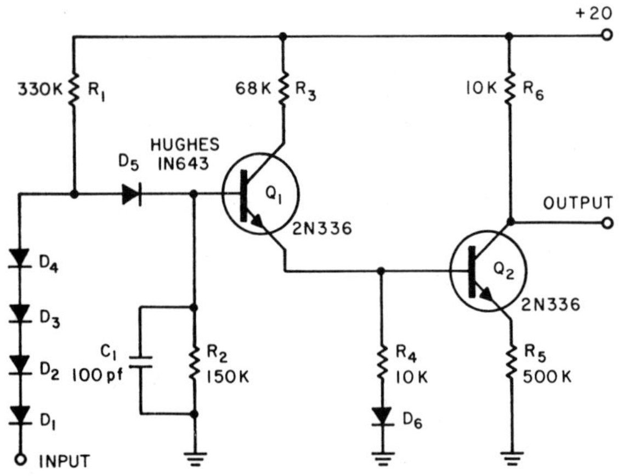

ZERO CROSSOVER—Gives output when positive-going signal is within 0.4 V of zero crossover, over temperature range of −55 to 80 C, for input signal peaks of up to 100 V in both directions and frequencies from d-c to 3,000 Hz. To reduce detection range to within 0.2 V of zero, diodes should be selected to have same forward voltage characteristics.—F. E. Olson, Zero Crossover Detector Shows High Sensitivity, *Electronic Design*, Dec. 7, 1964, p 67—68.

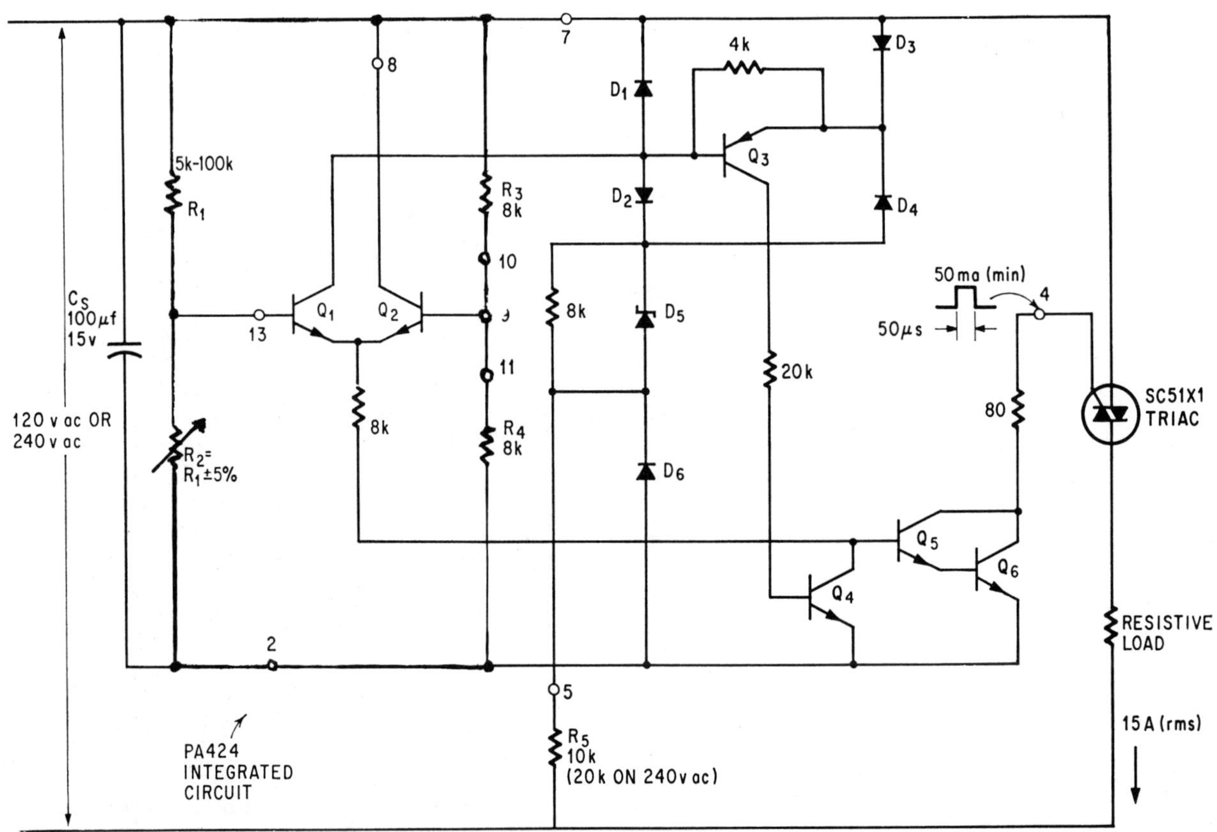

IC WITH TRIAC CONTROLS 1 KW—Uses GE PA424 IC with only five external components, by taking advantage of zero-voltage switching. Triac is fired only at zero-crossing points between half-cycles of a-c voltage. Requires no d-c power supply, and can control up to 15 A through resistive load. Article gives other power control applications for this IC. For temperature control, thermistor is used for R1.—F. W. Gutzwiller and J. H. Galloway, Power Grab By Linear IC's, *Electronics*, Aug. 21, 1967, p 81—86.

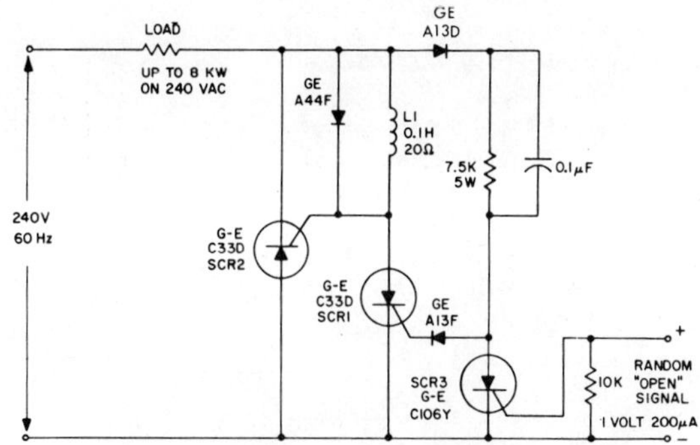

ZERO-VOLTAGE 8-KW SWITCHING—Combination of scr slaving circuit and synchronous switching insures that load voltage is always applied in essentially complete cycles, so voltage is zero at instant of switching and r-f interference is minimum. SCR2 fires at beginning of next half-cycle after SCR1 fires, to deliver even number of half-cycles and thereby reduce magnetic saturation effects in inductive load.—"SCR Manual," 4th Edition, General Electric, 1967, p 149.

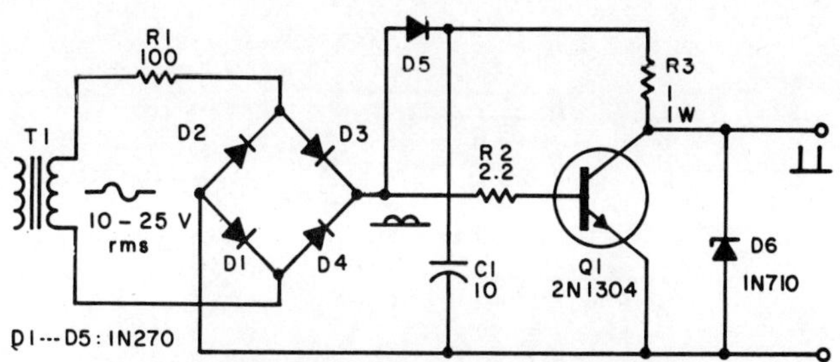

SYNC FOR FIRING SCR—Simple, inexpensive circuit requires no supply voltage or center-tapped transformer and can be used with any waveform. Used when precise synchronization with a-c line frequency is required, as in scr firing circuits. Output pulse is about 200 μs wide, with rise time of 20 μs. Q1 is normally ON; when signal level drops below that for conduction, in vicinity of zero crossing, Q1 cuts off and positive-going pulse appears at collector and output. —R. Billon, Zero-Crossing Detector Needs No Supply Voltage, *Electronic Design*, Jan. 4, 1968, p 144–145.

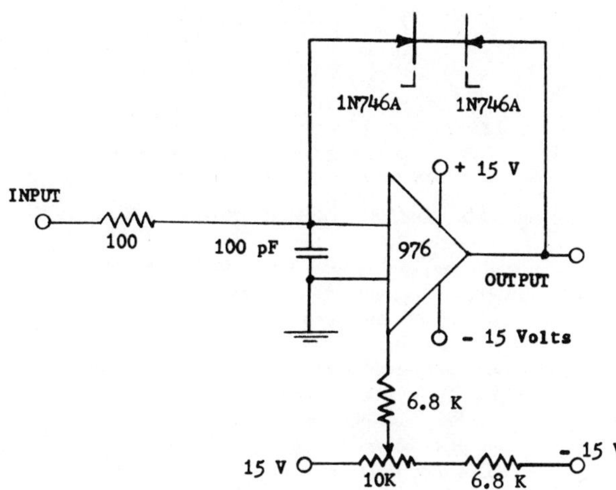

HIGH-SPEED ZERO-CROSSING DETECTOR—Uses OEI Model 976 opamp having slewing rate of 250 V per μs and minimum gain of 50 dB at 1 MHz. Requires negative input signal up to 1 V maximum and is inverting, with output of approximately 3.3 V when input is negative and with output transition occurring within nanoseconds of input zero crossing.—A High Speed Zero Crossing Detector Using an Operational Amplifier, Optical Electronics, Tucson, Ariz., No. 10041.

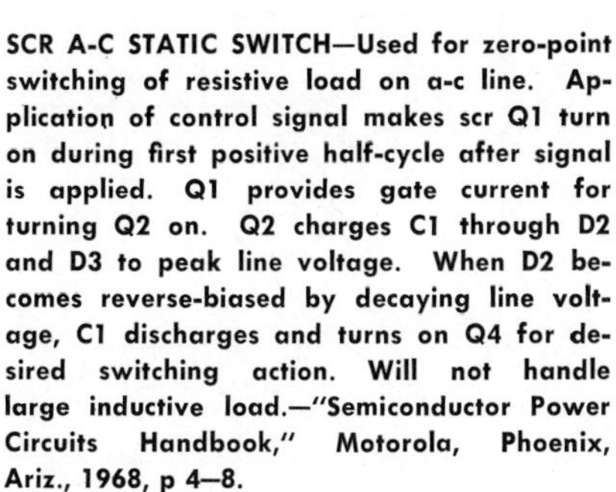

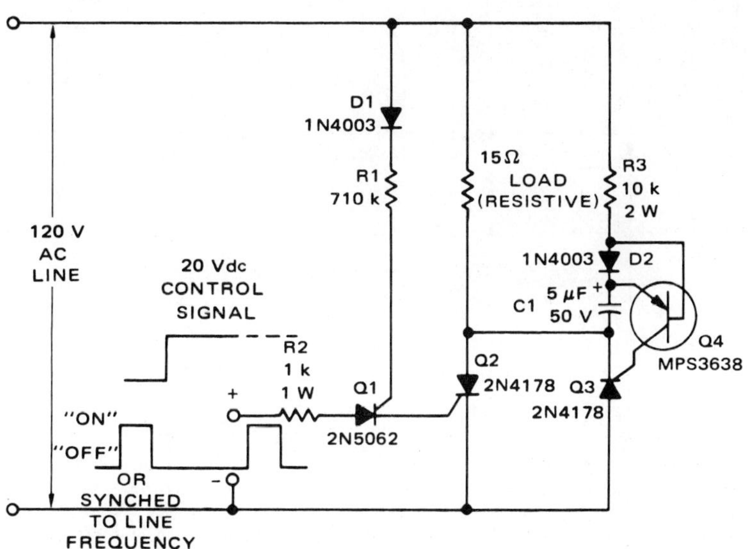

SCR A-C STATIC SWITCH—Used for zero-point switching of resistive load on a-c line. Application of control signal makes scr Q1 turn on during first positive half-cycle after signal is applied. Q1 provides gate current for turning Q2 on. Q2 charges C1 through D2 and D3 to peak line voltage. When D2 becomes reverse-biased by decaying line voltage, C1 discharges and turns on Q4 for desired switching action. Will not handle large inductive load.—"Semiconductor Power Circuits Handbook," Motorola, Phoenix, Ariz., 1968, p 4–8.

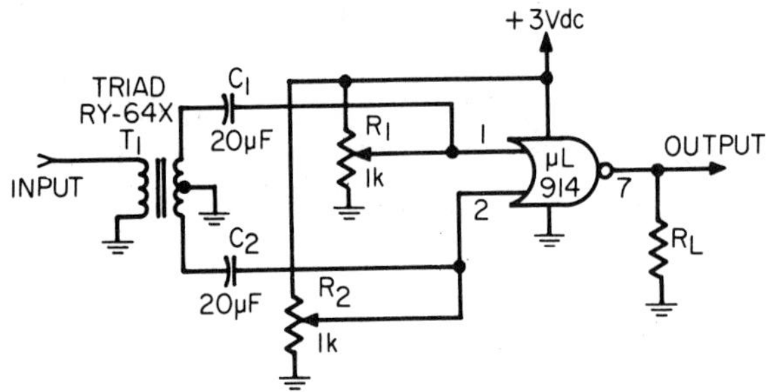

200–10,000 HZ ZERO-VOLTAGE DETECTOR—Delivers output pulse whenever a-c input waveform goes through zero. Applications include counters, phase-control circuits, and some types of analog-digital converters. Provides 1.2 V peak output for 1 V rms input.—T. Polaneczky and A. Brand, IC NOR Gate Detects Zero-Axis Crossing, *EEE*, April 1968, p 107.

PRECISION ZERO-CROSSING DETECTOR—Uses OEI Model 9186 opamp with feedback diodes that limit output to 0.5 V with either polarity, depending on polarity of input before crossing zero. Output lags actual zero crossing by 90 deg because of amplifier phase shift, which means that detector output will be zero 95 ns after input is zero for 10-MHz signal.—A Precision Zero Crossing Detector, Optical Electronics, Tucson, Ariz., No. 10114.

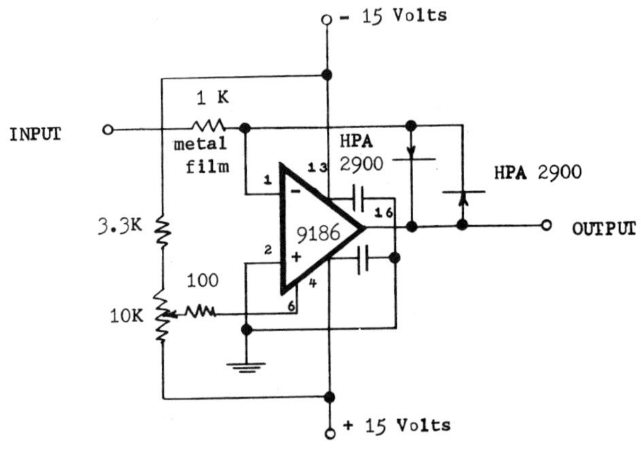

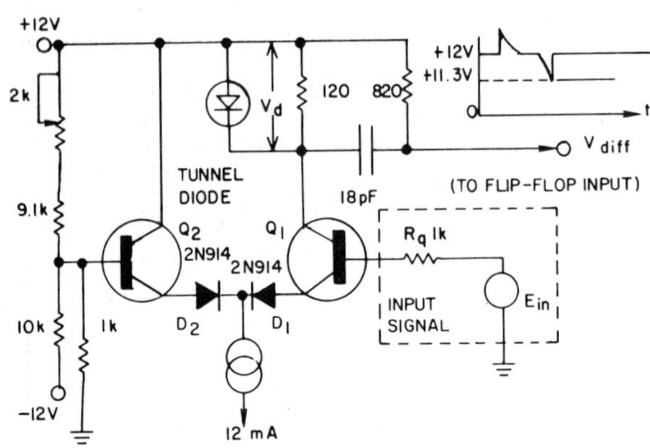

ZERO-CROSSING DISCRIMINATOR — High-speed circuit has broad dynamic range, high input resistance, and high input sensitivity. Collector currents of Q1 and Q2 are equal only when input signal is zero. When negative input signal is fed to Q1, collector current and voltage drop Vd decrease. When drop goes below tunnel diode voltage, it switches from high to low state, corresponding to low-level discrimination. With tunnel diode also in Q2 collector circuit, zero crossings of sine-wave input can be discriminated. —M. Sampaleanu, High-Speed Zero Crossing Detector Uses Tunnel Diodes, *Electronic Design*, March 15, 1970, p 214 and 216.

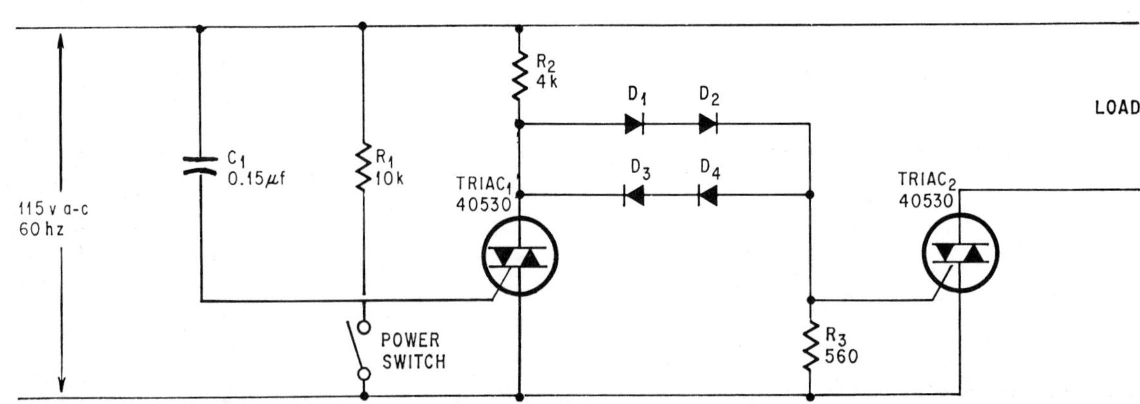

NOISE-FREE TRIAC A-C SWITCH—Permits switching of a-c voltages and currents only at zero points, to prevent generation of rfi that could destroy transistors.—W. B. Miles, Gated Semiconductors Clean A-C Switching, *Electronics*, May 27, 1968, p 105–106.

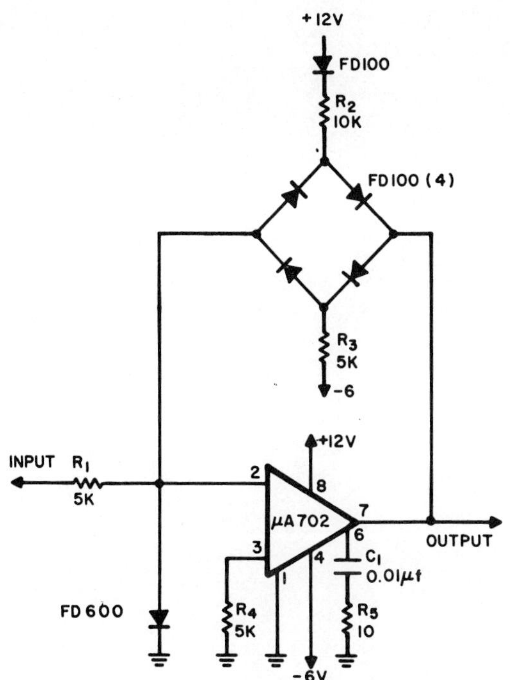

ZERO-CROSSING DETECTOR—Uses Fairchild IC opamp to perform power spectrum analysis of analog signal waveform, within specified passband, that is extracted from broadband signal and noise. Amplifier is driven to maximum output of 1.5 V for input voltage excursions as small as 500 μV to give uniform clipping of random analog waveform with negligible hysteresis and negligible loss of average reference level.—L. A. Watts, The Integrated Operational Amplifier: A Versatile and Economical Circuit, "Microelectronic Design," Hayden Book Co., N.Y., 1966, p 189–194.

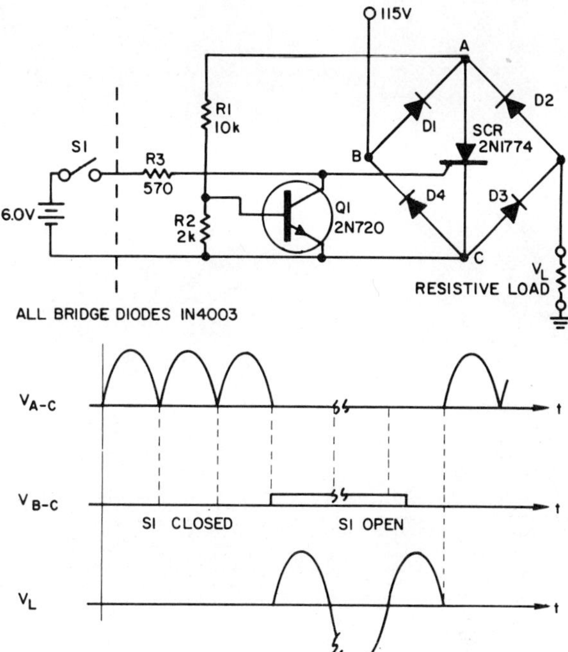

ZERO-VOLTAGE SWITCHING—Regardless of time S1 is closed, scr is turned on or off only at zero-voltage crossover point of a-c line voltage, for minimizing power-line rfi.—A. J. Marek, Simple Zero Crossing Detector Minimizes Power-Line RFI, *Electronic Design*, March 1, 1970, p 81.

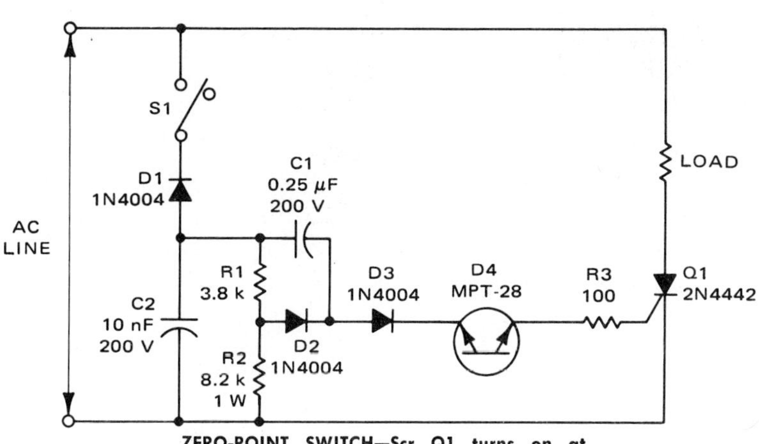

ZERO-POINT SWITCH—Scr Q1 turns on at start of first positive half-cycle following closing of S1, to prevent generation of electromagnetic interference. Book describes capacitor-charging action of circuit.—"Semiconductor Power Circuits Handbook," Motorola, Phoenix, Ariz., 1968, p 6–5.

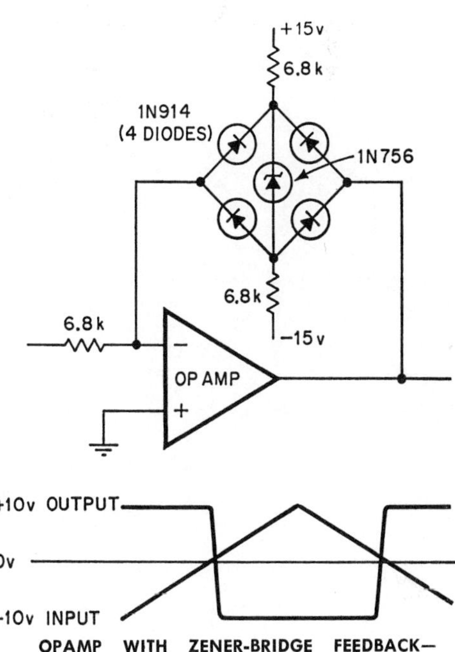

OPAMP WITH ZENER-BRIDGE FEEDBACK—Clips and squares edges of a-c inputs each time zero crossover is detected. Useful in phase-sensitive demodulation networks. Positive amplitudes of input generate negative output pulse, while negative inputs generate positive voltage level.—R. Liu, Zener Diode in Op Amp's Loop Enables Symmetrical Clipping, *Electronics*, Feb. 16, 1970, p 105.

Author Index

Subject Index